For Reference

Not to be taken from this room

The College Blue Book®

36th Edition

Scholarships, Fellowships, Grants, and Loans

The College Blue Book®

36th Edition

Scholarships, Fellowships, Grants, and Loans

MACMILLAN REFERENCE USA
A part of Gale, Cengage Learning

GALE
CENGAGE Learning™

Detroit • New York • San Francisco • New Haven, Conn • Waterville, Maine • London

GALE
CENGAGE Learning™

The College Blue Book, 36th Edition
Volume 5

Project Editor: Bohdan Romaniuk

Editorial Support Services: Wayne Fong

Composition and Electronic Prepress: Gary Leach

Manufacturing: Rita Wimberley

Product Management: Jenai Mynatt

© 2009 Macmillan Reference USA, a part of Gale, Cengage Learning

For product information and technology assistance, contact us at
Gale Customer Support, 1-800-877-4253.
For permission to use material from this text or product,
submit all requests online at **www.cengage.com/permissions.**
Further permissions questions can be emailed to
permissionrequest@cengage.com

Gale
27500 Drake Rd.
Farmington Hills, MI, 48331-3535

ISBN-13: 978-0-02-866074-5 (6 vol. set)
ISBN-10: 0-02-866074-9 (6 vol. set)
ISBN-13: 978-0-02-866079-0 (vol. 5)
ISBN-10: 0-02-866079-x (vol. 5)

ISSN 0198-8409

This title is also available as an e-book.
ISBN-13: 978-0-02-866142-1 (set)
ISBN-10: 0-02-866142-7 (set)
Contact your Gale sales representative for ordering information.

Printed in the United States of America
1 2 3 4 5 6 7 12 11 10 09 08

Contents

The College Blue Book® has been a standard, professional reference on higher education since it was first published in 1923. New features have been added during the intervening years to keep pace with the changing needs for information about our educational facilities. The information, especially in the areas of tuition, room and board, enrollment figures, library holdings, is constantly changing. It is difficult to maintain up-to-date figures in these areas, as many schools change tuition and related costs on an ongoing basis. We therefore urge our readers to check directly with the schools for the most current cost information.

CONTENTS OF EACH VOLUME

Volume 1: Narrative Descriptions

Nearly 4,200 colleges in the United States and Canada are fully described. Entrance requirements are detailed and campus facilities and costs are described. A map of each U.S. state and Canadian province is included and each college has a grid index for easy location. Web sites are also listed.

Volume 2: Tabular Data

Colleges are listed alphabetically by state or province. Information about costs, accreditation, enrollment figures, faculty, and names of the chief administrative officers are given for each school.

Volume 3: Degrees Offered by College and Subject

In Part I, the name of each college is listed alphabetically by state or province, with a list of the subject areas for which degrees are offered. Part II includes an alphabetical listing of subject areas for which degrees are granted by one or more institutions of higher education.

Volume 4: Occupational Education

More than 6,300 schools in the United States that provide occupational or technical training are fully described, offering such information as tuition costs, enrollment figures,

and entrance requirements. Two indexes are provided: an alphabetical listing of schools in the "Index of Occupational Education Schools," in addition to the "Curricula and Areas of Instruction" index.

Volume 5: Scholarships, Fellowships, Grants, and Loans

This volume provides a listing of more than 4,700 different sources of financial aid for students wishing to further their education. Split alphabetically into eight broad subject areas (each containing several more specialized concentrations of study), as well as a general section, each listing provides basic information about a specific award, including eligibility requirements, amount of award, and application deadlines.

Volume 6: Distance Learning Programs

Responding to this rapidly growing trend in postsecondary education, this volume features comprehensive profiles of more than 900 institutions offering distance learning programs within the United States and Canada, providing both basic information as well as in-depth descriptions of certain institutions.

FOR MORE INFORMATION

We are always open to suggestions and recommendations for improvement of The College Blue Book® from our readers and from the educational professions. Please write or call: Editor, The College Blue Book

Macmillan Reference USA

27500 Drake Rd.

Farmington Hills, MI 48331-3535

Phone: (248)699-4253

Toll-free: 800-347-GALE

Fax: (248)699-8075

Email: blue.book@gale.com

Web site: www.gale.cengage.com

The value of higher education, including highly specialized education in technical and vocational fields, has proved to be an absolute necessity. Through this edition of *Scholarships, Fellowships, Grants, and Loans,* students, counselors, and parents will find a wide variety of sources committed to funding all phases of postsecondary education. Those seeking financial help should make use of as many sources of information as possible, including the Internet, but should be aware that many scholarships and other sources of funding are available in their local area or through the institution they plan to attend.

Scholarships, Fellowships, Grants, and Loans is divided into eight broad subject areas. These are preceded by a "General" section, listing sponsors who do not restrict their awards to the study of a specific subject. Each of the eight categories is then divided into more specific areas of interest within that field. Under these more specific headings are the award entries, listed alphabetically by sponsoring organization. These entries assume a standard format throughout this volume.

All the information in the entry should be studied carefully; it is submitted directly by the sponsoring organization. If, under "Eligibility Requirements," only female descendants of Confederate soldiers are ruled eligible for the award, it is a waste of time for others to apply. On the other hand, if there is some indication of eligibility, prospective applicants should inquire further. You will speed the process of getting information if you enclose a stamped, self-addressed envelope. Some organizations will not respond unless they receive a stamped, self-addressed envelope.

The broad subject area listings are followed by four comprehensive indexes: "Title Index," "Sponsoring Organization," "Level of Education," and "Subject Index." By using the first index, the reader can locate specific awards with which they are already familiar. The second index lists sponsoring organizations and all the awards given by them. The "Level of Education Index" groups the awards by the various levels for which the funds are allocated. The "Subject Index" enables prospective applicants to determine awards that are given in specific subject areas.

Although *Scholarships, Fellowships, Grants, and Loans* lists, for the most part, private sources of financial aid, much assistance is still provided by the federal government, the states, and increasingly, the schools involved.

Federal aid, in the form of scholarships, outright grants, work study and various guaranteed loan programs has declined during the past decade; however, all postsecondary students should order an extremely useful publication, *The Student Guide*, from: ED Pubs

PO Box 1398

Jessup, MD 20794-1398

877-4-ED-PUBS

http://www.edpubs.org

Applications for federal student aid (FAFSA) are available from high schools, colleges, career schools, or The Federal Student Aid Information Center (800-433-3243). The FAFSA is also available on the web at: http://www.fafsa.ed.gov/

State governments are also sources of scholarships, grants and guaranteed loans, and students should contact their state department of education for details of what is offered. Programs and education budgets vary considerably from state to state.

Finally, the schools are themselves a major source of aid. Their financial aid programs have become as innovative as their curricula. Usually, all forms of aid are available, from outright grants to loans and work-study.

In determining need, most schools require an independent assessment of the student's, or if dependent, the family's, ability to help finance tuition and living costs. The College Board provides the CSS/Financial Aid PROFILE, a financial aid application service. PROFILE is required by select private colleges and some public institutions. All students should file the FAFSA (Free Application for Federal Student Aid). FAFSA is necessary to receive consideration for federal aid, many state grants, college scholarships, and other private aid programs. For specific filing requirements, the financial aid officer of the student's college of choice should be contacted.

The College Board

45 Columbus Ave.

New York, NY 10023-6992

(212)713-8000

www.collegeboard.com

Many civic, fraternal, educational, and business groups give scholarships in their local communities. Sometimes these are limited to a specific high school, but more often they are given to a local area which includes several high schools. These awards can be of significant help to graduating high school seniors. While one award may be as low as

$250-$500, the student is usually eligible for more than one award.

Finally, students should be aware that many scholarships are also awarded (nationally) only to those that are already in college and entering their sophomore, junior, or senior year.

Scholarships, Fellowships, Grants, and Loans is both a key and a stepping stone to financing higher education which has become almost a necessity in the United States. Despite budget cuts and an increase in competition for scarce financial resources, funds are available to the enterprising student determined to explore every avenue in pursuit of an education.

1 ■ 101ST AIRBORNE DIVISION ASSOCIATION
PO Box 929
Fort Campbell, KY 42223-0929
Tel: (931)431-0199
E-mail: 101stairbornedivisionassociation@comcast.net
Web Site: http://www.screamingeagle.org
To provide financial assistance to students who have the potential of becoming assets to the nation.
Title of Award: Chappie Hall Scholarship Program **Area, Field, or Subject:** General Studies. **Level of Education for which Award is Granted:** Graduate, Postgraduate, Undergraduate **Number Awarded:** 11. **Funds Available:** $1,000. **Duration:** Annual.
Eligibility Requirements: Applicant's parents, grandparents, spouse, living or deceased must be a former or present member of the 101st Airborne Division; must have at least 2.5 GPA; must demonstrate financial need. **Application Requirements:** Applicant must submit complete application package. **Deadline for Receipt:** May 31. **Additional Information:** Executive Secretary-Treasurer, phone: 270-439-0445, email: sambass101@comcast.net.

2 ■ THE FREDERICK B. ABRAMSON MEMORIAL FOUNDATION
1050 Connecticut Ave. NW, Ste. 200
Washington, DC 20036
Tel: (202)828-6490
Fax: (202)828-6490
E-mail: info@abramsonfoundation.org
Web Site: http://www.abramsonfoundation.org
To help defer college expenses at a four-year accredited institution.
Title of Award: The Frederick B. Abramson Memorial Foundation Scholarships **Area, Field, or Subject:** General studies. **Level of Education for which Award is Granted:** Undergraduate **Funds Available:** $10,000.
Eligibility Requirements: Applicants must be graduating from a public senior high school located in the District of Columbia; applicants must have demonstrated commitment to community service and social change; applicants must have demonstrated financial need; applicants must have at least 2.75 GPA or better; at least 1000 between math and verbal SATs and at least a score of 3 and above in the essay section; must have a family income of less than $70,000. **Application Requirements:** Applicants must submit an application form; essay; two letters of recommendation in which one is from the councilor and one is from the teacher; a copy of College Financial Aid Application or Student Aid Report; official transcript through midterm period of second semester of senior year including the SAT scores; budget for preferred college; letter of acceptance from college of choice; and a financial aid award letter from college of choice. **Deadline for Receipt:** April 14.

3 ■ ADOPTIVE FAMILIES TODAY
PO Box 1726
Barrington, IL 60011-1726
Tel: (847)382-0858
Fax: (847)382-0831
E-mail: adoptivefamiliestoday@hotmail.com
Web Site: http://adoptivefamiliestoday.com
To provide financial assistance to a foster child who is a current year high school graduate or GED recipient who plans to attend a technical/vocational college, junior college or a four year accredited college or university.
Title of Award: Adoptive Families Today Commemorative Scholarships **Area, Field, or Subject:** General studies. **Level of Education for which Award is Granted:** Undergraduate **Funds Available:** $1,785.
Eligibility Requirements: Applicant must live in foster care in one of the following Illinois counties: Cook, Lake, Kane, McHenry or DuPage who is graduating high school senior or GED recipient with a maintained GPA of 2.0 or above and demonstrates leadership in one or more of these areas: academics, student government, athletics, high school organizations and clubs, community service and employment. **Application Requirements:** Applicants must submit completed application form (for graduating senior); for GED recipient, test scores from the institution administering the exam; verification of wardship in writing; and reference form should be sent directly to the Scholarship Committee. **Deadline for Receipt:** May 15.

4 ■ ADVERTISING PRODUCTION CLUB OF NEW YORK
428 E State St.
Long Beach, NY 11561
Tel: (212)671-2975
Fax: (718)228-8202
E-mail: admin@apc-ny.org
Web Site: http://www.apc-ny.org
To provide assistance to students with financial need.
Title of Award: APC Tuition-Assist Scholarship Awards **Area, Field, or Subject:** General studies. **Level of Education for which Award is Granted:** Graduate, Undergraduate **Funds Available:** No specific amount.
Eligibility Requirements: Applicant must be a resident of New York City metro area enrolled as a full-time student in an accredited degree-granting program in any college in the U.S. **Application Requirements:** Guidelines and application forms are available from the Advertising Production Club office or can be downloaded from the APC website. Applicants must submit a completed hard copy application with the APC office together with registration receipt for the new semester, college transcript and acceptance letter. **Deadline for Receipt:** October 15.

5 ■ AHEPA BUCKEYE SCHOLARSHIP FOUNDATION
6437 Tylers Crossing
West Chester, OH 45069
Tel: (513)779-0842
Web Site: http://www.ahepadistrict11.org
To provide financial assistance to deserving students entering college or in undergraduate school.
Title of Award: Ahepa Buckeye Scholarship Awards **Area, Field, or Subject:** General studies. **Level of Education for which Award is Granted:** Undergraduate **Funds Available:** No amount mentioned.
Eligibility Requirements: Applicant must be an active member of the AHEPA, Daughters of Penelope, Sons of Pericles, Maids of Athena, or whose parent(s) have been active members of the Senior Orders for three consecutive years. **Application Requirements:** Applicant must submit

the completed application form along with a letter of recommendation from the counselor, principal, or other appropriate school official.

6 ■ AHEPA DISTRICT NO. 1 SCHOLARSHIP FOUNDATION

18 Riverdale Dr.
Charleston, SC 29407
Tel: (843)571-4181
Web Site: http://www.ahepadistrict1.org
To promote, encourage, induce and advance education at the college, university and graduate school level.
Title of Award: Ahepa District No. 1 Scholarship Program **Area, Field, or Subject:** General studies. **Level of Education for which Award is Granted:** Graduate, Undergraduate **Funds Available:** $500 to $1,500.
Eligibility Requirements: Applicant must be a student in the graduating class of his/her high school and planning to attend full time an accredited college or university during the current calendar year; a high school graduate planning to attend full time an accredited college or university during the calendar year; or attending an accredited college or university and will continue to attend full time during the calendar year. **Application Requirements:** Applicant must complete the application form and submit it with the required materials asked in order to apply for the scholarship. **Deadline for Receipt:** January 10.

7 ■ AIR FORCE SERGEANTS ASSOCIATION

5211 Auth Rd.
Suitland, MD 20746
Tel: (301)899-3500
Free: 800-638-0594
Fax: (301)899-8136
E-mail: staff@afsahq.org
Web Site: http://www.afsahq.org
To financially assist the undergraduate studies of eligible, dependent children of the Air Force Sergeants Association.
Title of Award: AFSA Scholarship Program **Area, Field, or Subject:** General studies. **Level of Education for which Award is Granted:** Undergraduate **Funds Available:** $500-$3,000.
Eligibility Requirements: Applicants must be a dependent youth of an AFSA or AFSA Auxiliary members. **Application Requirements:** Applicants must submit a completed application form; a copy of proof of sponsor's military status (copy of DD 214, copy of the sponsor's ID and discharge letter); official transcript of grades (high school graduates must include all grades from 9th to 12th grades, college applicants must include cumulative record of grades); a letter of recommendation written on the official school stationary with original signature (for high school graduate, letter must be written by the school principal or counselor; for college student, letter must be written by a college professor); a typed paragraph of the applicant's objectives (double-spaced) answering the question, "What do you plan to do with the education you receive?"; an essay (double-spaced) answering the question, "What is the most urgent problem facing society today?" and a typed, double-spaced two-page essay about a current, controversial issue; two self-addressed, stamped, blank postcards. High school graduate must include a valid record of combined SAT I or ACT scores (must be recorded on an official school transcript). **Deadline for Receipt:** March 31. **Additional Information:** AFSA/CMSAF/AMF Scholarship Program, 5211 Auth Rd., Suitland, Maryland 20746.

8 ■ AIR FORCE SERGEANTS ASSOCIATION-CHAPTER 155

PO Box 422
Dover, NH 03821
E-mail: redolbec@comcast.net
Web Site: http://www.afsa155.org
To enhance education opportunities for AFSA members and their families.
Title of Award: AFSA Chapter 155 Division 1 Scholarships - Category 1 **Area, Field, or Subject:** General studies. **Level of Education for which Award is Granted:** Undergraduate **Number Awarded:** 1. **Funds Available:** $500.
Eligibility Requirements: Applicants must be graduating high school senior entering 1st year college; the parents, grandparents and/or guardians are current members of AFSA/Auxiliary; have a GPA of 3.0. **Application Requirements:** Applicants must submit a completed application form (available at the website) **Deadline for Receipt:** April. **Additional Information:** Susan L. Williams, Scholarship Chair, 419 Ocean Rd. Portsmouth, NH 03801-6020.

9 ■ AIR FORCE SERGEANTS ASSOCIATION-CHAPTER 155

PO Box 422
Dover, NH 03821
E-mail: redolbec@comcast.net
Web Site: http://www.afsa155.org
To enhance education opportunities for AFSA members and their families.
Title of Award: AFSA Chapter 155 Division 1 Scholarships - Category 2 **Area, Field, or Subject:** General studies. **Level of Education for which Award is Granted:** Undergraduate **Number Awarded:** 1. **Funds Available:** $500.
Eligibility Requirements: Applicants must be 2nd, 3rd and 4th year college student up to 26 years age; the parents, grandparents and/or guardians are current members of AFSA/Auxiliary; have a GPA of 3.0. **Application Requirements:** Applicants must submit a completed application form (available at the website) **Deadline for Receipt:** April. **Additional Information:** Susan L. Williams, Scholarship Chair, 419 Ocean Rd. Portsmouth, NH 03801-6020.

10 ■ AIR FORCE SERGEANTS ASSOCIATION-CHAPTER 155

PO Box 422
Dover, NH 03821
E-mail: redolbec@comcast.net
Web Site: http://www.afsa155.org
To enhance education opportunities for AFSA members and their families.
Title of Award: AFSA Chapter 155 Division 1 Scholarships - Category 3 **Area, Field, or Subject:** General studies. **Level of Education for which Award is Granted:** Undergraduate **Number Awarded:** 1. **Funds Available:** $500.
Eligibility Requirements: Applicants must be AFSA/Auxiliary members seeking to complete advanced schooling at credited college or trade school. **Application Requirements:** Applicants must submit a completed application form (available at the website) **Deadline for Receipt:** April. **Additional Information:** Susan L. Williams, Scholarship Chair, 419 Ocean Rd. Portsmouth, NH 03801-6020.

11 ■ AIR FORCE SERGEANTS ASSOCIATION-CHAPTER 155

PO Box 422
Dover, NH 03821
E-mail: redolbec@comcast.net
Web Site: http://www.afsa155.org
To enhance education opportunities for AFSA members and their families.
Title of Award: Master Sergeant Neal E. Powers Memorial Scholarships **Area, Field, or Subject:** General studies. **Level of Education for which Award is Granted:** Undergraduate **Number Awarded:** 1. **Funds Available:** $500.
Eligibility Requirements: Applicants must be members or dependents of members of Chapter 155/A155; accepted and will be entering first post secondary education program. **Application Requirements:** Applicants must submit a completed application form (available at the website). **Deadline for Receipt:** June 30. **Additional Information:** Susan L. Williams, Scholarship Chair, 419 Ocean Rd. Portsmouth, NH 03801-6020.

12 ■ AIR FORCE SERGEANTS ASSOCIATION-CHAPTER 155

PO Box 422
Dover, NH 03821
E-mail: redolbec@comcast.net
Web Site: http://www.afsa155.org
To enhance education opportunities for AFSA members and their families.
Title of Award: Master Sergeant William Sowers Memorial Scholarships **Area, Field, or Subject:** General studies. **Level of Education for which Award is Granted:** Undergraduate **Number Awarded:** 1. **Funds Available:** $500.
Eligibility Requirements: Applicants must be members or dependents of members of Chapter 155/A155; enrolled in an accredited institution and have completed at least one semester or term. **Application Requirements:** Applicants must submit a completed application form (available at the website). **Deadline for Receipt:** June 30. **Additional Information:** Susan L. Williams, Scholarship Chair, 419 Ocean Rd. Portsmouth, NH 03801-6020.

13 ■ AIR TRAFFIC CONTROL ASSOCIATION

1101 King St., Ste. 300
Alexandria, VA 22314

Tel: (703)299-2430
Fax: (703)299-2437
E-mail: info@atca.org
Web Site: http://www.atca.org
To provide financial assistance to students enrolled in an aviation related program of study leading to a bachelor's degree or greater.
Title of Award: Air Traffic Control Association Non-employee Student Scholarships **Area, Field, or Subject:** Traffic management. **Level of Education for which Award is Granted:** Undergraduate **Funds Available:** No amount mentioned.
Eligibility Requirements: Applicants must have attendance equal to at least half-time (6 semester hours or the equivalent) and a minimum of 30 semester or 45 hours still to be completed before graduation; must be enrolled or accepted in a two-year or greater air traffic control program at an institution approved and/or listed by the Federal Aviation Administration as directly supporting the FAA's college training initiative; must be enrolled or accepted in an accredited college or university and planning to continue the following academic year; must be enrolled in course work related to his/her aviation-related career and leading to a bachelor's degree or greater; must be engaged in full-time employment in an aviation-related field; must be enrolled in course work designed to enhance the applicant's skill in an air traffic control or other aviation-related discipline. **Application Requirements:** Applicants must provide two letters of recommendation (from present or previous teachers, professors, instructors, supervisors, or managers) from within the last 12 months; submit certified transcript of all college coursework. If less than 30 semester or 45 quarter hours of college coursework have been completed, all high school transcripts also are required, work or experience that supports your educational and/or aviation career goals must be addressed in the application and/or essay; financial need must be addressed in your application and/or essay; submit a paper on the subject, "How My Education Efforts Will Enhance My Potential Contribution To Aviation." which should be typed, doubled spaced, 400 words maximum.

14 ■ AIR TRAFFIC CONTROL ASSOCIATION
1101 King St., Ste. 300
Alexandria, VA 22314
Tel: (703)299-2430
Fax: (703)299-2437
E-mail: info@atca.org
Web Site: http://www.atca.org
To provide financial assistance to students enrolled in air traffic control curriculum at FAA approved institution.
Title of Award: Gabe A. Hartl Scholarships **Area, Field, or Subject:** Traffic management. **Level of Education for which Award is Granted:** Undergraduate **Funds Available:** No amount mentioned.
Eligibility Requirements: Applicants must have attendance equal to at least half-time (6 semester hours or the equivalent) and a minimum of 30 semester or 45 hours still to be completed before graduation; must be enrolled or accepted in a two-year or greater air traffic control program at an institution approved and/or listed by the Federal Aviation Administration as directly supporting the FAA's college training initiative; must be enrolled or accepted in an accredited college or university and planning to continue the following academic year; must be enrolled in course work related to his/her aviation-related career and leading to a bachelor's degree or greater; must be engaged in full-time employment in an aviation-related field; must be enrolled in course work designed to enhance the applicant's skill in an air traffic control or other aviation-related disciplines. **Application Requirements:** Applicants must provide two letters of recommendation (from present or previous teachers, professors, instructors, supervisors, or managers) from within the last 12 months; submit certified transcript of all college coursework. If less than 30 semester or 45 quarter hours of college coursework have been completed, all high school transcripts also are required, work or experience that supports your educational and/or aviation career goals must be addressed in the application and/or essay; financial need must be addressed in your application and/or essay; submit a paper on the subject, "How My Education Efforts Will Enhance My Potential Contribution To Aviation." which should be typed, doubled spaced, 400 words maximum.

15 ■ AIRPORTS COUNCIL INTERNATIONAL-NORTH AMERICA
1775 K St. NW, Ste. 500
Washington, DC 20006

Tel: (202)293-8500; 888-424-7767
Fax: (202)331-1362
E-mail: nzimini@aci-na.org
Web Site: http://www.aci-na.org
To provide educational assistance for students at an accredited educational institution working towards a degree and a career in airport management or airport administration.
Title of Award: Airports Council International-North America Scholarship **Area, Field, or Subject:** General studies. **Level of Education for which Award is Granted:** Graduate, Undergraduate **Number Awarded:** 3. **Funds Available:** $2,500.
Eligibility Requirements: Applicants must be officially enrolled in an accredited college or university in either an undergraduate program focused on airport management and/or airport operations, or a graduate program focused on research on airport management or airport operations; must reside and attend school in the U.S. or Canada and must maintain a minimum GPA of 3.0 at the time of application. **Application Requirements:** Applicants must submit scholarship application (Form 101-06); official school transcript; two recent letters of recommendation, with one from a former or current professor/instructor and the other letter from someone other than a professor/instructor that has knowledge of the student's leadership qualities; a 300-500 word personal statement along with the application, with an emphasis on the applicant's interest in airport management or airport operations; and a current resume (maximum of two pages).

16 ■ ALABAMA COMMISSION ON HIGHER EDUCATION
PO Box 302000
Montgomery, AL 36130-2000
Tel: (334)242-1998
Fax: (334)242-0268
Web Site: http://www.ache.alabama.gov
To support the education of Alabama students.
Title of Award: ACHE/American Legion Auxiliary Scholarships **Area, Field, or Subject:** General studies. **Level of Education for which Award is Granted:** Undergraduate **Funds Available:** No specific amount.
Eligibility Requirements: Applicants must be either the son, daughter, grandson, granddaughter of veterans of World War I, World War II, Korea, or Vietnam and who are residents of Alabama; and must be attending an institutions having on-campus housing. **Application Requirements:** Applications are available from the American Legion Department Headquarters, American Legion Auxiliary, 120 North Jackson Street, Montgomery, AL 36104. **Deadline for Receipt:** April 1. **Additional Information:** 334-262-1176.

17 ■ ALABAMA COMMISSION ON HIGHER EDUCATION
PO Box 302000
Montgomery, AL 36130-2000
Tel: (334)242-1998
Fax: (334)242-0268
Web Site: http://www.ache.alabama.gov
To support the education of Alabama students.
Title of Award: ACHE/American Legion Scholarships **Area, Field, or Subject:** General studies. **Level of Education for which Award is Granted:** Undergraduate **Funds Available:** No specific amount.
Eligibility Requirements: Applicants must be either the son, daughter, grandson, granddaughter of veterans of World War I, World War II, Korea, or Vietnam and who are residents of Alabama; and must be attending an institutions having on-campus housing. **Application Requirements:** Applications are available from the Department Adjutant, The American Legion, P.O. Box 1069, Montgomery, AL 36192. **Deadline for Receipt:** May 1. **Additional Information:** 334-262-6638.

18 ■ ALABAMA COMMISSION ON HIGHER EDUCATION
PO Box 302000
Montgomery, AL 36130-2000
Tel: (334)242-1998
Fax: (334)242-0268
Web Site: http://www.ache.alabama.gov
To support the education of Alabama students.
Title of Award: ACHE Junior and Community College Athletic Scholarships **Area, Field, or Subject:** General studies. **Level of Education for

which Award is Granted: Undergraduate Funds Available: Not to exceed total tuition and books. Duration: One academic year.

Eligibility Requirements: Applicant must be full-time student enrolled in public junior and community colleges in Alabama. Application Requirements: Applicants must contact the coach, athletic director, or financial aid officer at any public junior or community college in Alabama in order to be considered.

19 ■ ALABAMA COMMISSION ON HIGHER EDUCATION
PO Box 302000
Montgomery, AL 36130-2000
Tel: (334)242-1998
Fax: (334)242-0268
Web Site: http://www.ache.alabama.gov
To assist the education of the dependents or spouses of police officers or firefighters killed in the line of duty in Alabama.
Title of Award: ACHE Police Officers and Firefighters Survivors' Educational Assistance Programs Area, Field, or Subject: General studies. Level of Education for which Award is Granted: Undergraduate Funds Available: Covers tuition, fees, books and supplies.
Eligibility Requirements: Applicant must be the dependent or the spouse of a police officer or firefighter killed in the line of duty; enrolled in an undergraduate program at a public postsecondary educational institution in Alabama. Application Requirements: Application forms may be obtained from the Alabama Commission on Higher Education. Additional Information: 334-242-2273.

20 ■ ALABAMA COMMISSION ON HIGHER EDUCATION
PO Box 302000
Montgomery, AL 36130-2000
Tel: (334)242-1998
Fax: (334)242-0268
Web Site: http://www.ache.alabama.gov
To support Alabama senior citizens with educational pursuits.
Title of Award: ACHE Senior Adult Scholarships Area, Field, or Subject: General studies. Level of Education for which Award is Granted: Two Year College, Undergraduate Funds Available: Full-tuition.
Eligibility Requirements: Applicant must be a senior citizen (aged 60 and over) who meet the admission requirements and attend public two-year postsecondary institutions in Alabama. Application Requirements: Applicants must contact the financial aid office at any public two-year postsecondary educational institution in Alabama in order to be considered.

21 ■ ALABAMA COMMISSION ON HIGHER EDUCATION
PO Box 302000
Montgomery, AL 36130-2000
Tel: (334)242-1998
Fax: (334)242-0268
Web Site: http://www.ache.alabama.gov
To support students with educational pursuits.
Title of Award: ACHE Two-Year College Academic Scholarships Area, Field, or Subject: General studies. Level of Education for which Award is Granted: Two Year College, Undergraduate Funds Available: Not to exceed in-state tuition and books. Duration: One academic year.
Eligibility Requirements: Applicant must be student accepted for enrollment at public two-year postsecondary educational institutions in Alabama. Application Requirements: Application forms are available at the financial aid office at any public two-year postsecondary educational institution in Alabama.

22 ■ ALABAMA COMMISSION ON HIGHER EDUCATION
PO Box 302000
Montgomery, AL 36130-2000
Tel: (334)242-1998
Fax: (334)242-0268
Web Site: http://www.ache.alabama.gov
To support the education of Alabama students.
Title of Award: Alabama Gi Dependents Educational Benefit Programs Area, Field, or Subject: General studies. Level of Education for which Award is Granted: Undergraduate Funds Available: Tuition, fees and book assistance.
Eligibility Requirements: Applicant must be a dependent or spouses of eligible Alabama veterans attending a public postsecondary educational institutions in Alabama; enrolled as an undergraduate student. Application Requirements: Application forms may be obtained from the Alabama State Department of Veterans Affairs, PO Box 1509, Montgomery, AL 36102-1509, or from any county veterans service officer. Additional Information: Alabama State Department of Veterans Affairs, at 334-242-5077.

23 ■ ALABAMA COMMISSION ON HIGHER EDUCATION
PO Box 302000
Montgomery, AL 36130-2000
Tel: (334)242-1998
Fax: (334)242-0268
Web Site: http://www.ache.alabama.gov
To assist Alabama National Guard members to attend a public postsecondary educational institution in Alabama.
Title of Award: Alabama National Guard Educational Assistance Programs Area, Field, or Subject: General studies. Level of Education for which Award is Granted: Undergraduate Funds Available: $500-$1000.
Eligibility Requirements: Applicants must be a student who is an active member in good standing with a federally recognized unit of the Alabama National Guard. Application Requirements: Applications are available from Alabama National Guard units. Forms must be signed by a representative of the Alabama Military Department and the financial aid officer at the college/university the applicant plans to attend.

24 ■ ALABAMA COMMISSION ON HIGHER EDUCATION
PO Box 302000
Montgomery, AL 36130-2000
Tel: (334)242-1998
Fax: (334)242-0268
Web Site: http://www.ache.alabama.gov
To support the education of students from families in which the head of the family is blind and whose family income is insufficient to provide educational benefits.
Title of Award: Alabama Scholarships for Dependents of Blind Parents Area, Field, or Subject: General studies. Level of Education for which Award is Granted: Undergraduate Funds Available: Covers instructional fees and tuition.
Eligibility Requirements: Applicant must be an Alabama resident; having a family in which the head of the family is blind or with family income is insufficient to provide educational benefits for attendance at an Alabama postsecondary institution. Application Requirements: Applications are available from Debra Culver, Rehab. Specialist, Alabama Department of Rehabilitation Services, 2129 East South Blvd., Montgomery, AL 36116-2455. Additional Information: Students must apply within two years of high school graduation. Additional Information: 800-441-7607, 334-613-2248, or 256-362-0638.

25 ■ ALABAMA COMMISSION ON HIGHER EDUCATION
PO Box 302000
Montgomery, AL 36130-2000
Tel: (334)242-1998
Fax: (334)242-0268
Web Site: http://www.ache.alabama.gov
To support the education of Alabama students.
Title of Award: Alabama Student Assistance Programs Area, Field, or Subject: General studies. Level of Education for which Award is Granted: Undergraduate Funds Available: $300-$2500. Duration: One academic year.
Eligibility Requirements: Applicant must be undergraduate student; an Alabama resident attending an eligible Alabama institution. Application Requirements: Applicants must submit the Free Application for Federal Student Aid available from high school guidance office or the financial aid office at the institution planning to attend.

26 ■ ALABAMA COMMISSION ON HIGHER EDUCATION
PO Box 302000
Montgomery, AL 36130-2000
Tel: (334)242-1998
Fax: (334)242-0268
Web Site: http://www.ache.alabama.gov
To support the education of Alabama students.

Title of Award: Alabama Student Grant Programs **Area, Field, or Subject:** General studies. **Level of Education for which Award is Granted:** Undergraduate **Funds Available:** Up to $1200. **Duration:** One academic year.
Eligibility Requirements: Applicant must be part-time or full-time undergraduate student; an Alabama resident; and attending Birmingham-Southern College, Concordia College, Faulkner University, Huntingdon College, Judson College, Miles College, Oakwood College, Samford University, Selma University, Southeastern Bible College, Southern Vocational College, Spring Hill College, Stillman College, or the University of Mobile. **Application Requirements:** Applications are available from the financial aid office at the institution the applicant is planning to attend.

27 ■ ALABAMA HORSE COUNCIL
PO Box 260
Morris, AL 35116
800-945-8033
E-mail: info@alabamahorsecouncil.org
Web Site: http://www.alabamahorsecouncil.org
To support the education of AHC members and their children.
Title of Award: Tagged for Greatness Scholarships **Area, Field, or Subject:** General studies. **Level of Education for which Award is Granted:** Undergraduate **Funds Available:** $1000-$1500. **Duration:** One year.
Eligibility Requirements: Applicants must be high school senior and accepted to a 4-year university; must be children or grandchildren of ASA members for two consecutive years. **Application Requirements:** Applicants must submit a completed application form. **Additional Information:** Funded by the Alabama Cattlemen's Foundation through the sale of the "Cowboy Tag". **Deadline for Receipt:** December. **Additional Information:** Martha Davis.

28 ■ ALASKA COMMUNITY FOUNDATION
400 L St., Ste. 100
Anchorage, AK 99501
Tel: (907)334-6700
Fax: (907)334-5780
E-mail: info@alaskacf.org
Web Site: http://www.alaskacf.org/index.php
To encourage scholastic performance, cross-country skiing, and participation in community ski activities.
Title of Award: Nordic Ski Association of Anchorage Scholarships **Area, Field, or Subject:** General studies. **Level of Education for which Award is Granted:** Undergraduate **Funds Available:** $1,500.
Eligibility Requirements: Applicants must be Alaska residents who are high school seniors or currently enrolled college students; must be members of the high school cross-country ski team during their junior and senior years and must have individual or family memberships in the NSAA; and must have a cumulative GPA of at least 2.7 on a 4.0 scale.
Application Requirements: Application forms are available at Nordic Skiing Association of Anchorage, 203 W 15th Ave., No. 204, Anchorage, AK 99501. Applicants must have a letter of recommendation, list of personal achievements and honors, a brief statement describing any community service, a maximum 500 word essay on the "benefits you have received from skiing", and a copy of official transcript from all high school or university work. **Deadline for Receipt:** April 1.

29 ■ ALASKA PULP SCHOLARSHIP FOUNDATION
PO Box 651
Wrangell, AK 99929
Tel: (907)874-3395
Web Site: http://www.apc-foundation.com
To provide financial assistance for furthering education.
Title of Award: APC Scholarships **Area, Field, or Subject:** General studies. **Level of Education for which Award is Granted:** Undergraduate **Funds Available:** $10,000.
Eligibility Requirements: Applicant must be a senior student in good standing at Wrangell and Sitka High School who plans to pursue post-secondary education. **Application Requirements:** Applicant must submit completed application form along with the biography tackling about his/her career plans, family, special talents, interests and financial need and must include a recent photo, an original transcript, latest SAT and ACT test scores and two letters of recommendation.

30 ■ ALBERTA 4-H
97 E Lake Ramp NE
Airdrie, AB, Canada T4A 0C3
Tel: (403)948-8510
Fax: (403)948-2069
E-mail: marquerite.stark@gov.ab.ca
Web Site: http://www.4h.ab.ca
To financially support deserving student members of the Organization who seek for continuing education.
Title of Award: Grande Prairie 4-H District Scholarships **Area, Field, or Subject:** General studies. **Level of Education for which Award is Granted:** Undergraduate **Number Awarded:** 2. **Funds Available:** $1,500.
Eligibility Requirements: Applicant must be a Grande Prairie 4-H District member student and a resident of Alberta based on Student Finance Regulations who have minimum year residency in Alberta immediately prior to the application date and enrolled full-time in a post secondary program recognized by Alberta Advanced Education. **Application Requirements:** Applicants must submit complete Provincial 4-H Scholarship application and NADC scholarship application. **Additional Information:** In partnership with Northern Alberta Development Council (NADC). **Deadline for Receipt:** May 5.

31 ■ ALBERTA 4-H
97 E Lake Ramp NE
Airdrie, AB, Canada T4A 0C3
Tel: (403)948-8510
Fax: (403)948-2069
E-mail: marquerite.stark@gov.ab.ca
Web Site: http://www.4h.ab.ca
To financially support deserving student members of the Organization who seek to continuing their education.
Title of Award: Provincial and Regional 4-H Scholarships **Area, Field, or Subject:** General studies. **Level of Education for which Award is Granted:** Undergraduate **Number Awarded:** 100. **Funds Available:** $80,000.
Eligibility Requirements: Applicant must be a past or present member of Alberta 4-H Club and/or a full-time post-secondary student at an officially recognized institution. **Application Requirements:** Applicants must submit a completed type-written scholarship application form and must include original photo along with the official transcript request for the last year's education. **Deadline for Receipt:** May 5.

32 ■ ALBERTA 4-H
97 E Lake Ramp NE
Airdrie, AB, Canada T4A 0C3
Tel: (403)948-8510
Fax: (403)948-2069
E-mail: marquerite.stark@gov.ab.ca
Web Site: http://www.4h.ab.ca
To provide financial assistance for Alberta 4-H members to further education.
Title of Award: Servus Credit Union 4-H Scholarships **Area, Field, or Subject:** General studies. **Level of Education for which Award is Granted:** Undergraduate **Number Awarded:** 2. **Funds Available:** $500.
Eligibility Requirements: Applicants must be Alberta 4-H members who have been involved for a minimum of three years; entering their first year of study at a postsecondary institution in Alberta within one year of graduation from high school; and reside in the following Servus Credit Union trade areas: Andrew, Devon, Drayton Valley, Elk Point, Entwistle, Fort Saskatchewan, Gibbons, Lamont, Leduc, Legal, Morinville, Mundare, Myrnam, Plamondon, Sangudo, St. Paul, Stony Plain and Wabamun. **Application Requirements:** Applicants must submit application form and the complete materials needed to avail the scholarship. **Deadline for Receipt:** May 5.

33 ■ ALBERTA LEARNING INFORMATION SERVICE - ALBERTA SCHOLARSHIP PROGRAM
Box 28000 Sta. Main
Edmonton, AB, Canada T5J 4R4
Tel: (780)427-8640
Fax: (780)427-1288
E-mail: scholarship@gov.ab.ca

Web Site: http://www.alis.alberta.ca
To commemorate the Province of Alberta's Centennial.
Title of Award: Alberta Centennial Premier's Scholarships - Alberta **Area, Field, or Subject:** General studies. **Level of Education for which Award is Granted:** Undergraduate **Funds Available:** No specific amount.
Eligibility Requirements: Applicants must: be Canadian citizens or permanent residents of Canada and Alberta; entering any level of postsecondary study at any university, college, technical institute or apprenticeship program in Canada. **Application Requirements:** Nominations are submitted by high school counselors. **Deadline for Receipt:** June 15. **Additional Information:** Alberta Scholarship Program at the above address.

34 ■ ALBERTA LEARNING INFORMATION SERVICE - ALBERTA SCHOLARSHIP PROGRAM
Box 28000 Sta. Main
Edmonton, AB, Canada T5J 4R4
Tel: (780)427-8640
Fax: (780)427-1288
E-mail: scholarship@gov.ab.ca
Web Site: http://www.alis.alberta.ca
To recognize the academic excellence of a student from Crowsnest Pass high School in the area of the sciences.
Title of Award: Janet and Horace Allen Scholarship **Area, Field, or Subject:** Science. **Level of Education for which Award is Granted:** Undergraduate **Funds Available:** $1,500.
Eligibility Requirements: Applicants must be Alberta residents and plan to enroll full-time in a post-secondary program of at least one semester in length. **Application Requirements:** Applicants may obtain an application form from Alberta Scholarship Programs and Crowsnest Pass High School. **Deadline for Receipt:** June 1.

35 ■ ALBERTA LEARNING INFORMATION SERVICE - ALBERTA SCHOLARSHIP PROGRAM
Box 28000 Sta. Main
Edmonton, AB, Canada T5J 4R4
Tel: (780)427-8640
Fax: (780)427-1288
E-mail: scholarship@gov.ab.ca
Web Site: http://www.alis.alberta.ca
To reward the accomplishments of an aboriginal student from Blue Quills First Nations College.
Title of Award: Theodore R. Campbell Scholarship **Area, Field, or Subject:** General studies. **Level of Education for which Award is Granted:** Undergraduate **Funds Available:** $1,500.
Eligibility Requirements: Applicants must be Alberta residents and have completed the first year towards an Education degree at Blue Quills First Nations College. **Application Requirements:** Application forms are available from Alberta Scholarship Programs and from the Research and Planning Office at Blue Quills First Nations College. **Deadline for Receipt:** June 1. **Additional Information:** Alberta Scholarship Program at the above address.

36 ■ ALBERTA LEARNING INFORMATION SERVICE - ALBERTA SCHOLARSHIP PROGRAM
Box 28000 Sta. Main
Edmonton, AB, Canada T5J 4R4
Tel: (780)427-8640
Fax: (780)427-1288
E-mail: scholarship@gov.ab.ca
Web Site: http://www.alis.alberta.ca
To help Alberta's needy students access this bursary and reduce their debt load.
Title of Award: Canada Millennium Bursary **Area, Field, or Subject:** General studies. **Level of Education for which Award is Granted:** Undergraduate **Funds Available:** $2,250-$3,000.
Eligibility Requirements: Students must be enrolled full-time at a Canadian post-secondary institution attending their second or subsequent year of undergraduate study or any year of a professional program. **Application Requirements:** Students do not need to apply for this scholarship separately. Students are automatically considered for Canada Millennium Bursaries when they apply for a student loan. **Additional Information:** Alberta Scholarship Program at the above address.

37 ■ ALBERTA LEARNING INFORMATION SERVICE - ALBERTA SCHOLARSHIP PROGRAM
Box 28000 Sta. Main
Edmonton, AB, Canada T5J 4R4
Tel: (780)427-8640
Fax: (780)427-1288
E-mail: scholarship@gov.ab.ca
Web Site: http://www.alis.alberta.ca
To recognize the accomplishments of students who attended Carmangay School and to commemorate the closing of the school.
Title of Award: Carmangay Home and School Association Scholarships **Area, Field, or Subject:** General studies. **Level of Education for which Award is Granted:** Undergraduate **Funds Available:** $2,500.
Eligibility Requirements: Applicants must: be Canadian citizens or landed immigrants and residents of Alberta according to Alberta Heritage Scholarship Fund regulations; have attended Carmangay School for at least one complete school year; have achieved a high academic standing in their Grade 12 year at an Alberta high school; and plan on entering full-time studies at a recognized post-secondary institution. **Application Requirements:** Application forms are available from regional school counselors and from the office of Alberta Scholarship Programs. Applicants must mail their application form to Alberta Scholarship Programs. **Deadline for Receipt:** August 1. **Additional Information:** Alberta Scholarship Programs at the above address.

38 ■ ALBERTA LEARNING INFORMATION SERVICE - ALBERTA SCHOLARSHIP PROGRAM
Box 28000 Sta. Main
Edmonton, AB, Canada T5J 4R4
Tel: (780)427-8640
Fax: (780)427-1288
E-mail: scholarship@gov.ab.ca
Web Site: http://www.alis.alberta.ca
To recognize those post-secondary students who have demonstrated outstanding dedication and leadership to fellow students and to their community.
Title of Award: Laurence Decore Awards for Student Leadership **Area, Field, or Subject:** General studies. **Level of Education for which Award is Granted:** Undergraduate **Funds Available:** $500.
Eligibility Requirements: Applicants must be Alberta residents who are currently enrolled in a minimum of three courses at a designated Alberta post-secondary institution. **Application Requirements:** Applicants do not need to apply. Schools may submit a nomination for this scholarship. **Deadline for Receipt:** March 1. **Additional Information:** Alberta Scholarship Programs at the above address.

39 ■ ALBERTA LEARNING INFORMATION SERVICE - ALBERTA SCHOLARSHIP PROGRAM
Box 28000 Sta. Main
Edmonton, AB, Canada T5J 4R4
Tel: (780)427-8640
Fax: (780)427-1288
E-mail: scholarship@gov.ab.ca
Web Site: http://www.alis.alberta.ca
To recognize the top male and female Alberta students who have excelled in track and field.
Title of Award: Earl and Countess of Wessex - World Championships in Athletics Scholarships **Area, Field, or Subject:** Athletics. **Level of Education for which Award is Granted:** Undergraduate **Funds Available:** $3,000.
Eligibility Requirements: Applicants must be Canadian citizens or landed immigrants and residents of Alberta, according to Alberta Scholarship Programs regulations. Applicants must have completed Grade 12 in Alberta in the same year they apply for the scholarship. Student must be planning on continuing their studies at a post-secondary institution in Alberta and participating on that institution's track and field team. **Application Requirements:** Applicants may obtain an application form from all Alberta high schools and from Alberta Scholarship Programs. **Deadline for Receipt:** October 1. **Additional Information:** Alberta Scholarship Program at the above address.

40 ■ ALBERTA LEARNING INFORMATION SERVICE - ALBERTA SCHOLARSHIP PROGRAM
Box 28000 Sta. Main
Edmonton, AB, Canada T5J 4R4

Tel: (780)427-8640
Fax: (780)427-1288
E-mail: scholarship@gov.ab.ca
Web Site: http://www.alis.alberta.ca
To recognize the accomplishments of intern, co-op, practicum, apprentice-ship, and research students.
Title of Award: International Education Awards - Ukraine **Area, Field, or Subject:** General studies. **Level of Education for which Award is Granted:** Undergraduate **Number Awarded:** 5. **Funds Available:** $5,000.
Eligibility Requirements: Applicant must be a post-secondary student or an apprenticeship student taking a practicum, internship, co-op or ap-prenticeship program, or may be a student conducting research. **Application Requirements:** Application forms will also be available from the Alberta Scholarship Programs' office, Alberta Colleges and Universities, the Canadian Embassy in Kyiv, and the Ministry of Education of Ukraine. In total, five copies of the completed application form must be submitted (an original plus four photocopies). This requirement does not apply to academic transcripts and reference letters. **Deadline for Receipt:** Febru-ary 1. **Additional Information:** Alberta Scholarship Program at the above address.

41 ■ ALBERTA LEARNING INFORMATION SERVICE - ALBERTA SCHOLARSHIP PROGRAM
Box 28000 Sta. Main
Edmonton, AB, Canada T5J 4R4
Tel: (780)427-8640
Fax: (780)427-1288
E-mail: scholarship@gov.ab.ca
Web Site: http://www.alis.alberta.ca
To assist student from Olds High School to pursue a post-secondary education.
Title of Award: Helen and George Kilik Scholarship **Area, Field, or Subject:** General studies. **Level of Education for which Award is Granted:** Undergraduate **Funds Available:** $1,000.
Eligibility Requirements: Candidate must be an Alberta resident, have completed all high school studies at Olds High school and intend to pursue post-secondary studies. The selected student must demonstrate financial need, and involvement in extracurricular activities. **Application Requirements:** Applicants may obtain an application from Olds High School or Alberta Scholarship Programs. **Deadline for Receipt:** June 1. **Additional Information:** Alberta Scholarship Programs at the above address.

42 ■ ALBERTA LEARNING INFORMATION SERVICE - ALBERTA SCHOLARSHIP PROGRAM
Box 28000 Sta. Main
Edmonton, AB, Canada T5J 4R4
Tel: (780)427-8640
Fax: (780)427-1288
E-mail: scholarship@gov.ab.ca
Web Site: http://www.alis.alberta.ca
To recognize and reward the academic excellence of a student entering a Faculty of Education.
Title of Award: Anna and John Kolesay Memorial Scholarship **Area, Field, or Subject:** General studies. **Level of Education for which Award is Granted:** Undergraduate **Funds Available:** $1,200.
Eligibility Requirements: Applicant must be: a Canadian citizen or permanent resident and an Alberta resident; from a family where neither parent obtained a university degree; enrolling full-time in the first year of a program in a Faculty of Education. **Application Requirements:** Applica-tion form can be obtained from Alberta Scholarship Programs and at Alberta high schools. **Deadline for Receipt:** July 1. **Additional Informa-tion:** Alberta Scholarship Program at the above address.

43 ■ ALBERTA LEARNING INFORMATION SERVICE - ALBERTA SCHOLARSHIP PROGRAM
Box 28000 Sta. Main
Edmonton, AB, Canada T5J 4R4
Tel: (780)427-8640
Fax: (780)427-1288
E-mail: scholarship@gov.ab.ca
Web Site: http://www.alis.alberta.ca

To recognize exceptional academic achievement and encourage outstanding students to continue their studies at the post-secondary level.
Title of Award: Louise McKinney Post-secondary Scholarship **Area, Field, or Subject:** General studies. **Level of Education for which Award is Granted:** Undergraduate **Funds Available:** $2,500.
Eligibility Requirements: Applicants must be residents of Alberta and in their second or subsequent year of full-time study. Alberta students study-ing outside the province because their program of study is not offered in Alberta will be considered for a scholarship if their class standing is in the top two percent of their program. **Application Requirements:** Students studying in-province are nominated by the Student Awards Office at participating Alberta post-secondary institutions. Other students may contact the Awards Office to determine their eligibility. **Additional Information:** Alberta Scholarship Programs at the above address.

44 ■ ALBERTA LEARNING INFORMATION SERVICE - ALBERTA SCHOLARSHIP PROGRAM
Box 28000 Sta. Main
Edmonton, AB, Canada T5J 4R4
Tel: (780)427-8640
Fax: (780)427-1288
E-mail: scholarship@gov.ab.ca
Web Site: http://www.alis.alberta.ca
To encourage students to pursue a post-secondary education and to recognize and reward exceptional academic at the senior high school level.
Title of Award: Dr. Ernest and Minnie Mehl Scholarship **Area, Field, or Subject:** General studies. **Level of Education for which Award is Granted:** Undergraduate **Funds Available:** $3,500.
Eligibility Requirements: Applicants must be Canadian citizens or landed immigrants who have completed their Grade 12 in Alberta at a school that follows the Alberta Education Curriculum. Applicants must be continuing their studies at a degree granting post-secondary institution in Canada. University transfer programs are acceptable. **Application Requirements:** Applicants may obtain an application form from high school counselors and from Alberta Scholarship Programs. **Deadline for Receipt:** June 1. **Additional Information:** Alberta Scholarship Programs at the above address.

45 ■ ALBERTA LEARNING INFORMATION SERVICE - ALBERTA SCHOLARSHIP PROGRAM
Box 28000 Sta. Main
Edmonton, AB, Canada T5J 4R4
Tel: (780)427-8640
Fax: (780)427-1288
E-mail: scholarship@gov.ab.ca
Web Site: http://www.alis.alberta.ca
To provide financial assistance to rural Albertans attending a designated post-secondary institution in Canada.
Title of Award: Millennium Alberta Rural Incentive Bursary Award **Area, Field, or Subject:** General studies. **Level of Education for which Award is Granted:** Undergraduate **Funds Available:** $1,000.
Eligibility Requirements: Applicants must: have attended a rural high school in Alberta; have lived in rural Alberta for a minimum of 12 months immediately prior to starting post-secondary studies; be attending a designated post-secondary institution in Canada; be enrolled in the first or second year of an undergraduate program of at least two years in length; be eligible for a minimum of $1,000 in student loan funding. **Application Requirements:** Students must complete both an Application for Financial Assistance and the Schedule 3 of the application for financial assistance. **Additional Information:** Alberta Scholarship Programs at the above ad-dress.

46 ■ ALBERTA LEARNING INFORMATION SERVICE - ALBERTA SCHOLARSHIP PROGRAM
Box 28000 Sta. Main
Edmonton, AB, Canada T5J 4R4
Tel: (780)427-8640
Fax: (780)427-1288
E-mail: scholarship@gov.ab.ca
Web Site: http://www.alis.alberta.ca
To reward academic excellence and provide opportunities for Albertans to pursue studies at Harvard University.

Title of Award: Charles S. Noble Scholarships for Study at Harvard **Area, Field, or Subject:** General studies. **Level of Education for which Award is Granted:** Undergraduate **Funds Available:** May 15.
Eligibility Requirements: Applicants must be Alberta residents who plan to apply or are enrolled full-time in any year of study in an undergraduate program at Harvard. **Application Requirements:** Applicants may obtain an application form from the Office of Admissions at Harvard and from the Alberta Heritage Scholarship Fund. **Deadline for Receipt:** May 15. **Additional Information:** Alberta Scholarship Programs at the above address.

47 ■ ALBERTA LEARNING INFORMATION SERVICE - ALBERTA SCHOLARSHIP PROGRAM
Box 28000 Sta. Main
Edmonton, AB, Canada T5J 4R4
Tel: (780)427-8640
Fax: (780)427-1288
E-mail: scholarship@gov.ab.ca
Web Site: http://www.alis.alberta.ca
To increase the number of trained professionals in Northern Alberta and to encourage students from Northern Alberta to obtain a post-secondary education.
Title of Award: Northern Alberta Development Council Bursary Award **Area, Field, or Subject:** General studies. **Level of Education for which Award is Granted:** Undergraduate **Funds Available:** $1,750.
Eligibility Requirements: Applicants must be residents of Alberta, and planning to enroll in a full-time post-secondary program. Applicants must also be within two years of completion of their post-secondary program. **Application Requirements:** Applicants may obtain an application form from www.benorth.ca. Application forms for these bursaries are also available from Alberta Scholarship Programs, Student Awards Offices and from the Northern Alberta Development Council. **Deadline for Receipt:** May 15. **Additional Information:** Northern Alberta Development Council, 2nd Fl., Provincial Bldg. 9621 - 96 Ave. Postal Bag 900-14 Peace River, AB T8S 1T4; 780-624-6545; nadc.council@gov.ab.ca.

48 ■ ALBERTA LEARNING INFORMATION SERVICE - ALBERTA SCHOLARSHIP PROGRAM
Box 28000 Sta. Main
Edmonton, AB, Canada T5J 4R4
Tel: (780)427-8640
Fax: (780)427-1288
E-mail: scholarship@gov.ab.ca
Web Site: http://www.alis.alberta.ca
To assist students in pursuing a post-secondary education.
Title of Award: Northern Alberta Development Council Bursary Partnership Program **Area, Field, or Subject:** General studies. **Level of Education for which Award is Granted:** Undergraduate **Funds Available:** $1,750. **Duration:** One year.
Eligibility Requirements: Applicants must be residents of Alberta and plan to enroll full-time in a post-secondary program. In addition, applicants must demonstrate financial need and be willing to live and work in northern Alberta after completion of the program. **Application Requirements:** Applicants may obtain an application form from www.benorth.ca. Application form for these bursaries are also available from Alberta Scholarship Programs, Student Awards Offices and from the Northern Alberta Development Council. **Deadline for Receipt:** May 15. **Additional Information:** Northern Alberta Development Council, 2nd Fl., Provincial Bldg. 9621 - 96 Ave. Postal Bag 900-14 Peace River, AB T8S 1T4; 780-624-6545; nadc.council@gov.ab.ca.

49 ■ ALBERTA LEARNING INFORMATION SERVICE - ALBERTA SCHOLARSHIP PROGRAM
Box 28000 Sta. Main
Edmonton, AB, Canada T5J 4R4
Tel: (780)427-8640
Fax: (780)427-1288
E-mail: scholarship@gov.ab.ca
Web Site: http://www.alis.alberta.ca
To provide incentive for Northern Alberta students with high financial need to enter post-secondary programs.
Title of Award: Northern Student Supplement **Area, Field, or Subject:** General studies. **Level of Education for which Award is Granted:** Undergraduate **Funds Available:** $500-$1,500.

Eligibility Requirements: Student must be: first time, first or second year post-secondary students; attending an educational institution participating in the Alberta Opportunities Bursary (AOB) program. Applicants are considered a northern Alberta resident if they have lived in the Northern Alberta Development Council (NADC) area for two consecutive years immediately prior to beginning their present post-secondary program. **Application Requirements:** Students will automatically be assessed for the supplement if they complete and submit the appropriate schedule with their online application for student financial assistance. Students applying on a paper application must complete and attach a separate application for the Northern Student Supplement. **Additional Information:** Northern Alberta Development Council, 2nd Fl., Provincial Bldg. 9621 - 96 Ave. Postal Bag 900-14 Peace River, AB T8S 1T4; 780-624-6545; nadc.council@gov.ab.ca.

50 ■ ALBERTA LEARNING INFORMATION SERVICE - ALBERTA SCHOLARSHIP PROGRAM
Box 28000 Sta. Main
Edmonton, AB, Canada T5J 4R4
Tel: (780)427-8640
Fax: (780)427-1288
E-mail: scholarship@gov.ab.ca
Web Site: http://www.alis.alberta.ca
To assist students whose studies will ultimately contribute to the advancement of women, or who are studying in fields where members of their gender are traditionally few in number.
Title of Award: Persons Case Scholarships **Area, Field, or Subject:** General studies. **Level of Education for which Award is Granted:** Undergraduate **Funds Available:** $5,000.
Eligibility Requirements: Applicants must be residents of Alberta and enrolled full-time at a post-secondary institution in Alberta. In addition, applicants must be enrolled in a program that is either non-traditional for their sex, or a program that will contribute to the advancement of women. Students studying out-of-province may be considered for this award if their program of study is not available in Alberta. **Application Requirements:** Applicant must submit the following requirements with their complete application form: official transcript of all-post secondary studies; short essay of two or three pages outlining why the issues they are studying are important to them and how their studies, activities and community contribute to the advancement of women; curriculum vitae/resume outlining academic achievement, volunteer experience, awards won, etc. In total, submit six copies of the completed application form, and six copies of all attachments (the original and five photocopies). **Additional Information:** Established in 1979. **Deadline for Receipt:** September 30. **Additional Information:** Alberta Scholarship Program at the above address.

51 ■ ALBERTA LEARNING INFORMATION SERVICE - ALBERTA SCHOLARSHIP PROGRAM
Box 28000 Sta. Main
Edmonton, AB, Canada T5J 4R4
Tel: (780)427-8640
Fax: (780)427-1288
E-mail: scholarship@gov.ab.ca
Web Site: http://www.alis.alberta.ca
To reward the athletic and academic excellence of baseball players and to provide an incentive and means for these players to continue with their post-secondary education.
Title of Award: Prairie Baseball Academy Scholarships **Area, Field, or Subject:** General studies. **Level of Education for which Award is Granted:** Undergraduate **Funds Available:** $500-$2,500.
Eligibility Requirements: Applicants must be Alberta residents and enrolled full-time at a post-secondary institution in Alberta. Applicants must be participants in the Prairie Baseball Academy and must have achieved a minimum GPA of 2.0 on a 4.0 scale in the previous semester. **Application Requirements:** Applicant may obtain an application form from Alberta Scholarship Programs, and from the Prairie Baseball Academy. **Deadline for Receipt:** October 15. **Additional Information:** Alberta Scholarship Programs at the above address.

52 ■ ALBERTA LEARNING INFORMATION SERVICE - ALBERTA SCHOLARSHIP PROGRAM
Box 28000 Sta. Main
Edmonton, AB, Canada T5J 4R4

Tel: (780)427-8640
Fax: (780)427-1288
E-mail: scholarship@gov.ab.ca
Web Site: http://www.alis.alberta.ca
To recognize the accomplishments of Alberta high school students taking the Registered Apprenticeship Program (RAP) and to encourage recipients to continue their apprenticeship training after completing high school.
Title of Award: Registered Apprenticeship Program (RAP) Scholarships **Area, Field, or Subject:** General studies. **Level of Education for which Award is Granted:** Undergraduate **Funds Available:** $1,000.
Eligibility Requirements: Applicant must: be a Canadian citizen or landed immigrant, and a resident of Alberta; have completed the requirements for high school graduation in Alberta; be registered as an Alberta apprentice in a trade while still attending high school; have completed a minimum of 250 hours of on-the-job training and work experience in their chosen trade; plan to continue in an approved regular apprenticeship program after completing high school; have not been awarded a RAP Scholarship previously. **Application Requirements:** Application form can be obtained from Alberta Scholarship Program. Applications must be supported by: one or two paragraph (written or typed) autobiography confirming plans to continue their apprenticeship program and detailing why a career in that trade is a good fit for them; completed employer recommendation form; recommendation letter from a high school teacher or counselor. **Deadline for Receipt:** July 15. **Additional Information:** Alberta Scholarship Programs at the above address.

53 ■ ALBERTA LEARNING INFORMATION SERVICE - ALBERTA SCHOLARSHIP PROGRAM
Box 28000 Sta. Main
Edmonton, AB, Canada T5J 4R4
Tel: (780)427-8640
Fax: (780)427-1288
E-mail: scholarship@gov.ab.ca
Web Site: http://www.alis.alberta.ca
To recognize excellence in an individual involved in leadership development and safety in the mountain community.
Title of Award: Robin Rousseau Memorial Mountain Achievement Scholarship **Area, Field, or Subject:** General studies. **Level of Education for which Award is Granted:** Undergraduate **Funds Available:** No specific amount.
Eligibility Requirements: Applicants must be Alberta residents and active in the mountain community and plan to study in any recognized Mountain Leadership and Safety program. **Application Requirements:** Applicants may obtain an application form from Alberta Scholarship Programs. **Deadline for Receipt:** January 30. **Additional Information:** Alberta Scholarship Programs at the above address.

54 ■ ALBERTA LEARNING INFORMATION SERVICE - ALBERTA SCHOLARSHIP PROGRAM
Box 28000 Sta. Main
Edmonton, AB, Canada T5J 4R4
Tel: (780)427-8640
Fax: (780)427-1288
E-mail: scholarship@gov.ab.ca
Web Site: http://www.alis.alberta.ca
To reward the best Alexander Rutherford Scholarship recipients.
Title of Award: Rutherford Scholars **Area, Field, or Subject:** General studies. **Level of Education for which Award is Granted:** Undergraduate **Funds Available:** $2,500.
Eligibility Requirements: Applicants must be in the top ten students as determined on the first writing of Diploma Examination. **Application Requirements:** No application is required. Recipients are selected from all Alexander Rutherford Scholarship applications received before the deadline. **Deadline for Receipt:** August 1. **Additional Information:** Alberta Scholarship Programs at the above address.

55 ■ ALBERTA LEARNING INFORMATION SERVICE - ALBERTA SCHOLARSHIP PROGRAM
Box 28000 Sta. Main
Edmonton, AB, Canada T5J 4R4
Tel: (780)427-8640
Fax: (780)427-1288

E-mail: scholarship@gov.ab.ca
Web Site: http://www.alis.alberta.ca
To recognize and reward academic achievement at the senior high school level and to encourage students to pursue post-secondary studies.
Title of Award: Alexander Rutherford Scholarships for High School Achievement **Area, Field, or Subject:** General studies. **Level of Education for which Award is Granted:** Undergraduate **Funds Available:** $2,500.
Eligibility Requirements: Applicants must be Canadian citizens or permanent residents and Alberta residents and plan to enroll full-time in a post-secondary program or apprenticeship program. Students must have a minimum combined average based on five designated courses in at least one grade: Grade 10, 11 or 12. The minimum average, value of the award, and courses that can be used depend on the student's graduation year. **Application Requirements:** There is no limit to apply for the scholarship except that the applicant must be planning to pursue post-secondary studies. Students who apply after the application deadline may not be recognized at their high school awards ceremony. High school grades obtained through upgrading at a post-secondary institution are not accepted. Eligible students who complete high school outside of Alberta must submit an official transcript of their high school marks from that province. **Deadline for Receipt:** May 1. **Additional Information:** Alberta Scholarship programs at the above address.

56 ■ ALBERTA PRESS COUNCIL
PO Box 2576
Medicine Hat, AB, Canada T1A 8G8
Tel: (403)580-4104; 888-580-4104
Fax: (403)580-4010
E-mail: abpress@telus.net
Web Site: http://www.albertapresscouncil.ca
To assist high school students in pursuing post-secondary studies.
Title of Award: Alberta Press Council Scholarships **Area, Field, or Subject:** General studies. **Level of Education for which Award is Granted:** Undergraduate **Funds Available:** $1,500 for the winning essay.
Eligibility Requirements: Applicants must be Canadian citizens or permanent residents; must have been residents of Alberta for at least one year prior to time of application; must be students currently attending Grade 12 in a recognized school in Alberta or students who are enrolled full-time in a postsecondary degree or diploma program. Family members of newspaper staff are eligible to apply; relatives of current Press Council Members are not. Scholarship is open to any field of study. Applicants must agree to allow the publishing of their essay on the Alberta Press Council's website and on Newswire Services. **Application Requirements:** Essay must be typed, double spaced, 12 point font, 1,000-1,100 words. It is essential that essays be carefully checked/proofread before submission, and neat and tidy word processed on standard size paper (8 1/2 x 11). Six copies of the essay and the application form, with only one cover page, are to be sent to the Selection Committee, Alberta Press Council. Please submit by regular mail or express post, faxed applications will not be accepted. **Deadline for Receipt:** February 28. **Additional Information:** Alberta Press council at the above address.

57 ■ ALBUQUERQUE COMMUNITY FOUNDATION
PO Box 36960
Albuquerque, NM 87176-6960
Tel: (505)883-6240
Fax: (505)883-3629
E-mail: foundation@albuquerquefoundation.org
Web Site: http://www.swcp.com
To provide financial support to those deserving students.
Title of Award: Robby Baker Memorial Scholarships **Area, Field, or Subject:** General Studies. **Level of Education for which Award is Granted:** Undergraduate **Funds Available:** No specific amount.
Eligibility Requirements: Applicants must be coping with dyslexia or other reading disability; must have earned a minimum of 2.5 GPA and must be enrolled as full time students in an accredited college or university. **Application Requirements:** Applicants must submit a completed application form and two references from teachers or counselors. **Additional Information:** Albuquerque Community Foundation at the above address

---

58 ■ ALBUQUERQUE COMMUNITY FOUNDATION

PO Box 36960
Albuquerque, NM 87176-6960
Tel: (505)883-6240
Fax: (505)883-3629
E-mail: foundation@albuquerquefoundation.org
Web Site: http://www.swcp.com
To provide financial assistance to those students who are in need.
Title of Award: Notah Begay III Scholarship Program **Area, Field, or Subject:** General Studies. **Level of Education for which Award is Granted:** Undergraduate **Funds Available:** $2,000.
Eligibility Requirements: Applicants must be Native American scholar athletes; must have a minimum GPA 3.0; must attend a community college, 4 year college or university full time. **Application Requirements:** Applicants must submit the following: copy of FAFSA, Student Aid Report or statement of financial aid; proof of tribal enrollment or Certificate of Indian Blood (minimum 25%); one reference from a current academic teacher or counselor; one reference from an athletic coach; include in your personal statement how you plan to give back to your community after college. **Additional Information:** Albuquerque Community Foundation at the above address

59 ■ ALBUQUERQUE COMMUNITY FOUNDATION

PO Box 36960
Albuquerque, NM 87176-6960
Tel: (505)883-6240
Fax: (505)883-3629
E-mail: foundation@albuquerquefoundation.org
Web Site: http://www.swcp.com
To support the education of graduating senior varsity soccer players.
Title of Award: Bryan Cline Memorial Soccer Scholarship Program **Area, Field, or Subject:** General Studies. **Level of Education for which Award is Granted:** Undergraduate **Funds Available:** No specific amount.
Eligibility Requirements: Applicants must attend a college or university full time. **Application Requirements:** Applicants must submit a completed application form including the name of your varsity soccer team coach and two letters of reference- one from a teacher or counselor and one from a soccer coach. **Additional Information:** This scholarship is for Eldorado High School students only. **Additional Information:** Albuquerque Community Foundation at the above address

60 ■ ALBUQUERQUE COMMUNITY FOUNDATION

PO Box 36960
Albuquerque, NM 87176-6960
Tel: (505)883-6240
Fax: (505)883-3629
E-mail: foundation@albuquerquefoundation.org
Web Site: http://www.swcp.com
To assist individuals who demonstrate a commitment towards reaching a career goal.
Title of Award: Excel Staffing Companies Scholarships for Excellence in Continuing Education **Area, Field, or Subject:** General Studies. **Level of Education for which Award is Granted:** Undergraduate **Funds Available:** $1,000.
Eligibility Requirements: Applicants must be individuals who are employed full time while attending school part time; must be residents of Albuquerque; must have a minimum of 3.0 GPA; must be working with a minimum of 30 hours per week. **Application Requirements:** Applicants must check the available website for the required materials. **Additional Information:** Albuquerque Community Foundation at the above address

61 ■ ALBUQUERQUE COMMUNITY FOUNDATION

PO Box 36960
Albuquerque, NM 87176-6960
Tel: (505)883-6240
Fax: (505)883-3629
E-mail: foundation@albuquerquefoundation.org
Web Site: http://www.swcp.com
To provide scholarship awards to New Mexico high school graduates residing in a manufactured home.
Title of Award: New Mexico Manufactured Housing Association Scholarship Program **Area, Field, or Subject:** General Studies. **Level of Education for which Award is Granted:** Undergraduate **Funds Available:** $1,000.
Eligibility Requirements: Applicants must live in a mobile/manufactured home; must have earned a minimum GPA 3.0; must attend a college or university full time. **Application Requirements:** Applicants must submit the following: written statement of financial need; proof of residency in a mobile/manufactured home: a copy of title or rental agreement or retail installment contract or county tax assessment; one reference from a teacher or counselor (1 page, 1 side only). **Additional Information:** Albuquerque Community Foundation at the above address

62 ■ ALBUQUERQUE COMMUNITY FOUNDATION

PO Box 36960
Albuquerque, NM 87176-6960
Tel: (505)883-6240
Fax: (505)883-3629
E-mail: foundation@albuquerquefoundation.org
Web Site: http://www.swcp.com
To provide financial assistance to address the gap in financial aid packages for both students beginning their college careers and those continuing their undergraduate work.
Title of Award: Sussman-Miller Educational Assistance Award Program **Area, Field, or Subject:** General Studies. **Level of Education for which Award is Granted:** Undergraduate **Funds Available:** No specific amount.
Eligibility Requirements: Applicants must attend a college or university full-time; must be graduating high school seniors or currently enrolled in college/university; must be federal financial aid recipients. **Application Requirements:** Applicants must check the available website for the required materials. **Deadline for Receipt:** April 24; July 1. **Additional Information:** Albuquerque Community Foundation at the above address

63 ■ HORATIO ALGER ASSOCIATION

99 Canal Center Plaza, Ste. 320
Alexandria, VA 22314
Tel: (703)684-9444
Fax: (703)548-3822
Web Site: http://www.horatioalger.com
To provide financial assistance to students in the state of Nebraska and western Iowa.
Title of Award: Horatio Alger Ak-Sar-Ben Scholarships **Area, Field, or Subject:** General studies. **Level of Education for which Award is Granted:** Undergraduate **Number Awarded:** 50. **Funds Available:** $5,000.
Eligibility Requirements: Applicants must be enrolled full time as a high school senior, progressing normally toward graduation, and planning to enter college no later than the fall following graduation; must have a strong commitment to pursue a bachelor's degree at an accredited institution (students may start their studies at a two-year institution and then transfer to a four-year institution); must have critical financial need ($50,000 or less adjusted gross income per family is preferred; if higher, an explanation must be provided); must be involved in co-curricular and community activities; must have a minimum grade point average of 2.0; must be a resident of Nebraska or western Iowa; be a citizen or permanent resident of the United States. **Application Requirements:** Applicants must have one letter of support and must be logged in to the application process at the HAA website. Faxes/emails will not be accepted. Students must download the certification page from the HAA web site, complete it and obtain the proper signatures prior to mailing.

64 ■ HORATIO ALGER ASSOCIATION

99 Canal Center Plaza, Ste. 320
Alexandria, VA 22314
Tel: (703)684-9444
Fax: (703)548-3822
Web Site: http://www.horatioalger.com
To provide financial assistance to students in the state of Alabama who exhibited integrity and perseverance in overcoming personal adversity and aspire to pursue higher education.
Title of Award: Horatio Alger Alabama Scholarships **Area, Field, or Subject:** General studies. **Level of Education for which Award is Granted:** Undergraduate **Number Awarded:** 12. **Funds Available:** $5,000.
Eligibility Requirements: Applicants must be enrolled full time as a high school senior, progressing normally toward graduation, and planning to

enter college no later than the fall following graduation; must have a strong commitment to pursue a bachelor's degree at an accredited institution (students may start their studies at a two-year institution and then transfer to a four-year institution); must have critical financial need ($50,000 or less adjusted gross income per family is preferred; if higher, an explanation must be provided); must be involved in co-curricular and community activities; must have a minimum grade point average of 2.0; be a resident of Alabama; and be a citizen or permanent resident of the United States. **Application Requirements:** Applicants must have one letter of support and must be logged in to the application process at the HAA website. Faxes/emails will not be accepted. Students must download the certification page from the HAA web site, complete it and obtain the proper signatures prior to mailing.

65 ■ HORATIO ALGER ASSOCIATION

99 Canal Center Plaza, Ste. 320
Alexandria, VA 22314
Tel: (703)684-9444
Fax: (703)548-3822
Web Site: http://www.horatioalger.com
To provide financial assistance to students in the state of California who have exhibited integrity and perseverance in overcoming personal adversity and aspire to pursue higher education.
Title of Award: Horatio Alger California and California Orange County Scholarships **Area, Field, or Subject:** General studies. **Level of Education for which Award is Granted:** Undergraduate **Number Awarded:** 50-Orange county Residents; 100-California Residents outside Orange County. **Funds Available:** $5,000 for Orange County residents; $2,500 for California residents outside Orange County.
Eligibility Requirements: Applicants must be enrolled full time as a high school senior, progressing normally toward graduation, and planning to enter college no later than the fall following graduation; must have a strong commitment to pursue a bachelor's degree at an accredited institution (students may start their studies at a two-year institution and then transfer to a four-year institution); must have critical financial need ($50,000 or less adjusted gross income per family is preferred; if higher, an explanation must be provided); must be involved in co-curricular and community activities; must have a minimum grade point average of 2.0; be a resident of California; and be a citizen or permanent resident of the United States. **Application Requirements:** Applicants must have one letter of support and must be logged in to the application process at the HAA website. Faxes/emails will not be accepted. Students must download the certification page from the HAA web site, complete it and obtain the proper signatures prior to mailing.

66 ■ HORATIO ALGER ASSOCIATION

99 Canal Center Plaza, Ste. 320
Alexandria, VA 22314
Tel: (703)684-9444
Fax: (703)548-3822
Web Site: http://www.horatioalger.com
To provide financial assistance to students in the state of Delaware.
Title of Award: Horatio Alger Delaware Scholarships **Area, Field, or Subject:** General studies. **Level of Education for which Award is Granted:** Undergraduate **Number Awarded:** 25. **Funds Available:** $5,000.
Eligibility Requirements: Applicants must be enrolled full time as a high school senior, progressing normally toward graduation, and planning to enter college no later than the fall following graduation; must have a strong commitment to pursue a bachelor's degree at an accredited institution (students may start their studies at a two-year institution and then transfer to a four-year institution); must have critical financial need ($50,000 or less adjusted gross income per family is preferred; if higher, an explanation must be provided); must be involved in co-curricular and community activities; must have a minimum grade point average of 2.0; be a resident of Delaware; and be a citizen or permanent resident of the United States. **Application Requirements:** Applicants must have one letter of support and must be logged in to the application process at the HAA website. Faxes/emails will not be accepted. Students must download the certification page from the HAA web site, complete it and obtain the proper signatures prior to mailing.

67 ■ HORATIO ALGER ASSOCIATION

99 Canal Center Plaza, Ste. 320
Alexandria, VA 22314
Tel: (703)684-9444
Fax: (703)548-3822
Web Site: http://www.horatioalger.com
To recognize deserving students from the Washington D.C., Metro area in the following counties: District of Columbia, Maryland, Virginia.
Title of Award: Horatio Alger District of Columbia, Maryland, and Virginia Scholarships **Area, Field, or Subject:** General studies. **Level of Education for which Award is Granted:** Undergraduate **Number Awarded:** 25. **Funds Available:** $2,500.
Eligibility Requirements: Applicants must be enrolled full time as a high school senior, progressing normally toward graduation, and planning to enter college no later than the fall following graduation; must have a strong commitment to pursue a bachelor's degree at an accredited institution (students may start their studies at a two-year institution and then transfer to a four-year institution); must have critical financial need ($50,000 or less adjusted gross income per family is preferred; if higher, an explanation must be provided); must be involved in co-curricular and community activities; must have a minimum grade point average of 2.0; and be a citizen or permanent resident of the United States. **Application Requirements:** Applicants must have one letter of support and must be logged in to the application process at the HAA website. Faxes/emails will not be accepted. Students must download the certification page from the HAA web site, complete it and obtain the proper signatures prior to mailing.

68 ■ HORATIO ALGER ASSOCIATION

99 Canal Center Plaza, Ste. 320
Alexandria, VA 22314
Tel: (703)684-9444
Fax: (703)548-3822
Web Site: http://www.horatioalger.com
To provide financial assistance to students in the counties of Broward, Martin, and St. Lucie in the state of Florida.
Title of Award: Horatio Alger Florida Scholarships **Area, Field, or Subject:** General studies. **Level of Education for which Award is Granted:** Undergraduate **Number Awarded:** 50. **Funds Available:** $5,000.
Eligibility Requirements: Applicants must be enrolled full time as a high school senior, progressing normally toward graduation, and planning to enter college no later than the fall following graduation; must have a strong commitment to pursue a bachelor's degree at an accredited institution (students may start their studies at a two-year institution and then transfer to a four-year institution); must have critical financial need ($50,000 or less adjusted gross income per family is preferred; if higher, an explanation must be provided); must be involved in co-curricular and community activities; must have a minimum grade point average of 2.0; and be a citizen or permanent resident of the United States. **Application Requirements:** Applicants must have one letter of support and must be logged in to the application process at the HAA website. Faxes/emails will not be accepted. Students must download the certification page from the HAA web site, complete it and obtain the proper signatures prior to mailing.

69 ■ HORATIO ALGER ASSOCIATION

99 Canal Center Plaza, Ste. 320
Alexandria, VA 22314
Tel: (703)684-9444
Fax: (703)548-3822
Web Site: http://www.horatioalger.com
To provide financial assistance to high school seniors in the state of Pennsylvania.
Title of Award: Horatio Alger Franklin Scholarships **Area, Field, or Subject:** General studies. **Level of Education for which Award is Granted:** Undergraduate **Number Awarded:** 25. **Funds Available:** $10,000.
Eligibility Requirements: Applicants must reside and attend high school in the state of Pennsylvania; must be enrolled full time as a high school senior, progressing normally toward graduation, and planning to enter college no later than the fall following graduation; must have a strong commitment to pursue a bachelor's degree at an accredited institution

(students may start their studies at a two-year institution and then transfer to a four-year institution); must have critical financial need ($50,000 or less adjusted gross income per family is preferred; if higher, an explanation must be provided); must be involved in co-curricular and community activities; must have a minimum grade point average of 2.0; and be a citizen or permanent resident of the United States. **Application Requirements:** Applicants must have one letter of support and must be logged in to the application process at the HAA website. Faxes/emails will not be accepted. Students must download the certification page from the HAA web site, complete it and obtain the proper signatures prior to mailing.

70 ■ HORATIO ALGER ASSOCIATION

99 Canal Center Plaza, Ste. 320
Alexandria, VA 22314
Tel: (703)684-9444
Fax: (703)548-3822
Web Site: http://www.horatioalger.com
To provide financial assistance to students in the state of Georgia.
Title of Award: Horatio Alger Georgia Scholarships **Area, Field, or Subject:** General studies. **Level of Education for which Award is Granted:** Undergraduate **Number Awarded:** 5. **Funds Available:** $5,000.
Eligibility Requirements: Applicants must be enrolled full time as a high school senior, progressing normally toward graduation, and planning to enter college no later than the fall following graduation; must have a strong commitment to pursue a bachelor's degree at an accredited institution (students may start their studies at a two-year institution and then transfer to a four-year institution); must have critical financial need ($50,000 or less adjusted gross income per family is preferred; if higher, an explanation must be provided); must be involved in co-curricular and community activities; must have a minimum grade point average of 2.0; and be a citizen or permanent resident of the United States. **Application Requirements:** Applicants must have one letter of support and must be logged in to the application process at the HAA website. Faxes/emails will not be accepted. Students must download the certification page from the HAA web site, complete it and obtain the proper signatures prior to mailing.

71 ■ HORATIO ALGER ASSOCIATION

99 Canal Center Plaza, Ste. 320
Alexandria, VA 22314
Tel: (703)684-9444
Fax: (703)548-3822
Web Site: http://www.horatioalger.com
To provide financial assistance to students entering their final two years of study in the College of Business at Idaho State University.
Title of Award: Horatio Alger Idaho University Scholarships **Area, Field, or Subject:** General studies. **Level of Education for which Award is Granted:** Undergraduate **Number Awarded:** 5. **Funds Available:** $5,000.
Eligibility Requirements: Applicants must attend Idaho State University and be enrolled in the College of Business; must have critical financial need based on the Student Aid Report; must be a resident of the State of Idaho; must have a minimum cumulative grade point average of 2.25 or better. **Application Requirements:** Applicants must have one letter of support and must be logged in to the application process at the HAA website. Faxes/emails will not be accepted. Students must download the certification page from the HAA web site, complete it and obtain the proper signatures prior to mailing. **Deadline for Receipt:** May 9.

72 ■ HORATIO ALGER ASSOCIATION

99 Canal Center Plaza, Ste. 320
Alexandria, VA 22314
Tel: (703)684-9444
Fax: (703)548-3822
Web Site: http://www.horatioalger.com
To provide financial assistance to students in the state of Illinois.
Title of Award: Horatio Alger Illinois Scholarships **Area, Field, or Subject:** General studies. **Level of Education for which Award is Granted:** Undergraduate **Number Awarded:** 25. **Funds Available:** $5,000.
Eligibility Requirements: Applicants must be enrolled full time as a high school senior, progressing normally toward graduation, and planning to

enter college no later than the fall following graduation; must have a strong commitment to pursue a bachelor's degree at an accredited institution (students may start their studies at a two-year institution and then transfer to a four-year institution); must have critical financial need ($50,000 or less adjusted gross income per family is preferred; if higher, an explanation must be provided); must be involved in co-curricular and community activities; must have a minimum grade point average of 2.0; be a resident of Illinois; and be a citizen or permanent resident of the United States. **Application Requirements:** Applicants must have one letter of support and must be logged in to the application process at the HAA website. Faxes/emails will not be accepted. Students must download the certification page from the HAA web site, complete it and obtain the proper signatures prior to mailing.

73 ■ HORATIO ALGER ASSOCIATION

99 Canal Center Plaza, Ste. 320
Alexandria, VA 22314
Tel: (703)684-9444
Fax: (703)548-3822
Web Site: http://www.horatioalger.com
To financial assistance to students in the state of Indiana.
Title of Award: Horatio Alger Indiana Scholarships **Area, Field, or Subject:** General studies. **Level of Education for which Award is Granted:** Undergraduate **Number Awarded:** 8. **Funds Available:** $5,000.
Eligibility Requirements: Applicants must be enrolled full time as a high school senior, progressing normally toward graduation, and planning to enter college no later than the fall following graduation; must have a strong commitment to pursue a bachelor's degree at an accredited institution (students may start their studies at a two-year institution and then transfer to a four-year institution); must have critical financial need ($50,000 or less adjusted gross income per family is preferred; if higher, an explanation must be provided); must be involved in co-curricular and community activities; must have a minimum grade point average of 2.0; be a resident of Indiana; and be a citizen or permanent resident of the United States. **Application Requirements:** Applicants must have one letter of support and must be logged in to the application process at the HAA website. Faxes/emails will not be accepted. Students must download the certification page from the HAA web site, complete it and obtain the proper signatures prior to mailing.

74 ■ HORATIO ALGER ASSOCIATION

99 Canal Center Plaza, Ste. 320
Alexandria, VA 22314
Tel: (703)684-9444
Fax: (703)548-3822
Web Site: http://www.horatioalger.com
To provide financial assistance to students in the state of Iowa.
Title of Award: Horatio Alger Iowa Scholarships **Area, Field, or Subject:** General studies. **Level of Education for which Award is Granted:** Undergraduate **Number Awarded:** 100. **Funds Available:** $3,000.
Eligibility Requirements: Applicants must be enrolled full time as a high school senior, progressing normally toward graduation, and planning to enter college no later than the fall following graduation; must have a strong commitment to pursue a bachelor's degree at an accredited institution (students may start their studies at a two-year institution and then transfer to a four-year institution); must have critical financial need ($50,000 or less adjusted gross income per family is preferred; if higher, an explanation must be provided); must be involved in co-curricular and community activities; must have a minimum grade point average of 2.0; and be a citizen or permanent resident of the United States. **Application Requirements:** Applicants must have one letter of support and must be logged in to the application process at the HAA website. Faxes/emails will not be accepted. Students must download the certification page from the HAA web site, complete it and obtain the proper signatures prior to mailing.

75 ■ HORATIO ALGER ASSOCIATION

99 Canal Center Plaza, Ste. 320
Alexandria, VA 22314
Tel: (703)684-9444
Fax: (703)548-3822
Web Site: http://www.horatioalger.com

To provide financial assistance to students in the state of Kentucky.
Title of Award: Horatio Alger Kentucky Scholarships **Area, Field, or Subject:** General studies. **Level of Education for which Award is Granted:** Undergraduate **Number Awarded:** 8. **Funds Available:** $5,000.
Eligibility Requirements: Applicants must be enrolled full time as a high school senior, progressing normally toward graduation, and planning to enter college no later than the fall following graduation; must have a strong commitment to pursue a bachelor's degree at an accredited institution (students may start their studies at a two-year institution and then transfer to a four-year institution); must have critical financial need ($50,000 or less adjusted gross income per family is preferred; if higher, an explanation must be provided); must be involved in co-curricular and community activities; must have a minimum grade point average of 2.0; be a resident of Kentucky; and be a citizen or permanent resident of the United States. **Application Requirements:** Applicants must have one letter of support and must be logged in to the application process at the HAA website. Faxes/emails will not be accepted. Students must download the certification page from the HAA web site, complete it and obtain the proper signatures prior to mailing.

76 ■ HORATIO ALGER ASSOCIATION
99 Canal Center Plaza, Ste. 320
Alexandria, VA 22314
Tel: (703)684-9444
Fax: (703)548-3822
Web Site: http://www.horatioalger.com
To provide scholarships to students in the State of Idaho.
Title of Award: Horatio Alger Lola and Duane Hagadone Idaho Scholarships **Area, Field, or Subject:** General studies. **Level of Education for which Award is Granted:** Undergraduate **Number Awarded:** 25. **Funds Available:** $5,000.
Eligibility Requirements: Applicants must be enrolled full time as a high school senior, progressing normally toward graduation, and planning to enter college no later than the fall following graduation; must have a strong commitment to pursue a bachelor's degree at an accredited institution (students may start their studies at a two-year institution and then transfer to a four-year institution); must have critical financial need ($50,000 or less adjusted gross income per family is preferred; if higher, an explanation must be provided); must be involved in co-curricular and community activities; must have a minimum grade point average of 2.0; and be a resident of Benewah, Boundary, Bonner, Kootenai, Latah, or Shoshone counties in the State of Idaho. Recipients must pursue a bachelor's degree at the University of Idaho or Lewis-Clark State College. **Application Requirements:** Applicants must have one letter of support and must be logged in to the application process at the HAA website. Faxes/emails will not be accepted. Students must download the certification page from the HAA web site, complete it and obtain the proper signatures prior to mailing.

77 ■ HORATIO ALGER ASSOCIATION
99 Canal Center Plaza, Ste. 320
Alexandria, VA 22314
Tel: (703)684-9444
Fax: (703)548-3822
Web Site: http://www.horatioalger.com
To provide financial assistance to students in the state of Louisiana.
Title of Award: Horatio Alger Louisiana Scholarships **Area, Field, or Subject:** General studies. **Level of Education for which Award is Granted:** Undergraduate **Number Awarded:** 50. **Funds Available:** $10,500.
Eligibility Requirements: Applicants must be enrolled full time as a high school senior, progressing normally toward graduation, and planning to enter college no later than the fall following graduation; must have a strong commitment to pursue a bachelor's degree at an accredited institution (students may start their studies at a two-year institution and then transfer to a four-year institution); must have critical financial need ($50,000 or less adjusted gross income per family is preferred; if higher, an explanation must be provided); must be involved in co-curricular and community activities; must have a minimum grade point average of 2.0; be a citizen or permanent resident of the United States. Students must plan to attend and enroll in one of the following five schools to be awarded the Louisiana Scholarship: Loyola University - New Orleans; McNeese

State University; Tulane University; University of New Orleans; Xavier University. **Application Requirements:** Applicants must have one letter of support and must be logged in to the application process at the HAA website. Faxes/emails will not be accepted. Students must download the certification page from the HAA web site, complete it and obtain the proper signatures prior to mailing.

78 ■ HORATIO ALGER ASSOCIATION
99 Canal Center Plaza, Ste. 320
Alexandria, VA 22314
Tel: (703)684-9444
Fax: (703)548-3822
Web Site: http://www.horatioalger.com
To provide financial assistance to students in the state of Minnesota.
Title of Award: Horatio Alger Minnesota Scholarships **Area, Field, or Subject:** General studies. **Level of Education for which Award is Granted:** Undergraduate **Number Awarded:** 42. **Funds Available:** $4,000.
Eligibility Requirements: Applicants must be enrolled full time as a high school senior, progressing normally toward graduation, and planning to enter college no later than the fall following graduation; must have a strong commitment to pursue a bachelor's degree at an accredited institution (students may start their studies at a two-year institution and then transfer to a four-year institution); must have critical financial need ($50,000 or less adjusted gross income per family is preferred; if higher, an explanation must be provided); must be involved in co-curricular and community activities; must have a minimum grade point average of 2.0; must be a resident of Anoka, Carver, Dakota, Hennepin, Ramsey, Scott, and Washington counties; and be a citizen or permanent resident of the United States. **Application Requirements:** Applicants must have one letter of support and must be logged in to the application process at the HAA website. Faxes/emails will not be accepted. Students must download the certification page from the HAA web site, complete it and obtain the proper signatures prior to mailing.

79 ■ HORATIO ALGER ASSOCIATION
99 Canal Center Plaza, Ste. 320
Alexandria, VA 22314
Tel: (703)684-9444
Fax: (703)548-3822
Web Site: http://www.horatioalger.com
To provide financial assistance to students in the state of Mississippi.
Title of Award: Horatio Alger Mississippi Scholarships **Area, Field, or Subject:** General studies. **Level of Education for which Award is Granted:** Undergraduate **Number Awarded:** 12. **Funds Available:** $5,000.
Eligibility Requirements: Applicants must be enrolled full time as a high school senior, progressing normally toward graduation, and planning to enter college no later than the fall following graduation; must have a strong commitment to pursue a bachelor's degree at an accredited institution (students may start their studies at a two-year institution and then transfer to a four-year institution); must have critical financial need ($50,000 or less adjusted gross income per family is preferred; if higher, an explanation must be provided); must be involved in co-curricular and community activities; must have a minimum grade point average of 2.0; be a resident of Mississippi; and be a citizen or permanent resident of the United States. **Application Requirements:** Applicants must have one letter of support and must be logged in to the application process at the HAA website. Faxes/emails will not be accepted. Students must download the certification page from the HAA web site, complete it and obtain the proper signatures prior to mailing.

80 ■ HORATIO ALGER ASSOCIATION
99 Canal Center Plaza, Ste. 320
Alexandria, VA 22314
Tel: (703)684-9444
Fax: (703)548-3822
Web Site: http://www.horatioalger.com
To provide financial assistance to students in the state Missouri.
Title of Award: Horatio Alger Missouri Scholarships **Area, Field, or Subject:** General studies. **Level of Education for which Award is Granted:** Undergraduate **Number Awarded:** 50. **Funds Available:** $5,000.

Eligibility Requirements: Applicants must be enrolled full time as a high school senior, progressing normally toward graduation, and planning to enter college no later than the fall following graduation; must have a strong commitment to pursue a bachelor's degree at an accredited institution (students may start their studies at a two-year institution and then transfer to a four-year institution); must have critical financial need ($50,000 or less adjusted gross income per family is preferred; if higher, an explanation must be provided); must be involved in co-curricular and community activities; must have a minimum grade point average of 2.0; must be a resident of Missouri; and be a citizen or permanent resident of the United States. Application Requirements: Applicants must have one letter of support and must be logged in to the application process at the HAA website. Faxes/emails will not be accepted. Students must download the certification page from the HAA web site, complete it and obtain the proper signatures prior to mailing.

81 ■ HORATIO ALGER ASSOCIATION

99 Canal Center Plaza, Ste. 320
Alexandria, VA 22314
Tel: (703)684-9444
Fax: (703)548-3822
Web Site: http://www.horatioalger.com
To provide financial assistance to students in the state of Montana.
Title of Award: Horatio Alger Montana Scholarships Area, Field, or Subject: General studies. Level of Education for which Award is Granted: Undergraduate Number Awarded: 50. Funds Available: $5,000.
Eligibility Requirements: Applicants must be enrolled full time as a high school senior, progressing normally toward graduation, and planning to enter college no later than the fall following graduation; must have a strong commitment to pursue a bachelor's degree at an accredited institution (students may start their studies at a two-year institution and then transfer to a four-year institution); must have critical financial need ($50,000 or less adjusted gross income per family is preferred; if higher, an explanation must be provided); must be involved in co-curricular and community activities; must have a minimum grade point average of 2.0; must be a resident of Montana; and be a citizen or permanent resident of the United States. Recipients must pursue a bachelor's degree at the University of Montana, The University of Montana-Western, The University of Montana-Missoula College of Technology, Helena College of Technology of The University of Montana, or Montana Tech of The University of The University of Montana. Application Requirements: Applicants must have one letter of support and must be logged in to the application process at the HAA website. Faxes/emails will not be accepted. Students must download the certification page from the HAA web site, complete it and obtain the proper signatures prior to mailing.

82 ■ HORATIO ALGER ASSOCIATION

99 Canal Center Plaza, Ste. 320
Alexandria, VA 22314
Tel: (703)684-9444
Fax: (703)548-3822
Web Site: http://www.horatioalger.com
To assist high school students who have faced and overcome great obstacles in their young lives.
Title of Award: Horatio Alger National Scholarships Area, Field, or Subject: General studies. Level of Education for which Award is Granted: Undergraduate Funds Available: $20,000.
Eligibility Requirements: Applicants must be enrolled full time as a high school senior, progressing normally toward graduation, and planning to enter college no later than the fall following graduation; must have a strong commitment to pursue a bachelor's degree at an accredited institution (students may start their studies at a two-year institution and then transfer to a four-year institution); must have critical financial need ($50,000 or less adjusted gross income per family is preferred; if higher, an explanation must be provided); must be involved in co-curricular and community activities; must have a minimum grade point average of 2.0; and be a citizen or permanent resident of the United States. Application Requirements: Applicants must have one letter of support and must be logged in to the application process at the HAA website. Faxes/emails will not be accepted. Students must download the certification page from the HAA web site, complete it and obtain the proper signatures prior to mailing.

83 ■ HORATIO ALGER ASSOCIATION

99 Canal Center Plaza, Ste. 320
Alexandria, VA 22314
Tel: (703)684-9444
Fax: (703)548-3822
Web Site: http://www.horatioalger.com
To provide financial assistance to students in the state of New Jersey.
Title of Award: Horatio Alger New Jersey Scholarships Area, Field, or Subject: General studies. Level of Education for which Award is Granted: Undergraduate Number Awarded: 5. Funds Available: $5,000.
Eligibility Requirements: Applicants must be enrolled full time as a high school senior, progressing normally toward graduation, and planning to enter college no later than the fall following graduation; must have a strong commitment to pursue a bachelor's degree at an accredited institution (students may start their studies at a two-year institution and then transfer to a four-year institution); must have critical financial need ($50,000 or less adjusted gross income per family is preferred; if higher, an explanation must be provided); must be involved in co-curricular and community activities; must have a minimum grade point average of 2.0; and be a citizen or permanent resident of the United States. Application Requirements: Applicants must have one letter of support and must be logged in to the application process at the HAA website. Faxes/emails will not be accepted. Students must download the certification page from the HAA web site, complete it and obtain the proper signatures prior to mailing.

84 ■ HORATIO ALGER ASSOCIATION

99 Canal Center Plaza, Ste. 320
Alexandria, VA 22314
Tel: (703)684-9444
Fax: (703)548-3822
Web Site: http://www.horatioalger.com
To provide financial assistance to students in the state of New York.
Title of Award: Horatio Alger New York Scholarships Area, Field, or Subject: General studies. Level of Education for which Award is Granted: Undergraduate Number Awarded: 5. Funds Available: $5,000.
Eligibility Requirements: Applicants must be enrolled full time as a high school senior, progressing normally toward graduation, and planning to enter college no later than the fall following graduation; must have a strong commitment to pursue a bachelor's degree at an accredited institution (students may start their studies at a two-year institution and then transfer to a four-year institution); must have critical financial need ($50,000 or less adjusted gross income per family is preferred; if higher, an explanation must be provided); must be involved in co-curricular and community activities; must have a minimum grade point average of 2.0; and be a citizen or permanent resident of the United States. Application Requirements: Applicants must have one letter of support and must be logged in to the application process at the HAA website. Faxes/emails will not be accepted. Students must download the certification page from the HAA web site, complete it and obtain the proper signatures prior to mailing.

85 ■ HORATIO ALGER ASSOCIATION

99 Canal Center Plaza, Ste. 320
Alexandria, VA 22314
Tel: (703)684-9444
Fax: (703)548-3822
Web Site: http://www.horatioalger.com
To provide financial assistance to students in the state of North Dakota.
Title of Award: Horatio Alger North Dakota Scholarships Area, Field, or Subject: General studies. Level of Education for which Award is Granted: Undergraduate Number Awarded: 25. Funds Available: $5,000.
Eligibility Requirements: Applicants must be enrolled full time as a high school senior, progressing normally toward graduation, and planning to enter college no later than the fall following graduation; must have a strong commitment to pursue a bachelor's degree at an accredited institution (students may start their studies at a two-year institution and then transfer to a four-year institution); must have critical financial need ($50,000 or less adjusted gross income per family is preferred; if higher, an explanation must be provided); must be involved in co-curricular and

community activities; must have a minimum grade point average of 2.0; be a resident of North Dakota; and be a citizen or permanent resident of the United States. **Application Requirements:** Applicants must have one letter of support and must be logged in to the application process at the HAA website. Faxes/emails will not be accepted. Students must download the certification page from the HAA web site, complete it and obtain the proper signatures prior to mailing.

86 ■ HORATIO ALGER ASSOCIATION

99 Canal Center Plaza, Ste. 320
Alexandria, VA 22314
Tel: (703)684-9444
Fax: (703)548-3822
Web Site: http://www.horatioalger.com
To provide financial assistance to students in the state of Oregon.
Title of Award: Horatio Alger Oregon Scholarships **Area, Field, or Subject:** General studies. **Level of Education for which Award is Granted:** Undergraduate **Number Awarded:** 5. **Funds Available:** $5,000.

Eligibility Requirements: Applicants must be enrolled full time as a high school senior, progressing normally toward graduation, and planning to enter college no later than the fall following graduation; must have a strong commitment to pursue a bachelor's degree at an accredited institution (students may start their studies at a two-year institution and then transfer to a four-year institution); must have critical financial need ($50,000 or less adjusted gross income per family is preferred; if higher, an explanation must be provided); must be involved in co-curricular and community activities; must have a minimum grade point average of 2.0; be a resident of Oregon; and be a citizen or permanent resident of the United States. **Application Requirements:** Applicants must have one letter of support and must be logged in to the application process at the HAA website. Faxes/emails will not be accepted. Students must download the certification page from the HAA web site, complete it and obtain the proper signatures prior to mailing.

87 ■ HORATIO ALGER ASSOCIATION

99 Canal Center Plaza, Ste. 320
Alexandria, VA 22314
Tel: (703)684-9444
Fax: (703)548-3822
Web Site: http://www.horatioalger.com
To provide financial assistance to students in the State of Pennsylvania.
Title of Award: Horatio Alger Pennsylvania Scholarships **Area, Field, or Subject:** General studies. **Level of Education for which Award is Granted:** Undergraduate **Number Awarded:** 50. **Funds Available:** $5,000.
Eligibility Requirements: Applicants must be enrolled full time as a high school senior, progressing normally toward graduation, and planning to enter college no later than the fall following graduation; must have a strong commitment to pursue a bachelor's degree at an accredited institution (students may start their studies at a two-year institution and then transfer to a four-year institution); must have critical financial need ($50,000 or less adjusted gross income per family is preferred; if higher, an explanation must be provided); must be involved in co-curricular and community activities; must have a minimum grade point average of 2.0; be a resident of Pennsylvania; and be a citizen or permanent resident of the United States. **Application Requirements:** Applicants must have one letter of support and must be logged in to the application process at the HAA website. Faxes/emails will not be accepted. Students must download the certification page from the HAA web site, complete it and obtain the proper signatures prior to mailing.

88 ■ HORATIO ALGER ASSOCIATION

99 Canal Center Plaza, Ste. 320
Alexandria, VA 22314
Tel: (703)684-9444
Fax: (703)548-3822
Web Site: http://www.horatioalger.com
To provide financial assistance to students in the state of South Dakota.
Title of Award: Horatio Alger South Dakota Scholarships **Area, Field, or Subject:** General studies. **Level of Education for which Award is Granted:** Undergraduate **Number Awarded:** 25. **Funds Available:** $5,000.

Eligibility Requirements: Applicants must be enrolled full time as a high school senior, progressing normally toward graduation, and planning to enter college no later than the fall following graduation; must have a strong commitment to pursue a bachelor's degree at an accredited institution (students may start their studies at a two-year institution and then transfer to a four-year institution); must have critical financial need ($50,000 or less adjusted gross income per family is preferred; if higher, an explanation must be provided); must be involved in co-curricular and community activities; must have a minimum grade point average of 2.0; be a resident of South Dakota; and be a citizen or permanent resident of the United States. **Application Requirements:** Applicants must have one letter of support and must be logged in to the application process at the HAA website. Faxes/emails will not be accepted. Students must download the certification page from the HAA web site, complete it and obtain the proper signatures prior to mailing.

89 ■ HORATIO ALGER ASSOCIATION

99 Canal Center Plaza, Ste. 320
Alexandria, VA 22314
Tel: (703)684-9444
Fax: (703)548-3822
Web Site: http://www.horatioalger.com
To provide financial assistance to students from Fort Worth, Texas.
Title of Award: Horatio Alger Texas - Fort Worth Scholarships **Area, Field, or Subject:** General studies. **Level of Education for which Award is Granted:** Undergraduate **Number Awarded:** 12. **Funds Available:** $5,000.

Eligibility Requirements: Applicants must be enrolled full time as a high school senior, progressing normally toward graduation, and planning to enter college no later than the fall following graduation; must have a strong commitment to pursue a bachelor's degree at an accredited institution (students may start their studies at a two-year institution and then transfer to a four-year institution); must have critical financial need ($50,000 or less adjusted gross income per family is preferred; if higher, an explanation must be provided); must be involved in co-curricular and community activities; must have a minimum grade point average of 2.0; and be a citizen or permanent resident of the United States. **Application Requirements:** Applicants must have one letter of support and must be logged in to the application process at the HAA website. Faxes/emails will not be accepted. Students must download the certification page from the HAA web site, complete it and obtain the proper signatures prior to mailing.

90 ■ HORATIO ALGER ASSOCIATION

99 Canal Center Plaza, Ste. 320
Alexandria, VA 22314
Tel: (703)684-9444
Fax: (703)548-3822
Web Site: http://www.horatioalger.com
To provide financial assistance to students in the state of Texas.
Title of Award: Horatio Alger Texas Scholarships **Area, Field, or Subject:** General studies. **Level of Education for which Award is Granted:** Undergraduate **Number Awarded:** 28. **Funds Available:** $5,000.

Eligibility Requirements: Applicants must be enrolled full time as a high school senior, progressing normally toward graduation, and planning to enter college no later than the fall following graduation; must have a strong commitment to pursue a bachelor's degree at an accredited institution (students may start their studies at a two-year institution and then transfer to a four-year institution); must have critical financial need ($50,000 or less adjusted gross income per family is preferred; if higher, an explanation must be provided); must be involved in co-curricular and community activities; must have a minimum grade point average of 2.0; be a resident of Texas; and be a citizen or permanent resident of the United States. **Application Requirements:** Applicants must have one letter of support and must be logged in to the application process at the HAA website. Faxes/emails will not be accepted. Students must download the certification page from the HAA web site, complete it and obtain the proper signatures prior to mailing.

91 ■ HORATIO ALGER ASSOCIATION

99 Canal Center Plaza, Ste. 320
Alexandria, VA 22314

Tel: (703)684-9444
Fax: (703)548-3822
Web Site: http://www.horatioalger.com
To provide financial assistance to students in the state of Utah.
Title of Award: Horatio Alger Utah Scholarships **Area, Field, or Subject:** General studies. **Level of Education for which Award is Granted:** Undergraduate **Number Awarded:** 25. **Funds Available:** $5,000.
Eligibility Requirements: Applicants must be enrolled full time as a high school senior, progressing normally toward graduation, and planning to enter college no later than the fall following graduation; must have a strong commitment to pursue a bachelor's degree at an accredited institution (students may start their studies at a two-year institution and then transfer to a four-year institution); must have critical financial need ($50,000 or less adjusted gross income per family is preferred; if higher, an explanation must be provided); must be involved in co-curricular and community activities; must have a minimum grade point average of 2.0; and be a citizen or permanent resident of the United States. **Application Requirements:** Applicants must have one letter of support and must be logged in to the application process at the HAA website. Faxes/emails will not be accepted. Students must download the certification page from the HAA web site, complete it and obtain the proper signatures prior to mailing.

92 ■ HORATIO ALGER ASSOCIATION
99 Canal Center Plaza, Ste. 320
Alexandria, VA 22314
Tel: (703)684-9444
Fax: (703)548-3822
Web Site: http://www.horatioalger.com
To provide financial assistance to students in the state of Washington.
Title of Award: Horatio Alger Washington Scholarships **Area, Field, or Subject:** General studies. **Level of Education for which Award is Granted:** Undergraduate **Number Awarded:** 5. **Funds Available:** $5,000.
Eligibility Requirements: Applicants must be enrolled full time as a high school senior, progressing normally toward graduation, and planning to enter college no later than the fall following graduation; must have a strong commitment to pursue a bachelor's degree at an accredited institution (students may start their studies at a two-year institution and then transfer to a four-year institution); must have critical financial need ($50,000 or less adjusted gross income per family is preferred; if higher, an explanation must be provided); must be involved in co-curricular and community activities; must have a minimum grade point average of 2.0; be a resident of Washington; and be a citizen or permanent resident of the United States. **Application Requirements:** Applicants must have one letter of support and must be logged in to the application process at the HAA website. Faxes/emails will not be accepted. Students must download the certification page from the HAA web site, complete it and obtain the proper signatures prior to mailing.

93 ■ HORATIO ALGER ASSOCIATION
99 Canal Center Plaza, Ste. 320
Alexandria, VA 22314
Tel: (703)684-9444
Fax: (703)548-3822
Web Site: http://www.horatioalger.com
To provide financial assistance to students in the state of Wyoming.
Title of Award: Horatio Alger Wyoming Scholarships **Area, Field, or Subject:** General studies. **Level of Education for which Award is Granted:** Undergraduate **Number Awarded:** 5. **Funds Available:** $5,000.
Eligibility Requirements: Applicants must be enrolled full time as a high school senior, progressing normally toward graduation, and planning to enter college no later than the fall following graduation; must have a strong commitment to pursue a bachelor's degree at an accredited institution (students may start their studies at a two-year institution and then transfer to a four-year institution); must have critical financial need ($50,000 or less adjusted gross income per family is preferred; if higher, an explanation must be provided); must be involved in co-curricular and community activities; must have a minimum grade point average of 2.0; and be a citizen or permanent resident of the United States. **Application Requirements:** Applicants must have one letter of support and must be logged in to the application process at the HAA website. Faxes/emails will

not be accepted. Students must download the certification page from the HAA web site, complete it and obtain the proper signatures prior to mailing.

94 ■ ALLEN UNIVERSITY
1530 Harden St.
Columbia, SC 29204
Tel: (803)376-5700
Web Site: http://www.allenuniversity.edu
To provide educational assistance for honor students.
Title of Award: Legislative Incentive for Future Excellence (LIFE) Scholarships **Area, Field, or Subject:** General studies. **Level of Education for which Award is Granted:** Undergraduate **Funds Available:** No specific amount.
Eligibility Requirements: Applicants must be U.S. citizens or legal permanent residents and must be South Carolina residents at the time of high school graduation and at the time of college enrollment. **Application Requirements:** Applicants must have earned a cumulative 3.0 grade point average (GPA) based on the SC Uniform Grading Scale upon high school graduation. **Additional Information:** Allen University's academic regulations specify the minimum cumulative grade point average a student must earn in order to avoid being placed on academic probation or suspension.

95 ■ ALLIANCE FOR CHOICE IN EDUCATION
1201 E Colfax Ave., Ste. 302
Denver, CO 80218
Tel: (303)573-1603
Fax: (720)266-6798
E-mail: mcooke@acescholarships.org
Web Site: http://www.acescholarships.org
To provide financial assistance to deserving students and to increase the access to high quality educational options.
Title of Award: ACE K-12 Scholarships Program **Area, Field, or Subject:** General Studies. **Level of Education for which Award is Granted:** High School **Funds Available:** Maximum of $2,000.
Eligibility Requirements: Applicants must be grades K-12; must be Colorado residents. **Application Requirements:** Applicants must submit the scholarship application form and must check the available website for more information. **Additional Information:** Alliance for Choice in Education at the above address

96 ■ ALPHA CHI
Harding University Box 12249
900 E Ctr.
Searcy, AR 72149-0001
Web Site: http://www.harding.edu
To provide financial support for the education of senior undergraduate students.
Title of Award: Gaston Scholarships **Area, Field, or Subject:** General studies. **Level of Education for which Award is Granted:** Undergraduate **Number Awarded:** 2. **Funds Available:** $2,000.
Eligibility Requirements: Nominee must be a senior year undergraduate student. **Application Requirements:** Nominee must submit the official nomination form completed, signed by the sponsor, and included with the entry; a letter of application from the student outlining his/her plans for study and detailing his/her extracurricular activities, maximum length of two pages, double-spaced; an academic paper or other appropriate work in the student's major field; one letter of recommendation/evaluation from a faculty member in the field represented by the paper or project addressed to the significance of the work; a self-addressed, stamped envelope. **Deadline for Receipt:** February 22.

97 ■ ALPHA CHI
Harding University Box 12249
900 E Ctr.
Searcy, AR 72149-0001
Web Site: http://www.harding.edu
To provide financial support for the education of senior undergraduate students.
Title of Award: Nolle Scholarships **Area, Field, or Subject:** General studies. **Level of Education for which Award is Granted:** Undergraduate **Number Awarded:** 10. **Funds Available:** $1,500.

Eligibility Requirements: Nominee must be a senior year undergraduate student. **Application Requirements:** Nominee must submit the official nomination form completed, signed by the sponsor, and included with the entry; a letter of application from the student outlining his/her plans for study and detailing his/her extracurricular activities, maximum length of two pages, double-spaced; an academic paper or other appropriate work in the student's major field; one letter of recommendation/evaluation from a faculty member in the field represented by the paper or project addressed to the significance of the work; a self-addressed, stamped envelope. **Deadline for Receipt:** February 22.

98 ■ ALPHA CHI SIGMA
2141 N Franklin Rd.
Indianapolis, IN 46219
800-ALC-HEMY
E-mail: foundation@alphachisigma.org
Web Site: http://alphachisigma.org
To encourage and recognize outstanding scholarship among Collegiate members of Alpha Chi Sigma Fraternity.
Title of Award: Alpha Chi Sigma Scholarship Award **Area, Field, or Subject:** General studies. **Level of Education for which Award is Granted:** Graduate, Undergraduate **Funds Available:** $1,000.
Eligibility Requirements: Nominee must have been a member of Alpha Chi Sigma Fraternity for one year, and enrolled in an institution of higher learning at the time of nomination. Undergraduate nominees must have completed the Junior year at the time of nomination. Graduate nominees may be nominated based upon both their undergraduate and graduate records upon the completion of their first year of graduate study. Graduate students may also be nominated, based upon their graduate records alone, after admission to candidacy for the terminal degree in the field of graduate study. **Application Requirements:** Application process is done through nomination.

99 ■ ALPHA KAPPA ALPHA - EDUCATIONAL ADVANCEMENT FOUNDATION
5656 S Stony Island Ave.
Chicago, IL 60637
Tel: 800-653-6528
Fax: (773)947-0277
E-mail: akaeaf@akaeaf.net
Web Site: http://www.akaeaf.org
To provide financial support to undergraduate and graduate students for the advancement of education and to promote life-long learning.
Title of Award: Alpha Kappa Alpha - Educational Advancement Foundation Financial Need-Based Scholarships **Area, Field, or Subject:** General studies. **Level of Education for which Award is Granted:** Graduate, Undergraduate **Funds Available:** $750 to $2,500. **Duration:** One year.
Eligibility Requirements: Applicants must be full-time undergraduate students, sophomores or beyond, currently enrolled in an accredited campus-based degree-granting institution of higher learning or currently enrolled, full-time graduate students; must have a minimum 2.5 GPA or C+ average. **Application Requirements:** Applicants must submit all the required application information. **Deadline for Receipt:** April 15 for the undergraduates' applications; August 15 for graduates' applications.

100 ■ ALPHA KAPPA ALPHA - EDUCATIONAL ADVANCEMENT FOUNDATION
5656 S Stony Island Ave.
Chicago, IL 60637
Tel: 800-653-6528
Fax: (773)947-0277
E-mail: akaeaf@akaeaf.net
Web Site: http://www.akaeaf.org
To provide financial support to undergraduate and graduate students for the advancement of education and to promote life-long learning.
Title of Award: Alpha Kappa Alpha - Educational Advancement Foundation Merit Scholarships **Area, Field, or Subject:** General studies. **Level of Education for which Award is Granted:** Graduate, Undergraduate **Funds Available:** $1,000 to $2,000.
Eligibility Requirements: Applicants must be full-time and currently enrolled undergraduate students with at least sophomore standing at an accredited campus-based degree-granting institution or full-time and currently enrolled graduate students at an accredited campus-based degree-

granting institution. Both must possess a minimum grade point average of 3.0. **Application Requirements:** Applicants must submit all the required application information. **Deadline for Receipt:** April 15 for undergraduates' applications; August 15 for graduates' applications.

101 ■ ALPHA KAPPA ALPHA - EDUCATIONAL ADVANCEMENT FOUNDATION
5656 S Stony Island Ave.
Chicago, IL 60637
Tel: 800-653-6528
Fax: (773)947-0277
E-mail: akaeaf@akaeaf.net
Web Site: http://www.akaeaf.org
To provide financial support to undergraduate and graduate students for the advancement of education and to promote life-long learning.
Title of Award: Youth Partners Accessing Capital (P.A.C.) **Area, Field, or Subject:** General studies. **Level of Education for which Award is Granted:** Graduate, Undergraduate **Funds Available:** $1,000 up to $3,000.
Eligibility Requirements: Applicants must be members of the Alpha Kappa Alpha Sorority, Inc.; at least college sophomores who have a minimum 3.0 of GPA. **Application Requirements:** Applicants must submit all the required application information. **Deadline for Receipt:** April 15.

102 ■ ALPHA PHI SIGMA
3301 College Ave.
Fort Lauderdale, FL 33314
Tel: (954)262-7004
Fax: (954)262-3646
E-mail: headquarters@alphaphisigma.org
Web Site: http://www.gannon.edu/resource/other/org/APSDP/index.html
To assist students in their educational pursuits.
Title of Award: Commander James Carr Forensic Science Scholarships **Area, Field, or Subject:** General studies. **Level of Education for which Award is Granted:** Undergraduate **Number Awarded:** 1. **Funds Available:** $1000.
Eligibility Requirements: Applicants must be Alpha Phi Sigma members. **Application Requirements:** Applicants must submit required materials and documents following the stipulated guidelines. **Deadline for Receipt:** January 31.

103 ■ ALPHA PHI SIGMA
3301 College Ave.
Fort Lauderdale, FL 33314
Tel: (954)262-7004
Fax: (954)262-3646
E-mail: headquarters@alphaphisigma.org
Web Site: http://www.gannon.edu/resource/other/org/APSDP/index.html
To assist students in their educational pursuits.
Title of Award: V.A. Leonard Scholarships **Area, Field, or Subject:** General studies. **Level of Education for which Award is Granted:** Graduate, Undergraduate **Number Awarded:** 1. **Funds Available:** $1000.
Eligibility Requirements: Applicants must be Alpha Phi Sigma members. **Application Requirements:** Applicants must submit required materials and documents following the stipulated guidelines. **Additional Information:** Established in 1982 in honor and recognition of Dr. Leonard's leadership and hard work in the field of Criminal Justice. **Deadline for Receipt:** January 31.

104 ■ ALPHA PHI SIGMA
3301 College Ave.
Fort Lauderdale, FL 33314
Tel: (954)262-7004
Fax: (954)262-3646
E-mail: headquarters@alphaphisigma.org
Web Site: http://www.gannon.edu/resource/other/org/APSDP/index.html
To assist students in their educational pursuits.
Title of Award: Public Agency Training Council Criminal Justice Scholarships **Area, Field, or Subject:** General studies. **Level of Education for which Award is Granted:** Undergraduate **Number Awarded:** 1. **Funds Available:** $1000.

Eligibility Requirements: Applicants must be Alpha Phi Sigma members. **Application Requirements:** Applicants must submit required materials and documents following the stipulated guidelines. **Additional Information:** Established in 1987. **Deadline for Receipt:** January 31.

105 ■ ALPHA PHI SIGMA

3301 College Ave.
Fort Lauderdale, FL 33314
Tel: (954)262-7004
Fax: (954)262-3646
E-mail: headquarters@alphaphisigma.org
Web Site: http://www.gannon.edu/resource/other/org/APSDP/index.html
To assist students in their educational pursuits.
Title of Award: Detective Cheryl Seiden Memorial Scholarships **Area, Field, or Subject:** General studies. **Level of Education for which Award is Granted:** Undergraduate **Number Awarded:** 1. **Funds Available:** $1000.
Eligibility Requirements: Applicants must be Alpha Phi Sigma members. **Application Requirements:** Applicants must submit required materials and documents following the stipulated guidelines. **Additional Information:** In memory of Metro-Dade Police Detective Cheryl Seiden, killed in the line of duty. **Deadline for Receipt:** January 31.

106 ■ ALPHA PHI SIGMA

3301 College Ave.
Fort Lauderdale, FL 33314
Tel: (954)262-7004
Fax: (954)262-3646
E-mail: headquarters@alphaphisigma.org
Web Site: http://www.gannon.edu/resource/other/org/APSDP/index.html
To assist students in their educational pursuits.
Title of Award: Regina B. Shearn Scholarships **Area, Field, or Subject:** General studies. **Level of Education for which Award is Granted:** Graduate, Undergraduate **Number Awarded:** 1. **Funds Available:** $1000.
Eligibility Requirements: Applicants must be Alpha Phi Sigma members. Applicants are not eligible to receive the same scholarship two years in succession. **Application Requirements:** Applicants must submit required materials and documents following the stipulated guidelines. **Additional Information:** Established in 2001, named after the first National Executive Director of Alpha Phi Sigma. **Deadline for Receipt:** January 31.

107 ■ AMERICAN ASSOCIATION OF BLACKS IN ENERGY

1625 K St. NW, Ste. 405
Washington, DC 20006
Tel: (202)371-9530
Fax: (202)371-9218
E-mail: info@aabe.org
Web Site: http://www.aabe.org
To help increase the number of African Americans and other misrepresented minorities in energy-related fields.
Title of Award: American Association of Blacks in Energy Scholarships **Area, Field, or Subject:** Energy-related areas. **Level of Education for which Award is Granted:** Undergraduate **Number Awarded:** 6. **Funds Available:** $1,500. **Duration:** One year.
Eligibility Requirements: Applicants must have at least an overall "B" academic average and a "B" average in mathematics and science courses; must be graduating high school seniors who have applied to one or more accredited colleges/universities; must be planning to major in engineering, mathematics, or the physical sciences; must demonstrate financial need; and must be members of one of the underrepresented minority groups in the sciences and related areas of technology. **Application Requirements:** Applicants must submit completed AABE application form; high school transcript; two letters of reference (one academic, one non-academic); and parent(s) or guardian(s) official verification of income (copy of signed tax return for previous year or W2 or a verified FAFSA form).

108 ■ AMERICAN ASSOCIATION OF FAMILY AND CONSUMER SCIENCES

400 N Columbus St., Ste. 202
Alexandria, VA 22314
Tel: (703)706-4600
Free: 800-424-8080
Fax: (703)706-4663
E-mail: staff@aafcs.org
Web Site: http://www.aafcs.org
To encourage undergraduate study in family and consumer sciences and its subspecialties.
Title of Award: American Association of Family and Consumer Sciences Scholarships **Area, Field, or Subject:** Sciences. **Level of Education for which Award is Granted:** Undergraduate **Funds Available:** $5,000.
Eligibility Requirements: Applicants must be citizens or permanent residents of the United States; must be planning to pursue or currently pursuing a degree in family and consumer sciences or its specialties at the undergraduate level on a full-time basis; must be currently enrolled in an undergraduate program that will continue into the coming academic year or have been admitted to an undergraduate program for the coming academic year; must be willing to commit themselves to meet the specific requirements of the scholarship for which they are applying. **Application Requirements:** Applicants must complete the application form; must have a maximum of three evaluators; must obtain official or unofficial copies of transcript; must mail five hard copies of labeled CDs of the completed application form. **Deadline for Receipt:** January 7.

109 ■ AMERICAN ASSOCIATION OF HEALTHCARE ADMINISTRATIVE MANAGEMENT

11240 Waples Mill Rd., Ste. 200
Fairfax, VA 22030
Tel: (703)281-4043
Fax: (703)359-7562
E-mail: moayad@aaham.org
Web Site: http://www.aaham.org
To provide educational scholarship to individual AAHAM members and their dependents.
Title of Award: National AAHAM Scholarships **Area, Field, or Subject:** General studies. **Level of Education for which Award is Granted:** Undergraduate **Funds Available:** $2,500.
Eligibility Requirements: Applicants must be individuals who have been National AAHAM members for at least one year and have paid their current dues by March 30 of the year in which applications are submitted. **Application Requirements:** Applicants must submit all the required application information.

110 ■ AMERICAN ASSOCIATION FOR THE IMPROVEMENT OF BOXING

86 Fletcher Ave.,
Mount Vernon, NY 10552-3319
Tel: (914)664-4571
Fax: (914)664-3164
E-mail: aaib@verizon.net
Web Site: http://www.aaib.org
To provide educational opportunities and financial assistance to working students.
Title of Award: AAIB Scholarships **Area, Field, or Subject:** General Studies. **Level of Education for which Award is Granted:** Undergraduate **Number Awarded:** 1. **Funds Available:** No specific amount. **Duration:** Annual.
Eligibility Requirements: Program is open to high school seniors who must be accepted by an accredited college or university; must be nominated by a current paid member. **Application Requirements:** Application form is available in the website. **Deadline for Receipt:** May 1.

111 ■ AMERICAN ASSOCIATION OF OCCUPATIONAL HEALTH NURSES

2920 Brandywine Rd., Ste. 100
Atlanta, GA 30341
Tel: (770)455-7757
Fax: (770)455-7271
E-mail: don@aaohn.org
Web Site: http://www.aaohn.org
To provide opportunities to further professional education for occupational and environment health professionals.
Title of Award: AAOHN Academic Study Scholarships **Area, Field, or Subject:** Occupational safety and health. **Level of Education for which Award is Granted:** Graduate, Undergraduate **Number Awarded:** 4. **Funds Available:** $2,500-$3,000.

Eligibility Requirements: Undergraduate candidate must be a registered nurse enrolled full or part time in a nationally accredited school of nursing baccalaureate program and demonstrate an interest in, and commitment to, occupational and environmental health. Graduate candidate must be a registered nurse enrolled full or part time in a graduate program that has application to occupational and environmental health. Applicants must submit documentation of enrollment status. **Application Requirements:** Applicants must submit a 500 word or less narrative (double-spaced with one-inch margins in 12-point font) addressing: professional goals as they pertain to academic activity and the field of occupational and environmental health; impact of education on career. **Deadline for Receipt:** December 1. **Additional Information:** Don Bollmer, Dir. of Business Affairs, at the above address.

112 ■ AMERICAN ASSOCIATION OF PEOPLE WITH DISABILITIES
1629 K St. NW, Ste. 503
Washington, DC 20006
Tel: (202)457-0046
Free: 800-840-8844
E-mail: aapd@aol.com
Web Site: http://www.aapd.com
To provide educational assistance for black students at the undergraduate or graduate level pursuing careers in the area of actuarial sciences.
Title of Award: Actuarial Scholarships for Minority Students **Area, Field, or Subject:** Actuarial science. **Level of Education for which Award is Granted:** Undergraduate **Funds Available:** No specific amount.
Eligibility Requirements: Applicants must be students of African descent in the actuarial profession and must be originating from the United States, Canada, Caribbean or African Nations; must have a GPA of at least 3.0 on a 4.0 scale; must have a Math SAT score of at least 600 or an ACT Math score of at least 28; and must be junior, senior or graduate students. **Application Requirements:** Applicants must complete the application form and submit along with two nomination forms; an official, sealed current college transcript; an official sealed record of any educational examination scores taken; a Student Aid Report; and a copy of the page in college or university catalog or an information sheet showing an estimate of tuition, fees, and other expenses. **Deadline for Receipt:** May 21. **Additional Information:** iabafdvp@blackactuaries.org.

113 ■ AMERICAN ASSOCIATION OF POLICE POLYGRAPHISTS
PO Box 657
Waynesville, OH 45068
Tel: (937)728-7827; 888-743-5479
Fax: (937)488-1046
E-mail: nom@policepolygraph.org
Web Site: http://www.policepolygraph.org
To provide financial assistance for deserving graduating high school senior or student currently attending college.
Title of Award: William "Buddy" Sentner Scholarship Awards **Area, Field, or Subject:** General studies. **Level of Education for which Award is Granted:** Undergraduate **Funds Available:** Scholarship amount not specified. **Duration:** One year.
Eligibility Requirements: Applicants must be a graduating high school senior or a college student; must be a relative of a full, life, or honorably retired member in good standing with the AAPP. **Application Requirements:** Applicants must submit a completed application form; a recent official transcript of all courses and grades; and two character reference letters (from current institution's faculty and from a non-relative). Completed application package must be sent to the AAPP's Office. **Deadline for Receipt:** March 31. **Additional Information:** aappnom@hughes.net.

114 ■ AMERICAN ASSOCIATION OF RAILROAD SUPERINTENDENTS
PO Box 200
LaFox, IL 60147
Tel: (331)643-3369
Fax: (630)762-0755
E-mail: aars@supt.org
Web Site: http://www.railroadsuperintendents.org
To support the education of students enrolled at an accredited college or university in the U.S. or Canada.
Title of Award: Frank J. Richter Scholarships **Area, Field, or Subject:** Transportation. **Level of Education for which Award is Granted:** Gradu-

ate, Undergraduate **Number Awarded:** 1. **Funds Available:** $1000. **Duration:** One year.
Eligibility Requirements: Applicant must be enrolled full-time undergraduate or graduate student at an accredited college or university; demonstrated successful completion of the previous year's study by maintaining at least a 2.75 accumulated GPA on a scale of 1 to 4 with an "A" equal to 4; have accumulate enough credits from accredited schools in time for the Fall Semester to have obtained at least a sophomore level standing at the college or university of enrollment. **Application Requirements:** Applicants must submit a completed application form together with an official transcript from the schools attended; and two letters of recommendation. The application and narrative statement are to be submitted in one envelope. The transcripts and letters of recommendation must be sent directly to AARS from the appropriate person. **Deadline for Receipt:** June 1.

115 ■ AMERICAN ASSOCIATION OF SCHOOL ADMINISTRATORS
801 N Quincy St., Ste. 700
Arlington, VA 22203-1730
Tel: (703)528-0700
Fax: (703)841-1543
E-mail: info@aasa.org
Web Site: http://www.aasa.org
To recognize students involved in the fight against hunger in America.
Title of Award: Stop Hunger Scholarships **Area, Field, or Subject:** General studies. **Level of Education for which Award is Granted:** Undergraduate **Funds Available:** $3,000.
Eligibility Requirements: Applicants must be enrolled in an accredited education institution (kindergarten through college) in the United States; and must have demonstrated ongoing commitment to their community by performing volunteer services impacting hunger in the United States at least within the last 12 months. **Application Requirements:** Applicants and nominators must supply a valid e-mail address; applicants must submit a completed application form. **Deadline for Receipt:** January 1-February 29.

116 ■ AMERICAN BUS ASSOCIATION
700 13th St. NW, Ste. 575
Washington, DC 20005-5923
Tel: (202)842-1645
Fax: (202)842-0850
E-mail: abainfo@buses.org
Web Site: http://www.buses.org
To financially assist deserving students who has a potential to be future leaders in the transportation, travel, and tourism industry.
Title of Award: ABA Academic Merit Scholarships **Area, Field, or Subject:** Transportation; Travel and tourism. **Level of Education for which Award is Granted:** Undergraduate **Number Awarded:** 2. **Funds Available:** $2,500. **Duration:** One Academic year.
Eligibility Requirements: Applicants must completed first year of studies and majoring or have a course of study relevant to the transportation, travel, and tourism industry at an accredited university; must have a minimum of 3.4 GPA or higher. **Application Requirements:** Application process is online (please visit the website). Applicants must also submit an essay (500 words) discussing the role they will play in advancing the future of the transportation, motorcoach, travel, and tourism/hospitality industry. **Additional Information:** James Simon.

117 ■ AMERICAN BUS ASSOCIATION
700 13th St. NW, Ste. 575
Washington, DC 20005-5923
Tel: (202)842-1645
Fax: (202)842-0850
E-mail: abainfo@buses.org
Web Site: http://www.buses.org
To promote understanding and to mobilize greater involvement in the transportation industry.
Title of Award: ABA Diversity Scholarships **Area, Field, or Subject:** Transportation; Travel and tourism. **Level of Education for which Award is Granted:** Undergraduate **Number Awarded:** 2. **Funds Available:** $2,500. **Duration:** One academic year.
Eligibility Requirements: Applicants must completed first year of studies and majoring or have a course of study relevant to the transportation,

travel, and tourism industry at an accredited university; must have a minimum of 3.0 GPA. **Application Requirements:** Application process is online (please visit the website). **Additional Information:** James Simon.

118 ■ AMERICAN BUS ASSOCIATION
700 13th St. NW, Ste. 575
Washington, DC 20005-5923
Tel: (202)842-1645
Fax: (202)842-0850
E-mail: abainfo@buses.org
Web Site: http://www.buses.org
To financially assist deserving students who have potentials to be future leaders in the transportation, travel, and tourism industry.
Title of Award: ABA Members Scholarships (ABA Bus and Tour Operators Only) **Area, Field, or Subject:** General studies. **Level of Education for which Award is Granted:** Undergraduate **Number Awarded:** 13. **Funds Available:** $2,500.
Eligibility Requirements: Applicant must be a member or a dependent of ABA bus and tour member companies employed for at least one year; must be entering fist year of college, university, or professional training school by fall; must have a minimum of 3.0 GPA or an average of B. **Application Requirements:** Application process is online (please visit the website). **Additional Information:** James Simon.

119 ■ AMERICAN BUS ASSOCIATION
700 13th St. NW, Ste. 575
Washington, DC 20005-5923
Tel: (202)842-1645
Fax: (202)842-0850
E-mail: abainfo@buses.org
Web Site: http://www.buses.org
To financially assist deserving students who have potentials to be future leaders in the transportation, travel and tourism industry.
Title of Award: ABA Members Scholarships (All ABA Member Companies) **Area, Field, or Subject:** Transportation; Travel and tourism. **Level of Education for which Award is Granted:** Undergraduate **Number Awarded:** 13. **Funds Available:** $2,500.
Eligibility Requirements: Applicants must be a member or a dependent of ABA members companies employed for at least one year; must completed first year of studies and majoring or have a course of study relevant to the transportation, travel and tourism industry; must have a minimum of 3.0 GPA or an average of B. **Application Requirements:** Application process is online (please visit the website). **Additional Information:** James Simon.

120 ■ AMERICAN BUS ASSOCIATION
700 13th St. NW, Ste. 575
Washington, DC 20005-5923
Tel: (202)842-1645
Fax: (202)842-0850
E-mail: abainfo@buses.org
Web Site: http://www.buses.org
To honor the contribution of bus drivers, mechanics and maintenance personnel to the motorcoach industry.
Title of Award: Peter L. Picknelly Honorary Scholarships **Area, Field, or Subject:** Transportation; Travel and tourism. **Level of Education for which Award is Granted:** Undergraduate **Number Awarded:** 2. **Funds Available:** $2,500. **Duration:** One academic year.
Eligibility Requirements: Applicants must be a bus driver or maintenance personnel, or dependents of ABA operator members; must be in a technical school with two-years or more transportation-related education programs. **Application Requirements:** Application process is online (please visit the website). **Additional Information:** James Simon.

121 ■ AMERICAN BUSINESS TRAVEL ASSOCIATION
7301 Burnet Rd., Ste. 102
Austin, TX 78757
Tel: (512)356-7154
E-mail: info@austinbta.org
Web Site: http://www.austinbta.org
To award scholarship to local high school students applying for higher education support.
Title of Award: Educational and Professional Achievement Scholarships **Area, Field, or Subject:** General studies. **Level of Education for which Award is Granted:** Undergraduate **Funds Available:** $1,500.

Eligibility Requirements: Applicants must be senior students currently registered and attending classes in the Greater Austin Metropolitan Area, including students in public schools, home-schooled students and students attending private educational institutions; must be planning to further their education or professional development by enrolling in an accredited college or university, a community college, a professional, technical or vocational institute or school. **Application Requirements:** Applicants may download an application form on-line. Applicants must submit the following requirements: a transcript of grades with a minimum cumulative GPA of 3.0; complete scholarship application form; at least three, but not more than five personal evaluations; a 500-word personal essay titled "Building My Future"; a resume detailing activities at school, work, community service, sports, clubs, etc.; a brief (less than 200 words), creative autobiographical statement. **Deadline for Receipt:** February 16. **Additional Information:** Kevin Maguire, Scholarship Committee Chair, Austin Business Travel Association, 512-272-7023, kevin1maguire@yahoo.com.

122 ■ AMERICAN CLAN GREGOR SOCIETY
238 W 1220 N
American Fork, UT 84003
Web Site: http://acgs.thecapitalscot.com/
To provide educational assistance to incoming college students.
Title of Award: Harry and Edith Blunt Scholarships **Area, Field, or Subject:** General studies. **Level of Education for which Award is Granted:** Undergraduate **Funds Available:** $1,000. **Duration:** One year.
Eligibility Requirements: Applicants must be ACGS members or children of ACGS members. **Application Requirements:** Applicants must submit their transcript of record, college acceptance and personal letter about activities and educational plans. **Deadline for Receipt:** April 1. **Additional Information:** Susan Tichy stichy@gmu.edu.

123 ■ AMERICAN COMPOSITES MANUFACTURERS ASSOCIATION
1010 North Glebe Rd., Ste. 450
Arlington, VA 22201
Tel: (703)525-0511
Fax: (703)525-0743
E-mail: info@acmanet.org
Web Site: http://www.acmanet.org
To support individuals involved in the composites industry.
Title of Award: American Composites Manufacturers Association Scholarships **Area, Field, or Subject:** General studies. **Level of Education for which Award is Granted:** Undergraduate **Funds Available:** $2,000.
Eligibility Requirements: Applicants must be graduating high school seniors planning to pursue a degree in accredited four-year colleges or universities. **Application Requirements:** Application forms are available at ACMA website (www.acmanet.org).

124 ■ AMERICAN COMPOSITES MANUFACTURERS ASSOCIATION
1010 North Glebe Rd., Ste. 450
Arlington, VA 22201
Tel: (703)525-0511
Fax: (703)525-0743
E-mail: info@acmanet.org
Web Site: http://www.acmanet.org
To provide special services and networking opportunities to member companies in the 13 most western states.
Title of Award: American Composites Manufacturers Association Western Chapter Scholarships **Area, Field, or Subject:** General Studies. **Level of Education for which Award is Granted:** Undergraduate **Funds Available:** $2,000.
Eligibility Requirements: Applicants must be employees, spouses, children or grandchildren of individuals who are employed by a company located in the 13 most western states (Alaska, Arizona, California, Colorado, Hawaii, Idaho, Montana, New Mexico, Nevada, Oregon, Utah, Washington, or Wyoming) that is a member of the ACMA; must be registered full-time students (minimum 12 hours) at an accredited college or university. **Application Requirements:** Applicants must submit the completed application form; transcript of all college work; statement of educational goals; career intentions and resume of extracurricular activities; work experience; community involvement; and two letters of reference (personal reference and a reference from a professor or teacher).

Deadline for Receipt: December 31. **Additional Information:** ACMA at the above address.

125 ■ AMERICAN CONGRESS ON SURVEYING AND MAPPING
6 Montgomery Village Ave., Ste. 403
Gaithersburg, MD 20879
Tel: (240)632-9716
Fax: (240)632-1321
E-mail: curtis.summer@acsm.net
Web Site: http://www.acsm.net
CSM Scholarships are designed to encourage, recognize, and support exceptional surveying and mapping students.
Title of Award: AAGS Graduate Fellowship Award **Area, Field, or Subject:** Surveying. **Level of Education for which Award is Granted:** Undergraduate **Funds Available:** $2,000.
Eligibility Requirements: Applicants must be enrolled in or accepted to a graduate program in geodetic surveying or geodesy. **Application Requirements:** Applicants must complete the application form; applicants must provide a proof of membership in ACSM; a brief yet complete statement indicating educational objectives, future plans of study or research, professional activities and financial need; at least three letters of recommendation (minimum of two from faculty members familiar with the student's work); a complete original official transcript through year prior to when the award will be presented. **Deadline for Receipt:** October 1. **Additional Information:** dawn.james@asm.net; American Congress on Surveying and Mapping at the above address.

126 ■ AMERICAN CONGRESS ON SURVEYING AND MAPPING
6 Montgomery Village Ave., Ste. 403
Gaithersburg, MD 20879
Tel: (240)632-9716
Fax: (240)632-1321
E-mail: curtis.summer@acsm.net
Web Site: http://www.acsm.net
CSM Scholarships are designed to encourage, recognize, and support exceptional surveying and mapping students.
Title of Award: AAGS Joseph F. Dracup Scholarship Award **Area, Field, or Subject:** Surveying. **Level of Education for which Award is Granted:** Undergraduate **Funds Available:** $2,000.
Eligibility Requirements: Applicants must be enrolled in two-year or four-year-surveying (and closely related) degree program, either full or part-time. **Application Requirements:** Applicants must complete the application form; applicants must provide a proof of membership in ACSM; a brief yet complete statement indicating educational objectives, future plans of study or research, professional activities and financial need; at least three letters of recommendation (minimum of two from faculty members familiar with the student's work); a complete original official transcript through year prior to when the award will be presented. **Deadline for Receipt:** October 1. **Additional Information:** dawn. james@asm.net; American Congress on Surveying and Mapping at the above address.

127 ■ AMERICAN CONGRESS ON SURVEYING AND MAPPING
6 Montgomery Village Ave., Ste. 403
Gaithersburg, MD 20879
Tel: (240)632-9716
Fax: (240)632-1321
E-mail: curtis.summer@acsm.net
Web Site: http://www.acsm.net
To encourage, recognize, and support exceptional surveying and mapping students.
Title of Award: ACSM Fellowship Scholarships **Area, Field, or Subject:** Surveying. **Level of Education for which Award is Granted:** Undergraduate **Funds Available:** $2,000.
Eligibility Requirements: Applicants must be junior or higher standing in any of the ACSM disciplines. **Application Requirements:** Applicants must complete the application form; applicants must provide a proof of membership in ACSM; a brief yet complete statement indicating educational objectives, future plans of study or research, professional activities and financial need; at least three letters of recommendation (minimum of two from faculty members familiar with the student's work); a complete original official transcript through year prior to when the award will be presented. **Deadline for Receipt:** October 1. **Additional Informa-**

tion: dawn.james@asm.net; American Congress on Surveying and Mapping at the above address.

128 ■ AMERICAN CONGRESS ON SURVEYING AND MAPPING
6 Montgomery Village Ave., Ste. 403
Gaithersburg, MD 20879
Tel: (240)632-9716
Fax: (240)632-1321
E-mail: curtis.summer@acsm.net
Web Site: http://www.acsm.net
To encourage, recognize and support exceptional surveying and mapping students.
Title of Award: The Bernsten International Scholarships in Surveying Technology **Area, Field, or Subject:** Surveying. **Level of Education for which Award is Granted:** Undergraduate **Number Awarded:** October 1. **Funds Available:** $500.
Eligibility Requirements: Applicant must be enrolled in two-year degree programs in surveying technology. **Application Requirements:** Applicants must complete the application form; applicants must provide a proof of membership in ACSM; a brief yet complete statement indicating educational objectives, future plans of study or research, professional activities and financial need; at least three letters of recommendation (minimum of two from faculty members familiar with the student's work); a complete original official transcript through year prior to when the award will be presented. **Deadline for Receipt:** October 1. **Additional Information:** dawn.james@asm.net; American Congress on Surveying and Mapping at the above address.

129 ■ AMERICAN CONGRESS ON SURVEYING AND MAPPING
6 Montgomery Village Ave., Ste. 403
Gaithersburg, MD 20879
Tel: (240)632-9716
Fax: (240)632-1321
E-mail: curtis.summer@acsm.net
Web Site: http://www.acsm.net
To provide financial assistance to a United States citizen.
Title of Award: Nettie Dracup Memorial Scholarships **Area, Field, or Subject:** Surveying. **Level of Education for which Award is Granted:** Undergraduate **Funds Available:** $2,000.
Eligibility Requirements: Applicants must be undergraduate student who is enrolled in Geodetic Surveying in an accredited college or university. **Application Requirements:** Applicants must complete the application form; applicants must provide a proof of membership in ACSM; a brief yet complete statement indicating educational objectives, future plans of study or research, professional activities and financial need; at least three letters of recommendation (minimum of two from faculty members familiar with the student's work); a complete original official transcript through year prior to when the award will be presented. **Deadline for Receipt:** October 1. **Additional Information:** dawn. james@asm.net; American Congress on Surveying and Mapping at the above address.

130 ■ AMERICAN CONGRESS ON SURVEYING AND MAPPING
6 Montgomery Village Ave., Ste. 403
Gaithersburg, MD 20879
Tel: (240)632-9716
Fax: (240)632-1321
E-mail: curtis.summer@acsm.net
Web Site: http://www.acsm.net
To encourage, recognize, and support exceptional surveying and mapping students.
Title of Award: Kris M. Kunze Memorial Scholarships **Area, Field, or Subject:** Surveying. **Level of Education for which Award is Granted:** Undergraduate **Funds Available:** $1,000.
Eligibility Requirements: Applicants must be licensed Professional Land Surveyors of Certified Photogrammetrists pursuing college level courses in Business Administration or Business Management or applicants must be full-time students enrolled in a two or four-year degree program in Surveying and Mapping pursuing a course of study including Business Administration or Business Management. **Application Requirements:** Applicants must complete the application form; applicants must provide a proof of membership in ACSM; a brief yet complete statement indicating educational objectives, future plans of study or research, professional

activities and financial need; at least three letters of recommendation (minimum of two from faculty members familiar with the student's work); a complete original official transcript through year prior to when the award will be presented. **Deadline for Receipt:** October 1. **Additional Information:** dawn.james@asm.net; American Congress on Surveying and Mapping at the above address.

131 ■ AMERICAN CONGRESS ON SURVEYING AND MAPPING

6 Montgomery Village Ave., Ste. 403
Gaithersburg, MD 20879
Tel: (240)632-9716
Fax: (240)632-1321
E-mail: curtis.summer@acsm.net
Web Site: http://www.acsm.net
To encourage, recognize, and support exceptional surveying and mapping students.

Title of Award: The Lowell H. and Dorothy Loving Undergraduate Scholarships **Area, Field, or Subject:** Surveying. **Level of Education for which Award is Granted:** Undergraduate **Funds Available:** $2,500.

Eligibility Requirements: Applicants must be junior or senior standing in a four-year program at a university or college in the United States. **Application Requirements:** Applicants must complete the application form; applicants must provide a proof of membership in ACSM; a brief yet complete statement indicating educational objectives, future plans of study or research, professional activities and financial need; at least three letters of recommendation (minimum of two from faculty members familiar with the student's work); a complete original official transcript through year prior to when the award will be presented. **Deadline for Receipt:** October 1. **Additional Information:** dawn.james@asm.net; American Congress on Surveying and Mapping at the above address.

132 ■ AMERICAN CONGRESS ON SURVEYING AND MAPPING

6 Montgomery Village Ave., Ste. 403
Gaithersburg, MD 20879
Tel: (240)632-9716
Fax: (240)632-1321
E-mail: curtis.summer@acsm.net
Web Site: http://www.acsm.net
To encourage, recognize, and support exceptional surveying and mapping students.

Title of Award: The Cady McDonnell Memorial Scholarships **Area, Field, or Subject:** Surveying. **Level of Education for which Award is Granted:** Undergraduate **Funds Available:** $1,000.

Eligibility Requirements: Applicants must be a resident of one of the following western states; Montana, Idaho, Washington, Oregon, Wyoming, Colorado, Utah, Nevada, California, Arizona, New Mexico, Alaska, and Hawaii; applicants must be a woman student enrolled in the field of surveying. **Application Requirements:** Applicants must complete the application form; applicants must provide a proof of membership in ACSM; a brief yet complete statement indicating educational objectives, future plans of study or research, professional activities and financial need; at least three letters of recommendation (minimum of two from faculty members familiar with the student's work); a complete original official transcript through year prior to when the award will be presented. **Deadline for Receipt:** October 1. **Additional Information:** dawn.james@asm.net; American Congress on Surveying and Mapping at the above address.

133 ■ AMERICAN CONGRESS ON SURVEYING AND MAPPING

6 Montgomery Village Ave., Ste. 403
Gaithersburg, MD 20879
Tel: (240)632-9716
Fax: (240)632-1321
E-mail: curtis.summer@acsm.net
Web Site: http://www.acsm.net
To encourage, recognize, and support exceptional surveying and mapping students.

Title of Award: NSPS Board of Governors Scholarships **Area, Field, or Subject:** Surveying. **Level of Education for which Award is Granted:** Undergraduate **Funds Available:** $1,000.

Eligibility Requirements: Applicants must be enrolled in studies in surveying entering their junior year of study in a four-year degree program of their choice; applicants must maintain a minimum 3.0 grade point aver-

age. **Application Requirements:** Applicants must complete the application form; applicants must provide a proof of membership in ACSM; a brief yet complete statement indicating educational objectives, future plans of study or research, professional activities and financial need; at least three letters of recommendation (minimum of two from faculty members familiar with the student's work); a complete original official transcript through year prior to when the award will be presented. **Deadline for Receipt:** October 1. **Additional Information:** dawn.james@asm.net; American Congress on Surveying and Mapping at the above address.

134 ■ AMERICAN CONGRESS ON SURVEYING AND MAPPING

6 Montgomery Village Ave., Ste. 403
Gaithersburg, MD 20879
Tel: (240)632-9716
Fax: (240)632-1321
E-mail: curtis.summer@acsm.net
Web Site: http://www.acsm.net
To recognize outstanding students enrolled full-time in undergraduate surveying programs.

Title of Award: The NSPS Scholarships **Area, Field, or Subject:** Surveying. **Level of Education for which Award is Granted:** Undergraduate **Funds Available:** $1,000.

Eligibility Requirements: Applicants must complete the application form; applicants must provide a proof of membership in ACSM; a brief yet complete statement indicating educational objectives, future plans of study or research, professional activities and financial need; at least three letters of recommendation (minimum of two from faculty members familiar with the students work); a complete original official transcript through year prior to when the award. **Application Requirements:** Applicants must complete the application form; applicants must provide a proof of membership in ACSM; a brief yet complete statement indicating educational objectives, future plans of study or research, professional activities and financial need; at least three letters of recommendation (minimum of two from faculty members familiar with the student's work); a complete original official transcript through year prior to when the award will be presented. **Deadline for Receipt:** October 1. **Additional Information:** dawn.james@asm.net; American Congress on Surveying and Mapping at the above address.

135 ■ AMERICAN CONGRESS ON SURVEYING AND MAPPING

6 Montgomery Village Ave., Ste. 403
Gaithersburg, MD 20879
Tel: (240)632-9716
Fax: (240)632-1321
E-mail: curtis.summer@acsm.net
Web Site: http://www.acsm.net
ACSM Scholarships are designed to encourage, recognize, and support exceptional surveying and mapping students.

Title of Award: The Schonstedt Scholarships in Surveying **Area, Field, or Subject:** Surveying. **Level of Education for which Award is Granted:** Undergraduate **Funds Available:** 1,500.

Eligibility Requirements: Applicant must be junior or senior student enrolled in a college or university. **Application Requirements:** Applicants must complete the application form; applicants must provide a proof of membership in ACSM; a brief yet complete statement indicating educational objectives, future plans of study or research, professional activities and financial need; at least three letters of recommendation (minimum of two from faculty members familiar with the student's work); a complete original official transcript through year prior to when the award will be presented. **Deadline for Receipt:** October 1.

136 ■ AMERICAN COPY EDITORS SOCIETY

333 W State St.
Milwaukee, WI 53203
Web Site: http://www.copyblock.com/acesdenver
To encourage young individuals to continue their career as potential professional copy editors.

Title of Award: Aubespin Scholarships **Area, Field, or Subject:** Editors and editing. **Level of Education for which Award is Granted:** Undergraduate **Funds Available:** $2,500.

Eligibility Requirements: Applicant must be a junior, senior or graduate student in the fall, graduating student who will take full-time copy editing jobs or internships. **Application Requirements:** Application forms are available on the website. Applicant must send a list of course work relevant to copy editing, list of copy editing experience, including work on student and professional publications; must provide an essay (750 words, double spaced); must have two recommendation letters: one from a faculty member or adviser and one from someone on a college or professional publicaton; must have two copies of five to 10 headlines; must submit a copy of a story that demonstrate the applicant's ability. Application form and other supporting documents must be sent to: ACES Scholarships, Milwaukee Journal Sentinel, 333 W State St., Milwaukee, WI 53203. **Deadline for Receipt:** November 15.

137 ■ AMERICAN CULINARY FEDERATION
The American Academy of Chefs
180 Center Place Way
St. Augustine, FL 32095
Tel: (904)824-4468
Free: 800-624-9458
Fax: (904)825-4758
E-mail: academy@acfchefs.net
Web Site: http://www.acfchefs.org
to provide financial assistance to those studying culinary arts.
Title of Award: Balestreri/Cutino Scholarships **Area, Field, or Subject:** Culinary arts. **Level of Education for which Award is Granted:** Undergraduate **Funds Available:** No specific amount.
Eligibility Requirements: Applicants must be an exemplary student currently enrolled in an accredited, post-secondary college, with a major in either culinary or pastry arts, or be an ACF registered apprentice. Applicant must have completed a grading or marking period (trimester, semester or quarter) and must have a career goal of becoming a chef or pastry chef. **Application Requirements:** Applicants must submit a completed application form; two letters of recommendation from industry and/or culinary professionals (may not be related to the applicant in any manner); a Financial Aid Release Form completed by the financial aid office; sealed official transcript showing current GPA; and signed photo and/or photo in ACF publications. **Deadline for Receipt:** December 31.

138 ■ AMERICAN CULINARY FEDERATION
The American Academy of Chefs
180 Center Place Way
St. Augustine, FL 32095
Tel: (904)824-4468
Free: 800-624-9458
Fax: (904)825-4758
E-mail: academy@acfchefs.net
Web Site: http://www.acfchefs.org
to provide financial assistance to those studying culinary arts.
Title of Award: Chaine des Rotisseurs Scholarships **Area, Field, or Subject:** Culinary arts. **Level of Education for which Award is Granted:** Undergraduate **Funds Available:** No specific amount.
Eligibility Requirements: Applicants must be an exemplary student currently enrolled in an accredited, post-secondary college, with a major in either culinary or pastry arts, or be an ACF registered apprentice. Applicant must have completed a grading or marking period (trimester, semester or quarter) and must have a career goal of becoming a chef or pastry chef. **Application Requirements:** Applicants must submit a completed application form; two letters of recommendation from industry and/or culinary professionals (may not be related to the applicant in any manner); a Financial Aid Release Form completed by the financial aid office; sealed official transcript showing current GPA; and signed photo and/or photo in ACF publications. **Deadline for Receipt:** December 31.

139 ■ AMERICAN CULINARY FEDERATION
The American Academy of Chefs
180 Center Place Way
St. Augustine, FL 32095
Tel: (904)824-4468
Free: 800-624-9458
Fax: (904)825-4758
E-mail: academy@acfchefs.net
Web Site: http://www.acfchefs.org
to provide financial assistance to those studying culinary arts.
Title of Award: Julia Child Memorial Scholarships **Area, Field, or Subject:** Culinary arts. **Level of Education for which Award is Granted:** Undergraduate **Funds Available:** No specific amount.

Eligibility Requirements: Applicants must be an exemplary student currently enrolled in an accredited, post-secondary college, with a major in either culinary or pastry arts, or be an ACF registered apprentice. Applicant must have completed a grading or marking period (trimester, semester or quarter) and must have a career goal of becoming a chef or pastry chef. **Application Requirements:** Applicants must submit a completed application form; two letters of recommendation from industry and/or culinary professionals (may not be related to the applicant in any manner); a Financial Aid Release Form completed by the financial aid office; sealed official transcript showing current GPA; and signed photo and/or photo in ACF publications. **Deadline for Receipt:** December 31.

140 ■ AMERICAN CULINARY FEDERATION
The American Academy of Chefs
180 Center Place Way
St. Augustine, FL 32095
Tel: (904)824-4468
Free: 800-624-9458
Fax: (904)825-4758
E-mail: academy@acfchefs.net
Web Site: http://www.acfchefs.org
to provide financial assistance to those studying culinary arts.
Title of Award: Linda Cullen Memorial Scholarships **Area, Field, or Subject:** Culinary arts. **Level of Education for which Award is Granted:** High School **Funds Available:** No specific amount.
Eligibility Requirements: Applicants must be an exemplary senior high school student eligible to graduate the same year as the scholarship is applied for. Applicants must be currently accepted to an accredited, post-secondary college, with a major in either culinary or pastry arts, or must be an ACF registered apprentice; have a career goal of becoming a chef or pastry chef. **Application Requirements:** Applicants must submit a completed application form; two letters of recommendation from industry and/or culinary professionals (may not be related to the applicant in any manner); a Financial Aid Release Form completed by the financial aid office; sealed official high school transcript showing current GPA; and signed photo and/or photo in ACF publications. **Deadline for Receipt:** March 31.

141 ■ AMERICAN CULINARY FEDERATION
The American Academy of Chefs
180 Center Place Way
St. Augustine, FL 32095
Tel: (904)824-4468
Free: 800-624-9458
Fax: (904)825-4758
E-mail: academy@acfchefs.net
Web Site: http://www.acfchefs.org
to provide financial assistance to those studying culinary arts.
Title of Award: Stanley "Doc" Jensen Scholarships **Area, Field, or Subject:** Culinary arts. **Level of Education for which Award is Granted:** High School **Funds Available:** No specific amount.
Eligibility Requirements: Applicants must be an exemplary senior high school student eligible to graduate the same year as the scholarship is applied for. Applicants must be currently accepted to an accredited, post-secondary college, with a major in either culinary or pastry arts, or must be an ACF registered apprentice; have a career goal of becoming a chef or pastry chef. **Application Requirements:** Applicants must submit a completed application form; two letters of recommendation from industry and/or culinary professionals (may not be related to the applicant in any manner); a Financial Aid Release Form completed by the financial aid office; sealed official high school transcript showing current GPA; and signed photo and/or photo in ACF publications. **Deadline for Receipt:** March 31.

142 ■ AMERICAN CULINARY FEDERATION
The American Academy of Chefs
180 Center Place Way
St. Augustine, FL 32095
Tel: (904)824-4468
Free: 800-624-9458
Fax: (904)825-4758
E-mail: academy@acfchefs.net
Web Site: http://www.acfchefs.org

to provide financial assistance to those studying culinary arts.
Title of Award: Andrew Macrina Scholarships **Area, Field, or Subject:** Culinary arts. **Level of Education for which Award is Granted:** High School **Funds Available:** No specific amount.

Eligibility Requirements: Applicants must be an exemplary senior high school student eligible to graduate the same year as the scholarship is applied for. Applicants must be currently accepted to an accredited, post-secondary college, with a major in either culinary or pastry arts, or must be an ACF registered apprentice; have a career goal of becoming a chef or pastry chef. **Application Requirements:** Applicants must submit a completed application form; two letters of recommendation from industry and/or culinary professionals (may not be related to the applicant in any manner); a Financial Aid Release Form completed by the financial aid office; sealed official high school transcript showing current GPA; and signed photo and/or photo in ACF publications. **Deadline for Receipt:** March 31.

143 ■ AMERICAN CULINARY FEDERATION

The American Academy of Chefs
180 Center Place Way
St. Augustine, FL 32095
Tel: (904)824-4468
Free: 800-624-9458
Fax: (904)825-4758
E-mail: academy@acfchefs.net
Web Site: http://www.acfchefs.org
to provide financial assistance to those studying culinary arts.

Title of Award: Ray and Gertrude Marshall Scholarships **Area, Field, or Subject:** Culinary arts. **Level of Education for which Award is Granted:** Undergraduate **Funds Available:** No specific amount.

Eligibility Requirements: Applicants must be an exemplary student currently enrolled in an accredited, post-secondary college, with a major in either culinary or pastry arts, or be an ACF registered apprentice. Applicant must have completed a grading or marking period (trimester, semester or quarter) and must have a career goal of becoming a chef or pastry chef. **Application Requirements:** Applicants must submit a completed application form; two letters of recommendation from industry and/or culinary professionals (may not be related to the applicant in any manner); a Financial Aid Release Form completed by the financial aid office; sealed official transcript showing current GPA; and signed photo and/or photo in ACF publications. **Deadline for Receipt:** December 31.

144 ■ AMERICAN CULINARY FEDERATION

The American Academy of Chefs
180 Center Place Way
St. Augustine, FL 32095
Tel: (904)824-4468
Free: 800-624-9458
Fax: (904)825-4758
E-mail: academy@acfchefs.net
Web Site: http://www.acfchefs.org
to provide financial assistance to those studying culinary arts.

Title of Award: Tomato Fest Scholarship Grants **Area, Field, or Subject:** Culinary arts. **Level of Education for which Award is Granted:** Undergraduate **Funds Available:** No specific amount.

Eligibility Requirements: Applicants must be an exemplary student currently enrolled in an accredited, post-secondary college, with a major in either culinary or pastry arts, or be an ACF registered apprentice. Applicant must have completed a grading or marking period (trimester, semester or quarter) and must have a career goal of becoming a chef or pastry chef. **Application Requirements:** Applicants must submit a completed application form; two letters of recommendation from industry and/or culinary professionals (may not be related to the applicant in any manner); a Financial Aid Release Form completed by the financial aid office; sealed official transcript showing current GPA; and signed photo and/or photo in ACF publications. **Deadline for Receipt:** December 31.

145 ■ AMERICAN FLORAL INDUSTRY ASSOCIATION

PO Box 420244
Dallas, TX 75342-0244
Tel: (214)742-2747
Fax: (214)742-2648
E-mail: afia@afia.net

Web Site: http://www.afia.net
To provide financial support to graduating high school seniors planning to continue their education in an accredited school.

Title of Award: AFIA Scholarships **Area, Field, or Subject:** General studies. **Level of Education for which Award is Granted:** Undergraduate **Number Awarded:** 2. **Funds Available:** $1,000. **Duration:** One academic year.

Eligibility Requirements: Applicants must be an employee or a dependent of an AFIA member company in good standing; must be high school seniors graduating from an accredited high school; have a minimum of a 3.0 GPA on a 4.0 grading system. **Application Requirements:** Applicants must submit a completed application form; an official high school transcript; two letters of recommendation; and a stated objective. **Deadline for Receipt:** May 4. **Additional Information:** rpoling@afia.net.

146 ■ AMERICAN FOREIGN SERVICE ASSOCIATION

2101 E St. NW
Washington, DC 20037
Tel: (202)338-4045
Free: 800-704-AFSA
Fax: (202)338-6820
E-mail: member@afsa.org
Web Site: http://www.afsa.org
To provide financial assistance for college education of deserving students who are dependents of the active, retired with pension, deceased or separated US government Foreign Service employees who served or serving at least a year abroad in a foreign affairs agencies.

Title of Award: American Foreign Service Association Scholarship Fund **Area, Field, or Subject:** General studies. **Level of Education for which Award is Granted:** Undergraduate **Number Awarded:** 55. **Funds Available:** $1,000 to $4,500.

Eligibility Requirements: Applicants must be students who attended or will be attending full-time (12 credit hours or more) as an undergraduate at a 2 or 4 year accredited college, university, community college, art school or conservatory (stateside or overseas); have cumulative 2.0 GPA on a 4.0 scale; must complete undergraduate in four years; and must demonstrate financial need. **Application Requirements:** Applicants must submit the Scholarship Application accompanied with a copy of high school/college transcripts; students or parents must complete the CSS PROFILE. **Deadline for Receipt:** February 6. **Additional Information:** Lori Dec, Scholarship Director, at the above address.

147 ■ AMERICAN GI FORUM OF SAN JOSE

765 Story Rd.
San Jose, CA 95122
Tel: (408)288-9470
Fax: (408)288-9473
E-mail: sjgif@sjgif.org
Web Site: http://www.sjgif.org
To establish a program of financial assistance for qualified students of Hispanic descent that reside in the County of Santa Clara, California.

Title of Award: American GI Forum of San Jose Scholarships **Area, Field, or Subject:** General Studies. **Level of Education for which Award is Granted:** Undergraduate **Funds Available:** No specific amount.

Eligibility Requirements: Applicants must be graduating from a high school located in Santa Clara County; must be enrolled or plan to enroll in an accredited college or university leading to an associate or bachelor's degree; and must have a minimum grade point average of 2.5. **Application Requirements:** Applicants must submit completed application form; wallet size senior picture; official copy of high school transcript; biographical data sheet; an autobiographical essay; and a copy of parent's most recent Federal Income Tax or Student Aid Application for California.

148 ■ AMERICAN HANDEL SOCIETY

School of Music, University of Maryland
College Park, MD 20742
Tel: (909)607-3568
E-mail: info@americanhandelsociety.org
Web Site: http://www.americanhandelsociety.org
To support work in the area of Handel or other related research.

Title of Award: J. Merrill Knapp Research Fellowships **Area, Field, or Subject:** General studies. **Level of Education for which Award is

Granted: Undergraduate **Funds Available:** $2,000.
Eligibility Requirements: Applicant must be students at North American universities and residents of North America. **Application Requirements:** Applicant must submit a curriculum vitae, a description of the project (not to exceed 750 words), a budget showing how and when the applicant plans to use the funds, and a description of other grants applied for or received for the same project; must have two recommendation letters. Application and other materials must be sent to: School of Music, University of Maryland, College Park **Deadline for Receipt:** March 15. **Additional Information:** Richard King.

149 ▪ AMERICAN HOTEL AND LODGING EDUCATIONAL FOUNDATION
1201 New York Ave. NW., Ste. 600
Washington, DC 20005-3931
Tel: (202)289-3100
Fax: (202)289-3199
E-mail: chammond@ahlef.org
Web Site: http://www.ahlef.org
To provide educational assistance to hospitality management students.
Title of Award: The AAA (American Automobile Association) Five Diamond Hospitality Scholarships **Area, Field, or Subject:** Hotel, institutional, and restaurant management. **Level of Education for which Award is Granted:** Undergraduate **Funds Available:** $5,000.
Eligibility Requirements: Applicants must be enrolled in at least 12 credit hours for the upcoming Fall and Spring semesters; at least a sophomore at the time of nomination; have a minimum 3.0 GPA; and must be U.S. citizens or permanent U.S. residents. **Application Requirements:** Applicants must complete all the required sections of the application. **Deadline for Receipt:** May 1.

150 ▪ AMERICAN HOTEL AND LODGING EDUCATIONAL FOUNDATION
1201 New York Ave. NW., Ste. 600
Washington, DC 20005-3931
Tel: (202)289-3100
Fax: (202)289-3199
E-mail: chammond@ahlef.org
Web Site: http://www.ahlef.org
To provide educational assistance for current lodging employees and their dependents.
Title of Award: The American Express Scholarship Competition **Area, Field, or Subject:** Hotel, institutional, and restaurant management. **Level of Education for which Award is Granted:** Undergraduate **Funds Available:** Baccalaureate Majors - $2,000 full-time enrollment; or $1,000 part-time; Associate Majors - $1,000 full-time enrollment; or $500 part- time.
Eligibility Requirements: Applicants must be enrolled full-time or part-time; must be working a minimum of 20-hours per week at an AH & LA member hotel and with at least 12 months hotel experience. **Application Requirements:** Applicants must complete all the required sections of the application. **Additional Information:** Founded by American Express in 1994. **Deadline for Receipt:** May 1. **Additional Information:** Crystal Hammond, manager of the Foundation's programs, at chammond@ahlef.org.

151 ▪ AMERICAN HOTEL AND LODGING EDUCATIONAL FOUNDATION
1201 New York Ave. NW., Ste. 600
Washington, DC 20005-3931
Tel: (202)289-3100
Fax: (202)289-3199
E-mail: chammond@ahlef.org
Web Site: http://www.ahlef.org
To provide financial aid to minority students pursuing a degree in hotel management.
Title of Award: The Hyatt Hotels Fund For Minority Lodging Management Students **Area, Field, or Subject:** Hotel, institutional, and restaurant management. **Level of Education for which Award is Granted:** Undergraduate **Number Awarded:** 18. **Funds Available:** $2,000.
Eligibility Requirements: Applicant must be enrolled in at least 12 credit hours for the upcoming Fall and Spring semesters, or just the Fall semester if graduating this December; at least a sophomore in a four-year program at the time of application; a minority descent: African-American,

Hispanic, American Indian, Alaskan Native, Asian or Pacific Islander; a U.S. citizen or permanent U.S. resident. **Application Requirements:** Applicants must complete all the required sections of the application. **Additional Information:** Established by Hyatt in 1988. **Deadline for Receipt:** May 1.

152 ▪ AMERICAN HOTEL AND LODGING EDUCATIONAL FOUNDATION
1201 New York Ave. NW., Ste. 600
Washington, DC 20005-3931
Tel: (202)289-3100
Fax: (202)289-3199
E-mail: chammond@ahlef.org
Web Site: http://www.ahlef.org
To provide educational assistance to hospitality management students.
Title of Award: The Steve Hymans Extended Stay Scholarship Program **Area, Field, or Subject:** Hotel, institutional, and restaurant management. **Level of Education for which Award is Granted:** Undergraduate **Funds Available:** Baccalaureate Majors - $2,000 full-time enrollment; or $1,000 part-time. Associate Majors - $1,000 full-time enrollment; or $500 part-time.
Eligibility Requirements: Applicant must be enrolled full-time or part-time; have a minimum of 3.0 GPA; be a U.S. citizen or permanent U.S. resident; and have at least some experience either working or interning (paid or unpaid) at a lodging property. **Application Requirements:** Applicants must complete all the required sections of the application. **Additional Information:** Established in honor of Steve Hymans. **Deadline for Receipt:** May 1.

153 ▪ AMERICAN HOTEL AND LODGING EDUCATIONAL FOUNDATION
1201 New York Ave. NW., Ste. 600
Washington, DC 20005-3931
Tel: (202)289-3100
Fax: (202)289-3199
E-mail: chammond@ahlef.org
Web Site: http://www.ahlef.org
To provide educational assistance to students pursuing a degree in hospitality-related degree programs.
Title of Award: Lodging Management Program (LMP) Scholarships **Area, Field, or Subject:** Hotel, institutional, and restaurant management. **Level of Education for which Award is Granted:** Undergraduate **Funds Available:** $1,000 per scholarship.
Eligibility Requirements: Applicants must be graduating high school seniors and have completed Year 1 and 2 of the LMP; must have a minimum 2.0 GPA. **Application Requirements:** Applications are self nominated which means students do not have to attend a particular school or be nominated by their respective schools. Applicants must complete all sections of the AH&LEF scholarship application form. **Additional Information:** Email Crystal Hammond, manager of the Foundation's programs, at chammond@ahlef.org.

154 ▪ AMERICAN HOTEL AND LODGING EDUCATIONAL FOUNDATION
1201 New York Ave. NW., Ste. 600
Washington, DC 20005-3931
Tel: (202)289-3100
Fax: (202)289-3199
E-mail: chammond@ahlef.org
Web Site: http://www.ahlef.org
To provide educational assistance for lodging management students.
Title of Award: The Arthur J. Packard Memorial Scholarship Competition **Area, Field, or Subject:** Hotel, institutional, and restaurant management. **Level of Education for which Award is Granted:** Undergraduate **Funds Available:** First-place winner $5,000; Second-place $3,000; Third-place $2,000.
Eligibility Requirements: Applicants must be enrolled full-time for the upcoming Fall and Spring semesters; have a minimum GPA of 3.5 or higher; and must be U.S. residents. **Application Requirements:** Applicants must complete all the required sections of the application. **Additional Information:** Established in honor of Arthur J. Packard. **Deadline for Receipt:** May 1. **Additional Information:** Crystal Hammond at 202-289-3188 or chammond@ahlef.org.

155 ■ AMERICAN HOTEL AND LODGING EDUCATIONAL FOUNDATION

1201 New York Ave. NW., Ste. 600
Washington, DC 20005-3931
Tel: (202)289-3100
Fax: (202)289-3199
E-mail: chammond@ahlef.org
Web Site: http://www.ahlef.org
To provide educational assistance to students pursuing a degree in hospitality-related degree programs.
Title of Award: Pepsi Scholarships **Area, Field, or Subject:** Hotel, institutional, and restaurant management. **Level of Education for which Award is Granted:** Undergraduate **Funds Available:** $500-$3,000 depending upon enrollment. Funds must be used exclusively for tuition, fees and books.
Eligibility Requirements: Applicants must be graduates of the Hospitality High School in Washington, D.C.; enrolled in at least 12 credit hours for the upcoming Fall and Spring semesters; worked at least 250 hours in the hotel/hospitality industry; and have a minimum 2.5 GPA. **Application Requirements:** Applicants must complete all the required sections of the application. **Additional Information:** Created by PepsiCo Foundation. **Deadline for Receipt:** May 1. **Additional Information:** 202-312-2007.

156 ■ AMERICAN HOTEL AND LODGING EDUCATIONAL FOUNDATION

1201 New York Ave. NW., Ste. 600
Washington, DC 20005-3931
Tel: (202)289-3100
Fax: (202)289-3199
E-mail: chammond@ahlef.org
Web Site: http://www.ahlef.org
To provide educational assistance to lodging management students.
Title of Award: Rama Scholarships for the American Dream **Area, Field, or Subject:** Hotel, institutional, and restaurant management. **Level of Education for which Award is Granted:** Graduate, Undergraduate **Funds Available:** $1,000-$3,000.
Eligibility Requirements: Applicants must be enrolled in at least 9-credit hours for the upcoming Fall and Spring semesters or just the Fall semester if graduating in December; undergraduate or graduate hospitality management majors; have a minimum 2.5 GPA; be U.S. citizens or permanent U.S. residents. **Application Requirements:** Applicants must complete all the required sections of the application. **Additional Information:** Established by JHM Hotels, Inc. **Deadline for Receipt:** May 1. **Additional Information:** Crystal Hammond at 202-289-3188 or email at chammond@ahlef.org.

157 ■ AMERICAN INDIAN COLLEGE FUND

8333 Greenwood Blvd.
Denver, CO 80221
Tel: (303)426-8900
Free: 800-776-3863
Fax: (303)426-1200
E-mail: info@collegefund.org
Web Site: http://www.collegefund.org
To provide financial assistance for American Indian students who are pursuing postsecondary education.
Title of Award: Cartwright Scholarships Program **Area, Field, or Subject:** General studies. **Level of Education for which Award is Granted:** Undergraduate **Funds Available:** $2,000.
Eligibility Requirements: Applicants must be male students who have at least a 3.0 grade point average; must commit to mentoring other male students and encouraging them to attend college; must be American Indian or Alaskan Native with proof of enrollment or descendancy; must be enrolled full-time at an eligible tribal college; and must have demonstrated exceptional academic achievement and financial need. **Application Requirements:** Applicants must check the available website for the required materials and for the online application process. **Additional Information:** In 2004, Dorwin "Doc" and Barbara Cartwright's passion for education compelled them to establish an endowment through the American Indian College Fund. **Additional Information:** American Indian College Fund at the above address.

158 ■ AMERICAN INDIAN COLLEGE FUND

8333 Greenwood Blvd.
Denver, CO 80221

Tel: (303)426-8900
Free: 800-776-3863
Fax: (303)426-1200
E-mail: info@collegefund.org
Web Site: http://www.collegefund.org
To provide students with exposure to career options, leadership skills and information on the education and commitment necessary to succeed in the business world.
Title of Award: Citi Foundation Scholarships Program **Area, Field, or Subject:** General studies. **Level of Education for which Award is Granted:** Undergraduate **Funds Available:** $4,000.
Eligibility Requirements: Applicants must have at least a 3.0 grade point average; must commit to organizing and participating in a career exploration day; must be American Indian or Alaskan Native with proof of enrollment or descendancy; must be enrolled full-time at an eligible tribal college; and must have demonstrated exceptional academic achievement and financial need. **Application Requirements:** Applicants must check the available website for the required materials and for the application process online. **Additional Information:** American Indian College Fund at the above address.

159 ■ AMERICAN INDIAN COLLEGE FUND

8333 Greenwood Blvd.
Denver, CO 80221
Tel: (303)426-8900
Free: 800-776-3863
Fax: (303)426-1200
E-mail: info@collegefund.org
Web Site: http://www.collegefund.org
To provide financial assistance for students who are in need.
Title of Award: Coca-Cola First Generation Scholarships **Area, Field, or Subject:** General studies. **Level of Education for which Award is Granted:** Undergraduate **Funds Available:** $5,000.
Eligibility Requirements: Applicants must have at least a 3.0 grade point average; must be in first or second semester of college; must be the first member of their immediate family to attend college; must be American Indian or Alaskan Native with proof of enrollment or descendancy; must be enrolled full-time at an eligible tribal college; and must have demonstrated exceptional academic achievement and financial need. **Application Requirements:** Applicants must check the available website for the application process online and for the required materials. **Additional Information:** American Indian College Fund at the above address.

160 ■ AMERICAN INDIAN COLLEGE FUND

8333 Greenwood Blvd.
Denver, CO 80221
Tel: (303)426-8900
Free: 800-776-3863
Fax: (303)426-1200
E-mail: info@collegefund.org
Web Site: http://www.collegefund.org
To provide need-based scholarships for outstanding American Indian students who are currently enrolled at a tribal college in Minnesota or New Mexico.
Title of Award: General Mills Foundation Scholarships **Area, Field, or Subject:** General studies. **Level of Education for which Award is Granted:** Undergraduate **Funds Available:** $2,000.
Eligibility Requirements: Applicants must have at least a 2.5 grade point average; must be American Indian or Alaskan Native with proof of enrollment or descendancy; must be enrolled full-time at an eligible Minnesota or New Mexico tribal college; and must have demonstrated exceptional academic achievement and financial need. **Application Requirements:** Applicants must check the available website for the required materials. **Additional Information:** American Indian College Fund at the above address.

161 ■ AMERICAN INDIAN COLLEGE FUND

8333 Greenwood Blvd.
Denver, CO 80221
Tel: (303)426-8900
Free: 800-776-3863
Fax: (303)426-1200
E-mail: info@collegefund.org

Web Site: http://www.collegefund.org
To award need-based scholarships to outstanding American Indian youth who will be entering freshmen at a tribal college.
Title of Award: Hilton Tribal College Diversity Scholarships **Area, Field, or Subject:** General studies. **Level of Education for which Award is Granted:** Undergraduate **Funds Available:** $2,500.
Eligibility Requirements: Applicants must have at least a 3.0 grade point average; must be high school graduates; must be American Indian or Alaskan Native with proof of enrollment or descendancy; must be enrolled full-time at an eligible tribal college; and must have demonstrated exceptional academic achievement and financial need. **Application Requirements:** Applicants must check the available website to fill out the application form online. **Additional Information:** American Indian College Fund at the above address.

162 ■ AMERICAN INDIAN COLLEGE FUND
8333 Greenwood Blvd.
Denver, CO 80221
Tel: (303)426-8900
Free: 800-776-3863
Fax: (303)426-1200
E-mail: info@collegefund.org
Web Site: http://www.collegefund.org
To award scholarships to outstanding American Indian students who are currently enrolled in tribal colleges.
Title of Award: Nissan North America, Inc. Scholarships **Area, Field, or Subject:** General studies. **Level of Education for which Award is Granted:** Undergraduate **Funds Available:** $3,000. **Duration:** One year.
Eligibility Requirements: Applicants must have at least a 2.5 grade point average; must be enrolled full-time at an eligible tribal college; must be American Indian or Alaskan Native with proof of enrollment or descendancy; and must have demonstrated exceptional academic achievement. **Application Requirements:** Applicants must check the available website to download the application form. **Additional Information:** American Indian College Fund at the above address.

163 ■ AMERICAN INDIAN COLLEGE FUND
8333 Greenwood Blvd.
Denver, CO 80221
Tel: (303)426-8900
Free: 800-776-3863
Fax: (303)426-1200
E-mail: info@collegefund.org
Web Site: http://www.collegefund.org
To award scholarships to American Indian students who are enrolled in a tribal college.
Title of Award: Sovereign Nations Scholarship Fund **Area, Field, or Subject:** General studies. **Level of Education for which Award is Granted:** Undergraduate **Funds Available:** $2,000.
Eligibility Requirements: Applicants must have demonstrated exceptional academic achievement by maintaining a 3.0 or higher G.P.A.; must commit to working for their tribe or an Indian organization upon completion of their degree; must be enrolled full-time at an eligible tribal college; and must be American Indian or Alaskan Native with proof of enrollment or descendancy. **Application Requirements:** Applicants must check the available website for the application process online. **Additional Information:** American Indian College Fund at the above address.

164 ■ AMERICAN INDIAN COLLEGE FUND
8333 Greenwood Blvd.
Denver, CO 80221
Tel: (303)426-8900
Free: 800-776-3863
Fax: (303)426-1200
E-mail: info@collegefund.org
Web Site: http://www.collegefund.org
To award scholarships for outstanding American Indian students who are enrolled in a tribal college.
Title of Award: Time Warner Tribal Scholars Program **Area, Field, or Subject:** General studies. **Level of Education for which Award is Granted:** Undergraduate **Funds Available:** $2,500. **Duration:** One year.
Eligibility Requirements: Applicants must have at least a 2.5 grade point average; must be enrolled full time at an eligible tribal college; and must

be American Indian or Alaskan Native with proof of enrollment or descendancy. **Application Requirements:** Applicants must check the available website to download the application form. **Additional Information:** American Indian College Fund at the above address.

165 ■ AMERICAN INDIAN COLLEGE FUND
8333 Greenwood Blvd.
Denver, CO 80221
Tel: (303)426-8900
Free: 800-776-3863
Fax: (303)426-1200
E-mail: info@collegefund.org
Web Site: http://www.collegefund.org
To award a scholarship to the best and the brightest American Indian student attending a tribal college.
Title of Award: Woksape Oyate: "Wisdom of the People" Distinguished Scholars Award **Area, Field, or Subject:** General studies. **Level of Education for which Award is Granted:** Undergraduate **Number Awarded:** 1. **Funds Available:** $8,000.
Eligibility Requirements: Program is open to valedictorians or salutatorians of their high school class; must be American Indian or Alaskan Native with proof of enrollment or descendancy; must be enrolled full-time at an eligible tribal college; and must have demonstrated exceptional academic achievement. **Application Requirements:** Applicants must check the available website to download the application form. **Additional Information:** American Indian College Fund at the above address.

166 ■ AMERICAN INDIAN EDUCATION FOUNDATION
2401 Eglin St.
Rapid City, SD 57703
Tel: (866)866-8642; (866)866-8642
Fax: (605)342-4113
E-mail: info@programs.org
Web Site: http://www.nrcprograms.org
To award scholarship to Native American undergraduates of any major.
Title of Award: Association on American Indian Affairs Emergency Aid Scholarship **Area, Field, or Subject:** General studies. **Level of Education for which Award is Granted:** Undergraduate **Number Awarded:** 20. **Funds Available:** $100-$400.
Eligibility Requirements: Applicants must be enrolled members of a federally recognized tribe. **Application Requirements:** Applicants must: complete AIEF Scholarship Application; provide documentation of tribal enrollment for themselves or their parents; provide transcripts with ACT and GPA scores; attach an essay that outlines the following information: introduction, academics, career plans, service to the Native American community, leadership/community service, financial needs and unique circumstances. **Deadline for Receipt:** April 4. **Additional Information:** Association on American Indian Affairs, ENA Scholarship, 966 Hungerford Dr. Ste. 12 B Rockeville, MD 20850. 240-314-7155.

167 ■ AMERICAN INDIAN EDUCATION FOUNDATION
2401 Eglin St.
Rapid City, SD 57703
Tel: (866)866-8642; (866)866-8642
Fax: (605)342-4113
E-mail: info@programs.org
Web Site: http://www.nrcprograms.org
To give American Indian students the tools, resources and opportunities to learn and succeed.
Title of Award: Daughters of the American Revolution American Indian Scholarships **Area, Field, or Subject:** General studies. **Level of Education for which Award is Granted:** Undergraduate **Number Awarded:** 60. **Funds Available:** $500.
Eligibility Requirements: Applicants must be: Native Americans who can show proof of ancestry; undergraduate or graduate students who have a GPA of 2.75 or higher; may be in any major. **Application Requirements:** Applicants must submit an application to the American Indian Scholarship, 1776 D St. NW Washington, DC 20006-5303; 202-628-1776; www.dar.org. **Deadline for Receipt:** April 1.

168 ■ AMERICAN INDIAN EDUCATION FOUNDATION
2401 Eglin St.
Rapid City, SD 57703

Tel: (866)866-8642; (866)866-8642
Fax: (605)342-4113
E-mail: info@programs.org
Web Site: http://www.nrcprograms.org
To give American Indian students the tools, resources and opportunities to learn and succeed.
Title of Award: International Order of the King's Daughters and Sons North American Indian Scholarship Program **Area, Field, or Subject:** General studies. **Level of Education for which Award is Granted:** Undergraduate **Funds Available:** $650.
Eligibility Requirements: Applicants must be: Native Americans who have (or whose parents have) a reservation number; undergraduates of any major. **Application Requirements:** Applicants must: complete AIEF Scholarship Application; provide documentation of tribal enrollment for themselves or their parents; provide transcripts with ACT and GPA scores; attach an essay that outlines the following information: introduction, academics, career plans, service to the Native American community, leadership/community service, financial needs and unique circumstances.
Deadline for Receipt: April 1. **Additional Information:** International Order of the King's Daughters and Sons. Attn: Director, North American Indian Department PO Box 1040 Chautauqua, NY 14722-1040; 716-357-4951.

169 ■ AMERICAN INDIAN EDUCATION FOUNDATION
2401 Eglin St.
Rapid City, SD 57703
Tel: (866)866-8642; (866)866-8642
Fax: (605)342-4113
E-mail: info@programs.org
Web Site: http://www.nrcprograms.org
To give American Indian students the tools, resources and opportunities to learn and succeed.
Title of Award: Native American Education Grants **Area, Field, or Subject:** General studies. **Level of Education for which Award is Granted:** Graduate, Undergraduate **Funds Available:** $200-$3,000.
Eligibility Requirements: Applicants must be: enrolled members of federally recognized tribes; undergraduate or graduate students of any major. **Application Requirements:** Applicants must: complete AIEF Scholarship Application; provide documentation of tribal enrollment for themselves or their parents; provide transcripts with ACT and GPA scores; attach an essay that outlines the following information: introduction, academics, career plans, service to the Native American community, leadership/community service, financial needs and unique circumstances.
Deadline for Receipt: June 1. **Additional Information:** Frances Cook, Native American Education Grants, Presbyterian Church-USA, 100 Witherspoon St. Rm M052B, Louisville, KY 40202; 888-728-7228 x 5776.

170 ■ AMERICAN INDIAN EDUCATION FOUNDATION
2401 Eglin St.
Rapid City, SD 57703
Tel: (866)866-8642; (866)866-8642
Fax: (605)342-4113
E-mail: info@programs.org
Web Site: http://www.nrcprograms.org
To give American Indian students the tools, resources and opportunities to learn and succeed.
Title of Award: Jackie Robinson Foundation Minority Scholarship **Area, Field, or Subject:** General studies. **Level of Education for which Award is Granted:** Undergraduate **Funds Available:** $6,000.
Eligibility Requirements: Applicants must be high school seniors entering an accredited college or university as freshmen. **Application Requirements:** Applicants must: complete AIEF Scholarship Application; provide documentation of tribal enrollment for themselves or their parents; provide transcripts with ACT and GPA scores; attach an essay that outlines the following information: introduction, academics, career plans, service to the Native American community, leadership/community service, financial needs and unique circumstances. **Deadline for Receipt:** April 1.
Additional Information: Jackie Robinson Foundation, Attn: Scholarship Coordinator, 3 W 35th St. 11th Fl. New York, NY 10001; 212-290-8600; www.jackierobinson.org.

171 ■ AMERICAN INDIAN EDUCATION FOUNDATION
2401 Eglin St.
Rapid City, SD 57703

Tel: (866)866-8642; (866)866-8642
Fax: (605)342-4113
E-mail: info@programs.org
Web Site: http://www.nrcprograms.org
To give American Indian Students the tools, resources and opportunities to learn and succeed.
Title of Award: U.S. BIA Indian Higher Education Grants **Area, Field, or Subject:** General studies. **Level of Education for which Award is Granted:** Undergraduate **Funds Available:** $300-$900.
Eligibility Requirements: Applicants must be: Native American undergraduate students of any major; enrolled in a federally recognized tribe. **Application Requirements:** Applicants must: complete AIEF Scholarship Application; provide documentation of tribal enrollment for themselves or their parents; provide transcripts with ACT and GPA scores; attach an essay that outlines the following information: introduction, academics, career plans, service to the Native American community, leadership/community service, financial needs and unique circumstances. Applicants may contact their tribe's education office for more information.

172 ■ AMERICAN JERSEY CATTLE ASSOCIATION
6486 E Main St.
Reynoldsburg, OH 43068-2362
Tel: (614)861-3636
Fax: (614)861-8040
Web Site: http://www.usjersey.com
To financially support secondary students entering college freshmen through graduate school.
Title of Award: Cedarcrest Farms Scholarships **Area, Field, or Subject:** General studies. **Level of Education for which Award is Granted:** Undergraduate **Funds Available:** $10,000.
Eligibility Requirements: Applicants must be junior member or lifetime member of the American Jersey Cattle Association. **Application Requirements:** Applicants must submit complete scholarship application form and a copy of most recent transcript listing all completed coursework.
Deadline for Receipt: July 7.

173 ■ AMERICAN JERSEY CATTLE ASSOCIATION
6486 E Main St.
Reynoldsburg, OH 43068-2362
Tel: (614)861-3636
Fax: (614)861-8040
Web Site: http://www.usjersey.com
To financially support secondary students entering as college freshmen through graduate school.
Title of Award: Reuben R. Cowles Youth Awards **Area, Field, or Subject:** General studies. **Level of Education for which Award is Granted:** Undergraduate **Funds Available:** $10,000.
Eligibility Requirements: Applicants must be junior member or lifetime member of the American Jersey Cattle Association. **Application Requirements:** Applicants must submit complete scholarship application form and a copy of most recent transcript listing all completed coursework.
Deadline for Receipt: July 7.

174 ■ THE AMERICAN LEGION
PO Box 1055
Indianapolis, IN 46206
Tel: (317)630-1200
Fax: (317)630-1223
Web Site: http://www.legion.org
To financially support the education of the dependents of active duty United States military and guard and reserve personnel
Title of Award: The American Legion Legacy Scholarships **Area, Field, or Subject:** General studies. **Level of Education for which Award is Granted:** Undergraduate **Funds Available:** Varies.
Eligibility Requirements: Applicant must be the dependent of active duty United States military and guard and reserve personnel who were federalized and killed on active duty on or after September 11, 2001. **Application Requirements:** Applicants must submit a completed scholarship application with a photocopy of the deceased veteran's Certificate of Death (DD 1300). **Deadline for Receipt:** April 15.

175 ■ THE AMERICAN LEGION
PO Box 1055
Indianapolis, IN 46206

Tel: (317)630-1200
Fax: (317)630-1223
Web Site: http://www.legion.org
To support the education of deserving high school students.
Title of Award: The American Legion National High School Oratorical Scholarships Contest **Area, Field, or Subject:** General studies. **Level of Education for which Award is Granted:** Undergraduate **Number Awarded:** Varies. **Funds Available:** 1st place: $18,000; 2nd place: $16,000; 3rd place: $14,000. Each Department (State) winner in the first round will receive a $1,500 scholarship. Each first round winner that does not advance to the Final Round will receive an additional $1,500 scholarship.
Eligibility Requirements: Candidate must be a high school student. **Application Requirements:** Applicants may contact their Department (State) or the National Organization of the American Legion for more information about the scholarships. **Additional Information:** The awards may be used to attend any college or university in the United States.

176 ■ THE AMERICAN LEGION
PO Box 1055
Indianapolis, IN 46206
Tel: (317)630-1200
Fax: (317)630-1223
Web Site: http://www.legion.org
To assist the education of a child, grandchild, great grandchild, etc. or a legally adopted child of a U.S. wartime veteran.
Title of Award: Samsung American Legion Scholarships **Area, Field, or Subject:** General studies. **Level of Education for which Award is Granted:** Undergraduate **Number Awarded:** Varies. **Funds Available:** In 2007, ten $20,000 scholarships and 88 $1,000 scholarships were awarded.
Eligibility Requirements: Applicant must be a high school junior who participates in either an American Legion Boys State or American Legion Auxiliary Girls State Program and be a direct descendant (child, grandchild, great grandchild, etc. or a legally adopted child) of a U.S. wartime veteran who served on active duty during one or more of the periods of war officially designated as eligibility dates for membership in The American Legion by the United States government. **Application Requirements:** Applicants must submit a completed scholarship application along with a photocopy of the veteran's Certification of Release or Discharge from Active Duty (DD-214), to Boys/Girls State program. **Additional Information:** In cooperation with Samsung.

177 ■ AMERICAN MILITARY RETIREES ASSOCIATION
5436 Peru St., Ste. 1
Plattsburgh, NY 12901
Tel: (518)563-9479; (180)0424-2969
Fax: (518)324-5204
E-mail: info@amra1973.org
Web Site: http://www.amra1973.org
To protect and improve the benefits of the military retirees.
Title of Award: Sergeant Major Douglas R. Drum Memorial Scholarship Fund **Area, Field, or Subject:** General studies. **Level of Education for which Award is Granted:** Undergraduate **Number Awarded:** 24. **Funds Available:** $1,000; $2,500; $5,000. **Duration:** two semester.
Eligibility Requirements: Applicants must be a current member of AMRA, his/her dependent, child or grandchild; he/she must pursuing a degree in an accredited college or university. **Application Requirements:** Applicants must present the award letter to the college/university and request that AMRA be billed for half the scholarship for the first semester and half the scholarship for the second semester; an applicant must submit a 500 word or less essay telling why an applicant deserve a scholarship from AMRA stating the Educational plans, achievements, leadership abilities, extracurricular and community activities, work experiences, character and citizenship traits, or any other circumstance that assist the committee during the selection process; an applicant must submit a letter of recommendation either from a teacher or professor, non-family member, past or current employer, from a project coordinator or a team leader. **Deadline for Receipt:** April 4.

178 ■ AMERICAN PAINT HORSE FOUNDATION
PO Box 961023
Fort Worth, TX 76161-0023

Tel: (817)834-2742
Fax: (817)222-8488
E-mail: rteate@apha.com
Web Site: http://www.aphfoundation.org
To promote educational and social growth of young horsemen and women.
Title of Award: American Paint Horse Foundation Scholarships **Area, Field, or Subject:** General studies. **Level of Education for which Award is Granted:** Undergraduate **Funds Available:** No specific amount.
Eligibility Requirements: Applicants must have at least a B average in high school; must pass the college entrance exam; must be APHA members in good standing; must have at least 3.0 cumulative grade point average; and must be enrolled in at least 12 credits hours per semesters. **Application Requirements:** Applicants must provide three letters of reference and an essay explaining their educational plans. **Deadline for Receipt:** March 1.

179 ■ AMERICAN PET PRODUCTS MANUFACTURERS ASSOCIATION
255 Glenville Rd.
Greenwich, CT 06831
Tel: (203)532-0000
Free: 800-452-1225
Fax: (203)532-0551
Web Site: http://www.appma.org
To aid deserving students who are eligible based on their parent's employment with an APPMA member firm.
Title of Award: APPMA's Jules Schwimmer Scholarship Program **Area, Field, or Subject:** General studies. **Level of Education for which Award is Granted:** Undergraduate **Number Awarded:** 8. **Funds Available:** $1,500.
Eligibility Requirements: Applicant must be a dependent of a full-time employee of an APPMA member firm. Parent of the applicant must still be an employee of the APPMA member firm by the time the winners are selected. **Application Requirements:** Applicants must obtain and submit online at www.scholarshipadministrators.net and use the ID code "APPMA". **Deadline for Receipt:** May 4.

180 ■ AMERICAN POLYGRAPH ASSOCIATION
PO Box 8037
Chattanooga, TN 37414-0037
Tel: (423)892-3992
Free: 800-APA-0037
Fax: (423)894-5435
E-mail: manager@polygraph.org
Web Site: http://www.polygraph.org
To provide financial assistance to deserving students.
Title of Award: William J. Yankee Memorial Scholarships **Area, Field, or Subject:** General studies. **Level of Education for which Award is Granted:** Undergraduate **Funds Available:** $5,000. **Duration:** One year.
Eligibility Requirements: Applicants must have a 4-year degree from an accredited college or university; must attend an APA accredited basic polygraph examiner training course; must qualify for APA membership upon completion of training. **Application Requirements:** Applicants must submit an essay of up to 1000 words on detection of deception, interviewing, interrogation or related fields; must have at least two letters of recommendation. **Deadline for Receipt:** June 1.

181 ■ AMERICAN PSYCHIATRIC ASSOCIATION ALLIANCE
c/o Angela Poblocki, Executive Director
PO Box 285
North Boston, NY 14110
Tel: (703)907-7304
E-mail: ang3689@aol.com
Web Site: http://www.apaalliance.org
To provide financial assistance for post secondary educational needs of a spouse/partner or dependents of impaired, disabled, or deceased physicians unable to provide family income.
Title of Award: Elsa Barton Educational Scholarships Fund **Area, Field, or Subject:** General Studies. **Level of Education for which Award is Granted:** Undergraduate **Funds Available:** No specific amount.
Eligibility Requirements: Program is open for the spouse, partner, widow, or child of an impaired, disabled or deceased physician who could

exhibit a need for additional financial resources in acquiring a post secondary education or vocational training. **Application Requirements:** Applicants must submit completed application form available on the website; a brief statement (300 words or less) on the applicant's professional or vocational goals, explanation of financial situation, amount of funding needed and purpose, and list of financial aid or scholarships applicant receives or will be receiving; verification of financial need: CSS Financial Aid Profile, or FAFSA, and applicant's Federal Income Tax returns for years 2006 and 2007 (If applicant is a child of a physician, also include copies of both parents' Federal Income Tax Returns for years 2006 and 2007); Proof of physician's inability to practice or a death certificate; and the applicant's relevant high school, university, or course of study transcripts. Mail completed application with supporting documents to: Elsa Barton Scholarship, American Psychiatric Association Alliance, P.O. Box 285, N. Boston, NY 14110. **Deadline for Receipt:** April 15. **Additional Information:** Angela Poblocki.

182 ■ AMERICAN PUBLIC POWER ASSOCIATION

1875 Connecticut Ave. NW, Ste. 1200
Washington, DC 20009-5715
Tel: (202)467-2900
Fax: (202)467-2910
Web Site: http://www.appanet.org
To promote the involvement of students in studying energy-related disciplines in the public power industry, and to provide host utilities with technical assistance.
Title of Award: DEED Student Research Grant/Internships **Area, Field, or Subject:** Energy-related areas. **Level of Education for which Award is Granted:** Graduate, Undergraduate **Funds Available:** $4,000. **Duration:** One year.
Eligibility Requirements: Applicants must be graduate or undergraduate students studying in energy-related disciplines from accredited colleges or universities; must be willing to work in a state with at least one sponsor DEED member. **Application Requirements:** Applicants must complete the information on the DEED Student Research Grant/Internship application coversheet available online; must submit the original signature of the student, utility authority and school official as well as other information requested in required signature section; must have a single transcript of the student's academic record. Application form and other requirements must be sent to DEED Administrator, American Public Power Association, 1875 Connecticut Ave. NW, Ste. 1200, Washington, DC 20009-5715. **Deadline for Receipt:** February 15 and October 1.

183 ■ AMERICAN RESEARCH INSTITUTE IN TURKEY

3260 S St.
Philadelphia, PA 19104-6324
Tel: (215)898-3474
Fax: (215)898-0657
E-mail: leinwand@sas.upenn.edu
Web Site: http://www.ccat.sas.upenn.edu
To promote American and Turkish research and exchange related to Turkey.
Title of Award: Fellowships for Intensive Advanced Turkish Language Study in Turkey **Area, Field, or Subject:** General Studies. **Level of Education for which Award is Granted:** Undergraduate **Funds Available:** $2,375. **Duration:** 1 year.
Eligibility Requirements: Applicants must be citizens or national/permanent residents of the United States; must be currently enrolled in an undergraduate or graduate level academic program; must have a minimum B average in studies; must perform at the high-intermediate level on a proficiency-based admission examination. **Application Requirements:** Applicants must submit complete application information; three letters of recommendation; letters of reference; and a copy of graduate transcript. **Deadline for Receipt:** February 11. **Additional Information:** Erika H. Gilson at 110 Jones Hall, Princeton University, Princeton, NJ 08544-1008.

184 ■ AMERICAN RISK AND INSURANCE ASSOCIATION

716 Providence Rd.
Malvern, PA 19355-3402
Tel: (610)640-1997
Fax: (610)725-1007
E-mail: aria@cpcuiia.org

Web Site: http://www.aria.org
To advance knowledge in Risk Management and Insurance; To enhance the career development of its members; to provide programs, awards, and services that expand risk management and insurance knowledge; to improve academic instruction and position its members.
Title of Award: Griffith Foundation Scholarships **Area, Field, or Subject:** Management. **Level of Education for which Award is Granted:** Undergraduate **Number Awarded:** 8. **Funds Available:** $2,000.
Eligibility Requirements: All applicants must be students enrolled in college majoring in actuarial science, business, or non-business making a commitment to take a risk in management and insurance course; he must be a U.S. citizen; must be at least sophomore and enrolled in an insurance, risk management, actuarial science or other related program; have a cumulative point of average of 3.0 above. **Application Requirements:** Applicant must fill out the application form and mail to the above address. **Deadline for Receipt:** March 10. **Additional Information:** The Griffith Foundation for Insurance Education 623, High Street Worthington, Ohio 43085; 614-880-9870; 614-880-9872; info@griffithfoundation.org.

185 ■ AMERICAN ROAD AND TRANSPORTATION BUILDERS ASSOCIATION

The ARTBA Building
1219 28th St. NW
Washington, DC 20007-3389
Tel: (202)289-4434
E-mail: artbadc@aol.com
Web Site: http://www.artba.org
To provide financial assistance to help the children or legally adopted children of highway workers killed or permanently disabled in the line of duty to pursue post-highschool education.
Title of Award: Highway Worker Memorial Scholarship Program **Area, Field, or Subject:** General studies. **Level of Education for which Award is Granted:** Undergraduate **Number Awarded:** 1. **Funds Available:** $2000.
Eligibility Requirements: Applicants must be sons, daughters or legally adopted children of highway workers who died or became permanently disabled in roadway construction zone accidents and their parents have been employed by a transportation construction firm or a transportation public agency at the time of his or her death or disabling injury. **Application Requirements:** Candidates must submit completed and signed award application form; proof of parent's death in line of duty; if parent is permanently disabled, must submit documentation that shows disability work-related; proof of guardianship if not living with surviving parent; an official copy of transcript and grade report from the school currently attended or most recently attended; a brief, typewritten statement explaining reasons for wanting to continue education accompanied by recent photo; completed and signed "Free Application for Federal Student Aid" (FAFSA) forms for the current year; federal tax return copy; copy of acceptance letter from the college, university, technical school where the applicants plan to attend; and two letters of recommendation from teachers in support of their application. **Deadline for Receipt:** February 29.

186 ■ AMERICAN ROMANIAN ORTHODOX YOUTH

8033 N Kenton Ave., Apt. 1W
Skokie, IL 60076
Tel: (330)519-6187
E-mail: lnemes@aroy.org
Web Site: http://www.aroy.org
To support the continuing education of student members.
Title of Award: A.R.F.O.R.A. Undergraduate Scholarships for Women **Area, Field, or Subject:** General studies. **Level of Education for which Award is Granted:** Undergraduate **Number Awarded:** 2. **Funds Available:** $1000.
Eligibility Requirements: Applicant must be a female voting member of a parish of the Romanian Orthodox Episcopate of America; a graduate of a duly accredited university/college; and accepted by a graduate school or a duly accredited university and specify her course of study. **Application Requirements:** Applicants must send a request for application to ARFORA/Martha Gavrila Scholarship c/o 222 Orchard Park Dr New Castle, PA 16105. Three letters of recommendation must be mailed sealed, directly to the attention of the Scholarship Committee. A photo must be included and a formal letter projecting the plans of the applicant. **Deadline for Receipt:** April 30.

187 ■ AMERICAN ROMANIAN ORTHODOX YOUTH
8033 N Kenton Ave., Apt. 1W
Skokie, IL 60076
Tel: (330)519-6187
E-mail: lnemes@aroy.org
Web Site: http://www.aroy.org
To support the continuing education of student members.
Title of Award: A.R.O.Y. Stanitz Scholarships **Area, Field, or Subject:** General studies. **Level of Education for which Award is Granted:** Undergraduate **Number Awarded:** 2. **Funds Available:** $1000. **Duration:** Annually.
Eligibility Requirements: Applicant must be an active AROY member; a high school graduate; and a college student or one who intends to enroll in a school or college of university level. **Application Requirements:** Applicants must submit a biographical history including family; an educational background and grades; list of AROY and church activities; list of extra-curricular interests or achievements; reasons why applying for the scholarship; a photograph; and a letter of recommendation from parish priest or AROY advisors regarding parish and AROY activities. Send all materials to William R Stanitz/AROY Scholarship The Romanian Orthodox Episcopate of America PO Box 309 Grass Lake, MI 49240-0309. **Additional Information:** Established in 1971. **Deadline for Receipt:** July 1.

188 ■ AMERICAN ROMANIAN ORTHODOX YOUTH
8033 N Kenton Ave., Apt. 1W
Skokie, IL 60076
Tel: (330)519-6187
E-mail: lnemes@aroy.org
Web Site: http://www.aroy.org
To support the education of students seeking ordination into priesthood or wish to serve the Church in a professional manner.
Title of Award: Bujea Memorial Scholarships **Area, Field, or Subject:** Religion. **Level of Education for which Award is Granted:** Undergraduate **Number Awarded:** 1. **Funds Available:** %500.
Eligibility Requirements: Applicant must be a Canadian student; and a communicant voting member of The Romanian Orthodox Episcopate of America. **Application Requirements:** Applicants must send a request for application to Bujea Memorial Scholarship Committee PO Box 1341 Regina SK S4P 3B8 Canada. **Deadline for Receipt:** April 30.

189 ■ AMERICAN ROMANIAN ORTHODOX YOUTH
8033 N Kenton Ave., Apt. 1W
Skokie, IL 60076
Tel: (330)519-6187
E-mail: lnemes@aroy.org
Web Site: http://www.aroy.org
To support the continuing education of student members.
Title of Award: R.O.E.A. Dumitru Golea Goldy-Gemu Scholarships **Area, Field, or Subject:** General studies. **Level of Education for which Award is Granted:** Undergraduate **Number Awarded:** 2. **Funds Available:** $1500.
Eligibility Requirements: Applicant must be of Romanian descent and a citizen or permanent resident of the U.S. or Canada. **Application Requirements:** Applicants must submit a completed application form together with a high school administration form/transcript of grades/letter of acceptance; an essay; and a photograph. Send application materials to Goldy Scholarship Committee PO Box 309 Grass Lake, MI 49240-0309. **Deadline for Receipt:** May 31.

190 ■ AMERICAN SMALL BUSINESSES ASSOCIATION
PO Box 300777
Chicago, IL 60630-0777
877-906-2722
E-mail: info@asbaonline.org
Web Site: http://www.asbaonline.org
To provide educational financial aid to members and their grandchildren.
Title of Award: ASBA College Scholarship Program **Area, Field, or Subject:** General studies. **Level of Education for which Award is Granted:** Undergraduate **Funds Available:** $1,000.
Eligibility Requirements: Applicant must be a dependent or grandchild of an ASBA member; enrolled at least one year in college or university. **Application Requirements:** Applicant must submit an application form

(please visit the website); an essay; two letters of recommendation; high school/college transcript. **Deadline for Receipt:** May.

191 ■ AMERICAN SOCIETY OF BREWING CHEMISTS
3340 Pilot Knob Rd.
St. Paul, MN 55121
Tel: (651)454-7250
Fax: (651)454-0766
E-mail: asbc@scisoc.org
Web Site: http://www.asbcnet.org
To provide financial support to a student who is a daughter or son of an active ASBC member.
Title of Award: ASBC Foundation Undergraduate Scholarships **Area, Field, or Subject:** General studies. **Level of Education for which Award is Granted:** Undergraduate **Funds Available:** $1,000. **Duration:** One year.
Eligibility Requirements: Candidates must be the daughter or son of an active ASBC member. Candidates must be enrolled as an undergraduate student at a college or university and be actively pursuing a bachelor's degree. For full-time undergraduate students, candidates must be enrolled in an academic schedule that meets the minimum requirements of the attending college or university. **Application Requirements:** Applicants must submit a completed application form; copies of transcripts; a letter of application describing career plans; and three letters of recommendation with at least two from the academic adviser and/or faculty members familiar with the applicant's academic record. The confidential letter(s) should include a general appraisal of the scholarship, extracurricular activities and abilities in particular relation to the purposes and eligibility requirements of the scholarships. **Deadline for Receipt:** March 1. **Additional Information:** Beth Elliott.

192 ■ AMERICAN SOCIETY FOR ENOLOGY AND VITICULTURE
PO Box 1855
Davis, CA 95617-1855
Tel: (530)753-3142
Fax: (530)753-3318
Web Site: http://www.asev.org
To define questions in the wine industry and work towards answers based on the relevant and scientifically rigorous information on selected topics.
Title of Award: American Society for Enology and Viticulture Scholarships **Area, Field, or Subject:** Viticulture. **Level of Education for which Award is Granted:** Undergraduate **Funds Available:** No specific amount. **Duration:** one semester.
Eligibility Requirements: All applicants must be undergraduate and graduate students and enrolled in or accepted into a full-time accredited four year college or university program; applicant should be a minimum of junior status for the upcoming academic year(45/06 quarter units); undergraduate students must have a minimum cumulative grade point average of 3.0; graduate students must have a minimum overall grade point average of 3.2. These averages must be based on a scale maximum of 4.0; applicants must be enrolled in a major or in a graduate group emphasizing enology or viviculture, or in a curriculum emphasizing a science basic to the wine and grape industry. **Application Requirements:** Applicant must download the scholarship application form or contact ASEV office; fill out the application form after receiving the packet; an applicant must send the application, copies of transcript, and two original letters of recommendation to the ASEV office; an applicant must submit a list of planned courses for the upcoming academic year. **Deadline for Receipt:** March 1.

193 ■ AMERICAN SOCIETY FOR MICROBIOLOGY
1752 N St. NW
Washington, DC 20036-2904
Tel: (202)942-9207
Fax: (202)942-9333
E-mail: chouston@utmb.edu
Web Site: http://www.asm.org
To support programs for education, training, and public information.
Title of Award: American Society for Microbiology Undergraduate Research Fellowships **Area, Field, or Subject:** General Studies. **Level of Education for which Award is Granted:** Undergraduate **Funds Available:** $4,000; $1,000-travel support.
Eligibility Requirements: Applicants must be enrolled as full-time matriculating undergraduate in an accredited U.S. institution; must be

involved in a research project; must have ASM members in their home institutions willing to serve as a mentor; must not have receive any financial support for research. **Application Requirements:** Applicants must submit a complete application form. **Deadline for Receipt:** February 1.

194 ■ AMERICAN SOCIETY OF SAFETY ENGINEERS

1800 E Oakton St.
Des Plaines, IL 60018
Tel: (847)699-2929
Fax: (847)768-3434
E-mail: customerservice@asse.org
Web Site: http://www.asse.org
To provide financial support to deserving students.
Title of Award: America Responds Memorial Scholarships **Area, Field, or Subject:** Occupational safety and health. **Level of Education for which Award is Granted:** Undergraduate **Funds Available:** $1,000. **Duration:** One year.
Eligibility Requirements: Applicant must be a U.S citizen; must be pursuing an undergraduate degree in occupational safety and health. **Application Requirements:** Applicants must submit a transcript of record; for further information about the application form and requirements, applicants are advised to contact the ASSE Foundation at 1800 E Oakton St., Des Plaines, IL 60018. **Deadline for Receipt:** December 1.

195 ■ AMERICAN SOCIETY OF SAFETY ENGINEERS

1800 E Oakton St.
Des Plaines, IL 60018
Tel: (847)699-2929
Fax: (847)768-3434
E-mail: customerservice@asse.org
Web Site: http://www.asse.org
To provide financial support to deserving students.
Title of Award: ASSE Construction Safety Scholarships **Area, Field, or Subject:** Occupational safety and health; Construction. **Level of Education for which Award is Granted:** Undergraduate **Funds Available:** $1,000. **Duration:** One year.
Eligibility Requirements: Applicant must be a student pursuing an undergraduate degree in occupational safety and health with an emphasis in construction safety. **Application Requirements:** Applicants must submit a transcript of record; for further information about the application form and requirements, applicants are advised to contact the ASSE Foundation at 1800 E Oakton St., Des Plaines, IL 60018. **Deadline for Receipt:** December 1.

196 ■ AMERICAN SOCIETY OF SAFETY ENGINEERS

1800 E Oakton St.
Des Plaines, IL 60018
Tel: (847)699-2929
Fax: (847)768-3434
E-mail: customerservice@asse.org
Web Site: http://www.asse.org
To provide financial support to deserving students.
Title of Award: ASSE Diversity Committee Scholarships **Area, Field, or Subject:** Occupational safety and health. **Level of Education for which Award is Granted:** Graduate, Undergraduate **Funds Available:** $1,000. **Duration:** One year.
Eligibility Requirements: Applicant must be a student pursuing an undergraduate or graduate degree in occupational safety & health or a closely related field. **Application Requirements:** Applicants must submit a transcript of record; for further information about the application form and requirements, applicants are advised to contact the ASSE Foundation at 1800 E Oakton St., Des Plaines, IL 60018. **Deadline for Receipt:** December 1.

197 ■ AMERICAN SOCIETY OF SAFETY ENGINEERS

1800 E Oakton St.
Des Plaines, IL 60018
Tel: (847)699-2929
Fax: (847)768-3434
E-mail: customerservice@asse.org
Web Site: http://www.asse.org
To provide financial support to deserving students.

Title of Award: Bechtel Group Foundation Scholarship for Safety & Health **Area, Field, or Subject:** Occupational safety and health; Construction. **Level of Education for which Award is Granted:** Undergraduate **Funds Available:** $8,000. **Duration:** One year.
Eligibility Requirements: Applicant must be a student pursuing an undergraduate degree in occupational safety and health with an emphasis in construction safety. **Application Requirements:** Applicants must submit a transcript of record; for further information about the application form and requirements, applicants are advised to contact the ASSE Foundation at 1800 E Oakton St., Des Plaines, IL 60018. **Deadline for Receipt:** December 1.

198 ■ AMERICAN SOCIETY OF SAFETY ENGINEERS

1800 E Oakton St.
Des Plaines, IL 60018
Tel: (847)699-2929
Fax: (847)768-3434
E-mail: customerservice@asse.org
Web Site: http://www.asse.org
To provide financial support to deserving students.
Title of Award: Warren K. Brown Scholarships **Area, Field, or Subject:** Occupational safety and health. **Level of Education for which Award is Granted:** Undergraduate **Funds Available:** $1,000. **Duration:** One year.
Eligibility Requirements: Applicant must be a student pursuing an undergraduate degree in occupational safety & health or a closely related field at Murray State University in Murray, KY or Indiana State University in Terre Haute, IN. **Application Requirements:** Applicants must submit a transcript of record; for further information about the application form and requirements, applicants are advised to contact the ASSE Foundation at 1800 E Oakton St., Des Plaines, IL 60018. **Deadline for Receipt:** December 1.

199 ■ AMERICAN SOCIETY OF SAFETY ENGINEERS

1800 E Oakton St.
Des Plaines, IL 60018
Tel: (847)699-2929
Fax: (847)768-3434
E-mail: customerservice@asse.org
Web Site: http://www.asse.org
To provide financial support to deserving students.
Title of Award: Central Indiana ASSE Scholarships **Area, Field, or Subject:** Occupational safety and health. **Level of Education for which Award is Granted:** Graduate, Undergraduate **Funds Available:** $1,000. **Duration:** One year.
Eligibility Requirements: Applicant must be a student pursuing an undergraduate or graduate degree in occupational safety & health or a closely related field. **Application Requirements:** Applicants must submit a transcript of record; for further information about the application form and requirements, applicants are advised to contact the ASSE Foundation at 1800 E Oakton St., Des Plaines, IL 60018. **Deadline for Receipt:** December 1.

200 ■ AMERICAN SOCIETY OF SAFETY ENGINEERS

1800 E Oakton St.
Des Plaines, IL 60018
Tel: (847)699-2929
Fax: (847)768-3434
E-mail: customerservice@asse.org
Web Site: http://www.asse.org
To provide financial support to deserving students.
Title of Award: CNA Foundation Scholarships **Area, Field, or Subject:** Occupational safety and health. **Level of Education for which Award is Granted:** Graduate, Undergraduate **Number Awarded:** 2. **Funds Available:** $4,000. **Duration:** One year.
Eligibility Requirements: Applicant must be a student pursuing an undergraduate or graduate degree in occupational safety & health or a closely related field. **Application Requirements:** Applicants must submit a transcript of record; for further information about the application form and requirements, applicants are advised to contact the ASSE Foundation at 1800 E Oakton St., Des Plaines, IL 60018. **Deadline for Receipt:** December 1.

201 ■ AMERICAN SOCIETY OF SAFETY ENGINEERS

1800 E Oakton St.
Des Plaines, IL 60018

Tel: (847)699-2929
Fax: (847)768-3434
E-mail: customerservice@asse.org
Web Site: http://www.asse.org
To provide financial support to deserving students.
Title of Award: Scott Dominguez - Craters of the Moon Chapter Scholarships **Area, Field, or Subject:** Occupational safety and health. **Level of Education for which Award is Granted:** Graduate, Undergraduate **Funds Available:** $1,000. **Duration:** One year.
Eligibility Requirements: Applicant must be a student pursuing an undergraduate or graduate degree in occupational safety & health or a closely related field. **Application Requirements:** Applicants must submit a transcript of record; for further information about the application form and requirements, applicants are advised to contact the ASSE Foundation at 1800 E Oakton St., Des Plaines, IL 60018. **Deadline for Receipt:** December 1.

202 ■ AMERICAN SOCIETY OF SAFETY ENGINEERS
1800 E Oakton St.
Des Plaines, IL 60018
Tel: (847)699-2929
Fax: (847)768-3434
E-mail: customerservice@asse.org
Web Site: http://www.asse.org
To provide financial support to deserving students.
Title of Award: Georgia Chapter of ASSE Annual Scholarships **Area, Field, or Subject:** Occupational safety and health. **Level of Education for which Award is Granted:** Undergraduate **Funds Available:** $1,000. **Duration:** One year.
Eligibility Requirements: Applicant must be a student pursuing an undergraduate degree in occupational safety & health or a closely related field; must be a Georgia resident. **Application Requirements:** Applicants must submit a transcript of record; for further information about the application form and requirements, applicants are advised to contact the ASSE Foundation at 1800 E Oakton St., Des Plaines, IL 60018. **Deadline for Receipt:** December 1.

203 ■ AMERICAN SOCIETY OF SAFETY ENGINEERS
1800 E Oakton St.
Des Plaines, IL 60018
Tel: (847)699-2929
Fax: (847)768-3434
E-mail: customerservice@asse.org
Web Site: http://www.asse.org
To provide financial support to deserving students.
Title of Award: Gold Country Section & Region II Scholarships **Area, Field, or Subject:** Occupational safety and health. **Level of Education for which Award is Granted:** Graduate, Undergraduate **Funds Available:** $1,000. **Duration:** One year.
Eligibility Requirements: Applicant must be a student pursuing an undergraduate or graduate degree in occupational safety & health or a closely related field; must be a student that resides within the Region II (MT, ID, WY, CO, UT, NV, AZ, NM) area. **Application Requirements:** Applicants must submit a transcript of record; for further information about the application form and requirements, applicants are advised to contact the ASSE Foundation at 1800 E Oakton St., Des Plaines, IL 60018. **Deadline for Receipt:** December 1.

204 ■ AMERICAN SOCIETY OF SAFETY ENGINEERS
1800 E Oakton St.
Des Plaines, IL 60018
Tel: (847)699-2929
Fax: (847)768-3434
E-mail: customerservice@asse.org
Web Site: http://www.asse.org
To provide financial support to deserving students.
Title of Award: Greater Baton Rouge Chapter - Don Jones Excellence in Safety Scholarships **Area, Field, or Subject:** Occupational safety and health. **Level of Education for which Award is Granted:** Undergraduate **Funds Available:** $1,000. **Duration:** One year.
Eligibility Requirements: Applicant must be a student pursuing a degree in occupational safety & health or a closely related field. **Application Requirements:** Applicants must submit a transcript of record; for further

information about the application form and requirements, applicants are advised to contact the ASSE Foundation at 1800 E Oakton St., Des Plaines, IL 60018. **Deadline for Receipt:** December 1.

205 ■ AMERICAN SOCIETY OF SAFETY ENGINEERS
1800 E Oakton St.
Des Plaines, IL 60018
Tel: (847)699-2929
Fax: (847)768-3434
E-mail: customerservice@asse.org
Web Site: http://www.asse.org
To provide financial support to deserving students.
Title of Award: Gulf Coast Past President's Scholarships **Area, Field, or Subject:** Occupational safety and health. **Level of Education for which Award is Granted:** Undergraduate **Number Awarded:** 2. **Funds Available:** $1,000. **Duration:** One year.
Eligibility Requirements: Applicant must be a student pursuing an undergraduate degree in occupational safety and health or a closely related field. **Application Requirements:** Applicants must submit a transcript of record; for further information about the application form and requirements, applicants are advised to contact the ASSE Foundation at 1800 E Oakton St., Des Plaines, IL 60018. **Deadline for Receipt:** December 1.

206 ■ AMERICAN SOCIETY OF SAFETY ENGINEERS
1800 E Oakton St.
Des Plaines, IL 60018
Tel: (847)699-2929
Fax: (847)768-3434
E-mail: customerservice@asse.org
Web Site: http://www.asse.org
To provide financial support to deserving students.
Title of Award: George Gustafson HSE Memorial Scholarships **Area, Field, or Subject:** Occupational safety and health. **Level of Education for which Award is Granted:** Graduate, Undergraduate **Funds Available:** $2,500. **Duration:** One year.
Eligibility Requirements: Applicant must be a student pursuing an undergraduate or graduate degree in occupational safety & health or a closely related field. **Application Requirements:** Applicants must submit a transcript of record; for further information about the application form and requirements, applicants are advised to contact the ASSE Foundation at 1800 E Oakton St., Des Plaines, IL 60018. **Deadline for Receipt:** December 1.

207 ■ AMERICAN SOCIETY OF SAFETY ENGINEERS
1800 E Oakton St.
Des Plaines, IL 60018
Tel: (847)699-2929
Fax: (847)768-3434
E-mail: customerservice@asse.org
Web Site: http://www.asse.org
To provide financial support to deserving students.
Title of Award: David Iden Memorial Safety Scholarships **Area, Field, or Subject:** Occupational safety and health. **Level of Education for which Award is Granted:** Undergraduate **Number Awarded:** 4. **Funds Available:** $4,000. **Duration:** One year.
Eligibility Requirements: Applicant must be a student pursuing an undergraduate degree in occupational safety & health or a closely related field. **Application Requirements:** Applicants must submit a transcript of record; for further information about the application form and requirements, applicants are advised to contact the ASSE Foundation at 1800 E Oakton St., Des Plaines, IL 60018. **Deadline for Receipt:** December 1.

208 ■ AMERICAN SOCIETY OF SAFETY ENGINEERS
1800 E Oakton St.
Des Plaines, IL 60018
Tel: (847)699-2929
Fax: (847)768-3434
E-mail: customerservice@asse.org
Web Site: http://www.asse.org
To provide financial support to deserving students.
Title of Award: Karl A. Jacobson Scholarships **Area, Field, or Subject:** Occupational safety and health. **Level of Education for which Award is Granted:** Undergraduate **Funds Available:** $2,000. **Duration:** One year.

Eligibility Requirements: Applicant must be a student pursuing an undergraduate degree in occupational safety & health or a closely related field. **Application Requirements:** Applicants must submit a transcript of record; for further information about the application form and requirements; applicants are advised to contact the ASSE Foundation at 1800 E Oakton St., Des Plaines, IL 60018. **Deadline for Receipt:** December 1.

209 ■ AMERICAN SOCIETY OF SAFETY ENGINEERS
1800 E Oakton St.
Des Plaines, IL 60018
Tel: (847)699-2929
Fax: (847)768-3434
E-mail: customerservice@asse.org
Web Site: http://www.asse.org
To provide financial support to deserving students.
Title of Award: Liberty Mutual Scholarships **Area, Field, or Subject:** Occupational safety and health. **Level of Education for which Award is Granted:** Undergraduate **Number Awarded:** 2. **Funds Available:** $3,000. **Duration:** One year.
Eligibility Requirements: Applicant must be a student pursuing an undergraduate degree in occupational safety & health or a closely related field. **Application Requirements:** Applicants must submit a transcript of record; for further information about the application form and requirements, applicants are advised to contact the ASSE Foundation at 1800 E Oakton St., Des Plaines, IL 60018. **Deadline for Receipt:** December 1.

210 ■ AMERICAN SOCIETY OF SAFETY ENGINEERS
1800 E Oakton St.
Des Plaines, IL 60018
Tel: (847)699-2929
Fax: (847)768-3434
E-mail: customerservice@asse.org
Web Site: http://www.asse.org
To provide financial support to deserving students.
Title of Award: Medina Scholarships for Hispanics in Safety **Area, Field, or Subject:** Occupational safety and health. **Level of Education for which Award is Granted:** Graduate, Undergraduate **Number Awarded:** 2. **Funds Available:** $2,000. **Duration:** One year.
Eligibility Requirements: Applicant must be a student pursuing an undergraduate or graduate degree in occupational safety & health or a closely related field; must be a bilingual student. **Application Requirements:** Applicants must submit a transcript of record; for further information about the application form and requirements, applicants are advised to contact the ASSE Foundation at 1800 E Oakton St., Des Plaines, IL 60018. **Deadline for Receipt:** December 1.

211 ■ AMERICAN SOCIETY OF SAFETY ENGINEERS
1800 E Oakton St.
Des Plaines, IL 60018
Tel: (847)699-2929
Fax: (847)768-3434
E-mail: customerservice@asse.org
Web Site: http://www.asse.org
To provide financial support to deserving students.
Title of Award: North Florida Chapter Safety Education Scholarships **Area, Field, or Subject:** Occupational safety and health. **Level of Education for which Award is Granted:** Graduate, Undergraduate **Funds Available:** $1,000. **Duration:** One year.
Eligibility Requirements: Applicant must be a student pursuing an undergraduate or graduate degree in occupational safety & health or a closely related field. **Application Requirements:** Applicants must submit a transcript of record; for further information about the application form and requirements, applicants are advised to contact the ASSE Foundation at 1800 E Oakton St., Des Plaines, IL 60018. **Deadline for Receipt:** December 1.

212 ■ AMERICAN SOCIETY OF SAFETY ENGINEERS
1800 E Oakton St.
Des Plaines, IL 60018
Tel: (847)699-2929
Fax: (847)768-3434
E-mail: customerservice@asse.org
Web Site: http://www.asse.org

To provide financial support to deserving students.
Title of Award: Northeastern Illinois Chapter Scholarships **Area, Field, or Subject:** Occupational safety and health. **Level of Education for which Award is Granted:** Graduate, Undergraduate **Number Awarded:** 2. **Funds Available:** $2,000. **Duration:** One year.
Eligibility Requirements: Applicant must be a student pursuing an undergraduate or graduate degree in occupational safety & health or a closely related field. **Application Requirements:** Applicants must submit a transcript of record; for further information about the application form and requirements, applicants are advised to contact the ASSE Foundation at 1800 E Oakton St., Des Plaines, IL 60018. **Deadline for Receipt:** December 1.

213 ■ AMERICAN SOCIETY OF SAFETY ENGINEERS
1800 E Oakton St.
Des Plaines, IL 60018
Tel: (847)699-2929
Fax: (847)768-3434
E-mail: customerservice@asse.org
Web Site: http://www.asse.org
To provide financial support to deserving students.
Title of Award: PDC Scholarships **Area, Field, or Subject:** Occupational safety and health. **Level of Education for which Award is Granted:** Undergraduate **Number Awarded:** 2. **Funds Available:** $1,200. **Duration:** One year.
Eligibility Requirements: Applicant must be a student pursuing a degree in occupational safety & health or a closely related field. **Application Requirements:** Applicants must submit a transcript of record; for further information about the application form and requirements, applicants are advised to contact the ASSE Foundation at 1800 E Oakton St., Des Plaines, IL 60018. **Deadline for Receipt:** December 1.

214 ■ AMERICAN SOCIETY OF SAFETY ENGINEERS
1800 E Oakton St.
Des Plaines, IL 60018
Tel: (847)699-2929
Fax: (847)768-3434
E-mail: customerservice@asse.org
Web Site: http://www.asse.org
To provide financial support to deserving students.
Title of Award: Harold F. Polston Scholarships **Area, Field, or Subject:** Occupational safety and health. **Level of Education for which Award is Granted:** Undergraduate **Funds Available:** $2,000. **Duration:** One year.
Eligibility Requirements: Applicant must be a student pursuing an undergraduate or graduate degree in occupational safety & health or a closely related field. **Application Requirements:** Applicants must submit a transcript of record; for further information about the application form and requirements, applicants are advised to contact the ASSE Foundation at 1800 E Oakton St., Des Plaines, IL 60018. **Deadline for Receipt:** December 1.

215 ■ AMERICAN SOCIETY OF SAFETY ENGINEERS
1800 E Oakton St.
Des Plaines, IL 60018
Tel: (847)699-2929
Fax: (847)768-3434
E-mail: customerservice@asse.org
Web Site: http://www.asse.org
To provide financial support to deserving students.
Title of Award: William C. Ray, CIH, CSP Arizona Scholarships **Area, Field, or Subject:** Occupational safety and health. **Level of Education for which Award is Granted:** Graduate, Undergraduate **Funds Available:** $1,000. **Duration:** One year.
Eligibility Requirements: Applicant must be a student pursuing an undergraduate or graduate degree in occupational safety & health or a closely related field; must reside in Arizona. **Application Requirements:** Applicants must submit a transcript of record; for further information about the application form and requirements, applicants are advised to contact the ASSE Foundation at 1800 E Oakton St., Des Plaines, IL 60018. **Deadline for Receipt:** December 1.

216 ■ AMERICAN SOCIETY OF SAFETY ENGINEERS
1800 E Oakton St.
Des Plaines, IL 60018

Tel: (847)699-2929
Fax: (847)768-3434
E-mail: customerservice@asse.org
Web Site: http://www.asse.org
To provide financial support to deserving students.
Title of Award: Marsh Risk Consulting Scholarships **Area, Field, or Subject:** Occupational safety and health. **Level of Education for which Award is Granted:** Undergraduate **Funds Available:** $1,000. **Duration:** One year.
Eligibility Requirements: Applicant must be a student pursuing an undergraduate degree in occupational safety & health or a closely related field. **Application Requirements:** Applicants must submit a transcript of record; for further information about the application form and requirements, applicants are advised to contact the ASSE Foundation at 1800 E Oakton St., Des Plaines, IL 60018. **Deadline for Receipt:** December 1.

217 ■ AMERICAN SOCIETY OF SAFETY ENGINEERS
1800 E Oakton St.
Des Plaines, IL 60018
Tel: (847)699-2929
Fax: (847)768-3434
E-mail: customerservice@asse.org
Web Site: http://www.asse.org
To provide financial support to deserving students.
Title of Award: Southwest Chapter Roy Kinslow Scholarships **Area, Field, or Subject:** Occupational safety and health. **Level of Education for which Award is Granted:** Undergraduate **Funds Available:** $1,000. **Duration:** One year.
Eligibility Requirements: Applicant must be a student pursuing an undergraduate degree in occupational safety & health or a closely related field at Southeastern Oklahoma State University in Durat, OK or for any student from the Southwest Chapter area attending a school within the Region III boundaries. **Application Requirements:** Applicants must submit a transcript of record; for further information about the application form and requirements, applicants are advised to contact the ASSE Foundation at 1800 E Oakton St., Des Plaines, IL 60018. **Deadline for Receipt:** December 1.

218 ■ AMERICAN SOCIETY OF SAFETY ENGINEERS
1800 E Oakton St.
Des Plaines, IL 60018
Tel: (847)699-2929
Fax: (847)768-3434
E-mail: customerservice@asse.org
Web Site: http://www.asse.org
To provide financial support to deserving students.
Title of Award: Harry Taback 9/11 Memorial Scholarships **Area, Field, or Subject:** Occupational safety and health. **Level of Education for which Award is Granted:** Undergraduate **Funds Available:** $1,000. **Duration:** One year.
Eligibility Requirements: Applicant must be a student pursuing an undergraduate or graduate degree in occupational safety & health or a closely related field; must be a natural born U.S citizen. **Application Requirements:** Applicants must submit transcript of record; for further information about the application form and requirements, applicants are advised to contact the ASSE Foundation at 1800 E Oakton St., Des Plaines, IL 60018. **Deadline for Receipt:** December 1.

219 ■ AMERICAN SOCIETY OF SAFETY ENGINEERS
1800 E Oakton St.
Des Plaines, IL 60018
Tel: (847)699-2929
Fax: (847)768-3434
E-mail: customerservice@asse.org
Web Site: http://www.asse.org
To provide financial support to deserving students.
Title of Award: UPS Diversity Scholarships **Area, Field, or Subject:** Occupational safety and health. **Level of Education for which Award is Granted:** Undergraduate **Number Awarded:** 2. **Funds Available:** $5,250. **Duration:** One year.
Eligibility Requirements: Applicant must be a student pursuing an undergraduate degree in occupational safety & health or a closely relative field; must be of a minority ethnic or racial group and must be a United

States citizen. **Application Requirements:** Applicants must submit a transcript of record; for further information about the application form and requirements, applicants are advised to contact the ASSE Foundation at 1800 E Oakton St., Des Plaines, IL 60018. **Deadline for Receipt:** December 1.

220 ■ AMERICAN SOCIETY OF SAFETY ENGINEERS
1800 E Oakton St.
Des Plaines, IL 60018
Tel: (847)699-2929
Fax: (847)768-3434
E-mail: customerservice@asse.org
Web Site: http://www.asse.org
To provide financial support to deserving students.
Title of Award: Washington Group International Safety Scholarships **Area, Field, or Subject:** Occupational safety and health; Construction. **Level of Education for which Award is Granted:** Undergraduate **Funds Available:** $1,000. **Duration:** One year.
Eligibility Requirements: Applicant must be a student pursuing an undergraduate degree in occupational safety & health with an emphasis in construction safety. **Application Requirements:** Applicants must submit a transcript of record; for further information about the application form and requirements, applicants are advised to contact the ASSE Foundation at 1800 E Oakton St., Des Plaines, IL 60018. **Deadline for Receipt:** December 1.

221 ■ AMERICAN SOCIETY OF TRAVEL AGENTS
1101 King St.
Alexandria, VA 22314
E-mail: askasta@asta.org
Web Site: http://www.asta.org
To encourage people to go into the travel and tourism business as their profession.
Title of Award: Alaska Airlines Scholarships **Area, Field, or Subject:** Travel and Tourism. **Level of Education for which Award is Granted:** Undergraduate **Funds Available:** $2,000.
Eligibility Requirements: Applicants must be travel/tourism students in either a four-year college/university or propriety travel school; must have at least 2.5 GPA on a 4.0 scale; must have relevant training in basic statistics or other social research method courses; must have at least basic computer skills; and must be residents, citizens, or legal aliens of the United States or Canada. **Application Requirements:** Applicants must submit proof of enrollment/acceptance at a travel school, community/junior college, college or university; an official school-printed description or listing of the curriculum where they are enrolled; proof of enrollments in travel and tourism courses, or letter from business colleague that can attest to the applicant's desire to pursue a career in the travel and tourism industry; four identical collated copies of applications and required materials (one original and three photocopies); and a 500-word paper on why the applicant is pursuing a career in the travel and tourism industry, which must include at least two career goals.

222 ■ AMERICAN SOCIETY OF TRAVEL AGENTS
1101 King St.
Alexandria, VA 22314
E-mail: askasta@asta.org
Web Site: http://www.asta.org
To encourage the pursuit of education and the growth and development of tomorrow's travel/tourism work force.
Title of Award: American Express Travel Scholarships **Area, Field, or Subject:** Travel and Tourism. **Level of Education for which Award is Granted:** Undergraduate **Funds Available:** No specific amount.
Eligibility Requirements: Applicants must be travel/tourism students in either a two or four-year college/university or propriety travel school; must have at least 3.0 GPA on a 4.0 scale; must have relevant training in basic statistics or other social research method courses; must have at least basic computer skills; and must be residents, citizens, or legal aliens of the United States or Canada. **Application Requirements:** Applicants must submit a proof of enrollment/acceptance at a travel school, community/junior college, college or university; an official school-printed description or listing of the curriculum where they enrolled; proof of enrollments in travel and tourism courses, or letter from business colleague that can attest to the applicant's desire to pursue a career in the travel and

tourism industry; four identical collated copies of applications and required materials (one original and three photocopies); and a 500-word statement detailing the student's plans in travel and tourism as well as the student's view of the travel industry's future.

223 ■ AMERICAN SOCIETY OF TRAVEL AGENTS

1101 King St.
Alexandria, VA 22314
E-mail: askasta@asta.org
Web Site: http://www.asta.org
To help future travel professionals meet the need for broader business management skills, beyond those dealing solely with travel and tourism issues.
Title of Award: American Society of Travel Agents AVIS Scholarships **Area, Field, or Subject:** Travel and Tourism. **Level of Education for which Award is Granted:** Graduate, Professional, Undergraduate **Number Awarded:** 1. **Funds Available:** $2,000.
Eligibility Requirements: Applicants must have a minimum of two years of full-time travel industry experience or an undergraduate degree in travel/tourism; may be currently employed in the travel industry; or may be currently enrolled in a minimum of two courses per semester in an accredited undergraduate or graduate level degree program in business or equivalent degree program. **Application Requirements:** Applicants must provide a proof of current employment in the travel industry; transcript from last academic term with proof of a GPA of 3.0 on a 4.0 scale, or if the applicant is returning to school after time spent in the workforce, applicant must submit transcript showing a GPA of 3.0 on 4.0 scale; and a brief essay (500-750 words) explaining how the degree program relates to applicant's future career in the travel industry.

224 ■ AMERICAN SOCIETY OF TRAVEL AGENTS

1101 King St.
Alexandria, VA 22314
E-mail: askasta@asta.org
Web Site: http://www.asta.org
To encourage serious academic study in the field of travel and tourism.
Title of Award: Arizona Chapter Gold Scholarships **Area, Field, or Subject:** Travel and Tourism. **Level of Education for which Award is Granted:** Undergraduate **Funds Available:** $3,000.
Eligibility Requirements: Applicants must be travel/tourism students in either a two or four-year college/university or propriety travel school; must have at least 2.5 GPA on a 4.0 scale; must have relevant training in basic statistics or other social research method courses; must have at least basic computer skills; and must be residents, citizens, or legal aliens of the United States or Canada. **Application Requirements:** Applicants must submit a proof of enrollment/acceptance at a travel school, community/junior college, college or university; an official school-printed description or listing of the curriculum where they are enrolled; proof of enrollments in travel and tourism courses, or letter from business colleague that can attest to the applicant's desire to pursue a career in the travel and tourism industry; four identical collated copies of applications and required materials (one original and three photocopies); and a 500-word statement detailing the student's plans in travel and tourism as well as the student's view of the travel industry's future.

225 ■ AMERICAN SOCIETY OF TRAVEL AGENTS

1101 King St.
Alexandria, VA 22314
E-mail: askasta@asta.org
Web Site: http://www.asta.org
To encourage academic research in the tourism field.
Title of Award: David J. Hallissey Memorial Scholarships **Area, Field, or Subject:** Travel and Tourism. **Level of Education for which Award is Granted:** Undergraduate **Funds Available:** No specific amount.
Eligibility Requirements: Applicants must be travel/tourism students from Washington, DC metro area colleges/universities in undergraduate or graduate travel or tourism programs; must have at least 3.0 GPA on a 4.0 scale; must have relevant training in basic statistics or other social research method courses; must have at least basic computer skills; and must be residents, citizens, or legal aliens of the United States or Canada. **Application Requirements:** Applicants must submit a proof of enrollment/acceptance at a travel school, community/junior college, college or university; an official school-printed description or listing of the cur-

riculum where he/she is enrolled; proof of enrollments in travel and tourism courses, or letter from a business colleague that can attest to the applicant's desire to pursue a career in the travel and tourism industry. Complete application must consist of four identical collated copies of applications and required materials (one original and three photocopies).

226 ■ AMERICAN SOCIETY OF TRAVEL AGENTS

1101 King St.
Alexandria, VA 22314
E-mail: askasta@asta.org
Web Site: http://www.asta.org
To encourage serious academic study in the field of travel and tourism.
Title of Award: Healy Scholarships **Area, Field, or Subject:** Travel and Tourism. **Level of Education for which Award is Granted:** Undergraduate **Funds Available:** $2,000.
Eligibility Requirements: Applicants must be travel/tourism students in either a four-year college/university or propriety travel school; must have at least 2.5 GPA on a 4.0 scale; must have relevant training in basic statistics or other social research method courses; must have at least basic computer skills; and must be residents, citizens, or legal aliens of the United States or Canada. **Application Requirements:** Applicants must submit a proof of enrollment/acceptance at a travel school, community/junior college, college or university; an official school-printed description or listing of the curriculum where they are enrolled; proof of enrollments in travel and tourism courses, or letter from business colleague that can attest to the applicant's desire to pursue a career in the travel and tourism industry; four identical collated copies of applications and required materials (one original and three photocopies); and a 500-word statement suggesting improvements in the travel industry.

227 ■ AMERICAN SOCIETY OF TRAVEL AGENTS

1101 King St.
Alexandria, VA 22314
E-mail: askasta@asta.org
Web Site: http://www.asta.org
To provide funding support for research projects in the travel and tourism field.
Title of Award: Holland America Line-Westours Research Grants **Area, Field, or Subject:** Travel and Tourism. **Level of Education for which Award is Granted:** Undergraduate **Funds Available:** No specific amount.
Eligibility Requirements: Applicant must be a resident, a citizen, or a legal alien of the United States or Canada and have an, at least, 2.5 grade point of average on a 4.0 scale. **Application Requirements:** Applicant must submit a proof of enrollment/acceptance at a travel school, community/junior college, or university; an official school-printed description or listing of the curriculum where he/she is enrolled; a proof of enrollment in travel and tourism courses; and a letter of recommendation from a professor, employer, or business colleague that can attest to the applicant's desire to pursue a career in the travel and tourism industry.

228 ■ AMERICAN SOCIETY OF TRAVEL AGENTS

1101 King St.
Alexandria, VA 22314
E-mail: askasta@asta.org
Web Site: http://www.asta.org
To encourage people to go into the travel and tourism business as their profession.
Title of Award: Pleasant Hawaiian Holidays Scholarships **Area, Field, or Subject:** Travel and Tourism. **Level of Education for which Award is Granted:** Undergraduate **Funds Available:** $2,500.
Eligibility Requirements: Applicants must be travel/tourism students in either a four-year college/university or propriety travel school; must have at least 2.5 GPA on a 4.0 scale; must have relevant training in basic statistics or other social research method courses; must have at least basic computer skills; and must be residents, citizens, or legal aliens of the United States or Canada. **Application Requirements:** Applicants must submit a proof of enrollment/acceptance at a travel school, community/junior college, college or university; an official school-printed description or listing of the curriculum where they are enrolled; proof of enrollments in travel and tourism courses, or letter from business colleague that can attest to the applicant's desire to pursue a career in the travel and tourism industry; four identical collated copies of applications

and required materials (one original and three photocopies); and a 500-word paper stating the applicant's career goals.

229 ■ AMERICAN SOCIETY OF TRAVEL AGENTS
1101 King St.
Alexandria, VA 22314
E-mail: askasta@asta.org
Web Site: http://www.asta.org
To encourage people to go into the travel and tourism business as their profession.
Title of Award: Stan and Leone Pollard Scholarships **Area, Field, or Subject:** Travel and Tourism. **Level of Education for which Award is Granted:** Undergraduate **Number Awarded:** 2. **Funds Available:** $2,000.
Eligibility Requirements: Applicants must be travel/tourism students in either a two or four-year college/university or propriety travel school; must have at least 2.5 GPA on a 4.0 scale; must have relevant training in basic statistics or other social research method courses; must have at least basic computer skills; must be residents, citizens, or legal aliens of the United States or Canada. **Application Requirements:** Applicants must submit proof of enrollment/acceptance at a travel school, community/junior college, college or university; an official school-printed description or listing of the curriculum where they are enrolled; proof of enrollments in travel and tourism courses, or letter from business colleague that can attest to the applicant's desire to pursue a career in the travel and tourism industry; four identical collated copies of applications and required materials (one original and three photocopies); and a 500-word paper on the student's objectives in the travel and tourism industry.

230 ■ AMERICAN SOCIETY OF TRAVEL AGENTS
1101 King St.
Alexandria, VA 22314
E-mail: askasta@asta.org
Web Site: http://www.asta.org
To help educate future travel agents.
Title of Award: George Reinke Scholarships **Area, Field, or Subject:** Travel and Tourism. **Level of Education for which Award is Granted:** Undergraduate **Number Awarded:** 6. **Funds Available:** $2,000.
Eligibility Requirements: Applicants must be travel/tourism students in either a two or four-year college/university or propriety travel school; must have at least 2.5 GPA on a 4.0 scale; must have a relevant training in basic statistics or other social research method courses; must have at least basic computer skills; and must be residents, citizens, or legal aliens of the United States or Canada. **Application Requirements:** Applicants must submit proof of enrollment/acceptance at a travel school, community/junior college, college or university; an official school-printed description or listing of the curriculum where they are enrolled; proof of enrollments in travel and tourism courses, or letter from business colleague that can attest to the applicant's desire to pursue a career in the travel and tourism industry; four identical collated copies of applications and required materials (one original and three photocopies); and a 500-word paper explaining why applicant needs the scholarship.

231 ■ AMERICAN SOCIETY OF TRAVEL AGENTS
1101 King St.
Alexandria, VA 22314
E-mail: askasta@asta.org
Web Site: http://www.asta.org
To fund research projects in the travel and tourism field.
Title of Award: Nancy Stewart Scholarships **Area, Field, or Subject:** Travel and Tourism. **Level of Education for which Award is Granted:** Undergraduate **Number Awarded:** 4. **Funds Available:** $400.
Eligibility Requirements: Applicants must have a minimum of three years of full-time travel industry experience; must be pursuing one of the Travel Institute's four certification program: CTC accreditation, Destination Specialist, Travel Career Development, Professional Management. **Application Requirements:** Applicants must provide a proof of current employment in the travel industry; transcript from last academic term with proof of a GPA of 3.0 on a 4.0 scale or if the applicant is returning to school after time spent in the workforce, submit a cover letter explaining why applicant is returning to school; a letter of intent to enroll in a Travel Institute course within one year and explaining what benefits they hope to obtain from the Travel Institute program or an application to the ASTA

educational program; a letter of recommendation from the official ASTA employer to confirm the employment status; and an original headshot picture. **Additional Information:** scholarships@asta.org.

232 ■ AMERICAN SOCIETY OF WOMEN ACCOUNTANTS
8405 Greensboro Dr., Ste. 800
McLean, VA 22102
Tel: (703)506-3265
Free: 800-326-2163
Fax: (703)506-3266
E-mail: aswa@aswa.org
Web Site: http://www.aswa.org
To provide financial assistance to students attending Community, State or 2-year Colleges in accounting or finance degree.
Title of Award: ASWA 2-Year College Scholarships **Area, Field, or Subject:** Accounting; Finance. **Level of Education for which Award is Granted:** Undergraduate **Funds Available:** Scholarship amount not specified.
Eligibility Requirements: Applicants must be community college students entering their second year of an Associates Degree Program who have completed 15 semester hours or equivalent; must have a minimum cumulative GPA of 3.0 on a 4.0 scale; and must be majoring in accounting or finance. **Application Requirements:** Applicants must submit a completed application form; seventy-five word essay about the his/her goals and objectives, what impact he/she wants to have on the accounting world and most likes about accounting; three references (two references must be from accounting faculty); and a copy and the original Academic Transcript from school. **Deadline for Receipt:** April.

233 ■ AMERICAN SOCIETY OF WOMEN ACCOUNTANTS
8405 Greensboro Dr., Ste. 800
McLean, VA 22102
Tel: (703)506-3265
Free: 800-326-2163
Fax: (703)506-3266
E-mail: aswa@aswa.org
Web Site: http://www.aswa.org
To provide financial assistance to students attending Community, State or 2-year Colleges in accounting or finance degree.
Title of Award: ASWA Undergraduate Scholarships **Area, Field, or Subject:** Accounting; Finance. **Level of Education for which Award is Granted:** Undergraduate **Funds Available:** Scholarship amount not specified.
Eligibility Requirements: Applicants must be students who have completed their sophomore year of college and are majoring in accounting or finance. **Application Requirements:** Applicants must submit a completed application form; seventy-five word essay about the his/her goals and objectives, what impact he/she wants to have on the accounting world and most likes about accounting; three references (two references must be from accounting faculty); and a copy and the original Academic Transcript from school. **Deadline for Receipt:** April.

234 ■ AMERICAN VETERANS
4647 Forbes Blvd.
Lanham, MD 20706-4380
Tel: (301)459-9600; 877-726-8387
Fax: (301)459-7924
E-mail: amvets@amvets.org
Web Site: http://www.amvets.org
To assist deserving children and grandchildren of veterans in attaining post-secondary education.
Title of Award: AMVETS National Scholarships - Entering College Freshmen **Area, Field, or Subject:** General studies. **Level of Education for which Award is Granted:** Undergraduate **Number Awarded:** 6. **Funds Available:** $1,000 each year. **Duration:** Four years.
Eligibility Requirements: Applicant must be a graduating high school senior entering at the college freshmen level; must have a minimum high school GPA of 3.0; must be the child or grandchild of a United States veteran; must be a U.S. citizen; must have demonstrated academic promise and financial need; and must agree to authorize AMVETS to publicize the scholarship award, if selected. **Application Requirements:** Applicants must submit a copy of the veteran's honorable discharge (Form DD 214). Dependents of current military personnel must submit a

letter from the base commander certifying the active duty status of the parent; an official high school transcript (must be in the 4.0 grade scale, or if in a different system, translated to the 4.0 scales); SAT and/or ACT scores; a complete and signed copy of the parent(s)'/guardian(s)' 1040 tax form (applicant's name must appear on the tax form); a copy of the applicant's Free Application For Federal Student Aid (FAFSA); essay (50-100 words); acceptance letter from the accredited school to be attended; proof of college expenses; and a resume detailing extracurricular activities, volunteer activities, community services, and jobs held during the past four years. **Deadline for Receipt:** April 15. **Additional Information:** at the above address.

235 ■ AMERICAN VETERANS
4647 Forbes Blvd.
Lanham, MD 20706-4380
Tel: (301)459-9600; 877-726-8387
Fax: (301)459-7924
E-mail: amvets@amvets.org
Web Site: http://www.amvets.org
To assist veterans who have exhausted government aid or who might not otherwise have the financial means to further their education.
Title of Award: AMVETS National Scholarships - For Veterans **Area, Field, or Subject:** General studies. **Level of Education for which Award is Granted:** Undergraduate **Number Awarded:** 3. **Funds Available:** $1,000 each year. **Duration:** Four years.
Eligibility Requirements: Applicant must be a U.S. veteran; a U.S. citizen; must demonstrate financial need; and must agree to authorize AMVETS to publicize the scholarship award, if selected. **Application Requirements:** Applicants must submit a copy of the veteran's honorable discharge or a letter certifying current service and eligibility for release from active duty prior to attending school; official college transcripts for all courses attempted and any degrees or certificates awarded (must be in the 4.0 grade scale, or if in a different system, translated to the 4.0 scales); a complete and signed copy of the applicant's 1040 tax form; a copy of the Free Application For Federal Student Aid (FAFSA); an essay (50-100 words); acceptance letter, or a letter stating current student status from an accredited school; proof of college expenses; and a resume detailing military duty and awards, volunteer activities, community services, and jobs held during the past four years. **Deadline for Receipt:** April 15. **Additional Information:** at the above address.

236 ■ AMERICAN VETERANS
4647 Forbes Blvd.
Lanham, MD 20706-4380
Tel: (301)459-9600; 877-726-8387
Fax: (301)459-7924
E-mail: amvets@amvets.org
Web Site: http://www.amvets.org
To support Junior ROTC cadets in pursuing study at an undergraduate college or university.
Title of Award: AMVETS National Scholarships - JROTC **Area, Field, or Subject:** General studies. **Level of Education for which Award is Granted:** Undergraduate **Number Awarded:** 1. **Funds Available:** $1,000. **Duration:** One year.
Eligibility Requirements: Applicant must be an active JROTC cadet and currently a high school senior; have a minimum high school GPA of 3.0; be the child or grandchild of a U.S. veteran; a U.S. citizen; have demonstrated academic promise and financial need; and agree to authorize AMVETS to publicize the scholarship award, if selected. **Application Requirements:** Applicant must submit a copy of the veteran's honorable discharge (Form DD 214). Dependents of current military personnel must submit a letter from the base commander certifying the active duty status of the parent; an official transcript including the first grading period of the current school year (must be in the 4.0 grade scale, or if in a different system, translated to the 4.0 scale); SAT and/or ACT scores; a complete and signed copy of the parent(s)'/guardian(s)'s 1040 tax form; a copy of the Free Application For Federal Student Aid (FAFSA); the essay (50-100 words); acceptance letter from the accredited school to attend; proof of college expenses; a letter from program commander verifying participation in ROTC/JROTC activities; and a resume detailing extracurricular activities, volunteer activities, community services and jobs held during the past four years. **Deadline for Receipt:** April 15. **Additional Information:** at the above address.

237 ■ AMERICAN VETERANS
4647 Forbes Blvd.
Lanham, MD 20706-4380
Tel: (301)459-9600; 877-726-8387
Fax: (301)459-7924
E-mail: amvets@amvets.org
Web Site: http://www.amvets.org
To provide financial assistance for veterans/guardsmen/reservists who have exhausted government aid, or who might not otherwise have the financial means to further their education.
Title of Award: Dr. Aurelio M. Caccomo Family Foundation Memorial Scholarships **Area, Field, or Subject:** General studies. **Level of Education for which Award is Granted:** Undergraduate **Number Awarded:** 2. **Funds Available:** $3,000.
Eligibility Requirements: Applicant must be a U.S. veteran or member of the National Guard or Reserves; a U.S. citizen; have demonstrated financial need; have a high school diploma or GED; agree to authorize AMVETS to publicize the scholarship award, if selected; enrolled or accepted for enrollment to an eligible program; must not be in default on a federal student loan; and not convicted under state or federal law of sale or possession of illegal drugs. **Application Requirements:** Applicants must submit a copy of the veteran's honorable discharge or a letter from the commanding officer certifying current Guard or Reserve status; an official college transcript for all courses attempted and any degrees or certificates awarded. (must be in the 4.0 grade scale or if in a different system, translated to the 4.0 scale); a complete and signed copy of the applicant's 1040 tax form; a copy of the Free Application for Federal Student Aid (FAFSA); an Essay (50-100 words); acceptance letter or a letter stating current student status from an accredited program; proof of expenses; and a resume detailing military duty and awards, volunteer activities, community services, and jobs held during the past four years. **Deadline for Receipt:** April 15. **Additional Information:** at the above address.

238 ■ AMERICAN WATER RESOURCES ASSOCIATION
PO Box 1626
Middleburg, VA 20118
Tel: (540)687-8390
Fax: (540)687-8395
E-mail: info@awra.org
Web Site: http://www.awra.org
To enhance the education in water resources.
Title of Award: Richard A. Herbert Memorial Scholarships **Area, Field, or Subject:** Water Resources. **Level of Education for which Award is Granted:** Undergraduate **Number Awarded:** 2. **Funds Available:** $4,000.
Eligibility Requirements: Applicant must be a national AWRA member; an applicant must be undergraduate student working toward his/her undergraduate degree enrolled in a program related to water resources; or applicant must be a full-time graduate student enrolled in a program relating to water resources. **Application Requirements:** Applicant should prepare a title page and two-page summary of their academic interests and their achievements, extracurricular interests, and career goals; he/she must include three-letters of reference(preferably from professors and/or advisors); a transcript of record including full name, permanent mailing address, e-mail address, and a phone number at which applicant may be easily reached. **Deadline for Receipt:** April 23,2008.

239 ■ AMERICAN WATER SKI EDUCATIONAL FOUNDATION
1251 Holy Cow Rd.
Polk City, FL 33868-8200
Tel: (863)324-2472
Fax: (863)324-3996
E-mail: info@waterskihalloffame.com
Web Site: http://www.waterskihalloffame.com
To preserve the traditions of one America's most popular family recreational activities; to encourage and to educate the safe enjoyment of the challenges of water skiing.
Title of Award: American Water Ski Educational Foundation Scholarships **Area, Field, or Subject:** General Studies. **Level of Education for which Award is Granted:** Undergraduate **Number Awarded:** 6. **Funds Available:** $1,500.
Eligibility Requirements: Applicant must be enrolled with a minimum of two year course in the secondary education; he/she must be a U.S.

citizen who is a current member of USA Water Ski Foundation. **Application Requirements:** Applicant must fill out the application form; he/she must submit two letters of reference; a 500 word essay on topic "AWSEF has a beautiful new facility"; an official transcript of grades; an official high school transcript. **Deadline for Receipt:** April 1.

240 ■ AMERICANS FOR INFORMED DEMOCRACY

701 Cathedral St., Ste. L3
Baltimore, MD 21201
Tel: (410)962-8773
E-mail: info@globalscholar.org
Web Site: http://www.aidemocracy.org
To provide financial assistance for students from all different fields, backgrounds and interests who have a strong academic record.
Title of Award: Americans for Informed Democracy Global Scholar Tuition **Area, Field, or Subject:** General studies. **Level of Education for which Award is Granted:** Undergraduate **Funds Available:** $2,000. **Duration:** Two weeks.
Eligibility Requirements: Applicants must be junior or senior students who have experienced with honors or advanced placement-level courses. **Application Requirements:** Applicants must file online application. Applicants must also submit a short essay explaining "what issue in international affairs he/she has most interest, why and how will it fit into his or her future plans?"

241 ■ ANAHEIM POLICE ASSOCIATION

508 N Anaheim Blvd.
Anaheim, CA 92805
Tel: (714)635-0272
Fax: (714)635-3240
E-mail: office@anaheimpoliceassociation.org
Web Site: http://www.anaheimpoliceassociation.org
To provide financial assistance for family and the children of any Anaheim Police Officers who could lose their life while in the performance of their job through education.
Title of Award: Anaheim Police Survivors and Scholarship Fund **Area, Field, or Subject:** General studies. **Level of Education for which Award is Granted:** Undergraduate **Funds Available:** $250 to $1,000.
Eligibility Requirements: Applicants must be entering students or recently high school graduates; continuing students (already enrolled in College Program) or a returning students (entering college after a break in educational experience); children (natural or adopted) of Anaheim Police Officers or Anaheim Reserve Officers enrolled in at least twelve units; must have cumulative GPA of 3.0 or higher. **Application Requirements:** Applicants must submit completed application form and a short essay of 500 words or less on need for scholarship and goals. **Deadline for Receipt:** April 1.

242 ■ WILBUR H. ANDERSON MEMORIAL SCHOLARSHIP FOUNDATION, INC.

2443 Skyland Place, SE
Washington, DC 20020
Tel: (202)678-8830
E-mail: info@whamscholarship.org
Web Site: http://www.whamscholarship.org
To provide financial assistance to deserving students who want to pursue their studies.
Title of Award: Wilbur H. Anderson Memorial Scholarships **Area, Field, or Subject:** General studies. **Level of Education for which Award is Granted:** Undergraduate **Funds Available:** $500.
Eligibility Requirements: Applicant must be living in the greater Metropolitan Washington, DC Area; must have a cumulative GPA of 2.5 or above. **Application Requirements:** Applicant must complete the application form available online; must submit an official copy of the recent transcript or record; must provide proof of enrollment confirmation from an accredited academic institution; must submit a letter of recommendation from the church pastor and/or church mentor, two copies of FAFSA/SAR, statement of financial need, and recent photograph. Application form and other supporting documents must be sent to The Wilbur H. Anderson, Scholarship Foundation, Inc., c/o Pastor Giles H. Jackson, 2443 Skyland Place SE, Washington, DC 20020. **Deadline for Receipt:** April 30.

243 ■ ARIZONA ASSOCIATION OF STUDENT FINANCIAL AID ADMINISTRATORS

PMB No. 123
4939 W Ray Rd., Ste. 4
Chandler, AZ 85226-2099
E-mail: support@aasfaa.org
Web Site: http://www.aasfaa.org
To provide quality services to the Hopi people by enhancing a full range of educational opportunities; to maintain efforts to increase the number of employable, degree-holding Hopi professionals; to maintain retention services which will enable students to complete programs.
Title of Award: BIA Higher Education Grants **Area, Field, or Subject:** General studies. **Level of Education for which Award is Granted:** Undergraduate **Funds Available:** $2,500.
Eligibility Requirements: Applicants must be students pursuing an associate, baccalaureate, graduate, or post-graduate degree; must be entering freshmen with a GPA of 2.5 for high school course work or a minimum composite of 50% on the GED exam; must have 2.5 GPA for all college work. **Application Requirements:** Applicants must submit an official high school transcript or original GED scores; must submit an official transcript from all post-secondary schools; must submit a Program of Study (POS) or Letter of Acceptance (LOA). **Deadline for Receipt:** July 1; December 1; April 1. **Additional Information:** 928-734-3533.

244 ■ ARIZONA ASSOCIATION OF STUDENT FINANCIAL AID ADMINISTRATORS

PMB No. 123
4939 W Ray Rd., Ste. 4
Chandler, AZ 85226-2099
E-mail: support@aasfaa.org
Web Site: http://www.aasfaa.org
To develop leadership and personal skills and acquire educational or pre-occupational experiences.
Title of Award: Educational Enrichment Awards **Area, Field, or Subject:** General studies. **Level of Education for which Award is Granted:** Undergraduate **Funds Available:** $500.
Eligibility Requirements: Applicants must be students in fifth grade through post-secondary level education. **Application Requirements:** Applicants must submit an official high school transcript or original GED scores; must submit an official transcript from all post-secondary schools; must submit a Program of Study (POS) or Letter of Acceptance (LOA). **Deadline for Receipt:** July 1; December 1; April 1. **Additional Information:** 928-734-3533.

245 ■ ARIZONA ASSOCIATION OF STUDENT FINANCIAL AID ADMINISTRATORS

PMB No. 123
4939 W Ray Rd., Ste. 4
Chandler, AZ 85226-2099
E-mail: support@aasfaa.org
Web Site: http://www.aasfaa.org
To encourage Hopi students to achieve and maintain a high level of academic excellence at an accredited private high school.
Title of Award: Private High School Awards **Area, Field, or Subject:** General studies. **Level of Education for which Award is Granted:** Undergraduate **Number Awarded:** 10. **Funds Available:** $4,000.
Eligibility Requirements: High school applicants must have an eighth grade education with a GPA of 3.50 while continuing students must have a GPA of 3.25. **Application Requirements:** Applicants must submit an official high school transcript or original GED scores; must submit an official transcript from all post-secondary schools; must submit a Program of Study (POS) or Letter of Acceptance (LOA) (if applicable). **Deadline for Receipt:** July 1; December 1; April 1. **Additional Information:** 928-734-3533.

246 ■ ARIZONA ASSOCIATION OF STUDENT FINANCIAL AID ADMINISTRATORS

PMB No. 123
4939 W Ray Rd., Ste. 4
Chandler, AZ 85226-2099
E-mail: support@aasfaa.org
Web Site: http://www.aasfaa.org

To encourage Hopi college students to obtain degrees in subject areas of priority interest to Hopi Tribal Goals and Objectives.
Title of Award: Tribal Priority Scholarships **Area, Field, or Subject:** General studies. **Level of Education for which Award is Granted:** Undergraduate **Number Awarded:** 5. **Funds Available:** $1,500.
Eligibility Requirements: Applicants must be junior and senior undergraduate, graduate, post-graduate and professional students in the areas of priority interest to the Hopi Tribe; must have an at least 3.5 GPA. **Application Requirements:** Applicants must submit an official high school transcript or original GED scores; must submit an official transcript from all post-secondary schools; must submit a Program of Study (POS) or Letter of Acceptance (LOA). **Deadline for Receipt:** July 1; December 1; April 1. **Additional Information:** 928-734-3533.

247 ■ ARIZONA CHRISTIAN SCHOOL TUITION ORGANIZATION
PO Box 6580
Chandler, AZ 85246
Tel: (480)820-0403
Fax: (480)820-2027
Web Site: http://www.acsto.org
To support students planning to attend K-12.
Title of Award: Arizona Christian School Tuition Organization Scholarships **Area, Field, or Subject:** General studies. **Level of Education for which Award is Granted:** Undergraduate **Funds Available:** No specific amount.
Eligibility Requirements: Student must be planning to attend K-12 in a Christian private school. **Application Requirements:** Students must submit a completed application form. **Additional Information:** All scholarships awarded will be sent directly to the student's school to be applied towards tuition. **Deadline for Receipt:** June, October, February.

248 ■ ARIZONA PARKS AND RECREATION ASSOCIATION
1422 N 44th St., Ste. 211
Phoenix, AZ 85008
Tel: (602)335-1962
Fax: (602)335-1965
E-mail: apra@azpra.org
Web Site: http://azpra.affiniscape.com
To enhance the professional development of individuals in the field.
Title of Award: Arizona Parks and Recreation Educational Scholarship Program **Area, Field, or Subject:** Parks and Recreation. **Level of Education for which Award is Granted:** Graduate, Undergraduate **Number Awarded:** 4. **Funds Available:** $500.
Eligibility Requirements: Applicants must be full-time undergraduate or graduate students in good standing who are enrolled in a professional degree program in parks and recreation or a related field. **Application Requirements:** Applicants must submit: completed application form; a professional resume including education and employment history; letter of recommendation from current faculty member; and copy of their most recent transcript. **Deadline for Receipt:** August 17. **Additional Information:** Vern Biaett at the above address.

249 ■ ARMENIAN EDUCATIONAL FOUNDATION
600 W Broadway, Ste. 130
Glendale, CA 91204
Tel: (818)242-4154
E-mail: aef@aefweb.org
Web Site: http://www.instantweb.com/a/aef
To provide financial support to qualified students of Armenian parentage.
Title of Award: Richard R. Tufenkian Memorial Scholarships **Area, Field, or Subject:** General studies. **Level of Education for which Award is Granted:** Undergraduate **Number Awarded:** 5. **Funds Available:** $2000.
Eligibility Requirements: Applicants should have Armenian origin; have a 3.0 GPA; and be an undergraduate student. **Application Requirements:** Applicants must submit an application form; proof of acceptance to the university or college; first two pages of income return of the applicant and parents of previous year; sealed official transcript; a letter of reference from university or college and from Armenian community service; and an essay. **Deadline for Receipt:** July 30.

250 ■ ARMENIAN SCHOLARSHIP FOUNDATION
14 Sandrick Rd.
Belmont, MA 02478

E-mail: leon@armenianscholarships.org
Web Site: http://www.armenianscholarships.org
To support the education of Armenian students in the U.S.
Title of Award: Armenian Scholarship Foundation Scholarships **Area, Field, or Subject:** General studies. **Level of Education for which Award is Granted:** Graduate, Undergraduate **Number Awarded:** 2. **Funds Available:** $750.
Eligibility Requirements: Applicant must be an Armenian student living in the U.S. and attending an undergraduate or graduate program in the U.S.; must demonstrate financial need and merit. **Application Requirements:** Applicants must submit: completed scholarship application form; high school or college official or unofficial transcript; an essay; and letters of recommendation (must be in a sealed envelope, signed by the recommender, included inside the application packet). **Deadline for Receipt:** May 15.

251 ■ ARMENIAN SCHOLARSHIP FOUNDATION
14 Sandrick Rd.
Belmont, MA 02478
E-mail: leon@armenianscholarships.org
Web Site: http://www.armenianscholarships.org
To support the education of Armenian students in the U.S.
Title of Award: Leon and Talin Barsoumian Scholarships **Area, Field, or Subject:** General studies. **Level of Education for which Award is Granted:** Graduate, Undergraduate **Number Awarded:** 1. **Funds Available:** $500.
Eligibility Requirements: Applicant must be an Armenian student living in the U.S. and attending an undergraduate or graduate program in the U.S. who demonstrates financial need and merit. **Application Requirements:** Applicants must submit: completed scholarship application form; high school or college official or unofficial transcript; an essay; and letters of recommendation (must be in a sealed envelope, signed by the recommender, included inside the application packet). **Additional Information:** Named after ASF president and his wife. **Deadline for Receipt:** May 15.

252 ■ ARMENIAN SCHOLARSHIP FOUNDATION
14 Sandrick Rd.
Belmont, MA 02478
E-mail: leon@armenianscholarships.org
Web Site: http://www.armenianscholarships.org
To support the education of Armenian students in the U.S.
Title of Award: Norair M. Kebabjian Memorial Scholarships **Area, Field, or Subject:** General studies. **Level of Education for which Award is Granted:** Undergraduate **Number Awarded:** 1. **Funds Available:** $500.
Eligibility Requirements: Applicant must be an Armenian student living in the U.S. and attending an undergraduate program in the U.S.; must demonstrate financial need and merit. **Application Requirements:** Applicants must submit: completed scholarship application form; high school or college official or unofficial transcript; an essay; and letters of recommendation (must be in a sealed envelope, signed by the recommender, included inside the application packet). **Deadline for Receipt:** May 15.

253 ■ ARMENIAN STUDENTS' ASSOCIATION OF AMERICA
333 Atlantic Ave.
Warwick, RI 02888
Tel: (401)461-6114
E-mail: asa@asainc.org
Web Site: http://www.asainc.org
To provide financial assistance to those students who are in need.
Title of Award: Armenian American Citizen's League Scholarships **Area, Field, or Subject:** General Studies. **Level of Education for which Award is Granted:** Undergraduate **Funds Available:** $500-$1,500.
Eligibility Requirements: Applicants must be permanent residents of the United States who have been living in California for at least two years and are enrolled full-time in an accredited college or university; minimum GPA of 3.0 (B average) is required. **Application Requirements:** Applicants must check the available website for the required materials. **Deadline for Receipt:** February 1. **Additional Information:** For more information, contact: Mrs. Dorothy Deradoorian. Co-Chairperson Educational and Scholarship Fund; P.O. Box 14, Moorpark, CA 93020-0014

254 ■ ARMENIAN STUDENTS' ASSOCIATION OF AMERICA
333 Atlantic Ave.
Warwick, RI 02888

Tel: (401)461-6114
E-mail: asa@asainc.org
Web Site: http://www.asainc.org
To provide financial assistance to those students who are in need.
Title of Award: Armenian General Athletic Union Scholarships **Area, Field, or Subject:** General Studies. **Level of Education for which Award is Granted:** Undergraduate **Funds Available:** $1,000.
Eligibility Requirements: Applicants must be high school students entering college; must be permanent U.S residents. **Application Requirements:** Applicants must check the available website for the required materials. **Deadline for Receipt:** May 15. **Additional Information:** Mrs. Ann Ajemian at 211 Grand Boulevard, Emerson, NJ 07630-1170.

255 ■ ARMENIAN STUDENTS' ASSOCIATION OF AMERICA
333 Atlantic Ave.
Warwick, RI 02888
Tel: (401)461-6114
E-mail: asa@asainc.org
Web Site: http://www.asainc.org
To provide financial assistance to those students who are in need.
Title of Award: Armenian Relief Society Scholarships **Area, Field, or Subject:** General Studies. **Level of Education for which Award is Granted:** Graduate, Undergraduate **Funds Available:** No specific amount.
Eligibility Requirements: Applicants must be undergraduate or graduate students in a four-year college or university. **Application Requirements:** Applicants must check the available website for the required materials. **Additional Information:** For more information, please contact: Mr. Sonanz Papazian at 617-926-02472.

256 ■ ARMENIAN STUDENTS' ASSOCIATION OF AMERICA
333 Atlantic Ave.
Warwick, RI 02888
Tel: (401)461-6114
E-mail: asa@asainc.org
Web Site: http://www.asainc.org
To provide financial assistance to those students who are in need.
Title of Award: Michael M. Assarian Scholarships **Area, Field, or Subject:** General studies. **Level of Education for which Award is Granted:** Undergraduate **Funds Available:** No specific amount.
Eligibility Requirements: Applicants must be full-time students of Armenian descent enrolled at Wayne State University. **Application Requirements:** Applicants must check the available website for the required materials. **Deadline for Receipt:** April 29. **Additional Information:** Private Scholarship Coordinator Office of Scholarships and Financial Aid Detroit, MI 48202; Tel: 313-577-4969

257 ■ ARMENIAN STUDENTS' ASSOCIATION OF AMERICA
333 Atlantic Ave.
Warwick, RI 02888
Tel: (401)461-6114
E-mail: asa@asainc.org
Web Site: http://www.asainc.org
To provide financial assistance to those students who are in need.
Title of Award: John M. Azarian Memorial Armenian Youth Scholarships Fund **Area, Field, or Subject:** General Studies. **Level of Education for which Award is Granted:** Undergraduate **Funds Available:** $500-$3,000.
Eligibility Requirements: Applicants must be full time enrolled in an accredited college or university; must be permanent residents of the United States. **Application Requirements:** Applicants must submit a completed application form and two letters of reference. **Deadline for Receipt:** May 1. **Additional Information:** Mr. John M. Azarian, Jr. c/o Azarian Management and Development Company at 6 Prospect Street, Suite 1B, Midland Park, NJ 07432.

258 ■ ARMENIAN STUDENTS' ASSOCIATION OF AMERICA
333 Atlantic Ave.
Warwick, RI 02888
Tel: (401)461-6114
E-mail: asa@asainc.org
Web Site: http://www.asainc.org
To provide financial assistance to those students who are in need.

Title of Award: Hagop Bogigian Scholarship Fund **Area, Field, or Subject:** General studies. **Level of Education for which Award is Granted:** Undergraduate **Funds Available:** No specific amount.
Eligibility Requirements: Applicants must be students of Armenian descent who are enrolled in a four-year Bachelor of Arts degree program at Mt. Holyoke College; must maintain over a 3.0 GPA, and demonstrate financial need. **Application Requirements:** Applicants should apply directly to the financial aid office for financial aid and should indicate on the form that they are of Armenian descent. **Deadline for Receipt:** March 1. **Additional Information:** Mt. Holyoke College Financial Aid Office, South Hadley, MA 01075 Tel: 413-538-2457.

259 ■ ARMENIAN STUDENTS' ASSOCIATION OF AMERICA
333 Atlantic Ave.
Warwick, RI 02888
Tel: (401)461-6114
E-mail: asa@asainc.org
Web Site: http://www.asainc.org
To provide financial assistance to those students who are in need.
Title of Award: Armen H. Bululian Scholarships **Area, Field, or Subject:** General Studies. **Level of Education for which Award is Granted:** Undergraduate **Funds Available:** $1,000.
Eligibility Requirements: Applicants must be graduating high school seniors or enrolled full-time undergraduate students in an accredited college or university; must be residents of Monmouth or Ocean Counties in New Jersey. **Application Requirements:** Applicants must check the available website for the required materials. **Deadline for Receipt:** June 30. **Additional Information:** For more information, Please contact: Mr. Harout Karakashian at 1184 Ocean Avenue, Elberon, NJ 07740.

260 ■ ARMENIAN STUDENTS' ASSOCIATION OF AMERICA
333 Atlantic Ave.
Warwick, RI 02888
Tel: (401)461-6114
E-mail: asa@asainc.org
Web Site: http://www.asainc.org
To provide financial assistance to those students who are in need.
Title of Award: Constantinople Armenian Relief Society (C.A.R.S.) Scholarships **Area, Field, or Subject:** General studies. **Level of Education for which Award is Granted:** Undergraduate **Number Awarded:** 20. **Funds Available:** $400-$600.
Eligibility Requirements: Applicants must be undergraduate students of Armenian descent; must have a minimum of 3.0 GPA; must be attending college in or residing in the NY/NJ area. **Application Requirements:** Applicants must check the available website for the required materials. **Deadline for Receipt:** June 30. **Additional Information:** For inquiries, please contact: Talin Sesetyan CARS Scholarship Committee at PO Box 769 Times Square Station New York, NY 10108 e-mail: talins11@hotmail.com

261 ■ ARMENIAN STUDENTS' ASSOCIATION OF AMERICA
333 Atlantic Ave.
Warwick, RI 02888
Tel: (401)461-6114
E-mail: asa@asainc.org
Web Site: http://www.asainc.org
To provide financial assistance to those students who are in need.
Title of Award: George & Isabelle Elanjian Scholarships **Area, Field, or Subject:** General Studies. **Level of Education for which Award is Granted:** Undergraduate **Number Awarded:** 2. **Funds Available:** $700 for tuition to one incoming first year student; $2,000 for one continuing upper-class student.
Eligibility Requirements: Applicants must be incoming freshmen students or enrolled for at least one year at the University of Michigan-Dearborn. **Application Requirements:** Applicants must be incoming students and should apply to the UM-D Admissions Office and upperclassmen should apply to the UM-D Financial Aid Office. Applicants must check the available website for the required materials. **Deadline for Receipt:** February 1. **Additional Information:** Armenian Students' Association of America at the above address

262 ■ ARMENIAN STUDENTS' ASSOCIATION OF AMERICA
333 Atlantic Ave.
Warwick, RI 02888

Tel: (401)461-6114
E-mail: asa@asainc.org
Web Site: http://www.asainc.org
To provide financial assistance to those students who are in need.
Title of Award: Hai Guin Scholarships Association **Area, Field, or Subject:** General Studies. **Level of Education for which Award is Granted:** Undergraduate **Funds Available:** $1,000.
Eligibility Requirements: Applicants must be students of Armenian descent, must reside in and attend school in Massachusetts. **Application Requirements:** Applicants must check the available website for the required materials. **Deadline for Receipt:** October 25. **Additional Information:** For inquiries, please contact: Hasmig Maserjian (Scholarship Chairperson) at P.O. Box 509, Belmont, MA 02478.

263 ■ ARMENIAN STUDENTS' ASSOCIATION OF AMERICA
333 Atlantic Ave.
Warwick, RI 02888
Tel: (401)461-6114
E-mail: asa@asainc.org
Web Site: http://www.asainc.org
To provide financial assistance to those students who are in need.
Title of Award: Calouste Gulbenkian Foundation Scholarships **Area, Field, or Subject:** General Studies. **Level of Education for which Award is Granted:** Graduate, Undergraduate **Funds Available:** No specific amount. **Duration:** Renewable for up to three years of study.
Eligibility Requirements: Applicants must be sophomores or above who are enrolled full-time in an accredited college or university. **Application Requirements:** Applicants must check the available website for the required materials. **Additional Information:** Calouste Sarkis Gulbenkian was an Armenian businessman and philanthropist, he played a major role in making the petroleum reserves of the Middle East available to Western development. By the end of his life he had become one of the world's wealthiest individuals and his art acquisitions are considered one of the greatest private collections. **Deadline for Receipt:** Between February 15 and April 1. **Additional Information:** Department of Armenian Communities Avenida de Berna 45-A, P-1067 Lisboa Codex, Portugal Fax: 351-793-4080.

264 ■ ARMENIAN STUDENTS' ASSOCIATION OF AMERICA
333 Atlantic Ave.
Warwick, RI 02888
Tel: (401)461-6114
E-mail: asa@asainc.org
Web Site: http://www.asainc.org
To help those students who demonstrate extreme financial need.
Title of Award: Sophia Hagopian Memorial Fund **Area, Field, or Subject:** General Studies. **Level of Education for which Award is Granted:** Undergraduate **Number Awarded:** 6. **Funds Available:** $2,000.
Eligibility Requirements: Applicants must be students of Armenian descent demonstrating financial need; must provide service to the community by being involved in Armenian organizations and/or activities; and must be full-time students in their junior or senior year of undergraduate studies at an accredited California college or university. **Application Requirements:** Applicants must check the available website for the required materials. **Deadline for Receipt:** April 15. **Additional Information:** 600 West Broadway, Suite 130, Glendale, CA 91204 Tel: 818-242-4154.

265 ■ ARMENIAN STUDENTS' ASSOCIATION OF AMERICA
333 Atlantic Ave.
Warwick, RI 02888
Tel: (401)461-6114
E-mail: asa@asainc.org
Web Site: http://www.asainc.org
To provide financial assistance to those students who are in need.
Title of Award: Hirair and Anna Hovnanian Foundation Presidential Scholarships **Area, Field, or Subject:** General Studies. **Level of Education for which Award is Granted:** Undergraduate **Funds Available:** No specific amount.
Eligibility Requirements: Applicants must be students of Armenian ethnic origin who demonstrate financial need and outstanding academic achievements; must maintain a minimum 2.75 GPA. **Application**

Requirements: Applicants must check the available website for the required materials. **Additional Information:** Villanova University; Office of Student Financial Assistance
Free: 800 Lancaster Avenue, Villanova, PA 19085

266 ■ ARMENIAN STUDENTS' ASSOCIATION OF AMERICA
333 Atlantic Ave.
Warwick, RI 02888
Tel: (401)461-6114
E-mail: asa@asainc.org
Web Site: http://www.asainc.org
To provide financial assistance to those students who are in need.
Title of Award: Hirair and Anna Hovnanian Foundation Scholarships **Area, Field, or Subject:** General Studies. **Level of Education for which Award is Granted:** Undergraduate **Funds Available:** No specific amount.
Eligibility Requirements: Applicants must be full-time students enrolled at the Women's College at Georgian Court University, preferably of Armenian descent, who exhibit financial need. **Application Requirements:** Applicants must check the contact information for inquiries. **Additional Information:** For more information please contact the Financial Aid Office of Georgian Court University at Tel: 908-364-2200, ext. 258

267 ■ ARMENIAN STUDENTS' ASSOCIATION OF AMERICA
333 Atlantic Ave.
Warwick, RI 02888
Tel: (401)461-6114
E-mail: asa@asainc.org
Web Site: http://www.asainc.org
To provide financial assistance to those students who are in need.
Title of Award: National Association for Armenian Studies and Research Scholarships **Area, Field, or Subject:** General Studies. **Level of Education for which Award is Granted:** Undergraduate **Funds Available:** No specific amount.
Eligibility Requirements: Applicants must be graduates or post-graduates doing research about Armenian Studies. **Application Requirements:** Awards will be given to those who meet the criteria. **Additional Information:** For more information, please contact: Mr. Manoog S. Young, Chairman, Board of Directors; 395 Concord Avenue, Belmont, MA 02478 Fax: 617-484-1759 Tel: 617-489-1610.

268 ■ ARMENIAN STUDENTS' ASSOCIATION OF AMERICA
333 Atlantic Ave.
Warwick, RI 02888
Tel: (401)461-6114
E-mail: asa@asainc.org
Web Site: http://www.asainc.org
To provide financial assistance to those students who are in need.
Title of Award: St. James Armenian Church Memorial Scholarships **Area, Field, or Subject:** General Studies. **Level of Education for which Award is Granted:** Undergraduate **Funds Available:** $250-$2,000.
Eligibility Requirements: Applicants must be affiliated with St. James Armenian Church by being a graduate of the Sunday school, a Sunday school teacher, a church choir member for at least one year, or in some other way acceptable to the scholarship committee. **Application Requirements:** Applicants must check the available website for the required materials. **Deadline for Receipt:** April 1. **Additional Information:** Ms. Anita Assarian; 465 Mount Auburn Street, Watertown, MA 02172 Tel: 617-923-8860 Fax: 617-926-5503.

269 ■ ARMENIAN STUDENTS' ASSOCIATION OF AMERICA
333 Atlantic Ave.
Warwick, RI 02888
Tel: (401)461-6114
E-mail: asa@asainc.org
Web Site: http://www.asainc.org
To provide financial assistance to those who are in need.
Title of Award: Hazaros Tabakoglu Scholarship Fund **Area, Field, or Subject:** General Studies. **Level of Education for which Award is Granted:** Undergraduate **Funds Available:** $1,000-$5,000.
Eligibility Requirements: Applicants must be full-time undergraduates of Armenian descent who are or will be enrolled at colleges in the United States. **Application Requirements:** Applicants must check the available

website for the required materials. **Deadline for Receipt:** May 1. **Additional Information:** 2 Park Avenue, New York, NY 1016 Tel: 212-686-0010.

270 ■ ARMENIAN STUDENTS' ASSOCIATION OF AMERICA

333 Atlantic Ave.
Warwick, RI 02888
Tel: (401)461-6114
E-mail: asa@asainc.org
Web Site: http://www.asainc.org
To provide financial assistance to those students who are in need.
Title of Award: Aram Torossian Memorial Scholarships **Area, Field, or Subject:** General studies. **Level of Education for which Award is Granted:** Undergraduate **Funds Available:** $300-$3,000.
Eligibility Requirements: Applicant must be a full-time student of Armenian parentage attending the University of California, Berkley. **Application Requirements:** Applicants must check the available website for the required materials. **Additional Information:** Armenian Students' Association of America at the above address

271 ■ ARMENIAN STUDENTS' ASSOCIATION OF AMERICA

333 Atlantic Ave.
Warwick, RI 02888
Tel: (401)461-6114
E-mail: asa@asainc.org
Web Site: http://www.asainc.org
To provide financial assistance to those students who are in need.
Title of Award: Union of Marash Armenian Scholarships **Area, Field, or Subject:** General Studies. **Level of Education for which Award is Granted:** Graduate, Undergraduate **Funds Available:** $500-$1,000.
Eligibility Requirements: Applicants must be matriculated, full-time undergraduate or graduate students accepted at an accredited institution of higher education. Must demonstrate academic excellence; be of good moral character; be in financial need; and show involvement in community; and must be a descendant of a Marashtsi (a part of Armenia/Asia Minor). **Application Requirements:** Applicants must check the available website for the required materials. **Additional Information:** Mrs. Siroon P. Shahinian, Ph.D.; Secretary, The Student Fund; One Sussex Road, Great Neck, NY 11020-1828.

272 ■ ARMENIAN STUDENTS' ASSOCIATION OF AMERICA

333 Atlantic Ave.
Warwick, RI 02888
Tel: (401)461-6114
E-mail: asa@asainc.org
Web Site: http://www.asainc.org
To provide financial assistance to those students who are in need.
Title of Award: Harry and Angel Zerigian Scholarships **Area, Field, or Subject:** Accounting. **Level of Education for which Award is Granted:** Undergraduate **Funds Available:** No specific amount.
Eligibility Requirements: Applicant must be a full-time student with financial need and of Armenian ancestry; must be day-division sophomores majoring in Accounting at Bentley College who have satisfactorily completed all course work through the fall of sophomore year. **Application Requirements:** Applicants must check the available website for the required materials.

273 ■ ARMY AVIATION ASSOCIATION OF AMERICA

755 Main St., Ste. 4D
Monroe, CT 06468-2830
Tel: (203)268-2450
Fax: (203)268-5870
E-mail: aaaa@quad-a.org
Web Site: http://www.quad-a.org
To provide grants and loans to members who seek further education as well as the member's family who sought college-entry financial aid.
Title of Award: AAAA Scholarship Program **Area, Field, or Subject:** General studies. **Level of Education for which Award is Granted:** Undergraduate **Number Awarded:** Varies. **Funds Available:** $1,000-$10,000.
Eligibility Requirements: Applicants must be a member of AAAA, the spouse of an AAAA member or deceased member, the unmarried son or daughter of an AAAA member or deceased member or the unmarried

grandchild of an AAAA member or deceased member. Applicants must be attending an accredited college or university or selected for Fall entry as an undergraduate or graduate. **Application Requirements:** Applicants must submit the completed application including the applicant's references made by two individuals; school recommendation; teacher's recommendation; academic reporting form; current transcripts of grades; and a photograph. For graduate students, applicants must submit a 250-word essay about the applicant's life experiences, work history and aspirations. **Deadline for Receipt:** May 1.

274 ■ ARMY SCHOLARSHIP FOUNDATION

6412 Brandon Ave., Ste. 201
Springfield, VA 22150
Fax: (703)451-1257
E-mail: contactus@armyscholarshipfoundation.org
Web Site: http://www.armyscholarshipfoundation.org
To financially assist deserving sons/daughters of current or former United States Army personnel in their pursuit of higher education.
Title of Award: First Lieutenant Scott McClean Love Memorial Scholarship - Children of Soldiers **Area, Field, or Subject:** General studies. **Level of Education for which Award is Granted:** Undergraduate **Funds Available:** $500-$2,000. **Duration:** One year.
Eligibility Requirements: Applicant must be the son/daughter of a serving regular active duty, active duty Reserve, or active duty National Guard U.S. Army member in good standing, or the son/daughter of a former U.S. Army member who received an Honorable Discharge or Medical Discharge, or was killed while serving in the U.S. Army. Must be a U.S. citizen not reaching 24th birthday by application deadline; and a high school senior, high school graduate, or registered as an undergraduate student at an accredited college or vocational/technical institution. **Application Requirements:** Applicants must submit a completed scholarship application form along with a Free Application for Federal Student Aid (FAFSA); a signed copy of the appropriate income tax return for the previous year; a certificate of good service or the parent's/spouse's DD 214; a high school transcript and transcripts from all post high school educational institutions (if applicable); an essay; and a photograph. **Additional Information:** In memory of First Lieutenant Scott McClean Love. **Deadline for Receipt:** May 1.

275 ■ ARMY SCHOLARSHIP FOUNDATION

6412 Brandon Ave., Ste. 201
Springfield, VA 22150
Fax: (703)451-1257
E-mail: contactus@armyscholarshipfoundation.org
Web Site: http://www.armyscholarshipfoundation.org
To financially assist deserving spouses of current or former United States Army personnel in their pursuit of higher education.
Title of Award: First Lieutenant Scott McClean Love Memorial Scholarship - Spouses of Soldiers **Area, Field, or Subject:** General studies. **Level of Education for which Award is Granted:** Undergraduate **Funds Available:** $500-$2000. **Duration:** One year.
Eligibility Requirements: Applicant must be spouse of a serving enlisted regular active duty, active duty Reserve, or active duty National Guard U.S. Army member in good standing. Must be a U.S. citizen not reaching 30th birthday by application deadline; and a high school senior, high school graduate, or registered as an undergraduate student at an accredited college or vocational/technical institution. **Application Requirements:** Applicants must submit a completed scholarship application form along with a Free Application for Federal Student Aid (FAFSA); a signed copy of the appropriate income tax return for the previous year; a certificate of good service or the parent's/spouse's DD 214; a high school transcript and transcripts from all post high school educational institutions (if applicable); an essay; and a photograph. **Additional Information:** In memory of First Lieutenant Scott McClean Love. **Deadline for Receipt:** May 1.

276 ■ ARMY SCHOLARSHIP FOUNDATION

6412 Brandon Ave., Ste. 201
Springfield, VA 22150
Fax: (703)451-1257
E-mail: contactus@armyscholarshipfoundation.org
Web Site: http://www.armyscholarshipfoundation.org

To financially assist deserving sons/daughters of current or former United States Army personnel in their pursuit of higher education. **Title of Award:** Captain Jennifer Shafer Odom Memorial Scholarships - Children of Soldiers **Area, Field, or Subject:** General studies. **Level of Education for which Award is Granted:** Undergraduate **Funds Available:** $500-$2,000. **Duration:** One year. **Eligibility Requirements:** Applicant must be the son/daughter of a serving regular active duty, active duty Reserve, or active duty National Guard U.S. Army member in good standing, or the son/daughter of a former U.S. Army member who received an Honorable Discharge or Medical Discharge, or was killed while serving in the U.S. Army. Must be a U.S. citizen not reaching 24th birthday by application deadline; and a high school senior, high school graduate, or registered undergraduate student at an accredited college or vocational/technical institution. **Application Requirements:** Applicants must submit a completed scholarship application form along with a Free Application for Federal Student Aid (FAFSA); a signed copy of the appropriate income tax return for the previous year; a certificate of good service or the parent's/spouse's DD 214; a high school transcript and transcripts from all post-high school educational institutions (if applicable); an essay; and a photograph. **Additional Information:** In memory of Captain Jennifer Shafer Odom. **Deadline for Receipt:** May 1.

277 ■ ARMY SCHOLARSHIP FOUNDATION

6412 Brandon Ave., Ste. 201
Springfield, VA 22150
Fax: (703)451-1257
E-mail: contactus@armyscholarshipfoundation.org
Web Site: http://www.armyscholarshipfoundation.org
To financially assist deserving spouses of current or former United States Army personnel in their pursuit of higher education. **Title of Award:** Captain Jennifer Shafer Odom Memorial Scholarships - Spouses of Soldiers **Area, Field, or Subject:** General studies. **Level of Education for which Award is Granted:** Undergraduate **Funds Available:** $500-$2,000. **Duration:** One year. **Eligibility Requirements:** Applicant must be spouse of a serving enlisted regular active duty, active duty Reserve, or active duty National Guard U. S. Army member in good standin. Must be a U.S. citizen not reaching 30th birthday by application deadline; and a high school senior, high school graduate, or registered as an undergraduate student at an accredited college or vocational/technical institution. **Application Requirements:** Applicants must submit a completed scholarship application form along with a Free Application for Federal Student Aid (FAFSA); a signed copy of the appropriate income tax return for the previous year; a certificate of good service or the parent's/spouse's DD 214; a high school transcript and transcripts from all post high school educational institutions (if applicable); an essay; and a photograph. **Additional Information:** In memory of Captain Jennifer Shafer Odom. **Deadline for Receipt:** May 1.

278 ■ AARON ARNOLDSEN MEMORIAL SCHOLARSHIP FUND

1325 Airmotive Way, Ste. 220
Reno, NV 89502
E-mail: info@aamemorial.com
Web Site: http://aamemorial.com
To provide financial support to aid students educational endeavor. **Title of Award:** Aaron Edward Arnoldsen Memorial Scholarships **Area, Field, or Subject:** General studies. **Level of Education for which Award is Granted:** Undergraduate **Funds Available:** $25,000. **Eligibility Requirements:** Applicant must be a male or a female; junior or senior class standing; graduate of Nevada High School; have 3.0 GPA or below; a full time student at the University of Nevada, Reno; and continuing employment through the forthcoming school-year. **Application Requirements:** Applicants must submit completed application form and the other requirements needed.

279 ■ ASIAN AND PACIFIC ISLANDER AMERICAN SCHOLARSHIP FUND

1900 L St. NW, Ste. 210
Washington, DC 20036-5002
Tel: (202)986-6892
Fax: (202)530-6843
E-mail: info@apiasf.org
Web Site: http://www.apiasf.org

To support and encourage all Asian and Pacific Islander American students to pursue higher education by developing future leaders who will contribute back to their communities. **Title of Award:** APIASF Scholarships **Area, Field, or Subject:** General studies. **Level of Education for which Award is Granted:** Undergraduate **Number Awarded:** 200. **Funds Available:** $2,500. **Eligibility Requirements:** Applicant must be of Asian and/or Pacific Islander ethnicity as defined by 2000 census; a U.S. citizen, U.S. National, legal permanent resident or a citizen of the Federated States of Micronesia, Republic of the Marshall Islands or the Republic of Palau; a first-time, incoming college student; enrolled full-time in a two or four-year program at a U.S. accredited college or university in the U.S., Guam, American Samoa, or the Commonwealth of the Northern Mariana Islands for the coming school year. (In the Freely Associated States, this includes the Community Colleges of the Federated States of Micronesia, the Republic of Marshall Islands and the Republic of Palau.) Applicants must have cumulative, unweighted grade point average (GPA) of 2.7 or higher on a 4.0 scale. **Application Requirements:** Applicants must complete the application form online, available at the website of APIASF, www. apiasf.org/apply. **Deadline for Receipt:** January 22.

280 ■ ASIS INTERNATIONAL

1625 Prince St.
Alexandria, VA 22314-2818
Tel: (703)519-6200
Fax: (703)519-6299
E-mail: asis@asisonline.org
Web Site: http://www.asisonline.org
To provide educational assistance to chapter members, student members or student nonmembers pursuing a security career. **Title of Award:** ASIS Foundation Chapter Matching Scholarships **Area, Field, or Subject:** General studies. **Level of Education for which Award is Granted:** Undergraduate **Funds Available:** $1,000. **Eligibility Requirements:** Applicants must be part- or full-time students who have completed one year of study at an accredited college, university or community college towards a career in security profession; must be undergraduate students (their chapter will set the grade point average required, for them to be qualified for the scholarship) or graduate students who earned at least a 3.0 GPA on a 4.0 scale. **Application Requirements:** Applicants must submit all the required application information.

281 ■ ASSOCIATION OF AMERICAN GEOGRAPHERS

1710 16th St. NW
Washington, DC 20009-3198
Tel: (202)324-1450
Fax: (202)234-2744
E-mail: aagguide@aag.org
Web Site: http://www.aag.org
To support college and university student career development in the academic areas of applied spatial data analysis or geographic information systems (GIS). **Title of Award:** AAG IGIF Graduate Research Awards **Area, Field, or Subject:** Geography. **Level of Education for which Award is Granted:** Graduate, Undergraduate **Funds Available:** $500. **Duration:** One year. **Eligibility Requirements:** Applicants must be full-time students who are currently registered in an undergraduate or graduate degree program providing either a degree or explicit specialization in some area of applied spatial data analysis or GIS study at a duly accredited and recognized college, university or other educational institution located within the United States. **Application Requirements:** Applications for an AAG IGIF Graduate Research Award must consist of the following: (a) Abstract of research intent; (b) Statement of problem and relevancy; (c) Context of proposed research in the literature; (d) Methodology/research design; (e) Anticipated results and significance of such results; (e) Schedule of research; (f) Budget; (g) A letter of recommendation from a faculty member. **Deadline for Receipt:** December 31. **Additional Information:** Application form and other supporting materials must be sent to Association of American Geographers, Hess Scholarship, 1710 16th Street NW, Washington, DC 20009-3198.

282 ■ ASSOCIATION OF AMERICAN GEOGRAPHERS

1710 16th St. NW
Washington, DC 20009-3198

Tel: (202)324-1450
Fax: (202)234-2744
E-mail: aagguide@aag.org
Web Site: http://www.aag.org
To support college and university student career development in the academic areas of applied spatial data analysis or geographic information systems (GIS).
Title of Award: AAG IGIF Student Travel Grants **Area, Field, or Subject:** Geography. **Level of Education for which Award is Granted:** Graduate, Undergraduate **Funds Available:** $500. **Duration:** One year.
Eligibility Requirements: Applicants must be full-time students who are currently registered in an undergraduate or graduate degree program providing either a degree or explicit specialization in some area of applied spatial data analysis or GIS study at a duly accredited and recognized college, university or other educational institution located within the United States. **Application Requirements:** Applicants must submit a letter of no more than three pages in length which may be supplemented by no more than two pages of supporting illustrations (letter should specifically address how the grant funds will be used and should indicate the career goals of the student and how these funds will assist in meeting those goals); must provide a letter from the student's faculty advisor including an endorsement from the chairperson of the applicable program; must have a brief curriculum vita and recent transcript of records. Application form and other supporting materials must be sent to Association of American Geographers, Hess Scholarship, 1710 16th Street NW, Washington, DC 200093198. **Deadline for Receipt:** December 31.

283 ■ ASSOCIATION OF AMERICAN GEOGRAPHERS

1710 16th St. NW
Washington, DC 20009-3198
Tel: (202)324-1450
Fax: (202)234-2744
E-mail: aagguide@aag.org
Web Site: http://www.aag.org
To provide financial assistance to qualified individuals who want to pursue their education.
Title of Award: Darrel Hess Community College Geography Scholarships **Area, Field, or Subject:** Geography. **Level of Education for which Award is Granted:** Undergraduate **Number Awarded:** 2. **Funds Available:** $1,000. **Duration:** One year.
Eligibility Requirements: Applicants must be students currently enrolled at a US community college, junior college, city college, or similar two-year educational institution; must have completed at least two transfer courses in geography and plan to transfer to a four-year institution as a geography major during the coming academic year. **Application Requirements:** Applicants must complete the scholarship application available online at www.aag.org/grantsawards/hessform.rtf; must submit a two page personal statement describing the applicant's academic and personal background, as well as the applicant's academic goals and interest in pursuing geography as a major at a baccalaureate institution; must have two letters of recommendation from college instructors; must have a copy of the applicant's current unofficial transcripts. Application form and other supporting materials must be sent to Association of American Geographers, Hess Scholarship, 1710 16th St. NW, Washington, DC 20009-3198. **Deadline for Receipt:** December 31.

284 ■ ASSOCIATION OF CALIFORNIA WATER AGENCIES

910 K St., Ste. 100
Sacramento, CA 95814-3577
Tel: (916)441-4545; 888-666-2292
Fax: (916)325-4849
E-mail: acwabox@acwa.com
Web Site: http://www.acwa.com
To promote study focusing on water resources.
Title of Award: Association of California Water Agencies Scholarships **Area, Field, or Subject:** Water resources. **Level of Education for which Award is Granted:** Undergraduate **Number Awarded:** 2. **Funds Available:** $3,000. **Duration:** One year.
Eligibility Requirements: Applicant must be a resident of California attending one of the selected California schools full-time as a junior or senior during the current academic year. **Application Requirements:** Applicants must submit a completed scholarship application form along with an essay. **Deadline for Receipt:** April 1. **Additional Information:** ACWA at acwabox@acwa.com, or 916-441-4545.

285 ■ ASSOCIATION OF CALIFORNIA WATER AGENCIES

910 K St., Ste. 100
Sacramento, CA 95814-3577
Tel: (916)441-4545; 888-666-2292
Fax: (916)325-4849
E-mail: acwabox@acwa.com
Web Site: http://www.acwa.com
To promote study focusing on water resources.
Title of Award: Clair A. Hill Scholarships **Area, Field, or Subject:** Water resources. **Level of Education for which Award is Granted:** Undergraduate **Funds Available:** $5,000.
Eligibility Requirements: Applicant must be a resident of California attending one of the selected California schools full-time as a sophomore, junior or senior during the current academic year. **Application Requirements:** Applicants must submit a completed scholarship application. **Deadline for Receipt:** February 1. **Additional Information:** Meggan Reed, Rancho California Water District, at 951-396-6922, or e-mail at reedm@ranchowater.com, or by fax at 951-296-6922.

286 ■ ASSOCIATION OF COLLEGE UNIONS INTERNATIONAL

One City Center, Ste. 200
120 W 7th St.
Bloomington, IN 47404
Tel: (812)245-2284
Fax: (812)245-6710
E-mail: acui@acui.org
Web Site: http://www.acui.org
To encourage graduate students to submit professional quality articles in the field of college unions and students activities.
Title of Award: Gretchen Laatsch Scholarships **Area, Field, or Subject:** General studies. **Level of Education for which Award is Granted:** Undergraduate **Funds Available:** $500. **Duration:** One year.
Eligibility Requirements: Applicants must be recognized by an institution as students in pursuit of graduate degrees in any academic area. **Application Requirements:** Applicants must submit an article containing a minimum of 500 words; must have a letter of recommendation from a college union or student activities professional. Application form and requirements must be sent to Association of College Unions International, Gretchen Laatsch Scholarship, One City Center, Ste. 200, 120 W 7th St., Bloomington, IN 47404. **Additional Information:** Scholarship was established by former ACUI President Gretchen Laatsch from the University of Akron and her husband, Jim Switzer.

287 ■ ASSOCIATION OF COLLEGE AND UNIVERSITY AUDITORS

342 N Main St., Ste. 301
West Hartford, CT 06117
Tel: (860)586-7561
Fax: (860)586-7550
E-mail: info@acua.org
Web Site: http://www.acua.org
To assist students in their education leading to careers in accounting, auditing, finance, or higher education administration.
Title of Award: ACUA Scholarships **Area, Field, or Subject:** Accounting; Finance; Educational administration. **Level of Education for which Award is Granted:** Graduate, Undergraduate **Number Awarded:** 2. **Funds Available:** $500.
Eligibility Requirements: Applicants must be a undergraduate or graduate student in a degree program leading to careers in accounting, auditing, finance, or higher education administration. **Application Requirements:** Applicants must submit a completed application form together with a single page essay; written recommendation; and a copy of transcript. **Deadline for Receipt:** May 31. **Additional Information:** Larry Mandel, ACUA Scholarship Chair, lmandel@calstate.edu.

288 ■ ASSOCIATION FOR COMPENSATORY EDUCATORS OF TEXAS

PO Box 4987
Whitefish, MT 59937
Tel: (406)862-3275
Fax: (406)862-3276
E-mail: wburroughs@bresnan.net
Web Site: http://acetx.org
To provide financial assistance for deserving students.
Title of Award: Association for Compensatory Educators of Texas Paraprofessionals Scholarships **Area, Field, or Subject:** General studies.

Level of Education for which Award is Granted: Undergraduate **Number Awarded:** 4. **Funds Available:** No specific amount. **Duration:** Annually.

Eligibility Requirements: Applicants must be paraprofessionals who wish to return to school to pursue a degree and teacher certification. They must be currently working with a school district in a compensatory program. **Application Requirements:** Applicants must submit proof of a high school diploma or GED and must check the available website to download the scholarship application, information letter, scoring rubric and scoring grid. **Deadline for Receipt:** March 10. **Additional Information:** Applications must be submitted in one envelope as one complete document to: Jeanne Walker 1302 Oak Creek Dr. Ennis, TX 75119.

289 ■ ASSOCIATION FOR COMPENSATORY EDUCATORS OF TEXAS
PO Box 4987
Whitefish, MT 59937
Tel: (406)862-3275
Fax: (406)862-3276
E-mail: wburroughs@bresnan.net
Web Site: http://acetx.org
To provide remedial assistance and support for students who have failed TAKS or are at-risk of dropping out of school.
Title of Award: Association for Compensatory Educators of Texas Scholarships **Area, Field, or Subject:** General studies. **Level of Education for which Award is Granted:** Undergraduate **Number Awarded:** 20. **Funds Available:** $1,000.
Eligibility Requirements: Applicants must be students who historically have more difficult time in school due to language, economic and other barriers. **Application Requirements:** Applicants must submit a completed application form. **Deadline for Receipt:** March 10. **Additional Information:** Applications must be submitted in one envelope as one complete document to: Jeanne Walker 1302 Oak Creek Dr. Ennis, TX 75119.

290 ■ ASSOCIATION FOR EDUCATION AND REHABILITATION OF THE BLIND AND VISUALLY IMPAIRED
1703 N Beauregard St., Ste. 440
Alexandria, VA 22311
Tel: (703)671-4500; 877-492-2708
Fax: (703)671-6391
E-mail: aer@aerbvi.org
Web Site: http://www.aerbvi.org
To support the education of selected students who are blind.
Title of Award: William and Dorothy Ferrell Scholarship Program **Area, Field, or Subject:** Visual impairment. **Level of Education for which Award is Granted:** Undergraduate **Number Awarded:** 2. **Funds Available:** $500.
Eligibility Requirements: Applicant must be legally blind; must be studying at the post-secondary level for a career in the field of services to persons who are blind or visually impaired. **Application Requirements:** Applicants must submit an application form (available at the website) to scholarships@aerbvi.org; a signed certification of visual status; and original letters of recommendation at the above address. **Deadline for Receipt:** February 15.

291 ■ ASSOCIATION OF ENERGY ENGINEERS FOUNDATION
4025 Pleasantdale Rd., Ste. 420
Atlanta, GA 30340
Tel: (770)447-5083
Fax: (770)446-3969
E-mail: maryelise@aeecenter.org
Web Site: http://www.aeecenter.org
To encourage qualified practitioners in energy engineering and energy management by awarding scholarships to further education in the field.
Title of Award: Association of Energy Engineers Foundation Scholarship Program **Area, Field, or Subject:** Energy-related areas. **Level of Education for which Award is Granted:** Graduate, Undergraduate **Funds Available:** No specific amount.
Eligibility Requirements: Applicants must be undergraduate and graduate degree candidates who are enrolled in engineering or management programs at accredited colleges or universities. **Application Requirements:** Applicants must submit all the required application information. **Deadline for Receipt:** May 1.

292 ■ ASSOCIATION FOR FINANCIAL TECHNOLOGY
34 N High St.
New Albany, OH 43054
Tel: (614)895-1208
Fax: (614)895-3466
Web Site: http://www.aftweb.com
To provide educational support for members and members' dependents.
Title of Award: James E. Stoner Memorial Scholarships **Area, Field, or Subject:** General studies. **Level of Education for which Award is Granted:** Undergraduate **Funds Available:** $3000. **Duration:** One year.
Eligibility Requirements: Applicants are the employees and their dependents. **Application Requirements:** Applicants must submit a completed application form available at the website. **Deadline for Receipt:** July 2.

293 ■ ASSOCIATION OF FOOD AND DRUG OFFICIALS
2550 Kingston Rd., Ste. 311
York, PA 17402
Tel: (717)757-2888
Fax: (717)755-8089
E-mail: afdo@afdo.org
Web Site: http://www.afdo.org
To provide financial assistance for students to further their education.
Title of Award: George M. Burditt Scholarships **Area, Field, or Subject:** General studies. **Level of Education for which Award is Granted:** Undergraduate **Funds Available:** $1,500.
Eligibility Requirements: Applicants must be sophomores preparing to enter junior year or juniors preparing to enter senior year. **Application Requirements:** Applicant must submit completed application form; official and complete college transcript, and two letters of recommendation from faculty members. **Deadline for Receipt:** February 1.

294 ■ ASSOCIATION OF FOOD AND DRUG OFFICIALS
2550 Kingston Rd., Ste. 311
York, PA 17402
Tel: (717)757-2888
Fax: (717)755-8089
E-mail: afdo@afdo.org
Web Site: http://www.afdo.org
To provide financial assistance for students to further their education.
Title of Award: Betsy B. Woodward Scholarships **Area, Field, or Subject:** General studies. **Level of Education for which Award is Granted:** Undergraduate **Funds Available:** $1,500.
Eligibility Requirements: Applicants must be sophomores preparing to enter junior year or juniors preparing to enter senior year. **Application Requirements:** Applicants must submit completed application form, official and complete college transcript; and two letters of recommendation from faculty members. **Deadline for Receipt:** February 1.

295 ■ ASSOCIATION OF FORMER INTELLIGENCE OFFICERS
6723 Whittier Ave., Ste. 303A
McLean, VA 22101-4533
Tel: (703)790-0320
Fax: (703)991-1278
E-mail: afio@afio.com
Web Site: http://www.afio.com
To provide funding for graduate and undergraduate study in a number of targeted countries and fields.
Title of Award: David L. Boren Undergraduate Scholarships **Area, Field, or Subject:** General studies. **Level of Education for which Award is Granted:** Graduate, Undergraduate **Funds Available:** $10,000 up to $20,000.
Eligibility Requirements: Applicants must be students currently enrolled in undergraduate study or graduates planning to attend graduate school; and must have desire to study foreign languages in addition to any major-related study. **Application Requirements:** Applicants must complete official application form which can be obtained from the Loyola College faculty representative. Applicants must also submit application forms online together with the 3 letters of recommendation, and 4 semesters' worth of transcripts. **Deadline for Receipt:** February 10.

296 ■ ASSOCIATION OF FORMER INTELLIGENCE OFFICERS
6723 Whittier Ave., Ste. 303A
McLean, VA 22101-4533

Tel: (703)790-0320
Fax: (703)991-1278
E-mail: afio@afio.com
Web Site: http://www.afio.com
To assist minority, disabled and non-disabled deserving students to increase knowledge and academic skills.
Title of Award: CIA Undergraduate Scholarships **Area, Field, or Subject:** General studies. **Level of Education for which Award is Granted:** Undergraduate **Funds Available:** $18,000.
Eligibility Requirements: Applicants must be high school seniors planning to enroll in a 4- or 5-year college program, or college sophomores enrolled in a 4- or 5-year college program. **Application Requirements:** Applicants must apply online and must successfully complete medical and psychological exam, polygraph interview and extensive background investigation.

297 ■ ASSOCIATION OF INDEPENDENT COLLEGES AND UNIVERSITIES OF PENNSYLVANIA
101 N Front St.
Harrisburg, PA 17101-1405
Tel: (717)232-8649
Fax: (717)233-8574
E-mail: duck@aicup.org
Web Site: http://www.aicup.org
To provide scholarship to the students who have shown an extraordinary commitment to community service and who have demonstrated creativity in shaping their volunteer activities.
Title of Award: Commonwealth "Good Citizen" Scholarships **Area, Field, or Subject:** General studies. **Level of Education for which Award is Granted:** Undergraduate **Number Awarded:** 7. **Funds Available:** $1,000.
Eligibility Requirements: Applicant must be a full-time undergraduate student with an extraordinary commitment to community service and who has demonstrated creativity in shaping his/her volunteer activities. **Application Requirements:** Applicants must write a brief essay describing their college experience, and focusing upon the answers to the following: what volunteer/extracurricular activities do they participate in, either on or off campus; how do their community service activities relate to their major and what leadership roles have they taken; what are their career/academic goals upon graduation; how will they remain involved in their community upon graduation. Applicants should include any additional information that they feel will be helpful in choosing them as a recipients of the Commonwealth "Good Citizen" Scholarship; must limit essay to two double-spaced pages (essay must have 1-inch margins) with a font that is easily readable and set no smaller than 11. Completed applications should be returned to applicants' Financial Aid Office. **Additional Information:** Mary Maronic, 717-232-8649 ext. 232; maronic@aicup.org.

298 ■ ASSOCIATION FOR INTERNATIONAL TRAINING
10400 Little Patuxent Parkway, Ste. 250
Columbia, MD 21044-3519
Tel: (410)992-3924
Fax: (410)992-3924
E-mail: aipt@aipt.org
Web Site: http://www.aipt.org
To help defray some of the costs associated with relocating overseas.
Title of Award: IAESTE United States Scholarships **Area, Field, or Subject:** General studies. **Level of Education for which Award is Granted:** Undergraduate **Number Awarded:** 3. **Funds Available:** No specific amount.
Eligibility Requirements: An applicant must be of IAESTE United States at the time of internship. **Application Requirements:** Applicant must submit a scholarship application form; a photo of the internship experience; a 500 word essay explaining the meaning and value of IAESTE internship. **Deadline for Receipt:** December 1. **Additional Information:** outbound@aipt.org.

299 ■ ASSOCIATION FOR IRON AND STEEL TECHNOLOGY
186 Thorn Hill Rd.
Warrendale, PA 15086-7528
Tel: (724)776-6040
Fax: (724)776-1880
E-mail: info@aist.org

Web Site: http://www.aist.org
To provide financial assistance to students who are planning to enter an accredited North American school.
Title of Award: AIST San Francisco Chapter Scholarships **Area, Field, or Subject:** General studies. **Level of Education for which Award is Granted:** Undergraduate **Number Awarded:** 1. **Funds Available:** $1,500. **Duration:** One year.
Eligibility Requirements: Applicant must be related to a San Francisco Chapter member; must be planning to attend or currently enrolled at an accredited university or college (full-time course only). **Application Requirements:** Applicants must submit an application form available at the website; resume; a recommendation/evaluation from a counselor, teacher or professor; copy of SAT/ACT scores; copy of transcripts; an essay (not more than 250 words) that answers the question, "Why are you motivated to attend college and how do you hope to utilize your degree after you graduate?". All requirements must be sent to: Frank Martucci Department Manager - Project Development USS-POSCO Industries 900 Loveridge Rd. Pittsburg, CA 94565. **Deadline for Receipt:** April 30. **Additional Information:** Frank Martucci at 925-439-6708 fmartucci@ussposco.com.

300 ■ ASSOCIATION FOR IRON AND STEEL TECHNOLOGY
186 Thorn Hill Rd.
Warrendale, PA 15086-7528
Tel: (724)776-6040
Fax: (724)776-1880
E-mail: info@aist.org
Web Site: http://www.aist.org
To provide educational assistance to non-engineering students.
Title of Award: Midwest Chapter Scholarships - Non-Engineering **Area, Field, or Subject:** General studies. **Level of Education for which Award is Granted:** Undergraduate **Number Awarded:** 1. **Funds Available:** $1,500. **Duration:** One year.
Eligibility Requirements: Applicant must be a graduating high school student or a full-time freshman, sophomore or junior student in good academic standing from an accredited institution. **Application Requirements:** Applicants must submit an application form available at the website; a resume; a recommendation/evaluation from a Counselor, Teacher or Professor; copy of SAT/ACT scores; a copy of transcripts; and an essay (maximum of 2 pages) describing the applicant's objectives for college and career. Requirements should be sent to: AIST Midwest Member Chapter Scholarships c/o Barry Felton 250 W US Highway 12 Burns Harbor, IN 46304. **Deadline for Receipt:** March 15. **Additional Information:** Barry Felton barry.felton@arcelormittal, 219-787-4280.

301 ■ ASSOCIATION FOR IRON AND STEEL TECHNOLOGY
186 Thorn Hill Rd.
Warrendale, PA 15086-7528
Tel: (724)776-6040
Fax: (724)776-1880
E-mail: info@aist.org
Web Site: http://www.aist.org
To provide educational assistance to both engineering and non-engineering students.
Title of Award: Midwest Chapter Scholarships - Western States Award **Area, Field, or Subject:** General studies. **Level of Education for which Award is Granted:** Undergraduate **Number Awarded:** 1. **Funds Available:** $3,000. **Duration:** One year.
Eligibility Requirements: Applicant must be a graduating high school student or a full-time freshman, sophomore or junior in good academic standing from an accredited institution. **Application Requirements:** Applicants must submit an application form available at the website; a resume; a recommendation/evaluation from a counselor, teacher or professor; copy of SAT/ACT scores; copy of transcripts; and an essay (maximum of 2 pages) describing the applicant's objectives for college and career. Requirements should be sent to: AIST Midwest Member Chapter Scholarships c/o Barry Felton 250 W US Highway 12 Burns Harbor, IN 46304. **Deadline for Receipt:** March 15. **Additional Information:** Barry Felton barry.felton@arcelormittal, 219-787-4280.

302 ■ ASSOCIATION OF JEWISH LIBRARIES
PO Box 1118
Teaneck, NJ 07666

Tel: (212)725-5359; 877-395-9257

E-mail: ajlibs@osu.edu

Web Site: http://www.jewishlibraries.org

To encourage students to train for, and enter, the field of Judaica librarianship.

Title of Award: AJL Scholarship Program **Area, Field, or Subject:** Archival science. **Level of Education for which Award is Granted:** Undergraduate **Funds Available:** $500.

Eligibility Requirements: Applicants must be attending an ALA-accredited library school or equivalent; should have an interest in, and demonstrate a potential for, pursuing a career in Judaica librarianship. **Application Requirements:** Applicants must complete and submit the application form available online and a brief statement about the involvement in Judaic activities. Submit requirements via e-mail, fax, or regular mail to: Lynn Feinman, 92nd St. Y 1395 Lexington Ave. New York, NY 10128, lfainman@92Y.org, fax: 212427-6119. **Deadline for Receipt:** March 15.

303 ■ ASSOCIATION OF OCCUPATIONAL HEALTH PROFESSIONALS IN HEALTHCARE

109 VIP Dr., Ste. 220

Wexford, PA 15090

800-362-4347

Fax: (724)935-1560

E-mail: info@aohp.org

Web Site: http://www.aohp.org

To provide annual education scholarships to subsidize the educational efforts of members.

Title of Award: Sandra Bobbitt Continuing Education Scholarships **Area, Field, or Subject:** General studies. **Level of Education for which Award is Granted:** Undergraduate **Funds Available:** $2,000.

Eligibility Requirements: Applicant must be an AOHP active member in good standing. **Application Requirements:** Applicants must submit essay typewritten, double-spaced, and limited to 1,000 words. Provide a formal title for the project. State the one category from the following list that best describes the area the research project will address: employment examinations, medical surveillance, immunizations, infectious diseases, employee health records, work injuries, administration, marketing occupational health services, or other healthcare-related topics. Briefly describe the impact/ significance of the research project to the occupational health professional in a healthcare setting. List the objectives and goal of the research project. Describe the activities that will be implemented to achieve the goals of the project, e.g., questionnaire. As appropriate, describe the target population, e.g., clinical (nursing, etc.) nonclinical employees. **Deadline for Receipt:** July 15.

304 ■ ASSOCIATION OF SCHOOL BUSINESS OFFICIALS OF MARYLAND AND THE DISTRICT OF COLUMBIA

PO Box 943

Rockville, MD 20848-0943

Tel: (301)318-4969

E-mail: asbomddc@comcast.net

Web Site: http://www.asbo.org

To assist individuals who need financial assistance for college education.

Title of Award: Dwight P. Jacobus Scholarships **Area, Field, or Subject:** General studies. **Level of Education for which Award is Granted:** Undergraduate **Number Awarded:** 4. **Funds Available:** $1000. **Duration:** One year.

Eligibility Requirements: Applicants must be residents of Maryland or District of Columbia for at least one year preceding the date of the award; must be accepted for admission as a full-time student; must demonstrate financial need; and must have a minimum 3.0 overall GPA. **Application Requirements:** Applicants must submit a completed application form and other supporting documents. **Deadline for Receipt:** March 1.

305 ■ ASSOCIATION OF SEVENTH-DAY ADVENTIST LIBRARIANS

James White Library, Andrews University

Berrien Springs, MI 49104-1400

E-mail: helmsc@andrews.edu

Web Site: http://www.asdal.org

To encourage employment of potential leaders in a Seventh-day Adventist Library while upholding excellence in scholarship.

Title of Award: D. Glenn Hilts Scholarships Program **Area, Field, or Subject:** General studies; Library and archival sciences. **Level of Educa-**tion for which Award is Granted: Graduate, Undergraduate **Funds Available:** $1,200.

Eligibility Requirements: Applicant must be a Seventh-Day Adventist in good standing; be accepted in an American Library Association accredited library school; and must be a full-time student. **Application Requirements:** Applicant must submit completed application form available at the website; submit a copy of the acceptance letter from the ALA-accredited library; GRE scores; an essay (maximum of three pages); high school and college transcripts; three letters of reference (there must be one from the applicant's Seventh-day Adventist pastor). **Deadline for Receipt:** June 15. **Additional Information:** Cynthia Mae Helms, Scholarship and Awards Committee at the above address.

306 ■ ASSOCIATION OF UNIVERSITIES AND COLLEGES OF CANADA

350 Albert St., Ste. 600

Ottawa, ON, Canada K1R 1B1

Tel: (613)563-1236

Fax: (613)563-9745

E-mail: info@aucc.ca

Web Site: http://www.aucc.ca

To foster and promote the interest of higher education.

Title of Award: Association of Universities and Colleges of Canada Public Scholarships **Area, Field, or Subject:** General studies. **Level of Education for which Award is Granted:** Undergraduate **Funds Available:** No specific amount.

Eligibility Requirements: Applicants must be interested in pursuing their postsecondary studies in Canada or abroad and must be Canadian citizens or permanent residents of Canada. **Application Requirements:** Applicants must complete the application form and submit along with an official, sealed or stamped and signed transcript; letters of reference; essays; and community service. **Additional Information:** 613-563-9745.

307 ■ ATHLETIC EQUIPMENT MANAGERS ASSOCIATION

460 Hunt Hill Rd.

Freeville, NY 13068

Tel: (607)539-6300

Fax: (607)539-6340

E-mail: aema@frontiernet.net

Web Site: http://www.aema1.com

To develop further the professional ability of each of its members.

Title of Award: Athletic Equipment Managers Association College Scholarships **Area, Field, or Subject:** General studies. **Level of Education for which Award is Granted:** Undergraduate **Number Awarded:** 6. **Funds Available:** $500. **Duration:** One year.

Eligibility Requirements: Applicant must be full-time college student with one year of collegiate athletic equipment management experience; displays an interest in the field of Athletic Equipment Management. **Application Requirements:** Applicants must submit a completed application form along with the required materials. **Additional Information:** March 15. **Additional Information:** Dorothy Cutting.

308 ■ ATLANTIC PROVINCES LIBRARY ASSOCIATION

166 Bedford Hwy.

Halifax, NS, Canada B3M 2J6

Tel: (902)457-6108

E-mail: Donna.Bourne-Tyson@msvu.ca

Web Site: http://www.apla.ca

To support the education of Canadian students with financial need.

Title of Award: Carin Alma E. Somers Scholarship Trust **Area, Field, or Subject:** Library and Information Studies. **Level of Education for which Award is Granted:** Undergraduate **Funds Available:** $2,000.

Eligibility Requirements: Applicants must be Canadian citizens; must be residents of Atlantic Provinces; and must have demonstrated financial need. **Application Requirements:** Applicants must submit a completed application form. **Additional Information:** Successful applicants will have been accepted in a School of Graduate Studies as candidates for a Master's degree in Library and Information Studies accredited by the American Library Association. The award will normally be announced at the Annual Atlantic Provinces Library Association Spring Conference. **Additional Information:** Atlantic Provinces Library Association at the above address.

309 ■ BALTIMORE CITY COLLEGE
600 E Lombard St., Rm. 206
Baltimore, MD 21202
Tel: (410)986-5518
Fax: (410)986-5510
Web Site: http://www.bccc.edu
To provide financial assistance to individuals who have the desire and commitment to pursue their educational goals.
Title of Award: BCCC Foundation Scholarships **Area, Field, or Subject:** General studies. **Level of Education for which Award is Granted:** Undergraduate **Funds Available:** No specific amount.
Eligibility Requirements: Applicants must be graduating high school students with at least 6 credits at BCCC with 2.5 GPA. **Application Requirements:** Applicants must submit completed scholarship application along with personal statement and copy of unofficial transcript.

310 ■ BALTIMORE CITY COLLEGE
600 E Lombard St., Rm. 206
Baltimore, MD 21202
Tel: (410)986-5518
Fax: (410)986-5510
Web Site: http://www.bccc.edu
To provide financial assistance to those who have the desire and commitment to pursue their educational goals.
Title of Award: BCCC Foundation Workforce Scholarships **Area, Field, or Subject:** General studies. **Level of Education for which Award is Granted:** Undergraduate **Funds Available:** No specific amount.
Eligibility Requirements: Applicants must be US citizens and residents of Maryland working at least 20 hours a week; must have a 2.5 GPA enrolled in at least three credits per semester if pursuing credit courses; and must demonstrate financial need through submission of FAFSA. **Application Requirements:** Applicants must submit completed scholarship application along with 300-500 word essay and a copy of transcript.

311 ■ BARRIENTOS SCHOLARSHIP FOUNDATION
PO Box 7173
Omaha, NE 68107
Tel: (402)215-5106
E-mail: info@barrientosscholarship.org
Web Site: http://www.barrientosscholarship.org
To provide financial assistance to qualified students who want to pursue their studies.
Title of Award: General Scholarship Awards **Area, Field, or Subject:** Interdisciplinary studies. **Level of Education for which Award is Granted:** Undergraduate **Number Awarded:** No specific amount. **Funds Available:** $250-$500. **Duration:** One year.
Eligibility Requirements: Applicants must be students pursuing higher education and career goals that focus on disciplines other than arts; must be of Latino Heritage; must be high school graduating seniors, currently enrolled in college, or adults ready to pursue college; must plan to enroll in at least two classes and attend an accredited community college, university, or technical or vocational school in the State of Nebraska or surrounding greater Omaha Metropolitan area; must have a minimum of a 2.5 cumulative GPA. **Application Requirements:** Applicants must have the application form available online; must have a personal essay with a minimum of two pages; must submit a letter of recommendation and official high school or college transcript. Application form and requirements must be sent to Barrientos Scholarship Foundation, P.O Box 7173, Omaha, NE 68107. **Deadline for Receipt:** May 15.

312 ■ BEACON OF HOPE SCHOLARSHIP FOUNDATION
7230 Medical Center Dr., Ste. 300
West Hills, CA 91307
Tel: (818)716-7003
Web Site: http://www.beaconhope.org
To provide financial assistance to qualified, underprivileged, college-bound African American high school students.
Title of Award: Beacon of Hope Scholarships **Area, Field, or Subject:** General studies. **Level of Education for which Award is Granted:** Undergraduate **Funds Available:** $1,000.
Eligibility Requirements: Applicants must be African American graduating high school students; must be residents of Mississippi and/or Los Angeles, California; must have at least a "B" average and verification of

acceptance and attendance at a four-year college or university in the United States; must participate in any scholarship-related public relations activities. **Application Requirements:** Applicants must submit the completed application form along with one certified copy of high school academic transcript; one original photograph; and a hard copy of an essay of at least 1,000 words entitled "Why I am Deserving of the Beacon of Hope Scholarship".

313 ■ BECA FOUNDATION
830 E Grand Ave., Ste. B
Escondido, CA 92025
Tel: (760)741-8246
E-mail: sdbeca@sbcglobal.net
Web Site: http://www.becafoundation.org
To seek promising students and provide them with the necessary financial assistance, moral support and guidance to complete their education, thereby promoting higher educational and leadership standards within the Hispanic community.
Title of Award: BECA Foundation-CUSM Scholarships **Area, Field, or Subject:** General studies. **Level of Education for which Award is Granted:** Undergraduate **Funds Available:** $1,000.
Eligibility Requirements: Applicants must be Latino students enrolled at CSU San Marcos. **Application Requirements:** Applicants must complete the application form. **Deadline for Receipt:** March 3. **Additional Information:** sdbeca@sbcglobal.net; 760-741-8246.

314 ■ BECA FOUNDATION
830 E Grand Ave., Ste. B
Escondido, CA 92025
Tel: (760)741-8246
E-mail: sdbeca@sbcglobal.net
Web Site: http://www.becafoundation.org
To seek promising students and provide them with the necessary financial assistance, moral support and guidance to complete their education, thereby promoting higher educational and leadership standards within the Hispanic community.
Title of Award: BECA Foundation General Scholarships Fund **Area, Field, or Subject:** General studies. **Level of Education for which Award is Granted:** Undergraduate **Funds Available:** $1,000.
Eligibility Requirements: Applicant must be a San Diego County High School graduate who is entering college. **Application Requirements:** Applicants must complete the application form. **Deadline for Receipt:** March 3. **Additional Information:** sdbeca@sbcglobal.net; 760-741-8246.

315 ■ BENTON COUNTY FOUNDATION
PO Box 911
Corvallis, OR 97339
Tel: (541)753-1603
Web Site: http://www.bentoncountyfoundation.org
To provide scholarship opportunity to the students from OSU.
Title of Award: Joel R. Friend Scholarship **Area, Field, or Subject:** General studies. **Level of Education for which Award is Granted:** Undergraduate **Funds Available:** No specific amount.
Eligibility Requirements: Applicants must be foreign students from Thailand, Taiwan (Republic of China) in attendance at OSU in any field of study; must qualify for financial assistance as defined by the Financial Aid Office of OSU. **Application Requirements:** Applicant may contact the Foundation for application form and other requirements. **Additional Information:** Benton County Foundation at the above address.

316 ■ BENTON COUNTY FOUNDATION
PO Box 911
Corvallis, OR 97339
Tel: (541)753-1603
Web Site: http://www.bentoncountyfoundation.org
To provide scholarship to the students of Oregon State University.
Title of Award: William Harrison Gill Education Fund **Area, Field, or Subject:** General studies. **Level of Education for which Award is Granted:** Undergraduate **Funds Available:** No specific amount.
Eligibility Requirements: Applicant must: be of Native American descent and must be an American citizen with a permanent or guardian residence in one of the following states: Arizona, California, Colorado, Idaho, Montana, Nevada, New Mexico, Oregon, Utah, Washington or Wyoming.

Application Requirements: Applicant may contact the Foundation for application process and other requirements.

317 ■ BENTON COUNTY FOUNDATION
PO Box 911
Corvallis, OR 97339
Tel: (541)753-1603
Web Site: http://www.bentoncountyfoundation.org
To award scholarship to the foreign students of ethnic Chinese descent. **Title of Award:** Lucy Hsu Ho Scholarship **Area, Field, or Subject:** General studies. **Level of Education for which Award is Granted:** Undergraduate **Funds Available:** No specific amount.
Eligibility Requirements: Applicants must be foreign students of ethnic Chinese descent; pimary preference in awarding the scholarship shall be given to those candidates who have demonstrated leadership in student and/or community activities and organizations, as well as the desire to serve others in the candidate's future chosen field of work. Secondary preference shall be determined by level of financial need; must re-apply for this scholarship each year; must qualify for financial assistance as defined by the Financial Aid Office of OSU. **Application Requirements:** Applicant may contact the Foundation for application form and other requirements. **Additional Information:** Benton County Foundation at the above address.

318 ■ BENTON COUNTY FOUNDATION
PO Box 911
Corvallis, OR 97339
Tel: (541)753-1603
Web Site: http://www.bentoncountyfoundation.org
To provide scholarship opportunity to the students enrolled at Oregon State University.
Title of Award: Kilbuck Family Native American Scholarship **Area, Field, or Subject:** General studies. **Level of Education for which Award is Granted:** Undergraduate **Funds Available:** No specific amount.
Eligibility Requirements: Applicant must have a cumulative GPA of 3.0 or above; have at least 1/16 enrolled or documented tribal affiliation; must be a graduate of Oregon or Alaska high schools. Scholarship is renewable for up to 12 terms if a 3.0 cumulative GPA is maintained. **Application Requirements:** Applicant may contact the Foundation for application process and other requirements.

319 ■ BENTON COUNTY FOUNDATION
PO Box 911
Corvallis, OR 97339
Tel: (541)753-1603
Web Site: http://www.bentoncountyfoundation.org
To provide scholarship to the students of Oregon State University.
Title of Award: David W. Schacht Native American Student Scholarship **Area, Field, or Subject:** General studies. **Level of Education for which Award is Granted:** Undergraduate **Funds Available:** No specific amount.
Eligibility Requirements: Applicants must: be students of Native American descent, defined as self-identified individuals with tribal affiliation; have demonstrated ability and scholarship during high school or during previous college years; must qualify for financial assistance as defined by the Financial Aid Office of OSU. **Application Requirements:** Applicant may contact the Foundation for application form and other requirements.

320 ■ BENTON COUNTY FOUNDATION
PO Box 911
Corvallis, OR 97339
Tel: (541)753-1603
Web Site: http://www.bentoncountyfoundation.org
To provide scholarship to the students pursuing their first baccalaureate or graduate degree in any field of study.
Title of Award: Helen J. and Harold Gilman Smith Scholarship **Area, Field, or Subject:** General study. **Level of Education for which Award is Granted:** Graduate, Undergraduate **Funds Available:** No specific amount.
Eligibility Requirements: Applicant must: be a Native American student; have a minimum GPA of 2.75 for their undergraduate freshman year. Graduate students must maintain the minimum GPA level required by their college graduate degree program. Preference is given to students

graduating from an American Indian high school. Applicant must qualify for financial assistance as defined by the Financial Aid Office of OSU. **Application Requirements:** Applicant may contact the Foundation for application form and other requirements. **Additional Information:** Benton County Foundation at the above address.

321 ■ BENTON COUNTY FOUNDATION
PO Box 911
Corvallis, OR 97339
Tel: (541)753-1603
Web Site: http://www.bentoncountyfoundation.org
To provide scholarship to the students who are current citizens of Nepal. **Title of Award:** Hugh and Helen Wood Nepales Scholarship **Area, Field, or Subject:** General studies. **Level of Education for which Award is Granted:** Undergraduate **Funds Available:** No specific amount.
Eligibility Requirements: Applicants must be current students who are citizens of Nepal; primary preference in awarding the scholarship shall be given to those candidates who agree to become a public servant in Nepal for at least five years following graduation. Other requirements include: a 3.5 GPA; a minimum TOEFL score of 550 or other language competency score satisfactory to the university: and all preparatory work completed in Nepal. Secondary consideration will be given to African American students if no Nepalese students meet the requirements. **Application Requirements:** Applicant may contact the Foundation for application form and other requirements. **Additional Information:** Benton County Foundation at the above address.

322 ■ BETA THETA PI
PO Box 6277
Oxford, OH 45056
Tel: (513)523-7591
Free: 800-800-BETA
E-mail: beta@betathetapi.org
Web Site: http://www.betathetapi.org
To financially assist students in their pursuit of academic achievement.
Title of Award: William H. Bates Oxford Cup Scholarships **Area, Field, or Subject:** General Studies. **Level of Education for which Award is Granted:** Graduate, Undergraduate **Number Awarded:** 1. **Funds Available:** $1475. **Duration:** One academic year.
Eligibility Requirements: Applicant must be undergraduate or graduate student; a member of Beta Theta Pi enrolled as full-time student. Previous recipients are not qualified. **Application Requirements:** Applicants must submit a completed standard application form along with transcript of grades and a passport type photo (head and shoulders, wallet size, in coat and tie). **Deadline for Receipt:** April 1.

323 ■ BETA THETA PI
PO Box 6277
Oxford, OH 45056
Tel: (513)523-7591
Free: 800-800-BETA
E-mail: beta@betathetapi.org
Web Site: http://www.betathetapi.org
To financially assist students in their pursuit of academic achievement.
Title of Award: Stephen D. Bechtel Oxford Cup Scholarships **Area, Field, or Subject:** General Studies. **Level of Education for which Award is Granted:** Graduate, Undergraduate **Number Awarded:** 1. **Funds Available:** $700. **Duration:** One academic year.
Eligibility Requirements: Applicant must be undergraduate or graduate student; a member of Beta Theta Pi enrolled as full-time student. Previous recipients are not qualified. **Application Requirements:** Applicants must submit a completed standard application form along with transcript of grades and a passport type photo (head and shoulders, wallet size, in coat and tie). **Deadline for Receipt:** April 1. **Additional Information:** Laura Lednik, at laura.lednik@betathetapi.org.

324 ■ BETA THETA PI
PO Box 6277
Oxford, OH 45056
Tel: (513)523-7591
Free: 800-800-BETA
E-mail: beta@betathetapi.org
Web Site: http://www.betathetapi.org

To financially assist students in their pursuit of academic achievement. **Title of Award:** Bertram W. Bennett Memorial Scholarships **Area, Field, or Subject:** General Studies. **Level of Education for which Award is Granted:** Graduate, Undergraduate **Number Awarded:** 2. **Funds Available:** $1050. **Duration:** One academic year.

Eligibility Requirements: Applicant must be undergraduate or graduate student; a member of Beta Theta Pi enrolled as full-time student. Previous recipients are not qualified. **Application Requirements:** Applicants must submit a completed standard application form along with transcript of grades and a passport type photo (head and shoulders, wallet size, in coat and tie). **Deadline for Receipt:** April 1.

325 ■ BETA THETA PI
PO Box 6277
Oxford, OH 45056
Tel: (513)523-7591
Free: 800-800-BETA
E-mail: beta@betathetapi.org
Web Site: http://www.betathetapi.org
To financially assist students in their pursuit of academic achievement. **Title of Award:** Seth R. and Corrine H. Brooks Memorial Scholarships **Area, Field, or Subject:** General Studies. **Level of Education for which Award is Granted:** Graduate, Undergraduate **Number Awarded:** 2. **Funds Available:** $1350. **Duration:** One academic year.

Eligibility Requirements: Applicant must be undergraduate or graduate student; a member of Beta Theta Pi enrolled as full-time student; and a son or daughter of a Beta alumnus. Previous recipients are not qualified. **Application Requirements:** Applicants must submit a completed standard application form along with transcript of grades and a passport type photo (head and shoulders, wallet size, in coat and tie). **Deadline for Receipt:** April 1. **Additional Information:** Laura Lednik, at laura.lednik@betathetapi.org.

326 ■ BETA THETA PI
PO Box 6277
Oxford, OH 45056
Tel: (513)523-7591
Free: 800-800-BETA
E-mail: beta@betathetapi.org
Web Site: http://www.betathetapi.org
To financially assist students in their pursuit of academic achievement. **Title of Award:** Edward M. Brown Oxford Cup Memorial Scholarships **Area, Field, or Subject:** General Studies. **Level of Education for which Award is Granted:** Graduate, Undergraduate **Number Awarded:** 2. **Funds Available:** $1050. **Duration:** One academic year.

Eligibility Requirements: Applicant must be undergraduate or graduate student; a member of Beta Theta Pi enrolled as full-time student. Previous recipients are not qualified. **Application Requirements:** Applicants must submit a completed standard application form along with transcript of grades and a passport type photo (head and shoulders, wallet size, in coat and tie). **Deadline for Receipt:** April 1.

327 ■ BETA THETA PI
PO Box 6277
Oxford, OH 45056
Tel: (513)523-7591
Free: 800-800-BETA
E-mail: beta@betathetapi.org
Web Site: http://www.betathetapi.org
To financially assist students in their pursuit of academic achievement. **Title of Award:** Adam S. Burford Memorial Scholarships **Area, Field, or Subject:** General Studies. **Level of Education for which Award is Granted:** Graduate, Undergraduate **Number Awarded:** 1. **Funds Available:** $400. **Duration:** One academic year.

Eligibility Requirements: Applicant must be undergraduate or graduate student; a member of Beta Theta Pi enrolled as full-time student. Previous recipients are not qualified. **Application Requirements:** Applicants must submit a completed standard application form along with transcript of grades and a passport type photo (head and shoulders, wallet size, in coat and tie). **Deadline for Receipt:** April 1. **Additional Information:** Laura Lednik, at laura.lednik@betathetapi.org.

328 ■ BETA THETA PI
PO Box 6277
Oxford, OH 45056

Tel: (513)523-7591
Free: 800-800-BETA
E-mail: beta@betathetapi.org
Web Site: http://www.betathetapi.org
To financially assist students in their pursuit of academic achievement. **Title of Award:** Thad Byrne Memorial Scholarships **Area, Field, or Subject:** General Studies. **Level of Education for which Award is Granted:** Graduate, Undergraduate **Number Awarded:** 1. **Funds Available:** $1475. **Duration:** One academic year.

Eligibility Requirements: Applicant must be undergraduate or graduate student; a member of Beta Theta Pi enrolled as full-time student. Previous recipients are not qualified. **Application Requirements:** Applicants must submit a completed standard application form along with transcript of grades and a passport type photo (head and shoulders, wallet size, in coat and tie). **Deadline for Receipt:** April 1. **Additional Information:** Laura Lednik, at laura.lednik@betathetapi.org.

329 ■ BETA THETA PI
PO Box 6277
Oxford, OH 45056
Tel: (513)523-7591
Free: 800-800-BETA
E-mail: beta@betathetapi.org
Web Site: http://www.betathetapi.org
To financially assist students in their pursuit of academic achievement. **Title of Award:** Thomas D. and Karen Cassady Scholarships **Area, Field, or Subject:** General Studies. **Level of Education for which Award is Granted:** Graduate, Undergraduate **Number Awarded:** 1. **Funds Available:** $1000. **Duration:** One academic year.

Eligibility Requirements: Applicant must be undergraduate or graduate student; a member of Beta Theta Pi enrolled as full-time student. Previous recipients are not qualified. **Application Requirements:** Applicants must submit a completed standard application form along with transcript of grades and a passport type photo (head and shoulders, wallet size, in coat and tie). **Deadline for Receipt:** April 1. **Additional Information:** Laura Lednik, at laura.lednik@betathetapi.org.

330 ■ BETA THETA PI
PO Box 6277
Oxford, OH 45056
Tel: (513)523-7591
Free: 800-800-BETA
E-mail: beta@betathetapi.org
Web Site: http://www.betathetapi.org
To financially assist students in their pursuit of academic achievement. **Title of Award:** Oscar Chapman Memorial Scholarships **Area, Field, or Subject:** General Studies. **Level of Education for which Award is Granted:** Graduate, Undergraduate **Number Awarded:** 1. **Funds Available:** $1200. **Duration:** One academic year.

Eligibility Requirements: Applicant must be undergraduate or graduate student; a member of Beta Theta Pi enrolled as full-time student. Previous recipients are not qualified. **Application Requirements:** Applicants must submit a completed standard application form along with transcript of grades and a passport type photo (head and shoulders, wallet size, in coat and tie). **Deadline for Receipt:** April 1. **Additional Information:** Laura Lednik, at laura.lednik@betathetapi.org.

331 ■ BETA THETA PI
PO Box 6277
Oxford, OH 45056
Tel: (513)523-7591
Free: 800-800-BETA
E-mail: beta@betathetapi.org
Web Site: http://www.betathetapi.org
To financially assist students in their pursuit of academic achievement. **Title of Award:** Cleveland Alumni Association Scholarships **Area, Field, or Subject:** General Studies. **Level of Education for which Award is Granted:** Graduate, Undergraduate **Number Awarded:** 4. **Funds Available:** $1050. **Duration:** One academic year.

Eligibility Requirements: Applicant must be undergraduate or graduate student; a member of Beta Theta Pi enrolled as full-time student. Previous recipients are not qualified. **Application Requirements:** Applicants must submit a completed standard application form along with transcript of grades and a passport type photo (head and shoulders, wallet size, in coat and tie). **Deadline for Receipt:** April 1.

332 ■ BETA THETA PI
PO Box 6277
Oxford, OH 45056
Tel: (513)523-7591
Free: 800-800-BETA
E-mail: beta@betathetapi.org
Web Site: http://www.betathetapi.org
To financially assist students in their pursuit of academic achievement.
Title of Award: L. Robert Clough Memorial Scholarships **Area, Field, or Subject:** General Studies. **Level of Education for which Award is Granted:** Graduate, Undergraduate **Number Awarded:** 1. **Funds Available:** $1000. **Duration:** One academic year.
Eligibility Requirements: Applicant must be undergraduate or graduate student; a member of Beta Theta Pi enrolled as full-time student; a Gamma Alpha at South Dakota. Previous recipients are not qualified. **Application Requirements:** Applicants must submit a completed standard application form along with transcript of grades and a passport type photo (head and shoulders, wallet size, in coat and tie). **Deadline for Receipt:** April 1.

333 ■ BETA THETA PI
PO Box 6277
Oxford, OH 45056
Tel: (513)523-7591
Free: 800-800-BETA
E-mail: beta@betathetapi.org
Web Site: http://www.betathetapi.org
To financially assist students in their pursuit of academic achievement.
Title of Award: William W. Dawson Memorial Scholarships **Area, Field, or Subject:** General Studies. **Level of Education for which Award is Granted:** Graduate, Undergraduate **Number Awarded:** 2. **Funds Available:** $1000. **Duration:** One academic year.
Eligibility Requirements: Applicant must be undergraduate or graduate student; a member of Beta Theta Pi enrolled as full-time student. Previous recipients are not qualified. **Application Requirements:** Applicants must submit a completed standard application form along with transcript of grades and a passport type photo (head and shoulders, wallet size, in coat and tie). **Deadline for Receipt:** April 1. **Additional Information:** Laura Lednik, at laura.lednik@betathetapi.org.

334 ■ BETA THETA PI
PO Box 6277
Oxford, OH 45056
Tel: (513)523-7591
Free: 800-800-BETA
E-mail: beta@betathetapi.org
Web Site: http://www.betathetapi.org
To financially assist students in their pursuit of academic achievement.
Title of Award: Delta Tau Chapter Scholarships **Area, Field, or Subject:** General Studies. **Level of Education for which Award is Granted:** Graduate, Undergraduate **Number Awarded:** 1. **Funds Available:** $725. **Duration:** One academic year.
Eligibility Requirements: Applicant must be undergraduate or graduate student; a member of Beta Theta Pi enrolled as full-time student. Previous recipients are not qualified. **Application Requirements:** Applicants must submit a completed standard application form along with transcript of grades and a passport type photo (head and shoulders, wallet size, in coat and tie). **Deadline for Receipt:** April 1. **Additional Information:** Laura Lednik, at laura.lednik@betathetapi.org.

335 ■ BETA THETA PI
PO Box 6277
Oxford, OH 45056
Tel: (513)523-7591
Free: 800-800-BETA
E-mail: beta@betathetapi.org
Web Site: http://www.betathetapi.org
To financially assist students in their pursuit of academic achievement.
Title of Award: John Holt Duncan Memorial Scholarships **Area, Field, or Subject:** General Studies. **Level of Education for which Award is

Granted: Graduate, Undergraduate **Number Awarded:** 1. **Funds Available:** $2375. **Duration:** One academic year.
Eligibility Requirements: Applicant must be undergraduate or graduate student; a member of Beta Theta Pi enrolled as full-time student. Previous recipients are not qualified. **Application Requirements:** Applicants must submit a completed standard application form along with transcript of grades and a passport type photo (head and shoulders, wallet size, in coat and tie). **Additional Information:** Funded by the estate of Robert C. Lafferty, Ohio Wesleyan '28. **Deadline for Receipt:** April 1. **Additional Information:** Laura Lednik, at laura.lednik@betathetapi.org.

336 ■ BETA THETA PI
PO Box 6277
Oxford, OH 45056
Tel: (513)523-7591
Free: 800-800-BETA
E-mail: beta@betathetapi.org
Web Site: http://www.betathetapi.org
To financially assist students in their pursuit of academic achievement.
Title of Award: Todd Elias Memorial Scholarships **Area, Field, or Subject:** General Studies. **Level of Education for which Award is Granted:** Graduate, Undergraduate **Number Awarded:** 1. **Funds Available:** $1625. **Duration:** One academic year.
Eligibility Requirements: Applicant must be undergraduate or graduate student; a member of Beta Theta Pi enrolled as full-time student. Previous recipients are not qualified. **Application Requirements:** Applicants must submit a completed standard application form along with transcript of grades and a passport type photo (head and shoulders, wallet size, in coat and tie). **Deadline for Receipt:** April 1.

337 ■ BETA THETA PI
PO Box 6277
Oxford, OH 45056
Tel: (513)523-7591
Free: 800-800-BETA
E-mail: beta@betathetapi.org
Web Site: http://www.betathetapi.org
To financially assist students in their pursuit of academic achievement.
Title of Award: James L. Gavin Memorial Scholarships **Area, Field, or Subject:** General Studies. **Level of Education for which Award is Granted:** Graduate, Undergraduate **Number Awarded:** 3. **Funds Available:** $1125. **Duration:** One academic year.
Eligibility Requirements: Applicant must be undergraduate or graduate student; a member of Beta Theta Pi enrolled as full-time student. Previous recipients are not qualified. **Application Requirements:** Applicants must submit a completed standard application form along with transcript of grades and a passport type photo (head and shoulders, wallet size, in coat and tie). **Deadline for Receipt:** April 1. **Additional Information:** Laura Lednik, at laura.lednik@betathetapi.org.

338 ■ BETA THETA PI
PO Box 6277
Oxford, OH 45056
Tel: (513)523-7591
Free: 800-800-BETA
E-mail: beta@betathetapi.org
Web Site: http://www.betathetapi.org
To financially assist students in their pursuit of academic achievement.
Title of Award: Thomas Boston Gordon Memorial Scholarships **Area, Field, or Subject:** General Studies. **Level of Education for which Award is Granted:** Graduate, Undergraduate **Number Awarded:** 1. **Funds Available:** $2375. **Duration:** One academic year.
Eligibility Requirements: Applicant must be undergraduate or graduate student; a member of Beta Theta Pi enrolled as full-time student. Previous recipients are not qualified. **Application Requirements:** Applicants must submit a completed standard application form along with transcript of grades and a passport type photo (head and shoulders, wallet size, in coat and tie). **Additional Information:** Funded by the estate of Robert C. Lafferty, Ohio Wesleyan '28. **Deadline for Receipt:** April 1. **Additional Information:** Laura Lednik, at laura.lednik@betathetapi.org.

339 ■ BETA THETA PI
PO Box 6277
Oxford, OH 45056

Tel: (513)523-7591
Free: 800-800-BETA
E-mail: beta@betathetapi.org
Web Site: http://www.betathetapi.org
To financially assist students in their pursuit of academic achievement.
Title of Award: Charles Henry Hardin Memorial Scholarships **Area, Field, or Subject:** General Studies. **Level of Education for which Award is Granted:** Graduate, Undergraduate **Number Awarded:** 1. **Funds Available:** $2375. **Duration:** One academic year.
Eligibility Requirements: Applicant must be undergraduate or graduate student; a member of Beta Theta Pi enrolled as full-time student. Previous recipients are not qualified. **Application Requirements:** Applicants must submit a completed standard application form along with transcript of grades and a passport type photo (head and shoulders, wallet size, in coat and tie). **Additional Information:** Funded by the estate of Robert C. Lafferty, Ohio Wesleyan '28. **Deadline for Receipt:** April 1. **Additional Information:** Laura Lednik, at laura.lednik@betathetapi.org.

340 ■ BETA THETA PI
PO Box 6277
Oxford, OH 45056
Tel: (513)523-7591
Free: 800-800-BETA
E-mail: beta@betathetapi.org
Web Site: http://www.betathetapi.org
To financially assist students in their pursuit of academic achievement.
Title of Award: Ronald, Randall and Roger Helman Scholarships **Area, Field, or Subject:** General Studies. **Level of Education for which Award is Granted:** Graduate, Undergraduate **Number Awarded:** 1. **Funds Available:** $850. **Duration:** One academic year.
Eligibility Requirements: Applicant must be undergraduate or graduate student; a member of Beta Theta Pi enrolled as full-time student. Previous recipients are not qualified. **Application Requirements:** Applicants must submit a completed standard application form along with transcript of grades and a passport type photo (head and shoulders, wallet size, in coat and tie). **Deadline for Receipt:** April 1. **Additional Information:** Laura Lednik, at laura.lednik@betathetapi.org.

341 ■ BETA THETA PI
PO Box 6277
Oxford, OH 45056
Tel: (513)523-7591
Free: 800-800-BETA
E-mail: beta@betathetapi.org
Web Site: http://www.betathetapi.org
To financially assist students in their pursuit of academic achievement.
Title of Award: Douglas W. Hill, Jr. Memorial Scholarships **Area, Field, or Subject:** General Studies. **Level of Education for which Award is Granted:** Graduate, Undergraduate **Number Awarded:** 2. **Funds Available:** $1250. **Duration:** One academic year.
Eligibility Requirements: Applicant must be undergraduate or graduate student; a member of Beta Theta Pi enrolled as full-time student. Previous recipients are not qualified. **Application Requirements:** Applicants must submit a completed standard application form along with transcript of grades and a passport type photo (head and shoulders, wallet size, in coat and tie). **Deadline for Receipt:** April 1. **Additional Information:** Laura Lednik, at laura.lednik@betathetapi.org.

342 ■ BETA THETA PI
PO Box 6277
Oxford, OH 45056
Tel: (513)523-7591
Free: 800-800-BETA
E-mail: beta@betathetapi.org
Web Site: http://www.betathetapi.org
To financially assist students in their pursuit of academic achievement.
Title of Award: John A. Hill Memorial Scholarships **Area, Field, or Subject:** General Studies. **Level of Education for which Award is Granted:** Graduate, Undergraduate **Number Awarded:** 1. **Funds Available:** $1100. **Duration:** One academic year.
Eligibility Requirements: Applicant must be undergraduate or graduate student; a member of Beta Theta Pi enrolled as full-time student; and a member of Alpha Zeta at Denver. Previous recipients are not qualified.

Application Requirements: Applicants must submit a completed standard application form along with transcript of grades and a passport type photo (head and shoulders, wallet size, in coat and tie). **Deadline for Receipt:** April 1.

343 ■ BETA THETA PI
PO Box 6277
Oxford, OH 45056
Tel: (513)523-7591
Free: 800-800-BETA
E-mail: beta@betathetapi.org
Web Site: http://www.betathetapi.org
To financially assist students in their pursuit of academic achievement.
Title of Award: James P. Kirkgasser Memorial Scholarships **Area, Field, or Subject:** General Studies. **Level of Education for which Award is Granted:** Graduate, Undergraduate **Number Awarded:** 1. **Funds Available:** $625. **Duration:** One academic year.
Eligibility Requirements: Applicant must be undergraduate or graduate student; a member of Beta Theta Pi enrolled as full-time student; and a Beta from District IV schools. Previous recipients are not qualified. **Application Requirements:** Applicants must submit a completed standard application form along with transcript of grades and a passport type photo (head and shoulders, wallet size, in coat and tie). **Deadline for Receipt:** April 1. **Additional Information:** Laura Lednik, at laura.lednik@betathetapi.org.

344 ■ BETA THETA PI
PO Box 6277
Oxford, OH 45056
Tel: (513)523-7591
Free: 800-800-BETA
E-mail: beta@betathetapi.org
Web Site: http://www.betathetapi.org
To financially assist students in their pursuit of academic achievement.
Title of Award: John Reily Knox Memorial Scholarships **Area, Field, or Subject:** General Studies. **Level of Education for which Award is Granted:** Graduate, Undergraduate **Number Awarded:** 1. **Funds Available:** $2375. **Duration:** One academic year.
Eligibility Requirements: Applicant must be undergraduate or graduate student; a member of Beta Theta Pi enrolled as full-time student. Previous recipients are not qualified. **Application Requirements:** Applicants must submit a completed standard application form along with transcript of grades and a passport type photo (head and shoulders, wallet size, in coat and tie). **Additional Information:** Funded by the estate of Robert C. Lafferty, Ohio Wesleyan '28. **Deadline for Receipt:** April 1.

345 ■ BETA THETA PI
PO Box 6277
Oxford, OH 45056
Tel: (513)523-7591
Free: 800-800-BETA
E-mail: beta@betathetapi.org
Web Site: http://www.betathetapi.org
To financially assist students in their pursuit of academic achievement.
Title of Award: Carl A. Kroch Oxford Cup Memorial Scholarships **Area, Field, or Subject:** General Studies. **Level of Education for which Award is Granted:** Graduate, Undergraduate **Number Awarded:** 2. **Funds Available:** $1200. **Duration:** One academic year.
Eligibility Requirements: Applicant must be undergraduate or graduate student; a member of Beta Theta Pi enrolled as full-time student. Previous recipients are not qualified. **Application Requirements:** Applicants must submit a completed standard application form along with transcript of grades and a passport type photo (head and shoulders, wallet size, in coat and tie). **Deadline for Receipt:** April 1. **Additional Information:** Laura Lednik, at laura.lednik@betathetapi.org.

346 ■ BETA THETA PI
PO Box 6277
Oxford, OH 45056
Tel: (513)523-7591
Free: 800-800-BETA
E-mail: beta@betathetapi.org
Web Site: http://www.betathetapi.org

To financially assist students in their pursuit of academic achievement. **Title of Award:** Otho E. Lane Memorial Scholarships **Area, Field, or Subject:** General Studies. **Level of Education for which Award is Granted:** Graduate, Undergraduate **Number Awarded:** 1. **Funds Available:** $1400. **Duration:** One academic year.

Eligibility Requirements: Applicant must be undergraduate or graduate student; a member of Beta Theta Pi enrolled as full-time student. Previous recipients are not qualified. **Application Requirements:** Applicants must submit a completed standard application form along with transcript of grades and a passport type photo (head and shoulders, wallet size, in coat and tie). **Deadline for Receipt:** April 1. **Additional Information:** Laura Lednik, at laura.lednik@betathetapi.org.

347 ■ BETA THETA PI
PO Box 6277
Oxford, OH 45056
Tel: (513)523-7591
Free: 800-800-BETA
E-mail: beta@betathetapi.org
Web Site: http://www.betathetapi.org
To financially assist students in their pursuit of academic achievement. **Title of Award:** David Linton Memorial Scholarships **Area, Field, or Subject:** General Studies. **Level of Education for which Award is Granted:** Graduate, Undergraduate **Number Awarded:** 1. **Funds Available:** $2375. **Duration:** One academic year.

Eligibility Requirements: Applicant must be undergraduate or graduate student; a member of Beta Theta Pi enrolled as full-time student. Previous recipients are not qualified. **Application Requirements:** Applicants must submit a completed standard application form along with transcript of grades and a passport type photo (head and shoulders, wallet size, in coat and tie). **Additional Information:** Funded by the estate of Robert C. Lafferty, Ohio Wesleyan '28. **Deadline for Receipt:** April 1.

348 ■ BETA THETA PI
PO Box 6277
Oxford, OH 45056
Tel: (513)523-7591
Free: 800-800-BETA
E-mail: beta@betathetapi.org
Web Site: http://www.betathetapi.org
To financially assist students in their pursuit of academic achievement. **Title of Award:** Horace G. Lozier Memorial Scholarships **Area, Field, or Subject:** General Studies. **Level of Education for which Award is Granted:** Graduate, Undergraduate **Number Awarded:** 1. **Funds Available:** $1800. **Duration:** One academic year.

Eligibility Requirements: Applicant must be undergraduate or graduate student; a member of Beta Theta Pi enrolled as full-time student. Previous recipients are not qualified. **Application Requirements:** Applicants must submit a completed standard application form along with transcript of grades and a passport type photo (head and shoulders, wallet size, in coat and tie). **Deadline for Receipt:** April 1.

349 ■ BETA THETA PI
PO Box 6277
Oxford, OH 45056
Tel: (513)523-7591
Free: 800-800-BETA
E-mail: beta@betathetapi.org
Web Site: http://www.betathetapi.org
To financially assist students in their pursuit of academic achievement. **Title of Award:** Samuel Taylor Marshall Memorial Scholarships **Area, Field, or Subject:** General Studies. **Level of Education for which Award is Granted:** Graduate, Undergraduate **Number Awarded:** 1. **Funds Available:** $2375. **Duration:** One academic year.

Eligibility Requirements: Applicant must be undergraduate or graduate student; a member of Beta Theta Pi enrolled as full-time student. Previous recipients are not qualified. **Application Requirements:** Applicants must submit a completed standard application form along with transcript of grades and a passport type photo (head and shoulders, wallet size, in coat and tie). **Additional Information:** Funded by the estate of Robert C. Lafferty, Ohio Wesleyan '28. **Deadline for Receipt:** April 1. **Additional Information:** Laura Lednik, at laura.lednik@betathetapi.org.

350 ■ BETA THETA PI
PO Box 6277
Oxford, OH 45056
Tel: (513)523-7591
Free: 800-800-BETA
E-mail: beta@betathetapi.org
Web Site: http://www.betathetapi.org
To financially assist students in their pursuit of academic achievement. **Title of Award:** Steven Craig Merrill Memorial Scholarships **Area, Field, or Subject:** General Studies. **Level of Education for which Award is Granted:** Graduate, Undergraduate **Number Awarded:** 1. **Funds Available:** $1050. **Duration:** One academic year.

Eligibility Requirements: Applicant must be undergraduate or graduate student; a member of Beta Theta Pi enrolled as full-time student; and a member of Omicron at Virginia. Previous recipients are not qualified. **Application Requirements:** Applicants must submit a completed standard application form along with transcript of grades and a passport type photo (head and shoulders, wallet size, in coat and tie). **Deadline for Receipt:** April 1. **Additional Information:** Laura Lednik, at laura.lednik@betathetapi.org.

351 ■ BETA THETA PI
PO Box 6277
Oxford, OH 45056
Tel: (513)523-7591
Free: 800-800-BETA
E-mail: beta@betathetapi.org
Web Site: http://www.betathetapi.org
To financially assist students in their pursuit of academic achievement. **Title of Award:** Edith Cantor Morrison Memorial Scholarships **Area, Field, or Subject:** Education--Curricula. **Level of Education for which Award is Granted:** Graduate, Undergraduate **Number Awarded:** 1. **Funds Available:** $600. **Duration:** One academic year.

Eligibility Requirements: Applicant must be undergraduate or graduate student; a member of Beta Theta Pi enrolled as full-time student; and a Beta majoring in education. Previous recipients are not qualified. **Application Requirements:** Applicants must submit a completed standard application form along with transcript of grades and a passport type photo (head and shoulders, wallet size, in coat and tie). **Deadline for Receipt:** April 1. **Additional Information:** Laura Lednik, at laura.lednik@betathetapi.org.

352 ■ BETA THETA PI
PO Box 6277
Oxford, OH 45056
Tel: (513)523-7591
Free: 800-800-BETA
E-mail: beta@betathetapi.org
Web Site: http://www.betathetapi.org
To financially assist students in their pursuit of academic achievement. **Title of Award:** Douglas J. Neeley Memorial Scholarships **Area, Field, or Subject:** General Studies. **Level of Education for which Award is Granted:** Graduate, Undergraduate **Number Awarded:** 2. **Funds Available:** $1125. **Duration:** One academic year.

Eligibility Requirements: Applicant must be undergraduate or graduate student; a member of Beta Theta Pi at Kenyon and enrolled as full-time student. Previous recipients are not qualified. **Application Requirements:** Applicants must submit a completed standard application form along with transcript of grades and a passport type photo (head and shoulders, wallet size, in coat and tie). **Deadline for Receipt:** April 1. **Additional Information:** Laura Lednik, at laura.lednik@betathetapi.org.

353 ■ BETA THETA PI
PO Box 6277
Oxford, OH 45056
Tel: (513)523-7591
Free: 800-800-BETA
E-mail: beta@betathetapi.org
Web Site: http://www.betathetapi.org
To financially assist students in their pursuit of academic achievement. **Title of Award:** E. William Palmer Memorial Scholarships **Area, Field, or Subject:** General Studies. **Level of Education for which Award is Granted:** Graduate, Undergraduate **Number Awarded:** 1. **Funds Available:** $1300. **Duration:** One academic year.

Eligibility Requirements: Applicant must be undergraduate or graduate student; a member of Beta Theta Pi enrolled as full-time student. Previous recipients are not qualified. **Application Requirements:** Applicants must submit a completed standard application form along with transcript of grades and a passport type photo (head and shoulders, wallet size, in coat and tie). **Deadline for Receipt:** April 1. **Additional Information:** Laura Lednik, at laura.lednik@betathetapi.org.

354 ■ BETA THETA PI
PO Box 6277
Oxford, OH 45056
Tel: (513)523-7591
Free: 800-800-BETA
E-mail: beta@betathetapi.org
Web Site: http://www.betathetapi.org
To financially assist students in their pursuit of academic achievement.
Title of Award: John J. and Elizabeth Rhodes Scholarships **Area, Field, or Subject:** General Studies. **Level of Education for which Award is Granted:** Graduate, Undergraduate **Number Awarded:** 1. **Funds Available:** $1625. **Duration:** One academic year.
Eligibility Requirements: Applicant must be undergraduate or graduate student; a member of Beta Theta Pi enrolled as full-time student. Previous recipients are not qualified. **Application Requirements:** Applicants must submit a completed standard application form along with transcript of grades and a passport type photo (head and shoulders, wallet size, in coat and tie). **Deadline for Receipt:** April 1.

355 ■ BETA THETA PI
PO Box 6277
Oxford, OH 45056
Tel: (513)523-7591
Free: 800-800-BETA
E-mail: beta@betathetapi.org
Web Site: http://www.betathetapi.org
To financially assist students in their pursuit of academic achievement.
Title of Award: Ben C. Rich Memorial Scholarships **Area, Field, or Subject:** General Studies. **Level of Education for which Award is Granted:** Graduate, Undergraduate **Number Awarded:** 2. **Funds Available:** $1000. **Duration:** One academic year.
Eligibility Requirements: Applicant must be undergraduate or graduate student; a member of Beta Theta Pi enrolled as full-time student. Previous recipients are not qualified. **Application Requirements:** Applicants must submit a completed standard application form along with transcript of grades and a passport type photo (head and shoulders, wallet size, in coat and tie). **Deadline for Receipt:** April 1. **Additional Information:** Laura Lednik, at laura.lednik@betathetapi.org.

356 ■ BETA THETA PI
PO Box 6277
Oxford, OH 45056
Tel: (513)523-7591
Free: 800-800-BETA
E-mail: beta@betathetapi.org
Web Site: http://www.betathetapi.org
To financially assist students in their pursuit of academic achievement.
Title of Award: Michael Clarkson Ryan Memorial Scholarships **Area, Field, or Subject:** General Studies. **Level of Education for which Award is Granted:** Graduate, Undergraduate **Number Awarded:** 1. **Funds Available:** $2375. **Duration:** One academic year.
Eligibility Requirements: Applicant must be undergraduate or graduate student; a member of Beta Theta Pi enrolled as full-time student. Previous recipients are not qualified. **Application Requirements:** Applicants must submit a completed standard application form along with transcript of grades and a passport type photo (head and shoulders, wallet size, in coat and tie). **Additional Information:** Funded by the estate of Robert C. Lafferty, Ohio Wesleyan '28. **Deadline for Receipt:** April 1. **Additional Information:** Laura Lednik, at laura.lednik@betathetapi.org.

357 ■ BETA THETA PI
PO Box 6277
Oxford, OH 45056
Tel: (513)523-7591
Free: 800-800-BETA

E-mail: beta@betathetapi.org
Web Site: http://www.betathetapi.org
To financially assist students in their pursuit of academic achievement.
Title of Award: William C. Scheetz Family Scholarships **Area, Field, or Subject:** General Studies. **Level of Education for which Award is Granted:** Graduate, Undergraduate **Number Awarded:** 2. **Funds Available:** $1325. **Duration:** One academic year.
Eligibility Requirements: Applicant must be undergraduate or graduate student; a member of Beta Theta Pi enrolled as full-time student. Previous recipients are not qualified. **Application Requirements:** Applicants must submit a completed standard application form along with transcript of grades and a passport type photo (head and shoulders, wallet size, in coat and tie). **Deadline for Receipt:** April 1. **Additional Information:** Laura Lednik, at laura.lednik@betathetapi.org.

358 ■ BETA THETA PI
PO Box 6277
Oxford, OH 45056
Tel: (513)523-7591
Free: 800-800-BETA
E-mail: beta@betathetapi.org
Web Site: http://www.betathetapi.org
To financially assist students in their pursuit of academic achievement.
Title of Award: Fred A. Seaton Memorial Scholarships **Area, Field, or Subject:** General Studies. **Level of Education for which Award is Granted:** Graduate, Undergraduate **Number Awarded:** 3. **Funds Available:** $1000. **Duration:** One academic year.
Eligibility Requirements: Applicant must be undergraduate or graduate student; a member of Beta Theta Pi enrolled as full-time student. Previous recipients are not qualified. **Application Requirements:** Applicants must submit a completed standard application form along with transcript of grades and a passport type photo (head and shoulders, wallet size, in coat and tie). **Deadline for Receipt:** April 1. **Additional Information:** Laura Lednik, at laura.lednik@betathetapi.org.

359 ■ BETA THETA PI
PO Box 6277
Oxford, OH 45056
Tel: (513)523-7591
Free: 800-800-BETA
E-mail: beta@betathetapi.org
Web Site: http://www.betathetapi.org
To financially assist students in their pursuit of academic achievement.
Title of Award: Misty and Sally Shoop Scholarships **Area, Field, or Subject:** General Studies. **Level of Education for which Award is Granted:** Graduate, Undergraduate **Number Awarded:** 1. **Funds Available:** $825. **Duration:** One academic year.
Eligibility Requirements: Applicant must be undergraduate or graduate student; a member of Beta Theta Pi enrolled as full-time student. Previous recipients are not qualified. **Application Requirements:** Applicants must submit a completed standard application form along with transcript of grades and a passport type photo (head and shoulders, wallet size, in coat and tie). **Deadline for Receipt:** April 1. **Additional Information:** Laura Lednik, at laura.lednik@betathetapi.org.

360 ■ BETA THETA PI
PO Box 6277
Oxford, OH 45056
Tel: (513)523-7591
Free: 800-800-BETA
E-mail: beta@betathetapi.org
Web Site: http://www.betathetapi.org
To financially assist students in their pursuit of academic achievement.
Title of Award: John R. Simpson Memorial Scholarships **Area, Field, or Subject:** General Studies. **Level of Education for which Award is Granted:** Graduate, Undergraduate **Number Awarded:** 8. **Funds Available:** $1050. **Duration:** One academic year.
Eligibility Requirements: Applicant must be undergraduate or graduate student; a member of Beta Theta Pi enrolled as full-time student. Previous recipients are not qualified. **Application Requirements:** Applicants must submit a completed standard application form along with transcript of grades and a passport type photo (head and shoulders, wallet size, in coat and tie). **Deadline for Receipt:** April 1. **Additional Information:** Laura Lednik, at laura.lednik@betathetapi.org.

361 ■ BETA THETA PI
PO Box 6277
Oxford, OH 45056
Tel: (513)523-7591
Free: 800-800-BETA
E-mail: beta@betathetapi.org
Web Site: http://www.betathetapi.org
To financially assist students in their pursuit of academic achievement.
Title of Award: James George Smith Memorial Scholarships **Area, Field, or Subject:** General Studies. **Level of Education for which Award is Granted:** Graduate, Undergraduate **Number Awarded:** 1. **Funds Available:** $2375. **Duration:** One academic year.
Eligibility Requirements: Applicant must be undergraduate or graduate student; a member of Beta Theta Pi enrolled as full-time student. Previous recipients are not qualified. **Application Requirements:** Applicants must submit a completed standard application form along with transcript of grades and a passport type photo (head and shoulders, wallet size, in coat and tie). **Additional Information:** Funded by the estate of Robert C. Lafferty, Ohio Wesleyan '28. **Deadline for Receipt:** April 1. **Additional Information:** Laura Lednik, at laura.lednik@betathetapi.org.

362 ■ BETA THETA PI
PO Box 6277
Oxford, OH 45056
Tel: (513)523-7591
Free: 800-800-BETA
E-mail: beta@betathetapi.org
Web Site: http://www.betathetapi.org
To financially assist students in their pursuit of academic achievement.
Title of Award: H. Hiram Stephenson Oxford Cup Scholarships **Area, Field, or Subject:** General Studies. **Level of Education for which Award is Granted:** Graduate, Undergraduate **Number Awarded:** 1. **Funds Available:** $500. **Duration:** One academic year.
Eligibility Requirements: Applicant must be undergraduate or graduate student; a member of Beta Theta Pi enrolled as full-time student. Previous recipients are not qualified. **Application Requirements:** Applicants must submit a completed standard application form along with transcript of grades and a passport type photo (head and shoulders, wallet size, in coat and tie). **Deadline for Receipt:** April 1. **Additional Information:** Laura Lednik, at laura.lednik@betathetapi.org.

363 ■ BETA THETA PI
PO Box 6277
Oxford, OH 45056
Tel: (513)523-7591
Free: 800-800-BETA
E-mail: beta@betathetapi.org
Web Site: http://www.betathetapi.org
To financially assist students in their pursuit of academic achievement.
Title of Award: Hugh E. Stephenson Oxford Cup Scholarships **Area, Field, or Subject:** General Studies. **Level of Education for which Award is Granted:** Graduate, Undergraduate **Number Awarded:** 1. **Funds Available:** $550. **Duration:** One academic year.
Eligibility Requirements: Applicant must be undergraduate or graduate student; a member of Beta Theta Pi enrolled as full-time student. Previous recipients are not qualified. **Application Requirements:** Applicants must submit a completed standard application form along with transcript of grades and a passport type photo (head and shoulders, wallet size, in coat and tie). **Deadline for Receipt:** April 1. **Additional Information:** Laura Lednik, at laura.lednik@betathetapi.org.

364 ■ BETA THETA PI
PO Box 6277
Oxford, OH 45056
Tel: (513)523-7591
Free: 800-800-BETA
E-mail: beta@betathetapi.org
Web Site: http://www.betathetapi.org
To financially assist students in their pursuit of academic achievement.
Title of Award: Michael W. Toennis Scholarships **Area, Field, or Subject:** General Studies. **Level of Education for which Award is Granted:** Graduate, Undergraduate **Number Awarded:** 1. **Funds Available:** $650. **Duration:** One academic year.

Eligibility Requirements: Applicant must be undergraduate or graduate student; a member of Beta Theta Pi enrolled as full-time student. Previous recipients are not qualified. **Application Requirements:** Applicants must submit a completed standard application form along with transcript of grades and a passport type photo (head and shoulders, wallet size, in coat and tie). **Deadline for Receipt:** April 1.

365 ■ BETA THETA PI
PO Box 6277
Oxford, OH 45056
Tel: (513)523-7591
Free: 800-800-BETA
E-mail: beta@betathetapi.org
Web Site: http://www.betathetapi.org
To financially assist students in their pursuit of academic achievement.
Title of Award: Gupton A. Vogt Oxford Cup Memorial Scholarships **Area, Field, or Subject:** General Studies. **Level of Education for which Award is Granted:** Graduate, Undergraduate **Number Awarded:** 1. **Funds Available:** $875. **Duration:** One academic year.
Eligibility Requirements: Applicant must be undergraduate or graduate student; a member of Beta Theta Pi enrolled as full-time student. Previous recipients are not qualified. **Application Requirements:** Applicants must submit a completed standard application form along with transcript of grades and a passport type photo (head and shoulders, wallet size, in coat and tie). **Deadline for Receipt:** April 1. **Additional Information:** Laura Lednik, at laura.lednik@betathetapi.org.

366 ■ BETHUNE-COOKMAN UNIVERSITY
640 Dr. Mary McLeod Bethune Blvd.
Daytona Beach, FL 32114
Tel: (386)481-2000
Web Site: http://www.cookman.edu
To provide financial assistance for students intending to pursue their education.
Title of Award: Bethune-Cookman University Excelsior Scholarships **Area, Field, or Subject:** General studies. **Level of Education for which Award is Granted:** Undergraduate **Funds Available:** Funds may cover the cost of full-time tuition that is not covered by federal or state financial aid and other non-institutional scholarships. **Duration:** One year.
Eligibility Requirements: Applicants must be completing high school in spring; must be incoming freshmen at a university; and must maintain a 3.4 cumulative GPA. **Application Requirements:** Applicants must apply for admission to be considered. **Deadline for Receipt:** February 1.

367 ■ BETHUNE-COOKMAN UNIVERSITY
640 Dr. Mary McLeod Bethune Blvd.
Daytona Beach, FL 32114
Tel: (386)481-2000
Web Site: http://www.cookman.edu
To provide financial assistance to students intending to pursue their education.
Title of Award: Bethune-Cookman University Presidential Scholarships **Area, Field, or Subject:** General studies. **Level of Education for which Award is Granted:** Undergraduate **Funds Available:** Fund may be used for full-time tuition, room, boarding fees, and a $500 per semester book voucher only. **Duration:** Annual.
Eligibility Requirements: Applicants must be completing high school in spring; must incoming freshmen at any university; and must maintain a 3.5 cumulative GPA. **Application Requirements:** Applicants must apply for admission to be considered. **Deadline for Receipt:** February 1.

368 ■ BIG SANDY COMMUNITY AND TECHNICAL COLLEGE
1 Bert T. Combs Dr.
Prestonsburg, KY 41653
Tel: (606)886-3863; 888-641-4132
Web Site: http://www.bigsandy.kctcs.edu
To provide financial support for deserving Kentucky high school students and GED recipients intending to pursue their education.
Title of Award: Kentucky Educational Excellence Scholarships **Area, Field, or Subject:** General studies. **Level of Education for which Award is Granted:** Graduate, Undergraduate **Funds Available:** Varies.
Eligibility Requirements: Applicants be high school students; must be U.S. citizens, national or permanent residents; must be residents of

Kentucky; must have earned at least a 2.5 GPA in any year of high school while meeting the KEES curriculum requirements; must attend and graduate from a certified Kentucky high school or other approved high school; and must not be a convicted felon. High school graduates applying for a KEES bonus award must have at least an ACT composite score of 15 or a score of 710 or higher on the SAT and must have earned at least a 2.5 GPA in any year of high school while meeting the KEES curriculum requirements. Home school graduates applying for a KEES bonus award must have an ACT composite score of 15 or better on a national exam; must be U.S citizens, national or permanent residents; must be residents of Kentucky; must be enrolled in a participating college; and must not be a convicted felon. GED graduate applicants must have an ACT composite score of 15 or better on a national exam; must have earned a GED in Kentucky within five years of turning 18 years old; must be U.S citizens, national or permanent residents; must be residents of Kentucky; must be enrolled in a participating college within five years of receiving a GED; and must not be a convicted felon. **Application Requirements:** Applicants are advised to contact KEES for scholarship information and instructions at kees@kheaa.com.

369 ■ BIG SANDY COMMUNITY AND TECHNICAL COLLEGE

1 Bert T. Combs Dr.
Prestonsburg, KY 41653
Tel: (606)886-3863; 888-641-4132
Web Site: http://www.bigsandy.kctcs.edu
To help students offset the high tuition charges at independent colleges.
Title of Award: Kentucky Tuition Grants **Area, Field, or Subject:** General studies. **Level of Education for which Award is Granted:** Undergraduate **Funds Available:** $2,000-$3,000. **Duration:** One academic year.
Eligibility Requirements: Applicants must be residents of Kentucky who are enrolled in the Commonwealth's independent colleges. Institutions must be accredited by a regional accrediting association recognized by U.S Department of Education and must not be comprised solely of religious instruction; must be full-time undergraduates enrolled in an associate or baccalaureate degree program and must have no past due financial obligations to KHEAA to any Title IV program. **Application Requirements:** Applicants must complete the Application for Federal Student Aid form. Applicants are advised to contact the Federal Student Aid Information Center at 800-433-3243 for further information.

370 ■ BIG SANDY COMMUNITY AND TECHNICAL COLLEGE

1 Bert T. Combs Dr.
Prestonsburg, KY 41653
Tel: (606)886-3863; 888-641-4132
Web Site: http://www.bigsandy.kctcs.edu
To improve educational opportunities for Kentuckians.
Title of Award: Mary Jo Young Scholarships **Area, Field, or Subject:** General studies. **Level of Education for which Award is Granted:** Undergraduate **Funds Available:** No specific amount.
Eligibility Requirements: Program is open to high school students in grades 9 thru 12 enrolled in dual credit classes at any college or university or to students taking Advanced Placement courses through the Kentucky Virtual High School. **Application Requirements:** Applicants must send completed application to: KHEAA Mary Jo Young Scholarship Program, PO Box 798, Frankfort, KY 40602-0798. **Deadline for Receipt:** May 1.

371 ■ BIRMINGHAM PUBLIC SCHOOL

550 W Merrill St.
Birmingham, MI 48009
Tel: (248)203-3000
E-mail: webmaster-main@birmingham.k12.mi.us
Web Site: http://www.birmingham.k12.mi.us
To provide college financial assistance for students who reside within the boundaries of the Birmingham School District upon high school graduation.
Title of Award: Birmingham Student Scholarship Fund Association **Area, Field, or Subject:** General studies. **Level of Education for which Award is Granted:** Undergraduate **Number Awarded:** Varies **Funds Available:** $750-$2,000.
Eligibility Requirements: Applicants must have their primary residence within the boundaries of the Birmingham Public School or private school district during that year. **Application Requirements:** Applicants must submit completed application to the student's high school counselor prior

to the filing date set by the Scholar Board each year. The application must be signed by both the student and one parent certifying the truth of the application. The application requires student's and parents' current income tax information, as well as information regarding family housing, Unless there is independent written verification of an established pattern of non-support by a parent; scholarship grants will be reduced by 50 percent if information is not received from both parents. The application and instructions can be printed from the web page. **Deadline for Receipt:** March 1. **Additional Information:** BPS at the above address.

372 ■ BLACK ALLIANCE FOR EDUCATIONAL OPTIONS

888 16th St. NW, Ste. 800
Washington, DC 20006
Tel: (202)429-2236
Fax: (202)349-9879
Web Site: http://www.baeo.org
To provide partial tuition assistance for low-income families to send their children to private schools.
Title of Award: BAEO Children's Scholarship Fund **Area, Field, or Subject:** General Studies. **Level of Education for which Award is Granted:** High School **Funds Available:** No specific amount.
Eligibility Requirements: Applicants must be: 5 years of age or older; from low-income families; students from kindergarten-8th grade. **Application Requirements:** Applicants must check the available website for the required materials. **Additional Information:** Black Alliance for Educational Options at the above address.

373 ■ BLACK ALLIANCE FOR EDUCATIONAL OPTIONS

888 16th St. NW, Ste. 800
Washington, DC 20006
Tel: (202)429-2236
Fax: (202)349-9879
Web Site: http://www.baeo.org
To provide financial assistance and support services to Washington DC metropolitan area African-American students.
Title of Award: Black Student Fund **Area, Field, or Subject:** General Studies. **Level of Education for which Award is Granted:** High School **Funds Available:** No specific amount.
Eligibility Requirements: Applicants must be African American students; must be in grades pre-kindergarten to 12; must be residents in Greater Washington area. **Application Requirements:** Applicants must check the available website for more information. **Additional Information:** For more information, contact Gwen Thompson, Director, at 202-387-1414 or mail@blackstudentfund.org.

374 ■ BLACK BUSINESS AND PROFESSIONAL ASSOCIATION

675 King St. W, Ste. 210
Toronto, ON, Canada M5V 1M9
Tel: (416)504-4097
Fax: (416)504-7343
E-mail: bbpa@bellnet.ca
Web Site: http://www.bbpa.org
To provide support for Black Canadian students.
Title of Award: Hon. Lincoln Alexander Scholarships **Area, Field, or Subject:** General studies. **Level of Education for which Award is Granted:** Undergraduate **Funds Available:** $2,000. **Duration:** One year.
Eligibility Requirements: Applicant must be a Canadian citizen or a permanent resident; must be 17 to 30 years of age; and must be enrolled in a full-time degree (graduate or undergraduate), diploma or certificate program at a Canadian college or university for the academic year. **Application Requirements:** Applicants must submit completed application form; a letter describing the reasons why they would be worthy recipients of a BBPA National Scholarship; a completed financial information schedule stating their budget for the coming year including information on their expected sources of funding, family income and related information; and a letter of reference from the two individuals named in their application (must be a teacher from their high school, college or university, and an individual who is familiar with their community service). Application form and requirements must be sent to The Board of Trustees, BBPA National Scholarship Fund, 675 King St., W, Ste. 210, Toronto, ON M5V 1M9. **Deadline for Receipt:** May 30.

375 ■ BLACK BUSINESS AND PROFESSIONAL ASSOCIATION

675 King St. W, Ste. 210
Toronto, ON, Canada M5V 1M9

Tel: (416)504-4097
Fax: (416)504-7343
E-mail: bbpa@bellnet.ca
Web Site: http://www.bbpa.org
To provide support to Black Canadian students.
Title of Award: Louise Bennett-Coverley Scholarships **Area, Field, or Subject:** General studies. **Level of Education for which Award is Granted:** Undergraduate **Funds Available:** $2,000. **Duration:** One year. **Eligibility Requirements:** Applicant must be a Canadian citizen or a permanent resident; must be 17 to 30 years of age; must be enrolled in a full time degree (graduate or undergraduate), diploma or certificate program at a Canadian college or university for the academic year. **Application Requirements:** Applicants must complete the application form, submit a letter describing the reasons why they would be a worthy recipient of a BBPA National Scholarship; must provide the completed financial information schedule stating their budget for the coming year including information on their expected sources of funding, family income and related information; must have a letter of reference from the two individuals named in their application (must be a teacher from their high school, college or university, and an individual who is familiar with their community service). Application form and requirements must be sent to The Board of Trustees, BBPA National Scholarship Fund, 675 King St., W, Ste. 210, Toronto, ON M5V 1M9. **Deadline for Receipt:** May 30.

376 ■ BLACK BUSINESS AND PROFESSIONAL ASSOCIATION
675 King St. W, Ste. 210
Toronto, ON, Canada M5V 1M9
Tel: (416)504-4097
Fax: (416)504-7343
E-mail: bbpa@bellnet.ca
Web Site: http://www.bbpa.org
To provide support for Black Canadian students.
Title of Award: BMO Financial Group Scholarships **Area, Field, or Subject:** General studies. **Level of Education for which Award is Granted:** Undergraduate **Number Awarded:** 2. **Funds Available:** $5,000. **Duration:** One year.
Eligibility Requirements: Applicants must be students with academic achievements who have demonstrated social responsibility; must be Canadian citizens or permanent residents; must be 17 to 30 years of age; and must be enrolled in a full-time degree (graduate or undergraduate), diploma or certificate program at a Canadian college or university for the academic year. **Application Requirements:** Applicants must complete the application form and submit along with a letter describing the reasons why they would be a worthy recipient of a BBPA National Scholarship; a completed financial information schedule stating their budget for the coming year including information on their expected sources of funding, family income and related information; and a letter of reference from the two individuals named in their application (must be a teacher from their high school, college or university, and an individual who is familiar with their community service). Application form and requirements must be sent to The Board of Trustees, BBPA National Scholarship Fund, 675 King St., W, Ste. 210, Toronto, ON M5V 1M9. **Deadline for Receipt:** May 30.

377 ■ BLACK BUSINESS AND PROFESSIONAL ASSOCIATION
675 King St. W, Ste. 210
Toronto, ON, Canada M5V 1M9
Tel: (416)504-4097
Fax: (416)504-7343
E-mail: bbpa@bellnet.ca
Web Site: http://www.bbpa.org
To provide support to Black Canadian students.
Title of Award: Herb Carnegie Scholarships **Area, Field, or Subject:** General studies. **Level of Education for which Award is Granted:** Undergraduate **Funds Available:** $2,000. **Duration:** One year.
Eligibility Requirements: Applicants must be a Canadian citizen or a permanent resident; must be 17 to 30 years of age; must be enrolled in a full time degree (graduate or undergraduate), diploma or certificate program at a Canadian college or university for the academic year. **Application Requirements:** Applicants must complete the application form, submit a letter describing the reasons why they would be a worthy recipient of a BBPA National Scholarship; must provide the completed financial information schedule stating their budget for the coming year including information on their expected sources of funding, family income and

related information; must have a letter of reference from the two individuals named in their application (must be a teacher from their high school, college or university, and an individual who is familiar with their community service). Application form and requirements must be sent to The Board of Trustees, BBPA National Scholarship Fund, 675 King St., W, Ste. 210, Toronto, ON M5V 1M9. **Deadline for Receipt:** May 30.

378 ■ BLACK BUSINESS AND PROFESSIONAL ASSOCIATION
675 King St. W, Ste. 210
Toronto, ON, Canada M5V 1M9
Tel: (416)504-4097
Fax: (416)504-7343
E-mail: bbpa@bellnet.ca
Web Site: http://www.bbpa.org
To provide support for Black Canadian students.
Title of Award: Fraser Milner Casgrain LLP Scholarships **Area, Field, or Subject:** General studies. **Level of Education for which Award is Granted:** Undergraduate **Funds Available:** $5,000. **Duration:** One year. **Eligibility Requirements:** Applicants must be Canadian citizens or permanent residents; must be 17 to 30 years of age; and must be enrolled in a full time degree (graduate or undergraduate), diploma or certificate program at a Canadian college or university for the academic year. **Application Requirements:** Applicants must complete the application form and submit along with a letter describing the reasons why they would be worthy recipients of a BBPA National Scholarship; a completed financial information schedule stating their budget for the coming year including information on their expected sources of funding, family income and related information; and a letter of reference from the two individuals named in their application (must be a teacher from their high school, college or university, and an individual who is familiar with their community service). Application form and requirements must be sent to The Board of Trustees, BBPA National Scholarship Fund, 675 King St., W, Ste. 210, Toronto, ON M5V 1M9. **Deadline for Receipt:** May 30.

379 ■ BLACK BUSINESS AND PROFESSIONAL ASSOCIATION
675 King St. W, Ste. 210
Toronto, ON, Canada M5V 1M9
Tel: (416)504-4097
Fax: (416)504-7343
E-mail: bbpa@bellnet.ca
Web Site: http://www.bbpa.org
To provide support for Black Canadian students.
Title of Award: CIBC Scholarships **Area, Field, or Subject:** General studies. **Level of Education for which Award is Granted:** Undergraduate **Funds Available:** $5,000. **Duration:** One year.
Eligibility Requirements: Applicants must be students attending college or university who have shown academic achievement, leadership potential and a commitment to helping in the community; must be Canadian citizens or permanent residents; must be 17 to 30 years of age; and must be enrolled in a full-time degree (graduate or undergraduate), diploma or certificate program at a Canadian college or university for the academic year. **Application Requirements:** Applicants must complete the application form and submit along with a letter describing the reasons why they would be a worthy recipient of a BBPA National Scholarship; a completed financial information schedule stating their budget for the coming year including information on their expected sources of funding, family income and related information; and a letter of reference from the two individuals named in their application (must be a teacher from their high school, college or university, and an individual who is familiar with their community service). Application form and requirements must be sent to The Board of Trustees, BBPA National Scholarship Fund, 675 King St., W, Ste. 210, Toronto, ON M5V 1M9. **Deadline for Receipt:** May 30.

380 ■ BLACK BUSINESS AND PROFESSIONAL ASSOCIATION
675 King St. W, Ste. 210
Toronto, ON, Canada M5V 1M9
Tel: (416)504-4097
Fax: (416)504-7343
E-mail: bbpa@bellnet.ca
Web Site: http://www.bbpa.org
To provide support for Black Canadian students.
Title of Award: Erma Collins Scholarships **Area, Field, or Subject:** General studies. **Level of Education for which Award is Granted:** Undergraduate **Funds Available:** $1,000. **Duration:** One year.

Eligibility Requirements: Applicants must be students attending community college; must be Canadian citizens or permanent residents; must be 17 to 30 years of age; and must be enrolled in a full time degree (graduate or undergraduate), diploma or certificate program at a Canadian college or university for the academic year. **Application Requirements:** Applicants must complete the application form and submit along with a letter describing the reasons why they would be worthy recipients of a BBPA National Scholarship; a completed financial information schedule stating their budget for the coming year including information on their expected sources of funding, family income and related information; and a letter of reference from the two individuals named in their application (must be a teacher from their high school, college or university, and an individual who is familiar with their community service). Application form and requirements must be sent to The Board of Trustees, BBPA National Scholarship Fund, 675 King St., W, Ste. 210, Toronto, ON M5V 1M9. **Deadline for Receipt:** May 30.

381 ■ BLACK BUSINESS AND PROFESSIONAL ASSOCIATION

675 King St. W, Ste. 210
Toronto, ON, Canada M5V 1M9
Tel: (416)504-4097
Fax: (416)504-7343
E-mail: bbpa@bellnet.ca
Web Site: http://www.bbpa.org
To provide support for Black Canadian students.
Title of Award: Harry Gairey Scholarships **Area, Field, or Subject:** General studies. **Level of Education for which Award is Granted:** Undergraduate **Number Awarded:** 2. **Funds Available:** $2,000. **Duration:** One year.
Eligibility Requirements: Applicant must be a Canadian citizen or a permanent resident; must be 17 to 30 years of age; must be enrolled in a full time degree (graduate or undergraduate), diploma or certificate program at a Canadian college or university for the academic year. **Application Requirements:** Applicants must complete the application form, letter describing the reasons why they would be worthy recipients of a BBPA National Scholarship; a completed financial information schedule stating their budget for the coming year including information on their expected sources of funding, family income and related information; and a letter of reference from the two individuals named in their application (must be a teacher from their high school, college or university, and an individual who is familiar with their community service). Application form and requirements must be sent to The Board of Trustees, BBPA National Scholarship Fund, 675 King St., W, Ste. 210, Toronto, ON M5V 1M9. **Deadline for Receipt:** May 30.

382 ■ BLACK BUSINESS AND PROFESSIONAL ASSOCIATION

675 King St. W, Ste. 210
Toronto, ON, Canada M5V 1M9
Tel: (416)504-4097
Fax: (416)504-7343
E-mail: bbpa@bellnet.ca
Web Site: http://www.bbpa.org
To provide support for Black Canadian students.
Title of Award: Lucille May Gopie Scholarships **Area, Field, or Subject:** General studies. **Level of Education for which Award is Granted:** Undergraduate **Funds Available:** $2,000. **Duration:** One year.
Eligibility Requirements: Applicant must be a person who has been encouraged by a single parent to pursue higher education; must be a Canadian citizen or a permanent resident; must be 17 to 30 years of age; and must be enrolled in a full-time degree (graduate or undergraduate), diploma or certificate program at a Canadian college or university for the academic year. **Application Requirements:** Applicants must complete the application form and submit along with a letter describing the reasons why they would be a worthy recipient of a BBPA National Scholarship; a completed financial information schedule stating their budget for the coming year including information on their expected sources of funding, family income and related information; and a letter of reference from the two individuals named in their application (must be a teacher from their high school, college or university, and an individual who is familiar with their community service). Application form and requirements must be sent to The Board of Trustees, BBPA National Scholarship Fund, 675 King St., W, Ste. 210, Toronto, ON M5V 1M9. **Deadline for Receipt:** May 30.

383 ■ BLACK BUSINESS AND PROFESSIONAL ASSOCIATION

675 King St. W, Ste. 210
Toronto, ON, Canada M5V 1M9
Tel: (416)504-4097
Fax: (416)504-7343
E-mail: bbpa@bellnet.ca
Web Site: http://www.bbpa.org
To provide support for Black Canadian students.
Title of Award: Al Hamilton Scholarships **Area, Field, or Subject:** General studies. **Level of Education for which Award is Granted:** Undergraduate **Funds Available:** $2,000. **Duration:** One year.
Eligibility Requirements: Applicants must be a Canadian citizen or a permanent resident; must be 17 to 30 years of age; must be enrolled in a full time degree (graduate or undergraduate), diploma or certificate program at a Canadian college or university for the academic year. **Application Requirements:** Applicants must submit a completed application form, a letter describing the reasons why they would be worthy recipients of a BBPA National Scholarship; a completed financial information schedule stating their budget for the coming year including information on their expected sources of funding, family income and related information; and a letter of reference from the two individuals named in their application (must be a teacher from their high school, college or university, and an individual who is familiar with their community service). Application form and requirements must be sent to The Board of Trustees, BBPA National Scholarship Fund, 675 King St., W, Ste. 210, Toronto, ON M5V 1M9. **Deadline for Receipt:** May 30.

384 ■ BLACK BUSINESS AND PROFESSIONAL ASSOCIATION

675 King St. W, Ste. 210
Toronto, ON, Canada M5V 1M9
Tel: (416)504-4097
Fax: (416)504-7343
E-mail: bbpa@bellnet.ca
Web Site: http://www.bbpa.org
To provide support for Black Canadian students.
Title of Award: William Peyton Hubbard Scholarships **Area, Field, or Subject:** General studies. **Level of Education for which Award is Granted:** Undergraduate **Funds Available:** $2,000. **Duration:** One year.
Eligibility Requirements: Applicant must be a Canadian citizen or a permanent resident; must be 17 to 30 years of age; and must be enrolled in a full-time degree (graduate or undergraduate), diploma or certificate program at a Canadian college or university for the academic year. **Application Requirements:** Applicants must complete the application form and submit along with a letter describing the reasons why they would be a worthy recipient of a BBPA National Scholarship; a completed financial information schedule stating their budget for the coming year including information on their expected sources of funding, family income and related information; and a letter of reference from the two individuals named in their application (must be a teacher from their high school, college or university, and an individual who is familiar with their community service). Application form and requirements must be sent to The Board of Trustees, BBPA National Scholarship Fund, 675 King St., W, Ste. 210, Toronto, ON M5V 1M9. **Deadline for Receipt:** May 30.

385 ■ BLACK BUSINESS AND PROFESSIONAL ASSOCIATION

675 King St. W, Ste. 210
Toronto, ON, Canada M5V 1M9
Tel: (416)504-4097
Fax: (416)504-7343
E-mail: bbpa@bellnet.ca
Web Site: http://www.bbpa.org
To provide support for Black Canadian students.
Title of Award: Right Hon. Michaelle Jean Scholarships **Area, Field, or Subject:** General studies. **Level of Education for which Award is Granted:** Undergraduate **Funds Available:** $2,000. **Duration:** One year.
Eligibility Requirements: Applicant must be a Canadian citizen or a permanent resident; must be 17 to 30 years of age; and must be enrolled in a full-time degree (graduate or undergraduate), diploma or certificate program at a Canadian college or university for the academic year. **Application Requirements:** Applicants must complete the application form and submit along with a letter describing the reasons why they would be worthy recipients of a BBPA National Scholarship; a completed financial information schedule stating their budget for the coming year including

information on their expected sources of funding, family income and related information; and a letter of reference from the two individuals named in their application (must be a teacher from their high school, college or university, and an individual who is familiar with their community service). Application form and requirements must be sent to The Board of Trustees, BBPA National Scholarship Fund, 675 King St., W, Ste. 210, Toronto, ON M5V 1M9. **Deadline for Receipt:** May 30.

386 ■ BLACK BUSINESS AND PROFESSIONAL ASSOCIATION
675 King St. W, Ste. 210
Toronto, ON, Canada M5V 1M9
Tel: (416)504-4097
Fax: (416)504-7343
E-mail: bbpa@bellnet.ca
Web Site: http://www.bbpa.org
To provide support for Black Canadian students.
Title of Award: Harry Jerome Scholarships **Area, Field, or Subject:** General studies. **Level of Education for which Award is Granted:** Undergraduate **Funds Available:** $5,000. **Duration:** One year.
Eligibility Requirements: Applicant must be a Canadian citizen or a permanent resident; must be 17 to 30 years of age; and must be enrolled in a full-time degree (graduate or undergraduate), diploma or certificate program at a Canadian college or university for the academic year. **Application Requirements:** Applicants must complete the application form and submit along with a letter describing the reasons why they would be worthy recipients of a BBPA National Scholarship; a completed financial information schedule stating their budget for the coming year including information on their expected sources of funding, family income and related information; and a letter of reference from the two individuals named in their application (must be a teacher from their high school, college or university, and an individual who is familiar with their community service). Application form and requirements must be sent to The Board of Trustees, BBPA National Scholarship Fund, 675 King St., W, Ste. 210, Toronto, ON M5V 1M9. **Deadline for Receipt:** May 30.

387 ■ BLACK BUSINESS AND PROFESSIONAL ASSOCIATION
675 King St. W, Ste. 210
Toronto, ON, Canada M5V 1M9
Tel: (416)504-4097
Fax: (416)504-7343
E-mail: bbpa@bellnet.ca
Web Site: http://www.bbpa.org
To provide support for Black Canadian students.
Title of Award: Beverly Mascoll Scholarships **Area, Field, or Subject:** General studies. **Level of Education for which Award is Granted:** Undergraduate **Funds Available:** $2,000. **Duration:** One year.
Eligibility Requirements: Applicant must be a Canadian citizen or a permanent resident; must be 17 to 30 years of age; and must be enrolled in a full-time degree (graduate or undergraduate), diploma or certificate program at a Canadian college or university for the academic year. **Application Requirements:** Applicants must complete the application form and submit along with a letter describing the reasons why they would be worthy recipients of a BBPA National Scholarship; a completed financial information schedule stating their budget for the coming year including information on their expected sources of funding, family income and related information; and a letter of reference from the two individuals named in their application (must be a teacher from their high school, college or university, and an individual who is familiar with their community service). Application form and requirements must be sent to The Board of Trustees, BBPA National Scholarship Fund, 675 King St., W, Ste. 210, Toronto, ON M5V 1M9. **Deadline for Receipt:** May 30.

388 ■ BLACK BUSINESS AND PROFESSIONAL ASSOCIATION
675 King St. W, Ste. 210
Toronto, ON, Canada M5V 1M9
Tel: (416)504-4097
Fax: (416)504-7343
E-mail: bbpa@bellnet.ca
Web Site: http://www.bbpa.org
To provide support for Black Canadian students.
Title of Award: Minerva Scholarships **Area, Field, or Subject:** General studies. **Level of Education for which Award is Granted:** Undergraduate **Number Awarded:** 2-4. **Funds Available:** $2,000-$4,000. **Duration:** One year.

Eligibility Requirements: Applicant must be a Canadian citizen or a permanent resident; must be 17 to 30 years of age; and must be enrolled in a full-time degree (graduate or undergraduate), diploma or certificate program at a Canadian college or university for the academic year. **Application Requirements:** Applicants must complete the application form and submit along with a letter describing the reasons why they would be a worthy recipient of a BBPA National Scholarship; a completed financial information schedule stating their budget for the coming year including information on their expected sources of funding, family income and related information; and a letter of reference from the two individuals named in their application (must be a teacher from their high school, college or university, and an individual who is familiar with their community service). Application form and requirements must be sent to The Board of Trustees, BBPA National Scholarship Fund, 675 King St., W, Ste. 210, Toronto, ON M5V 1M9. **Deadline for Receipt:** May 30.

389 ■ BLACK BUSINESS AND PROFESSIONAL ASSOCIATION
675 King St. W, Ste. 210
Toronto, ON, Canada M5V 1M9
Tel: (416)504-4097
Fax: (416)504-7343
E-mail: bbpa@bellnet.ca
Web Site: http://www.bbpa.org
To provide support for Black Canadian students.
Title of Award: Portia White Scholarships **Area, Field, or Subject:** General studies. **Level of Education for which Award is Granted:** Undergraduate **Funds Available:** $2,000. **Duration:** One year.
Eligibility Requirements: Applicant must be a Canadian citizen or a permanent resident; must be 17 to 30 years of age; and must be enrolled in a full-time degree (graduate or undergraduate), diploma or certificate program at a Canadian college or university for the academic year. **Application Requirements:** Applicants must complete the application form and submit along with a letter describing the reasons why they would be worthy recipients of a BBPA National Scholarship; a completed financial information schedule stating their budget for the coming year including information on their expected sources of funding, family income and related information; and a letter of reference from the two individuals named in their application (must be a teacher from their high school, college or university, and an individual who is familiar with their community service). Application form and requirements must be sent to The Board of Trustees, BBPA National Scholarship Fund, 675 King St., W, Ste. 210, Toronto, ON M5V 1M9. **Deadline for Receipt:** May 30.

390 ■ BLACK BUSINESS AND PROFESSIONAL ASSOCIATION
675 King St. W, Ste. 210
Toronto, ON, Canada M5V 1M9
Tel: (416)504-4097
Fax: (416)504-7343
E-mail: bbpa@bellnet.ca
Web Site: http://www.bbpa.org
To provide support for Black Canadian students.
Title of Award: Dwight Whylie Scholarships **Area, Field, or Subject:** General studies. **Level of Education for which Award is Granted:** Undergraduate **Funds Available:** $2,000. **Duration:** One year.
Eligibility Requirements: Applicant must be a Canadian citizen or a permanent resident; must be 17 to 30 years of age; and must be enrolled in a full-time degree (graduate or undergraduate), diploma or certificate program at a Canadian college or university for the academic year. **Application Requirements:** Applicants must submit completed application form; a letter describing the reasons why they would be worthy recipients of a BBPA National Scholarship; a completed financial information schedule stating their budget for the coming year including information on their expected sources of funding, family income and related information; and a letter of reference from the two individuals named in their application (must be a teacher from their high school, college or university, and an individual who is familiar with their community service). Application form and requirements must be sent to The Board of Trustees, BBPA National Scholarship Fund, 675 King St., W, Ste. 210, Toronto, ON M5V 1M9. **Deadline for Receipt:** May 30.

391 ■ BLACK WOMEN IN SISTERHOOD FOR ACTION
PO Box 1529
Washington, DC 20013

Tel: (202)543-5719
Fax: (202)543-5719
E-mail: info@bisa-hq.org
Web Site: http://www.bisa-hq.org
To provide financial assistance for prospective college students who have been accepted for admission to a college or university and who are in need of financial assistance.
Title of Award: BISA's Scholarship Assistance Program **Area, Field, or Subject:** General studies. **Level of Education for which Award is Granted:** Undergraduate **Funds Available:** $1,000. **Duration:** 4 years.
Eligibility Requirements: Black female high school graduates (currently graduating from high school in the year of application) are eligible to apply. **Application Requirements:** Applicants must submit transcript of records and SAT or ACT Scores; parent's Income Tax Submission to IRS (with W-2 Statement); Financial Aid Award Letter; and two typed double-spaced pages or one single-spaced page highlighting where you expect to be in your career development in ten years. **Deadline for Receipt:** April 6.

392 ■ BLACK WOMEN IN SISTERHOOD FOR ACTION
PO Box 1592
Washington, DC 20013
Tel: (202)543-6013
Fax: (202)543-5719
E-mail: info@bisa-hq.org
Web Site: http://www.bisa-hq.org
To provide financial assistance to college students who have been accepted for admission to a college or university and need financial assistance.
Title of Award: BISA's Scholarships Assistance Program **Area, Field, or Subject:** General studies. **Level of Education for which Award is Granted:** High School **Funds Available:** $1,000. **Duration:** One year.
Eligibility Requirements: Applicants must be black females; must be graduates or graduating high school seniors. **Application Requirements:** Applicants must submit completed application form; transcript; SAT or ACT scores; parents' income tax submission to IRS (with W-2 Statement); financial aid award letter; and written self-portrait (two typed double spaced pages or one single spaced page) highlighting where they expect to be in their career development in 10 years. **Deadline for Receipt:** April 6.

393 ■ BLOOD ASSURANCE FOUNDATION
705 E 4th St.
Chattanooga, TN 37403-1916
Tel: (423)756-0966
Free: 800-962-0628
Fax: (423)752-8460
E-mail: wlf@bloodassurance.org
Web Site: http://www.bloodassurance.org
To encourage educational pursuits by providing financial assistance.
Title of Award: The Crystal Green Blood Assurance Scholarships **Area, Field, or Subject:** General studies. **Level of Education for which Award is Granted:** Undergraduate **Number Awarded:** 12. **Funds Available:** $1,500. **Duration:** 1 year.
Eligibility Requirements: Applicants must be high school senior students planning to enter an accredited two or four-year college or university; and must have an, at least, "B" average and score at least 20 on the ACT or 1100 on the SAT cumulative. **Application Requirements:** Applicants must submit a detailed marketing plan for a new drive promotion; applicants must secure two letters of recommendation and obtain an official high school transcript which includes the first semester senior grades and ACT/SAT test scores.

394 ■ BOYS AND GIRLS CLUB OF OTTAWA
2825 Dumaurier Ave.
Ottawa, ON, Canada K2B 7W3
Tel: (613)232-0925
E-mail: sbradford@bgcottawa.org
Web Site: http://www.bgcottawa.org
To promote, encourage and sponsor promising individuals who would otherwise experience extreme hardships in pursuing a post-secondary education.
Title of Award: Brian Smith Scholarship **Area, Field, or Subject:** General studies. **Level of Education for which Award is Granted:** Undergraduate **Number Awarded:** 2. **Funds Available:** $2,500-$5,000.

Eligibility Requirements: Applicants must be graduating students from a high school in the Ottawa area planning to attend any university or college in the city of Ottawa. **Application Requirements:** Applicants must submit: a completed application form; completed expenses and income form; up-to-date resume; two letters of recommendation; copy of most recent school transcript; proof of citizenship status; copy of letter of acceptance to an accredited post-secondary school; professional quality color photo; and a 300-1,000 word essay discussing their community involvement, financial need, accomplishment and academics. **Deadline for Receipt:** March 30.

395 ■ BRAIN TUMOR FOUNDATION FOR CHILDREN
6065 Roswell Rd. NE, Ste. 505
Atlanta, GA 30328
Tel: (404)252-4107
Fax: (404)252-4108
E-mail: info@braintumorkids.org
Web Site: http://www.braintumorkids.org
To encourage educational pursuits among survivors of a pediatric brain or spinal cord tumor by providing financial support.
Title of Award: Larry Dean Davis Scholarships Program **Area, Field, or Subject:** General Studies. **Level of Education for which Award is Granted:** Undergraduate **Number Awarded:** 2. Varies. **Funds Available:** 2,500. **Duration:** Annual.
Eligibility Requirements: Candidates must be survivors of pediatric brain or spinal cord tumor who are residents of the state of Georgia; must be entering or currently enrolled in an advanced educational program at a college, university, vocational school, or other setting; must demonstrate a need for financial assistance. **Application Requirements:** Applicants must submit completed application available on the website, along with two qualified recommendations to: Brain Tumor Foundation for Children, Inc., 6065 Roswell Road, Suite 505; Atlanta, GA 30328-4015; Applicants may call the foundation for further information or to request an application. **Deadline for Receipt:** April 15. **Additional Information:** Brain Tumor Foundation for Children, Inc., tel: 404-252-4107.

396 ■ BRETZLAFF FOUNDATION
1550 N Milford Rd.
Milford, MI 48381
Tel: (248)684-3408
Fax: (248)684-2648
Web Site: http://www.hebf.org
To provide scholarships that will be a credit to American Society.
Title of Award: Hilda E. Bretzlaff Foundation Scholarships **Area, Field, or Subject:** General studies. **Level of Education for which Award is Granted:** Undergraduate **Funds Available:** No specific amount.
Eligibility Requirements: Applicants must have a 2.0 cumulative grade point average or better. **Application Requirements:** All applications are by invitation only. Interested students my contact the OPBEA office for more information.

397 ■ BRITISH AMERICAN FOUNDATION OF TEXAS
PO Box 421234
Houston, TX 77242
Tel: (713)587-9900
Fax: (713)784-7712
E-mail: info@baftx.org
Web Site: http://baftx.org
To assist the students seeking financial resources for their education.
Title of Award: BAFTX Early Starters Awards **Area, Field, or Subject:** General studies. **Level of Education for which Award is Granted:** Undergraduate **Funds Available:** $500 up to $1,000.
Eligibility Requirements: Applicants must be permanent residents of Texas; enrolled in full-time education; between 11 and 14 years old and must maintain a competitive GPA and hold an excellent school attendance record. **Application Requirements:** Applicants must submit the completed application form; essay between 300 and 500 words regarding a British person (past or present) whom they admire; current transcript signed by a member of their teaching staff; letter of recommendation which must come from a teacher in whose class they were enrolled within the past year, or from a guidance counselor at their school (letter must be on school letterhead paper); and a recent photograph.

398 ■ BRITISH AMERICAN FOUNDATION OF TEXAS

PO Box 421234
Houston, TX 77242
Tel: (713)587-9900
Fax: (713)784-7712
E-mail: info@baftx.org
Web Site: http://baftx.org
To provide financial assistance to aspiring individuals from Great Britain or Texas, USA that are intent on furthering their education in their chosen field.
Title of Award: BAFTX Graduate Awards **Area, Field, or Subject:** General studies. **Level of Education for which Award is Granted:** Undergraduate **Funds Available:** No specific amount.
Eligibility Requirements: Applicants must be permanent residents of Texas; enrolled in full time education; between 21 and 25 years old; must hold an undergraduate degree with a GPA of 3.5 or above for U.S. applicants and 2:1 (65+) for U.K. applicants. **Application Requirements:** Applicants must submit completed application form; essay, not less than 1,000 words, on one of the topics from the application form found at the website of BAFTX; current transcript of academic performance signed by a member of the teaching staff; letter of recommendation from a graduate or undergraduate professor in whose class they were enrolled or from a guidance counselor at their university (letter must be on university letterhead paper); financial statement declaring their eligibility for the program; budget outline stating the sum being requested for tuition fees and other costs associated with graduate tuition; and a recent photograph.

399 ■ BRITISH AMERICAN FOUNDATION OF TEXAS

PO Box 421234
Houston, TX 77242
Tel: (713)587-9900
Fax: (713)784-7712
E-mail: info@baftx.org
Web Site: http://baftx.org
To provide a summer study program for academically adept students from low-income families in the Houston area.
Title of Award: BAFTX Junior Achievers Awards **Area, Field, or Subject:** General studies. **Level of Education for which Award is Granted:** Undergraduate **Funds Available:** No specific amount.
Eligibility Requirements: Applicants must be permanent residents of Texas; enrolled in full-time education; between 16 and 17 years old; and must maintain a competitive GPA and excellent school attendance record. **Application Requirements:** Applicants must submit completed application form; an essay between 500 and 750 words regarding a British person (past or present) whom they admire; current transcript of academic performance signed by a member of the teaching staff; letter of recommendation which must come from a teacher in whose class they were enrolled within the past year or from a guidance counselor at their school (letter must be on school letterhead); and a recent photograph.

400 ■ BRITISH AMERICAN FOUNDATION OF TEXAS

PO Box 421234
Houston, TX 77242
Tel: (713)587-9900
Fax: (713)784-7712
E-mail: info@baftx.org
Web Site: http://baftx.org
To alleviate the financial burden of college fees.
Title of Award: BAFTX Undergraduate Awards **Area, Field, or Subject:** General studies. **Level of Education for which Award is Granted:** Undergraduate **Funds Available:** No specific amount.
Eligibility Requirements: Applicants must be permanent residents of Texas; enrolled in full time education; between 18 and 22 years old; and must maintain a GPA of 3.5. **Application Requirements:** Applicants must submit an essay, not less than 1,000 words, on one of the topics given in the application form found at the website of BAFTX; a letter of recommendation which must come from a teacher in whose class they were enrolled within the past year or from a guidance counselor at their university (letter must be on university letterhead paper); current transcript of their academic performance signed by a member of the teaching staff; financial statement declaring their eligibility for the program; budget outline stating the sum being requested for tuition fees and other costs associated with their education for one semester; and a recent photograph.

401 ■ RON BROWN SCHOLAR PROGRAM

1160 Pepsi Place Ste. 206
Charlottesville, VA 22901
Tel: (434)964-1588
Fax: (434)964-1589
Web Site: http://www.ronbrown.org
To identify African-American high school seniors who will make significant contributions to society; to provide financial support to those who are in need.
Title of Award: Ron Brown Scholars Program **Area, Field, or Subject:** General Studies. **Level of Education for which Award is Granted:** High School **Funds Available:** $10,000 annually. **Duration:** 4 years.
Eligibility Requirements: Applicants must be senior high school students; must excel academically; exhibit exceptional leadership potential; participate in community service activities and demonstrate financial need; must be US a citizen or hold a permanent resident visa card. **Application Requirements:** Applicants must mail the application materials in one packet. Transcripts and letters of recommendation should not be sent under separate cover; incomplete, e-mailed or faxed applications will not be considered. **Deadline for Receipt:** November 1. **Additional Information:** CAP Charitable Foundation at the above address

402 ■ SUSAN THOMPSON BUFFETT FOUNDATION

222 Kiewit Plz.
Omaha, NE 68131
Tel: (402)943-1300
Web Site: http://www.buffettscholarships.org
To provide financial assistance to qualified individuals.
Title of Award: Susan Thompson Buffett Foundation Scholarships **Area, Field, or Subject:** General studies. **Level of Education for which Award is Granted:** Undergraduate **Funds Available:** $3,200 plus a textbook allowance of $400. **Duration:** One year.
Eligibility Requirements: Applicants must be residents of the State of Nebraska; must be graduating high school seniors or undergraduate students who have not already earned a bachelor's degree; must be attending or applying to a Nebraska state public school; must be in need of financial assistance; must have maintained at least a 2.5 GPA throughout high school; must have applied for federal financial aid and have already received back the Student Aid Report that contains their Expected Family Contribution. **Application Requirements:** Applicants must complete the application form available online; must submit a high school or college transcript; two letters of reference from teachers, employers or clergy members; must have a copy of the Information Summary of their financial aid; must provide one-page handwritten background and personal information. **Deadline for Receipt:** March 1.

403 ■ BUILDING OWNERS AND MANAGERS ASSOCIATION OF GREATER NEW YORK

11 Penn Plz., 22nd Fl., Ste. 2201
New York, NY 10001
Tel: (212)239-3662
Fax: (212)268-7441
E-mail: mary@bomany.com
Web Site: http://www.bomany.org
To financially assist students to further their professional education.
Title of Award: BOMA/NY Scholarships **Area, Field, or Subject:** General studies. **Level of Education for which Award is Granted:** Undergraduate **Funds Available:** No specific amount.
Eligibility Requirements: Applicants must be currently enrolled RPA, FMA, SMA, or SMT students, taking home study, classroom study or accelerated courses; must be employed by a BOMA/NY member firm and working within the 5 Boroughs of New York. **Application Requirements:** Applicants must submit completed application form along with a one page essay and letter of recommendation from current employer. **Deadline for Receipt:** June 22.

404 ■ BUSINESS AND PROFESSIONAL WOMEN'S FOUNDATION

1900 M St. NW, Ste. 310
Washington, DC 20036
Tel: (202)293-1100
Fax: (202)861-0298
E-mail: foundation@bpwfoundation.org
Web Site: http://www.bpwusa.org

To provide financial assistance to disadvantaged women seeking to further their education.
Title of Award: Career Advancement Scholarships **Area, Field, or Subject:** General studies. **Level of Education for which Award is Granted:** Undergraduate **Funds Available:** No specific amount.
Eligibility Requirements: Applicant must be a female at least 25 years of age; must be a U.S citizen or U.S national; must demonstrate critical financial need; must have an expected family contribution (EFC) of $2,500 or less; must be officially accepted into an accredited U.S college or university, including those in American Samoa, Puerto Rico, and the Virgin Islands; must demonstrate clear career plans; must not be earning a doctoral-level or terminal degree. **Application Requirements:** Scholarship application and other supporting documents must be sent to BPW foundation. **Additional Information:** The Business and Professional Women's Foundation established the Career Advancement Scholarship Program in 1969 to provide scholarships, grants and loans to women seeking to improve their lives. **Deadline for Receipt:** April 15.

405 ■ CALHOUN COMMUNITY COLLEGE
PO Box 2216
Decatur, AL 35609
Tel: (256)306-2500
Free: 800-626-3628
Web Site: http://www.calhoun.edu
To provide educational assistance for Calhoun students.
Title of Award: Calhoun Scholarships **Area, Field, or Subject:** General studies. **Level of Education for which Award is Granted:** Undergraduate **Funds Available:** $1,500 for full-tuition.
Eligibility Requirements: Applicants must be enrolled at the Calhoun College. **Application Requirements:** Applicants must complete a FAFSA (Free Application for Federal Student Aid) by March 1 in order to be considered. Applicants must also complete the online scholarship application and submit along with other required materials and information. **Deadline for Receipt:** March 1. **Additional Information:** Student Financial Services, 256-306-2624.

406 ■ CALIFORNIA ASSOCIATION OF PRIVATE POSTSECONDARY SCHOOLS
400 Capitol Mall, Ste. 1560
Sacramento, CA 95814
Tel: (916)447-5500; 888-92-CAPPS
Fax: (916)440-8970
E-mail: info@cappsonline.org
Web Site: http://www.cappsonline.org
To ensure that the needs of the entire sector, from small registered schools to large institutions are met from an educational, policy and business perspective.
Title of Award: California Association of Private Postsecondary Schools Scholarships **Area, Field, or Subject:** Cosmetology. **Level of Education for which Award is Granted:** Undergraduate **Number Awarded:** 4. **Funds Available:** $5,000.
Eligibility Requirements: Applicants must be enrolled in a cosmetology, massage, aesthetics, or allied health program at a CAPP's member School; must be U.S. citizens and residents of California; and must have a high school diploma. **Application Requirements:** Applicants must submit one to two-page essay along with the completed application form, transcript and three letters of recommendation. **Deadline for Receipt:** June 1. **Additional Information:** info@cappsonline.com.

407 ■ CALIFORNIA GROCERS ASSOCIATION
1415 L St., Ste. 450
Sacramento, CA 95814-3910
Tel: (916)448-3545
Fax: (916)448-2793
Web Site: http://www.cagrocers.com
To provide proactive leadership, education, advocacy and information.
Title of Award: Lou Amen Legacy Scholarship **Area, Field, or Subject:** General studies. **Level of Education for which Award is Granted:** Undergraduate **Funds Available:** $1,000.
Eligibility Requirements: Applicants must be full-time college students at an accredited, non-profit college or university in the United States. **Application Requirements:** Applicants must submit a completed application form.

408 ■ CALIFORNIA GROCERS ASSOCIATION
1415 L St., Ste. 450
Sacramento, CA 95814-3910
Tel: (916)448-3545
Fax: (916)448-2793
Web Site: http://www.cagrocers.com
To provide proactive leadership, education, advocacy and information.
Title of Award: Don C. Beaver Memorial Scholarship **Area, Field, or Subject:** General studies. **Level of Education for which Award is Granted:** Undergraduate **Funds Available:** $2,000.
Eligibility Requirements: Applicants must be full-time college students at an accredited, non-profit college or university in the United States. **Application Requirements:** Applicants must submit a completed application form.

409 ■ CALIFORNIA GROCERS ASSOCIATION
1415 L St., Ste. 450
Sacramento, CA 95814-3910
Tel: (916)448-3545
Fax: (916)448-2793
Web Site: http://www.cagrocers.com
To provide proactive leadership, education, advocacy and information.
Title of Award: Jack H. Brown Scholarship **Area, Field, or Subject:** General studies. **Level of Education for which Award is Granted:** Undergraduate **Funds Available:** $1,000.
Eligibility Requirements: Applicants must be full-time college students at an accredited, non-profit college or university in the United States. **Application Requirements:** Applicants must submit a completed application form.

410 ■ CALIFORNIA GROCERS ASSOCIATION
1415 L St., Ste. 450
Sacramento, CA 95814-3910
Tel: (916)448-3545
Fax: (916)448-2793
Web Site: http://www.cagrocers.com
To provide proactive leadership, education, advocacy and information.
Title of Award: California Shopping Cart Retrieval Corporation Inc. Scholarships **Area, Field, or Subject:** General studies. **Level of Education for which Award is Granted:** Undergraduate **Number Awarded:** 1. **Funds Available:** $2,500.
Eligibility Requirements: Applicants must be full-time college students at an accredited, non-profit college or university in the United States. **Application Requirements:** Applicants must submit a completed application form.

411 ■ CALIFORNIA GROCERS ASSOCIATION
1415 L St., Ste. 450
Sacramento, CA 95814-3910
Tel: (916)448-3545
Fax: (916)448-2793
Web Site: http://www.cagrocers.com
To provide proactive leadership, education, advocacy and information.
Title of Award: Classic Wines of California Scholarships **Area, Field, or Subject:** General studies. **Level of Education for which Award is Granted:** Undergraduate **Number Awarded:** 2. **Funds Available:** $2,000.
Eligibility Requirements: Applicants must be full-time college students at an accredited, non-profit college or university in the United States. **Application Requirements:** Applicants must submit a completed application form.

412 ■ CALIFORNIA GROCERS ASSOCIATION
1415 L St., Ste. 450
Sacramento, CA 95814-3910
Tel: (916)448-3545
Fax: (916)448-2793
Web Site: http://www.cagrocers.com
To provide proactive leadership, education, advocacy and information.
Title of Award: Joey and Florence Franco Legacy Scholarship **Area, Field, or Subject:** General studies. **Level of Education for which Award is Granted:** Undergraduate **Funds Available:** $1,000.
Eligibility Requirements: Applicants must be full-time college students at an accredited, non-profit college or university in the United States. **Ap-**

plication Requirements: Applicants must submit a completed application form.

413 ■ CALIFORNIA GROCERS ASSOCIATION
1415 L St., Ste. 450
Sacramento, CA 95814-3910
Tel: (916)448-3545
Fax: (916)448-2793
Web Site: http://www.cagrocers.com
To provide proactive leadership, education, advocacy and information.
Title of Award: Hall of Achievement Scholarships **Area, Field, or Subject:** General studies. **Level of Education for which Award is Granted:** Undergraduate **Funds Available:** $2,000.
Eligibility Requirements: Applicants must be full-time college students at an accredited, non-profit college or university in the United States. **Application Requirements:** Applicants must submit a completed application form.

414 ■ CALIFORNIA GROCERS ASSOCIATION
1415 L St., Ste. 450
Sacramento, CA 95814-3910
Tel: (916)448-3545
Fax: (916)448-2793
Web Site: http://www.cagrocers.com
To provide proactive leadership, education, advocacy and information.
Title of Award: Roger K. Hughes Legacy Scholarship **Area, Field, or Subject:** General studies. **Level of Education for which Award is Granted:** Undergraduate **Funds Available:** $1,000.
Eligibility Requirements: Applicants must be full-time college students at an accredited, non-profit college or university in the United States. **Application Requirements:** Applicants must submit a completed application form.

415 ■ CALIFORNIA GROCERS ASSOCIATION
1415 L St., Ste. 450
Sacramento, CA 95814-3910
Tel: (916)448-3545
Fax: (916)448-2793
Web Site: http://www.cagrocers.com
To provide proactive leadership, education, advocacy and information.
Title of Award: Paul A. Hughes Memorial Scholarship **Area, Field, or Subject:** General studies. **Level of Education for which Award is Granted:** Undergraduate **Number Awarded:** 1. **Funds Available:** $1,000.
Eligibility Requirements: Applicants must be full-time college students at an accredited, non-profit college or university in the United States. **Application Requirements:** Applicants must submit a completed application form.

416 ■ CALIFORNIA GROCERS ASSOCIATION
1415 L St., Ste. 450
Sacramento, CA 95814-3910
Tel: (916)448-3545
Fax: (916)448-2793
Web Site: http://www.cagrocers.com
To provide proactive leadership, education, advocacy and information.
Title of Award: Illuminator Educational Foundation Scholarships **Area, Field, or Subject:** General studies. **Level of Education for which Award is Granted:** Undergraduate **Number Awarded:** 10. **Funds Available:** $1,000.
Eligibility Requirements: Applicants must be full-time college students at an accredited, non-profit college or university in the United States. **Application Requirements:** Applicants must submit a completed application form.

417 ■ CALIFORNIA GROCERS ASSOCIATION
1415 L St., Ste. 450
Sacramento, CA 95814-3910
Tel: (916)448-3545
Fax: (916)448-2793
Web Site: http://www.cagrocers.com
To provide proactive leadership, education, advocacy and information.
Title of Award: Don Kaplan Legacy Scholarship **Area, Field, or Subject:** General studies. **Level of Education for which Award is Granted:** Undergraduate **Funds Available:** $1,000.

Eligibility Requirements: Applicants must be full-time college students at an accredited, non-profit college or university in the United States. **Application Requirements:** Applicants must submit a completed application form.

418 ■ CALIFORNIA GROCERS ASSOCIATION
1415 L St., Ste. 450
Sacramento, CA 95814-3910
Tel: (916)448-3545
Fax: (916)448-2793
Web Site: http://www.cagrocers.com
To provide proactive leadership, education, advocacy and information.
Title of Award: Peter and Jody Larkin Legacy Scholarship **Area, Field, or Subject:** General studies. **Level of Education for which Award is Granted:** Undergraduate **Funds Available:** $1,000.
Eligibility Requirements: Applicants must be full-time college students at an accredited, non-profit college or university in the United States. **Application Requirements:** Applicants must submit a completed application form.

419 ■ CALIFORNIA GROCERS ASSOCIATION
1415 L St., Ste. 450
Sacramento, CA 95814-3910
Tel: (916)448-3545
Fax: (916)448-2793
Web Site: http://www.cagrocers.com
To provide proactive leadership, education, advocacy and information.
Title of Award: Bill MacAloney Legacy Scholarship **Area, Field, or Subject:** General studies. **Level of Education for which Award is Granted:** Undergraduate **Funds Available:** $1,000.
Eligibility Requirements: Applicants must be full-time college students at an accredited, non-profit college or university in the United States. **Application Requirements:** Applicants must submit a completed application form.

420 ■ CALIFORNIA GROCERS ASSOCIATION
1415 L St., Ste. 450
Sacramento, CA 95814-3910
Tel: (916)448-3545
Fax: (916)448-2793
Web Site: http://www.cagrocers.com
To provide proactive leadership, education, advocacy and information.
Title of Award: Al Plamann Legacy Scholarship **Area, Field, or Subject:** General studies. **Level of Education for which Award is Granted:** Undergraduate **Funds Available:** $1,000.
Eligibility Requirements: Applicants must be full-time college students at an accredited, non-profit college or university in the United States. **Application Requirements:** Applicants must submit a completed application form.

421 ■ CALIFORNIA GROCERS ASSOCIATION
1415 L St., Ste. 450
Sacramento, CA 95814-3910
Tel: (916)448-3545
Fax: (916)448-2793
Web Site: http://www.cagrocers.com
To provide proactive leadership, education, advocacy and information.
Title of Award: Save Mart Legacy Scholarships **Area, Field, or Subject:** General studies. **Level of Education for which Award is Granted:** Undergraduate **Funds Available:** $1,000.
Eligibility Requirements: Applicants must be full-time college students at an accredited, non-profit college or university in the United States. **Application Requirements:** Applicants must submit a completed application form.

422 ■ CALIFORNIA GROCERS ASSOCIATION
1415 L St., Ste. 450
Sacramento, CA 95814-3910
Tel: (916)448-3545
Fax: (916)448-2793
Web Site: http://www.cagrocers.com
To provide proactive leadership, education, advocacy and information.
Title of Award: Trelut Family Legacy Scholarships **Area, Field, or Subject:** General studies. **Level of Education for which Award is Granted:** Undergraduate **Funds Available:** $1,000.

Eligibility Requirements: Applicants must be full-time college students at an accredited, non-profit college or university in the United States. **Application Requirements:** Applicants must submit a completed application form.

423 ■ CALIFORNIA GROCERS ASSOCIATION
1415 L St., Ste. 450
Sacramento, CA 95814-3910
Tel: (916)448-3545
Fax: (916)448-2793
Web Site: http://www.cagrocers.com
To provide proactive leadership, education, advocacy and information.
Title of Award: Bob Wilson Legacy Scholarship **Area, Field, or Subject:** General studies. **Level of Education for which Award is Granted:** Undergraduate **Funds Available:** $1,000.
Eligibility Requirements: Applicants must be full-time college students at an accredited, non-profit college or university in the United States. **Application Requirements:** Applicants must submit a completed application form.

424 ■ CALIFORNIA GROUNDWATER ASSOCIATION
PO Box 14369
Santa Rosa, CA 95402-6369
Tel: (707)578-4408
Fax: (707)546-4906
E-mail: wellguy@groundh2o.org
Web Site: http://www.groundh2o.org
To provide financial assistance to those students who are in need.
Title of Award: California Groundwater Association Scholarships **Area, Field, or Subject:** General Studies. **Level of Education for which Award is Granted:** Undergraduate **Funds Available:** $1,000.
Eligibility Requirements: Applicants must be California residents; must demonstrate an interest in some facet of groundwater technology. **Application Requirements:** Applicants must obtain a CGA sponsor and provide a 500 word essay about their interest in the groundwater field or their chosen field of study. Applicants must check the available website for the additional requirements. **Additional Information:** Please call at 707-578-4408 for details.

425 ■ CALIFORNIA LIBRARY ASSOCIATION
717 20th St., Ste. 200
Sacramento, CA 95811
Tel: (916)447-8541
Fax: (916)447-8394
E-mail: info@cla-net.org
Web Site: http://www.cla-net.org
To enable more than 100 new librarians to get on the fast track to ALA and professional leadership.
Title of Award: Emerging Leaders Scholarships **Area, Field, or Subject:** General studies. **Level of Education for which Award is Granted:** Undergraduate **Funds Available:** $1,500.
Eligibility Requirements: Applicant must be under 35 years of age or be a new librarian of any age with fewer than five years post-MLS experience; must have recent MLS degree from an ALA or NCATE accredited or be in an MLS program; must attend both ALA conferences and work virtually in between each; must be prepared to commit to serve on an ALA, divisions, chapter, or round table committee, taskforce or workgroup upon completion of the program; must be an ALA member or join upon selection if not already a member. **Application Requirements:** Applicants must submit a completed application form. **Deadline for Receipt:** June 20.

426 ■ CALIFORNIA POLICE YOUTH CHARITIES
3800 Watt Ave., Ste. 125
Sacramento, CA 95821
Tel: (916)482-4245
Fax: (916)482-4246
E-mail: cbuzzeaton@sbcglobal.net
Web Site: http://www.calpyc.com
To provide spirit lifting opportunities to critically ill children with the purpose of enhancing their quality of life while allowing them to experience something unique and important also to their families.
Title of Award: Herbie Morici Memorial Scholarships **Area, Field, or Subject:** General studies. **Level of Education for which Award is Granted:** Undergraduate **Funds Available:** $500.

Eligibility Requirements: Applicants must be high school seniors in each California's 58 counties. **Application Requirements:** Applicants must submit a completed application form.

427 ■ CALIFORNIA POLICE YOUTH CHARITIES
3800 Watt Ave., Ste. 125
Sacramento, CA 95821
Tel: (916)482-4245
Fax: (916)482-4246
E-mail: cbuzzeaton@sbcglobal.net
Web Site: http://www.calpyc.com
To recognize twelfth grade students who have engaged in meaningful leadership and citizenship volunteer activities during the past year.
Title of Award: Youth Leadership Scholarships **Area, Field, or Subject:** General studies. **Level of Education for which Award is Granted:** Undergraduate **Number Awarded:** 20. **Funds Available:** $1,000.
Eligibility Requirements: Applicants must be high school seniors who wish to pursue their studies in college; must be residents of California, sons, daughters or wards of an active or retired California Peace Officer. **Application Requirements:** Applicants must submit a completed application form and essay. **Deadline for Receipt:** May 1. **Additional Information:** cbuzzeaton@msn.com.

428 ■ CALIFORNIA SCHOOL LIBRARY ASSOCIATION
1300 Baker St.
Bakersfield, CA 93305
Tel: (661)631-4808
E-mail: yoons@bcsd.com
Web Site: http://www.csla.net
To assist Northern California students.
Title of Award: Jewels Gardiner Scholarships **Area, Field, or Subject:** Library and archival sciences. **Level of Education for which Award is Granted:** Undergraduate **Number Awarded:** 2. **Funds Available:** $1,000. **Duration:** One year.
Eligibility Requirements: Applicants must be enrolled in a Library Media Teacher Credential program. **Application Requirements:** Application forms are available online. Applicants must submit a letter of recommendation. Application form and requirements must be sent to Chair, Jewel Gardiner Memorial Fund, California School Library Association, 1001 26th St., Sacramento, CA 95816. **Deadline for Receipt:** August 1 and November 1.

429 ■ CALIFORNIA SCOTTISH RITE FOUNDATION
855 Elm Ave.
Long Beach, CA 90813
Web Site: http://www.scottishritecalifornia.org
To provide financial assistance to young men and women who want to pursue their education at university and graduate level.
Title of Award: California Scottish Rite Foundation Scholarships **Area, Field, or Subject:** General studies. **Level of Education for which Award is Granted:** Undergraduate **Funds Available:** $1,500. **Duration:** One year.
Eligibility Requirements: Applicants must be undergraduate students who are residents of California state with ages ranging from 17 to 25 years old; must have a grade point average of 3.0 or better. **Application Requirements:** Applicants must submit completed application form along with certified transcript of grades for previous semester; typed letter with handwritten signature by student of their employment, planned courses in the coming quarter/semester and current mailing address. **Deadline for Receipt:** March 14.

430 ■ CALIFORNIA STATE UNIVERSITY SAN MACROS ALUMNI ASSOCIATION
Cal State San Macros
333 S Twin Oaks Valley Rd.
San Marcos, CA 92096
Tel: (760)750-4405
E-mail: alumni@csusm.edu
Web Site: http://www.csusmalumni.org
To support fellow and future alumni in furthering their education.
Title of Award: Cal State San Macros Alumna Scholarships **Area, Field, or Subject:** General studies. **Level of Education for which Award is Granted:** Undergraduate **Number Awarded:** 1. **Funds Available:** $500. **Duration:** One year.

Eligibility Requirements: Applicant must be admitted to a degree or certificate program and enrolled in at least six units. **Application Requirements:** Applicant must submit an application to the Financial Aid and Scholarship Office. **Additional Information:** Financial Aid and Scholarship Office, 760-750-4850.

431 ■ CALIFORNIA STATE UNIVERSITY SAN MACROS ALUMNI ASSOCIATION

Cal State San Macros
333 S Twin Oaks Valley Rd.
San Marcos, CA 92096
Tel: (760)750-4405
E-mail: alumni@csusm.edu
Web Site: http://www.csusmalumni.org
To support fellow and future alumni in furthering their education.
Title of Award: Cost-of-Books Relief Scholarships **Area, Field, or Subject:** General studies. **Level of Education for which Award is Granted:** Undergraduate **Number Awarded:** 1. **Funds Available:** $500. **Duration:** One year.
Eligibility Requirements: Applicant must be a student with financial need, enrolled in at least 6 units and have a GPA of 3.0. **Application Requirements:** Applicant must submit an application and a 250-500 word essay to the Financial Aid and Scholarship Office. **Additional Information:** Financial Aid and Scholarship Office, 760-750-4850.

432 ■ CALISTA CORPORATION

301 Calista Ct., Ste. A
Anchorage, AK 99518-3028
Tel: (907)279-5516
Fax: (907)272-5060
E-mail: calista@calistacorp.com
Web Site: http://www.calistacorp.com
To provide financial assistance to Alaska Natives to enable them to participate in continuing educational activities, formal programs of study and programs to improve their status.
Title of Award: Calista Scholarships **Area, Field, or Subject:** General studies. **Level of Education for which Award is Granted:** Undergraduate **Funds Available:** $500-$1,000. **Duration:** One year.
Eligibility Requirements: Applicant must be accepted to an accredited school and enrolling on a full-time basis; must be a high school graduate or have earned a GED and be in good academic standing with an at least 2.0 GPA; must be employees of Calista Corporation or their descendants. **Application Requirements:** Applicant must complete the application form available online; must have the official transcript of record; must have a copy of birth certificate or Certificate of Indian Blood; must have a letter of acceptance from their college, university or vocational school; must provide an essay (up to 500 words) describing their educational and career goals, their reasons for attending school and what they hope to accomplish in the future using the knowledge gained from their educational experience. Application form and other supporting documents must be sent to Calista Scholarship Fund, 301 Calista Ct., Ste. A, Anchorage, AK 99518-3028. **Deadline for Receipt:** June 30.

433 ■ CALVIN ALUMNI ASSOCIATION

3201 Burton St. SE
Grand Rapids, MI 49546
Tel: (616)526-6000
Free: 800-688-0122
Fax: (616)526-8551
E-mail: alumni@calvin.edu
Web Site: http://www.calvin.edu
To build community among Calvin College alumni and friends; to provide opportunities for service and aspiring alumni to answer God's call in life and vocation.
Title of Award: Calvin Alumni Association Arizona Central Chapter Scholarships **Area, Field, or Subject:** General studies. **Level of Education for which Award is Granted:** Undergraduate **Funds Available:** $1,000.
Eligibility Requirements: Applicants must be high school seniors who have applied to Calvin and live in central Arizona. **Application Requirements:** Applicants must answer all questions on the application; must submit a transcript that shows the two most recent years of education; must attach a written references. **Deadline for Receipt:** March 1. **Additional Information:** 480-785-9852.

434 ■ CALVIN ALUMNI ASSOCIATION

3201 Burton St. SE
Grand Rapids, MI 49546
Tel: (616)526-6000
Free: 800-688-0122
Fax: (616)526-8551
E-mail: alumni@calvin.edu
Web Site: http://www.calvin.edu
To build community among Calvin College alumni and friends; to provide opportunities for service and aspiring alumni to answer God's call in life and vocation.
Title of Award: Calvin Alumni Association-Black Alumni Chapter Scholarships **Area, Field, or Subject:** General studies. **Level of Education for which Award is Granted:** Undergraduate **Funds Available:** No specific amount.
Eligibility Requirements: Applicants must be current Calvin College black students who have completed two semesters; must be in good standing; must be enrolled in a full-time status. **Application Requirements:** Applicants must submit a completed application form. **Deadline for Receipt:** April 15.

435 ■ CALVIN ALUMNI ASSOCIATION

3201 Burton St. SE
Grand Rapids, MI 49546
Tel: (616)526-6000
Free: 800-688-0122
Fax: (616)526-8551
E-mail: alumni@calvin.edu
Web Site: http://www.calvin.edu
To build community among Calvin College alumni and friends; to provide opportunities for service and aspiring alumni to answer God's call in life and vocation.
Title of Award: Calvin Alumni Association British Columbia Scholarships **Area, Field, or Subject:** General studies. **Level of Education for which Award is Granted:** Undergraduate **Funds Available:** $500.
Eligibility Requirements: Applicants must be enrolled as freshmen students. **Application Requirements:** Applicants must submit a completed application form.

436 ■ CALVIN ALUMNI ASSOCIATION

3201 Burton St. SE
Grand Rapids, MI 49546
Tel: (616)526-6000
Free: 800-688-0122
Fax: (616)526-8551
E-mail: alumni@calvin.edu
Web Site: http://www.calvin.edu
To build community among Calvin College alumni and friends; to provide opportunities for service and aspiring alumni to answer God's call in life and vocation.
Title of Award: Calvin Alumni Association California- Bay Area Scholarships **Area, Field, or Subject:** General studies. **Level of Education for which Award is Granted:** Undergraduate **Funds Available:** No specific amount.
Eligibility Requirements: Applicants must be current high school seniors; must live in the LA/Inland Empire Chapter area; must have a minimum GPA of 3.0. **Application Requirements:** Applicants must submit a completed application form. **Deadline for Receipt:** April 15. **Additional Information:** 526-461-1489.

437 ■ CALVIN ALUMNI ASSOCIATION

3201 Burton St. SE
Grand Rapids, MI 49546
Tel: (616)526-6000
Free: 800-688-0122
Fax: (616)526-8551
E-mail: alumni@calvin.edu
Web Site: http://www.calvin.edu
To build community among Calvin College alumni and friends; to provide opportunities for service and aspiring alumni to answer God's call in life and vocation.
Title of Award: Calvin Alumni Association Colorado Chapter Scholarships **Area, Field, or Subject:** General studies. **Level of Education for which Award is Granted:** Undergraduate **Number Awarded:** 7. **Funds Available:** $1,000.

Eligibility Requirements: Applicants must be students who are in good standing, leader in the church community and will continue attributes at Calvin College. **Application Requirements:** Applicants must submit a completed application form; must submit a typed essay, completed evaluation/Letter from Youth Pastor/Minister; completed evaluation/Letter from High School Teacher/Counselor High School Transcript and signature of applicant. **Deadline for Receipt:** March 14.

438 ■ CALVIN ALUMNI ASSOCIATION

3201 Burton St. SE
Grand Rapids, MI 49546
Tel: (616)526-6000
Free: 800-688-0122
Fax: (616)526-8551
E-mail: alumni@calvin.edu
Web Site: http://www.calvin.edu
To build community among Calvin College alumni and friends; to provide opportunities for service and inspiring alumni to answer God's call in life and vocation.
Title of Award: Calvin Alumni Association Florida-Gulf Coast Scholarships **Area, Field, or Subject:** General studies. **Level of Education for which Award is Granted:** Undergraduate **Funds Available:** No stated amount.
Eligibility Requirements: Applicants must be first year students from the Gulf Coast Florida; must live within the Gulf Coast Chapter area. **Application Requirements:** Applicants must submit a completed application form. **Deadline for Receipt:** March 14. **Additional Information:** 941-794-3016.

439 ■ CALVIN ALUMNI ASSOCIATION

3201 Burton St. SE
Grand Rapids, MI 49546
Tel: (616)526-6000
Free: 800-688-0122
Fax: (616)526-8551
E-mail: alumni@calvin.edu
Web Site: http://www.calvin.edu
To build community among Calvin College alumni and friends; to provide opportunities for service and inspiring alumni to answer God's call in life and vocation.
Title of Award: Calvin Alumni Association-Illinois Scholarships **Area, Field, or Subject:** General studies. **Level of Education for which Award is Granted:** Undergraduate **Funds Available:** $1,000.
Eligibility Requirements: Applicants must be first year students from the Chicagoland Areas. **Application Requirements:** Applicants must submit a completed application form; two completed recommendation forms; must submit a completed recommendation from their school Principal or Counselor; must submit an official high school transcript. **Deadline for Receipt:** April 4. **Additional Information:** 630-462-0406.

440 ■ CALVIN ALUMNI ASSOCIATION

3201 Burton St. SE
Grand Rapids, MI 49546
Tel: (616)526-6000
Free: 800-688-0122
Fax: (616)526-8551
E-mail: alumni@calvin.edu
Web Site: http://www.calvin.edu
To build community among Calvin College alumni and friends; to provide opportunities for service and inspiring alumni to answer God's call in life and vocation.
Title of Award: Calvin Alumni Association-Iowa/Pella Scholarships **Area, Field, or Subject:** General studies. **Level of Education for which Award is Granted:** Undergraduate **Funds Available:** No stated amount.
Eligibility Requirements: Applicants must be first year students entering Calvin College and students living within the Pella Chapter area are eligible to apply. **Application Requirements:** Applicants must submit a completed application form, academic recommendation form and character recommendation form. **Deadline for Receipt:** April 1. **Additional Information:** jkuy05@iowatelecom.net.

441 ■ CALVIN ALUMNI ASSOCIATION

3201 Burton St. SE
Grand Rapids, MI 49546

Tel: (616)526-6000
Free: 800-688-0122
Fax: (616)526-8551
E-mail: alumni@calvin.edu
Web Site: http://www.calvin.edu
To build community among Calvin College alumni and friends; to provide opportunities for service and inspiring alumni to answer God's call in life and vocation.
Title of Award: Calvin Alumni Association-Maryland/Baltimore Scholarships **Area, Field, or Subject:** General studies. **Level of Education for which Award is Granted:** Undergraduate **Number Awarded:** 9. **Funds Available:** $2,500.
Eligibility Requirements: Applicants must be first year students entering Calvin College; must have at least 2.5 GPA; must attend a high school in Kent County. **Application Requirements:** Applicants must submit a completed application form and three recommendation from non-relatives. **Deadline for Receipt:** January 30. **Additional Information:** alumnievents@calvin.edu.

442 ■ CALVIN ALUMNI ASSOCIATION

3201 Burton St. SE
Grand Rapids, MI 49546
Tel: (616)526-6000
Free: 800-688-0122
Fax: (616)526-8551
E-mail: alumni@calvin.edu
Web Site: http://www.calvin.edu
To build a community among Calvin College alumni and friends; to provide opportunities for service and inspiring alumni to answer God's call in life and vocation.
Title of Award: Calvin Alumni Association-Michigan Lakeshore Scholarships **Area, Field, or Subject:** General studies. **Level of Education for which Award is Granted:** Undergraduate **Funds Available:** $1,000.
Eligibility Requirements: Applicants must be first year students entering Calvin College; must attend a high school on Ottawa, Muskegon or Allegan Counties. **Application Requirements:** Applicants must submit a completed application form, short essay, transcript of records and two reference letter. **Deadline for Receipt:** March 21. **Additional Information:** 231-557-1311.

443 ■ CALVIN ALUMNI ASSOCIATION

3201 Burton St. SE
Grand Rapids, MI 49546
Tel: (616)526-6000
Free: 800-688-0122
Fax: (616)526-8551
E-mail: alumni@calvin.edu
Web Site: http://www.calvin.edu
To build community among Calvin College alumni and friends; to provide opportunities for service and inspiring alumni to answer God's call in life and vocation.
Title of Award: Calvin Alumni Association-Michigan, Lansing Scholarships **Area, Field, or Subject:** General studies. **Level of Education for which Award is Granted:** Undergraduate **Funds Available:** $1,000.
Eligibility Requirements: Applicants must be first year students entering Calvin College; must have at least 2.5 GPA or better; must live in Mid-Michigan Chapter area. **Application Requirements:** Applicants must submit a completed application form and two written references. **Deadline for Receipt:** February 1. **Additional Information:** 517-487-6326.

444 ■ CALVIN ALUMNI ASSOCIATION

3201 Burton St. SE
Grand Rapids, MI 49546
Tel: (616)526-6000
Free: 800-688-0122
Fax: (616)526-8551
E-mail: alumni@calvin.edu
Web Site: http://www.calvin.edu
To build community among Calvin College alumni and friends; to provide opportunities for service and inspiring alumni to answer God's call in life and vocation.
Title of Award: Calvin Alumni Association-New Jersey Scholarships **Area, Field, or Subject:** General studies. **Level of Education for which Award is Granted:** Undergraduate **Funds Available:** $1,000.

Eligibility Requirements: Applicants must be students planning to attend Calvin for the first time; must be from local area (New Jersey or New York City metro area). **Application Requirements:** Applicants must submit a completed application and recommendation form. **Deadline for Receipt:** March 31. **Additional Information:** 201-444-0844.

445 ■ CALVIN ALUMNI ASSOCIATION

3201 Burton St. SE
Grand Rapids, MI 49546
Tel: (616)526-6000
Free: 800-688-0122
Fax: (616)526-8551
E-mail: alumni@calvin.edu
Web Site: http://www.calvin.edu
To build community among Calvin College alumni and friends; to provide opportunities for service and inspiring alumni to answer God's call in life and vocation.

Title of Award: Calvin Alumni Association-New York, Rochester Scholarships **Area, Field, or Subject:** General studies. **Level of Education for which Award is Granted:** Undergraduate **Funds Available:** $750. **Eligibility Requirements:** Applicants must be first year Calvin students; must live in Rochester area. **Application Requirements:** Applicants must submit a completed application form, completed references from Pastor/ Youth Leader and Teacher/Counselor and transcript of grades. **Deadline for Receipt:** March 14. **Additional Information:** 585-671-8735.

446 ■ CALVIN ALUMNI ASSOCIATION

3201 Burton St. SE
Grand Rapids, MI 49546
Tel: (616)526-6000
Free: 800-688-0122
Fax: (616)526-8551
E-mail: alumni@calvin.edu
Web Site: http://www.calvin.edu
To build community among Calvin College alumni and friends; to provide opportunities for service and inspiring alumni to answer God's call in life and vocation.

Title of Award: Calvin Alumni Association-South Florida Scholarships **Area, Field, or Subject:** General studies. **Level of Education for which Award is Granted:** Undergraduate **Funds Available:** No stated amount. **Eligibility Requirements:** Applicants must be first year students entering Calvin college; students from Palm Beach and surrounding counties are eligible. **Application Requirements:** Applicants must submit a completed application form. **Deadline for Receipt:** February 15. **Additional Information:** wierengap@bellsouth.net.

447 ■ CALVIN ALUMNI ASSOCIATION

3201 Burton St. SE
Grand Rapids, MI 49546
Tel: (616)526-6000
Free: 800-688-0122
Fax: (616)526-8551
E-mail: alumni@calvin.edu
Web Site: http://www.calvin.edu
To build community among Calvin College alumni and friends; to provide opportunities for service and inspiring alumni to answer God's call in life and vocation.

Title of Award: Calvin Alumni Association-South Florida Sophomore Scholarships **Area, Field, or Subject:** General studies. **Level of Education for which Award is Granted:** Undergraduate **Funds Available:** $500. **Eligibility Requirements:** Applicants must be students from Palm Beach and surrounding counties who will be sophomores at Calvin; must have an accumulated GPA of at least 2.0. **Application Requirements:** Applicants must submit a completed application form; must write a brief letter of application including name, local Florida address, majors and a copy of the most current Calvin transcript. **Deadline for Receipt:** February 14. **Additional Information:** wierenap@bellsouth.net.

448 ■ CALVIN ALUMNI ASSOCIATION

3201 Burton St. SE
Grand Rapids, MI 49546
Tel: (616)526-6000

Free: 800-688-0122
Fax: (616)526-8551
E-mail: alumni@calvin.edu
Web Site: http://www.calvin.edu
To build community among Calvin College alumni and friends; to provide opportunities for service and inspiring alumni to answer God's call in life and vocation.

Title of Award: Calvin Alumni Association-Southeast Michigan Scholarships **Area, Field, or Subject:** General studies. **Level of Education for which Award is Granted:** Undergraduate **Funds Available:** $1,000. **Eligibility Requirements:** Applicants must be first year students entering Calvin College; must living in Southeast Michigan Chapter area. **Application Requirements:** Applicants must submit a completed application form and two written references. **Deadline for Receipt:** March 1. **Additional Information:** 734-945-0683.

449 ■ CALVIN ALUMNI ASSOCIATION

3201 Burton St. SE
Grand Rapids, MI 49546
Tel: (616)526-6000
Free: 800-688-0122
Fax: (616)526-8551
E-mail: alumni@calvin.edu
Web Site: http://www.calvin.edu
To build community among Calvin College alumni and friends; to provide opportunities for service and inspiring alumni to answer God's call in life and vocation.

Title of Award: Calvin Alumni Association-Southeastern Wisconsin Scholarships **Area, Field, or Subject:** General studies. **Level of Education for which Award is Granted:** Undergraduate **Funds Available:** No stated amount. **Eligibility Requirements:** Applicants must be undergraduate college students who have completed at least two years of undergraduate education; must be residents of Dodge, Jefferson, Kenosha, Milwaukee, Ozaukee, Racine, Walworth, Washington, or Waukesha County, Wisconsin who attended a church in one of those counties; must intend to attend Calvin College during the next academic year. **Application Requirements:** Applicants must submit a complete application form, a complete "Statement of Ways and Means" and a certified copy of transcript from each of the colleges attended. **Deadline for Receipt:** March 31. **Additional Information:** alumni@calvin.edu.

450 ■ CALVIN ALUMNI ASSOCIATION

3201 Burton St. SE
Grand Rapids, MI 49546
Tel: (616)526-6000
Free: 800-688-0122
Fax: (616)526-8551
E-mail: alumni@calvin.edu
Web Site: http://www.calvin.edu
To build community among Calvin College alumni and friends; to provide opportunities for service and aspiring alumni to answer God's call in life and vocation.

Title of Award: Calvin Alumni Association Southern California Chapter Scholarships **Area, Field, or Subject:** General studies. **Level of Education for which Award is Granted:** Undergraduate **Number Awarded:** 1. **Funds Available:** $1,000. **Eligibility Requirements:** Applicants must be current high school senior students; must live within the Southern California Chapter area; must have a GPA of 3.0. **Application Requirements:** Applicants must submit a completed application form. **Deadline for Receipt:** March 14. **Additional Information:** trena@boonstras.com.

451 ■ CALVIN ALUMNI ASSOCIATION

3201 Burton St. SE
Grand Rapids, MI 49546
Tel: (616)526-6000
Free: 800-688-0122
Fax: (616)526-8551
E-mail: alumni@calvin.edu
Web Site: http://www.calvin.edu
To build community among Calvin College alumni and friends; to provide opportunities for service and inspiring alumni to answer God's call in life and vocation.

Title of Award: Calvin Alumni Association-Southwest Michigan, Kalamazoo Scholarships **Area, Field, or Subject:** General studies. **Level of Education for which Award is Granted:** Undergraduate **Funds Available:** No stated amount.
Eligibility Requirements: Applicants must be high school senior students who live in Southwest Michigan Chapter area. **Application Requirements:** Applicants must submit a completed application form including activities and awards. **Deadline for Receipt:** April 14. **Additional Information:** 269-388-8052.

452 ■ CALVIN ALUMNI ASSOCIATION
3201 Burton St. SE
Grand Rapids, MI 49546
Tel: (616)526-6000
Free: 800-688-0122
Fax: (616)526-8551
E-mail: alumni@calvin.edu
Web Site: http://www.calvin.edu
To build community among Calvin College alumni and friends; to provide opportunities for service and inspiring alumni to answer God's call in life and vocation.
Title of Award: Calvin Alumni Association-Washington, D.C. Scholarships **Area, Field, or Subject:** General studies. **Level of Education for which Award is Granted:** Undergraduate **Funds Available:** No stated amount.
Eligibility Requirements: Applicants must be incoming first year or transfer Calvin students in the greater D.C./Baltimore area who will be entering Calvin. **Application Requirements:** Applicants must complete the application form and three copies of recommendation form. **Deadline for Receipt:** March 14. **Additional Information:** 209-401-3331.

453 ■ CALVIN ALUMNI ASSOCIATION
3201 Burton St. SE
Grand Rapids, MI 49546
Tel: (616)526-6000
Free: 800-688-0122
Fax: (616)526-8551
E-mail: alumni@calvin.edu
Web Site: http://www.calvin.edu
To build community among Calvin College alumni and friends; to provide opportunities for service and inspiring alumni to answer God's call in life and vocation.
Title of Award: Calvin Alumni Association-Washington, Lynden Scholarships **Area, Field, or Subject:** General studies. **Level of Education for which Award is Granted:** Undergraduate **Funds Available:** $500.
Eligibility Requirements: Applicants must be students living within the lynden Chapter area; must be high school seniors entering Calvin College with a minimum GPA of 2.50. **Application Requirements:** Applicants must complete the application form. **Deadline for Receipt:** March 15. **Additional Information:** matterdj@msn.com.

454 ■ CALVIN ALUMNI ASSOCIATION
3201 Burton St. SE
Grand Rapids, MI 49546
Tel: (616)526-6000
Free: 800-688-0122
Fax: (616)526-8551
E-mail: alumni@calvin.edu
Web Site: http://www.calvin.edu
To build community among Calvin College alumni and friends; to provide opportunities for service and inspiring alumni to answer God's call in life and vocation.
Title of Award: Calvin Alumni Association-Washington-Seattle/Tacoma Scholarships **Area, Field, or Subject:** General studies. **Level of Education for which Award is Granted:** Undergraduate **Funds Available:** No stated amount.
Eligibility Requirements: Applicants must be first year students including transferee entering Calvin and must living within the Seattle/Tacoma Chapter. **Application Requirements:** Applicants must submit a completed application form. **Deadline for Receipt:** April 25. **Additional Information:** b_wolt@yahoo.com.

455 ■ CAMDEN COUNTY COLLEGE
200 N Broadway
Camden, NJ 08102-1185

Tel: (856)338-1817
Web Site: http://www.camdencc.edu
To provide financial assistance to individuals who want to continue their studies at CCC.
Title of Award: Scott Bonners Memorial Scholarships **Area, Field, or Subject:** General studies. **Level of Education for which Award is Granted:** Undergraduate **Funds Available:** No specific amount. **Duration:** One year.
Eligibility Requirements: Applicant must be full time, single parent with financial need; must have a minimum of GPA 3.0. **Application Requirements:** Applicants must submit one recommendation from a faculty member or administrator at Camden County College. Application forms are available online and must be sent to Camden County College Foundation, PO Box 200, College Dr., Blackwood, NJ 08012. **Deadline for Receipt:** February 18.

456 ■ CAMDEN COUNTY COLLEGE
200 N Broadway
Camden, NJ 08102-1185
Tel: (856)338-1817
Web Site: http://www.camdencc.edu
To provide support to qualified individuals who want to pursue an education at CCC.
Title of Award: Camden County College Employee Memorial Scholarships **Area, Field, or Subject:** General studies. **Level of Education for which Award is Granted:** Undergraduate **Funds Available:** No specific amount. **Duration:** One academic year.
Eligibility Requirements: Applicants must have a cumulative GPA of 3.0. **Application Requirements:** Applicants must submit one recommendation from a faculty member or administrator at Camden County College. Application forms are available online and must be sent to Camden County College Foundation, PO Box 200, College Dr., Blackwood, NJ 08012. **Deadline for Receipt:** February 18.

457 ■ CAMDEN COUNTY COLLEGE
200 N Broadway
Camden, NJ 08102-1185
Tel: (856)338-1817
Web Site: http://www.camdencc.edu
To provide support to the outstanding individuals who want to pursue higher education and career goals at CCC.
Title of Award: Camden County College Foundation Scholarships **Area, Field, or Subject:** General studies. **Level of Education for which Award is Granted:** Undergraduate **Number Awarded:** 2. **Funds Available:** No specific amount. **Duration:** One academic year.
Eligibility Requirements: Applicants must be full-time or part-time students returning to CCC; must have a minimum of 3.0 GPA; must have completed a 12 college credits. **Application Requirements:** Applicants must submit one recommendation from a faculty member or administrator at Camden County College. Application forms are available online and must be sent to Camden County College Foundation, PO Box 200, College Dr., Blackwood, NJ 08012. **Deadline for Receipt:** February 18.

458 ■ CAMDEN COUNTY COLLEGE
200 N Broadway
Camden, NJ 08102-1185
Tel: (856)338-1817
Web Site: http://www.camdencc.edu
To provide financial assistance to qualified individuals who wants to pursue an education at CCC.
Title of Award: Camden County Retired Educators Association Scholarships **Area, Field, or Subject:** General studies. **Level of Education for which Award is Granted:** Undergraduate **Number Awarded:** 2. **Funds Available:** No specific amount. **Duration:** One academic year.
Eligibility Requirements: Applicants must be a full time education students returning to CCC. **Application Requirements:** Applicants must submit one recommendation from a faculty member or administrator at Camden County College. Application forms are available online and must be sent to Camden County College Foundation, PO Box 200, College Dr., Blackwood, NJ 08012. **Deadline for Receipt:** February 18.

459 ■ CAMDEN COUNTY COLLEGE
200 N Broadway
Camden, NJ 08102-1185

Tel: (856)338-1817
Web Site: http://www.camdencc.edu
To encourage a widowed or divorced non-traditional students to continue their studies at CCC.
Title of Award: James & Maryetta Cook Scholarships **Area, Field, or Subject:** General studies. **Level of Education for which Award is Granted:** Undergraduate **Funds Available:** No specific amount. **Duration:** One academic year.
Eligibility Requirements: Applicants must be widowed or divorced non-traditional students and returning to CCC; must demonstrates a motivation to succeed despite personal pr professional obstacles; must have a minimum GPA of 3.0. **Application Requirements:** Applicants must submit one recommendation from a faculty member or administrator at Camden County College. Application forms are available online and must be sent to Camden County College Foundation, PO Box 200, College Dr., Blackwood, NJ 08012. **Deadline for Receipt:** February 18.

460 ■ CAMDEN COUNTY COLLEGE
200 N Broadway
Camden, NJ 08102-1185
Tel: (856)338-1817
Web Site: http://www.camdencc.edu
To provide financial support to qualified individuals who wants to pursue their studies.
Title of Award: Garden State Rotary Club of Cherry Hill Scholarships **Area, Field, or Subject:** General studies. **Level of Education for which Award is Granted:** Undergraduate **Funds Available:** No specific amount. **Duration:** One academic year.
Eligibility Requirements: Applicants must have a minimum GPA of 3.0. **Application Requirements:** Applicants must submit one recommendation from a faculty member or administrator at Camden County College. Application forms are available online and must be sent to Camden County College Foundation, PO Box 200, College Dr., Blackwood, NJ 08012. **Deadline for Receipt:** February 18.

461 ■ CAMDEN COUNTY COLLEGE
200 N Broadway
Camden, NJ 08102-1185
Tel: (856)338-1817
Web Site: http://www.camdencc.edu
To provide financial assistance to qualified individuals who want to pursue their career.
Title of Award: Dr. Martin Luther King & Coretta Scott King Student Leadership Scholarships **Area, Field, or Subject:** General studies. **Level of Education for which Award is Granted:** Undergraduate **Funds Available:** No specific amount. **Duration:** One academic year.
Eligibility Requirements: Applicants must have completed a minimum of 12 college credits; must have a cumulative GPA of 3.0. **Application Requirements:** Applicants must submit one recommendation from a faculty member or administrator at Camden County College. Application forms are available online and must be sent to Camden County College Foundation, PO Box 200, College Dr., Blackwood, NJ 08012. **Deadline for Receipt:** February 18.

462 ■ CAMDEN COUNTY COLLEGE
200 N Broadway
Camden, NJ 08102-1185
Tel: (856)338-1817
Web Site: http://www.camdencc.edu
To encourage individuals to pursue an education at CCC.
Title of Award: Carolyn Murray Memorial Scholarships **Area, Field, or Subject:** General studies. **Level of Education for which Award is Granted:** Undergraduate **Funds Available:** No specific amount. **Duration:** One academic year.
Eligibility Requirements: Applicants must be students returning to CCC; must have a minimum GPA of 3.0. **Application Requirements:** Applicants must submit one recommendation from a faculty member or administrator at Camden County College. Application forms are available online and must be sent to Camden County College Foundation, PO Box 200, College Dr., Blackwood, NJ 08012. **Deadline for Receipt:** February 18.

463 ■ CAMDEN COUNTY COLLEGE
200 N Broadway
Camden, NJ 08102-1185

Tel: (856)338-1817
Web Site: http://www.camdencc.edu
To provide financial support to male students who wants to pursue an education at CCC.
Title of Award: H.N. Neal Memorial Scholarships **Area, Field, or Subject:** General studies. **Level of Education for which Award is Granted:** Undergraduate **Funds Available:** No specific amount. **Duration:** One academic year.
Eligibility Requirements: Applicants must be male students with a minimum cumulative GPA of 3.0. **Application Requirements:** Applicants must submit one recommendation from a faculty member or administrator at Camden County College. Application forms are available online and must be sent to Camden County College Foundation, PO Box 200, College Dr., Blackwood, NJ 08012. **Deadline for Receipt:** February 18.

464 ■ CAMDEN COUNTY COLLEGE
200 N Broadway
Camden, NJ 08102-1185
Tel: (856)338-1817
Web Site: http://www.camdencc.edu
To encourage African-American students to pursue their education.
Title of Award: Jerrothia Allenfonzo Riggs & Anna & Dorothy Mae Barnes Scholarships **Area, Field, or Subject:** General studies. **Level of Education for which Award is Granted:** Undergraduate **Funds Available:** No specific amount. **Duration:** One academic year.
Eligibility Requirements: Applicants must be an African-American female; must be a first-generation high school graduate and resident of Camden City; must have a minimum GPA of 3.0. **Application Requirements:** Applicants must submit one recommendation from a faculty member or administrator at Camden County College. Application forms are available online and must be sent to Camden County College Foundation, PO Box 200, College Dr., Blackwood, NJ 08012. **Deadline for Receipt:** February 18.

465 ■ CAMDEN COUNTY COLLEGE
200 N Broadway
Camden, NJ 08102-1185
Tel: (856)338-1817
Web Site: http://www.camdencc.edu
To provide financial assistance to qualified individuals who want to continue their studies at CCC.
Title of Award: Madlyn D. Thompson Memorial Scholarships **Area, Field, or Subject:** General studies. **Level of Education for which Award is Granted:** Undergraduate **Funds Available:** No specific amount. **Duration:** One academic year.
Eligibility Requirements: Applicants must be a single female parent returning to CCC; must have completed at least 30 credits toward degree and be residents of Camden; must have a minimum GPA of 3.0. **Application Requirements:** Applicants must submit one recommendation from a faculty member or administrator at Camden County College. Application forms are available online and must be sent to Camden County College Foundation, PO Box 200, College Dr., Blackwood, NJ 08012. **Deadline for Receipt:** February 18.

466 ■ CAMDEN COUNTY COLLEGE
200 N Broadway
Camden, NJ 08102-1185
Tel: (856)338-1817
Web Site: http://www.camdencc.edu
To provide financial assistance to qualified individuals.
Title of Award: Mercedes Laurie Wade Scholarships **Area, Field, or Subject:** General studies. **Level of Education for which Award is Granted:** Undergraduate **Funds Available:** No specific amount. **Duration:** One academic year.
Eligibility Requirements: Applicants must be female athletes, must be currently enrolled full time and with financial need; must have a minimum GPA of 2.5. **Application Requirements:** Applicants must submit one recommendation from a faculty member or administrator at Camden County College. Application forms are available online and must be sent to Camden County College Foundation, PO Box 200, College Dr., Blackwood, NJ 08012. **Deadline for Receipt:** February 18.

467 ■ CAMDEN COUNTY COLLEGE
200 N Broadway
Camden, NJ 08102-1185

Tel: (856)338-1817
Web Site: http://www.camdencc.edu
To provide financial assistance to individuals who want to pursue an education at CCC.
Title of Award: Watsontown Volunteer Fire Company Scholarships **Area, Field, or Subject:** General studies. **Level of Education for which Award is Granted:** Undergraduate **Funds Available:** No specific amount. **Duration:** One year.
Eligibility Requirements: Applicants must be students who want to return to CCC; must have a minimum cumulative GPA 3.0. **Application Requirements:** Applicants must submit one recommendation from a faculty member or administrator at Camden County College. Application forms are available online and must be sent to Camden County College Foundation, PO Box 200, College Dr., Blackwood, NJ 08012. **Deadline for Receipt:** February 18.

468 ■ CAMECO CORPORATION
2121-11th St. W
Saskatoon, SK, Canada S7M 1J3
Tel: (306)956-6290
Fax: (306)956-6201
Web Site: http://www.cameco.com
To provide financial assistance to deserving individuals in northern Saskatchewan who want to pursue their education.
Title of Award: Cameco Northern Scholarships - Technical Institute **Area, Field, or Subject:** General studies. **Level of Education for which Award is Granted:** Undergraduate **Funds Available:** $5,000. **Duration:** One year.
Eligibility Requirements: Applicant must be a resident of northern Saskatchewan and must have lived in the north for a minimum of five years; must be enrolled as a full-time student in a program of study leading to certification from a recognized technical institute located in Saskatchewan. **Application Requirements:** Applicant must complete the scholarship application available online; must submit a letter that includes the following: (1) a statement regarding the applicant's academic plans; (2) a list of the courses the applicant plans to take; (3) the name of the institution at which the applicant plans to enroll (or is enrolled); (4) the applicant's career objectives; (5) reference to the applicant's academic, social and athletic interests; (6) the applicant's goals for the future. Application form and other supporting documents must be sent to Cameco Corporation, Northern Affairs Office, PO Box 1049, La Ronge, SK S0J 1L0. **Deadline for Receipt:** June 30.

469 ■ CAMECO CORPORATION
2121-11th St. W
Saskatoon, SK, Canada S7M 1J3
Tel: (306)956-6290
Fax: (306)956-6201
Web Site: http://www.cameco.com
To provide financial assistance to deserving individuals in north Saskatchewan who want to pursue their education.
Title of Award: Cameco Northern Scholarships - University **Area, Field, or Subject:** General studies. **Level of Education for which Award is Granted:** Undergraduate **Funds Available:** $750. **Duration:** One year.
Eligibility Requirements: Applicant must be a resident of northern Saskatchewan and must have lived in the north for a minimum of five years; must be enrolled as a full-time student in a program of study leading to a degree from a Saskatchewan university, or from another Canadian university in situations where the student's program of study is not available in Saskatchewan. **Application Requirements:** Applicant must complete the scholarship application available online; must submit a letter that includes the following: (1) a statement regarding the applicant's academic plans; (2) a list of the courses the applicant plans to take; (3) the name of the institution at which the applicant plans to enroll (or is enrolled); (4) the applicant's career objectives; (5) reference to the applicant's academic, social and athletic interests; (6) the applicant's goals for the future. Application form and other supporting documents must be sent to Cameco Corporation, Northern Affairs Office, PO Box 1049, La Ronge, SK S0J 1L0. **Deadline for Receipt:** June 30.

470 ■ CANADA MILLENNIUM SCHOLARSHIP FOUNDATION
1000 Sherboke St. W, Ste. 800
Montreal, QC, Canada H3A 3R2

Tel: (514)985-0026; 877-786-3999
Fax: (514)985-5987
E-mail: millennium.foundation@bm-ms.org
Web Site: http://www.millenniumscholarships.ca
To complement provincial and territorial student assistance programs.
Title of Award: Canada Millennium Scholarship Foundation Millennium Bursary Award **Area, Field, or Subject:** General studies. **Level of Education for which Award is Granted:** Undergraduate **Funds Available:** $1,000.
Eligibility Requirements: Applicants must be post-secondary students who demonstrate merit and financial need. **Application Requirements:** Applicants may apply for the student financial assistance from their province or territory of residence. In some cases, students must indicate on their student assistance application that they wish to be considered for a millennium bursars. In most cases, students do not need to apply; their names are automatically considered when they apply from their home province or territorial governments which then provide the foundation with the names of eligible students. **Additional Information:** CMSF at the above address.

471 ■ CANADIAN ANESTHESIOLOGISTS' SOCIETY
1 Eglinton Ave. E, Ste. 208
Toronto, ON, Canada M4P 3A1
Tel: (416)480-0602
Fax: (416)480-0320
E-mail: director@cas.ca
Web Site: http://www.cas.ca
To provide financial support to students pursuing college.
Title of Award: Frank Newman Leadership Awards **Area, Field, or Subject:** General studies. **Level of Education for which Award is Granted:** Undergraduate **Number Awarded:** 2. **Funds Available:** $5,000.
Eligibility Requirements: Applicants must be undergraduate students at Campus Compact member colleges and universities. **Application Requirements:** Applicants must complete the online application form. Prepare a student-written essay; letter of nomination from applicant's president/chancellor; mentoring plan; and a recent head-and-shoulder photo. **Additional Information:** awards2008@compact.org.

472 ■ CANADIAN CARTOGRAPHIC ASSOCIATION
PO Box 3050
Victoria, BC, Canada V8W 3P5
Web Site: http://www.cca-acc.org
To recognize and encourage exceptional student achievement and ability in any aspect of cartography.
Title of Award: Norman Nicholson Scholarships **Area, Field, or Subject:** Cartography. **Level of Education for which Award is Granted:** Undergraduate **Funds Available:** $5,000. **Duration:** One year.
Eligibility Requirements: Applicant must be a full-time student in a recognized college or university program; must be a Canadian citizen or landed immigrant. **Application Requirements:** Applicants must submit an official transcript of all college or university courses complete with grades received; letters of recommendation from two faculty members who are familiar with the student's works and capabilities; one-page statement from the student regarding plans for continuing education in cartography. Application and attachments must be sent to: Canadian Cartographic Association 66 Meredith Dr., PO Box 225, Ilderton, ON N0M 2A0. **Deadline for Receipt:** March 15. **Additional Information:** Alberta Auringer Wood.

473 ■ CANADIAN COUNCIL FOR ABORIGINAL BUSINESS
250 The Esplanade, Ste. 204
Toronto, ON, Canada M5A 1J2
Tel: (416)961-8663
Fax: (416)961-3995
E-mail: info@ccab.com
Web Site: http://www.ccab.com
To provide scholarship assistance to qualified individuals who want to pursue their post-secondary education.
Title of Award: Foundation for the Advancement of Aboriginal Youth Bursary Program **Area, Field, or Subject:** General studies. **Level of Education for which Award is Granted:** Undergraduate **Funds Available:** $750. **Duration:** One year.

Eligibility Requirements: Applicant must be a Canadian resident, of First Nation, Metis or Inuit heritage and attending either a high school or a post-secondary institute full-time within Canada. **Application Requirements:** Applicant must complete the application form available online; must be provide proof of First Nations, Inuit or Metis ancestry; must have two signed, original letters of support; must provide a copy of the most recent official school transcripts and report card; must include a letter of acceptance; must provide a recent color photo. Application form and other supporting documents must be sent to the Foundation for the Advancement of Aboriginal Youth, c/o Canadian Council for Aboriginal Business, 250 The Esplanade, Ste. 204, Toronto, ON M5A 1J2. **Deadline for Receipt:** October 15.

474 ■ CANADIAN COUNCIL FOR ABORIGINAL BUSINESS
250 The Esplanade, Ste. 204
Toronto, ON, Canada M5A 1J2
Tel: (416)961-8663
Fax: (416)961-3995
E-mail: info@ccab.com
Web Site: http://www.ccab.com
To provide scholarship assistance to qualified individuals who want to pursue their post-secondary education.
Title of Award: Foundation for the Advancement of Aboriginal Youth Scholarships **Area, Field, or Subject:** General studies. **Level of Education for which Award is Granted:** Undergraduate **Funds Available:** $2,500. **Duration:** One year.
Eligibility Requirements: Applicant must be a Canadian resident, of First Nation, Metis or Inuit heritage and attending either high school or a post-secondary institute full-time within Canada. **Application Requirements:** Applicant must complete the application form available online; must provide proof of First Nation, Inuit or Metis ancestry; must have two signed, original letters of support; must provide a copy of the most recent official school transcripts and report card; must include a letter of acceptance; must provide a recent color photo. Application form and other supporting documents must be sent to Foundation for the Advancement of Aboriginal Youth, c/o Canadian Council for Aboriginal Business, 250 The Esplanade, Ste. 204, Toronto, ON M5A 1J2. **Deadline for Receipt:** October 15.

475 ■ CANADIAN FEDERATION OF INDEPENDENT GROCERS
2235 Sheppard Ave. E, Ste. 902
Willowdale, ON, Canada M2J 5B5
Tel: (416)492-2311
Free: 800-661-2344
Fax: (416)492-2347
E-mail: info@cfig.ca
Web Site: http://www.cfig.ca
To provide financial assistance to residents and students of Canada for their further educational enrichment.
Title of Award: CFIG National Scholarships **Area, Field, or Subject:** General studies. **Level of Education for which Award is Granted:** Undergraduate **Funds Available:** $8,000.
Eligibility Requirements: Applicants must be Canadian residents studying in Canada; enrolled or expecting to be enrolled in a postsecondary program of at least 2 years. High school applicants must be in their last year of secondary studies; college or university applicants must be enrolled in at least one more full year of study as of spring. **Application Requirements:** Applicants must submit a 1,000-word essay on topic given by the scholarship committee; list of academic achievements, awards, and extracurricular activities; official grade transcript of the last completed year; and the completed application form with all pertinent information properly filled in.

476 ■ CANADIAN HARD OF HEARING ASSOCIATION
2415 Holly Ln., Ste. 205
Ottawa, ON, Canada K1V 7P2
Tel: (613)526-1584
Free: 800-263-8068
Fax: (613)526-4718
E-mail: chhanational@chha.ca
Web Site: http://www.chha.ca
To offer financial assistance and recognition to hard of hearing and deafened students.

Title of Award: Canadian Hard of Hearing Association Scholarships **Area, Field, or Subject:** General studies. **Level of Education for which Award is Granted:** Undergraduate **Funds Available:** $1,000.
Eligibility Requirements: Applicants must be students registered in a full-time program at a recognized Canadian college or university, with a goal of obtaining a diploma or degree; must be either hard of hearing, deafened or orally deaf. **Application Requirements:** Application forms are available online. Applicants must submit a copy of the most recent school transcript; must have a personal statement, and two letters of reference. **Additional Information:** Established in 2002. **Deadline for Receipt:** January 31.

477 ■ CANADIAN HEMOPHILIA SOCIETY
625 Pres. Kennedy Ave., Ste. 505
Montreal, QC, Canada H3A 1K2
Tel: (514)848-0503
Free: 800-668-2686
Fax: (514)848-9661
E-mail: chs@hemophilia.ca
Web Site: http://www.hemophilia.ca
To bring young volunteers into the CHS while recognizing the importance of education.
Title of Award: CHS - Bursary Program Scholarships **Area, Field, or Subject:** General studies. **Level of Education for which Award is Granted:** Undergraduate **Funds Available:** $4,000.
Eligibility Requirements: Applicants must possess academic proficiency; must have experience in community service at volunteer level; and must possess leadership qualities. **Application Requirements:** Applicant must provide three letters of reference with the application stating the abilities and suitability of the candidate; must provide a letter from his/her physician or any medical authority confirming his/her medical status; must submit an original essay (500 words) to emphasize the logical thinking and adequate writing skills of the applicant; and must submit the original transcript of grades for the last year in secondary school. Application forms are available from the website. **Deadline for Receipt:** April 30.

478 ■ CANADIAN HEMOPHILIA SOCIETY
625 Pres. Kennedy Ave., Ste. 505
Montreal, QC, Canada H3A 1K2
Tel: (514)848-0503
Free: 800-668-2686
Fax: (514)848-9661
E-mail: chs@hemophilia.ca
Web Site: http://www.hemophilia.ca
To bring young volunteers into the CHS while recognizing the importance of education.
Title of Award: CHS Scholarships **Area, Field, or Subject:** General studies. **Level of Education for which Award is Granted:** Undergraduate **Funds Available:** $4,000.
Eligibility Requirements: Applicants must possess academic proficiency (GPA of 3.0 on a 4.0 scale); must have experience in community service at a volunteer level; and must possess leadership qualities. **Application Requirements:** Applicant must provide three letters of reference with the application stating the abilities and suitability of the candidate; must provide a letter from his/her physician or any medical authority confirming his/her medical status; must submit an original essay (500 words) to emphasize the logical thinking and adequate writing skills of the applicant; and must submit the original transcript of grades for the last year in secondary school. Application forms are available from the website. **Deadline for Receipt:** April 30.

479 ■ CANADIAN HOSPITALITY FOUNDATION
300 Adelaide St. E, No. 399
Toronto, ON, Canada M5A 1N1
Tel: (416)363-3401
Fax: (416)363-3403
E-mail: chf@theohi.ca
Web Site: http://www.chfscholarships.com
To provide scholarship to the students enrolled in the first or second year of a community college.
Title of Award: Applied Hospitality Degree Scholarships **Area, Field, or Subject:** Hotel, institutional, and restaurant management; Travel and tourism. **Level of Education for which Award is Granted:** Undergraduate **Funds Available:** $2,500.

Eligibility Requirements: Applicants must be college students currently enrolled in the first or second year of a community college. Applicants must be Canadian citizens or permanent residents. **Application Requirements:** Applicants must complete the application form on-line. In addition, students must submit hard copies of the following documents (please note that missing or incomplete documents may be grounds for elimination): Most current official transcripts of your complete academic history at the college you are enrolled in at this time; one or more letters of recommendation from an instructor and/or administrator form your college; One letters of recommendation from past or present employers; Resume; An essay on one of the topics listed on application form (600 words). Employer and school letters must include telephone numbers and, where possible, e-mail addresses. **Deadline for Receipt:** April 30. **Additional Information:** CHF at the above address.

480 ■ CANADIAN HOSPITALITY FOUNDATION

300 Adelaide St. E, No. 399
Toronto, ON, Canada M5A 1N1
Tel: (416)363-3401
Fax: (416)363-3403
E-mail: chf@theohi.ca
Web Site: http://www.chfscholarships.com
To provide scholarship to the High School students in their final year of school.

Title of Award: Canadian Hospitality Foundation College Entrance Scholarships **Area, Field, or Subject:** Culinary arts; Hotel, institutional, and restaurant management; Travel and tourism. **Level of Education for which Award is Granted:** Undergraduate **Funds Available:** $3,000.

Eligibility Requirements: Applicants must be high school students in their final year of school and who are enrolling in a minimum two-year college program in one of the following areas of training or study: Accommodation; Chef; Cook; Culinary; Events; Food and Beverages; Golf Club; Hospitality; Hotel; Resort; Restaurant; Tourism; Applicants must be Canadian citizens or permanent residents. **Application Requirements:** Applicants must complete the application form on-line. In addition, students must submit hard copies of the following documents (please note that missing or incomplete documents may be grounds for elimination): Final-year official transcripts from your previous academic year and report card from your current academic year (first semester/first term); Letter/s of recommendation from your school principal, teacher or guidance counselor; Letter/s of recommendation form past or present employers. School and employer letters must include telephone numbers and, where possible, e-mail addresses. **Deadline for Receipt:** April 30. **Additional Information:** CHF at the above address.

481 ■ CANADIAN HOSPITALITY FOUNDATION

300 Adelaide St. E, No. 399
Toronto, ON, Canada M5A 1N1
Tel: (416)363-3401
Fax: (416)363-3403
E-mail: chf@theohi.ca
Web Site: http://www.chfscholarships.com
To provide scholarships to High School students in their final year of school.

Title of Award: Canadian Hospitality Foundation University Entrance Scholarships **Area, Field, or Subject:** Hotel, institutional, and restaurant management; Travel and tourism. **Level of Education for which Award is Granted:** Undergraduate **Funds Available:** $3,500.

Eligibility Requirements: Applicants must be high school students in their final year of school who are enrolling in a university degree program in one of the following areas of training or study: Hospitality; Hotel; Tourism. Applicants must be Canadian citizens or permanent residents. **Application Requirements:** Applicants must complete the application form on-line; in addition, students must submit hard copies of the following documents (please note that missing or incomplete documents may be grounds for elimination): Final-year official transcripts from your previous academic year and report card from your current academic year (first semester/first term); Letter/s of recommendation from your school principal, teacher or guidance counselor; Letter/s of recommendation form past or present employers. School and employer letters must include telephone numbers and, where possible, e-mail addresses. **Deadline for Receipt:** April 30. **Additional Information:** CHF at the above address.

482 ■ CANADIAN HOSPITALITY FOUNDATION

300 Adelaide St. E, No. 399
Toronto, ON, Canada M5A 1N1
Tel: (416)363-3401
Fax: (416)363-3403
E-mail: chf@theohi.ca
Web Site: http://www.chfscholarships.com
To provide scholarship to the students enrolled in a one-year culinary program.

Title of Award: Culinary (1-Year Program) Scholarships **Area, Field, or Subject:** Culinary arts. **Level of Education for which Award is Granted:** Undergraduate **Funds Available:** $1,500.

Eligibility Requirements: Applicants must: be college students currently enrolled in a one-year (minimum ten months) culinary certificate program; not have received any other Canadian Hospitality Foundation scholarships; be Canadian citizens or permanent residents. **Application Requirements:** Applicants must complete the application form on-line. In addition, students must submit hard copies of the following documents (please note that missing or incomplete documents may be grounds for elimination): Final-year official transcripts from your previous academic year and report card from your current academic year (first semester/first term); Letter/s of recommendation from your school principal, teacher or guidance counselor; Letter/s of recommendation form past or present employers. School and employer letters must include telephone numbers and, where possible, e-mail addresses. **Deadline for Receipt:** April 30. **Additional Information:** CHF at the above address.

483 ■ CANADIAN PARKING ASSOCIATION

350-2255 St. Laurent Blvd.
Ottawa, ON, Canada K1G 4K3
Tel: (613)727-0700
Fax: (613)727-3183
E-mail: info@canadianparking.ca
Web Site: http://www.canadianparking.ca
To provide financial assistance to students in their pursuit of academic excellence and to encourage post-secondary study that enhances the parking industry in Canada.

Title of Award: Canadian Parking Association Scholarships **Area, Field, or Subject:** General studies. **Level of Education for which Award is Granted:** Undergraduate **Number Awarded:** 10. **Funds Available:** $2,000. **Duration:** One academic year.

Eligibility Requirements: Applicants must be registered CPA members whose job function is 50% related to parking, their spouses and dependents, members' employees whose job function is 50% related to parking, their spouses and dependents with a minimum average of 70% in the last three semesters of studies (non-academic courses such as career or personal development related courses will not be considered). **Application Requirements:** Applicants must submit the completed application form; official transcript of the last three semesters of available marks; description of extracurricular activities or volunteer/community involvement; two signed letters of reference; and the parental consent form. **Deadline for Receipt:** May 15.

484 ■ CANADIAN SANITATION SUPPLY ASSOCIATION

910 Dundas St., W
PO Box 10009
Whitby, ON, Canada L1P 1P7
Tel: (905)430-7267
Fax: (905)430-6418
Web Site: http://cssa.com
To provide scholarship assistance to qualified Canadian students who will be attending college or university in Canada.

Title of Award: Canadian Sanitation Supply Association Scholarships **Area, Field, or Subject:** General studies. **Level of Education for which Award is Granted:** Undergraduate **Number Awarded:** 6. **Funds Available:** $2,000 offered in each of the six regions: Atlantic Canada, Quebec, Ontario, Manitoba & Saskatchewan, Alberta, British Columbia. **Duration:** One year.

Eligibility Requirements: Applicant must be a student who will be graduating high school; must be an individual who is already enrolled in a college or university in Canada; must be a young Canadian who has achieved a high level of academic and leadership standards. **Application Requirements:** Applicant must complete the application form available online; must have a photograph, and official high school or college transcript; must provide an essay on: "What does your school custodian or facilities manager think about the Green cleaning Movement?"; must have a typed resume with name, planned occupation or profession, high school information, college or university information, employment history, activity and leadership record, and applicant evaluation form completed by a counselor or teacher. **Deadline for Receipt:** June 1.

485 ■ CANADIAN SANITATION SUPPLY ASSOCIATION

910 Dundas St., W
PO Box 10009
Whitby, ON, Canada L1P 1P7
Tel: (905)430-7267
Fax: (905)430-6418
Web Site: http://cssa.com
To provide scholarship assistance to qualified Canadian students who will be attending college or university in Canada.
Title of Award: International Sanitary Supply Association Foundation Scholarships **Area, Field, or Subject:** General studies. **Level of Education for which Award is Granted:** High School **Funds Available:** $2,000. **Duration:** One year.
Eligibility Requirements: Applicant must be a student who will be graduating high school; must be an individual who is already enrolled in a college or university in Canada; must be a young Canadian who has achieved a high level of academic and leadership standards. **Application Requirements:** Applicant must complete the application form available online; must have a photograph, and official high school or college transcript; must provide an essay on: "What does your school custodian or facilities manager think about the Green cleaning Movement?"; must have a typed resume with name, planned occupation or profession, high school information, college or university information, employment history, activity and leadership record, and applicant evaluation form completed by a counselor or teacher. **Deadline for Receipt:** June 1.

486 ■ CANADIAN WATER RESOURCES ASSOCIATION

280 Albert St., Ste. 900
Ottawa, ON, Canada K1P 5G8
Tel: (613)237-9363
Fax: (613)594-5190
E-mail: services@aic.ca
Web Site: http://www.cwra.org
To raise awareness of the value of water; to promote responsible and effective water resource management in Canada.
Title of Award: Ken Thomson Scholarships **Area, Field, or Subject:** Water resources. **Level of Education for which Award is Granted:** Undergraduate **Funds Available:** $2,000.
Eligibility Requirements: Applicant must be the second-highest ranked graduate student whose program of study focuses upon applied, natural or social science aspects of water resources; must be Canadian citizen or landed immigrant attending a Canadian University or college; must be enrolled in full-time graduate studies in any discipline. **Application Requirements:** Applicants must provide a statement from the chairman/director of the department which verifies that the application is reflective of the project; a 500-word statement which outlines the applicant's research project and its relevance to sustainable water resources; official transcript of records; two references to be sent directly to the Scholarship Committee by the referees or appropriate official of the university or college; a statement from the program chairman or director endorsing the application from that program, including confirmation of the applicant's full-time registration; and completed application form. **Deadline for Receipt:** February 29.

487 ■ CANCER SURVIVORS FUND

PO Box 792
Missouri City, TX 77459
Tel: (281)437-7142
Fax: (281)437-9568
E-mail: csf@cancersurvivorsfund.org
Web Site: http://www.cancersurvivorsfund.org
To augment the expenses associated with the college education of young cancer survivors.
Title of Award: Cancer Survivors' Fund Scholarships **Area, Field, or Subject:** General Studies. **Level of Education for which Award is Granted:** Undergraduate **Funds Available:** No specific amount.

Eligibility Requirements: Applicants must be cancer survivors or currently diagnosed with cancer; must be enrolled in or accepted for enrollment in an undergraduate school. **Application Requirements:** Applicants must complete the online scholarship application; must submit two letters of recommendation from two different academic teachers addressing why they should receive the scholarship; a letter from your attending physician verifying your medical history and current medical situation; must agree to do volunteer work to use their cancer experience to help other young cancer patients and survivors coping with a life threatening or life-altering event; Must submit an essay discussing the following question. HOW HAS MY EXPERIENCE WITH CANCER IMPACTED MY LIFE VALUES AND CAREER GOALS? Essays must be a minimum of 500 words and a maximum of 1200 words. **Additional Information:** The applicants and their parents if they are minors, must sign a release, that they agree to have their name and photo published in the news media or any CSF publication as a recipient of Cancer Survivors' Fund scholarship and that they agree to have their name, photo and success story to be published on this website or in any CSF publication. **Additional Information:** Cancer Survivors' Fund at the above address

488 ■ CAPE CORAL COMMUNITY FOUNDATION

4729 Vincennes Blvd.
Cape Coral, FL 33904
Tel: (239)542-5594
E-mail: cccf@capecoralcf.org
Web Site: http://capecoralcf.planyourlegacy.org
To assist eligible high school seniors to further their education by attending college.
Title of Award: The Rotary Club of Cape Coral Goldcoast Scholarships Fund **Area, Field, or Subject:** General Studies. **Level of Education for which Award is Granted:** Undergraduate **Number Awarded:** 3. **Funds Available:** $4,000. **Duration:** 4 years.
Eligibility Requirements: Applicants must be graduating seniors of any high school in Lee County; must have a 3.2 GPA or better; must be accepted to at least one accredited junior college, college or university; must be residents of Cape Coral; must be U.S. citizens and active in school and community. **Application Requirements:** Applicants must submit a completed application form. **Deadline for Receipt:** April 1.

489 ■ CAPE FEAR COMMUNITY COLLEGE FOUNDATION

411 N Front St.
Wilmington, NC 28401
Tel: (910)362-7207
Web Site: http://cfcc.edu/foundation
To assist the local high school students of North Carolina throughout the course of their studies.
Title of Award: Cape Fear Community College Merit Scholarships **Area, Field, or Subject:** General studies. **Level of Education for which Award is Granted:** Undergraduate **Number Awarded:** 10. **Funds Available:** $1,800. **Duration:** One year.
Eligibility Requirements: Applicants must be U.S. citizen high school senior students who have applied for or been approved to enroll in Cape Fear Community College in a curriculum program and possess academic potential as shown by high school grades, rank in class. **Application Requirements:** Applicants must submit all required application information including the letter of recommendation from high school principal, guidance counselor or high school teacher. **Deadline for Receipt:** April 1.

490 ■ CARIBBEAN HOTEL ASSOCIATION

2655 Le Juene Rd., Ste. 910
Coral Gables, FL 33134
Tel: (305)443-3040
Fax: (305)443-3005
E-mail: executive@caribbeanhotelassociation.com
Web Site: http://www.caribbeanhotelassociation.com
To provide people throughout the Caribbean region with an awareness of the industry's varied career opportunities a well as technical and professional development.
Title of Award: Caribbean Hotel Association Academic Scholarships **Area, Field, or Subject:** Hotel, Institutional, and Restaurant Management. **Level of Education for which Award is Granted:** Undergraduate **Funds Available:** No stated amount.
Eligibility Requirements: Applicants must be full-time or must be secondary school graduates pursuing a diploma or degree in hotel and

restaurant management or culinary arts in a two-year or four-year program at an affiliated CHA institution; or either be full-time students who are currently pursuing a diploma or degree in hotel and restaurant management, culinary arts in a two-year, four-year, or a graduate program at an affiliated CHA institution and who has completed first semester of the program; must be born in the Caribbean and registered as a Caribbean National. **Application Requirements:** Applicants must complete the application form; must submit a copy of certificates or awards; must include a current photo; must submit a references or recommendation. **Deadline for Receipt:** March 15.

491 ■ CHI PHI FRATERNITY
1160 Satellite Blvd.
Suwanee, GA 30024
Tel: (404)231-1824
Fax: (404)237-5090
E-mail: chiphi@chiphi.org
Web Site: http://www.chiphi.org
To encourage the Chi Phi members to pursue their education.
Title of Award: Chi Phi Educational Trust **Area, Field, or Subject:** General studies. **Level of Education for which Award is Granted:** Undergraduate **Funds Available:** Over $80,000.
Eligibility Requirements: Applicants must be Chi Phi members. **Application Requirements:** Applicant must provide a cover letter, summarize the applicant's qualifications and provide a description of his future aspirations and goals; must have the current academic transcript and recommendation letter from one faculty member and from the chapter Alpha. **Deadline for Receipt:** May 1.

492 ■ CHICANA/LATINA FOUNDATION
1419 Burlingame Ave. Ste. N
Burlingame, CA 94010
Tel: (650)373-1083
Fax: (650)373-1090
E-mail: olga@chicanalatina.org
Web Site: http://www.chicanalatina.org
To assist Latina students in completing their undergraduate and graduate college education.
Title of Award: Chicana Latina Scholarship Fund **Area, Field, or Subject:** General Studies. **Level of Education for which Award is Granted:** Graduate, Undergraduate **Funds Available:** No specific amount.
Eligibility Requirements: Applicants must be Chicana/Latina women of the Northern California counties; must be enrolled in accredited colleges, universities and community colleges in one of the listed Northern California counties; must have been residents for at least two years in one of the listed Northern California counties; must be enrolled as full-time college students, have completed a minimum of 15 college semester units after high school graduation, and have at least a 2.5 GPA; must have demonstrated leadership and civic/community involvement. **Application Requirements:** Applicants must check the available website to download the application form. **Additional Information:** Chicana Latina Foundation at the above address

493 ■ CHILDREN'S HOSPITAL OF PHILADELPHIA
34th St. and Civic Center Blvd.
Philadelphia, PA 19104-4399
Tel: (215)590-1000
Free: 800-879-2467
E-mail: fordg@email.edu
Web Site: http://www.chop.edu
To support the financial needs of young adults who are impacted by cancer and seeking higher education.
Title of Award: Vera Yip Memorial Scholarships **Area, Field, or Subject:** General Studies. **Level of Education for which Award is Granted:** Undergraduate **Funds Available:** Varies.
Eligibility Requirements: Applicant must be 35 years or younger at the time of application; must be young adult who has lost a parent/guardian to cancer or has a parent/guardian with cancer or the parent/guardian has experienced a cancer diagnosis between the ages of 15 and 35; must be currently attending or planning to attend a four-year college, university or vocational program and seeking a bachelor's degree or higher; and must have demonstrated leadership abilities and commitment to their com-

munity. **Application Requirements:** Applicants must accomplish complete application.

494 ■ CHRISTIAN RECORD SERVICES
PO Box 6097
Lincoln, NE 68506-0097
Tel: (402)488-0981
Fax: (402)488-7582
E-mail: info@christianrecord.org
Web Site: http://www.christianrecord.org
To assist blind young people who wish to pursue their college education.
Title of Award: CRS Scholarships **Area, Field, or Subject:** General studies. **Level of Education for which Award is Granted:** Undergraduate **Funds Available:** $500. **Duration:** One academic year.
Eligibility Requirements: Applicants must be legally blind; planning to attend college as a full-time student on the undergraduate level. **Application Requirements:** Applicants must submit a completed Scholarship application and character reference forms. **Deadline for Receipt:** April 1. **Additional Information:** Shelly Kittleson.

495 ■ CINCINNATI SCHOLARSHIP FOUNDATION
652 Main St.
Cincinnati, OH 45202
Tel: (513)345-6701
Fax: (513)345-6705
Web Site: http://www.cincinnatischolarshipfoundation.org
To encourage students to achieve their highest academic potential.
Title of Award: Cincinnati High School Scholarships **Area, Field, or Subject:** General studies. **Level of Education for which Award is Granted:** High School **Funds Available:** A monthly stipend based on GPA.
Eligibility Requirements: Applicant must attend a Cincinnati Public School in grades 7-12; meet the Federal Poverty Income Guidelines; maintains a minimum 2.50 GPA with no "Fs", "Xs" or "Is" in any subject; and be referred by a designated counselor or school representative. **Application Requirements:** Applications are only available from the representative at the student's school. The CSF representatives provide applications to students they recommend for the program. **Additional Information:** Started in 1918. The program works only for students attending Cincinnati Public Schools.

496 ■ CINCINNATI SCHOLARSHIP FOUNDATION
652 Main St.
Cincinnati, OH 45202
Tel: (513)345-6701
Fax: (513)345-6705
Web Site: http://www.cincinnatischolarshipfoundation.org
To help students from Greater Cincinnati area to achieve their dream of a college education.
Title of Award: Cincinnati Scholarship Foundation CFT/ACPSOP Scholarships **Area, Field, or Subject:** General studies. **Level of Education for which Award is Granted:** Undergraduate **Funds Available:** No specific amount.
Eligibility Requirements: Applicant must be a resident of Greater Cincinnati, and attending college as a full-time student. **Application Requirements:** Applicants must submit a completed scholarship application form along with a copy of recent transcript; expected Family Contribution (EFC) from Student Aid Report (SAR), which comes as a result of filing the FAFSA; and a copy of Financial Aid Award Letter from the chosen college to be attended. **Additional Information:** Faxed applications will not be considered. **Deadline for Receipt:** April 30.

497 ■ CINCINNATI SCHOLARSHIP FOUNDATION
652 Main St.
Cincinnati, OH 45202
Tel: (513)345-6701
Fax: (513)345-6705
Web Site: http://www.cincinnatischolarshipfoundation.org
To help students from Greater Cincinnati area to achieve the dream of a college education.
Title of Award: CSF Ach Family Scholarships **Area, Field, or Subject:** General studies. **Level of Education for which Award is Granted:** Undergraduate **Funds Available:** No specific amount.

Eligibility Requirements: Applicant must be a resident of Greater Cincinnati, and attending college as a full-time student. **Application Requirements:** Applicants must submit a completed scholarship application form along with a copy of recent transcript; expected Family Contribution (EFC) from Student Aid Report (SAR), which comes as a result of filing the FAFSA; and a copy of Financial Aid Award Letter from the chosen college to be attended. **Additional Information:** Faxed applications will not be considered. **Deadline for Receipt:** April 30.

498 ■ CINCINNATI SCHOLARSHIP FOUNDATION
652 Main St.
Cincinnati, OH 45202
Tel: (513)345-6701
Fax: (513)345-6705
Web Site: http://www.cincinnatischolarshipfoundation.org
To help students from Greater Cincinnati area to achieve the dream of a college education.
Title of Award: CSF Barr Foundation Scholarships **Area, Field, or Subject:** General studies. **Level of Education for which Award is Granted:** Undergraduate **Funds Available:** No specific amount.
Eligibility Requirements: Applicant must be a resident of Greater Cincinnati, and attending college as a full-time student. **Application Requirements:** Applicants must submit a completed scholarship application form along with a copy of recent transcript; expected Family Contribution (EFC) from Student Aid Report (SAR), which comes as a result of filing the FAFSA; and a copy of Financial Aid Award Letter from the chosen college to be attended. **Additional Information:** Faxed applications will not be considered. **Deadline for Receipt:** April 30.

499 ■ CINCINNATI SCHOLARSHIP FOUNDATION
652 Main St.
Cincinnati, OH 45202
Tel: (513)345-6701
Fax: (513)345-6705
Web Site: http://www.cincinnatischolarshipfoundation.org
To help students from Greater Cincinnati area to achieve the dream of a college education.
Title of Award: CSF Barrett Family Scholarships **Area, Field, or Subject:** General studies. **Level of Education for which Award is Granted:** Undergraduate **Funds Available:** No specific amount.
Eligibility Requirements: Applicant must be a resident of Greater Cincinnati, and attending college as a full-time student. **Application Requirements:** Applicants must submit a completed scholarship application form along with a copy of recent transcript; expected Family Contribution (EFC) from Student Aid Report (SAR), which comes as a result of filing the FAFSA; and a copy of Financial Aid Award Letter from the chosen college to be attended. **Additional Information:** Faxed applications will not be considered. **Deadline for Receipt:** April 30.

500 ■ CINCINNATI SCHOLARSHIP FOUNDATION
652 Main St.
Cincinnati, OH 45202
Tel: (513)345-6701
Fax: (513)345-6705
Web Site: http://www.cincinnatischolarshipfoundation.org
To help students from Greater Cincinnati area to achieve the dream of a college education.
Title of Award: CSF Bigg's/Curtis Breeden Scholarships **Area, Field, or Subject:** General studies. **Level of Education for which Award is Granted:** Undergraduate **Funds Available:** No specific amount.
Eligibility Requirements: Applicant must be a resident of Greater Cincinnati, and attending college as a full-time student. **Application Requirements:** Applicants must submit a completed scholarship application form along with a copy of recent transcript; expected Family Contribution (EFC) from Student Aid Report (SAR), which comes as a result of filing the FAFSA; and a copy of Financial Aid Award Letter from the chosen college to be attended. **Additional Information:** Faxed applications will not be considered. **Deadline for Receipt:** April 30.

501 ■ CINCINNATI SCHOLARSHIP FOUNDATION
652 Main St.
Cincinnati, OH 45202
Tel: (513)345-6701

Fax: (513)345-6705
Web Site: http://www.cincinnatischolarshipfoundation.org
To help students from Greater Cincinnati area to achieve the dream of a college education.
Title of Award: CSF Bob and Linda Kohlhepp Scholarships **Area, Field, or Subject:** General studies. **Level of Education for which Award is Granted:** Undergraduate **Funds Available:** No specific amount.
Eligibility Requirements: Applicant must be a resident of Greater Cincinnati, and attending college as a full-time student. **Application Requirements:** Applicants must submit a completed scholarship application form along with a copy of recent transcript; expected Family Contribution (EFC) from Student Aid Report (SAR), which comes as a result of filing the FAFSA; and a copy of Financial Aid Award Letter from the chosen college to be attended. **Additional Information:** Faxed applications will not be considered. **Deadline for Receipt:** April 30.

502 ■ CINCINNATI SCHOLARSHIP FOUNDATION
652 Main St.
Cincinnati, OH 45202
Tel: (513)345-6701
Fax: (513)345-6705
Web Site: http://www.cincinnatischolarshipfoundation.org
To help students from Greater Cincinnati area to achieve the dream of a college education.
Title of Award: CSF Borden Inc. Scholarships **Area, Field, or Subject:** General studies. **Level of Education for which Award is Granted:** Undergraduate **Funds Available:** No specific amount.
Eligibility Requirements: Applicant must be a resident of Greater Cincinnati, and attending college as a full-time student. **Application Requirements:** Applicants must submit a completed scholarship application form along with a copy of recent transcript; expected Family Contribution (EFC) from Student Aid Report (SAR), which comes as a result of filing the FAFSA; and a copy of Financial Aid Award Letter from the chosen college to be attended. **Additional Information:** Faxed applications will not be considered. **Deadline for Receipt:** April 30.

503 ■ CINCINNATI SCHOLARSHIP FOUNDATION
652 Main St.
Cincinnati, OH 45202
Tel: (513)345-6701
Fax: (513)345-6705
Web Site: http://www.cincinnatischolarshipfoundation.org
To help students from Greater Cincinnati area to achieve the dream of a college education.
Title of Award: CSF Carl H. Linder Family Scholarships **Area, Field, or Subject:** General studies. **Level of Education for which Award is Granted:** Undergraduate **Funds Available:** No specific amount.
Eligibility Requirements: Applicant must be a resident of Greater Cincinnati, and attending college as a full-time student. **Application Requirements:** Applicants must submit a completed scholarship application form along with a copy of recent transcript; expected Family Contribution (EFC) from Student Aid Report (SAR), which comes as a result of filing the FAFSA; and a copy of Financial Aid Award Letter from the chosen college to be attended. **Additional Information:** Faxed applications will not be considered. **Deadline for Receipt:** April 30.

504 ■ CINCINNATI SCHOLARSHIP FOUNDATION
652 Main St.
Cincinnati, OH 45202
Tel: (513)345-6701
Fax: (513)345-6705
Web Site: http://www.cincinnatischolarshipfoundation.org
To help students from Greater Cincinnati area to achieve the dream of a college education.
Title of Award: CSF Castellini Foundation Scholarships **Area, Field, or Subject:** General studies. **Level of Education for which Award is Granted:** Undergraduate **Funds Available:** No specific amount.
Eligibility Requirements: Applicant must be a resident of Greater Cincinnati, and attending college as a full-time student. **Application Requirements:** Applicants must submit a completed scholarship application form along with a copy of recent transcript; expected Family Contribution (EFC) from Student Aid Report (SAR), which comes as a result of filing the FAFSA; and a copy of Financial Aid Award Letter from the chosen college

to be attended. **Additional Information:** Faxed applications will not be considered. **Deadline for Receipt:** April 30.

505 ■ CINCINNATI SCHOLARSHIP FOUNDATION
652 Main St.
Cincinnati, OH 45202
Tel: (513)345-6701
Fax: (513)345-6705
Web Site: http://www.cincinnatischolarshipfoundation.org
To help students from Greater Cincinnati area to achieve their dream of a college education.
Title of Award: CSF Charles and Claire Phillips Scholarships **Area, Field, or Subject:** General studies. **Level of Education for which Award is Granted:** Undergraduate **Funds Available:** No specific amount.
Eligibility Requirements: Applicant must be a resident of Greater Cincinnati, and attending college as a full-time student. **Application Requirements:** Applicants must submit a completed scholarship application form along with a copy of recent transcript; expected Family Contribution (EFC) from Student Aid Report (SAR), which comes as a result of filing the FAFSA; and a copy of Financial Aid Award Letter from the chosen college to be attended. **Additional Information:** Faxed applications will not be considered. **Deadline for Receipt:** April 30.

506 ■ CINCINNATI SCHOLARSHIP FOUNDATION
652 Main St.
Cincinnati, OH 45202
Tel: (513)345-6701
Fax: (513)345-6705
Web Site: http://www.cincinnatischolarshipfoundation.org
To help students from Greater Cincinnati area to achieve their dream of a college education.
Title of Award: CSF Charlotte R. Schmidlapp Scholarships **Area, Field, or Subject:** General studies. **Level of Education for which Award is Granted:** Undergraduate **Funds Available:** No specific amount.
Eligibility Requirements: Applicant must be a resident of Greater Cincinnati, and attending college as a full-time student. **Application Requirements:** Applicants must submit a completed scholarship application form along with a copy of recent transcript; expected Family Contribution (EFC) from Student Aid Report (SAR), which comes as a result of filing the FAFSA; and a copy of Financial Aid Award Letter from the chosen college to be attended. **Additional Information:** Faxed applications will not be considered. **Deadline for Receipt:** April 30.

507 ■ CINCINNATI SCHOLARSHIP FOUNDATION
652 Main St.
Cincinnati, OH 45202
Tel: (513)345-6701
Fax: (513)345-6705
Web Site: http://www.cincinnatischolarshipfoundation.org
To help students from Greater Cincinnati area to achieve the dream of a college education.
Title of Award: CSF Christopher Todd Grant Memorial Scholarships **Area, Field, or Subject:** General studies. **Level of Education for which Award is Granted:** Undergraduate **Funds Available:** No specific amount.
Eligibility Requirements: Applicant must be a resident of Greater Cincinnati, and attending college as a full-time student. **Application Requirements:** Applicants must submit a completed scholarship application form along with a copy of recent transcript; expected Family Contribution (EFC) from Student Aid Report (SAR), which comes as a result of filing the FAFSA; and a copy of Financial Aid Award Letter from the chosen college to be attended. **Additional Information:** Faxed applications will not be considered. **Deadline for Receipt:** April 30.

508 ■ CINCINNATI SCHOLARSHIP FOUNDATION
652 Main St.
Cincinnati, OH 45202
Tel: (513)345-6701
Fax: (513)345-6705
Web Site: http://www.cincinnatischolarshipfoundation.org
To help students from Greater Cincinnati area to achieve the dream of a college education.

Title of Award: CSF Cincinnati Bell Scholarships **Area, Field, or Subject:** General studies. **Level of Education for which Award is Granted:** Undergraduate **Funds Available:** No specific amount.
Eligibility Requirements: Applicant must be a resident of Greater Cincinnati, and attending college as a full-time student. **Application Requirements:** Applicants must submit a completed scholarship application form along with a copy of recent transcript; expected Family Contribution (EFC) from Student Aid Report (SAR), which comes as a result of filing the FAFSA; and a copy of Financial Aid Award Letter from the chosen college to be attended. **Additional Information:** Faxed applications will not be considered. **Deadline for Receipt:** April 30.

509 ■ CINCINNATI SCHOLARSHIP FOUNDATION
652 Main St.
Cincinnati, OH 45202
Tel: (513)345-6701
Fax: (513)345-6705
Web Site: http://www.cincinnatischolarshipfoundation.org
To help students from Greater Cincinnati area to achieve the dream of a college education.
Title of Award: CSF Cincinnati Financial Corporation Scholarships **Area, Field, or Subject:** General studies. **Level of Education for which Award is Granted:** Undergraduate **Funds Available:** No specific amount.
Eligibility Requirements: Applicant must be a resident of Greater Cincinnati, and attending college as a full-time student. **Application Requirements:** Applicants must submit a completed scholarship application form along with a copy of recent transcript; expected Family Contribution (EFC) from Student Aid Report (SAR), which comes as a result of filing the FAFSA; and a copy of Financial Aid Award Letter from the chosen college to be attended. **Additional Information:** Faxed applications will not be considered. **Deadline for Receipt:** April 30.

510 ■ CINCINNATI SCHOLARSHIP FOUNDATION
652 Main St.
Cincinnati, OH 45202
Tel: (513)345-6701
Fax: (513)345-6705
Web Site: http://www.cincinnatischolarshipfoundation.org
To help students from Greater Cincinnati area to achieve the dream of a college education.
Title of Award: CSF Cincinnati Milacron Scholarships **Area, Field, or Subject:** General studies. **Level of Education for which Award is Granted:** Undergraduate **Funds Available:** No specific amount.
Eligibility Requirements: Applicant must be a resident of Greater Cincinnati, and attending college as a full-time student. **Application Requirements:** Applicants must submit a completed scholarship application form along with a copy of recent transcript; expected Family Contribution (EFC) from Student Aid Report (SAR), which comes as a result of filing the FAFSA; and a copy of Financial Aid Award Letter from the chosen college to be attended. **Additional Information:** Faxed applications will not be considered. **Deadline for Receipt:** April 30.

511 ■ CINCINNATI SCHOLARSHIP FOUNDATION
652 Main St.
Cincinnati, OH 45202
Tel: (513)345-6701
Fax: (513)345-6705
Web Site: http://www.cincinnatischolarshipfoundation.org
To help students from Greater Cincinnati area to achieve the dream of a college education.
Title of Award: CSF Corwin Nixon Scholarships **Area, Field, or Subject:** General studies. **Level of Education for which Award is Granted:** Undergraduate **Funds Available:** No specific amount.
Eligibility Requirements: Applicant must be a resident of Greater Cincinnati, and attending college as a full-time student. **Application Requirements:** Applicants must submit a completed scholarship application form along with a copy of recent transcript; expected Family Contribution (EFC) from Student Aid Report (SAR), which comes as a result of filing the FAFSA; and a copy of Financial Aid Award Letter from the chosen college to be attended. **Additional Information:** Faxed applications will not be considered. **Deadline for Receipt:** April 30.

512 ■ CINCINNATI SCHOLARSHIP FOUNDATION
652 Main St.
Cincinnati, OH 45202
Tel: (513)345-6701
Fax: (513)345-6705
Web Site: http://www.cincinnatischolarshipfoundation.org
To help students from Greater Cincinnati area to achieve the dream of a college education.
Title of Award: CSF Crosset Family Scholarships **Area, Field, or Subject:** General studies. **Level of Education for which Award is Granted:** Undergraduate **Funds Available:** No specific amount.
Eligibility Requirements: Applicant must be a resident of Greater Cincinnati, and attending college as a full-time student. **Application Requirements:** Applicants must submit a completed scholarship application form along with a copy of recent transcript; expected Family Contribution (EFC) from Student Aid Report (SAR), which comes as a result of filing the FAFSA; and a copy of Financial Aid Award Letter from the chosen college to be attended. **Additional Information:** Faxed applications will not be considered. **Deadline for Receipt:** April 30.

513 ■ CINCINNATI SCHOLARSHIP FOUNDATION
652 Main St.
Cincinnati, OH 45202
Tel: (513)345-6701
Fax: (513)345-6705
Web Site: http://www.cincinnatischolarshipfoundation.org
To help students from Greater Cincinnati area to achieve the dream of a college education.
Title of Award: CSF Dater Foundation Scholarships **Area, Field, or Subject:** General studies. **Level of Education for which Award is Granted:** Undergraduate **Funds Available:** No specific amount.
Eligibility Requirements: Applicant must be a resident of Greater Cincinnati, and attending college as a full-time student. **Application Requirements:** Applicants must submit a completed scholarship application form along with a copy of recent transcript; expected Family Contribution (EFC) from Student Aid Report (SAR), which comes as a result of filing the FAFSA; and a copy of Financial Aid Award Letter from the chosen college to be attended. **Additional Information:** Faxed applications will not be considered. **Deadline for Receipt:** April 30.

514 ■ CINCINNATI SCHOLARSHIP FOUNDATION
652 Main St.
Cincinnati, OH 45202
Tel: (513)345-6701
Fax: (513)345-6705
Web Site: http://www.cincinnatischolarshipfoundation.org
To help students from Greater Cincinnati area to achieve the dream of a college education.
Title of Award: CSF David J. Joseph Company Scholarships **Area, Field, or Subject:** General studies. **Level of Education for which Award is Granted:** Undergraduate **Funds Available:** No specific amount.
Eligibility Requirements: Applicant must be a resident of Greater Cincinnati, and attending college as a full-time student. **Application Requirements:** Applicants must submit a completed scholarship application form along with a copy of recent transcript; expected Family Contribution (EFC) from Student Aid Report (SAR), which comes as a result of filing the FAFSA; and a copy of Financial Aid Award Letter from the chosen college to be attended. **Additional Information:** Faxed applications will not be considered. **Deadline for Receipt:** April 30.

515 ■ CINCINNATI SCHOLARSHIP FOUNDATION
652 Main St.
Cincinnati, OH 45202
Tel: (513)345-6701
Fax: (513)345-6705
Web Site: http://www.cincinnatischolarshipfoundation.org
To help students from Greater Cincinnati area to achieve the dream of a college education.
Title of Award: CSF Dee Wacksman Memorial Scholarships **Area, Field, or Subject:** General studies. **Level of Education for which Award is Granted:** Undergraduate **Funds Available:** No specific amount.
Eligibility Requirements: Applicant must be a resident of Greater Cincinnati, and attending college as a full-time student. **Application Require-**

ments: Applicants must submit a completed scholarship application form along with a copy of recent transcript; expected Family Contribution (EFC) from Student Aid Report (SAR), which comes as a result of filing the FAFSA; and a copy of Financial Aid Award Letter from the chosen college to be attended. **Additional Information:** Faxed applications will not be considered. **Deadline for Receipt:** April 30.

516 ■ CINCINNATI SCHOLARSHIP FOUNDATION
652 Main St.
Cincinnati, OH 45202
Tel: (513)345-6701
Fax: (513)345-6705
Web Site: http://www.cincinnatischolarshipfoundation.org
To help students from Greater Cincinnati area to achieve the dream of a college education.
Title of Award: CSF Duke Energy Scholarships **Area, Field, or Subject:** General studies. **Level of Education for which Award is Granted:** Undergraduate **Funds Available:** No specific amount.
Eligibility Requirements: Applicant must be a resident of Greater Cincinnati, and attending college as a full-time student. **Application Requirements:** Applicants must submit a completed scholarship application form along with a copy of recent transcript; expected Family Contribution (EFC) from Student Aid Report (SAR), which comes as a result of filing the FAFSA; and a copy of Financial Aid Award Letter from the chosen college to be attended. **Additional Information:** Faxed applications will not be considered. **Deadline for Receipt:** April 30.

517 ■ CINCINNATI SCHOLARSHIP FOUNDATION
652 Main St.
Cincinnati, OH 45202
Tel: (513)345-6701
Fax: (513)345-6705
Web Site: http://www.cincinnatischolarshipfoundation.org
To help students from Greater Cincinnati area to achieve the dream of a college education.
Title of Award: CSF Dwight Hibbard Scholarships **Area, Field, or Subject:** General studies. **Level of Education for which Award is Granted:** Undergraduate **Funds Available:** No specific amount.
Eligibility Requirements: Applicant must be a resident of Greater Cincinnati, and attending college as a full-time student. **Application Requirements:** Applicants must submit a completed scholarship application form along with a copy of recent transcript; expected Family Contribution (EFC) from Student Aid Report (SAR), which comes as a result of filing the FAFSA; and a copy of Financial Aid Award Letter from the chosen college to be attended. **Additional Information:** Faxed applications will not be considered. **Deadline for Receipt:** April 30.

518 ■ CINCINNATI SCHOLARSHIP FOUNDATION
652 Main St.
Cincinnati, OH 45202
Tel: (513)345-6701
Fax: (513)345-6705
Web Site: http://www.cincinnatischolarshipfoundation.org
To help students from Greater Cincinnati area to achieve the dream of a college education.
Title of Award: CSF Ella Wilson Johnson Scholarships **Area, Field, or Subject:** General studies. **Level of Education for which Award is Granted:** Undergraduate **Funds Available:** No specific amount.
Eligibility Requirements: Applicant must be a resident of Greater Cincinnati, and attending college as a full-time student. **Application Requirements:** Applicants must submit a completed scholarship application form along with a copy of recent transcript; expected Family Contribution (EFC) from Student Aid Report (SAR), which comes as a result of filing the FAFSA; and a copy of Financial Aid Award Letter from the chosen college to be attended. **Additional Information:** Faxed applications will not be considered. **Deadline for Receipt:** April 30.

519 ■ CINCINNATI SCHOLARSHIP FOUNDATION
652 Main St.
Cincinnati, OH 45202
Tel: (513)345-6701
Fax: (513)345-6705
Web Site: http://www.cincinnatischolarshipfoundation.org

To help students from Greater Cincinnati area to achieve the dream of a college education.
Title of Award: CSF Estelle Davis Memorial Scholarships **Area, Field, or Subject:** General studies. **Level of Education for which Award is Granted:** Undergraduate **Funds Available:** No specific amount.
Eligibility Requirements: Applicant must be a resident of Greater Cincinnati, and attending college as a full-time student. **Application Requirements:** Applicants must submit a completed scholarship application form along with a copy of recent transcript; expected Family Contribution (EFC) from Student Aid Report (SAR), which comes as a result of filing the FAFSA; and a copy of Financial Aid Award Letter from the chosen college to be attended. **Additional Information:** Faxed applications will not be considered. **Deadline for Receipt:** April 30.

520 ■ CINCINNATI SCHOLARSHIP FOUNDATION
652 Main St.
Cincinnati, OH 45202
Tel: (513)345-6701
Fax: (513)345-6705
Web Site: http://www.cincinnatischolarshipfoundation.org
To help students from Greater Cincinnati area to achieve the dream of a college education.
Title of Award: CSF Eugene Carroll Scholarships **Area, Field, or Subject:** General studies. **Level of Education for which Award is Granted:** Undergraduate **Funds Available:** No specific amount.
Eligibility Requirements: Applicant must be a resident of Greater Cincinnati, and attending college as a full-time student. **Application Requirements:** Applicants must submit a completed scholarship application form along with a copy of recent transcript; expected Family Contribution (EFC) from Student Aid Report (SAR), which comes as a result of filing the FAFSA; and a copy of Financial Aid Award Letter from the chosen college to be attended. **Additional Information:** Faxed applications will not be considered. **Deadline for Receipt:** April 30.

521 ■ CINCINNATI SCHOLARSHIP FOUNDATION
652 Main St.
Cincinnati, OH 45202
Tel: (513)345-6701
Fax: (513)345-6705
Web Site: http://www.cincinnatischolarshipfoundation.org
To help students from Greater Cincinnati area to achieve the dream of a college education.
Title of Award: CSF E.W. Scripps Scholarships **Area, Field, or Subject:** General studies. **Level of Education for which Award is Granted:** Undergraduate **Funds Available:** No specific amount.
Eligibility Requirements: Applicant must be a resident of Greater Cincinnati, and attending college as a full-time student. **Application Requirements:** Applicants must submit a completed scholarship application form along with a copy of recent transcript; expected Family Contribution (EFC) from Student Aid Report (SAR), which comes as a result of filing the FAFSA; and a copy of Financial Aid Award Letter from the chosen college to be attended. **Additional Information:** Faxed applications will not be considered. **Deadline for Receipt:** April 30.

522 ■ CINCINNATI SCHOLARSHIP FOUNDATION
652 Main St.
Cincinnati, OH 45202
Tel: (513)345-6701
Fax: (513)345-6705
Web Site: http://www.cincinnatischolarshipfoundation.org
To help students from Greater Cincinnati area to achieve the dream of a college education.
Title of Award: CSF Farmer Family Foundation Scholarships **Area, Field, or Subject:** General studies. **Level of Education for which Award is Granted:** Undergraduate **Funds Available:** No specific amount.
Eligibility Requirements: Applicant must be a resident of Greater Cincinnati, and attending college as a full-time student. **Application Requirements:** Applicants must submit a completed scholarship application form along with a copy of recent transcript; expected Family Contribution (EFC) from Student Aid Report (SAR), which comes as a result of filing the FAFSA; and a copy of Financial Aid Award Letter from the chosen college to be attended. **Additional Information:** Faxed applications will not be considered. **Deadline for Receipt:** April 30.

523 ■ CINCINNATI SCHOLARSHIP FOUNDATION
652 Main St.
Cincinnati, OH 45202
Tel: (513)345-6701
Fax: (513)345-6705
Web Site: http://www.cincinnatischolarshipfoundation.org
To help students from Greater Cincinnati area to achieve the dream of a college education.
Title of Award: CSF Fifth Third Bank Combined Scholarships **Area, Field, or Subject:** General studies. **Level of Education for which Award is Granted:** Undergraduate **Funds Available:** No specific amount.
Eligibility Requirements: Applicant must be a resident of Greater Cincinnati, and attending college as a full-time student. **Application Requirements:** Applicants must submit a completed scholarship application form along with a copy of recent transcript; expected Family Contribution (EFC) from Student Aid Report (SAR), which comes as a result of filing the FAFSA; and a copy of Financial Aid Award Letter from the chosen college to be attended. **Additional Information:** Faxed applications will not be considered. **Deadline for Receipt:** April 30.

524 ■ CINCINNATI SCHOLARSHIP FOUNDATION
652 Main St.
Cincinnati, OH 45202
Tel: (513)345-6701
Fax: (513)345-6705
Web Site: http://www.cincinnatischolarshipfoundation.org
To help students from Greater Cincinnati area to achieve the dream of a college education.
Title of Award: CSF Fletemeyer Family Scholarships **Area, Field, or Subject:** General studies. **Level of Education for which Award is Granted:** Undergraduate **Funds Available:** No specific amount.
Eligibility Requirements: Applicant must be a resident of Greater Cincinnati, and attending college as a full-time student. **Application Requirements:** Applicants must submit a completed scholarship application form along with a copy of recent transcript; expected Family Contribution (EFC) from Student Aid Report (SAR), which comes as a result of filing the FAFSA; and a copy of Financial Aid Award Letter from the chosen college to be attended. **Additional Information:** Faxed applications will not be considered. **Deadline for Receipt:** April 30.

525 ■ CINCINNATI SCHOLARSHIP FOUNDATION
652 Main St.
Cincinnati, OH 45202
Tel: (513)345-6701
Fax: (513)345-6705
Web Site: http://www.cincinnatischolarshipfoundation.org
To help students from Greater Cincinnati area to achieve the dream of a college education.
Title of Award: CSF Florette B. Hoffheimer Scholarships **Area, Field, or Subject:** General studies. **Level of Education for which Award is Granted:** Undergraduate **Funds Available:** No specific amount.
Eligibility Requirements: Applicant must be a resident of Greater Cincinnati, and attending college as a full-time student. **Application Requirements:** Applicants must submit a completed scholarship application form along with a copy of recent transcript; expected Family Contribution (EFC) from Student Aid Report (SAR), which comes as a result of filing the FAFSA; and a copy of Financial Aid Award Letter from the chosen college to be attended. **Additional Information:** Faxed applications will not be considered. **Deadline for Receipt:** April 30.

526 ■ CINCINNATI SCHOLARSHIP FOUNDATION
652 Main St.
Cincinnati, OH 45202
Tel: (513)345-6701
Fax: (513)345-6705
Web Site: http://www.cincinnatischolarshipfoundation.org
To help students from Greater Cincinnati area to achieve the dream of a college education.
Title of Award: CSF Frank Foster Skillman Scholarships **Area, Field, or Subject:** General studies. **Level of Education for which Award is Granted:** Undergraduate **Funds Available:** No specific amount.
Eligibility Requirements: Applicant must be a resident of Greater Cincinnati, and attending college as a full-time student. **Application Require-**

ments: Applicants must submit a completed scholarship application form along with a copy of recent transcript; expected Family Contribution (EFC) from Student Aid Report (SAR), which comes as a result of filing the FAFSA; and a copy of Financial Aid Award Letter from the chosen college to be attended. **Additional Information:** Faxed applications will not be considered. **Deadline for Receipt:** April 30.

527 ■ CINCINNATI SCHOLARSHIP FOUNDATION
652 Main St.
Cincinnati, OH 45202
Tel: (513)345-6701
Fax: (513)345-6705
Web Site: http://www.cincinnatischolarshipfoundation.org
To help students from Greater Cincinnati area to achieve the dream of a college education.
Title of Award: CSF Gardner Foundation Scholarships **Area, Field, or Subject:** General studies. **Level of Education for which Award is Granted:** Undergraduate **Funds Available:** No specific amount.
Eligibility Requirements: Applicant must be a resident of Greater Cincinnati, and attending college as a full-time student. **Application Requirements:** Applicants must submit a completed scholarship application form along with a copy of recent transcript; expected Family Contribution (EFC) from Student Aid Report (SAR), which comes as a result of filing the FAFSA; and a copy of Financial Aid Award Letter from the chosen college to be attended. **Additional Information:** Faxed applications will not be considered. **Deadline for Receipt:** April 30.

528 ■ CINCINNATI SCHOLARSHIP FOUNDATION
652 Main St.
Cincinnati, OH 45202
Tel: (513)345-6701
Fax: (513)345-6705
Web Site: http://www.cincinnatischolarshipfoundation.org
To help students from Greater Cincinnati area to achieve the dream of a college education.
Title of Award: CSF G.E. Aircraft Engines Scholarships **Area, Field, or Subject:** General studies. **Level of Education for which Award is Granted:** Undergraduate **Funds Available:** No specific amount.
Eligibility Requirements: Applicant must be a resident of Greater Cincinnati, and attending college as a full-time student. **Application Requirements:** Applicants must submit a completed scholarship application form along with a copy of recent transcript; expected Family Contribution (EFC) from Student Aid Report (SAR), which comes as a result of filing the FAFSA; and a copy of Financial Aid Award Letter from the chosen college to be attended. **Additional Information:** Faxed applications will not be considered. **Deadline for Receipt:** April 30.

529 ■ CINCINNATI SCHOLARSHIP FOUNDATION
652 Main St.
Cincinnati, OH 45202
Tel: (513)345-6701
Fax: (513)345-6705
Web Site: http://www.cincinnatischolarshipfoundation.org
To help students from Greater Cincinnati area to achieve the dream of a college education.
Title of Award: CSF George and Amy Polley Scholarships **Area, Field, or Subject:** General studies. **Level of Education for which Award is Granted:** Undergraduate **Funds Available:** No specific amount.
Eligibility Requirements: Applicant must be a resident of Greater Cincinnati, and attending college as a full-time student. **Application Requirements:** Applicants must submit a completed scholarship application form along with a copy of recent transcript; expected Family Contribution (EFC) from Student Aid Report (SAR), which comes as a result of filing the FAFSA; and a copy of Financial Aid Award Letter from the chosen college to be attended. **Additional Information:** Faxed applications will not be considered. **Deadline for Receipt:** April 30.

530 ■ CINCINNATI SCHOLARSHIP FOUNDATION
652 Main St.
Cincinnati, OH 45202
Tel: (513)345-6701
Fax: (513)345-6705
Web Site: http://www.cincinnatischolarshipfoundation.org

To help students from Greater Cincinnati area to achieve the dream of a college education.
Title of Award: CSF Goldman, Sachs and Company Scholarships **Area, Field, or Subject:** General studies. **Level of Education for which Award is Granted:** Undergraduate **Funds Available:** No specific amount.
Eligibility Requirements: Applicant must be a resident of Greater Cincinnati, and attending college as a full-time student. **Application Requirements:** Applicants must submit a completed scholarship application form along with a copy of recent transcript; expected Family Contribution (EFC) from Student Aid Report (SAR), which comes as a result of filing the FAFSA; and a copy of Financial Aid Award Letter from the chosen college to be attended. **Additional Information:** Faxed applications will not be considered. **Deadline for Receipt:** April 30.

531 ■ CINCINNATI SCHOLARSHIP FOUNDATION
652 Main St.
Cincinnati, OH 45202
Tel: (513)345-6701
Fax: (513)345-6705
Web Site: http://www.cincinnatischolarshipfoundation.org
To help students from Greater Cincinnati area to achieve the dream of a college education.
Title of Award: CSF Greater Cincinnati Scholarships Association **Area, Field, or Subject:** General studies. **Level of Education for which Award is Granted:** Undergraduate **Funds Available:** No specific amount.
Eligibility Requirements: Applicant must be a resident of Greater Cincinnati, and attending college as a full-time student. **Application Requirements:** Applicants must submit a completed scholarship application form along with a copy of recent transcript; expected Family Contribution (EFC) from Student Aid Report (SAR), which comes as a result of filing the FAFSA; and a copy of Financial Aid Award Letter from the chosen college to be attended. **Additional Information:** Faxed applications will not be considered. **Deadline for Receipt:** April 30.

532 ■ CINCINNATI SCHOLARSHIP FOUNDATION
652 Main St.
Cincinnati, OH 45202
Tel: (513)345-6701
Fax: (513)345-6705
Web Site: http://www.cincinnatischolarshipfoundation.org
To help students from Greater Cincinnati area to achieve the dream of a college education.
Title of Award: CSF H.C. Schott Foundation Scholarships **Area, Field, or Subject:** General studies. **Level of Education for which Award is Granted:** Undergraduate **Funds Available:** No specific amount.
Eligibility Requirements: Applicant must be a resident of Greater Cincinnati, and attending college as a full-time student. **Application Requirements:** Applicants must submit a completed scholarship application form along with a copy of recent transcript; expected Family Contribution (EFC) from Student Aid Report (SAR), which comes as a result of filing the FAFSA; and a copy of Financial Aid Award Letter from the chosen college to be attended. **Additional Information:** Faxed applications will not be considered. **Deadline for Receipt:** April 30.

533 ■ CINCINNATI SCHOLARSHIP FOUNDATION
652 Main St.
Cincinnati, OH 45202
Tel: (513)345-6701
Fax: (513)345-6705
Web Site: http://www.cincinnatischolarshipfoundation.org
To help students from Greater Cincinnati area to achieve the dream of a college education.
Title of Award: CSF HCRTA/Glen O. and Wyllabeth Wise Scholarships **Area, Field, or Subject:** General studies. **Level of Education for which Award is Granted:** Undergraduate **Funds Available:** No specific amount.
Eligibility Requirements: Applicant must be a resident of Greater Cincinnati, and attending college as a full-time student. **Application Requirements:** Applicants must submit a completed scholarship application form along with a copy of recent transcript; expected Family Contribution (EFC) from Student Aid Report (SAR), which comes as a result of filing the

FAFSA; and a copy of Financial Aid Award Letter from the chosen college to be attended. **Additional Information:** Faxed applications will not be considered. **Deadline for Receipt:** April 30.

534 ■ CINCINNATI SCHOLARSHIP FOUNDATION
652 Main St.
Cincinnati, OH 45202
Tel: (513)345-6701
Fax: (513)345-6705
Web Site: http://www.cincinnatischolarshipfoundation.org
To help students from Greater Cincinnati area to achieve the dream of a college education.
Title of Award: CSF Heidelberg Distributing Co. Scholarships **Area, Field, or Subject:** General studies. **Level of Education for which Award is Granted:** Undergraduate **Funds Available:** No specific amount.
Eligibility Requirements: Applicant must be a resident of Greater Cincinnati, and attending college as a full-time student. **Application Requirements:** Applicants must submit a completed scholarship application form along with a copy of recent transcript; expected Family Contribution (EFC) from Student Aid Report (SAR), which comes as a result of filing the FAFSA; and a copy of Financial Aid Award Letter from the chosen college to be attended. **Additional Information:** Faxed applications will not be considered. **Deadline for Receipt:** April 30.

535 ■ CINCINNATI SCHOLARSHIP FOUNDATION
652 Main St.
Cincinnati, OH 45202
Tel: (513)345-6701
Fax: (513)345-6705
Web Site: http://www.cincinnatischolarshipfoundation.org
To help students from Greater Cincinnati area to achieve the dream of a college education.
Title of Award: CSF Heinz Pet Products Scholarships **Area, Field, or Subject:** General studies. **Level of Education for which Award is Granted:** Undergraduate **Funds Available:** No specific amount.
Eligibility Requirements: Applicant must be a resident of Greater Cincinnati, and attending college as a full-time student. **Application Requirements:** Applicants must submit a completed scholarship application form along with a copy of recent transcript; expected Family Contribution (EFC) from Student Aid Report (SAR), which comes as a result of filing the FAFSA; and a copy of Financial Aid Award Letter from the chosen college to be attended. **Additional Information:** Faxed applications will not be considered. **Deadline for Receipt:** April 30.

536 ■ CINCINNATI SCHOLARSHIP FOUNDATION
652 Main St.
Cincinnati, OH 45202
Tel: (513)345-6701
Fax: (513)345-6705
Web Site: http://www.cincinnatischolarshipfoundation.org
To help students from Greater Cincinnati area to achieve the dream of a college education.
Title of Award: CSF Helen Steiner Rice Scholarships **Area, Field, or Subject:** General studies. **Level of Education for which Award is Granted:** Undergraduate **Funds Available:** No specific amount.
Eligibility Requirements: Applicant must be a resident of Greater Cincinnati, and attending college as a full-time student. **Application Requirements:** Applicants must submit a completed scholarship application form along with a copy of recent transcript; expected Family Contribution (EFC) from Student Aid Report (SAR), which comes as a result of filing the FAFSA; and a copy of Financial Aid Award Letter from the chosen college to be attended. **Additional Information:** Faxed applications will not be considered. **Deadline for Receipt:** April 30.

537 ■ CINCINNATI SCHOLARSHIP FOUNDATION
652 Main St.
Cincinnati, OH 45202
Tel: (513)345-6701
Fax: (513)345-6705
Web Site: http://www.cincinnatischolarshipfoundation.org
To help students from Greater Cincinnati area to achieve the dream of a college education.

Title of Award: CSF Johnny Bench Scholarships **Area, Field, or Subject:** General studies. **Level of Education for which Award is Granted:** Undergraduate **Funds Available:** No specific amount.
Eligibility Requirements: Applicant must be a resident of Greater Cincinnati, and attending college as a full-time student. **Application Requirements:** Applicants must submit a completed scholarship application form along with a copy of recent transcript; expected Family Contribution (EFC) from Student Aid Report (SAR), which comes as a result of filing the FAFSA; and a copy of Financial Aid Award Letter from the chosen college to be attended. **Additional Information:** Faxed applications will not be considered. **Deadline for Receipt:** April 30.

538 ■ CINCINNATI SCHOLARSHIP FOUNDATION
652 Main St.
Cincinnati, OH 45202
Tel: (513)345-6701
Fax: (513)345-6705
Web Site: http://www.cincinnatischolarshipfoundation.org
To help students from Greater Cincinnati area to achieve the dream of a college education.
Title of Award: CSF Joseph S. Stern, Jr. Scholarships **Area, Field, or Subject:** General studies. **Level of Education for which Award is Granted:** Undergraduate **Funds Available:** No specific amount.
Eligibility Requirements: Applicant must be a resident of Greater Cincinnati, and attending college as a full-time student. **Application Requirements:** Applicants must submit a completed scholarship application form along with a copy of recent transcript; expected Family Contribution (EFC) from Student Aid Report (SAR), which comes as a result of filing the FAFSA; and a copy of Financial Aid Award Letter from the chosen college to be attended. **Additional Information:** Faxed applications will not be considered. **Deadline for Receipt:** April 30.

539 ■ CINCINNATI SCHOLARSHIP FOUNDATION
652 Main St.
Cincinnati, OH 45202
Tel: (513)345-6701
Fax: (513)345-6705
Web Site: http://www.cincinnatischolarshipfoundation.org
To help students from Greater Cincinnati area to achieve the dream of a college education.
Title of Award: CSF Judge Benjamin Schwartz Scholarships **Area, Field, or Subject:** General studies. **Level of Education for which Award is Granted:** Undergraduate **Funds Available:** No specific amount.
Eligibility Requirements: Applicant must be a resident of Greater Cincinnati, and attending college as a full-time student. **Application Requirements:** Applicants must submit a completed scholarship application form along with a copy of recent transcript; expected Family Contribution (EFC) from Student Aid Report (SAR), which comes as a result of filing the FAFSA; and a copy of Financial Aid Award Letter from the chosen college to be attended. **Additional Information:** Faxed applications will not be considered. **Deadline for Receipt:** April 30.

540 ■ CINCINNATI SCHOLARSHIP FOUNDATION
652 Main St.
Cincinnati, OH 45202
Tel: (513)345-6701
Fax: (513)345-6705
Web Site: http://www.cincinnatischolarshipfoundation.org
To help students from Greater Cincinnati area to achieve the dream of a college education.
Title of Award: CSF Juilfs Foundation Scholarships **Area, Field, or Subject:** General studies. **Level of Education for which Award is Granted:** Undergraduate **Funds Available:** No specific amount.
Eligibility Requirements: Applicant must be a resident of Greater Cincinnati, and attending college as a full-time student. **Application Requirements:** Applicants must submit a completed scholarship application form along with a copy of recent transcript; expected Family Contribution (EFC) from Student Aid Report (SAR), which comes as a result of filing the FAFSA; and a copy of Financial Aid Award Letter from the chosen college to be attended. **Additional Information:** Faxed applications will not be considered. **Deadline for Receipt:** April 30.

541 ■ CINCINNATI SCHOLARSHIP FOUNDATION
652 Main St.
Cincinnati, OH 45202

Tel: (513)345-6701
Fax: (513)345-6705
Web Site: http://www.cincinnatischolarshipfoundation.org
To help students from Greater Cincinnati area to achieve the dream of a college education.
Title of Award: CSF Kroger Cincinnati/Dayton Scholarships **Area, Field, or Subject:** General studies. **Level of Education for which Award is Granted:** Undergraduate **Funds Available:** No specific amount.
Eligibility Requirements: Applicant must be a resident of Greater Cincinnati, and attending college as a full-time student. **Application Requirements:** Applicants must submit a completed scholarship application form along with a copy of recent transcript; expected Family Contribution (EFC) from Student Aid Report (SAR), which comes as a result of filing the FAFSA; and a copy of Financial Aid Award Letter from the chosen college to be attended. **Additional Information:** Faxed applications will not be considered. **Deadline for Receipt:** April 30.

542 ■ CINCINNATI SCHOLARSHIP FOUNDATION
652 Main St.
Cincinnati, OH 45202
Tel: (513)345-6701
Fax: (513)345-6705
Web Site: http://www.cincinnatischolarshipfoundation.org
To help students from Greater Cincinnati area to achieve the dream of a college education.
Title of Award: CSF L and T Woolfolk Memorial Scholarships **Area, Field, or Subject:** General studies. **Level of Education for which Award is Granted:** Undergraduate **Funds Available:** No specific amount.
Eligibility Requirements: Applicant must be a resident of Greater Cincinnati, and attending college as a full-time student. **Application Requirements:** Applicants must submit a completed scholarship application form along with a copy of recent transcript; expected Family Contribution (EFC) from Student Aid Report (SAR), which comes as a result of filing the FAFSA; and a copy of Financial Aid Award Letter from the chosen college to be attended. **Additional Information:** Faxed applications will not be considered. **Deadline for Receipt:** April 30.

543 ■ CINCINNATI SCHOLARSHIP FOUNDATION
652 Main St.
Cincinnati, OH 45202
Tel: (513)345-6701
Fax: (513)345-6705
Web Site: http://www.cincinnatischolarshipfoundation.org
To help students from Greater Cincinnati area to achieve the dream of a college education.
Title of Award: CSF Lazarus/Federated Scholarships **Area, Field, or Subject:** General studies. **Level of Education for which Award is Granted:** Undergraduate **Funds Available:** No specific amount.
Eligibility Requirements: Applicant must be a resident of Greater Cincinnati, and attending college as a full-time student. **Application Requirements:** Applicants must submit a completed scholarship application form along with a copy of recent transcript; expected Family Contribution (EFC) from Student Aid Report (SAR), which comes as a result of filing the FAFSA; and a copy of Financial Aid Award Letter from the chosen college to be attended. **Additional Information:** Faxed applications will not be considered. **Deadline for Receipt:** April 30.

544 ■ CINCINNATI SCHOLARSHIP FOUNDATION
652 Main St.
Cincinnati, OH 45202
Tel: (513)345-6701
Fax: (513)345-6705
Web Site: http://www.cincinnatischolarshipfoundation.org
To help students from Greater Cincinnati area to achieve the dream of a college education.
Title of Award: CSF L.B. Zapoleon Scholarships **Area, Field, or Subject:** General studies. **Level of Education for which Award is Granted:** Undergraduate **Funds Available:** No specific amount.
Eligibility Requirements: Applicant must be a resident of Greater Cincinnati, and attending college as a full-time student. **Application Requirements:** Applicants must submit a completed scholarship application form along with a copy of recent transcript; expected Family Contribution (EFC)

from Student Aid Report (SAR), which comes as a result of filing the FAFSA; and a copy of Financial Aid Award Letter from the chosen college to be attended. **Additional Information:** Faxed applications will not be considered. **Deadline for Receipt:** April 30.

545 ■ CINCINNATI SCHOLARSHIP FOUNDATION
652 Main St.
Cincinnati, OH 45202
Tel: (513)345-6701
Fax: (513)345-6705
Web Site: http://www.cincinnatischolarshipfoundation.org
To help students from Greater Cincinnati area to achieve the dream of a college education.
Title of Award: CSF Lowe Simpson Scholarships **Area, Field, or Subject:** General studies. **Level of Education for which Award is Granted:** Undergraduate **Funds Available:** No specific amount.
Eligibility Requirements: Applicant must be a resident of Greater Cincinnati, and attending college as a full-time student. **Application Requirements:** Applicants must submit a completed scholarship application form along with a copy of recent transcript; expected Family Contribution (EFC) from Student Aid Report (SAR), which comes as a result of filing the FAFSA; and a copy of Financial Aid Award Letter from the chosen college to be attended. **Additional Information:** Faxed applications will not be considered. **Deadline for Receipt:** April 30.

546 ■ CINCINNATI SCHOLARSHIP FOUNDATION
652 Main St.
Cincinnati, OH 45202
Tel: (513)345-6701
Fax: (513)345-6705
Web Site: http://www.cincinnatischolarshipfoundation.org
To help students from Greater Cincinnati area to achieve the dream of a college education.
Title of Award: CSF Lyle and Arlene Everingham Scholarships **Area, Field, or Subject:** General studies. **Level of Education for which Award is Granted:** Undergraduate **Funds Available:** No specific amount.
Eligibility Requirements: Applicant must be a resident of Greater Cincinnati, and attending college as a full-time student. **Application Requirements:** Applicants must submit a completed scholarship application form along with a copy of recent transcript; expected Family Contribution (EFC) from Student Aid Report (SAR), which comes as a result of filing the FAFSA; and a copy of Financial Aid Award Letter from the chosen college to be attended. **Additional Information:** Faxed applications will not be considered. **Deadline for Receipt:** April 30.

547 ■ CINCINNATI SCHOLARSHIP FOUNDATION
652 Main St.
Cincinnati, OH 45202
Tel: (513)345-6701
Fax: (513)345-6705
Web Site: http://www.cincinnatischolarshipfoundation.org
To help students from Greater Cincinnati area to achieve the dream of a college education.
Title of Award: CSF Lyle Everingham Scholarships **Area, Field, or Subject:** General studies. **Level of Education for which Award is Granted:** Undergraduate **Funds Available:** No specific amount.
Eligibility Requirements: Applicant must be a resident of Greater Cincinnati, and attending college as a full-time student. **Application Requirements:** Applicants must submit a completed scholarship application form along with a copy of recent transcript; expected Family Contribution (EFC) from Student Aid Report (SAR), which comes as a result of filing the FAFSA; and a copy of Financial Aid Award Letter from the chosen college to be attended. **Additional Information:** Faxed applications will not be considered. **Deadline for Receipt:** April 30.

548 ■ CINCINNATI SCHOLARSHIP FOUNDATION
652 Main St.
Cincinnati, OH 45202
Tel: (513)345-6701
Fax: (513)345-6705
Web Site: http://www.cincinnatischolarshipfoundation.org

To help students from Greater Cincinnati area to achieve the dream of a college education.
Title of Award: CSF M and E Brown Scholarships **Area, Field, or Subject:** General studies. **Level of Education for which Award is Granted:** Undergraduate **Funds Available:** No specific amount.
Eligibility Requirements: Applicant must be a resident of Greater Cincinnati, and attending college as a full-time student. **Application Requirements:** Applicants must submit a completed scholarship application form along with a copy of recent transcript; expected Family Contribution (EFC) from Student Aid Report (SAR), which comes as a result of filing the FAFSA; and a copy of Financial Aid Award Letter from the chosen college to be attended. **Additional Information:** Faxed applications will not be considered. **Deadline for Receipt:** April 30.

549 ■ CINCINNATI SCHOLARSHIP FOUNDATION

652 Main St.
Cincinnati, OH 45202
Tel: (513)345-6701
Fax: (513)345-6705
Web Site: http://www.cincinnatischolarshipfoundation.org
To help students from Greater Cincinnati area to achieve the dream of a college education.
Title of Award: CSF M. Kantor and Brothers Scholarships **Area, Field, or Subject:** General studies. **Level of Education for which Award is Granted:** Undergraduate **Funds Available:** No specific amount.
Eligibility Requirements: Applicant must be a resident of Greater Cincinnati, and attending college as a full-time student. **Application Requirements:** Applicants must submit a completed scholarship application form along with a copy of recent transcript; expected Family Contribution (EFC) from Student Aid Report (SAR), which comes as a result of filing the FAFSA; and a copy of Financial Aid Award Letter from the chosen college to be attended. **Additional Information:** Faxed applications will not be considered. **Deadline for Receipt:** April 30.

550 ■ CINCINNATI SCHOLARSHIP FOUNDATION

652 Main St.
Cincinnati, OH 45202
Tel: (513)345-6701
Fax: (513)345-6705
Web Site: http://www.cincinnatischolarshipfoundation.org
To help students from Greater Cincinnati area to achieve the dream of a college education.
Title of Award: CSF Martha W. Tanner Memorial Scholarships **Area, Field, or Subject:** General studies. **Level of Education for which Award is Granted:** Undergraduate **Funds Available:** No specific amount.
Eligibility Requirements: Applicant must be a resident of Greater Cincinnati, and attending college as a full-time student. **Application Requirements:** Applicants must submit a completed scholarship application form along with a copy of recent transcript; expected Family Contribution (EFC) from Student Aid Report (SAR), which comes as a result of filing the FAFSA; and a copy of Financial Aid Award Letter from the chosen college to be attended. **Additional Information:** Faxed applications will not be considered. **Deadline for Receipt:** April 30.

551 ■ CINCINNATI SCHOLARSHIP FOUNDATION

652 Main St.
Cincinnati, OH 45202
Tel: (513)345-6701
Fax: (513)345-6705
Web Site: http://www.cincinnatischolarshipfoundation.org
To help students from Greater Cincinnati area to achieve the dream of a college education.
Title of Award: CSF Marvin Rammelsberg Memorial Scholarships **Area, Field, or Subject:** General studies. **Level of Education for which Award is Granted:** Undergraduate **Funds Available:** No specific amount.
Eligibility Requirements: Applicant must be a resident of Greater Cincinnati, and attending college as a full-time student. **Application Requirements:** Applicants must submit a completed scholarship application form along with a copy of recent transcript; expected Family Contribution (EFC) from Student Aid Report (SAR), which comes as a result of filing the FAFSA; and a copy of Financial Aid Award Letter from the chosen college

to be attended. **Additional Information:** Faxed applications will not be considered. **Deadline for Receipt:** April 30.

552 ■ CINCINNATI SCHOLARSHIP FOUNDATION

652 Main St.
Cincinnati, OH 45202
Tel: (513)345-6701
Fax: (513)345-6705
Web Site: http://www.cincinnatischolarshipfoundation.org
To help students from Greater Cincinnati area to achieve the dream of a college education.
Title of Award: CSF Mary Roberts Scholarships **Area, Field, or Subject:** General studies. **Level of Education for which Award is Granted:** Undergraduate **Funds Available:** No specific amount.
Eligibility Requirements: Applicant must be a resident of Greater Cincinnati, and attending college as a full-time student. **Application Requirements:** Applicants must submit a completed scholarship application form along with a copy of recent transcript; expected Family Contribution (EFC) from Student Aid Report (SAR), which comes as a result of filing the FAFSA; and a copy of Financial Aid Award Letter from the chosen college to be attended. **Additional Information:** Faxed applications will not be considered. **Deadline for Receipt:** April 30.

553 ■ CINCINNATI SCHOLARSHIP FOUNDATION

652 Main St.
Cincinnati, OH 45202
Tel: (513)345-6701
Fax: (513)345-6705
Web Site: http://www.cincinnatischolarshipfoundation.org
To help students from Greater Cincinnati area to achieve the dream of a college education.
Title of Award: CSF McCall Educational Scholarships **Area, Field, or Subject:** General studies. **Level of Education for which Award is Granted:** Undergraduate **Funds Available:** No specific amount.
Eligibility Requirements: Applicant must be a resident of Greater Cincinnati, and attending college as a full-time student. **Application Requirements:** Applicants must submit a completed scholarship application form along with a copy of recent transcript; expected Family Contribution (EFC) from Student Aid Report (SAR), which comes as a result of filing the FAFSA; and a copy of Financial Aid Award Letter from the chosen college to be attended. **Additional Information:** Faxed applications will not be considered. **Deadline for Receipt:** April 30.

554 ■ CINCINNATI SCHOLARSHIP FOUNDATION

652 Main St.
Cincinnati, OH 45202
Tel: (513)345-6701
Fax: (513)345-6705
Web Site: http://www.cincinnatischolarshipfoundation.org
To help students from Greater Cincinnati area to achieve the dream of a college education.
Title of Award: CSF Michael Bany Memorial Scholarships **Area, Field, or Subject:** General studies. **Level of Education for which Award is Granted:** Undergraduate **Funds Available:** No specific amount.
Eligibility Requirements: Applicant must be a resident of Greater Cincinnati, and attending college as a full-time student. **Application Requirements:** Applicants must submit a completed scholarship application form along with a copy of recent transcript; expected Family Contribution (EFC) from Student Aid Report (SAR), which comes as a result of filing the FAFSA; and a copy of Financial Aid Award Letter from the chosen college to be attended. **Additional Information:** Faxed applications will not be considered. **Deadline for Receipt:** April 30.

555 ■ CINCINNATI SCHOLARSHIP FOUNDATION

652 Main St.
Cincinnati, OH 45202
Tel: (513)345-6701
Fax: (513)345-6705
Web Site: http://www.cincinnatischolarshipfoundation.org
To help students from Greater Cincinnati area to achieve the dream of a college education.
Title of Award: CSF Midland Company Scholarships **Area, Field, or Subject:** General studies. **Level of Education for which Award is Granted:** Undergraduate **Funds Available:** No specific amount.

Eligibility Requirements: Applicant must be a resident of Greater Cincinnati, and attending college as a full-time student. **Application Requirements:** Applicants must submit a completed scholarship application form along with a copy of recent transcript; expected Family Contribution (EFC) from Student Aid Report (SAR), which comes as a result of filing the FAFSA; and a copy of Financial Aid Award Letter from the chosen college to be attended. **Additional Information:** Faxed applications will not be considered. **Deadline for Receipt:** April 30.

556 ■ CINCINNATI SCHOLARSHIP FOUNDATION
652 Main St.
Cincinnati, OH 45202
Tel: (513)345-6701
Fax: (513)345-6705
Web Site: http://www.cincinnatischolarshipfoundation.org
To help students from Greater Cincinnati area to achieve the dream of a college education.
Title of Award: CSF Nelson Schwab Jr. Family Scholarships **Area, Field, or Subject:** General studies. **Level of Education for which Award is Granted:** Undergraduate **Funds Available:** No specific amount.
Eligibility Requirements: Applicant must be a resident of Greater Cincinnati, and attending college as a full-time student. **Application Requirements:** Applicants must submit a completed scholarship application form along with a copy of recent transcript; expected Family Contribution (EFC) from Student Aid Report (SAR), which comes as a result of filing the FAFSA; and a copy of Financial Aid Award Letter from the chosen college to be attended. **Additional Information:** Faxed applications will not be considered. **Deadline for Receipt:** April 30.

557 ■ CINCINNATI SCHOLARSHIP FOUNDATION
652 Main St.
Cincinnati, OH 45202
Tel: (513)345-6701
Fax: (513)345-6705
Web Site: http://www.cincinnatischolarshipfoundation.org
To help students from Greater Cincinnati area to achieve the dream of a college education.
Title of Award: CSF Nethercott Family Scholarships **Area, Field, or Subject:** General studies. **Level of Education for which Award is Granted:** Undergraduate **Funds Available:** No specific amount.
Eligibility Requirements: Applicant must be a resident of Greater Cincinnati, and attending college as a full-time student. **Application Requirements:** Applicants must submit a completed scholarship application form along with a copy of recent transcript; expected Family Contribution (EFC) from Student Aid Report (SAR), which comes as a result of filing the FAFSA; and a copy of Financial Aid Award Letter from the chosen college to be attended. **Additional Information:** Faxed applications will not be considered. **Deadline for Receipt:** April 30.

558 ■ CINCINNATI SCHOLARSHIP FOUNDATION
652 Main St.
Cincinnati, OH 45202
Tel: (513)345-6701
Fax: (513)345-6705
Web Site: http://www.cincinnatischolarshipfoundation.org
To help students from Greater Cincinnati area to achieve the dream of a college education.
Title of Award: CSF Ohio National Foundation Scholarships **Area, Field, or Subject:** General studies. **Level of Education for which Award is Granted:** Undergraduate **Funds Available:** No specific amount.
Eligibility Requirements: Applicant must be a resident of Greater Cincinnati, and attending college as a full-time student. **Application Requirements:** Applicants must submit a completed scholarship application form along with a copy of recent transcript; expected Family Contribution (EFC) from Student Aid Report (SAR), which comes as a result of filing the FAFSA; and a copy of Financial Aid Award Letter from the chosen college to be attended. **Additional Information:** Faxed applications will not be considered. **Deadline for Receipt:** April 30.

559 ■ CINCINNATI SCHOLARSHIP FOUNDATION
652 Main St.
Cincinnati, OH 45202
Tel: (513)345-6701

Fax: (513)345-6705
Web Site: http://www.cincinnatischolarshipfoundation.org
To help students from Greater Cincinnati area to achieve the dream of a college education.
Title of Award: CSF Pepper Family Scholarships **Area, Field, or Subject:** General studies. **Level of Education for which Award is Granted:** Undergraduate **Funds Available:** No specific amount.
Eligibility Requirements: Applicant must be a resident of Greater Cincinnati, and attending college as a full-time student. **Application Requirements:** Applicants must submit a completed scholarship application form along with a copy of recent transcript; expected Family Contribution (EFC) from Student Aid Report (SAR), which comes as a result of filing the FAFSA; and a copy of Financial Aid Award Letter from the chosen college to be attended. **Additional Information:** Faxed applications will not be considered. **Deadline for Receipt:** April 30.

560 ■ CINCINNATI SCHOLARSHIP FOUNDATION
652 Main St.
Cincinnati, OH 45202
Tel: (513)345-6701
Fax: (513)345-6705
Web Site: http://www.cincinnatischolarshipfoundation.org
To help students from Greater Cincinnati area to achieve the dream of a college education.
Title of Award: CSF Pichler Family Scholarships **Area, Field, or Subject:** General studies. **Level of Education for which Award is Granted:** Undergraduate **Funds Available:** No specific amount.
Eligibility Requirements: Applicant must be a resident of Greater Cincinnati, and attending college as a full-time student. **Application Requirements:** Applicants must submit a completed scholarship application form along with a copy of recent transcript; expected Family Contribution (EFC) from Student Aid Report (SAR), which comes as a result of filing the FAFSA; and a copy of Financial Aid Award Letter from the chosen college to be attended. **Additional Information:** Faxed applications will not be considered. **Deadline for Receipt:** April 30.

561 ■ CINCINNATI SCHOLARSHIP FOUNDATION
652 Main St.
Cincinnati, OH 45202
Tel: (513)345-6701
Fax: (513)345-6705
Web Site: http://www.cincinnatischolarshipfoundation.org
To help students from Greater Cincinnati area to achieve the dream of a college education.
Title of Award: CSF PNC Bank Scholarships **Area, Field, or Subject:** General studies. **Level of Education for which Award is Granted:** Undergraduate **Funds Available:** No specific amount.
Eligibility Requirements: Applicant must be a resident of Greater Cincinnati, and attending college as a full-time student. **Application Requirements:** Applicants must submit a completed scholarship application form along with a copy of recent transcript; expected Family Contribution (EFC) from Student Aid Report (SAR), which comes as a result of filing the FAFSA; and a copy of Financial Aid Award Letter from the chosen college to be attended. **Additional Information:** Faxed applications will not be considered. **Deadline for Receipt:** April 30.

562 ■ CINCINNATI SCHOLARSHIP FOUNDATION
652 Main St.
Cincinnati, OH 45202
Tel: (513)345-6701
Fax: (513)345-6705
Web Site: http://www.cincinnatischolarshipfoundation.org
To help students from Greater Cincinnati area to achieve the dream of a college education.
Title of Award: CSF Priscilla Gamble Scholarships **Area, Field, or Subject:** General studies. **Level of Education for which Award is Granted:** Undergraduate **Funds Available:** No specific amount.
Eligibility Requirements: Applicant must be a resident of Greater Cincinnati, and attending college as a full-time student. **Application Requirements:** Applicants must submit a completed scholarship application form along with a copy of recent transcript; expected Family Contribution (EFC) from Student Aid Report (SAR), which comes as a result of filing the FAFSA; and a copy of Financial Aid Award Letter from the chosen college

to be attended. **Additional Information:** Faxed applications will not be considered. **Deadline for Receipt:** April 30.

563 ■ CINCINNATI SCHOLARSHIP FOUNDATION
652 Main St.
Cincinnati, OH 45202
Tel: (513)345-6701
Fax: (513)345-6705
Web Site: http://www.cincinnatischolarshipfoundation.org
To help students from Greater Cincinnati area to achieve the dream of a college education.
Title of Award: CSF Procter and Gamble Scholarships **Area, Field, or Subject:** General studies. **Level of Education for which Award is Granted:** Undergraduate **Funds Available:** No specific amount.
Eligibility Requirements: Applicant must be a resident of Greater Cincinnati, and attending college as a full-time student. **Application Requirements:** Applicants must submit a completed scholarship application form along with a copy of recent transcript; expected Family Contribution (EFC) from Student Aid Report (SAR), which comes as a result of filing the FAFSA; and a copy of Financial Aid Award Letter from the chosen college to be attended. **Additional Information:** Faxed applications will not be considered. **Deadline for Receipt:** April 30.

564 ■ CINCINNATI SCHOLARSHIP FOUNDATION
652 Main St.
Cincinnati, OH 45202
Tel: (513)345-6701
Fax: (513)345-6705
Web Site: http://www.cincinnatischolarshipfoundation.org
To help students from Greater Cincinnati area to achieve the dream of a college education.
Title of Award: CSF Raymond and Augusta Klink Scholarships **Area, Field, or Subject:** General studies. **Level of Education for which Award is Granted:** Undergraduate **Funds Available:** No specific amount.
Eligibility Requirements: Applicant must be a resident of Greater Cincinnati, and attending college as a full-time student. **Application Requirements:** Applicants must submit a completed scholarship application form along with a copy of recent transcript; expected Family Contribution (EFC) from Student Aid Report (SAR), which comes as a result of filing the FAFSA; and a copy of Financial Aid Award Letter from the chosen college to be attended. **Additional Information:** Faxed applications will not be considered. **Deadline for Receipt:** April 30.

565 ■ CINCINNATI SCHOLARSHIP FOUNDATION
652 Main St.
Cincinnati, OH 45202
Tel: (513)345-6701
Fax: (513)345-6705
Web Site: http://www.cincinnatischolarshipfoundation.org
To help students from Greater Cincinnati area to achieve the dream of a college education.
Title of Award: CSF Richard Heekin Scholarships **Area, Field, or Subject:** General studies. **Level of Education for which Award is Granted:** Undergraduate **Funds Available:** No specific amount.
Eligibility Requirements: Applicant must be a resident of Greater Cincinnati, and attending college as a full-time student. **Application Requirements:** Applicants must submit a completed scholarship application form along with a copy of recent transcript; expected Family Contribution (EFC) from Student Aid Report (SAR), which comes as a result of filing the FAFSA; and a copy of Financial Aid Award Letter from the chosen college to be attended. **Additional Information:** Faxed applications will not be considered. **Deadline for Receipt:** April 30.

566 ■ CINCINNATI SCHOLARSHIP FOUNDATION
652 Main St.
Cincinnati, OH 45202
Tel: (513)345-6701
Fax: (513)345-6705
Web Site: http://www.cincinnatischolarshipfoundation.org
To help students from Greater Cincinnati area to achieve the dream of a college education.
Title of Award: CSF Robert H. Reakirt Foundation Scholarships **Area, Field, or Subject:** General studies. **Level of Education for which**

Award is Granted: Undergraduate **Funds Available:** No specific amount.
Eligibility Requirements: Applicant must be a resident of Greater Cincinnati, and attending college as a full-time student. **Application Requirements:** Applicants must submit a completed scholarship application form along with a copy of recent transcript; expected Family Contribution (EFC) from Student Aid Report (SAR), which comes as a result of filing the FAFSA; and a copy of Financial Aid Award Letter from the chosen college to be attended. **Additional Information:** Faxed applications will not be considered. **Deadline for Receipt:** April 30.

567 ■ CINCINNATI SCHOLARSHIP FOUNDATION
652 Main St.
Cincinnati, OH 45202
Tel: (513)345-6701
Fax: (513)345-6705
Web Site: http://www.cincinnatischolarshipfoundation.org
To help students from Greater Cincinnati area to achieve the dream of a college education.
Title of Award: CSF Roger and Joyce Howe Family Scholarships **Area, Field, or Subject:** General studies. **Level of Education for which Award is Granted:** Undergraduate **Funds Available:** No specific amount.
Eligibility Requirements: Applicant must be a resident of Greater Cincinnati, and attending college as a full-time student. **Application Requirements:** Applicants must submit a completed scholarship application form along with a copy of recent transcript; expected Family Contribution (EFC) from Student Aid Report (SAR), which comes as a result of filing the FAFSA; and a copy of Financial Aid Award Letter from the chosen college to be attended. **Additional Information:** Faxed applications will not be considered. **Deadline for Receipt:** April 30.

568 ■ CINCINNATI SCHOLARSHIP FOUNDATION
652 Main St.
Cincinnati, OH 45202
Tel: (513)345-6701
Fax: (513)345-6705
Web Site: http://www.cincinnatischolarshipfoundation.org
To help students from Greater Cincinnati area to achieve the dream of a college education.
Title of Award: CSF S. David Shor Scholarships **Area, Field, or Subject:** General studies. **Level of Education for which Award is Granted:** Undergraduate **Funds Available:** No specific amount.
Eligibility Requirements: Applicant must be a resident of Greater Cincinnati, and attending college as a full-time student. **Application Requirements:** Applicants must submit a completed scholarship application form along with a copy of recent transcript; expected Family Contribution (EFC) from Student Aid Report (SAR), which comes as a result of filing the FAFSA; and a copy of Financial Aid Award Letter from the chosen college to be attended. **Additional Information:** Faxed applications will not be considered. **Deadline for Receipt:** April 30.

569 ■ CINCINNATI SCHOLARSHIP FOUNDATION
652 Main St.
Cincinnati, OH 45202
Tel: (513)345-6701
Fax: (513)345-6705
Web Site: http://www.cincinnatischolarshipfoundation.org
To help students from Greater Cincinnati area to achieve the dream of a college education.
Title of Award: CSF SC Johnson, A Family Company Scholarships **Area, Field, or Subject:** General studies. **Level of Education for which Award is Granted:** Undergraduate **Funds Available:** No specific amount.
Eligibility Requirements: Applicant must be a resident of Greater Cincinnati, and attending college as a full-time student. **Application Requirements:** Applicants must submit a completed scholarship application form along with a copy of recent transcript; expected Family Contribution (EFC) from Student Aid Report (SAR), which comes as a result of filing the FAFSA; and a copy of Financial Aid Award Letter from the chosen college to be attended. **Additional Information:** Faxed applications will not be considered. **Deadline for Receipt:** April 30.

570 ■ CINCINNATI SCHOLARSHIP FOUNDATION
652 Main St.
Cincinnati, OH 45202
Tel: (513)345-6701
Fax: (513)345-6705
Web Site: http://www.cincinnatischolarshipfoundation.org
To help students from Greater Cincinnati area to achieve the dream of a college education.
Title of Award: CSF Scripps Headliners Scholarships **Area, Field, or Subject:** General studies. **Level of Education for which Award is Granted:** Undergraduate **Funds Available:** No specific amount.
Eligibility Requirements: Applicant must be a resident of Greater Cincinnati, and attending college as a full-time student. **Application Requirements:** Applicants must submit a completed scholarship application form along with a copy of recent transcript; expected Family Contribution (EFC) from Student Aid Report (SAR), which comes as a result of filing the FAFSA; and a copy of Financial Aid Award Letter from the chosen college to be attended. **Additional Information:** Faxed applications will not be considered. **Deadline for Receipt:** April 30.

571 ■ CINCINNATI SCHOLARSHIP FOUNDATION
652 Main St.
Cincinnati, OH 45202
Tel: (513)345-6701
Fax: (513)345-6705
Web Site: http://www.cincinnatischolarshipfoundation.org
To help students from Greater Cincinnati area to achieve the dream of a college education.
Title of Award: CSF Semple Foundation Scholarships **Area, Field, or Subject:** General studies. **Level of Education for which Award is Granted:** Undergraduate **Funds Available:** No specific amount.
Eligibility Requirements: Applicant must be a resident of Greater Cincinnati, and attending college as a full-time student. **Application Requirements:** Applicants must submit a completed scholarship application form along with a copy of recent transcript; expected Family Contribution (EFC) from Student Aid Report (SAR), which comes as a result of filing the FAFSA; and a copy of Financial Aid Award Letter from the chosen college to be attended. **Additional Information:** Faxed applications will not be considered. **Deadline for Receipt:** April 30.

572 ■ CINCINNATI SCHOLARSHIP FOUNDATION
652 Main St.
Cincinnati, OH 45202
Tel: (513)345-6701
Fax: (513)345-6705
Web Site: http://www.cincinnatischolarshipfoundation.org
To help students from Greater Cincinnati area to achieve the dream of a college education.
Title of Award: CSF Thomas J. Emery Memorial Scholarships **Area, Field, or Subject:** General studies. **Level of Education for which Award is Granted:** Undergraduate **Funds Available:** No specific amount.
Eligibility Requirements: Applicant must be a resident of Greater Cincinnati, and attending college as a full-time student. **Application Requirements:** Applicants must submit a completed scholarship application form along with a copy of recent transcript; expected Family Contribution (EFC) from Student Aid Report (SAR), which comes as a result of filing the FAFSA; and a copy of Financial Aid Award Letter from the chosen college to be attended. **Additional Information:** Faxed applications will not be considered. **Deadline for Receipt:** April 30.

573 ■ CINCINNATI SCHOLARSHIP FOUNDATION
652 Main St.
Cincinnati, OH 45202
Tel: (513)345-6701
Fax: (513)345-6705
Web Site: http://www.cincinnatischolarshipfoundation.org
To help students from Greater Cincinnati area to achieve the dream of a college education.
Title of Award: CSF T.L. Conlan Memorial Scholarships **Area, Field, or Subject:** General studies. **Level of Education for which Award is Granted:** Undergraduate **Funds Available:** No specific amount.
Eligibility Requirements: Applicant must be a resident of Greater Cincinnati, and attending college as a full-time student. **Application Require-

ments:** Applicants must submit a completed scholarship application form along with a copy of recent transcript; expected Family Contribution (EFC) from Student Aid Report (SAR), which comes as a result of filing the FAFSA; and a copy of Financial Aid Award Letter from the chosen college to be attended. **Additional Information:** Faxed applications will not be considered. **Deadline for Receipt:** April 30.

574 ■ CINCINNATI SCHOLARSHIP FOUNDATION
652 Main St.
Cincinnati, OH 45202
Tel: (513)345-6701
Fax: (513)345-6705
Web Site: http://www.cincinnatischolarshipfoundation.org
To help students from Greater Cincinnati area to achieve the dream of a college education.
Title of Award: CSF Union Central 135th Anniversary Scholarships **Area, Field, or Subject:** General studies. **Level of Education for which Award is Granted:** Undergraduate **Funds Available:** No specific amount.
Eligibility Requirements: Applicant must be a resident of Greater Cincinnati, and attending college as a full-time student. **Application Requirements:** Applicants must submit a completed scholarship application form along with a copy of recent transcript; expected Family Contribution (EFC) from Student Aid Report (SAR), which comes as a result of filing the FAFSA; and a copy of Financial Aid Award Letter from the chosen college to be attended. **Additional Information:** Faxed applications will not be considered. **Deadline for Receipt:** April 30.

575 ■ CINCINNATI SCHOLARSHIP FOUNDATION
652 Main St.
Cincinnati, OH 45202
Tel: (513)345-6701
Fax: (513)345-6705
Web Site: http://www.cincinnatischolarshipfoundation.org
To help students from Greater Cincinnati area to achieve the dream of a college education.
Title of Award: CSF U.S. Bank N.A. Scholarships **Area, Field, or Subject:** General studies. **Level of Education for which Award is Granted:** Undergraduate **Funds Available:** No specific amount.
Eligibility Requirements: Applicant must be a resident of Greater Cincinnati, and attending college as a full-time student. **Application Requirements:** Applicants must submit a completed scholarship application form along with a copy of recent transcript; expected Family Contribution (EFC) from Student Aid Report (SAR), which comes as a result of filing the FAFSA; and a copy of Financial Aid Award Letter from the chosen college to be attended. **Additional Information:** Faxed applications will not be considered. **Deadline for Receipt:** April 30.

576 ■ CINCINNATI SCHOLARSHIP FOUNDATION
652 Main St.
Cincinnati, OH 45202
Tel: (513)345-6701
Fax: (513)345-6705
Web Site: http://www.cincinnatischolarshipfoundation.org
To help students from Greater Cincinnati area to achieve the dream of a college education.
Title of Award: CSF Walter and Marilyn Bartlett Scholarships **Area, Field, or Subject:** General studies. **Level of Education for which Award is Granted:** Undergraduate **Funds Available:** No specific amount.
Eligibility Requirements: Applicant must be a resident of Greater Cincinnati, and attending college as a full-time student. **Application Requirements:** Applicants must submit a completed scholarship application form along with a copy of recent transcript; expected Family Contribution (EFC) from Student Aid Report (SAR), which comes as a result of filing the FAFSA; and a copy of Financial Aid Award Letter from the chosen college to be attended. **Additional Information:** Faxed applications will not be considered. **Deadline for Receipt:** April 30.

577 ■ CINCINNATI SCHOLARSHIP FOUNDATION
652 Main St.
Cincinnati, OH 45202
Tel: (513)345-6701

Fax: (513)345-6705
Web Site: http://www.cincinnatischolarshipfoundation.org
To help students from Greater Cincinnati area to achieve the dream of a college education.
Title of Award: CSF Western-Southern Foundation Scholarships **Area, Field, or Subject:** General studies. **Level of Education for which Award is Granted:** Undergraduate **Funds Available:** No specific amount.
Eligibility Requirements: Applicant must be a resident of Greater Cincinnati, and attending college as a full-time student. **Application Requirements:** Applicants must submit a completed scholarship application form along with a copy of recent transcript; expected Family Contribution (EFC) from Student Aid Report (SAR), which comes as a result of filing the FAFSA; and a copy of Financial Aid Award Letter from the chosen college to be attended. **Additional Information:** Faxed applications will not be considered. **Deadline for Receipt:** April 30.

578 ■ CINCINNATI SCHOLARSHIP FOUNDATION
652 Main St.
Cincinnati, OH 45202
Tel: (513)345-6701
Fax: (513)345-6705
Web Site: http://www.cincinnatischolarshipfoundation.org
To help students from Greater Cincinnati area to achieve the dream of a college education.
Title of Award: CSF William A. Friedlander Scholarships **Area, Field, or Subject:** General studies. **Level of Education for which Award is Granted:** Undergraduate **Funds Available:** No specific amount.
Eligibility Requirements: Applicant must be a resident of Greater Cincinnati, and attending college as a full-time student. **Application Requirements:** Applicants must submit a completed scholarship application form along with a copy of recent transcript; expected Family Contribution (EFC) from Student Aid Report (SAR), which comes as a result of filing the FAFSA; and a copy of Financial Aid Award Letter from the chosen college to be attended. **Additional Information:** Faxed applications will not be considered. **Deadline for Receipt:** April 30.

579 ■ CINCINNATI SCHOLARSHIP FOUNDATION
652 Main St.
Cincinnati, OH 45202
Tel: (513)345-6701
Fax: (513)345-6705
Web Site: http://www.cincinnatischolarshipfoundation.org
To help students from Greater Cincinnati area to achieve the dream of a college education.
Title of Award: CSF Wm. J. Rielly/MCURC Scholarships **Area, Field, or Subject:** General studies. **Level of Education for which Award is Granted:** Undergraduate **Funds Available:** No specific amount.
Eligibility Requirements: Applicant must be a resident of Greater Cincinnati, and attending college as a full-time student. **Application Requirements:** Applicants must submit a completed scholarship application form along with a copy of recent transcript; expected Family Contribution (EFC) from Student Aid Report (SAR), which comes as a result of filing the FAFSA; and a copy of Financial Aid Award Letter from the chosen college to be attended. **Additional Information:** Faxed applications will not be considered. **Deadline for Receipt:** April 30.

580 ■ CINCINNATI SCHOLARSHIP FOUNDATION
652 Main St.
Cincinnati, OH 45202
Tel: (513)345-6701
Fax: (513)345-6705
Web Site: http://www.cincinnatischolarshipfoundation.org
To help students from Greater Cincinnati area to achieve the dream of a college education.
Title of Award: CSF Woodward Trustees Scholarships **Area, Field, or Subject:** General studies. **Level of Education for which Award is Granted:** Undergraduate **Funds Available:** No specific amount.
Eligibility Requirements: Applicant must be a resident of Greater Cincinnati, and attending college as a full-time student. **Application Requirements:** Applicants must submit a completed scholarship application form along with a copy of recent transcript; expected Family Contribution (EFC) from Student Aid Report (SAR), which comes as a result of filing the

FAFSA; and a copy of Financial Aid Award Letter from the chosen college to be attended. **Additional Information:** Faxed applications will not be considered. **Deadline for Receipt:** April 30.

581 ■ CINCINNATI SCHOLARSHIP FOUNDATION
652 Main St.
Cincinnati, OH 45202
Tel: (513)345-6701
Fax: (513)345-6705
Web Site: http://www.cincinnatischolarshipfoundation.org
To help students from Greater Cincinnati area to achieve the dream of a college education.
Title of Award: CSF Wynne Family Memorial Scholarships **Area, Field, or Subject:** General studies. **Level of Education for which Award is Granted:** Undergraduate **Funds Available:** No specific amount.
Eligibility Requirements: Applicant must be a resident of Greater Cincinnati, and attending college as a full-time student. **Application Requirements:** Applicants must submit a completed scholarship application form along with a copy of recent transcript; expected Family Contribution (EFC) from Student Aid Report (SAR), which comes as a result of filing the FAFSA; and a copy of Financial Aid Award Letter from the chosen college to be attended. **Additional Information:** Faxed applications will not be considered. **Deadline for Receipt:** April 30.

582 ■ CIVITAN INTERNATIONAL
PO Box 130744
Birmingham, AL 35213-0744
Tel: (205)591-8910
Free: 800-CIV-ITAN
E-mail: civitan@civitan.org
Web Site: http://www.civitan.com
To provide financial assistance to students enrolled in undergraduate or graduate studies.
Title of Award: Civitan Shropshire Scholarships **Area, Field, or Subject:** General studies. **Level of Education for which Award is Granted:** Undergraduate **Funds Available:** $2,000. **Duration:** One year.
Eligibility Requirements: Applicants must be Civitans (or Civitans' children or grandchildren) and must have been Civitan for at least two years and/or must be or have been Junior Civitans for no less than two years; must be students pursuing careers which help further the ideals and purposes of Civitan International as embodied in its Creed; must be enrolled in a degreed or certificate program at an accredited community college, vocational school, four-year college or graduate school. **Application Requirements:** Applicants must submit all required application information. **Deadline for Receipt:** January 31.

583 ■ CLUB MANAGERS ASSOCIATION OF AMERICA
1733 King St.
Alexandria, VA 22314
Tel: (703)739-9500
Fax: (703)739-0124
E-mail: cmaa@cmaa.org
Web Site: http://www.cmaa.org
To financially support the professional development of club managers through education, training and research initiatives.
Title of Award: Joe Perdue Scholarships **Area, Field, or Subject:** Management. **Level of Education for which Award is Granted:** Undergraduate **Funds Available:** No specific amount.
Eligibility Requirements: Candidates must be pursuing managerial careers in the private club industry; must have completed freshman year of college and be enrolled for the full academic year in an accredited four-year institution; must have achieved and maintained a grade point average of at least 2.5 on a 4.0 scale, or 4.5 on a 6.0 scale. **Application Requirements:** Candidates must submit an official application available from the website; a sealed copy of official college transcripts; a recommendation form and recommendation letter from a faculty advisor/ professor and a private club industry professional; a resume; an essay (500-1000 words) addressing the following components: 1) your career objectives and goals; 2) the characteristics you possess that will enable you to succeed as a club manager; 3) your perception of CMAA and the private club industry; 4) your specific interests within the private club management field; 5) why you feel that you should be a Club Foundation Scholarship recipient. **Deadline for Receipt:** May 1. **Additional Information:** joeperduescholarship@clubfoundation.org.

584 ■ COALITION OF HIGHER EDUCATION ASSISTANCE ORGANIZATIONS

1101 Vermont Ave. NW, Ste. 400
Washington, DC 20005-3586
Tel: (202)289-3910
Fax: (202)371-0197
Web Site: http://www.coheao.org
To provide financial assistance to those students who are in need.
Title of Award: COHEAO Scholarships **Area, Field, or Subject:** General Studies. **Level of Education for which Award is Granted:** Undergraduate **Funds Available:** No specific amount.
Eligibility Requirements: Applicants must be U.S citizens; must attend a COHEAO member school; must have a minimum GPA of 3.75 on a 4.0 scale. Only undergraduate students who are entering their sophomore, junior or senior year are eligible to apply; freshmen and graduate students are not eligible. **Application Requirements:** Applicants must check the available website for the application process online. **Additional Information:** Coalition of Higher Education Assistance Organizations at the above address

585 ■ COASTAL BEND COMMUNITY FOUNDATION

600 Leopard St., Ste. 1716
Corpus Christi, TX 78473
Tel: (361)882-9745
Fax: (361)882-2865
Web Site: http://www.cbcfoundation.org
To provide resources for educational opportunities including vocational schools and two and four-year universities.
Title of Award: Alejandro "Alex" Abecia Reaching High Scholarships **Area, Field, or Subject:** General studies. **Level of Education for which Award is Granted:** Undergraduate **Number Awarded:** 4. **Funds Available:** $100.
Eligibility Requirements: Applicants must be senior members of the Mary Caroll High School Band or graduating senior members of the Mary Caroll High School soccer team; must be members of the A/B Honor Roll; must have taken honor classes in high school and maintained a courseload of at least 12 hours per semester. **Application Requirements:** Applicants must download the applications from the website of the Foundation. **Deadline for Receipt:** March 14.

586 ■ COASTAL BEND COMMUNITY FOUNDATION

600 Leopard St., Ste. 1716
Corpus Christi, TX 78473
Tel: (361)882-9745
Fax: (361)882-2865
Web Site: http://www.cbcfoundation.org
To provide financial assistance to graduating seniors at W.B. Ray High School to attend college.
Title of Award: Chris Nance Adler Scholarship Fund **Area, Field, or Subject:** General studies. **Level of Education for which Award is Granted:** High School **Number Awarded:** 2. **Funds Available:** $500.
Eligibility Requirements: Applicants must be graduating seniors at W.B. Ray High School and chosen by the Hall of Honor Selection Committee from the students named to the permanent honor roll. **Application Requirements:** Applicants must obtain applications from the Ray High School counselor's Office. **Deadline for Receipt:** April 20.

587 ■ COASTAL BEND COMMUNITY FOUNDATION

600 Leopard St., Ste. 1716
Corpus Christi, TX 78473
Tel: (361)882-9745
Fax: (361)882-2865
Web Site: http://www.cbcfoundation.org
To provide resources for educational opportunities including vocational schools and two and four-year universities.
Title of Award: Allen - Marty Allen Scholarships **Area, Field, or Subject:** General studies. **Level of Education for which Award is Granted:** High School, Undergraduate **Number Awarded:** 1. **Funds Available:** $200.
Eligibility Requirements: Applicants must be graduating seniors of a Coastal Bend high school or college students who attended a Coastal Bend high school; must be majoring in music; must maintain GPA of 2.5 and course load of at least 12 college credits per semester. **Application Requirements:** Applicants must submit all the required application information. **Deadline for Receipt:** March 14.

588 ■ COASTAL BEND COMMUNITY FOUNDATION

600 Leopard St., Ste. 1716
Corpus Christi, TX 78473
Tel: (361)882-9745
Fax: (361)882-2865
Web Site: http://www.cbcfoundation.org
To provide educational assistance to students seeking a bachelor's degree in building construction.
Title of Award: O.J. Beck, Jr. Memorial Scholarships **Area, Field, or Subject:** Construction. **Level of Education for which Award is Granted:** Undergraduate **Number Awarded:** 1. **Funds Available:** $2,000.
Eligibility Requirements: Applicants must be students at Texas A&M University - College Station who are seeking a bachelor's degree in building construction; must have maintained residency in the area served by the South Texas Chapter of Associated General Contractors. **Application Requirements:** Applicants must obtain application form from the Associated General Contractors office located at 518 S Enterprise Pkwy., Corpus Christi, TX 78405; Phone number: 361-289-0996.

589 ■ COASTAL BEND COMMUNITY FOUNDATION

600 Leopard St., Ste. 1716
Corpus Christi, TX 78473
Tel: (361)882-9745
Fax: (361)882-2865
Web Site: http://www.cbcfoundation.org
To provide financial assistance to students who are determined to succeed and planning to attend college.
Title of Award: Beecroft Family Scholarships **Area, Field, or Subject:** General studies. **Level of Education for which Award is Granted:** High School **Number Awarded:** 2. **Funds Available:** $1,500.
Eligibility Requirements: Applicants must be graduating high school seniors in Nueces or San Patricio County, recipients of a GED certificate or currently attending college; must maintain at least 12 credit hours per semester at Del Mar College or Texas A&M-Corpus Christi. **Application Requirements:** Applicants must download applications from the website of the Foundation. **Deadline for Receipt:** March 14.

590 ■ COASTAL BEND COMMUNITY FOUNDATION

600 Leopard St., Ste. 1716
Corpus Christi, TX 78473
Tel: (361)882-9745
Fax: (361)882-2865
Web Site: http://www.cbcfoundation.org
To provide financial support to graduating seniors from a Coastal Bend high school.
Title of Award: Reverend E.F. Bennett Scholarships **Area, Field, or Subject:** General studies. **Level of Education for which Award is Granted:** High School **Number Awarded:** 1. **Funds Available:** $300.
Eligibility Requirements: Applicants must be: graduating seniors from a Coastal Bend high school; in the top 10% of their graduating class; attending Del Mar College, Texas A&M University-Corpus Christi or Texas A&M University-Kingsville. **Application Requirements:** Applicants must download the application form from the website of the Foundation or obtain it by calling the Foundation office at 361-882-9745. **Deadline for Receipt:** March 15.

591 ■ COASTAL BEND COMMUNITY FOUNDATION

600 Leopard St., Ste. 1716
Corpus Christi, TX 78473
Tel: (361)882-9745
Fax: (361)882-2865
Web Site: http://www.cbcfoundation.org
To provide financial assistance to teenage parents in Coastal Bend to pursue a college education while raising and supporting their children.
Title of Award: Marion Luna Brem/Pat McNeil Teen Parent Scholarships **Area, Field, or Subject:** General studies. **Level of Education for which Award is Granted:** Undergraduate **Number Awarded:** 2. **Funds Available:** $1,000. **Duration:** One year.
Eligibility Requirements: Applicants must be: teenage parents who have attended high school in Coastal Bend; pursuing college education while raising and supporting a child; recipients of a high school diploma or GED certification; must attend Coastal Bend College, Del Mar College, Texas

A&M University-Corpus Christi or Texas A&M University-Kingsville; must maintain a 2.0 GPA on a 4.0 scale and a minimum of 9 credit hours per semester. **Application Requirements:** Applicants must submit all the required application information. **Deadline for Receipt:** March 14.

592 ■ COASTAL BEND COMMUNITY FOUNDATION

600 Leopard St., Ste. 1716
Corpus Christi, TX 78473
Tel: (361)882-9745
Fax: (361)882-2865
Web Site: http://www.cbcfoundation.org
To provide educational support for students who graduated from a Victoria ISD high school.
Title of Award: Justin Forrest Cox "Beat the Odds" Memorial Scholarships **Area, Field, or Subject:** General studies. **Level of Education for which Award is Granted:** Undergraduate **Number Awarded:** 1. **Funds Available:** $2,500.
Eligibility Requirements: Applicants must be students who graduated from a Victoria ISD high school; have a "C" average or better; be pursuing a four-year baccalaureate degree; complete at least 12 credit hours per semester; have overcome a significant difficulty in graduating from high school and have maintained a 2.5 GPA. **Application Requirements:** Applicants must obtain application form from Making the Grade-Victoria, 1908 Laurent Tower, Ste. 290 (PO Box 105), Victoria, TX 77902; Phone or Fax: 361-578-0270. **Additional Information:** Scholarship is to be used for books and tuition only. **Deadline for Receipt:** February 24.

593 ■ COASTAL BEND COMMUNITY FOUNDATION

600 Leopard St., Ste. 1716
Corpus Christi, TX 78473
Tel: (361)882-9745
Fax: (361)882-2865
Web Site: http://www.cbcfoundation.org
To provide financial assistance to graduates of Mathis High School and current Mathis High School students to further their education in college.
Title of Award: D.C. and Virginia Brown Scholarships **Area, Field, or Subject:** General studies. **Level of Education for which Award is Granted:** High School, Undergraduate **Number Awarded:** 4. **Funds Available:** $4,000. **Duration:** One year.
Eligibility Requirements: Applicants must be graduates or current students of Mathis High School who have earned their GED certificate and who have good potential and character; must maintain a course load of 12 semester hours and a 2.5 GPA on a 4.0 scale. **Application Requirements:** Applicants must download application form from the website of the Foundation or obtain it from Mathis High School counseling office. **Deadline for Receipt:** March 15.

594 ■ COASTAL BEND COMMUNITY FOUNDATION

600 Leopard St., Ste. 1716
Corpus Christi, TX 78473
Tel: (361)882-9745
Fax: (361)882-2865
Web Site: http://www.cbcfoundation.org
To assist outstanding high school students of W.B. Ray High School who have a passion for soccer.
Title of Award: Derek Lee Dean Soccer Scholarships **Area, Field, or Subject:** General studies. **Level of Education for which Award is Granted:** High School **Funds Available:** $500.
Eligibility Requirements: Applicants must be outstanding W.B. Ray High School students and members of the soccer team who exhibit love for soccer, teamwork and sportsmanship. **Application Requirements:** Applicants must download the application form from the website of the Foundation or obtain it from the W.B. Ray High School counselor's office. **Deadline for Receipt:** April 1.

595 ■ COASTAL BEND COMMUNITY FOUNDATION

600 Leopard St., Ste. 1716
Corpus Christi, TX 78473
Tel: (361)882-9745
Fax: (361)882-2865
Web Site: http://www.cbcfoundation.org
To promote educational excellence in Coastal Bend.
Title of Award: Doraine Pursuit of Educational Excellence Scholarships **Area, Field, or Subject:** General studies. **Level of Education for which

Award is Granted:** High School **Number Awarded:** 1. **Funds Available:** $2,000.
Eligibility Requirements: Applicants must be graduating high school seniors in the Coastal Bend; must be in the top 10% of the graduating class; and have maintained a GPA of 3.0 and enrolled in at least 12 hours per semester. **Application Requirements:** Applicants must download applications found at the website of the Foundation. **Deadline for Receipt:** March 14.

596 ■ COASTAL BEND COMMUNITY FOUNDATION

600 Leopard St., Ste. 1716
Corpus Christi, TX 78473
Tel: (361)882-9745
Fax: (361)882-2865
Web Site: http://www.cbcfoundation.org
To provide financial assistance to graduating Alice High School senior students in pursuing college.
Title of Award: Jay Downes Memorial Scholarships **Area, Field, or Subject:** General studies. **Level of Education for which Award is Granted:** High School **Number Awarded:** 1. **Funds Available:** $1,000.
Eligibility Requirements: Applicants must be graduating Alice High School seniors who lettered in UIL-sanctioned golf for at least two years; have an overall high school GPA of "B" or better; participated in extracurricular activities other than athletics; have high ideals, and spirit of good conduct and sportsmanship benefiting the "Fighting Alice Coyote"; must attend a four-year college or university, register for at least 12 hours of classes and maintain a minimum college GPA of 2.5 on 4.0 scale. **Application Requirements:** Applicants must be nominated by the athletic director and head golf coach at Alice High School.

597 ■ COASTAL BEND COMMUNITY FOUNDATION

600 Leopard St., Ste. 1716
Corpus Christi, TX 78473
Tel: (361)882-9745
Fax: (361)882-2865
Web Site: http://www.cbcfoundation.org
To provide financial assistance to graduating seniors of Corpus Christi, Flour Bluff or Tuloso-Midway ISD high schools in furthering their education.
Title of Award: Barney Flynn Memorial Scholarships **Area, Field, or Subject:** General studies. **Level of Education for which Award is Granted:** High School **Number Awarded:** 1. **Funds Available:** $1,000.
Eligibility Requirements: Applicants must be graduating seniors of Corpus Christi, Flour Bluff or Tuloso-Midway ISD high schools; must be members of the high school band with a high performance level in band. **Application Requirements:** Applicants must submit all the required application information. **Deadline for Receipt:** March 14.

598 ■ COASTAL BEND COMMUNITY FOUNDATION

600 Leopard St., Ste. 1716
Corpus Christi, TX 78473
Tel: (361)882-9745
Fax: (361)882-2865
Web Site: http://www.cbcfoundation.org
To financially assist students in completing high school and attending college.
Title of Award: Food for Thought Scholarships **Area, Field, or Subject:** General studies. **Level of Education for which Award is Granted:** High School **Number Awarded:** 1. **Funds Available:** $1,250. **Duration:** One year.
Eligibility Requirements: Applicants must be ninth-grade, at-risk high school students in Coastal Bend or graduates from high school. **Application Requirements:** Applicants must obtain applications by contacting Dee Haven at 361-884-5802.

599 ■ COASTAL BEND COMMUNITY FOUNDATION

600 Leopard St., Ste. 1716
Corpus Christi, TX 78473
Tel: (361)882-9745
Fax: (361)882-2865
Web Site: http://www.cbcfoundation.org
To provide educational assistance to senior students of Mary Caroll High School.

Title of Award: Melissa Guerra Scholarships **Area, Field, or Subject:** General studies. **Level of Education for which Award is Granted:** Undergraduate **Funds Available:** $1,000.
Eligibility Requirements: Applicants must be Mary Carroll High School seniors; must attend a publicly funded college or university in Texas; and maintain a minimum of a 3.0 GPA and 12 credit hours per semester. **Application Requirements:** Applicants must submit all the required application information. **Deadline for Receipt:** March 14.

600 ■ COASTAL BEND COMMUNITY FOUNDATION

600 Leopard St., Ste. 1716
Corpus Christi, TX 78473
Tel: (361)882-9745
Fax: (361)882-2865
Web Site: http://www.cbcfoundation.org
To provide the high school graduating senior students of Roy Miller High School financial assistance for their college education.
Title of Award: Manuel Hernandez, Jr. Foundation Scholarships **Area, Field, or Subject:** General studies. **Level of Education for which Award is Granted:** High School **Number Awarded:** 4. **Funds Available:** $500.
Eligibility Requirements: Applicants must be graduating seniors of Roy Miller High School; must have been accepted at a college, university, trade or vocational institution. **Application Requirements:** Applicants must submit all the required application information. **Deadline for Receipt:** March 14.

601 ■ COASTAL BEND COMMUNITY FOUNDATION

600 Leopard St., Ste. 1716
Corpus Christi, TX 78473
Tel: (361)882-9745
Fax: (361)882-2865
Web Site: http://www.cbcfoundation.org
To assist high school students who are seeking financial resources to further their college education.
Title of Award: Casey Laine Armed Forces Scholarships **Area, Field, or Subject:** General studies. **Level of Education for which Award is Granted:** High School **Number Awarded:** 1. **Funds Available:** $200.
Eligibility Requirements: Applicants must graduate in top 50% of high school class; maintain a GPA of 2.5 and enrolled in at least 12 hours per semester; must be graduating seniors or current graduates from a Coastal Bend high school, or members or honorably discharged veterans of the armed services, or R.O.T.C. members (high school seniors must agree to join an R.O.T.C. program upon entering college). **Application Requirements:** Applicants must submit all the required application information. **Deadline for Receipt:** March 14.

602 ■ COASTAL BEND COMMUNITY FOUNDATION

600 Leopard St., Ste. 1716
Corpus Christi, TX 78473
Tel: (361)882-9745
Fax: (361)882-2865
Web Site: http://www.cbcfoundation.org
To assist high school seniors seeking financial resources to further their education.
Title of Award: Sue Kay Lay Memorial Scholarships **Area, Field, or Subject:** General studies. **Level of Education for which Award is Granted:** High School **Number Awarded:** 5. **Funds Available:** $1,500.
Eligibility Requirements: Applicants must be high school seniors graduating at the end of the spring semester; must be enrolled in college full-time (12 hours or more); must have high school GPA of 3.5; have graduated from a high school in Coastal Bend; and maintain a permanent residence in the Coastal Bend. **Application Requirements:** Applicants must submit all the required application information. **Deadline for Receipt:** March 14.

603 ■ COASTAL BEND COMMUNITY FOUNDATION

600 Leopard St., Ste. 1716
Corpus Christi, TX 78473
Tel: (361)882-9745
Fax: (361)882-2865
Web Site: http://www.cbcfoundation.org

To assist high school juniors or seniors attending a Coastal Bend high school.
Title of Award: Brian and Colleen Miller Scholarships **Area, Field, or Subject:** General studies. **Level of Education for which Award is Granted:** High School **Number Awarded:** 1. **Funds Available:** $500.
Eligibility Requirements: Applicants must be high school juniors or seniors attending a Coastal Bend high school; must attend any accredited four-year college or university. **Application Requirements:** Applicants must submit completed application form along with the documentation of participation and/or awards in the areas of mathematics and/or science. **Deadline for Receipt:** March 14.

604 ■ COASTAL BEND COMMUNITY FOUNDATION

600 Leopard St., Ste. 1716
Corpus Christi, TX 78473
Tel: (361)882-9745
Fax: (361)882-2865
Web Site: http://www.cbcfoundation.org
To provide financial assistance to students in continuing their education in college.
Title of Award: Puedo Scholarships - Joseph Huerta **Area, Field, or Subject:** General studies. **Level of Education for which Award is Granted:** High School **Number Awarded:** 10. **Funds Available:** $1,000 to $5,000. **Duration:** One year.
Eligibility Requirements: Applicants must have graduated from a CCISD high school and have a high school GPA of at least 90 percent on a 100-point scale; must be enrolled as full-time college students (at least 12 semester credits) at a four-year accredited college or university; and must maintain a course load of at least 12 college credits per semester and a GPA of 3.0 or higher. **Application Requirements:** Applicants must submit all the required application information. Application form can be downloaded at the website of the Foundation, www.cbcfoundation.org. **Deadline for Receipt:** March 14.

605 ■ COASTAL BEND COMMUNITY FOUNDATION

600 Leopard St., Ste. 1716
Corpus Christi, TX 78473
Tel: (361)882-9745
Fax: (361)882-2865
Web Site: http://www.cbcfoundation.org
To provide graduating CCISD high school seniors financial assistance for their college education.
Title of Award: J.J. Rains Memorial Scholarships **Area, Field, or Subject:** General studies. **Level of Education for which Award is Granted:** High School **Number Awarded:** 1. **Funds Available:** $1,000.
Eligibility Requirements: Applicants must be graduating CCISD high school seniors with preference for students who have participated in speech or debate; have a cumulative high school GPA of 2.5; must maintain a cumulative college GPA of 2.5 on a 4.0 scale and enroll in a minimum of 12 semester hours. **Application Requirements:** Applicants must submit all the required application information. **Deadline for Receipt:** March 14.

606 ■ COASTAL BEND COMMUNITY FOUNDATION

600 Leopard St., Ste. 1716
Corpus Christi, TX 78473
Tel: (361)882-9745
Fax: (361)882-2865
Web Site: http://www.cbcfoundation.org
To provide financial assistance for graduating seniors of W.B. Ray High School.
Title of Award: W.B. Ray HS Class of '56 Averill Johnson Scholarships **Area, Field, or Subject:** General studies. **Level of Education for which Award is Granted:** High School **Number Awarded:** 1. **Funds Available:** $500.
Eligibility Requirements: Applicants must be W.B. Ray high school seniors in the top 10% of their graduating class; enrolled as full-time (12 semester hours) students in an accredited college or university in the United States in the fall semester following graduation. **Application Requirements:** Applicants must submit all the required application information. **Deadline for Receipt:** March 14.

607 ■ COASTAL BEND COMMUNITY FOUNDATION

600 Leopard St., Ste. 1716
Corpus Christi, TX 78473

Tel: (361)882-9745
Fax: (361)882-2865
Web Site: http://www.cbcfoundation.org
To advance higher education in the immediate Corpus Christi area.
Title of Award: Rotary Club of Corpus Christi Scholarships **Area, Field, or Subject:** General studies. **Level of Education for which Award is Granted:** High School **Number Awarded:** 2. **Funds Available:** $2,500 to $3,000.
Eligibility Requirements: Applicants must be graduating seniors from the following: all CCISD high schools, Tuloso-Midway, Calallen, West Oso or Flour Bluff high schools, Incarnate Word Academy, Corpus Christi Academy or Annapolis Christian Academy; must attend Texas A&M Corpus Christi or Del Mar College; must maintain a minimum GPA of 2.0 on a 4.0 scale and courseload of at least 12 hours per semester. **Application Requirements:** Applicants must submit all the required application information and application form can be downloaded from the website of the Foundation. **Deadline for Receipt:** March 14.

608 ■ COASTAL BEND COMMUNITY FOUNDATION
600 Leopard St., Ste. 1716
Corpus Christi, TX 78473
Tel: (361)882-9745
Fax: (361)882-2865
Web Site: http://www.cbcfoundation.org
To provide financial assistance for Coastal Bend students who are home-schooled and need financial aid.
Title of Award: Seaman Family Scholarships **Area, Field, or Subject:** General studies. **Level of Education for which Award is Granted:** High School **Funds Available:** $500.
Eligibility Requirements: Applicant must be a Coastal Bend or Calhoun County home-schooled student who demonstrates financial need; must be accepted at an accredited college or university; and must maintain a courseload of 12 semester hours. **Application Requirements:** Applicants must submit completed application form; essay of 500 words about the topic "Freedom." **Deadline for Receipt:** March 14.

609 ■ COASTAL BEND COMMUNITY FOUNDATION
600 Leopard St., Ste. 1716
Corpus Christi, TX 78473
Tel: (361)882-9745
Fax: (361)882-2865
Web Site: http://www.cbcfoundation.org
To assist graduating high school senior students in Coastal Bend, financially, to continue their education.
Title of Award: Judge Terry Shamsie Scholarships **Area, Field, or Subject:** General studies. **Level of Education for which Award is Granted:** High School **Number Awarded:** 4. **Funds Available:** $1,000.
Eligibility Requirements: Applicants must be graduating high school seniors in the Coastal Bend (Arkansas, Bee Jim Wells, Kleberg, Nueces, Refugio, San Patricio). **Application Requirements:** Applicants must submit completed applications which can be downloaded from the website of the Foundation. **Deadline for Receipt:** March 14.

610 ■ COASTAL BEND COMMUNITY FOUNDATION
600 Leopard St., Ste. 1716
Corpus Christi, TX 78473
Tel: (361)882-9745
Fax: (361)882-2865
Web Site: http://www.cbcfoundation.org
To provide financial assistance to further the education of eligible students in Coastal Bend.
Title of Award: South Texas Lighthouse for the Blind Scholarships **Area, Field, or Subject:** General studies. **Level of Education for which Award is Granted:** Undergraduate **Funds Available:** $5,000.
Eligibility Requirements: Applicants must be graduating seniors from a Coastal Bend high school or employees or immediate family members of employees of the South Texas Lighthouse for the Blind; must have high school GPA of at least 80% on a 100% scale; must be enrolled in an accredited college or university of the United States; and must maintain a courseload of 12 college credits per semester and cumulative college GPA of at least 3.0 on a 4.0 scale. **Application Requirements:** Applicant must submit a completed application form that can be downloaded from the website of the Foundation. **Deadline for Receipt:** March 14.

611 ■ COASTAL BEND COMMUNITY FOUNDATION
600 Leopard St., Ste. 1716
Corpus Christi, TX 78473
Tel: (361)882-9745
Fax: (361)882-2865
Web Site: http://www.cbcfoundation.org
To provide financial assistance to high school seniors and college students who are descendants of volunteer firefighters in Coastal Bend.
Title of Award: Stewart Title Firefighters Scholarships **Area, Field, or Subject:** General studies. **Level of Education for which Award is Granted:** High School, Undergraduate **Number Awarded:** 2. **Funds Available:** $1,000.
Eligibility Requirements: Applicants must be high school seniors or college students in Coastal Bend; must be children of uniformed and volunteer firefighters for a fire department located in Coastal Bend; and must have maintained a 3.0 GPA and complete at least 12 credit hours per semester. **Application Requirements:** Applicants must submit all the required application information. **Deadline for Receipt:** March 14.

612 ■ COASTAL BEND COMMUNITY FOUNDATION
600 Leopard St., Ste. 1716
Corpus Christi, TX 78473
Tel: (361)882-9745
Fax: (361)882-2865
Web Site: http://www.cbcfoundation.org
To provide financial assistance to deserving accounting students of Texas for furthering their education in the field.
Title of Award: Talbert Family Memorial Accounting Scholarships **Area, Field, or Subject:** Accounting. **Level of Education for which Award is Granted:** Undergraduate **Funds Available:** $2,000.
Eligibility Requirements: Applicants must be full-time college juniors majoring in accounting at a Texas college with 3.25 grade point average; must have graduated from a Coastal Bend high school and permanently reside in Coastal Bend. **Application Requirements:** Applicants must submit all the required application information. **Deadline for Receipt:** March 14.

613 ■ COASTAL BEND COMMUNITY FOUNDATION
600 Leopard St., Ste. 1716
Corpus Christi, TX 78473
Tel: (361)882-9745
Fax: (361)882-2865
Web Site: http://www.cbcfoundation.org
To provide an opportunity for people permanently confined to a wheelchair to attend college or technical school.
Title of Award: Wheelchair Success Foundation Scholarships **Area, Field, or Subject:** General school. **Level of Education for which Award is Granted:** Undergraduate **Number Awarded:** 1. **Funds Available:** $500.
Eligibility Requirements: Applicants must be graduates or GED certificate holders who attended a Coastal Bend high school; permanently confined to a wheelchair; must maintain nine credit hours per semester with GPA of 2.5 while attending an accredited university, college or technical school. **Application Requirements:** Applicants must download application form from the website of CBC Foundation or inquire through telephone call to the Foundation. **Deadline for Receipt:** March 14.

614 ■ COCA-COLA SCHOLARS FOUNDATION
PO Box 442
Atlanta, GA 30301-0442
800-306-2653
Fax: (404)733-5439
E-mail: scholars@na.ko.com
Web Site: http://www.coca-colascholars.org
To provide scholarships to high school seniors.
Title of Award: Coca-Cola Scholars Foundation Four-Year Award for Seniors **Area, Field, or Subject:** General studies. **Level of Education for which Award is Granted:** Undergraduate **Number Awarded:** 50-200. **Funds Available:** $10,000-$20,000.
Eligibility Requirements: Applicants must be high school seniors attending school in the US; must be U.S. citizens; must be seniors anticipating completion of a high school diploma during the academic year in which application is made; must be seniors planning to pursue a degree at an

accredited U.S. postsecondary institution; and must be carrying a minimum 3.0 GPA at the end of their junior year of high school. **Application Requirements:** Applicants may apply online. They must complete all parts of the application process. **Deadline for Receipt:** October 31. **Additional Information:** Coca-Cola at the above address.

615 ■ COLLEGE STUDENT EDUCATORS INTERNATIONAL

One Dupont Circle NW, Ste. 300
Washington, DC 20036-1188
Tel: (202)835-2272
Fax: (202)296-3286
E-mail: info@acpa.nche.edu
Web Site: http://www.acpa.nche.edu
To enhance the student affairs profession; to generate and disseminate knowledge about college students.
Title of Award: Educational Leadership Foundation Grants **Area, Field, or Subject:** General studies. **Level of Education for which Award is Granted:** Undergraduate **Funds Available:** $60,000.
Eligibility Requirements: Applicants must be currently enrolled in a college, university and institution. **Application Requirements:** Applicants must complete the online application form including the name and contact information. **Deadline for Receipt:** February 1. **Additional Information:** lwillett@coastal.edu.

616 ■ COLORADO CHRISTIAN UNIVERSITY ALUMNI ASSOCIATION

8787 W Alameda Ave.
Lakewood, CO 80226
Tel: (303)963-3330
Free: 800-44-FAITH
Fax: (303)963-3331
E-mail: ccualumni@ccu.edu
Web Site: http://www.ccu.edu/alumni
To assist students with the cost of post-secondary education.
Title of Award: CCU Alumni Endowed Scholarships **Area, Field, or Subject:** General studies. **Level of Education for which Award is Granted:** Undergraduate **Funds Available:** No specific amount.
Eligibility Requirements: Applicant must be pursuing a baccalaureate degree; completed at least 85 credits, with a minimum of 24 credits earned at CCU; have a GPA of 3.3 or above; demonstrated the need of financial assistance; shows local church or community involvement; and have an alumni sponsor. **Application Requirements:** Contact the Alumni Relations for more details on the scholarship. **Additional Information:** Funds was established by the CCU Alumni Association.

617 ■ COLORADO HOTEL AND LODGING ASSOCIATION

730 17th St., Ste. 920
Denver, CO 80202
Tel: (303)297-8335
Fax: (303)297-8104
E-mail: info@chla.com
Web Site: http://www.coloradolodging.com
To offer college students an opportunity to apply for this scholarship to overcome financial need.
Title of Award: Karl Mehlmann Scholarships **Area, Field, or Subject:** Culinary Arts. **Level of Education for which Award is Granted:** Undergraduate **Funds Available:** No specific amount.
Eligibility Requirements: Applicants must be enrolled in an accredited four-year university or college and be majoring in hotel and/or restaurant management; must also be enrolled in the final year at the Culinary Institute of America; must be freshmen, sophomores, juniors, or seniors who are going to graduate school; must carry a minimum workload of 12 hours per quarter or semester; must have maintain a minimum overall GPA of 3.0 on a 4.0 scale; must be U.S. citizens. **Application Requirements:** Applicants must submit one official transcript from current school, or most recent if not currently attending school; must submit a brief autobiography; one-page, typewritten essay answering why you've selected the hospitality industry for your career and what definition of hospitality is; must submit a type, signed and on letterhead recommendation letter from College or University; signature from Director/Dean. **Deadline for Receipt:** April 25. **Additional Information:** stephanie@chla.com

618 ■ COLUMBUS CITIZENS FOUNDATION

8 E 69th St.
New York, NY 10021

Tel: (212)249-9923
Fax: (212)737-4413
E-mail: ccf@columbuscitizens.org
Web Site: http://www.columbuscitizensfd.org
To provide financial assistance to underwrite the cost of Italian descent students' college tuition.
Title of Award: Columbus Citizens Foundation College Scholarships **Area, Field, or Subject:** General studies. **Level of Education for which Award is Granted:** Undergraduate **Funds Available:** No specific amount. **Duration:** Four years.
Eligibility Requirements: Applicants must be students who are of Italian descent and who are from households where the total gross income does not exceed $30,000 per capita; must have a minimum grade average of 85% or a 3.0 GPA; and must be residents of one of the following states: NY, NJ, DE, DC, MD, PA, VT, RI, ME, MA, NH, or CT. **Application Requirements:** Application is available for download in .pfd format and must be sent to the Private School Aid Service. **Deadline for Receipt:** February 1.

619 ■ COLUMBUS CITIZENS FOUNDATION

8 E 69th St.
New York, NY 10021
Tel: (212)249-9923
Fax: (212)737-4413
E-mail: ccf@columbuscitizens.org
Web Site: http://www.columbuscitizensfd.org
To provide educational assistance for students of Italian descent.
Title of Award: Columbus Citizens Foundation High School Scholarships **Area, Field, or Subject:** General studies. **Level of Education for which Award is Granted:** High School **Funds Available:** No specific amount.
Eligibility Requirements: Applicants must be students of Italian descent and must come from households where the total gross income does not exceed $25,000 per capita. Applicants must maintain a 3.0 GPA and demonstrate that they have performed community service activities. **Application Requirements:** Application is available for download in .pdf format and must be sent to the Private School Aid Service **Deadline for Receipt:** March 14.

620 ■ COMMUNICATIONS WORKERS OF AMERICA

7B-1050 Baxter Rd.
Ottawa, ON, Canada K2C 3P1
Tel: (613)820-9777; 877-486-4292
Fax: (613)820-8188
E-mail: info@cwa-scacanada.ca
Web Site: http://www.cwa-scacanada.ca
To raise professional standards and promote ethical business and journalistic practices.
Title of Award: Communications Workers of America Scholarships **Area, Field, or Subject:** General studies. **Level of Education for which Award is Granted:** Undergraduate **Funds Available:** $1,000.
Eligibility Requirements: Applicants must be full-time students at an accredited college, university, community college, technical or trade school. **Application Requirements:** Applicants must complete the application form. **Deadline for Receipt:** October 31.

621 ■ COMMUNITY FOUNDATION OF CALHOUN COUNTY

PO Box 1826
Anniston, AL 36202-1826
Tel: (256)231-5160
Fax: (256)231-5161
E-mail: info@yourcommunityfirst.org
Web Site: http://www.yourcommunityfirst.org
To help young men and women secure a college education.
Title of Award: Joe Bynum/Raymond James Investment Services Technical Excellence Scholarships Fund **Area, Field, or Subject:** General studies. **Level of Education for which Award is Granted:** Undergraduate **Funds Available:** $2,500.
Eligibility Requirements: Applicants must be graduates of Oxford High School in Calhoun County; must have a 2.5 average on a 4.0 scale; must be enrolled as part- or full-time students. **Application Requirements:** Applicants must submit a completed application form and an essay describing their personal aspirations, educational or career goals and how this scholarship will help in achieving their career goals. **Deadline for Receipt:** February 1.

622 ■ COMMUNITY FOUNDATION OF CALHOUN COUNTY
PO Box 1826
Anniston, AL 36202-1826
Tel: (256)231-5160
Fax: (256)231-5161
E-mail: info@yourcommunityfirst.org
Web Site: http://www.yourcommunityfirst.org
To provide financial resources enabling local students to pursue higher education at Auduburn University.
Title of Award: Calhoun County Auduburn University Scholarships **Area, Field, or Subject:** General studies. **Level of Education for which Award is Granted:** Undergraduate **Funds Available:** No specific amount.
Eligibility Requirements: Applicants must be graduates of any accredited public or private high school within Calhoun County; must have maintained 2.5 GPA on a 4.0 scale. **Application Requirements:** Applicants must submit a completed application form and an essay describing their personal aspirations, educational and career goals. **Deadline for Receipt:** February 1. **Additional Information:** info@yourcommunityfirst.org.

623 ■ COMMUNITY FOUNDATION OF CALHOUN COUNTY
PO Box 1826
Anniston, AL 36202-1826
Tel: (256)231-5160
Fax: (256)231-5161
E-mail: info@yourcommunityfirst.org
Web Site: http://www.yourcommunityfirst.org
To encourage young people to follow their dreams and to help lessen some of life's challenges.
Title of Award: Melanie and Todd Edmonson Memorial Scholarship **Area, Field, or Subject:** General studies. **Level of Education for which Award is Granted:** Undergraduate **Funds Available:** No specific amount.
Eligibility Requirements: Applicants must be graduates of Oxford High School or its successor; must have 3.0 or "B" average; must be actively involved in their community, school and religious activities; must be full or part-time enrolled students at an accredited institution of higher learning in the United States; may be pursuing any field of academic study or technical training. **Application Requirements:** Applicants must submit a completed application form, transcript of records, an essay describing their personal aspirations, educational or career goals and how this scholarship will help in achieving their career goals. **Deadline for Receipt:** February 1. **Additional Information:** info@yourcommunityfirst.org.

624 ■ COMMUNITY FOUNDATION OF CALHOUN COUNTY
PO Box 1826
Anniston, AL 36202-1826
Tel: (256)231-5160
Fax: (256)231-5161
E-mail: info@yourcommunityfirst.org
Web Site: http://www.yourcommunityfirst.org
To encourage high school seniors to attain a four-year college degree.
Title of Award: Farley Moody Galbraith Scholarship Fund **Area, Field, or Subject:** General studies. **Level of Education for which Award is Granted:** Undergraduate **Funds Available:** $2,500.
Eligibility Requirements: Applicants must be graduating seniors from any public or private high school including home school; must have 3.0 average on a 4.0 scale; must be enrolled as part- or full-time students. **Application Requirements:** Applicants must submit a completed application form and an essay describing their personal aspirations, educational or career goals and how this scholarship will help in achieving their career goals. **Deadline for Receipt:** February 1.

625 ■ COMMUNITY FOUNDATION OF CALHOUN COUNTY
PO Box 1826
Anniston, AL 36202-1826
Tel: (256)231-5160
Fax: (256)231-5161
E-mail: info@yourcommunityfirst.org
Web Site: http://www.yourcommunityfirst.org
To provide supplement funding for full- or part-time enrolled students at an accredited state college or university within Alabama.
Title of Award: Whitney Laine Gallahar Memorial Scholarship Fund **Area, Field, or Subject:** General studies. **Level of Education for which Award is Granted:** Undergraduate **Funds Available:** $1,000.
Eligibility Requirements: Applicants must be graduating seniors of Ohatchee High school or its successor institution; must have 2.5 GPA; must be enrolled as part- or full-time. **Application Requirements:** Applicants must submit a completed application form and an essay describing their personal aspirations, educational or career goals and how this scholarship will help in achieving their career goals. **Deadline for Receipt:** February 1.

626 ■ COMMUNITY FOUNDATION OF CALHOUN COUNTY
PO Box 1826
Anniston, AL 36202-1826
Tel: (256)231-5160
Fax: (256)231-5161
E-mail: info@yourcommunityfirst.org
Web Site: http://www.yourcommunityfirst.org
To provide full or supplemental funding for full-time enrolled students at an accredited state college or university within Alabama.
Title of Award: Cleve Holloway Memorial Scholarship Fund **Area, Field, or Subject:** General studies. **Level of Education for which Award is Granted:** Undergraduate **Funds Available:** No specific amount.
Eligibility Requirements: Applicants must be graduating seniors of Anniston High School or its successor institution; must maintain high personal standards and moral character; must have a minimum of 2.5 or "C" average on a 4.0 scale; must be enrolled full-time. **Application Requirements:** Applicants must submit a completed application form, transcript of records and an essay describing their personal aspirations, educational or career goals and how this scholarship will help in achieving their career goals. **Additional Information:** info@yourcommunityfirst.org.

627 ■ COMMUNITY FOUNDATION OF CALHOUN COUNTY
PO Box 1826
Anniston, AL 36202-1826
Tel: (256)231-5160
Fax: (256)231-5161
E-mail: info@yourcommunityfirst.org
Web Site: http://www.yourcommunityfirst.org
To provide supplement funding for full or part-time enrolled students at any accredited two-or-four-year college or university within the United States.
Title of Award: E.C. Lloyd and J.C.U. Johnson Scholarships Fund **Area, Field, or Subject:** General studies. **Level of Education for which Award is Granted:** Undergraduate **Funds Available:** $2,500.
Eligibility Requirements: Applicants must be graduating seniors from any public or private high school including home schools; must have 2.5 or "C" average on a 4.0 scale; must be enrolled as part- or full-time students. **Application Requirements:** Applicants must submit a completed application form and an essay describing their personal aspirations, educational or career goals and how this scholarship will help in achieving the career goal. **Deadline for Receipt:** February 1.

628 ■ COMMUNITY FOUNDATION OF CALHOUN COUNTY
PO Box 1826
Anniston, AL 36202-1826
Tel: (256)231-5160
Fax: (256)231-5161
E-mail: info@yourcommunityfirst.org
Web Site: http://www.yourcommunityfirst.org
To foster hope, self-confidence and ambition in the graduates of Anniston High School.
Title of Award: Reverend John S. Nettled Scholarship **Area, Field, or Subject:** General studies. **Level of Education for which Award is Granted:** Undergraduate **Funds Available:** No specific amount.
Eligibility Requirements: Applicants must be graduating seniors from Anniston high School; must have 2.5 GPA or above on a 4.0 scale. **Application Requirements:** Applicants must submit a completed application form and an essay describing the personal aspirations, educational and career goals. **Deadline for Receipt:** February 1. **Additional Information:** info@yourcommunityfirst.org.

629 ■ COMMUNITY FOUNDATION OF CALHOUN COUNTY
PO Box 1826
Anniston, AL 36202-1826
Tel: (256)231-5160
Fax: (256)231-5161
E-mail: info@yourcommunityfirst.org
Web Site: http://www.yourcommunityfirst.org
To support tuition assistance for students attending Sacred Heart of Jesus Catholic School in Anniston, Alabama.
Title of Award: Gerald Powell Scholarship **Area, Field, or Subject:** General studies. **Level of Education for which Award is Granted:** Undergraduate **Funds Available:** No specific amount.
Eligibility Requirements: Applicants must be enrolled on a full-time basis at Sacred Heart of Jesus Catholic School either in elementary or high school levels; must maintain a GPA of 2.5 or "C" on a 4.0 scale.
Application Requirements: Applicants must submit a completed application form. **Deadline for Receipt:** May 1.

630 ■ COMMUNITY FOUNDATION OF CALHOUN COUNTY
PO Box 1826
Anniston, AL 36202-1826
Tel: (256)231-5160
Fax: (256)231-5161
E-mail: info@yourcommunityfirst.org
Web Site: http://www.yourcommunityfirst.org
To foster educational opportunities for graduates of Saks High School; to provide full or supplemental funding for full-time enrolled students over a four-year period at an accredited college or university within the United States.
Title of Award: Joseph and Amelia Saks Scholarship Fund **Area, Field, or Subject:** General studies. **Level of Education for which Award is Granted:** Undergraduate **Funds Available:** No specific amount.
Eligibility Requirements: Applicants must be graduating senior students of Saks High School or it's successor institution; must have maintained high personal standards and moral character; must have a minimum of 2.5 or "C" average on a 4.0 scale; must be full-time students completing academics aligned with their specific major or degree. **Application Requirements:** Applicants must submit: a completed application form; an essay describing their personal aspirations, educational or career goals and how this scholarship will help in achieving their career goals; a signed letter of acceptance; certified proof of enrollment from an institution and confirmation that the recipient is enrolled; and an official college or university transcript at the end of academic term. **Deadline for Receipt:** February 1. **Additional Information:** info@yourcommunityfirst.org.

631 ■ COMMUNITY FOUNDATION OF CALHOUN COUNTY
PO Box 1826
Anniston, AL 36202-1826
Tel: (256)231-5160
Fax: (256)231-5161
E-mail: info@yourcommunityfirst.org
Web Site: http://www.yourcommunityfirst.org
To provide tuition assistance for students attending Sacred Heart of Jesus Catholic School in Anniston, Alabama.
Title of Award: Mark Dauglas Sawyer Memorial Scholarship **Area, Field, or Subject:** General studies. **Level of Education for which Award is Granted:** High School **Funds Available:** No specific amount.
Eligibility Requirements: Applicants must be enrolled on a full-time basis at the School of Sacred Heart of Jesus Catholic School either at the elementary or high school level; must have a "C" or 2.5 average on a 4.0 scale. **Application Requirements:** Applicants must submit a completed application form. **Deadline for Receipt:** May 1.

632 ■ COMMUNITY FOUNDATION OF CALHOUN COUNTY
PO Box 1826
Anniston, AL 36202-1826
Tel: (256)231-5160
Fax: (256)231-5161
E-mail: info@yourcommunityfirst.org
Web Site: http://www.yourcommunityfirst.org
To recognize the value of higher education and provide support for graduates of Anniston High School.
Title of Award: Leslie and Mary Ella Scales Memorial Scholarship **Area, Field, or Subject:** General studies. **Level of Education for which**

Award is Granted: Undergraduate Funds Available: No specific amount.
Eligibility Requirements: Applicants must be full-time or part-time students attending any accredited institution of higher learning in United States; may pursue any field of academic study or technical training. **Application Requirements:** Applicants must submit a completed application form. **Additional Information:** info@yourcommunityfirst.org.

633 ■ COMMUNITY FOUNDATION OF CALHOUN COUNTY
PO Box 1826
Anniston, AL 36202-1826
Tel: (256)231-5160
Fax: (256)231-5161
E-mail: info@yourcommunityfirst.org
Web Site: http://www.yourcommunityfirst.org
To provide supplemental funding for full or part-time enrolled students at an accredited college, university or technical institution within United States.
Title of Award: Nathan Sparks Memorial Scholarship **Area, Field, or Subject:** General studies. **Level of Education for which Award is Granted:** Undergraduate **Funds Available:** $1,000.
Eligibility Requirements: Applicants must be graduating seniors of Saks High School or its successor institution. **Application Requirements:** Applicants must submit a completed application form, an essay describing their personal character and two letters of recommendation. **Additional Information:** info@yourcommunityfirst.org.

634 ■ COMMUNITY FOUNDATION OF CALHOUN COUNTY
PO Box 1826
Anniston, AL 36202-1826
Tel: (256)231-5160
Fax: (256)231-5161
E-mail: info@yourcommunityfirst.org
Web Site: http://www.yourcommunityfirst.org
To supplement tuition at the baccalaureate level.
Title of Award: H.T. and Terrell Stanford Scholarship **Area, Field, or Subject:** General studies. **Level of Education for which Award is Granted:** Undergraduate **Funds Available:** No specific amount.
Eligibility Requirements: Applicants must be graduating senior students from Oxford High School; must maintain a GPA of 2.5 and have strong moral character as attested to by recommendations; must be recognized for school and community service. **Application Requirements:** Applicants must submit a completed application form and other documents are available at the guidance office of Oxford High School. **Deadline for Receipt:** February 1. **Additional Information:** info@yourcommunityfirst.org.

635 ■ COMMUNITY FOUNDATION OF CALHOUN COUNTY
PO Box 1826
Anniston, AL 36202-1826
Tel: (256)231-5160
Fax: (256)231-5161
E-mail: info@yourcommunityfirst.org
Web Site: http://www.yourcommunityfirst.org
To enhance the quality of life in Calhoun County, Alabama.
Title of Award: Mary Katherine "Kathy" Williamson Scholarship Fund **Area, Field, or Subject:** General studies. **Level of Education for which Award is Granted:** Undergraduate **Funds Available:** No specific amount.
Eligibility Requirements: Applicants must be individuals who have a diploma from any accredited public or private high school or who have earned the General Education Development (GED) certificate; must be residents of Calhoun County; must have a 2.5 overall GPA or better on a 4.0 scale. **Application Requirements:** Applicants must submit a completed application form, transcript of records, and an essay describing their personal aspirations, educational or career goals and how this scholarship will help in achieving their career goals. **Deadline for Receipt:** February 1. **Additional Information:** info@yourcommunityfirst.org.

636 ■ COMMUNITY FOUNDATION OF THE EASTERN SHORE
1324 Belmont Ave.
Salisbury, MD 21804

Tel: (410)742-9911
Fax: (410)742-6638
E-mail: info@cfes.org
Web Site: http://www.cfes.org
To empower donors to make a profound difference in the quality of life in Maryland's Lower Eastern Shore; to provide community leadership through grants, non-profit support programs, charitable partnerships and local initiatives in Somerset, Wicomico and Worcester counties.
Title of Award: William R. Bowen Scholarship **Area, Field, or Subject:** General studies. **Level of Education for which Award is Granted:** Undergraduate **Funds Available:** $1,000.
Eligibility Requirements: Applicants must be graduating seniors of Snow Hill High School. **Application Requirements:** Applicants must submit a completed application form.

637 ■ COMMUNITY FOUNDATION OF THE EASTERN SHORE
1324 Belmont Ave.
Salisbury, MD 21804
Tel: (410)742-9911
Fax: (410)742-6638
E-mail: info@cfes.org
Web Site: http://www.cfes.org
To empower donors to make a profound difference in the quality of life in Maryland's Lower Eastern Shore; to provide community leadership through grants, non-profit support programs, charitable partnerships and local initiatives in Somerset, Wicomico and Worcester counties.
Title of Award: William T. Burbage Family Memorial Scholarship **Area, Field, or Subject:** General studies. **Level of Education for which Award is Granted:** Undergraduate **Funds Available:** $1,000.
Eligibility Requirements: Applicants must be graduating seniors of Stephen Decatur High School who have selected their college and have been accepted for admission as full-time students; must have 3.0 GPA. **Application Requirements:** Applicants must submit a completed application form; an official high school transcript of grades; letter of acceptance from college or university; two letters of recommendation from non-family members; a detailed listing by high school year of activities and an essay explaining how growing up on the Eastern Shore has contributed the individual leadership style. **Deadline for Receipt:** April 15.

638 ■ COMMUNITY FOUNDATION OF THE EASTERN SHORE
1324 Belmont Ave.
Salisbury, MD 21804
Tel: (410)742-9911
Fax: (410)742-6638
E-mail: info@cfes.org
Web Site: http://www.cfes.org
To empower donors to make a profound difference in the quality of life in Maryland's Lower Eastern Shore; to provide community leadership through grants, non-profit support programs, charitable partnerships and local initiatives in Somerset, Wicomico and Worcester counties.
Title of Award: Irene Culver Collins and Louis Franklin Collins Scholarship **Area, Field, or Subject:** General studies. **Level of Education for which Award is Granted:** Undergraduate **Funds Available:** $5,000.
Eligibility Requirements: Applicants must be post-graduates or current 12th grade students of Parkside High School, Wicomico County, Maryland who have been accepted for admission as full-time college students; must have successfully completed a minimum of three advanced placement social studies during the enrollment at Parkside High School. **Application Requirements:** Applicants must submit a completed application form; an official high school transcript of grades; letter of acceptance from college or university; an essay describing the personal character and two letters of recommendation from non-family members. **Deadline for Receipt:** April 15.

639 ■ COMMUNITY FOUNDATION OF THE EASTERN SHORE
1324 Belmont Ave.
Salisbury, MD 21804
Tel: (410)742-9911
Fax: (410)742-6638
E-mail: info@cfes.org
Web Site: http://www.cfes.org
To empower donors to make a profound difference in the quality of life in Maryland's Lower Eastern Shore; to provide community leadership

through grants, non-profit support programs, charitable partnerships and local initiatives in Somerset, Wicomico and Worcester counties.
Title of Award: Eastern Shore Builder's Association Scholarships **Area, Field, or Subject:** General studies. **Level of Education for which Award is Granted:** Undergraduate **Funds Available:** $500.
Eligibility Requirements: Applicants must be current 12th grade students of high schools in Eastern Shore of Maryland counties of Kent, Queen Anne's, Caroline, Talbot, Dorchester, Somerset and Worcester who have been accepted for admission as full-time students; must have a minimum of 2.5 GPA on a 4.0 scale; must be participated in some extracurricular activities. **Application Requirements:** Applicants must submit a completed application form; an official high school transcript of grades; letter of acceptance from college or university; must submit an essay describing the reasons of choosing the career path and two letters of recommendation from non-family members. **Deadline for Receipt:** April 1.

640 ■ COMMUNITY FOUNDATION OF THE EASTERN SHORE
1324 Belmont Ave.
Salisbury, MD 21804
Tel: (410)742-9911
Fax: (410)742-6638
E-mail: info@cfes.org
Web Site: http://www.cfes.org
To empower donors to make a profound difference in the quality of life in Maryland's Lower Eastern Shore; to provide community leadership through grants, non-profit support programs, charitable partnerships and local initiatives in Somerset, Wicomico and Worcester counties.
Title of Award: Federalsburg Rotary Club Scholarships **Area, Field, or Subject:** General studies. **Level of Education for which Award is Granted:** Undergraduate **Funds Available:** $500.
Eligibility Requirements: Applicants must be graduating seniors of Colonel Richardson High School who have selected their college and have been accepted for admission as full-time students; must have 2.5 GPA. **Application Requirements:** Applicants must submit a completed application form; an official high school transcript of grades and letter of acceptance from college or university.

641 ■ COMMUNITY FOUNDATION OF THE EASTERN SHORE
1324 Belmont Ave.
Salisbury, MD 21804
Tel: (410)742-9911
Fax: (410)742-6638
E-mail: info@cfes.org
Web Site: http://www.cfes.org
To empower donors to make a profound difference in the quality of life in Maryland's Lower Eastern Shore; to provide community leadership through grants, non-profit support programs, charitable partnerships and local initiatives in Somerset, Wicomico and Worcester counties.
Title of Award: Green Hill Yacht and Country Club Scholarships **Area, Field, or Subject:** General studies. **Level of Education for which Award is Granted:** Undergraduate **Funds Available:** $1,000.
Eligibility Requirements: Applicants must be graduating seniors of any Wicomico, Somerset or Worcester County School; must be past graduates or current 12th grade students who have been accepted for admission as full-time students in an accredited four-year college or university or accredited two-year educational/vocational institution. **Application Requirements:** Applicants must submit a completed application form, an official high school transcript of grades and two letters of recommendation from non-family member. **Deadline for Receipt:** April 15.

642 ■ COMMUNITY FOUNDATION OF THE EASTERN SHORE
1324 Belmont Ave.
Salisbury, MD 21804
Tel: (410)742-9911
Fax: (410)742-6638
E-mail: info@cfes.org
Web Site: http://www.cfes.org
To empower donors to make a profound difference in the quality of life in Maryland's Lower Eastern Shore; to provide community leadership through grants, non-profit support programs, charitable partnerships and local initiatives in Somerset, Wicomico and Worcester counties.

Title of Award: Gruwell Scholarships **Area, Field, or Subject:** General studies. **Level of Education for which Award is Granted:** Undergraduate **Funds Available:** $1,000.

Eligibility Requirements: Applicants must be residents of Lake Forest School District, Kent County, Delaware who have selected their college and have been accepted for admission as full-time students. **Application Requirements:** Applicants must submit a completed application form, an official high school transcript of grades and letter of acceptance from college or university; must submit a copy of parent/guardian and student's most recent income tax return and two letters of recommendation from non-family members.

643 ■ COMMUNITY FOUNDATION OF THE EASTERN SHORE
1324 Belmont Ave.
Salisbury, MD 21804
Tel: (410)742-9911
Fax: (410)742-6638
E-mail: info@cfes.org
Web Site: http://www.cfes.org
To empower donors to make a profound difference in the quality of life in Maryland's Lower Eastern Shore; to provide community leadership through grants, non-profit support programs, charitable partnerships and local initiatives in Somerset, Wicomico and Worcester counties.

Title of Award: Hancock Family Snow Hill High School Scholarships **Area, Field, or Subject:** General studies. **Level of Education for which Award is Granted:** Undergraduate **Funds Available:** $2,000.

Eligibility Requirements: Applicants must be graduating seniors at Snow Hill High School who have been accepted by an Accredited academic college program; must have 2.5 GPA in appropriate course work indicating the students are able to be successful at the college level; must have three or more year residents of Snow Hill area; must be active in school activity, church, community and youth clubs; must have good moral character. **Application Requirements:** Applicants must submit a completed application form; an official high school transcript of grades; letter of acceptance from college or university; a copy of parent/guardian and student's most recent income tax return and two letters of recommendation from non-family members. **Deadline for Receipt:** April 21.

644 ■ COMMUNITY FOUNDATION OF THE EASTERN SHORE
1324 Belmont Ave.
Salisbury, MD 21804
Tel: (410)742-9911
Fax: (410)742-6638
E-mail: info@cfes.org
Web Site: http://www.cfes.org
To empower donors to make a profound difference in the quality of life in Maryland's Lower Eastern Shore; to provide community leadership through grants, non-profit support programs, charitable partnerships and local initiatives in Somerset, Wicomico and Worcester counties.

Title of Award: Martin S. Kane Memorial Community Service Award Scholarships **Area, Field, or Subject:** General studies. **Level of Education for which Award is Granted:** Undergraduate **Funds Available:** $600.

Eligibility Requirements: Applicants must be from Wicomico High School. **Application Requirements:** Applicants must submit a completed application form.

645 ■ COMMUNITY FOUNDATION OF THE EASTERN SHORE
1324 Belmont Ave.
Salisbury, MD 21804
Tel: (410)742-9911
Fax: (410)742-6638
E-mail: info@cfes.org
Web Site: http://www.cfes.org
To empower donors to make a profound difference in the quality of life in Maryland's Lower Eastern Shore; to provide community leadership through grants, non-profit support programs, charitable partnerships and local initiatives in Somerset, Wicomico and Worcester counties.

Title of Award: TFC Edward A. Plank, Jr. Memorial Scholarship **Area, Field, or Subject:** General studies. **Level of Education for which Award is Granted:** Undergraduate **Funds Available:** $1,000.

Eligibility Requirements: Applicants must be graduating seniors of any Wicomico, Somerset or Worcester County School; must have 3.0 overall GPA; must be accepted in a full-time basis at an accredited two-to-four-year college. **Application Requirements:** Applicants must submit a completed application form, a "500-word" essay on how crimes and/or drug abuse have affected today's society and personal letters of recommendation from two responsible adults other than relatives. **Deadline for Receipt:** March 31.

646 ■ COMMUNITY FOUNDATION OF THE EASTERN SHORE
1324 Belmont Ave.
Salisbury, MD 21804
Tel: (410)742-9911
Fax: (410)742-6638
E-mail: info@cfes.org
Web Site: http://www.cfes.org
To empower donors to make a profound difference in the quality of life in Maryland's Lower Eastern Shore; to provide community leadership through grants, non-profit support programs, charitable partnerships and local initiatives in Somerset, Wicomico and Worcester counties.

Title of Award: Progress Lane Scholarships **Area, Field, or Subject:** General studies. **Level of Education for which Award is Granted:** Undergraduate **Funds Available:** $500.

Eligibility Requirements: Applicants must be current graduating 12th grade students of Washington High School, Princess Anne, Maryland who are financially advantaged and have been accepted for admission as students with a minimum of six credit hours in a course of study that will serve the educational requirements for their chosen career. **Application Requirements:** Applicants must submit a completed application form; an official high school transcript of grades; a letter of acceptance from college; university or training institute and "250-word" essay describing the reasons of wanting to attend college. **Deadline for Receipt:** April 1.

647 ■ COMMUNITY FOUNDATION OF THE EASTERN SHORE
1324 Belmont Ave.
Salisbury, MD 21804
Tel: (410)742-9911
Fax: (410)742-6638
E-mail: info@cfes.org
Web Site: http://www.cfes.org
To empower donors to make a profound difference in the quality of life in Maryland's Lower Eastern Shore; to provide community leadership through grants, non-profit support programs, charitable partnerships and local initiatives in Somerset, Wicomico and Worcester counties.

Title of Award: Duane V. Puerde Memorial Scholarship **Area, Field, or Subject:** General studies. **Level of Education for which Award is Granted:** Undergraduate **Funds Available:** $500.

Eligibility Requirements: Applicants must be past graduates or current 12th grade students of Parkside High school who are residents of rural Eastern Wicomico County, Maryland including but not exclusive to the communities of Parsonburg, Pittsville, Powellville, Williards or Melson who have been accepted for admission as full-time college students or vocational school. **Application Requirements:** Applicants must submit a completed application form, an official high school transcript of grades and two letters of recommendation from non-family members.

648 ■ COMMUNITY FOUNDATION OF THE EASTERN SHORE
1324 Belmont Ave.
Salisbury, MD 21804
Tel: (410)742-9911
Fax: (410)742-6638
E-mail: info@cfes.org
Web Site: http://www.cfes.org
To empower donors to make a profound difference in the quality of life in Maryland's Lower Eastern Shore; to provide community leadership through grants, non-profit support programs, charitable partnerships and local initiatives in Somerset, Wicomico and Worcester counties.

Title of Award: Elizabeth Pusey Scholarship **Area, Field, or Subject:** General studies. **Level of Education for which Award is Granted:** Undergraduate **Funds Available:** $1,000.

Eligibility Requirements: Applicants must be graduating seniors at any Wicomico County high school who have selected their college and have been accepted from admission as full-time students; must be in the top 10% of their class. **Application Requirements:** Applicants must submit a completed application form, an official transcript of grades ad letter of acceptance from college or university. **Deadline for Receipt:** April 1.

649 ■ COMMUNITY FOUNDATION OF THE EASTERN SHORE
1324 Belmont Ave.
Salisbury, MD 21804
Tel: (410)742-9911
Fax: (410)742-6638
E-mail: info@cfes.org
Web Site: http://www.cfes.org
To empower donors to make a profound difference in the quality of life in Maryland's Lower Eastern Shore; to provide community leadership through grants, non-profit support programs, charitable partnerships and local initiatives in Somerset, Wicomico and Worcester counties.
Title of Award: Lana K. Rinehart Scholarship **Area, Field, or Subject:** General studies. **Level of Education for which Award is Granted:** Undergraduate **Funds Available:** $1,000.
Eligibility Requirements: Applicants must be graduating senior students at Parkside High School. **Application Requirements:** Applicants must submit a completed application form.

650 ■ COMMUNITY FOUNDATION OF THE EASTERN SHORE
1324 Belmont Ave.
Salisbury, MD 21804
Tel: (410)742-9911
Fax: (410)742-6638
E-mail: info@cfes.org
Web Site: http://www.cfes.org
To empower donors to make a profound difference in the quality of life in Maryland's Lower Eastern Shore; to provide community leadership through grants, non-profit support programs, charitable partnerships and local initiatives in Somerset, Wicomico and Worcester counties.
Title of Award: Drew Smith Memorial Scholarship **Area, Field, or Subject:** General studies. **Level of Education for which Award is Granted:** Undergraduate **Funds Available:** $1,000.
Eligibility Requirements: Applicants must be adults or graduating public or private high school seniors who are pursuing a degree in golf turf management from an accredited college or university and must be domiciled residents of the Eastern Shore Counties of Maryland and Virginia or the State of Delaware; must be enrolled in college for a minimum of six credit hours per scholastic year. **Application Requirements:** Applicants must submit a completed application form. **Deadline for Receipt:** July 14.

651 ■ COMMUNITY FOUNDATION OF THE EASTERN SHORE
1324 Belmont Ave.
Salisbury, MD 21804
Tel: (410)742-9911
Fax: (410)742-6638
E-mail: info@cfes.org
Web Site: http://www.cfes.org
To empower donors to make a profound difference in the quality of life in Maryland's Lower Eastern Shore; to provide community leadership through grants, non-profit support programs, charitable partnerships and local initiatives in Somerset, Wicomico and Worcester counties.
Title of Award: Esther M. Smith Scholarship **Area, Field, or Subject:** General studies. **Level of Education for which Award is Granted:** Undergraduate **Funds Available:** $2,000. **Duration:** One year.
Eligibility Requirements: Applicants must be graduating seniors with a disability as accepted defined by the Americans with Disabilities Act (ADA) who attended in Wicomico County; must be nominated by their school principal, guidance counselor or teacher; must have a minimum GPA of 2.0 and have been accepted for admission as full-time students at an accredited four-year college or university or a two-year education or career training institution. **Application Requirements:** Applicants must submit completed application form; an official high school transcript of grades and letter of recommendation from non-family members. **Deadline for Receipt:** April 1.

652 ■ COMMUNITY FOUNDATION OF THE EASTERN SHORE
1324 Belmont Ave.
Salisbury, MD 21804
Tel: (410)742-9911
Fax: (410)742-6638
E-mail: info@cfes.org
Web Site: http://www.cfes.org
To empower donors to make a profound difference in the quality of life in Maryland's Lower Eastern Shore; to provide community leadership through grants, non-profit support programs, charitable partnerships and local initiatives in Somerset, Wicomico and Worcester counties.
Title of Award: Wicomico High School Class of '55 Scholarships **Area, Field, or Subject:** General studies. **Level of Education for which Award is Granted:** Undergraduate **Funds Available:** $1,000.
Eligibility Requirements: Applicants must be graduating senior students of Wicomico High School who have spent at least their junior and senior years in that school's program; must have selected their college and have been accepted for admission as full-time students; must have 3.0 cumulative GPA. **Application Requirements:** Applicants must submit a completed application form; an official high school transcript of grades; letter of acceptance from college or university; three letters of recommendation from non-family members and "250-word" essay on "How they can make a difference". **Deadline for Receipt:** April 15.

653 ■ COMMUNITY FOUNDATION OF THE EASTERN SHORE
1324 Belmont Ave.
Salisbury, MD 21804
Tel: (410)742-9911
Fax: (410)742-6638
E-mail: info@cfes.org
Web Site: http://www.cfes.org
To empower donors to make a profound difference in the quality of life in Maryland's Lower Eastern Shore; to provide community leadership through grants, non-profit support programs, charitable partnerships and local initiatives in Somerset, Wicomico and Worcester counties.
Title of Award: M. William and Frances J. Tilghman Scholarship **Area, Field, or Subject:** General studies. **Level of Education for which Award is Granted:** Undergraduate **Funds Available:** $1,500.
Eligibility Requirements: Applicants must be graduating high school senior students of Somerset County. **Application Requirements:** Applicants must submit a completed application form; an official high school transcript of grades; letter of acceptance from a college or university and two letters of recommendation from non-family members. **Deadline for Receipt:** April 15.

654 ■ COMMUNITY FOUNDATION OF THE FOX RIVER VALLEY
111 W Downer Place, Ste. 312
Aurora, IL 60506-6106
E-mail: info@communityfoundationfrv.org
Web Site: http://www.communityfoundationfrv.org
To enhance and support the quality of life in the Fox River Valley of Illinois.
Title of Award: Community Foundation of the Fox River Valley Scholarships **Area, Field, or Subject:** General studies. **Level of Education for which Award is Granted:** Undergraduate **Funds Available:** No specific amount.
Eligibility Requirements: Applicants must be students who will attend an accredited institution of higher learning on a full-time basis and whose permanent residence is within the Foundation's service area. **Application Requirements:** Applicants must submit a completed application form. **Additional Information:** 630-896-7800.

655 ■ COMMUNITY FOUNDATION FOR GREATER NEW HAVEN
70 Audubon St.
New Haven, CT 06510-9755
Tel: (203)777-2386
Fax: (203)787-6584
E-mail: contactus@cfgnh.org
Web Site: http://www.cfgnh.org
To create positive and sustainable change in Greater New Haven by increasing the amount of and enhancing the impact of community philanthropy and to provide college scholarships based on financial need.
Title of Award: Bambey Bailey Scholarships **Area, Field, or Subject:** General studies. **Level of Education for which Award is Granted:** Undergraduate **Funds Available:** No specific amount.
Eligibility Requirements: Applicants must be students from New Haven who may not consider college as an option; must demonstrate an interest and ability in writing; must attend or plan to attend Wellesley College. **Application Requirements:** Applicants must complete the application form and attach a personal essay; academic verification; letter of recommenda-

tion; and Parent/Guardian IRS Form. **Deadline for Receipt:** March 21. **Additional Information:** 203-777-7097; 203-787-6584.

656 ■ COMMUNITY FOUNDATION FOR GREATER NEW HAVEN

70 Audubon St.
New Haven, CT 06510-9755
Tel: (203)777-2386
Fax: (203)787-6584
E-mail: contactus@cfgnh.org
Web Site: http://www.cfgnh.org
To create positive and sustainable change in Greater New Haven by increasing the amount of and enhancing the impact of community philanthropy.
Title of Award: George J. Bysiewicz Scholarship Fund **Area, Field, or Subject:** General studies. **Level of Education for which Award is Granted:** Undergraduate **Funds Available:** No specific amount.
Eligibility Requirements: Applicants must be students from New Haven, Catholic School planning to attend Sacred Heart Academy and Notre Dame High School. **Application Requirements:** Applicants must complete the application form and attach a personal essay; academic verification; letter of recommendation; and Parent/Guardian IRS Form. **Deadline for Receipt:** March 21. **Additional Information:** 203-777-7097; 203-787-6584.

657 ■ COMMUNITY FOUNDATION FOR GREATER NEW HAVEN

70 Audubon St.
New Haven, CT 06510-9755
Tel: (203)777-2386
Fax: (203)787-6584
E-mail: contactus@cfgnh.org
Web Site: http://www.cfgnh.org
To create positive and sustainable change in Greater New Haven by increasing the amount of and enhancing the impact of community philanthropy.
Title of Award: Murtha Cullina Scholarships **Area, Field, or Subject:** General Studies. **Level of Education for which Award is Granted:** Undergraduate **Funds Available:** No specific amount.
Eligibility Requirements: Applicants must be students from the greater New Haven area planning to attend a college or university. **Application Requirements:** Applicants must complete the application form and attach a personal essay; academic verification; letter of recommendation; and Parent/Guardian IRS Form. **Deadline for Receipt:** March 21. **Additional Information:** 203-777-7097; 203-787-6584.

658 ■ COMMUNITY FOUNDATION FOR GREATER NEW HAVEN

70 Audubon St.
New Haven, CT 06510-9755
Tel: (203)777-2386
Fax: (203)787-6584
E-mail: contactus@cfgnh.org
Web Site: http://www.cfgnh.org
To create positive and sustainable change in Greater New Haven by increasing the amount of and enhancing the impact of community philanthropy.
Title of Award: John S. Martinez and Family Scholarships Fund **Area, Field, or Subject:** General studies. **Level of Education for which Award is Granted:** Undergraduate **Funds Available:** No specific amount.
Eligibility Requirements: Applicants must be students in an institution or university. **Application Requirements:** Applicants must complete the application form and must attach a personal essay; academic verification; letter of recommendation; and Parent/Guardian IRS Form. **Deadline for Receipt:** March 21. **Additional Information:** 203-777-7097; 203-787-6584.

659 ■ COMMUNITY FOUNDATION FOR GREATER NEW HAVEN

70 Audubon St.
New Haven, CT 06510-9755
Tel: (203)777-2386
Fax: (203)787-6584
E-mail: contactus@cfgnh.org
Web Site: http://www.cfgnh.org

To create positive and sustainable change in Greater New Haven by increasing the amount of and enhancing the impact of community philanthropy.
Title of Award: Charles L. Terrell/New Haven Savings Bank Scholarship Fund **Area, Field, or Subject:** General studies. **Level of Education for which Award is Granted:** Undergraduate **Funds Available:** No specific amount.
Eligibility Requirements: Applicants must be high school students with financial need who have demonstrated a commitment to community service. **Application Requirements:** Applicants must complete the application form and attach a personal essay; academic verification; letter of recommendation; and parent/Guardian IRS Form. **Deadline for Receipt:** March 21. **Additional Information:** 203-777-7097; 203-787-6584.

660 ■ COMMUNITY FOUNDATION FOR GREATER NEW HAVEN

70 Audubon St.
New Haven, CT 06510-9755
Tel: (203)777-2386
Fax: (203)787-6584
E-mail: contactus@cfgnh.org
Web Site: http://www.cfgnh.org
To create positive and sustainable change in Greater New Haven by increasing the amount of and enhancing the impact of community philanthropy.
Title of Award: Ruth and Sherman Zudekoff Scholarships **Area, Field, or Subject:** General studies. **Level of Education for which Award is Granted:** Undergraduate **Funds Available:** No specific amount.
Eligibility Requirements: Applicants must be students graduating from secondary school in regions served by the foundation. **Application Requirements:** Applicants must complete the application form and attach a personal essay; academic verification; letter of recommendation; and Parent/Guardian IRS Form. **Deadline for Receipt:** March 21. **Additional Information:** 203-777-7097; 203-787-6584.

661 ■ COMMUNITY FOUNDATION OF GREENE COUNTY

PO Box 768
Waynesburg, PA 15370
Tel: (724)627-2010
Fax: (724)627-2011
E-mail: cfgcpa@gmail.com
Web Site: http://www.cfgcpa.org
To maintain and enhance the educational, social, cultural, health and civic resources of the community through support of qualified non-profit organizations.
Title of Award: The William H. Davis, Jr. Scholarship Fund **Area, Field, or Subject:** General studies. **Level of Education for which Award is Granted:** Undergraduate **Number Awarded:** 2. **Funds Available:** $500.
Eligibility Requirements: Applicants must be graduating seniors of Southeastern Greene School District or its equivalent; must be accepted students at Westmoreland County Community College as full-time students or registered for a minimum of 12 credit hours; must be qualified for no more than three-quarters financial aid. **Application Requirements:** Applicants must submit five copies of their FAFSA, Special Condition Form, verification of GPA from the guidance counselor, copy of acceptance letter from WCCC and attendance record.

662 ■ COMMUNITY FOUNDATION OF GREENE COUNTY

PO Box 768
Waynesburg, PA 15370
Tel: (724)627-2010
Fax: (724)627-2011
E-mail: cfgcpa@gmail.com
Web Site: http://www.cfgcpa.org
To maintain and enhance the educational, social, cultural, health and civic resources of the community through support of qualified non-profit organizations.
Title of Award: The Thelma S. Hoge Memorial Scholarship Fund **Area, Field, or Subject:** General studies. **Level of Education for which Award is Granted:** Undergraduate **Funds Available:** $1,000.
Eligibility Requirements: Applicants must be graduating seniors from West Greene; must be accepted at a post-secondary or four-year college degree program; must have a minimum GPA of 3.0. **Application Requirements:** Applicants must provide a brief essay about themselves; copy of high school transcript and two character references.

663 ■ COMMUNITY FOUNDATION OF GREENE COUNTY
PO Box 768
Waynesburg, PA 15370
Tel: (724)627-2010
Fax: (724)627-2011
E-mail: cfgcpa@gmail.com
Web Site: http://www.cfgcpa.org
To provide an annual need-based scholarship to the Jefferson-Morgan High School.
Title of Award: The Renardo A. Matteucci Scholarship Fund **Area, Field, or Subject:** General studies. **Level of Education for which Award is Granted:** Undergraduate **Funds Available:** $1,000.
Eligibility Requirements: Applicants must be graduating students from Jefferson-Morgan High School; must be planning to pursue a Bachelor Degree, an Associate Degree or a Diploma from a trade school; must have a minimum GPA of 2.75. **Application Requirements:** Applicants must submit five copies of their FAFSA, Special Condition Form, verification of their GPA from guidance counselor, an official attendance record and post-secondary acceptance letter. **Deadline for Receipt:** April 15.

664 ■ COMMUNITY FOUNDATION OF GREENE COUNTY
PO Box 768
Waynesburg, PA 15370
Tel: (724)627-2010
Fax: (724)627-2011
E-mail: cfgcpa@gmail.com
Web Site: http://www.cfgcpa.org
To assist graduating senior class members of Carmichaels High School to continue post-secondary education.
Title of Award: The Walter Samek III Memorial Scholarship Fund **Area, Field, or Subject:** General studies. **Level of Education for which Award is Granted:** Undergraduate **Funds Available:** No specific amount.
Eligibility Requirements: Applicants must be Carmichaels senior boys or girls who are enrolled in an approved post-secondary college/university; must have a 3.5 GPA. **Application Requirements:** Applicants must submit a completed application form. **Deadline for Receipt:** April 15.

665 ■ THE COMMUNITY FOUNDATION OF MIDDLE TENNESSEE
3833 Cleghorn Ave., Ste. 400
Nashville, TN 37215-2519
Tel: (615)321-4939; 888-540-5200
E-mail: mail@cfmt.org
Web Site: http://www.cfmt.org
To help students in planning their postsecondary education.
Title of Award: Lt. Holly Adams Memorial Scholarship **Area, Field, or Subject:** General studies. **Level of Education for which Award is Granted:** Undergraduate **Funds Available:** No specific amount.
Eligibility Requirements: Applicants must be students from the Page High School area in Williamson County who not only achieve, but also possess the integrity, courage, and caring spirit to help others achieve. **Application Requirements:** Applicants must complete the application form. Applicants must submit two applicant appraisals; transcript of grades; student essay describing educational plans and how these will help in career goals. Applicants must submit one recent photograph. **Deadline for Receipt:** March 15. **Additional Information:** pcole@cfmt.org

666 ■ THE COMMUNITY FOUNDATION OF MIDDLE TENNESSEE
3833 Cleghorn Ave., Ste. 400
Nashville, TN 37215-2519
Tel: (615)321-4939; 888-540-5200
E-mail: mail@cfmt.org
Web Site: http://www.cfmt.org
To help students in planning their postsecondary education.
Title of Award: Kathy D. and Stephen J. Anderson Scholarships **Area, Field, or Subject:** General studies. **Level of Education for which Award is Granted:** Undergraduate **Funds Available:** Maximum amount of $10,000.
Eligibility Requirements: Applicants must be graduate students from the Page High School area in Williamson County, who have attended for a minimum of three years. Applicants must be in good standing as citizens

in the school and community. Applicants must have a 3.2 or better GPA and minimum ACT score of 22 or SAT of 1100. Applicants must be involved in at least one extracurricular activity. **Application Requirements:** Applicants must complete the application form. Applicants must submit two applicant appraisals; transcript of grades; student essay describing educational plans and how these will help in career goals. Applicants must submit one recent photograph. **Deadline for Receipt:** March 15. **Additional Information:** pcole@cfmt.org

667 ■ THE COMMUNITY FOUNDATION OF MIDDLE TENNESSEE
3833 Cleghorn Ave., Ste. 400
Nashville, TN 37215-2519
Tel: (615)321-4939; 888-540-5200
E-mail: mail@cfmt.org
Web Site: http://www.cfmt.org
To help students in planning their postsecondary education.
Title of Award: Dody Boyd Scholarships **Area, Field, or Subject:** General studies. **Level of Education for which Award is Granted:** Undergraduate **Funds Available:** No specific amount.
Eligibility Requirements: Applicants must be seniors graduating from Cheatham County Central High School and wishing to attend a two-year community college/technical school or four-year university. Applicants must have a GPA of at least 2.5 or better and an ACT score of 20 or better. **Application Requirements:** Applicants must complete the application form. Applicants must submit two applicant appraisals; transcript of grades; student essay describing educational plans and how these will help in career goals. Applicants must submit one recent photograph. **Deadline for Receipt:** March 15. **Additional Information:** pcole@cfmt.org

668 ■ THE COMMUNITY FOUNDATION OF MIDDLE TENNESSEE
3833 Cleghorn Ave., Ste. 400
Nashville, TN 37215-2519
Tel: (615)321-4939; 888-540-5200
E-mail: mail@cfmt.org
Web Site: http://www.cfmt.org
To help students in planning their postsecondary education.
Title of Award: JoAhn Brown-Nash Memorial Scholarships **Area, Field, or Subject:** General studies. **Level of Education for which Award is Granted:** Undergraduate **Funds Available:** No specific amount.
Eligibility Requirements: Applicants must be female students at Fisk University, entering their junior year, who exemplify outstanding leadership skills, with a GPA of 3.2 or above. **Application Requirements:** Applicants must complete the application form. Applicants must submit two applicant appraisals; transcript of grades; student essay describing educational plans and how these will help in career goals. Applicants must submit one recent photograph. **Deadline for Receipt:** March 15. **Additional Information:** pcole@cfmt.org

669 ■ THE COMMUNITY FOUNDATION OF MIDDLE TENNESSEE
3833 Cleghorn Ave., Ste. 400
Nashville, TN 37215-2519
Tel: (615)321-4939; 888-540-5200
E-mail: mail@cfmt.org
Web Site: http://www.cfmt.org
To help students in planning their postsecondary education.
Title of Award: William and Clara Bryan Scholarships **Area, Field, or Subject:** General studies. **Level of Education for which Award is Granted:** Undergraduate **Funds Available:** No specific amount.
Eligibility Requirements: Applicants must be high school seniors, or college freshmen, sophomores or juniors who are from Giles County, Tennessee and have lived there for the majority of their pre-college schooling. **Application Requirements:** Applicants must complete the application form. Applicants must submit two applicant appraisals; transcript of grades; student essay describing educational plans and how these will help in career goals. Applicants must submit one recent photograph. **Deadline for Receipt:** March 15. **Additional Information:** pcole@cfmt.org

670 ■ THE COMMUNITY FOUNDATION OF MIDDLE TENNESSEE
3833 Cleghorn Ave., Ste. 400
Nashville, TN 37215-2519
Tel: (615)321-4939; 888-540-5200

E-mail: mail@cfmt.org
Web Site: http://www.cfmt.org
To help students in planning their postsecondary education.
Title of Award: Cheatham County Scholarships **Area, Field, or Subject:** General Studies. **Level of Education for which Award is Granted:** Undergraduate **Funds Available:** No specific amount.
Eligibility Requirements: Applicants must be Cheatham County, Tennessee residents for a minimum period of one year. Applicants must have a high school diploma or GED with a GPA of 2.0 or better. Applicants must attend an accredited college, university, or technical school and maintain a grade point average of 2.0 or better. **Application Requirements:** Applicants must complete the application form. Applicants must submit two applicant appraisals; transcript of grades; student essay describing educational plans and how these will help in career goals. Applicants must submit one recent photograph. **Deadline for Receipt:** March 15. **Additional Information:** pcole@cfmt.org

671 ■ THE COMMUNITY FOUNDATION OF MIDDLE TENNESSEE
3833 Cleghorn Ave., Ste. 400
Nashville, TN 37215-2519
Tel: (615)321-4939; 888-540-5200
E-mail: mail@cfmt.org
Web Site: http://www.cfmt.org
To help students in planning their postsecondary education.
Title of Award: Choose Your Future Scholarships **Area, Field, or Subject:** General studies. **Level of Education for which Award is Granted:** Undergraduate **Funds Available:** No specific amount.
Eligibility Requirements: Applicants must be graduates of the Metropolitan Nashville Public School of Davidson County with a minimum GPA of 2.5 and a score of 21 on the ACT. Applicants must be attending a college or university in the United States. **Application Requirements:** Applicants must complete the application form. Applicants must submit two applicant appraisals; transcript of grades; student essay describing educational plans and how these will help in career goals. Applicants must submit one recent photograph. **Deadline for Receipt:** March 15. **Additional Information:** pcole@cfmt.org

672 ■ THE COMMUNITY FOUNDATION OF MIDDLE TENNESSEE
3833 Cleghorn Ave., Ste. 400
Nashville, TN 37215-2519
Tel: (615)321-4939; 888-540-5200
E-mail: mail@cfmt.org
Web Site: http://www.cfmt.org
To help students in planning their postsecondary education.
Title of Award: The Community Foundation DBI Scholarships **Area, Field, or Subject:** General studies. **Level of Education for which Award is Granted:** Undergraduate **Funds Available:** No specific amount.
Eligibility Requirements: Applicants must be graduating high school seniors, undergraduates and graduates enrolling or enrolled at an accredited college/university, junior college or technical/vocational school on a full-time basis, maintaining a B average or better. **Application Requirements:** Applicants must complete the application form. Applicants must submit two applicant appraisals; transcript of grades; student essay describing educational plans and how these will help in career goals. Applicants must submit one recent photograph. **Deadline for Receipt:** March 15. **Additional Information:** pcole@cfmt.org

673 ■ THE COMMUNITY FOUNDATION OF MIDDLE TENNESSEE
3833 Cleghorn Ave., Ste. 400
Nashville, TN 37215-2519
Tel: (615)321-4939; 888-540-5200
E-mail: mail@cfmt.org
Web Site: http://www.cfmt.org
To help students in planning their postsecondary education.
Title of Award: The Community Foundation Student Education Loans **Area, Field, or Subject:** General studies. **Level of Education for which Award is Granted:** Undergraduate **Funds Available:** No specific amount.
Eligibility Requirements: Applicants must be young men or women whose parents have discontinued financial support for their education because they are gay or lesbian. **Application Requirements:** Applicants must complete the application form. Applicants must submit two applicant

appraisals; transcript of grades; student essay describing the educational plans and how these will help in career goals. Applicants must submit one recent photograph. **Deadline for Receipt:** March 15. **Additional Information:** pcole@cfmt.org

674 ■ THE COMMUNITY FOUNDATION OF MIDDLE TENNESSEE
3833 Cleghorn Ave., Ste. 400
Nashville, TN 37215-2519
Tel: (615)321-4939; 888-540-5200
E-mail: mail@cfmt.org
Web Site: http://www.cfmt.org
To help students in planning their postsecondary education.
Title of Award: B.J. Dean Scholarships **Area, Field, or Subject:** General studies. **Level of Education for which Award is Granted:** Undergraduate **Funds Available:** No specific amount.
Eligibility Requirements: Applicants must be a female preparing for full-time ministry, but scholarship is not limited to those seeking ordination or serving in any particular denomination. Applicant must be a resident of Tennessee or Texas or be enrolled in Yale Dignity School. **Application Requirements:** Applicants must complete the application form. Applicants must submit two applicant appraisals; transcript of grades; student essay describing educational plans and how these will help in career goals. Applicants must submit one recent photograph. **Deadline for Receipt:** March 15. **Additional Information:** pcole@cfmt.org

675 ■ THE COMMUNITY FOUNDATION OF MIDDLE TENNESSEE
3833 Cleghorn Ave., Ste. 400
Nashville, TN 37215-2519
Tel: (615)321-4939; 888-540-5200
E-mail: mail@cfmt.org
Web Site: http://www.cfmt.org
To help students in planning their postsecondary education.
Title of Award: Jimmy Edwards Scholarships **Area, Field, or Subject:** General studies. **Level of Education for which Award is Granted:** Undergraduate **Funds Available:** No specific amount.
Eligibility Requirements: Applicants must be past students or graduates of Donelson High School, and descendents of alumni of Donelson High School. **Application Requirements:** Applicants must complete the application form. Applicants must submit two applicant appraisals; transcript of grades; student essay describing educational plans and how these will help in career goals. Applicants must submit one recent photograph. **Deadline for Receipt:** March 15. **Additional Information:** pcole@cfmt.org

676 ■ THE COMMUNITY FOUNDATION OF MIDDLE TENNESSEE
3833 Cleghorn Ave., Ste. 400
Nashville, TN 37215-2519
Tel: (615)321-4939; 888-540-5200
E-mail: mail@cfmt.org
Web Site: http://www.cfmt.org
To help students in planning their postsecondary education.
Title of Award: Pauline LaFon Gore Scholarships **Area, Field, or Subject:** General studies. **Level of Education for which Award is Granted:** Undergraduate **Funds Available:** No specific amount.
Eligibility Requirements: Applicants must be high school seniors and current college underclassmen who are from Smith County, Tennessee and have lived there for the majority of their pre-college schooling. **Application Requirements:** Applicants must complete the application form. Applicants must submit two applicant appraisals; transcript of grades; student essay describing educational plans and how these will help in career goals. Applicants must submit one recent photograph. **Deadline for Receipt:** March 15. **Additional Information:** pcole@cfmt.org

677 ■ THE COMMUNITY FOUNDATION OF MIDDLE TENNESSEE
3833 Cleghorn Ave., Ste. 400
Nashville, TN 37215-2519
Tel: (615)321-4939; 888-540-5200
E-mail: mail@cfmt.org
Web Site: http://www.cfmt.org
To help students in planning their postsecondary education.
Title of Award: Frank and Charlene Harris Scholarships **Area, Field, or Subject:** General studies. **Level of Education for which Award is Granted:** Undergraduate **Funds Available:** No specific amount.

Eligibility Requirements: Applicants must be seniors of Cumberland Gap High School in Clairborne County, TN. Applicants should have a GPA of 3.0 or higher at the time of the application. **Application Requirements:** Applicants must complete the application form. Applicants must submit two applicant appraisals; transcript of grades; student essay describing educational plans and how these will help in career goals. Applicants must submit one recent photograph. **Deadline for Receipt:** March 15. **Additional Information:** pcole@cfmt.org

678 ■ THE COMMUNITY FOUNDATION OF MIDDLE TENNESSEE
3833 Cleghorn Ave., Ste. 400
Nashville, TN 37215-2519
Tel: (615)321-4939; 888-540-5200
E-mail: mail@cfmt.org
Web Site: http://www.cfmt.org
To help students in planning their postsecondary education.
Title of Award: Jennifer Ingrum Scholarships **Area, Field, or Subject:** General studies. **Level of Education for which Award is Granted:** Undergraduate **Number Awarded:** 2. **Funds Available:** $2,000.
Eligibility Requirements: Applicants must be students who qualify academically for college but need financial assistance. **Application Requirements:** Applicants must complete the application form. Applicants must submit two applicant appraisals; transcript of grades; student essay describing educational plans and how these will help in career goals. Applicants must submit one recent photograph. **Deadline for Receipt:** March 15. **Additional Information:** pcole@cfmt.org

679 ■ THE COMMUNITY FOUNDATION OF MIDDLE TENNESSEE
3833 Cleghorn Ave., Ste. 400
Nashville, TN 37215-2519
Tel: (615)321-4939; 888-540-5200
E-mail: mail@cfmt.org
Web Site: http://www.cfmt.org
To help students in planning their postsecondary education.
Title of Award: Knox-Hume Scholarships **Area, Field, or Subject:** General studies. **Level of Education for which Award is Granted:** Undergraduate **Funds Available:** No specific amount.
Eligibility Requirements: Applicants must be graduates of Hume-Fogg High School who exhibit academic merit and financial need. **Application Requirements:** Applicants must complete the application form. Applicants must submit two applicant appraisals; transcript of grades; student essay describing educational plans and how these will help in career goals. Applicants must submit one recent photograph. **Deadline for Receipt:** March 15. **Additional Information:** pcole@cfmt.org

680 ■ THE COMMUNITY FOUNDATION OF MIDDLE TENNESSEE
3833 Cleghorn Ave., Ste. 400
Nashville, TN 37215-2519
Tel: (615)321-4939; 888-540-5200
E-mail: mail@cfmt.org
Web Site: http://www.cfmt.org
To help students in planning their postsecondary education.
Title of Award: Michael B. Kruse Scholarships **Area, Field, or Subject:** Accounting. **Level of Education for which Award is Granted:** Undergraduate **Funds Available:** No specific amount.
Eligibility Requirements: Applicants must be rising juniors, seniors, and graduate students majoring in accounting. Applicants must be residents of Tennessee and attend an accredited college/university in the State of Tennessee. Applicants must maintain a minimum GPA of 3.2 or better. **Application Requirements:** Applicants must complete the application form. Applicants must submit two applicant appraisals; transcript of grades; student essay describing educational plans and how these will help in career goals. Applicants must submit one recent photograph. **Deadline for Receipt:** March 15. **Additional Information:** pcole@cfmt.org

681 ■ THE COMMUNITY FOUNDATION OF MIDDLE TENNESSEE
3833 Cleghorn Ave., Ste. 400
Nashville, TN 37215-2519
Tel: (615)321-4939; 888-540-5200
E-mail: mail@cfmt.org
Web Site: http://www.cfmt.org
To help students in planning their postsecondary education.
Title of Award: Heloise Werthan Kuhn Scholarships **Area, Field, or Subject:** General studies. **Level of Education for which Award is Granted:** Undergraduate **Funds Available:** No specific amount.

Eligibility Requirements: Applicants must be pregnant or parenting teens. Applicants must be enrolled or planning to enroll in postsecondary education at an accredited college, university, junior college, technical school, or job training program as a way to increase their job skills and become more employable. **Application Requirements:** Applicants must complete the application form. Applicants must submit two applicant appraisals; transcript of grades; student essay describing the educational plans and how these will help in career goals. Applicants must submit one recent photograph. **Deadline for Receipt:** March 15. **Additional Information:** pcole@cfmt.org

682 ■ THE COMMUNITY FOUNDATION OF MIDDLE TENNESSEE
3833 Cleghorn Ave., Ste. 400
Nashville, TN 37215-2519
Tel: (615)321-4939; 888-540-5200
E-mail: mail@cfmt.org
Web Site: http://www.cfmt.org
To help students in planning their postsecondary education. To provide financial assistance to students who would be otherwise unable to take qualifying entrance exams to institutions of higher learning and to provide gifted students financial assistance to attend academic programs that offer intellecutally-accelerated content.
Title of Award: Diane G. Lowe and John Gomez, IV Scholarships **Area, Field, or Subject:** General studies. **Level of Education for which Award is Granted:** Undergraduate **Funds Available:** No specific amount.
Eligibility Requirements: Applicants must be students with financial need in Grades 6-12 who reside in Rutherford, Cannon, Dekalb, or Wilson Counties. **Application Requirements:** Applicants must complete the application form. Applicants must submit two applicant appraisals; transcript of grades; student essay describing educational plans and how these will help in career goals. Applicants must submit one recent photograph. **Deadline for Receipt:** March 15. **Additional Information:** pcole@cfmt.org

683 ■ THE COMMUNITY FOUNDATION OF MIDDLE TENNESSEE
3833 Cleghorn Ave., Ste. 400
Nashville, TN 37215-2519
Tel: (615)321-4939; 888-540-5200
E-mail: mail@cfmt.org
Web Site: http://www.cfmt.org
To help students in planning their postsecondary education.
Title of Award: Juliann and Joseph Maxwell Scholarships **Area, Field, or Subject:** General studies. **Level of Education for which Award is Granted:** Undergraduate **Funds Available:** No specific amount.
Eligibility Requirements: Applicants must be high school seniors, college freshmen, sophomores, and juniors who are dependent children, including adopted and stepchildren of employees, or full-time or part-time employees of the Tractor Supply Company. **Application Requirements:** Applicants must complete the application form. Applicants must submit two applicant appraisals; transcript of grades; student essay describing their educational plans and how these will help in career goals. Applicants must submit one recent photograph. **Deadline for Receipt:** March 15. **Additional Information:** pcole@cfmt.org

684 ■ THE COMMUNITY FOUNDATION OF MIDDLE TENNESSEE
3833 Cleghorn Ave., Ste. 400
Nashville, TN 37215-2519
Tel: (615)321-4939; 888-540-5200
E-mail: mail@cfmt.org
Web Site: http://www.cfmt.org
To help students in planning their postsecondary education.
Title of Award: Juliann King Maxwell Scholarships for Students in White County, Arkansas **Area, Field, or Subject:** General studies. **Level of Education for which Award is Granted:** Undergraduate **Funds Available:** No specific amount.
Eligibility Requirements: Applicants must be graduating seniors from Riverview High School or prior recipients of this scholarship. **Application Requirements:** Applicants must complete the application form. Applicants must submit two applicant appraisals; transcript of grades; student essay describing educational plans and how these will help in career goals. Applicants must submit one recent photograph. **Deadline for Receipt:** March 15. **Additional Information:** pcole@cfmt.org

685 ■ THE COMMUNITY FOUNDATION OF MIDDLE TENNESSEE
3833 Cleghorn Ave., Ste. 400
Nashville, TN 37215-2519
Tel: (615)321-4939; 888-540-5200
E-mail: mail@cfmt.org
Web Site: http://www.cfmt.org
To help students in planning their postsecondary education.
Title of Award: John E. Mayfield ABLE Scholarships **Area, Field, or Subject:** General studies. **Level of Education for which Award is Granted:** Undergraduate **Funds Available:** No specific amount.
Eligibility Requirements: Applicants must be graduating seniors and be participants of the ABLE program. **Application Requirements:** Applicants must complete the application form. Applicants must submit two applicant appraisals; transcript of grades; student essay describing educational plans and how these will help in career goals. Applicants must submit one recent photograph. **Deadline for Receipt:** March 15. **Additional Information:** pcole@cfmt.org

686 ■ THE COMMUNITY FOUNDATION OF MIDDLE TENNESSEE
3833 Cleghorn Ave., Ste. 400
Nashville, TN 37215-2519
Tel: (615)321-4939; 888-540-5200
E-mail: mail@cfmt.org
Web Site: http://www.cfmt.org
To help students in planning their postsecondary education.
Title of Award: John E. Mayfield Scholarships for Cheatham County Central High School **Area, Field, or Subject:** General studies. **Level of Education for which Award is Granted:** Undergraduate **Funds Available:** No specific amount.
Eligibility Requirements: Applicants must be alumni and/or graduating seniors of Cheatham County Central High School in Cheatham County, Tennessee; Applicants must be residents of Cheatham County and have a grade point average of 2.0 or better. **Application Requirements:** Applicants must complete the application form. Applicants must submit two applicant appraisals; transcript of grades; student essay describing educational plans and how these will help in career goals. Applicants must submit one recent photograph. **Deadline for Receipt:** March 15. **Additional Information:** pcole@cfmt.org

687 ■ THE COMMUNITY FOUNDATION OF MIDDLE TENNESSEE
3833 Cleghorn Ave., Ste. 400
Nashville, TN 37215-2519
Tel: (615)321-4939; 888-540-5200
E-mail: mail@cfmt.org
Web Site: http://www.cfmt.org
To help students in planning their postsecondary education.
Title of Award: John E. Mayfield Scholarships for Harpeth High School **Area, Field, or Subject:** General studies. **Level of Education for which Award is Granted:** Undergraduate **Funds Available:** No specific amount.
Eligibility Requirements: Applicants must be alumni and/or graduating seniors of Harpeth High School in Cheatham County, Tennessee. Applicants must be residents of Cheatham County and have a GPA of 2.0 or better. **Application Requirements:** Applicants must complete the application form. Applicants must submit two applicant appraisals; transcript of grades; student essay describing educational plans and how these will help in career goals. Applicants must submit one recent photograph. **Deadline for Receipt:** March 15. **Additional Information:** pcole@cfmt.org

688 ■ THE COMMUNITY FOUNDATION OF MIDDLE TENNESSEE
3833 Cleghorn Ave., Ste. 400
Nashville, TN 37215-2519
Tel: (615)321-4939; 888-540-5200
E-mail: mail@cfmt.org
Web Site: http://www.cfmt.org
To help students in planning their postsecondary education.
Title of Award: John E. Mayfield Scholarships Pleasant View Christian School **Area, Field, or Subject:** General studies. **Level of Education for which Award is Granted:** Undergraduate **Funds Available:** No specific amount.
Eligibility Requirements: Applicants must be alumni and/or graduating seniors of Pleasant View Christian School in Cheatham County, Tennes-

see. Applicants must be residents of Cheatham County and have a GPA of 2.0 or better. **Application Requirements:** Applicants must complete the application form. Applicants must submit two applicant appraisals; transcript of grades; student essay describing educational plans and how these will help in career goals. Applicants must submit one recent photograph. **Deadline for Receipt:** March 15. **Additional Information:** pcole@cfmt.org

689 ■ THE COMMUNITY FOUNDATION OF MIDDLE TENNESSEE
3833 Cleghorn Ave., Ste. 400
Nashville, TN 37215-2519
Tel: (615)321-4939; 888-540-5200
E-mail: mail@cfmt.org
Web Site: http://www.cfmt.org
To help students in planning their postsecondary education.
Title of Award: John E. Mayfield Scholarships for Sycamore High School **Area, Field, or Subject:** General studies. **Level of Education for which Award is Granted:** Undergraduate **Funds Available:** No specific amount.
Eligibility Requirements: Applicants must be alumni and/or graduating seniors of Sycamore High School in Cheatham County, Tennessee. Applicants must be residents of Cheatham County and have a GPA of 2.0 or better. **Application Requirements:** Applicants must complete the application form. Applicants must submit two applicant appraisals; transcript of grades; student essay describing educational plans and how these will help in career goals. Applicants must submit one recent photograph. **Deadline for Receipt:** March 15. **Additional Information:** pcole@cfmt.org

690 ■ THE COMMUNITY FOUNDATION OF MIDDLE TENNESSEE
3833 Cleghorn Ave., Ste. 400
Nashville, TN 37215-2519
Tel: (615)321-4939; 888-540-5200
E-mail: mail@cfmt.org
Web Site: http://www.cfmt.org
To help students in planning their postsecondary education.
Title of Award: Archie Hartwell Nash Memorial Scholarships **Area, Field, or Subject:** General studies. **Level of Education for which Award is Granted:** Undergraduate **Funds Available:** No specific amount.
Eligibility Requirements: Applicants must be Middle Tennessee State University sophomores or above including graduate students who are working at a minimum of 20 hours and have a GPA of 2.0 or better. **Application Requirements:** Applicants must complete the application form. Applicants must submit two applicant appraisals; transcript of grades; student essay describing educational plans and how these will help in career goals. Applicants must submit one recent photograph. **Deadline for Receipt:** March 15. **Additional Information:** pcole@cfmt.org

691 ■ THE COMMUNITY FOUNDATION OF MIDDLE TENNESSEE
3833 Cleghorn Ave., Ste. 400
Nashville, TN 37215-2519
Tel: (615)321-4939; 888-540-5200
E-mail: mail@cfmt.org
Web Site: http://www.cfmt.org
To help students in planning their postsecondary education.
Title of Award: Jerry Newson Scholarships **Area, Field, or Subject:** General studies. **Level of Education for which Award is Granted:** Undergraduate **Funds Available:** No specific amount.
Eligibility Requirements: Applicants must currently reside in Davidson County, Tennessee. High school graduates and adults are encouraged to apply. Applicants must be pursuing a degree in the social sciences or areas where they will be helping and giving back to their community. **Application Requirements:** Applicants must complete the application form. Applicants must submit two applicant appraisals; transcript of grades; student essay describing educational plans and how these will help in career goals. Applicants must submit one recent photograph. **Deadline for Receipt:** March 15. **Additional Information:** pcole@cfmt.org

692 ■ THE COMMUNITY FOUNDATION OF MIDDLE TENNESSEE
3833 Cleghorn Ave., Ste. 400
Nashville, TN 37215-2519
Tel: (615)321-4939; 888-540-5200
E-mail: mail@cfmt.org

Web Site: http://www.cfmt.org
To help students in planning their postsecondary education.
Title of Award: Buster Pool Memorial Scholarships **Area, Field, or Subject:** General studies. **Level of Education for which Award is Granted:** Undergraduate **Funds Available:** No specific amount.
Eligibility Requirements: Applicants must be graduating seniors of Meridian High School in Meridian, Mississippi and/or previous recipients of this scholarship. Applicants must have a GPA of 2.5 or higher at the time of application. **Application Requirements:** Applicants must complete the application form. Applicants must submit two applicant appraisals; transcript of grades; student essay describing educational plans and how these will help in career goals. Applicants must submit one recent photograph. **Deadline for Receipt:** March 15. **Additional Information:** pcole@cfmt.org

693 ■ THE COMMUNITY FOUNDATION OF MIDDLE TENNESSEE
3833 Cleghorn Ave., Ste. 400
Nashville, TN 37215-2519
Tel: (615)321-4939; 888-540-5200
E-mail: mail@cfmt.org
Web Site: http://www.cfmt.org
To help students in planning their postsecondary education.
Title of Award: Barbara Hagan Richards Scholarships **Area, Field, or Subject:** General studies. **Level of Education for which Award is Granted:** Undergraduate **Funds Available:** No specific amount.
Eligibility Requirements: Applicants must be graduating seniors, undergraduates, and/or graduate students currently enrolled in a college/university and/or alumni of any high school located and serving Giles County, Tennessee. Applicants must have a GPA of 3.0. **Application Requirements:** Applicants must complete the application form. Applicants must submit two applicant appraisals; transcript of grades; student essay describing educational plans and how these will help in career goals. Applicants must submit one recent photograph. **Deadline for Receipt:** March 15. **Additional Information:** pcole@cfmt.org

694 ■ THE COMMUNITY FOUNDATION OF MIDDLE TENNESSEE
3833 Cleghorn Ave., Ste. 400
Nashville, TN 37215-2519
Tel: (615)321-4939; 888-540-5200
E-mail: mail@cfmt.org
Web Site: http://www.cfmt.org
To help students in planning their postsecondary education.
Title of Award: James Edward "Bill" Richards Scholarships **Area, Field, or Subject:** General studies. **Level of Education for which Award is Granted:** Undergraduate **Funds Available:** No specific amount.
Eligibility Requirements: Applicants must be graduating seniors, undergraduates, and/or alumni of East High School in Nashville, Tennessee. Applicants must have a GPA of at least 3.0. **Application Requirements:** Applicants must complete the application form. Applicants must submit two applicant appraisals; transcript of grades; student essay describing educational plans and how these will help in career goals. Applicants must submit one recent photograph. **Deadline for Receipt:** March 15. **Additional Information:** pcole@cfmt.org

695 ■ THE COMMUNITY FOUNDATION OF MIDDLE TENNESSEE
3833 Cleghorn Ave., Ste. 400
Nashville, TN 37215-2519
Tel: (615)321-4939; 888-540-5200
E-mail: mail@cfmt.org
Web Site: http://www.cfmt.org
To help students in planning their postsecondary education.
Title of Award: Meyer and Dorothy Silverman Scholarships **Area, Field, or Subject:** General studies. **Level of Education for which Award is Granted:** Undergraduate **Funds Available:** No specific amount.
Eligibility Requirements: Applicants must be students in Grade 7 to 12 in Oak Ridge Public Schools who are committed to developing their talents as string instrument players but who, otherwise, would be financially unable to take private string instruction. **Application Requirements:** Applicants must complete the application form. Applicants must submit two applicant appraisals; transcript of grades; student essay describing educational plans and how these will help in career goals. Applicants must submit one recent photograph. **Deadline for Receipt:** March 15. **Additional Information:** pcole@cfmt.org

696 ■ THE COMMUNITY FOUNDATION OF MIDDLE TENNESSEE
3833 Cleghorn Ave., Ste. 400
Nashville, TN 37215-2519
Tel: (615)321-4939; 888-540-5200
E-mail: mail@cfmt.org
Web Site: http://www.cfmt.org
To help students in planning their postsecondary education.
Title of Award: Richie Stevenson Scholarships **Area, Field, or Subject:** General studies. **Level of Education for which Award is Granted:** Undergraduate **Funds Available:** No specific amount.
Eligibility Requirements: Applicants must be graduates of Benton Hall School who wish to attend a technical school, vocational school, community college, junior or four-year college or university. **Application Requirements:** Applicants must complete the application form. Applicants must submit two applicant appraisals; transcript of grades; student essay describing educational plans and how these will help in career goals. Applicants must submit one recent photograph. **Deadline for Receipt:** March 15. **Additional Information:** pcole@cfmt.org

697 ■ THE COMMUNITY FOUNDATION OF MIDDLE TENNESSEE
3833 Cleghorn Ave., Ste. 400
Nashville, TN 37215-2519
Tel: (615)321-4939; 888-540-5200
E-mail: mail@cfmt.org
Web Site: http://www.cfmt.org
To help students in planning their postsecondary education.
Title of Award: Tennessee Trucking Association Scholarships **Area, Field, or Subject:** General studies. **Level of Education for which Award is Granted:** Undergraduate **Funds Available:** No specific amount.
Eligibility Requirements: Applicants must be Tennessee residents who are dependent children, spouses or employees who are members in good standing of the Tennessee Trucking Association. Applicants must be entering their junior or senior years at accredited colleges or universities located in the State of Tennessee. **Application Requirements:** Applicants must complete the application form. Applicants must submit two applicant appraisals; transcript of grades; student essay describing the educational plans and how these will help in career goals. Applicants must submit one recent photograph. **Deadline for Receipt:** March 15. **Additional Information:** pcole@cfmt.org

698 ■ THE COMMUNITY FOUNDATION OF MIDDLE TENNESSEE
3833 Cleghorn Ave., Ste. 400
Nashville, TN 37215-2519
Tel: (615)321-4939; 888-540-5200
E-mail: mail@cfmt.org
Web Site: http://www.cfmt.org
To help students in planning their postsecondary education.
Title of Award: Teddy Wilburn Scholarships **Area, Field, or Subject:** General studies. **Level of Education for which Award is Granted:** Undergraduate **Funds Available:** No specific amount.
Eligibility Requirements: Applicants must be students enrolling or currently enrolled at Tennessee State University or Vanderbilt University; Applicants must have at least a B grade average overall during the last two years of high school; must have attended high school within the 40 counties of Middle Tennessee for the majority of high school. **Application Requirements:** Applicants must complete the application form. Applicants must submit two applicant appraisals; transcript of grades; student essay describing educational plans and how these will help in career goals. Applicants must submit one recent photograph. **Deadline for Receipt:** March 15. **Additional Information:** pcole@cfmt.org

699 ■ THE COMMUNITY FOUNDATION OF MIDDLE TENNESSEE
3833 Cleghorn Ave., Ste. 400
Nashville, TN 37215-2519
Tel: (615)321-4939; 888-540-5200
E-mail: mail@cfmt.org
Web Site: http://www.cfmt.org
To help students in planning their postsecondary education.
Title of Award: The Woman's Club of Nashville Scholarships **Area, Field, or Subject:** General studies. **Level of Education for which Award is Granted:** Undergraduate **Funds Available:** No specific amount.
Eligibility Requirements: Applicants must be women residing in Davidson County, Tennessee. Applicants must be graduating high school

seniors or high school graduates with a GPA of 3.0 or higher. **Application Requirements:** Applicants must complete the application form. Applicants must submit two applicant appraisals; transcript of grades; student essay describing educational plans and how these will help in career goals. Applicants must submit one recent photograph. **Deadline for Receipt:** March 15. **Additional Information:** pcole@cfmt.org

700 ■ COMMUNITY FOUNDATION OF NORTHERN ILLINOIS

946 N 2nd St.
Rockford, IL 61107
Tel: (815)962-2110
Fax: (815)962-2116
Web Site: http://www.cfnil.org
To serve the four county area (Boone, Ogle, Stephenson and Winnebago) through philanthropy; to provide leadership in meeting charitable needs and to be a responsible steward to the Foundation's donors and of the Foundation's endowment.
Title of Award: Richard L. Bernardi Memorial Scholarship **Area, Field, or Subject:** General studies. **Level of Education for which Award is Granted:** Undergraduate **Funds Available:** No specific amount.
Eligibility Requirements: Applicants must be attending or planning to attend Rock Valley College; must be committed to completing a bachelor's degree; must have an at least 2.0 GPA. **Application Requirements:** Applicants must submit a completed application form, verification form, an official college transcript in a sealed envelope and two completed recommendation forms. **Deadline for Receipt:** March 1. **Additional Information:** jpatterson@cfnil.org.

701 ■ COMMUNITY FOUNDATION OF NORTHERN ILLINOIS

946 N 2nd St.
Rockford, IL 61107
Tel: (815)962-2110
Fax: (815)962-2116
Web Site: http://www.cfnil.org
To serve the four county area (Boone, Ogle, Stephenson and Winnebago) through philanthropy; to provide leadership in meeting charitable needs and to be a responsible steward to the Foundation's donors and of the Foundation's endowment.
Title of Award: Lindsay Buster Memorial Scholarship **Area, Field, or Subject:** General studies. **Level of Education for which Award is Granted:** Undergraduate **Funds Available:** No specific amount.
Eligibility Requirements: Applicants must be graduating senior athletes from Jefferson High school who have participated in high school sports for a minimum of three years including their senior year; must have 2.5 or higher cumulative GPA; must have plans to attend a two-or-four year college or university. **Application Requirements:** Applicants must submit a completed application form, verification form, an official transcript in a sealed envelope and two letters of recommendation. **Deadline for Receipt:** March 1. **Additional Information:** jpatterson@cfnil.org.

702 ■ COMMUNITY FOUNDATION OF NORTHERN ILLINOIS

946 N 2nd St.
Rockford, IL 61107
Tel: (815)962-2110
Fax: (815)962-2116
Web Site: http://www.cfnil.org
To serve the four county area (Boone, Ogle, Stephenson and Winnebago) through philanthropy; to provide leadership in meeting charitable needs and to be a responsible steward to the Foundation's donors and of the Foundation's endowment.
Title of Award: Joe Carnes Scholarship **Area, Field, or Subject:** General studies. **Level of Education for which Award is Granted:** Undergraduate **Funds Available:** No specific amount.
Eligibility Requirements: Applicants must be graduating senior students at Crystal Lake South High School with a GPA of at least 3.0. **Application Requirements:** Applicants must submit a completed application form, verification form, an official transcript in a sealed envelope, two letters of recommendation and a copy of their FAFSA. **Deadline for Receipt:** March 1. **Additional Information:** jpatterson@cfnil.org.

703 ■ COMMUNITY FOUNDATION OF NORTHERN ILLINOIS

946 N 2nd St.
Rockford, IL 61107

Tel: (815)962-2110
Fax: (815)962-2116
Web Site: http://www.cfnil.org
To serve the four county area (Boone, Ogle, Stephenson and Winnebago) through philanthropy; to provide leadership in meeting charitable needs and to be a responsible steward to the Foundation's donors and of the Foundation's endowment.
Title of Award: May Cassioppi Scholarship **Area, Field, or Subject:** General studies. **Level of Education for which Award is Granted:** Undergraduate **Funds Available:** No specific amount.
Eligibility Requirements: Applicants must be former Guilford High school swimmers and/or divers; must exhibit character traits of strength, discipline, leadership, teamwork and loyalty. **Application Requirements:** Applicants must submit a completed application form, verification form, an official transcript in a sealed envelope, two letters of recommendation and a copy of their FAFSA. **Deadline for Receipt:** March 1. **Additional Information:** jpatterson@cfnil.org.

704 ■ COMMUNITY FOUNDATION OF NORTHERN ILLINOIS

946 N 2nd St.
Rockford, IL 61107
Tel: (815)962-2110
Fax: (815)962-2116
Web Site: http://www.cfnil.org
To serve the four county area (Boone, Ogle, Stephenson and Winnebago) through philanthropy; to provide leadership in meeting charitable needs and to be a responsible steward to the Foundation's donors and of the Foundation's endowment.
Title of Award: Harry H. and Floy B. Chapin Scholarship **Area, Field, or Subject:** General studies. **Level of Education for which Award is Granted:** Undergraduate **Funds Available:** No specific amount.
Eligibility Requirements: Applicants must be graduating senior students from Durand, Dakota or Pecatonica High school; must rank in top 15% of graduating class; must plan to attend a recognized college or university. **Application Requirements:** Applicants must submit a completed application form, verification form, an official transcript in a sealed envelope and two letters of recommendation. **Deadline for Receipt:** March 1. **Additional Information:** jpatterson@cfnil.org.

705 ■ COMMUNITY FOUNDATION OF NORTHERN ILLINOIS

946 N 2nd St.
Rockford, IL 61107
Tel: (815)962-2110
Fax: (815)962-2116
Web Site: http://www.cfnil.org
To serve the four county area (Boone, Ogle, Stephenson and Winnebago) through philanthropy; to provide leadership in meeting charitable needs and to be a responsible steward to the Foundation's donors and of the Foundation's endowment.
Title of Award: Community Foundation Scholarships **Area, Field, or Subject:** General studies. **Level of Education for which Award is Granted:** Undergraduate **Funds Available:** No specific amount.
Eligibility Requirements: Applicants must be graduating senior students and residents of Winnebago county; must have an at least 2.75 or higher GPA and have plans to attend a college, university or trade school. **Application Requirements:** Applicants must submit a completed application form, verification form, an official transcript in a sealed envelope, two letters of recommendation and a copy of their FAFSA. **Deadline for Receipt:** March 1. **Additional Information:** jpatterson@cfnil.org.

706 ■ COMMUNITY FOUNDATION OF NORTHERN ILLINOIS

946 N 2nd St.
Rockford, IL 61107
Tel: (815)962-2110
Fax: (815)962-2116
Web Site: http://www.cfnil.org
To serve the four county area (Boone, Ogle, Stephenson and Winnebago) through philanthropy; to provide leadership in meeting charitable needs and to be a responsible steward to the Foundation's donors and of the Foundation's endowment.
Title of Award: Margaret T. Craig Community Service Scholarship **Area, Field, or Subject:** General studies. **Level of Education for which Award is Granted:** Undergraduate **Funds Available:** No specific amount.

Eligibility Requirements: Applicants must be high school graduates under the age of 23 or graduating seniors with a permanent address in Winnebago County; must have a plan to pursue a two or four-year degree at an accredited college, university or trade school; must have a minimum of 2.75 GPA. **Application Requirements:** Applicants must submit a completed application form, verification form, an official transcript in a sealed envelope and two letters of recommendation. **Deadline for Receipt:** March 1. **Additional Information:** jpatterson@cfnil.org.

707 ■ COMMUNITY FOUNDATION OF NORTHERN ILLINOIS
946 N 2nd St.
Rockford, IL 61107
Tel: (815)962-2110
Fax: (815)962-2116
Web Site: http://www.cfnil.org
To serve the four county area (Boone, Ogle, Stephenson and Winnebago) through philanthropy; to provide leadership in meeting charitable needs and to be a responsible steward to the Foundation's donors and of the Foundation's endowment; to provide educational resources to Pecatonica High School senior students who are pursuing higher education.
Title of Award: John Flynn Memorial Scholarship **Area, Field, or Subject:** General studies. **Level of Education for which Award is Granted:** Undergraduate **Funds Available:** No specific amount.
Eligibility Requirements: Applicants must be graduating Pecatonica High School senior students who are pursuing higher education; must have at least a 2.0 GPA on a 4.0 scale and have been involved in community service. **Application Requirements:** Applicants must submit a completed application form, verification form, an official transcript in a sealed envelope and two letters of recommendation. **Deadline for Receipt:** March 1. **Additional Information:** jpatterson@cfnil.org.

708 ■ COMMUNITY FOUNDATION OF NORTHERN ILLINOIS
946 N 2nd St.
Rockford, IL 61107
Tel: (815)962-2110
Fax: (815)962-2116
Web Site: http://www.cfnil.org
To serve the four county area (Boone, Ogle, Stephenson and Winnebago) through philanthropy; to provide leadership in meeting charitable needs and to be a responsible steward to the Foundation's donors and of the Foundation's endowment.
Title of Award: Susan Kay Munson Gilmore Memorial Scholarship **Area, Field, or Subject:** General studies. **Level of Education for which Award is Granted:** Undergraduate **Funds Available:** No specific amount.
Eligibility Requirements: Applicants must be graduating senior students or former graduates of a Guilford or Mendota Township high school; must have "C" or better average; and must be pursuing a vocational career. **Application Requirements:** Applicants must submit a completed application form, verification form, an official transcript in a sealed envelope, two letters of recommendation and a copy of their FAFSA. **Deadline for Receipt:** March 1. **Additional Information:** jpatterson@cfnil.org.

709 ■ COMMUNITY FOUNDATION OF NORTHERN ILLINOIS
946 N 2nd St.
Rockford, IL 61107
Tel: (815)962-2110
Fax: (815)962-2116
Web Site: http://www.cfnil.org
To serve the four county area (Boone, Ogle, Stephenson and Winnebago) through philanthropy; to provide leadership in meeting charitable needs and to be a responsible steward to the Foundation's donors and of the Foundation's endowment; to provide educational resources to graduating seniors, current college students or non-traditional students.
Title of Award: Nettie and Jesse Gorov Scholarship **Level of Education for which Award is Granted:** Undergraduate **Funds Available:** No specific amount.
Eligibility Requirements: Applicants must plan to attend an accredited two or four-year school. **Application Requirements:** Applicants must submit a completed application form, verification form, an official transcript in a sealed envelope, two letters of recommendation and a copy of their FAFSA. **Deadline for Receipt:** March 1. **Additional Information:** jpatterson@cfnil.org.

710 ■ COMMUNITY FOUNDATION OF NORTHERN ILLINOIS
946 N 2nd St.
Rockford, IL 61107
Tel: (815)962-2110
Fax: (815)962-2116
Web Site: http://www.cfnil.org
To serve the four county area (Boone, Ogle, Stephenson and Winnebago) through philanthropy; to provide leadership in meeting charitable needs and to be a responsible steward to the Foundation's donors and of the Foundation's endowment.
Title of Award: Amber Huber Memorial Scholarship **Area, Field, or Subject:** General studies. **Level of Education for which Award is Granted:** Undergraduate **Funds Available:** No specific amount.
Eligibility Requirements: Applicants must be graduating senior females from Byron High School who have participated in the Byron High School girls track program and/or Byron High School Cheerleading program for at least three seasons including their senior year; must have a minimum GPA of 5 on an 11 point scale or "C" average. **Application Requirements:** Applicants must submit a completed application form, verification form, an official transcript in a sealed envelope and two letters of recommendation. **Deadline for Receipt:** March 31. **Additional Information:** jpatterson@cfnil.org.

711 ■ COMMUNITY FOUNDATION OF NORTHERN ILLINOIS
946 N 2nd St.
Rockford, IL 61107
Tel: (815)962-2110
Fax: (815)962-2116
Web Site: http://www.cfnil.org
To serve the four county area (Boone, Ogle, Stephenson and Winnebago) through philanthropy; to provide leadership in meeting charitable needs and to be a responsible steward to the Foundation's donors and of the Foundation's endowment; to provide educational funds to support Auburn High school CAPA students planning to attend an accredited college or university.
Title of Award: Ashley E. Ketcher Memorial Scholarships **Area, Field, or Subject:** General studies. **Level of Education for which Award is Granted:** Undergraduate **Funds Available:** No specific amount.
Eligibility Requirements: Applicants must be graduating Auburn High School seniors in the CAPA program who have an interest in and prior experience in the performing arts; must have a cumulative GPA of at least 2.5. **Application Requirements:** Applicants must submit a completed application form, verification form, an official transcript in a sealed envelope, two letters of recommendation and a copy of FAFSA. **Deadline for Receipt:** March 1. **Additional Information:** jpatterson@cfnil.org.

712 ■ COMMUNITY FOUNDATION OF NORTHERN ILLINOIS
946 N 2nd St.
Rockford, IL 61107
Tel: (815)962-2110
Fax: (815)962-2116
Web Site: http://www.cfnil.org
To serve the four county area (Boone, Ogle, Stephenson and Winnebago) through philanthropy; to provide leadership in meeting charitable needs and to be a responsible steward to the Foundation's donors and of the Foundation's endowment.
Title of Award: Leopold Education Project Scholarships **Area, Field, or Subject:** General studies. **Level of Education for which Award is Granted:** Undergraduate **Funds Available:** No specific amount.
Eligibility Requirements: Applicants must be graduating high school seniors or high school graduates who are enrolled or planning to enroll in a full-time course of study at an accredited four-year college or university in a natural resources filed. **Application Requirements:** Applicants must contact Jackie Falkenstein for more information. **Additional Information:** 815-544-2677.

713 ■ COMMUNITY FOUNDATION OF NORTHERN ILLINOIS
946 N 2nd St.
Rockford, IL 61107
Tel: (815)962-2110
Fax: (815)962-2116
Web Site: http://www.cfnil.org

To serve the four county area (Boone, Ogle, Stephenson and Winnebago) through philanthropy; to provide leadership in meeting charitable needs and to be a responsible steward to the Foundation's donors and of the Foundation's endowment; to provide awards to worthy scholars who otherwise might not receive a college or university education. **Title of Award:** Keith Miffioli Scholarship **Area, Field, or Subject:** General studies. **Level of Education for which Award is Granted:** Undergraduate **Funds Available:** No specific amount. **Eligibility Requirements:** Applicants must be graduating senior students from a Boone, Stephenson, Ogle or Winnebago County School who have a cumulative GPA of 3.0 or higher. **Application Requirements:** Applicants must submit a completed application form, verification form, an official transcript in a sealed envelope, two letters of recommendation and a copy of their FAFSA. **Deadline for Receipt:** March 1. **Additional Information:** jpatterson@cfnil.org.

714 ■ COMMUNITY FOUNDATION OF NORTHERN ILLINOIS

946 N 2nd St.
Rockford, IL 61107
Tel: (815)962-2110
Fax: (815)962-2116
Web Site: http://www.cfnil.org
To serve the four county area (Boone, Ogle, Stephenson and Winnebago) through philanthropy; to provide leadership in meeting charitable needs and to be a responsible steward to the Foundation's donors and of the Foundation's endowment.
Title of Award: Northwest Community Center Scholarships **Area, Field, or Subject:** General studies. **Level of Education for which Award is Granted:** Undergraduate **Funds Available:** No specific amount. **Eligibility Requirements:** Applicants must be graduating senior students or graduates from a Rockford high school who have a GPA of at least 2.0; must have plans to attend a college, university or trade school; must be residents of northwest Rockford or have a history of involvement at the Northwest Community Center as either a volunteer or participant. **Application Requirements:** Applicants must submit a completed application form, verification form, an official transcript in a sealed envelope, two letters of recommendation and a copy of their FAFSA. **Deadline for Receipt:** March 1. **Additional Information:** jpatterson@cfnil.org.

715 ■ COMMUNITY FOUNDATION OF NORTHERN ILLINOIS

946 N 2nd St.
Rockford, IL 61107
Tel: (815)962-2110
Fax: (815)962-2116
Web Site: http://www.cfnil.org
To serve the four county area (Boone, Ogle, Stephenson and Winnebago) through philanthropy; to provide leadership in meeting charitable needs and to be a responsible steward to the Foundation's donors and of the Foundation's endowment.
Title of Award: Katharine H. Obye Scholarship Award **Area, Field, or Subject:** General studies. **Level of Education for which Award is Granted:** Undergraduate **Funds Available:** No specific amount. **Eligibility Requirements:** Applicants must be female students who are graduating from a public high school within Boone or Winnebago county who have plans to teach at any level or in any field; must have done outstanding work on a high school publication staff such as newspaper or yearbook. **Application Requirements:** Applicants must submit a completed application form, verification form, an official transcript in a sealed envelope, two letters of recommendation and a copy of their FAFSA. **Deadline for Receipt:** March 1. **Additional Information:** jpatterson@cfnil.org.

716 ■ COMMUNITY FOUNDATION OF NORTHERN ILLINOIS

946 N 2nd St.
Rockford, IL 61107
Tel: (815)962-2110
Fax: (815)962-2116
Web Site: http://www.cfnil.org
To serve the four county area (Boone, Ogle, Stephenson and Winnebago) through philanthropy; to provide leadership in meeting charitable needs and to be a responsible steward to the Foundation's donors and of the Foundation's endowment.
Title of Award: Rockford Area Habitat for Humanity College Scholarships **Area, Field, or Subject:** General studies. **Level of Education for which**

Award is Granted: Undergraduate **Funds Available:** No specific amount.
Eligibility Requirements: Applicants must have plans to attend an accredited junior college or university; must be current homeowner residents or dependents of homeowner residents of a home built by Rockford Area Habitat for Humanity; must be residing in that home at time of scholarship application. **Application Requirements:** Applicants must submit a completed application form, verification form, an official transcript in a sealed envelope, two letters of recommendation and a copy of FAFSA. **Deadline for Receipt:** March 1. **Additional Information:** jpatterson@cfnil.org.

717 ■ COMMUNITY FOUNDATION OF NORTHERN ILLINOIS

946 N 2nd St.
Rockford, IL 61107
Tel: (815)962-2110
Fax: (815)962-2116
Web Site: http://www.cfnil.org
To serve the four county area (Boone, Ogle, Stephenson and Winnebago) through philanthropy; to provide leadership in meeting charitable needs and to be a responsible steward to the Foundation's donors and of the Foundation's endowment.
Title of Award: Rockford Chapter Daughters of the American Revolution Memorial Scholarships **Area, Field, or Subject:** General studies. **Level of Education for which Award is Granted:** Undergraduate **Funds Available:** No specific amount.
Eligibility Requirements: Applicants must be graduating seniors from Winnebago or Boone County pursuing a two or four year degree. **Application Requirements:** Applicants must contact Audrey Johnson for more information.

718 ■ COMMUNITY FOUNDATION OF NORTHERN ILLINOIS

946 N 2nd St.
Rockford, IL 61107
Tel: (815)962-2110
Fax: (815)962-2116
Web Site: http://www.cfnil.org
To serve the four county area (Boone, Ogle, Stephenson and Winnebago) through philanthropy; to provide leadership in meeting charitable needs and to be a responsible steward to the Foundation's donors and of the Foundation's endowment.
Title of Award: Deborah Jean Rydberg Memorial Scholarship **Area, Field, or Subject:** General studies. **Level of Education for which Award is Granted:** Undergraduate **Funds Available:** No specific amount.
Eligibility Requirements: Applicants must be graduating female senior athletes at Guilford High school who have at least a "C" or better average and have plans to attend college. **Application Requirements:** Applicants must submit a completed application form, verification form, an official transcript in a sealed envelope and two letters of recommendation. **Deadline for Receipt:** March 1. **Additional Information:** jpatterson@cfnil.org.

719 ■ COMMUNITY FOUNDATION OF NORTHERN ILLINOIS

946 N 2nd St.
Rockford, IL 61107
Tel: (815)962-2110
Fax: (815)962-2116
Web Site: http://www.cfnil.org
To serve the four county area (Boone, Ogle, Stephenson and Winnebago) through philanthropy; to provide leadership in meeting charitable needs and to be a responsible steward to the Foundation's donors and of the Foundation's endowment.
Title of Award: Elisabeth Seegmiller Recruitment Scholarship Grant **Area, Field, or Subject:** General studies. **Level of Education for which Award is Granted:** Undergraduate **Funds Available:** No specific amount.
Eligibility Requirements: Applicants must be female Rockford College sophomore or junior students who are pursuing a degree in education. **Application Requirements:** Applicants must submit a completed application form, verification form, an official transcript in a sealed envelope and two letters of recommendation. **Deadline for Receipt:** March 1. **Additional Information:** jpatterson@cfnil.org.

720 ■ COMMUNITY FOUNDATION OF NORTHERN ILLINOIS
946 N 2nd St.
Rockford, IL 61107
Tel: (815)962-2110
Fax: (815)962-2116
Web Site: http://www.cfnil.org
To serve the four county area (Boone, Ogle, Stephenson and Winnebago) through philanthropy; to provide leadership in meeting charitable needs and to be a responsible steward to the Foundation's donors and of the Foundation's endowment.
Title of Award: Senior Memorial Scholarships **Area, Field, or Subject:** General studies. **Level of Education for which Award is Granted:** Undergraduate **Funds Available:** No specific Amount.
Eligibility Requirements: Applicants must be graduating senior students from a Rockford School District No. 205 high school; must plan to attend a college, university or higher institution of learning. **Application Requirements:** Applicants must submit a completed application form. **Deadline for Receipt:** March 1.

721 ■ COMMUNITY FOUNDATION OF NORTHERN ILLINOIS
946 N 2nd St.
Rockford, IL 61107
Tel: (815)962-2110
Fax: (815)962-2116
Web Site: http://www.cfnil.org
To serve the four county area (Boone, Ogle, Stephenson and Winnebago) through philanthropy; to provide leadership in meeting charitable needs and to be a responsible steward to the Foundation's donors and of the Foundation's endowment; to provide educational resources for residents in the four counties of Boone, Ogle, Stephenson and Winnebago.
Title of Award: Ernest and Charlene Stachowiak Memorial Scholarship **Area, Field, or Subject:** General studies. **Level of Education for which Award is Granted:** Undergraduate **Funds Available:** No specific amount.
Eligibility Requirements: Applicants must be graduating seniors or college students with a permanent address within Boone, Ogle, Stephenson or Winnebago county; must have a GPA of at least 2.5 on 4.0 sale. **Application Requirements:** Applicants must submit a completed application form, verification form, an official transcript in a sealed envelope, two letters of recommendation and a copy of their FAFSA. **Deadline for Receipt:** March 1. **Additional Information:** jpatterson@cfnil.org.

722 ■ COMMUNITY FOUNDATION OF NORTHERN ILLINOIS
946 N 2nd St.
Rockford, IL 61107
Tel: (815)962-2110
Fax: (815)962-2116
Web Site: http://www.cfnil.org
To serve the four county area (Boone, Ogle, Stephenson and Winnebago) through philanthropy; to provide leadership in meeting charitable needs and to be a responsible steward to the Foundation's donors and of the Foundation's endowment.
Title of Award: Carolyn Wones Recruitment Scholarships Grant **Area, Field, or Subject:** General studies. **Level of Education for which Award is Granted:** Undergraduate **Funds Available:** No specific amount.
Eligibility Requirements: Applicants must be females who graduated from a public high school within Boone or Winnebago county; must have plans to pursue a degree in secondary teaching; must exhibit academic potential and have participated in a number of high school activities. **Application Requirements:** Applicants must submit a completed application form, verification form, an official transcript in a sealed envelope and two letters of recommendation. **Deadline for Receipt:** March 1. **Additional Information:** jpatterson@cfnil.org.

723 ■ COMMUNITY FOUNDATION OF NORTHERN ILLINOIS
946 N 2nd St.
Rockford, IL 61107
Tel: (815)962-2110
Fax: (815)962-2116
Web Site: http://www.cfnil.org
To serve the four county area (Boone, Ogle, Stephenson and Winnebago) through philanthropy; to provide leadership in meeting charitable needs

and to be a responsible steward to the Foundation's donors and of the Foundation's endowment.
Title of Award: Margaret Wyeth Scholarship **Area, Field, or Subject:** General studies. **Level of Education for which Award is Granted:** Undergraduate **Funds Available:** No specific amount.
Eligibility Requirements: Applicants must be graduating public high school senior students and residing in Boone, Ogle or Winnebago County; must plan to attend a college or university. **Application Requirements:** Applicants must submit a completed application form, verification form, an official transcript in a sealed envelope, two letters of recommendation and a copy of their FAFSA. **Deadline for Receipt:** March 1. **Additional Information:** jpatterson@cfnil.org.

724 ■ COMMUNITY FOUNDATION OF NORTHERN ILLINOIS
946 N 2nd St.
Rockford, IL 61107
Tel: (815)962-2110
Fax: (815)962-2116
Web Site: http://www.cfnil.org
To serve the four county area (Boone, Ogle, Stephenson and Winnebago) through philanthropy; to provide leadership in meeting charitable needs and to be a responsible steward to the Foundation's donors and of the Foundation's endowment.
Title of Award: Zeta Chapter Memorial Scholarships Award **Area, Field, or Subject:** General studies. **Level of Education for which Award is Granted:** Undergraduate **Funds Available:** No specific amount.
Eligibility Requirements: Applicants must be females who are graduating from a public high school within Boone or Winnebago county; must have plans to teach at any level; must exhibit academic potential and have participated in a number of high school activities. **Application Requirements:** Applicants must submit a completed application form, verification form, an official transcript in a sealed envelope and two letters of recommendation. **Deadline for Receipt:** March 1. **Additional Information:** jpatterson@cfnil.org.

725 ■ COMMUNITY FOUNDATION OF PRINCE EDWARD ISLAND
119-121 Quenn St., Ste. 105
Charlottetown, PE, Canada C1A 1Z4
Tel: (902)892-3440
Free: 800-566-7307
Fax: (902)892-0880
E-mail: foundation@cfpei.ca
Web Site: http://www.cfpei.ca
To provide scholarship assistance to qualified individuals who want to pursue their studies.
Title of Award: Lorne and Ruby Bonnell Scholarships **Area, Field, or Subject:** General studies. **Level of Education for which Award is Granted:** Undergraduate **Funds Available:** $1,000. **Duration:** One year.
Eligibility Requirements: Applicant must be a graduate of a Prince Edward Island high school; must be a graduate of the University of Prince Edward Island with high academic standing; must be accepted into graduate studies in the sciences at a Canadian university. **Application Requirements:** Applicant must complete the application form available online; must submit an official letter of acceptance from a Canadian graduate school. Application form and other supporting documents must be sent to Lorne and Ruby Bonnell Scholarship Fund c/o The Community Foundation of Prince Edward Island, 119-121 Queen St. Ste. 105, Charlottetown, PE C1A 4B3. **Additional Information:** Scholarship Fund was established on December 14, 2000 by the Honorable M. Lorne Bonnell, a prominent Prince Edward Island medical doctor, past Cabinet Minister of the Provincial Legislature, and Senator. **Deadline for Receipt:** May 30.

726 ■ COMMUNITY FOUNDATION OF PRINCE EDWARD ISLAND
119-121 Quenn St., Ste. 105
Charlottetown, PE, Canada C1A 1Z4
Tel: (902)892-3440
Free: 800-566-7307
Fax: (902)892-0880
E-mail: foundation@cfpei.ca
Web Site: http://www.cfpei.ca
To provide financial assistance to qualified individuals who want to pursue their education.

Title of Award: Orin Carver Scholarships **Area, Field, or Subject:** General studies. **Level of Education for which Award is Granted:** Undergraduate **Funds Available:** No specific amount.

Eligibility Requirements: Applicants must be high school graduates in the top 25% of their class; must exhibit excellence and leadership in either athletics, arts and/or community service; must be accepted into a post-secondary program at UPEI or Holland College. **Application Requirements:** Applicants must complete the application form available online; must have a formal statement of academic standing and official academic transcript for most recent academic year, as verified by educational institute attended; must have two letters of reference (one from the educational institution and one from a community member); must provide a 500 word essay or portfolio of their excellent works. Application form and other supporting documents must be sent to Orin Carver Scholarship Selection Committee, c/o Community Foundation of PEI, 119-121 Queen St. Ste. 105, Charlottetown, PE C1A 4b3. **Deadline for Receipt:** May 30.

727 ■ COMMUNITY FOUNDATION OF PRINCE EDWARD ISLAND
119-121 Quenn St., Ste. 105
Charlottetown, PE, Canada C1A 1Z4
Tel: (902)892-3440
Free: 800-566-7307
Fax: (902)892-0880
E-mail: foundation@cfpei.ca
Web Site: http://www.cfpei.ca
To provide financial assistance to qualified individuals who want to pursue their education.

Title of Award: Phillips Scholarships **Area, Field, or Subject:** General studies. **Level of Education for which Award is Granted:** Undergraduate **Funds Available:** No specific amount.

Eligibility Requirements: Applicant must be a high school graduate from the Western School District with a physical disability; must be a resident of Prince County; must have financial need; must have been accepted at a recognized post-secondary institution. **Application Requirements:** Applicant must complete the application form available online; must submit a copy of their final grades; must have a brief description of their physical disability and what they hope to gain from their studies; must have a letter of acceptance for the next year's study. Application form and other supporting documents must be sent to Lowell Phillips Scholarship Award c/o Community Foundation of Prince Edward Island, 119-121 Queen St. Ste. 105, Charlottetown, PEI C1A 4B3. **Deadline for Receipt:** May 30.

728 ■ COMMUNITY FOUNDATION OF PRINCE EDWARD ISLAND
119-121 Quenn St., Ste. 105
Charlottetown, PE, Canada C1A 1Z4
Tel: (902)892-3440
Free: 800-566-7307
Fax: (902)892-0880
E-mail: foundation@cfpei.ca
Web Site: http://www.cfpei.ca
To provide financial assistance to qualified individuals who want to pursue their education.

Title of Award: Summerside-Natick Hockey Scholarships **Area, Field, or Subject:** General studies. **Level of Education for which Award is Granted:** Undergraduate **Funds Available:** No specific amount. **Duration:** One year.

Eligibility Requirements: Applicant must be a high school graduate of Prince Edward Island; must be accepted at a post-secondary institution; must be entering the first year of study; must have played in the Summerside Area Minor Hockey Association. **Application Requirements:** Applicant must complete the application form available online; must include a letter detailing how he/she meets the selection criteria; must have an official letter of acceptance from a recognized post-secondary institution; must submit two letters of reference; and most recent transcript. Application form and other supporting documents must be sent to The Summerside-Natick International Friendship Fund c/o The Community Foundation of Prince Edward Island, 119-121 Queen St. Ste. 105, Queen Square Place, Charlottetown, PE C1A 4B3. **Additional Information:** Founding members of the International Friendship Hockey Series Committee established the Summerside-Natick International Friendship Hockey Fund. **Deadline for Receipt:** May 30.

729 ■ COMMUNITY FOUNDATION OF SARASOTA COUNTY
PO Box 49587
Sarasota, FL 34237
Tel: (941)955-3000
Fax: (941)952-1951
E-mail: stewart@cfsarasota.org
Web Site: http://www.cfsarasota.org
To encourage and enable caring individuals to easily and effectively support the charitable causes that they care about.

Title of Award: Community Foundation of Sarasota County Adult Learner Scholarships **Area, Field, or Subject:** General studies. **Level of Education for which Award is Granted:** Undergraduate **Funds Available:** No specific amount.

Eligibility Requirements: Applicants must be adult learners who are returning to vocational school or college after having been out of high school for a number of years. **Application Requirements:** Applicants must complete the application form; must submit a parent or guardian's most recent 1040 federal tax form; and must provide two letters of reference from people who know the applicant well. **Deadline for Receipt:** September 15.

730 ■ COMMUNITY FOUNDATION OF SARASOTA COUNTY
PO Box 49587
Sarasota, FL 34237
Tel: (941)955-3000
Fax: (941)952-1951
E-mail: stewart@cfsarasota.org
Web Site: http://www.cfsarasota.org
To further education at a college, university, or institution of higher learning including education in advanced vocational training.

Title of Award: Father Connie Dougherty Scholarships **Area, Field, or Subject:** General studies. **Level of Education for which Award is Granted:** Undergraduate **Funds Available:** $5,000.

Eligibility Requirements: Applicants must be graduates of Sarasota County public and private school. **Application Requirements:** Applicants must submit a completed application form; an official transcript; SAT or ACT scores; copy of Student Aid Report; and three letters of recommendation (one must come from a teacher and one from a community member who is not a teacher or relative). **Deadline for Receipt:** April 1. **Additional Information:** mimi@sarasota.org

731 ■ COMMUNITY FOUNDATION OF SARASOTA COUNTY
PO Box 49587
Sarasota, FL 34237
Tel: (941)955-3000
Fax: (941)952-1951
E-mail: stewart@cfsarasota.org
Web Site: http://www.cfsarasota.org
To encourage and enable caring individuals to easily and effectively support the charitable causes that they care about and to provide scholarships for adult learners in Sarasota County to pursue a professional certificate in hairdressing.

Title of Award: James Franklin and Dorothy J. Warnell Scholarship Fund **Area, Field, or Subject:** General studies. **Level of Education for which Award is Granted:** Undergraduate **Funds Available:** No specific amount.

Eligibility Requirements: Applicants must be residents of Sarasota County and post high school students. **Application Requirements:** Applicants must submit completed application form; a parent or guardian's most recent 1040 federal tax form; two letters of reference from people who know the applicant well; official transcript of record; official acceptance letter from college or vocational school; and a copy of SAT and ACT scores.

732 ■ COMMUNITY FOUNDATION OF SARASOTA COUNTY
PO Box 49587
Sarasota, FL 34237
Tel: (941)955-3000
Fax: (941)952-1951
E-mail: stewart@cfsarasota.org
Web Site: http://www.cfsarasota.org
To encourage and enable caring individuals to easily and effectively support the charitable causes that they care about and to provide scholarships for adult learners in Sarasota County to pursue a professional certificate in hairdressing.

Title of Award: Helen F. "Jerri" Rand Memorial Scholarships **Area, Field, or Subject:** Cosmetology. **Level of Education for which Award is Granted:** Undergraduate **Funds Available:** No specific amount.
Eligibility Requirements: Applicants must be adult learners who are accepted to any accredited beauty school in Sarasota County. **Application Requirements:** Applicants must complete the application form; must submit a parent or guardian's most recent 1040 federal tax form; must provide two letters of reference from people who know the applicant well; must provide official transcript of record, official acceptance letter from college or vocational school; and must submit a copy of SAT and ACT scores.

733 ■ COMMUNITY FOUNDATION OF SARASOTA COUNTY

PO Box 49587
Sarasota, FL 34237
Tel: (941)955-3000
Fax: (941)952-1951
E-mail: stewart@cfsarasota.org
Web Site: http://www.cfsarasota.org
To encourage and enable caring individuals to easily and effectively support the charitable causes that they care about.
Title of Award: Traditional Student Scholarships **Area, Field, or Subject:** General studies. **Level of Education for which Award is Granted:** Undergraduate **Funds Available:** No specific amount.
Eligibility Requirements: Applicants must be high school seniors, or those who are 25 years old or younger who are currently attending college. **Application Requirements:** Applicants must complete the application form; must submit a parent or guardian's most recent 1040 federal tax form; and must provide two letters of reference from people who know the applicant well. **Deadline for Receipt:** March 1. **Additional Information:** rebekah@cfsarasota.org.

734 ■ COMMUNITY FOUNDATION FOR SOUTHEAST MICHIGAN

333 West Fort St., Ste. 2010
Detroit, MI 48226-3134
Tel: (313)961-6675
Fax: (313)961-2886
E-mail: cfsem@cfsem.org
Web Site: http://www.cfsem.org
To provide financial assistance to students of Southeast Michigan region for their education.
Title of Award: Detroit Economic Club Scholarships **Area, Field, or Subject:** General studies. **Level of Education for which Award is Granted:** Undergraduate **Number Awarded:** 2. **Funds Available:** $2,000. **Duration:** One year.
Eligibility Requirements: Applicants must be high school seniors in public or private high school in Wayne, Oakland or Macomb counties. **Application Requirements:** Applicants must first be nominated by his or her counselor and then invited to apply, for scholarship consideration. **Deadline for Receipt:** April 1.

735 ■ COMMUNITY FOUNDATION FOR SOUTHEAST MICHIGAN

333 West Fort St., Ste. 2010
Detroit, MI 48226-3134
Tel: (313)961-6675
Fax: (313)961-2886
E-mail: cfsem@cfsem.org
Web Site: http://www.cfsem.org
To provide financial assistance to students of Southeast Michigan region for education.
Title of Award: Detroit Tigers Willie Horton Scholarships **Area, Field, or Subject:** General studies. **Level of Education for which Award is Granted:** Undergraduate **Number Awarded:** 1. **Funds Available:** $5,000. **Duration:** One year.
Eligibility Requirements: Applicants must be graduating seniors at Northwestern High School in Detroit; must show leadership and character through extra curricular activities, volunteer involvement and work experience in school and in the community; have applied or have been accepted as full time students in an accredited educational institution in the United States. **Application Requirements:** Applicants must use a computer, typewriter or print neatly in blue or black ink all appropriate forms. **Deadline for Receipt:** April 1.

736 ■ COMMUNITY FOUNDATION FOR SOUTHEAST MICHIGAN

333 West Fort St., Ste. 2010
Detroit, MI 48226-3134
Tel: (313)961-6675
Fax: (313)961-2886
E-mail: cfsem@cfsem.org
Web Site: http://www.cfsem.org
To provide financial assistance to students of Southeast Michigan region for their education.
Title of Award: Robert Holmes Scholarships **Area, Field, or Subject:** General studies. **Level of Education for which Award is Granted:** Undergraduate **Number Awarded:** 6. **Funds Available:** $1,000.
Eligibility Requirements: Applicants must be dependents of eligible Michigan Teamsters and high school seniors who will attend a Michigan College or University as full time students. **Application Requirements:** Applicants must submit the completed application form and other required documents. **Deadline for Receipt:** April 1.

737 ■ COMMUNITY FOUNDATION FOR SOUTHEAST MICHIGAN

333 West Fort St., Ste. 2010
Detroit, MI 48226-3134
Tel: (313)961-6675
Fax: (313)961-2886
E-mail: cfsem@cfsem.org
Web Site: http://www.cfsem.org
To provide financial assistance to students in the Southeast Michigan region for their education.
Title of Award: Chris Kurzweil Scholarships **Area, Field, or Subject:** General studies. **Level of Education for which Award is Granted:** Undergraduate **Number Awarded:** 2. **Funds Available:** $1,500. **Duration:** One year.
Eligibility Requirements: Applicants must be dependents of members of the Intertape Polymer Group, formerly American Tape; and must be high school seniors. **Application Requirements:** Applicants must use a computer, typewriter or print neatly in blue or black ink all appropriate forms. **Deadline for Receipt:** April 1.

738 ■ COMMUNITY FOUNDATION FOR SOUTHEAST MICHIGAN

333 West Fort St., Ste. 2010
Detroit, MI 48226-3134
Tel: (313)961-6675
Fax: (313)961-2886
E-mail: cfsem@cfsem.org
Web Site: http://www.cfsem.org
To provide educational assistance to students who are graduates from public high schools in Fowlerville.
Title of Award: Imelda and Ralph LeMar Scholarship Program **Area, Field, or Subject:** General studies. **Level of Education for which Award is Granted:** Undergraduate **Funds Available:** $900.
Eligibility Requirements: Applicants must be members of a graduating class in a public high school in Fowlerville, Michigan; must demonstrates exemplary desire, ability and good grades; must show leadership and character through extra curricular activities, volunteer involvement and work experience in school and in the community; have applied or been accepted as full-time students in an accredited educational institution in the United States; must be planning to study chemistry, physics or electrical or mechanical engineering in college. **Application Requirements:** Applicants must use a computer, typewriter or print neatly in blue or black ink all appropriate forms. **Deadline for Receipt:** April 1.

739 ■ COMMUNITY FOUNDATION FOR SOUTHEAST MICHIGAN

333 West Fort St., Ste. 2010
Detroit, MI 48226-3134
Tel: (313)961-6675
Fax: (313)961-2886
E-mail: cfsem@cfsem.org
Web Site: http://www.cfsem.org
To provide financial assistance to students of Southeast Michigan region for their education.
Title of Award: Virgil K. Lobring Scholarships **Area, Field, or Subject:** General studies. **Level of Education for which Award is Granted:** Undergraduate **Funds Available:** $1,500.
Eligibility Requirements: Applicants must be members of the graduating class at Southwestern High School in Detroit, Michigan; must demonstrate

exemplary desire, ability and good grades; demonstrate leadership and character through extra curricular activities, volunteer involvement and work experience in school and in the community; have applied or been accepted as full-time students in an accredited educational institution in the United States; must be students who have demonstrated the greatest improvement from the time during freshman year in high school as determined by the Lobring Scholarship committee; must demonstrate financial need. **Application Requirements:** Applicants must submit the application containing scholarship guidelines and deadlines, student application, essay question, recommendation forms from counselor, teacher and community service forms; and transcripts release form. **Deadline for Receipt:** April 1.

740 ■ COMMUNITY FOUNDATION FOR SOUTHEAST MICHIGAN
333 West Fort St., Ste. 2010
Detroit, MI 48226-3134
Tel: (313)961-6675
Fax: (313)961-2886
E-mail: cfsem@cfsem.org
Web Site: http://www.cfsem.org
To provide financial assistance to the male varsity athlete from North Farmington High School student who best personifies school spirit and good sportsmanship.
Title of Award: Cary Moore Memorial Scholarship Fund **Area, Field, or Subject:** General studies. **Level of Education for which Award is Granted:** Undergraduate **Number Awarded:** 1. **Funds Available:** $1,500. **Duration:** One year.
Eligibility Requirements: Applicants must be members of the graduating class at North Farmington High School who demonstrates exemplary desire, ability and good grades; must be male athletes who show leadership, character and sportsmanship by participation in varsity athletics at North Farmington High School and Raiders Pride; have applied or been accepted as a full-time students in an accredited educational institution in the United States. **Application Requirements:** Applicants must use a computer, typewriter or print neatly in blue or black ink all appropriate forms. **Deadline for Receipt:** April 2.

741 ■ COMMUNITY FOUNDATION FOR SOUTHEAST MICHIGAN
333 West Fort St., Ste. 2010
Detroit, MI 48226-3134
Tel: (313)961-6675
Fax: (313)961-2886
E-mail: cfsem@cfsem.org
Web Site: http://www.cfsem.org
To provide financial assistance to students of Southeast Michigan region for their education.
Title of Award: Jean and Tom Rosenthal Scholarship Program **Area, Field, or Subject:** General studies. **Level of Education for which Award is Granted:** Undergraduate **Number Awarded:** 2. **Funds Available:** $1,000. **Duration:** One year.
Eligibility Requirements: Applicants must be members of the graduating class at Pontiac Northern High School or Pontiac Central High School demonstrating exemplary desire, ability and good grades of at least 2.5 or higher; must show leadership and character through extracurricular activities, volunteer involvement and work experience in school and in the community; have applied or been accepted as full-time students in an accredited educational institution in the United States. **Application Requirements:** Applicants must submit the application containing scholarship guidelines and deadlines, student application, essay question, recommendation forms from counselor, teacher and community service forms; and transcripts release form. **Deadline for Receipt:** April 1.

742 ■ COMMUNITY FOUNDATION OF WESTERN MASSACHUSETTS
PO Box 15769
Springfield, MA 01115
Tel: (413)732-2858
Fax: (413)733-8565
Web Site: http://www.communityfoundation.org
To help bring higher education within reach of residents in Massachusetts who might not otherwise be able to afford it.
Title of Award: Community Foundation of Western Massachusetts Community Scholarship Program **Area, Field, or Subject:** General studies. **Level of Education for which Award is Granted:** Undergraduate **Number Awarded:** 2. **Funds Available:** $10,000.

Eligibility Requirements: Applicants must be residents from Franklin, Hampden, Hampshire or combination or city/town; must be freshmen, sophomores, juniors, graduating seniors or graduates of specific high school. **Application Requirements:** Applicants must submit all the required application information.

743 ■ CONNECTICUT ASSOCIATION OF LAND SURVEYORS
78 Beaver Rd.
Wethersfield, CT 06109
Tel: (860)563-1990
Fax: (860)529-9700
E-mail: kathy@ctsurveyor.com
Web Site: http://www.ctsurveyor.com
To provide information about land surveying in Connecticut to the growing global surveying/internet community.
Title of Award: Connecticut Association of Land Surveyors Memorial Scholarships **Area, Field, or Subject:** Surveying. **Level of Education for which Award is Granted:** Undergraduate **Funds Available:** No stated amount.
Eligibility Requirements: Applicants must be residents of Connecticut; must be enrolled in a program leading to a degree in surveying or related fields; must be accepted to attend the program and could be a freshman; must show an interest or work history in being a part of the surveying profession. **Application Requirements:** Applicants must submit a statement outlining qualifications, transcript, resume and other pertinent information. **Deadline for Receipt:** June 1. **Additional Information:** 49 Arlington St., West Haven, CT 06516.

744 ■ CONNECTICUT CONSTRUCTION INDUSTRIES ASSOCIATION
912 Silas Deane Hwy.
Wethersfield, CT 06109
Tel: (860)529-6855
Fax: (860)563-0616
E-mail: ccia-info@ctconstruction.org
Web Site: http://www.ctconstruction.org
To provide constant resource of information services and educational seminars; to maintain strong working relationships with federal and state agencies; to utilize lobbying efforts focused on removing unnecessary regulatory inefficiencies and costly restrictions that hinder progress and stifle the economy.
Title of Award: Associated General Contractors of Connecticut Scholarships **Area, Field, or Subject:** Construction. **Level of Education for which Award is Granted:** Undergraduate **Funds Available:** $2,500.
Eligibility Requirements: Applicants must be graduating high school seniors entering college as freshmen or entering a two-year technical school with a construction course of study with the intent of entering a four-year college upon completion of the technical school; must desire a career in construction; must pursue a B.S. degree in construction technology or construction civil engineering; must be U.S. citizen or documented resident of the United States. **Application Requirements:** Applicants must complete the "four-page" signed application; must submit one faculty evaluation form completed by high school faculty member with scholastic achievement and school history, two personal evaluation forms and official transcript of records. **Deadline for Receipt:** March 30.

745 ■ CONNECTICUT CONSTRUCTION INDUSTRIES ASSOCIATION
912 Silas Deane Hwy.
Wethersfield, CT 06109
Tel: (860)529-6855
Fax: (860)563-0616
E-mail: ccia-info@ctconstruction.org
Web Site: http://www.ctconstruction.org
To assist students studying in the field of construction management including civil engineering at an accredited college in Connecticut.
Title of Award: John Costello Memorial Scholarships **Area, Field, or Subject:** Construction. **Level of Education for which Award is Granted:** Undergraduate **Funds Available:** $2,000. **Duration:** 4 years.
Eligibility Requirements: Applicants must be graduating senior high school students with a GPA of 2.5. **Application Requirements:** Applicants must submit a completed application form.

746 ■ COPPER AND BRASS SERVICE CENTER ASSOCIATION INC.
994 Old Eagle School Rd., Ste. 1019
Wayne, PA 19087-1802

Tel: (610)971-4850
Fax: (610)971-4859
E-mail: diana@cbsa.copper-brass.org
Web Site: http://www.cbsa.copper-brass.org
To provide financial educational assistance to employees of CBSA's service center or associate member companies.
Title of Award: Copper and Brass Service Center Inc. Scholarship Program **Area, Field, or Subject:** Education-Curricula. **Level of Education for which Award is Granted:** Undergraduate **Number Awarded:** 5. **Funds Available:** No specific amount.
Eligibility Requirements: Applicants must be dependents of an individual employed in CBSA's service center or any associate member company; must be college students entering Sophomore, Junior, or Senior year in the fall. **Application Requirements:** Applicants are advised to visit the website to apply online.

747 ■ COUNCIL ON SOCIAL WORK EDUCATION
1725 Duke St., Ste. 500
Alexandria, VA 22314-3457
Tel: (703)683-8080
Fax: (703)683-8099
E-mail: info@cswe.org
Web Site: http://www.cswe.org
To promote equity and social justice in social work.
Title of Award: Carl A. Scott Book Scholarships **Area, Field, or Subject:** General Studies. **Level of Education for which Award is Granted:** Undergraduate **Number Awarded:** 2. **Funds Available:** $500.
Eligibility Requirements: Applicants must be in the last year of study for a social work degree in a baccalaureate or master's degree program accredited by the Council on Social Work Education; must be African American, American Indian, Asian American, Mexican American or Puerto Rican; must have a cumulative GPA of at least 3.0 on a 4.0 scale; and must be enrolled in 12 credit hours. **Application Requirements:** Applicants must submit a two-three page, double-spaced, typewritten statement that include professional interests, and experiences; two letters of recommendation preferably from a professor, a field instructor, or a community-based leader; an official letter from the school's registrar verifying that you are enrolled and in good standing with the university or college; and an official academic transcript from university/college. **Deadline for Receipt:** May 5.

748 ■ CULINARY AND HOSPITALITY FOUNDATION OF SAN BENITO COUNTY
PO Box 1153
Tres Pinos, CA 95075
Tel: (831)628-3320
E-mail: info@chfsbc.com
Web Site: http://chfsbc.com
To encourage professional development within the culinary, hospitality, tourism or related industry.
Title of Award: Culinary and Hospitality Foundation of San Benito County Scholarships **Area, Field, or Subject:** Culinary Arts. **Level of Education for which Award is Granted:** Undergraduate **Number Awarded:** 2. **Funds Available:** $1,000.
Eligibility Requirements: Applicants must be high school senior students who are permanent residents of San Benito County and are graduating from an accredited high school; must plan to seek a career in the culinary, hospitality or tourism related industry; and must have a high school GPA of 2.0 or above. **Application Requirements:** Applicants must submit a completed application form; two letters of recommendation; official high school transcript; and a personal essay. **Deadline for Receipt:** April 15. **Additional Information:** PO Box 1153, Tres Pinos, CA 95075.

749 ■ THE CULINARY TRUST
PO Box 273
New York, NY 10013
Tel: (646)224-6989; 888-345-4666
E-mail: info@theculinarytrust.com
Web Site: http://www.theculinarytrust.com
To assist freshmen students pursuing a bachelor's degree in Culinary Arts at Kendall College.
Title of Award: Kendall College Bachelor of Arts in Culinary Arts Scholarships **Area, Field, or Subject:** Culinary arts. **Level of Education for**

which **Award is Granted:** Undergraduate **Number Awarded:** 1. **Funds Available:** $500.
Eligibility Requirements: Applicant must be a freshman student pursuing a degree in Culinary Arts; have a GPA of 3.0 or higher. **Application Requirements:** Applicants must submit a completed Culinary Trust Scholarship application form; a project proposal (two pages, double-spaced) illustrating their culinary goals; two letters of reference on business or personal letterhead; a current academic transcript; a non-refundable application fee of $25. **Additional Information:** For information about Kendall College visit www.kendall.edu. **Deadline for Receipt:** December 15. **Additional Information:** scholarships@theculinarytrust.com.

750 ■ CYSTIC FIBROSIS FOUNDATION
6931 Arlington Rd.
Bethesda, MD 20814
Tel: (301)951-4422
Free: 800-344-4823
E-mail: info@cff.org
Web Site: http://www.cff.org
To provide financial assistance to individuals with Cystic Fibrosis intending to pursue studies in undergraduate or vocational schools.
Title of Award: Cystic Fibrosis Foundation Scholarships **Area, Field, or Subject:** General studies. **Level of Education for which Award is Granted:** Undergraduate **Funds Available:** $1,000. **Duration:** Annual.
Eligibility Requirements: Applicants may either be individuals entering college or vocational school or those who have already completed two semesters of college or vocational school. **Application Requirements:** Application forms and instructions are available in the website. **Deadline for Receipt:** March 21. **Additional Information:** Cystic Fibrosis Scholarship Foundation, 1555 Sherman Avenue, 116 Evanston, IL 60201.

751 ■ CYSTIC FIBROSIS WORLDWIDE
210 Park Ave., No. 267
Worcester, MA 01609
Tel: (508)733-6120
E-mail: information@cfww.org
Web Site: http://www.cfww.org
To provide educational assistance to student athletes with cystic fibrosis.
Title of Award: Exercise For Life Athletic Scholarships Program **Area, Field, or Subject:** General studies. **Level of Education for which Award is Granted:** Undergraduate **Number Awarded:** 2. **Funds Available:** $10,000.
Eligibility Requirements: Applicants must be high school senior athletes pursuing undergraduate degrees. **Application Requirements:** Applicants must submit an application form (available at the website); EFL training log (print from website); an essay (one-page, single-spaced) on the importance of exercise and compliance; recent photo; letter from physician (on letterhead) confirming CF diagnosis and therapy routine; recent W2 form verification for both parents; high school transcript; letter of acceptance from a college institution; and signed waiver. Requirements must be mailed to: Boomer Esiason Foundation, Attn: Scholarship Program, 52 Vanderbilt Ave., 15th Fl., New York, NY 10017. **Deadline for Receipt:** June 27. **Additional Information:** jcahillbef@aol.com.

752 ■ CYSTIC FIBROSIS WORLDWIDE
210 Park Ave., No. 267
Worcester, MA 01609
Tel: (508)733-6120
E-mail: information@cfww.org
Web Site: http://www.cfww.org
To provide educational assistance to students engaged in arts.
Title of Award: Scholarships of the Arts **Area, Field, or Subject:** General studies. **Level of Education for which Award is Granted:** Graduate, Undergraduate **Funds Available:** No specific amount.
Eligibility Requirements: Applicants must be artists with cystic fibrosis (CF). **Application Requirements:** Applicants must submit an application form (available at the website); a recent photo; letter from the doctor confirming diagnosis of cystic fibrosis and list of daily medication routine; 2-part essay; an official/unofficial high school/college transcript; tuition breakdown; W2 form for verification for both parents and picture of the art entry. Applications and other requirements must be mailed to: Boomer Esiason Foundation, Attn: Scholarship Program, 52 Vanderbilt Ave. 15th Fl., New York, NY 10017. **Deadline for Receipt:** May 23.

753 ■ CYSTIC FIBROSIS WORLDWIDE

210 Park Ave., No. 267
Worcester, MA 01609
Tel: (508)733-6120
E-mail: information@cfww.org
Web Site: http://www.cfww.org
To provide educational assistance to students with cystic fibrosis.
Title of Award: Bonnie Strangio Education Scholarships **Area, Field, or Subject:** General studies. **Level of Education for which Award is Granted:** Graduate, Undergraduate **Funds Available:** $2,500.
Eligibility Requirements: Applicants must be undergraduate or graduate students who have cystic fibrosis. **Application Requirements:** Applicants must submit an application form (available at the website); an essay on post-graduation goals; a recent photo; a letter from a physician confirming CF diagnosis; most recent W2 form verification for both parents; transcript (high school, college, or graduate); and letter of acceptance from an academic institution. All requirements must be mailed to: Boomer Esiason Foundation, Attn: Scholarship Program, 52 Vanderbilt Ave., 15th Fl., New York, New York, 10017. **Deadline for Receipt:** June 13. **Additional Information:** jcahillbef@aol.com.

754 ■ DADE COMMUNITY FOUNDATION, INC.

200 S Biscayne Blvd., Ste. 505
Miami, FL 33131-2343
Tel: (305)371-2711
Fax: (305)371-5342
Web Site: http://www.dadecommunityfoundation.org
To provide financial assistance to Miami-Dade County minority students planning to continue their education at the university level and pursue a career in South Florida.
Title of Award: Judge Sidney M. Aronovitz Memorial Scholarships **Area, Field, or Subject:** General studies. **Level of Education for which Award is Granted:** High School **Number Awarded:** 1. **Funds Available:** $500. **Duration:** One year.
Eligibility Requirements: Applicants must be minority high school seniors or GED recipients no older than 19 years of age attending a Miami Dade County public school with a minimum high school grade point average of 3.0. **Application Requirements:** Applicants must submit the completed application form and enclose all proper attachments. **Deadline for Receipt:** March 19.

755 ■ DADE COMMUNITY FOUNDATION, INC.

200 S Biscayne Blvd., Ste. 505
Miami, FL 33131-2343
Tel: (305)371-2711
Fax: (305)371-5342
Web Site: http://www.dadecommunityfoundation.org
To provide educational opportunities for the children of current, full-time employees of The Continental Group, Inc and its subsidiaries.
Title of Award: The Continental Group Scholarship Fund **Area, Field, or Subject:** General studies. **Level of Education for which Award is Granted:** High School **Number Awarded:** 4. **Funds Available:** $1,000. **Duration:** Four years.
Eligibility Requirements: Applicants must be high school seniors graduating in 2008 with a minimum 3.0 grade point average and have a parent who is a fulltime employee of The Continental Group, Inc. or one of its Subsidiaries for at least one year. **Application Requirements:** Applicants must submit all the required application information. **Deadline for Receipt:** March 27.

756 ■ DADE COMMUNITY FOUNDATION, INC.

200 S Biscayne Blvd., Ste. 505
Miami, FL 33131-2343
Tel: (305)371-2711
Fax: (305)371-5342
Web Site: http://www.dadecommunityfoundation.org
To provide financial assistance to deserving students in Dade County who have successfully dealt with life's obstacles.
Title of Award: Alan R. Epstein "Reach for the Stars" Scholarships **Area, Field, or Subject:** General studies. **Level of Education for which Award is Granted:** Undergraduate **Funds Available:** $10,000. **Duration:** One year.
Eligibility Requirements: Applicants must be high school seniors graduating in June. **Application Requirements:** Applicants must submit

completed application form; high school official transcript; college acceptance letter(s); two letters of recommendation; volunteer/work experience and school activities; personal statement; one or two paragraphs describing the importance of scholarship. **Deadline for Receipt:** April 11.

757 ■ DADE COMMUNITY FOUNDATION, INC.

200 S Biscayne Blvd., Ste. 505
Miami, FL 33131-2343
Tel: (305)371-2711
Fax: (305)371-5342
Web Site: http://www.dadecommunityfoundation.org
To support minority high school students in need of financial assistance.
Title of Award: Samalot - Sebastian Scholarship Fund **Area, Field, or Subject:** General studies. **Level of Education for which Award is Granted:** High School **Number Awarded:** 3. **Funds Available:** $2,000. **Duration:** One year.
Eligibility Requirements: Applicants must be permanent residents or citizens of the U.S. and domiciled in South Florida; must have minimum high school grade point average of 3.5; must be enrolling as full-time students (minimum of 12 credit hours per semester) in a four-year college/university. **Application Requirements:** Applicants must submit all the required application information. **Deadline for Receipt:** April 4.

758 ■ DATATEL

4375 Fair Lakes Ct.
Fairfax, VA 22033
Tel: (703)968-9000
Free: 800-DAT-ATEL
Web Site: http://www.datatel.com
To support students who served the U.S. military and are attending an eligible Datatel client institution.
Title of Award: Datatel Angelfire Scholarships **Area, Field, or Subject:** General studies. **Level of Education for which Award is Granted:** Graduate, Undergraduate **Funds Available:** $1700.
Eligibility Requirements: Applicant must be an outstanding student currently attending an eligible Datatel client institution, who served the U.S. military in the Asian theater (Vietnam, Cambodia, or Laos during the 1964-1975 time-frame), or in Operation Desert Storm, Operation Enduring Freedom and/or Operation Iraqi Freedom; or a spouse or child of a Vietnam Veteran, or a refugee from Vietnam, Cambodia, or Laos. **Application Requirements:** Applicants must complete and submit an online application together with the essay. **Deadline for Receipt:** January 31. **Additional Information:** Jane H. Roth, Executive Director at scholars@datatel.com.

759 ■ DATATEL

4375 Fair Lakes Ct.
Fairfax, VA 22033
Tel: (703)968-9000
Free: 800-DAT-ATEL
Web Site: http://www.datatel.com
To help deserving students meet education goals.
Title of Award: Datatel Scholarships **Area, Field, or Subject:** General studies. **Level of Education for which Award is Granted:** Graduate, Undergraduate **Number Awarded:** 180 in 2008-2009 academic year. **Funds Available:** $1000, $1600, and $2400.
Eligibility Requirements: Applicant must be a student currently attending an eligible Datatel client institution; enrolled as full-time or part-time (taking at least six credit hours) undergraduate or graduate student. **Application Requirements:** Applicants must complete and submit an online application by the deadline; all applications and letters of recommendation are to be submitted electronically. **Deadline for Receipt:** January 31. **Additional Information:** Jane H. Roth, Executive Director at scholars@datatel.com.

760 ■ DATATEL

4375 Fair Lakes Ct.
Fairfax, VA 22033
Tel: (703)968-9000
Free: 800-DAT-ATEL
Web Site: http://www.datatel.com
To support returning students with their education.
Title of Award: Russ Griffith Memorial Scholarships **Area, Field, or Subject:** General studies. **Level of Education for which Award is**

Granted: Graduate, Undergraduate **Number Awarded:** 50. **Funds Available:** $2000.

Eligibility Requirements: Applicant must be an outstanding student attending an eligible Datatel client institution who has returned to school after an absence of five years or longer; full- and part-time, taking at least six credit hours, undergraduate or graduate student. **Application Requirements:** Applicants must complete and submit an on-line application together with the essay. **Additional Information:** Formerly called as Returning Student Scholarship. **Deadline for Receipt:** January 31. **Additional Information:** Jane H. Roth, Executive Director at scholars@datatel.com.

761 ■ DAVIS MEMORIAL FOUNDATION
1098 Foster City Blvd., No. 204
Foster City, CA 94404-2300
Tel: (650)570-5446
Fax: (650)570-5460
E-mail: dmf@wsrca.com
Web Site: http://www.davisfoundation.org
To develop qualified professionals through education and to award those who have the desire to continue to improve their quality of life.
Title of Award: Davis Memorial Foundation Scholarship Award Program **Area, Field, or Subject:** General studies. **Level of Education for which Award is Granted:** Graduate, Undergraduate **Number Awarded:** 5. **Funds Available:** $3,000.
Eligibility Requirements: Applicants must be high school students, undergraduate or graduate students or technical trade school students who are provisionally accepted as students into undergraduate or graduate degree programs for the coming academic year by accredited colleges or universities; must be WSRCA members in good standing, their employees or their respective immediate family (spouse or child). The child may be natural, legally adopted or a step child. **Application Requirements:** Applicants must submit 6 copies of each: official application form; official transcript of all high school and college records; letter from college, university or technical trade school where the undergraduate or graduate work will be undertaken, indicating provisional acceptance of the proposed course of study; and current picture. **Deadline for Receipt:** April 1.

762 ■ DELAWARE COMMUNITY FOUNDATION
PO Box 1636
Wilmington, DE 19899
Tel: (302)571-8004
Fax: (302)571-1553
E-mail: info@delcf.org
Web Site: http://www.delcf.org
To provide college scholarship assistance to those worthy students based on demonstrated academic ability, leadership traits and financial need.
Title of Award: Chrysler Technical Scholarships Fund **Area, Field, or Subject:** General Studies. **Level of Education for which Award is Granted:** Undergraduate **Funds Available:** $1,000 per academic year.
Eligibility Requirements: Applicants must be residents of Delaware; must have an at least 2.75 GPA and provide evidence of a commitment to leadership in the community; must plan to obtain a degree or certificate from a community college, trade school or university in a technical field related to the design, engineering, manufacturing or repair of automotive products, including but not limited to, automotive repair, skilled trades, and engineering. **Application Requirements:** Applicants must download and fill out the application form at the Delaware Community Foundation website. **Deadline for Receipt:** July 31.

763 ■ DELTA DELTA DELTA
PO Box 5987
Arlington, TX 76005-5987
Tel: (817)633-8001
Fax: (817)652-0212
E-mail: info@trideltaeo.org
Web Site: http://www.tridelta.org
To provide financial assistance to qualified undergraduate students.
Title of Award: Nancy Ashley Adams/Ashley Adams Koetje Scholarships **Area, Field, or Subject:** General studies. **Level of Education for which Award is Granted:** Undergraduate **Funds Available:** $500-$1,500. **Duration:** One academic year.

Eligibility Requirements: Applicant must be a Alpha Eta chapter member in Florida State University; must be an initiated sophomore or junior member. **Application Requirements:** Application forms are available on the website. Applicant must provide a personal statement about their educational and vocational goals; must have a recommendation letter from a faculty member; must have an official transcript from each undergraduate institution. Application materials must be sent to: Delta Delta Delta, PO Box 5987, Arlington, TX 76005. **Deadline for Receipt:** March 15.

764 ■ DELTA DELTA DELTA
PO Box 5987
Arlington, TX 76005-5987
Tel: (817)633-8001
Fax: (817)652-0212
E-mail: info@trideltaeo.org
Web Site: http://www.tridelta.org
To provide financial assistance to qualified undergraduate students.
Title of Award: Adams Family Scholarships **Area, Field, or Subject:** General studies. **Level of Education for which Award is Granted:** Undergraduate **Funds Available:** $500-$1,500. **Duration:** One academic year.
Eligibility Requirements: Applicant must be a Chi member at the University of Mississippi chapter; must be an initiated sophomore or junior member. **Application Requirements:** Application forms are available in the website. Applicant must provide a personal statement about educational and vocational goals; must have a recommendation letter from a faculty member; must have an official transcript from each undergraduate institutions. Application materials must be sent to: Delta Delta Delta, PO Box 5987, Arlington, TX 76005. **Deadline for Receipt:** March 15.

765 ■ DELTA DELTA DELTA
PO Box 5987
Arlington, TX 76005-5987
Tel: (817)633-8001
Fax: (817)652-0212
E-mail: info@trideltaeo.org
Web Site: http://www.tridelta.org
To provide financial assistance to qualified undergraduate students.
Title of Award: Alpha Eta Scholarships **Area, Field, or Subject:** General studies. **Level of Education for which Award is Granted:** Undergraduate **Funds Available:** $500-$1,500. **Duration:** One academic year.
Eligibility Requirements: Applicant must be a member of Alpha Eta chapter member at Florida State University; must be an initiated sophomore or junior member. **Application Requirements:** Application forms are available on the website. Applicant must provide a personal statement about their educational and vocational goals; must have a recommendation letter from a faculty member; must have an official transcript from each undergraduate institution. Application materials must be sent to: Delta Delta Delta, PO Box 5987, Arlington, TX 76005. **Deadline for Receipt:** March 15.

766 ■ DELTA DELTA DELTA
PO Box 5987
Arlington, TX 76005-5987
Tel: (817)633-8001
Fax: (817)652-0212
E-mail: info@trideltaeo.org
Web Site: http://www.tridelta.org
To provide financial assistance to qualified undergraduate students.
Title of Award: Alpha Rho Leadership Scholarships **Area, Field, or Subject:** General studies. **Level of Education for which Award is Granted:** Undergraduate **Funds Available:** $500-$1,500. **Duration:** One academic year.
Eligibility Requirements: Applicant must be a Alpha Rho chapter member at the University of Georgia; must be an initiated sophomore or junior member. **Application Requirements:** Application forms are available on the website. Applicant must provide a personal statement about their educational and vocational goals; must have a recommendation letter from a faculty member; must have an official transcript from each undergraduate institution. Application materials must be sent to: Delta Delta Delta, PO Box 5987, Arlington, TX 76005. **Deadline for Receipt:** March 15.

767 ■ DELTA DELTA DELTA
PO Box 5987
Arlington, TX 76005-5987
Tel: (817)633-8001
Fax: (817)652-0212
E-mail: info@trideltaeo.org
Web Site: http://www.tridelta.org
To provide financial assistance to qualified undergraduate students.
Title of Award: Jane E. Anderson Scholarships **Area, Field, or Subject:** General studies. **Level of Education for which Award is Granted:** Undergraduate **Funds Available:** $500-$1,500. **Duration:** One academic year.
Eligibility Requirements: Applicant must be a Kappa chapter member at the University of Nebraska; must have academic achievement at the collegiate level; must be "without favor or prejudice"; must be an initiated sophomore or junior member. **Application Requirements:** Application forms are available on the website. Applicant must provide a personal statement about educational and vocational goals; must have a recommendation letter from a faculty member; must have an official transcript from each undergraduate institution. Application materials must be sent to: Delta Delta Delta, PO Box 5987, Arlington, TX 76005. **Deadline for Receipt:** March 15.

768 ■ DELTA DELTA DELTA
PO Box 5987
Arlington, TX 76005-5987
Tel: (817)633-8001
Fax: (817)652-0212
E-mail: info@trideltaeo.org
Web Site: http://www.tridelta.org
To provide financial assistance to qualified undergraduate students.
Title of Award: Atlanta Alumnae Achievement Scholarships **Area, Field, or Subject:** General studies. **Level of Education for which Award is Granted:** Undergraduate **Funds Available:** $500-$1,500. **Duration:** One academic year.
Eligibility Requirements: Applicant must be currently enrolled in an undergraduate Tri Delta member in good standing at any public or private college or university; must be a collegiate member who graduated from a Georgia high school in one of the following four counties: Fulton, Dekalb, Cobb or Gwinnett; must be a junior during the application year. **Application Requirements:** Application forms are available on the website. Applicant must provide a personal statement about educational and vocational goals; must have a recommendation letter from a faculty member; must have an official transcript from each undergraduate institution. Application materials must be sent to: Delta Delta Delta, PO Box 5987, Arlington, TX 76005. **Deadline for Receipt:** March 15.

769 ■ DELTA DELTA DELTA
PO Box 5987
Arlington, TX 76005-5987
Tel: (817)633-8001
Fax: (817)652-0212
E-mail: info@trideltaeo.org
Web Site: http://www.tridelta.org
To provide financial assistance to qualified undergraduate students.
Title of Award: Beta Gamma Memorial Scholarship Fund **Area, Field, or Subject:** General studies. **Level of Education for which Award is Granted:** Undergraduate **Funds Available:** $500-$1,500. **Duration:** One academic year.
Eligibility Requirements: Applicant must be a Beta Gamma chapter member at Jacksonville University; must be a full time undergraduate at Jacksonville University; must have a minimum GPA of 2.5; must be a member who has overcome personal hardship or life struggle. **Application Requirements:** Application forms are available on the website. Applicant must provide a personal statement about their educational and vocational goals; must have a recommendation letter from a faculty member; must have an official transcript from each undergraduate institution. Application materials must be sent to: Delta Delta Delta, PO Box 5987, Arlington, TX 76005. **Deadline for Receipt:** March 15.

770 ■ DELTA DELTA DELTA
PO Box 5987
Arlington, TX 76005-5987

Tel: (817)633-8001
Fax: (817)652-0212
E-mail: info@trideltaeo.org
Web Site: http://www.tridelta.org
To provide financial assistance to a qualified undergraduate students.
Title of Award: Chi Chapter Undergraduate Scholarships **Area, Field, or Subject:** General studies. **Level of Education for which Award is Granted:** Undergraduate **Funds Available:** $500-$1,500. **Duration:** One academic year.
Eligibility Requirements: Applicant must be Chi member at the University of Mississippi chapter; must be an initiated sophomore or junior member. **Application Requirements:** Application forms are available on the website. Applicant must provide a personal statement about their educational and vocational goals; must have a recommendation letter from a faculty member; must have an official transcript from each undergraduate institutions. Application materials must be sent to: Delta Delta Delta, PO Box 5987, Arlington, TX 76005. **Deadline for Receipt:** March 15.

771 ■ DELTA DELTA DELTA
PO Box 5987
Arlington, TX 76005-5987
Tel: (817)633-8001
Fax: (817)652-0212
E-mail: info@trideltaeo.org
Web Site: http://www.tridelta.org
To provide financial assistance to qualified undergraduate students.
Title of Award: Louise Bales Gallagher Scholarships **Area, Field, or Subject:** General studies. **Level of Education for which Award is Granted:** Undergraduate **Funds Available:** $500-$1,500. **Duration:** One academic year.
Eligibility Requirements: Applicant must be a Delta Epsilon chapter member at Millikin University; must be an initiated sophomore or junior members. **Application Requirements:** Application forms are available on the website. Applicant must provide a personal statement about educational and vocational goals; must have a recommendation letter from a faculty member; must have an official transcript from each undergraduate institutions. Application materials must be sent to: Delta Delta Delta, PO Box 5987, Arlington, TX 76005. **Deadline for Receipt:** March 15.

772 ■ DELTA DELTA DELTA
PO Box 5987
Arlington, TX 76005-5987
Tel: (817)633-8001
Fax: (817)652-0212
E-mail: info@trideltaeo.org
Web Site: http://www.tridelta.org
To provide financial assistance to qualified undergraduate students.
Title of Award: Peg Hart Harrison Memorial Scholarships **Area, Field, or Subject:** General studies. **Level of Education for which Award is Granted:** Undergraduate **Funds Available:** $500-$1,500. **Duration:** One academic year.
Eligibility Requirements: Applicant must be a Beta Lambda chapter member at the University of Central Florida; must be a member who has overcome insurmountable odds; must be an initiated sophomore or junior member. **Application Requirements:** Application forms are available in the website. Applicant must provide a personal statement about their educational and vocational goals; must have a recommendation letter from a faculty member; must have an official transcript from each undergraduate institution. Application materials must be sent to: Delta Delta Delta, PO Box 5987, Arlington, TX 76005. **Deadline for Receipt:** March 15.

773 ■ DELTA DELTA DELTA
PO Box 5987
Arlington, TX 76005-5987
Tel: (817)633-8001
Fax: (817)652-0212
E-mail: info@trideltaeo.org
Web Site: http://www.tridelta.org
To provide financial assistance to qualified undergraduate students.
Title of Award: Erin Kumelos Heard Memorial Scholarships **Area, Field, or Subject:** General studies. **Level of Education for which Award is**

Granted: Undergraduate **Funds Available:** $500-$1,500. **Duration:** One academic year.
Eligibility Requirements: Applicant must be a member of the Beta Pi chapter at California/Davis; must be an initiated sophomore or junior member in good standing with the foundation; must be a full-time student and active member. **Application Requirements:** Application forms are available in the website. Applicant must provide a personal statement about educational and vocational goals; must have a recommendation letter from a faculty member; must have an official transcript from each undergraduate institutions. Application materials must be sent to: Delta Delta Delta, PO Box 5987, Arlington, TX 76005. **Deadline for Receipt:** March 15.

774 ■ DELTA DELTA DELTA
PO Box 5987
Arlington, TX 76005-5987
Tel: (817)633-8001
Fax: (817)652-0212
E-mail: info@trideltaeo.org
Web Site: http://www.tridelta.org
To provide financial assistance to qualified undergraduate students.
Title of Award: Houston Alumnae Undergraduate Tri Delta Scholarships **Area, Field, or Subject:** General studies. **Level of Education for which Award is Granted:** Undergraduate **Funds Available:** $500-$1,500. **Duration:** One academic year.
Eligibility Requirements: Applicant must be a collegiate member from the Houston Alumnae chapter zip-code area; must be an initiated sophomore or junior member. **Application Requirements:** Application forms are available on the website. Applicant must provide a personal statement about educational and vocational goals; must have a recommendation letter from a faculty member; must have an official transcript from each undergraduate institution. Application materials must be sent to: Delta Delta Delta, PO Box 5987, Arlington, TX 76005. **Deadline for Receipt:** March 15.

775 ■ DELTA DELTA DELTA
PO Box 5987
Arlington, TX 76005-5987
Tel: (817)633-8001
Fax: (817)652-0212
E-mail: info@trideltaeo.org
Web Site: http://www.tridelta.org
To provide financial assistance to qualified undergraduate students.
Title of Award: Kappa Chapter Centennial Scholarships **Area, Field, or Subject:** General studies. **Level of Education for which Award is Granted:** Undergraduate **Funds Available:** $500-$1,500. **Duration:** One academic year.
Eligibility Requirements: Applicant must be a Kappa chapter member at the University of Nebraska; must be an initiated sophomore or junior member. **Application Requirements:** Application forms are available on the website. Applicant must provide a personal statement about educational and vocational goals; must have a recommendation letter from a faculty member; must have an official transcript from each undergraduate institution. Application materials must be sent to: Delta Delta Delta, PO Box 5987, Arlington, TX 76005. **Deadline for Receipt:** March 15.

776 ■ DELTA DELTA DELTA
PO Box 5987
Arlington, TX 76005-5987
Tel: (817)633-8001
Fax: (817)652-0212
E-mail: info@trideltaeo.org
Web Site: http://www.tridelta.org
To provide financial assistance to qualified undergraduate students.
Title of Award: Luella Akins Key Scholarships **Area, Field, or Subject:** General studies. **Level of Education for which Award is Granted:** Undergraduate **Funds Available:** $500-$1,500. **Duration:** One academic year.
Eligibility Requirements: Applicant must be an initiated sophomore or junior member in good standing of Delta Delta; must be a full-time student and active member. **Application Requirements:** Application forms are available on the website. Applicant must provide a personal statement

about educational and vocational goals; must have a recommendation letter from a faculty member; must have an official transcript from each undergraduate institution. Application materials must be sent to: Delta Delta Delta, PO Box 5987, Arlington, TX 76005. **Deadline for Receipt:** March 15.

777 ■ DELTA DELTA DELTA
PO Box 5987
Arlington, TX 76005-5987
Tel: (817)633-8001
Fax: (817)652-0212
E-mail: info@trideltaeo.org
Web Site: http://www.tridelta.org
To provide financial assistance to qualified undergraduate students.
Title of Award: Sarah Shinn Marshall Scholarships **Area, Field, or Subject:** General studies. **Level of Education for which Award is Granted:** Undergraduate **Funds Available:** $500-$1,500. **Duration:** One academic year.
Eligibility Requirements: Applicant must be an initiated sophomore or junior member in good standing of Delta Delta; must be a full-time student and active member. **Application Requirements:** Application forms are available on the website. Applicant must provide a personal statement about educational and vocational goals; must have a recommendation letter from a faculty member; must have an official transcript from each undergraduate institution. Application materials must be sent to: Delta Delta Delta, PO Box 5987, Arlington, TX 76005. **Deadline for Receipt:** March 15.

778 ■ DELTA DELTA DELTA
PO Box 5987
Arlington, TX 76005-5987
Tel: (817)633-8001
Fax: (817)652-0212
E-mail: info@trideltaeo.org
Web Site: http://www.tridelta.org
To provide financial assistance to qualified undergraduate students.
Title of Award: Martin Sisters Scholarships **Area, Field, or Subject:** General studies. **Level of Education for which Award is Granted:** Undergraduate **Funds Available:** $500-$1,500. **Duration:** One academic year.
Eligibility Requirements: Applicant must be an initiated sophomore or junior members in good standing of Delta Delta; must be a full-time student and active member. **Application Requirements:** Application forms are available in the website. Applicant must provide a personal statement about educational and vocational goals; must have a recommendation letter from a faculty member; must have an official transcript from each undergraduate institutions. Application materials must be sent to: Delta Delta Delta, PO Box 5987, Arlington, TX 76005. **Deadline for Receipt:** March 15.

779 ■ DELTA DELTA DELTA
PO Box 5987
Arlington, TX 76005-5987
Tel: (817)633-8001
Fax: (817)652-0212
E-mail: info@trideltaeo.org
Web Site: http://www.tridelta.org
To provide financial assistance to qualified undergraduate students.
Title of Award: McKinney Sisters Undergraduate Scholarships **Area, Field, or Subject:** General studies. **Level of Education for which Award is Granted:** Undergraduate **Funds Available:** $500-$1,500. **Duration:** One academic year.
Eligibility Requirements: Applicant must be a graduate from high school in San Antonio, TX or has permanent residence in San Antonio; must be an initiated sophomore or junior member. **Application Requirements:** Application forms are available on the website. Applicant must provide a personal statement about educational and vocational goals; must have a recommendation letter from a faculty member; must have an official transcript from each undergraduate institution. Application materials must be sent to: Delta Delta Delta, PO Box 5987, Arlington, TX 76005. **Deadline for Receipt:** March 15.

780 ■ DELTA DELTA DELTA
PO Box 5987
Arlington, TX 76005-5987

Tel: (817)633-8001
Fax: (817)652-0212
E-mail: info@trideltaeo.org
Web Site: http://www.tridelta.org
To provide financial assistance to qualified undergraduate students.
Title of Award: Northern Virginia Alumnae Chapter Scholarships **Area, Field, or Subject:** General studies. **Level of Education for which Award is Granted:** Undergraduate **Funds Available:** $500-$1,500. **Duration:** One academic year.
Eligibility Requirements: Applicant must have academic achievement of 3.0 or better GPA; must have a financial need; must be an initiated sophomore or junior member. **Application Requirements:** Application forms are available on the website. Applicant must provide a personal statement about educational and vocational goals; must have a recommendation letter from a faculty member; must have an official transcript from each undergraduate institution. Application materials must be sent to: Delta Delta Delta, PO Box 5987, Arlington, TX 76005. **Deadline for Receipt:** March 15.

781 ■ DELTA DELTA DELTA
PO Box 5987
Arlington, TX 76005-5987
Tel: (817)633-8001
Fax: (817)652-0212
E-mail: info@trideltaeo.org
Web Site: http://www.tridelta.org
To provide financial assistance to qualified undergraduate students.
Title of Award: Cissy McDaniel Parker Scholarships **Area, Field, or Subject:** General studies. **Level of Education for which Award is Granted:** Undergraduate **Funds Available:** $500-$1,500. **Duration:** One academic year.
Eligibility Requirements: Applicant must be a Theta Zeta chapter member at the University of Texas; must have an academic achievement of 3.0 or better GPA; must be an initiated sophomore or junior members. **Application Requirements:** Application forms are available on the website. Applicant must provide a personal statement about educational and vocational goals; must have a recommendation letter from a faculty member; must have an official transcript from each undergraduate institution. Application materials must be sent to: Delta Delta Delta, PO Box 5987, Arlington, TX 76005. **Deadline for Receipt:** March 15.

782 ■ DELTA DELTA DELTA
PO Box 5987
Arlington, TX 76005-5987
Tel: (817)633-8001
Fax: (817)652-0212
E-mail: info@trideltaeo.org
Web Site: http://www.tridelta.org
To provide financial assistance to qualified undergraduate students.
Title of Award: Zoe Gore Perrin Scholarships **Area, Field, or Subject:** General studies. **Level of Education for which Award is Granted:** Undergraduate **Funds Available:** $500-$1,500. **Duration:** One academic year.
Eligibility Requirements: Applicant must be an initiated sophomore and junior member in good standing of Delta Delta; must be a full-time student and active member. **Application Requirements:** Application forms are available on the website. Applicant must provide a personal statement about their educational and vocational goals; must have a recommendation letter from a faculty member; must have an official transcript from each undergraduate institution. Application materials must be sent to: Delta Delta Delta, PO Box 5987, Arlington, TX 76005. **Deadline for Receipt:** March 15.

783 ■ DELTA DELTA DELTA
PO Box 5987
Arlington, TX 76005-5987
Tel: (817)633-8001
Fax: (817)652-0212
E-mail: info@trideltaeo.org
Web Site: http://www.tridelta.org
To provide financial assistance to qualified undergraduate students.
Title of Award: Cheryl White Pryor Memorial Scholarships **Area, Field, or Subject:** General studies. **Level of Education for which Award is Granted:** Undergraduate **Funds Available:** $500. **Duration:** One academic year.

Eligibility Requirements: Applicant must be a member of Delta Sigma chapter member at Tennessee; must be an initiated sophomore or junior members. **Application Requirements:** Application forms are available on the website. Applicant must provide a personal statement about educational and vocational goals; must have a recommendation letter from a faculty member; must have an official transcript from each undergraduate institution. Application materials must be sent to: Delta Delta Delta, PO Box 5987, Arlington, TX 76005. **Deadline for Receipt:** March 15.

784 ■ DELTA DELTA DELTA
PO Box 5987
Arlington, TX 76005-5987
Tel: (817)633-8001
Fax: (817)652-0212
E-mail: info@trideltaeo.org
Web Site: http://www.tridelta.org
To provide financial assistance to a qualified undergraduate student.
Title of Award: Susan E. Riley Scholarships **Area, Field, or Subject:** General studies. **Level of Education for which Award is Granted:** Undergraduate **Funds Available:** $500-$1,500. **Duration:** One academic year.
Eligibility Requirements: Applicant must be a Theta Mu chapter member at Oregon State University; must be currently a Tri Delta member in good standing; must show academic achievements at the collegiate level; must participate in community service; must be an initiated sophomore or junior member. **Application Requirements:** Application forms are available on the website. Applicant must provide a personal statement about their educational and vocational goals; must have a recommendation letter from a faculty member; must have an official transcript from each undergraduate institution. Application materials must be sent to: Delta Delta Delta, PO Box 5987, Arlington, TX 76005. **Deadline for Receipt:** March 15.

785 ■ DELTA DELTA DELTA
PO Box 5987
Arlington, TX 76005-5987
Tel: (817)633-8001
Fax: (817)652-0212
E-mail: info@trideltaeo.org
Web Site: http://www.tridelta.org
To provide financial assistance to qualified undergraduate students.
Title of Award: Jean Wiggin Roach Scholarships **Area, Field, or Subject:** General studies. **Level of Education for which Award is Granted:** Undergraduate **Funds Available:** $500-$1,500. **Duration:** One academic year.
Eligibility Requirements: Applicant must be a Phi Lambda chapter member at Texas Christian University; must have academic achievement at the collegiate level; must be an initiated sophomore and junior members. **Application Requirements:** Application forms are available on the website. Applicant must provide a personal statement about educational and vocational goals; must have a recommendation letter from a faculty member; must have an official transcript from each undergraduate institution. Application materials must be sent to: Delta Delta Delta, PO Box 5987, Arlington, TX 76005. **Deadline for Receipt:** March 15.

786 ■ DELTA DELTA DELTA
PO Box 5987
Arlington, TX 76005-5987
Tel: (817)633-8001
Fax: (817)652-0212
E-mail: info@trideltaeo.org
Web Site: http://www.tridelta.org
To provide financial assistance to qualified undergraduate students.
Title of Award: Jeanne Graves Ryland Scholarships **Area, Field, or Subject:** General studies. **Level of Education for which Award is Granted:** Undergraduate **Funds Available:** $500-$1,500. **Duration:** One academic year.
Eligibility Requirements: Applicant must be a Phi Theta chapter member at Auburn University; must be an initiated sophomore or junior member. **Application Requirements:** Application forms are available on the website. Applicant must provide a personal statement about

educational and vocational goals; must have a recommendation letter from a faculty member; must have an official transcript from each undergraduate institution. Application materials must be sent to: Delta Delta Delta, PO Box 5987, Arlington, TX 76005. **Deadline for Receipt:** March 15.

787 ■ DELTA DELTA DELTA
PO Box 5987
Arlington, TX 76005-5987
Tel: (817)633-8001
Fax: (817)652-0212
E-mail: info@trideltaeo.org
Web Site: http://www.tridelta.org
To provide financial assistance to qualified undergraduate students.
Title of Award: Julie Anne Sadlier Memorial Scholarships **Area, Field, or Subject:** General studies. **Level of Education for which Award is Granted:** Undergraduate **Funds Available:** $500-$1,500. **Duration:** One academic year.
Eligibility Requirements: Applicant must be a Theta Pi chapter member at UCLA; must have overcome a personal hardship or life struggle; must be an initiated sophomore or junior members. **Application Requirements:** Application forms are available on the website. Applicant must provide a personal statement about educational and vocational goals; must have a recommendation letter from a faculty member; must have an official transcript from each undergraduate institution. Application materials must be sent to: Delta Delta Delta, PO Box 5987, Arlington, TX 76005. **Deadline for Receipt:** March 15.

788 ■ DELTA DELTA DELTA
PO Box 5987
Arlington, TX 76005-5987
Tel: (817)633-8001
Fax: (817)652-0212
E-mail: info@trideltaeo.org
Web Site: http://www.tridelta.org
To provide financial assistance to qualified undergraduate students.
Title of Award: Virginia Hartford Saharov Memorial Scholarships **Area, Field, or Subject:** General studies. **Level of Education for which Award is Granted:** Undergraduate **Funds Available:** $500-$1,500. **Duration:** One academic year.
Eligibility Requirements: Applicant must be a Delta Pi chapter member at Illinois; must be an initiated sophomore or junior member. **Application Requirements:** Application forms are available on the website. Applicant must provide a personal statement about educational and vocational goals; must have a recommendation letter from a faculty member; must have an official transcript from each undergraduate institution. Application materials must be sent to: Delta Delta Delta, PO Box 5987, Arlington, TX 76005. **Deadline for Receipt:** March 15.

789 ■ DELTA DELTA DELTA
PO Box 5987
Arlington, TX 76005-5987
Tel: (817)633-8001
Fax: (817)652-0212
E-mail: info@trideltaeo.org
Web Site: http://www.tridelta.org
To provide financial assistance to a qualified undergraduate students.
Title of Award: Edith Scandlyn/Sammie Lynn Scandlyn Puett Memorial Scholarships **Area, Field, or Subject:** General studies. **Level of Education for which Award is Granted:** Undergraduate **Funds Available:** $500-$1,500. **Duration:** One academic year.
Eligibility Requirements: Applicant must be a Delta Sigma chapter member at the University of Tennessee; must be an initiated sophomore or junior members. **Application Requirements:** Application forms are available on the website. Applicant must provide a personal statement about educational and vocational goals; must have a recommendation letter from a faculty member; must have an official transcript from each undergraduate institution. Application materials must be sent to: Delta Delta Delta, PO Box 5987, Arlington, TX 76005. **Deadline for Receipt:** March 15.

790 ■ DELTA DELTA DELTA
PO Box 5987
Arlington, TX 76005-5987

Tel: (817)633-8001
Fax: (817)652-0212
E-mail: info@trideltaeo.org
Web Site: http://www.tridelta.org
To provide financial assistance to qualified undergraduate students.
Title of Award: Teri Wenglein-Callender Undergraduate Scholarships **Area, Field, or Subject:** General studies. **Level of Education for which Award is Granted:** Undergraduate **Funds Available:** $500-$1,500. **Duration:** One academic year.
Eligibility Requirements: Applicant must be a Theta Zeta chapter member at the University of Texas; must be an initiated sophomore or junior member. **Application Requirements:** Application forms are available on the website. Applicant must provide a personal statement about educational and vocational goals; must have a recommendation letter from a faculty member; must have an official transcript from each undergraduate institution. Application materials must be sent to: Delta Delta Delta, PO Box 5987, Arlington, TX 76005. **Deadline for Receipt:** March 15.

791 ■ DELTA DELTA DELTA
PO Box 5987
Arlington, TX 76005-5987
Tel: (817)633-8001
Fax: (817)652-0212
E-mail: info@trideltaeo.org
Web Site: http://www.tridelta.org
To provide financial assistance to qualified undergraduate students.
Title of Award: Donna Axum Whitworth Scholarships **Area, Field, or Subject:** General studies. **Level of Education for which Award is Granted:** Undergraduate **Funds Available:** $500-$1,500. **Duration:** One academic year.
Eligibility Requirements: Applicant must be a Delta Iota member at Arkansas; must be an initiated sophomore or junior member. **Application Requirements:** Application forms are available on the website. Applicant must provide a personal statement about educational and vocational goals; must have a recommendation letter from a faculty member; must have an official transcript from each undergraduate institutions. Application materials must be sent to: Delta Delta Delta, PO Box 5987, Arlington, TX 76005. **Deadline for Receipt:** March 15.

792 ■ DELTA EPSILON SIGMA
11300 NE 2nd Ave.
Miami, FL 33161
Web Site: http://www.deltaepsilonsigma.org
To provide financial support for the education of member students.
Title of Award: Fitzgerald Fellowships **Area, Field, or Subject:** General studies. **Level of Education for which Award is Granted:** Undergraduate **Funds Available:** $1,000.
Eligibility Requirements: Applicants must be junior year members. **Application Requirements:** Applicants must submit typed application accompanied by three letters of recommendation including one from the Chapter Advisor and official transcripts of all college work through the current fall semester. **Deadline for Receipt:** April 1.

793 ■ DELTA EPSILON SIGMA
11300 NE 2nd Ave.
Miami, FL 33161
Web Site: http://www.deltaepsilonsigma.org
To provide financial support for the education of member students.
Title of Award: Fitzgerald Scholarships **Area, Field, or Subject:** General studies. **Level of Education for which Award is Granted:** Undergraduate **Funds Available:** $1,000.
Eligibility Requirements: Applicants must be junior year members. **Application Requirements:** Applicants must submit typed application accompanied by three letters of recommendation including one from the Chapter Advisor and official transcripts of all college work through the current fall semester. **Deadline for Receipt:** April 1.

794 ■ DELTA GAMMA
PO Box 21397
Columbus, OH 43221
Tel: (614)481-8149
Fax: (614)481-0133

Web Site: http://www.deltagamma.org
To encourage the Delta Gammas to pursue a career in Science.
Title of Award: Delta Gamma Scholarships **Area, Field, or Subject:** Science. **Level of Education for which Award is Granted:** Undergraduate **Funds Available:** No specific amount.
Eligibility Requirements: Candidates must have a 3.0 or higher GPA; must be participants in chapter, campus and community leadership activities; must have completed at least three semester or four quarter of college work. **Application Requirements:** For more information on Delta Gamma scholarship, applicants are advised to contact the Director of Scholarships and Fellowships, Betty Plaggemier Guthrie (at FNScholarFellow@deltagamma.org), or contact Executive Offices at 3250 Riverside Drive, PO Box 21397, Columbus OH 43221-0397. **Deadline for Receipt:** February 15.

795 ■ DELTA NU ALPHA TRANSPORTATION FRATERNITY
435 Pennsylvannia Ave. 102
Glen Ellyn, IL 60137
Tel: (630)653-3622
Fax: (630)653-3632
E-mail: admin@deltanualpha.org
Web Site: http://www.deltanualpha.org
To emphasize financial assistance and mentoring for students, excellent continuing education opportunities for the work force, and vigilance in communicating changes in regulations.
Title of Award: Delta Nu Alpha Foundation Scholarships **Area, Field, or Subject:** Transportation; Logistics. **Level of Education for which Award is Granted:** Undergraduate **Funds Available:** No specific amount.
Eligibility Requirements: Program is open to all students studying in the field of Transportation, Logistics and Supply Chain Management. Students pursuing associate and bachelor degrees are encouraged to apply. **Application Requirements:** Applicants must submit completed application form along with transcripts of all college/university level work completed and two letters of recommendation (one should be from the transportation, logistics or supply chain management instructor). **Deadline for Receipt:** May 31. **Additional Information:** Tom Bock DNA Foundation Scholarship Chair, 4123 Apple blossom Rd. Lutz, FL 33558.

796 ■ DELTA PHI EPSILON
251 S Camc St.
Philadelphia, PA 19107
Tel: (215)732-5901
E-mail: info@dphie.org
Web Site: http://www.dphie.org
To develop a social conscience and a willingness to think in terms of the common good in order to assure for its members continuous development and achievement in the collegiate and fraternity world.
Title of Award: Delta Phi Epsilon Educational Foundation Scholarships **Area, Field, or Subject:** General studies. **Level of Education for which Award is Granted:** Undergraduate **Funds Available:** No specific amount. **Duration:** One academic year.
Eligibility Requirements: Applicants must be members of Delta Phi Epsilon or the sons or daughters of members; must be enrolled in undergraduate studies during the academic year. **Application Requirements:** Application forms are available on the website. Applicant must submit an official transcript of grades, letter of introduction and need for scholarship, typed autobiographical sketch (1,000 word max), two recent photos suitable for publication, letter of recommendation from (must provide at least 2): (1) Chapter President; (2) Chapter Advisor; (3) College Professor or Administrator; (4) High School Teacher/Principal; (5) Alumna; (6) Employer. Applicant must provide a name and address of financial aid director for the school. Application materials must be mailed to: Delta Phi Epsilon Educational Foundation, 251 S Camac St., Philadelphia, PA 19107. **Deadline for Receipt:** April 15.

797 ■ DELTA TAU LAMBDA SORORITY
PO Box 7714
Ann Arbor, MI 48107
E-mail: dtl-info@deltataulambda.org
Web Site: http://www.deltataulambda.org
To assist young Latinas in reaching goals using education as their tool.
Title of Award: Lydia Cruz and Sandra Maria Ramos Scholarships **Area, Field, or Subject:** General studies. **Level of Education for which**

Award is Granted: Undergraduate **Funds Available:** No specific amount.
Eligibility Requirements: Applicants must be current Latina high school seniors who are entering their first year of college at a two or four year higher learning institution. **Application Requirements:** Applicant must complete the application form available on the website; must provide the official high school transcript and a copy of University/College Acceptance Latter. Scholarship application materials must be sent to: Delta Tau Lambda Sorority, Inc., PO Box 7714, Ann Arbor, MI 48107. **Deadline for Receipt:** For more information on requirements and deadlines contact the foundation at DTL-info@deltataulambda.org.

798 ■ DELTA ZETA SORORITY
202 E Church St.
Oxford, OH 45056
Tel: (513)523-7597
Web Site: http://www.deltazeta.org
To provide financial assistance to all qualified undergraduate students.
Title of Award: Sandra Sebrell Bailey Scholarships **Area, Field, or Subject:** General studies. **Level of Education for which Award is Granted:** Undergraduate **Funds Available:** $1,000-$2,500. **Duration:** One academic year.
Eligibility Requirements: Applicant must be a junior or senior woman who has been an initiated member at least one year and is in good standing. **Application Requirements:** Scholarship applications are available on the website and must be completed properly. Applicant must have the FAFSA reply form. **Deadline for Receipt:** February 15.

799 ■ DELTA ZETA SORORITY
202 E Church St.
Oxford, OH 45056
Tel: (513)523-7597
Web Site: http://www.deltazeta.org
To provide financial assistance for qualified graduate students.
Title of Award: Charline Chilson Scholarships **Area, Field, or Subject:** Science. **Level of Education for which Award is Granted:** Undergraduate **Funds Available:** $1,000-$2,500. **Duration:** One academic year.
Eligibility Requirements: Applicant must be a Delta Zeta member in good standing; must be in their junior or senior year or as graduate students; must have a high grade point in their major; must show financial need; must have a history of active leadership and participation in Delta Zeta activities; and must have a commitment to a degree in science. **Application Requirements:** Scholarship applications are available on the website and must be completed properly. Applicant must have the FAFSA reply form. **Deadline for Receipt:** February 15.

800 ■ DELTA ZETA SORORITY
202 E Church St.
Oxford, OH 45056
Tel: (513)523-7597
Web Site: http://www.deltazeta.org
To provide financial assistance to all qualified undergraduate students.
Title of Award: Delta Zeta Undergraduate Scholarships **Area, Field, or Subject:** General studies. **Level of Education for which Award is Granted:** Undergraduate **Funds Available:** $1,000-$2,500. **Duration:** one academic year.
Eligibility Requirements: Applicant must be an initiated, active, continuing member of Delta Zeta entering junior or senior year; must be outstanding in campus and chapter activities, and have maintained at least a B average (3.0). **Application Requirements:** Scholarship applications are available on the website and must be completed properly. Applicant must have the FAFSA reply form. **Deadline for Receipt:** February 15.

801 ■ DELTA ZETA SORORITY
202 E Church St.
Oxford, OH 45056
Tel: (513)523-7597
Web Site: http://www.deltazeta.org
To provide financial assistance to all qualified undergraduate students.
Title of Award: Lavonne Heghinian Scholarships **Area, Field, or Subject:** General studies. **Level of Education for which Award is Granted:** Undergraduate **Funds Available:** $1,000-$2,500. **Duration:** One academic year.

Eligibility Requirements: Applicant must be an initiated, active, continuing member of Delta Zeta in need of financial assistance; must have a 3.0 average. **Application Requirements:** Scholarship applications are available on the website and must be completed properly. Applicant must have the FAFSA reply form. **Deadline for Receipt:** February 15.

802 ■ DELTA ZETA SORORITY
202 E Church St.
Oxford, OH 45056
Tel: (513)523-7597
Web Site: http://www.deltazeta.org
To provide financial assistance to all qualified undergraduate students.
Title of Award: John L. and Eleanore I. Mckinley Scholarships **Area, Field, or Subject:** General studies. **Level of Education for which Award is Granted:** Undergraduate **Funds Available:** $1,000-$2,500. **Duration:** One academic year.
Eligibility Requirements: Applicant must be a junior or senior Delta Zeta member in good standing; must have earned a B or better average at the conclusion of their sophomore year; must have achieved a high level of service to the Delta Zeta Sorority and her college community. **Application Requirements:** Scholarship applications are available on the website and must be completed properly. Applicant must have the FAFSA reply form. **Deadline for Receipt:** February 15.

803 ■ DELTA ZETA SORORITY
202 E Church St.
Oxford, OH 45056
Tel: (513)523-7597
Web Site: http://www.deltazeta.org
To provide financial assistance to all qualified undergraduate student.
Title of Award: Gail Patrick Charitable Trust Scholarships **Area, Field, or Subject:** General studies. **Level of Education for which Award is Granted:** Undergraduate **Funds Available:** $2,500. **Duration:** One academic year.
Eligibility Requirements: Applicant must be an initiated, active, continuing Delta Zeta member in need of financial assistance; must be entering her junior or senior year. **Application Requirements:** Scholarship applications are available on the website and must be completed properly. Applicant must have the FAFSA reply form. **Deadline for Receipt:** February 15.

804 ■ DELTA ZETA SORORITY
202 E Church St.
Oxford, OH 45056
Tel: (513)523-7597
Web Site: http://www.deltazeta.org
To provide financial assistance to all qualified undergraduate students.
Title of Award: Elizabeth Coulter Stephenson Scholarships **Area, Field, or Subject:** General studies. **Level of Education for which Award is Granted:** Undergraduate **Funds Available:** $500. **Duration:** One academic year.
Eligibility Requirements: Applicant must be outstanding in campus and chapter activities; must have held, or must currently hold, an executive board position; must have at least 3.0 average; must have been adversely affected, or parents have been adversely affected by a disaster. **Application Requirements:** Application forms are available in the website. Applicant must provide the official transcript; must have statement about special service to Delta Zeta, campus activities and/or community involvement, and academic honors; must have the list of employment record; must submit a recommendation letter from the college chapter director (CCD) and if chapter has no CCD, a letter from RCC will suffice. Application materials must be sent to: Delta Zeta Foundation, 202 E Church St., Oxford, OH 45056. **Deadline for Receipt:** February 15.

805 ■ DELTA ZETA SORORITY
202 E Church St.
Oxford, OH 45056
Tel: (513)523-7597
Web Site: http://www.deltazeta.org
To provide financial assistance to all qualified undergraduate students.
Title of Award: Thornberg/Havens Scholarships **Area, Field, or Subject:** General studies. **Level of Education for which Award is Granted:** Undergraduate **Funds Available:** $1,000-$2,500. **Duration:** One academic year.

Eligibility Requirements: Applicant must be an undergraduate and/or graduate Delta Zeta in good standing; must be an initiated member in need of financial assistance who has shown outstanding campus and chapter activities; must have at least 3.0 undergraduate average. **Application Requirements:** Scholarship applications are available on the website and must be completed properly. Applicant must have the FAFSA reply form. **Deadline for Receipt:** February 15.

806 ■ DEMOLAY INTERNATIONAL
10200 NW Ambassador Dr.
Kansas City, MO 64153
Tel: (816)891-8333
Free: 800-336-6529
Fax: (816)891-9062
E-mail: demolay@demolay.org
Web Site: http://www.demolay.org
To provide financial assistance for eligible members of Demolay.
Title of Award: Frank S. Land Scholarships **Area, Field, or Subject:** General studies. **Level of Education for which Award is Granted:** Undergraduate **Number Awarded:** 1. **Funds Available:** $800.
Eligibility Requirements: Applicants must be active members of DeMolay who have not yet reached their majority or 21st birthday. **Application Requirements:** Applicants may download the scholarship application form from the Foundation's website. **Deadline for Receipt:** April 1.

807 ■ DEMOLAY INTERNATIONAL
10200 NW Ambassador Dr.
Kansas City, MO 64153
Tel: (816)891-8333
Free: 800-336-6529
Fax: (816)891-9062
E-mail: demolay@demolay.org
Web Site: http://www.demolay.org
To support the post-baccalaureate education of the members of Demolay.
Title of Award: York Rite Grand Chapter Royal Arch Masons Scholarships **Area, Field, or Subject:** General studies. **Level of Education for which Award is Granted:** Undergraduate **Funds Available:** $1,000.
Eligibility Requirements: Applicants must be active senior DeMolay members. **Application Requirements:** Applicants may download scholarship application form from the foundation's website. **Deadline for Receipt:** April 1.

808 ■ DENVER SCHOLARSHIP FOUNDATION
303 E 17th Ave., Ste. 200
Denver, CO 80203
Tel: (303)951-4140
Fax: (303)951-4143
E-mail: info@denverscholarship.org
Web Site: http://www.denverscholarship.org
To inspire and empower Denver Public School (DPS) students to achieve their post-secondary goals.
Title of Award: Denver Scholarship Foundation Scholarships **Area, Field, or Subject:** General studies. **Level of Education for which Award is Granted:** Undergraduate **Funds Available:** No specific amount.
Eligibility Requirements: Applicant must be a DPS graduate, enrolled and included in the State Census (October 1st Count) at a participating DPS school for at least one year immediately preceding graduation; and eligible to receive federal student financial aid (must be U.S. citizen, permanent resident or other eligible non-citizen). **Application Requirements:** Applicants must complete and submit the DSF Scholarship Application online. **Additional Information:** All mailings, fax coversheets, or e-mail messages must include the student's full name, student ID number, phone number, and e-mail address. **Deadline for Receipt:** March 31.

809 ■ BILL DICKEY SCHOLARSHIP ASSOCIATION
1140 E Washington St. Ste. 103
Phoenix, AZ 85034
Tel: (602)258-7851
Fax: (602)258-3412
E-mail: andrea@bdscholar.org
Web Site: http://www.nmjgsa.org

To provide financial support to deserving undergraduate students. **Title of Award:** Bill Dickey Scholarship Association Scholarships **Area, Field, or Subject:** General studies. **Level of Education for which Award is Granted:** Undergraduate **Funds Available:** Maximum award amount: $6,000. **Duration:** Annually.

Eligibility Requirements: Applicants must be high school seniors who are already in BDSA database as well as undergraduate students that previously received a scholarship as freshmen are eligible to apply. **Application Requirements:** Applicants must check the available website to enter their database profile and to gain information regarding this award. **Additional Information:** Bill Dickey Scholarship Association at the above address

810 ■ DISABLED AMERICAN VETERANS

PO Box 14301
Cincinnati, OH 45250-0301
Tel: (859)441-7300; 877-426-2838
Web Site: http://www.dav.org
To provide financial assistance to young volunteers who play active roles in the Department of Veterans Affairs Voluntary Service programs to continue their education.

Title of Award: Jesse Brown Memorial Youth Scholarship Program **Area, Field, or Subject:** General studies. **Level of Education for which Award is Granted:** Undergraduate **Funds Available:** No specific amount.

Eligibility Requirements: Applicants must be any volunteers who are at the age of 21 or younger and have volunteered for a minimum of 100 hours at a VA medical center during the previous year; immediate family members of the DAV national organization are also eligible. **Application Requirements:** Nominations must be submitted by the Voluntary Service Program Manager at the VA medical center, DAV Department Commander, or the student must submit a self-nomination form, which is available online, including an essay and any supporting documentation.

811 ■ DOLPHIN SCHOLARSHIP FOUNDATION

5040 Virginia Beach Blvd., Ste. 104A
Virginia Beach, VA 23462
Tel: (757)671-3200
Fax: (757)671-3330
E-mail: info@dolphinscholarship.org
Web Site: http://www.dolphinscholarship.org
To support the education of children/stepchildren of members or former members of the Submarine Force or who have served in the Submarine Force.

Title of Award: Dolphin Scholarships **Area, Field, or Subject:** General studies. **Level of Education for which Award is Granted:** Undergraduate **Number Awarded:** Varies. **Funds Available:** Varies.

Eligibility Requirements: Applicant must be a high school senior or college student; child or stepchild of a member or former member of the U.S. Navy Submarine Force; unmarried; under age 24; must attend a four-year accredited college or university and intend to work toward a BS or BA degree. **Application Requirements:** Applicants must submit a completed scholarship application form.

812 ■ DULUTH SUPERIOR AREA COMMUNITY FOUNDATION

324 W Superior St., Ste. 212
Duluth, MN 55802
Tel: (218)726-0232
Fax: (218)726-0257
E-mail: info@communityfoundation.com
Web Site: http://www.dsacommunityfoundation.com
To provide financial assistance to the non-traditional, older students in financial resources for their education.

Title of Award: Darrell and Palchie Asselin Scholarships **Area, Field, or Subject:** General studies. **Level of Education for which Award is Granted:** Undergraduate **Funds Available:** $2,000. **Duration:** One year.

Eligibility Requirements: Applicants must be students over the age of 22 who are the primary care givers to one or more children under the age of 18; must have a grade point average of 2.5 (based on a 4.0 system) or higher for a completed of at least 50% of the course of instruction at the time of the award. **Application Requirements:** Applicants must complete the application form, available online and must submit one recommendation from a teacher, advisor, counselor or administrator; a current

transcript indicating the success in completing the course of study; and Federal 1040 form. **Deadline for Receipt:** January 15.

813 ■ DULUTH SUPERIOR AREA COMMUNITY FOUNDATION

324 W Superior St., Ste. 212
Duluth, MN 55802
Tel: (218)726-0232
Fax: (218)726-0257
E-mail: info@communityfoundation.com
Web Site: http://www.dsacommunityfoundation.com
To provide assistance to Jewish and Roman Catholic students who are in need financial of aid for their college education.

Title of Award: Bernard and Mary Brusin Scholarships **Area, Field, or Subject:** General studies. **Level of Education for which Award is Granted:** Undergraduate **Funds Available:** $4,500. **Duration:** One year.

Eligibility Requirements: Applicants must be either Jewish or Roman Catholic graduating seniors from St. Louis County public or private high schools who are in the top 25% of their high school. **Application Requirements:** Applicants must submit all the required application information. **Additional Information:** The award is co-payable to the institution and the recipient. **Deadline for Receipt:** January 15.

814 ■ DULUTH SUPERIOR AREA COMMUNITY FOUNDATION

324 W Superior St., Ste. 212
Duluth, MN 55802
Tel: (218)726-0232
Fax: (218)726-0257
E-mail: info@communityfoundation.com
Web Site: http://www.dsacommunityfoundation.com
To provide financial assistance to students entering/attending any post secondary vocational college, community college or other college or university.

Title of Award: Duluth Building and Construction Trades Council Scholarships **Area, Field, or Subject:** General studies. **Level of Education for which Award is Granted:** Undergraduate **Number Awarded:** 2. **Funds Available:** $2,500. **Duration:** One year.

Eligibility Requirements: Applicants must be graduating high school seniors, whose parent/guardian is a member of one of the 17 unions affiliated with the Duluth Building Trades Council; must have grade point average of 2.75, based on 4.0 scale, or higher. **Application Requirements:** Applicants must submit all the required application information. **Additional Information:** The award is co-payable to the institution and the recipient. **Deadline for Receipt:** January 15.

815 ■ DULUTH SUPERIOR AREA COMMUNITY FOUNDATION

324 W Superior St., Ste. 212
Duluth, MN 55802
Tel: (218)726-0232
Fax: (218)726-0257
E-mail: info@communityfoundation.com
Web Site: http://www.dsacommunityfoundation.com
To assist the worthy student who customarily would be eliminated from scholarship consideration on the basis of level achievement attained in class work.

Title of Award: Duluth Central HS Alumni Scholarships **Area, Field, or Subject:** General studies. **Level of Education for which Award is Granted:** Undergraduate **Number Awarded:** 1. **Funds Available:** $1,000. **Duration:** One year.

Eligibility Requirements: Applicants must be graduating seniors from Duluth Central High School who will attend the College of St. Scholastica, University of Minnesota-Duluth, University of Wisconsin-Superior, Lake Superior College, or Wisconsin Indianhead Technical College. **Application Requirements:** Applicants must submit all the required application information. **Additional Information:** The Award is co-payable to the institution and the recipient. **Deadline for Receipt:** January 15.

816 ■ DULUTH SUPERIOR AREA COMMUNITY FOUNDATION

324 W Superior St., Ste. 212
Duluth, MN 55802
Tel: (218)726-0232
Fax: (218)726-0257
E-mail: info@communityfoundation.com
Web Site: http://www.dsacommunityfoundation.com

To provide financial assistance for post-secondary education to the children of employees of Ulland Brothers.

Title of Award: Peter M. Gargano Scholarship Fund **Area, Field, or Subject:** General studies. **Level of Education for which Award is Granted:** Undergraduate **Number Awarded:** 1. **Funds Available:** $2,000. **Duration:** One year.

Eligibility Requirements: Applicants must be children of Ulland Brothers employees who have been employed with the company for a minimum of two years (for salaried employees) or for a minimum of two seasons (for seasonal employees); must be students who are unmarried child under age 25 who is not self-supporting and who are full-time high school seniors or post-secondary students; must have a grade point average of 3.0 (based on 4.0 system) or higher. **Application Requirements:** Applicants must submit completed application form and recently completed Student Aid Report (SAR) from the Free Application for Federal Student Aid (FAFSA). **Additional Information:** The award is co-payable to the institution and the recipient. **Deadline for Receipt:** January 15.

817 ■ DULUTH SUPERIOR AREA COMMUNITY FOUNDATION
324 W Superior St., Ste. 212
Duluth, MN 55802
Tel: (218)726-0232
Fax: (218)726-0257
E-mail: info@communityfoundation.com
Web Site: http://www.dsacommunityfoundation.com
To provide financial assistance to graduating female seniors from Denfeld High School or the Marshall School who exemplifies the characteristics and life exhibited by Patricia Gustafson.

Title of Award: Patricia S. Gustafson '56 Memorial Scholarships **Area, Field, or Subject:** General studies. **Level of Education for which Award is Granted:** Undergraduate **Funds Available:** $800. **Duration:** One year.

Eligibility Requirements: Applicants must be young women who will graduate from Denfeld High School or Marshall High School; must plan to attend either the University of Minnesota Duluth, Lake Superior College or the College of St. Scholastica; must have a high school grade point average of 3.4 or higher; must be active participants or leaders in school activities; must have some measure of financial need. **Application Requirements:** Applicants must submit a completed application form and a personal statement answering the question "Considering what you know of Patricia Gustafson, why do you think you would be a worthy recipient of a scholarship honoring her memory?" **Additional Information:** The award is co-payable to the institution and the recipient.

818 ■ DULUTH SUPERIOR AREA COMMUNITY FOUNDATION
324 W Superior St., Ste. 212
Duluth, MN 55802
Tel: (218)726-0232
Fax: (218)726-0257
E-mail: info@communityfoundation.com
Web Site: http://www.dsacommunityfoundation.com
To provide assistance to students with financial need.

Title of Award: Jeanne H. Hemmingway Scholarships **Area, Field, or Subject:** General studies. **Level of Education for which Award is Granted:** Undergraduate **Funds Available:** $2,250. **Duration:** One year.

Eligibility Requirements: Applicants must be graduate seniors of public or private high schools in St. Louis, Lake and Cook counties who are planning to attend UMD; must be in the top 15% of their high school. **Application Requirements:** Applicants must submit a completed application form and a recently completed Student Aid Report (SAR) from the Free Application for Federal Student Aid (FAFSA). **Additional Information:** The award is co-payable to the institution and the recipient. **Deadline for Receipt:** $2,250.

819 ■ DULUTH SUPERIOR AREA COMMUNITY FOUNDATION
324 W Superior St., Ste. 212
Duluth, MN 55802
Tel: (218)726-0232
Fax: (218)726-0257
E-mail: info@communityfoundation.com
Web Site: http://www.dsacommunityfoundation.com
To provide financial assistance for students of all backgrounds to enable them to pursue higher education.

Title of Award: Max and Julia Houghton Duluth Central Scholarships **Area, Field, or Subject:** General studies. **Level of Education for which Award is Granted:** Undergraduate **Number Awarded:** 3. **Funds Available:** $2,500. **Duration:** One year.

Eligibility Requirements: Applicants must be graduating seniors from Duluth Central High School who are in the top 25% of their high school class. **Application Requirements:** Applicants must submit all the required application information. **Additional Information:** The award is co-payable to the institution and the recipient. **Deadline for Receipt:** January 15.

820 ■ DULUTH SUPERIOR AREA COMMUNITY FOUNDATION
324 W Superior St., Ste. 212
Duluth, MN 55802
Tel: (218)726-0232
Fax: (218)726-0257
E-mail: info@communityfoundation.com
Web Site: http://www.dsacommunityfoundation.com
To provide opportunities to students who are seeking for financial resources for their education in college.

Title of Award: Greg Irons Student Scholarships **Area, Field, or Subject:** General studies. **Level of Education for which Award is Granted:** Undergraduate **Number Awarded:** 2. **Funds Available:** $1,000. **Duration:** One year.

Eligibility Requirements: Applicants must be graduating seniors from Denfeld, East, Central and Unity high schools who are planning to attend an accredited college or university. **Application Requirements:** Application forms are available on the Foundation's website and from the Duluth Public School Offices. **Additional Information:** The award is co-payable to the institution and the recipient. **Deadline for Receipt:** January 15.

821 ■ DULUTH SUPERIOR AREA COMMUNITY FOUNDATION
324 W Superior St., Ste. 212
Duluth, MN 55802
Tel: (218)726-0232
Fax: (218)726-0257
E-mail: info@communityfoundation.com
Web Site: http://www.dsacommunityfoundation.com
To provide financial assistance to the residents of Hermantown and graduates of Hermantown High School.

Title of Award: The Jackson Club Scholarships **Area, Field, or Subject:** General studies. **Level of Education for which Award is Granted:** Undergraduate **Number Awarded:** 5. **Funds Available:** $500. **Duration:** One year.

Eligibility Requirements: Applicants must be residents of Hermantown and graduates of Hermantown High School planning to attend any accredited post-secondary institution on a full-time basis; must have a 2.3 grade point average. **Application Requirements:** Applicants must submit all the required application information. **Additional Information:** The award is co-payable to the institution and the recipient. **Deadline for Receipt:** January 15.

822 ■ DULUTH SUPERIOR AREA COMMUNITY FOUNDATION
324 W Superior St., Ste. 212
Duluth, MN 55802
Tel: (218)726-0232
Fax: (218)726-0257
E-mail: info@communityfoundation.com
Web Site: http://www.dsacommunityfoundation.com
To provide financial assistance to students who intend to pursue further education or training at any accredited university, college or technical school.

Title of Award: Cory Jam Awards **Area, Field, or Subject:** General studies. **Level of Education for which Award is Granted:** Undergraduate **Number Awarded:** 1. **Funds Available:** $800-$1,000. **Duration:** One year.

Eligibility Requirements: Applicants must be graduating seniors from Duluth East High School who attended Congdon Park Elementary School, Homecroft Elementary School or Lowell Elementary School; must have participated in at least two extracurricular activities sponsored by Duluth East High School and at least one community based activity during their high school enrollment years; must intend to pursue education or training at any accredited university, college or technical school; must possess a

3.5 grade point average or higher based on 4.0 system. **Application Requirements:** Applicants must submit all the required application information. **Additional Information:** The payment is co-payable to the institution and recipient. **Deadline for Receipt:** January 15.

823 ■ DULUTH SUPERIOR AREA COMMUNITY FOUNDATION
324 W Superior St., Ste. 212
Duluth, MN 55802
Tel: (218)726-0232
Fax: (218)726-0257
E-mail: info@communityfoundation.com
Web Site: http://www.dsacommunityfoundation.com
To provide financial assistance to high school seniors residing within Minnesota Power's service territory.
Title of Award: Minnesota Power Community Involvement Scholarships **Area, Field, or Subject:** General studies. **Level of Education for which Award is Granted:** Undergraduate **Number Awarded:** 25. **Funds Available:** $2,000. **Duration:** One year.
Eligibility Requirements: Applicants must be high school seniors residing within Minnesota Power's service territory; must be full-time high school students who have a 2.5 GPA (on a 4.0 scale) or above. **Application Requirements:** Applicants must submit application information. **Additional Information:** The award is co-payable to the institution and the recipient. **Deadline for Receipt:** January 15.

824 ■ DULUTH SUPERIOR AREA COMMUNITY FOUNDATION
324 W Superior St., Ste. 212
Duluth, MN 55802
Tel: (218)726-0232
Fax: (218)726-0257
E-mail: info@communityfoundation.com
Web Site: http://www.dsacommunityfoundation.com
To provide financial assistance to students with their educational needs.
Title of Award: Modern Woodmen of America Scholarships **Area, Field, or Subject:** General studies. **Level of Education for which Award is Granted:** Undergraduate **Number Awarded:** 1. **Funds Available:** $1,000. **Duration:** One year.
Eligibility Requirements: Applicants must be single parents who are the primary care-givers to one or more children; must have completed at least 50 percent of their course of instruction at the time of the award. **Application Requirements:** Applicants must submit all the required application information. **Additional Information:** The award is co-payable to the institution and the recipient. **Deadline for Receipt:** January 15.

825 ■ DULUTH SUPERIOR AREA COMMUNITY FOUNDATION
324 W Superior St., Ste. 212
Duluth, MN 55802
Tel: (218)726-0232
Fax: (218)726-0257
E-mail: info@communityfoundation.com
Web Site: http://www.dsacommunityfoundation.com
To provide educational opportunities for students who are in financial need.
Title of Award: Amelia and Emanuel Nessell Scholarships **Area, Field, or Subject:** General studies. **Level of Education for which Award is Granted:** Undergraduate **Funds Available:** $500. **Duration:** One year.
Eligibility Requirements: Applicants must be graduating seniors of Duluth public or private high schools; must be Jewish students who are planning to pursue a post-secondary education, including community colleges and four-year colleges and universities; must be in the top 25% of their high school class. **Application Requirements:** Applicants must submit a completed DSACF Common Scholarship Application form along with a recently completed Student Aid Report (SAR) from the Free Application for Federal Student Aid (FAFSA). **Additional Information:** The award is co-payable to the institution and the recipient. **Deadline for Receipt:** January 15.

826 ■ DULUTH SUPERIOR AREA COMMUNITY FOUNDATION
324 W Superior St., Ste. 212
Duluth, MN 55802
Tel: (218)726-0232
Fax: (218)726-0257
E-mail: info@communityfoundation.com

Web Site: http://www.dsacommunityfoundation.com
To provide financial assistance for students to achieve higher education.
Title of Award: Anderson Niskanen Scholarships **Area, Field, or Subject:** General studies. **Level of Education for which Award is Granted:** Undergraduate **Number Awarded:** 3. **Funds Available:** $2,000. **Duration:** One year.
Eligibility Requirements: Applicants must be graduating seniors from Duluth public high schools who will attend either the University of Minnesota-Duluth or the University of Minnesota-Twin Cities. **Application Requirements:** Applicants must submit all the required application information. **Deadline for Receipt:** January 15.

827 ■ DULUTH SUPERIOR AREA COMMUNITY FOUNDATION
324 W Superior St., Ste. 212
Duluth, MN 55802
Tel: (218)726-0232
Fax: (218)726-0257
E-mail: info@communityfoundation.com
Web Site: http://www.dsacommunityfoundation.com
To help future generations of Marshall School students to pursue their educational goals.
Title of Award: Dr. Mark Rathke Family Scholarships **Area, Field, or Subject:** General studies. **Level of Education for which Award is Granted:** Undergraduate **Number Awarded:** 1. **Funds Available:** $1,000. **Duration:** One year.
Eligibility Requirements: Applicants must be graduating seniors of the Marshall School who will be attending a college or university as full-time students; must have a grade point average of 2.75 (on a 4.0 scale) or higher. **Application Requirements:** Applicants must submit all the required application information. **Deadline for Receipt:** January 15.

828 ■ DULUTH SUPERIOR AREA COMMUNITY FOUNDATION
324 W Superior St., Ste. 212
Duluth, MN 55802
Tel: (218)726-0232
Fax: (218)726-0257
E-mail: info@communityfoundation.com
Web Site: http://www.dsacommunityfoundation.com
To provide financial assistance to students pursuing a college degree.
Title of Award: Lawrence E. & Mabel Jackson Rudberg Scholarships **Area, Field, or Subject:** General studies. **Level of Education for which Award is Granted:** Undergraduate **Funds Available:** $5,000. **Duration:** One year.
Eligibility Requirements: Applicants must be graduating seniors from Duluth public and Two Harbors Senior High; must intend to pursue post-secondary education at an accredited four-year public or private college or university. **Application Requirements:** Applicants must submit a completed DSACF Common Scholarship Application form along with a recently completed Student Aid Report (SAR) from the Free Application for Federal Student Aid (FAFSA). **Additional Information:** The award is co-payable to the institution and the recipient. **Deadline for Receipt:** January 15.

829 ■ DULUTH SUPERIOR AREA COMMUNITY FOUNDATION
324 W Superior St., Ste. 212
Duluth, MN 55802
Tel: (218)726-0232
Fax: (218)726-0257
E-mail: info@communityfoundation.com
Web Site: http://www.dsacommunityfoundation.com
To provide financial assistance to graduates of Duluth Denfeld High School.
Title of Award: Marie V. Saltwick Scholarships **Area, Field, or Subject:** General studies. **Level of Education for which Award is Granted:** Undergraduate **Funds Available:** $2,000. **Duration:** One year.
Eligibility Requirements: Applicants must graduating seniors from Denfeld High School who are intending to pursue post-secondary education at a vocational college, community college, or other college or university on a full-time basis; must have achieved a 2.8 or higher cumulative GPA (on a 4.0 scale) in high school. **Application Requirements:** Applicants must submit a completed DSACF Common Scholarship Application form along with a recently completed Student Aid Report (SAR) from the Free Application for Federal Student Aid (FAFSA). **Additional**

Information: The award is co-payable to the institution and the recipient. **Deadline for Receipt:** January 15.

830 ■ DULUTH SUPERIOR AREA COMMUNITY FOUNDATION
324 W Superior St., Ste. 212
Duluth, MN 55802
Tel: (218)726-0232
Fax: (218)726-0257
E-mail: info@communityfoundation.com
Web Site: http://www.dsacommunityfoundation.com
To provide financial assistance to those in need to pursue trade or career.
Title of Award: Phil Shykes Memorial Scholarships **Area, Field, or Subject:** General studies. **Level of Education for which Award is Granted:** Undergraduate **Funds Available:** $1,000. **Duration:** One year. **Eligibility Requirements:** Applicants must be graduating seniors from Hermantown High School who are intending to pursue post-secondary education at a vocational college, community college, or other college or university on a full-time basis; must have achieved a 2.8 or higher cumulative GPA (on a 4.0 scale) in high school. **Application Requirements:** Applicants must submit a completed DSACF Common Scholarship Application form along with a recently completed Student Aid Report (SAR) from the Free Application for Federal Student Aid (FAFSA). **Additional Information:** The award is co-payable to the institution and the recipient. **Deadline for Receipt:** January 15.

831 ■ DULUTH SUPERIOR AREA COMMUNITY FOUNDATION
324 W Superior St., Ste. 212
Duluth, MN 55802
Tel: (218)726-0232
Fax: (218)726-0257
E-mail: info@communityfoundation.com
Web Site: http://www.dsacommunityfoundation.com
To provide financial assistance for graduating high school seniors living in or attending school in the central areas of Duluth.
Title of Award: Dale and Betty George Sola Scholarships **Area, Field, or Subject:** General studies. **Level of Education for which Award is Granted:** Undergraduate **Funds Available:** $2,000. **Duration:** One year. **Eligibility Requirements:** Applicants must be students of Duluth Central High School, the Marshall School, and alternative schools (including Unity School, and the Harbor City International School) in the central areas of Duluth; or, graduates residing within the Central Hillside or Park Point areas who have a grade point average of 2.75 (on a 4.0 scale) or higher. **Application Requirements:** Applicants must complete the DSACF Common Scholarship Application available from the Guidance Offices and must submit a recently completed Student Aid Report (SAR) from the Free Application for Federal Student Aid (FAFSA). **Deadline for Receipt:** January 15.

832 ■ DULUTH SUPERIOR AREA COMMUNITY FOUNDATION
324 W Superior St., Ste. 212
Duluth, MN 55802
Tel: (218)726-0232
Fax: (218)726-0257
E-mail: info@communityfoundation.com
Web Site: http://www.dsacommunityfoundation.com
To provide financial assistance to students who are going to attend college.
Title of Award: Robert B. and Sophia Whiteside Scholarships **Area, Field, or Subject:** General studies. **Level of Education for which Award is Granted:** Undergraduate **Funds Available:** $6,000. **Duration:** One year. **Eligibility Requirements:** Applicants must be high school seniors graduating from schools, including home schools, in Duluth and seek admission to any fully-accredited, degree granting college or university. **Application Requirements:** Applicants must submit all the completed required application information. **Deadline for Receipt:** January 15.

833 ■ EAR FOUNDATION
PO Box 330867
Nashville, TN 37203
Tel: (615)627-2724
Free: 800-545-HEAR
Fax: (615)627-2728
E-mail: info@earfoundation.org
Web Site: http://www.earfoundation.org
To provide educational fund to an impaired person.
Title of Award: Minnie Pearl Scholarship Program **Area, Field, or Subject:** General Studies. **Level of Education for which Award is Granted:** Undergraduate **Funds Available:** $2,500. **Duration:** Annual. **Eligibility Requirements:** Applicant must be a current high school senior with at least a 3.0 cumulative GPA; intending to attend a junior college, university or technical school on a full-time basis (12 hours per quarter or semester); have significant (severe to profound) bilateral hearing loss; must be a mainstreamed hearing-impaired student; and must be a United States citizen. **Application Requirements:** Applicant must be submit completed application, copy of audiology report for both ears performed within the last 12 months; certified high school transcript (may be sent separately); two letters of recommendation from teachers; one letter of recommendation from a non-family member; and a recent photo. Submit collated documents to: Minnie Pearl Scholarship Program, The EAR Foundation, PO Box 330867, Nashville, TN 37203. **Deadline for Receipt:** February 15.

834 ■ EAST TENNESSEE FOUNDATION
625 Market St., Ste. 1400
Knoxville, TN 37902
Tel: (865)524-1223; 877-524-1223
Fax: (865)637-6039
Web Site: http://www.easttennesseefoundation.org
To assist students who possess the potential for excellence but may require some additional support in achieving their educational goals.
Title of Award: Steven L. Coffey Memorial Scholarships **Area, Field, or Subject:** General Studies. **Level of Education for which Award is Granted:** Undergraduate **Funds Available:** $1,200 Annually. **Duration:** 4 years. **Eligibility Requirements:** Applicants must either be Anderson County residents and graduates of Anderson County High School, Clinton Senior High School or Oak Ridge High School. **Application Requirements:** Applicants must check the application online for the required materials. **Deadline for Receipt:** April 18. **Additional Information:** East Tennessee Foundation at the above address

835 ■ EAST TENNESSEE FOUNDATION
625 Market St., Ste. 1400
Knoxville, TN 37902
Tel: (865)524-1223; 877-524-1223
Fax: (865)637-6039
Web Site: http://www.easttennesseefoundation.org
To benefit graduating seniors of Anderson County High School who wish to pursue an advanced degree.
Title of Award: R.G Crossno Memorial Scholarships **Area, Field, or Subject:** General studies. **Level of Education for which Award is Granted:** Undergraduate **Funds Available:** $1,400. **Eligibility Requirements:** Applicants must be enrolled as full-time students in an accredited public or private not-for-profit university or community college. **Application Requirements:** Applicants must check the application process online as well as the required materials. **Additional Information:** Mr. R.G. Crossno, past mayor of Norris, Tennessee and 21-year member of the Anderson County School Board dedicated his life to promoting better education throughout the state of Tennessee. **Deadline for Receipt:** April 11. **Additional Information:** East Tennessee Foundation at the above address

836 ■ EAST TENNESSEE FOUNDATION
625 Market St., Ste. 1400
Knoxville, TN 37902
Tel: (865)524-1223; 877-524-1223
Fax: (865)637-6039
Web Site: http://www.easttennesseefoundation.org
To recognize and benefit students who demonstrate leadership or achievement in a balanced array of activities, including the arts, athletics, citizenship, community/religious service and academics.
Title of Award: Michael D. Curtin Renaissance Student Memorial Scholarships **Area, Field, or Subject:** General Studies. **Level of Education for which Award is Granted:** Undergraduate **Funds Available:** Up to $1,000.

Eligibility Requirements: Applicants must be enrolled as full time students in an accredited public or private not-for-profit university. **Application Requirements:** Applicants must check the application process online. **Deadline for Receipt:** March 14.

837 ■ EDMONTON EPILEPSY ASSOCIATION
11007-124 St.
Edmonton, AB, Canada T5M 0J5
Tel: (780)488-9600; (866)374-5377
Fax: (780)447-5486
E-mail: info@edmontonepilepsy.org
Web Site: http://www.edmontonepilepsy.org
To open doors for incoming or continuing Canadian college students who are under epilepsy care.
Title of Award: Edmonton Epilepsy Continuing Education Scholarships **Area, Field, or Subject:** General studies. **Level of Education for which Award is Granted:** Undergraduate **Funds Available:** $1,000.
Eligibility Requirements: Applicants must be Greater-Edmonton area students aged 17-29 years of age who are Canadian Citizens or who have Landed Immigrant status and who are currently under a Canadian physician's care for epilepsy. Visa students are not eligible for this award. **Application Requirements:** Applicants must submit a completed application form available from the website; a short essay (600-1,200 words) on "How Can I Personally Help Increase Epilepsy Education in my Community?"; three letters of recommendation of which one must come from someone from academia; copy of immigration papers (if landed immigrant); an unofficial copy of the current academic transcript; and a copy of university, college, or graduate school application(s)/acceptance letter, or confirmation of enrollment. Complete application package must be submitted to: Scholarship Awards, Edmonton Epilepsy Association, 11007-124 St., Edmonton, AB T5M 0J5. **Deadline for Receipt:** March 1.

838 ■ EDUCATIONAL FOUNDATION FOR WOMEN IN ACCOUNTING
PO Box 1925
Southeastern, PA 19399-1925
Tel: (610)407-9229
Fax: (610)644-3713
E-mail: info@efwa.org
Web Site: http://www.efwa.org
To provide financial assistance to female reentry students who wish to pursue a degree in accounting.
Title of Award: Michele L. McDonald Scholarships **Area, Field, or Subject:** Accounting. **Level of Education for which Award is Granted:** Undergraduate **Funds Available:** $1,000. **Duration:** One year.
Eligibility Requirements: Applicants must be women returning to college from the work force or after raising children. **Application Requirements:** Applicants must submit a completed application with all attachments (scholastic record; employment record; volunteer activities; professional activities; honors; career goals; personal goals; financial need; tax returns; references; and complete school contact information) to Educational Foundation for Women in Accounting. **Additional Information:** Established by the Albuquerque chapter of the American Society of Women Accountants in memory of one of their members and was transferred to EFWA in 2006. **Deadline for Receipt:** April 15.

839 ■ EDUCATIONAL FOUNDATION FOR WOMEN IN ACCOUNTING
PO Box 1925
Southeastern, PA 19399-1925
Tel: (610)407-9229
Fax: (610)644-3713
E-mail: info@efwa.org
Web Site: http://www.efwa.org
To provide financial assistance to female reentry students who wish to pursue a degree in accounting.
Title of Award: Rowling, Dold and Associates LLP Scholarships **Area, Field, or Subject:** Accounting. **Level of Education for which Award is Granted:** Undergraduate **Funds Available:** $1,000. **Duration:** One year.
Eligibility Requirements: Applicants must be women returning to school with undergraduate status; incoming, current, or reentry junior or seniors; or minority women. **Application Requirements:** Applicants must submit a completed application with all attachments (scholastic record; employment record; volunteer activities; professional activities; honors; career goals; personal goals; financial need; tax returns; references; and

complete school contact information) to Educational Foundation for Women in Accounting. **Deadline for Receipt:** April 15.

840 ■ EDUCATIONAL FOUNDATION FOR WOMEN IN ACCOUNTING
PO Box 1925
Southeastern, PA 19399-1925
Tel: (610)407-9229
Fax: (610)644-3713
E-mail: info@efwa.org
Web Site: http://www.efwa.org
To provide financial assistance to female reentry students who wish to pursue a degree in accounting.
Title of Award: Women In Need Scholarships **Area, Field, or Subject:** Accounting. **Level of Education for which Award is Granted:** Undergraduate **Number Awarded:** 1. **Funds Available:** $2,000. **Duration:** One year.
Eligibility Requirements: Applicants should be incoming, current, or reentry juniors or seniors. **Application Requirements:** Applicants must submit a completed application with all attachments (scholastic record; employment record; volunteer activities; professional activities; honors; career goals; personal goals; financial need; tax returns; references; and complete school contact information) to Educational Foundation for Women in Accounting. **Additional Information:** Created by the Board of Trustees in 2000. **Deadline for Receipt:** April 15.

841 ■ EDUCATIONAL FOUNDATION FOR WOMEN IN ACCOUNTING
PO Box 1925
Southeastern, PA 19399-1925
Tel: (610)407-9229
Fax: (610)644-3713
E-mail: info@efwa.org
Web Site: http://www.efwa.org
To provide financial assistance to female reentry students who wish to pursue a degree in accounting.
Title of Award: Women In Transition Scholarships **Area, Field, or Subject:** Accounting. **Level of Education for which Award is Granted:** Undergraduate **Number Awarded:** 1. **Funds Available:** Up to $4,000. **Duration:** One year.
Eligibility Requirements: Applicants should be incoming or current freshmen and women returning to school with a freshman status. **Application Requirements:** Applicants must submit a completed application with all attachments (scholastic record; employment record; volunteer activities; professional activities; honors; career goals; personal goals; financial need; tax returns; references; and complete school contact information) to Educational Foundation for Women in Accounting. **Additional Information:** Established in 1990 to commemorate the 25th Anniversary of the Educational Foundation. **Deadline for Receipt:** April 15. **Additional Information:** Cynthia Hires.

842 ■ EDUCATIONAL PORTAL OF THE AMERICAS
1889 F St. NW
Washington, DC 20006
Tel: (202)458-6166
E-mail: portal@oas.org
Web Site: http://www.educoas.org
To award a person to undertake undergraduate or graduate studies that lead to a degree and/or graduate research in a university or higher learning institution of member state.
Title of Award: Educational Portal of the Americas Undergraduate Scholarships **Area, Field, or Subject:** General Studies. **Level of Education for which Award is Granted:** Undergraduate **Funds Available:** $30,000.
Eligibility Requirements: Applicants must be accepted into the university where he/she plans to study for the last two years of undergraduate degree. **Application Requirements:** Applicants must present complete application form. **Additional Information:** scholarships@oas.org.

843 ■ EISENHOWER INSTITUTE
915 15th St. NW, 8th Fl.
Washington, DC 20005
Tel: (202)628-4444
Fax: (202)628-4445

E-mail: ei@eisenhowerinstitute.org
Web Site: http://www.eisenhowerinstitute.org
To help students obtain undergraduate degrees in furtherance of education and leadership skills.
Title of Award: Ann Cook Whitman Scholarships for Perry High School **Area, Field, or Subject:** General studies. **Level of Education for which Award is Granted:** Undergraduate **Number Awarded:** 2. **Funds Available:** $4000 each year for four years. **Duration:** Annually.
Eligibility Requirements: Applicant must be a high school senior student at Perry High School planning to receive an undergraduate education; and have an average of B and above (can be waived for applicants with strong needs or qualifications). **Application Requirements:** Applicants must submit an academic transcript; a resume; a statement of career aspirations (maximum of 1,000 words); a letter of recommendation from the candidate's faculty advisor or guidance counselor; another letter of recommendation from a member of the Perry, Ohio community, other than a family member; and documentation from Perry High School on its needs-based assessment procedures for its nominees. Submit materials at the Perry High School. **Deadline for Receipt:** March 1.

844 ■ EISENHOWER INSTITUTE

915 15th St. NW, 8th Fl.
Washington, DC 20005
Tel: (202)628-4444
Fax: (202)628-4445
E-mail: ei@eisenhowerinstitute.org
Web Site: http://www.eisenhowerinstitute.org
To assist graduating African-American seniors from the District of Columbia public education system in obtaining an undergraduate degree in furtherance of their education and leadership skills.
Title of Award: Ann Cook Whitman Washington, DC Scholarships **Area, Field, or Subject:** General studies. **Level of Education for which Award is Granted:** Undergraduate **Number Awarded:** 2. **Funds Available:** $4000 each year for four years. **Duration:** Annually.
Eligibility Requirements: Applicant must be an African-American senior student from any of four eligible high schools (Spingarn, H.D. Woodson, Ballou, and Eastern) pursuing an undergraduate education; and have an average of B and above (can be waived for applicants with strong needs or qualifications). **Application Requirements:** Applicants must submit a completed application form; academic transcript; a statement of career aspirations (maximum of 500 words); identification of colleges/universities applied to; a letter of recommendation from a faculty member or the guidance counselor; and another letter of recommendation from a member of the Washington, DC community, other than a family member. Submit materials at the applicant's respective high school. **Deadline for Receipt:** March 1.

845 ■ ELKS NATIONAL FOUNDATION

2750 N Lakeview Ave.
Chicago, IL 60614-2256
Tel: (773)755-4728
Fax: (773)755-4729
E-mail: enf@elks.org
Web Site: http://www.elks.org
To build stronger communities.
Title of Award: Elks National Foundation Scholarships **Area, Field, or Subject:** General studies. **Level of Education for which Award is Granted:** Undergraduate **Funds Available:** Maximum amount of $15,000.
Eligibility Requirements: Applicants must be undergraduates in an institution, college, or university. **Application Requirements:** Applicants must complete the application form. **Additional Information:** scholarship@elks.org

846 ■ ENLISTED ASSOCIATION OF NATIONAL GUARD OF THE UNITED STATES

3133 Mount Vernon Ave.
Alexandria, VA 22305-2640
Tel: (703)519-3846
Free: 800-234-3264
Fax: (703)519-3849
E-mail: eangus@eangus.org
Web Site: http://www.eangus.org

To support the education of EANGUS members, their spouses and their unmarried children.
Title of Award: CSM Virgil R. Williams Scholarships **Area, Field, or Subject:** General studies. **Level of Education for which Award is Granted:** Undergraduate **Number Awarded:** 2. **Funds Available:** $2,000. **Duration:** One year.
Eligibility Requirements: Applicant must be EANGUS Auxiliary members; must be unmarried, dependent sons and daughters of EANGUS Auxiliary members; must be spouses of EANGUS Auxiliary members. **Application Requirements:** Applicant must submit a transcript of high school credits and/or a transcript of college credits for applicants already in an institution of higher learning; must have a letter from the applicant with personal, specific facts as to his/ her desire to continue his/ her educationand why financial assistance is required; must have three letters of academic recommendation verifying the application and giving moral, personal and leadership traits. Application form and other documents must be submitted electronically via the internet to the Chairman of the Scholarship Committee except the school transcript. **Deadline for Receipt:** July 1.

847 ■ EPILEPSY NEWFOUNDLAND AND LABRADOR

26 O'Leary Ave.
St. John's, NL, Canada A1B 2C7
Tel: (709)722-0502
Fax: (709)722-0999
E-mail: info@epilepsynl.com
Web Site: http://www.epilepsynl.com
To widen horizons of ENL student members by providing financial support as they pursue college or university studies.
Title of Award: Jim Hierlihy Memorial Scholarships **Area, Field, or Subject:** General studies. **Level of Education for which Award is Granted:** Undergraduate **Number Awarded:** 1. **Funds Available:** $1,000. **Duration:** Two years.
Eligibility Requirements: Applicants must be diagnosed with epilepsy and be members in good standing of Epilepsy Newfoundland and Labrador at the time of scholarship application. Scholarship is not open to current ENL board and staff members. Former board or staff members and/or their family members may apply for scholarships if they have been out of the service of Epilepsy Newfoundland and Labrador for two years. **Application Requirements:** Applicants must submit the completed application form available from the website along with a copy of the most recent academic transcript to: Epilepsy Newfoundland and Labrador, 26 O'Leary Ave., St. John's, NF A1B 2C7. **Deadline for Receipt:** November 1.

848 ■ EPILEPSY NEWFOUNDLAND AND LABRADOR

26 O'Leary Ave.
St. John's, NL, Canada A1B 2C7
Tel: (709)722-0502
Fax: (709)722-0999
E-mail: info@epilepsynl.com
Web Site: http://www.epilepsynl.com
To widen horizons of ENL student members by providing financial support as they pursue college or university studies.
Title of Award: Mature Student Scholarships **Area, Field, or Subject:** General studies. **Level of Education for which Award is Granted:** Undergraduate **Number Awarded:** 1. **Funds Available:** $1,000. **Duration:** Two years.
Eligibility Requirements: Applicants must be 21 years or older; must be diagnosed with epilepsy; and be a member in good standing of Epilepsy Newfoundland and Labrador at the time of the scholarship application. Scholarship is not open to current ENL board and staff members. Former board or staff members and/or their family members can apply for scholarships if they have been out of the service of Epilepsy Newfoundland and Labrador for two years. **Application Requirements:** Applicants must complete application form available at the website and submit it along with a copy of the most recent academic transcript to: Epilepsy Newfoundland and Labrador, 26 O'Leary Ave., St. John's, NF A1B 2C7. **Deadline for Receipt:** November 1.

849 ■ EQUITY FOUNDATION

P.O Box 5696
Portland, OR 97228

Tel: (503)231-5759
E-mail: info@equityfoundation.org
Web Site: http://www.equityfoundation.org
To provide financial assistance to those post secondary LGBT students.
Title of Award: Just Out Scholarship Fund **Area, Field, or Subject:**
General Studies. **Level of Education for which Award is Granted:**
Undergraduate **Funds Available:** No specific amount.
Eligibility Requirements: Applicants must be members of the gay,
lesbian, bisexual or transgendered communities. **Application Require-
ments:** Applicants must check the available website for the required
materials. **Deadline for Receipt:** June 30. **Additional Information:**
Equity Foundation at the above address

850 ■ EQUITY FOUNDATION
P.O Box 5696
Portland, OR 97228
Tel: (503)231-5759
E-mail: info@equityfoundation.org
Web Site: http://www.equityfoundation.org
To provide financial assistance to those students who are in need.
Title of Award: Orchard-Hoyman Fund for GLBT Student Scholarships
Area, Field, or Subject: General Studies. **Level of Education for which
Award is Granted:** Undergraduate **Number Awarded:** 2. **Funds Avail-
able:** $1,000.
Eligibility Requirements: Applicants must be GLBT students ages 20
and under, who reside in Lane County, Oregon and need financial as-
sistance to attain their post secondary educational goals. **Application
Requirements:** Applicants must check the application process online.
Deadline for Receipt: August 31. **Additional Information:** Equity
Foundation at the above address

851 ■ EQUITY FOUNDATION
P.O Box 5696
Portland, OR 97228
Tel: (503)231-5759
E-mail: info@equityfoundation.org
Web Site: http://www.equityfoundation.org
To provide financial assistance to those post secondary LGBT students.
Title of Award: Portland Area Business Association Scholarships **Area,
Field, or Subject:** General Studies. **Level of Education for which
Award is Granted:** Undergraduate **Funds Available:** No specific
amount.
Eligibility Requirements: Applicants must be members of the gay,
lesbian, bisexual or transgendered communities. **Application Require-
ments:** Applicants must check the available website for the required
materials. **Deadline for Receipt:** June 30. **Additional Information:**
Equity Foundation at the above address

852 ■ EQUITY FOUNDATION
P.O Box 5696
Portland, OR 97228
Tel: (503)231-5759
E-mail: info@equityfoundation.org
Web Site: http://www.equityfoundation.org
To provide financial assistance to those students who are in need.
Title of Award: Pride of the Rose Scholarships Fund **Area, Field, or
Subject:** General studies. **Level of Education for which Award is
Granted:** Undergraduate **Funds Available:** No specific amount.
Eligibility Requirements: Applicants must be post-secondary education
to members of the gay, lesbian, bisexual, and transgender communities
and their children residing in the Quad-county area of Portland, OR and
Clark County, WA. **Application Requirements:** Applicants must check
the application process online. **Deadline for Receipt:** July 31. **Additional
Information:** Equity Foundation at the above address

853 ■ EXECUTIVE WOMEN INTERNATIONAL
515 S 700 E, Ste. 2A
Salt Lake City, UT 84102
Tel: (801)355-2800; 877-4394-669
Fax: (801)355-2852
E-mail: ewi@executivewomen.org
Web Site: http://www.executivewomen.org
To financially help qualified applicants to achieve their academic goals.

Title of Award: Executive Women International Scholarship Program
(EWISP) **Area, Field, or Subject:** General studies. **Level of Education
for which Award is Granted:** High School **Funds Available:** $10,000.
Eligibility Requirements: Applicant must be a high school junior expecting to graduate from high school; and pursuing a degree in an accredited
post-secondary institution. **Application Requirements:** Applicants must
submit a completed application form available at the website; two letters
of recommendation (use the Personal Recommendation Form) and official
transcript of grades. Applications are to be submitted to the EWI chapter
near the applicant's residency.

854 ■ FAMILIES OF FREEDOM SCHOLARSHIP FUND
PO Box 297
St. Peter, MN 56082
877-862-0136
Fax: (507)931-8924
E-mail: familiesoffreedom@scholarshipamerica.org
Web Site: http://www.familiesoffreedom.org
To provide education assistance for post-secondary study to dependents -
children and spouses - of those killed of permanently disabled as a result
of terrorist attacks on September 11, 2001 and during the rescue activities
to those attacks.
Title of Award: Families of Freedom Scholarship Fund - America
Scholarships **Area, Field, or Subject:** General studies. **Level of Educa-
tion for which Award is Granted:** Undergraduate **Funds Available:**
$1,000. **Duration:** One year.
Eligibility Requirements: Applicants must be dependents of those killed
or permanently disabled as a result of the terrorist attacks on September
11, 2001, and during the rescue activities relating to those attacks.
Specifically, families of Freedom benefits children and spouses of the
victims, including airplane crew and passengers, World Trade Center and
Pentagon workers and visitors, and relief workers, including firefighters
and emergency medical personnel and law enforcement personnel.
Participants must enroll in a course of study at an accredited two- or four-
year college, university or vocational-technical school based in the United
States. **Application Requirements:** Applicants must submit all the
required application information.

855 ■ FEDERAL COMMUNICATION BAR ASSOCIATION FOUNDA-
TION
1020 19th St. NW, Ste. 325
Washington, DC 20036-6101
Tel: (202)293-4000
Fax: (202)293-4317
E-mail: fcba@fcba.org
Web Site: http://www.fcba.org
To provide financial assistance for local high school students intending to
pursue college studies.
Title of Award: FCBA Foundation Scholarships **Area, Field, or Subject:**
General studies. **Level of Education for which Award is Granted:**
Undergraduate **Funds Available:** No specific amount.
Eligibility Requirements: Applicants must be high school students at-
tending in any of the 8 high schools located in the District of Columbia.
Application Requirements: Applicants must complete the application.
Please make sure that you have completed and attached all information
required by the application. If an applicant does not have certain information specified, that applicant should so note, and provide a brief explanation. Please note that applicants are required to certify that he or she is a
legal resident of the United States or must explain, in detail, their
residency status in order to be considered for an FCBA Foundation
scholarship. Applicants must attach copies of any essays, awards, letters
of recommendation or appreciation (in addition to the recommendations
specified in the application), or any other documentation or representation
of excellence or achievement that demonstrates their future potential or
would provide additional insight to the foundation as it reviews the written
applications according to the criteria. **Deadline for Receipt:** March 3. **Additional Information:** Kerry Loughney, FCBA Foundation; kerry@fcba.
org

856 ■ FEDERAL LAW ENFORCEMENT OFFICERS ASSOCIATION
PO Box 326
Lewisberry, PA 17339
Tel: (717)938-2300

Fax: (717)932-2262
E-mail: fleoa@fleoa.org
Web Site: http://www.fleoa.org
To provide educational assistance for the children of current, retired or deceased Federal Law Enforcement Officers.
Title of Award: FLEOA Foundation Scholarship Program **Area, Field, or Subject:** General studies. **Level of Education for which Award is Granted:** Undergraduate **Number Awarded:** 15. **Funds Available:** $1,000.
Eligibility Requirements: Applicants must be high school graduates; dependents of a current, retired or deceased Federal Law Enforcement Officer. **Application Requirements:** Applicants must submit completed application form available from the website; transcript of records (with class ranking, SAT scores); and an acceptance letter from a college or university. Submit applications with a self addressed stamped envelope to: FLEOA Foundation PO Box 1306 Grand Central Station New York, NY 10163. **Deadline for Receipt:** August.

857 ■ FEDERAL MANAGERS ASSOCIATION
1641 Prince St.
Alexandria, VA 22314-2818
Tel: (703)683-8700
Fax: (703)683-8707
E-mail: info@fedmanagers.org
Web Site: http://www.fedmanagers.org
To provide financial assistance for the educational pursuits of current civilian employees and retirees who are FMA members and their dependent family members.
Title of Award: FMA-FEEA Scholarship Program **Area, Field, or Subject:** General studies. **Level of Education for which Award is Granted:** Undergraduate **Funds Available:** No specific amount.
Eligibility Requirements: Applicants must be at least college freshmen by the fall of 2008 semester; must have a 3.0 cumulative grade point average on 4.0 scale; must be current high school seniors or college students working toward an accredited degree and enrolled in two- or four-year post-secondary, graduate or postgraduate program; full-time students (if dependents); and part-time students (if federal employees). **Application Requirements:** Applicants must submit complete application package containing the FMA-FEEA Scholarship Application Form; essay; written recommendation/character reference; transcript of scholastic record; brief description of awards, extracurricular and community service activities; copy of ACT, SAT or other examination scores; copy of most recent standard Form 50 "Notice of Personnel Action"; and two self-addressed, stamped, No. 10 business-size envelopes with first class postage properly affixed. **Deadline for Receipt:** March 28.

858 ■ FEDERATION OF AMERICAN CONSUMERS AND TRAVELERS
318 Hillsboro Ave.
PO Box 104
Edwardsville, IL 62025
Tel: (618)656-5369
E-mail: cservice@usafact.org
Web Site: http://www.usafact.org
To assure the continuation of FACT's selfless intents and purposes; to maintain high level of professionalism at the director level; to prevent any special-interest groups or self-serving individuals from assuming control of FACT for their own gain.
Title of Award: FACT Graduating Senior Scholarship Program **Area, Field, or Subject:** General studies. **Level of Education for which Award is Granted:** Undergraduate **Number Awarded:** 4. **Funds Available:** $10,000 and $2,500.
Eligibility Requirements: Program is open to FACT members. Applicants must be graduating from an accredited public, private or parochial high school or equivalent during the 2007-2008 school year; must maintain a "C" grade point average to remain in the funds (if considered). Applicants may be students currently enrolled in 2- or 4-year education in accredited colleges or universities. **Application Requirements:** Applicants must submit completed application form; Release Authorization and Membership Verification Form; Certification Form; Official Copy of High School Transcript signed by the applicant's high school principal or academic advisor; and a two-page, double-spaced essay. **Deadline for Receipt:** January 15. **Additional Information:** FACT Membership Office at the above address.

859 ■ FIRST COMMUNITY FOUNDATION OF PENNSYLVANIA, WILLIAMSPORT-LYCOMING
330 Pine St., Suite 401
Williamsport, PA 17701
Tel: (570)321-1500; (866)901-2372
Fax: (570)321-6434
E-mail: fcfpa@fcfpa.org
Web Site: http://www.wlfoundation.org
To provide scholarship for Danville Area High School seniors who have been accepted or will attend an accredited 4-year college, full-time.
Title of Award: Ken and Pat Ackerman Family Scholarship Fund **Area, Field, or Subject:** General studies. **Level of Education for which Award is Granted:** Undergraduate **Funds Available:** No specific amount.
Eligibility Requirements: Applicants must have been a varsity wrestler and/or varsity football player and have the highest cumulative 4-year average in English. **Application Requirements:** Applicants may request an application from the guidance counselor of Danville Area School District. **Additional Information:** Gary Grozier, Guidance Counselor of Danville Area School District, 600 Walnut St., Danville, PA 17821; 570-271-3268 ext. 2006; ggrozier@danville.k12.pa.us.

860 ■ FIRST COMMUNITY FOUNDATION OF PENNSYLVANIA, WILLIAMSPORT-LYCOMING
330 Pine St., Suite 401
Williamsport, PA 17701
Tel: (570)321-1500; (866)901-2372
Fax: (570)321-6434
E-mail: fcfpa@fcfpa.org
Web Site: http://www.wlfoundation.org
To provide financial assistance for Montoursville Area High School seniors who are seeking higher education beyond graduation from high school (full-time) and who represent the top 10% GPA of graduating seniors.
Title of Award: Ruth D. Adams Fund **Area, Field, or Subject:** General studies. **Level of Education for which Award is Granted:** Undergraduate **Funds Available:** No specific amount.
Eligibility Requirements: Applicants shall be approved for full-time admission to any accredited two or four-year college or university of their choice and be enrolled in a course of study of their choice which leads to a degree. **Application Requirements:** Applicants may contact and request an application from the Montoursville Area High School. **Additional Information:** Ronda Albert, Montoursville Area High School, 100 N Arch St, Montoursville, PA 17754; 570-368-3509; ralbert@montoursville. k12.pa.us.

861 ■ FIRST COMMUNITY FOUNDATION OF PENNSYLVANIA, WILLIAMSPORT-LYCOMING
330 Pine St., Suite 401
Williamsport, PA 17701
Tel: (570)321-1500; (866)901-2372
Fax: (570)321-6434
E-mail: fcfpa@fcfpa.org
Web Site: http://www.wlfoundation.org
To provide scholarship for graduating seniors from Mount Carmel Area High School and Montoursville Area High School respectively, who have been accepted into a full-time undergraduate, business or technical program at an accredited institution of higher education.
Title of Award: Anne L. Alexander and Blaise Robert Alexander Memorial Scholarships **Area, Field, or Subject:** General studies. **Level of Education for which Award is Granted:** Undergraduate **Funds Available:** No specific amount.
Eligibility Requirements: Applicants must have exhibited good citizenship and community involvement; must be a leader with a sense of humor; must be grounded; must show tolerance to others; must be honest; must have integrity; and must make a difference in the school community. **Application Requirements:** Applicants may contact and request an application from the Montoursville Area High School. **Additional Information:** Ronda Albert, Montoursville Area High School, 100 N Arch St, Montoursville, PA 17754; 570-368-3509; ralbert@montoursville.k12.pa.us.

862 ■ FIRST COMMUNITY FOUNDATION OF PENNSYLVANIA, WILLIAMSPORT-LYCOMING
330 Pine St., Suite 401
Williamsport, PA 17701

Tel: (570)321-1500; (866)901-2372
Fax: (570)321-6434
E-mail: fcfpa@fcfpa.org
Web Site: http://www.wlfoundation.org
To provide financial assistance for graduates who have been in the foster care system or have legal adopted status and who have shown remarkable achievement despite the obstacles in their life.
Title of Award: B-Brave McMahon/Stratton Scholarship Fund **Area, Field, or Subject:** General studies. **Level of Education for which Award is Granted:** Undergraduate **Funds Available:** No specific amount.
Eligibility Requirements: Applicant must be a graduating senior from a Lycoming County High School or Clinton County High School that has believed in herself/himself; must have been accepted into a full-time continuing education program, preferably in Pennsylvania; must have exhibited good citizenship and have no known drug or alcohol record or juvenile offenses; have an unmet financial need; and must show evidence that they have a current minimum GPA of 2.8. **Application Requirements:** Candidates must complete the application and submit it along with any requested additional information to the Williamsport-Lycoming Community Foundation. **Deadline for Receipt:** April 1. **Additional Information:** Candy Bower, Manager of Program and Scholarship Services candyb@fcfpa.org.

863 ■ FIRST COMMUNITY FOUNDATION OF PENNSYLVANIA, WILLIAMSPORT-LYCOMING
330 Pine St., Suite 401
Williamsport, PA 17701
Tel: (570)321-1500; (866)901-2372
Fax: (570)321-6434
E-mail: fcfpa@fcfpa.org
Web Site: http://www.wlfoundation.org
To provide financial assistance for honor students from the Danville Area High School.
Title of Award: Bloch-Selinger Education Fund **Area, Field, or Subject:** General studies. **Level of Education for which Award is Granted:** Undergraduate **Funds Available:** No specific amount. **Duration:** Annual.
Eligibility Requirements: Applicants must be attending a full-time accredited school or university and be in good standing. **Application Requirements:** Applicants may request an application from the guidance counselor of Danville Area School District. **Additional Information:** Gary Grozier, Guidance Counselor of Danville Area School District, 600 Walnut St., Danville, PA 17821; 570-271-3268 ext. 2006; ggrozier@danville.k12. pa.us.

864 ■ FIRST COMMUNITY FOUNDATION OF PENNSYLVANIA, WILLIAMSPORT-LYCOMING
330 Pine St., Suite 401
Williamsport, PA 17701
Tel: (570)321-1500; (866)901-2372
Fax: (570)321-6434
E-mail: fcfpa@fcfpa.org
Web Site: http://www.wlfoundation.org
To provide scholarship to the Danville Area High School seniors.
Title of Award: Diane Booth Memorial Scholarships **Area, Field, or Subject:** General studies. **Level of Education for which Award is Granted:** Undergraduate **Funds Available:** No specific amount.
Eligibility Requirements: Applicants must be accepted into a full-time undergraduate, associate or technical program in an institution of higher education; have exhibited good citizenship and community involvement; and a strong potential for success. **Application Requirements:** Applicants may request an application from the Danville Area School District. **Additional Information:** Gary Grozier, Guidance Counselor, Danville Area School District, 570-271-3268; ggrozier@danville.k12.pa.us.

865 ■ FIRST COMMUNITY FOUNDATION OF PENNSYLVANIA, WILLIAMSPORT-LYCOMING
330 Pine St., Suite 401
Williamsport, PA 17701
Tel: (570)321-1500; (866)901-2372
Fax: (570)321-6434
E-mail: fcfpa@fcfpa.org
Web Site: http://www.wlfoundation.org

To provide scholarship for Danville Area High School seniors who will attend an accredited 2 or 4-year college.
Title of Award: Cotner Family Scholarships **Area, Field, or Subject:** Agricultural economics. **Level of Education for which Award is Granted:** Undergraduate **Funds Available:** No specific amount.
Eligibility Requirements: Applicants must be high school seniors attending an accredited 2 or 4-year college and must be pursuing studies in agriculture or agricultural related fields on a full-time basis. **Application Requirements:** Applicants may request an application from the Guidance Counselor of Danville Area School District. **Additional Information:** Gary Grozier, Guidance Counselor of Danville Area School District, 600 Walnut St., Danvilled, PA 17821; 570-271-3268 ext. 2006; ggrozier@danville.k12. pa.us.

866 ■ FIRST COMMUNITY FOUNDATION OF PENNSYLVANIA, WILLIAMSPORT-LYCOMING
330 Pine St., Suite 401
Williamsport, PA 17701
Tel: (570)321-1500; (866)901-2372
Fax: (570)321-6434
E-mail: fcfpa@fcfpa.org
Web Site: http://www.wlfoundation.org
To provide financial assistance for Danville Area High School seniors who have been accepted into a full-time undergraduate program at an accredited institution of higher education, preferably in Pennsylvania.
Title of Award: Danville Education Association Scholarship Fund **Area, Field, or Subject:** General studies. **Level of Education for which Award is Granted:** Undergraduate **Funds Available:** No specific amount.
Eligibility Requirements: Applicants must have exhibited good citizenship and community involvement; must have unmet financial need; and must have not been the recipient of other major scholarship awards. **Application Requirements:** Applicants may request an application from the Guidance Counselor of Danville Area School District. **Additional Information:** Gary Grozier, Guidance Counselor of Danville Area School District, 600 Walnut St., Danvilled, PA 17821; 570-271-3268 ext. 2006; ggrozier@ danville.k12.pa.us.

867 ■ FIRST COMMUNITY FOUNDATION OF PENNSYLVANIA, WILLIAMSPORT-LYCOMING
330 Pine St., Suite 401
Williamsport, PA 17701
Tel: (570)321-1500; (866)901-2372
Fax: (570)321-6434
E-mail: fcfpa@fcfpa.org
Web Site: http://www.wlfoundation.org
To provide financial assistance for Danville Area High School seniors who have been accepted and will be pursuing a Bachelor of Arts or Sciences degree in an accredited institution of higher education.
Title of Award: Danville High School Class of 1963 Scholarship Fund **Area, Field, or Subject:** General studies. **Level of Education for which Award is Granted:** Undergraduate **Funds Available:** No specific amount.
Eligibility Requirements: Applicants must have exhibited good citizenship and community involvement. The recipients must have experience with community service and volunteering. **Application Requirements:** Applicants may request application form from the Guidance Counselor of Danville Area School District. **Additional Information:** Gary Grozier, Guidance Counselor of Danville Area School District, 600 Walnut St., Danvilled, PA 17821; 570-271-3268 ext. 2006; ggrozier@danville.k12.pa. us.

868 ■ FIRST COMMUNITY FOUNDATION OF PENNSYLVANIA, WILLIAMSPORT-LYCOMING
330 Pine St., Suite 401
Williamsport, PA 17701
Tel: (570)321-1500; (866)901-2372
Fax: (570)321-6434
E-mail: fcfpa@fcfpa.org
Web Site: http://www.wlfoundation.org
To provide financial assistance for Danville Area High School seniors who have been accepted and will attend an accredited 2 or 4-year college as full-time students.

Title of Award: Danville Rotary Scholarships **Area, Field, or Subject:** General studies. **Level of Education for which Award is Granted:** Undergraduate **Funds Available:** No specific amount.

Eligibility Requirements: Applicants must have exhibited good citizenship, honesty, integrity, and volunteerism in the community and/or charity that demonstrate the Rotary's motto. **Application Requirements:** Applicants may request an application from the Guidance Counselor of Danville Area School District. **Additional Information:** Gary Grozier, Guidance Counselor of Danville Area School District, 600 Walnut St., Danvilled, PA 17821; 570-271-3268 ext. 2006; ggrozier@danville.k12.pa.us.

869 ■ FIRST COMMUNITY FOUNDATION OF PENNSYLVANIA, WILLIAMSPORT-LYCOMING

330 Pine St., Suite 401
Williamsport, PA 17701
Tel: (570)321-1500; (866)901-2372
Fax: (570)321-6434
E-mail: fcfpa@fcfpa.org
Web Site: http://www.wlfoundation.org
To provide financial assistance for South Williamsport Area High School seniors who are pursuing a higher education degree at an accredited college or university.

Title of Award: Nolan W. Feeser Scholarship Fund **Area, Field, or Subject:** General studies. **Level of Education for which Award is Granted:** Undergraduate **Number Awarded:** 2. **Funds Available:** No specific amount.

Eligibility Requirements: Applicants must have displayed academic achievements; must have unmet financial need; and must be planning to enroll at or pursuing a degree at Lycoming College, Gettysburg College or Pennsylvania College of Technology. **Application Requirements:** Applicants may contact and request an application from the South Williamsport Area High School. **Additional Information:** Verna Correll, Guidance Counselor, South Williamsport Jr./Sr. High School, 700 Percy St., S Williamsport, PA 17702; 570-326-2684; vcorrell@mounties.k12.pa.us.

870 ■ FIRST COMMUNITY FOUNDATION OF PENNSYLVANIA, WILLIAMSPORT-LYCOMING

330 Pine St., Suite 401
Williamsport, PA 17701
Tel: (570)321-1500; (866)901-2372
Fax: (570)321-6434
E-mail: fcfpa@fcfpa.org
Web Site: http://www.wlfoundation.org
To encourage educational pursuits by providing scholarship for Indian Valley High School seniors.

Title of Award: Daniel G. and Helen I. Fultz Scholarship Fund **Area, Field, or Subject:** General studies. **Level of Education for which Award is Granted:** Undergraduate **Funds Available:** No specific amount.

Eligibility Requirements: Program is open to Indian Valley High School seniors who have been accepted into a full-time undergraduate program at Lycoming College, Williamsport, PA. If there are no applicants from Indian Valley High School, then applicants may be chosen from Lewistown High School in Mifflin County, again, who have been accepted into a full-time undergraduate degree program at Lycoming College, Williamsport, PA. Applicants must have good citizenship and community involvement; be a leader with a sense of humor; be grounded; must show tolerance of others; be honest; have integrity; and make a difference in the school community. Unmet financial need is also considered. **Application Requirements:** Applicants may contact and request an application from the Indian Valley High School. **Deadline for Receipt:** April 15. **Additional Information:** Jane A. Floor, Guidance Counselor, Indian Valley High School, 717-248-5444, jaf53@mcsdk12.org; Frank A. Zook, Guidance Counselor, Lewistown High School, 717-242-1401, faz42@mcsdk12.org.

871 ■ FIRST COMMUNITY FOUNDATION OF PENNSYLVANIA, WILLIAMSPORT-LYCOMING

330 Pine St., Suite 401
Williamsport, PA 17701
Tel: (570)321-1500; (866)901-2372

Fax: (570)321-6434
E-mail: fcfpa@fcfpa.org
Web Site: http://www.wlfoundation.org
To provide scholarship for Danville Area High School seniors who have been accepted into a full-time undergraduate program.

Title of Award: Adam Hampton Memorial Scholarship Fund **Area, Field, or Subject:** General studies. **Level of Education for which Award is Granted:** Undergraduate **Funds Available:** No specific amount.

Eligibility Requirements: Applicants must have good citizenship and community involvement; must be a leader with a sense of humor; must be grounded; must show tolerance of others; must be honest; must have integrity; and must make a difference in the school community. Applicants must also have an unmet financial need and must hold a "B" average or above. **Application Requirements:** Applicants may request an application from the Guidance Counselor of Danville Area School District. **Additional Information:** Gary Grozier, Guidance Counselor of Danville Area School District, 600 Walnut St., Danville, PA 17821; 570-271-3268 ext. 2006; ggrozier@danville.k12.pa.us.

872 ■ FIRST COMMUNITY FOUNDATION OF PENNSYLVANIA, WILLIAMSPORT-LYCOMING

330 Pine St., Suite 401
Williamsport, PA 17701
Tel: (570)321-1500; (866)901-2372
Fax: (570)321-6434
E-mail: fcfpa@fcfpa.org
Web Site: http://www.wlfoundation.org
To provide financial assistance for Lycoming County young adults who demonstrate the potential to succeed in pursuing higher education goals.

Title of Award: Morton Harrison Scholarship Fund **Area, Field, or Subject:** General studies. **Level of Education for which Award is Granted:** Undergraduate **Funds Available:** No specific amount.

Eligibility Requirements: Candidates shall be young adults who, as a result of legal offenses as juveniles or young adults, have come to the attention of Lycoming County's Probation Department; must demonstrate a strong willingness to make positive changes in their lives and pursue educational and/or job training goals that will enable them to fulfill their human potential; and plan to attend a qualified institution of higher education, including but not limited to a 2- or 4-year college or university, a technical college, trade school, or other approved education or training program. **Application Requirements:** Candidates must complete the application and submit it along with any requested additional information to the Williamsport-Lycoming Community Foundation. **Additional Information:** Candy Bower, Manager of Program and Scholarship Services candyb@fcfpa.org.

873 ■ FIRST COMMUNITY FOUNDATION OF PENNSYLVANIA, WILLIAMSPORT-LYCOMING

330 Pine St., Suite 401
Williamsport, PA 17701
Tel: (570)321-1500; (866)901-2372
Fax: (570)321-6434
E-mail: fcfpa@fcfpa.org
Web Site: http://www.wlfoundation.org
To provide scholarship for Montgomery Area High School seniors and/or graduated alumni who have been accepted and will attend an accredited 2 or 4-year college or university, full-time or part-time.

Title of Award: Carl and Lucille Jarrett Scholarship Fund **Area, Field, or Subject:** General studies. **Level of Education for which Award is Granted:** Graduate, Undergraduate **Funds Available:** $1,000.

Eligibility Requirements: The applicants must exhibit good citizenship; must be honest; must have integrity; must have shown through job or volunteer history his/her ability to succeed; must be self-motivated; and must have strong ethics. **Application Requirements:** Applicants must complete the application. Applicants may request an application by contacting the Guidance Counselors of Montgomery Area High School or download it through the Foundation's web site. **Deadline for Receipt:** May 1. **Additional Information:** Tara Bozella or Stacey Roman, Guidance Counselors, Montgomery Area High School, 570-547-1608 ext. 116; tbozella@montasd.org; sroman@montasd.org.

874 ■ FIRST COMMUNITY FOUNDATION OF PENNSYLVANIA, WILLIAMSPORT-LYCOMING

330 Pine St., Suite 401
Williamsport, PA 17701
Tel: (570)321-1500; (866)901-2372
Fax: (570)321-6434
E-mail: fcfpa@fcfpa.org
Web Site: http://www.wlfoundation.org
To provide financial assistance for Danville Area High School seniors who have been accepted into a full-time undergraduate program at an accredited institution of higher education, preferably in Pennsylvania.
Title of Award: Carl J. Marrara Memorial Scholarship Fund **Area, Field, or Subject:** General studies. **Level of Education for which Award is Granted:** Undergraduate **Funds Available:** No specific amount.
Eligibility Requirements: Applicants must have exhibited good citizenship and community involvement; must be a leader with a sense of humor; must be grounded; must show tolerance of others; must be honest; must have integrity and make a difference in the school community; and must have an unmet financial need. **Application Requirements:** Applicants may request an application from the guidance counselor of Danville Area School District. **Additional Information:** Gary Grozier, Guidance Counselor of Danville Area School District, 600 Walnut St., Danville, PA 17821; 570-271-3268 ext. 2006; ggrozier@danville.k12.pa.us.

875 ■ FIRST COMMUNITY FOUNDATION OF PENNSYLVANIA, WILLIAMSPORT-LYCOMING

330 Pine St., Suite 401
Williamsport, PA 17701
Tel: (570)321-1500; (866)901-2372
Fax: (570)321-6434
E-mail: fcfpa@fcfpa.org
Web Site: http://www.wlfoundation.org
To provide financial assistance for Danville Area High School seniors who have been accepted into a full-time undergraduate program at an accredited institution of higher education, preferably in Pennsylvania.
Title of Award: Walter A. and Nan C. McCloskey Memorial Scholarships **Area, Field, or Subject:** General studies. **Level of Education for which Award is Granted:** Undergraduate **Funds Available:** No specific amount.
Eligibility Requirements: Applicants must have attained a Boys or Girls letter in basketball (or football or baseball in the event basketball is discontinued at Danville High School). The award recipient shall be a good school and community citizen in addition to his/her scholastic and athletic qualities. **Application Requirements:** Applicants may request an application from the guidance counselor of Danville Area School District. **Additional Information:** Gary Grozier, Guidance Counselor of Danville Area School District, 600 Walnut St., Danville, PA 17821; 570-271-3268 ext. 2006; ggrozier@danville.k12.pa.us.

876 ■ FIRST COMMUNITY FOUNDATION OF PENNSYLVANIA, WILLIAMSPORT-LYCOMING

330 Pine St., Suite 401
Williamsport, PA 17701
Tel: (570)321-1500; (866)901-2372
Fax: (570)321-6434
E-mail: fcfpa@fcfpa.org
Web Site: http://www.wlfoundation.org
To provide financial assistance for Sullivan County High School seniors who have been accepted into a full-time undergraduate program at an accredited institution of higher education, preferably in Pennsylvania.
Title of Award: Missigman Scholarship Fund **Area, Field, or Subject:** General studies. **Level of Education for which Award is Granted:** Undergraduate **Funds Available:** No specific amount.
Eligibility Requirements: Candidate must be a graduating senior at Sullivan County High School and must demonstrate a strong potential to succeed in pursuing their higher education objectives. **Application Requirements:** Applicants may request an application from the Sullivan County High School or from the First Community Foundation of Pennsylvania. **Additional Information:** Jill Sysock, Guidance Office, Sullivan County High School, Beech and South St., Laporte, PA 18626, 570-947-7001, sysojill@sulcosd.k12.pa.us.

877 ■ FIRST COMMUNITY FOUNDATION OF PENNSYLVANIA, WILLIAMSPORT-LYCOMING

330 Pine St., Suite 401
Williamsport, PA 17701
Tel: (570)321-1500; (866)901-2372
Fax: (570)321-6434
E-mail: fcfpa@fcfpa.org
Web Site: http://www.wlfoundation.org
To provide financial assistance for Muncy High School seniors who have been accepted into a full-time continuing education program.
Title of Award: Muncy Rotary Club Scholarship Fund **Area, Field, or Subject:** General studies. **Level of Education for which Award is Granted:** Undergraduate **Funds Available:** No specific amount.
Eligibility Requirements: Applicants must have exhibited community involvement. Other than a strong potential for success, such factors as class rank and GPA will not be criteria in making a selection unless, in the judgment of the Muncy Rotary Club Scholarship Committee, such factors are needed to distinguish between multiple potential candidates. **Application Requirements:** Applicants may request an application from Erik Berthold of Muncy High School. **Deadline for Receipt:** April 1. **Additional Information:** Erik Berthold, Guidance Counselor, Muncy High School, 200 West Penn St., Muncy, PA 17756, 570-546-3127 ext. 3260, eberthold@muncysd.org.

878 ■ FIRST COMMUNITY FOUNDATION OF PENNSYLVANIA, WILLIAMSPORT-LYCOMING

330 Pine St., Suite 401
Williamsport, PA 17701
Tel: (570)321-1500; (866)901-2372
Fax: (570)321-6434
E-mail: fcfpa@fcfpa.org
Web Site: http://www.wlfoundation.org
To provide financial assistance for graduating seniors in the Muncy Area School District who have completed grades 9, 10, and 11 at the Muncy High School and who have been accepted and will attend a 4-year college, full-time.
Title of Award: Muncy Scholars Award Fund **Area, Field, or Subject:** General studies. **Level of Education for which Award is Granted:** Undergraduate **Funds Available:** No specific amount.
Eligibility Requirements: Applicants must have exhibited continued growth in his/her citizenship; must be a leader; must be honest; must have integrity; and must be determined to succeed. **Application Requirements:** Applicants will be selected from the top 10 academic performers and must have attained at least one varsity letter (either n sports or band). **Additional Information:** Erik Berthold, guidance counselor, Muncy High School, 200 W Penn St., Muncy, PA 17756; 570-546-3127 ext. 3260; eberthold@muncysd.org.

879 ■ FIRST COMMUNITY FOUNDATION OF PENNSYLVANIA, WILLIAMSPORT-LYCOMING

330 Pine St., Suite 401
Williamsport, PA 17701
Tel: (570)321-1500; (866)901-2372
Fax: (570)321-6434
E-mail: fcfpa@fcfpa.org
Web Site: http://www.wlfoundation.org
To provide scholarship for Montoursville Area High School seniors who are planning to attend a vocational/technical college or a two or four-year accredited college.
Title of Award: Kimberly Marie Rogers Memorial Scholarship Fund **Area, Field, or Subject:** General studies. **Level of Education for which Award is Granted:** Undergraduate **Funds Available:** No specific amount.
Eligibility Requirements: Applicants must be Montoursville Area High School seniors who are planning to attend a vocational/technical college or a two or four-year accredited college. Their major should fall under the vocational/technical field. **Application Requirements:** Applicants may contact and request an application from the Montoursville Area High School. **Additional Information:** Ronda Albert, Montoursville Area High School, 100 N Arch St, Montoursville, PA 17754; 570-368-3509; ralbert@montoursville.k12.pa.us.

880 ■ FIRST COMMUNITY FOUNDATION OF PENNSYLVANIA, WILLIAMSPORT-LYCOMING
330 Pine St., Suite 401
Williamsport, PA 17701
Tel: (570)321-1500; (866)901-2372
Fax: (570)321-6434
E-mail: fcfpa@fcfpa.org
Web Site: http://www.wlfoundation.org
To provide financial assistance for Loyalsock High School seniors intending to attend a qualified institution of higher education in pursuit of a career in education who have a demonstrated interest in working with children and who exhibit an appreciation of the arts.
Title of Award: Dr. Wayne F. Rose Scholarship Fund **Area, Field, or Subject:** General studies. **Level of Education for which Award is Granted:** Undergraduate **Funds Available:** No specific amount.
Eligibility Requirements: Applicants must demonstrate family financial need; must demonstrate active involvement working or volunteering with children outside of their own school and typical class responsibilities; must demonstrate participation in the arts while in school and/or through extracurricular activities; and must be in good academic standing with potential for success. **Application Requirements:** Applicants may request an application to the Loyalsock Township High School. Applicants must have a recommendation of at least one teacher. **Additional Information:** Diane Stanzione, Loyalsock Township High School, 1801 Loyalsock Drive, Williamsport, PA 17701, 570-326-3581 ext. 1307, dstanzio@ltsd.k12.pa.us.

881 ■ FIRST COMMUNITY FOUNDATION OF PENNSYLVANIA, WILLIAMSPORT-LYCOMING
330 Pine St., Suite 401
Williamsport, PA 17701
Tel: (570)321-1500; (866)901-2372
Fax: (570)321-6434
E-mail: fcfpa@fcfpa.org
Web Site: http://www.wlfoundation.org
To provide financial assistance for South Williamsport Area High School seniors who have been accepted into a full-time undergraduate program at an accredited institution of higher education, preferably in Pennsylvania.
Title of Award: John A. Savoy Scholarship Fund **Area, Field, or Subject:** General studies. **Level of Education for which Award is Granted:** Undergraduate **Funds Available:** $500. **Duration:** Annual.
Eligibility Requirements: Applicants must have exhibited good citizenship and community involvement; have unmet financial need; and must not have been the recipient of other major scholarship awards. **Application Requirements:** Scholarship is renewable as long as the recipient remains in good standing at an accredited college or university but shall not exceed a maximum of 4 years. Applicant must submit an application to the Guidance Counselor's Office; must include a cover letter (not to exceed two pages) outlining why he or she is applying for the scholarship and summarizing his/her ultimate career objectives; must provide at least one letter of reference; and must provide proof that he or she has been accepted to a qualified two or four-year college/university. **Deadline for Receipt:** May 1. **Additional Information:** Verna Correll, Guidance Counselor, South Williamsport Jr./Sr. High School, 700 Percy St., S Williamsport, PA 17702; 570-326-2684; vcorrell@mounties.k12.pa.us.

882 ■ FIRST COMMUNITY FOUNDATION OF PENNSYLVANIA, WILLIAMSPORT-LYCOMING
330 Pine St., Suite 401
Williamsport, PA 17701
Tel: (570)321-1500; (866)901-2372
Fax: (570)321-6434
E-mail: fcfpa@fcfpa.org
Web Site: http://www.wlfoundation.org
To defray all or a portion of the costs of attending college or other undergraduate institutions of higher learning beyond the secondary level for Warrior Run High School seniors.
Title of Award: Ralph and Josephine Smith Scholarship Fund **Area, Field, or Subject:** General studies. **Level of Education for which Award is Granted:** Undergraduate **Number Awarded:** 4. **Funds Available:** $625. **Duration:** One semester.
Eligibility Requirements: Candidate must maintain a GPA of 2.5. Candidate's financial needs shall always be a primary consideration.

Extra-curricular activities will not be considered in the selection process. **Application Requirements:** Applicants may request an application from the Guidance Office of Warrior Run High School. **Additional Information:** Jenna Brown or Jim Houser, Guidance Office, Warrior Run High School, 4800 Susquehanna Trail, Turbotville, PA 17772, 570-649-5166 ext. 105, jbrown@wrsd.org or jhouser@wrsd.org.

883 ■ FIRST COMMUNITY FOUNDATION OF PENNSYLVANIA, WILLIAMSPORT-LYCOMING
330 Pine St., Suite 401
Williamsport, PA 17701
Tel: (570)321-1500; (866)901-2372
Fax: (570)321-6434
E-mail: fcfpa@fcfpa.org
Web Site: http://www.wlfoundation.org
To provide financial assistance for Muncy High School seniors who are pursuing higher education.
Title of Award: Margaret E. Waldron Scholarship Fund **Area, Field, or Subject:** General studies. **Level of Education for which Award is Granted:** Undergraduate **Funds Available:** $3,000 - freshman and sophomore years; $4,000 - junior and senior years. **Duration:** One year.
Eligibility Requirements: Candidates must have completed grades 10, 11, 12 at Muncy High School and have graduated from academic courses at Muncy High School; must rank in upper 1/5 of the class during junior and senior years; must present letter of acceptance from a postsecondary institution of higher learning. **Application Requirements:** Applicants may contact Guidance Office of Muncy High School to request an application or download the application from the Foundation's web site. Applicant must submit a copy of his/her parents' current U.S. Individual Income Tax Return and a copy of his or her school transcript through the third marking period of his or her senior year. **Deadline for Receipt:** April 1. **Additional Information:** Erik Berthold, Guidance Counselor, Muncy High School, 200 W Penn St., Muncy, PA 17756, 570-546-3127 ext. 3260, eberthold@muncysd.org.

884 ■ FIRST COMMUNITY FOUNDATION OF PENNSYLVANIA, WILLIAMSPORT-LYCOMING
330 Pine St., Suite 401
Williamsport, PA 17701
Tel: (570)321-1500; (866)901-2372
Fax: (570)321-6434
E-mail: fcfpa@fcfpa.org
Web Site: http://www.wlfoundation.org
To provide financial assistance for Williamsport Area High School seniors intending to attend a college, university, or vocational school that offers an at least two-year degree or certification program.
Title of Award: Williamsport High School Class of 1970 Scholarship Fund **Area, Field, or Subject:** General studies. **Level of Education for which Award is Granted:** Undergraduate **Funds Available:** No specific amount.
Eligibility Requirements: Candidates must be in need of financial assistance and shall not have received any other scholarship totaling more than $250. Preference is given to applicant who is not necessarily the most outstanding scholar nor the most sensational athlete; but rather, the student who has worked diligently to master his/her selection of academic courses, has earned the respect of his/her teachers and fellow students because he/she possesses unquestionable integrity and who consistently displays compassion or kindness to others. **Application Requirements:** Applicants may request an application from the Head Principal of Williamsport Area High School. **Additional Information:** Head Principal, Williamsport Area High School, 2990 WFourth St., Williamsport, PA 17701, 5703238411.

885 ■ FIRST COMMUNITY FOUNDATION OF PENNSYLVANIA, WILLIAMSPORT-LYCOMING
330 Pine St., Suite 401
Williamsport, PA 17701
Tel: (570)321-1500; (866)901-2372
Fax: (570)321-6434
E-mail: fcfpa@fcfpa.org
Web Site: http://www.wlfoundation.org
To provide academic support for students who are attending Pennsylvania College and have graduated from Bradford County, Clinton County, Lycoming County, Potter County, Sullivan County or Tioga County.

Title of Award: Williamsport-Lycoming Community Foundation - Benjamin Franklin Scholarships **Area, Field, or Subject:** General studies. **Level of Education for which Award is Granted:** Undergraduate **Funds Available:** No specific amount.

Eligibility Requirements: Applicants must be enrolled at the Pennsylvania College of Technology; must be enrolled in an approved Tech prep high school program and subsequently enroll in a Certificate, Associate or Bachelor's Degree program at the Pennsylvania College of Technology. In schools without approved Tech Prep programs, students must enroll in a high school vocational-technical program and subsequently enroll in a Certificate, Associate, or Bachelor's Degree program at the Pennsylvanian College of Technology. Applicants must have a GPA of "B" or higher and must be enrolled full-time. Preference will be given to continuing students in subsequent years if a cumulative GPA of 2.80 is maintained in the program. **Application Requirements:** Applicants must submit a writing sample as defined by the Pennsylvania College of Technology Prep office. **Additional Information:** Joan Kay, Executive Director, Pennsylvania College of Technology Foundation, Inc., One College Ave., Williamsport, PA 17701-5799; 570-320-8020; jkay@pct.edu.

886 ■ ALLISON E. FISHER MEMORIAL FUND

PO Box 43402
Baltimore, MD 21236
Tel: (410)679-0595
E-mail: fishers@verizon.net
Web Site: http://www.allisonfisherfund.org
To provide financial assistance to graduating senior students who have been accepted to a two-year community college or four-year college or university.

Title of Award: St. Stephen A.M.E. Allison E. Fisher Book Awards **Area, Field, or Subject:** General studies. **Level of Education for which Award is Granted:** Undergraduate **Funds Available:** $300. **Duration:** One year.

Eligibility Requirements: Applicants must be graduating senior students who attended St. Stephen A.M.E. and who have been accepted to a two-year community college or four-year college or university. **Application Requirements:** Applicants must submit all the required application information.

887 ■ ALLISON E. FISHER MEMORIAL FUND

PO Box 43402
Baltimore, MD 21236
Tel: (410)679-0595
E-mail: fishers@verizon.net
Web Site: http://www.allisonfisherfund.org
To provide financial assistance and recognize graduating seniors at Perry Hall High School.

Title of Award: Spirit of Allison Graduation Award **Area, Field, or Subject:** General studies. **Level of Education for which Award is Granted:** High School **Funds Available:** $500.

Eligibility Requirements: Applicants must be graduating seniors at Perry Hall High School. **Application Requirements:** Applicants must submit all the application information.

888 ■ FOUNDATION FOR THE CAROLINAS

217 S Tryon St.
Charlotte, NC 28202
Tel: (704)973-4500
Free: 800-973-7244
Web Site: http://www.fftc.org
To provide educational assistance for deserving students with financial need who are residents of Union County, NC.

Title of Award: Henry S. and Carolyn Adams Scholarship Fund **Area, Field, or Subject:** General studies. **Level of Education for which Award is Granted:** Undergraduate **Funds Available:** $4,000. **Duration:** One year.

Eligibility Requirements: Applicants must have a minimum cumulative grade point average of 3.0 (on a 4.0 scale); must be legal residents of Union County, NC; must be nominated by the principal of their high school; and must demonstrate a substantial need for financial assistance. **Application Requirements:** Applicants must submit completed application form; official copy of high school transcript(s), including SAT/ACT scores; one to two-paged typed statement expressing qualifications for the scholarship, educational goals and financial need for scholarship assistance; two completed recommendation forms including at least one from a current teacher; and a copy of SAR from FAFSA. **Deadline for Receipt:** March 15.

889 ■ FOUNDATION FOR THE CAROLINAS

217 S Tryon St.
Charlotte, NC 28202
Tel: (704)973-4500
Free: 800-973-7244
Web Site: http://www.fftc.org
To provide financial assistance for students at the University of North Carolina at Charlotte who have expressed an interest in the multi-family housing field.

Title of Award: Herb Adrian Memorial Scholarship Fund **Area, Field, or Subject:** Finance; Construction; Management. **Level of Education for which Award is Granted:** Undergraduate **Funds Available:** No specific amount.

Eligibility Requirements: Applicants must be rising UNC Charlotte juniors or seniors; must have interest in the multi-housing industry, including but not limited to finance, construction and management; and must demonstrate financial need. **Application Requirements:** Applicants must contact the UNC Charlotte Student Financial Aid Office at 704687-2461 for application.

890 ■ FOUNDATION FOR THE CAROLINAS

217 S Tryon St.
Charlotte, NC 28202
Tel: (704)973-4500
Free: 800-973-7244
Web Site: http://www.fftc.org
To provide financial support and encouragement for adult women age 25 and older who are raising school-age children (grades K-12) and hope to earn a two-year nursing degree or a four-year undergraduate degree in the field of their choice.

Title of Award: Andersen Nontraditional Scholarship for Women's Education and Retraining **Area, Field, or Subject:** General studies. **Level of Education for which Award is Granted:** Undergraduate **Funds Available:** No specific amount. **Duration:** One year.

Eligibility Requirements: Applicants must be nontraditional female students age 25 or older at the time of the application deadline; legal residents of Mecklenburg County, NC or contiguous county in North Carolina or South Carolina; enrolled or planning to enroll as full-time, degree-seeking students at an accredited institution in North Carolina or South Carolina. **Application Requirements:** Applicants must submit a completed application form; copy of the Student Aid Report from FAFSA; official transcripts of grades for the applicant's most recently completed coursework; three recommendation forms from non-related adults such as instructors or other campus administrators, employers, mentors, etc.; updated, typed resume; one to two-page typed personal statement expressing why the applicant is applying for the scholarship and the applicant's educational and career goals; and copy of the applicant's federal tax return for the preceding year showing dependents and adjusted gross income. **Deadline for Receipt:** April 2.

891 ■ FOUNDATION FOR THE CAROLINAS

217 S Tryon St.
Charlotte, NC 28202
Tel: (704)973-4500
Free: 800-973-7244
Web Site: http://www.fftc.org
To provide financial support for children of the employees of Hanes Companies, Inc., USA.

Title of Award: Donald H. Bernstein/John B. Talbert, Jr. Scholarship Fund **Area, Field, or Subject:** General studies. **Level of Education for which Award is Granted:** Undergraduate **Funds Available:** $1,000 to $2,500. **Duration:** One year.

Eligibility Requirements: Applicants must be graduating high school seniors who have a minimum cumulative grade point average of 3.0 (on a 4.0 scale). Parents or legal guardians of applicants must be employees who have completed at least two years (24 months) of full-time service with Hanes Companies, Inc. USA prior to the application deadline. Children of employees shall be defined to include natural-born or legally-adopted dependent children and stepchildren and wards of employees. **Application Requirements:** Applicants must submit completed application form; copy of high school transcript(s), including SAT/ACT scores; three recommendation forms (two from teachers or other school personnel and one from an employer or other non-related adult); one to two-paged typed statement expressing the reason for applying for the scholarship, qualifications, and educational/career goals; and letter from an official of Hanes Companies, Inc. USA where parent or legally-appointed guardians are employed.

892 ■ FOUNDATION FOR THE CAROLINAS
217 S Tryon St.
Charlotte, NC 28202
Tel: (704)973-4500
Free: 800-973-7244
Web Site: http://www.fftc.org
To provide financial assistance for accounting students at East Carolina University.
Title of Award: T. Frank Booth Memorial Scholarship Fund **Area, Field, or Subject:** Accounting. **Level of Education for which Award is Granted:** Undergraduate **Funds Available:** No specific amount.
Eligibility Requirements: Applicants must be legal residents of North Carolina who are juniors or seniors with a 3.0 minimum cumulative grade point average (on 4.0 scale) who have declared major in accounting. **Application Requirements:** Applicants must submit all the required application information. **Additional Information:** East Carolina University Department of Accounting, 252-328-6055.

893 ■ FOUNDATION FOR THE CAROLINAS
217 S Tryon St.
Charlotte, NC 28202
Tel: (704)973-4500
Free: 800-973-7244
Web Site: http://www.fftc.org
To provide financial assistance for high school seniors graduating from Charlotte-Mecklenburg high schools (public or private) who have experienced the death of one or both parents.
Title of Award: Kasie Ford Capling Memorial Scholarship Endowment Fund **Area, Field, or Subject:** General studies. **Level of Education for which Award is Granted:** Undergraduate **Funds Available:** No specific amount.
Eligibility Requirements: Applicants must be graduating high school seniors from a high school located in Mecklenburg County, NC (public or private) planning to enter a four-year degree program at an accredited institution; must be legal residents of Mecklenburg County, NC; and must have experienced the death of one or both parents. **Application Requirements:** Applicants must submit all the required application information.

894 ■ FOUNDATION FOR THE CAROLINAS
217 S Tryon St.
Charlotte, NC 28202
Tel: (704)973-4500
Free: 800-973-7244
Web Site: http://www.fftc.org
To support the children of employees of member firms of the Carolinas-Virginias Region of the National Retail Hardware Association.
Title of Award: Carolinas-Virginias Retail Hardware Scholarship Fund **Area, Field, or Subject:** General studies. **Level of Education for which Award is Granted:** Undergraduate **Funds Available:** $500 up to $2,000. **Duration:** One year.
Eligibility Requirements: Applicants must have a minimum cumulative grade point average of 2.5 on a 4.0 scale; whose parents or legally-appointed guardians are employees who have completed at least two years of full-time service with a member firm of the Carolinas-Virginias Region of the National Retail Hardware Association; children of employees shall be defined to include natural-born or legally-adopted dependent children and stepchildren and wards of employees. **Application Requirements:** Applicants must submit completed application form; copy of the Student Aid Report (SAR) from FAFSA; official transcript(s) of high school and/or college coursework and grades for at least the last two years, including SAT/ACT scores if taken; three recommendation forms, two from teachers or other school personnel and one from an employer or other non-related adult; one to two-page typed statement expressing the

reason on why applicant is applying for the scholarship, qualifications and educational and career goals; a letter from an official of the member firm of the Carolinas-Virginias Region of the National Retail Hardware Association where parent or legally-appointed guardian is employed. **Deadline for Receipt:** February 15.

895 ■ FOUNDATION FOR THE CAROLINAS
217 S Tryon St.
Charlotte, NC 28202
Tel: (704)973-4500
Free: 800-973-7244
Web Site: http://www.fftc.org
To provide educational assistance for young residents of housing owned or managed by the Charlotte Housing Authority.
Title of Award: Charlotte Housing Authority Scholarship Fund (CHASF) **Area, Field, or Subject:** General studies. **Level of Education for which Award is Granted:** Undergraduate **Funds Available:** $500 up to $3,400. **Duration:** One year.
Eligibility Requirements: Applicants must be residents of public housing owned or managed by the Charlotte Housing Authority. Applicants attending college, vocational or technical school for the first time must not be over 21 years of age as of September 1 of the school year for which the scholarship award is to be made; those who have previously attended a college, vocational or technical school must not be over 24 years of age as of September 1 of the school year for which the scholarship award is to be made. **Application Requirements:** Applicants must submit completed application form; official transcript(s) of coursework and grades for at least the first two years, including SAT/ACT scores if taken; three recommendation forms (one from an adult in the housing community where the applicant lives, one from a teacher, counselor or other school administrator, and one from an employer, minister, community leader or other non-related adult); one to two pages typed personal statement expressing the applicant's educational and career goals and financial need for scholarship assistance; and copy of the applicant's FAFSA or student aid report. **Deadline for Receipt:** March 1.

896 ■ FOUNDATION FOR THE CAROLINAS
217 S Tryon St.
Charlotte, NC 28202
Tel: (704)973-4500
Free: 800-973-7244
Web Site: http://www.fftc.org
To provide motivation and encouragement for Charlotte-Mecklenburg public high school students with financial need to stay in school, graduate and pursue postsecondary education.
Title of Award: Charlotte-Mecklenburg Schools Scholarship Incentive Program **Area, Field, or Subject:** General studies. **Level of Education for which Award is Granted:** Undergraduate **Funds Available:** $800 to $1,500. **Duration:** One year.
Eligibility Requirements: Applicants must be graduating seniors at a Charlotte-Mecklenburg public high school; must be participants in the Communities In Schools ThinkCOLLEGE Program or the Charlotte-Mecklenburg Schools AVID Program; must be legal residents of Mecklenburg County, NC; and must have 2.5 minimum cumulative grade point average on a 4.0 scale. **Application Requirements:** Applicants must submit completed application form; official copy of high school transcript(s), including SAT/ACT scores; two recommendation forms from a teacher, counselor or other school administrator, and the other one from an employer, community leader or non-related adult; one to two pages typed personal statement; and copy of SAR from FAFSA. **Deadline for Receipt:** March 1.

897 ■ FOUNDATION FOR THE CAROLINAS
217 S Tryon St.
Charlotte, NC 28202
Tel: (704)973-4500
Free: 800-973-7244
Web Site: http://www.fftc.org
To assist children in grades K-8 intending to attend tuition-based schools which their families could not otherwise afford.
Title of Award: Children's Scholarship Fund of Charlotte **Area, Field, or Subject:** General studies. **Level of Education for which Award is Granted:** High School **Funds Available:** No specific amount.

Eligibility Requirements: Applicants must be legal resident children of Mecklenburg County, NC in grades K-8 attending or planning to attend a tuition-based school in the Charlotte-Mecklenburg region. **Application Requirements:** Applicants must submit all the required application information. **Deadline for Receipt:** October 1.

898 ■ FOUNDATION FOR THE CAROLINAS
217 S Tryon St.
Charlotte, NC 28202
Tel: (704)973-4500
Free: 800-973-7244
Web Site: http://www.fftc.org
To increase the number of high school graduates from Richmond County, NC pursuing post-secondary education.
Title of Award: Cole Foundation Undergraduate Scholarship Program **Area, Field, or Subject:** General studies. **Level of Education for which Award is Granted:** Undergraduate **Number Awarded:** 2. **Funds Available:** $2,000 for two-year scholarship; $4,000 for four-year scholarships. **Duration:** One year.
Eligibility Requirements: Applicants must be legal residents of Richmond County, NC; must be high school seniors scheduled to graduate in the spring of the current school year. Students applying for four-year scholarships must have a minimum cumulative grade point average of 3.0 (on 4.0 scale). Students applying for two-year scholarships must have a minimum cumulative grade point average of 2.5 (on a 4.0 scale). **Application Requirements:** Applicants must submit completed application form; copy of SAR from FAFSA; official copy of the applicant's high school transcript(s), including SAT/ACT scores if taken; type-written statement expressing educational and career goals, reasons for applying for the scholarship and why they deserve the scholarship; and copy of both parents' federal tax return(s) for the preceding year showing dependents and adjusted gross income. **Deadline for Receipt:** March 1.

899 ■ FOUNDATION FOR THE CAROLINAS
217 S Tryon St.
Charlotte, NC 28202
Tel: (704)973-4500
Free: 800-973-7244
Web Site: http://www.fftc.org
To provide financial assistance for children of employees of general contracting companies headquartered in Mecklenburg County, NC.
Title of Award: Crowder Scholarship Fund **Area, Field, or Subject:** General studies. **Level of Education for which Award is Granted:** Undergraduate **Funds Available:** $1,000. **Duration:** One year.
Eligibility Requirements: Children of employees are defined as natural-born or legally-adopted dependent children and stepchildren and wards of employees. Parents or legally-appointed guardians of applicants must have worked for their respective general contracting company for at least three years prior to the application deadline. A minimum cumulative grade point average of 2.0 (on a 4.0 scale) is required. **Application Requirements:** Applicants must submit completed application form; copy of SAR from FAFSA; official transcript(s) of high school and/or college coursework and grades for at least the last two years, including SAT/ACT scores if taken; three recommendation forms; a one to two-paged typed statement expressing why the applicant is applying for the scholarship, applicant's qualifications and the applicant's educational and career goals; a letter from an official of the general contracting company where the applicant's parent is employed, certifying that the parent is an employee and stating the employee's position and length of service; and a copy of both parents' federal tax return for the preceding year showing dependents and adjusted gross income. **Deadline for Receipt:** February 15.

900 ■ FOUNDATION FOR THE CAROLINAS
217 S Tryon St.
Charlotte, NC 28202
Tel: (704)973-4500
Free: 800-973-7244
Web Site: http://www.fftc.org
To provide financial assistance for undergraduate students who "fall between the cracks" of financial aid and/or scholarship programs.
Title of Award: The E.R. and Lilian B. Dimmette Scholarship Fund **Area, Field, or Subject:** General studies. **Level of Education for which Award is Granted:** Undergraduate **Funds Available:** $1,000 to $4,000. **Duration:** One year.

Eligibility Requirements: Applicants must be nominated by the Superintendent of Schools in their county; must have a minimum cumulative grade point average of 2.5 (on a 4.0 scale); and must be legal residents of Gaston, Iredell, Mecklenburg, Rowan or Wilkes County, North Carolina. **Application Requirements:** Applicants must submit completed application form; copy of the SAR from FAFSA; official copy of high school transcript(s), including SAT/ACT scores; three recommendation forms (two from teachers or other school personnel and one from an employer or other non-related adult); one to two-paged typed statement expressing qualifications for the scholarship, educational goals and financial need for scholarship assistance; copy of both parents' federal tax return for the preceding year showing dependents and adjusted gross income; and copy of estimated expense budget for tuition, fees, room, board, books, etc. for the school planning to attend. **Deadline for Receipt:** February 15.

901 ■ FOUNDATION FOR THE CAROLINAS
217 S Tryon St.
Charlotte, NC 28202
Tel: (704)973-4500
Free: 800-973-7244
Web Site: http://www.fftc.org
To provide financial assistance for students intending to pursue college but who are not capable of paying the school expenses.
Title of Award: Foundation for the Carolinas Rotary Scholarship Fund **Area, Field, or Subject:** General studies. **Level of Education for which Award is Granted:** Undergraduate **Funds Available:** $1,000 to $2,000. **Duration:** One year.
Eligibility Requirements: Applicants must be at least college juniors or seniors at a four-year institution enrolling as full-time students; must have a minimum 3.0 cumulative grade point average (on a 4.0 scale); and must demonstrate financial need. **Application Requirements:** Applicants must submit completed application form; copy of Student Aid Report (SAR) from Free Application for Federal Student Aid; official transcript(s) of academic coursework and grades for at least the last two years; three recommendation forms (two from instructors or other campus administrators and one from an employer or other non-related individual in Charlotte-Mecklenburg area); one to two-paged typed statement expressing reasons for applying for the scholarship; and a copy of the estimated expense budget for tuition, room and board, books, etc. **Deadline for Receipt:** April 2.

902 ■ FOUNDATION FOR THE CAROLINAS
217 S Tryon St.
Charlotte, NC 28202
Tel: (704)973-4500
Free: 800-973-7244
Web Site: http://www.fftc.org
To provide financial assistance for undergraduate students who have shown a career interest or demonstrate practical experiences in the plastics industry.
Title of Award: Richard Goolsby Scholarship Fund **Area, Field, or Subject:** General studies. **Level of Education for which Award is Granted:** Undergraduate **Funds Available:** $4,000. **Duration:** One year.
Eligibility Requirements: Applicants must be full-time rising college sophomore, junior or senior students at a four-year college or two-year technical school, who are in good academic standing and majoring in or taking courses that would be suited to a career in the plastics industry. **Application Requirements:** Applicants must submit completed application form; copy of the Student Aid Report (SAR) from Free Application for Federal Student Aid; official transcript(s) of academic coursework and grades for at least the last two years; three recommendation forms (two from teachers or other school administrators and one from an employer or other non-related individual); and a personal statement expressing reasons for applying for the scholarship, qualifications, educational and career goals in plastics industry. **Deadline for Receipt:** February 15.

903 ■ FOUNDATION FOR THE CAROLINAS
217 S Tryon St.
Charlotte, NC 28202
Tel: (704)973-4500
Free: 800-973-7244
Web Site: http://www.fftc.org

To provide financial assistance for students at Pfeiffer University in Misenheimer, NC and Mitchell Community College in Statesville, NC. **Title of Award:** James V. Johnson Scholarship Fund **Area, Field, or Subject:** General studies. **Level of Education for which Award is Granted:** Undergraduate **Funds Available:** No specific amount. **Eligibility Requirements:** Applicants must be legal residents of Iredell or Alexander County in North Carolina who are incoming freshmen at Pfeiffer University in Misenheimer, NC or first-year students at Mitchell Community College in Statesville, NC. **Application Requirements:** Applicants must submit all the required application information. **Additional Information:** Pfeiffer University Office Admissions and Financial Aid, 704-463-1360 or the Mitchell Community College Office of Financial Aid, 704-878-3200.

904 ■ FOUNDATION FOR THE CAROLINAS
217 S Tryon St.
Charlotte, NC 28202
Tel: (704)973-4500
Free: 800-973-7244
Web Site: http://www.fftc.org
To provide undergraduate scholarships for students of Queens University of Charlotte in Charlotte, NC and Brevard College in Brevard, NC.
Title of Award: Annabel Lambeth Jones Scholarship Fund **Area, Field, or Subject:** General studies. **Level of Education for which Award is Granted:** Undergraduate **Funds Available:** No specific amount. **Eligibility Requirements:** Applicants must be incoming freshmen; must have high academic merit; and must have demonstrated leadership potential. **Application Requirements:** Applicants must submit all the required application information.

905 ■ FOUNDATION FOR THE CAROLINAS
217 S Tryon St.
Charlotte, NC 28202
Tel: (704)973-4500
Free: 800-973-7244
Web Site: http://www.fftc.org
To support deserving students with financial need who are residents of Anson or Union Countries in North Carolina.
Title of Award: Mary and Millard Kiker Scholarship Fund **Area, Field, or Subject:** General studies. **Level of Education for which Award is Granted:** Undergraduate **Funds Available:** $1,000 to $4,000. **Duration:** One year.
Eligibility Requirements: Applicants must be legal residents of Anson or Union County, NC who are nominated by the Superintendent of Schools in their county with a minimum cumulative grade point average of 2.5 (on a 4.0 scale) and must demonstrate substantial need for financial assistance. **Application Requirements:** Applicants must submit completed application form; copy of the Student Aid Report from FAFSA; official copy of high school transcript(s), including SAT/ACT scores; three recommendation forms (two from teachers or other school personnel and one from an employer or other non-related adult); one to two-paged typed statement expressing qualifications for the scholarship, educational goals and financial need for scholarship assistance; and a copy of both parents' federal tax return for the preceding year showing dependents and adjusted gross income. **Deadline for Receipt:** April 2.

906 ■ FOUNDATION FOR THE CAROLINAS
217 S Tryon St.
Charlotte, NC 28202
Tel: (704)973-4500
Free: 800-973-7244
Web Site: http://www.fftc.org
To provide motivation and encouragement to George T. Lewis, Jr. Academic Center graduates intending to pursue postsecondary education or training.
Title of Award: George T. Lewis, Jr. Academic Scholarship Fund **Area, Field, or Subject:** General studies. **Level of Education for which Award is Granted:** Undergraduate **Funds Available:** $1,500. **Duration:** One year.
Eligibility Requirements: Applicants must meet or exceed the benchmark goals for attendance set for the George T. Lewis, Jr. Academic Center during their senior year; must have earned a minimum 2.0 cumulative grade point average (on a 4.0 scale) at the end of the first semester of

senior year; and must be graduating seniors at the George T. Lewis, Jr. Academic Center and must have at least one full academic year of enrollment and participation in the ThinkCOLLEGE Program (upon graduation). **Application Requirements:** Applicants must submit completed application form; copy of the SAR from FAFSA; official copy of high school transcript(s), including SAT/ACT scores; two recommendation forms (one from a teacher, counselor or other school administrator and one from employer, community leader or other non-related adult); a one to two-paged typed personal statement on one of the following topics: (1) Discuss who or what has been the biggest influence on your decisions to attend college and why or (2) Present and explain the 'personal mission' or 'personal vision' you have adopted for yourself and discuss why you think these goals are important; and a copy of the applicant's completed FAFSA. **Deadline for Receipt:** March 1.

907 ■ FOUNDATION FOR THE CAROLINAS
217 S Tryon St.
Charlotte, NC 28202
Tel: (704)973-4500
Free: 800-973-7244
Web Site: http://www.fftc.org
To assist high school athletes from Mecklenburg County, NC and Spartanburg County, SC who wish to pursue a four-year undergraduate degree.
Title of Award: Carolina Panthers Players Sam Mills Memorial Scholarship Fund **Area, Field, or Subject:** General studies. **Level of Education for which Award is Granted:** Undergraduate **Number Awarded:** 2. **Funds Available:** $5,100. **Duration:** One year.
Eligibility Requirements: Applicants must be graduate senior athletes at high schools (public or private) located in Mecklenburg County, NC or Spartanburg County, SC; have earned a varsity letter in high school; with 3.0 minimum cumulative unweighted grade point average on a 4.0 scale; and demonstrated outstanding leadership and citizenship. **Application Requirements:** Applicants must submit completed application form; copy of the Student Aid Report (SAR) from Free Application for FAFSA; official copy of high school transcript, including SAT/ACT scores; three recommendation forms, one from a faculty member/school official and one from a member of the coaching staff of the sport in which the athletes participate; a one to two-page statement expressing the reason why applicant is applying for the scholarship, their involvement in athletics, and educational and career goals. **Deadline for Receipt:** April 30.

908 ■ FOUNDATION FOR THE CAROLINAS
217 S Tryon St.
Charlotte, NC 28202
Tel: (704)973-4500
Free: 800-973-7244
Web Site: http://www.fftc.org
To provide undergraduate scholarships for graduating seniors at North Mecklenburg High School in Huntersville, NC.
Title of Award: Ted H. Ousley Scholarship Fund **Area, Field, or Subject:** General studies. **Level of Education for which Award is Granted:** Undergraduate **Funds Available:** No specific amount.
Eligibility Requirements: Applicants must be graduating seniors at North Mecklenburg High School; must have a minimum cumulative grade point average of 2.5 (on a 4.0 scale); and must be planning to attend a postsecondary institution in North Carolina. **Application Requirements:** Applicants must submit all the required application information. **Additional Information:** Scholarship Coordinator at North Mecklenburg High School, 980-343-3840.

909 ■ FOUNDATION FOR THE CAROLINAS
217 S Tryon St.
Charlotte, NC 28202
Tel: (704)973-4500
Free: 800-973-7244
Web Site: http://www.fftc.org
To provide financial support for students from Lancaster County, SC intending to attend Winthrop University.
Title of Award: Henry DeWitt Plyler Scholarship Fund **Area, Field, or Subject:** General studies. **Level of Education for which Award is Granted:** Undergraduate **Funds Available:** $500 to $1,000. **Duration:** One year.

Eligibility Requirements: Applicants must be graduating seniors or graduates of Lancaster County public high schools; must have a 3.0 minimum cumulative grade point average (on a 4.0 scale); and must be legal residents of Lancaster County, SC. **Application Requirements:** Applicants must submit completed application form; copy of the SAR from FAFSA; official transcript(s) of high school and/or college coursework and grades for at least the last two years, including SAT/ACT scores if taken; three recommendation forms (two from teachers or other school personnel and one from employer or other non-related adult); one to two-paged typed statement expressing reason for applying for the scholarship, qualifications and the educational and career goals. **Deadline for Receipt:** February 1.

910 ■ FOUNDATION FOR THE CAROLINAS
217 S Tryon St.
Charlotte, NC 28202
Tel: (704)973-4500
Free: 800-973-7244
Web Site: http://www.fftc.org
To assist graduates of high schools in Charlotte-Mecklenburg (public or private schools) to attend the University of North Carolina at Chapel Hill. **Title of Award:** Ben Robinette Scholarship Endowment Fund **Area, Field, or Subject:** General studies. **Level of Education for which Award is Granted:** Undergraduate **Funds Available:** No specific amount. **Eligibility Requirements:** Applicants must be graduating seniors at public or private high school in Charlotte-Mecklenburg with minimum of 3.0 grade point average on 4.0 scale. **Application Requirements:** Applicants must submit all the required application information. **Additional Information:** UNC Chapel Hill Office of Scholarships and Student Aid, 919-962-8396.

911 ■ FOUNDATION FOR THE CAROLINAS
217 S Tryon St.
Charlotte, NC 28202
Tel: (704)973-4500
Free: 800-973-7244
Web Site: http://www.fftc.org
To provide financial support for graduating seniors at Providence High School in Charlotte, NC. **Title of Award:** Tacy Ana Smith Memorial Scholarship Fund **Area, Field, or Subject:** General studies. **Level of Education for which Award is Granted:** Undergraduate **Funds Available:** No specific amount. **Eligibility Requirements:** Applicants must be graduating seniors at Providence High School with a 2.5 minimum cumulative grade point average (on a 4.0 scale), planning to attend a four-year college or university. **Application Requirements:** Applicants must submit all the required application information. **Additional Information:** Scholarship Coordinator at Providence High School, 980-343-5390.

912 ■ FOUNDATION FOR THE CAROLINAS
217 S Tryon St.
Charlotte, NC 28202
Tel: (704)973-4500
Free: 800-973-7244
Web Site: http://www.fftc.org
To provide financial assistance for undergraduate students who demonstrate aptitude and career potential in arts. **Title of Award:** The Spirit Square Center for Arts and Education Scholarship Fund **Area, Field, or Subject:** General studies. **Level of Education for which Award is Granted:** Undergraduate **Funds Available:** $4,000. **Duration:** One year. **Eligibility Requirements:** Applicants must be rising college junior or senior students in good academic standing who have demonstrated talent and a declared major that indicates potential for a significant career contribution to arts. **Application Requirements:** Applicants must submit completed application form; official transcript(s) of academic coursework and grades for at least the last two years; three recommendation forms, two of which must come from individuals who are able to evaluate the applicants' aptitude and career potential in arts; one to two pages typed statement expressing 1) reasons for applying for the scholarship, 2) interest in arts, 3) educational and career goals in arts; and 4) a copy of the estimated expense budget for tuition, room and board, books, etc. **Deadline for Receipt:** March 1.

913 ■ FOUNDATION FOR THE CAROLINAS
217 S Tryon St.
Charlotte, NC 28202
Tel: (704)973-4500
Free: 800-973-7244
Web Site: http://www.fftc.org
To provide financial support for students who graduate from a public high school located in Hoke County, NC. **Title of Award:** Mary Stewart and William T. Covington, Jr. Scholarship Fund **Area, Field, or Subject:** General studies. **Level of Education for which Award is Granted:** Undergraduate **Funds Available:** No specific amount. **Eligibility Requirements:** Applicants must be legal residents of Hoke county, NC who are graduating seniors at Hoke County High School; must have 2.75 minimum cumulative grade point average (on a 4.0 scale); and must attend a four-year college or university. **Application Requirements:** Applicants must submit all the required application information and materials. **Additional Information:** Scholarship Coordinator at Hoke County High School, 910-875-2156.

914 ■ FOUNDATION FOR THE CAROLINAS
217 S Tryon St.
Charlotte, NC 28202
Tel: (704)973-4500
Free: 800-973-7244
Web Site: http://www.fftc.org
To provide scholarship assistance for ThinkCOLLEGE Program participants planning to attend Central Piedmont Community College. **Title of Award:** Jack Tate/ThinkCOLLEGE Scholarship Fund **Area, Field, or Subject:** General studies. **Level of Education for which Award is Granted:** Undergraduate **Funds Available:** $800. **Duration:** One year. **Eligibility Requirements:** Applicants must achieve 90% of the benchmark goal for attendance set for their high school during their senior year (Charlotte-Mecklenburg School System sets individual school goals each year for attendance, academics and behavior, copies are available in the school offices); must have earned a minimum 2.5 cumulative grade point average (on a 4.0 scale) at the end of the first semester of senior year; must be graduating seniors at a Communities In Schools site; and must have at least one full academic year of enrollment and participation in the ThinkCOLLEGE Program (upon graduation). **Application Requirements:** Applicants must submit completed application form; official copy of high school transcript(s), including SAT/ACT scores; two recommendation forms (one from a teacher, counselor or other school administrator and one from an employer, community leader or other non-related adult); one to two-paged typed personal statement; and a copy of Student Aid Report from Free Application for Federal Student Aid (FAFSA). **Deadline for Receipt:** March 1.

915 ■ FOUNDATION FOR THE CAROLINAS
217 S Tryon St.
Charlotte, NC 28202
Tel: (704)973-4500
Free: 800-973-7244
Web Site: http://www.fftc.org
To provide financial assistance for children of Charlotte, NC firefighters. **Title of Award:** Laramie Walden Memorial Fund **Area, Field, or Subject:** General studies. **Level of Education for which Award is Granted:** Undergraduate **Funds Available:** $500. **Duration:** One year. **Eligibility Requirements:** Applicants must be seniors scheduled to graduate in the spring of the academic year; must have 3.5 minimum cumulative weighted grade point average (on a 4.0 scale) whose parent(s) are full-time employees of the Charlotte Fire Department with at least one year of service; and must participate in state-sanctioned school sport. **Application Requirements:** Applicants must submit completed application form; official transcript(s) of academic coursework and grades for at least the last two years; three recommendation forms (two from instructor or other school administrator and one from a non-related adult in the Charlotte-Mecklenburg area such as an employer, coach, scout leader, etc.); and a one-paged typed statement expressing the reason for applying for the scholarship, qualifications, and educational and career goals.

916 ■ FOUNDATION FOR THE CAROLINAS
217 S Tryon St.
Charlotte, NC 28202

Tel: (704)973-4500

Free: 800-973-7244

Web Site: http://www.fftc.org

To provide undergraduate college and/or vocational scholarships for children of employees of Wikoff Color Corporation and its subsidiaries.

Title of Award: Fred C. Wikoff, Jr. Scholarship Fund **Area, Field, or Subject:** General studies. **Level of Education for which Award is Granted:** Undergraduate **Funds Available:** $500 to $2,000. **Duration:** One year.

Eligibility Requirements: Applicants must be children of employees (defined to include natural-born or legally-adopted dependent children and stepchildren and wards of employees). Parents or legally-appointed guardians of applicants must be full-time employees who have worked for Wikoff Color Corporation for at least two years prior to the application deadline. Applicants enrolled in high school at the time of application must have a minimum cumulative grade point average 2.5 (on a 4.0 scale). Applicants enrolled in college at the time of application must have a minimum cumulative grade point average of 2.0 (on a 4.0 scale). Applicant's age must not be over 25 as of the application deadline but a student over the age of 25 will be considered on a case to case basis if the student is permanently disabled or has some other special circumstance that requires him or her to be financially dependent upon their parents. **Application Requirements:** Applicants must submit completed application form; copy of SAR from FAFSA; official transcript(s) of high school and/or college coursework and grades for at least the last two years, including SAT/ACT scores if taken; three recommendation forms (two from teachers or other school personnel and one from an employer or other non-related adult); one to two-page typed statement expressing the reason for applying for the scholarship, qualifications and educational and career goals; and a letter from an official of Wikoff Color Corporation where parents or legally appointed guardians are employed. **Deadline for Receipt:** February 15.

917 ■ FOUNDATION FOR THE CAROLINAS

217 S Tryon St.

Charlotte, NC 28202

Tel: (704)973-4500

Free: 800-973-7244

Web Site: http://www.fftc.org

To provide financial support for the most gifted future leaders who have the capability, desire, energy, enthusiasm and determination to improve our civilization and to enhance the quality of all life cultural, civic, and ecological.

Title of Award: Mary and Elliot Wood Foundation Undergraduate Scholarship Fund **Area, Field, or Subject:** General studies. **Level of Education for which Award is Granted:** Undergraduate **Funds Available:** No specific amount.

Eligibility Requirements: Applicants must be students graduating from high schools in the districts in Guilford County, Davidson County, Randolph County, Moore County. **Application Requirements:** Applicants must submit completed application form and all other required materials for the scholarship. **Deadline for Receipt:** January 15.

918 ■ FOUNDATION FOR COMMUNITY ASSOCIATION RESEARCH

225 Reinekers Ln., Ste. 300

Alexandria, VA 22314

Tel: (703)548-8600; 888-224-4321

Fax: (703)684-1581

E-mail: foundation@caionline.org

Web Site: http://www.cairf.org

To promote positive charge for all stakeholders who live in homeowner associations by discovering future trends and opportunities; to support and conduct research; to facilitate and promote cooperation among industry partners and provide resources that help educate the public.

Title of Award: Byron Hanke Fellowships **Area, Field, or Subject:** General studies. **Level of Education for which Award is Granted:** Undergraduate **Funds Available:** Maximum amount of $4,000.

Eligibility Requirements: Applicants must be enrolled in an accredited master's, doctoral or law program in United the States of America or Canada. **Application Requirements:** Applicants must submit a completed application form and research proposal.

919 ■ FOUNDATION FOR ENHANCING COMMUNITIES

200 N Third St., PO Box 678

Harrisburg, PA 17108-0678

Tel: (717)236-5040

Fax: (717)231-4463

E-mail: dawn@tfec.org

Web Site: http://www.ghf.org

To provide financial assistance for a Dauphin County high school senior planning to attend a four-year college or university.

Title of Award: G. Thomas Balsbaugh Memorial Scholarship Fund **Area, Field, or Subject:** General studies. **Level of Education for which Award is Granted:** Undergraduate **Funds Available:** $1,000.

Eligibility Requirements: Applicants must have high academic standing and achievement; must exemplify good character; must exhibit a variety of interests and activities in both academic and personal life; and must demonstrate financial need. **Application Requirements:** Application for the scholarship should include: official academic transcript issued by school; completed personal information; completed financial statement; and personal statement describing current interests and activities as well as future goals and ambitions. **Deadline for Receipt:** March 31. **Additional Information:** Dawn Morris, Program Officer; 717-236-5040; dawn@tfec.org.

920 ■ FOUNDATION FOR ENHANCING COMMUNITIES

200 N Third St., PO Box 678

Harrisburg, PA 17108-0678

Tel: (717)236-5040

Fax: (717)231-4463

E-mail: dawn@tfec.org

Web Site: http://www.ghf.org

To provide financial support for a graduating senior of Cedar Cliff High School who attended Hillside Elementary School.

Title of Award: Robbie Baron Memorial Scholarships **Area, Field, or Subject:** General studies. **Level of Education for which Award is Granted:** Undergraduate **Funds Available:** No specific amount. **Duration:** Annual.

Eligibility Requirements: Applicant must be a graduating senior at Cedar Cliff High School and have attended Hillside Elementary. **Application Requirements:** Applicants may download the application at the TFEC web site. Applicants must submit the following required attachments: completed student application; high school transcript; completed student essay (question attached); and one personal reference letter. Applicants may return their completed application to the High School Guidance Office. **Deadline for Receipt:** April 30. **Additional Information:** Dawn Morris, Program Officer; 717-236-5040; dawn@tfec.org.

921 ■ FOUNDATION FOR ENHANCING COMMUNITIES

200 N Third St., PO Box 678

Harrisburg, PA 17108-0678

Tel: (717)236-5040

Fax: (717)231-4463

E-mail: dawn@tfec.org

Web Site: http://www.ghf.org

To promote Christian initiatives through education and athletics.

Title of Award: CODY Foundation Fund **Area, Field, or Subject:** General studies. **Level of Education for which Award is Granted:** Undergraduate **Number Awarded:** 1. **Funds Available:** $250.

Eligibility Requirements: Applicants must be graduating high school senior students from Greenwood High School, Susquenita High School, West Perry High School or Newport High School. **Application Requirements:** Applicants must complete the required attachments: completed application; official high school transcript; FAFSA student aid report; completed student essay; and two personal reference letters. **Additional Information:** Dawn Morris, Program Officer; 717-236-5040; dawn@tfec.org.

922 ■ FOUNDATION FOR ENHANCING COMMUNITIES

200 N Third St., PO Box 678

Harrisburg, PA 17108-0678

Tel: (717)236-5040

Fax: (717)231-4463

E-mail: dawn@tfec.org

Web Site: http://www.ghf.org

To assist students with their college tuition expenses.
Title of Award: Jan DiMartino Delany Memorial Scholarship Fund **Area, Field, or Subject:** General studies. **Level of Education for which Award is Granted:** Undergraduate **Funds Available:** $2,000.
Eligibility Requirements: Applicant must be a graduating senior of Cumberland Valley High School who will attend a two or four-year institution of higher learning. **Application Requirements:** Applicants must complete and submit the application to the Cumberland Valley High School Guidance Office. Include an official transcript of complete high school record, including GPA, through the first half of final year, on which the raised school seal is imprinted. On a separate sheet of paper, list your most significant extracurricular or nonacademic activities, noting work experience and community service with the dates of these activities. Attach an essay answering the question: "What are some of the obstacles that you have overcome or challenges that you have met in your life and how do they impact your future goals?" The essay should be titled, typewritten, double-spaced and must not exceed 300 words. Return the completed application and attachments to the CVHS Guidance Department. **Deadline for Receipt:** April 4. **Additional Information:** Dawn Morris, Program Officer; 717-236-5040; dawn@tfec.org.

923 ■ FOUNDATION FOR ENHANCING COMMUNITIES

200 N Third St., PO Box 678
Harrisburg, PA 17108-0678
Tel: (717)236-5040
Fax: (717)231-4463
E-mail: dawn@tfec.org
Web Site: http://www.ghf.org
To assist students with travel expenses for educational or service trips.
Title of Award: Sue and Ken Dyer Foundation Travel Scholarship Award **Area, Field, or Subject:** Travel and tourism. **Level of Education for which Award is Granted:** Undergraduate **Funds Available:** $2,000.
Eligibility Requirements: Applicants must be junior or senior students enrolled at one of the following schools: Cedar Cliff, Camp Hill, Mechanicsburg, Trinity or the Harrisburg Academy. **Application Requirements:** Applicants must complete and return the application and required attachments to the Foundation. Required attachments include: scholastic record and extracurricular activities; an essay on the topic: "The purpose of my proposed trip and what I expect to gain from this experience"; two reference letters from individuals who can speak to the quality of your character, your academic prowess and/or your likelihood of utilizing the proposed travel experience as a tool for personal growth; also include financial information. **Deadline for Receipt:** April 14. **Additional Information:** Dawn Morris, Program Officer; 717-236-5040; dawn@tfec.org.

924 ■ FOUNDATION FOR ENHANCING COMMUNITIES

200 N Third St., PO Box 678
Harrisburg, PA 17108-0678
Tel: (717)236-5040
Fax: (717)231-4463
E-mail: dawn@tfec.org
Web Site: http://www.ghf.org
To award scholarship to a graduating senior of Harrisburg High School.
Title of Award: Educational Opportunity Fund **Area, Field, or Subject:** General studies. **Level of Education for which Award is Granted:** Undergraduate **Funds Available:** $1,250.
Eligibility Requirements: Applicant must be a graduating senior of Harrisburg High School who will attend a four-year college or university. Scholarship is renewable for up to eight semesters total, providing the student maintains a minimum GPA of 2.5 on a 4.0 scale. **Application Requirements:** Applicants must complete and return the application and required attachments to the guidance counselor at Harrisburg High School. Required attachments include: scholastic record and extracurricular activities; an essay on the topic: "How I am Preparing for My Life Goals"; and a FAFSA Student Aid Report. **Deadline for Receipt:** April 5. **Additional Information:** Dawn Morris, Program Officer; 717-236-5040; dawn@tfec.org.

925 ■ FOUNDATION FOR ENHANCING COMMUNITIES

200 N Third St., PO Box 678
Harrisburg, PA 17108-0678
Tel: (717)236-5040

Fax: (717)231-4463
E-mail: dawn@tfec.org
Web Site: http://www.ghf.org
To assist students with their college expenses.
Title of Award: Friends of Megan Bolton Memorial Fund **Area, Field, or Subject:** General studies. **Level of Education for which Award is Granted:** Undergraduate **Funds Available:** No specific amount.
Eligibility Requirements: Program is open to graduating high school seniors. **Application Requirements:** Application form can be obtained online. Applicants must submit an official school transcript of their complete high school record, including GPA, through the first half of final year, on which the raised school seal is imprinted. Students should indicate evidence of meaningful leadership and positive character traits, volunteer work or involvement in community or church activities/charities that contribute to the betterment of that community or organization. Submit a resume if available, though not required, and a reference letter written by one of the contacts from the resume. Students are also asked to submit an essay (300 words or less) describing his or her idea of friendship and the significance of having close friends in their lives. **Deadline for Receipt:** April 16. **Additional Information:** Dawn Morris, Program Officer; 717-236-5040; dawn@tfec.org.

926 ■ FOUNDATION FOR ENHANCING COMMUNITIES

200 N Third St., PO Box 678
Harrisburg, PA 17108-0678
Tel: (717)236-5040
Fax: (717)231-4463
E-mail: dawn@tfec.org
Web Site: http://www.ghf.org
To assist students with tuition expenses.
Title of Award: Friendship Scholarship Fund **Area, Field, or Subject:** General studies. **Level of Education for which Award is Granted:** Undergraduate **Funds Available:** No specific amount.
Eligibility Requirements: Applicants must be graduating seniors of Harrisburg High School who will attend a four-year college or university or will further their vocational training at an accredited institution. **Application Requirements:** Applicants must complete and submit the application and attachments on or before the deadline. **Deadline for Receipt:** March 31. **Additional Information:** Dawn Morris, Program Officer; 717-236-5040; dawn@tfec.org.

927 ■ FOUNDATION FOR ENHANCING COMMUNITIES

200 N Third St., PO Box 678
Harrisburg, PA 17108-0678
Tel: (717)236-5040
Fax: (717)231-4463
E-mail: dawn@tfec.org
Web Site: http://www.ghf.org
To award scholarships for deserving students attending Cumberland Valley High School.
Title of Award: Erin L. Jenkins Memorial Scholarship Fund **Area, Field, or Subject:** General studies. **Level of Education for which Award is Granted:** Undergraduate **Funds Available:** No specific amount.
Eligibility Requirements: Students must reside in the area defined by the Cumberland Valley School District or its successor. **Application Requirements:** Students must complete and return the application and attachments to the Foundation. Students must also submit the following: official school transcript; two recommendations; and a list of most memorable community services. (Please write an essay on what meant most to you.) Application form can be obtained online. **Deadline for Receipt:** April 18. **Additional Information:** Dawn Morris, Program Officer at the above address.

928 ■ FOUNDATION FOR ENHANCING COMMUNITIES

200 N Third St., PO Box 678
Harrisburg, PA 17108-0678
Tel: (717)236-5040
Fax: (717)231-4463
E-mail: dawn@tfec.org
Web Site: http://www.ghf.org
To assist students with their college tuition expenses.
Title of Award: Sam Mizrahi Memorial Scholarships **Area, Field, or Subject:** General studies. **Level of Education for which Award is Granted:** Undergraduate **Funds Available:** No specific amount.

Eligibility Requirements: Applicants must demonstrate financial need; must have a minimum 2.5 GPA; and must have a high moral character. **Application Requirements:** Applicants must complete the attached form and any other requested supporting documents and return on or before the deadline to the guidance counselor at Northern York High School. Applicants must include an official transcript of complete high school record, including GPA, through first half of final year, on which the raised school seal is imprinted. On a separate sheet of paper, list the most significant extracurricular or nonacademic activities, noting work experience and community service with the dates of these activities. Applicants must also write a one to two-page essay on the subject "My biggest life challenge and what I learned from the experience". **Deadline for Receipt:** April 1. **Additional Information:** Dawn Morris, Program Officer at the above address.

929 ■ FOUNDATION FOR ENHANCING COMMUNITIES
200 N Third St., PO Box 678
Harrisburg, PA 17108-0678
Tel: (717)236-5040
Fax: (717)231-4463
E-mail: dawn@tfec.org
Web Site: http://www.ghf.org
To assist students with their college tuition expenses.
Title of Award: Leo F. Moro Baseball Memorial Scholarships **Area, Field, or Subject:** General studies. **Level of Education for which Award is Granted:** Undergraduate **Funds Available:** No specific amount.
Eligibility Requirements: Applicants must demonstrate financial need, sportsmanship and leadership; must demonstrate academic achievement based on GPA and SAT scores; and must have a potential for success in the sport of baseball. **Application Requirements:** Applicants must complete and return the attached form and other requested supporting documents to the foundation. Applicants must include an official transcript of complete high school record, including GPA, through the first half of final year, on which the raised school seal is imprinted. On a separate sheet of paper, list the most significant extracurricular or nonacademic activities, noting work experience and community service with the dates of these activities. Please include a photocopy of your FAFSA with your completed scholarship application. Application form can be obtained online. **Deadline for Receipt:** April 27. **Additional Information:** Dawn Morris, Program Officer at the above address.

930 ■ FOUNDATION FOR ENHANCING COMMUNITIES
200 N Third St., PO Box 678
Harrisburg, PA 17108-0678
Tel: (717)236-5040
Fax: (717)231-4463
E-mail: dawn@tfec.org
Web Site: http://www.ghf.org
To assist students with business, technical or trade school tuition expenses.
Title of Award: Ollie Rosenberg Educational Trust **Area, Field, or Subject:** General studies. **Level of Education for which Award is Granted:** Undergraduate **Funds Available:** $2,000.
Eligibility Requirements: Students must attend a state supported school in Pennsylvania; must have a job; must have a Pennsylvania student loan; and must demonstrate financial need. **Application Requirements:** Applicants must complete and submit the application and required documents to the Foundation. Required documents include official transcript of the complete high school record, including GPA, through first half of final year, on which the raised school seal is imprinted, and a 300-word essay explaining how applicant has overcome the challenges in life and how he or she will apply these lessons to his or her vocation. Applicants must list their most significant extracurricular or nonacademic activities, emphasizing work experience and community volunteer service. **Deadline for Receipt:** April 6. **Additional Information:** Dawn Morris, Program Officer at the above address.

931 ■ FOUNDATION FOR ENHANCING COMMUNITIES
200 N Third St., PO Box 678
Harrisburg, PA 17108-0678
Tel: (717)236-5040
Fax: (717)231-4463
E-mail: dawn@tfec.org

Web Site: http://www.ghf.org
To assist students with business, technical or trade school tuition expenses.
Title of Award: Ollie Rosenberg Scholarship Travel Fund **Area, Field, or Subject:** Travel and tourism. **Level of Education for which Award is Granted:** Undergraduate **Funds Available:** No specific amount.
Eligibility Requirements: Applicants must be graduating seniors who wish to travel to Israel to study traditional Jewish customs and culture. **Application Requirements:** Applicants must complete the following required attachments: completed student background sheet, verification of family income, completed student essay and two personal reference letters. One letter should be from your Guidance Counselor and the other letter should be from an individual who can speak to your ability to successfully complete your studies, such as a teacher, employer, or mentor. Your letter of reference should not be from a family member. **Deadline for Receipt:** April 11. **Additional Information:** Dawn Morris, Program Officer at the above address.

932 ■ FOUNDATION FOR ENHANCING COMMUNITIES
200 N Third St., PO Box 678
Harrisburg, PA 17108-0678
Tel: (717)236-5040
Fax: (717)231-4463
E-mail: dawn@tfec.org
Web Site: http://www.ghf.org
To provide aid for needy and deserving students who otherwise would not have the financial means to obtain a four-year college education.
Title of Award: J. Ward Sleichter and Frances F. Sleichter Memorial Scholarship Fund **Area, Field, or Subject:** General studies. **Level of Education for which Award is Granted:** Undergraduate **Funds Available:** No specific amount.
Eligibility Requirements: Applicants must be full-time students who maintain a B average or equivalent. Students must reside in the area defined by the Shippensburg Area School District, or its successor. **Application Requirements:** Applicants must complete the following required attachments: application; official school transcript; two recommendations (one from the student's guidance counselor and one from a teacher who can discuss the student's personal characteristics such as motivation, character, ability, and potential); and FAFSA Student Aid Report (make sure to include the cover letter of the report, which will indicate the student's Estimated Family contribution). **Deadline for Receipt:** April 6. **Additional Information:** Erica Frontino, Guidance Counselor, Shippensburg Area High School, 317 N. Morris St., Shippensburg, PA 17257.

933 ■ FOUNDATION FOR ENHANCING COMMUNITIES
200 N Third St., PO Box 678
Harrisburg, PA 17108-0678
Tel: (717)236-5040
Fax: (717)231-4463
E-mail: dawn@tfec.org
Web Site: http://www.ghf.org
To provide assistance for female seniors of Chambersburg Area Senior High School.
Title of Award: Soroptimist International of Chambersburg Scholarship Fund **Area, Field, or Subject:** General studies. **Level of Education for which Award is Granted:** Undergraduate **Funds Available:** $500.
Eligibility Requirements: Recipients must be accepted at an accredited college or university at the time the awards are made. **Application Requirements:** Applicants must complete the required attachments. Required attachments include: application; two letters of recommendation (one from your guidance counselor, containing your GPA, course of study and general character assessment and the other from one of your teacher containing a general character assessment of you as a person and a student); FAFSA Student Aid Report; a paragraph of approximately 150 words answering the question "Why I Have Chosen to Continue My Education". **Deadline for Receipt:** April 18. **Additional Information:** Chris Butler, Guidance Counselor, Chambersburg Area Senior High School, 511 S Sixth High School, Chambersburg, PA 17201.

934 ■ FOUNDATION FOR ENHANCING COMMUNITIES
200 N Third St., PO Box 678
Harrisburg, PA 17108-0678

Tel: (717)236-5040
Fax: (717)231-4463
E-mail: dawn@tfec.org
Web Site: http://www.ghf.org
To assist students with their college tuition expenses.
Title of Award: Jack and Edna May Yost Scholarship Fund **Area, Field, or Subject:** General studies. **Level of Education for which Award is Granted:** Undergraduate **Funds Available:** No specific amount.
Eligibility Requirements: Applicants must be graduating seniors of a Dauphin or Cumberland County High School who will attend a two or four-year accredited college; must have a minimum SAT score of 1,000; must have an overall average between C+ and B-; must be full-time students planning to attend a two or four-year accredited college; must be graduates of any Dauphin or Cumberland County high school; and must be able to demonstrate past or current community service and willingness to work to attain future goals. **Application Requirements:** Applicants must complete and submit the following attachments: official transcript of complete high school record, including GPA, through the first half of final year, on which the raised school seal is imprinted; a FAFSA Student Aid Report; and list of most significant extracurricular activities, noting work experience and community service with the dates of these activities. **Deadline for Receipt:** April 14. **Additional Information:** Dawn Morris, Program Officer at the above address.

935 ■ FOUNDATION OF THE FEDERAL BAR ASSOCIATION
1220 N Fillmore St., Ste. 444
Arlington, VA 22201
Tel: (571)481-9100
Web Site: http://www.fedbar.org
To provide financial assistance for high school students continuing higher education.
Title of Award: Foundation of the Federal Bar Association Public Service Scholarships **Area, Field, or Subject:** General studies. **Level of Education for which Award is Granted:** Undergraduate **Funds Available:** $5,000.
Eligibility Requirements: Applicants must be graduating high school seniors planning to attend a four-year college or university; must be students currently enrolled full-time at a four-year college or university; or graduate students enrolled full-time in a graduate or professional degree program. At least one of the applicant's parents or guardians must be a current federal government attorney or federal judge and member of the Federal Bar Association. **Application Requirements:** Applicants must submit completed application along with most recent transcripts (official copy); letter of acceptance from their college, university or graduate/professional school for new enrollees; and an essay. **Deadline for Receipt:** March 3.

936 ■ JOE FRANCIS HAIRCARE SCHOLARSHIP FOUNDATION
PO Box 50625
Minneapolis, MN 55405
Tel: (651)769-1757
E-mail: mklarson@qwest.net
Web Site: http://www.joefrancis.com/jfh
To provide support to deserving students who want to pursue their professional training in hairstyling.
Title of Award: Joe Francis Haircare Scholarships **Area, Field, or Subject:** Cosmetology. **Level of Education for which Award is Granted:** Undergraduate **Funds Available:** $1,000. **Duration:** One year.
Eligibility Requirements: Applicant must be actively enrolled in cosmetology school, or planning to enroll in school. **Application Requirements:** Applicant must complete the application form available online; must have a letter of recommendation from an employer, instructor, counselor, or someone qualified to offer testimony of his/her character. Application form and other supporting documents must be sent to Joe Francis Haircare Scholarship Foundation Program, PO Box 50625, Minneapolis, MN 55405. **Deadline for Receipt:** June 1.

937 ■ FREEDOM ALLIANCE
22570 Market Court, Ste. 240
Dulles, VA 20166
Tel: (703)444-7940
Free: 800-475-6620
Fax: (703)444-9893

Web Site: http://www.freedomalliance.org
To support the children of American heroes.
Title of Award: Freedom Alliance Scholarships **Area, Field, or Subject:** General studies. **Level of Education for which Award is Granted:** Undergraduate **Funds Available:** No specific amount.
Eligibility Requirements: Applicant must be a dependent child of an active service member killed or disabled as the result of an operational mission/training accident; a senior high school, high school graduate or enrolled in an institution of higher learning; and must be 26 years old and below. **Application Requirements:** Applicants must complete online application and forward a copy of Government Issued Photo Identification (drivers License, ID Card); must submit a certificate of death or rating letter from the Veterans Administration disability; an essay; scholastic record; and a photo (photo of parents are optional). **Additional Information:** Freedom of Alliance will mail scholarship check to the school.

938 ■ FUNERAL SERVICE FOUNDATION
13625 Bishop's Dr.
Brookfield, WI 53005
Tel: 877-402-5900
Fax: (262)789-6977
E-mail: info@funeralservicefoundation.org
Web Site: http://www.funeralservicefoundation.org
To provide financial assistance for mortuary science school students.
Title of Award: Joseph E. Hagan Memorial Scholarships **Area, Field, or Subject:** Mortuary science. **Level of Education for which Award is Granted:** Undergraduate **Number Awarded:** 2. **Funds Available:** $1,000. **Duration:** One year.
Eligibility Requirements: Applicants must be full-time students who will be enrolled or have been accepted for enrollment in the Fall semester in programs accredited by the American Board of Funeral Service Education. **Application Requirements:** Applicants must submit all the required application information.

939 ■ FUNERAL SERVICE FOUNDATION
13625 Bishop's Dr.
Brookfield, WI 53005
Tel: 877-402-5900
Fax: (262)789-6977
E-mail: info@funeralservicefoundation.org
Web Site: http://www.funeralservicefoundation.org
To provide financial assistance for top-scoring mortuary science students via the Key Memories scholarship essay contest.
Title of Award: Key Memories Scholarships **Area, Field, or Subject:** Mortuary science. **Level of Education for which Award is Granted:** Undergraduate **Number Awarded:** 5. **Funds Available:** $1,000. **Duration:** One year.
Eligibility Requirements: Applicants must be students who are enrolled or accepted for enrollment in a mortuary science school accredited by the American Board of Funeral Service Education. **Application Requirements:** Applicants must submit an essay and must complete application.

940 ■ GAY AND LESBIAN BUSINESS ASSOCIATION OF SANTA BARBARA
PO Box 90907
Santa Barbara, CA 93190
E-mail: glba@prideguide.net
Web Site: http://www.glbasb.com
To provide financial assistance to those students who are in need.
Title of Award: Carl Joseph Adelhardt Memorial Scholarships **Area, Field, or Subject:** General Studies. **Level of Education for which Award is Granted:** Undergraduate **Funds Available:** No specific amount.
Eligibility Requirements: Applicants must have the contribution to the Santa Barbara gay and lesbian community, career goals and financial need. **Application Requirements:** Applicants must submit the following: completion of an application, including statements of community involvement and financial need; an autobiography/personal statement; a copy of current college and/or high school transcript of records; two letters of recommendation: one from a community member and the other from a teacher or faculty member at your institution. **Deadline for Receipt:** July 30. **Additional Information:** GLBA Santa Barbara at the above address.

941 ■ GAY AND LESBIAN BUSINESS ASSOCIATION OF SANTA BARBARA
PO Box 90907
Santa Barbara, CA 93190
E-mail: glba@prideguide.net
Web Site: http://www.glbasb.com
To provide exceptional and ongoing support to those GLBA students.
Title of Award: Raffin Gathercole Scholarships **Area, Field, or Subject:** General Studies. **Level of Education for which Award is Granted:** Undergraduate **Funds Available:** No specific amount.
Eligibility Requirements: Applicants must have the contribution to the Santa Barbara gay and lesbian community, career goals and financial need. **Application Requirements:** Applicants must submit the following: completion of an application, including statements of community involvement and financial need; an autobiography/personal statement; a copy of current college and/or high school transcript of records; two letters of recommendation: one from a community member and the other from a teacher or faculty member at your institution. **Deadline for Receipt:** July 30. **Additional Information:** GLBA Santa Barbara at the above address

942 ■ GAY AND LESBIAN BUSINESS ASSOCIATION OF SANTA BARBARA
PO Box 90907
Santa Barbara, CA 93190
E-mail: glba@prideguide.net
Web Site: http://www.glbasb.com
To provide financial assistance to students who are in need.
Title of Award: Stephen Logan Memorial Scholarships **Area, Field, or Subject:** General studies. **Level of Education for which Award is Granted:** Undergraduate **Funds Available:** No specific amount.
Eligibility Requirements: Applicants must have the contribution to the Santa Barbara gay and lesbian community, career goals and financial need. **Application Requirements:** Applicants must submit the following: completion of an application, including statements of community involvement and financial need; an autobiography/personal statement; a copy of current college and/or high school transcript of records; two letters of recommendation: one from a community member and the other from a teacher or faculty member at your institution. **Deadline for Receipt:** July 30. **Additional Information:** GLBA Santa Barbara at the above address.

943 ■ GEMOLOGICAL INSTITUTE OF AMERICA
The Robert Mouawad Campus
5345 Amada Dr.
Carlsbad, CA 92008
Tel: (760)603-4031
Free: 800-421-7250
E-mail: financialaid@gia.edu
Web Site: http://www.gia.edu
To provide educational assistance to students.
Title of Award: Peter Hess Scholarships **Area, Field, or Subject:** General studies. **Level of Education for which Award is Granted:** Undergraduate **Number Awarded:** 1. **Funds Available:** $1000.
Eligibility Requirements: Applicant must be U.S. citizen and permanent resident; at least 17 years old; must be a member, related to a member or planning to join California Jewelers Association; have a high school diploma or GED equivalency; currently employed or planning to enter in the jewelry industry; applying for any On Campus or Distance Education course or program; past recipient of GIA scholarship within last five years are not eligible. **Application Requirements:** Applicant must complete the GIA Scholarship application (available at the website), with a letter of recommendation from a person in the jewelry industry. Send application and supporting documents to: Gemological Institute of America, Office of Student Financial Assistance, MS 7 The Robert Mouawad Campus 5345 Armada Drive Carlsbad, CA 92008. **Deadline for Receipt:** June 15 - October 15. **Additional Information:** Financial aid representative, 800-421-7250 x-4175, financialaid@gia.edu.

944 ■ GEMOLOGICAL INSTITUTE OF AMERICA
The Robert Mouawad Campus
5345 Amada Dr.
Carlsbad, CA 92008
Tel: (760)603-4031
Free: 800-421-7250
E-mail: financialaid@gia.edu
Web Site: http://www.gia.edu
To provide educational assistance to students.
Title of Award: Lone Star GIA Associate and Alumni Scholarships **Area, Field, or Subject:** General studies. **Level of Education for which Award is Granted:** Undergraduate **Number Awarded:** 1. **Funds Available:** $500.
Eligibility Requirements: Applicant must be U.S. citizen and permanent resident; at least 17 years old; have a high school diploma or GED equivalency; currently employed or planning to enter in the jewelry industry; applying for any On Campus, Distance Education, or Lab course or program; past recipient of GIA scholarship within last five years are not eligible. **Application Requirements:** Applicant must complete the GIA Scholarship application (available at the website), with a letter of recommendation from a person in the jewelry industry. Send application and supporting documents to: Gemological Institute of America, Office of Student Financial Assistance, MS 7 The Robert Mouawad Campus 5345 Armada Drive Carlsbad, CA 92008. **Deadline for Receipt:** June 15 - October 15. **Additional Information:** Financial aid representative, 800-421-7250 x-4175, financialaid@gia.edu.

945 ■ GEMOLOGICAL INSTITUTE OF AMERICA
The Robert Mouawad Campus
5345 Amada Dr.
Carlsbad, CA 92008
Tel: (760)603-4031
Free: 800-421-7250
E-mail: financialaid@gia.edu
Web Site: http://www.gia.edu
To provide educational assistance to students.
Title of Award: Eunice Miles Scholarships **Area, Field, or Subject:** General studies. **Level of Education for which Award is Granted:** Undergraduate **Number Awarded:** 2. **Funds Available:** $500.
Eligibility Requirements: Applicant must be U.S. citizen and permanent resident; at least 17 years old; have a high school diploma or GED equivalency; currently employed or planning to enter in the jewelry industry; applying for any On Campus School or Distance Education course or program; past recipient of GIA scholarship within last five years are not eligible. **Application Requirements:** Applicant must complete the GIA Scholarship application (available at the website), with a letter of recommendation from a person in the jewelry industry. Send application and supporting documents to: Gemological Institute of America, Office of Student Financial Assistance, MS 7 The Robert Mouawad Campus 5345 Armada Drive Carlsbad, CA 92008. **Deadline for Receipt:** June 15 October 15. **Additional Information:** Financial aid representative, 800-421-7250 x-4175, financialaid@gia.edu.

946 ■ GEMOLOGICAL INSTITUTE OF AMERICA
The Robert Mouawad Campus
5345 Amada Dr.
Carlsbad, CA 92008
Tel: (760)603-4031
Free: 800-421-7250
E-mail: financialaid@gia.edu
Web Site: http://www.gia.edu
To provide educational assistance to students.
Title of Award: North Texas GIA Alumni Association Scholarships **Area, Field, or Subject:** General studies. **Level of Education for which Award is Granted:** Undergraduate **Number Awarded:** 1. **Funds Available:** $1500.
Eligibility Requirements: Applicant must be U.S. citizen and a resident of Texas; at least 17 years old; have a high school diploma or GED equivalency; currently employed or planning to enter in the jewelry industry; applying for any On Campus, Distance Education, or Lab course or program; past recipient of GIA scholarship within last five years are not eligible. **Application Requirements:** Applicant must complete the GIA Scholarship application (available at the website), with a letter of recommendation from a person in the jewelry industry. Send application and supporting documents to: Gemological Institute of America, Office of Student Financial Assistance, MS 7 The Robert Mouawad Campus 5345 Armada Drive Carlsbad, CA 92008. **Deadline for Receipt:** June 15 October 15. **Additional Information:** Financial aid representative, 800-421-7250 x-4175, financialaid@gia.edu.

947 ■ GEMOLOGICAL INSTITUTE OF AMERICA

The Robert Mouawad Campus
5345 Amada Dr.
Carlsbad, CA 92008
Tel: (760)603-4031
Free: 800-421-7250
E-mail: financialaid@gia.edu
Web Site: http://www.gia.edu
To provide educational assistance to students.

Title of Award: Robert B. Westover Scholarships **Area, Field, or Subject:** General studies. **Level of Education for which Award is Granted:** Undergraduate **Number Awarded:** 1. **Funds Available:** $1000. **Eligibility Requirements:** Applicant must be U.S. citizen and permanent resident; at least 17 years old; must be a member, related to a member or planning to join California Jewelers Association; have a high school diploma or GED equivalency; currently employed or planning to enter in the jewelry industry; applying for any On Campus or Distance Education course or program; past recipient of GIA scholarship within last five years are not eligible. **Application Requirements:** Applicant must complete the GIA Scholarship application (available at the website), with a letter of recommendation from a person in the jewelry industry. Send application and supporting documents to: Gemological Institute of America, Office of Student Financial Assistance, MS 7 The Robert Mouawad Campus 5345 Armada Drive Carlsbad, CA 92008. **Deadline for Receipt:** June 15 - October 15. **Additional Information:** Financial aid representative, 800-421-7250 x-4175, financialaid@gia.edu.

948 ■ GEMOLOGICAL INSTITUTE OF AMERICA

The Robert Mouawad Campus
5345 Amada Dr.
Carlsbad, CA 92008
Tel: (760)603-4031
Free: 800-421-7250
E-mail: financialaid@gia.edu
Web Site: http://www.gia.edu
To provide educational assistance to students.

Title of Award: Milton Wolf Scholarships **Area, Field, or Subject:** General studies. **Level of Education for which Award is Granted:** Undergraduate **Number Awarded:** 1. **Funds Available:** $500. **Eligibility Requirements:** Applicant must be U.S. citizen and a legal resident of California; at least 17 years old; have a high school diploma or GED equivalency; currently employed or planning to enter in the jewelry industry; applying for any On Campus educational course or program taken at the GIA Carlsbad campus; past recipient of GIA scholarship within last five years are not eligible. **Application Requirements:** Applicant must complete the GIA Scholarship application (available at the website), with a letter of recommendation from a person in the jewelry industry. Send application and supporting documents to: Gemological Institute of America, Office of Student Financial Assistance, MS 7 The Robert Mouawad Campus 5345 Armada Drive Carlsbad, CA 92008. **Deadline for Receipt:** June 15 - October 15. **Additional Information:** Financial aid representative, 800-421-7250 x-4175, financialaid@gia.edu.

949 ■ GEMOLOGICAL INSTITUTE OF AMERICA

The Robert Mouawad Campus
5345 Amada Dr.
Carlsbad, CA 92008
Tel: (760)603-4031
Free: 800-421-7250
E-mail: financialaid@gia.edu
Web Site: http://www.gia.edu
To provide educational assistance to students.

Title of Award: Zale Corporation Scholarships **Area, Field, or Subject:** General studies. **Level of Education for which Award is Granted:** Undergraduate **Number Awarded:** 1. **Funds Available:** $5000. **Eligibility Requirements:** Applicant must be U.S. citizen and permanent resident; at least 17 years old; have a high school diploma or GED equivalency; currently employed or planning to enter in the jewelry industry; applying for any On Campus or Distance Education course or program; past recipient of GIA scholarship within last five years are not eligible. **Application Requirements:** Applicant must complete the GIA Scholarship application (available at the website), with a letter of recommendation from a person in the jewelry industry. Send application and

supporting documents to: Gemological Institute of America, Office of Student Financial Assistance, MS 7 The Robert Mouawad Campus 5345 Armada Drive Carlsbad, CA 92008. **Deadline for Receipt:** June 15 October 15. **Additional Information:** Financial aid representative, 800-421-7250 x-4175, financialaid@gia.edu.

950 ■ GERBER FOUNDATION

4747 W 48th St., Ste. 153
Fremont, MI 49412-8119
Tel: (231)924-3175
Fax: (231)924-7906
E-mail: tgf@ncresa.org
Web Site: http://www.gerberfoundation.org
To assist graduating students from one of the five school districts in Newaygo County, Michigan.

Title of Award: Gerber Foundation Merit Scholarships **Area, Field, or Subject:** General studies. **Level of Education for which Award is Granted:** Undergraduate **Funds Available:** $2,000. **Eligibility Requirements:** Students must have a GPA of 3.70 or below. **Application Requirements:** Applications may be submitted online or by sending the application forms to the Foundation. Application forms can be obtained from the high school counselor's office or from the Foundation office. Applicants must also submit the following: educational report from Counselor (Form S-1); high school transcript; 1st Recommendation (Form S-2 or letter); 2nd Recommendation (Form S-2 or letter); personal information and financial summary (Form S-3); and personal essay (typed, 500-1000 word essay). **Deadline for Receipt:** February 28. **Additional Information:** Gerber Foundation at the above address.

951 ■ GERBER FOUNDATION

4747 W 48th St., Ste. 153
Fremont, MI 49412-8119
Tel: (231)924-3175
Fax: (231)924-7906
E-mail: tgf@ncresa.org
Web Site: http://www.gerberfoundation.org
To assist graduating students from one of the five school districts in Newaygo County, Michigan.

Title of Award: Daniel Gerber, Sr. Medallion Scholarships **Area, Field, or Subject:** General studies. **Level of Education for which Award is Granted:** Undergraduate **Funds Available:** $8,000. **Eligibility Requirements:** Students must have a GPA of 3.71 or higher. **Application Requirements:** Applications may be submitted online or by sending the application forms to the Foundation. Application forms can be obtained from the high school counselor's office or from the Foundation office. Applicants must also submit the following: educational report from Counselor (Form S-1); high school transcript; 1st Recommendation (Form S-2 or letter); 2nd Recommendation (Form S-2 or letter); personal information and financial summary (Form S-3); and personal essay (typed, 500-1000 word essay). **Deadline for Receipt:** July 1. **Additional Information:** Gerber foundation at the above address.

952 ■ GERMAN ACADEMIC EXCHANGE SERVICE

871 United Nations Plz.
New York, NY 10017
Tel: (212)758-3223
Fax: (212)755-5780
E-mail: daadny@daad.org
Web Site: http://www.daad.org
To support undergraduate US and Canadian students interested in studying, doing research, or completing an internship in Germany.

Title of Award: DAAD Undergraduate Scholarship Program **Area, Field, or Subject:** General studies. **Level of Education for which Award is Granted:** Undergraduate **Funds Available:** No specific amount. **Eligibility Requirements:** Applicant must currently be a second or third year student. Students are eligible with outstanding academic records and personal integrity, as evinced by both their grades and letters of recommendation; must be a U.S. or Canadian citizen or permanent residents; has interest in contemporary German and European affairs; full-time students in an undergraduate degree-granting program at an accredited North American college or university; younger than 32 before the grant starts. **Application Requirements:** Applicants must submit: the DAAD language evaluation form with signature, supplemental documents and materials, 3 copies; resume; Project Proposal (approximately 3 pages); recommendation letter from major professors; any of: Acceptance into Study Abroad Program, Exchange Program, letter by mentor or invitation from a German university; transcripts; Language Evaluation Certificate. Application and other supporting document must be sent to: German Academic Exchange Service/DAAD New York, 871 United Nations Plaza, New York, NY 10017-USA. **Deadline for Receipt:** January 31.

953 ■ GLEANER LIFE INSURANCE ASSOCIATION

5200 West Us Hwy. 223
Adrian, MI 49221-7984
Tel: 800-992-1894
Fax: (517)265-6191
E-mail: membercare@gleanerlife.org
Web Site: http://www.gleanerlife.org
To strengthen the brotherhood.
Title of Award: Gleaner Life Insurance Scholarship Foundation **Area, Field, or Subject:** General studies. **Level of Education for which Award is Granted:** Undergraduate **Number Awarded:** 1. **Funds Available:** No specific amount.
Eligibility Requirements: An applicant must be senior high school student or graduate; he or she is planning to attend the college of education; an applicant must be full time which requires ten or more credit hours. **Application Requirements:** Applicant must fill out the application form and present any information and/or reasons for applying; applicant should attach an official transcript of high school records (applicants already graduated from high school are also required to submit high school transcript or attach an official transcript of college record if applicable); applicant must submit a list of scholastic awards won (local, county, district, state or national); result of an aptitude test at junior or senior level; evaluation of student (leadership, perseverance, prediction of post-high school success). **Deadline for Receipt:** April 1.

954 ■ GODPARENTS FOR TANZANIA

PO Box 20221
Roanoke, VA 24018
E-mail: tellmemore@godparents4tz.org
Web Site: http://www.agpsf.org
To provide financial assistance for projects that are intended to help educate young people.
Title of Award: Godparents for Tanzania Scholarships **Area, Field, or Subject:** General studies. **Level of Education for which Award is Granted:** Undergraduate **Funds Available:** No specific amount.
Eligibility Requirements: Applicants must be Tanzanian citizens from the Kilimanjaro or Karatu areas of Tanzania; must demonstrate a satisfactory academic record at current level of education; must be attending school in Tanzania; must be studying on the secondary or first degree university level; and must agree to work in Tanzania for five years following graduation. **Application Requirements:** Applicants must submit completed application along with a letter of reference from a non-related adult, preferably an educator or clergy person.

955 ■ GOLDEN KEY INTERNATIONAL HONOUR SOCIETY

621 Noeth Ave. NE., Ste. C-100
Atlanta, GA 30308
Tel: (404)377-2400
Free: 800-377-2401
Fax: (678)420-6757
E-mail: memberservices@goldenkey.org
Web Site: http://www.goldenkey.org
To support a Golden Key new member with their education.
Title of Award: Golden Key International Honour Society New Graduate Member Scholarships **Area, Field, or Subject:** General studies. **Level of Education for which Award is Granted:** Undergraduate **Number Awarded:** 5. **Funds Available:** $1000.
Eligibility Requirements: Applicant must be a new U.S. Golden Key graduate student members; have accepted Golden Key membership during the 2007-2008 academic year; and enrolled in classes in a degree-granting program. **Application Requirements:** Applicants must complete the online application form. **Additional Information:** A Golden Key Member ID is required to complete the application. **Deadline for Receipt:** May 15 and December 14. **Additional Information:** awards@goldenkey.org.

956 ■ GOLDEN KEY INTERNATIONAL HONOUR SOCIETY

621 Noeth Ave. NE., Ste. C-100
Atlanta, GA 30308
Tel: (404)377-2400
Free: 800-377-2401
Fax: (678)420-6757
E-mail: memberservices@goldenkey.org
Web Site: http://www.goldenkey.org
To assist members who participate in a study abroad program.
Title of Award: Golden Key International Honour Society Study Abroad Scholarships **Area, Field, or Subject:** General studies. **Level of Education for which Award is Granted:** Undergraduate **Number Awarded:** 10. **Funds Available:** $1000. **Duration:** One year.
Eligibility Requirements: Applicants must be undergraduate members currently enrolled in a study abroad program; or will be enrolled the academic year immediately following the granting of the award. **Application Requirements:** Applicants must register scholarship application online. Print the cover page from the online registration and use it as a cover for the entire application and attach a description of the planned academic program (maximum of 5 pages), a one-page statement signed by a professor, and a current comprehensive official academic transcript. **Deadline for Receipt:** April 15. **Additional Information:** awards@goldenkey.org.

957 ■ GOLDEN KEY INTERNATIONAL HONOUR SOCIETY

621 Noeth Ave. NE., Ste. C-100
Atlanta, GA 30308
Tel: (404)377-2400
Free: 800-377-2401
Fax: (678)420-6757
E-mail: memberservices@goldenkey.org
Web Site: http://www.goldenkey.org
To assist members with their thesis research or presenting their research at professional conferences or student research symposia.
Title of Award: Golden Key International Honour Society Undergraduate Research Grants **Area, Field, or Subject:** General studies. **Level of Education for which Award is Granted:** Undergraduate **Number Awarded:** 10. **Funds Available:** $500. **Duration:** One year.
Eligibility Requirements: Applicants must be undergraduate student members. **Application Requirements:** Applicants must register scholarship applications online. Print the cover page from the online registration and use it as a cover for the entire application and attach a description of the proposed research presentation, a summarized budget of overall cost of attending the conference, and a current comprehensive official academic transcript. **Deadline for Receipt:** April 15 and October 15. **Additional Information:** awards@goldenkey.org.

958 ■ GOLDEN KEY INTERNATIONAL HONOUR SOCIETY

621 Noeth Ave. NE., Ste. C-100
Atlanta, GA 30308
Tel: (404)377-2400
Free: 800-377-2401
Fax: (678)420-6757
E-mail: memberservices@goldenkey.org
Web Site: http://www.goldenkey.org
To provide opportunities for members to explore some of the most beautiful natural and cultural environments in the world.
Title of Award: ProWorld Study Abroad Scholarships **Area, Field, or Subject:** General studies. **Level of Education for which Award is Granted:** Undergraduate **Number Awarded:** 3. **Funds Available:** $1000.
Eligibility Requirements: Applicant must be a member in the Australia, Canada or the United States; currently enrolled in a full-time or part-time undergraduate course of study at an accredited four year college or university; and accepted to a ProWorld semester long program. **Application Requirements:** Applicants must submit a ProWorld Scholarship Application to scholarships@myproworld.org. **Deadline for Receipt:** April 30.

959 ■ GONJA ASSOCIATION OF NORTH AMERICA

PO Box 403
Lithonia, GA 30058
Web Site: http://www.geocities.com/mumuni/index.htm
To assist Gonjaland to reach its fullest potential by utilizing its vast fertile land in the field of Agriculture, and Industry. To assist the people of

Gonjaland to participate in educational, political, social and economic well-being of the traditional area and the nation in general. **Title of Award:** GANA Scholarship Program **Area, Field, or Subject:** General studies. **Level of Education for which Award is Granted:** Undergraduate **Number Awarded:** Six. **Funds Available:** $100,00. **Duration:** Award is for not more than two years.

Eligibility Requirements: Applicant must be the first generation (example illiterate parenthood) Jr./Snr. High School including sixth form; must maintain an overall average grade of 80% and above; must originate from Gonjaland; must exhibit financial need. **Application Requirements:** Applicant must complete the application form available on the website address; must sent a short essay and recommendation letter from the current/last teacher. Application and other materials must be sent to: GANA, Po Box 403, Lithonia, GA, 30058.

960 ■ GOODMAN AND COMPANY, LLP

One Commercial Pl., Ste. 800
Norfolk, VA 23510
Tel: (757)624-5100; (866)455-3261
Fax: (757)624-5233
Web Site: http://www.goodmanco.com
To help promising students pursue public accounting as a profession.
Title of Award: Goodman and Company, LLP Annual Scholarships **Area, Field, or Subject:** Accounting. **Level of Education for which Award is Granted:** Undergraduate **Number Awarded:** 1. **Funds Available:** $2,500.

Eligibility Requirements: Applicant must be a U.S. citizen; a junior or senior accounting major; currently enrolled in an accredited Virginia college or university with the intent to take the CPA Exam; and have a minimum overall and accounting GPA of 3.0 or higher. **Application Requirements:** Applicants must submit a completed scholarship application together with the essay; letter of recommendation from a faculty member; a current resume; and recent official transcript reflecting GPA; application must be typed or printed. **Deadline for Receipt:** January 10.

961 ■ GOVERNMENT FINANCE OFFICERS ASSOCIATION OF UNITED STATES AND CANADA

203 N LaSalle St., Ste. 2700
Chicago, IL 60601-1210
Tel: (312)977-9700
Fax: (312)977-4806
Web Site: http://www.gfoa.org
To recognize outstanding performance by minority students preparing for careers in state and local government finance.
Title of Award: Minorities in Government Finance Scholarships **Area, Field, or Subject:** Finance. **Level of Education for which Award is Granted:** Graduate, Undergraduate **Funds Available:** $5,000.

Eligibility Requirements: Applicants must be current full- or part-time upper-division undergraduate or graduate students in public administration, accounting, finance, political science, economics or business administration (with a specific focus on government or nonprofit management); must belong to one of the following groups (as defined by the U.S. Census Bureau): Black or African American, American Indian or Alaska Native, Asian, Native Hawaiian or other Pacific islander, Hispanic or Latino; must be citizens or permanent residents of the United States or Canada; must be recommended by academic advisor, the dean of the graduate program (graduate students) or department chair (undergraduate students); must be students who have not received scholarships administered by the Government Finance Officers Association of the United States and Canada. **Application Requirements:** Applicants must submit application form; statement of proposed state and local government finance career plan and if applicable, plan of graduate study; undergraduate and graduate grade transcripts; resume; and academic advisor's, department chair's or dean's letter of recommendation; and other letters of recommendation (optional). **Deadline for Receipt:** February 29.

962 ■ GRAND HAVEN AREA COMMUNITY FOUNDATION

1 S. Harbor Dr.
Grand Haven, MI 49417
Tel: (616)842-6378
Fax: (616)842-9518
E-mail: bpost@ghacf.org

Web Site: http://www.ghacf.org
To improve and enhance the quality of life in the Tri-Cities area by serving as a leader, catalyst and resource for philanthropy; to strive for community improvement through strategic grantmaking in such fields as arts, education, health, environment, youth, social services and other human needs.
Title of Award: Charles A. Bassett Endowed Memorial Scholarship Fund **Area, Field, or Subject:** General studies. **Level of Education for which Award is Granted:** Undergraduate **Funds Available:** No specific amount.

Eligibility Requirements: Applicants must be graduating seniors who have played on the tennis team. **Application Requirements:** Applicants must submit: completed application form; current high school or college transcript; Student Aid Report (SAR) from the Free Application for Federal Student Aid (FAFSA); and letter of recommendation. **Deadline for Receipt:** March 7. **Additional Information:** 616-842-6378.

963 ■ GRAND HAVEN AREA COMMUNITY FOUNDATION

1 S. Harbor Dr.
Grand Haven, MI 49417
Tel: (616)842-6378
Fax: (616)842-9518
E-mail: bpost@ghacf.org
Web Site: http://www.ghacf.org
To assist men and women in the Tri-Cities in returning to school to further their education after a period of working.
Title of Award: James W. Jr.and Jane T. Brown Scholarship Fund **Area, Field, or Subject:** General studies. **Level of Education for which Award is Granted:** Undergraduate **Funds Available:** No specific amount.

Eligibility Requirements: Applicants must be over the age of 21. **Application Requirements:** Applicants must submit: completed application form; current high school or college transcript; Student Aid Report (SAR) from the Free Application for Federal Student Aid (FAFSA), unless applying for scholarships that do not consider financial need; and letter of recommendation. **Deadline for Receipt:** March 7. **Additional Information:** 616-842-6378.

964 ■ GRAND HAVEN AREA COMMUNITY FOUNDATION

1 S. Harbor Dr.
Grand Haven, MI 49417
Tel: (616)842-6378
Fax: (616)842-9518
E-mail: bpost@ghacf.org
Web Site: http://www.ghacf.org
To improve and enhance the quality of life in the Tri-Cities area by serving as a leader, catalyst and resource for philanthropy; to strive for community improvement through strategic grantmaking in such fields as arts, education, health, environment, youth, social services and other human needs.
Title of Award: Geri Coccodrilli Culinary Scholarship Fund **Area, Field, or Subject:** Culinary Arts. **Level of Education for which Award is Granted:** Undergraduate **Funds Available:** No specific amount.

Eligibility Requirements: Applicants must be graduating high school seniors from the Tri-Cities area and Fruitport High School who wish to pursue studies in the Culinary Arts. **Application Requirements:** Applicants must submit: completed application form; current high school or college transcript; Student Aid Report (SAR) from the Free Application for Federal Student Aid (FAFSA); and letter of recommendation. **Deadline for Receipt:** March 7. **Additional Information:** 616-842-6378.

965 ■ GRAND HAVEN AREA COMMUNITY FOUNDATION

1 S. Harbor Dr.
Grand Haven, MI 49417
Tel: (616)842-6378
Fax: (616)842-9518
E-mail: bpost@ghacf.org
Web Site: http://www.ghacf.org
To improve and enhance the quality of life in the Tri-Cities area by serving as a leader, catalyst and resource for philanthropy; to strive for community improvement through strategic grantmaking in such fields as arts, education, health, environment, youth, social services and other human needs; to assist high school graduating seniors of northwest Ottawa County to pursue a college education.
Title of Award: John and Victory E. Frantz Scholarship Fund **Area, Field, or Subject:** General studies. **Level of Education for which Award is

Granted: Undergraduate **Funds Available:** No specific amount.
Eligibility Requirements: Applicants must be high school graduating seniors of northwest Ottawa County. **Application Requirements:** Applicants must submit: completed application form; current high school or college transcript; Student Aid Report (SAR) from the Free Application for Federal Student Aid (FAFSA), unless applying for scholarships that do not consider financial need; and letter of recommendation. **Deadline for Receipt:** March 7. **Additional Information:** 616-842-6378.

966 ■ GRAND HAVEN AREA COMMUNITY FOUNDATION
1 S. Harbor Dr.
Grand Haven, MI 49417
Tel: (616)842-6378
Fax: (616)842-9518
E-mail: bpost@ghacf.org
Web Site: http://www.ghacf.org
To provide educational assistance to a student planning to pursue an advanced degree in Library science.
Title of Award: Friends of Loutit District Library Scholarships Fund **Area, Field, or Subject:** Library science. **Level of Education for which Award is Granted:** Undergraduate **Funds Available:** No specific amount.
Eligibility Requirements: Applicants must be enrolled in an ALA-accredited graduate program in Library Science. **Application Requirements:** Applicants must submit: completed application form; current high school or college transcript; Student Aid Report (SAR) from the Free Application for Federal Student Aid (FAFSA), unless applying for scholarships that do not consider financial need; and letter of recommendation. **Deadline for Receipt:** March 7. **Additional Information:** 616-842-6378.

967 ■ GRAND HAVEN AREA COMMUNITY FOUNDATION
1 S. Harbor Dr.
Grand Haven, MI 49417
Tel: (616)842-6378
Fax: (616)842-9518
E-mail: bpost@ghacf.org
Web Site: http://www.ghacf.org
To improve and enhance the quality of life in the Tri-Cities area by serving as a leader, catalyst and resource for philanthropy; to strive for community improvement through strategic grantmaking in such fields as arts, education, health, environment, youth, social services and other human needs.
Title of Award: Tim Gifford Scholarship Fund **Area, Field, or Subject:** General studies. **Level of Education for which Award is Granted:** Undergraduate **Funds Available:** No specific amount.
Eligibility Requirements: Applicants must be graduates of Spring Lake High School; must have been SLHS students for three semesters immediately prior to graduation and must have attended for at least three years; must plan to attend Amherest College within 30 months of high school graduation. **Application Requirements:** Applicants must submit: completed application form; current high school or college transcript; Student Aid Report (SAR) from the Free Application for Federal Student Aid (FAFSA), unless applying for scholarships that do not consider financial need; and letter of recommendation. **Deadline for Receipt:** March 7. **Additional Information:** 616-842-6378.

968 ■ GRAND HAVEN AREA COMMUNITY FOUNDATION
1 S. Harbor Dr.
Grand Haven, MI 49417
Tel: (616)842-6378
Fax: (616)842-9518
E-mail: bpost@ghacf.org
Web Site: http://www.ghacf.org
To improve and enhance the quality of life in the Tri-Cities area by serving as a leader, catalyst and resource for philanthropy; to strive for community improvement through strategic grantmaking in such fields as arts, education, health, environment, youth, social services and other human needs.
Title of Award: Barbara and Nicole Heicox Foreign Travel and Study Scholarships Fund **Area, Field, or Subject:** Travel and tourism. **Level of Education for which Award is Granted:** Undergraduate **Funds Available:** No specific amount.
Eligibility Requirements: Applicants must be junior, high school and/or college students wishing to pursue educational opportunities in foreign countries. **Application Requirements:** Applicants must submit: completed application form; current high school or college transcript;

Student Aid Report (SAR) from the Free Application for Federal Student Aid (FAFSA), unless applying for scholarships that do not consider financial need; and letter of recommendation. **Deadline for Receipt:** March 7. **Additional Information:** 616-842-6378.

969 ■ GRAND HAVEN AREA COMMUNITY FOUNDATION
1 S. Harbor Dr.
Grand Haven, MI 49417
Tel: (616)842-6378
Fax: (616)842-9518
E-mail: bpost@ghacf.org
Web Site: http://www.ghacf.org
To improve and enhance the quality of life in the Tri-Cities area by serving as a leader, catalyst and resource for philanthropy; to strive for community improvement through strategic grantmaking in such fields as arts, education, health, environment, youth, social services and other human needs.
Title of Award: Michael Herman Memorial Scholarship Fund **Area, Field, or Subject:** General studies. **Level of Education for which Award is Granted:** Undergraduate **Funds Available:** No specific amount.
Eligibility Requirements: Applicants must be soccer players and coaches of younger students who are interested in learning soccer; must be current high school graduates of any Tri-Cities area public or private high school intending to pursue degree or certification at any two-or four-year accredited college, university, vocational or technical school; first consideration shall be given to students who played on a soccer team and wish to continue playing in college on an intramural, club or college team. **Application Requirements:** Applicants must submit: completed application form; current high school or college transcript; Student Aid Report (SAR) from the Free Application for Federal Student Aid (FAFSA), unless applying for scholarships that do not consider financial need; and letter of recommendation. **Deadline for Receipt:** March 7. **Additional Information:** 616-842-6378.

970 ■ GRAND HAVEN AREA COMMUNITY FOUNDATION
1 S. Harbor Dr.
Grand Haven, MI 49417
Tel: (616)842-6378
Fax: (616)842-9518
E-mail: bpost@ghacf.org
Web Site: http://www.ghacf.org
To improve and enhance the quality of life in the Tri-Cities area by serving as a leader, catalyst and resource for philanthropy; to strive for community improvement through strategic grantmaking in such fields as arts, education, health, environment, youth, social services and other human needs.
Title of Award: Hoffman Family Scholarships Fund **Area, Field, or Subject:** General studies. **Level of Education for which Award is Granted:** Undergraduate **Funds Available:** No specific amount.
Eligibility Requirements: Applicants must be graduating high school seniors at Grand Haven, Spring Lake or Fruitport high schools; must have a 3.0 GPA; special consideration will be given to an individual who is a member of the first generation in their family to attend college. **Application Requirements:** Applicants must submit: completed application form; current high school or college transcript; Student Aid Report (SAR) from the Free Application for Federal Student Aid (FAFSA), unless applying for scholarships that do not consider financial need; and letter of recommendation. **Deadline for Receipt:** March 7. **Additional Information:** 616-842-6378.

971 ■ GRAND HAVEN AREA COMMUNITY FOUNDATION
1 S. Harbor Dr.
Grand Haven, MI 49417
Tel: (616)842-6378
Fax: (616)842-9518
E-mail: bpost@ghacf.org
Web Site: http://www.ghacf.org
To provide educational financial assistance to a graduating senior from Central High School.
Title of Award: Seth Koehler Central High School Scholarship Fund **Area, Field, or Subject:** General studies. **Level of Education for which Award is Granted:** Undergraduate **Funds Available:** No specific amount.
Eligibility Requirements: Applicants must be graduating seniors from Central High School; must plan to attend any two-to-four year college,

university, vocational or technical school. **Application Requirements:** Applicants must submit: completed application form; current high school or college transcript; Student Aid Report (SAR) from the Free Application for Federal Student Aid (FAFSA), unless applying for scholarships that do not consider financial need; and letter of recommendation. **Deadline for Receipt:** March 7. **Additional Information:** 616-842-6378.

972 ■ GRAND HAVEN AREA COMMUNITY FOUNDATION
1 S. Harbor Dr.
Grand Haven, MI 49417
Tel: (616)842-6378
Fax: (616)842-9518
E-mail: bpost@ghacf.org
Web Site: http://www.ghacf.org
To improve and enhance the quality of life in the Tri-Cities area by serving as a leader, catalyst and resource for philanthropy; to strive for community improvement through strategic grantmaking in such fields as arts, education, health, environment, youth, social services and other human needs. **Title of Award:** Jack W. Leatherman Family Scholarship Fund **Area, Field, or Subject:** General studies. **Level of Education for which Award is Granted:** Undergraduate **Funds Available:** No specific amount.
Eligibility Requirements: Applicants must be Grand Haven area public school graduates. **Application Requirements:** Applicants must submit: completed application form; current high school or college transcript; Student Aid Report (SAR) from the Free Application for Federal Student Aid (FAFSA), unless applying for scholarships that do not consider financial need; and letter of recommendation. **Deadline for Receipt:** March 7. **Additional Information:** 616-842-6378.

973 ■ GRAND HAVEN AREA COMMUNITY FOUNDATION
1 S. Harbor Dr.
Grand Haven, MI 49417
Tel: (616)842-6378
Fax: (616)842-9518
E-mail: bpost@ghacf.org
Web Site: http://www.ghacf.org
To improve and enhance the quality of life in the Tri-Cities area by serving as a leader, catalyst and resource for philanthropy; to strive for community improvement through strategic grantmaking in such fields as arts, education, health, environment, youth, social services and other human needs. **Title of Award:** Pat and John MacTavish Scholarship Fund **Area, Field, or Subject:** Science. **Level of Education for which Award is Granted:** Undergraduate **Funds Available:** No specific amount.
Eligibility Requirements: Applicants must be high school or college students seeking to pursue any of the following areas of study: math, chemistry, geology, technical writing, physics or computer science. **Application Requirements:** Applicants must submit: completed application form; current high school or college transcript; Student Aid Report (SAR) from the Free Application for Federal Student Aid (FAFSA), unless applying for scholarships that do not consider financial need; and letter of recommendation. **Deadline for Receipt:** March 7. **Additional Information:** 616-842-6378.

974 ■ GRAND HAVEN AREA COMMUNITY FOUNDATION
1 S. Harbor Dr.
Grand Haven, MI 49417
Tel: (616)842-6378
Fax: (616)842-9518
E-mail: bpost@ghacf.org
Web Site: http://www.ghacf.org
To provide assistance to a Grand Haven High School graduating senior student.
Title of Award: Kyle Moreland Memorial Endowment Scholarships Fund **Area, Field, or Subject:** General studies. **Level of Education for which Award is Granted:** Undergraduate **Funds Available:** No specific amount.
Eligibility Requirements: Applicants must be Grand Haven High School graduating seniors planning to attend a two or four-year college degree program; must be active in their Christian faith community; must have participated on the high school golf or tennis team; must have a 3.0 GPA or above. Scholarship is also open to current graduates of Spring Lake High School and/or Western Christian Michigan High School. **Application**

Requirements: Applicants must submit: completed application form; current high school or college transcript; Student Aid Report (SAR) from the Free Application for Federal Student Aid (FAFSA), unless applying for scholarships that do not consider financial need; and letter of recommendation. **Deadline for Receipt:** March 7. **Additional Information:** 616-842-6378.

975 ■ GRAND HAVEN AREA COMMUNITY FOUNDATION
1 S. Harbor Dr.
Grand Haven, MI 49417
Tel: (616)842-6378
Fax: (616)842-9518
E-mail: bpost@ghacf.org
Web Site: http://www.ghacf.org
To improve and enhance the quality of life in the Tri-Cities area by serving as a leader, catalyst and resource for philanthropy; to strive for community improvement through strategic grantmaking in such fields as arts, education, health, environment, youth, social services and other human needs. **Title of Award:** P.E.O. Chapter Scholarship Fund **Area, Field, or Subject:** General studies. **Level of Education for which Award is Granted:** Undergraduate **Funds Available:** No specific amount.
Eligibility Requirements: Applicants must be graduating female students or non-traditional students who graduated from any Tri-Cities area public or private high school; must plan to pursue a degree or certification at any two or four-year accredited college, university, vocational or technical school. **Application Requirements:** Applicants must submit: completed application form; current high school or college transcript; Student Aid Report (SAR) from the Free Application for Federal Student Aid (FAFSA), unless applying for scholarships that do not consider financial need; and letter of recommendation. **Deadline for Receipt:** March 7. **Additional Information:** 616-842-6378.

976 ■ GRAND HAVEN AREA COMMUNITY FOUNDATION
1 S. Harbor Dr.
Grand Haven, MI 49417
Tel: (616)842-6378
Fax: (616)842-9518
E-mail: bpost@ghacf.org
Web Site: http://www.ghacf.org
To provide scholarship assistance to a Grand Haven High School student. **Title of Award:** Jacob L. Reinecke Memorial Scholarship Fund **Area, Field, or Subject:** General studies. **Level of Education for which Award is Granted:** Undergraduate **Funds Available:** No specific amount.
Eligibility Requirements: Applicants must be Grand Haven High School graduating seniors planning to attend a two-to-four year college, university or trade school; consideration will be given to male students who participated in high school athletics, specifically basketball or baseball; must have a 3.0 GPA or above. **Application Requirements:** Applicants must submit: completed application form; current high school or college transcript; Student Aid Report (SAR) from the Free Application for Federal Student Aid (FAFSA), unless applying for scholarships that do not consider financial need; and letter of recommendation. **Deadline for Receipt:** March 7. **Additional Information:** 616-842-6378.

977 ■ GRAND HAVEN AREA COMMUNITY FOUNDATION
1 S. Harbor Dr.
Grand Haven, MI 49417
Tel: (616)842-6378
Fax: (616)842-9518
E-mail: bpost@ghacf.org
Web Site: http://www.ghacf.org
To improve and enhance the quality of life in the Tri-Cities area by serving as a leader, catalyst and resource for philanthropy; to strive for community improvement through strategic grantmaking in such fields as arts, education, health, environment, youth, social services and other human needs. **Title of Award:** Daniel L. Reiss Memorial Scholarship Fund **Area, Field, or Subject:** General studies. **Level of Education for which Award is Granted:** Undergraduate **Funds Available:** No specific amount.
Eligibility Requirements: Applicants must be graduating Grand Haven High School students who have at least a 3.8 GPA; must plan to pursue studies at Grand Valley State University or Western Michigan University. **Application Requirements:** Applicants must submit: completed applica-

tion form; current high school or college transcript; Student Aid Report (SAR) from the Free Application for Federal Student Aid (FAFSA), unless applying for scholarships that do not consider financial need; and letter of recommendation. **Deadline for Receipt:** March 7. **Additional Information:** 616-842-6378.

978 ■ GRAND HAVEN AREA COMMUNITY FOUNDATION

1 S. Harbor Dr.
Grand Haven, MI 49417
Tel: (616)842-6378
Fax: (616)842-9518
E-mail: bpost@ghacf.org
Web Site: http://www.ghacf.org

To improve and enhance the quality of life in the Tri-Cities area by serving as a leader, catalyst and resource for philanthropy; to strive for community improvement through strategic grantmaking in such fields as arts, education, health, environment, youth, social services and other human needs. **Title of Award:** Harold and Eleonor Ringelberg Scholarship Fund **Area, Field, or Subject:** General studies. **Level of Education for which Award is Granted:** Undergraduate **Funds Available:** No specific amount.

Eligibility Requirements: Applicants must be Grand Haven High School graduating seniors with a minimum 3.8 GPA; must plan to pursue a college degree at Michigan State University; must have attended Grand Haven Christian School prior to high school. **Application Requirements:** Applicants must submit: completed application form; current high school or college transcript; Student Aid Report (SAR) from the Free Application for Federal Student Aid (FAFSA), unless applying for scholarships that do not consider financial need; and letter of recommendation. **Deadline for Receipt:** March 7. **Additional Information:** 616-842-6378.

979 ■ GRAND HAVEN AREA COMMUNITY FOUNDATION

1 S. Harbor Dr.
Grand Haven, MI 49417
Tel: (616)842-6378
Fax: (616)842-9518
E-mail: bpost@ghacf.org
Web Site: http://www.ghacf.org

To improve and enhance the quality of life in the Tri-Cities area by serving as a leader, catalyst and resource for philanthropy; to strive for community improvement through strategic grantmaking in such fields as arts, education, health, environment, youth, social services and other human needs. **Title of Award:** Charles and Eleonor Rycenga Education Scholarships Fund **Area, Field, or Subject:** General studies. **Level of Education for which Award is Granted:** Undergraduate **Funds Available:** No specific amount.

Eligibility Requirements: Applicants must be graduating seniors of Grand Haven, Spring Lake or Western Christian High School; must have the desire to continue their education at an accredited four-year college, junior college, trade school or apprenticeship, preferably in Michigan. **Application Requirements:** Applicants must submit: completed application form; current high school or college transcript; Student Aid Report (SAR) from the Free Application for Federal Student Aid (FAFSA), unless applying for scholarships that do not consider financial need; and letter of recommendation. **Deadline for Receipt:** March 7. **Additional Information:** 616-842-6378.

980 ■ GRAND HAVEN AREA COMMUNITY FOUNDATION

1 S. Harbor Dr.
Grand Haven, MI 49417
Tel: (616)842-6378
Fax: (616)842-9518
E-mail: bpost@ghacf.org
Web Site: http://www.ghacf.org

To improve and enhance the quality of life in the Tri-Cities area by serving as a leader, catalyst and resource for philanthropy; to strive for community improvement through strategic grantmaking in such fields as the arts, education, health, environment, youth, social services and other human needs. **Title of Award:** Millicent M. Schaffner Endowed Memorial Scholarship **Area, Field, or Subject:** General studies. **Level of Education for which Award is Granted:** Undergraduate **Funds Available:** No specific amount.

Eligibility Requirements: Applicants must be female students who have a strong motivation to continue their education at an accredited four-year college. **Application Requirements:** Applicants must submit: completed application form; current high school or college transcript; Student Aid Report (SAR) from the Free Application for Federal Student Aid (FAFSA), unless applying for scholarships that do not consider financial need; and letter of recommendation. **Deadline for Receipt:** March 7. **Additional Information:** 616-842-6378.

981 ■ GRAND HAVEN AREA COMMUNITY FOUNDATION

1 S. Harbor Dr.
Grand Haven, MI 49417
Tel: (616)842-6378
Fax: (616)842-9518
E-mail: bpost@ghacf.org
Web Site: http://www.ghacf.org

To improve and enhance the quality of life in the Tri-Cities area by serving as a leader, catalyst and resource for philanthropy; to strive for community improvement through strategic grantmaking in such fields as arts, education, health, environment, youth, social services and other human needs. **Title of Award:** David and Ginny Schultz Family Scholarship Fund **Area, Field, or Subject:** General studies. **Level of Education for which Award is Granted:** Undergraduate **Funds Available:** No specific amount.

Eligibility Requirements: Applicants must be graduating seniors who wish to continue their education at a four-year college, junior college, trade school or apprenticeship. **Application Requirements:** Applicants must submit: completed application form; current high school or college transcript; Student Aid Report (SAR) from the Free Application for Federal Student Aid (FAFSA), unless applying for scholarships that do not consider financial need; and letter of recommendation. **Deadline for Receipt:** March 7. **Additional Information:** 616-842-6378.

982 ■ GRAND HAVEN AREA COMMUNITY FOUNDATION

1 S. Harbor Dr.
Grand Haven, MI 49417
Tel: (616)842-6378
Fax: (616)842-9518
E-mail: bpost@ghacf.org
Web Site: http://www.ghacf.org

To improve and enhance the quality of life in the Tri-Cities area by serving as a leader, catalyst and resource for philanthropy; to strive for community improvement through strategic grantmaking in such fields as arts, education, health, environment, youth, social services and other human needs. **Title of Award:** Ken and Sandy Sharkey Family Scholarship Fund **Area, Field, or Subject:** General studies. **Level of Education for which Award is Granted:** Undergraduate **Funds Available:** No specific amount.

Eligibility Requirements: Applicants must be graduating seniors from Grand Haven High School who demonstrate civic responsibility and plan to be involved in improving their community in the future. **Application Requirements:** Applicants must submit: completed application form; current high school or college transcript; Student Aid Report (SAR) from the Free Application for Federal Student Aid (FAFSA), unless applying for scholarships that do not consider financial need; and letter of recommendation. **Deadline for Receipt:** March 7. **Additional Information:** 616-842-6378.

983 ■ GRAND HAVEN AREA COMMUNITY FOUNDATION

1 S. Harbor Dr.
Grand Haven, MI 49417
Tel: (616)842-6378
Fax: (616)842-9518
E-mail: bpost@ghacf.org
Web Site: http://www.ghacf.org

To improve and enhance the quality of life in the Tri-Cities area by serving as a leader, catalyst and resource for philanthropy; to strive for community improvement through strategic grantmaking in such fields as arts, education, health, environment, youth, social services and other human needs. **Title of Award:** H. Wayne Van Agtmael Cosmetology Scholarship Fund **Area, Field, or Subject:** Cosmetology. **Level of Education for which Award is Granted:** Undergraduate **Funds Available:** No specific amount.

Eligibility Requirements: Applicants must be students planning to attend a Cosmetology School. **Application Requirements:** Applicants must submit: completed application form; current high school or college transcript; Student Aid Report (SAR) from the Free Application for Federal Student Aid (FAFSA), unless applying for scholarships that do not consider financial need; and letter of recommendation. **Deadline for Receipt:** March 7. **Additional Information:** 616-842-6378.

984 ■ GRAND HAVEN AREA COMMUNITY FOUNDATION
1 S. Harbor Dr.
Grand Haven, MI 49417
Tel: (616)842-6378
Fax: (616)842-9518
E-mail: bpost@ghacf.org
Web Site: http://www.ghacf.org
To improve and enhance the quality of life in the Tri-Cities area by serving as a leader, catalyst and resource for philanthropy; to strive for community improvement through strategic grantmaking in such fields as the arts, education, health, environment, youth, social services and other human needs.
Title of Award: Woman's Club of Grand Haven Scholarships Fund **Area, Field, or Subject:** General studies. **Level of Education for which Award is Granted:** Undergraduate **Funds Available:** No specific amount.
Eligibility Requirements: Applicants may be traditional and non-traditional students. Traditional students must be graduating from a Tri-Cities area high school with a minimum 2.5 GPA; non-traditional must be female, ages 21 or older. **Application Requirements:** Applicants must submit: completed application form; current high school or college transcript; Student Aid Report (SAR) from the Free Application for Federal Student Aid (FAFSA), unless applying for scholarships that do not consider financial need; and letter of recommendation. **Deadline for Receipt:** March 7. **Additional Information:** 616-842-6378.

985 ■ GRAND HAVEN AREA COMMUNITY FOUNDATION
1 S. Harbor Dr.
Grand Haven, MI 49417
Tel: (616)842-6378
Fax: (616)842-9518
E-mail: bpost@ghacf.org
Web Site: http://www.ghacf.org
To provide assistance to students to further their education.
Title of Award: Zenko Family Scholarship Fund **Level of Education for which Award is Granted:** Undergraduate **Funds Available:** No specific amount.
Eligibility Requirements: Applicants must be graduates of Spring Lake, Grand Haven or Fruitport High School. **Application Requirements:** Applicants must submit: completed application form; current high school or college transcript; Student Aid Report (SAR) from the Free Application for Federal Student Aid (FAFSA), unless applying for scholarships that do not consider financial need; and letter of recommendation. **Deadline for Receipt:** March 7. **Additional Information:** 616-842-6378.

986 ■ GRAND RAPIDS COMMUNITY FOUNDATION
161 Ottawa Ave. NW
Ste. 209-C Waters Bldg.
Grand Rapids, MI 49503
Tel: (616)454-1751
Fax: (616)454-6455
E-mail: grfound@grfoundation.org
Web Site: http://www.grfoundation.org
To provide financial support to those students who are in need.
Title of Award: Altrusa International of Grand Rapids Scholarships **Area, Field, or Subject:** General Studies. **Level of Education for which Award is Granted:** Undergraduate **Funds Available:** No specific amount.
Eligibility Requirements: Applicants must be students from Kent, Allegan, Iona, Ottawa, Montcalm or Muskegon counties. Applicants must be entering or returning to college after sitting out of school for two years. Applicants must demonstrate financial need. **Application Requirements:** Applicants must check the available website for the required materials. **Additional Information:** Grand Rapids Community Foundation at the above address

987 ■ GRAND RAPIDS COMMUNITY FOUNDATION
161 Ottawa Ave. NW
Ste. 209-C Waters Bldg.
Grand Rapids, MI 49503
Tel: (616)454-1751
Fax: (616)454-6455
E-mail: grfound@grfoundation.org
Web Site: http://www.grfoundation.org
To provide financial support to those students who are in need.
Title of Award: Geraldine Geistert Boss Scholarships **Area, Field, or Subject:** General Studies. **Level of Education for which Award is Granted:** Undergraduate **Funds Available:** No specific amount.
Eligibility Requirements: Applicants must be full-time students with financial need residing in Kent County (5 year minimum) and pursuing an undergraduate degree at an accredited college in Michigan. Applicants must have a minimum of 3.0 GPA. **Application Requirements:** Applicants must check the available website for the required materials. **Additional Information:** Grand Rapids Community Foundation at the above address

988 ■ GRAND RAPIDS COMMUNITY FOUNDATION
161 Ottawa Ave. NW
Ste. 209-C Waters Bldg.
Grand Rapids, MI 49503
Tel: (616)454-1751
Fax: (616)454-6455
E-mail: grfound@grfoundation.org
Web Site: http://www.grfoundation.org
To provide financial assistance to those students who are in need.
Title of Award: Orrie & Dorothy Cassada Scholarships **Area, Field, or Subject:** General Studies. **Level of Education for which Award is Granted:** Undergraduate **Funds Available:** No specific amount.
Eligibility Requirements: Applicants must be residents of Kent County who will be attending Aquinas, Calvin, Cornerstone, Davenport, GRCC, GVSU or Kendall. Applicants must have financial need and a 3.0 minimum GPA. **Application Requirements:** Applicants must check the available website for more information. **Additional Information:** Grand Rapids Community Foundation at the above address

989 ■ GRAND RAPIDS COMMUNITY FOUNDATION
161 Ottawa Ave. NW
Ste. 209-C Waters Bldg.
Grand Rapids, MI 49503
Tel: (616)454-1751
Fax: (616)454-6455
E-mail: grfound@grfoundation.org
Web Site: http://www.grfoundation.org
To provide financial assistance to those students who are in need.
Title of Award: Thomas D. Coffield Scholarships **Area, Field, or Subject:** General Studies. **Level of Education for which Award is Granted:** Undergraduate **Funds Available:** No specific amount.
Eligibility Requirements: Applicants must be senior students at Central High School who will be entering a two or four-year accredited college or university; must have a 2.5 minimum GPA; must have demonstrated financial need. **Application Requirements:** Applicants must check the available website for more information. **Additional Information:** Grand Rapids Community Foundation at the above address

990 ■ GRAND RAPIDS COMMUNITY FOUNDATION
161 Ottawa Ave. NW
Ste. 209-C Waters Bldg.
Grand Rapids, MI 49503
Tel: (616)454-1751
Fax: (616)454-6455
E-mail: grfound@grfoundation.org
Web Site: http://www.grfoundation.org
To provide financial assistance to those students who are in need.
Title of Award: Achille & Irene Despres, William & Andre Scholarships **Area, Field, or Subject:** General Studies. **Level of Education for which Award is Granted:** Undergraduate **Funds Available:** No specific amount.
Eligibility Requirements: Applicants must be of Mexican heritage; must be Kent or Ottawa residents; must be enrolled in an accredited college or university; must have demonstrated financial need; must have a cumula-

tive GPA of at least 2.75. **Application Requirements:** Applicants must check the available website for the required materials. **Additional Information:** Grand Rapids Community Foundation at the above address

991 ■ GRAND RAPIDS COMMUNITY FOUNDATION

161 Ottawa Ave. NW
Ste. 209-C Waters Bldg.
Grand Rapids, MI 49503
Tel: (616)454-1751
Fax: (616)454-6455
E-mail: grfound@grfoundation.org
Web Site: http://www.grfoundation.org
To provide financial support to those students who are in need.
Title of Award: Virginia Valk Fehsenfeld Scholarships **Area, Field, or Subject:** General Studies. **Level of Education for which Award is Granted:** Undergraduate **Funds Available:** No specific amount.
Eligibility Requirements: Applicants must be full-time undergraduate students pursuing a degree in Dietetics, Nutrition, Education or General Human Services. Applicants must be residents of Kent County, must have financial need and a 3.4 GPA is required. **Application Requirements:** Applicants must check the available website for the required materials. **Additional Information:** Grand Rapids Community Foundation at the above address

992 ■ GRAND RAPIDS COMMUNITY FOUNDATION

161 Ottawa Ave. NW
Ste. 209-C Waters Bldg.
Grand Rapids, MI 49503
Tel: (616)454-1751
Fax: (616)454-6455
E-mail: grfound@grfoundation.org
Web Site: http://www.grfoundation.org
To provide financial assistance to those students who are in need.
Title of Award: Melbourne & Alice E. Frontjes Scholarships **Area, Field, or Subject:** General Studies. **Level of Education for which Award is Granted:** Undergraduate **Funds Available:** No specific amount.
Eligibility Requirements: Applicants must be Kent County residents who are pursuing an undergraduate degree at Central Michigan University, Western Michigan University , GRCC, University of Michigan or Michigan State University. Applicants must have demonstrated financial need and have a minimum of 2.75 GPA. **Application Requirements:** Applicants must check the available website for the required materials. **Additional Information:** Grand Rapids Community Foundation at the above address

993 ■ GRAND RAPIDS COMMUNITY FOUNDATION

161 Ottawa Ave. NW
Ste. 209-C Waters Bldg.
Grand Rapids, MI 49503
Tel: (616)454-1751
Fax: (616)454-6455
E-mail: grfound@grfoundation.org
Web Site: http://www.grfoundation.org
To provide financial support to those students who are in need.
Title of Award: Carolyn Gallmeyer Scholarships **Area, Field, or Subject:** General Studies. **Level of Education for which Award is Granted:** Undergraduate **Funds Available:** No specific amount.
Eligibility Requirements: Applicants must be Kent County residents who are pursuing an undergraduate degree at any U.S college. **Application Requirements:** Applicants must check the available website for the required materials. **Additional Information:** Grand Rapids Community Foundation at the above address

994 ■ GRAND RAPIDS COMMUNITY FOUNDATION

161 Ottawa Ave. NW
Ste. 209-C Waters Bldg.
Grand Rapids, MI 49503
Tel: (616)454-1751
Fax: (616)454-6455
E-mail: grfound@grfoundation.org
Web Site: http://www.grfoundation.org
To provide financial assistance to those students who are in need.
Title of Award: Grand Rapids Scholarship Association **Area, Field, or Subject:** General Studies. **Level of Education for which Award is Granted:** Undergraduate **Funds Available:** No specific amount.

Eligibility Requirements: Applicants must be Kent County residents who will be attending Aquinas, Calvin, Cornerstone, Davenport, GRCC, GVSU or Kendall. Applicants must have financial need and must have a 3.0 minimum GPA. **Application Requirements:** Applicants must check the available website for the required materials. **Additional Information:** Grand Rapids Community Foundation at the above address

995 ■ GRAND RAPIDS COMMUNITY FOUNDATION

161 Ottawa Ave. NW
Ste. 209-C Waters Bldg.
Grand Rapids, MI 49503
Tel: (616)454-1751
Fax: (616)454-6455
E-mail: grfound@grfoundation.org
Web Site: http://www.grfoundation.org
To provide financial support to those students who are in need.
Title of Award: Guy D. & Mary Edith Halladay Graduate Scholarships **Area, Field, or Subject:** General Studies. **Level of Education for which Award is Granted:** Undergraduate **Funds Available:** No specific amount.
Eligibility Requirements: Applicants must be residents of Kent County and must be graduate level students at a Michigan college. Applicants must have demonstrated financial need and must have a minimum of 3.0 GPA. **Application Requirements:** Applicants must check the available website for more information. **Additional Information:** Grand Rapids Community Foundation at the above address

996 ■ GRAND RAPIDS COMMUNITY FOUNDATION

161 Ottawa Ave. NW
Ste. 209-C Waters Bldg.
Grand Rapids, MI 49503
Tel: (616)454-1751
Fax: (616)454-6455
E-mail: grfound@grfoundation.org
Web Site: http://www.grfoundation.org
To provide financial support to those students who are in need.
Title of Award: Harry and Lucille Brown Scholarships **Area, Field, or Subject:** General Studies. **Level of Education for which Award is Granted:** Undergraduate **Funds Available:** No specific amount.
Eligibility Requirements: Applicants must be residents of Kent County; must have financial need; must be pursuing an undergraduate degree at any accredited college in the U.S; must have a minimum of 3.3 GPA. **Application Requirements:** Applicants must check the available website for the required materials. **Additional Information:** Grand Rapids Community Foundation at the above address

997 ■ GRAND RAPIDS COMMUNITY FOUNDATION

161 Ottawa Ave. NW
Ste. 209-C Waters Bldg.
Grand Rapids, MI 49503
Tel: (616)454-1751
Fax: (616)454-6455
E-mail: grfound@grfoundation.org
Web Site: http://www.grfoundation.org
To provide financial assistance to those students who are in need.
Title of Award: Donald & Florence Hunting Scholarships **Area, Field, or Subject:** General Studies. **Level of Education for which Award is Granted:** Undergraduate **Funds Available:** No specific amount.
Eligibility Requirements: Applicants must be senior students at Rockford High School who will be entering college in the fall. Applicants must have demonstrated financial need. **Application Requirements:** Applicants must check the available website for more information. **Additional Information:** Grand Rapids Community Foundation at the above address

998 ■ GRAND RAPIDS COMMUNITY FOUNDATION

161 Ottawa Ave. NW
Ste. 209-C Waters Bldg.
Grand Rapids, MI 49503
Tel: (616)454-1751
Fax: (616)454-6455
E-mail: grfound@grfoundation.org
Web Site: http://www.grfoundation.org

To provide financial assistance to those students who are in need.
Title of Award: Jack Family Scholarships **Area, Field, or Subject:** General Studies. **Level of Education for which Award is Granted:** Undergraduate **Funds Available:** No specific amount.
Eligibility Requirements: Applicants must be undergraduate students residing in Kent County who demonstrate financial need. Applicants must have a minimum of 3.3 GPA. **Application Requirements:** Applicants must check the available website for more information. **Additional Information:** Grand Rapids Community Foundation at the above address

999 ■ GRAND RAPIDS COMMUNITY FOUNDATION

161 Ottawa Ave. NW
Ste. 209-C Waters Bldg.
Grand Rapids, MI 49503
Tel: (616)454-1751
Fax: (616)454-6455
E-mail: grfound@grfoundation.org
Web Site: http://www.grfoundation.org
To provide financial support to those deserving students.
Title of Award: Camilla C. Johnson Scholarships **Area, Field, or Subject:** General Studies. **Level of Education for which Award is Granted:** Undergraduate **Funds Available:** No specific amount.
Eligibility Requirements: Applicants must be senior students at Union High School entering college full-time in the fall. Applicants must have financial need. Applicants must have a cumulative of 2.6 GPA. **Application Requirements:** Applicants must check the available website for the required materials. **Additional Information:** Grand Rapids Community Foundation at the above address

1000 ■ GRAND RAPIDS COMMUNITY FOUNDATION

161 Ottawa Ave. NW
Ste. 209-C Waters Bldg.
Grand Rapids, MI 49503
Tel: (616)454-1751
Fax: (616)454-6455
E-mail: grfound@grfoundation.org
Web Site: http://www.grfoundation.org
To provide financial assistance to those students who are in need.
Title of Award: Lavina Laible Scholarships **Area, Field, or Subject:** General Studies. **Level of Education for which Award is Granted:** Undergraduate **Funds Available:** No specific amount.
Eligibility Requirements: Applicants must be female students in their third year or above of undergraduate studies at the University of Michigan. Applicants must be Kent County residents. Applicants must have financial need. Applicants must have a minimum of 3.0 GPA. **Application Requirements:** Applicants must check the available website for the required materials. **Additional Information:** Grand Rapids Community Foundation at the above address

1001 ■ GRAND RAPIDS COMMUNITY FOUNDATION

161 Ottawa Ave. NW
Ste. 209-C Waters Bldg.
Grand Rapids, MI 49503
Tel: (616)454-1751
Fax: (616)454-6455
E-mail: grfound@grfoundation.org
Web Site: http://www.grfoundation.org
To provide financial assistance to those students who are in need.
Title of Award: Stephen Lankester Scholarships **Area, Field, or Subject:** General Studies. **Level of Education for which Award is Granted:** Undergraduate **Funds Available:** No specific amount.
Eligibility Requirements: Applicants must be Kent County residents; must be attending an undergraduate program at a Michigan college; must have financial need; must have a minimum of 3.0 GPA. **Application Requirements:** Applicants must check the available website for more information. **Additional Information:** Grand Rapids Community Foundation at the above address

1002 ■ GRAND RAPIDS COMMUNITY FOUNDATION

161 Ottawa Ave. NW
Ste. 209-C Waters Bldg.
Grand Rapids, MI 49503
Tel: (616)454-1751

Fax: (616)454-6455
E-mail: grfound@grfoundation.org
Web Site: http://www.grfoundation.org
To provide financial assistance to deserving students.
Title of Award: Shepard L. & Mabel C. Lepard Scholarships **Area, Field, or Subject:** General Studies. **Level of Education for which Award is Granted:** Undergraduate **Funds Available:** No specific amount.
Eligibility Requirements: Applicants must be pursuing an undergraduate degree at any accredited college or university in the U.S; must be Kent County residents; must have demonstrated financial need; must have a minimum of 3.3 GPA. **Application Requirements:** Applicants must check the available website for the required materials. **Additional Information:** Grand Rapids Community Foundation at the above address

1003 ■ GRAND RAPIDS COMMUNITY FOUNDATION

161 Ottawa Ave. NW
Ste. 209-C Waters Bldg.
Grand Rapids, MI 49503
Tel: (616)454-1751
Fax: (616)454-6455
E-mail: grfound@grfoundation.org
Web Site: http://www.grfoundation.org
To provide financial assistance to students who are in need.
Title of Award: John T. & Frances Maghielse Scholarships **Area, Field, or Subject:** General Studies. **Level of Education for which Award is Granted:** Undergraduate **Funds Available:** No specific amount.
Eligibility Requirements: Applicants must be graduates of Grand Rapids Public High School; must be Kent County residents; must be currently pursuing a full-time undergraduate degree in the field of Education at any Michigan public or private college/ university. Applicants must have financial need and must have a minimum of 3.0 GPA. **Application Requirements:** Applicants must check the available website for the required materials. **Additional Information:** Grand Rapids Community Foundation at the above address

1004 ■ GRAND RAPIDS COMMUNITY FOUNDATION

161 Ottawa Ave. NW
Ste. 209-C Waters Bldg.
Grand Rapids, MI 49503
Tel: (616)454-1751
Fax: (616)454-6455
E-mail: grfound@grfoundation.org
Web Site: http://www.grfoundation.org
To provide financial assistance to deserving students.
Title of Award: Robert L. & Hilda Treasure Mitchell Scholarships **Area, Field, or Subject:** General Studies. **Level of Education for which Award is Granted:** Undergraduate **Funds Available:** No specific amount.
Eligibility Requirements: Applicants must be pursuing an undergraduate degree at any accredited college or university in the U.S; must be Kent County residents; must demonstrate financial need; must have a minimum of 3.3 GPA. **Application Requirements:** Applicants must check the available website for the required materials. **Additional Information:** Grand Rapids Community Foundation at the above address

1005 ■ GRAND RAPIDS COMMUNITY FOUNDATION

161 Ottawa Ave. NW
Ste. 209-C Waters Bldg.
Grand Rapids, MI 49503
Tel: (616)454-1751
Fax: (616)454-6455
E-mail: grfound@grfoundation.org
Web Site: http://www.grfoundation.org
To provide financial support to those students who are in need.
Title of Award: Josephine Ringold Scholarships **Area, Field, or Subject:** General Studies. **Level of Education for which Award is Granted:** Undergraduate **Funds Available:** No specific amount.
Eligibility Requirements: Applicants must be Kent County residents who will be attending Aquinas, Calvin, Cornerstone, Davenport, GRCC, GVSU or Kendall. Applicants must have financial need and a 3.0 minimum GPA is required. **Application Requirements:** Applicants must check the available website for more information. **Additional Information:** Grand Rapids Community Foundation at the above address

1006 ■ GRAND RAPIDS COMMUNITY FOUNDATION
161 Ottawa Ave. NW
Ste. 209-C Waters Bldg.
Grand Rapids, MI 49503
Tel: (616)454-1751
Fax: (616)454-6455
E-mail: grfound@grfoundation.org
Web Site: http://www.grfoundation.org
To provide financial assistance to those students who are in need.
Title of Award: Margery J. Seeger Scholarships **Area, Field, or Subject:** General Studies. **Level of Education for which Award is Granted:** Undergraduate **Funds Available:** No specific amount.
Eligibility Requirements: Applicants must be Kent County residents who are pursuing an undergraduate degree at any accredited college in the U.S. Applicants must have financial need. Applicants must have a minimum of 3.3 GPA. **Application Requirements:** Applicants must check the available website for the required materials. **Additional Information:** Grand Rapids Community Foundation at the above address

1007 ■ GRAND RAPIDS COMMUNITY FOUNDATION
161 Ottawa Ave. NW
Ste. 209-C Waters Bldg.
Grand Rapids, MI 49503
Tel: (616)454-1751
Fax: (616)454-6455
E-mail: grfound@grfoundation.org
Web Site: http://www.grfoundation.org
To provide financial support to those students who are in need.
Title of Award: Gladys Snauble Scholarships **Area, Field, or Subject:** General Studies. **Level of Education for which Award is Granted:** Undergraduate **Funds Available:** No specific amount.
Eligibility Requirements: Applicants must be senior students at Cedar Springs High School who will be entering college in the fall. Applicants must have financial need. **Application Requirements:** Applicants must check the available website for the required materials. **Additional Information:** Grand Rapids Community Foundation at the above address

1008 ■ GRAND RAPIDS COMMUNITY FOUNDATION
161 Ottawa Ave. NW
Ste. 209-C Waters Bldg.
Grand Rapids, MI 49503
Tel: (616)454-1751
Fax: (616)454-6455
E-mail: grfound@grfoundation.org
Web Site: http://www.grfoundation.org
To provide financial support to those students who are in need.
Title of Award: Christine Soper Scholarships **Area, Field, or Subject:** General Studies. **Level of Education for which Award is Granted:** Undergraduate **Funds Available:** No specific amount.
Eligibility Requirements: Applicants must be Kent County residents who will be attending Aquinas, Calvin, Cornerstone, Davenport, GRCC, GVSU or Kendall. Applicants must have financial need. Applicants must have a cumulative of 3.0 GPA. **Application Requirements:** Applicants must check the available website for the required materials. **Additional Information:** Grand Rapids Community Foundation at the above address

1009 ■ GRAND RAPIDS COMMUNITY FOUNDATION
161 Ottawa Ave. NW
Ste. 209-C Waters Bldg.
Grand Rapids, MI 49503
Tel: (616)454-1751
Fax: (616)454-6455
E-mail: grfound@grfoundation.org
Web Site: http://www.grfoundation.org
To provide financial assistance to those students who are in need.
Title of Award: Dorothy B. & Charles E. Thomas Scholarships **Area, Field, or Subject:** General Studies. **Level of Education for which Award is Granted:** Undergraduate **Funds Available:** No specific amount.
Eligibility Requirements: Applicants must be Kent County residents who will be attending Aquinas, Calvin, Cornerstone, Davenport, GRCC, GVSU or Kendall. Applicants must have a minimum of 3.0 GPA. Applicants must have financial need. **Application Requirements:** Applicants must check the available website for the application process and for the required

materials. **Additional Information:** Grand Rapids Community Foundation at the above address

1010 ■ GRAND RAPIDS COMMUNITY FOUNDATION
161 Ottawa Ave. NW
Ste. 209-C Waters Bldg.
Grand Rapids, MI 49503
Tel: (616)454-1751
Fax: (616)454-6455
E-mail: grfound@grfoundation.org
Web Site: http://www.grfoundation.org
To provide financial assistance to those students who are in need.
Title of Award: Dorothy J. Thurston Graduate Scholarships **Area, Field, or Subject:** General Studies. **Level of Education for which Award is Granted:** Undergraduate **Funds Available:** No specific amount.
Eligibility Requirements: Applicants must be Kent County residents who are pursuing full or part-time study at any accredited school in Michigan. Applicants must have financial need. Applicants must have a minimum of 3.0 GPA. **Application Requirements:** Applicants must check the available website for more information. **Additional Information:** Grand Rapids Community Foundation at the above address

1011 ■ GRAND RAPIDS COMMUNITY FOUNDATION
161 Ottawa Ave. NW
Ste. 209-C Waters Bldg.
Grand Rapids, MI 49503
Tel: (616)454-1751
Fax: (616)454-6455
E-mail: grfound@grfoundation.org
Web Site: http://www.grfoundation.org
To provide financial support to those students who are in need.
Title of Award: Mildred E. Troske Music Scholarships **Area, Field, or Subject:** General Studies. **Level of Education for which Award is Granted:** Undergraduate **Funds Available:** No specific amount.
Eligibility Requirements: Applicants must be residents of Kent County who are studying music at a camp or are undergraduate music majors. Applicants must have demonstrated financial need. Applicants must have a minimum of 3.0 GPA. **Application Requirements:** Applicants must check the available website for the required materials. **Additional Information:** Grand Rapids Community Foundation at the above address

1012 ■ GRAND RAPIDS COMMUNITY FOUNDATION
161 Ottawa Ave. NW
Ste. 209-C Waters Bldg.
Grand Rapids, MI 49503
Tel: (616)454-1751
Fax: (616)454-6455
E-mail: grfound@grfoundation.org
Web Site: http://www.grfoundation.org
To provide financial assistance to those students who are in need.
Title of Award: Keith C. Vanderhyde Scholarships **Area, Field, or Subject:** General Studies. **Level of Education for which Award is Granted:** Undergraduate **Funds Available:** No specific amount.
Eligibility Requirements: Applicants must be senior students or graduates of Ottawa Hills High School who are pursuing a full-time undergraduate degree. Applicants must demonstrate financial need. Applicants must have a minimum of 3.0 GPA. **Application Requirements:** Applicants must check the available website for the required materials. **Additional Information:** Grand Rapids Community Foundation at the above address

1013 ■ GRAND RAPIDS COMMUNITY FOUNDATION
161 Ottawa Ave. NW
Ste. 209-C Waters Bldg.
Grand Rapids, MI 49503
Tel: (616)454-1751
Fax: (616)454-6455
E-mail: grfound@grfoundation.org
Web Site: http://www.grfoundation.org
To provide financial assistance to those students who are in need.
Title of Award: Jacob R. & Mary M. VanLoo & Lenore K. VanLoo Scholarships **Area, Field, or Subject:** General Studies. **Level of Education for which Award is Granted:** Undergraduate **Funds Available:** No specific amount.

Eligibility Requirements: Applicants must be Kent County residents who will be attending Aquinas, Calvin, Cornerstone, Davenport, GRCC, GVSU or Kendall. Applicants must have financial need. Applicants must have a minimum of 3.0 GPA. **Application Requirements:** Applicants must check the available website for the required materials. **Additional Information:** Grand Rapids Community Foundation at the above address

1014 ■ GRAND RAPIDS COMMUNITY FOUNDATION
161 Ottawa Ave. NW
Ste. 209-C Waters Bldg.
Grand Rapids, MI 49503
Tel: (616)454-1751
Fax: (616)454-6455
E-mail: grfound@grfoundation.org
Web Site: http://www.grfoundation.org
To provide financial assistance to those students who are in need.
Title of Award: Donald M. Wells Scholarships **Area, Field, or Subject:** General Studies. **Level of Education for which Award is Granted:** Undergraduate **Funds Available:** No specific amount.
Eligibility Requirements: Applicants must be senior students or graduates of Central High School who are pursuing undergraduate studies at GRCC, University of Chicago or University of Michigan. Applicants must have financial need and must have a minimum of 2.5 GPA. **Application Requirements:** Applicants must check the available website for more information regarding this award. **Additional Information:** Grand Rapids Community Foundation at the above address

1015 ■ GRAND RAPIDS COMMUNITY FOUNDATION
161 Ottawa Ave. NW
Ste. 209-C Waters Bldg.
Grand Rapids, MI 49503
Tel: (616)454-1751
Fax: (616)454-6455
E-mail: grfound@grfoundation.org
Web Site: http://www.grfoundation.org
To provide financial support to those students who are in need.
Title of Award: Elmo Wierenga Alumni Scholarships **Area, Field, or Subject:** General Studies. **Level of Education for which Award is Granted:** Undergraduate **Funds Available:** No specific amount.
Eligibility Requirements: Applicants must be senior students at Ottawa Hills High School pursuing full-time undergraduate studies at any 2 or 4-year accredited school in the U.S. Applicants must have financial need and a minimum of 2.5 GPA. **Application Requirements:** Applicants must check the available website for the required materials. **Additional Information:** Grand Rapids Community Foundation at the above address

1016 ■ GRANDMOTHERS FOR PEACE INTERNATIONAL
PO Box 580788
Elk Grove, CA 95758
Tel: (916)730-6476
E-mail: lorraine@grandmothersforpeace.org
Web Site: http://www.grandmothersforpeace.org
To provide financial assistance to students across the United States, Africa, Kyrgzstan, Canada, Norway and the Ukraine.
Title of Award: Barbara Wiedner and Dorothy Vandercook Memorial Peace Scholarships **Area, Field, or Subject:** General studies. **Level of Education for which Award is Granted:** Undergraduate **Funds Available:** $250.
Eligibility Requirements: Applicant must be a high school senior or in first year of college. **Application Requirements:** Applicants must submit completed application form; brief autobiography of activities relating to peace and social justice, nuclear disarmament issues, or conflict resolution; two letters of recommendation; and must describe how will they contribute to a peaceful and just society in the future. **Deadline for Receipt:** March 1.

1017 ■ GRANGER BUSINESS ASSOCIATION
PO Box 427
Granger, IN 46530
E-mail: info@grangertoday.com
Web Site: http://www.grangertoday.com
To award scholarships to area students to help defray college expenses.
Title of Award: Granger Business Association College Scholarships **Area, Field, or Subject:** General Studies. **Level of Education for which**

Award is Granted: Undergraduate **Number Awarded:** 10. **Funds Available:** $1,000.
Eligibility Requirements: Applicants must reside in the 46530 zip code and demonstrate financial need. **Application Requirements:** Applicants must check the application process online. **Additional Information:** Granger Business Association at the above address.

1018 ■ GREAT SEATTLE BUSINESS ASSOCIATION
400 E Pine St., Ste. 322
Seattle, WA 98122
Tel: (206)363-9188
Fax: (206)568-3123
E-mail: office@thegsba.org
Web Site: http://www.thegsba.org
To support undergraduate students by providing financial resources to pursue their educational goals.
Title of Award: Greater Seattle Business Association Scholarships **Area, Field, or Subject:** General studies. **Level of Education for which Award is Granted:** Undergraduate **Funds Available:** $3,000 up to $10,000. **Duration:** One year.
Eligibility Requirements: Applicant must be a current resident of Washington pursuing an undergraduate degree at any college in the US. **Application Requirements:** Applicants must complete and return scholarship application, letters of reference and transcripts by application deadline. **Deadline for Receipt:** October.

1019 ■ THE GREATER TACOMA COMMUNITY FOUNDATION
PO Box 1995
Tacoma, WA 98401
Tel: (253)383-5622
Web Site: http://www.tacomafoundation.org
To benefit students from Pierce County high schools and help tomorrow's leaders reach their goals and fulfill their dreams.
Title of Award: Clay Huntington Sports Communications Scholarships **Area, Field, or Subject:** General studies. **Level of Education for which Award is Granted:** Undergraduate **Funds Available:** No specific amount.
Eligibility Requirements: Applicants must be graduating seniors at Pierce County High School; must intend to declare a major in radio/television production and/or broadcast editorial journalism or a similar communications-related field. **Application Requirements:** Applicants must request an application form at Tacoma Athletic Commission. **Additional Information:** PO Box 11304, Tacoma, WA 98411.

1020 ■ THE GREATER TACOMA COMMUNITY FOUNDATION
PO Box 1995
Tacoma, WA 98401
Tel: (253)383-5622
Web Site: http://www.tacomafoundation.org
To provide assistance for students.
Title of Award: Anna M. Rundquist Memorial Scholarship **Area, Field, or Subject:** General studies. **Level of Education for which Award is Granted:** Undergraduate **Funds Available:** No specific amount.
Eligibility Requirements: Applicants must be graduating students from Highline Community College, Olympic College, South Puget Sound Community College or Tacoma Community College; must be enrolled at a four-year college or university to pursue a nursing career. **Application Requirements:** Applicants must submit a completed application form available at the guidance office.

1021 ■ THE GREATER TACOMA COMMUNITY FOUNDATION
PO Box 1995
Tacoma, WA 98401
Tel: (253)383-5622
Web Site: http://www.tacomafoundation.org
To foster generosity by connecting people who care with causes that matter.
Title of Award: The Tacoma Athletic Commission Scholarships **Area, Field, or Subject:** Athletics. **Level of Education for which Award is Granted:** Undergraduate **Funds Available:** No specific amount.
Eligibility Requirements: Applicants must be current graduating senior students at Pierce County High School; must be enrolled at a vocational school or a two or four-year college. **Application Requirements:** Ap-

plicants must request an application form at Tacoma Athletic Commission. **Additional Information:** PO Box 11304, Tacoma, WA 98411.

1022 ■ GREEN KNIGHT ECONOMIC DEVELOPMENT CORPORATION
PO Box 4
Pen Argyl, PA 18072
E-mail: gkedc@gkedc.com
Web Site: http://www.gkedc.com
To financially support a student living in the Pen Argyl School District who wishes to continue higher education.
Title of Award: Green Knight Economic Development Corporation (GKEDC) Scholarships **Area, Field, or Subject:** General studies. **Level of Education for which Award is Granted:** Undergraduate **Funds Available:** $4,000 each year. **Duration:** Four years.
Eligibility Requirements: Applicant must be a graduating high school senior who lives in the Pen Argyl School District and will be continuing his/her education in a college program; must take at least 24 credits per year and must maintain, at a minimum, a cumulative GPA of 2.5. **Application Requirements:** Applicants must submit a completed scholarship application form together with a one-page essay. **Additional Information:** Community Relations Committee at comm@gkedc.com.

1023 ■ GRIFFIN FOUNDATION
303 W Prospect Rd.
Fort Collins, CO 80526
Tel: (970)482-3030
Fax: (970)484-6648
E-mail: carol.wood@thegriffinfoundation.org
Web Site: http://www.thegriffinfoundation.org
To award scholarship to qualified applicants who have an associate degree from a junior or community college.
Title of Award: Griffin Foundation Scholarships **Area, Field, or Subject:** General studies. **Level of Education for which Award is Granted:** Undergraduate **Funds Available:** $5,000.
Eligibility Requirements: Applicants must have an associate degree or at least 60 hours from a junior or community college and are seeking to complete a baccalaureate degree. **Application Requirements:** Application form can be downloaded from the Griffin Foundation website. Applicants must type or print their application legibly; applicants must attach three letters of recommendation, at least one of which is from a college faculty member, counselor or administrator who can comment on applicant qualifications (be sure recommendations are signed). Applicants must attach an official copy of grade transcript(s) from each college attended. Scholarship can only be used at Colorado State University (Fort Collins Campus), the University of Northern Colorado, or the University of Wyoming (Larimie Campus). **Deadline for Receipt:** March 1. **Additional Information:** Carol Wood, Program Dir. at the above address.

1024 ■ GEORGE AND MARY JOSEPHINE HAMMAN FOUNDATION
3336 Richmond, Ste. 310
Houston, TX 77098
Tel: (713)522-9891
Fax: (713)522-9693
E-mail: hammanfdn@aol.com
Web Site: http://www.hammanfoundation.org
To provide undergraduate scholarships for Houston area high school seniors.
Title of Award: George and Mary Josephine Hamman Foundation Scholarships **Area, Field, or Subject:** General studies. **Level of Education for which Award is Granted:** High School **Funds Available:** No specific amount.
Eligibility Requirements: Applicants must be Houston area high school seniors who attend schools or are homeschooled in the following eight counties: Brazoria, Chambers, Fort Bend, Galveston, Harris, Liberty, Montgomery or Waller; must be US citizens. **Application Requirements:** Applicants must write for the one-page scholarship application and the two-page financial qualification statement or it may be downloaded from the website. Completed scholarship applications must be submitted with these documents (in the following order): (1) Financial Qualification Statement, (2) complete, legible, signed copy of parents'/guardians' and student's most recent federal income tax return (including all schedules) plus, if applicable, corporate or partnership returns, (3) proof of ACT

and/or SAT results, and (4) high school transcript (unofficial is okay). Mail to: George and Mary Josephine Hamman Foundation, 3336 Richmond, Suite 310, Houston, TX 77098. **Deadline for Receipt:** February 29.

1025 ■ HARNESS HORSE YOUTH FOUNDATION
16575 Carey Rd.
Westfield, IN 46074
Tel: (317)867-5877
Fax: (317)867-5896
E-mail: ellen@hhyf.org
Web Site: http://www.hhyf.org
To provide financial assistance to the children or relatives of racing officials who were members of the North American Judges and Stewards and licensed pari-mutuel officials.
Title of Award: Charles Bradley Memorial Scholarships **Area, Field, or Subject:** General studies. **Level of Education for which Award is Granted:** Undergraduate **Funds Available:** No amount mentioned.
Eligibility Requirements: Applicants must be at least in high school and children or relatives of racing officials who were members of the North American Judges and Stewards Association and/or licensed USTA pari-mutuel officials in the following categories: presiding judges, associate judges, paddock judges, and starters. **Application Requirements:** Applicants must complete and submit application form. **Deadline for Receipt:** April 30.

1026 ■ HARNESS HORSE YOUTH FOUNDATION
16575 Carey Rd.
Westfield, IN 46074
Tel: (317)867-5877
Fax: (317)867-5896
E-mail: ellen@hhyf.org
Web Site: http://www.hhyf.org
To provide financial assistance to the eligible children of harness horse trainers or licensed caretakers.
Title of Award: Gallo Blue Chip Scholarships **Area, Field, or Subject:** General studies. **Level of Education for which Award is Granted:** Undergraduate **Funds Available:** No specific amount.
Eligibility Requirements: Applicant must be at least a senior high school student and a child of harness horse trainer or caretaker licensed in New York and/or New Jersey raised and/or reside in the two-state region. **Application Requirements:** Applicants must submit complete application form. **Deadline for Receipt:** April 30.

1027 ■ HARNESS HORSE YOUTH FOUNDATION
16575 Carey Rd.
Westfield, IN 46074
Tel: (317)867-5877
Fax: (317)867-5896
E-mail: ellen@hhyf.org
Web Site: http://www.hhyf.org
To provide financial support for senior high school students who may or may not be pursuing harness racing but demonstrates passion for the sport.
Title of Award: Curt Greene Memorial Scholarships **Area, Field, or Subject:** General studies. **Level of Education for which Award is Granted:** Undergraduate **Funds Available:** No amount mentioned.
Eligibility Requirements: Applicant must be at least a high school senior. **Application Requirements:** Applicants must complete and submit application form. **Deadline for Receipt:** April 30.

1028 ■ HARNESS TRACKS OF AMERICA
4640 E Sunrise, Ste. 200
Tucson, AZ 85718
Tel: (520)529-2525; (520)529-3235
E-mail: info@harnesstracks.com
Web Site: http://www.harnesstracks.com
To provide financial assistance to students for post-secondary education.
Title of Award: Harness Tracks of America Scholarship Fund **Area, Field, or Subject:** General studies. **Level of Education for which Award is Granted:** Undergraduate **Number Awarded:** 5. **Funds Available:** $5,000.
Eligibility Requirements: Applicants must be sons or daughters of licensed drivers, trainers, caretakers, management or young people

actively engaged in the harness racing industry. **Application Requirements:** Applicants must submit complete application form. **Deadline for Receipt:** June 15.

1029 ■ HARTFORD FOUNDATION FOR PUBLIC GIVING
10 Columbus Blvd., 8th Flr.
Hartford, CT 06106
Tel: (860)548-1888
Fax: (860)524-8346
E-mail: hfpg@hfpg.org
Web Site: http://www.hfpg.org
To provide scholarship for graduating high school seniors of Greater Hartford area.
Title of Award: Frederick G. Adams Scholarships **Area, Field, or Subject:** General studies. **Level of Education for which Award is Granted:** Undergraduate **Funds Available:** $3,000.
Eligibility Requirements: Applicants must be graduating seniors who live in or are attending school in Greater Hartford; must be entering a four-year college or university (full-time enrollment); must have a financial need; must be on a top third of the class or a good academic record; and must be active volunteer in school, community, or other extracurricular activities. **Application Requirements:** Applicants must download and fill out the online application and attach the following requirements: letter of recommendation from your guidance counselor or a teacher; official high school transcript, including SAT or ACT scores; copy of the essay you submitted with your college application (if you did not have to submit one, write a brief essay, no more than 2 pages, regarding your future goals); copy of pages 1 and 2 of your parents' 2006 or most recent completed federal tax form 1040; and mail everything to Hartford Foundation College Scholarship Program. **Deadline for Receipt:** February 6. **Additional Information:** Hartford Foundation College Scholarship Program, Scholarship Management Services, Scholarship America, One Scholarship Way, PO Box 297, St. Peter, MN 56082. 800-537-4180.

1030 ■ HARTFORD FOUNDATION FOR PUBLIC GIVING
10 Columbus Blvd., 8th Flr.
Hartford, CT 06106
Tel: (860)548-1888
Fax: (860)524-8346
E-mail: hfpg@hfpg.org
Web Site: http://www.hfpg.org
To provide scholarships for graduating seniors from a public high school in Hartford.
Title of Award: Alliance for Academic Achievement Program Scholarships **Area, Field, or Subject:** General studies. **Level of Education for which Award is Granted:** Undergraduate **Number Awarded:** 15. **Funds Available:** $5,000. **Duration:** One year.
Eligibility Requirements: Applicants must be Hartford residents; must be entering Howard University, Trinity College or University of Connecticut; must have academic excellence and financial need (FAFSA required). **Application Requirements:** Applicants must complete the General Scholarship Application Form and include a brief personal statement indicating what you intend to study in college and why. **Deadline for Receipt:** February 29. **Additional Information:** Ruth E. Torres, The Alliance Program, College Relations, One Hartford Plaza (HO-1-06), Hartford, CT 06155, 860-757-1538, ruth.torres@thehartford.com.

1031 ■ HARTFORD FOUNDATION FOR PUBLIC GIVING
10 Columbus Blvd., 8th Flr.
Hartford, CT 06106
Tel: (860)548-1888
Fax: (860)524-8346
E-mail: hfpg@hfpg.org
Web Site: http://www.hfpg.org
To award scholarships for graduating high school seniors.
Title of Award: American Fire Sprinkler Association Scholarships **Area, Field, or Subject:** General studies. **Level of Education for which Award is Granted:** Undergraduate **Number Awarded:** 2. **Funds Available:** $1,000.
Eligibility Requirements: Applicants must be Connecticut residents who are entering a four-year college or university. **Application Requirements:** Applicants must complete and submit an application and essay to the association. Applicants may obtain application materials from the American

Fire Sprinkler Association, CT Chapter. **Deadline for Receipt:** March 22. **Additional Information:** David K. Thompson, American fire Sprinkler Association, Connecticut Chapter, PO Box 2350, Hartford, CT 06146. 860-246-7711. dave@thesprink.com.

1032 ■ HARTFORD FOUNDATION FOR PUBLIC GIVING
10 Columbus Blvd., 8th Flr.
Hartford, CT 06106
Tel: (860)548-1888
Fax: (860)524-8346
E-mail: hfpg@hfpg.org
Web Site: http://www.hfpg.org
To award scholarships for students who demonstrate financial need.
Title of Award: American Savings Foundation Scholarships **Area, Field, or Subject:** General science. **Level of Education for which Award is Granted:** Undergraduate **Funds Available:** $1,000-$2,000.
Eligibility Requirements: Applicants must have a 2.5 minimum GPA or top 1/3 of class; must have academic potential and community service; must live in one of the 64 towns served by the American Savings Foundation, including Avon, Andover, Bloomfield, Bolton, Burlington, Canton, East Hartford, Farmington, Glastonbury, Granby, Hebron, Manchester, Marlborough, Newington, New Britain, Simsbury, Tolland, West Hartford, Wethersfield (partial list). **Application Requirements:** Applicants may apply online at www.asfdn.org or call Senior Program Officer of American Savings Foundation. **Deadline for Receipt:** March 31. **Additional Information:** Maria Falvo, Senior Program Officer, Scholarships, American Savings Foundation 185 Main St., New Britain, CT 06051. 860-827-2572. mfalvo@asfdn.org.

1033 ■ HARTFORD FOUNDATION FOR PUBLIC GIVING
10 Columbus Blvd., 8th Flr.
Hartford, CT 06106
Tel: (860)548-1888
Fax: (860)524-8346
E-mail: hfpg@hfpg.org
Web Site: http://www.hfpg.org
To award educational assistance for students enrolled as undergraduate at Amherst College.
Title of Award: Amherst College Connecticut Alumni Scholarships **Area, Field, or Subject:** General studies. **Level of Education for which Award is Granted:** Undergraduate **Funds Available:** $1,000.
Eligibility Requirements: Applicants must be residents of Connecticut; must demonstrate financial need; and must demonstrate academic excellence. **Application Requirements:** Applicants may obtain an application to the Scholarship Chairman of Gordon Muir and Foley, LLP. **Deadline for Receipt:** December 31. **Additional Information:** Robert J. O'Brien, scholarship Chairman, Gordon Muir and Foley, LLP. 10 Columbus Blvd., Hartford, CT 06106. 860-525-4849.

1034 ■ HARTFORD FOUNDATION FOR PUBLIC GIVING
10 Columbus Blvd., 8th Flr.
Hartford, CT 06106
Tel: (860)548-1888
Fax: (860)524-8346
E-mail: hfpg@hfpg.org
Web Site: http://www.hfpg.org
To provide educational assistance for students presently enrolled at Hampton University.
Title of Award: John Bell and Lawrence Thornton Scholarship Fund **Area, Field, or Subject:** General studies. **Level of Education for which Award is Granted:** Undergraduate **Number Awarded:** Varies. **Funds Available:** No specific amount.
Eligibility Requirements: Applicant must be a Greater Hartford resident; must demonstrate academic excellence, financial need, extra curricular activities and community service; must have a GPA of 3.0 and above; and must be rising sophomore and rising junior status. **Application Requirements:** Applicants may obtain application materials from Connecticut River Valley Chapter National Hampton University Alumni Association, Inc. Scholarship Committee, PO Box 2734 Hartford, CT 06146-2734. **Deadline for Receipt:** march 23. **Additional Information:** hamptonalumnict@yahoo.com.

1035 ■ HARTFORD FOUNDATION FOR PUBLIC GIVING
10 Columbus Blvd., 8th Flr.
Hartford, CT 06106

Tel: (860)548-1888
Fax: (860)524-8346
E-mail: hfpg@hfpg.org
Web Site: http://www.hfpg.org
To provide educational assistance for students entering or enrolled in an accredited medical school at a college or university.
Title of Award: Dr. Francis Anthony Beneventi Medical Scholarships **Area, Field, or Subject:** General studies. **Level of Education for which Award is Granted:** Undergraduate **Number Awarded:** 1. **Funds Available:** $5,000.
Eligibility Requirements: Applicants must have a minimum of 3.25 GPA.
Application Requirements: Application materials (for Connecticut residents) may be obtained by sending a self-addressed stamped envelope to NSDAR Scholarship Committee, 215 Loomis Rd. N Granby, CT 06060. **Deadline for Receipt:** April 15. **Additional Information:** Mrs. Michael L. Stewart, CT State Chairperson. 860-653-4203. L2stew@yahoo.com.

1036 ■ HARTFORD FOUNDATION FOR PUBLIC GIVING

10 Columbus Blvd., 8th Flr.
Hartford, CT 06106
Tel: (860)548-1888
Fax: (860)524-8346
E-mail: hfpg@hfpg.org
Web Site: http://www.hfpg.org
To provide educational assistance for graduating high school seniors from Rockville, Tolland or Ellington High Schools.
Title of Award: Lebbeus F. Bissell Scholarships **Area, Field, or Subject:** General studies. **Level of Education for which Award is Granted:** Undergraduate **Number Awarded:** 3. **Funds Available:** $4,000.
Eligibility Requirements: Applicants must demonstrate academic excellence, financial need, extracurricular activities and community service.
Application Requirements: Applicants may obtain application materials from Guidance Departments of Rockville, Tolland or Ellington High Schools or from Lebbeus F. Bissel Scholarship Advisory Committee, 183 Reservoir Rd. Vermon, CT 06066. **Deadline for Receipt:** March 20. **Additional Information:** Thomas Mason, Chairman. 860-875-0527 or 860-548-1888.

1037 ■ HARTFORD FOUNDATION FOR PUBLIC GIVING

10 Columbus Blvd., 8th Flr.
Hartford, CT 06106
Tel: (860)548-1888
Fax: (860)524-8346
E-mail: hfpg@hfpg.org
Web Site: http://www.hfpg.org
To provide scholarship for graduating high school seniors.
Title of Award: Boy Scouts of America General Scholarships **Area, Field, or Subject:** General studies. **Level of Education for which Award is Granted:** Undergraduate **Funds Available:** No specific amount.
Eligibility Requirements: Applicants must be participating in Boy Scout program; must be an Eagle Scout; and must demonstrate financial need and community service. **Application Requirements:** Applicants may obtain application materials from www.nesa.org or contact the Program Director of Connecticut Rivers Council, BSA. **Deadline for Receipt:** January 31. **Additional Information:** Connecticut Rivers Council, BSA PO Box 280098 60 Darlin St. E Hartford, CT 06128. 860-290-8860.

1038 ■ HARTFORD FOUNDATION FOR PUBLIC GIVING

10 Columbus Blvd., 8th Flr.
Hartford, CT 06106
Tel: (860)548-1888
Fax: (860)524-8346
E-mail: hfpg@hfpg.org
Web Site: http://www.hfpg.org
To provide scholarship for graduating high school senior who lives in or attends school in Greater Hartford.
Title of Award: W. Philip Braender and Nancy Coleman Braender Scholarships **Area, Field, or Subject:** General studies. **Level of Education for which Award is Granted:** Undergraduate **Number Awarded:** 1. **Funds Available:** $3,000.
Eligibility Requirements: Applicants must be entering a four-year college or university (full-time enrollment); must demonstrate financial need;

must be in the top third with good academic record; and must be active volunteer in school, community, or other extracurricular activities. **Application Requirements:** Application form can be downloaded on-line. Applicants must complete the scholarship application. Applicants must also attach the following requirements: letter of recommendation from your guidance counselor or a teacher; official high school transcript. Including SAT or ACT scores; copy of the essay you submitted with your college application. If you did not have to submit one, write a brief (no more than two pages) essay regarding your future goals; copy of pages 1 and 2 of your parents' 2006 or most recent completed federal tax form 1040. Mail everything to Hartford Foundation College Scholarship Program. **Deadline for Receipt:** February 6. **Additional Information:** Hartford Foundation College Scholarship Program, Scholarship Management Services, Scholarship America, One Scholarship Way, PO Box 297, St. Peter, MN 56082. 800-537-4180.

1039 ■ HARTFORD FOUNDATION FOR PUBLIC GIVING

10 Columbus Blvd., 8th Flr.
Hartford, CT 06106
Tel: (860)548-1888
Fax: (860)524-8346
E-mail: hfpg@hfpg.org
Web Site: http://www.hfpg.org
To provide scholarship for graduating high school seniors from Windsor High School (all cluster).
Title of Award: Casabella Family Memorial Scholarships **Area, Field, or Subject:** General studies. **Level of Education for which Award is Granted:** Undergraduate **Number Awarded:** 3-6. **Funds Available:** $3,000.
Eligibility Requirements: Applicants must be accepted to a two or four-year college, university or an accredited professional or technical school and must demonstrate financial need, academic or technical ability and athletic achievement. **Application Requirements:** Applicants may obtain the Casabella Family Scholarship Brochure at the Windsor High School guidance office. Applicants must complete the General Scholarship Application and include: Portfolio of relevant work with 500-word written description of projects; additional copy of letter of acceptance to educational institution and submit to Casabella Family Scholarship Windsor High School Guidance Office, 50 Sage Park Rd. Windsor, CT 06095. **Deadline for Receipt:** May 1. **Additional Information:** aford@windsorct.org; fax: 860-687-2029; phone: 860-687-2020 ext. 371.

1040 ■ HARTFORD FOUNDATION FOR PUBLIC GIVING

10 Columbus Blvd., 8th Flr.
Hartford, CT 06106
Tel: (860)548-1888
Fax: (860)524-8346
E-mail: hfpg@hfpg.org
Web Site: http://www.hfpg.org
To provide scholarship to the graduating high school senior who has earned the Gold award.
Title of Award: Emily Chaison Gold Award Scholarships **Area, Field, or Subject:** General studies. **Level of Education for which Award is Granted:** Undergraduate **Number Awarded:** 1. **Funds Available:** $750.
Eligibility Requirements: Applicants must be a registered in Girl Scouts and be a Connecticut resident. **Application Requirements:** Applicants may obtain application materials from Girl Scouts of Connecticut 340 Washington St. Hartford, CT 06106. www.gsofct.org. **Deadline for Receipt:** April 15. **Additional Information:** Girl Scout of Connecticut, 860-522-0163.

1041 ■ HARTFORD FOUNDATION FOR PUBLIC GIVING

10 Columbus Blvd., 8th Flr.
Hartford, CT 06106
Tel: (860)548-1888
Fax: (860)524-8346
E-mail: hfpg@hfpg.org
Web Site: http://www.hfpg.org
To provide scholarship for graduating high school students.
Title of Award: The College Club of Hartford Scholarships **Area, Field, or Subject:** General studies. **Level of Education for which Award is Granted:** Undergraduate **Funds Available:** $1,000.
Eligibility Requirements: Applicants must be graduating public high school seniors residing in Avon, Bloomfield, Canton, East Hartford,

Farmington, Glastonbury, Hartford, Manchester, Newington, Rocky Hill, Simsbury, West Hartford, Wethersfield or Windsor; must be attending in an accredited twoor four-year school; must demonstrate financial need and community service; must be on a class rank upper 10% (Applicant's grades through 2nd quarter of senior year are required); and must be students who attend Trinity College or St. Joseph College in Connecticut. **Application Requirements:** Applicants may obtain application materials from their high school guidance office and submit it to Scholarship Committee, Mrs. Carolyn Holgerson, Chairman, 391 Robbins Ave. Newington, CT 06111. 860666-9586. **Deadline for Receipt:** March 15.

1042 ■ HARTFORD FOUNDATION FOR PUBLIC GIVING
10 Columbus Blvd., 8th Flr.
Hartford, CT 06106
Tel: (860)548-1888
Fax: (860)524-8346
E-mail: hfpg@hfpg.org
Web Site: http://www.hfpg.org
To award scholarship to the students entering or enrolled as undergraduate in an accredited college or university.
Title of Award: Connecticut Association of Latinos in Higher Education Scholarships **Area, Field, or Subject:** General studies. **Level of Education for which Award is Granted:** Undergraduate **Number Awarded:** 10. **Funds Available:** $1,000.
Eligibility Requirements: Applicants must be residents of Connecticut; must be of Latino background; must have financial need and community service; and must have an academic excellence ("B" average). **Application Requirements:** Applicants must complete the General Scholarship Application and include the following requirements: a copy of your Student Aid Report; a two-page typed, double-space essay on "How you feel education is going to impact your ability to continue assisting others to pursue an education." **Deadline for Receipt:** April 18. **Additional Information:** CALAHE Scholarship Chair c/o Office of Dean of Students, Dr. Wilson Luna, Gateway Community College, 60 Sargent Drive New Haven, CT 06511. 203-285-2210. wilsonluna@aol.com.

1043 ■ HARTFORD FOUNDATION FOR PUBLIC GIVING
10 Columbus Blvd., 8th Flr.
Hartford, CT 06106
Tel: (860)548-1888
Fax: (860)524-8346
E-mail: hfpg@hfpg.org
Web Site: http://www.hfpg.org
To provide scholarship for graduating high school seniors.
Title of Award: Connecticut Capitol Scholarship Program **Area, Field, or Subject:** General studies. **Level of Education for which Award is Granted:** Undergraduate **Funds Available:** $300-$3,000.
Eligibility Requirements: Applicants must be residents of Connecticut entering in a Connecticut college or a college located in one of the following states: District of Columbia, Maine, Massachusetts, New Hampshire, Pennsylvania, Rhode Island, or Vermont; must demonstrate academic excellence being on a class rank of top 20% or SAT above 1800. **Application Requirements:** Applicants may obtain application materials from high school guidance counselor or from Connecticut Department of Higher Education. **Deadline for Receipt:** February 15. **Additional Information:** Connecticut Department of Higher Education, 61 Woodland St. Hartford, CT 06105; Phone: 860-947-1855 Fax: 860-947-1313; csp@ctdhe.org.

1044 ■ HARTFORD FOUNDATION FOR PUBLIC GIVING
10 Columbus Blvd., 8th Flr.
Hartford, CT 06106
Tel: (860)548-1888
Fax: (860)524-8346
E-mail: hfpg@hfpg.org
Web Site: http://www.hfpg.org
To provide scholarship for graduating high school seniors or college students enrolled in a Horticulture degree program.
Title of Award: Connecticut Nurserymen's Foundation Scholarships **Area, Field, or Subject:** Horticulture. **Level of Education for which Award is Granted:** Undergraduate **Number Awarded:** 1. **Funds Available:** $5,000.
Eligibility Requirements: Applicants must be Connecticut residents entering a two or four-year college program in Horticulture; must

demonstrate financial need and academic excellence; must have a work experience and Future Farmers of American membership helpful, but not necessary. **Application Requirements:** Applicants may obtain the application materials from their high school guidance counselor or from Connecticut Nurserymen's Foundation. **Deadline for Receipt:** March 14. **Additional Information:** Judy Mattson, Scholarship Committee Chairman, 131 Hollister St. Manchester, CT 06042, Phone: 860-643-8363 Fax: 860-643-2778; jmattson.negs@sbcglobal.net.

1045 ■ HARTFORD FOUNDATION FOR PUBLIC GIVING
10 Columbus Blvd., 8th Flr.
Hartford, CT 06106
Tel: (860)548-1888
Fax: (860)524-8346
E-mail: hfpg@hfpg.org
Web Site: http://www.hfpg.org
To provide scholarship for college junior or senior or graduate students enrolled in a full-time program to teach blind and visually impaired students in Connecticut.
Title of Award: Brian Cummins Memorial Scholarships **Area, Field, or Subject:** General studies. **Level of Education for which Award is Granted:** Undergraduate **Number Awarded:** 1. **Funds Available:** $5,000.
Eligibility Requirements: Applicants must demonstrate financial need, community service, and academic excellence. **Application Requirements:** Applicants may obtain scholarship materials from National Federation of the Blind of Connecticut 477 Connecticut Blvd. Ste. 217 E Hartford, CT 06108. **Deadline for Receipt:** October 15. **Additional Information:** National Federation of the Blind of Connecticut, Phone: 860-298-1971 Fax: 860-291-2795; info@nfbct.org.

1046 ■ HARTFORD FOUNDATION FOR PUBLIC GIVING
10 Columbus Blvd., 8th Flr.
Hartford, CT 06106
Tel: (860)548-1888
Fax: (860)524-8346
E-mail: hfpg@hfpg.org
Web Site: http://www.hfpg.org
To provide scholarship to the graduating students from A.I. Prince Technical, Bloomfield, Bulkeley, Hartford Public, Windsor, or Weaver High School.
Title of Award: Delta Sigma Theta Hartford Alumnae Scholarships **Area, Field, or Subject:** General studies. **Level of Education for which Award is Granted:** Undergraduate **Funds Available:** $2,000.
Eligibility Requirements: Applicants must be Black/African American female high school senior planning to attend a four-year college or university. Applicants must have a leadership abilities, academic excellence, top 25th percentile and community service. **Application Requirements:** Applicants may obtain scholarship materials from their high school guidance counselor and submit to the Delta Sigma Theta Sorority, Inc., Hartford Alumnae Chapter. **Deadline for Receipt:** March 1. **Additional Information:** Mrs. Shirley Harrison, Scholarship Chairperson, PO Box 2163 Hartford, CT 06145-2163. Phone: 860-985-5501 Fax: 860-833-8804.

1047 ■ HARTFORD FOUNDATION FOR PUBLIC GIVING
10 Columbus Blvd., 8th Flr.
Hartford, CT 06106
Tel: (860)548-1888
Fax: (860)524-8346
E-mail: hfpg@hfpg.org
Web Site: http://www.hfpg.org
To provide scholarship for students who are legally blind.
Title of Award: C. Rodney Demarest Memorial Scholarships **Area, Field, or Subject:** General studies. **Level of Education for which Award is Granted:** Undergraduate **Number Awarded:** 1. **Funds Available:** $3,000.
Eligibility Requirements: Applicants must be graduating high school seniors or college students residing or attending school full-time in Connecticut. Applicants must demonstrate financial need, community service and academic excellence. **Application Requirements:** Applicants may obtain application materials from National Federation of the Blind of CT,

477 Connecticut Blvd. Ste. 217 E Hartford, CT 06108. 860289-1971. info@nfbct.org. www.nfbct.org. **Deadline for Receipt:** September 15.

1048 ■ HARTFORD FOUNDATION FOR PUBLIC GIVING
10 Columbus Blvd., 8th Flr.
Hartford, CT 06106
Tel: (860)548-1888
Fax: (860)524-8346
E-mail: hfpg@hfpg.org
Web Site: http://www.hfpg.org
To provide scholarship to the graduating senior.
Title of Award: Albert and Jane Dewey Scholarships **Area, Field, or Subject:** General studies. **Level of Education for which Award is Granted:** Undergraduate **Funds Available:** $1,000-$4,000.
Eligibility Requirements: Applicants must be residents of Manchester who demonstrate financial need. Preference will be given to minority student. **Application Requirements:** Applicants may obtain application materials from Manchester Scholarship Foundation Inc., 20 Hartford Rd. Manchester, CT 06040. Phone: 860645-1673
Fax; 860432-9136; www.manchesterscholarship.org. **Deadline for Receipt:** Mid-April.

1049 ■ HARTFORD FOUNDATION FOR PUBLIC GIVING
10 Columbus Blvd., 8th Flr.
Hartford, CT 06106
Tel: (860)548-1888
Fax: (860)524-8346
E-mail: hfpg@hfpg.org
Web Site: http://www.hfpg.org
To provide scholarship to a high school senior who lives in or attends school in the Greater Hartford area.
Title of Award: Harry A. Donn Scholarships **Area, Field, or Subject:** General studies. **Level of Education for which Award is Granted:** Undergraduate **Number Awarded:** 1. **Funds Available:** $3,000.
Eligibility Requirements: Applicants must: be entering a four-year college or university (full-time enrollment); demonstrate financial need; be on a class rank - top third with good academic record; be active volunteer in school, community, or other extracurricular activities. **Application Requirements:** Application form can be downloaded online. Applicants must complete the scholarship application. Applicants must also attach the following requirements: letter of recommendation from your guidance counselor or a teacher; official high school transcript. Including SAT or ACT scores; copy of the essay you submitted with your college application. If you did not have to submit one, write a brief (no more than two pages) essay regarding your future goals; copy of pages 1 and 2 of your parents' most recent completed federal tax form 1040. Mail everything to Hartford Foundation College Scholarship Program. **Deadline for Receipt:** February 6. **Additional Information:** Hartford Foundation College Scholarship Program, Scholarship Management Services, Scholarship America, 1505 Riverview Rd., PO Box 297, St. Peter, MN 56082. 800-537-4180.

1050 ■ HARTFORD FOUNDATION FOR PUBLIC GIVING
10 Columbus Blvd., 8th Flr.
Hartford, CT 06106
Tel: (860)548-1888
Fax: (860)524-8346
E-mail: hfpg@hfpg.org
Web Site: http://www.hfpg.org
To provide scholarship to the students entering or enrolled in a four-year college or university.
Title of Award: Priscilla Maxwell Endicott Scholarships **Area, Field, or Subject:** General studies. **Level of Education for which Award is Granted:** Undergraduate **Number Awarded:** 4. **Funds Available:** $3,000.
Eligibility Requirements: Applicants must: be a resident of Connecticut; be a female; be active junior golfer with golf handicap; demonstrate financial need and academic excellence. **Application Requirements:** Applicants may download an application form from www.cwga.org. **Deadline for Receipt:** April 20. **Additional Information:** Deborah Boynton, Scholarship Chairwoman, 52 Mountain Spring Rd., Farmington, CT 06032. 860-826-4008. deb@creedmonarch.com.

1051 ■ HARTFORD FOUNDATION FOR PUBLIC GIVING
10 Columbus Blvd., 8th Flr.
Hartford, CT 06106
Tel: (860)548-1888
Fax: (860)524-8346
E-mail: hfpg@hfpg.org
Web Site: http://www.hfpg.org
To provide scholarship to the students who will be attending a four-year college or university.
Title of Award: Farmington UNICO Scholarships **Area, Field, or Subject:** General studies. **Level of Education for which Award is Granted:** Undergraduate **Number Awarded:** 4. **Funds Available:** $1,500.
Eligibility Requirements: Applicants must: be a Farmington or West Hartford resident; be a graduating high school senior; demonstrated financial need and academic excellence. **Application Requirements:** Applicants may obtain application materials from their high school guidance office or Farmington Chapter of UNICO National, Scholarship Committee, 11 Parkview Rd. West Hartford, CT 06110. **Deadline for Receipt:** March 15. **Additional Information:** Jim Kane. Phone: 860-229-0301 Fax: 860-826-1997.

1052 ■ HARTFORD FOUNDATION FOR PUBLIC GIVING
10 Columbus Blvd., 8th Flr.
Hartford, CT 06106
Tel: (860)548-1888
Fax: (860)524-8346
E-mail: hfpg@hfpg.org
Web Site: http://www.hfpg.org
To provide scholarship to the graduating high school senior who lives in or attends school in Greater Hartford.
Title of Award: Symee Ruth Feinburg Memorial Scholarships **Area, Field, or Subject:** Human relations. **Level of Education for which Award is Granted:** Undergraduate **Number Awarded:** 1. **Funds Available:** $3,000.
Eligibility Requirements: Applicants must: be entering a four-year college or university; pursuing a career in human services; be in a class rank- top third with good academic record; be an active volunteer in school. community, or other extracurricular activities. **Application Requirements:** Application form can be downloaded online. Applicants must complete the scholarship application. Applicants must also attach the following requirements: letter of recommendation from your guidance counselor or a teacher; official high school transcript. Including SAT or ACT scores; copy of the essay you submitted with your college application. If you did not have to submit one, write a brief (no more than two pages) essay regarding your future goals; copy of pages 1 and 2 of your parents' 2006 or most recent completed federal tax form 1040. Mail everything to Hartford Foundation College Scholarship Program. **Deadline for Receipt:** February 6. **Additional Information:** Hartford Foundation College Scholarship Program, Scholarship Management Services, Scholarship America, 1505 Riverview Rd., PO Box 297, St. Peter, MN 56082. 800-537-4180.

1053 ■ HARTFORD FOUNDATION FOR PUBLIC GIVING
10 Columbus Blvd., 8th Flr.
Hartford, CT 06106
Tel: (860)548-1888
Fax: (860)524-8346
E-mail: hfpg@hfpg.org
Web Site: http://www.hfpg.org
To provide scholarship to the graduating seniors from any public high school in the City of Hartford.
Title of Award: First Church of Christ in Wethersfield - Metcalf Scholarships **Area, Field, or Subject:** General studies. **Level of Education for which Award is Granted:** Undergraduate **Funds Available:** $625. **Duration:** 1 semester.
Eligibility Requirements: Applicants must demonstrate financial need; extracurricular activities; have a potential for completing a four-year undergraduate program; have an interview with selection committee members. **Application Requirements:** Applicants may obtain application materials from their high school guidance office or contact First Church of Christ in Wethersfield, Metcalf Scholarship Chairperson 250 Main St., Wethersfield, CT 06109. Phone 860529-1575 ext. 212

Fax: 860721-7861. **Deadline for Receipt:** March 1.

1054 ■ HARTFORD FOUNDATION FOR PUBLIC GIVING
10 Columbus Blvd., 8th Flr.
Hartford, CT 06106
Tel: (860)548-1888
Fax: (860)524-8346
E-mail: hfpg@hfpg.org
Web Site: http://www.hfpg.org
To provide scholarship to the graduating high school senior.
Title of Award: Jacob and Lewis Fox Scholarships **Area, Field, or Subject:** General studies. **Level of Education for which Award is Granted:** Undergraduate **Number Awarded:** 18. **Funds Available:** $3,000.
Eligibility Requirements: Applicants must: be a graduating high school senior; be a students attend Bulkeley, Hartford Public, or Weaver High School; entering a four-year college or university; have leadership abilities, financial need, spirit of reverence and academic excellence. **Application Requirements:** Applicants may obtain application materials from their high school guidance office. No direct application sent from Foundation. **Deadline for Receipt:** December 15. **Additional Information:** Jacob and Lewis Fox Foundation, 860-633-1429.

1055 ■ HARTFORD FOUNDATION FOR PUBLIC GIVING
10 Columbus Blvd., 8th Flr.
Hartford, CT 06106
Tel: (860)548-1888
Fax: (860)524-8346
E-mail: hfpg@hfpg.org
Web Site: http://www.hfpg.org
To provide scholarship to the graduating high school senior.
Title of Award: Marcus Garvey Scholarships **Area, Field, or Subject:** General studies. **Level of Education for which Award is Granted:** Undergraduate **Number Awarded:** 1. **Funds Available:** $1,000.
Eligibility Requirements: Applicants must: be of West Indian parentage; demonstrate financial need, community service and academic excellence. **Application Requirements:** Applicants must submit a complete application and an essay on "The significance of the life of Marcus Garvey" to the Foundation. **Deadline for Receipt:** June 30. **Additional Information:** West Indian Foundation, Inc. Scholarship Committee, PO Box 320394 Hartford, CT 06132. 860-241-0379. westindian@snet.net.

1056 ■ HARTFORD FOUNDATION FOR PUBLIC GIVING
10 Columbus Blvd., 8th Flr.
Hartford, CT 06106
Tel: (860)548-1888
Fax: (860)524-8346
E-mail: hfpg@hfpg.org
Web Site: http://www.hfpg.org
To provide scholarship to the graduating high school senior who lives in or attends school in Greater Hartford.
Title of Award: Hartford Foundation College Scholarship Program **Area, Field, or Subject:** General studies. **Level of Education for which Award is Granted:** Undergraduate **Number Awarded:** 30-40. **Funds Available:** $3,000.
Eligibility Requirements: Applicants must: be entering a four-year college or university (full-time enrollment); demonstrate financial need; be on the class rank - top third with good academic record; be an active volunteer in school, community, or other extracurricular activities. **Application Requirements:** Application form can be downloaded on-line. Applicants must complete the scholarship application. Applicants must also attach the following requirements: letter of recommendation from your guidance counselor or a teacher; official high school transcript. Including SAT or ACT scores; copy of the essay you submitted with your college application. If you did not have to submit one, write a brief (no more than two pages) essay regarding your future goals; copy of pages 1 and 2 of your parents' most recent completed federal tax form 1040. Mail everything to Hartford Foundation College Scholarship Program. **Deadline for Receipt:** February 6. **Additional Information:** Hartford Foundation College Scholarship Program, Scholarship Management Services, Scholarship America, One Scholarship Way, PO Box 297, St. Peter, MN 56082. 800-537-4180.

1057 ■ HARTFORD FOUNDATION FOR PUBLIC GIVING
10 Columbus Blvd., 8th Flr.
Hartford, CT 06106
Tel: (860)548-1888
Fax: (860)524-8346
E-mail: hfpg@hfpg.org
Web Site: http://www.hfpg.org
To award scholarship to a graduating high school senior form a public high school in the City of Hartford.
Title of Award: Hartford Grammar School Scholarships **Area, Field, or Subject:** General studies. **Level of Education for which Award is Granted:** Undergraduate **Number Awarded:** 1-3. **Funds Available:** $3,000. **Duration:** Renewable.
Eligibility Requirements: Applicants must be entering a four-year college or university (full-time enrollment); demonstrate financial need; be on class rank with good academic record; be an active volunteer in school, community, or other extracurricular activities. **Application Requirements:** Application form can be downloaded on-line. Applicants must complete the scholarship application. Applicants must also attach the following requirements: letter of recommendation from your guidance counselor or a teacher; official high school transcript. Including SAT or ACT scores; copy of the essay you submitted with your college application. If you did not have to submit one, write a brief (no more than two pages) essay regarding your future goals; copy of pages 1 and 2 of your parents' 2006 or most recent completed federal tax form 1040. Mail everything to Hartford Foundation College Scholarship Program. **Deadline for Receipt:** February 13. **Additional Information:** Hartford Foundation College Scholarship Program, Scholarship Management Services, Scholarship America, One Scholarship Way, PO Box 297, St. Peter, MN 56082. 800-537-4180.

1058 ■ HARTFORD FOUNDATION FOR PUBLIC GIVING
10 Columbus Blvd., 8th Flr.
Hartford, CT 06106
Tel: (860)548-1888
Fax: (860)524-8346
E-mail: hfpg@hfpg.org
Web Site: http://www.hfpg.org
To provide scholarship to the students entering or enrolled in a four-year college or university.
Title of Award: Hartford Whalers Booster Club Scholarships **Area, Field, or Subject:** General studies. **Level of Education for which Award is Granted:** Undergraduate **Number Awarded:** 1. **Funds Available:** $1,000.
Eligibility Requirements: Applicants must: intend to play collegiate hockey; have an outstanding hockey abilities; be a Connecticut resident; have an academic excellence. **Application Requirements:** Applicants must complete the General Scholarship Application and include a letter of recommendation from your hockey coach outlining your hockey performance and submit to Hartford Whalers Booster Club. **Deadline for Receipt:** March 20. **Additional Information:** Heather Turner Scholarship Coordinator, PO Box 273 Hartford, CT 06141. Phone: 860-643-0842. hartfordwhalersboosterclub@hotmail.com.

1059 ■ HARTFORD FOUNDATION FOR PUBLIC GIVING
10 Columbus Blvd., 8th Flr.
Hartford, CT 06106
Tel: (860)548-1888
Fax: (860)524-8346
E-mail: hfpg@hfpg.org
Web Site: http://www.hfpg.org
To provide scholarship students who are legally blind.
Title of Award: Doris E. Higley Memorial Scholarships **Area, Field, or Subject:** General studies. **Level of Education for which Award is Granted:** Undergraduate **Number Awarded:** 1. **Funds Available:** $8,000.
Eligibility Requirements: Applicants must: be a graduating high school senior or college student residing or attending school full-time in Connecticut; be legally blind; demonstrate financial need. **Application Requirements:** Applicants may obtain application materials from National Federation of the Blind of Connecticut 477 Connecticut Blvd. Ste. 217, East Hartford, CT 06108; www.nfbct.org; info@nfbct.org Fax: 860291-2795; Phone: 860289-1971. **Deadline for Receipt:** September 15.

1060 ■ HARTFORD FOUNDATION FOR PUBLIC GIVING
10 Columbus Blvd., 8th Flr.
Hartford, CT 06106
Tel: (860)548-1888
Fax: (860)524-8346
E-mail: hfpg@hfpg.org
Web Site: http://www.hfpg.org
To provide scholarship to a graduating high school senior.
Title of Award: Cecilia Hillman Scholarships **Area, Field, or Subject:** General studies. **Level of Education for which Award is Granted:** Undergraduate **Number Awarded:** 1-2. **Funds Available:** $1,000-$2,000.
Eligibility Requirements: Applicants must: be a Greater Hartford resident; be a Jewish student; be a middle third of graduating class. **Application Requirements:** Applicants may obtain application materials from Jewish Community Foundation of Greater Hartford. **Deadline for Receipt:** April 15. **Additional Information:** Michael Elfenbaum, 333 Bloomfield Ave. Ste. D, West Hartford, CT 06117; Phone: 860-523-7460 Fax: 860-231-0576; melfenbaum@jcfhartford.org.

1061 ■ HARTFORD FOUNDATION FOR PUBLIC GIVING
10 Columbus Blvd., 8th Flr.
Hartford, CT 06106
Tel: (860)548-1888
Fax: (860)524-8346
E-mail: hfpg@hfpg.org
Web Site: http://www.hfpg.org
To provide scholarship to a graduating Jewish female high school senior.
Title of Award: Ernest and Charlotte Hirst Family Scholarships **Area, Field, or Subject:** General studies. **Level of Education for which Award is Granted:** Undergraduate **Number Awarded:** 1-2. **Funds Available:** $3,000-$10,000. **Duration:** Renewable.
Eligibility Requirements: Applicants must: be attending a four-year college or university; be a Greater Hartford resident; have a minimum B average; be an active involvement in the Jewish community. **Application Requirements:** Applicants may obtain application materials from Jewish Community Foundation of Greater Hartford. **Deadline for Receipt:** April 15. **Additional Information:** Michael Elfenbaum, 333 Bloomfield Ave. Ste. D, West Hartford, CT 06117; Phone: 860-523-7460 Fax: 860-231-0576; melfenbaum@jcfhartford.org.

1062 ■ HARTFORD FOUNDATION FOR PUBLIC GIVING
10 Columbus Blvd., 8th Flr.
Hartford, CT 06106
Tel: (860)548-1888
Fax: (860)524-8346
E-mail: hfpg@hfpg.org
Web Site: http://www.hfpg.org
To award scholarship to the graduating senior from eligible Greater Hartford area high school.
Title of Award: Doc Hurley Scholarships **Area, Field, or Subject:** General studies. **Level of Education for which Award is Granted:** Undergraduate **Funds Available:** $2,000-$10,000.
Eligibility Requirements: Student must be entering college in the fall semester after graduation. Eligible school can be found on www.docscholar.org. Students demonstrate financial need, academic excellence and community service. **Application Requirements:** Applicants may obtain application materials from eligible high school guidance office. Applications will not be mailed to students. Valid applications must include: Student Air Report (SAR) from FAFSA showing Estimated Family Contribution (EFC); Three letter of recommendation (teacher, guidance counselor, and non-educational person); typed essay (no more than 1 1/2 pages); High School Transcript; SAT or ACT scores. All materials must be submitted to Doc Hurley Scholarship Foundation, Inc. **Deadline for Receipt:** March. **Additional Information:** Muriel Hurley - Carter, Executive Dir. PO Box 4008 Hartford, CT 06147. Phone: 860-549-5012 Fax: 860-549-5955; dhsf@docscholar.org.

1063 ■ HARTFORD FOUNDATION FOR PUBLIC GIVING
10 Columbus Blvd., 8th Flr.
Hartford, CT 06106
Tel: (860)548-1888
Fax: (860)524-8346
E-mail: hfpg@hfpg.org

Web Site: http://www.hfpg.org
To provide scholarships to students entering a four-year college or university.
Title of Award: Interracial Scholarship Fund of Greater Hartford **Area, Field, or Subject:** General studies. **Level of Education for which Award is Granted:** Undergraduate **Number Awarded:** 1. **Funds Available:** $3,000. **Duration:** Renewable.
Eligibility Requirements: Applicants must: be graduating high school senior who lives in or attends school in Greater Hartford; be on a class rank - top third with good academic record; be active volunteer in school, community, or other extracurricular activities; be involved in community service. **Application Requirements:** Application form can be downloaded online. Applicants must complete the scholarship application. Applicants must also attach the following requirements: letter of recommendation from your guidance counselor or a teacher; official high school transcript. Including SAT or ACT scores; copy of the essay you submitted with your college application. If you did not have to submit one, write a brief (no more than two pages) essay regarding your future goals; copy of pages 1 and 2 of your parents' most recent completed federal tax form 1040. Mail everything to Hartford Foundation College Scholarship Program. **Deadline for Receipt:** February 13. **Additional Information:** Hartford Foundation College Scholarship Program, Scholarship Management Services, Scholarship America, One Scholarship Way, PO Box 297, St. Peter, MN 56082. 800-537-4180.

1064 ■ HARTFORD FOUNDATION FOR PUBLIC GIVING
10 Columbus Blvd., 8th Flr.
Hartford, CT 06106
Tel: (860)548-1888
Fax: (860)524-8346
E-mail: hfpg@hfpg.org
Web Site: http://www.hfpg.org
To provide scholarship for graduating high school seniors.
Title of Award: J and K Foundation Scholarships **Area, Field, or Subject:** General studies. **Level of Education for which Award is Granted:** Undergraduate **Number Awarded:** 1-3. **Funds Available:** $1,000-$5,000.
Eligibility Requirements: Applicants must be residents of Hartford or East Hartford; must be attending a four-year college or university; must demonstrate financial need; and must be on class rank in top quarter. **Application Requirements:** Applicants must complete the General Scholarship Application and include College acceptance letter and Financial aid award letter. Submit all requirements to J and K Thomas Foundation 74 Boysenberry Court, Suffield, CT 06078; JandKschol@cox.net. **Deadline for Receipt:** April 29.

1065 ■ HARTFORD FOUNDATION FOR PUBLIC GIVING
10 Columbus Blvd., 8th Flr.
Hartford, CT 06106
Tel: (860)548-1888
Fax: (860)524-8346
E-mail: hfpg@hfpg.org
Web Site: http://www.hfpg.org
To award scholarship to the graduating high school who have arthritis or rheumatic disease.
Title of Award: Juvenile Arthritis Scholarships **Area, Field, or Subject:** General studies. **Level of Education for which Award is Granted:** Undergraduate **Number Awarded:** 3-4. **Funds Available:** $1,000.
Eligibility Requirements: Applicants must; be a graduating Connecticut, Maine, New Hampshire, Rhode Island or Vermont high school senior or college undergraduate; must have arthritis or rheumatic disease; have a school or community volunteer service. **Application Requirements:** Applicants may obtain application materials from Arthritis Foundation, Northern and Southern New England Chapter, 35 Cold Spring Rd., Rocky Hill, CT 06067; Phone: 860563-1177 ext. 102 Fax: 860563-6018; info.sne@arthritis.org. **Deadline for Receipt:** March 30.

1066 ■ HARTFORD FOUNDATION FOR PUBLIC GIVING
10 Columbus Blvd., 8th Flr.
Hartford, CT 06106
Tel: (860)548-1888
Fax: (860)524-8346

E-mail: hfpg@hfpg.org
Web Site: http://www.hfpg.org
To award scholarship to the graduating high school senior from a public high school of Hartford, West Hartford, or Plainfield.
Title of Award: Walter Kapala Scholarships **Area, Field, or Subject:** General studies. **Level of Education for which Award is Granted:** Undergraduate **Funds Available:** No specific amount.
Eligibility Requirements: Applicants must be entering a four-year college or university in the fall after high school graduation; demonstrate financial need and have an academic excellence. **Application Requirements:** Applicants must complete the General Scholarship Application and mail to Merrill Lynch Trust Company, Walter Kapala Scholarship, Hopewell Charitable Trust Center, 1300 Merill Lynch Drive, Pennington, NJ 08534. **Deadline for Receipt:** May 1. **Additional Information:** Merill Lynch Trust Company, 800-513-0742.

1067 ■ HARTFORD FOUNDATION FOR PUBLIC GIVING

10 Columbus Blvd., 8th Flr.
Hartford, CT 06106
Tel: (860)548-1888
Fax: (860)524-8346
E-mail: hfpg@hfpg.org
Web Site: http://www.hfpg.org
To provide scholarship to the eligible high school senior or college students.
Title of Award: Dr. Leizon and Barbara Kessel Scholarships **Area, Field, or Subject:** General studies. **Level of Education for which Award is Granted:** Undergraduate **Number Awarded:** 1-15. **Funds Available:** $1,000-$5,000.
Eligibility Requirements: Applicants must: be a Jewish high school senior or college student; a resident of Greater Hartford; demonstrate financial need. **Application Requirements:** Applicants may obtain an application materials from Jewish Community Foundation of Greater Hartford. **Deadline for Receipt:** April 15. **Additional Information:** Michael Elfenbaum, 333 Bloomfield Ave. Ste. D, West Hartford, CT06117. Phone: 860-523-7460
Fax: 860-231-0576; melbenbaum@jchartford.org.

1068 ■ HARTFORD FOUNDATION FOR PUBLIC GIVING

10 Columbus Blvd., 8th Flr.
Hartford, CT 06106
Tel: (860)548-1888
Fax: (860)524-8346
E-mail: hfpg@hfpg.org
Web Site: http://www.hfpg.org
To award scholarship to a graduating high school senior who lives in or attends school in Greater Hartford.
Title of Award: Herman P. Kopplemann Scholarships **Area, Field, or Subject:** General studies. **Level of Education for which Award is Granted:** Undergraduate **Number Awarded:** 1-4. **Funds Available:** $3,000. **Duration:** Renewable.
Eligibility Requirements: Applicants must: be entering a four-year college or university; demonstrate financial need; be on a top third with good academic record; be an active volunteer in school, community, or other extracurricular activities; has been a newspaper carrier in Hartford County. **Application Requirements:** Application form can be downloaded on-line. Applicants must complete the scholarship application. Applicants must also attach the following requirements: letter of recommendation from your guidance counselor or a teacher; official high school transcript. Including SAT or ACT scores; copy of the essay you submitted with your college application. If you did not have to submit one, write a brief (no more than two pages) essay regarding your future goals; copy of pages 1 and 2 of your parents' 2006 or most recent completed federal tax form 1040. Mail everything to Scholarship America, Hartford Foundation College Scholarship Program, Scholarship Management Services, 1505 Riverview Rd, PO Box 297, St. Peter, MN 56082. 800537-4180. **Deadline for Receipt:** February 6.

1069 ■ HARTFORD FOUNDATION FOR PUBLIC GIVING

10 Columbus Blvd., 8th Flr.
Hartford, CT 06106
Tel: (860)548-1888
Fax: (860)524-8346

E-mail: hfpg@hfpg.org
Web Site: http://www.hfpg.org
To award scholarship to the graduating high school senior from Greater Hartford region.
Title of Award: Lazarus Foundation Scholarships **Area, Field, or Subject:** General studies. **Level of Education for which Award is Granted:** Undergraduate **Number Awarded:** 2. **Funds Available:** $3,000.
Eligibility Requirements: Applicants must: be a current undergraduate student; have a GPA of 2.23; have 100 hours of demonstrated community service activities. **Application Requirements:** Applicants must complete the General Scholarship Application and submit it to West Indian Foundation, Inc., Scholarship Committee, 1229 Albany Ave. PO Box 320394 Hartford, CT 06132-0394. **Deadline for Receipt:** June 30. **Additional Information:** West Indian Foundation, Inc. westindian@snet.net; 860-241-0379.

1070 ■ HARTFORD FOUNDATION FOR PUBLIC GIVING

10 Columbus Blvd., 8th Flr.
Hartford, CT 06106
Tel: (860)548-1888
Fax: (860)524-8346
E-mail: hfpg@hfpg.org
Web Site: http://www.hfpg.org
To provide scholarship to the graduating senior residing in Hartford, East Hartford, Windsor, Bloomfield, Newington, West Hartford, or Wethersfield.
Title of Award: H.B. Paul Lowenberg Lions Scholarships **Area, Field, or Subject:** General studies. **Level of Education for which Award is Granted:** Undergraduate **Number Awarded:** 3. **Funds Available:** $500-$750.
Eligibility Requirements: Applicants must: be entering or enrolled in a two- or four-year college or university; demonstrate financial need and academic excellence. Preference is given to entering college students with an interest in music and the arts. **Application Requirements:** Applicants must complete the General Scholarship Application and submit it together with your Student Aid Report (SAR) to Hartford Host Lions Club. **Deadline for Receipt:** April 30. **Additional Information:** Atty. Bruce Bergman, Lions Scholarship Chairperson. 63 Imlay St. Hartford, CT 06105. Phone: 860-522-1436
Fax: 860-522-9077.

1071 ■ HARTFORD FOUNDATION FOR PUBLIC GIVING

10 Columbus Blvd., 8th Flr.
Hartford, CT 06106
Tel: (860)548-1888
Fax: (860)524-8346
E-mail: hfpg@hfpg.org
Web Site: http://www.hfpg.org
To provide scholarship to the graduating senior or college student residing or attending school full-time in Connecticut.
Title of Award: Mary Main Memorial Scholarships **Area, Field, or Subject:** General studies. **Level of Education for which Award is Granted:** Undergraduate **Number Awarded:** 1. **Funds Available:** $3,000.
Eligibility Requirements: Applicants must be legally blind and demonstrate financial need, community service, and academic excellence. **Application Requirements:** Applicants may obtain application materials from National Federation of the Blind of Connecticut 477 Connecticut Blvd. Ste. 217, East Hartford, CT 06108; www.nfbct.org; info@nfbct.org
Fax: 860291-2795; Phone: 860289-1971. **Deadline for Receipt:** September 15.

1072 ■ HARTFORD FOUNDATION FOR PUBLIC GIVING

10 Columbus Blvd., 8th Flr.
Hartford, CT 06106
Tel: (860)548-1888
Fax: (860)524-8346
E-mail: hfpg@hfpg.org
Web Site: http://www.hfpg.org
To award scholarship to the graduating senior residing in Manchester.
Title of Award: Manchester Scholarship Foundation Scholarships **Area, Field, or Subject:** General studies. **Level of Education for which Award is Granted:** Undergraduate **Number Awarded:** 80. **Funds Available:** %500-$4,000.

Eligibility Requirements: Applicants must: demonstrate financial need; have an academic excellence; be involved in community and school activities. **Application Requirements:** Mid-April. **Deadline for Receipt:** Students may obtain application materials from their Guidance Office or from Manchester Scholarship Foundation, Inc. 20 Hartford Rd. Manchester, CT 06040. **Additional Information:** Manchester Scholarship Foundation, Inc., Phone: 860-645-1673 Fax: 860-432-9136.

1073 ■ HARTFORD FOUNDATION FOR PUBLIC GIVING
10 Columbus Blvd., 8th Flr.
Hartford, CT 06106
Tel: (860)548-1888
Fax: (860)524-8346
E-mail: hfpg@hfpg.org
Web Site: http://www.hfpg.org
To provide scholarship to the students entering or enrolled in a four-year college or university.
Title of Award: Dr. Cladwell McCoy, Jr. Memorial Scholarships **Area, Field, or Subject:** Engineering, Mathematics and mathematical sciences; Science. **Level of Education for which Award is Granted:** Undergraduate **Number Awarded:** 5. **Funds Available:** $1,000.
Eligibility Requirements: Applicants must be graduating high school senior attending Bloomfield, Bulkeley, Hartford Public, Weaver, or Windsor High School. **Application Requirements:** Applicants must complete the General Scholarship Application and submit to Dr. Caldwell Mccoy, Jr. Foundation, Inc. **Deadline for Receipt:** May 15. **Additional Information:** Mr. Calvin C. Cole, Chairman and CEO, 19 Durnham St. Hartford, CT 06112. 860-243-8004.

1074 ■ HARTFORD FOUNDATION FOR PUBLIC GIVING
10 Columbus Blvd., 8th Flr.
Hartford, CT 06106
Tel: (860)548-1888
Fax: (860)524-8346
E-mail: hfpg@hfpg.org
Web Site: http://www.hfpg.org
To provide scholarship to the students attending the University of Connecticut.
Title of Award: Michaels Jewelers Foundation General Scholarships **Area, Field, or Subject:** General studies. **Level of Education for which Award is Granted:** Undergraduate **Number Awarded:** 9. **Funds Available:** $500.
Eligibility Requirements: Applicants must: be a graduating senior from Avon, Amity, Bristol Central, Ridgefield, Brookfield, Guilford, Laurelton Hall, Masuk, Nonnewaug, Simsbury, or Torrington high school; demonstrate financial need; have at least "C" GPA, making a maximum academic effort. **Application Requirements:** Applicants may obtain application materials from their high school guidance counselor at the selected school. **Deadline for Receipt:** March 1. **Additional Information:** Michael Jewelers Foundation, 203-597-4905. gems@michaelsjewelers.com.

1075 ■ HARTFORD FOUNDATION FOR PUBLIC GIVING
10 Columbus Blvd., 8th Flr.
Hartford, CT 06106
Tel: (860)548-1888
Fax: (860)524-8346
E-mail: hfpg@hfpg.org
Web Site: http://www.hfpg.org
To award scholarship to the students attending a two- or four-year college or university.
Title of Award: O'Meara Foundation Scholarships **Area, Field, or Subject:** General studies. **Level of Education for which Award is Granted:** Undergraduate **Number Awarded:** 100. **Funds Available:** $500-$3,000. **Duration:** Renewable.
Eligibility Requirements: Applicants must: be a graduating high school senior; be a resident of Hartford County; demonstrate financial need. **Application Requirements:** Applicants may obtain application materials from O'Meara Foundation, Inc. Claude-Evalyne Odiaka, 1900 Berlin Turnpike Wethersfield, CT 06109. **Deadline for Receipt:** June 1. **Additional Information:** O'Meara Foundation, Inc. Phone: 860-563-2918 Fax: 860-563-9300; bpiincmax@aol.com.

1076 ■ HARTFORD FOUNDATION FOR PUBLIC GIVING
10 Columbus Blvd., 8th Flr.
Hartford, CT 06106
Tel: (860)548-1888
Fax: (860)524-8346
E-mail: hfpg@hfpg.org
Web Site: http://www.hfpg.org
To provide scholarship to the graduating high school senior.
Title of Award: Fitzroy and Mildred Parkinson Memorial Scholarships **Area, Field, or Subject:** General studies. **Level of Education for which Award is Granted:** Undergraduate **Funds Available:** No specific amount.
Eligibility Requirements: Applicants must be of West Indian Heritage and demonstrate community service. **Application Requirements:** Applicants must complete the General Scholarship Application and submit it to West Indian Foundation, Inc. 1229 Albany Ave. PO Box 320394 Harford, CT 0132-0394. westindian@snet.net. 860241-0379. **Deadline for Receipt:** June 30.

1077 ■ HARTFORD FOUNDATION FOR PUBLIC GIVING
10 Columbus Blvd., 8th Flr.
Hartford, CT 06106
Tel: (860)548-1888
Fax: (860)524-8346
E-mail: hfpg@hfpg.org
Web Site: http://www.hfpg.org
To award scholarship to students accepted at and plan to attend Brown University.
Title of Award: Dorothy E. Hofmann Pembroke Scholarships **Area, Field, or Subject:** General studies. **Level of Education for which Award is Granted:** Undergraduate **Funds Available:** $5,000-$7,000.
Eligibility Requirements: Applicants must: be a graduating female senior from Hartford Public, Bulkeley, Weaver high school, or any female graduating senior who is a resident of Hartford; have an academic excellence; have extracurricular activities. **Application Requirements:** Applicants may obtain application materials from Bank of America, 777 Main St. Hartford, CT 06115. **Deadline for Receipt:** April 15. **Additional Information:** Brenda Betancourt, Trust Assistant, CT2-102-22-02; 860-952-7387; brenda.l.betancourt@bankofamerica.com

1078 ■ HARTFORD FOUNDATION FOR PUBLIC GIVING
10 Columbus Blvd., 8th Flr.
Hartford, CT 06106
Tel: (860)548-1888
Fax: (860)524-8346
E-mail: hfpg@hfpg.org
Web Site: http://www.hfpg.org
To provide scholarship to the graduating high school senior in the City of Hartford.
Title of Award: Day Pitney LLP Scholarships **Area, Field, or Subject:** General studies. **Level of Education for which Award is Granted:** Undergraduate **Number Awarded:** 1. **Funds Available:** $3,000.
Eligibility Requirements: Applicants must: be entering a four-year college or university (full-time enrollment); demonstrate financial need; be on the class rank - top third with good academic record; be active volunteer in school, community, or other extracurricular activities. **Application Requirements:** Application form can be downloaded on-line. Applicants must complete the scholarship application. Applicants must also attach the following requirements: letter of recommendation from your guidance counselor or a teacher; official high school transcript. Including SAT or ACT scores; copy of the essay you submitted with your college application. If you did not have to submit one, write a brief (no more than two pages) essay regarding your future goals; copy of pages 1 and 2 of your parents' 2006 or most recent completed federal tax form 1040. Mail everything to Hartford Foundation College Scholarship Program. **Deadline for Receipt:** February 6. **Additional Information:** Hartford Foundation College Scholarship Program, Scholarship Management Services, Scholarship America, 1505 Riverview Rd., PO Box 297, St. Peter, MN 56082. 800-537-4180.

1079 ■ HARTFORD FOUNDATION FOR PUBLIC GIVING
10 Columbus Blvd., 8th Flr.
Hartford, CT 06106

Tel: (860)548-1888
Fax: (860)524-8346
E-mail: hfpg@hfpg.org
Web Site: http://www.hfpg.org
To award financial support to the graduating high school senior.
Title of Award: Mary C. Rawlins Scholarships **Area, Field, or Subject:** General studies. **Level of Education for which Award is Granted:** Undergraduate **Number Awarded:** 1. **Funds Available:** $500.
Eligibility Requirements: Applicants must: be a resident of Connecticut; graduating high school senior; be entering a two- or four-year college or university; have a GPA of 2.5 or higher at end of Fall semester. **Application Requirements:** Applicants may obtain application materials from Division of Criminal Justice, The CTAAAP Scholarship Committee, 300 Corporate Place Rocky Hill, CT 06067. **Deadline for Receipt:** April 30. **Additional Information:** Patricia Alston-Tyson, 860-258-5800; patricia. alston-tyson@po.state.ct.us.

1080 ■ HARTFORD FOUNDATION FOR PUBLIC GIVING
10 Columbus Blvd., 8th Flr.
Hartford, CT 06106
Tel: (860)548-1888
Fax: (860)524-8346
E-mail: hfpg@hfpg.org
Web Site: http://www.hfpg.org
To provide scholarship to the graduating high school seniors attending public or private schools in Hartford County.
Title of Award: Bro. Dr. Frank T. Simpson **Area, Field, or Subject:** General studies. **Level of Education for which Award is Granted:** Undergraduate **Number Awarded:** 1-4. **Funds Available:** $1,500.
Eligibility Requirements: Applicants must: students who will be enrolled in a two- or four-year college or university; have an academic excellence, class rank with a minimum of 3.0 GPA; have documentation of community service and other extracurricular activities within the community and school. **Application Requirements:** Applicants may obtain application materials from their high school guidance counselor, or download from the website at www.hartfordalphas.com. Applicants must submit all requirements to Scholarship Committee Chairman BSL Educational Foundation, Inc. Alpha Phi Fraternity, Inc. PO Box 335 Hartford, CT 06141-0330. www. hartford.ocm **Deadline for Receipt:** March 31.

1081 ■ HARTFORD FOUNDATION FOR PUBLIC GIVING
10 Columbus Blvd., 8th Flr.
Hartford, CT 06106
Tel: (860)548-1888
Fax: (860)524-8346
E-mail: hfpg@hfpg.org
Web Site: http://www.hfpg.org
To award scholarship to the female adult learner - age 24 or older.
Title of Award: Town and County Club Scholarships **Area, Field, or Subject:** General studies. **Level of Education for which Award is Granted:** Undergraduate **Funds Available:** $2,000.
Eligibility Requirements: Applicant must be a resident of Greater Hartford region; must be enrolled full or part-time in an accredited community undergraduate college or university in the Greater Hartford region; must have a completion of 15 semester hours or the equivalent of academic work with a 2.5 GPA; and must demonstrate financial need. **Application Requirements:** Students may contact the Town and County Club or access the website www.townncounty.com for application form. **Deadline for Receipt:** March 3. **Additional Information:** Town and County Club, Scholarship Committee, 22 Woodland St. Hartford, CT 06105. Phone: 860-522-1109
Fax: 860-728-0758; office@towncounty.com.

1082 ■ HARTFORD FOUNDATION FOR PUBLIC GIVING
10 Columbus Blvd., 8th Flr.
Hartford, CT 06106
Tel: (860)548-1888
Fax: (860)524-8346
E-mail: hfpg@hfpg.org
Web Site: http://www.hfpg.org
To provide scholarship for entering freshmen or enrolled sophomores of Tunxis Community College.
Title of Award: Tunxis Community College Foundation Scholarships **Area, Field, or Subject:** General studies. **Level of Education for which**

Award is Granted: Undergraduate **Funds Available:** No specific amount.
Eligibility Requirements: Applicants must demonstrate financial need, community service and academic excellence. **Application Requirements:** Applicants may obtain application materials from Tunxis Community College, 271 Scott Swamp Rd. Farmington, CT 06032. **Deadline for Receipt:** August 1. **Additional Information:** David Welsh, Phone: 860-255-3513
Fax: 860-676-8906; dwelsh@txcc.commnet.edu.

1083 ■ HARTFORD FOUNDATION FOR PUBLIC GIVING
10 Columbus Blvd., 8th Flr.
Hartford, CT 06106
Tel: (860)548-1888
Fax: (860)524-8346
E-mail: hfpg@hfpg.org
Web Site: http://www.hfpg.org
To provide scholarship for graduating high school seniors.
Title of Award: West Indian Migrant Farm Workers Memorial Scholarships **Area, Field, or Subject:** General studies. **Level of Education for which Award is Granted:** Undergraduate **Funds Available:** $3,000.
Eligibility Requirements: Applicants must be of West Indian Heritage and must demonstrate academic excellence and financial need. **Application Requirements:** Applicants may obtain application materials from West Indian Foundation, Inc. Scholarship Committee, PO Box 320394 Hartford, CT 06132-0394. westindian@snet.net; www.westindianfoundation.org
Fax: 860241-0379. **Deadline for Receipt:** June 30.

1084 ■ HARTFORD FOUNDATION FOR PUBLIC GIVING
10 Columbus Blvd., 8th Flr.
Hartford, CT 06106
Tel: (860)548-1888
Fax: (860)524-8346
E-mail: hfpg@hfpg.org
Web Site: http://www.hfpg.org
To award scholarship to students entering a four-year college or university.
Title of Award: Elmer Cooke Young - Taylor Young Scholarships **Area, Field, or Subject:** General studies. **Level of Education for which Award is Granted:** Undergraduate **Number Awarded:** 6. **Funds Available:** $3,000.
Eligibility Requirements: Students must be graduating seniors from Glastonbury or Windsor High School; must demonstrate financial need; must be on a class rank - top third with good academic record; and must be active volunteers in school, community, or other extracurricular activities. **Application Requirements:** Application forms can be downloaded on-line. Applicants must complete the scholarship application. Applicants must also attach the following requirements: letter of recommendation from your guidance counselor or a teacher; official high school transcript (including SAT or ACT scores); copy of the essay you submitted with your college application (If you did not have to submit one, write a brief essay of no more than two pages regarding your future goals); copy of pages 1 and 2 of your parents' 2006 or most recent completed federal tax form 1040. Mail everything to Hartford Foundation College Scholarship Program. **Deadline for Receipt:** February 6. **Additional Information:** Hartford Foundation College Scholarship Program, Scholarship Management Services, Scholarship America, One Scholarship Way, PO Box 297, St. Peter, MN 56082. 800-537-4180.

1085 ■ HAWAII HOTEL AND LODGING ASSOCIATION
2270 Kalakaua Ave., Ste. 1506
Honolulu, HI 96815-2552
Tel: (808)923-0407
Fax: (808)924-3843
E-mail: hhla@hawaiihotels.org
Web Site: http://www.hawaiihotels.org
To provide support to students with dedication and leadership potential to work toward the standard of excellence.
Title of Award: R.W. "Bob" Holden Scholarships **Area, Field, or Subject:** Hotel, institutional, and restaurant management. **Level of Education for which Award is Granted:** Undergraduate **Funds Available:** No specific amount. **Duration:** One year.

Eligibility Requirements: Applicant must be a resident of Hawaii and a U.S citizen; must be a junior or senior attending an accredited university or college and accepted in a hotel management program; must have a minimum of 3.0 grade. **Application Requirements:** Applicants must submit a current transcript, letter of recommendation from a college professor, counselor or dean; must provide an autobiography, photograph, and career goals essay. Application form and other supporting documents must be sent to R.W. Bob Holden Scholarship Committee, Hawaii Hotel Industry Foundation, 2270 Kalakaua Ave., Ste. 1506, Honolulu, HI 96815. **Deadline for Receipt:** June 30.

1086 ■ HAWAII HOTEL AND LODGING ASSOCIATION
2270 Kalakaua Ave., Ste. 1506
Honolulu, HI 96815-2552
Tel: (808)923-0407
Fax: (808)924-3843
E-mail: hhla@hawaiihotels.org
Web Site: http://www.hawaiihotels.org
To provide support to students with dedication and leadership potential to work toward the standard of excellence.
Title of Award: Clem Judd Jr. Memorial Scholarships **Area, Field, or Subject:** Hotel, institutional, and restaurant management. **Level of Education for which Award is Granted:** Undergraduate **Funds Available:** No specific amount. **Duration:** One year.
Eligibility Requirements: Applicant must provide proof of Hawaiian ancestry; must be a resident of Hawaii; must be a junior or senior attending an accredited university or college and accepted in a hotel management program; must maintain a minimum 2.8 grade point average. **Application Requirements:** Applicants must have a proof of residency, proof of U.S. citizenship, and proof of Hawaiian ancestry; must have a current transcript of record; must have an autobiography and photograph; must provide a career goals essay; must have a letter of recommendation from a college professor, counselor or dean. Application forms and other supporting documents must be sent to Clem Judd Jr. Memorial Scholarship Committee, Hawaii Hotel Industry Foundation, 2270 Kalakaua Ave., Ste. 1506, Honolulu, HI 96815. **Deadline for Receipt:** July 1.

1087 ■ HAWAII HOTEL AND LODGING ASSOCIATION
2270 Kalakaua Ave., Ste. 1506
Honolulu, HI 96815-2552
Tel: (808)923-0407
Fax: (808)924-3843
E-mail: hhla@hawaiihotels.org
Web Site: http://www.hawaiihotels.org
To provide support to undergraduate students who wants to pursue their education.
Title of Award: Native Hawaiian Scholarships **Area, Field, or Subject:** Hotel, institutional, and restaurant management. **Level of Education for which Award is Granted:** Undergraduate **Funds Available:** No specific amount. **Duration:** One year.
Eligibility Requirements: Applicant must provide a proof of Native Hawaiian ancestry; must be a resident of Hawaii; must be a graduating senior accepted an accredited university or college; must maintain a minimum 2.8 grade point average. **Application Requirements:** Applicants must provide a proof of residency, proof of U.S. citizenship, and proof of Native Hawaii ancestry; must have a current high school report card or current college transcript (if transferring from 2 year to 4 year college); must have a autobiography, and photograph; must provide a letter of recommendation from a teacher, counselor or principal, and a career goal essay (500 words or less). Application form and other supporting documents must be sent to Native Hawaiian Scholarships Committee, Hawaii Hotel Industry Foundation, 2270 Kalakaua Ave., Ste. 1506, Honolulu, HI 96815. **Deadline for Receipt:** June 30.

1088 ■ HELLENIC NEWS OF AMERICA
26 W Chester Pike
Havertown, PA 19083
Tel: (610)446-1463
Fax: (610)446-3189
E-mail: info@hellenicnews.com
Web Site: http://www.hellenicnews.com
To encourage and support the educational aspirations of gifted high school graduates and university students of Hellenic descent and to recognize students of high scholastic achievement, and provide support for those who have financial need.
Title of Award: The PanHellenic Scholarships **Area, Field, or Subject:** General studies. **Level of Education for which Award is Granted:** Undergraduate **Funds Available:** Maximum amount of $250,000.
Eligibility Requirements: Applicants must be high school students or currently enrolled in any university. Applicant who is a high school graduate must have completed a state-certified high school, or equivalent and be registered to attend a university or educational institution of similar standing in the USA; Applicants who are currently enrolled in a university must have completed at least one year of full-time study at an accredited university in the USA. **Application Requirements:** Applicants must submit an essay that addresses the connections between Hellenic contributions to the world and America today. Applicants must complete the application form. **Deadline for Receipt:** August 31.

1089 ■ HELLENIC UNIVERSITY CLUB OF PHILADELPHIA
PO Box 42199
Philadelphia, PA 19101-2199
Tel: (215)483-7440
E-mail: hucphila@yahoo.com
Web Site: http://www.hucphila.org
To provide scholarships for students with outstanding academic qualifications and financial need.
Title of Award: Andrew G. Chressanthis Memorial Scholarships **Area, Field, or Subject:** General studies. **Level of Education for which Award is Granted:** Undergraduate **Funds Available:** $2,000.
Eligibility Requirements: Applicants must be of Greek descent; must be U.S. citizens; and must be undergraduate students who have declared majors in Greek studies. **Application Requirements:** Application form can be obtained from the HUCPhila website. Applicants must complete the application form and mail to the attention of the Scholarship Chairman. Applicants must also provide one letter of recommendation and scholastic transcripts. **Deadline for Receipt:** April 21. **Additional Information:** Scholarship Chairman at the above address.

1090 ■ HELLENIC UNIVERSITY CLUB OF PHILADELPHIA
PO Box 42199
Philadelphia, PA 19101-2199
Tel: (215)483-7440
E-mail: hucphila@yahoo.com
Web Site: http://www.hucphila.org
To provide scholarships for students with outstanding academic qualifications and financial need.
Title of Award: Christopher Demetris Scholarships **Area, Field, or Subject:** General studies. **Level of Education for which Award is Granted:** Undergraduate **Funds Available:** $1,200.
Eligibility Requirements: Applicant must be a student who is a Greek Orthodox and a U.S. citizen. **Application Requirements:** Application form can be obtained from the HUCPhila website. Applicants must complete the application form and mail to Scholarship Chairman. Applicants must also provide one letter of recommendation and scholastic transcripts. **Additional Information:** Funded by Jack and Olga Demetris in memory of their infant son. **Deadline for Receipt:** April 21. **Additional Information:** Scholarship Chairman at the above address.

1091 ■ HELLENIC UNIVERSITY CLUB OF PHILADELPHIA
PO Box 42199
Philadelphia, PA 19101-2199
Tel: (215)483-7440
E-mail: hucphila@yahoo.com
Web Site: http://www.hucphila.org
To provide scholarship for students with outstanding academic qualifications and financial need.
Title of Award: Dorizas Memorial Scholarships **Area, Field, or Subject:** General studies. **Level of Education for which Award is Granted:** Undergraduate **Funds Available:** $3,000.
Eligibility Requirements: Applicants must be enrolled full-time in a degree program at an accredited four-year college or university. High school seniors accepted for enrollment in such a degree program may also apply. **Application Requirements:** Application form can be obtained from the HUCPhila website. Applicants must complete the application form and mail to Scholarship Chairman. Applicants must also provide one

letter of recommendation and scholastic transcripts. **Additional Information:** Established in honor of the late Dr. Michael Dorizas, a widely respected Philadelphia educator and athlete. **Deadline for Receipt:** April 21. **Additional Information:** Scholarship Chairman at the above address.

1092 ■ HELLENIC UNIVERSITY CLUB OF PHILADELPHIA
PO Box 42199
Philadelphia, PA 19101-2199
Tel: (215)483-7440
E-mail: hucphila@yahoo.com
Web Site: http://www.hucphila.org
To provide scholarships for students pursuing undergraduate education at the Wharton School of the University of Pennsylvania.
Title of Award: George C. Liacouras Memorial Scholarships **Area, Field, or Subject:** General studies. **Level of Education for which Award is Granted:** Undergraduate **Funds Available:** $5,000.
Eligibility Requirements: Applicants must be of Greek descent; must be U.S. citizens; and must be enrolled full-time at the Wharton School of the University of Pennsylvania. **Application Requirements:** Application form can be obtained from the HUCPhila website. Applicants must complete the application form and mail to Scholarship Chairman. Applicants must also provide one letter of recommendation and scholastic transcripts. **Additional Information:** Established by Mrs. Effie Liacouras. **Deadline for Receipt:** April 21. **Additional Information:** Scholarship Chairman at the above address.

1093 ■ HELLENIC UNIVERSITY CLUB OF PHILADELPHIA
PO Box 42199
Philadelphia, PA 19101-2199
Tel: (215)483-7440
E-mail: hucphila@yahoo.com
Web Site: http://www.hucphila.org
To provide scholarships for students with outstanding academic qualifications and financial need.
Title of Award: Peter George Pitsakis Memorial Scholarships **Area, Field, or Subject:** General studies. **Level of Education for which Award is Granted:** Undergraduate **Funds Available:** $2,500.
Eligibility Requirements: Applicants must be of Greek descent; must be U.S. citizens; and must be undergraduate students who have declared majors in Greek studies. **Application Requirements:** Application form can be obtained from the HUCPhila website. Applicants must complete the application form and mail to Scholarship Chairman. Applicants must also provide one letter of recommendation and scholastic transcripts. **Additional Information:** Established in accordance with the request of and in memory of Peter G. Pitsakis, a past president of the Hellenic University Club. **Deadline for Receipt:** April 21. **Additional Information:** Scholarship Chairman at the above address.

1094 ■ HILLEL MONTREAL
3460 Stanley St.
Montreal, QC, Canada H3A 1R8
Tel: (514)845-9171
Fax: (514)345-6418
E-mail: romy@hillel.ca
Web Site: http://montreal.hillel.ca
To award annually the needy university students who require an additional assistance for living expenses.
Title of Award: Therese and David Bohbot Scholarship **Area, Field, or Subject:** General studies. **Level of Education for which Award is Granted:** Undergraduate **Funds Available:** No specific amount.
Eligibility Requirements: Applicants must be currently enrolled in a university. **Application Requirements:** Applicants must submit a letter explaining goals/reasons for request; proof of Quebec residency; transcript of records; acceptance letter to University; two letters of reference and Social Insurance Number. **Deadline for Receipt:** May 30.

1095 ■ HILLEL MONTREAL
3460 Stanley St.
Montreal, QC, Canada H3A 1R8
Tel: (514)845-9171
Fax: (514)345-6418
E-mail: romy@hillel.ca
Web Site: http://montreal.hillel.ca

To improve the quality and diversity of Hillel Montreal.
Title of Award: Marlene Brand Memorial Scholarship **Area, Field, or Subject:** General studies. **Level of Education for which Award is Granted:** Undergraduate **Funds Available:** $2,500.
Eligibility Requirements: Applicants must be students living and studying in Montreal. **Application Requirements:** Applicants must submit a letter stating the objectives and reasons for request, history of community involvement, proof of Quebec residency, letter of University acceptance, transcript of grades, two letters of recommendation from teachers or employers, Social Insurance number and Montreal address and telephone number. **Deadline for Receipt:** May 30.

1096 ■ HILLEL MONTREAL
3460 Stanley St.
Montreal, QC, Canada H3A 1R8
Tel: (514)845-9171
Fax: (514)345-6418
E-mail: romy@hillel.ca
Web Site: http://montreal.hillel.ca
To improve the quality and diversity of Hillel Montreal.
Title of Award: Dr. Oskar and Sally Schickler Scholarship **Area, Field, or Subject:** General studies. **Level of Education for which Award is Granted:** Undergraduate **Funds Available:** $1,000.
Eligibility Requirements: Applicants must be first year of CEGEP study. **Application Requirements:** Applicants must submit a letter stating the goals; reasons for request; proof of Quebec residency; high school transcript of records; acceptance letter; two letters of recommendation from professors and Social Insurance Number. **Deadline for Receipt:** May 30.

1097 ■ HISPANIC ASSOCIATION OF COLLEGES AND UNIVERSITIES
8415 Datapoint Dr., Ste. 400
San Antonio, TX 78229
Tel: (210)698-3805
Fax: (210)692-0823
E-mail: hacu@hacu.net
Web Site: http://www.hacu.net
To promote the development of member colleges and universities; to improve access to and the quality of post-secondary educational opportunities for Hispanic students; and to meet the needs of business, industry and government through the development and sharing of resources, information and expertise.
Title of Award: Daimler Chrysler Scholarships Award **Area, Field, or Subject:** General studies. **Level of Education for which Award is Granted:** Undergraduate **Funds Available:** $1,000.
Eligibility Requirements: Applicants must be full-time undergraduate students attending 2-to-4 year institutions; must possess a minimum cumulative GPA of 3.0. **Application Requirements:** Applicants must fill out the application form and must provide any documents showing that they are currently enrolled or accepted by a college, university, or institution. **Deadline for Receipt:** May 23.

1098 ■ HISPANIC ASSOCIATION OF COLLEGES AND UNIVERSITIES
8415 Datapoint Dr., Ste. 400
San Antonio, TX 78229
Tel: (210)698-3805
Fax: (210)692-0823
E-mail: hacu@hacu.net
Web Site: http://www.hacu.net
To promote the development of member colleges and universities; to improve access to and the quality of post-secondary educational opportunities for Hispanic students; and to meet the needs of business, industry and government through the development and sharing of resources, information and expertise.
Title of Award: HACU/Wal-Mart Achievers Scholarships **Area, Field, or Subject:** Business Administration; Management. **Level of Education for which Award is Granted:** Undergraduate **Funds Available:** $1,000.
Eligibility Requirements: Applicants must be full-time undergraduate students attending two or four year institutions and must possess a minimum cumulative GPA of 3.0. **Application Requirements:** Applicants must fill out the application form and must provide any documents show-

ing that they are currently enrolled or accepted by a college, university, or institution. **Deadline for Receipt:** May 23.

1099 ■ HISPANIC ASSOCIATION OF COLLEGES AND UNIVERSI-TIES
8415 Datapoint Dr., Ste. 400
San Antonio, TX 78229
Tel: (210)698-3805
Fax: (210)692-0823
E-mail: hacu@hacu.net
Web Site: http://www.hacu.net
To promote the development of member colleges and universities; to improve access to and the quality of post-secondary educational opportunities for Hispanic students; and to meet the needs of business, industry and government through the development and sharing of resources, information and expertise.
Title of Award: Hispanic Association of Colleges and Universities Scholarships **Area, Field, or Subject:** General studies. **Level of Education for which Award is Granted:** Undergraduate **Funds Available:** No specific amount.
Eligibility Requirements: Applicants must be Hispanic Association of Colleges and Universities member institutions; must be attending a HACU-member institution at the time applications are completed and scholarships are made. **Application Requirements:** Applicants must fill out the application form and must provide any documents showing that they are currently enrolled or accepted by a college, university, or institution. **Deadline for Receipt:** May 23.

1100 ■ HISPANIC ASSOCIATION OF COLLEGES AND UNIVERSI-TIES
8415 Datapoint Dr., Ste. 400
San Antonio, TX 78229
Tel: (210)698-3805
Fax: (210)692-0823
E-mail: hacu@hacu.net
Web Site: http://www.hacu.net
To promote the development of member colleges and universities; to improve access to and the quality of post-secondary educational opportunities for Hispanic students; and to meet the needs of business, industry and government through the development and sharing of resources, information and expertise.
Title of Award: Wachovia Scholarship Awards **Area, Field, or Subject:** Finance; Accounting; Business Administration. **Level of Education for which Award is Granted:** Undergraduate **Funds Available:** $1,000.
Eligibility Requirements: Applicants must be full-time undergraduate students attending two or four year institutions and must posses a minimum cumulative GPA of 3.0. **Application Requirements:** Applicants must fill out the application form and must provide any documents showing that they are currently enrolled or accepted by a college, university, or institution. **Deadline for Receipt:** May 23.

1101 ■ HISPANIC ASSOCIATION ON CORPORATE RESPONSIBILITY
1444 I St. NW, Ste. 850
Washington, DC 20005
Tel: (202)682-4012
Fax: (202)682-0086
E-mail: hacr@hacr.org
Web Site: http://www.hacr.org
To provide financial educational assistance to help the next generation of youth reach their full potential.
Title of Award: Hispanic Association on Corporate Responsibility Scholarship Program **Area, Field, or Subject:** General studies. **Level of Education for which Award is Granted:** Undergraduate **Funds Available:** $300,000. **Duration:** Three years.
Eligibility Requirements: Applicants must be member students of Hispanic Association of Colleges and Universities; must be full-time undergraduate students with minimum of 3.0 GPA at four-year HACU member higher education institutions who have completed at least 12 undergraduate units of any major with an interest in the entertainment, news, media, and telecommunications industries. **Application Requirements:** Applicants must submit all the required application information.

1102 ■ HISPANIC ASSOCIATION ON CORPORATE RESPONSIBILITY
1444 I St. NW, Ste. 850
Washington, DC 20005

Tel: (202)682-4012
Fax: (202)682-0086
E-mail: hacr@hacr.org
Web Site: http://www.hacr.org
To provide opportunities for students to achieve a higher education.
Title of Award: Vern W. Reeder Memorial Scholarships **Area, Field, or Subject:** General studies. **Level of Education for which Award is Granted:** Undergraduate **Funds Available:** $5,000.
Eligibility Requirements: Applicants must be accepted as full-time undergraduate or post-graduate students at a fully-accredited, non-profit vocational school, technical school, community college, college or university. **Application Requirements:** Applicants must submit all the required application information.

1103 ■ HISPANIC FACULTY STAFF ASSOCIATION
1 University Station, D5000
Austin, TX 78712
Tel: (512)471-1511
Fax: (512)471-0239
E-mail: alba.ortiz@mail.utexas.edu
Web Site: http://www.utexas.edu
To promote communication and to support networking; to serve as a voice for university, educational, professional and cultural Hispanic issues; to promote career growth, development and initial employment; and to provide opportunities for social and cultural interaction for Hispanic professionals.
Title of Award: Jamail/Long Challenge Grant Scholarships **Area, Field, or Subject:** General studies. **Level of Education for which Award is Granted:** Graduate, Undergraduate **Funds Available:** $1,000. **Duration:** One year.
Eligibility Requirements: Applicants must be Hispanic students enrolled as full-time undergraduate, graduate or transfer students at the University of Texas, Austin; must maintain satisfactory progress toward completion of their degree requirements as determined by the regular procedures of the Texas Exes. **Application Requirements:** Applicants must complete the online Continuing & Transfer Scholarship Application provided by the Office of Student Financial Services. Applicants must select "Texas Exes Scholarships" on the "Scholarship Choices" page of the application and then enter the correct scholarship code, ESA-HISPANIC, in the space provided. **Deadline for Receipt:** March 1.

1104 ■ HISPANIC NATIONAL BAR ASSOCIATION
1111 Pennysylvania Ave. NW
Washington, DC 20004
Tel: (202)223-4777
Web Site: http://www.hnba.com
To support and assist the Hispanic students on their education.
Title of Award: La Unidad Latina Foundation Scholarships **Area, Field, or Subject:** General studies. **Level of Education for which Award is Granted:** Graduate, Undergraduate **Funds Available:** $250-$1,000.
Eligibility Requirements: Applicants must be Hispanic; must have a grade point average between 2.80-3.60 out of a 4.0 GPA scale; must be enrolled in an eligible bachelor's or master's degree program at an accredited four-year college or university; must have at least one full-time year of study for undergraduate applicants, and at least one full-time semester of study for graduate applicants; must be residing in United States. **Application Requirements:** Applicants must submit the official university-issued academic transcript. Graduate students are required to submit graduate and undergraduate transcript. Applicants must have a letter of recommendation from university administrator/faculty or community leader demonstrating student leadership and commitment to civic service (200-350 words). Application form is available at the website. **Deadline for Receipt:** February 15 and October 15.

1105 ■ HISPANIC SCHOLARSHIP FUND
55 Second St., Ste. 1500
San Francisco, CA 94105
877-473-4636
Fax: (415)808-2302
E-mail: info@hsf.net
Web Site: http://www.hsf.net
To assist graduating high school seniors of Hispanic heritage obtain a bachelor's degree.

Title of Award: Ford Motor Company Scholarship Program **Area, Field, or Subject:** General studies. **Level of Education for which Award is Granted:** Undergraduate **Funds Available:** $2,500.
Eligibility Requirements: Applicant must be of Hispanic heritage; U.S. citizen or legal permanent resident with a valid permanent resident card or passport stamped I-551; graduating from high school in 2008; have a minimum GPA of 3.0 on a 4.0 scale or equivalent; enrolling full-time in a degree-seeking program at a four-year U.S. accredited institution in the U.S., Puerto Rico, U.S. Virgin Islands or Guam; must apply for federal financing aid using the Free Application for Federal Student Aid (FAFSA) at www.fafsa.ed.gov. **Application Requirements:** Applications must be submitted using the HSF online application system. **Additional Information:** In partnership with Ford Motor Company Fund. **Deadline for Receipt:** March 15. **Additional Information:** highschool@hsf.net.

1106 ■ HISPANIC SCHOLARSHIP FUND

55 Second St., Ste. 1500
San Francisco, CA 94105
877-473-4636
Fax: (415)808-2302
E-mail: info@hsf.net
Web Site: http://www.hsf.net
To assist students of Hispanic heritage obtain a college degree.
Title of Award: Hispanic Scholarship Fund (HSF) College Scholarship Program **Area, Field, or Subject:** General studies. **Level of Education for which Award is Granted:** Graduate, Undergraduate **Funds Available:** $1,000-$5,000.
Eligibility Requirements: Applicant must be of Hispanic heritage; U.S. citizen or legal permanent resident with a valid permanent resident card or passport stamped I-551; have a minimum 3.0 GPA on a 4.0 scale or the equivalent; must apply for federal financing aid using the Free Application for Federal Student Aid (FAFSA) at www.fafsa.ed.gov; must be pursuing his/her first undergraduate of graduate degree; must have plans to enroll full-time in a degree seeking program at a two-year or four-year U.S. accredited institution in the U.S., Puerto Rico, U.S. Virgin Islands or Guam. **Application Requirements:** Applications must be submitted using the HSF online application system. **Deadline for Receipt:** March 15. **Additional Information:** cctransfer@hsf.net.

1107 ■ HISPANIC SCHOLARSHIP FUND

55 Second St., Ste. 1500
San Francisco, CA 94105
877-473-4636
Fax: (415)808-2302
E-mail: info@hsf.net
Web Site: http://www.hsf.net
To assist outstanding Latinos who are heirs of the Atrisco Land Grant of New Mexico.
Title of Award: HSF/Atrisco Heritage Foundation Scholarship Program **Area, Field, or Subject:** General studies. **Level of Education for which Award is Granted:** Graduate, Undergraduate **Funds Available:** $2,000.
Eligibility Requirements: Applicant must be of Hispanic heritage; U.S. citizen or legal permanent resident with a valid permanent resident card or passport stamped I-551; have a minimum 2.0 GPA on a 4.0 scale or the equivalent; must apply for federal financing aid using the Free Application for Federal Student Aid (FAFSA) at www.fafsa.ed.gov; must be pursuing his/her first undergraduate of graduate degree; have plans to enroll full-time in a degree seeking program at a two or four year U.S. accredited institution in the U.S., Puerto Rico, U.S. Virgin Islands or Guam. **Application Requirements:** Applications must be submitted using the HSF online application system. **Deadline for Receipt:** March 15. **Additional Information:** cctransfer@hsf.net.

1108 ■ HISPANIC SCHOLARSHIP FUND

55 Second St., Ste. 1500
San Francisco, CA 94105
877-473-4636
Fax: (415)808-2302
E-mail: info@hsf.net
Web Site: http://www.hsf.net
To assist graduating Hispanic high school seniors in obtaining a bachelor's degree.
Title of Award: HSF/IDT Hope High School Scholarship Program **Area, Field, or Subject:** General studies. **Level of Education for which**

Award is Granted: Undergraduate **Funds Available:** $10,600. **Duration:** Four years.
Eligibility Requirements: Applicant must be of Hispanic heritage; US citizen or legal permanent resident with a valid permanent resident card or passport stamped I-551; graduating high school from New York City Metropolitan (Bergen, Essex, Hudson, Hunterdon, Middlesex, Passaic, and Somerset); have a minimum GPA of 3.0 on a 4.0 scale; enrolling full-time in a degree-seeking program at a four-year U.S. accredited institution in the U.S., Puerto Rico, U.S. Virgin Islands or Guam; must apply for federal financing aid using the Free Application for Federal Student Aid (FAFSA) at www.fafsa.ed.gov. **Application Requirements:** Applicants must submit application using the HSF online application system. **Deadline for Receipt:** March 15. **Additional Information:** highschool@hsf.net.

1109 ■ HISPANIC SCHOLARSHIP FUND

55 Second St., Ste. 1500
San Francisco, CA 94105
877-473-4636
Fax: (415)808-2302
E-mail: info@hsf.net
Web Site: http://www.hsf.net
To provide financial assistance to current high school seniors from Colorado and Texas.
Title of Award: Peierls Rising Star Scholarship Program **Area, Field, or Subject:** General studies. **Level of Education for which Award is Granted:** Undergraduate **Funds Available:** $5,000. **Duration:** Two years.
Eligibility Requirements: Applicant must be of Hispanic heritage; U.S. citizen or legal permanent resident with a valid permanent resident card or passport stamped I-551; have a minimum GPA of 2.50 and maximum of 2.99 on a 4.0 scale; enrolling full-time in a degree-seeking program at a four-year U.S. accredited institution in the U.S., Puerto Rico, U.S. Virgin Islands or Guam; must apply for federal financing aid using the Free Application for Federal Student Aid (FAFSA) at www.fafsa.ed.gov; reside in Colorado or Texas. Applicants must have participated in of the pre-collegiate programs: Colorado UpLift; CU-Denver Pre-Collegiate Program; College Summit Peer Leaders; Colorado "I Have A Dream"; Denver Scholarship Foundation; Big Brothers/Big Sisters of South Texas; CAMP; Communities in Schools; HSF Peer Counseling Program; UTSA Early Outreach Program; UTSA G-Force Student Mentorship; UTSA Talent Search; UTSA Upward Bound. **Application Requirements:** Applicants must apply online. Download and mail the HSF Recommender Form to Hispanic Scholarship Fund: Peierls Rising Star Scholarship Program 55 Second St., Ste. 1500 San Francisco, CA 94105. **Deadline for Receipt:** February 15. **Additional Information:** Email: highschool@hsf.net.

1110 ■ HISPANIC SCHOLARSHIP FUND

55 Second St., Ste. 1500
San Francisco, CA 94105
877-473-4636
Fax: (415)808-2302
E-mail: info@hsf.net
Web Site: http://www.hsf.net
To provide financial assistance to high school seniors entering The University of Texas at Austin.
Title of Award: TU@UT HSF College Scholarship Program **Area, Field, or Subject:** General studies. **Level of Education for which Award is Granted:** Undergraduate **Funds Available:** $2,500.
Eligibility Requirements: Applicant must be of Hispanic heritage; U.S. citizen or legal permanent resident with a valid permanent resident card or passport stamped I-551; must apply by March 1 for federal financing aid using the Free Application for Federal Student Aid (FAFSA) at www.fafsa.ed.gov; have demonstrated financial need; plan to enroll full-time at the University of Texas at Austin; be a graduate of one of the following high schools: Harlingen, Harlingen South, Rio Hondo, San Benito, Los Fresnos, Gladys Porter, Simon Rivera, James Pace, Homer Hanna, Lopez, John H. Reagan, Sidney Lanier, William B. Travis **Application Requirements:** Applications must be submitted using the HSF online application system. **Deadline for Receipt:** February 15. **Additional Information:** scholar1@hsf.net.

1111 ■ HISPANIC SCHOLARSHIP FUND
55 Second St., Ste. 1500
San Francisco, CA 94105
877-473-4636
Fax: (415)808-2302
E-mail: info@hsf.net
Web Site: http://www.hsf.net
To provide financial assistance to students who are classified as Georgia residents.
Title of Award: University Alliance HSF/UGA College Scholarship Program **Area, Field, or Subject:** General studies. **Level of Education for which Award is Granted:** Undergraduate **Funds Available:** $2,500.
Eligibility Requirements: Applicant must be of Hispanic heritage; U.S. citizen or legal permanent resident with a valid permanent resident card or passport stamped I-551; must apply by March 1 for federal financing aid using the Free Application for Federal Student Aid (FAFSA) at www.fafsa.ed.gov; must demonstrate financial need; have a minimum 3.0 GPA on a 4.0 scale; plan to enroll full-time at the University of Georgia. **Application Requirements:** Applicants must use the HSF online application system in applying for the scholarship. **Additional Information:** Students planning to enroll at University of Georgia must be continuing graduates or transfer students. **Deadline for Receipt:** March 15. **Additional Information:** scholar1@hsf.net.

1112 ■ HISPANIC SCHOLARSHIP FUND
55 Second St., Ste. 1500
San Francisco, CA 94105
877-473-4636
Fax: (415)808-2302
E-mail: info@hsf.net
Web Site: http://www.hsf.net
To assist high school seniors of Hispanic heritage from Hidalgo County in Texas obtain a bachelor's degree.
Title of Award: Valley Alliance of Mentors for Opportunities and Scholarship (VAMOS) Program **Area, Field, or Subject:** General studies. **Level of Education for which Award is Granted:** Undergraduate **Funds Available:** $5,000 per year. **Duration:** Four Years.
Eligibility Requirements: Applicants must be of Hispanic heritage; U.S. citizen or legal permanent resident with a valid permanent resident card or passport stamped I-551; graduating high school from Hidalgo County, Texas; belong to the top 25% of high school graduating class; have a minimum GPA of 3.0 on a 4.0 scale or equivalent; plan to enroll full-time in a degree-seeking program at a four-year U.S. accredited institution in the U.S., Puerto Rico, U.S. Virgin Islands or Guam; apply for federal financing aid using the Free Application for Federal Student Aid (FAFSA) at www.fafsa.ed.gov. **Application Requirements:** Applications must be submitted using the HSF online application system. **Deadline for Receipt:** February 29. **Additional Information:** highschool@hsf.net.

1113 ■ HISPANIC SCHOLARSHIP FUND
55 Second St., Ste. 1500
San Francisco, CA 94105
877-473-4636
Fax: (415)808-2302
E-mail: info@hsf.net
Web Site: http://www.hsf.net
To provide financial assistance to new students of Western Governors University.
Title of Award: Western Governors University Scholarship Program **Area, Field, or Subject:** General studies. **Level of Education for which Award is Granted:** Undergraduate **Funds Available:** $1,200.
Eligibility Requirements: Applicants must be of Hispanic heritage; U.S. citizen or legal permanent resident with a valid permanent resident card or passport stamped I-551; have a minimum 3.0 GPA on a 4.0 scale or the equivalent; must apply for federal financing aid using the Free Application for Federal Student Aid (FAFSA) at www.fafsa.ed.gov; be enrolled at Western Governors University. **Application Requirements:** Applicants must use the HSF online application system. **Deadline for Receipt:** 30th of each month. **Additional Information:** scholar1@hsf.net.

1114 ■ HOLOCAUST AND HUMAN RIGHTS CENTER OF MAINE
University of Maine at Augusta
46 University Dr.
Augusta, ME 04330-1644
Tel: (207)621-3530
E-mail: infohhrc@maine.edu
Web Site: http://www.hhrc.uma.edu
To provide financial assistance for high school students residing in Maine.
Title of Award: Lawrence Alan Spiegel Remembrance Scholarships **Area, Field, or Subject:** General studies. **Level of Education for which Award is Granted:** Undergraduate **Funds Available:** $1,000.
Eligibility Requirements: Applicants must be high school seniors or home-schoolers who are residents of Maine and who have been accepted at any accredited and Title IV eligible college, university or technical school. **Application Requirements:** Applicants must write an essay on "Why is it important that the remembrance, history and lessons of the Holocaust be passed to a new generation?" The essay is not to exceed four typed, double-spaced pages. The essay must be accompanied by a self-addressed, stamped envelope and a completed application. Applications may be downloaded from the website or may be requested by mail at: Holocaust and Human Rights Center of Maine, Michael Klahr Center, Lawrence Alan Spiegel Remembrance Scholarship, University of Maine at Augusta, 46 University Drive, Augusta, ME 04330. (When writing for an application, please include a stamped, self addressed envelope). **Deadline for Receipt:** March 31.

1115 ■ HERBERT HOOVER PRESIDENTIAL LIBRARY ASSOCIATION
PO Box 696
West Branch, IA 52358
Tel: (319)643-5327
Free: 800-828-0475
Fax: (319)634-2391
E-mail: info@hooverassociation.org
Web Site: http://www.hooverassociation.org
To encourage academic excellence and innovativeness among young students of Iowa by providing educational assistance.
Title of Award: Herbert Hoover Uncommon Student Awards **Area, Field, or Subject:** General Studies. **Level of Education for which Award is Granted:** Undergraduate **Number Awarded:** 3. **Funds Available:** $5,000.
Eligibility Requirements: Applicant must be a senior in an Iowa high school or a home schooled program in the fall of 2008; program is not open to the child or grandchild of a staff member or trustee of the Hoover Library Association, Library-Museum or National Historic Site. **Application Requirements:** Applicant must submit completed application available in the website, along with project proposal and two letters of recommendation (recommendation forms are available at the website and must be sent separately) to: Hoover Library Association, P.O. Box 696, West Branch, IA 52358. **Deadline for Receipt:** March 31. **Additional Information:** Patricia Hand, Mgr. of Academic Programs, Tel: 319-643-5327 or 800-828-0475, email: scholarship@hooverassociation.org.

1116 ■ HORMEL FOODS CORPORATION
Hormel Pl.
Austin, MN 55912
Tel: (507)437-5345
Free: 800-523-4635
E-mail: media@hormel.com
Web Site: http://www.hormelfoods.com
To help academically-talented students to obtain college scholarships.
Title of Award: Hormel Foods Charitable Trust Scholarships **Area, Field, or Subject:** General studies. **Level of Education for which Award is Granted:** Undergraduate **Funds Available:** Maximum amount of $3,000. **Duration:** 4 years.
Eligibility Requirements: Applicants must be high school senior students who will enter an accredited college. **Application Requirements:** Applicants must submit a complete application form and Preliminary Scholastic Aptitude Test Scores.

1117 ■ HOSPITALITY ASSOCIATION OF SOUTH CAROLINA
PO Box 7577
Columbia, SC 29201
Tel: (803)765-9000
Free: 800-803-4272
Fax: (803)252-7136
E-mail: tom@schospitality.org
Web Site: http://www.schospitality.org

To encourage educational pursuits by providing financial assistance.
Title of Award: Prostart National Certificate of Achievement Scholarships
Area, Field, or Subject: Culinary Arts. **Level of Education for which Award is Granted:** Undergraduate **Funds Available:** $2,000.
Eligibility Requirements: Applicants must be students who earned a Prostart National Certificate of Achievement; must be citizens or permanent residents of the United States of America; and must be graduating high school seniors or juniors who will study culinary arts and food service management at accredited culinary schools, colleges or universities. **Application Requirements:** Applicants must have a signed hard copy of the online application, signed by the parents or guardian if under 18; must submit typed case-study; a copy of current high school transcript of records; if you are graduating senior, transcript must include grades of senior year and a letter of acceptance from the culinary school, college or university; must include a letter of intent stating the plan to enroll in an accredited restaurant or food service program for a minimum of nine credits for high school juniors. **Deadline for Receipt:** August 15. **Additional Information:** 175 West Jackson Blvd., Ste. 1500 Chicago, IL 60604-2702.

1118 ■ HOSPITALITY ASSOCIATION OF SOUTH CAROLINA

PO Box 7577
Columbia, SC 29201
Tel: (803)765-9000
Free: 800-803-4272
Fax: (803)252-7136
E-mail: tom@schospitality.org
Web Site: http://www.schospitality.org
To provide educational assistance for students who demonstrate an interest in and commitment to the hospitality (restaurant, lodging tourism) industry.
Title of Award: South Carolina Tourism and Hospitality Educational Foundation Scholarships **Area, Field, or Subject:** Travel and tourism. **Level of Education for which Award is Granted:** Undergraduate **Funds Available:** No specific amount.
Eligibility Requirements: Applicants must be currently employed in the hospitality industry and/or enrolled in an industry-related educational program at an accredited institution. **Application Requirements:** Applicants must submit a completed application form; three letters of reference; three completed Character Reference Forms; current official transcript; and a double-spaced essay (minimum of 500 words and maximum of 1,000 words). **Deadline for Receipt:** April 11. **Additional Information:** PO Box 7577 Columbia, SC 29202.

1119 ■ HOSPITALITY ASSOCIATION OF SOUTH CAROLINA

PO Box 7577
Columbia, SC 29201
Tel: (803)765-9000
Free: 800-803-4272
Fax: (803)252-7136
E-mail: tom@schospitality.org
Web Site: http://www.schospitality.org
To encourage educational pursuits by providing financial assistance.
Title of Award: South Carolina Undergraduate Scholarships **Area, Field, or Subject:** Culinary arts. **Level of Education for which Award is Granted:** Undergraduate **Funds Available:** No specific amount.
Eligibility Requirements: Applicants must be enrolled in a post-secondary restaurant/hospitality program and must be attending an accredited post college or university in South Carolina. **Application Requirements:** Applicants must submit a completed application form along with a one-to-two-page essay outlining their career goals and dreams. **Additional Information:** monica@schospitality.org.

1120 ■ HOUGHTON MIFFLIN COMPANY

222 Berkeley St.
Boston, MA 02116
Tel: (617)351-5000
Web Site: http://www.hmco.com
To provide financial assistance to high school student working to affect change in the community.
Title of Award: Gerda and Kurt Klein Scholarships **Area, Field, or Subject:** General studies. **Level of Education for which Award is Granted:** High School **Number Awarded:** 1. **Funds Available:** $10,000.

Eligibility Requirements: Applicant must be a high school student who works to affect change in the community by fostering ethnic and religious tolerance and acting against bigotry and hatred. **Application Requirements:** Applicants must submit a completed scholarship application form, 500-word essay, letter of recommendation and official high school transcript in one envelope to Gerda and Kurt Klein Scholarships, c/o Houghton Mifflin Harcourt Scholarships 6277 Sea Harbor Drive Orlando, FL 32887. **Deadline for Receipt:** August 30.

1121 ■ HUNGARIAN AMERICAN COALITION

1120 Connecticut Ave. NW, Ste. 280
Washington, DC 20036
Tel: (202)296-9505
Fax: (202)775-5175
E-mail: hac@hacusa.org
Web Site: http://www.hacusa.org
To provide partial annual scholarships for Hungarian students who will be admitted at any U.S. college or university.
Title of Award: Dr. Elemer and Eva Kiss Scholarships Fund **Area, Field, or Subject:** General studies. **Level of Education for which Award is Granted:** Undergraduate **Number Awarded:** 2-4. **Funds Available:** $1,000. **Duration:** 1 year.
Eligibility Requirements: Applicant must be a citizen of Hungary or a member of an ethnic Hungarian community in Slovakia, Romania, Voivodina, Serbia, or Ukraine; must have gained admission as a full-time student to a U.S. college or university. **Application Requirements:** Applicants must provide proof of scholarship and other sources of financial support; record of excellent academic standing; and two letters of recommendation regarding the applicant's personal and academic achievements. **Additional Information:** Scholarship recipients are asked to provide a copy of their registration form and are expected to keep the Coalition informed of their academic progress. **Additional Information:** Hungarian American Coalition at the above address.

1122 ■ HYDROCEPHALUS ASSOCIATION

870 Market St., Ste. 705
San Francisco, CA 94102
Tel: (415)732-7040; 888-598-3789
Fax: (415)732-7044
E-mail: info@hydroassoc.org
Web Site: http://www.hydroassoc.org
To offer scholarships to young adults with hydrocephalus.
Title of Award: Anthony Abbene Scholarships **Area, Field, or Subject:** General studies. **Level of Education for which Award is Granted:** Undergraduate **Funds Available:** $500.
Eligibility Requirements: Applicants must be between 17 and 30 years old and have hydrocephalus. **Application Requirements:** Applicants must check the available website for details. **Additional Information:** This fund was established in 2002 by Anthony Abbene's extended family. Anthony is a teenager with hydrocephalus. This fund awards two scholarships in honor of Anthony and to help others with hydrocephalus with their education. **Deadline for Receipt:** April 1. **Additional Information:** Hydrocephalus Association at the above address

1123 ■ HYDROCEPHALUS ASSOCIATION

870 Market St., Ste. 705
San Francisco, CA 94102
Tel: (415)732-7040; 888-598-3789
Fax: (415)732-7044
E-mail: info@hydroassoc.org
Web Site: http://www.hydroassoc.org
To offer scholarships to young adults with hydrocephalus.
Title of Award: Justin Scot Alston Memorial Scholarships **Area, Field, or Subject:** General studies. **Level of Education for which Award is Granted:** Undergraduate **Funds Available:** $500.
Eligibility Requirements: Applicants must be between 17 and 30 years old and have hydrocephalus. **Application Requirements:** Applicants must check the available website for details. **Additional Information:** Gloria M. Alston established this scholarship in loving memory of her son, Justin Scot Alston, who died in 2004. Justin received a Hydrocephalus Association scholarship in 2002 and will be remembered for his tremendous upbeat attitude and for all that he accomplished during his short life. **Deadline for Receipt:** April 1. **Additional Information:** Hydrocephalus Association at the above address

1124 ■ HYDROCEPHALUS ASSOCIATION

870 Market St., Ste. 705
San Francisco, CA 94102
Tel: (415)732-7040; 888-598-3789
Fax: (415)732-7044
E-mail: info@hydroassoc.org
Web Site: http://www.hydroassoc.org
To offer scholarships to young adults with hydrocephalus.
Title of Award: Laura Beckley Barsotti Memorial Scholarships **Area, Field, or Subject:** General studies. **Level of Education for which Award is Granted:** Undergraduate **Funds Available:** $500.
Eligibility Requirements: Applicants must be between 17 and 30 years old and have hydrocephalus. **Application Requirements:** Applicants must check the available website for details. **Additional Information:** The Beckley-Clark family established this scholarship in 2008 in loving memory of Laura Beckley Barsotti. Of particular interest are candidates who express an interest in education or social work. **Deadline for Receipt:** April 1. **Additional Information:** Hydrocephalus Association at the above address

1125 ■ HYDROCEPHALUS ASSOCIATION

870 Market St., Ste. 705
San Francisco, CA 94102
Tel: (415)732-7040; 888-598-3789
Fax: (415)732-7044
E-mail: info@hydroassoc.org
Web Site: http://www.hydroassoc.org
To offer scholarships to young adults with hydrocephalus.
Title of Award: Gerard Swartz Fudge Memorial Scholarships **Area, Field, or Subject:** General studies. **Level of Education for which Award is Granted:** Undergraduate **Funds Available:** $500.
Eligibility Requirements: Applicants must be between 17 and 30 years old and have hydrocephalus. **Application Requirements:** Applicants must check the available website for details. **Additional Information:** This fund was established in 1994 by the Fudge family. Their son, Gerard, had hydrocephalus and died in 1992 at the age of 22 in the midst of his college experience. **Deadline for Receipt:** April 1. **Additional Information:** Hydrocephalus Association at the above address

1126 ■ HYDROCEPHALUS ASSOCIATION

870 Market St., Ste. 705
San Francisco, CA 94102
Tel: (415)732-7040; 888-598-3789
Fax: (415)732-7044
E-mail: info@hydroassoc.org
Web Site: http://www.hydroassoc.org
To offer scholarships to young adults with hydrocephalus.
Title of Award: Mario J. Tocco Hydrocephalus Foundation Scholarships **Area, Field, or Subject:** General studies. **Level of Education for which Award is Granted:** Undergraduate **Funds Available:** $500.
Eligibility Requirements: Applicants must be between 17 and 30 years old and have hydrocephalus. **Application Requirements:** Applicants must check the available website for details. **Additional Information:** Greg and Georgana Tocco and their families established this scholarship in 2007 in loving memory of Greg's grandfather, Mario, and in honor of the Hydrocephalus Foundation, Inc of Saugus, MA. **Deadline for Receipt:** April 1. **Additional Information:** Hydrocephalus Association at the above address

1127 ■ HYDROCEPHALUS ASSOCIATION

870 Market St., Ste. 705
San Francisco, CA 94102
Tel: (415)732-7040; 888-598-3789
Fax: (415)732-7044
E-mail: info@hydroassoc.org
Web Site: http://www.hydroassoc.org
To offer scholarships to young adults with hydrocephalus.
Title of Award: Morris and Rebecca Ziskind Memorial Scholarships **Area, Field, or Subject:** General studies. **Level of Education for which Award is Granted:** Undergraduate **Funds Available:** $500.
Eligibility Requirements: Applicants must be between 17 and 30 years old and have hydrocephalus. **Application Requirements:** Applicants must check the available website for details. **Additional Information:**
This fund was established in 2001 by Rebecca Ziskind and her family in memory of her husband, Dr. Morris Ziskind, who had NPH. After Rebecca Ziskind's death in 2005, their three surviving children and their spouses-Carrie and Dee Norton, Jerome and Rosemary Ziskind, and Janet and Charles Tarino-graciously funded one more scholarship in loving memory of their parents, so that two scholarships are now awarded from this fund. **Deadline for Receipt:** April 1. **Additional Information:** Hydrocephalus Association at the above address

1128 ■ ICE SKATING INSTITUTE OF AMERICA

17120 N Dallas Pkwy., Ste. 140
Dallas, TX 75248-1187
Tel: (972)735-8800
Fax: (972)735-8815
E-mail: isiaef@skateisi.org
Web Site: http://www.skateisi.com
To promote the intellectual growth of ISI member skaters.
Title of Award: Ice Skating Institute of America Education Foundation **Area, Field, or Subject:** General studies. **Level of Education for which Award is Granted:** Undergraduate **Number Awarded:** Varies. **Funds Available:** $4,000. **Duration:** Entire length of undergraduate study.
Eligibility Requirements: Applicants must have completed at least three years of high school or equivalent, with a minimum 3.0 grade point average (based on a 4.0 system) during the last two years; must be a current individual or professional member of the Ice Skating Institute and have been for a minimum of four years; must have participated in the ISI Recreational Skater Program at an ISI Administrative member (rink or club) program for a minimum of four years; must have participated in ISI group classes or ISI Endorsed Competitions within the last two years. Must have completed 120 hours of volunteer service, of which at least 60 hours must be in association with an ISI member facility; must enroll and carry the minimum number of credit hours necessary to be a full time undergraduate student. Teachers or instructors must be a current Professional Member of the Ice Skating Institute, teaching the ISI program at an ISI Administrative Member (rink or club). Instructor status must be verified by the ISI Administrative Member. **Application Requirements:** Applicants must submit completed application form, two evaluation forms (one from the supervisor at the site where a majority of the volunteer service took place and the second from an adult not associated with ice skating and not a relative of the applicant) and a statement of 500 words or less, typed or printed explaining "Why I should receive an ISIA Education Foundation Scholarship." **Deadline for Receipt:** March 1.

1129 ■ IDAHO COMMUNITY FOUNDATION

210 W State St.
Boise, ID 83702
Tel: (208)342-3535
Free: 800-657-5357
Fax: (208)342-3577
E-mail: info@idcomfdn.org
Web Site: http://www.idcomfdn.org
To promote greater understanding of the Holocaust among high school students in Idaho.
Title of Award: Goldmann Scholarships Fund **Area, Field, or Subject:** General studies. **Level of Education for which Award is Granted:** Undergraduate **Funds Available:** $1,200.
Eligibility Requirements: Applicants must be senior students in an accredited high school or home school in Idaho; must have plans to attend an accredited Idaho Institution of higher learning during the academic year. **Application Requirements:** Applicants must submit a formal research paper, bibliography and references. **Deadline for Receipt:** April 15.

1130 ■ IDAHO COMMUNITY FOUNDATION

210 W State St.
Boise, ID 83702
Tel: (208)342-3535
Free: 800-657-5357
Fax: (208)342-3577
E-mail: info@idcomfdn.org
Web Site: http://www.idcomfdn.org
To attract the best and brightest students to the profession pursuing an accounting degree at an Idaho school.

Title of Award: Idaho Society of CPA's Scholarships **Area, Field, or Subject:** Accounting. **Level of Education for which Award is Granted:** Undergraduate **Funds Available:** $1,000.
Eligibility Requirements: Applicants must be residents of Idaho; must be enrolled as full-time students at the junior or senior level of public or private college or university in the state of Idaho majoring in accounting; must have a cumulative GPA of 2.75 or above for all class work prior to the application. **Application Requirements:** Applicants must submit a completed application form. **Deadline for Receipt:** April 16.

1131 ■ IDAHO COMMUNITY FOUNDATION

210 W State St.
Boise, ID 83702
Tel: (208)342-3535
Free: 800-657-5357
Fax: (208)342-3577
E-mail: info@idcomfdn.org
Web Site: http://www.idcomfdn.org
To recognize and encourage outstanding Idaho students pursuing first certificates or degree in professional-technical education or professional-technical teacher education at Idaho Schools.
Title of Award: Roger C. Sathre Memorial Scholarship Fund **Area, Field, or Subject:** General studies. **Level of Education for which Award is Granted:** Undergraduate **Funds Available:** $500.
Eligibility Requirements: Applicants must be residents of Idaho; must have graduated from an accredited public or private high school in Idaho or equivalent; must have maintained a cumulative GPA of 2.5 or better during the previous two years of school at an accredited high school or post-secondary school; must be enrolled as full-time students as defined by the school in a professional-technical or professional-technical teacher education program at an accredited college or university in Idaho; must be pursuing an undergraduate course of consecutive attendance and leading to a first degree, technical certificate or other approved award. **Application Requirements:** Applicants must submit a completed application form; must write an essay identifying the reasons for wanting to pursue the chosen field; must obtain two letters of recommendation, report documenting financial need and portfolio of academic and technical achievement. **Deadline for Receipt:** February 1.

1132 ■ IDAHO COMMUNITY FOUNDATION

210 W State St.
Boise, ID 83702
Tel: (208)342-3535
Free: 800-657-5357
Fax: (208)342-3577
E-mail: info@idcomfdn.org
Web Site: http://www.idcomfdn.org
To further the education of students at an accredited college, university or technical college.
Title of Award: W.L. Shattuck Scholarship **Area, Field, or Subject:** General studies. **Level of Education for which Award is Granted:** Undergraduate **Funds Available:** $1,000.
Eligibility Requirements: Applicants must be students who are high school graduates of Idaho Falls School District 91 or Bonneville School District 93 not younger than 16 or older than 26 years old; must be accepted and enrolled at an accredited higher education or technical education program. **Application Requirements:** Applicants must submit a completed application form; an official high school transcript; two letters of recommendation; resume and short statement of educational goals; must also submit the names and addresses of higher education or technical education programs to be attended and three copies of an original completed application form. **Deadline for Receipt:** April 24. **Additional Information:** 208-525-7500 ext. 274.

1133 ■ ILLINOIS STUDENT ASSISTANCE COMMISSION

1755 Lake Cook Rd.
Deerfield, IL 60015-5209
Tel: 800-899-4722
E-mail: collegezone@isac.org
Web Site: http://www.collegezone.com
To provide financial support to deserving individuals who have outstanding academic achievements.
Title of Award: Robert C. Byrd Honors Scholarships **Area, Field, or Subject:** General studies. **Level of Education for which Award is**

Granted: Undergraduate **Funds Available:** $1,500. **Duration:** Four years.
Eligibility Requirements: Applicant must be a U.S citizen or an eligible non-citizen; must be an Illinois resident; must be an Illinois high school graduate; must be enrolled, or accepted for enrollment on a full-time basis, as an undergraduate student at a U.S Department of Education-approved college in the United States. **Application Requirements:** Applicant must complete the eligibility certification form and must be sent to ISAC, 775 Lake Cook Rd., Deerfield, IL 60015-5209. **Deadline for Receipt:** July 15.

1134 ■ ILLINOIS STUDENT ASSISTANCE COMMISSION

1755 Lake Cook Rd.
Deerfield, IL 60015-5209
Tel: 800-899-4722
E-mail: collegezone@isac.org
Web Site: http://www.collegezone.com
To provide financial support to qualified individuals intending to pursue their education.
Title of Award: Illinois Student Assistance Commission Merit Recognition Scholarships **Area, Field, or Subject:** General studies. **Level of Education for which Award is Granted:** Undergraduate **Funds Available:** $1,000. **Duration:** One academic year.
Eligibility Requirements: Applicant must be a U.S citizen or an eligible non-citizen; must be a resident of Illinois; must be in the top five percent of their high school class; must take the ACT, SAT or Prairie State Achievement Exam; must attend an approved, Illinois postsecondary institution as an undergraduate on at least a half-time basis, or attend one of the nation's four approved Military Science Academies; must comply with federal Selective Service registration requirements. **Application Requirements:** Scholarship application and application documents must be sent to ISAC, 1755 Lake Cook Rd., Deerfield, IL 60015-5209. **Deadline for Receipt:** June 15.

1135 ■ IMAGINE AMERICA FOUNDATION

1101 Connecticut Ave. NW, Ste. 901
Washington, DC 20036
Tel: (202)336-6800
Fax: (202)408-8102
E-mail: bobm@imagine-america.org
Web Site: http://www.imagine-america.org
To help high school seniors attend college.
Title of Award: Imagine America Online Scholarships **Area, Field, or Subject:** General studies. **Level of Education for which Award is Granted:** Undergraduate **Funds Available:** $1,000.
Eligibility Requirements: Applicants must be enrolled in an online/distance learning experience at a participating career in college. **Application Requirements:** Applicants must complete the online application form.

1136 ■ INDEPENDENT LUBRICANT MANUFACTURERS ASSOCIATION

400 N Columbus St., Ste. 201
Alexandria, VA 22314
Tel: (703)684-5574
Fax: (703)836-8503
Web Site: http://hwww.ilma.org
To provide financial assistance to deserving students.
Title of Award: Independent Lubricant Manufacturers Association Scholarships **Area, Field, or Subject:** General studies. **Level of Education for which Award is Granted:** Undergraduate **Funds Available:** $1,000.
Eligibility Requirements: Applicant must be a citizen in a North American country; must attend or be enrolled in a college or university in North America; must be registered as a full-time student (12 credit hours or more per semester, 9 credit hours per trimester or more); must have a minimum of 3.0 cumulative GPA. **Application Requirements:** Applicant must have a letter of recommendation from teacher or advisor. Application forms are available online. **Deadline for Receipt:** June 30.

1137 ■ INDEPENDENT ORDER OF FORESTERS

789 Don Mills Rd.
Toronto, ON, Canada M3C 1T9

Tel: (416)429-3000
Free: 800-828-1540
Fax: (416)429-3896
E-mail: service@forester.com
Web Site: http://www.foresters.com
To provide opportunity for Foresters members to pursue higher learning through financial support.

Title of Award: Foresters Scholarships **Area, Field, or Subject:** General Studies. **Level of Education for which Award is Granted:** Undergraduate **Funds Available:** Up to $8,000 to cover related to post-secondary education.

Eligibility Requirements: Applicants must be Foresters members or their biological or legally-adopted dependents or children, aged 25 years or under; Foresters members and/or their spouse, aged 25 years or under; Foresters member and/or their spouse who are mature students who are currently enrolled in full-time post-secondary studies. Applicants must have performed a minimum of forty hours of community service in the 2 years prior to application. **Application Requirements:** Applicant must have the Forester life, Foresters annuity, Social Fraternal membership and a registered non-voting member; must submit the application form together with official transcript, community service achievement list, two letters of reference and a member consent form. **Deadline for Receipt:** September-November.

1138 ■ INDIANA LIBRARY FEDERATION
941 ELLA.M86th St. Ste. 2
Indianapolis, IN 46240
Tel: (317)257-2040
Fax: (317)257-1389
E-mail: lkolb@ilfonline.org
Web Site: http://www.ilfonline.org
To provide funds for at least one scholarship applicant entering or currently enrolled in a program to receive educational certification in the field of School Library Media Services.

Title of Award: Indiana Library Federation AIME Scholarships **Area, Field, or Subject:** Library and archival sciences. **Level of Education for which Award is Granted:** Undergraduate **Funds Available:** $500.

Eligibility Requirements: Applicants must be currently enrolled in an undergraduate or graduate certification program for School Library Media Services; must meet the current criteria as set by the Indiana Professional Standards Board. **Application Requirements:** Applicants must submit three letters of recommendation from which one must come from librarian. Masters candidates must submit (a) transcript or copy of official grade report for any library science courses already completed, (b) transcripts of all undergraduate education and (c) transcripts from other graduate work (may be included, but are not required). Public library certification candidates must submit (a) a copy of the approved public library certification program, (b) transcripts from undergraduate education and/or high school and (c) transcript or copy of official grade report for any course already taken toward library certification. School library media candidates must submit (a) a transcript for any education and/or library science courses already completed, (b) a transcript for all undergraduate or graduate work completed and (c) transcripts from high school may be included by candidates that have not yet completed any graduate or undergraduate work. **Additional Information:** 317-257-2040.

1139 ■ INDIANA LIBRARY FEDERATION
941 ELLA.M86th St. Ste. 2
Indianapolis, IN 46240
Tel: (317)257-2040
Fax: (317)257-1389
E-mail: lkolb@ilfonline.org
Web Site: http://www.ilfonline.org
To foster the professional growth of its members and the promotion of all libraries in Indiana.

Title of Award: Esther Schlundt Memorial Scholarships **Area, Field, or Subject:** General studies. **Level of Education for which Award is Granted:** Undergraduate **Funds Available:** $1,000.

Eligibility Requirements: Applicants must be entering or currently enrolled in an ALA-accredited graduate degree program in library and information science; or must be entering or currently enrolled in an Indiana State Library-approved library certification program. **Application Requirements:** Applicants must submit three letters of recommendation

from which one must come from a librarian; must submit transcript or copy of official grade report for any library science courses already completed for masters candidates, all undergraduate transcripts and/or high school and transcripts and a copy of official grade report for any course already taken toward library certification. School library media candidates must submit transcripts for any education and/or library science courses already completed. **Additional Information:** 317-257-2040

1140 ■ INDIANA LIBRARY FEDERATION
941 ELLA.M86th St. Ste. 2
Indianapolis, IN 46240
Tel: (317)257-2040
Fax: (317)257-1389
E-mail: lkolb@ilfonline.org
Web Site: http://www.ilfonline.org
To foster the professional growth of its members and the promotion of all libraries in Indiana.

Title of Award: Sue Marsh Weller Memorial Scholarships **Area, Field, or Subject:** Library and archival sciences. **Level of Education for which Award is Granted:** Graduate, Postgraduate, Undergraduate **Funds Available:** No specific amount.

Eligibility Requirements: Applicants must be entering or currently enrolled in an ALA-accredited program of graduate study specializing in children librarianship. **Application Requirements:** Applicants must submit three letters of recommendation from which one must come from a librarian. Masters candidates must submit (a) transcript or copy of official grade report for any library science courses already completed, (b) transcripts of all undergraduate education and (c) transcripts from other graduate work (may be included, but are not required). Public library certification candidates must submit (a) a copy of the approved public library certification program, (b) transcripts from undergraduate education and/or high school and (c) transcript or copy of official grade report for any course already taken toward library certification. School library media candidates must submit (a) official grade report for any education and/or library science courses already completed (undergraduate and/or high school), (b) a transcript for all undergraduate or graduate work completed and (c) transcripts from high school may be included by candidates that have not yet completed any graduate or undergraduate work. **Additional Information:** 317-257-2040.

1141 ■ INDIANA STATE ALUMNI ASSOCIATION
200 N 7th St.
Terre Haute, IN 47809-9989
800-GO-TO-ISU
Web Site: http://www.indstate.edu/alum/alum_assoc.htm
To support educational pursuit of students.

Title of Award: Warren M. Anderson Scholarships **Area, Field, or Subject:** General studies. **Level of Education for which Award is Granted:** Undergraduate **Funds Available:** $1200. **Duration:** One year.

Eligibility Requirements: Applicant must be entering college as freshmen at the Indiana State University; belongs to the top 30 percent of the high school; or have a GPA of 3.0. **Application Requirements:** Applicant must submit an a list of high school/community accomplishments/activities, and a letter of recommendation from a high school councilor, civic leader, principal, or minister. **Deadline for Receipt:** Must be admitted before March 1. **Additional Information:** admissions@indstate.edu.

1142 ■ INDIANA STATE ALUMNI ASSOCIATION
200 N 7th St.
Terre Haute, IN 47809-9989
800-GO-TO-ISU
Web Site: http://www.indstate.edu/alum/alum_assoc.htm
To support educational pursuit of a dependent of an alumni.

Title of Award: Child of Alumni Book Voucher Awards **Area, Field, or Subject:** General studies. **Level of Education for which Award is Granted:** Undergraduate **Funds Available:** $500 ($250 in fall and another in spring).

Eligibility Requirements: Applicant must be entering college as freshmen at the Indiana State University and a dependent of an alumni. **Application Requirements:** Student must state that he/she is a dependent of an alumni in the admission application. **Deadline for Receipt:** Must be admitted before March 1. **Additional Information:** admissions@indstate.edu.

1143 ■ INDIANA STATE ALUMNI ASSOCIATION
200 N 7th St.
Terre Haute, IN 47809-9989
800-GO-TO-ISU
Web Site: http://www.indstate.edu/alum/alum_assoc.htm
To support educational pursuit of students.
Title of Award: Gongaware Scholarships College of Business **Area, Field, or Subject:** Insurance and insurance-related; Risk management. **Level of Education for which Award is Granted:** Undergraduate **Funds Available:** $2500, notebook computer, and professionals development account. **Duration:** One year.
Eligibility Requirements: Applicant must have a competitive GPA, class rank, SAT/ACT; majoring in insurance and risk management; and entering college as freshmen at the Indiana State University. **Application Requirements:** For application, call 812237-8633. **Additional Information:** Scholar will participate in two summer internship, be assigned an industry mentor, participate in an international experience, and be offered opportunities in developing leadership skills. Scholarship is funded by Don and Patricia Gongaware. **Deadline for Receipt:** Must be admitted before December 1. **Additional Information:** admissions@indstate.edu.

1144 ■ INDIANA STATE ALUMNI ASSOCIATION
200 N 7th St.
Terre Haute, IN 47809-9989
800-GO-TO-ISU
Web Site: http://www.indstate.edu/alum/alum_assoc.htm
To support educational pursuit of students.
Title of Award: Indiana State Alumni Association Dean's Scholarships **Area, Field, or Subject:** General studies. **Level of Education for which Award is Granted:** Undergraduate **Funds Available:** $2000. **Duration:** One year.
Eligibility Requirements: Applicant must rank in the top 25 percent of the high school class; or have a GPA of 3.5; accepted at the Indiana State University campus as a freshmen. **Application Requirements:** Student must be admitted to the Indiana State University and will be automatically qualified for the scholarship. **Additional Information:** No additional application required. **Deadline for Receipt:** Must be admitted before February 1. **Additional Information:** admissions@indstate.edu.

1145 ■ INDIANA STATE ALUMNI ASSOCIATION
200 N 7th St.
Terre Haute, IN 47809-9989
800-GO-TO-ISU
Web Site: http://www.indstate.edu/alum/alum_assoc.htm
To support educational pursuit of students.
Title of Award: Indiana State Alumni Association Incentive Scholarships **Area, Field, or Subject:** General studies. **Level of Education for which Award is Granted:** Undergraduate **Funds Available:** $4000 (out-of-state tuition). **Duration:** One year.
Eligibility Requirements: Applicant must be an out-of-state freshman; have a 3.0 GPA; has a competitive SAT/ACT scores and class rank. **Application Requirements:** Student must be admitted to the Indiana State University and will be automatically qualified for the scholarship. **Additional Information:** No additional application required. Students eligible for the Southern Illinois Free Waiver and reside in the 20 Illinois counties and not eligible for the award. **Deadline for Receipt:** Must be admitted before June 1. **Additional Information:** admissions@indstate.edu.

1146 ■ INDIANA STATE ALUMNI ASSOCIATION
200 N 7th St.
Terre Haute, IN 47809-9989
800-GO-TO-ISU
Web Site: http://www.indstate.edu/alum/alum_assoc.htm
To support educational pursuit of students.
Title of Award: Indiana State Alumni Association President's Academic Excellence Scholarships **Area, Field, or Subject:** General studies. **Level of Education for which Award is Granted:** Undergraduate **Funds Available:** Full tuition. **Duration:** One year.
Eligibility Requirements: Student must belong to the top ten percent of the high school class; have a GPA of 3.7; a high school graduate entering freshmen; studying 12 or more credit hours per semester; and accepted at the Indiana State University campus. **Application Requirements:** Student must be admitted to the Indiana State University and will be

automatically qualified for the scholarship. **Additional Information:** No additional application required. **Deadline for Receipt:** Must be admitted before December 1. **Additional Information:** admissions@indstate.edu.

1147 ■ INDIANA STATE ALUMNI ASSOCIATION
200 N 7th St.
Terre Haute, IN 47809-9989
800-GO-TO-ISU
Web Site: http://www.indstate.edu/alum/alum_assoc.htm
To support educational pursuit of students.
Title of Award: Indiana State Alumni Association President's Scholarships **Area, Field, or Subject:** General studies. **Level of Education for which Award is Granted:** Undergraduate **Funds Available:** Full tuition, room and board, books and supplies, personal laptop computer. **Duration:** One year.
Eligibility Requirements: Student must belong to the top ten percent of the high school class; have a GPA of 3.7; a high school graduate entering freshmen; studying 12 or more credit hours per semester; and accepted at the Indiana State University campus. **Application Requirements:** Student must be admitted to the Indiana State University and will be automatically qualified for the scholarship. **Additional Information:** No additional application required. **Deadline for Receipt:** Must be admitted before December 1. **Additional Information:** admissions@indstate.edu.

1148 ■ INDIANA STATE ALUMNI ASSOCIATION
200 N 7th St.
Terre Haute, IN 47809-9989
800-GO-TO-ISU
Web Site: http://www.indstate.edu/alum/alum_assoc.htm
To prepare and support student from rural Indiana to return in their hometown as a primary care physician.
Title of Award: Indiana State Alumni Association Rural Health Scholarships **Area, Field, or Subject:** Physiology. **Level of Education for which Award is Granted:** Undergraduate **Funds Available:** Full tuition.
Eligibility Requirements: Applicant must have a GPA of 3.5; scoring a combined 1200 in Critical Reading (CR) and Mathematics (M) sections of the SAT or 27 on the ACT; and resides in rural Indiana. **Application Requirements:** For application, call 812237-8633. **Additional Information:** To complete the program, scholar must maintain an average GPA of 3.5. **Additional Information:** admissions@indstate.edu.

1149 ■ INDIANA STATE ALUMNI ASSOCIATION
200 N 7th St.
Terre Haute, IN 47809-9989
800-GO-TO-ISU
Web Site: http://www.indstate.edu/alum/alum_assoc.htm
To support educational pursuit of students.
Title of Award: Indiana State Alumni Association Transfer Student Scholarships **Area, Field, or Subject:** General studies. **Level of Education for which Award is Granted:** Undergraduate **Funds Available:** $1500. **Duration:** One year.
Eligibility Requirements: Applicant must have a 3.0 GPA with a minimum of 32 transferable semester hours. **Application Requirements:** Student must be admitted to the Indiana State University and will be automatically qualified for the scholarship. The application for admission serves as the scholarship application. **Additional Information:** No additional application required. **Deadline for Receipt:** Must be admitted before June 1 (fall semester) or December 1 (spring semester). **Additional Information:** admissions@indstate.edu.

1150 ■ INDIANA STATE ALUMNI ASSOCIATION
200 N 7th St.
Terre Haute, IN 47809-9989
800-GO-TO-ISU
Web Site: http://www.indstate.edu/alum/alum_assoc.htm
To support educational pursuit of students.
Title of Award: Indiana Top Scholar Award **Area, Field, or Subject:** General studies. **Level of Education for which Award is Granted:** Undergraduate **Funds Available:** $4000. **Duration:** One year.
Eligibility Requirements: Applicant must be entering college as freshmen at the Indiana State University; ranking first to fifth in their senior class; have a GPA of 3.0; and have academic honors diplomas. **Application Requirements:** Student must be admitted to the Indiana State

University and will be automatically qualified for the scholarship. **Additional Information:** No additional application required. **Deadline for Receipt:** Must be admitted before March 1. **Additional Information:** admissions@indstate.edu.

1151 ■ INDIANA STATE ALUMNI ASSOCIATION

200 N 7th St.
Terre Haute, IN 47809-9989
800-GO-TO-ISU
Web Site: http://www.indstate.edu/alum/alum_assoc.htm
To provide students unique opportunities in experimental learning.
Title of Award: Lilly Fellow Scholarships **Area, Field, or Subject:** General studies. **Level of Education for which Award is Granted:** Undergraduate **Funds Available:** $5000. **Duration:** One year.
Eligibility Requirements: Applicant must have a GPA of 3.0 with 32 transferable credit hours. **Application Requirements:** Applicants must submit an essay on their interest of being a Lilly Fellow; a letter of recommendation; and a resume. **Additional Information:** A fellow will be working with a faculty mentor on research, community service, outreach and Lilly Fellow activities. **Additional Information:** University Center for Public Service and Community Engagement, 812-237-7900.

1152 ■ INDIANA STATE ALUMNI ASSOCIATION

200 N 7th St.
Terre Haute, IN 47809-9989
800-GO-TO-ISU
Web Site: http://www.indstate.edu/alum/alum_assoc.htm
To support educational pursuit of students.
Title of Award: Networks Scholarships College of Business **Area, Field, or Subject:** Finance. **Level of Education for which Award is Granted:** Undergraduate **Funds Available:** Full tuition, notebook computer, and professional development account. **Duration:** One year.
Eligibility Requirements: Applicant must be entering college as freshmen at the Indiana State University. **Application Requirements:** For application, call 812237-8633. **Additional Information:** Scholar will participate in a paid internship, attend leadership-development activities, have an international experience, and will be mentored. **Deadline for Receipt:** Must be admitted before December 1. **Additional Information:** admissions@indstate.edu.

1153 ■ INDIANA STATE ALUMNI ASSOCIATION

200 N 7th St.
Terre Haute, IN 47809-9989
800-GO-TO-ISU
Web Site: http://www.indstate.edu/alum/alum_assoc.htm
To support educational pursuit of students.
Title of Award: Sycamore Scholar Awards **Area, Field, or Subject:** General studies. **Level of Education for which Award is Granted:** Undergraduate **Funds Available:** Half the cost of in-state tuition.
Eligibility Requirements: Applicant must be entering college as freshmen at the Indiana State University; belongs to the top ten percent of their graduating class; have a minimum of 3.0 GPA; and have completed academic honors diploma. **Application Requirements:** Student must be admitted to the Indiana State University and will be automatically qualified for the scholarship. **Additional Information:** No additional application required. Recipients will be disqualified for the Indiana Top Scholar Award. **Deadline for Receipt:** Must be admitted before March 1. **Additional Information:** admissions@indstate.edu.

1154 ■ INSTITUTE OF MANAGEMENT ACCOUNTANTS

10 Paragon Dr.
Montvale, NJ 07645-1718
Tel: (201)573-9000
Free: 800-638-4427
Fax: (201)474-1600
E-mail: ima@imanet.org
Web Site: http://www.imanet.org
To help student members of IMA offset the high cost of education and pursue further studies in preparation for careers in accounting, management and finance.
Title of Award: Stuart Cameron and Margaret McLeod Memorial Scholarships (SCMS) **Area, Field, or Subject:** Accounting; Management; Finance. **Level of Education for which Award is Granted:** Graduate,

Undergraduate **Number Awarded:** 2. **Funds Available:** $5,000 and lodging, transportation and registrations costs for the Annual Conference in June and the Student Conference in November.
Eligibility Requirements: Applicants must be IMA student members (membership number must be indicated in the application); may either be a full or part-time student with strictly 12 credits per semester; must be physically located in the United States or Puerto Rico studying at regionally accredited institutions; have a minimum GPA of 3.0 throughout undergraduate/graduate academic career; pursuing a career in management accounting, financial management, or information. **Application Requirements:** Applicants must submit a one-page resume; official university transcripts with school seal and enclosed in a sealed envelope; two recommendations (from a current or past employer, a current or past professor or an IMA member) submitted on the attached form and sealed in an envelope with the reference's signature across the seal; two-page written statement indicating the applicant's reason for applying for the scholarship, reasons why she/he deserves the award, specific contributions to IMA and ideas on how he/she will promote awareness and increase membership and certification within IMA. **Additional Information:** Scholarship has two categories, undergraduate and graduate student category. **Deadline for Receipt:** February 15. **Additional Information:** Jodi Ryan at (800)638-4427, ext. 1556 or jryan@imanet.org.

1155 ■ INSTITUTE OF MANAGEMENT ACCOUNTANTS

10 Paragon Dr.
Montvale, NJ 07645-1718
Tel: (201)573-9000
Free: 800-638-4427
Fax: (201)474-1600
E-mail: ima@imanet.org
Web Site: http://www.imanet.org
To help student members of IMA offset the high cost of education and pursue further studies in preparation for careers in accounting, management and finance.
Title of Award: IMA Memorial Education Fund Scholarships (MEF) **Area, Field, or Subject:** Accounting; Management; Finance. **Level of Education for which Award is Granted:** Graduate, Undergraduate **Number Awarded:** 2. **Funds Available:** $1,000-$2,500.
Eligibility Requirements: Applicants must be IMA student members (membership number must be indicated in the application); must be physically located in the United States or Puerto Rico and is currently studying at regionally accredited institutions; must have a minimum GPA of 3.0 throughout undergraduate/graduate academic career; pursuing a career in management accounting, financial management, or information. **Application Requirements:** Applicants must submit a one-page resume; official university transcripts with school seal and enclosed in a sealed envelope; two letters of recommendations (from a current or past employer, a current or past professor or an IMA member) submitted on the attached form and sealed in an envelope with the reference's signature across the seal; two-page written statement indicating the applicant's reason for applying for the scholarship, statements why the applicant deserves the award, specific contributions to IMA, and suggestions on promoting awareness and increase membership and certification within IMA. **Additional Information:** Scholarship has two categories, undergraduate and graduate student category. **Deadline for Receipt:** February 15. **Additional Information:** Jodi Ryan at (800)638-4427, ext. 1556 or jryan@imanet.org.

1156 ■ INSTITUTE OF REAL ESTATE MANAGEMENT

430 N Michigan Ave.
Chicago, IL 60611
Tel: 800-837-0706
Fax: 800-338-4736
E-mail: custserv@irem.org
Web Site: http://www.irem.org
To facilitate increased minority participation in the real estate management industry by providing educational assistance.
Title of Award: George M. Brooker Collegiate Scholarships for Minorities **Area, Field, or Subject:** Real Estate; Management. **Level of Education for which Award is Granted:** Graduate, Postgraduate, Undergraduate **Number Awarded:** 2 (undergraduate); 1 (graduate). **Funds Available:** $1,000 (undergraduate); $2,500 (graduate). **Duration:** Annual.

Eligibility Requirements: Applicant must be a member of a minority (non-Caucasian) group; must be a citizen of the United States; must be beginning junior or senior year of undergraduate work or pursuing graduate or post-graduate studies; has declared a major in real estate or a related field; have a minimum GPA of 3.0 on a 4.0 scale within his or her major; and has completed two courses in real estate or indicate intent to complete such courses. **Application Requirements:** Applicant must submit complete application (available in the website), three letters of recommendation of which one must come from the college dean, written essay (not to exceed 500 words) explaining the applicant's interest in the industry, and a letter of recommendation from local IREM chapter president or officer. Forward materials to: IREM Foundation Administrator, Attn: Furbush Scholarship: CPM, 430 N. Michigan Ave., Chicago, IL 60611-4090. **Deadline for Receipt:** March 31.

1157 ■ INSTITUTE OF TURKISH STUDIES

Intercultural Center - Box 571033
Georgetown University
Washington, DC 20057-1033
Tel: (202)687-0295
Fax: (202)687-3780
Web Site: http://www.turkishstudies.org
To honor competent student to study in Turkey.
Title of Award: Institute of Turkish Studies Undergraduate Study Grants **Area, Field, or Subject:** General studies. **Level of Education for which Award is Granted:** Undergraduate **Funds Available:** $10,000.
Eligibility Requirements: Applicant must be a U.S. citizen; enrolled in college or university in United States. **Application Requirements:** Applicant must send grant application cover sheet (available at the website); a project proposal (maximum of 3 pages, double-spaced); and a budget. Applications must be sent electronically in MAS Word or PDF format to dcc@turkishstudies.org and the supporting documents by regular mail. **Deadline for Receipt:** March. **Additional Information:** dcc@turkishstudies.org.

1158 ■ INSURANCE SCHOLARSHIP FOUNDATION OF AMERICA

PO Box 866
Hendersonville, NC 28793-0866
Tel: (828)890-3328; (866)379-4732
Fax: (828)891-2997
E-mail: foundation@inssfa.org
Web Site: http://www.inssfa.org
To promote excellence in the insurance industry by underwriting the education of current and future employees.
Title of Award: Insurance Scholarship Foundation of America College Scholarships **Area, Field, or Subject:** Insurance and insurance-related fields. **Level of Education for which Award is Granted:** Undergraduate **Funds Available:** $500-$5,000.
Eligibility Requirements: Applicants must be candidates for a bachelor's or higher degree with a major in insurance, risk management, or actuarial science; must be currently attending a college or university and be completing or have completed the second year of college; must have successfully completed two insurance, risk management, or actuarial science courses having a minimum of three credit hours each; and must have achieved at least 3.0 grade point average on a 4.0 scale. **Application Requirements:** Applicants must submit a completed application form.

1159 ■ INSURANCE SCHOLARSHIP FOUNDATION OF AMERICA

PO Box 866
Hendersonville, NC 28793-0866
Tel: (828)890-3328; (866)379-4732
Fax: (828)891-2997
E-mail: foundation@inssfa.org
Web Site: http://www.inssfa.org
To promote excellence in the insurance industry by underwriting the education of current and future employees.
Title of Award: Marsh College Scholarships **Area, Field, or Subject:** Insurance and insurance-related fields. **Level of Education for which Award is Granted:** Undergraduate **Funds Available:** $500-$5,000.
Eligibility Requirements: Applicants must be candidates for a bachelor's or higher degree with a major in insurance, risk management or actuarial science; must be currently attending a college or university and be completing or have completed the second year of college; must have suc-

cessfully completed two insurance, risk management, or actuarial science courses having a minimum of three credit hours each; and must have achieved at least 3.0 grade point of average on a 4.0 scale. **Application Requirements:** Applicants must submit a completed application form.

1160 ■ INTERMEDIARIES AND REINSURANCE UNDERWRITERS ASSOCIATION

971 Rte. 202 N
Branchburg, NJ 08876
Tel: (908)203-0211
Fax: (908)203-0213
E-mail: info@irua.com
Web Site: http://www.irua.com
To provide an opportunity for college juniors and seniors to learn about the reinsurance industry and gain practical experience in its operation.
Title of Award: Intermediaries and Reinsurance Underwriters Association Scholarships **Area, Field, or Subject:** Insurance and insurance-related fields. **Level of Education for which Award is Granted:** Undergraduate **Funds Available:** $400. **Duration:** One week.
Eligibility Requirements: Applicants must be full-time students enrolled in an undergraduate program at an accredited four-year college or university; have at least one term remaining following completion of the intern program; have an overall GPA of at least 3.0 and two recommendations from faculty advisor, dean or department chairman; must be enrolled in degree program with a major in insurance, economics, business or a related field; and must be U.S. citizens of at least 18 years of age. **Application Requirements:** Applicants must submit all required application information.

1161 ■ INTERNATIONAL ALUMNI ASSOCIATION OF SHRI MAHAVIR JAIN VIDYALAYA

1119 Flanders St.
Garner, NC 27529
Tel: (919)772-8473
Web Site: http://www.iaamjv.org
To promote the cause of college education in the Jain community.
Title of Award: College Education Loan Scholarships For U.S. Resident Students **Area, Field, or Subject:** General studies. **Level of Education for which Award is Granted:** Undergraduate **Number Awarded:** 10. **Funds Available:** $2,000 for the first year and $1,000 annually for next three years of undergraduate studies.
Eligibility Requirements: Applicant must be born in Jain Family or actively practicing Jainism; graduating U.S. High School senior; have a minimum GPA of 3.0 on 4.0 scale; or a minimum SAT score of 1500 out of max. 2400; or Minimum ACT score of 20; enrolled full-time Undergraduate student in U.S.; a U.S. permanent resident or U.S. Citizen; and in need for financial assistance. **Application Requirements:** Applicants must submit a completed application form. **Additional Information:** This is an interest-free loan scholarship. **Deadline for Receipt:** June 30. **Additional Information:** Dr. Dinesh M. Shah Chairman, College Education Loan Committee 2034 Via Del Rey South Pasadena, CA 91030-4146.

1162 ■ INTERNATIONAL ASSOCIATION OF BLACK ACTUARIES

19 S LaSalle St., Ste. 1400
Chicago, IL 60603
Tel: (215)392-4598
Fax: (215)395-6400
E-mail: iaba_ed@blackactuaries.org
Web Site: http://www.blackactuaries.org
To provide scholarships among undergraduates or graduate level for qualified black students who are interested in pursuing actuarial careers.
Title of Award: International Association of Black Actuaries Scholarships **Area, Field, or Subject:** Actuarial science. **Level of Education for which Award is Granted:** Undergraduate **Funds Available:** No specific amount.
Eligibility Requirements: Applicants must be permanent residents or U.S./Canadian citizens; must be admitted to college or university which offers either a program in actuarial science or courses that will serve to prepare the students for actuarial career; must have demonstrated mathematical ability an interest in an actuarial career; must have at least 3.0 GPA on a 4.0 scale, a Math SAT score of at least 600 or an ACT Math score of at least 28; must have completed the calculus and probability courses; must be junior, senior or graduate students attempting or already

passed the exam; must have completed or completing the validation by educational experience(VEE) requirements; must have determination, self-motivation, excellent recommendations from mathematics-related instructors and familiarity with an actuarial profession demands. **Application Requirements:** Applicants must submit a completed online application form, two nomination forms completed by instructors and/or advisors at educational institution, an official, sealed record of any educational examination scores, Student Aid Report (SAR) showing the financial date and a copy of college or university catalog or information sheet showing an estimated expenses. **Deadline for Receipt:** May 21. **Additional Information:** iabafdvp@blackactuaries.org.

1163 ■ INTERNATIONAL ASSOCIATION OF EMERGENCY MANAGERS

201 Park Washington Court
Falls Church, VA 22046-4527
Tel: (703)538-1795
Fax: (703)241-5603
E-mail: shiley@iaem.com
Web Site: http://www.iaem.com
To further education on emergency management by developing students that possess the intellect and technical skills to advance and enhance the profession.
Title of Award: International Association of Emergency Managers Scholarships **Area, Field, or Subject:** Emergency and disaster Services. **Level of Education for which Award is Granted:** Undergraduate **Funds Available:** No specific amount.
Eligibility Requirements: Applicants must be full-time students pursuing an associate or diploma baccalaureate or graduate degree in emergency management or a closely related field. **Application Requirements:** Applicants must submit the following: original transcript with official seal (may be sent by the registrar or included in the application package); a verification that they are enrolled as full-time students based on the standards set by their study program (full-time student verification must be provided by the registrar and is deemed a separate document from the applicant's transcript); three references (at least one reference must be from a faculty member); description of applicant's major/program and course description (may be supplied by sending a school catalog, providing printed copies from a Web site, or submitting information sheets provided by the department). **Deadline for Receipt:** May 16. **Additional Information:** Dawn M. Shiley-Danziesen; 703-538-3542; shiley@iaem.com.

1164 ■ INTERNATIONAL ASSOCIATION OF WORKFORCE PROFESSIONALS

1801 Louisville Rd.
Frankfort, KY 40601
Tel: (502)223-4459; 888-898-9960
Fax: (502)223-4127
E-mail: iawp@iawponline.org
Web Site: http://www.iawponline.org
To provide financial assistance for IAWP student members or dependents of IAWP full members who wish to increase their knowledge, skills, and abilities in the area of leadership or workforce development.
Title of Award: Freddy L. Jacobs Scholarships **Area, Field, or Subject:** General Studies. **Level of Education for which Award is Granted:** Undergraduate **Funds Available:** $75; $150; $250.
Eligibility Requirements: Applicants must be pursuing an associate, undergraduate degree or other certification who are required to complete an extracurricular educational or training to program to obtain high school diploma. **Application Requirements:** Applicants must complete the scholarship application form and attach a brief explanation of how this course will increase their knowledge, skills and abilities in the area of leadership or workforce development. **Additional Information:** International Association of Workforce professionals at the above address.

1165 ■ INTERNATIONAL BROTHERHOOD OF ELECTRICAL WORKERS

263 Ward St.
East Windsor, NJ 08520
Tel: (609)443-4100
Fax: (609)448-8690
Web Site: http://www.local827.org
To provide educational support for children of IBEW members.

Title of Award: Local 827 Peter J. Casey Scholarships **Area, Field, or Subject:** General studies. **Level of Education for which Award is Granted:** Undergraduate **Funds Available:** $1,000.
Eligibility Requirements: Applicants must be dependents of an IBEW member and must be in their senior year of high school. **Application Requirements:** Applicants must submit a completed application form. **Deadline for Receipt:** January 31.

1166 ■ INTERNATIONAL CODE COUNCIL FOUNDATION

500 New Jersey Ave. NW, 6th Fl.
Washington, DC 20001-2070
Tel: 888-422-7233
E-mail: leslie@flash.org
Web Site: http://www.icc-foundation.org
To provide financial assistance for children of ICC governmental members.
Title of Award: C.D. Howard Scholarships **Area, Field, or Subject:** General studies. **Level of Education for which Award is Granted:** Undergraduate **Number Awarded:** 1. **Funds Available:** $1,000.
Eligibility Requirements: Applicants must be children of code enforcement agency personnel. The jurisdiction authority must be an active Governmental Member of the International Code Council. Children must be dependents as defined by the Internal Revenue Service. **Application Requirements:** Applicants must demonstrate financial need. Financial information will be required along with details of any other financial assistance the applicant is receiving. Applicants must also provide evidence of satisfactory scholastic achievement including grades, test scores and teacher recommendations. Applicants must complete the scholarship application. A one-page narrative on why the applicant should be awarded the scholarship is also required. **Deadline for Receipt:** June 30. **Additional Information:** International Code Council Foundation, Attn: Scholarships c/o: COO 900 Montclair Road Birmingham, AL 35213-1206; scholarships@iccsafe.org

1167 ■ INTERNATIONAL CODE COUNCIL FOUNDATION

500 New Jersey Ave. NW, 6th Fl.
Washington, DC 20001-2070
Tel: 888-422-7233
E-mail: leslie@flash.org
Web Site: http://www.icc-foundation.org
To provide financial assistance for children of ICC Governmental Members.
Title of Award: Charlie O'Meilia Scholarships **Area, Field, or Subject:** General studies. **Level of Education for which Award is Granted:** Undergraduate **Number Awarded:** 1. **Funds Available:** $1,000.
Eligibility Requirements: Applicants must be children of code enforcement agency personnel. The jurisdiction authority must be an active Governmental Member of the International Code Council; children must be dependents as defined by the Internal Revenue Service. Typically, this includes birth children, stepchildren, legally adopted children, or a legal ward financially supported by the employee. **Application Requirements:** Applications and instructions are available in the ICC and ICCF websites. Applicants must provide evidence of satisfactory scholastic achievement including grades, test scores and teacher recommendations. Applicants must complete the scholarship application. A one-page narrative on why the applicant should be awarded the scholarship is also required. **Additional Information:** The Charlie O'meilia Scholarship is awarded by the Palm Beach County chapter in honor of long-time member Charlie O'Meilia. **Deadline for Receipt:** June 30. **Additional Information:** International Code Council Foundation, Attn: Scholarships c/o: COO 900 Montclair Road Birmingham, AL 35213-1206; scholarships@iccsafe.org

1168 ■ INTERNATIONAL DOOR ASSOCIATION

PO Box 246
West Milton, OH 45383-0246
Tel: (937)698-8042
Free: 800-355-4432
Fax: (937)698-6153
E-mail: info@longmgt.com
Web Site: http://www.doors.org
To support advanced educational opportunities for scholastically eligible students.
Title of Award: International Door Association Scholarship Awards **Area, Field, or Subject:** General studies. **Level of Education for which**

Award is Granted: Undergraduate **Funds Available:** $2,000 for full-time; for part-time, award amount is to be determined by semester hours or equivalent taken, and not to exceed $1,000. **Duration:** One academic year.
Eligibility Requirements: Applicants must be a high school with senior standing, community college, an associate degree program, vocational school or similar certification/diploma program, undergraduate college or university; have a cumulative grade point average equal to or greater than 3.0 on a 4.0 scale (or equivalent); must be an immediate family member, an employee, or an immediate family member of an employee of an IDA Installing/Servicing Dealer Member or an IDA Primary Industry Manufacturer/Vendor Member in good standing. **Application Requirements:** Applicants must submit a completed scholarship application, official transcript, personal statement and three letters of recommendation. **Additional Information:** Scholarship has two criteria: Primary Full-Time and Secondary Part-Time. **Deadline for Receipt:** July 15. **Additional Information:** Peggy Sanders, Scholarship Administration, psanders@longmgt.com.

1169 ■ INTERNATIONAL EXECUTIVE HOUSE KEEPERS ASSOCIATION
1001 Eastwind Dr., Ste. 301
Westerville, OH 43081-3361
Tel: (614)895-7166
Free: 800-200-6342
Fax: (614)895-1248
E-mail: excel@ieha.org
Web Site: http://www.ieha.org
To provide educational assistance to IEHA members.
Title of Award: IEHA Education Foundation Scholarship Awards **Area, Field, or Subject:** General studies. **Level of Education for which Award is Granted:** Undergraduate **Funds Available:** $800.
Eligibility Requirements: Applicants must be an IEHA member enrolled in an undergraduate or associate degree or IEHA approved certification program. **Application Requirements:** Applicants must submit a completed application form; a manuscript, transcript of grades; curriculum of student showing classroom hours of coursework; and a letter from the school official or instructor verifying the enrollment of the applicant. **Deadline for Receipt:** January 10.

1170 ■ INTERNATIONAL EXECUTIVE HOUSE KEEPERS ASSOCIATION
1001 Eastwind Dr., Ste. 301
Westerville, OH 43081-3361
Tel: (614)895-7166
Free: 800-200-6342
Fax: (614)895-1248
E-mail: excel@ieha.org
Web Site: http://www.ieha.org
To provide educational assistance to the IEHA members and their immediate families.
Title of Award: Spartan Scholarship Awards **Area, Field, or Subject:** General studies. **Level of Education for which Award is Granted:** Undergraduate **Funds Available:** $1,500.
Eligibility Requirements: Applicants must be an IEHA member or an immediate family of an IEHA member. **Application Requirements:** Applicants must submit a completed application form and a letter stating the reasons for applying the funds, the use of the award, and explanation of career goals. **Deadline for Receipt:** September.

1171 ■ INTERNATIONAL FLIGHT SERVICES ASSOCIATION
1100 Johnson Ferry Rd., Ste. 300
Atlanta, GA 30342
Tel: (404)252-3663
Fax: (404)252-0774
E-mail: ifsa@kellencompany.com
Web Site: http://www.ifsanet.com
To provide opportunities for students involved in hospitality programs to further their education.
Title of Award: Lois Campbell Scholarship Award **Area, Field, or Subject:** General studies. **Level of Education for which Award is Granted:** Undergraduate **Funds Available:** $2,250.
Eligibility Requirements: Applicants must have completed a minimum of 20 hours of course study in a post-secondary, hospitality management program; must be in a "good" academic standing and exhibit high leadership potential in the hospitality industry; must able to pursue the chosen course of study beginning with the academic year following the recipient's acceptance of the award. **Application Requirements:** Applicants must provide an official transcript of records for all high school and post-secondary studies at an accredited institution; must provide three letters of recommendation preferably from college professors, clergy and employers; must provide official documentation noting cancer history or loss of a family member due to cancer. **Deadline for Receipt:** May 15.
Additional Information: Olena Eaton at the above address.

1172 ■ INTERNATIONAL FLIGHT SERVICES ASSOCIATION
1100 Johnson Ferry Rd., Ste. 300
Atlanta, GA 30342
Tel: (404)252-3663
Fax: (404)252-0774
E-mail: ifsa@kellencompany.com
Web Site: http://www.ifsanet.com
To provide opportunities for students involved in hospitality programs to further their education.
Title of Award: Tommy Depaola Scholarship Award **Area, Field, or Subject:** General studies. **Level of Education for which Award is Granted:** Undergraduate **Funds Available:** $2,250.
Eligibility Requirements: Applicants must have completed a minimum of 20 hours of course study in a post-secondary, hospitality management program; must be in a "good" academic standing and exhibit high leadership potential in the hospitality industry; must able to pursue the chosen course of study beginning with the academic year following the recipient's acceptance of the award. **Application Requirements:** Applicants must provide an official transcript of records for all high school and post-secondary studies at an accredited institution; must provide three letters of recommendation preferably from college professors, clergy and employers; must provide official documentation noting cancer history or loss of a family member due to cancer. **Deadline for Receipt:** May 15.
Additional Information: Olena Eaton at the above address.

1173 ■ INTERNATIONAL FRANCHISE ASSOCIATION
1501 K St. NW, Ste. 350
Washington, DC 20005
Tel: (202)628-8000
Fax: (202)628-0812
Web Site: http://www.franchise.org
To provide financial support to those students who are in need.
Title of Award: Don Debolt Franchising Scholarship Program **Area, Field, or Subject:** General Studies. **Level of Education for which Award is Granted:** Undergraduate **Number Awarded:** 2. **Funds Available:** $2,500.
Eligibility Requirements: Applicants must be graduating high school seniors who have an expressed interest in pursuing a degree in entrepreneurship and franchising. **Application Requirements:** Applicants must submit completed application form. **Additional Information:** The Don DeBolt Franchising Scholarship Program, named in honor of IFA's recently-retired president who served from 1995 to 2004, is being conducted in cooperation with DECA and Delta Epsilon. **Additional Information:** International Franchise Association at the above address

1174 ■ INTERNATIONAL GRENFELL ASSOCIATION
66 Birmingham St.
St. John, NL, Canada A1E 5M8
Tel: (709)745-6162
Fax: (709)745-6163
E-mail: iga@nfld.net
Web Site: http://www.iga.nf.net
To support the education of students with financial need who have been accepted into or are currently attending a post-secondary education institution.
Title of Award: International Grenfell Association Bursary **Area, Field, or Subject:** General studies. **Level of Education for which Award is Granted:** Undergraduate **Funds Available:** Varies.
Eligibility Requirements: Applicant must be a Canadian citizen in the IGA region (must have graduated from a high school within the region); must not already possess a post-secondary degree; and must complete at least four courses per semester. **Application Requirements:** Application

forms and information can be obtained from the Grenfell Scholarship Committee or may be obtained online. Applications must be completed by the student and returned to the committee on or before the deadline. **Deadline for Receipt:** May 15. **Additional Information:** Mr. Paul Canning at the above address.

1175 ■ INTERNATIONAL GRENFELL ASSOCIATION

66 Birmingham St.
St. John, NL, Canada A1E 5M8
Tel: (709)745-6162
Fax: (709)745-6163
E-mail: iga@nfld.net
Web Site: http://www.iga.nf.net
To support the education of high achievers who are planning to pursue college education.

Title of Award: International Grenfell Association Secondary/High School Scholarships **Area, Field, or Subject:** General studies. **Level of Education for which Award is Granted:** Undergraduate **Funds Available:** $6,000. **Duration:** Annual.

Eligibility Requirements: Applicants must be Canadian citizens residing in the IGA region; must be in regular attendance at high schools in the IGA region; must have achieved superior results in the previous year's final exams and the current year's midterms; must complete Level III examinations achieving grades consistent with previous attainment; must be eligible for entrance to a university; and must have taken a full course load (normally a minimum of 5 courses per semester). **Application Requirements:** Applications must be completed by the student and returned to the principal on or before the deadline. Application form can be downloaded online. **Deadline for Receipt:** February 15. **Additional Information:** Mr. Paul Canning at the above address.

1176 ■ INTERNATIONAL GRENFELL ASSOCIATION

66 Birmingham St.
St. John, NL, Canada A1E 5M8
Tel: (709)745-6162
Fax: (709)745-6163
E-mail: iga@nfld.net
Web Site: http://www.iga.nf.net
To support the education of high achievers and/or those with financial need who have completed one or more years of post-secondary education with one renewable scholarship.

Title of Award: International Grenfell Association University/College Scholarships **Area, Field, or Subject:** General studies. **Level of Education for which Award is Granted:** Undergraduate **Funds Available:** $6,000. **Duration:** Annual.

Eligibility Requirements: Applicant must be a Canadian citizen residing in the IGA region (must have graduated from a high school within the region); have completed one or more years of post-secondary education in a program leading to an undergraduate degree from a recognized university or diploma from a minimum of a three-year program at a recognized college; must achieve superior results in the current fall and winter semesters; must not already possess a post-secondary degree; and must undertake a full course load (minimum of 5 courses per semester). **Application Requirements:** Application forms and information can be obtained from the Grenfell Scholarship Committee or may be obtained online. The application must be completed by the student and returned to the committee on or before the deadline. **Deadline for Receipt:** May 15. **Additional Information:** Mr. Paul Canning at the above address.

1177 ■ INTERNATIONAL HARVESTER COLLECTORS

18324 Monroa Rd. 1073
Madison, MO 65263
Tel: (660)291-8742
E-mail: IHCCLUB@aol.com
Web Site: http://www.nationalihcollectors.com
To provide a worldwide collector's network for the preservation of history, products, literature and memorabilia of the International Harvester Company.

Title of Award: International Harvester Collectors Scholarships **Area, Field, or Subject:** General studies. **Level of Education for which Award is Granted:** Undergraduate **Number Awarded:** 2. **Funds Available:** $1,000-first place; $750-second place.

Eligibility Requirements: All applicants must be members, children of members, or grandchildren of members of the International Harvester Collectors Inc., Club; must be enrolled or accepted for enrollment in an accredited college, university, junior college, trade, or technical school, or other similar post-high school educational institution; must be graduating high school seniors on the year of the application. **Application Requirements:** Applicants are required to submit an essay of not less than 1,000 not more than 2,000 words discussing the historical significance of any aspect of the International Harvester Company. The topic shall be "The evolution of the Farmall"; Each applicant shall include separately information regarding the educational institution. This information shall include the complete mailing address and telephone number of that educational institution's financial aid office; an annotated bibliography that lists the sources of information for the essay; a cover letter stating the institution the applicant will be attending, how the scholarship will be used in achieving the student's goals, and the process by which the applicant acquired the information for the essay. **Deadline for Receipt:** May 15. **Additional Information:** Darell Darst; 18324 Country road 1073, Madison, MO 65263; Farmall130@socket.net.

1178 ■ INTERNATIONAL MILITARY COMMUNITY EXECUTIVES ASSOCIATION

1530 Dunwoody Village Pkwy., Ste. 203
Atlanta, GA 30338
Tel: (770)396-2101
Fax: (770)396-2198
E-mail: imcea@imcea.com
Web Site: http://www.imcea.com
To assist MWR professionals in continuing their education.

Title of Award: The Robert W. Brunsman Memorial Scholarships **Area, Field, or Subject:** General studies. **Level of Education for which Award is Granted:** Graduate, Undergraduate **Funds Available:** No specific amount.

Eligibility Requirements: Applicant must be a current IMCEA member enrolled in a college or university working towards an Associates Degree, Bachelors Degree or higher. **Application Requirements:** Applicants must mail the application form, with a two-page essay regarding, "What is the most important issue society is facing today?", a letter of acceptance to the college or university that the applicant is planning to attend, or a transcript from the college or university currently attended. **Deadline for Receipt:** February 15.

1179 ■ INTERNATIONAL MILITARY COMMUNITY EXECUTIVES ASSOCIATION

1530 Dunwoody Village Pkwy., Ste. 203
Atlanta, GA 30338
Tel: (770)396-2101
Fax: (770)396-2198
E-mail: imcea@imcea.com
Web Site: http://www.imcea.com
To assist young men and women in furthering their education beyond the high school level.

Title of Award: Roy C. and Dorothy Jean Olson Memorial Scholarships **Area, Field, or Subject:** General studies. **Level of Education for which Award is Granted:** Undergraduate **Funds Available:** No specific amount.

Eligibility Requirements: Applicant must be a son or daughter of a current Regular or Position IMCEA member, graduating from high school in the school year of application submission or to be currently enrolled in a college or university working toward an Associates Degree, Bachelors Degree or higher. **Application Requirements:** Applicants must mail the application form, with a two-page essay regarding, "What is the most important issue society is facing today?", a letter of acceptance to the college or university that the applicant is planning to attend, or a transcript from the college or university currently attended. **Deadline for Receipt:** February 15.

1180 ■ INTERNATIONAL RADIO AND TELEVISION SOCIETY FOUNDATION

420 Lexington Ave., Ste. 1601
New York, NY 10170
Tel: (212)867-6650
Fax: (212)867-6653

Web Site: http://www.irts.org

To financially assist students with their educational pursuit.

Title of Award: IRTS Foundation Summer Fellowship Program **Area, Field, or Subject:** General studies. **Level of Education for which Award is Granted:** Graduate, Undergraduate **Funds Available:** No specific amount.

Eligibility Requirements: Program is open to college juniors, seniors or graduate students at the time of application; must complete their junior year at the time of the Fellowship (June 2008); college seniors and graduate students cannot graduate prior to May 2008. **Application Requirements:** Applicants must complete the application form available at the website and send it via email attachment with the subject line format SFPO8.Last Name.First Name to: apply@irts.org. **Deadline for Receipt:** December 2.

1181 ■ INTERNATIONAL SAFETY EQUIPMENT ASSOCIATION

1901 N Moore St.
Arlington, VA 22209-1762
Tel: (703)525-1695; (703)528-2148
E-mail: isea@safetyequipment.org
Web Site: http://www.safetyequipment.org

To Provide financial assistance to the promising dependant of its members in the final year in college or universities.

Title of Award: Lincoln C. Bailey Memorial Scholarship Fund **Area, Field, or Subject:** General studies. **Level of Education for which Award is Granted:** Undergraduate **Funds Available:** $2,500.

Eligibility Requirements: Applicants must be in the first year or second year in college; a dependant of ISEA members. **Application Requirements:** Applicants must submit transcript and financial information. **Deadline for Receipt:** March 25.

1182 ■ INTERNATIONAL TRANSPORTATION MANAGEMENT ASSOCIATION

PO Box 924146
Houston, TX 77292-4146
Tel: (281)885-7135
Fax: (281)885-7026
E-mail: elizabeth.golden@hlag.com
Web Site: http://www.itma-houston.org

To provide educational assistance for qualified graduating high school seniors intending to pursue their studies.

Title of Award: James Costello Memorial Scholarships **Area, Field, or Subject:** Logistics. **Level of Education for which Award is Granted:** Undergraduate **Funds Available:** $500-$1,000.

Eligibility Requirements: Applicants must be graduating high school seniors and university students majoring in a logistics-related curriculum. **Application Requirements:** Applicants must complete and submit the electronic scholarship application form. An ITMA scholarship will not be considered unless all three of the following supporting documents are received by the commission deadline: a certified copy of college/university transcript or high school transcript; two letters of recommendation; and a 200-word essay. Both the completed scholarship application and the required three supporting documents must reach ITMA for the application to be processed and considered. **Deadline for Receipt:** April 25.

1183 ■ INTERNATIONAL UNION OF BRICKLAYERS AND ALLIED CRAFTWORKERS

620 F St. NW
Washington, DC 20004
Tel: (202)783-3788; 888-880-8222
E-mail: askbac@bacweb.org
Web Site: http://www.bacweb.org

To assist students pursuing their post-secondary education.

Title of Award: Union Plus Scholarship Program **Area, Field, or Subject:** General studies. **Level of Education for which Award is Granted:** Undergraduate **Funds Available:** $500-4,000.

Eligibility Requirements: Applicant must be a current or retired members of unions participating in any Union Plus program, their spouses and their dependent children (including foster children, step children, and any other child for whom the individual member provides greater than 50% of his or her support) can apply for a Union Plus Scholarship; must be accepted into an accredited college or university, community college or recognized technical or trade school. **Application Requirements:** Application forms are in the website. **Deadline for Receipt:** January 31.

1184 ■ INTERNATIONAL UNION OF BRICKLAYERS AND ALLIED CRAFTWORKERS

620 F St. NW
Washington, DC 20004
Tel: (202)783-3788; 888-880-8222
E-mail: askbac@bacweb.org
Web Site: http://www.bacweb.org

To assist the children of BAC members in pursuing a college education.

Title of Award: U.S. Bates Scholarship Program **Area, Field, or Subject:** General studies. **Level of Education for which Award is Granted:** Undergraduate **Number Awarded:** 3-4. **Funds Available:** $2,500. **Duration:** One year.

Eligibility Requirements: Applicant must be a son or daughter of U.S BAC members (in good standing) of U.S. BAC locals who will be juniors in high school; must take or plan to take the standardized PSAT exam in the fall of their junior year. **Application Requirements:** Applicant must apply during their junior year in high school. For further information, applicants are advised to contact BAC's Educational Department at askbac@bacweb.org or call 888880-8BAC.

1185 ■ JACK AND JILL OF AMERICA FOUNDATION

1930 17th St. NW
Washington, DC 20009
Tel: (202)232-5290
Fax: (202)232-1747
E-mail: administration@jackandjillfoundation.org
Web Site: http://www.jackandjillfoundation.org

To provide financial assistance to African American students in preparing them to reach their fullest potential through higher education.

Title of Award: National College Scholarship Award **Area, Field, or Subject:** General education. **Level of Education for which Award is Granted:** Undergraduate **Funds Available:** $1,500 to $2,500. **Duration:** One year.

Eligibility Requirements: Applicants must be African American high school seniors with a minimum GPA of 3.0 who will be pursuing a bachelor's degree at any accredited postsecondary institution in the United States. **Application Requirements:** Applicants must submit an essay, resume, academic transcript, letters of recommendation and confirmation of 60 hours or more of active community service. **Additional Information:** Applicants who are alumni of Jack and Jill of America, Inc. are ineligible to apply for the scholarship. **Deadline for Receipt:** March 14. **Additional Information:** United Negro College Fund, Inc., 8260 Willow Oaks Corporate Dr., Fairfax, VA 22031.

1186 ■ JACKSON COUNTY COMMUNITY FOUNDATION

One Jackson Square, 100 E Michigan Ave., Ste. 308
Jackson, MI 49201-1406
Tel: (517)787-1321
Fax: (517)787-4333
E-mail: jcf@jacksoncf.org
Web Site: http://www.jacksoncf.org

To assist all citizens of greater Jackson in improving the quality of their lives; to support its work as a community grantmaker and community leader.

Title of Award: Dennis J. Beck Memorial Scholarship **Area, Field, or Subject:** General studies. **Level of Education for which Award is Granted:** Undergraduate **Funds Available:** $1,000.

Eligibility Requirements: Applicants must be Ethnic minorities pursuing any field of study with special consideration given to those pursuing a degree in Manufacturing. **Application Requirements:** Applicants must submit a completed application form and must provide a proof of acceptance at an accredited college, university, vocational or technical school.

1187 ■ JACKSON COUNTY COMMUNITY FOUNDATION

One Jackson Square, 100 E Michigan Ave., Ste. 308
Jackson, MI 49201-1406
Tel: (517)787-1321
Fax: (517)787-4333
E-mail: jcf@jacksoncf.org
Web Site: http://www.jacksoncf.org

To assist all citizens of greater Jackson in improving the quality of their lives; to support its work as a community grantmaker and community leader.

Title of Award: The Eleonor A. Ernest Scholarship **Area, Field, or Subject:** General studies. **Level of Education for which Award is Granted:** Undergraduate **Funds Available:** $1,000.
Eligibility Requirements: Applicants must be valedictorian, salutatorian or students with highest GPA from a smaller Jackson County High School; must have a cumulative GPA of 3.0 or higher who participates in school activities and/or sports; must have a good citizenship, leadership and outside activities including work experience. **Application Requirements:** Applicants must submit a completed application form.

1188 ■ JACKSON COUNTY COMMUNITY FOUNDATION

One Jackson Square, 100 E Michigan Ave., Ste. 308
Jackson, MI 49201-1406
Tel: (517)787-1321
Fax: (517)787-4333
E-mail: jcf@jacksoncf.org
Web Site: http://www.jacksoncf.org
To assist all citizens of greater Jackson in improving the quality of their lives; to support its work as a community grantmaker and community leader.
Title of Award: Melissa Eleonor Ernest Scholarship **Area, Field, or Subject:** Cosmetology. **Level of Education for which Award is Granted:** Undergraduate **Funds Available:** $1,000.
Eligibility Requirements: Applicants must be Jackson County residents; must be adult returning to school, graduating high school senior students already enrolled in an accredited institution of Cosmetology; must be full- or part-time students with a cumulative 2.0 GPA or higher. **Application Requirements:** Applicants must submit a completed application form.

1189 ■ JACKSON COUNTY COMMUNITY FOUNDATION

One Jackson Square, 100 E Michigan Ave., Ste. 308
Jackson, MI 49201-1406
Tel: (517)787-1321
Fax: (517)787-4333
E-mail: jcf@jacksoncf.org
Web Site: http://www.jacksoncf.org
To assist all citizens of greater Jackson in improving the quality of their lives; to support its work as a community grantmaker and community leader.
Title of Award: Robert P. Ernest Scholarship **Area, Field, or Subject:** General studies. **Level of Education for which Award is Granted:** Undergraduate **Funds Available:** $1,000.
Eligibility Requirements: Applicants must be valedictorian, salutatorian or students with highest GPA from a smaller Jackson County High School; must have a cumulative GPA of 3.0 or higher who participates in school activities and/or sports; must have a good citizenship, leadership and outside activities including work experience. **Application Requirements:** Applicants must submit a completed application form.

1190 ■ JACKSON COUNTY COMMUNITY FOUNDATION

One Jackson Square, 100 E Michigan Ave., Ste. 308
Jackson, MI 49201-1406
Tel: (517)787-1321
Fax: (517)787-4333
E-mail: jcf@jacksoncf.org
Web Site: http://www.jacksoncf.org
To recognize a Hanover-Horton students for overall achievement and scholastic excellence.
Title of Award: Hanover-Horton High School Youth of Promise Scholarships **Area, Field, or Subject:** General studies. **Level of Education for which Award is Granted:** Undergraduate **Funds Available:** $1,000.
Eligibility Requirements: Applicants must be graduating Hanover-Horton High School senior students who hold a GPA of 3.0; must have attended the school for at least one full academic year and demonstrate good character with focused goals; must have the plan to be full-time students and carry a minimum of 12 credit hours or equivalent; must also have the plan to attend an accredited Michigan college or university. **Application Requirements:** Applicants must submit a completed application form.

1191 ■ JACKSON COUNTY COMMUNITY FOUNDATION

One Jackson Square, 100 E Michigan Ave., Ste. 308
Jackson, MI 49201-1406

Tel: (517)787-1321
Fax: (517)787-4333
E-mail: jcf@jacksoncf.org
Web Site: http://www.jacksoncf.org
To assist all citizens of greater Jackson in improving the quality of their lives; to support its work as a community grantmaker and community leader.
Title of Award: William and Beatrice Kavanaugh Scholarship **Area, Field, or Subject:** General studies. **Level of Education for which Award is Granted:** Undergraduate **Funds Available:** $1,000.
Eligibility Requirements: Applicants must be graduating students of Grass Lake High school seniors who attended the school for the full academic year; must have a cumulative GPA of 2.8 or higher; must have plan to be full-time students and carry at least 12 credit hours or equivalent; must be accepted at an accredited college or university and demonstrated a good citizenship qualities in school and/or community. **Application Requirements:** Applicants must submit a completed application form.

1192 ■ JACKSON COUNTY COMMUNITY FOUNDATION

One Jackson Square, 100 E Michigan Ave., Ste. 308
Jackson, MI 49201-1406
Tel: (517)787-1321
Fax: (517)787-4333
E-mail: jcf@jacksoncf.org
Web Site: http://www.jacksoncf.org
To further the education of the students; to assist all citizens of greater Jackson in improving the quality of their lives; to support it's work as a community grantmaker and community leader.
Title of Award: The Otis and Florence Lapham Memorial Scholarship **Area, Field, or Subject:** General studies. **Level of Education for which Award is Granted:** Undergraduate **Funds Available:** $1,000.
Eligibility Requirements: Applicants must be senior graduating students of Hanover-Horton High School who hold a minimum of 2.5 GPA; must demonstrate a good work history and participated in both school and extracurricular activities. **Application Requirements:** Applicants must submit a completed application form.

1193 ■ JACKSON COUNTY COMMUNITY FOUNDATION

One Jackson Square, 100 E Michigan Ave., Ste. 308
Jackson, MI 49201-1406
Tel: (517)787-1321
Fax: (517)787-4333
E-mail: jcf@jacksoncf.org
Web Site: http://www.jacksoncf.org
To further the education of the students; to assist all citizens of greater Jackson in improving the quality of their lives; to support its work as a community grantmaker and community leader.
Title of Award: Lucile E. McGee Scholarship **Area, Field, or Subject:** General studies. **Level of Education for which Award is Granted:** Undergraduate **Funds Available:** $1,000.
Eligibility Requirements: Applicants must be senior graduating students of Hanover-Horton High School who hold a minimum of 2.5 GPA; must demonstrate a good work history and participated in both school and extracurricular activities. **Application Requirements:** Applicants must submit a completed application form.

1194 ■ JACKSON COUNTY COMMUNITY FOUNDATION

One Jackson Square, 100 E Michigan Ave., Ste. 308
Jackson, MI 49201-1406
Tel: (517)787-1321
Fax: (517)787-4333
E-mail: jcf@jacksoncf.org
Web Site: http://www.jacksoncf.org
To recognize exceptional high school and college achievement in academics, citizenship and extracurricular activity.
Title of Award: Philip Guy Richardson Memorial Scholarship **Area, Field, or Subject:** General studies. **Level of Education for which Award is Granted:** Undergraduate **Funds Available:** $2,000.
Eligibility Requirements: Applicants must be Napoleon High school candidates for graduation with a minimum GPA of 3.0 or higher; must participated in school activities and/or sports. **Application Requirements:** Applicants must submit a completed application form.

1195 ■ JACKSON COUNTY COMMUNITY FOUNDATION
One Jackson Square, 100 E Michigan Ave., Ste. 308
Jackson, MI 49201-1406
Tel: (517)787-1321
Fax: (517)787-4333
E-mail: jcf@jacksoncf.org
Web Site: http://www.jacksoncf.org
To recognize students who demonstrate motivation in their pursuit of higher education, actively involved in their community and have financial need.
Title of Award: Faith Speckhard Scholarships **Area, Field, or Subject:** General studies. **Level of Education for which Award is Granted:** Undergraduate **Funds Available:** $5,000.
Eligibility Requirements: Applicants must be Jackson High School graduating seniors who are African-Americans or a women of any race; must have a minimum of 2.4 GPA and must be full or part-time students in an accredited college or university. **Application Requirements:** Applicants must submit a completed application form and proof of acceptance in an accredited college, university, vocational or technical institute.

1196 ■ JACKSON COUNTY COMMUNITY FOUNDATION
One Jackson Square, 100 E Michigan Ave., Ste. 308
Jackson, MI 49201-1406
Tel: (517)787-1321
Fax: (517)787-4333
E-mail: jcf@jacksoncf.org
Web Site: http://www.jacksoncf.org
To assist all citizens of greater Jackson in improving the quality of their lives; to support its work as a community grantmaker and community leader.
Title of Award: Barbara and Howard Thompson Scholarship **Area, Field, or Subject:** General studies. **Level of Education for which Award is Granted:** Undergraduate **Funds Available:** $5,000.
Eligibility Requirements: Applicants must be Jackson High School graduating seniors or previous recipients who have plan to pursue a degree in History and/or political science; must be accepted at an accredited two or four-year college or university; must have 3.0 GPA. **Application Requirements:** Applicants must submit a completed application form.

1197 ■ JAMAICAN CANADIAN ASSOCIATION
995 Arrow Rd.
Toronto, ON, Canada M9M 2Z5
Tel: (416)746-5772
Fax: (416)746-7035
E-mail: info@jcassoc.org
Web Site: http://www.jcassoc.org
To provide financial assistance to students from the Caribbean/ African community, who are pursuing postsecondary studies in Ontario universities/colleges.
Title of Award: Brown Dental Scholarships **Area, Field, or Subject:** General studies. **Level of Education for which Award is Granted:** Undergraduate **Funds Available:** $1,000. **Duration:** One year.
Eligibility Requirements: Applicants must be Canadian citizens or landed immigrants of Caribbean/African background; must be enrolled as full-time first-year students at an Ontario university/ college or other postsecondary institution; must demonstrate remarkable academic performance or progress in high school; must demonstrate involvement and leadership in campus and/or community activities; must demonstrate financial need. **Application Requirements:** Application forms are available online and must be sent to The Jamaican Canadian Association Center, 995 Arrow Rd., Toronto M9M 2Z5. **Additional Information:** Scholarship is donated by Dr. Lancelot A. Brown, who was born in Montreal to Jamaican parents. **Deadline for Receipt:** July 25.

1198 ■ JAMAICAN CANADIAN ASSOCIATION
995 Arrow Rd.
Toronto, ON, Canada M9M 2Z5
Tel: (416)746-5772
Fax: (416)746-7035
E-mail: info@jcassoc.org
Web Site: http://www.jcassoc.org

To provide financial assistance to students from the Caribbean/ African community, who are pursuing postsecondary studies in Ontario universities/colleges.
Title of Award: Mary Anne Chambers Scholarships **Area, Field, or Subject:** General studies. **Level of Education for which Award is Granted:** Undergraduate **Funds Available:** $1,200. **Duration:** One year.
Eligibility Requirements: Applicant must be a Canadian citizen or landed immigrant of Caribbean/African background; must be enrolled as a full-time first-year student at an Ontario university/ college or other postsecondary institution; must demonstrate remarkable academic performance or progress in high school; must demonstrate involvement and leadership in campus and/or community activities; must demonstrate financial need. **Application Requirements:** Application forms are available online and must be sent to The Jamaican Canadian Association Center, 995 Arrow Rd., Toronto M9M 2Z5. **Additional Information:** Sponsored by the Hon. Mary Ann Chambers, Minister of Training Colleges and Universities. **Deadline for Receipt:** July 25.

1199 ■ JAMAICAN CANADIAN ASSOCIATION
995 Arrow Rd.
Toronto, ON, Canada M9M 2Z5
Tel: (416)746-5772
Fax: (416)746-7035
E-mail: info@jcassoc.org
Web Site: http://www.jcassoc.org
To provide financial assistance to students from the Caribbean/ African community, who are pursuing postsecondary studies in Ontario universities/colleges.
Title of Award: Marcus Mosiah Garvey Scholarships **Area, Field, or Subject:** General studies. **Level of Education for which Award is Granted:** Undergraduate **Number Awarded:** 2. **Funds Available:** $1,000. **Duration:** One year.
Eligibility Requirements: Applicant must be a Canadian citizen or landed immigrant of Caribbean/African background; must be enrolled as a full-time first-year student at an Ontario university/ college or other postsecondary institution; must demonstrate remarkable academic performance or progress in high school; must demonstrate involvement and leadership in campus and/or community activities; must demonstrate financial need. **Application Requirements:** Applicants must submit a two-page essay on The Life and Times of Marcus Garvey. Application forms are available online and must be sent to The Jamaican Canadian Association Center, 995 Arrow Rd., Toronto M9M 2Z5. **Additional Information:** Sponsored by Professor Erma Collins. **Deadline for Receipt:** July 25.

1200 ■ JAMAICAN CANADIAN ASSOCIATION
995 Arrow Rd.
Toronto, ON, Canada M9M 2Z5
Tel: (416)746-5772
Fax: (416)746-7035
E-mail: info@jcassoc.org
Web Site: http://www.jcassoc.org
To provide financial assistance to students from the Caribbean/ African community, who are pursuing postsecondary studies in Ontario universities/colleges.
Title of Award: Humber College Institute of Technology and Advanced Learning Scholarships **Area, Field, or Subject:** General studies. **Level of Education for which Award is Granted:** Undergraduate **Funds Available:** $1,000. **Duration:** One year.
Eligibility Requirements: Applicant must be a Canadian citizen or landed immigrant of Caribbean/African background; must be enrolled as a full-time first-year student at an Ontario university/ college or other postsecondary institution; must demonstrate remarkable academic performance or progress in high school; must demonstrate involvement and leadership in campus and/or community activities; must demonstrate financial need. **Application Requirements:** Application forms are available online and must be sent to The Jamaican Canadian Association Center, 995 Arrow Rd., Toronto M9M 2Z5. **Additional Information:** Sponsored by Humber College for a first-year student attending that institution. **Deadline for Receipt:** July 25.

1201 ■ JAMAICAN CANADIAN ASSOCIATION
995 Arrow Rd.
Toronto, ON, Canada M9M 2Z5

Tel: (416)746-5772
Fax: (416)746-7035
E-mail: info@jcassoc.org
Web Site: http://www.jcassoc.org
To assist students with significant personal achievements beyond scholastic ability.

Title of Award: I Have a Dream Scholarships **Area, Field, or Subject:** General studies. **Level of Education for which Award is Granted:** Undergraduate **Number Awarded:** 2. **Funds Available:** $1,000. **Duration:** One year.

Eligibility Requirements: Applicant must be a Canadian citizen or landed immigrant of Caribbean/African background; must be enrolled as a full-time first-year student at an Ontario university/ college or other postsecondary institution; must demonstrate remarkable academic performance or progress in high school; must demonstrate involvement and leadership in campus and/or community activities; must demonstrate financial need. **Application Requirements:** Application forms are available online and must be sent to The Jamaican Canadian Association Center, 995 Arrow Rd., Toronto M9M 2Z5. **Deadline for Receipt:** July 25.

1202 ■ JAMAICAN CANADIAN ASSOCIATION
995 Arrow Rd.
Toronto, ON, Canada M9M 2Z5
Tel: (416)746-5772
Fax: (416)746-7035
E-mail: info@jcassoc.org
Web Site: http://www.jcassoc.org
To provide financial assistance to students from the Caribbean/ African community, who are pursuing postsecondary studies in Ontario universities/colleges.

Title of Award: Jamaica Day Basil Duncan Memorial Scholarships **Area, Field, or Subject:** General studies. **Level of Education for which Award is Granted:** Undergraduate **Funds Available:** $1,500. **Duration:** One year.

Eligibility Requirements: Applicant must be a Canadian citizen or landed immigrant of Caribbean/African background; must be enrolled as a full-time first-year student at an Ontario university/ college or other postsecondary institution; must demonstrate remarkable academic performance or progress in high school; must demonstrate involvement and leadership in campus and/or community activities; must demonstrate financial need. **Application Requirements:** Application forms are available online and must be sent to The Jamaican Canadian Association Center, 995 Arrow Rd., Toronto M9M 2Z5. **Additional Information:** Scholarship is donated by the Jamaica Day Event Board of Directors in honor of the late Basil Duncan, who was a member of that Board. **Deadline for Receipt:** July 25.

1203 ■ JAMAICAN CANADIAN ASSOCIATION
995 Arrow Rd.
Toronto, ON, Canada M9M 2Z5
Tel: (416)746-5772
Fax: (416)746-7035
E-mail: info@jcassoc.org
Web Site: http://www.jcassoc.org
To provide financial assistance to students from the Caribbean/ African community, who are pursuing postsecondary studies in Ontario universities/colleges.

Title of Award: Ryerson Scholarships **Area, Field, or Subject:** General studies. **Level of Education for which Award is Granted:** Undergraduate **Number Awarded:** 2. **Funds Available:** $1,000. **Duration:** One year.
Eligibility Requirements: Applicant must be a Canadian citizen or landed immigrant of Caribbean/African background; must be enrolled as a full-time first-year student at an Ontario university/ college or other postsecondary institution; must demonstrate remarkable academic performance or progress in high school; must demonstrate involvement and leadership in campus and/or community activities; must demonstrate financial need. **Application Requirements:** Application forms are available online and must be sent to The Jamaican Canadian Association Center, 995 Arrow Rd., Toronto M9M 2Z5. **Additional Information:** Sponsored by Ryerson University for one male and one female first-year student attending that university. **Deadline for Receipt:** July 25.

1204 ■ JAMAICAN CANADIAN ASSOCIATION
995 Arrow Rd.
Toronto, ON, Canada M9M 2Z5
Tel: (416)746-5772
Fax: (416)746-7035
E-mail: info@jcassoc.org
Web Site: http://www.jcassoc.org
To provide support to African-Canadian youth who are pursuing a postsecondary education.

Title of Award: Eva Smith Bursary **Area, Field, or Subject:** General studies. **Level of Education for which Award is Granted:** Undergraduate **Funds Available:** $750. **Duration:** One year.

Eligibility Requirements: Applicant must be a Canadian citizen or landed immigrant of Caribbean/African background; must be enrolled as a full-time first-year student at an Ontario university/ college or other postsecondary institution; must demonstrate remarkable academic performance or progress in high school; must demonstrate involvement and leadership in campus and/or community activities; must demonstrate financial need. **Application Requirements:** Application forms are available online and must be sent to The Jamaican Canadian Association Center, 995 Arrow Rd., Toronto M9M 2Z5. **Additional Information:** Bursary is named in honor of the late Eva Smith, a tireless community worker who dedicated her life to youth concerns, women's rights, immigration issues, education and community empowerment. **Deadline for Receipt:** July 25.

1205 ■ JAMAICAN CANADIAN ASSOCIATION
995 Arrow Rd.
Toronto, ON, Canada M9M 2Z5
Tel: (416)746-5772
Fax: (416)746-7035
E-mail: info@jcassoc.org
Web Site: http://www.jcassoc.org
To provide financial assistance to students from the Caribbean/ African community, who are pursuing postsecondary studies in Ontario universities/colleges.

Title of Award: Barbara Thomas Bursary **Area, Field, or Subject:** General studies. **Level of Education for which Award is Granted:** Undergraduate **Funds Available:** $500. **Duration:** One year.

Eligibility Requirements: Applicants must be a Canadian citizens or landed immigrants of Caribbean/African background; must be enrolled as full-time first-year students at an Ontario university/ college or other postsecondary institution; must demonstrate remarkable academic performance or progress in high school; must demonstrate involvement and leadership in campus and/or community activities; must demonstrate financial need. **Application Requirements:** Application forms are available online and must be sent to The Jamaican Canadian Association Center, 995 Arrow Rd., Toronto M9M 2Z5. **Deadline for Receipt:** July 25.

1206 ■ JAMAICAN CANADIAN ASSOCIATION
995 Arrow Rd.
Toronto, ON, Canada M9M 2Z5
Tel: (416)746-5772
Fax: (416)746-7035
E-mail: info@jcassoc.org
Web Site: http://www.jcassoc.org
To provide financial assistance to students from the Caribbean/ African community who are pursuing postsecondary studies in Ontario universities/colleges.

Title of Award: York Regional Police Scholarships **Area, Field, or Subject:** General studies. **Level of Education for which Award is Granted:** Undergraduate **Funds Available:** $1,000. **Duration:** One year.
Eligibility Requirements: Applicants must be Canadian citizens or landed immigrants of Caribbean/African background; must be enrolled as full-time first-year students at an Ontario university/ college or other postsecondary institution; must demonstrate remarkable academic performance or progress in high school; must demonstrate involvement and leadership in campus and/or community activities; must demonstrate financial need. **Application Requirements:** Application forms are available online and must be sent to The Jamaican Canadian Association Center, 995 Arrow Rd., Toronto M9M 2Z5. **Deadline for Receipt:** July 25.

1207 ■ JAMAICAN CANADIAN ASSOCIATION

995 Arrow Rd.
Toronto, ON, Canada M9M 2Z5
Tel: (416)746-5772
Fax: (416)746-7035
E-mail: info@jcassoc.org
Web Site: http://www.jcassoc.org
To provide financial assistance to students from the Caribbean/ African community, who are pursuing postsecondary studies in Ontario universities/colleges.
Title of Award: Youth Affairs Committee Rising Star Scholarships **Area, Field, or Subject:** General studies. **Level of Education for which Award is Granted:** Undergraduate **Funds Available:** $1,000. **Duration:** One year.
Eligibility Requirements: Applicant must be a Canadian citizen or landed immigrant of Caribbean/African background; must be enrolled as a full-time first-year student at an Ontario university/ college or other postsecondary institution; must demonstrate remarkable academic performance or progress in high school; must demonstrate involvement and leadership in campus and/or community activities; must demonstrate financial need. **Application Requirements:** Applicants must produce a 500-word essay on either one of following topics: (a) The Maroon In Jamaica; (b) The Haitian Revolution; (c) The Importance of Civic Engagement as a Youth; (d) The Importance of Youth Cultural Education. Application forms are available online and must be sent to The Jamaican Canadian Association Center, 995 Arrow Rd., Toronto M9M 2Z5. **Deadline for Receipt:** July 25.

1208 ■ JEWISH FOUNDATION FOR EDUCATION OF WOMEN

135 E 64th St.
New York, NY 10065
Tel: (212)288-3931
Fax: (212)288-5798
E-mail: info@jfew.org
Web Site: http://www.jfew.org
To provide financial assistance for Jewish students through a joint program with the Rose Biller Fund of UJA-Federation of New York.
Title of Award: JFEW/UJA-Federation Rose Biller Scholarships **Area, Field, or Subject:** General studies. **Level of Education for which Award is Granted:** Undergraduate **Funds Available:** $5,000. **Duration:** One year.
Eligibility Requirements: Applicants must be Jewish students, permanent residents of and attending colleges or graduate or professional schools in New York City or the countries of Nassau, Suffolk or Westchester. **Application Requirements:** Applicants must complete the application online with all required information. **Deadline for Receipt:** June 16.

1209 ■ JEWISH GUILD FOR THE BLIND

15 W 65th St.
New York, NY 10023
Tel: (212)769-6200
Free: 800-284-4422
Fax: (212)769-6266
E-mail: info@jgb.org
Web Site: http://www.jgb.org
To assist blind high school students to pursue college.
Title of Award: GuildScholar Awards **Area, Field, or Subject:** General studies. **Level of Education for which Award is Granted:** Undergraduate **Number Awarded:** 12-15. **Funds Available:** $15,000.
Eligibility Requirements: Applicants must be legally blind high school student and a U.S citizen. **Application Requirements:** Applicants must provide (in tif, jpeg or pdf format) proof of legal blindness; proof of U.S. citizenship; documentation of academic achievement; three letters of recommendations and two personal statements. Applicants are required to apply online. **Additional Information:** Applicants must choose a college that is accredited by a body recognized by the Council of Higher Education Accreditation. **Deadline for Receipt:** July 1. **Additional Information:** Gordon Rovins, 212-769-7801 or guildscholar@jgb.org.

1210 ■ JEWISH WAR VETERANS OF THE UNITED STATES OF AMERICA

1811 R St. NW
Washington, DC 20009
Tel: (202)265-6280
Fax: (202)234-5662
E-mail: jwv@jwv.org
Web Site: http://www.jwv.org
To provide financial support for the education of descendants of members of the Jewish War Veterans of the United States of America.
Title of Award: Bernard Rotberg Memorial Scholarships **Area, Field, or Subject:** General studies. **Level of Education for which Award is Granted:** Undergraduate **Funds Available:** $1,000.
Eligibility Requirements: Applicant must be a direct descendant (child, grandchild, great grandchild) of members in good standing of the Jewish War Veterans of the United States of America. If applicant's relative is deceased, member must have been in good standing at the time of his/her death. Applicant must be a high school senior accepted as a freshman entering in the fall semester by an accredited four-year college or university or a three-year hospital school of nursing; must be in the upper 25% of their high school graduating class; and must demonstrate involvement and leadership in extracurricular activities, in their Jewish community and the community at large. **Application Requirements:** Applicants must complete all sections of Part I of the Application Form which must be signed by the JWV member related to the applicant and the JWV member's Post Commander. After the signatures are obtained, the applicant should forward Part I and II of the application form to school officials along with a stamped envelope addressed to the appropriate Department Commander. The applicant's school must complete Part II of the application form. **Deadline for Receipt:** May 2.

1211 ■ JOURNYX

9011 Mountain Ridge Dr., Ste. 200
Austin, TX 78759
Tel: (512)834-8888
Free: 800-755-9878
Fax: (512)834-8858
Web Site: http://www.journyx.com
To improve the philosophy and the technology of project accounting.
Title of Award: Journyx Scholarships **Area, Field, or Subject:** Accounting. **Level of Education for which Award is Granted:** Graduate, Undergraduate **Number Awarded:** 1. **Funds Available:** $500.
Eligibility Requirements: Applicant must be over 18 years old; a resident of the United States; currently enrolled as a full-time graduate or undergraduate at a university in the United States. **Application Requirements:** Students must submit their entries (an essay of 1000 words or less), along with an official academic transcript containing the student's spring semester grades for the academic year in progress and a copy of student's resume that includes e-mail address, campus address and phone number, student ID number, permanent address and phone number, major and expected graduation date. Submit materials via e-mail. **Deadline for Receipt:** June 1. **Additional Information:** scholarship@journyx.com.

1212 ■ JUNIOR ACHIEVEMENT

One Education Way
Colorado Springs, CO 80906
Tel: (719)540-8000; 888-4JA-ALUM
Fax: (719)540-6299
E-mail: newmedia@ja.org
Web Site: http://www.ja.org
To allow educational advancements by providing financial assistance.
Title of Award: Joe Francomano Scholarships **Area, Field, or Subject:** General studies. **Level of Education for which Award is Granted:** Undergraduate **Number Awarded:** 1. **Funds Available:** $5,000 per year. **Duration:** Four years.
Eligibility Requirements: Applicants must be high school seniors graduating before June 30; must have a minimum GPA of 3.0; must have demonstrated leadership and excellent extracurricular and community activities; and must have financial need. **Application Requirements:** Applicants must submit a completed application form along with other supporting materials. **Additional Information:** In memory of Joseph Francomano, past president of JA. **Deadline for Receipt:** February 1. **Additional Information:** scholarships@ja.org.

1213 ■ JUNIOR ACHIEVEMENT

One Education Way
Colorado Springs, CO 80906

Tel: (719)540-8000; 888-4JA-ALUM
Fax: (719)540-6299
E-mail: newmedia@ja.org
Web Site: http://www.ja.org
To allow educational advancements by providing financial assistance.
Title of Award: Hugh B. Sweeny Scholarships **Area, Field, or Subject:** General studies. **Level of Education for which Award is Granted:** Undergraduate **Number Awarded:** 1. **Funds Available:** $5,000. **Duration:** One year.
Eligibility Requirements: Applicants must be high school seniors graduating before June 30; must have a minimum GPA of 3.0; and must exemplify achievement, citizenship, creativity, leadership, motivation, and financial need. **Application Requirements:** Applicants must submit a completed application form along with other supporting materials. **Deadline for Receipt:** February 1. **Additional Information:** scholarships@ja.org.

1214 ■ KAPPA KAPPA GAMMA
PO Box 38
Columbus, OH 43216-0038
Tel: (614)228-6515; (866)554-1870
Fax: (614)228-7809
E-mail: kkghq@kappa.org
Web Site: http://www.kappakappagamma.org
To deliver educational and leadership training, preserve the Fraternity's heritage from an historical perspective, and to provide financial assistance to members in need.
Title of Award: Kappa Kappa Gamma Undergraduate Scholarships **Area, Field, or Subject:** General studies. **Level of Education for which Award is Granted:** Undergraduate **Funds Available:** No specific amount.
Eligibility Requirements: Applicant must be a member of KappaKappa Gamma Fraternity who has a grade average of B or above (3.0 on 4.0 scale) and is in good standing. **Application Requirements:** Applicant must submit a personal essay or letter stating educational and career goals and financial need; must have official transcripts from all colleges or universities attended; two recommendation letters, one academic (professor, adviser, dean) and one chapter (President, Vice President-Standards or Chapter Council Adviser). Application materials must be sent to: Kappa Kappa Gamma Foundation, PO Box 38, Columbus, OH 43216-0038. **Deadline for Receipt:** February 1.

1215 ■ KAPPA OMICRON NU
4990 Northwind Dr., Ste. 140
East Lansing, MI 48823-5031
Tel: (517)351-8335
Fax: (517)351-8336
E-mail: dmitstifer@kon.org
Web Site: http://www.kon.org
To provide opportunity for its member to attend The LeaderShape Institute.
Title of Award: Kappa Omicron Nu Undergraduate Scholarships **Area, Field, or Subject:** Leadership, Institutional and community. **Level of Education for which Award is Granted:** Undergraduate **Number Awarded:** 1. **Funds Available:** $1000.
Eligibility Requirements: Applicant must be undergraduate student member with at least one more year in the undergraduate program of studies. **Application Requirements:** Applicants must submit a short statement of commitment to leadership on campus during 2008-2009 academic year, and a short description of academic status. Send materials electronically to dmitstifer@kon.org. **Deadline for Receipt:** February 15.

1216 ■ KAPPA OMICRON NU HONOR SOCIETY
4990 Northwind Dr., Ste. 140
East Lansing, MI 48823-5031
Tel: (517)351-8335
Fax: (517)351-8336
E-mail: dmitstifer@kon.org
Web Site: http://www.kon.org
To recognize and encourage excellence in scholarship, research, and leadership at the local level.
Title of Award: Kappa Omicron Nu Honor Society Scholars Program Grants **Area, Field, or Subject:** General studies. **Level of Education for which Award is Granted:** Undergraduate **Funds Available:** varies.

Eligibility Requirements: Applicants must be individuals who maintain good standing in the society and must be conducting undergraduate and/or graduate research. **Application Requirements:** Applicants must complete the application form and submit to National Kappa Omicron Nu. **Additional Information:** dmitstifer@kon.org; 517-351-8335.

1217 ■ KELLOGG COMMUNITY COLLEGE FOUNDATION
450 N Ave.
Battle Creek, MI 49017
Tel: (269)965-3931
Web Site: http://www.kellogg.edu
To generate and encourage philanthropic giving and manage funds to enhance the quality of education while building stronger communities.
Title of Award: Foundation Scholarships **Area, Field, or Subject:** General studies. **Level of Education for which Award is Granted:** Undergraduate **Funds Available:** No specific amount.
Eligibility Requirements: Applicants must have a cumulative GPA of 2.5 and be working towards their first college degree. **Application Requirements:** Applicants must submit a 150 word personal statement detailing their goals and achievements, a copy of transcript of records and three letters of recommendation from high school or college instructors, counselors or employers. **Deadline for Receipt:** March 10.

1218 ■ KELLOGG COMMUNITY COLLEGE FOUNDATION
450 N Ave.
Battle Creek, MI 49017
Tel: (269)965-3931
Web Site: http://www.kellogg.edu
To generate and encourage philanthropic giving and manage funds to enhance the quality of education while building stronger communities.
Title of Award: Gold Key Scholarships **Area, Field, or Subject:** General studies. **Level of Education for which Award is Granted:** Undergraduate **Funds Available:** $6,000.
Eligibility Requirements: Applicants must be students within the KCC district; must have completed no more than 24 credit hours of college; must have 3.2 cumulative GPA and ACT of 20 or higher. **Application Requirements:** Applicants must submit: a completed application form; an official high school and/or college transcript; three written letters of recommendation; ACT scores; 150 word written essay discussing achievements and future goals; and resume or employment information including activities, leadership, volunteer or school-related positions. **Deadline for Receipt:** February 1.

1219 ■ KELLOGG COMMUNITY COLLEGE FOUNDATION
450 N Ave.
Battle Creek, MI 49017
Tel: (269)965-3931
Web Site: http://www.kellogg.edu
To generate and encourage philanthropic giving and manage= funds to enhance the quality of education while building stronger communities.
Title of Award: Walter and Lucille Harper Scholarship **Area, Field, or Subject:** General studies. **Level of Education for which Award is Granted:** Undergraduate **Funds Available:** No specific amount.
Eligibility Requirements: Applicants must be second year KCC students graduating with an associate's degree; must have a minimum of 3.0 GPA; must be citizens of the United States. **Application Requirements:** Applicants must submit: a completed application form; a copy of transcript of records; 150 word personal statement detailing their future aspirations; and three written letters of recommendation from teachers, counselors and employers. **Deadline for Receipt:** March 10.

1220 ■ KELLOGG COMMUNITY COLLEGE FOUNDATION
450 N Ave.
Battle Creek, MI 49017
Tel: (269)965-3931
Web Site: http://www.kellogg.edu
To generate and encourage philanthropic giving and manage funds to enhance the quality of education while building stronger communities.
Title of Award: Kellogg Company Career Scholarships **Area, Field, or Subject:** General studies. **Level of Education for which Award is Granted:** Undergraduate **Funds Available:** $6,000.
Eligibility Requirements: Applicants must be citizens, legal permanent residents or nationals of the United States; must be residents of the

greater Battle Creek area; must have a cumulative GPA of 2.5 on a 4.0 scale; must be entering or have been admitted as full-time degree seeking students at Kellogg Community College; must have demonstrated leadership abilities through participation in community service, extracurricular or other activities; must be pursuing and completing an associate's degree in accounting or business management; must have fewer than 24 credit hours of college credit completed. **Application Requirements:** Applicants must submit: a completed application form; a transcript of grades; a minimum of 250 word personal statement detailing their future aspirations; and three written recommendations. **Deadline for Receipt:** April 10.

1221 ■ KELLOGG COMMUNITY COLLEGE FOUNDATION

450 N Ave.
Battle Creek, MI 49017
Tel: (269)965-3931
Web Site: http://www.kellogg.edu
To generate and encourage philanthropic giving and manage funds to enhance the quality of education while building stronger communities.
Title of Award: Trustee Scholarships **Area, Field, or Subject:** General studies. **Level of Education for which Award is Granted:** Undergraduate **Funds Available:** No specific amount.
Eligibility Requirements: Applicants must be graduating high school seniors within the KCC district; must be in the top 20% of graduating class and have at least a 3.0 GPA. **Application Requirements:** Applicants must submit a completed application form.

1222 ■ KENTUCKY FRIED CHICKEN FOUNDATION

PO Box 725489
Atlanta, GA 31139
800-225-5532
Web Site: http://www.kfcscholars.org
To provide funding for tuition, fees, books, room and board for eligible individuals to complete a bachelor's degree.
Title of Award: KFC Colonel's Scholars Program **Area, Field, or Subject:** General studies. **Level of Education for which Award is Granted:** Undergraduate **Funds Available:** $5,000.
Eligibility Requirements: Applicants must be graduates from high school in academic year between December 1, 2007 and August 31, 2008; must have earned a minimum cumulative high school GPA of 2.75; must be planning to pursue a bachelor's degree at a public, in-state college or university; must be U.S. citizens. **Application Requirements:** Applicants must submit all the required application information.

1223 ■ ALDEN KINDRED OF AMERICA

PO Box 2754
Duxbury, MA 02331-2754
Tel: (781)934-9092
Fax: (781)934-9149
Web Site: http://www.alden.org
To provide educational assistance to incoming college students.
Title of Award: Donnell B. Young Scholarships **Area, Field, or Subject:** General studies. **Level of Education for which Award is Granted:** Undergraduate **Number Awarded:** 1. **Funds Available:** $ 1,000.
Eligibility Requirements: Applicants must be graduating high school students who are lineage members of the Alden Kindred of America, Inc. **Application Requirements:** Applicants must submit their high school transcripts (mailed directly by their school). A typewritten research paper of 750-1,000 words is a strict requirement. The topic must be extracted from the Early American Period (1620-1750). The preface of the research paper should contain a short paragraph about the reason of the application for the scholarship. Footnotes and bibliography of references should be included. Volunteer work and personal information including hobbies and interests must also be provided. All application forms must have two references (one personal and one from the school). **Deadline for Receipt:** March 1.

1224 ■ SUSAN G. KOMEN BREAST CANCER FOUNDATION

5005 LBJ Freeway, Ste. 250
Dallas, TX 75244
877-465-6636
Web Site: http://www.komen.org
To assist young adults in their academic pursuits.

Title of Award: Susan G. Komen Breast Cancer Foundation College Scholarship Awards **Area, Field, or Subject:** General studies. **Level of Education for which Award is Granted:** Undergraduate **Funds Available:** $10,000. **Duration:** Four years.
Eligibility Requirements: Applicants must be U.S. citizens, high school or college graduate students who have lost a parent to breast cancer and planning to attend state-supported college or university in their state where they permanently reside and were never subjected to disciplinary action by any institution. **Application Requirements:** Applicants must send an email to Susan G. Komen Breast Cancer Foundation to apply for the application.

1225 ■ KOREAN AMERICAN SCHOLARSHIP FOUNDATION

1952 Gallows Rd., Ste. 340 B
Vienna, VA 22182
Tel: (703)748-5935
Fax: (703)748-1874
E-mail: national@kasf.org
Web Site: http://www.kasf.org
To help meet the financial needs of Korean-American students seeking higher education.
Title of Award: KASF Chair Scholarships **Area, Field, or Subject:** General studies. **Level of Education for which Award is Granted:** Graduate, Undergraduate **Funds Available:** An annual $1000 scholarship. **Duration:** Lifetime scholarship.
Eligibility Requirements: Applicant must be a Korean-American student currently enrolled in a full-time undergraduate or graduate program. **Application Requirements:** Applicants must submit a completed scholarship application to the respective KASF region (each region is designated by the state where school is located). **Deadline for Receipt:** Varies with the region.

1226 ■ KOREAN AMERICAN SCHOLARSHIP FOUNDATION

1952 Gallows Rd., Ste. 340 B
Vienna, VA 22182
Tel: (703)748-5935
Fax: (703)748-1874
E-mail: national@kasf.org
Web Site: http://www.kasf.org
To help meet the financial needs of Korean-American students seeking higher education in a specific field.
Title of Award: KASF Designated Scholarships **Area, Field, or Subject:** General studies. **Level of Education for which Award is Granted:** Graduate, Undergraduate **Funds Available:** $1000 or more. **Duration:** One-time or a continuous basis.
Eligibility Requirements: Applicant must be a Korean-American student currently enrolled in a full-time undergraduate or graduate program in a specific field. **Application Requirements:** Applicants must submit a completed scholarship application to the respective KASF region (each region is designated by the state where school is located). **Deadline for Receipt:** Varies with the region.

1227 ■ KOREAN AMERICAN SCHOLARSHIP FOUNDATION

1952 Gallows Rd., Ste. 340 B
Vienna, VA 22182
Tel: (703)748-5935
Fax: (703)748-1874
E-mail: national@kasf.org
Web Site: http://www.kasf.org
To help meet the financial needs of Korean-American students seeking higher education in various academic fields.
Title of Award: KASF General Scholarships **Area, Field, or Subject:** General studies. **Level of Education for which Award is Granted:** Graduate, Undergraduate **Funds Available:** $1000 or more.
Eligibility Requirements: Applicant must be a Korean-American student currently enrolled in a full-time undergraduate or graduate program in one of various academic fields. **Application Requirements:** Applicants must submit a completed scholarship application to the respective KASF region (each region is designated by the state where school is located). **Deadline for Receipt:** Varies with the region.

1228 ■ LAM RESEARCH CORPORATION

4650 Cushing Pkwy.
Fremont, CA 94538

Tel: (510)572-0200
E-mail: ehshelpdesk@lamresearch.com
Web Site: http://www.lamresearch.com
To further the education of students who exemplify the core values of the company.
Title of Award: Lam Research Corporation Core Value and Performance Scholarships for Interns **Area, Field, or Subject:** General studies. **Level of Education for which Award is Granted:** Undergraduate **Number Awarded:** 2. **Funds Available:** $2,500.
Eligibility Requirements: Applicants must be intern students at Lam. **Application Requirements:** Applicants may contact the Community Affairs department for more information about the scholarship. **Additional Information:** Lam Research Corporation Core Values: Achievement; Honesty and integrity; Innovation and continuous improvement; Mutual trust and respect; Open communication; Ownership and accountability; and Teamwork. **Additional Information:** communityaffairs@lamrc.com.

1229 ■ LAM RESEARCH CORPORATION
4650 Cushing Pkwy.
Fremont, CA 94538
Tel: (510)572-0200
E-mail: ehshelpdesk@lamresearch.com
Web Site: http://www.lamresearch.com
To further the education of students who exemplify the core values of the company.
Title of Award: Lam Research Corporation Core Values Scholarships **Area, Field, or Subject:** General studies. **Level of Education for which Award is Granted:** Undergraduate **Number Awarded:** 6. **Funds Available:** $10,000. **Duration:** Four years.
Eligibility Requirements: Applicants must be graduating seniors from each of the six high schools in Fremont, CA who best exemplifies Lam's Core Values. **Application Requirements:** Applicants may contact the Community Affairs department for more information about the scholarship. **Additional Information:** Lam Research Corporation Core Values: Achievement; Honesty and integrity; Innovation and continuous improvement; Mutual trust and respect; Open communication; Ownership and accountability; and Teamwork. **Additional Information:** communityaffairs@lamrc.com.

1230 ■ LAMBDA IOTA TAU
Ball State University
Muncie, IN 47306-0460
Tel: (765)285-8370
Fax: (765)285-3765
E-mail: ktaylor@bsu.edu
Web Site: http://www.bsu.edu/shapps/english/undergraduate/lit
To financially support student members with their education.
Title of Award: LIT Scholarships **Area, Field, or Subject:** General studies. **Level of Education for which Award is Granted:** Graduate, Undergraduate **Number Awarded:** 2. **Funds Available:** $1000. **Duration:** Annually.
Eligibility Requirements: Applicant must be undergraduate in the top 35% of their class and have a B average in at least 12 semester hours; or graduate students who have completed at least one semester or term with an A- average. Candidates must be nominated by a chapter sponsor. **Application Requirements:** Candidates must submit the nomination letter from the sponsor; an essay or piece of creative writing; and another essay of 1000 words or less on career goals and objectives. All materials must be received at the LIT Headquarters, c/o Professor Bruce W. Hozeski. **Deadline for Receipt:** May 31.

1231 ■ LANIER TECHNICAL COLLEGE
2990 Landrum Educational Dr.
Oakwood, GA 30566
Tel: (770)531-6300
Fax: (770)631-6328
E-mail: info@laniertech.edu
Web Site: http://www.laniertech.edu
To provide financial support to deserving students intending to pursue completion of their programs of study.
Title of Award: Kenneth H. Breeden Scholarships **Area, Field, or Subject:** General studies. **Level of Education for which Award is Granted:** Undergraduate **Funds Available:** $500. **Duration:** One academic year.

Eligibility Requirements: Applicants must have a previous approved for HOPE grant or HOPE Scholarship funding; must be in good academic standing in accordance with college guidelines. **Application Requirements:** Applicants must submit a Kenneth H. Breeden Scholarship application (available online) along with a letter of recommendation from an advisor or instructor. Application documents must be sent to the Financial Aid Office three weeks prior to registration for the quarter aid is requested.

1232 ■ LANIER TECHNICAL COLLEGE
2990 Landrum Educational Dr.
Oakwood, GA 30566
Tel: (770)531-6300
Fax: (770)631-6328
E-mail: info@laniertech.edu
Web Site: http://www.laniertech.edu
To help students offset their educational costs, specifically with books and supplies and to assist the students who are residents of Forsyth County.
Title of Award: Forsyth County United Way Scholarships **Area, Field, or Subject:** General studies. **Level of Education for which Award is Granted:** Undergraduate **Funds Available:** $250. **Duration:** One academic year.
Eligibility Requirements: Applicants must be in good academic standing in accordance with college and Financial Aid guidelines and must be residents of Forsyth County. **Application Requirements:** Applicant must submit a completed United Way Scholarship Application along with a letter of recommendation from an advisor, instructor or a responsible member of the community capable of reporting applicants' work record, leadership and notable skills. Application and other documentations must be submitted to the Financial Aid Office two weeks prior to registration for the quarter aid is requested.

1233 ■ LANIER TECHNICAL COLLEGE
2990 Landrum Educational Dr.
Oakwood, GA 30566
Tel: (770)531-6300
Fax: (770)631-6328
E-mail: info@laniertech.edu
Web Site: http://www.laniertech.edu
To encourage educational pursuits by providing financial assistance.
Title of Award: Lanier Merit Scholarships **Area, Field, or Subject:** General studies. **Level of Education for which Award is Granted:** Undergraduate **Funds Available:** No specific amount. **Duration:** One academic year.
Eligibility Requirements: Applicants must be able to demonstrate outstanding achievement. **Application Requirements:** Applicants must submit a completed scholarship application (available online); a letter of endorsement from instructor or community member; and a copy of high school transcript, GED scores and/or work record.

1234 ■ LANIER TECHNICAL COLLEGE
2990 Landrum Educational Dr.
Oakwood, GA 30566
Tel: (770)531-6300
Fax: (770)631-6328
E-mail: info@laniertech.edu
Web Site: http://www.laniertech.edu
To encourage educational pursuits by providing financial assistance.
Title of Award: Lanier Need-Based Scholarships **Area, Field, or Subject:** General studies. **Level of Education for which Award is Granted:** Undergraduate **Funds Available:** No specific amount. The Lanier Technical College Scholarship Committee will determine selection of the scholarship recipient. **Duration:** One academic year.
Eligibility Requirements: Program is open to individuals with financial need. **Application Requirements:** Applicants must complete the scholarship application form and submit along with an endorsement letter from instructor or community member and a letter of applicant explaining the need for financial assistance.

1235 ■ LANIER TECHNICAL COLLEGE
2990 Landrum Educational Dr.
Oakwood, GA 30566
Tel: (770)531-6300
Fax: (770)631-6328

E-mail: info@laniertech.edu
Web Site: http://www.laniertech.edu
To provide financial assistance for deserving students who are residents of Dawson or Lumpkin Counties.
Title of Award: Edna A. Noblin Dawsonville Lions Club Scholarships **Area, Field, or Subject:** General studies. **Level of Education for which Award is Granted:** Undergraduate **Funds Available:** No specific amount. **Duration:** One academic year.
Eligibility Requirements: Applicants must be residents of Dawson County or Lumpkin County. **Application Requirements:** Applicants must submit a completed scholarship application form; a short letter from applicant explaining the need for financial assistance; a list of specific costs for which the applicants require assistance; and a recommendation letter from faculty member or responsible member of the community capable of reporting applicant's work record, leadership, and notable skills.

1236 ■ LAPPER COUNTY COMMUNITY FOUNDATION
220 W Nepressing St., Ste. 202
Lapeer, MI 48446
Tel: (810)664-0691
E-mail: lccf@charterinternet.com
Web Site: http://www.lapeercountycommunityfoundation.org
To attract and manage permanently endowed funds serving a wide range of charitable purposes in order to strengthen the quality of life in Lapeer County.
Title of Award: The Clarke B. Adams Memorial Foundation Lapeer County Community Foundation Fund **Area, Field, or Subject:** General studies. **Level of Education for which Award is Granted:** Undergraduate **Funds Available:** No specific amount.
Eligibility Requirements: Applicants must be graduating at the end of the current school year from Lapeer East or Lapeer West High School; must be accepted and planning to enroll in an accredited post-secondary college, university or trade school; must have 2.5 or better GPA based on a 4.0 scale. **Application Requirements:** Applicants must submit a completed application form, transcript, resume, an essay and letter of recommendation from a teacher or community leader stating the personal qualities. **Deadline for Receipt:** April 21.

1237 ■ LAPPER COUNTY COMMUNITY FOUNDATION
220 W Nepressing St., Ste. 202
Lapeer, MI 48446
Tel: (810)664-0691
E-mail: lccf@charterinternet.com
Web Site: http://www.lapeercountycommunityfoundation.org
To support educational assistance to students from Almont Township or the Village of Almont and the Township of Dryden of the Village of Dryden.
Title of Award: Ross P. Broesamle Educational Scholarships Fund **Area, Field, or Subject:** General studies. **Level of Education for which Award is Granted:** Undergraduate **Funds Available:** No specific amount.
Eligibility Requirements: Applicants must reside in geographic areas stated and be accepted or enrolled in an accredited state approved degree granting institution. **Application Requirements:** Applicants must be prepared to participate in a brief interview; must submit a transcript of records, test scores, photos and federal tax return for self or family. **Deadline for Receipt:** April 15.

1238 ■ LAPPER COUNTY COMMUNITY FOUNDATION
220 W Nepressing St., Ste. 202
Lapeer, MI 48446
Tel: (810)664-0691
E-mail: lccf@charterinternet.com
Web Site: http://www.lapeercountycommunityfoundation.org
To advance the values of community education through the development and encouragement of teachers who best emulate the qualities of commitment to well-rounded education and social values at the elementary level.
Title of Award: Irma Gelhausen Scholarship Fund **Area, Field, or Subject:** General studies. **Level of Education for which Award is Granted:** Undergraduate **Funds Available:** No specific amount.
Eligibility Requirements: Applicants must be in the third or more year of college/university studies; must have a GPA of 3.0 or higher for post-secondary studies and must be residents of Lapeer County. **Application Requirements:** Applicants must submit a completed application form, a

"200-word" essay discussing the expectations to achieve as an educator; must attach the most recent transcript of records, verification of current GPA and standardized test scores, IRS federal tax return and current photo to be used for publicity purposes. **Deadline for Receipt:** August 30. **Additional Information:** Debbie Cady at the above address.

1239 ■ LEARNING DISABILITIES ASSOCIATION OF OTTAWA-CARLETON
160 Percy St., Rm. No. 2
Ottawa, ON, Canada K1R 6E5
Tel: (613)567-5864
Fax: (613)567-5979
E-mail: ldaoc@rogers.com
Web Site: http://ldao-c.ncf.ca
To accommodate and support students with permanent disabilities.
Title of Award: Canada Study Grant for the Accommodation of Students with Permanent Disabilities **Area, Field, or Subject:** General studies. **Level of Education for which Award is Granted:** Undergraduate **Funds Available:** $8,000.
Eligibility Requirements: Applicants must have appropriate medical documentation; and a need for exceptional education. **Application Requirements:** Applicants must qualify for full-time or part-time Canada Student Loan assistance and then complete a separate application form. **Additional Information:** LDAO-C at the above address.

1240 ■ LEWIS-CLARK STATE COLLEGE
500 8th Ave.
Lewiston, ID 83501
Tel: (208)792-5272
Web Site: http://www.lcsc.edu
To offset the educationally-related expenses of a Lewis-Clark State College student from the Culdesac-Lapwai area.
Title of Award: The "21" Endowed Scholarships **Area, Field, or Subject:** General studies. **Level of Education for which Award is Granted:** Undergraduate **Funds Available:** No specific amount.
Eligibility Requirements: Applicants must be entering first year students who have a cumulative GPA of at least 2.5. **Application Requirements:** Applicants must submit a general application. **Deadline for Receipt:** March 1.

1241 ■ LEWIS-CLARK STATE COLLEGE
500 8th Ave.
Lewiston, ID 83501
Tel: (208)792-5272
Web Site: http://www.lcsc.edu
To provide educational assistance for students who demonstrate consistency and improvement in their scholastic records.
Title of Award: Mamie Adams Memorial Awards **Area, Field, or Subject:** General studies. **Level of Education for which Award is Granted:** Undergraduate **Funds Available:** No specific amount.
Eligibility Requirements: Applicants must be high school seniors who are planning to attend college in the fall or undergraduate college students enrolled at a 2- or 4-year institution with at least a 2.5 GPA. **Application Requirements:** Applicants must accomplish a general application available at the website.

1242 ■ LEWIS-CLARK STATE COLLEGE
500 8th Ave.
Lewiston, ID 83501
Tel: (208)792-5272
Web Site: http://www.lcsc.edu
To acknowledge outstanding Idaho high school seniors who have participated in The American Legion of Idaho Boys and Girls State competition and who have selected Lewis-Clark State College as their school of choice.
Title of Award: American Legion Boys/Girls State Scholarships **Area, Field, or Subject:** General studies. **Level of Education for which Award is Granted:** Undergraduate **Funds Available:** $200.
Eligibility Requirements: Applicants must be outstanding senior students of Idaho High School who are currently enrolled in LCSC. **Application Requirements:** Applicants must accomplish a general application available at the website.

1243 ■ LEWIS-CLARK STATE COLLEGE
500 8th Ave.
Lewiston, ID 83501
Tel: (208)792-5272
Web Site: http://www.lcsc.edu
To benefit a non-traditional student that is a cancer survivor, is currently battling cancer, or who has had to deal with cancer in their immediate family.
Title of Award: Diana Brown Endowed Scholarships **Area, Field, or Subject:** General studies. **Level of Education for which Award is Granted:** Undergraduate **Funds Available:** No specific amount.
Eligibility Requirements: Applicants must be cancer survivors or are currently battling cancer and are registered degree-seeking, full-time students. **Application Requirements:** Applicants must submit general application. **Deadline for Receipt:** March 1.

1244 ■ LEWIS-CLARK STATE COLLEGE
500 8th Ave.
Lewiston, ID 83501
Tel: (208)792-5272
Web Site: http://www.lcsc.edu
To offset the educationally-related expenses of Lewis-Clark State College students.
Title of Award: Glen and Babs Carlson Endowed Scholarships **Area, Field, or Subject:** General studies. **Level of Education for which Award is Granted:** Undergraduate **Funds Available:** No specific amount.
Eligibility Requirements: Applicants must be students at Lewis-Clark State College with a cumulative GPA consistent with the minimum required for admission. **Application Requirements:** Applicants must submit a general application. **Deadline for Receipt:** March 1.

1245 ■ LEWIS-CLARK STATE COLLEGE
500 8th Ave.
Lewiston, ID 83501
Tel: (208)792-5272
Web Site: http://www.lcsc.edu
To provide financial assistance for the graduates of Emmett High School.
Title of Award: Walter & Elsie Carr Endowed Scholarships **Area, Field, or Subject:** General studies. **Level of Education for which Award is Granted:** Undergraduate **Funds Available:** No specific amount.
Eligibility Requirements: Applicants must be enrolled for at least 12 credits. **Application Requirements:** Applicants must submit a general application. **Deadline for Receipt:** March 1.

1246 ■ LEWIS-CLARK STATE COLLEGE
500 8th Ave.
Lewiston, ID 83501
Tel: (208)792-5272
Web Site: http://www.lcsc.edu
To provide financial assistance for students from Idaho High School.
Title of Award: Church Family Scholarships **Area, Field, or Subject:** General studies. **Level of Education for which Award is Granted:** Undergraduate **Funds Available:** No specific amount.
Eligibility Requirements: Applicants must be first year students from an Idaho high school with a cumulative high school GPA of at least 3.0.; must be enrolled full-time (12 credits) at Lewis-Clark State College; must have at least a 2.5 semester GPA at the end of their first semester at LCSC; and must maintain at least a 3.0 cumulative GPA by the end of the first year at LCSC and thereafter. **Application Requirements:** Applicant must submit general application. **Deadline for Receipt:** March 1.

1247 ■ LEWIS-CLARK STATE COLLEGE
500 8th Ave.
Lewiston, ID 83501
Tel: (208)792-5272
Web Site: http://www.lcsc.edu
To offset the educational expenses of Lewis-Clark State College students.
Title of Award: Fisher Clark Memorial Endowed Scholarships **Area, Field, or Subject:** General studies. **Level of Education for which Award is Granted:** Undergraduate **Funds Available:** No specific amount.
Eligibility Requirements: Applicants must be female students and must have a cumulative grade point average consistent with the minimum required for admission and for progress toward her major. **Application Requirements:** Applicants must submit a general application. **Deadline for Receipt:** March 1.

1248 ■ LEWIS-CLARK STATE COLLEGE
500 8th Ave.
Lewiston, ID 83501
Tel: (208)792-5272
Web Site: http://www.lcsc.edu
To inspire educational pursuits among less capable individuals by providing financial assistance.
Title of Award: Coeur d'Alene Alumni Scholarships **Area, Field, or Subject:** General studies. **Level of Education for which Award is Granted:** Undergraduate **Funds Available:** No specific amount.
Eligibility Requirements: Applicants must be attending the LCSC Couer d'Alene campus; must be currently enrolled in a minimum of six semester credits through the Coeur d'Alene program which includes credits from LCSC and NIC; must have completed at least one semester of course work through LCSC; and must have a minimum GPA of 3.0. **Application Requirements:** Applicants must accomplish a general application available at the website. **Deadline for Receipt:** March 1.

1249 ■ LEWIS-CLARK STATE COLLEGE
500 8th Ave.
Lewiston, ID 83501
Tel: (208)792-5272
Web Site: http://www.lcsc.edu
To offset the educationally-related expenses of Lewis-Clark State College students intending to pursue a career in the field of real estate.
Title of Award: The Rick Crane Group Real Estate Scholarships Fund **Area, Field, or Subject:** Real Estate; Business Administration. **Level of Education for which Award is Granted:** Undergraduate **Funds Available:** $100.
Eligibility Requirements: Program is open to individuals seeking a Bachelor's degree in Business, or an Associate of Applied Science degree in Business Management. Applicants must be serious about becoming a real estate agent or otherwise working in the field of real estate, have a grade point average of at least 3.5 with strong potential for academic achievement, and must be full-time students taking 12 or more credits. **Application Requirements:** Applicants must accomplish the required general application available in the website. **Deadline for Receipt:** March 1.

1250 ■ LEWIS-CLARK STATE COLLEGE
500 8th Ave.
Lewiston, ID 83501
Tel: (208)792-5272
Web Site: http://www.lcsc.edu
To provide financial assistance for the Idaho youth.
Title of Award: Laura Moore Cunningham Foundation General Scholarships **Area, Field, or Subject:** General studies. **Level of Education for which Award is Granted:** Undergraduate **Funds Available:** No specific amount.
Eligibility Requirements: Applicants must be classified as full-time students who are carrying 12 or more credits per semester and who have a minimum cumulative GPA of 3.0. and must also be Idaho residents. **Application Requirements:** Applicants must submit a general application. **Deadline for Receipt:** March 1.

1251 ■ LEWIS-CLARK STATE COLLEGE
500 8th Ave.
Lewiston, ID 83501
Tel: (208)792-5272
Web Site: http://www.lcsc.edu
To provide financial assistance for individuals intending to pursue an education.
Title of Award: Kenneth and Kathleen Davis Endowed Scholarships **Area, Field, or Subject:** General studies. **Level of Education for which Award is Granted:** Undergraduate **Number Awarded:** 1. **Funds Available:** $1500.
Eligibility Requirements: Applicants must be classified as full-time students, carrying 12 or more credits per semester and must have a minimum cumulative GPA of 3.5. **Application Requirements:** Applicants must submit general application. **Deadline for Receipt:** March 1.

1252 ■ LEWIS-CLARK STATE COLLEGE
500 8th Ave.
Lewiston, ID 83501
Tel: (208)792-5272
Web Site: http://www.lcsc.edu
To provide financial assistance for students and single parents who are in need and are intending to pursue higher education.
Title of Award: Dean A. Froehlich Endowed Scholarships **Area, Field, or Subject:** General studies. **Level of Education for which Award is Granted:** Undergraduate **Funds Available:** No specific amount.
Eligibility Requirements: Applicants must be enrolled for at least 12 credits and have a minimum 2.5 GPA. **Application Requirements:** Applicants must submit a general application. **Deadline for Receipt:** March 1.

1253 ■ LEWIS-CLARK STATE COLLEGE
500 8th Ave.
Lewiston, ID 83501
Tel: (208)792-5272
Web Site: http://www.lcsc.edu
To provide educational assistance for students from Lapwai High School.
Title of Award: Irene Carlson Gnaedinger Memorial Scholarships **Area, Field, or Subject:** General studies. **Level of Education for which Award is Granted:** Undergraduate **Funds Available:** No specific amount.
Eligibility Requirements: Applicants must be graduates of Lapwai High School; must demonstrate a minimum cumulative GPA of 2.5; and are enrolled for a minimum of 12 credits in a baccalaureate degree program. **Application Requirements:** Applicants must submit a general application. **Deadline for Receipt:** March 1.

1254 ■ LEWIS-CLARK STATE COLLEGE
500 8th Ave.
Lewiston, ID 83501
Tel: (208)792-5272
Web Site: http://www.lcsc.edu
To provide financial assistance to people who cannot afford college education.
Title of Award: Jack & Mary Lou Gruber Scholarships **Area, Field, or Subject:** General studies. **Level of Education for which Award is Granted:** Undergraduate **Funds Available:** No specific amount.
Eligibility Requirements: Applicants must have a minimum of 3.0 GPA and are enrolled for a minimum of 12 credits. **Application Requirements:** Applicants must submit a general application. **Deadline for Receipt:** March 1.

1255 ■ LEWIS-CLARK STATE COLLEGE
500 8th Ave.
Lewiston, ID 83501
Tel: (208)792-5272
Web Site: http://www.lcsc.edu
To offset the educationally-related expenses of Lewis-Clark State College students.
Title of Award: Henderson Memorial Endowed Scholarships **Area, Field, or Subject:** General studies. **Level of Education for which Award is Granted:** Undergraduate **Funds Available:** No specific amount.
Eligibility Requirements: Applicants must have completed at least one semester at LCSC and must have a cumulative GPA of at least 3.0. **Application Requirements:** Applicants must submit general application. **Deadline for Receipt:** March 1.

1256 ■ LEWIS-CLARK STATE COLLEGE
500 8th Ave.
Lewiston, ID 83501
Tel: (208)792-5272
Web Site: http://www.lcsc.edu
To support varsity players who are also good in academics.
Title of Award: Frank and Gladys Hopkins Endowed Scholarships **Area, Field, or Subject:** General studies. **Level of Education for which Award is Granted:** Undergraduate **Funds Available:** $1,000.
Eligibility Requirements: Applicants must be classified as full-time students who are participating on the LCSC baseball team. Applicants must also have a cumulative GPA consistent with the minimum required

for admission and for progress toward their selected major. **Application Requirements:** Applicants must accomplish the required general application available at the website. **Deadline for Receipt:** March 1.

1257 ■ LEWIS-CLARK STATE COLLEGE
500 8th Ave.
Lewiston, ID 83501
Tel: (208)792-5272
Web Site: http://www.lcsc.edu
To provide financial assistance to students who are in need.
Title of Award: Idaho Attorney General Scholarships **Area, Field, or Subject:** General studies. **Level of Education for which Award is Granted:** Undergraduate **Number Awarded:** 2. **Funds Available:** $750. **Duration:** One year.
Eligibility Requirements: Applicants must be freshmen and have had three years involvement in either Idaho FFA or 4-H. **Application Requirements:** Applicants must accomplish general application available in the website. **Deadline for Receipt:** March 1.

1258 ■ LEWIS-CLARK STATE COLLEGE
500 8th Ave.
Lewiston, ID 83501
Tel: (208)792-5272
Web Site: http://www.lcsc.edu
To inspire educational pursuits among less capable individuals by providing financial assistance.
Title of Award: Idaho Promise Category B Scholarships **Area, Field, or Subject:** General studies. **Level of Education for which Award is Granted:** Undergraduate **Funds Available:** No specific amount.
Eligibility Requirements: Applicants must graduate from an Idaho High School or its equivalent; must have a 3.0 or better cumulative high school GPA or ACT score of 20 or better; must be under the age of 22; and must be intending to attend as full-time students. **Application Requirements:** Applicants must accomplish a general application available in the website.

1259 ■ LEWIS-CLARK STATE COLLEGE
500 8th Ave.
Lewiston, ID 83501
Tel: (208)792-5272
Web Site: http://www.lcsc.edu
To provide financial assistance for the benefit of students from Lewiston, Idaho, Clarkston and Washington attending Lewis-Clark State College during the beginning stage of their college experience.
Title of Award: Lewiston Clarkston Kiwanis Club Scholarships **Area, Field, or Subject:** General studies. **Level of Education for which Award is Granted:** Undergraduate **Funds Available:** $100.
Eligibility Requirements: Applicants must have completed at least one semester at LCSC and must have a minimum cumulative 2.5 GPA. **Application Requirements:** Applicants must complete general application available at the website. **Deadline for Receipt:** March 1.

1260 ■ LEWIS-CLARK STATE COLLEGE
500 8th Ave.
Lewiston, ID 83501
Tel: (208)792-5272
Web Site: http://www.lcsc.edu
To offset the educationally-related expenses of Lewis-Clark State College students.
Title of Award: Lewis-Clark Coin Club Endowed Scholarships **Area, Field, or Subject:** General studies. **Level of Education for which Award is Granted:** Undergraduate **Funds Available:** No specific amount.
Eligibility Requirements: Applicants must be classified as full-time students carrying 12 or more credits per semester with a minimum cumulative GPA of 2.5. **Additional Information:** Annual awards are variable and are awarded in alternate award cycles to an academic and a professional technical student and may be renewed to students who continue to meet the above criteria. **Deadline for Receipt:** March 1.

1261 ■ LEWIS-CLARK STATE COLLEGE
500 8th Ave.
Lewiston, ID 83501
Tel: (208)792-5272

Web Site: http://www.lcsc.edu
To recognize students who have shown consistency and improvement in their scholastic records.
Title of Award: Lewis-Clark State College Foundation Scholars Scholarships **Area, Field, or Subject:** General studies. **Level of Education for which Award is Granted:** Undergraduate **Funds Available:** $2,500.
Eligibility Requirements: Applicants must have exceptional academic achievement, community involvement and leadership ability; must be outstanding Idaho and Asotin County, Washington high school seniors with a cumulative GPA of 3.5. **Application Requirements:** Applicants must accomplish a general application available at the website. **Deadline for Receipt:** March 1.

1262 ■ LEWIS-CLARK STATE COLLEGE
500 8th Ave.
Lewiston, ID 83501
Tel: (208)792-5272
Web Site: http://www.lcsc.edu
To inspire educational pursuits among less capable individuals by providing financial assistance.
Title of Award: Lewis-Clark State College Freshman Scholarships **Area, Field, or Subject:** General studies. **Level of Education for which Award is Granted:** Undergraduate **Funds Available:** $500. **Duration:** One year.
Eligibility Requirements: Applicants must be Idaho High School seniors planning to attend LCSC in their freshman year and must have a high school cumulative GPA of at least 3.5. **Application Requirements:** Students must be at least tentatively admitted to the college and have their 7th semester high school transcript on file with the Office of Admission prior to the Deadline. **Deadline for Receipt:** March 1.

1263 ■ LEWIS-CLARK STATE COLLEGE
500 8th Ave.
Lewiston, ID 83501
Tel: (208)792-5272
Web Site: http://www.lcsc.edu
To benefit junior and senior students of Idaho colleges and universities.
Title of Award: Lewis-Clark State College/Idaho Society of CPAs Scholarships Fund **Area, Field, or Subject:** Accounting. **Level of Education for which Award is Granted:** Undergraduate **Funds Available:** $1000. **Duration:** One Academic Year.
Eligibility Requirements: Applicants must be residents of Idaho and must have a cumulative grade point average of 2.75 or above for all class work prior to the application; must maintain the stated grade point for each semester. **Application Requirements:** Applicants must submit a general application. **Deadline for Receipt:** April 14. **Additional Information:** Melissa R. Nelson; 250 Bobwhite Court, Ste. 240 Boise, ID 83706 Fax 208-344-8984.

1264 ■ LEWIS-CLARK STATE COLLEGE
500 8th Ave.
Lewiston, ID 83501
Tel: (208)792-5272
Web Site: http://www.lcsc.edu
To assist non-traditional students who have been out of high school for at least 5 years at the time of their initial enrollment at Lewis-Clark State College.
Title of Award: Lewis-Clark State College Non-Traditional Student Scholarships **Area, Field, or Subject:** General studies. **Level of Education for which Award is Granted:** Undergraduate **Funds Available:** $500.
Eligibility Requirements: Program is open to full-time, degree seeking students who meet the non-traditional requirement. **Application Requirements:** Applicants must accomplish a general application available in the website.

1265 ■ LEWIS-CLARK STATE COLLEGE
500 8th Ave.
Lewiston, ID 83501
Tel: (208)792-5272
Web Site: http://www.lcsc.edu
To provide financial assistance for students who have shown improvement in their academic records.

Title of Award: Lewis-Clark State College Presidential Out-of-State Scholarships **Area, Field, or Subject:** General studies. **Level of Education for which Award is Granted:** Undergraduate **Funds Available:** No specific amount.
Eligibility Requirements: Program is open to promising new non-resident students with at least a high school or transfer cumulative GPA of 3.0; must maintain a 2.5 semester GPA, completing at least 12 credits per semester and registering for classes during advanced registration each semester. **Application Requirements:** Applicants must accomplish a general application available at the website. **Deadline for Receipt:** March 1 for Fall enrollment or November 1 for Spring enrollment.

1266 ■ LEWIS-CLARK STATE COLLEGE
500 8th Ave.
Lewiston, ID 83501
Tel: (208)792-5272
Web Site: http://www.lcsc.edu
To recognize promising Idaho High School seniors by providing educational assistance.
Title of Award: Lewis-Clark State College Provost Scholarships **Area, Field, or Subject:** General studies. **Level of Education for which Award is Granted:** Undergraduate **Funds Available:** $500. **Duration:** One year.
Eligibility Requirements: Applicants must have a cumulative GPA of 3.0-3.49; must maintain a 3.0 semester GPA while completing at least 12 credits each semester; and must be at least tentatively admitted to the college and have their 7th semester high school transcripts on file with the Office of Admission. **Application Requirements:** Applicants must accomplish general application available in the website. **Deadline for Receipt:** March 1. **Additional Information:** Financial Aid Office, LCSC, 500 8th Avenue, Lewiston, ID 83501, 800-933-5272 or 208-792-2224.

1267 ■ LEWIS-CLARK STATE COLLEGE
500 8th Ave.
Lewiston, ID 83501
Tel: (208)792-5272
Web Site: http://www.lcsc.edu
To assist transfer students intending to complete a bachelor's degree at Lewis-Clark State College.
Title of Award: Lewis-Clark State College Transfer Scholarships **Area, Field, or Subject:** General studies. **Level of Education for which Award is Granted:** Undergraduate **Funds Available:** $500.
Eligibility Requirements: Program is open to students who transfer from the following colleges: North Idaho College, Community Colleges in the Spokane area, College of Southern Idaho, Walla Walla Community College, and Treasure Valley Community College. Students must also be full-time, degree seeking students with a cumulative G.P.A. of 3.0 or higher. **Application Requirements:** Applicants must submit a general application.

1268 ■ LEWIS-CLARK STATE COLLEGE
500 8th Ave.
Lewiston, ID 83501
Tel: (208)792-5272
Web Site: http://www.lcsc.edu
To encourage educational pursuits among less capable students by providing educational assistance.
Title of Award: Lewis-Clark State College Valley Scholarships **Area, Field, or Subject:** General studies. **Level of Education for which Award is Granted:** Undergraduate **Funds Available:** No specific amount.
Eligibility Requirements: Program is open to promising Lewiston, Clarkston and Asotin High School seniors with a cumulative GPA of 3.0 and are planning to attend LCSC. **Application Requirements:** Applicants must submit a completed Application for Admission form, 7th semester transcripts and ACT/SAT scores. **Additional Information:** Financial Aid Office, LCSC, 500 8th Avenue, Lewiston, ID 83501. 800-933-5272 or 208-792-2224.

1269 ■ LEWIS-CLARK STATE COLLEGE
500 8th Ave.
Lewiston, ID 83501
Tel: (208)792-5272

Web Site: http://www.lcsc.edu
To encourage educational pursuits by providing financial assistance.
Title of Award: Lewiston Service League Memorial Scholarships **Area, Field, or Subject:** General studies. **Level of Education for which Award is Granted:** Undergraduate **Funds Available:** No specific amount.
Eligibility Requirements: Applicants must be full-time students with at least 12 credit hours; must show academic promise or ability to satisfactorily complete college work with a minimum grade point average of 3.0. **Application Requirements:** Applicants must accomplish general application available at the website. **Additional Information:** Lewiston Service League, P.O. Box 1811, Lewiston, ID 83501.

1270 ■ LEWIS-CLARK STATE COLLEGE
500 8th Ave.
Lewiston, ID 83501
Tel: (208)792-5272
Web Site: http://www.lcsc.edu
To provide educational support for young people who, for personal, financial, or other reasons discontinued their education, and for those who are in need of retraining who wish to return to school.
Title of Award: Elizabeth McKissick Memorial Scholarships **Area, Field, or Subject:** General Studies. **Level of Education for which Award is Granted:** Undergraduate **Funds Available:** No specific amount.
Eligibility Requirements: Applicants must be individuals who have graduated from or who attended Lewiston High School. Recipients of this scholarship must be at least 22 years of age at the time of application and must be classified as at least part-time students (taking 6 or more credits per semester). **Application Requirements:** Applicants must accomplish a general application available in the website. **Deadline for Receipt:** March 1.

1271 ■ LEWIS-CLARK STATE COLLEGE
500 8th Ave.
Lewiston, ID 83501
Tel: (208)792-5272
Web Site: http://www.lcsc.edu
To encourage educational pursuits among non-traditional students.
Title of Award: Robbie Miller Memorial Scholarships **Area, Field, or Subject:** General studies. **Level of Education for which Award is Granted:** Undergraduate **Funds Available:** No specific amount.
Eligibility Requirements: Program is open to non-traditional students who demonstrate a 2.5 cumulative GPA and must have a current standing of sophomore or above. **Application Requirements:** Applicants must accomplish a general application available in the website. **Deadline for Receipt:** March 1.

1272 ■ LEWIS-CLARK STATE COLLEGE
500 8th Ave.
Lewiston, ID 83501
Tel: (208)792-5272
Web Site: http://www.lcsc.edu
To provide financial assistance for individuals intending to pursue their educational goals.
Title of Award: Eugene Northrup Scholarships **Area, Field, or Subject:** General studies. **Level of Education for which Award is Granted:** Undergraduate **Number Awarded:** 2. **Funds Available:** $500. **Duration:** One year.
Eligibility Requirements: Program is open to graduating seniors of an area high school and who have a GPA of 3.0. **Application Requirements:** Applicants must write a 500-word essay on Unionism. **Deadline for Receipt:** March 1.

1273 ■ LEWIS-CLARK STATE COLLEGE
500 8th Ave.
Lewiston, ID 83501
Tel: (208)792-5272
Web Site: http://www.lcsc.edu
To provide financial assistance for individuals intending to pursue their educational goals.
Title of Award: Odd Fellows Lodge No. 8 Endowed Scholarships **Area, Field, or Subject:** General studies. **Level of Education for which Award is Granted:** Undergraduate **Funds Available:** $250.

Eligibility Requirements: Applicants must be full-time students carrying 12 or more credits per semester; must have a minimum cumulative GPA of 3.0. **Application Requirements:** Applicants must accomplish a general application available at the website. **Deadline for Receipt:** March 1.

1274 ■ LEWIS-CLARK STATE COLLEGE
500 8th Ave.
Lewiston, ID 83501
Tel: (208)792-5272
Web Site: http://www.lcsc.edu
To provide financial assistance for worthy community college and university students in timber-related fields.
Title of Award: Oregon Logging Conference Scholarships **Area, Field, or Subject:** General studies. **Level of Education for which Award is Granted:** Undergraduate **Funds Available:** No specific amount.
Eligibility Requirements: Applicants must be students in timber-related fields who are enrolled in a community college or university. **Application Requirements:** Applicants must accomplish a general application available at the website.

1275 ■ LEWIS-CLARK STATE COLLEGE
500 8th Ave.
Lewiston, ID 83501
Tel: (208)792-5272
Web Site: http://www.lcsc.edu
To offset the educationally-related expenses of Lewis-Clark State College students.
Title of Award: Eleanor Perry Memorial Endowed Scholarships **Area, Field, or Subject:** General studies. **Level of Education for which Award is Granted:** Undergraduate **Funds Available:** No specific amount.
Eligibility Requirements: Applicants must be full-time students; must have a minimum cumulative GPA of at least a 3.0. **Application Requirements:** Applicants must accomplish a general application available at the website. **Deadline for Receipt:** March 1.

1276 ■ LEWIS-CLARK STATE COLLEGE
500 8th Ave.
Lewiston, ID 83501
Tel: (208)792-5272
Web Site: http://www.lcsc.edu
To encourage educational pursuits among less capable students by providing educational assistance.
Title of Award: State of Idaho Scholarships Category A **Area, Field, or Subject:** General studies. **Level of Education for which Award is Granted:** Undergraduate **Funds Available:** $3,000.
Eligibility Requirements: Applicants must be outstanding Idaho High School graduates as evaluated through their rank in graduating class, ACT scores, and recommendations from high school officials. They must also intend to enroll in academic or vocational programs at eligible Idaho postsecondary educational institutions. **Application Requirements:** Application instructions are available in the website. **Deadline for Receipt:** January 15.

1277 ■ LEWIS-CLARK STATE COLLEGE
500 8th Ave.
Lewiston, ID 83501
Tel: (208)792-5272
Web Site: http://www.lcsc.edu
To encourage educational pursuits among less capable students by providing educational assistance.
Title of Award: Tschudy Family Scholarships **Area, Field, or Subject:** General studies. **Level of Education for which Award is Granted:** Undergraduate **Funds Available:** $2,500.
Eligibility Requirements: Applicants must be residents of Idaho; must be graduating Emmett High School seniors or have graduated within the last seven years from Emmett High School; and must be full-time academic students (at least 14 credit hours) at BSU, ISU, LCSC or UI. **Application Requirements:** Applicants must accomplish a general application available at the website.

1278 ■ LEWIS-CLARK STATE COLLEGE
500 8th Ave.
Lewiston, ID 83501

Tel: (208)792-5272
Web Site: http://www.lcsc.edu
To provide financial assistance for promising students in Washington.
Title of Award: Washington Reciprocity Out-of-State Scholarships **Area, Field, or Subject:** General studies. **Level of Education for which Award is Granted:** Undergraduate **Funds Available:** No specific amount.
Eligibility Requirements: Applicants must maintain a 2.5 semester GPA, completing at least 12 credits per semester and registering for classes during advanced registration each semester. **Application Requirements:** Applicants must accomplish a general application available at the website.

1279 ■ MARVIN LEWIS COMMUNITY FUND

Longworth Hall
700 W Pete Rose Way, Unit 37
Cincinnati, OH 45203
Tel: (513)381-5437
Fax: (513)381-5439
Web Site: http://www.marvinlewis.org
To recognize and honor outstanding male and female student athletes.
Title of Award: Marvin Lewis Scholarships **Area, Field, or Subject:** General studies. **Level of Education for which Award is Granted:** Undergraduate **Funds Available:** No specific amount.
Eligibility Requirements: Applicant must be a resident of Greater Cincinnati, and attending college as a full-time student. **Application Requirements:** Applicants must submit a completed scholarship application form along with a copy of recent transcript; Expected Family Contribution (EFC) from Student Aid Report (SAR) in the FAFSA; a copy of Financial Aid Award Letter from their chosen college; a 1000-word essay; and evidence of a varsity letter. Faxed applications will not be considered. **Additional Information:** In partnership with The Cincinnati Scholarship Foundation. **Deadline for Receipt:** April 30.

1280 ■ LEXINGTON COMMUNITY FOUNDATION

607 Washington St.
PO Box 422
Lexington, NE 68850
Tel: (308)324-6704
E-mail: lexfoundation@alltel.net
Web Site: http://www.lexfoundation.org
To promote community philanthropy by working with individuals, families and organizations to develop tailored giving plans that effectively meet the charitable goals and financial circumstances.
Title of Award: Lexington Alumni Scholarships **Area, Field, or Subject:** General studies. **Level of Education for which Award is Granted:** Undergraduate **Funds Available:** $750.
Eligibility Requirements: Applicants must be graduating senior students who rank in the upper 1/2 of their class. **Application Requirements:** Applicants must submit a completed application form; must provide three letters of recommendation and must attach a recent photo.

1281 ■ LEXINGTON COMMUNITY FOUNDATION

607 Washington St.
PO Box 422
Lexington, NE 68850
Tel: (308)324-6704
E-mail: lexfoundation@alltel.net
Web Site: http://www.lexfoundation.org
To promote community philanthropy by working with individuals, families and organizations to develop tailored giving plans that effectively meet the charitable goals and financial circumstances.
Title of Award: Lexington Community Foundation Annual Scholarships **Area, Field, or Subject:** General studies. **Level of Education for which Award is Granted:** Undergraduate **Funds Available:** $2,000.
Eligibility Requirements: Applicants must be graduating senior students who rank in the upper 1/3 of their class. **Application Requirements:** Applicants must submit a completed application form; must provide three letters of recommendation and must attach a recent photo.

1282 ■ LEXINGTON COMMUNITY FOUNDATION

607 Washington St.
PO Box 422
Lexington, NE 68850

Tel: (308)324-6704
E-mail: lexfoundation@alltel.net
Web Site: http://www.lexfoundation.org
To promote community philanthropy by working with individuals, families and organizations to develop tailored giving plans that effectively meet the charitable goals and financial circumstances.
Title of Award: Lexington Community Foundation/CCC Scholarships **Area, Field, or Subject:** General studies. **Level of Education for which Award is Granted:** Undergraduate **Funds Available:** $600.
Eligibility Requirements: Applicants must be graduating senior students who rank in the upper 1/2 of their class. **Application Requirements:** Applicants must submit a completed application form; must provide three letters of recommendation and must attach a recent photo.

1283 ■ LEXINGTON COMMUNITY FOUNDATION

607 Washington St.
PO Box 422
Lexington, NE 68850
Tel: (308)324-6704
E-mail: lexfoundation@alltel.net
Web Site: http://www.lexfoundation.org
To promote community philanthropy by working with individuals, families and organizations to develop tailored giving plans that effectively meet the charitable goals and financial circumstances.
Title of Award: Norall Scholarships Trust **Area, Field, or Subject:** General studies. **Level of Education for which Award is Granted:** Undergraduate **Funds Available:** No specific amount.
Eligibility Requirements: Applicants must be past graduates of high school in Dawson who are enrolled in a US. college. **Application Requirements:** Applicants must complete the application form, a copy of Dawson County High School transcript for first-time applicant, academic transcript for post-secondary education and three personal references. **Deadline for Receipt:** March 1. **Additional Information:** PO Box 890 Lexington, NE 68850.

1284 ■ LEXINGTON COMMUNITY FOUNDATION

607 Washington St.
PO Box 422
Lexington, NE 68850
Tel: (308)324-6704
E-mail: lexfoundation@alltel.net
Web Site: http://www.lexfoundation.org
To promote community philanthropy by working with individuals, families and organizations to develop tailored giving plans that effectively meet the charitable goals and financial circumstances.
Title of Award: Francelene Skinner Memorial Scholarship **Area, Field, or Subject:** General studies. **Level of Education for which Award is Granted:** Undergraduate **Funds Available:** $500.
Eligibility Requirements: Applicants must be graduating seniors who rank in the upper 1/3 of their class and must be U.S. citizens. **Application Requirements:** Applicants must submit a completed application form; must provide three letters of recommendation and must attach a recent photo.

1285 ■ LEXINGTON COMMUNITY FOUNDATION

607 Washington St.
PO Box 422
Lexington, NE 68850
Tel: (308)324-6704
E-mail: lexfoundation@alltel.net
Web Site: http://www.lexfoundation.org
To promote community philanthropy by working with individuals, families and organizations to develop tailored giving plans that effectively meet the charitable goals and financial circumstances.
Title of Award: Mark and Vera Turner Memorial Scholarship **Area, Field, or Subject:** General studies. **Level of Education for which Award is Granted:** Undergraduate **Funds Available:** $1,000.
Eligibility Requirements: Applicants must be graduating senior students who rank in the upper 1/2 of the class; must be graduating Lexington High School seniors who enroll in a university, college, community college or trade school within the state of Nebraska. **Application Requirements:** Applicants must submit a completed application form; must provide three letters of recommendation and must attach a recent photo.

1286 ■ LEXINGTON COMMUNITY FOUNDATION

607 Washington St.
PO Box 422
Lexington, NE 68850
Tel: (308)324-6704
E-mail: lexfoundation@alltel.net
Web Site: http://www.lexfoundation.org
To promote community philanthropy by working with individuals, families and organizations to develop tailored giving plans that effectively meet the charitable goals and financial circumstances.
Title of Award: Robert R. Wade Scholarship **Area, Field, or Subject:** General studies. **Level of Education for which Award is Granted:** Undergraduate **Funds Available:** $1,000.
Eligibility Requirements: Applicants must be graduating senior students who rank in the upper 1/2 of the class; must be U.S. citizens and must be graduating Lexington High School seniors who enroll in a public university, college, community college or trade school within the state of Nebraska. **Application Requirements:** Applicants must submit a completed application form; must provide three letters of recommendation and must attach a recent photo.

1287 ■ LIFE AND HEALTH INSURANCE FOUNDATION FOR EDUCATION

1655 N Fort Myer Dr., Ste. 610
Arlington, VA 22209
888-LIF-E777
Fax: (202)464-5011
E-mail: info@lifehappens.org
Web Site: http://www.lifehappens.org
To help deserving young people realize their dream of achieving a college education.
Title of Award: LIFE Lessons Scholarships Program **Area, Field, or Subject:** General Studies. **Level of Education for which Award is Granted:** Undergraduate **Funds Available:** $25,000.
Eligibility Requirements: Applicants must be: college students and college-bound high school seniors; legal residents of the fifty United States and the District of Columbia; between 17 and 24 years of age. Applicant must have experienced the death of a parent or legal guardian and be currently enrolled in or accepted to a college, university or trade school within the fifty United States or District of Columbia. A minor should have a parent's or legal guardian's permission to enter. **Application Requirements:** Applicants who qualify must submit essays or videos about how the death of a parent or guardian impacted their lives. **Deadline for Receipt:** March. **Additional Information:** Life and Health Insurance Foundation for Education at the above address.

1288 ■ LIGHTHOUSE INTERNATIONAL

111 E 59th St.
New York, NY 10022-1202
Tel: (212)821-9200
Free: 800-829-0500
Fax: (212)821-9707
E-mail: info@lighthouse.org
Web Site: http://www.lighthouse.org
To provide educational support to visually impaired students.
Title of Award: Christine H. Eide Memorial Scholarships **Area, Field, or Subject:** General studies. **Level of Education for which Award is Granted:** Graduate, Undergraduate **Funds Available:** A maximum of $1,000. **Duration:** One year.
Eligibility Requirements: Applicant must be a full-time undergraduate or graduate college student in an accredited college/university; and must be impaired visually. **Application Requirements:** Application form is available at the website. Applicants must complete and send the application to: Dr. Cynthia Stuen, Senior Vice President, Policy and Professional Affairs, New York Lighthouse Vision Rehabilitation Services 111 East 59th Street New York, NY 10022-1202. **Deadline for Receipt:** September for the fall semester and January for the spring semester. **Additional Information:** Gina Obando, gobando@lighthouse.org.

1289 ■ LIGHTHOUSE INTERNATIONAL

111 E 59th St.
New York, NY 10022-1202
Tel: (212)821-9200
Free: 800-829-0500
Fax: (212)821-9707
E-mail: info@lighthouse.org
Web Site: http://www.lighthouse.org
To provide support to visually impaired students to continue their education to college.
Title of Award: Lighthouse International Scholarships - College-bound Awards **Area, Field, or Subject:** General studies. **Level of Education for which Award is Granted:** High School **Funds Available:** $5,000.
Eligibility Requirements: Applicant must be a senior or high school graduate; legally blind; a U.S. citizen; not related to any Lighthouse employees and not a previous winners of program. **Application Requirements:** Applicant must send an application form (can be downloaded at the website); an essay; proof of the applicant's visual condition; transcripts; and two letters of recommendation. All materials must send thru email at sca@lighthouse.org. **Deadline for Receipt:** February. **Additional Information:** sca@lighthouse.org.

1290 ■ LIGHTHOUSE INTERNATIONAL

111 E 59th St.
New York, NY 10022-1202
Tel: (212)821-9200
Free: 800-829-0500
Fax: (212)821-9707
E-mail: info@lighthouse.org
Web Site: http://www.lighthouse.org
To provide support to visually impaired students to continue their education.
Title of Award: Lighthouse International Scholarships - Undergraduate Awards **Area, Field, or Subject:** General studies. **Level of Education for which Award is Granted:** Undergraduate **Funds Available:** $5,000.
Eligibility Requirements: Applicant must be a college student; legally blind; a U.S. citizen; not related to Lighthouse employees and not a previous winner of the program. **Application Requirements:** Applicant must send an application form (can be downloaded at the website); an essay; proof of the applicant's visual condition; transcripts; and two letters of recommendation. **Deadline for Receipt:** February.

1291 ■ LOGICORE CORPORATION

1015 Henderson Rd. NW
Huntsville, AL 35816
Tel: (256)533-5789
Fax: (256)533-5785
E-mail: hr@logicorehsv.com
Web Site: http://www.logicorehsv.com
To assist deserving young people of Madison County, Madison City, Huntsville City, Lawrence County and Limestone County.
Title of Award: Miranda Bouldin General Scholarships **Area, Field, or Subject:** General studies. **Level of Education for which Award is Granted:** Undergraduate **Number Awarded:** 4. **Funds Available:** $1,500.
Eligibility Requirements: Applicants must be U.S. citizens; graduating seniors from Madison County schools, Madison City schools, Huntsville City schools, Lawrence County schools, or Limestone County schools; have made a 4-year commitment to attend college or university in Alabama; and have cumulative GPA of 3.00 or higher and scored at least 21 on the ACT or 990 on the SAT. **Application Requirements:** Applicants must write an essay; must submit application form, and three letters of recommendation. A copy of transcript must be mailed directly from the application's school. **Additional Information:** Founded in 2006 by Miranda Bouldin, President and CEO of LogiCore Corporation. **Deadline for Receipt:** April 20.

1292 ■ LUSO-AMERICAN EDUCATION FOUNDATION

PO Box 2967
Dublin, CA 94568
Tel: (925)828-3883
Fax: (925)828-3883
E-mail: odom@luso-american.org
To provide financial assistance to qualified students to further their education.
Title of Award: Antonio Mattos Memorial Scholarships **Area, Field, or Subject:** General studies. **Level of Education for which Award is Granted:** Undergraduate **Number Awarded:** 1. **Funds Available:** $1,000. **Duration:** One year.

Eligibility Requirements: Applicants must be a high school graduating senior or enrolled in a four-year college or university; must have a GPA of 3.5 or higher; a Sacramento or East Bay area (CA) resident; member of the Luso-American Fraternal Federation - Luso-American Life Insurance Society and policy holder in good standing for a minimum of 2 years; excel in a sport during the 4 high school years; and active in the Fraternal Community. **Application Requirements:** Applicants must request for the application form available on the Foundation's office. Submit the completed application form together with an official transcript and three letters of recommendation to the Foundation's office. **Deadline for Receipt:** March 1.

1293 ■ LUSO-AMERICAN EDUCATION FOUNDATION
PO Box 2967
Dublin, CA 94568
Tel: (925)828-3883
Fax: (925)828-3883
E-mail: odom@luso-american.org
To provide financial assistance to qualified students to further their education.

Title of Award: Joaquin Pereira Memorial Scholarships **Area, Field, or Subject:** General studies. **Level of Education for which Award is Granted:** Undergraduate **Number Awarded:** 1. **Funds Available:** $1,000. **Duration:** One year.
Eligibility Requirements: Applicant must be a high school graduating senior or enrolled in a four-year college or university; must have a GPA of 3.5 or higher; a member of the Luso-American Fraternal Federation - Luso-American Life Insurance Society and policy holder in good standing for a minimum of 2 years. **Application Requirements:** Applicants must request for the application form available on the Foundation's office. Submit the completed application form together with an official transcript and three letters of recommendation to the Foundation's office. **Deadline for Receipt:** March 1.

1294 ■ LUSO-AMERICAN EDUCATION FOUNDATION
PO Box 2967
Dublin, CA 94568
Tel: (925)828-3883
Fax: (925)828-3883
E-mail: odom@luso-american.org
To provide financial assistance to qualified students who wish to further their education.

Title of Award: Ryan "Munchie" Taylor Memorial Scholarships **Area, Field, or Subject:** General studies. **Level of Education for which Award is Granted:** Undergraduate **Number Awarded:** 1. **Funds Available:** $1,000. **Duration:** One year.
Eligibility Requirements: Applicants must be a high school graduating senior or enrolled in a four-year college or university; must have a GPA of 3.5 or higher; must have held local or state youth office; a Stanislaus County (CA) resident; member of the Luso-American Fraternal Federation - Luso-American Life Insurance Society and policy holder in good standing for a minimum of 2 years; must participated in Fraternal Youth activities for 2 or more years or performed at State Conventions. **Application Requirements:** Applicants must request for the application form available on the Foundation's office. Submit the completed application form together with an official transcript and three letters of recommendation to the Foundation's office. **Deadline for Receipt:** March 1.

1295 ■ STEPHEN T. MARCHELLO SCHOLARSHIP FOUNDATION
1170 E Long Pl.
Centennial, CO 80122
Tel: (303)886-5018
E-mail: fmarchello@earthlink.net
Web Site: http://www.stmfoundation.org
To support the education of students who have a history of childhood cancer.

Title of Award: Stephen T. Marchello Scholarships **Area, Field, or Subject:** General studies. **Level of Education for which Award is Granted:** Undergraduate **Funds Available:** No specific amount.
Eligibility Requirements: Applicant must be a high school graduate in the states of AZ, CA, CO, and MT; must have survived childhood cancer. **Application Requirements:** Applicants must submit a completed scholarship application along with a copy of transcript (with GPA); SAT or

ACT test scores; a confirmation of the treatment by the doctor or by the hospital or clinic; and a reference letter (from someone other than a family member). **Deadline for Receipt:** March 15.

1296 ■ MARINE BIOLOGICAL LABORATORY
7 MBL St.
Woods Hole, MA 02543
Tel: (508)548-3705
E-mail: mdonovan@mbl.edu
Web Site: http://www.mbl.edu
To provide support for Physiology students.

Title of Award: Bruce and Betty Alberts Endowed Scholarships in Physiology **Area, Field, or Subject:** Physiology. **Level of Education for which Award is Granted:** Undergraduate **Funds Available:** No specific amount.
Eligibility Requirements: Applicants must be attending a Marine Biological Laboratory summer course. **Application Requirements:** Applicants must complete the application form.

1297 ■ MARINE BIOLOGICAL LABORATORY
7 MBL St.
Woods Hole, MA 02543
Tel: (508)548-3705
E-mail: mdonovan@mbl.edu
Web Site: http://www.mbl.edu
To provide support for students who are accepted in the physiology course.

Title of Award: Mountain Memorial Scholarships **Area, Field, or Subject:** Physiology. **Level of Education for which Award is Granted:** Undergraduate **Funds Available:** No specific amount.
Eligibility Requirements: Applicants must be attending a summer course at Marine Biological Laboratory. **Application Requirements:** Applicants must complete the application form.

1298 ■ MARINE CORPS LEAGUE FOUNDATION
PO Box 3070
Merrifield, VA 22116-3070
Tel: (972)272-6384
E-mail: corpsma@aol.com
Web Site: http://www.mclfoundation.org
To grant scholarship to qualified applicants pursuing full-time undergraduate or technical training at a recognized institution.

Title of Award: Marine Corps League National Scholarships **Area, Field, or Subject:** General studies. **Level of Education for which Award is Granted:** Undergraduate **Funds Available:** No specific amount. **Duration:** Maximum of four years.
Eligibility Requirements: Applicant must be the spouse, child, grandchild, great grandchild or step child of a Marine Corps League or Auxiliary member in good standing; or the child of a Marine who died in the line of duty; or a member of the Marine Corps League or Auxiliary in good standing or honorably discharged Marines in need of rehabilitation training not provided by government programs. Sponsors must be a member in good standing of the Marine Corps League or Auxiliary. **Application Requirements:** Applicants must submit a completed application form in which the sponsor has completely filled out their section. **Additional Information:** Do not staple any document to the application. **Deadline for Receipt:** July 1.

1299 ■ THURGOOD MARSHALL COLLEGE FUND
80 Maiden Ln., Ste. 2204
New York, NY 10038
Tel: (212)573-8888; 877-690-8673
Fax: (212)573-8497
Web Site: http://thurgoodmarshallfund.org
To support schools or specific areas of interest of a student.

Title of Award: TMCF Scholarships **Area, Field, or Subject:** General studies. **Level of Education for which Award is Granted:** Undergraduate **Funds Available:** $2,200. **Duration:** One semester.
Eligibility Requirements: The applicant must be a full-time U.S. citizen student pursuing a degree in any discipline at one of the 47 TMCF member schools who demonstrates commitment to academic excellence and community service with a high school GPA of not less than 3.0; a combined verbal/math score of 1650 or more on the Scholastic Aptitude

Test (SAT) or a score of 25 or higher on the American College Testing (ACT) examination, recommended by his high school as academically exceptional or outstanding in the creative and performing arts, and has financial need. **Application Requirements:** Applicants must submit general information form, enrollment/certification of academic standing, acceptance form, financial aid information together with high school transcript (for incoming freshman), undergraduate transcript (for graduate and law school), resume and/or personal information form recommendation letters, essay head shot or personal photograph.

1300 ■ GEORGE C. MARSHALL FOUNDATION
PO Box 1600
Lexington, VA 24450-1600
Tel: (540)463-7103
Fax: (540)464-5229
E-mail: marshallfoundation@marshallfoundation.org
Web Site: http://www.marshallfoundation.org
To promote primary research and study as the cornerstone of the library, archives, and educational programs.
Title of Award: Marshall Undergraduate Scholars Programs **Area, Field, or Subject:** General studies. **Level of Education for which Award is Granted:** Undergraduate **Funds Available:** $250 cash award plus travel expenses up to $300 for students from distant institutions. **Duration:** One year.
Eligibility Requirements: Applicant must be an undergraduate student at selected Virginia and Mid Atlantic colleges. **Application Requirements:** Applicants must complete the requirements on or before the deadline. **Deadline for Receipt:** May 12.

1301 ■ MASSACHUSETTS CHAPTER OF THE INTERNATIONAL AS-SOCIATION OF ARSON INVESTIGATORS (IAAI)
PO Box 237
Southbridge, MA 01550-0237
Tel: (978)567-3300
E-mail: miloseek@aol.com
Web Site: http://www.maiaai.com
To support the education of a member or an immediate family member or grandchild of a Massachusetts IAAI Chapter member.
Title of Award: Sgt. Michael F. Cherven Memorial Scholarships **Area, Field, or Subject:** General studies. **Level of Education for which Award is Granted:** Undergraduate **Number Awarded:** 2. **Funds Available:** $500.
Eligibility Requirements: Applicant must be members, immediate family members or grandchildren of a Massachusetts IAAI Chapter member in good standing; and must be graduating high school seniors or entering/currently enrolled at a college/university. **Application Requirements:** Applicants must submit a completed application form with the required supporting documents. **Deadline for Receipt:** June 4.

1302 ■ MATANUSKA-SUSITNA COLLEGE
PO Box 2889
Palmer, AK 99645
Tel: (907)745-9774
Fax: (907)745-9711
E-mail: info@matsu.alaska.edu
Web Site: http://www.matsu.alaska.edu
To provide support to deserving students in Alaska who want to pursue an education in any campus of the University of Alaska.
Title of Award: Alaska Native Medical Center Auxiliary Scholarships **Area, Field, or Subject:** General studies. **Level of Education for which Award is Granted:** Undergraduate **Funds Available:** $1,000.
Eligibility Requirements: Applicant must have graduated from a rural Alaska high school that is off the highway system in Alaska; must be a full-time student and in good academic standing with a minimum cumulative GPA of 2.0. **Application Requirements:** Applicant must complete the application forms available at the website; must attach a personal essay, two letters of recommendation, and current transcripts. **Deadline for Receipt:** February 15.

1303 ■ MATANUSKA-SUSITNA COLLEGE
PO Box 2889
Palmer, AK 99645
Tel: (907)745-9774

Fax: (907)745-9711
E-mail: info@matsu.alaska.edu
Web Site: http://www.matsu.alaska.edu
To provide support for deserving students in Alaska intending to pursue an education in any campus of the University of Alaska.
Title of Award: Alaska Visitors Association/Gomar Scholarships **Area, Field, or Subject:** Travel and tourism. **Level of Education for which Award is Granted:** Undergraduate **Funds Available:** $500.
Eligibility Requirements: Applicants must be enrolled in programs of study emphasizing travel and tourism. **Application Requirements:** Applicants must complete the application forms available in the website; must attach a personal essay, two letters of recommendation, and their current transcripts. **Deadline for Receipt:** February 15.

1304 ■ MATANUSKA-SUSITNA COLLEGE
PO Box 2889
Palmer, AK 99645
Tel: (907)745-9774
Fax: (907)745-9711
E-mail: info@matsu.alaska.edu
Web Site: http://www.matsu.alaska.edu
To provide support for deserving students in Alaska intending to pursue an education in any campus of the University of Alaska.
Title of Award: Alaska Yukon Pioneer Memorial Scholarships **Area, Field, or Subject:** General studies. **Level of Education for which Award is Granted:** Undergraduate **Funds Available:** $500.
Eligibility Requirements: Applicants must be full-time students and residents of Alaska or the Yukon Territory and must have graduated from high school either in Alaska or the Yukon Territory. **Application Requirements:** Applicants must complete the application forms available on the website; must attach a personal essay, two letters of recommendation, and their current transcripts. **Deadline for Receipt:** February 15.

1305 ■ MATANUSKA-SUSITNA COLLEGE
PO Box 2889
Palmer, AK 99645
Tel: (907)745-9774
Fax: (907)745-9711
E-mail: info@matsu.alaska.edu
Web Site: http://www.matsu.alaska.edu
To provide support to deserving students in Alaska who want to pursue an education in any campus of the University of Alaska.
Title of Award: Lawrence Bayer Business Administration Scholarships **Area, Field, or Subject:** Business administration. **Level of Education for which Award is Granted:** Undergraduate **Funds Available:** $500.
Eligibility Requirements: Applicant must be full-time students attending the University of Alaska at Fairbanks or the University of Alaska at Anchorage and have a minimum GPA of 3.0; must be a business administration major active in clubs and/or sports. **Application Requirements:** Applicant must complete the application forms available at the website; must attach a personal essay, two letters of recommendation, and current transcripts. **Deadline for Receipt:** February 15.

1306 ■ MATANUSKA-SUSITNA COLLEGE
PO Box 2889
Palmer, AK 99645
Tel: (907)745-9774
Fax: (907)745-9711
E-mail: info@matsu.alaska.edu
Web Site: http://www.matsu.alaska.edu
To provide support to deserving students in Alaska who want to pursue an education in any campus of the University of Alaska.
Title of Award: Bolick Foreign Student Scholarships **Area, Field, or Subject:** General studies. **Level of Education for which Award is Granted:** Undergraduate **Funds Available:** $1,000.
Eligibility Requirements: Applicant must be a full-time student holding exclusive citizenship in another country and attending the university on a student visa. **Application Requirements:** Applicant must complete the application forms available at the website; must attach a personal essay, two letters of recommendation, and current transcripts. **Deadline for Receipt:** February 15.

1307 ■ MATANUSKA-SUSITNA COLLEGE
PO Box 2889
Palmer, AK 99645

Tel: (907)745-9774
Fax: (907)745-9711
E-mail: info@matsu.alaska.edu
Web Site: http://www.matsu.alaska.edu
To provide financial assistance for tuition and other educational expenses to non-traditional students who are seeking degree completion or retraining at the Matanuska-Susitna College.
Title of Award: Dr. Betty J. Boyd-Beu & Edwin G. Beu, Jr. Scholarships **Area, Field, or Subject:** General studies. **Level of Education for which Award is Granted:** Undergraduate **Funds Available:** $2,500. **Duration:** One academic year.
Eligibility Requirements: Applicant must be a non-traditional student and have graduated from high school; must have worked prior to enrolling or returning to college, thus re-entering college to complete a degree or enrolling to retrain for another position in the workplace; must be in good academic standing with a minimum cumulative GPA of 3.0; must be formally admitted to a degreeseeking program; must be enrolled in the semester(s) for which the award is made. **Application Requirements:** Applicants must complete the MSC scholarship application; must attach a list of activities/community service in which they have participated; must attach a resume of their work experience over the past four years; must attach a personal essay; must attach two letters of recommendation and transcripts. Application forms must be submitted to: Dr. Betty Boyd-Beu & Edwin G. Beu Jr. Scholarship, Matanuska-Susitna College, Student Services, FSM 102, PO Box 2889, Palmer, AK 99645. **Deadline for Receipt:** May 31.

1308 ■ MATANUSKA-SUSITNA COLLEGE
PO Box 2889
Palmer, AK 99645
Tel: (907)745-9774
Fax: (907)745-9711
E-mail: info@matsu.alaska.edu
Web Site: http://www.matsu.alaska.edu
To provide support to deserving students in Alaska who want to pursue an education in any campus of the University of Alaska.
Title of Award: Charles E. Bunnell Scholarships **Area, Field, or Subject:** General studies. **Level of Education for which Award is Granted:** Undergraduate **Funds Available:** $1,000.
Eligibility Requirements: Applicants must be full-time students entering his/her junior or senior year with a declared major in an accredited field and have a minimum GPA of 3.2. **Application Requirements:** Applicant must submit an additional paragraph describing how they emulate the ideals of persistence, vision, selfsacrifice, concern for others and love of the North. Applicant must complete the application forms available at the website; must attach a personal essay, two letters of recommendation, and current transcripts. **Additional Information:** Named after Charles E. Bunnell, the first president of the University of Alaska. **Deadline for Receipt:** February 15.

1309 ■ MATANUSKA-SUSITNA COLLEGE
PO Box 2889
Palmer, AK 99645
Tel: (907)745-9774
Fax: (907)745-9711
E-mail: info@matsu.alaska.edu
Web Site: http://www.matsu.alaska.edu
To provide support to deserving students in Alaska who want to pursue an education in any campus of the University of Alaska.
Title of Award: Loyal D. Burkett Memorial Scholarships **Area, Field, or Subject:** General studies. **Level of Education for which Award is Granted:** Undergraduate **Funds Available:** $500.
Eligibility Requirements: Applicant must be a full-time student in good academic standing and demonstrate motivation, academic and leadership potential. **Application Requirements:** Applicant must complete the application forms available at the website; must attach a personal essay, two letters of recommendation, and current transcripts. **Deadline for Receipt:** February 15.

1310 ■ MATANUSKA-SUSITNA COLLEGE
PO Box 2889
Palmer, AK 99645
Tel: (907)745-9774

Fax: (907)745-9711
E-mail: info@matsu.alaska.edu
Web Site: http://www.matsu.alaska.edu
To provide support to deserving students in Alaska who want to pursue an education in any campus of the University of Alaska.
Title of Award: Excellence in Geographic Information Systems Scholarships **Area, Field, or Subject:** Geography. **Level of Education for which Award is Granted:** Undergraduate **Funds Available:** $500.
Eligibility Requirements: Applicant must be a full-time junior, senior, or graduate student in good standing with a minimum overall cumulative GPA of 2.88 or a major GPA of 3.2; must have declared interest in Geographic Information Systems or Mapping Science and be engaged in a directed or undirected project or class involving Geographic Information Systems during the award period. **Application Requirements:** Applicant must complete the application forms available at the website; must attach a personal essay, two letters of recommendation, and current transcripts. **Deadline for Receipt:** February 15.

1311 ■ MATANUSKA-SUSITNA COLLEGE
PO Box 2889
Palmer, AK 99645
Tel: (907)745-9774
Fax: (907)745-9711
E-mail: info@matsu.alaska.edu
Web Site: http://www.matsu.alaska.edu
To provide support to deserving students in Alaska who want to pursue an education in any campus of the University of Alaska.
Title of Award: Johnny and Sarah Frank Scholarships **Area, Field, or Subject:** General studies. **Level of Education for which Award is Granted:** Undergraduate **Funds Available:** $500.
Eligibility Requirements: Applicants must be of Gwich in Athabaskan descent; must have a minimum 2.5 GPA and must enroll for at least six credit hours. **Application Requirements:** Applicant must complete the application forms available at the website; must attach a personal essay, two letters of recommendation, and current transcripts. **Deadline for Receipt:** February 15.

1312 ■ MATANUSKA-SUSITNA COLLEGE
PO Box 2889
Palmer, AK 99645
Tel: (907)745-9774
Fax: (907)745-9711
E-mail: info@matsu.alaska.edu
Web Site: http://www.matsu.alaska.edu
To provide support to deserving students in Alaska who want to pursue an education in any campus of the University of Alaska.
Title of Award: Charles F. Gould Endowment Scholarships **Area, Field, or Subject:** General studies. **Level of Education for which Award is Granted:** Undergraduate **Funds Available:** $1,000.
Eligibility Requirements: Applicant must be a full-time Alaska Native student, preferably Eskimo, with a minimum GPA of 2.0. **Application Requirements:** Applicant must complete the application forms available at the website; must attach a personal essay, two letters of recommendation, and their current transcripts. **Deadline for Receipt:** February 15.

1313 ■ MATANUSKA-SUSITNA COLLEGE
PO Box 2889
Palmer, AK 99645
Tel: (907)745-9774
Fax: (907)745-9711
E-mail: info@matsu.alaska.edu
Web Site: http://www.matsu.alaska.edu
To provide support to deserving students in Alaska who want to pursue an education in any campus of the University of Alaska.
Title of Award: John B. Henderson Scholarships **Area, Field, or Subject:** General studies. **Level of Education for which Award is Granted:** Undergraduate **Funds Available:** $500.
Eligibility Requirements: Applicants must be full-time students attending any campus of the University of Alaska. **Application Requirements:** Applicant must complete the application forms available at the website; must attach a personal essay, two letters of recommendation, and current transcripts. **Deadline for Receipt:** February 15.

1314 ■ MATANUSKA-SUSITNA COLLEGE
PO Box 2889
Palmer, AK 99645
Tel: (907)745-9774
Fax: (907)745-9711
E-mail: info@matsu.alaska.edu
Web Site: http://www.matsu.alaska.edu
To provide support to deserving students in Alaska who want to pursue an education in any campus of the University of Alaska.
Title of Award: Iver & Cora Knapstad Scholarships **Area, Field, or Subject:** General studies. **Level of Education for which Award is Granted:** Undergraduate **Funds Available:** $1,000.
Eligibility Requirements: Applicants must be full-time students attending any University of Alaska campus. **Application Requirements:** Applicant must complete the application forms available at the website; must attach a personal essay, two letters of recommendation, and current transcripts. **Deadline for Receipt:** February 15.

1315 ■ MATANUSKA-SUSITNA COLLEGE
PO Box 2889
Palmer, AK 99645
Tel: (907)745-9774
Fax: (907)745-9711
E-mail: info@matsu.alaska.edu
Web Site: http://www.matsu.alaska.edu
To provide support to deserving students in Alaska who want to pursue an education in any campus of the University of Alaska.
Title of Award: Robert Wade Korn Endowed Scholarships **Area, Field, or Subject:** General studies. **Level of Education for which Award is Granted:** Undergraduate **Funds Available:** $1,000.
Eligibility Requirements: Applicants must be graduates of Cordova Alaska High School with a minimum of 2.0 average. **Application Requirements:** Applicant must complete the application forms available at the website; must attach a personal essay, two letters of recommendation, and current transcripts. **Deadline for Receipt:** February 15.

1316 ■ MATANUSKA-SUSITNA COLLEGE
PO Box 2889
Palmer, AK 99645
Tel: (907)745-9774
Fax: (907)745-9711
E-mail: info@matsu.alaska.edu
Web Site: http://www.matsu.alaska.edu
To provide support to deserving students in Alaska who want to pursue an education in any campus of the University of Alaska.
Title of Award: Austin E. Lathrop Scholarships **Area, Field, or Subject:** General studies. **Level of Education for which Award is Granted:** Undergraduate **Funds Available:** $1,000.
Eligibility Requirements: Applicants must be full-time students attending any campus of the University of Alaska. **Application Requirements:** Applicant must complete the application forms available at the website; must attach a personal essay, two letters of recommendation, and their current transcripts. **Deadline for Receipt:** February 15.

1317 ■ MATANUSKA-SUSITNA COLLEGE
PO Box 2889
Palmer, AK 99645
Tel: (907)745-9774
Fax: (907)745-9711
E-mail: info@matsu.alaska.edu
Web Site: http://www.matsu.alaska.edu
To provide support to deserving students in Alaska who want to pursue an education in any campus of the University of Alaska.
Title of Award: Franklin M. Leach Scholarships **Area, Field, or Subject:** General studies. **Level of Education for which Award is Granted:** Undergraduate **Funds Available:** $1,000.
Eligibility Requirements: Applicants must be full-time students seeking a degree in Aviation and have a minimum cumulative GPA of 2.0. **Application Requirements:** Applicant must complete the application forms available at the website; must attach a personal essay, two letters of recommendation, and current transcripts. **Deadline for Receipt:** February 15.

1318 ■ MATANUSKA-SUSITNA COLLEGE
PO Box 2889
Palmer, AK 99645
Tel: (907)745-9774
Fax: (907)745-9711
E-mail: info@matsu.alaska.edu
Web Site: http://www.matsu.alaska.edu
To provide support to deserving students in Alaska who want to pursue an education in any campus of the University of Alaska.
Title of Award: Matanuska-Susitna College Regent's Scholarships **Area, Field, or Subject:** General studies. **Level of Education for which Award is Granted:** Undergraduate **Funds Available:** $5,000.
Eligibility Requirements: Applicant must be junior, senior or graduate students in good academic standing whose application reflects demonstrated commitment and involvement in leadership and civic or professional service activities and recognized academic achievement. **Application Requirements:** Applicant must complete the application forms available at the website; must attach a personal essay, two letters of recommendation, and current transcripts. **Deadline for Receipt:** February 15.

1319 ■ MATANUSKA-SUSITNA COLLEGE
PO Box 2889
Palmer, AK 99645
Tel: (907)745-9774
Fax: (907)745-9711
E-mail: info@matsu.alaska.edu
Web Site: http://www.matsu.alaska.edu
To provide support to deserving students in Alaska who want to pursue an education in any campus of the University of Alaska.
Title of Award: Dave McCloud Aviation Memorial Scholarships **Area, Field, or Subject:** General studies. **Level of Education for which Award is Granted:** Undergraduate **Funds Available:** $500.
Eligibility Requirements: Applicants must be full-time students seeking a degree in Aviation and have a minimum cumulative GPA of 2.0; must be a resident of Alaska. **Application Requirements:** Applicant must complete the application forms available at the website; must attach a personal essay, two letters of recommendation, and current transcripts. **Deadline for Receipt:** February 15.

1320 ■ MATANUSKA-SUSITNA COLLEGE
PO Box 2889
Palmer, AK 99645
Tel: (907)745-9774
Fax: (907)745-9711
E-mail: info@matsu.alaska.edu
Web Site: http://www.matsu.alaska.edu
To provide support to deserving students in Alaska who want to pursue an education in any campus of the University of Alaska.
Title of Award: Richard Mellon Endowment Scholarships **Area, Field, or Subject:** General studies. **Level of Education for which Award is Granted:** Undergraduate **Funds Available:** $1,500.
Eligibility Requirements: Applicants must be full-time students. **Application Requirements:** Applicant must complete the application forms available at the website; must attach a personal essay, two letters of recommendation, and current transcripts. **Deadline for Receipt:** February 15.

1321 ■ MATANUSKA-SUSITNA COLLEGE
PO Box 2889
Palmer, AK 99645
Tel: (907)745-9774
Fax: (907)745-9711
E-mail: info@matsu.alaska.edu
Web Site: http://www.matsu.alaska.edu
To provide support to deserving students in Alaska who want to pursue an education in any campus of the University of Alaska.
Title of Award: Andrew Nerland Endowment Scholarships **Area, Field, or Subject:** General studies. **Level of Education for which Award is Granted:** Undergraduate **Funds Available:** $1,000.
Eligibility Requirements: Applicants must be full-time student. **Application Requirements:** Applicant must complete the application forms available at the website; must attach a personal essay, two letters of recommendation, and current transcripts. **Deadline for Receipt:** February 15.

1322 ■ MATANUSKA-SUSITNA COLLEGE
PO Box 2889
Palmer, AK 99645
Tel: (907)745-9774
Fax: (907)745-9711
E-mail: info@matsu.alaska.edu
Web Site: http://www.matsu.alaska.edu
To provide support to deserving students in Alaska who want to pursue an education in any campus of the University of Alaska.
Title of Award: Maureen E. Nolan-Cahill Memorial Scholarships **Area, Field, or Subject:** Science. **Level of Education for which Award is Granted:** Undergraduate **Funds Available:** $500.
Eligibility Requirements: Applicants must be a female students majoring in science with a GPA of at least 3.0; must demonstrate financial need.
Application Requirements: Applicant must complete the application forms available at the website; must attach a personal essay, two letters of recommendation, and current transcripts. **Deadline for Receipt:** February 15.

1323 ■ MATANUSKA-SUSITNA COLLEGE
PO Box 2889
Palmer, AK 99645
Tel: (907)745-9774
Fax: (907)745-9711
E-mail: info@matsu.alaska.edu
Web Site: http://www.matsu.alaska.edu
To provide support to deserving students in Alaska who want to pursue an education in any campus of the University of Alaska.
Title of Award: Don & Jan O'Dowd/SWAA Scholarships **Area, Field, or Subject:** General studies. **Level of Education for which Award is Granted:** Undergraduate **Funds Available:** $500.
Eligibility Requirements: Applicants must be full-time incoming freshmen students with a minimum GPA of 3.0; must be Alaska residents and graduates of an Alaska high school. **Application Requirements:** Applicant must complete the application forms available at the website; must attach a personal essay, two letters of recommendation, and current transcripts. **Deadline for Receipt:** February 15.

1324 ■ MATANUSKA-SUSITNA COLLEGE
PO Box 2889
Palmer, AK 99645
Tel: (907)745-9774
Fax: (907)745-9711
E-mail: info@matsu.alaska.edu
Web Site: http://www.matsu.alaska.edu
To provide support to deserving students in Alaska who want to pursue an education in any campus of the University of Alaska.
Title of Award: Alvin G. Ott Fish and Wildlife Scholarships **Area, Field, or Subject:** General studies. **Level of Education for which Award is Granted:** Undergraduate **Funds Available:** $500.
Eligibility Requirements: Applicants must be full-time students with a minimum GPA of 3.0 and majoring in a field related to fish and wildlife. **Application Requirements:** Applicant must complete the application forms available at the website; must attach a personal essay, two letters of recommendation, and current transcripts. **Deadline for Receipt:** February 15.

1325 ■ MATANUSKA-SUSITNA COLLEGE
PO Box 2889
Palmer, AK 99645
Tel: (907)745-9774
Fax: (907)745-9711
E-mail: info@matsu.alaska.edu
Web Site: http://www.matsu.alaska.edu
To provide support to deserving students in Alaska who want to pursue an education in any campus of the University of Alaska.
Title of Award: Point Lay Memorial Scholarships **Area, Field, or Subject:** General studies. **Level of Education for which Award is Granted:** Undergraduate **Funds Available:** $3,000.
Eligibility Requirements: Applicants must be full-time students and current or former residents of Pt. Lay, Alaska. **Application Requirements:** Applicant must complete the application forms available at the website; must attach a personal essay, two letters of recommendation, and current transcripts. **Deadline for Receipt:** February 15.

1326 ■ MATANUSKA-SUSITNA COLLEGE
PO Box 2889
Palmer, AK 99645
Tel: (907)745-9774
Fax: (907)745-9711
E-mail: info@matsu.alaska.edu
Web Site: http://www.matsu.alaska.edu
To provide support to deserving students in Alaska who want to pursue an education in any campus of the University of Alaska.
Title of Award: A.D. 'Al' Robertson Memorial Scholarships **Area, Field, or Subject:** General studies. **Level of Education for which Award is Granted:** Undergraduate **Funds Available:** $500.
Eligibility Requirements: Applicants must be full-time students and a member of the graduating class of Ketchikan High School in the year the scholarship is awarded; must have a minimum GPA of 2.5. **Application Requirements:** Applicant must complete the application forms available at the website; must attach a personal essay, two letters of recommendation, and current transcripts. **Deadline for Receipt:** February 15.

1327 ■ MATANUSKA-SUSITNA COLLEGE
PO Box 2889
Palmer, AK 99645
Tel: (907)745-9774
Fax: (907)745-9711
E-mail: info@matsu.alaska.edu
Web Site: http://www.matsu.alaska.edu
To provide support to deserving students in Alaska who want to pursue an education in any campus of the University of Alaska.
Title of Award: Pat and Cliff Rogers Nursing Scholarships **Area, Field, or Subject:** General studies. **Level of Education for which Award is Granted:** Undergraduate **Funds Available:** $500.
Eligibility Requirements: Applicants must be full-time students in his/her junior or senior year of a nursing program at any institution within the U.S. **Application Requirements:** Applicant must complete the application forms available in the website; must attach a personal essay, two letters of recommendation, and current transcripts. **Deadline for Receipt:** February 15.

1328 ■ MATANUSKA-SUSITNA COLLEGE
PO Box 2889
Palmer, AK 99645
Tel: (907)745-9774
Fax: (907)745-9711
E-mail: info@matsu.alaska.edu
Web Site: http://www.matsu.alaska.edu
To provide support to deserving students in Alaska who want to pursue an education in any campus of the University of Alaska.
Title of Award: Sourdough Reunion Memorial Scholarships **Area, Field, or Subject:** General studies. **Level of Education for which Award is Granted:** Undergraduate **Funds Available:** $500.
Eligibility Requirements: Applicants must be full-time students entering his/her junior or senior year with a minimum GPA of 3.0 and be residents of Alaska or the Yukon Territory; must have graduated from a high school in Alaska or the Yukon Territory. **Application Requirements:** Applicant must complete the application forms available at the website; must attach a personal essay, two letters of recommendation, and current transcripts. **Deadline for Receipt:** February 15.

1329 ■ MATANUSKA-SUSITNA COLLEGE
PO Box 2889
Palmer, AK 99645
Tel: (907)745-9774
Fax: (907)745-9711
E-mail: info@matsu.alaska.edu
Web Site: http://www.matsu.alaska.edu
To provide support to deserving students in Alaska who want to pursue an education in any campus of the University of Alaska.
Title of Award: Togiak Village Scholarships **Area, Field, or Subject:** General studies. **Level of Education for which Award is Granted:** Undergraduate **Funds Available:** $500.
Eligibility Requirements: Applicants must be full-time students who are residents of Togiak Village seeking a college education. **Application Requirements:** Applicant must complete the application forms available

at the website; must attach a personal essay, two letters of recommendation, and current transcripts. **Deadline for Receipt:** February 15.

1330 ■ MATANUSKA-SUSITNA COLLEGE
PO Box 2889
Palmer, AK 99645
Tel: (907)745-9774
Fax: (907)745-9711
E-mail: info@matsu.alaska.edu
Web Site: http://www.matsu.alaska.edu
To provide support to deserving students in Alaska who want to pursue an education in any campus of the University of Alaska.
Title of Award: Umialik Scholarships **Area, Field, or Subject:** General studies. **Level of Education for which Award is Granted:** Undergraduate **Funds Available:** $5,000.
Eligibility Requirements: Applicants must be full-time students attending any campus of the University of Alaska and be in good academic standing. **Application Requirements:** Applicant must complete the application forms available at the website; must attach a personal essay, two letters of recommendation, and current transcripts. **Deadline for Receipt:** February 15.

1331 ■ MATANUSKA-SUSITNA COLLEGE
PO Box 2889
Palmer, AK 99645
Tel: (907)745-9774
Fax: (907)745-9711
E-mail: info@matsu.alaska.edu
Web Site: http://www.matsu,alaska.edu
To provide an incentive for Alaska's middle and high school students intending to achieve academic excellence; to nourish efforts of schools to provide high quality education; and to encourage the top high school graduates from every community in Alaska to attend the University of Alaska.
Title of Award: University of Alaska Scholars Program **Area, Field, or Subject:** General studies. **Level of Education for which Award is Granted:** Undergraduate **Funds Available:** $1,375. **Duration:** Eight semesters.
Eligibility Requirements: Applicants must be US citizens or aliens lawfully admitted for permanent residence in the United States; must have successfully earned a high school diploma from a qualified Alaska high school; must be admitted into a certificate or degree program; must be enrolled as full-time, undergraduate students for the first fall semester following the graduation date of the class with which he or she designated and continuously thereafter; and must participate in or attend any mandatory orientation or program as may be required by the campus. **Application Requirements:** Applicants must submit the application form at the UA Scholars Program, University of Alaska, Butrovich Bldg., Ste. 207, Fairbanks, AK 99775. **Deadline for Receipt:** May 1.

1332 ■ MATANUSKA-SUSITNA COLLEGE
PO Box 2889
Palmer, AK 99645
Tel: (907)745-9774
Fax: (907)745-9711
E-mail: info@matsu.alaska.edu
Web Site: http://www.matsu.alaska.edu
To provide support to deserving students in Alaska who want to pursue an education in any campus of the University of Alaska.
Title of Award: William S. Wilson Memorial Scholarships **Area, Field, or Subject:** Science. **Level of Education for which Award is Granted:** Undergraduate **Funds Available:** $5,000.
Eligibility Requirements: Applicants must be full-time students majoring in science. **Application Requirements:** Applicant must complete the application forms available at the website; must attach a personal essay, two letters of recommendation, and current transcripts. **Deadline for Receipt:** February 15.

1333 ■ EDMUND F. MAXWELL FOUNDATION
P.O. Box 22537
Seattle, WA 98122-0537
E-mail: admin@maxwell.org
Web Site: http://www.maxwell.org

To provide assistance to those who have demonstrated financial need and have shown ability, aptitude and a promise of useful citizenship.
Title of Award: Edmund F. Maxwell Scholarships **Area, Field, or Subject:** General studies. **Level of Education for which Award is Granted:** Undergraduate **Funds Available:** Up to $5000. **Duration:** One year.
Eligibility Requirements: Applicant must be planning to attend an accredited independent college/university as freshman; a resident of Western Washington; and have a combined math and reading SAT score of over 1200. **Application Requirements:** Applicants must submit a completed scholarship application along with the 500-word essay; official, certified high school transcript; Certification of SAT/ACT scores; and Financial Aid Worksheet (to be completed by each College/University); applicants must also submit a Free Application For Student Aid form (FAFSA) to the institution that he/she is planning to attend. **Deadline for Receipt:** April 30.

1334 ■ RONALD MCDONALD HOUSE CHARITIES
One Kroc Dr.
Oak Brook, IL 60523
Tel: (630)623-7048
Fax: (630)623-7488
E-mail: info@rmhc.org
Web Site: http://www.rmhc.org
To help high school seniors attend college.
Title of Award: Ronald McDonald House Charities African American Future Achievers Scholarships **Area, Field, or Subject:** General studies. **Level of Education for which Award is Granted:** Undergraduate **Funds Available:** No specific amount.
Eligibility Requirements: Applicants must be high school seniors; must be younger than 21 years old; must be eligible to attend a two- or four-year college or university with a full course of study; must be legal residents of the United States; must be living in a participating local RMHS Chapter's geographic area; and must have at least one parent of African American or Black Caribbean heritage. **Application Requirements:** Applicants must complete the application form.

1335 ■ RONALD MCDONALD HOUSE CHARITIES
One Kroc Dr.
Oak Brook, IL 60523
Tel: (630)623-7048
Fax: (630)623-7488
E-mail: info@rmhc.org
Web Site: http://www.rmhc.org
To help high school seniors to attend college.
Title of Award: Ronald McDonald House Charities of Hispanic Heritage **Area, Field, or Subject:** General studies. **Level of Education for which Award is Granted:** Undergraduate **Funds Available:** No specific amount.
Eligibility Requirements: Applicants must be high school seniors; must be younger than 21 years old; must be eligible to attend a two- or four-year college or university with a full course of study; must be legal residents of the United States; must be living in a participating local RMHS Chapter's geographic area; and must have at least one parent of Hispanic heritage. **Application Requirements:** Applicants must complete the application form.

1336 ■ RONALD MCDONALD HOUSE CHARITIES
One Kroc Dr.
Oak Brook, IL 60523
Tel: (630)623-7048
Fax: (630)623-7488
E-mail: info@rmhc.org
Web Site: http://www.rmhc.org
To help high school seniors pursue educational goals.
Title of Award: Ronald McDonald House Charities Scholarships **Area, Field, or Subject:** General studies. **Level of Education for which Award is Granted:** Undergraduate **Funds Available:** No specific amount.
Eligibility Requirements: Applicants must be high school students. All students can apply regardless of race, color, creed, religion, sexual orientation, gender, disability or national origin. **Application Requirements:** Applicants must complete the application form.

1337 ■ RONALD MCDONALD HOUSE CHARITIES

One Kroc Dr.
Oak Brook, IL 60523
Tel: (630)623-7048
Fax: (630)623-7488
E-mail: info@rmhc.org
Web Site: http://www.rmhc.org
To help high school seniors to attend college.
Title of Award: Ronald McDonald House Charities Scholarships in Asia **Area, Field, or Subject:** General studies. **Level of Education for which Award is Granted:** Undergraduate **Funds Available:** No specific amount.
Eligibility Requirements: Applicants must be high school seniors; must be younger than 21 years old; must be eligible to attend a two- or four-year college or university with a full course of study; must be legal residents of the United States; must be living in a participating local RMHS Chapter's geographic area; and must have at least one parent of Asian/Pacific Islander heritage. **Application Requirements:** Applicants must complete the application form.

1338 ■ MCDONALD'S CORPORATION

2111 McDonald's Dr.
Oak Brook, IL 60523
800-244-6227
Web Site: http://www.mcdonalds.com
To recognize and support the McDonald's USA student-employees for their education.
Title of Award: McDonald's USA National Employee Scholarship Program **Area, Field, or Subject:** General studies. **Level of Education for which Award is Granted:** Undergraduate **Funds Available:** $1,000.
Eligibility Requirements: Applicants must be currently employed at a McDonald's restaurant and have at least four months continuous employment at the time of application; must work a minimum of 15 hours per week; must be high school seniors or college students planning to attend an accredited institution offering postsecondary education and/or career training and instruction in the fall; must be employed by McDonald's or a McDonald's owner/operator at the time the scholarship awards are announced. **Application Requirements:** Applicants must complete most of the application online and print out the rest. **Deadline for Receipt:** March 1.

1339 ■ RICHARD D. MCDONOUGH GOLF SCHOLARSHIP FOUNDA- TION

c/o Robert A. Provencher
243 Campbell St.
Manchester, NH 03104
Tel: (603)232-2345
E-mail: nhga@usga.org
Web Site: http://mcdonough.nhgolf.com
To support outstanding young men and women employed at New Hampshire golf courses in pursuing higher education.
Title of Award: Dr. George T. Bottomley Scholarships **Area, Field, or Subject:** General studies. **Level of Education for which Award is Granted:** Undergraduate **Funds Available:** No specific amount.
Eligibility Requirements: Applicant must have a minimum of 2 summers of successful work at a NH golf course as a caddie, in the Pro Shop, on the grounds crew, or in the clubhouse; must be a high school graduate at an accredited school; have a minimum GPA of 2.5 on a 4.0 scale; demonstrate promise of academic success; must be from the Seacoast area; and have financial need. **Application Requirements:** Applicants must be recommended by the golf club where they have been employed for a minimum of two seasons. Applicants must submit a completed scholarship application; official copy of high school transcript; a copy of acceptance letter; a copy of FAFSA form. **Additional Information:** Endowed in memory of Dr. George T. Bottomley by the Fuller Foundation. **Deadline for Receipt:** May 23. **Additional Information:** Mitchell B. Jean, Chairman McDonough Scholarship Committee.

1340 ■ RICHARD D. MCDONOUGH GOLF SCHOLARSHIP FOUNDA- TION

c/o Robert A. Provencher
243 Campbell St.
Manchester, NH 03104

Tel: (603)232-2345
E-mail: nhga@usga.org
Web Site: http://mcdonough.nhgolf.com
To support outstanding young men and women employed at New Hampshire golf courses in pursuing higher education.
Title of Award: Dr. Robert Elliott Memorial Scholarships **Area, Field, or Subject:** General studies. **Level of Education for which Award is Granted:** Undergraduate **Funds Available:** No specific amount.
Eligibility Requirements: Applicant must have a minimum of 2 summers of successful work at a NH golf course as a caddie, in the Pro Shop, on the grounds crew, or in the clubhouse; must be a high school graduate at an accredited school; have a minimum GPA of 2.5 on a 4.0 scale; demonstrate promise of academic success; and have financial need. **Application Requirements:** Applicants must be recommended by the golf club where they have been employed for a minimum of two seasons. Applicants must submit a completed scholarship application; an official copy of high school transcript; a copy of acceptance letter; and a copy of FAFSA form. **Additional Information:** Endowed in memory of Dr. Robert Elliott, president of The McDonough Foundation from 1960-1963. **Deadline for Receipt:** May 23. **Additional Information:** Mitchell B. Jean, Chairman McDonough Scholarship Committee.

1341 ■ RICHARD D. MCDONOUGH GOLF SCHOLARSHIP FOUNDA- TION

c/o Robert A. Provencher
243 Campbell St.
Manchester, NH 03104
Tel: (603)232-2345
E-mail: nhga@usga.org
Web Site: http://mcdonough.nhgolf.com
To support outstanding young men and women employed at New Hampshire golf courses in pursuing higher education.
Title of Award: Pauline Elliott Scholarships **Area, Field, or Subject:** General studies. **Level of Education for which Award is Granted:** Undergraduate **Funds Available:** No specific amount. **Duration:** One year.
Eligibility Requirements: Applicant must have a minimum of 2 summers of successful work at a NH golf course as a caddie, in the Pro Shop, on the grounds crew, or in the clubhouse; must be a high school graduate from an accredited school; have a minimum GPA of 2.5 on a 4.0 scale; demonstrate promise of academic success; and have financial need. **Application Requirements:** Applicants must be recommended by the golf club where they have been employed for a minimum of two seasons. Applicants must submit a completed scholarship application; an official copy of high school transcript; a copy of acceptance letter; a copy of FAFSA form. **Additional Information:** Endowed by the Manchester Country Club membership in honor of Mr. Lencki's 50 years of service to MCC. **Deadline for Receipt:** May 23. **Additional Information:** Mitchell B. Jean, Chairman McDonough Scholarship Committee.

1342 ■ RICHARD D. MCDONOUGH GOLF SCHOLARSHIP FOUNDA- TION

c/o Robert A. Provencher
243 Campbell St.
Manchester, NH 03104
Tel: (603)232-2345
E-mail: nhga@usga.org
Web Site: http://mcdonough.nhgolf.com
To support outstanding young men and women employed at New Hampshire golf courses in pursuing higher education.
Title of Award: Robert C. Erb Sr. Scholarships **Area, Field, or Subject:** General studies. **Level of Education for which Award is Granted:** Undergraduate **Funds Available:** No specific amount.
Eligibility Requirements: Applicant must have a minimum of 2 summers of successful work at a NH golf course as a caddie, in the Pro Shop, on the grounds crew, or in the clubhouse; must be a high school graduate at an accredited school; have a minimum GPA of 2.5 on a 4.0 scale; demonstrate promise of academic success; and have financial need. **Application Requirements:** Applicants must be recommended by the golf club where they have been employed for a minimum of two seasons. Applicants must submit a completed scholarship application; an official copy of high school transcript; a copy of acceptance letter; and a copy of FAFSA form. **Additional Information:** Endowed in memory of Robert C.

Erb Sr by his wife, Elizabeth P. Erb, and son, Bob Erb Jr. **Deadline for Receipt:** May 23. **Additional Information:** Mitchell B. Jean, Chairman McDonough Scholarship Committee.

1343 ■ RICHARD D. MCDONOUGH GOLF SCHOLARSHIP FOUNDATION

c/o Robert A. Provencher
243 Campbell St.
Manchester, NH 03104
Tel: (603)232-2345
E-mail: nhga@usga.org
Web Site: http://mcdonough.nhgolf.com
To support outstanding young men and women, employed at New Hampshire golf courses in pursuing higher education.
Title of Award: Phil Friel Scholarships **Area, Field, or Subject:** General studies. **Level of Education for which Award is Granted:** Undergraduate **Funds Available:** No specific amount. **Duration:** One year.
Eligibility Requirements: Applicant must have a minimum of 2 summers of successful work at a NH golf course as a caddie, in the Pro Shop, on the grounds crew, or in the clubhouse; must be a high school graduate from an accredited school; have a minimum GPA of 2.5 on a 4.0 scale; demonstrate promise of academic success; must be pursuing a career in the golf industry; and have financial need. **Application Requirements:** Applicants must be recommended by the golf club where they have been employed for a minimum of two seasons. Applicants must submit a completed scholarship application; an official copy of high school transcript; a copy of acceptance letter; and a copy of FAFSA form. **Deadline for Receipt:** May 23. **Additional Information:** Mitchell B. Jean, Chairman McDonough Scholarship Committee.

1344 ■ RICHARD D. MCDONOUGH GOLF SCHOLARSHIP FOUNDATION

c/o Robert A. Provencher
243 Campbell St.
Manchester, NH 03104
Tel: (603)232-2345
E-mail: nhga@usga.org
Web Site: http://mcdonough.nhgolf.com
To support outstanding young men and women employed at 45 New Hampshire golf courses in pursuing higher education.
Title of Award: Alex Gissler Memorial Scholarships **Area, Field, or Subject:** General studies. **Level of Education for which Award is Granted:** Undergraduate **Funds Available:** No specific amount.
Eligibility Requirements: Applicant must have a minimum of 2 summers of successful work at a NH golf course as a caddie, in the Pro Shop, on the grounds crew, or in the clubhouse; must be a high school graduate at an accredited school; have a minimum GPA of 2.5 on a 4.0 scale; demonstrate promise of academic success; work at Baker Hill Golf Club; and have financial need. **Application Requirements:** Applicants must be recommended by the golf club where they have been employed for a minimum of two seasons. Applicants must submit a completed scholarship application; an official copy of high school transcript; a copy of acceptance letter; and a copy of FAFSA form. **Additional Information:** Endowed by Baker Hill Golf Club membership in memory of Alex Gissler. **Deadline for Receipt:** May 23. **Additional Information:** Mitchell B. Jean, Chairman McDonough Scholarship Committee.

1345 ■ RICHARD D. MCDONOUGH GOLF SCHOLARSHIP FOUNDATION

c/o Robert A. Provencher
243 Campbell St.
Manchester, NH 03104
Tel: (603)232-2345
E-mail: nhga@usga.org
Web Site: http://mcdonough.nhgolf.com
To support outstanding young men and women employed at New Hampshire golf courses in pursuing higher education.
Title of Award: Stan Lencki Scholarships **Area, Field, or Subject:** General studies. **Level of Education for which Award is Granted:** Undergraduate **Funds Available:** No specific amount.
Eligibility Requirements: Applicant must have a minimum of 2 summers of successful work at a NH golf course as a caddie, in the Pro Shop, on the grounds crew, or in the clubhouse; must be a high school graduate at

an accredited school; have a minimum GPA of 2.5 on a 4.0 scale; demonstrate promise of academic success; and have financial need. **Application Requirements:** Applicants must be recommended by the golf club where they have been employed for a minimum of two seasons. Applicants must submit a completed scholarship application; an official copy of high school transcript; a copy of acceptance letter; and a copy of FAFSA form. **Additional Information:** Endowed by the Manchester Country Club membership in honor of Mr. Lencki's 50 years of service to MCC. **Deadline for Receipt:** May 23. **Additional Information:** Mitchell B. Jean, Chairman McDonough Scholarship Committee.

1346 ■ RICHARD D. MCDONOUGH GOLF SCHOLARSHIP FOUNDATION

c/o Robert A. Provencher
243 Campbell St.
Manchester, NH 03104
Tel: (603)232-2345
E-mail: nhga@usga.org
Web Site: http://mcdonough.nhgolf.com
To support outstanding young men and women employed at New Hampshire golf courses in pursuing higher education.
Title of Award: Rick Mahoney Scholarships **Area, Field, or Subject:** General studies. **Level of Education for which Award is Granted:** Undergraduate **Funds Available:** No specific amount.
Eligibility Requirements: Applicant must have a minimum of 2 summers of successful work at a NH golf course as a caddie, in the Pro Shop, on the grounds crew, or in the clubhouse; must be a high school graduate at an accredited school; have a minimum GPA of 2.5 on a 4.0 scale; demonstrate promise of academic success; be resident of Nashua, NH; and have financial need. **Application Requirements:** Applicants must be recommended by the golf club where they have been employed for a minimum of two seasons. Applicants must submit a completed scholarship application; an official copy of high school transcript; a copy of acceptance letter; and a copy of FAFSA form. **Additional Information:** Endowed by the McDonough Foundation is honor of Mr. Mahoney. **Deadline for Receipt:** May 23. **Additional Information:** Mitchell B. Jean, Chairman McDonough Scholarship Committee.

1347 ■ RICHARD D. MCDONOUGH GOLF SCHOLARSHIP FOUNDATION

c/o Robert A. Provencher
243 Campbell St.
Manchester, NH 03104
Tel: (603)232-2345
E-mail: nhga@usga.org
Web Site: http://mcdonough.nhgolf.com
To support outstanding young men and women employed at New Hampshire golf courses in pursuing higher education.
Title of Award: NHPGA Apprentice Scholarships **Area, Field, or Subject:** General studies. **Level of Education for which Award is Granted:** Undergraduate **Funds Available:** No specific amount.
Eligibility Requirements: Applicant must have a minimum of 2 summers of successful work at a NH golf course as a caddie, in the Pro Shop, on the grounds crew, or in the clubhouse; must be a high school graduate at an accredited school; have a minimum GPA of 2.5 on a 4.0 scale; demonstrate promise of academic success; and have financial need. **Application Requirements:** Applicants must be recommended by the golf club where they have been employed for a minimum of two seasons. Applicants must submit a completed scholarship application; an official copy of high school transcript; a copy of acceptance letter; and a copy of FAFSA form. **Additional Information:** Endowed by the New Hampshire Chapter of the New England PGA. **Deadline for Receipt:** May 23. **Additional Information:** Mitchell B. Jean, Chairman McDonough Scholarship Committee.

1348 ■ RICHARD D. MCDONOUGH GOLF SCHOLARSHIP FOUNDATION

c/o Robert A. Provencher
243 Campbell St.
Manchester, NH 03104
Tel: (603)232-2345
E-mail: nhga@usga.org
Web Site: http://mcdonough.nhgolf.com

To support outstanding young men and women employed at New Hampshire golf courses in pursuing higher education.
Title of Award: Walter T. Philippy Scholarships **Area, Field, or Subject:** General studies. **Level of Education for which Award is Granted:** Undergraduate **Funds Available:** No specific amount.
Eligibility Requirements: Applicant must have a minimum of 2 summers of successful work at a NH golf course as a caddie, in the Pro Shop, on the grounds crew, or in the clubhouse; must be a high school graduate at an accredited school; have a minimum GPA of 2.5 on a 4.0 scale; demonstrate promise of academic success; must be employed at Derryfield Country Club or a Manchester, NH, golf course; and must have financial need. **Application Requirements:** Applicants must be recommended by the golf club where they have been employed for a minimum of two seasons. Applicants must submit a completed scholarship application; an official copy of high school transcript; a copy of acceptance letter; and a copy of FAFSA form. **Additional Information:** Endowed by Matilda Philippy and her family in memory of Walter T. Philippy. **Deadline for Receipt:** May 23. **Additional Information:** Mitchell B. Jean, Chairman McDonough Scholarship Committee.

1349 ■ RICHARD D. MCDONOUGH GOLF SCHOLARSHIP FOUNDATION
c/o Robert A. Provencher
243 Campbell St.
Manchester, NH 03104
Tel: (603)232-2345
E-mail: nhga@usga.org
Web Site: http://mcdonough.nhgolf.com
To support outstanding young men and women employed at New Hampshire golf courses in pursuing higher education.
Title of Award: David J. Pollini Scholarships **Area, Field, or Subject:** General studies. **Level of Education for which Award is Granted:** Undergraduate **Funds Available:** No specific amount.
Eligibility Requirements: Applicant must have a minimum of 2 summers of successful work at a NH golf course as a caddie, in the Pro Shop, on the grounds crew, or in the clubhouse; must be a high school graduate at an accredited school; have a minimum GPA of 2.5 on a 4.0 scale; demonstrate promise of academic success; must be an employee of Kingswood Golf Club or Lakes Region golf course; and have financial need. **Application Requirements:** Applicants must be recommended by the golf club where they have been employed for a minimum of two seasons. Applicants must submit a completed scholarship application; an official copy of high school transcript; a copy of acceptance letter; and a copy of FAFSA form. **Additional Information:** Endowed by the Kingswood Golf Club membership and friends of Dave. **Deadline for Receipt:** May 23. **Additional Information:** Mitchell B. Jean, Chairman McDonough Scholarship Committee.

1350 ■ RICHARD D. MCDONOUGH GOLF SCHOLARSHIP FOUNDATION
c/o Robert A. Provencher
243 Campbell St.
Manchester, NH 03104
Tel: (603)232-2345
E-mail: nhga@usga.org
Web Site: http://mcdonough.nhgolf.com
To support outstanding young men and women employed at New Hampshire golf courses in pursuing higher education.
Title of Award: Pope Scholarships Award **Area, Field, or Subject:** General studies. **Level of Education for which Award is Granted:** Undergraduate **Funds Available:** No specific amount. **Duration:** One year.
Eligibility Requirements: Applicant must have a minimum of 2 summers of successful work at a NH golf course as a caddie, in the Pro Shop, on the grounds crew, or in the clubhouse; must be a high school graduate at an accredited school; have a minimum GPA of 2.5 on a 4.0 scale; demonstrate promise of academic success; and have financial need. **Application Requirements:** Applicants must be recommended by the golf club where they have been employed for a minimum of two seasons. Applicants must submit a completed scholarship application; an official copy of high school transcript; a copy of acceptance letter; and a copy of FAFSA form. **Additional Information:** Funded by the Foundation, together with the membership of Concord Country Club, in memory of the

former University of New Hampshire golf coach and Concord Country Club member, Ken Pope. **Deadline for Receipt:** May 23. **Additional Information:** Mitchell B. Jean, Chairman McDonough Scholarship Committee.

1351 ■ RICHARD D. MCDONOUGH GOLF SCHOLARSHIP FOUNDATION
c/o Robert A. Provencher
243 Campbell St.
Manchester, NH 03104
Tel: (603)232-2345
E-mail: nhga@usga.org
Web Site: http://mcdonough.nhgolf.com
To support outstanding young men and women employed at New Hampshire golf courses in pursuing higher education.
Title of Award: Jim Sheerin Scholarships **Area, Field, or Subject:** General studies. **Level of Education for which Award is Granted:** Undergraduate **Funds Available:** No specific amount.
Eligibility Requirements: Applicant must have a minimum of 2 summers of successful work at a NH golf course as a caddie, in the Pro Shop, on the grounds crew, or in the clubhouse; must be a high school graduate from an accredited school; have a minimum GPA of 2.5 on a 4.0 scale; demonstrate promise of academic success; must be employed at Abenaqui Country Club or at a Seacoast-area golf course; and have financial need. **Application Requirements:** Applicants must be recommended by the golf club where they have been employed for a minimum of two seasons. Applicants must submit a completed scholarship application; copy of high school transcript; copy of acceptance; a copy of FAFSA form. **Additional Information:** Endowed by Abenaqui Country Club membership and friends of Jim in honor of his many years of service as head golf professional and director of golf. **Deadline for Receipt:** May 23. **Additional Information:** Mitchell B. Jean, Chairman McDonough Scholarship Committee.

1352 ■ MCKELVEY FOUNDATION
200 Park Ave., 44th Fl.
New York, NY 10166
Tel: (212)847-7236; 877-625-3583
Fax: (212)847-7240
E-mail: info@mckelveyfoundation.org
Web Site: http://www.mckelveyfoundation.org
To assist the education of young entrepreneurs.
Title of Award: McKelvey Foundation Entrepreneurial Scholarships **Area, Field, or Subject:** General studies. **Level of Education for which Award is Granted:** Undergraduate **Number Awarded:** 150. **Funds Available:** Up to $10,000 per year. **Duration:** Four years.
Eligibility Requirements: Applicant must be a graduating senior of a U.S. high school or home-school program; plan to attend an accredited four-year college or university in the U.S.; have owned and operated a business for at least one year with at least one paid employee (excluding the applicant); and have generated sales revenue (unless non-profit). **Application Requirements:** Applicants must submit a completed online scholarship application. **Deadline for Receipt:** January 25.

1353 ■ MCKELVEY FOUNDATION
200 Park Ave., 44th Fl.
New York, NY 10166
Tel: (212)847-7236; 877-625-3583
Fax: (212)847-7240
E-mail: info@mckelveyfoundation.org
Web Site: http://www.mckelveyfoundation.org
To financially support the education of a student who is first in the family to pursue a college education.
Title of Award: McKelvey Scholarships **Area, Field, or Subject:** General studies. **Level of Education for which Award is Granted:** Undergraduate **Number Awarded:** 150. **Funds Available:** $3,000 each year. **Duration:** Four years.
Eligibility Requirements: Applicant must attend a partnering high school in the states of NY, PA or WV; be the first generation to attend college (neither mother nor father went to college); have financial need; show involvement in work and/or extracurricular activities; and plan to attend a four-year college within home state. **Application Requirements:** Applicants must submit a completed online scholarship application. **Deadline for Receipt:** December 1.

1354 ■ MEDICORP HEALTH SYSTEM

2300 Fall Hill Ave., Ste. 401
Fredericksburg, VA 22401
Tel: (540)899-5411; (866)860-0946
Fax: (540)741-2571
Web Site: http://www.medicorpcareers.org
To provide financial assistance to cover tuition, fees, housing, and textbooks for deserving students in their final year of education.
Title of Award: MHS Health Career Scholarships **Area, Field, or Subject:** Medical. **Level of Education for which Award is Granted:** Undergraduate **Funds Available:** No specific amount.
Eligibility Requirements: Applicants must be rising seniors who have at least a minimum GPA of 2.75 in profession courses and in good standing attending an accredited BSN, CRNA, PT, OT, SLP, radiology tech, or pharmacist program. **Application Requirements:** Applicants must submit resume; a copy of current CPR; two clinical letters of reference; top clinical areas of interest; statement of goals; current transcript; and the complete application packet.

1355 ■ MEETING PROFESSIONALS INTERNATIONAL-GREATER NEW YORK CHAPTER

7 Fox Run Rd.
Briarcliff Manor, NY 10510
Tel: (914)762-1456
Fax: (914)944-9227
E-mail: info@mpigny.org
Web Site: http://www.mpigny.org
To support the education of a student working towards degrees to enter into the hospitality industry.
Title of Award: Jay Magazine Memorial Fund (JMMF) College Scholarships **Area, Field, or Subject:** Hotel, institutional, and restaurant management. **Level of Education for which Award is Granted:** Undergraduate **Funds Available:** Membership to the chapter - $40; $1000 reimbursement of school expenses; and $100 in "MPI Dollars" to attend MPI Educational Events.
Eligibility Requirements: Applicant must be carrying a minimum class load of 6 credits in current semester or be working F/T with 3 credits in current semester. **Application Requirements:** Applicants must submit a completed application form along with the required documents to Donny Wancho at awards@mpigny.org, or via fax at 718361-09670. **Deadline for Receipt:** Jan 31.

1356 ■ MENTAL HEALTH ASSOCIATION OF TARRANT COUNTY

3136 W St.
Fort Worth, TX 76107
Tel: (817)335-5405
Fax: (817)334-0025
E-mail: mhatc@mhatc.org
Web Site: http://www.mhatc.org
To provide financial support to those students who have mental illnesses.
Title of Award: Lillian Cooper Droke Memorial Scholarships **Area, Field, or Subject:** General Studies. **Level of Education for which Award is Granted:** Undergraduate **Funds Available:** No specific amount.
Eligibility Requirements: Applicants must be enrolled in college or technical training; must have a mental illness. If no eligible mental health consumer applies, other students pursuing a career in the mental health field may also be considered. **Application Requirements:** Applicants must check the available website online to download the application form. **Additional Information:** Mental Health Association of Tarrant County at the above address.

1357 ■ MEXICAN AMERICAN GROCERS ASSOCIATION

405 N. San Fernando Rd.
Los Angeles, CA 90031
Tel: (323)227-1565
Fax: (323)227-6935
E-mail: maga727@sbcglobal.net
Web Site: http://www.maga.org
To provide financial assistance for financially needy students.
Title of Award: Mexican American Grocers Association Scholarships **Area, Field, or Subject:** General studies. **Level of Education for which Award is Granted:** Undergraduate **Funds Available:** No specific amount.

Eligibility Requirements: Applicants must demonstrate financial need. **Application Requirements:** Applicants must check the application process online. **Additional Information:** Mexican American Grocers Association at the above address.

1358 ■ MICHIGAN ASSOCIATION OF REALTORS

PO Box 40725
Lansing, MI 48901-7925
Tel: (517)372-8890
Free: 800-454-7842
Fax: (517)334-5568
E-mail: abates@mirealtors.com
Web Site: http://www.mirealtors.com
To encourage and support outstanding, highly-motivated students to specialize in the study of real estate.
Title of Award: Michigan Association of Realtors Scholarship Trust **Area, Field, or Subject:** Real estate. **Level of Education for which Award is Granted:** Undergraduate **Funds Available:** No specific amount. **Duration:** One year.
Eligibility Requirements: Applicants must have an average grade point of 2.0 on a 4.0 scale or equivalent of a "C" average and show evidence of academic achievement; must exemplify character, including demonstrated evidence of good citizenship; must agree to take courses which are related to the real estate field; must be full-time students, entering junior or senior year or post-graduate work at a major university or college. **Application Requirements:** Applicants must complete and submit the application before the deadline. Application form can be downloaded at the Michigan Association of Realtors web site. Applicants must also provide a copy of ACT or SAT test scores and a copy of their college transcript. **Deadline for Receipt:** July 1. **Additional Information:** Andrea Bates at the above address.

1359 ■ MICHIGAN COUNCIL OF WOMEN IN TECHNOLOGY

PO Box 214585
Auburn Hills, MI 48321
Tel: (248)654-3697
Fax: (248)281-5391
E-mail: info@mcwt.org
Web Site: http://www.mcwt.org
To provide financial assistance for deserving Michigan-based women.
Title of Award: Michigan Council of Women in Technology College Scholarship Program **Area, Field, or Subject:** General studies. **Level of Education for which Award is Granted:** Graduate, Undergraduate **Funds Available:** $5,000. **Duration:** One year.
Eligibility Requirements: Applicants must be Michigan-based women who are currently or will be enrolled in college or university-level courses. **Application Requirements:** Applicants must check the council's website for the required materials. **Deadline for Receipt:** February 28. **Additional Information:** Michigan Council of Women in Technology at the above address.

1360 ■ MICHIGAN COUNCIL OF WOMEN IN TECHNOLOGY

PO Box 214585
Auburn Hills, MI 48321
Tel: (248)654-3697
Fax: (248)281-5391
E-mail: info@mcwt.org
Web Site: http://www.mcwt.org
To provide educational assistance for high school girls who are currently or will be enrolled in college level courses.
Title of Award: Michigan Council of Women in Technology High School Scholarships Program **Area, Field, or Subject:** General studies. **Level of Education for which Award is Granted:** Undergraduate **Funds Available:** A total disbursement of up to $20,000. **Duration:** 4 years.
Eligibility Requirements: Applicants must be young women entering college. **Application Requirements:** Applicants must check the available website for the required materials. **Deadline for Receipt:** February 28. **Additional Information:** Michigan Council of Women in Technology at the above address

1361 ■ MICHIGAN EDUCATION ASSOCIATION

PO Box 2573
East Lansing, MI 48826-2573

Tel: (517)332-6551
Free: 800-292-1934
Fax: (517)337-5587
E-mail: mea-it@mea.org
Web Site: http://www.mea.org
To provide education, advancement of quality education and security of the rights of education employees.
Title of Award: Michigan Education Association Scholarships **Area, Field, or Subject:** General studies. **Level of Education for which Award is Granted:** Undergraduate **Funds Available:** No specific amount.
Eligibility Requirements: Applicants must be graduates of public schools; must be attending a Michigan public community/junior college, four-year degree granting institution, or a certification or license granting institution; or attend one of the approved private institutions. **Application Requirements:** Applicants must submit completed application form.

1362 ■ MICHIGAN STORMWATER-FLOODPLAIN ASSOCIATION

PO Box 14265
Lansing, MI 48901-4265
Tel: (810)341-7500
E-mail: bhaneline@roweincorp.com
Web Site: http://mi.floods.org
To promote the common interest in floodplain and stormwater management; enhance cooperation among various local, state, and federal governmental agencies; encourage effective and innovative approaches to managing the state's floodplain and stormwater management systems; to mitigate the losses, costs, and human suffering caused by flooding and to promote wise use of the natural and beneficial functions of floodplains.
Title of Award: Michigan Stormwater-Floodplain Association Scholarships **Area, Field, or Subject:** Water supply industry. **Level of Education for which Award is Granted:** Undergraduate **Funds Available:** $1,500.
Eligibility Requirements: Applicants must be full-time juniors, seniors, or graduate students in biosystems, civil, or environmental engineering with a specialization related to the mission and goals of the MSFA. **Application Requirements:** Applicants must submit a completed application form; a copy of their program of study showing courses remaining and photocopy of their transcript; a current resume that includes a statement of their career objectives and graduation date; a one page, typed essay highlighting their academic achievements, extracurricular activities, past and present work experiences, future occupation and commitment to the mission and goals of the MSFA; must submit a letter of recommendation from a faculty member of their department.

1363 ■ MICHIGAN SUGAR COMPANY

2600 S Euclid Ave.
Bay City, MI 48706
Tel: (989)686-0161
Fax: (989)671-3695
E-mail: info@michigansugar.com
Web Site: http://www.michigansugar.com
To provide academic support to high school seniors who have completed a documented Youth Sugarbeet Project.
Title of Award: Phil Brimhall Memorial Scholarships **Area, Field, or Subject:** General studies. **Level of Education for which Award is Granted:** Undergraduate **Funds Available:** $1,000.
Eligibility Requirements: Applicants must be residents of a county where sugarbeets are grown; must be high school graduating seniors; must have participated in the Michigan Sugar Youth Sugarbeet Program at one time and have completed a Sugarbeet Project. **Application Requirements:** Applicants must submit a completed application form available at Michigan Sugar Company web site. **Deadline for Receipt:** April 25.

1364 ■ MICHIGAN SUGAR COMPANY

2600 S Euclid Ave.
Bay City, MI 48706
Tel: (989)686-0161
Fax: (989)671-3695
E-mail: info@michigansugar.com
Web Site: http://www.michigansugar.com
To provide academic support to high school seniors who have completed a documented Youth Sugarbeet Project.

Title of Award: Albert Flegenheimer Memorial Scholarships **Area, Field, or Subject:** General studies. **Level of Education for which Award is Granted:** Undergraduate **Funds Available:** $2,500.
Eligibility Requirements: Applicants must be residents of a county where sugarbeets are grown; must be high school graduating seniors; must have participated in the Michigan Sugar Youth Sugarbeet Program at one time and have completed a Sugarbeet Project. **Application Requirements:** Applicants must submit a completed application form available at the Michigan Sugar Company web site. **Deadline for Receipt:** April 25.

1365 ■ MICHIGAN SUGAR COMPANY

2600 S Euclid Ave.
Bay City, MI 48706
Tel: (989)686-0161
Fax: (989)671-3695
E-mail: info@michigansugar.com
Web Site: http://www.michigansugar.com
To provide financial support to deserving students enrolled in the Hotel Restaurant/Resort Management program of study.
Title of Award: Michigan Sugar Company Hotel Restaurant/Resort Management Scholarships **Area, Field, or Subject:** Hotel, institutional, and restaurant management. **Level of Education for which Award is Granted:** Undergraduate **Funds Available:** $1,000.
Eligibility Requirements: Applicants must be enrolled full-time in the Hotel Restaurant/Resort Management program in any college or university. **Application Requirements:** For an application please contact the Financial Aid Office at Northwood University. **Additional Information:** Northwood University, 989-837-4230.

1366 ■ MICHIGAN SUGAR COMPANY

2600 S Euclid Ave.
Bay City, MI 48706
Tel: (989)686-0161
Fax: (989)671-3695
E-mail: info@michigansugar.com
Web Site: http://www.michigansugar.com
To provide academic support to Sugar Queen participants.
Title of Award: Michigan Sugar Queen Scholarships **Area, Field, or Subject:** General studies. **Level of Education for which Award is Granted:** Undergraduate **Funds Available:** $2,000.
Eligibility Requirements: Applicants must be female, at least 18 years old and not older than 23; must never have been married and have no minor dependents; must be serving as Michigan Sugar Queen or Court attendant for a full year from crowning; must be friendly, courteous, and not use tobacco, alcoholic beverages, or drugs when appearing at official functions as Michigan Queen or Court attendant; must be residents of a county where sugarbeets are grown (Arenac, Bay, Clare, Clinton, Genesee, Gladwin, Gratiot, Huron, Ionia, Iosco, Isabella, Lapeer, Macomb, Midland, Montcalm, Ogemaw, Saginaw, Sanilac, Shiawassee, St. Clair and Tuscola). A parent/guardian will be required to attend any overnight events as a chaperone. **Application Requirements:** Interested contestants need to complete an application and send it with a picture. Application form can be downloaded at MSC website. **Additional Information:** Barb Wallace, 989-686-0161.

1367 ■ MICHIGAN TURFGRASS FOUNDATION

3225 W. St.Joseph
Lansing, MI 48917
Tel: (517)327-9207
Fax: (517)321-0495
E-mail: litchfi9@msu.edu
Web Site: http://www.michiganturfgrass.org
To support the ongoing research, education and extension in the area of professional turfgrass management that will benefit all individuals who manage turfgrasses or derive pleasure from the results of such management.
Title of Award: Robert Hancock Memorial Scholarship Award **Area, Field, or Subject:** Management. **Level of Education for which Award is Granted:** Undergraduate **Number Awarded:** 1. **Funds Available:** $2,000.
Eligibility Requirements: Applicant must be a senior undergraduate in the four-year Turfgrass Management Program; and must have a 3.0 GPA

or higher. **Application Requirements:** Applicants must complete the application form and submit along with a cover letter, resume, questionnaire answers, and letter of recommendation. **Deadline for Receipt:** November 21. **Additional Information:** litchfi9@msu.edu.

1368 ■ MICHIGAN TURFGRASS FOUNDATION
3225 W. St.Joseph
Lansing, MI 48917
Tel: (517)327-9207
Fax: (517)321-0495
E-mail: litchfi9@msu.edu
Web Site: http://www.michiganturfgrass.org
To support the ongoing research, education and extension in the area of professional turfgrass management that will benefit all individuals who manage turfgrasses or derive pleasure from the results of such management.
Title of Award: Norman Kramer Scholarship Award **Area, Field, or Subject:** General studies. **Level of Education for which Award is Granted:** Undergraduate **Number Awarded:** 1. **Funds Available:** $2,500.
Eligibility Requirements: Applicants must be students with a minimum of 42 credits completed and who have a 3.0 GPA or higher. **Application Requirements:** Applicants must complete the application form and submit along with a cover letter, resume, questionnaire answers, and letter of recommendation. **Deadline for Receipt:** November 21. **Additional Information:** litchfi9@msu.edu

1369 ■ MICHIGAN TURFGRASS FOUNDATION
3225 W. St.Joseph
Lansing, MI 48917
Tel: (517)327-9207
Fax: (517)321-0495
E-mail: litchfi9@msu.edu
Web Site: http://www.michiganturfgrass.org
To support the ongoing research, education and extension in the area of professional turfgrass management that will benefit all individuals who manage turfgrasses or derive pleasure from the results of such management.
Title of Award: Kenyon T. Payne Outstanding Student Awards **Area, Field, or Subject:** Management. **Level of Education for which Award is Granted:** Undergraduate **Funds Available:** $2,000.
Eligibility Requirements: Applicants must be second year students in the Turfgass Management Program who have a 3.0 GPA or higher. **Application Requirements:** Applicants must complete the application form and submit along with a cover letter, resume, questionnaire answers, and letter of recommendation. **Deadline for Receipt:** November 21. **Additional Information:** litchfi9@msu.edu.

1370 ■ MIDWEST DAIRY ASSOCIATION
2015 Rice St.
St. Paul, MN 55113
800-642-3895
Web Site: http://www.midwestdairy.com
To provide financial assistance to college students within the Chicago Division.
Title of Award: Chicago Division Scholarships **Area, Field, or Subject:** General Studies. **Level of Education for which Award is Granted:** Undergraduate **Number Awarded:** 2. **Funds Available:** $1,000.
Eligibility Requirements: Applicants must be enrolled in an accredited college; must be immediate family members of dairy farmers. **Application Requirements:** Applicants must check the available website for the required materials. **Deadline for Receipt:** March 1. **Additional Information:** For more information, contact: Marla Behrends, Industry Relations Manager at 309-376-2196

1371 ■ MIDWEST DAIRY ASSOCIATION
2015 Rice St.
St. Paul, MN 55113
800-642-3895
Web Site: http://www.midwestdairy.com
To provide financial assistance to those students who are in need.
Title of Award: Minnesota Division Scholarships **Area, Field, or Subject:** General Studies. **Level of Education for which Award is Granted:** Undergraduate **Funds Available:** $1,000-$3,000.

Eligibility Requirements: Applicants must be enrolled students at the University of Minnesota CFANS in St. Paul or in Crookston. **Application Requirements:** Applicants must check the available website for the required materials. **Additional Information:** Midwest Dairy Association at the above address.

1372 ■ MIDWEST DAIRY ASSOCIATION
2015 Rice St.
St. Paul, MN 55113
800-642-3895
Web Site: http://www.midwestdairy.com
To provide financial support to those students who are in need.
Title of Award: Ozarks Division Scholarships **Area, Field, or Subject:** General Studies. **Level of Education for which Award is Granted:** Undergraduate **Number Awarded:** 4. **Funds Available:** $500.
Eligibility Requirements: Applicants must be enrolled in an accredited college. Applicants must be immediate family members of dairy farmers. **Application Requirements:** Applicants must check the available website for the required materials. **Deadline for Receipt:** March 1. **Additional Information:** For more information, contact: Stacy Dohle, Industry Relations Manager at 417-267-5039

1373 ■ MIDWEST DAIRY ASSOCIATION
2015 Rice St.
St. Paul, MN 55113
800-642-3895
Web Site: http://www.midwestdairy.com
To provide financial support to those students who are in need.
Title of Award: St. Louis Division Scholarships **Area, Field, or Subject:** General Studies. **Level of Education for which Award is Granted:** Undergraduate **Number Awarded:** 2. **Funds Available:** $1,000. **Duration:** One year.
Eligibility Requirements: Applicants must be enrolled in an accredited college. Applicants must be immediate family members of dairy farmers. **Application Requirements:** Applicants must check the available website for the required materials. **Deadline for Receipt:** March 1. **Additional Information:** For more information, contact: Marla Behrends, Industry Relations Manager at 309-376-2196

1374 ■ MIDWEST DAIRY ASSOCIATION
2015 Rice St.
St. Paul, MN 55113
800-642-3895
Web Site: http://www.midwestdairy.com
To provide financial support to those students who are in need.
Title of Award: South Dakota Division Scholarships **Area, Field, or Subject:** Dairy Science. **Level of Education for which Award is Granted:** Undergraduate **Number Awarded:** 2. **Funds Available:** $750.
Eligibility Requirements: Applicants must be incoming freshmen majoring in Dairy Science who are admitted at Dakota State University in Brookings. **Application Requirements:** Applicants must check the available website for the required materials. **Additional Information:** For more information, contact: Char Hovland, Industry Relations Manager at 605-692-4812

1375 ■ MILITARY INTELLIGENCE CORPS ASSOCIATION
6339 S Ranch Rd.
Hereford, AZ 85615
Tel: (520)456-6232
E-mail: info@micorps.org
Web Site: http://www.micorps.org
To provide educational assistance for family members of Active Duty, Reserve, National Guard and retired Military Intelligence Soldiers.
Title of Award: Military Intelligence Corps Association Scholarships **Area, Field, or Subject:** General studies. **Level of Education for which Award is Granted:** Undergraduate **Funds Available:** $500 - $1,000.
Eligibility Requirements: Applicants or their sponsors must be current MICA members in good standing. They must be pursuing post-secondary education through a college, university, vocational school or technical institution and must be accepted or enrolled in a qualified education program and who agree to complete at least one course or class. **Application Requirements:** Applications must contain the following documentation: scholarship application checklist; scholarship application

signed by the applicant; copy of MICA Membership Card (if copy of membership card is not available, please provide some proof of current membership); three letters of Recommendation (all letters of recommendation must be signed and include full point of contact information); essay (include a one-page essay detailing the applicant's educational goals and program of study); transcripts; and proof of acceptance by an educational institution. **Deadline for Receipt:** May 15. **Additional Information:** MICA Scholarship Chairman; 110 Rhea Street, Fort Huachuca, Arizona 85613-7080.

1376 ■ MILITARY OFFICERS ASSOCIATION OF AMERICA
201 N Washington St.
Alexandria, VA 22314
Tel: (703)549-2311
Free: 800-234-6622
E-mail: msc@moaa.org
Web Site: http://www.moaa.org
To help children of Uniformed Services members who died or was severley disabled while in active service as a member of the Regular, Guard or Reserve Forces.
Title of Award: MOAA American Patriot Scholarships **Area, Field, or Subject:** General studies. **Level of Education for which Award is Granted:** Undergraduate **Funds Available:** At least $2,500.
Eligibility Requirements: Applicant must be a child of a member of the Uniformed Services who died while in active service; must be under the age of 24 at the time of application (the maximum age for students who are serving or have served in the Armed Forces before completing college will be increased by the number of years served, for up to five years of service or 29 years of age); must be planning to attend an accredited college/university as a full-time student seeking their first undergraduate degree; and must have a cumulative GPA of 3.0 or higher on a 4.0 scale. **Application Requirements:** Applicants must apply for the scholarship online. **Deadline for Receipt:** March 3.

1377 ■ MILITARY OFFICERS ASSOCIATION OF AMERICA
201 N Washington St.
Alexandria, VA 22314
Tel: (703)549-2311
Free: 800-234-6622
E-mail: msc@moaa.org
Web Site: http://www.moaa.org
To help children of active Uniformed Services members.
Title of Award: MOAA Base/Post Scholarships **Area, Field, or Subject:** General studies. **Level of Education for which Award is Granted:** Undergraduate **Number Awarded:** 25. **Funds Available:** $1,000.
Eligibility Requirements: Applicant must be the dependent son/daughter (under age 24) of an active duty officer and enlisted military personnel. **Application Requirements:** Applicants must apply for the scholarship online. **Deadline for Receipt:** March 3.

1378 ■ MILITARY OFFICERS ASSOCIATION OF AMERICA
201 N Washington St.
Alexandria, VA 22314
Tel: (703)549-2311
Free: 800-234-6622
E-mail: msc@moaa.org
Web Site: http://www.moaa.org
To help children of Uniformed Services members.
Title of Award: General John Paul Ratay Educational Grants **Area, Field, or Subject:** General studies. **Level of Education for which Award is Granted:** Undergraduate **Funds Available:** $4,000.
Eligibility Requirements: Applicant must be the child of the surviving spouse of a retired officer. **Application Requirements:** Applicants must apply online. **Deadline for Receipt:** March 3.

1379 ■ MILLER THOMSON LLP
PO Box 1011
Toronto, ON, Canada M5H 3S1
Tel: (416)595-8500; 888-762-5559
Fax: (416)595-8695
E-mail: toronto@millerthomson.com
Web Site: http://www.millerthomson.com
To encourage and promote the attainment of higher education goals by top students in Canada.
Title of Award: Miller Thomson Foundation Scholarships **Area, Field, or Subject:** General studies. **Level of Education for which Award is Granted:** Undergraduate **Number Awarded:** 200. **Funds Available:** $1,000. **Duration:** One year.
Eligibility Requirements: Applicant must be a graduating student attending Canadian secondary schools and must be one of the top students in Canada who have demonstrated a high level of academic achievement and have made positive contribution to their school or community. **Application Requirements:** Applicants are advised to visit the foundation website at www.millerthomson.com for scholarship information and instructions or contact Mrs. Lesley A. Lawson, Executive Director, The Miller Thomson Foundation at llawson@millerthomson.com. **Additional Information:** Scholarship was created by Miller Thomson LLP in 1995 and funded annually by its partners. **Deadline for Receipt:** March 15.

1380 ■ MINNEAPOLIS JEWISH FEDERATION
13100 Wayzata Blvd., Ste. 200
Minnetonka, MN 55305
Tel: (952)593-2600
Fax: (952)593-2544
E-mail: webmaster@ujfc.org
Web Site: http://twincities.ujcfedweb.org
To provide financial assistance to those children with high financial need.
Title of Award: Minneapolis Camp Scholarships **Area, Field, or Subject:** General studies. **Level of Education for which Award is Granted:** Undergraduate **Funds Available:** No specific amount.
Eligibility Requirements: Applicants must be Jewish; must be residents of the greater Minneapolis area. **Application Requirements:** Applicants must submit a completed application form to the Minneapolis Jewish Federation office. **Deadline for Receipt:** March 28. **Additional Information:** Applications must be submitted to: Norma Kaplan, Camp Scholarships, 13100 Wayzata Blvd., Ste. 200, Minnetonka, MN 55305, or email nkaplan@mplsfed.org or call at 952-417-2335. Forms may also be downloaded from the Twin Cities website at www.jewishminnesota.org.

1381 ■ MINNESOTA ASSOCIATION OF PUBLIC ACCOUNTANTS
1711 W County Rd. B, Ste. 300N
Roseville, MN 55113
Tel: (651)635-0706
Free: 800-501-4521
Fax: (651)635-0307
E-mail: admin@mapamn.com
Web Site: http://www.mapa-mn.com
To further the knowledge of the practitioner and offer a source of current information and interplay of ideas among professionals.
Title of Award: Minnesota Association of Public Accountant Scholarships **Area, Field, or Subject:** Accounting. **Level of Education for which Award is Granted:** Undergraduate **Funds Available:** No specific amount.
Eligibility Requirements: Applicants must be undergraduate students entering their junior year; must be enrolled in a degree program at an accredited four-year college or university majoring in accounting with the intention to practice in the field of public accounting; must have at least a 2.5 or better grade point average; must be U.S. citizens attending a U.S. accredited school; and must be Minnesota residents. **Application Requirements:** Applicants must submit a completed application form; official transcript; and letters of recommendation from advisors or professors. **Deadline for Receipt:** April 1.

1382 ■ MINNESOTA CHAPTER AMERICAN PLANNING ASSOCIATION
9288 Beverly Dr.
Breezy Point, MN 56472
Tel: (763)576-2722; 888-882-5369
E-mail: mnapa_admin@tds.net
Web Site: http://www.mnapa.com
To foster the development of students in the planning field by providing student scholarship each year.
Title of Award: Gunnar Isberg Student Scholarships **Area, Field, or Subject:** General studies. **Level of Education for which Award is Granted:** Undergraduate **Funds Available:** $1,000.

Eligibility Requirements: Applicants must be pursuing education in planning or planning related fields in a degree program; must be residents of the State of Minnesota or attending a university or college within the State of Minnesota in a planning related program. **Application Requirements:** Applicants must submit a proof of enrollment; a recent transcript; letter of recommendation from a professor or job supervisor; a current resume including education, work experience, organizations, school activities, and professional skills; and a cover letter stating anticipated graduation date and professional goals. **Deadline for Receipt:** July 11. **Additional Information:** michele.mcpherson@co.mill-lacs.mn.us.

1383 ■ MIRACOSTA COLLEGE

1 Barnard Dr.
Oceanside, CA 92056
Tel: (760)757-2121; 888-201-8480
Web Site: http://www.miracosta.cc.ca.us
To provide educational support for qualified individuals intending to pursue a two-year degree.
Title of Award: MiraCosta College Two-Year Colleges Scholarships **Area, Field, or Subject:** General studies. **Level of Education for which Award is Granted:** Undergraduate **Number Awarded:** 350. **Funds Available:** $1,000. **Duration:** Two years.
Eligibility Requirements: Applicants must be U.S. citizens or permanent residents; must have a minimum of a 2.5 at time of nomination; must be planning to enroll in at least two course during the fall term at a two-year degree granting institution; and must be actively engaged in volunteer service or employed at least part-time. **Application Requirements:** Applicants must contact the scholarship at www.ptk.org for application and deadline information. **Deadline for Receipt:** May 31.

1384 ■ MOLINE FOUNDATION

817 11th Ave.
Moline, IL 61265
Tel: (309)736-3800
Fax: (309)736-3721
E-mail: molinefoundation@gconline.com
Web Site: http://www.molinefoundation.org
To provide grants to health, human services, education, community development, the arts, and other charitable organizations which benefit the citizens of Moline Foundations.
Title of Award: Cleam T. Hanson Scholarship Fund **Area, Field, or Subject:** General studies. **Level of Education for which Award is Granted:** Undergraduate **Funds Available:** No specific amount.
Eligibility Requirements: Applicants must be graduating high school seniors, or community college students preparing to transfer to four-year colleges. Applicants must intend to pursue a bachelor's degree on a full-time basis in any career field. Applicants must demonstrate financial need. Applicants must have achieved high school scholastic performance in the upper one-third of their class, or community college grade performance of 2.5 on a 4.0 scale, or equivalent. **Application Requirements:** Applicants must complete the application form. **Additional Information:** 309-736-3800.

1385 ■ MORRIS COUNTY PSYCHOLOGICAL ASSOCIATION

50 Maple Ave.
Morristown, NJ 07960
Tel: (973)644-0033
E-mail: info@mcpanj.com
Web Site: http://www.mcpanj.com
To stimulate and encourage the study of the behavioral sciences in high school students.
Title of Award: Morris County Psychological Association Scholarships **Area, Field, or Subject:** General Studies. **Level of Education for which Award is Granted:** Undergraduate **Funds Available:** No specific amount.
Eligibility Requirements: Applicants must be high school students who are taking classes related to the behavioral sciences including psychology, human and animal behavior, child development, sociology. **Application Requirements:** Applicants must check the available website for the required materials. **Additional Information:** Morris County Psychological Association at the above address.

1386 ■ JAMES B. MORRIS SCHOLARSHIP FUND

525 SW 5th St., Ste. A
Des Moines, IA 50309-4501

Tel: (515)282-8192
Fax: (515)282-9117
E-mail: morris@assoc-mgmt.com
Web Site: http://www.morrisscholarship.org
To provide assistance, motivation, and internship opportunities for minority students pursuing post-secondary and graduate degrees.
Title of Award: James B. Morris Scholarships **Area, Field, or Subject:** General studies. **Level of Education for which Award is Granted:** Undergraduate **Funds Available:** No specific amount. **Duration:** One year.
Eligibility Requirements: Program is open to individuals of minority ethnic status as defined by the Equal Employment Opportunity Commission who have a minimum 2.5 GPA. Eligible applicants may be: Iowa high school graduates and residents of Iowa who are attending any U.S. college or university; or non-Iowa residents who are attending Iowa colleges or universities. **Application Requirements:** Applicants must submit a copy of official high school transcripts (for graduating high school seniors only), official college transcript (most recent semester only); must provide one or more letters of references (at least one must be from an instructor); must provide a writing sample (an essay about the applicant and why they are applying for the scholarship); must complete the application form available online and must have a recent photograph (head and shoulder shot only). Application form and other supporting documents must be sent to Scholarship Committee Chairperson, James B. Morris Scholarship Fund, Inc., 525 SW 5th St., Ste. A, Des Moines, IA 50309-4501. **Deadline for Receipt:** April 1.

1387 ■ JOHN R. MOTT SCHOLARSHIP FOUNDATION

2550 M St. NW
Washington, DC 20037
E-mail: info@mottscholarship.org
Web Site: http://www.mottscholarship.org
To provide scholarship for higher education to students who are natives of Calabria.
Title of Award: John R. Mott Scholarships **Area, Field, or Subject:** General studies. **Level of Education for which Award is Granted:** Undergraduate **Funds Available:** $10,000. **Duration:** One year.
Eligibility Requirements: Applicants must be natives to the region of Calabria, Italy who are enrolled to attend any accredited post-secondary school; must be seeking an education leading to a degree or professional certificate. **Application Requirements:** Applicants must complete the application form available online. Applicants must submit an official transcript from the university attesting to academic performance. Application form and requirements must be sent to NIAF Mott Scholarships, 1860 19th St. NW. Washington, DC 20009. **Deadline for Receipt:** March 15.

1388 ■ ANTHONY MUNOZ FOUNDATION

Longworth Hall
700 West Pete Rose Way, Unit 54
Cincinnati, OH 45203
Tel: (513)772-4900
Fax: (513)772-4911
E-mail: info@munozfoundation.org
Web Site: http://munozfoundation.com
To support Tri-State youth in achieving their dreams of attending a local college or university.
Title of Award: Anthony Munoz Scholarships **Area, Field, or Subject:** General studies. **Level of Education for which Award is Granted:** Undergraduate **Funds Available:** No specific amount.
Eligibility Requirements: Applicant must be: a resident of any of the Tri-State region (Kentucky, Indiana, and Ohio); attending a local, Tri-State region, non-proprietary college, university or technical college; a graduating high school senior with at least a 2.0 GPA (or a G.E.D. recipient under the age of 23); of any race but of socio-economic need; must maintain a post-secondary GPA of at least a 2.0. **Application Requirements:** Applicants must submit a completed scholarship application form along with a copy of recent transcript; Expected Family Contribution (EFC) from Student Aid Report (SAR), which comes as a result of filing the FAFSA; and a copy of Financial Aid Award Letter from their chosen college. **Additional Information:** Faxed applications will not be considered. In partnership with The Cincinnati Scholarship Foundation. **Deadline for Receipt:** April 30.

1389 ■ DANIEL MURPHY SCHOLARSHIP FUND
228 S Wabash, Ste. 600
Chicago, IL 60604
Tel: (312)455-7800
Fax: (312)455-7801
E-mail: andrew@dmsf.org
Web Site: http://www.dmsf.org
To financially support disadvantaged Chicago students who demonstrate academic potential.
Title of Award: Daniel Murphy Scholarships **Area, Field, or Subject:** General studies. **Level of Education for which Award is Granted:** High School **Number Awarded:** 100-120. **Funds Available:** No specific amount. **Duration:** Four years.
Eligibility Requirements: Applicant must be a Chicago eighth grade student who has demonstrated academic potential, strong character and financial need; must reside within the city of Chicago. **Application Requirements:** Applicants must submit a completed scholarship application form. **Deadline for Receipt:** November 2.

1390 ■ NASHVILLE CATHOLIC BUSINESS WOMEN'S LEAGUE
PO Box 50994
Nashville, TN 37205-0994
E-mail: info@ncbwl.org
Web Site: http://www.ncbwl.org
To provide financial support to those students who are in need.
Title of Award: Aurella Varallo Mariani Scholarship Program **Area, Field, or Subject:** General studies. **Level of Education for which Award is Granted:** Undergraduate **Funds Available:** No specific amount.
Eligibility Requirements: Applicants must be deserving young Catholic women in the middle Tennessee area. **Application Requirements:** Applicants must check the available website for details. **Additional Information:** The scholarships are named in memory of Aurelia Varallo Mariani, a faithful and loving NCBWL member who graduated from St. Cecilia Academy in 1951. Her love for her alma mater and for this league continued until her untimely death in 1997. **Additional Information:** Nashville Catholic Business Women's League at the above address.

1391 ■ NASHVILLE CATHOLIC BUSINESS WOMEN'S LEAGUE
PO Box 50994
Nashville, TN 37205-0994
E-mail: info@ncbwl.org
Web Site: http://www.ncbwl.org
To provide scholarship assistance to deserving female students.
Title of Award: NCBWL Scholarships **Area, Field, or Subject:** General studies. **Level of Education for which Award is Granted:** High School **Funds Available:** No specific amount.
Eligibility Requirements: Applicants must be female students; must be enrolled at St. Cecilia Academy, Father Ryan High School or Pope John Paul II High School for their full four years of matriculation. **Application Requirements:** Applicants must submit a completed application form. **Additional Information:** Nashville Catholic Business Women's League at the above address.

1392 ■ NATIONAL ACTIVE AND RETIRED FEDERAL EMPLOYEES ASSOCIATION
606 N Washington St.
Alexandria, VA 22314
Tel: (703)838-7760
Fax: (703)838-7785
Web Site: http://www.narfe.org
To provide financial assistance for education of children and grandchildren of federal employees.
Title of Award: NARFE-FEEA Scholarship Awards Program **Area, Field, or Subject:** General studies. **Level of Education for which Award is Granted:** Undergraduate **Funds Available:** 1,000.
Eligibility Requirements: Applicant must be a child, grandchild, stepchild or great-grandchild of any NARFE member in good standing currently in high school and has at least a 3.0 grade point average on a 4.0 scale. **Application Requirements:** Applicant must submit copies of their American College Testing (ACT) or Scholastic Aptitude Testing (SAT) scores, or other entrance examination scores as applicable; a written letter of recommendation/character reference from a teacher, or counselor; a list and brief description of awards and/or community service activities on

a separate page; a typed, double-spaced, essay on a specific topic determined in the "Official Scholarship Application"; and two stamped, self-addressed No. 10 business-size envelopes. **Deadline for Receipt:** April 30.

1393 ■ NATIONAL AIR FILTRATION ASSOCIATION
PO Box 68639
Virginia Beach, VA 23471
Tel: (757)313-7400
Fax: (757)497-1895
E-mail: nafa@nafahq.org
Web Site: http://www.nafahq.org
To honor students who demonstrate outstanding personal and academic characteristics.
Title of Award: National Air Filtration Association Scholarship Fund **Area, Field, or Subject:** General studies. **Level of Education for which Award is Granted:** Undergraduate **Number Awarded:** 2. **Funds Available:** $1,000. Cash scholarships are used for college expenses. **Duration:** Entire length of undergraduate study.
Eligibility Requirements: Applicants must be immediate family members of NAFA members in good standing, or family members of employees of NAFA member firms. Grandchildren of NAFA members are also qualified. Incoming Freshmen must have a minimum ACT score of 22 or SAT score of 900 and rank in the top 35% of the graduating class. Transfer students must have a cumulative GPA of 2.75 on a 4.0 scale. **Application Requirements:** Applicants must submit a recent photo for press release purposes; a written essay of 1-2 typewritten pages that gives a brief biographical sketch of the individual along with reasons why they feel they should receive the scholarship; and two letters of recommendation, one of which must be from a recent teacher. Neither recommendation should be from a family member. **Deadline for Receipt:** August 1.

1394 ■ NATIONAL ALPHA LAMBDA DELTA
PO Box 4403
Macon, GA 31208-4403
800-9-ALPHA-1
E-mail: ald@nationalald.org
Web Site: http://www.nationalad.org
To provide financial support for ALD members pursuing a graduate or professional degree.
Title of Award: ALD Graduate Fellowships **Area, Field, or Subject:** General studies. **Level of Education for which Award is Granted:** Undergraduate **Number Awarded:** 23. **Funds Available:** $3,000 up to $7,500.
Eligibility Requirements: Applicant must be a member of Alpha Lambda Delta who has maintained a GPA of 3.5 on a 4.0 scale or equivalent until graduation. **Application Requirements:** Applicants must submit typed application, official transcript of all academic work, and list of not more than three persons from whom have requested letters of recommendation. **Deadline for Receipt:** January 31.

1395 ■ NATIONAL ALPHA LAMBDA DELTA
PO Box 4403
Macon, GA 31208-4403
800-9-ALPHA-1
E-mail: ald@nationalald.org
Web Site: http://www.nationalad.org
To provide financial assistance to qualified members for their education.
Title of Award: Jo Anne J. Trow Scholarships **Area, Field, or Subject:** General studies. **Level of Education for which Award is Granted:** Undergraduate **Funds Available:** $1,000 up to $3,000.
Eligibility Requirements: Applicants must be members of Alpha Lambda Delta who have maintained the cumulative grade point average of 3.5 on a 4.0 scale or equivalent. **Application Requirements:** Applicants must complete application form, prepare the supplemental materials, and submit original application and two complete photocopies of all application materials to ALD chapter's scholarship selection committee's advisor. **Deadline for Receipt:** April 1.

1396 ■ NATIONAL ASIAN AMERICAN SOCIETY OF ACCOUNTANTS
PO Box 8689
New York, NY 10116
Tel: (212)248-4888

Fax: (212)344-5636
E-mail: info@naasa.org
Web Site: http://www.naasa.org
To enhance the presence and influence of minorities in the accounting and finance profession; to encourage the development of finance professionals and students while serving as a collective voice for the minority communities in the field of accounting and finance; and to encourage their selection of accounting as a major and their ultimate entry into the profession.
Title of Award: AICPA Scholarships for Minority Accounting Students **Area, Field, or Subject:** Accounting; Finance. **Level of Education for which Award is Granted:** Undergraduate **Funds Available:** Maximum amount of $5,000.
Eligibility Requirements: Applicant must be a declared accounting major with the intention of pursuing the CPA credential; must be full-time undergraduate student with 12 semester hours or equivalent at a four year or upper division institution, unless completing his/her semester of study; must have successfully completed at least 30 semester hours or equivalent of college coursework including at least six semester hours in accounting; must at least obtain 3.3 GPA major and cumulative; must be Black or African American, Hispanic or Latino, Asian, American Indian or Alaska native, Native Hawaiian Islander, or two or more races; must be U.S. citizen or permanent resident; and must be an AICPA student affiliate member. **Application Requirements:** Applicants must complete the application form and submit along with a one-page, typed essay and a letter of recommendation. **Deadline for Receipt:** June 2.

1397 ■ NATIONAL ASIAN AMERICAN SOCIETY OF ACCOUNTANTS
PO Box 8689
New York, NY 10116
Tel: (212)248-4888
Fax: (212)344-5636
E-mail: info@naasa.org
Web Site: http://www.naasa.org
To recognize and inspire outstanding students.
Title of Award: ASCEND/ING Scholarships **Area, Field, or Subject:** Accounting; Finance. **Level of Education for which Award is Granted:** Undergraduate **Funds Available:** No specific amount.
Eligibility Requirements: Applicants must be current and active Ascend student members who are undergraduate or graduate students. Must either be juniors or seniors majoring in accountancy, finance, taxation, management information systems or business-related program in the academic year. They must have a strong academic standing and a 3.2 GPA or higher and community volunteer experience. **Application Requirements:** Applicants must submit a resume including current GPA; minimum of 500-word personal essay describing career goals; and unofficial college or university transcript. **Deadline for Receipt:** June 15. **Additional Information:** vanessa.manzano@naasa.org

1398 ■ NATIONAL ASIAN AMERICAN SOCIETY OF ACCOUNTANTS
PO Box 8689
New York, NY 10116
Tel: (212)248-4888
Fax: (212)344-5636
E-mail: info@naasa.org
Web Site: http://www.naasa.org
To enhance the presence and influence of Asian Americans in the accounting and finance profession and to encourage the development of finance professionals and students while serving as a collective voice for the Asian and Pacific Islander communities in the field of accounting and finance.
Title of Award: Ernst and Young/Ascend Leadership Scholarship Program **Area, Field, or Subject:** Accounting; Finance. **Level of Education for which Award is Granted:** Undergraduate **Number Awarded:** 5. **Funds Available:** $5,000.
Eligibility Requirements: Applicants must be students who demonstrate a desire to pursue a career in accounting and professional services. **Application Requirements:** Applicants must complete the application form. **Deadline for Receipt:** June 15. **Additional Information:** venessa.manzano@naasa.org.

1399 ■ NATIONAL ASSOCIATION FOR THE ADVANCEMENT OF COLORED PEOPLE
PO Box 1740
Alexandria, VA 22312
Tel: (703)684-6190
Fax: (703)619-0450
E-mail: naacp@naacpalexandria.org
Web Site: http://www.naacpalexandria.org
To provide financial aid for those who have successfully completed high school and are planning to continue their education in an institution of higher learning.
Title of Award: Annie B. Rose Educational Scholarships **Area, Field, or Subject:** General studies. **Level of Education for which Award is Granted:** Undergraduate **Number Awarded:** 3. **Funds Available:** $1,000. **Duration:** One year.
Eligibility Requirements: Applicant must be a resident of the City of Alexandria; must have a minimum "C" grade point average (2.5 or better); be a graduating senior or current college enrolled; must have applied to and received official notice of acceptance by an accredited school; must be willing to receive the scholarship award through the business office of his/her respective institution; and willing to uphold the goals and objectives of the NAACP. **Application Requirements:** Applicants must submit an official NAACP Scholarship Application; two letters of recommendation; official school transcript; and a 200-300 words personal essay. **Deadline for Receipt:** May 1.

1400 ■ NATIONAL ASSOCIATION OF CAMPUS ACTIVITIES
13 Harbison Way
Columbia, SC 29212
Tel: (803)732-6222
Fax: (803)749-1047
E-mail: info@naca.org
Web Site: http://www.naca.org
To support undergraduate or graduate students.
Title of Award: Tese Caldarelli Memorial Scholarships **Area, Field, or Subject:** General studies. **Level of Education for which Award is Granted:** Undergraduate **Funds Available:** No specific amount.
Eligibility Requirements: Applicants must be undergraduate students with a minimum cumulative GPA of 3.0 or better at the time of the application. **Application Requirements:** Applicants must submit a current resume and complete the application form; at least two letters of recommendation; official verification of the applicant's current enrollment status. **Deadline for Receipt:** November 1.

1401 ■ NATIONAL ASSOCIATION OF CAMPUS ACTIVITIES
13 Harbison Way
Columbia, SC 29212
Tel: (803)732-6222
Fax: (803)749-1047
E-mail: info@naca.org
Web Site: http://www.naca.org
To support undergraduate or graduate students.
Title of Award: Markey Scholarships **Area, Field, or Subject:** General studies. **Level of Education for which Award is Granted:** Undergraduate **Funds Available:** No specific amount.
Eligibility Requirements: Applicants must have a minimum of a 2.5 cumulative GPA; be junior, senior, or graduate students at a four-year school in the former NACA South Central Region. **Application Requirements:** Applicants must submit a current resume and any supporting materials that may enhance the applicant's candidacy. **Deadline for Receipt:** September 1.

1402 ■ NATIONAL ASSOCIATION OF CAMPUS ACTIVITIES
13 Harbison Way
Columbia, SC 29212
Tel: (803)732-6222
Fax: (803)749-1047
E-mail: info@naca.org
Web Site: http://www.naca.org
To assist students pursuing graduate or undergraduate studies leading to a career in student activities or a related student services field.
Title of Award: NACA East Coast Undergraduate Scholarships for Student Leaders **Area, Field, or Subject:** General studies. **Level of Education for which Award is Granted:** Undergraduate **Funds Available:** No specific amount.

Eligibility Requirements: Applicants must be matriculated undergraduates in good standing at the time of their application and during the semester in which the award is received; have a GPA of 2.5 on a 4.0 scale; have demonstrated significant leadership skills and ability; have made significant contributions via volunteer involvement, either on or off campus; be enrolled in a college or university within the former NACA East Coast region. **Application Requirements:** Applicants must submit at least two letters of recommendation; resume or description of the applicant's leadership activities, skills, and ability, training, and accomplishment; official transcript of the applicant's current enrollment status from the college or university. **Deadline for Receipt:** March 31.

1403 ■ NATIONAL ASSOCIATION OF CAMPUS ACTIVITIES

13 Harbison Way
Columbia, SC 29212
Tel: (803)732-6222
Fax: (803)749-1047
E-mail: info@naca.org
Web Site: http://www.naca.org
To assist students pursuing graduate or undergraduate studies leading to a career in student activities or a related student services field.
Title of Award: NACA Regional Council Student Leadership Scholarships **Area, Field, or Subject:** General studies. **Level of Education for which Award is Granted:** Undergraduate **Funds Available:** No specific amount.
Eligibility Requirements: Applicants must be matriculated undergraduate in good standing at the time of their application and during the semester in which the award is received; hold a significant leadership position on campus or in the community; have made significant contributions via volunteer involvement, either on or off the campus. **Application Requirements:** Applicants must submit at least two letters of recommendation; resume or description of the applicant's leadership activities, skills, and ability, training, and accomplishment; and official transcript of the applicant's current enrollment status from the college or university. **Deadline for Receipt:** May 1.

1404 ■ NATIONAL ASSOCIATION OF CAMPUS ACTIVITIES

13 Harbison Way
Columbia, SC 29212
Tel: (803)732-6222
Fax: (803)749-1047
E-mail: info@naca.org
Web Site: http://www.naca.org
To assist students pursuing graduate or undergraduate studies leading to a career in student activities or a related student services field; to recognize the achievements of undergraduate student leaders enrolled at colleges and universities in the former NACA Southeast Region.
Title of Award: NACA Southeast Student Leadership Scholarships **Area, Field, or Subject:** General Studies. **Level of Education for which Award is Granted:** Undergraduate **Number Awarded:** 4. **Funds Available:** No specific amount.
Eligibility Requirements: Applicants must be matriculated undergraduates in good standing at the time of their application and during the semester in which the award is received; have a GPA of 2.5 on a 4.0 scale; have demonstrated significant leadership skills and ability; hold a significant leadership position on campus or in the community; have made significant contributions via volunteer involvement, either on or off the campus. **Application Requirements:** Applicants must submit at least two letters of recommendation; resume or description of the applicant's leadership activities, skills, and ability, training, and accomplishment; and official transcript of the applicant's current enrollment status from the college or university. **Deadline for Receipt:** March 31.

1405 ■ NATIONAL ASSOCIATION OF CAMPUS ACTIVITIES

13 Harbison Way
Columbia, SC 29212
Tel: (803)732-6222
Fax: (803)749-1047
E-mail: info@naca.org
Web Site: http://www.naca.org
To assist students pursuing graduate or undergraduate studies leading to a career in student activities or a related student services field; to provide economic assistance to qualified underrepresented programmers; to

increase the participation of ethnic minority individuals in the field of campus activities.
Title of Award: National Association of Campus Activities Multicultural Scholarship Programs **Area, Field, or Subject:** General studies. **Level of Education for which Award is Granted:** Undergraduate **Funds Available:** No specific amount.
Eligibility Requirements: Applicants must be matriculated undergraduates in good standing at the time of their application and during the semester in which the award is received; must be a member of the African-American, Latina/Latino, Native American, Asian American, or Pacific Islander ethnic minorities; hold a significant leadership position on campus or in the community; have made significant contributions via volunteer involvement, either on or off the campus. **Application Requirements:** Applicants must submit at least two letters of recommendation; resume or description of the applicant's leadership activities, skills, and ability, training, and accomplishment; official transcript of the applicant's current enrollment status from the college or university. Applicants must submit a 350-600-word statement describing their leadership program and how their participation met their professional development objectives. **Deadline for Receipt:** May 1.

1406 ■ NATIONAL ASSOCIATION OF CAMPUS ACTIVITIES

13 Harbison Way
Columbia, SC 29212
Tel: (803)732-6222
Fax: (803)749-1047
E-mail: info@naca.org
Web Site: http://www.naca.org
To support undergraduate or graduate students.
Title of Award: National Association of Campus Activities Scholarships for Student Leaders **Area, Field, or Subject:** General studies. **Level of Education for which Award is Granted:** Undergraduate **Funds Available:** No specific amount.
Eligibility Requirements: Applicants must be undergraduate students in good standing at the time of the application and during the semester in which the award is received. **Application Requirements:** Applicants must submit a current resume and a letter of recommendation from the candidate's current supervisor. **Deadline for Receipt:** November 1.

1407 ■ NATIONAL ASSOCIATION OF CAMPUS ACTIVITIES

13 Harbison Way
Columbia, SC 29212
Tel: (803)732-6222
Fax: (803)749-1047
E-mail: info@naca.org
Web Site: http://www.naca.org
To recognize the achievements of undergraduate or graduate student leaders enrolled in colleges and universities located in the former NACA Pacific Northwest Region.
Title of Award: Lori Rhett Memorial Scholarships **Area, Field, or Subject:** General studies. **Level of Education for which Award is Granted:** Undergraduate **Funds Available:** No specific amount.
Eligibility Requirements: Applicants must be matriculated undergraduate or graduate students with a cumulative GPA of 2.5 or better at the time of application and during the semester in which the award is received. Applicants must demonstrate significant leadership skills and abilities; hold a significant leadership position on campus. Applicants must have made significant contributions via volunteer involvement, either on or off campus. Applicants must be enrolled in a college or university within the former NACA Pacific Northwest Region. **Application Requirements:** Applicants must complete the application form; at least two letters of recommendation; a resume; official verification of the applicant's current enrollment status and a copy of academic transcripts from the college or university. **Deadline for Receipt:** June 30.

1408 ■ NATIONAL ASSOCIATION OF CAMPUS ACTIVITIES

13 Harbison Way
Columbia, SC 29212
Tel: (803)732-6222
Fax: (803)749-1047
E-mail: info@naca.org
Web Site: http://www.naca.org

To assist students pursuing graduate or undergraduate studies leading to a related student services field.
Title of Award: Wisconsin Region Student Leadership Scholarships **Area, Field, or Subject:** General studies. **Level of Education for which Award is Granted:** Undergraduate **Funds Available:** No specific amount.
Eligibility Requirements: Applicants must be undergraduate or graduate students in good standing and enrolled in the equivalent of at least six semesters at the time of the application and during the semester in which the award is received; be either currently enrolled in or have received a degree from a college or university within Wisconsin or Upper Peninsula of Michigan; have demonstrated leadership skills and significant service to his/her campus and/or the community. **Application Requirements:** Applicants must complete the application form; obtain a 100-word biographical sketch; submit a resume or description of relevant educational experiences; and submit an official transcript of record and three letters of reference. **Deadline for Receipt:** January 15.

1409 ■ NATIONAL ASSOCIATION OF CAMPUS ACTIVITIES
13 Harbison Way
Columbia, SC 29212
Tel: (803)732-6222
Fax: (803)749-1047
E-mail: info@naca.org
Web Site: http://www.naca.org
To provide financial assistance to undergraduate or graduate student leaders enrolled in the former NACA Great Lakes Region.
Title of Award: Zagunis Student Leader Scholarships **Area, Field, or Subject:** General studies. **Level of Education for which Award is Granted:** Undergraduate **Funds Available:** No specific amount.
Eligibility Requirements: Applicants must be undergraduate students with a minimum cumulative GPA of 3.0 or better at the time of the application. **Application Requirements:** Applicants must submit a current resume and complete the application form. **Deadline for Receipt:** November 1.

1410 ■ NATIONAL ASSOCIATION OF CONTAINER DISTRIBUTORS
1601 Bond St., Ste. 101
Naperville, IL 60563
Tel: (630)544-5052
Fax: (630)544-5055
E-mail: info@nacd.net
Web Site: http://www.nacd.net
To provide assistance to students with financial need.
Title of Award: Henry Hoffman Memorial Scholarship Fund **Area, Field, or Subject:** General studies. **Level of Education for which Award is Granted:** Undergraduate **Funds Available:** No specific amount.
Eligibility Requirements: Applicants must be students who have completed their junior year in high school and are children of employees of member companies of NACD. Students must have a 3.0 grade point average and maintain a 2.5 GPA in college. As a pre-requisite for eligibility, a NACD member company must employ one of the applicant's parents at the time the application is made. **Application Requirements:** Applicants must submit a completed application form. **Deadline for Receipt:** February 1.

1411 ■ NATIONAL ASSOCIATION FOR COUNTY COMMUNITY AND ECONOMIC DEVELOPMENT
2025 M St. NW, Ste. 800
Washington, DC 20036-3309
Tel: (202)367-1149
Fax: (202)367-2149
E-mail: snusser@smithbucklin.com
Web Site: http://www.nacced.org
To provide financial assistance to undergraduate and graduate students.
Title of Award: NACCED Annual John C. Murphy Scholarships **Area, Field, or Subject:** Housing. **Level of Education for which Award is Granted:** Graduate, Undergraduate **Number Awarded:** 1. **Funds Available:** $2,000.
Eligibility Requirements: Applicants must be currently attending an American college or university with a chosen field of study including course work in the areas of affordable housing and/or community and economic development. Applicants must also exhibit financial need. **Ap-

plication Requirements:** All applicants must be nominated by a NACCED member in good standing. Candidates must submit a completed scholarship application; official school transcript with official grade point average; certification of financial need - with an attached Financial Aide Award letter from the university; collegiate letter of acceptance stating the date of enrollment; personal statement of approximately 500 words introducing the applicant; letter of recommendation from a teacher, faculty or civic leader; support letter from a NACCED member in good standing. **Deadline for Receipt:** August 1.

1412 ■ NATIONAL ASSOCIATION FOR EQUAL OPPORTUNITY IN HIGHER EDUCATION
209 3rd St. SE
Washington, DC 20003
Tel: (202)552-3300
Fax: (202)552-3330
Web Site: http://www.nafeo.org
To provide financial assistance for students and give them opportunities to gain valuable work experience to supplement coursework.
Title of Award: NAFEO Internship Program **Area, Field, or Subject:** General studies. **Level of Education for which Award is Granted:** Undergraduate **Funds Available:** No specific amount.
Eligibility Requirements: Applicants must be sophomore U.S. citizen students with a 3.0 cumulative grade point average; good credit rating; free of drug use, misdemeanors, or felonies in the last three years. **Application Requirements:** Applicants must submit completed application and resume to the NAFEO Internship Office. They should have their institutions forward an official transcript of their academic work and two letters of recommendation or recommendation forms completed by faculty members. **Deadline for Receipt:** March 1.

1413 ■ NATIONAL ASSOCIATION OF HEATING SERVICE MANAGERS
PO Box 67
East Petersburg, PA 17520-0067
888-552-0900
Fax: (717)625-3077
E-mail: info@naohsm.org
Web Site: http://www.naohsm.org
To educate and advance oil heat service professionals.
Title of Award: Dave Nelsen Scholarships **Area, Field, or Subject:** Heating, air conditioning, and refrigeration. **Level of Education for which Award is Granted:** Undergraduate **Number Awarded:** 9. **Funds Available:** $2,000.
Eligibility Requirements: Applicants must be currently attending or planning to attend a technical college or trade school and must be involved in the Oil Heating industry. **Application Requirements:** Applicants must submit completed application form and a 500-word essay stating their goals towards the heating industry. **Deadline for Receipt:** May 20.

1414 ■ NATIONAL ASSOCIATION OF NEGRO BUSINESS AND PROFESSIONAL WOMEN'S CLUBS
1806 New Hampshire Ave. NW
Washington, DC 20009
Tel: (202)483-4206
E-mail: info@nanbpwc.org
Web Site: http://www.nanbpwc.org
To provide financial assistance for African-American students pursuing their college education.
Title of Award: Dorothy G. Allsop Scholarships **Area, Field, or Subject:** General studies. **Level of Education for which Award is Granted:** Undergraduate **Funds Available:** No specific amount.
Eligibility Requirements: Applicants must be graduating African-American high school seniors residing in Connecticut who have a cumulative grade point average of 2.5 or above on a 4.0 scale. **Application Requirements:** Applicants must complete the scholarship application form online and must submit a typed essay of no less than 250 words on the topic "Why Cosmetology/Beauty Culture is important to me" **Deadline for Receipt:** March 1.

1415 ■ NATIONAL ASSOCIATION OF NEGRO BUSINESS AND PROFESSIONAL WOMEN'S CLUBS
1806 New Hampshire Ave. NW
Washington, DC 20009

Tel: (202)483-4206

E-mail: info@nanbpwc.org

Web Site: http://www.nanbpwc.org

To provide financial assistance for African-American students pursuing their college education.

Title of Award: Dr. Julianne Malveaux Scholarships **Area, Field, or Subject:** General studies. **Level of Education for which Award is Granted:** Undergraduate **Funds Available:** No specific amount.

Eligibility Requirements: Applicants must be United States citizens; must be African-American females; must be enrolled as college sophomores or juniors in an accredited college or university; must be majoring in journalism, economics or related field (public policy, creative writing, etc.); and must have a cumulative grade point average (GPA) of 3.0 or above on a 4.0 scale. **Application Requirements:** Applicants must complete the scholarship application online and submit a 1000-word essay on their career plans and their relevance to the Dr. Julianne Malveaux Program Theme: "Black Women's Hands Can Rock the World." **Deadline for Receipt:** March 1.

1416 ■ NATIONAL ASSOCIATION OF NEGRO BUSINESS AND PROFESSIONAL WOMEN'S CLUBS

1806 New Hampshire Ave. NW

Washington, DC 20009

Tel: (202)483-4206

E-mail: info@nanbpwc.org

Web Site: http://www.nanbpwc.org

To provide financial assistance for African-American students pursuing their college education.

Title of Award: NANBPWC National Scholarships **Area, Field, or Subject:** General studies. **Level of Education for which Award is Granted:** Undergraduate **Funds Available:** No specific amount.

Eligibility Requirements: Applicants must be graduating African-American high school seniors who have a cumulative grade point average of 3.0 or above on a 4.0 scale by February 1st in the year of graduation. **Application Requirements:** Applicants must complete the scholarship application form online and must submit a typed essay of no less than 300 words on the topic: "Why Education is Important to Me" **Deadline for Receipt:** March 1.

1417 ■ NATIONAL ASSOCIATION OF NEGRO BUSINESS AND PROFESSIONAL WOMEN'S CLUBS

1806 New Hampshire Ave. NW

Washington, DC 20009

Tel: (202)483-4206

E-mail: info@nanbpwc.org

Web Site: http://www.nanbpwc.org

To provide financial assistance for African American students pursuing their college education.

Title of Award: NANBPWC Woman of Substance Scholarships **Area, Field, or Subject:** General studies. **Level of Education for which Award is Granted:** Undergraduate **Funds Available:** No specific amount.

Eligibility Requirements: Applicants must be African American females who are residents of Michigan; must be undergraduate students enrolled in an accredited college or university; and must have a cumulative grade point average (GPA) 3.0 or above on a 4.0 scale. **Application Requirements:** Applicants must complete the scholarship application online and submit a 500-word essay on the topic: "Challenges to the Mature Student and How They'd Overcome Them." **Deadline for Receipt:** March 1.

1418 ■ NATIONAL ASSOCIATION OF PEDIATRIC NURSE PRACTITIONERS

20 Brace Rd., Ste. 200

Cherry Hill, NJ 08034-2634

Tel: (856)857-9700

Fax: (856)857-1600

E-mail: info@napnap.org

Web Site: http://www.napnap.org

To provide financial support to PNP students who plan on practicing in a rural or underserved geographical region for the first two years after he/she completes their PNP education.

Title of Award: NAPNAP McNeil Rural and Underserved Scholarships **Area, Field, or Subject:** General studies. **Level of Education for which Award is Granted:** Undergraduate **Funds Available:** $37,000.

Eligibility Requirements: Applicants must be planning on practicing in a rural or undeserved geographical region for the first two years after PNP education completed; registered nurse who has completed at least 2 semesters or quarters as defined by the university; enrolled at recognized Master's degree program; has no previous formal pediatric nurse practitioner education; and demonstrated financial need. **Application Requirements:** Applicants must submit five copies of the application and needed materials to NAPNAP Foundation. **Deadline for Receipt:** June 15.

1419 ■ NATIONAL ASSOCIATION OF RECREATION RESOURCE PLANNERS

PO Box 221

Marienville, PA 16239

Tel: (814)927-8212

Fax: (814)927-6659

E-mail: info@narrp.org

Web Site: http://www.narrp.org

To provide financial support for the advancement of recreation planning knowledge, skills and professional leadership of students in higher education.

Title of Award: NARRP Student Conference Scholarships **Area, Field, or Subject:** General studies. **Level of Education for which Award is Granted:** Graduate, Undergraduate **Funds Available:** $500.

Eligibility Requirements: Applicants must be undergraduate or graduate students enrolled full-time in an NRPA accredited recreation management, planning or closely related degree program. **Application Requirements:** Applicant must complete the application form along with the current resume and transcript; 500-word narrative statement of academic and career goals, and how attending the NARRP Conference will be helpful towards achieving these goals; and letter of recommendation from Major Professor/Academic Advisor. **Deadline for Receipt:** March 14.

1420 ■ NATIONAL ASSOCIATION FOR THE SELF-EMPLOYED

PO Box 612067

DFW Airport, TX 75261-2067

800-232-6273

Fax: 800-551-4446

E-mail: koberlander@nase.org

Web Site: http://www.nase.org

To assist members in sending their children to college.

Title of Award: National Association for the Self-Employed Scholarships **Area, Field, or Subject:** General studies. **Level of Education for which Award is Granted:** Undergraduate **Number Awarded:** 20. **Funds Available:** $4,000.

Eligibility Requirements: Applicant must be a legal dependent of a NASE member, aged 16-24; must be a high school student or college undergraduate. **Application Requirements:** Applicants must submit a completed application form and original copies of transcripts and test scores. **Deadline for Receipt:** May 15.

1421 ■ NATIONAL ASSOCIATION OF SEWER SERVICE COMPANIES

11521 Cronridge Dr., Ste. J

Owings Mills, MD 21117

Tel: (410)486-3500

Fax: (410)486-6838

E-mail: marc@logiball.com

Web Site: http://www.nassco.org

To improve the success rate of everyone involved in the pipeline rehabilitation industry through education, technical resources, and industry advocacy.

Title of Award: The NASSCO Jeffrey D. Ralston Memorial Scholarships **Area, Field, or Subject:** General studies. **Level of Education for which Award is Granted:** Undergraduate **Number Awarded:** 1. **Funds Available:** $2,000. **Duration:** Not stated.

Eligibility Requirements: Applicants must be a dependent of an active NASSCO member or an active participant in the sewer service industry. Applicants must have at least a 3.0 GPA. **Application Requirements:** Applicants must submit a completed application form. **Deadline for Receipt:** January 21. **Additional Information:** www.nassco.org

1422 ■ NATIONAL ASSOCIATION OF WOMEN IN CONSTRUCTION

327 S Adams St.

Fort Worth, TX 76104

Tel: (817)877-5551
Free: 800-552-3506
Fax: (817)877-0324
E-mail: nawic@nawic.org
Web Site: http://www.nawic.org
To promote education and contribute to the betterment of the construction industry.
Title of Award: Construction Trades Scholarships **Area, Field, or Subject:** Construction. **Level of Education for which Award is Granted:** Undergraduate **Funds Available:** $1,000-$2,000.
Eligibility Requirements: Applicant must be currently enrolled in a construction related degree program at a school in the United States or Canada. **Application Requirements:** Applicants must have the following: Complete and signed application form; must have the transcript of grades for three most recent semester; must have extracurricular activities and Employment history. Application and other supporting materials must be sent to: NAWIC Founders' Scholarship Foundation, 10130 Vivera Dr., La Mesa, CA 91941. **Deadline for Receipt:** March 15. **Additional Information:** Linda Young at the above address.

1423 ■ NATIONAL ASSOCIATION OF WOMEN IN CONSTRUCTION
327 S Adams St.
Fort Worth, TX 76104
Tel: (817)877-5551
Free: 800-552-3506
Fax: (817)877-0324
E-mail: nawic@nawic.org
Web Site: http://www.nawic.org
To promote education and contribute to the betterment of the construction industry. To encourage women to pursue and establish careers in the construction industry.
Title of Award: NAWIC Founders Undergraduate Scholarships **Area, Field, or Subject:** Construction. **Level of Education for which Award is Granted:** Undergraduate **Funds Available:** $1,000-$2,000.
Eligibility Requirements: Applicant must be currently enrolled in a construction-related degree program at a school in the United States or Canada, and must have at least one term remaining in an course of study leading to a degree or an associate degree in a construction-related field. Applicant must desire a career in a construction related field; must be enrolled full-time; must have a current cumulative GPA of 3.0 or higher to be considered for awards. **Application Requirements:** Applicants must have the following: Complete the signed application form; must have the transcript of grades for three most recent semester; must have extracurricular activities and employment history. Application and other supporting materials must be sent to: NAWIC Founders' Scholarship Foundation, 327 S Adams, Forth Worth, TX 76104. **Deadline for Receipt:** March 15.

1424 ■ NATIONAL BETA CLUB
151 Beta Club Way
Spartanburg, SC 29306-3012
800-845-8281
Fax: (864)542-9300
Web Site: http://www.betaclub.org
To provide financial assistance to Beta Club members in their senior year.
Title of Award: National Beta Club Scholarships **Area, Field, or Subject:** General studies. **Level of Education for which Award is Granted:** Undergraduate **Number Awarded:** 210. **Funds Available:** $1,000-$15,000. **Duration:** One year.
Eligibility Requirements: Applicants must be senior high school students who are active National Beta Club members and are registered with the national headquarters as of June 3; must be nominated by their Beta Club chapters to participate. **Application Requirements:** Applicants must submit all the required application information. **Deadline for Receipt:** December 10.

1425 ■ NATIONAL CENTER FOR LEARNING DISABILITIES
381 Park Ave. S, Ste. 1401
New York, NY 10016
Tel: (212)545-7510; 888-575-7373
Fax: (212)545-9665
Web Site: http://www.ncld.org
To assist students who are facing the challenges of living with a learning disability.

Title of Award: Anne Ford Scholarships **Area, Field, or Subject:** General studies. **Level of Education for which Award is Granted:** Undergraduate **Funds Available:** $10,000. **Duration:** Four years.
Eligibility Requirements: Applicant must have a GPA of 3.0 or higher; demonstrated financial assistance; a U.S. citizen; enrolled as a high school senior and pursuing a four year undergraduate degree. **Application Requirements:** Applicants must submit a completed application form; a personal statement; a high school transcript; three letters of recommendations; a financial statement; copies of SAT/ACT scores; and a current documentation of a learning disability that includes evaluation reports. **Deadline for Receipt:** December 31.

1426 ■ NATIONAL COAL TRANSPORTATION ASSOCIATION
4 W Meadow Lark Ln., Ste. 100
Littleton, CO 80127-5718
Tel: (303)979-2798
Fax: (303)973-1848
E-mail: tom@nationalcoaltransportation.org
Web Site: http://www.nationalcoaltransportation.org
To provide financial assistance to the dependents of employees of NCTA member companies.
Title of Award: National Coal Transportation Association At Large Scholarships **Area, Field, or Subject:** General studies. **Level of Education for which Award is Granted:** Undergraduate **Funds Available:** $1,500. **Duration:** 1 year.
Eligibility Requirements: Applicants must be dependents of full time employees of NCTA member companies; enrolled in college as a sophomore or junior. **Application Requirements:** Applicants must send an application form with school transcripts. **Deadline for Receipt:** June 30.

1427 ■ NATIONAL COLLEGIATE CANCER FOUNDATION
PO Box 14190
Silver Spring, MD 20911
Tel: (717)215-0943
Web Site: http://www.collegiatecancer.org
To provide financial support for college students who have a personal diagnosis with cancer and are seeking to continue their higher education.
Title of Award: National Collegiate Cancer Foundation Scholarships **Area, Field, or Subject:** General studies. **Level of Education for which Award is Granted:** Undergraduate **Funds Available:** $1,000.
Eligibility Requirements: Applicants must be college students who have been diagnosed with cancer and are seeking to continue their higher education. **Application Requirements:** Applicants must check the available website for the required materials. **Deadline for Receipt:** September. **Additional Information:** National Collegiate Cancer Foundation at the above address.

1428 ■ NATIONAL COSMETOLOGY ASSOCIATION
401 N Michigan Ave.
Chicago, IL 60611
Tel: (312)527-6765; (866)871-0656
Fax: (312)464-6118
E-mail: nca1@ncacares.org
Web Site: http://www.ncacares.org
To help students find satisfaction, build a career and reach out to others; to keep the cosmetology profession strong.
Title of Award: Sally Beauty Scholarships for High School Graduates **Area, Field, or Subject:** Cosmetology. **Level of Education for which Award is Granted:** Undergraduate **Number Awarded:** 10. **Funds Available:** $1,000.
Eligibility Requirements: Applicants must be high school graduates under the age of 26 who want to enter the cosmetology profession. **Application Requirements:** Applicants must submit a completed application form. **Deadline for Receipt:** January 15.

1429 ■ NATIONAL COSTUMERS ASSOCIATION
121 N Bosart Ave.
Indianapolis, IN 46201
Tel: (317)351-1940
Free: 800-NCA-1321
Fax: (317)351-1941
E-mail: office@costumers.org

Web Site: http://www.costumers.org
To promote the costume industry through education.
Title of Award: National Costumers Association Scholarships **Area, Field, or Subject:** General studies. **Level of Education for which Award is Granted:** Undergraduate **Number Awarded:** Varies. **Funds Available:** Dollar amounts of awards will be determined by the amount of funds available and the number of applicants meeting qualifications at the time of submission of application.
Eligibility Requirements: Applicants must be 17 years old and above, with a GPA of 2.75 or higher and enrolled in an accredited university or school. **Application Requirements:** Applicants must submit a completed and signed application form; proof of GPA; copy of online transcript; and one photo - preferably a headshot. Candidates must also submit a 100-word (max) biography and a 500-word (min) essay of the candidate's field of study and how it applies to the costume industry. **Deadline for Receipt:** April 1. **Additional Information:** Gary Broadrick at the above address.

1430 ■ NATIONAL COURT REPORTERS ASSOCIATION
8224 Old Courthouse Rd.
Vienna, VA 22182-3808
Tel: (703)556-6272
Fax: (703)556-6291
E-mail: misc@ncrahq.org
Web Site: http://www.ncraonline.org
To provide scholarships to NCRA students.
Title of Award: National Court Reporters Association Student Intern Scholarships **Area, Field, or Subject:** General studies. **Level of Education for which Award is Granted:** Undergraduate **Funds Available:** No specific amount.
Eligibility Requirements: The nominee must be a current NCRA student member and must be an intern in any of the three career paths: judicial, CART, and captioning. The nominee must also be enrolled in an NCRA-certified Court Reporter Training Program. The nominee in a judicial court reporting program must have passed at least one of the program's Q and A tests at a minimum of 190 words per minute. The nominee in a CART or captioning program must have passed at least one of the program's literary tests at a minimum of 160 words per minute. Nominee must have a GPA of at least 3.5 overall, based on a 4.0 standard or equivalent. **Application Requirements:** Nominator may download a nomination form via NCRA web site. **Deadline for Receipt:** October 31.

1431 ■ NATIONAL COURT REPORTERS ASSOCIATION
8224 Old Courthouse Rd.
Vienna, VA 22182-3808
Tel: (703)556-6272
Fax: (703)556-6291
E-mail: misc@ncrahq.org
Web Site: http://www.ncraonline.org
To provide scholarships to NCRA students.
Title of Award: Frank Sarli Memorial Scholarships **Area, Field, or Subject:** General studies. **Level of Education for which Award is Granted:** Undergraduate **Funds Available:** No specific amount.
Eligibility Requirements: The nominee must be a current NCRA student member and must be enrolled in an NCRA-certified court reporting program. The nominee must have also passed at least one of the court reporting program's Q and A tests at a minimum of 200 words per minute; must have a grade point average of at least a 3.5 overall, based on a 4.0 standard; must have a demonstrated need for financial assistance; must possess all the qualities exemplified by a professional court reporter, including professional attitude, demeanor, dress and motivation. All criteria must be confirmed and verified by the submitting court reporting program. **Application Requirements:** Nominator may nominate a student who meets the criteria for the scholarship. **Additional Information:** B.J. Shorak, Deputy Executive Director, bjshorak@ncrahq.org.

1432 ■ NATIONAL DEFENSE TRANSPORTATION ASSOCIATION
50 S Picket St., Ste. 220
Alexandria, VA 22304-7206
Tel: (703)751-5011
Fax: (703)823-8761
E-mail: info@ndtahq.com
Web Site: http://www.ndtahq.com

To encourage college students to study transportation and logistics.
Title of Award: Academic Scholarship Program A **Area, Field, or Subject:** Transportation; Logistics. **Level of Education for which Award is Granted:** Undergraduate **Funds Available:** No specific amount.
Eligibility Requirements: Applicants must be members of NDTA or dependents of an NDTA member in good standing. **Application Requirements:** Applicants must note that at the time of filing his/her application, the student must have satisfactorily completed 45 semester hours of work at regionally accredited colleges or universities. The regionally accredited college/university, which the applicant plans to attend must offer a minimum of 15 semester hours in transportation, supply chain management, or logistics or some combination of the above. The applicant must indicate on his/her application the transportation/physical distribution, logistics or information technology courses he/she plans to incorporate into his/her degree program. These courses must comprise at least 15 semester hours of the student's required hours for a degree. A brief statement from a responsible administrator stating that the proposed courses will constitute acceptable work toward a degree must be attached to the application. Blank application forms may be obtained by the NDTA member from: The forum, Education and Professional Development Committee; NDTA Headquarters; or his/her local Chapter. completed applications must be submitted to the Forum, Education and Professional Development Committee. **Deadline for Receipt:** April 16.

1433 ■ NATIONAL DEFENSE TRANSPORTATION ASSOCIATION
50 S Picket St., Ste. 220
Alexandria, VA 22304-7206
Tel: (703)751-5011
Fax: (703)823-8761
E-mail: info@ndtahq.com
Web Site: http://www.ndtahq.com
To assist freshmen college students and high school graduates to achieve academic goals.
Title of Award: Academic Scholarship Program B **Area, Field, or Subject:** Transportation; Logistics. **Level of Education for which Award is Granted:** Undergraduate **Funds Available:** No specific amount.
Eligibility Requirements: Applicants must be NDTA members or financial dependents under the IRS code of an NDTA member. **Application Requirements:** Blank application forms may be obtained by the NDTA member from: The forum, Education and Professional Development Committee; NDTA Headquarters; or his/her local Chapter. Completed applications must be submitted to the Forum, Education and Professional Development Committee. **Deadline for Receipt:** April 16.

1434 ■ NATIONAL DRUG ENFORCEMENT OFFICERS ASSOCIATION
PO Box 1475
Quantico, VA 22134-1475
Tel: (704)770-2050
Fax: (704)770-2051
E-mail: steven.r.peterson@usdoj.gov
Web Site: http://www.ndeoa.org
To financially support the education of a child of a NDEOA member.
Title of Award: NDEOA Scholarships **Area, Field, or Subject:** General Studies. **Level of Education for which Award is Granted:** Undergraduate **Funds Available:** $1,000.
Eligibility Requirements: Applicant must be graduating from high school; or a college student pursuing an undergraduate degree; have a GPA of 2.75 in a 4.0 scale; must be a dependent of an NDEOA member in good standing. **Application Requirements:** Applicant must submit a completed application form; three letters of recommendation; transcript; and a written essay about the applicant's plans and goals, and why the applicant deserves the scholarship. **Deadline for Receipt:** July 1.

1435 ■ NATIONAL EAGLE SCOUT ASSOCIATION
PO Box 152079
Irving, TX 75015-2079
Tel: (972)580-2114
E-mail: eagletter@netbsa.org
Web Site: http://www.nesa.org
To support the education of a student active in Boy Scouting, Varsity Scouting, or Venturing.
Title of Award: American Legion Eagle Scout of the Year Scholarships **Area, Field, or Subject:** General studies. **Level of Education for which**

Award is Granted: High School **Number Awarded:** One recipient and three second placers. **Funds Available:** $10,000 and $2500.
Eligibility Requirements: Applicant must have received the Eagle Scout Award and the religious emblem awarded by his religious institution; have demonstrated practical citizenship in church, school, Scouting, and the community; son or grandson of an American Legion or American Legion Auxiliary member; or must be a member of a Scouting unit chartered to a Legion post, an Auxiliary unit, or a Sons of the American Legion squadron. **Application Requirements:** Applicants must complete and file the nomination form. **Additional Information:** Awarded by The American Legion. **Deadline for Receipt:** March 1. **Additional Information:** Contact the American Legion department in their state.

1436 ■ NATIONAL EAGLE SCOUT ASSOCIATION

PO Box 152079
Irving, TX 75015-2079
Tel: (972)580-2114
E-mail: eagletter@netbsa.org
Web Site: http://www.nesa.org
To support the education of a student active in Boy Scouting, Varsity Scouting, or Venturing.
Title of Award: Rick Arkans Eagle Scout Scholarships **Area, Field, or Subject:** General studies. **Level of Education for which Award is Granted:** High School **Number Awarded:** 1. **Funds Available:** $1000.
Eligibility Requirements: Applicant must be currently registered and active in Boy Scouting, Varsity Scouting, or Venturing; have earned the Eagle Scout Award; have earned the Ner Tamid or Etz Chaim religious emblem; active in a synagogue; have demonstrated practical citizenship in the synagogue, school, Scouting unit, and community; have demonstrate financial need; and be enrolled in an accredited high school and in his final year. **Application Requirements:** Applicants must submit a complete application. **Additional Information:** Sponsored by the National Jewish Committee on Scouting. **Deadline for Receipt:** February 28.

1437 ■ NATIONAL EAGLE SCOUT ASSOCIATION

PO Box 152079
Irving, TX 75015-2079
Tel: (972)580-2114
E-mail: eagletter@netbsa.org
Web Site: http://www.nesa.org
To assist the education of an Eagle scout student.
Title of Award: Birmingham-Southern College Eagle Scout Scholarships **Area, Field, or Subject:** General studies. **Level of Education for which Award is Granted:** Undergraduate **Funds Available:** $2500 per year.
Eligibility Requirements: Applicant must be an incoming freshmen at the Birmingham Southern College; and an Eagle Scout. **Application Requirements:** Applicant must forward a letter of interest and student resume at the BSC Admissions Office. **Additional Information:** Award is given by BirminghamSouthern College, Birmingham, Ala. **Deadline for Receipt:** January 15. **Additional Information:** Admission Office, BirminghamSouthern College Box 549008 Birmingham, AL 35254, at 800-523-5793.

1438 ■ NATIONAL EAGLE SCOUT ASSOCIATION

PO Box 152079
Irving, TX 75015-2079
Tel: (972)580-2114
E-mail: eagletter@netbsa.org
Web Site: http://www.nesa.org
To support the education of high school seniors who are currently registered and active in Boy Scouting, Varsity Scouting, or Venturing.
Title of Award: Emmett J. Doerr Memorial Distinguished Scout Scholarships **Area, Field, or Subject:** General studies. **Level of Education for which Award is Granted:** High School **Number Awarded:** 3. **Funds Available:** $1000-$2500. **Duration:** One year.
Eligibility Requirements: Applicants must be outstanding Catholic high-school seniors currently registered and active in Boy Scouting, Varsity Scouting, or Venturing; have earned the Eagle Scout Award or the Silver Award; have earned the Ad Altare Dei or Pope Pius XII religious emblem; have held a Scouting leadership position; and have served in parish. **Application Requirements:** Applicants must submit a complete application. **Additional Information:** Sponsored by the National Catholic Committee on Scouting. **Deadline for Receipt:** April 1. **Additional Information:** Barb Nestel, National Catholic Committee on Scouting, nccs@netbsa.org.

1439 ■ NATIONAL EAGLE SCOUT ASSOCIATION

PO Box 152079
Irving, TX 75015-2079
Tel: (972)580-2114
E-mail: eagletter@netbsa.org
Web Site: http://www.nesa.org
To assist the education of an Eagle Scout student.
Title of Award: Dofflemyer Scholarships **Area, Field, or Subject:** General studies. **Level of Education for which Award is Granted:** Undergraduate **Funds Available:** Varies.
Eligibility Requirements: Applicant must be an Eagle Scout entering Stanford University. **Application Requirements:** Applicants must follow the university's standard application process. **Additional Information:** Awarded by Stanford University, Stanford, Calif. **Deadline for Receipt:** February 1. **Additional Information:** Financial Aid Office, Stanford University, Montag Hall 355 Galvez St. Stanford, CA 94305-6106, at 888-326-3773, or financialaid@stanford.edu.

1440 ■ NATIONAL EAGLE SCOUT ASSOCIATION

PO Box 152079
Irving, TX 75015-2079
Tel: (972)580-2114
E-mail: eagletter@netbsa.org
Web Site: http://www.nesa.org
To support the education of a student active in Scouting, Varsity Scouting, or Venturing.
Title of Award: Eastern Orthodox Scouting Scholarships **Area, Field, or Subject:** General studies. **Level of Education for which Award is Granted:** High School **Number Awarded:** 3. **Funds Available:** $1000.
Eligibility Requirements: Applicant must be registered and active in Boy Scouting or Girl Scouting; must have earned the Eagle Scout Award (Boy Scouts) or the Gold Award (Girl Scouts); active in an Eastern Orthodox church; have earned the Alpha Omega religious emblem; and enrolled in an accredited high school, in the final year. **Application Requirements:** Applicants must submit four letters of recommendation with the application. **Additional Information:** Awarded by the Eastern Orthodox Committee on Scouting. **Deadline for Receipt:** May 1. **Additional Information:** George N. Boulukos, 862 Guy Lombardo Ave. Freeport, New York 11520, at 516-868-4050.

1441 ■ NATIONAL EAGLE SCOUT ASSOCIATION

PO Box 152079
Irving, TX 75015-2079
Tel: (972)580-2114
E-mail: eagletter@netbsa.org
Web Site: http://www.nesa.org
To assist the education of an Eagle Scout student.
Title of Award: Epsilon Tau Pi's Soaring Eagle Scholarships **Area, Field, or Subject:** General studies. **Level of Education for which Award is Granted:** Undergraduate **Funds Available:** $500.
Eligibility Requirements: Applicant must be an Eagle Scout entering as freshman at the University of Dayton; have demonstrated leadership ability in Scouting, and has a strong record of community participation beyond Scouting; have a SAT score of at least 1600 or an ACT score of at least 25. **Application Requirements:** Applicants must visit the Epsilon Tau Pi Alpha Chapter website for the details of application. **Additional Information:** Awarded by Epsilon Tau Pi Alpha Chapter, University of Dayton, Dayton, Ohio. **Deadline for Receipt:** August 3. **Additional Information:** Soaring Eagle Scholarship, Epsilon Tau Pi, 1915 Trinity Ave. Dayton, OH 45409

1442 ■ NATIONAL EAGLE SCOUT ASSOCIATION

PO Box 152079
Irving, TX 75015-2079
Tel: (972)580-2114
E-mail: eagletter@netbsa.org
Web Site: http://www.nesa.org
To assist the education of an Eagle Scout student.
Title of Award: Gaebe Eagle Scout Awards **Area, Field, or Subject:** General studies. **Level of Education for which Award is Granted:** Undergraduate **Funds Available:** $1000.
Eligibility Requirements: Applicant must be entering as freshman at Johnson and Wales University and must be an Eagle Scout. **Application**

Requirements: Applications are available at JWU's NSO Office; submit application and a transcript of grades to the NSO Office. **Additional Information:** The scholarship may be used at JWU's campuses in Providence, R.I.; North Miami, Fla.; Denver, Colo.; and Charlotte, N.C. Awarded by Johnson and Wales University, Providence, R.I. **Deadline for Receipt:** February 1. **Additional Information:** National Student Organizations, Johnson and Wales University, 8 Abbott Park Place Providence, RI 02903, at 800-342-5598, x-2345.

1443 ■ NATIONAL EAGLE SCOUT ASSOCIATION

PO Box 152079
Irving, TX 75015-2079
Tel: (972)580-2114
E-mail: eagletter@netbsa.org
Web Site: http://www.nesa.org
To assist the education of a boy and girl scout student.

Title of Award: Gold Award/Eagle Scout Scholarships **Area, Field, or Subject:** General studies. **Level of Education for which Award is Granted:** Undergraduate **Funds Available:** $1000 ($500 per semester). **Eligibility Requirements:** Applicant must have a high-school core GPA of at least 2.5 as calculated by Mississippi State University, or at least 48 hours of transferable community college course credit with a minimum cumulative GPA of 2.5; a Mississippi resident or have received the Eagle Scout Award or Gold Award in a Mississippi-based Scouting council. **Application Requirements:** Applicants must follow the university's standard application process. **Additional Information:** Awarded by the Mississippi State University, Mississippi State, Miss. **Deadline for Receipt:** August 1. **Additional Information:** Office of Admissions and Scholarships, Mississippi State University P.O. Box 6334 Mississippi State, MS 39762-6334, at 662-325-2224, or admit@msstate.edu.

1444 ■ NATIONAL EAGLE SCOUT ASSOCIATION

PO Box 152079
Irving, TX 75015-2079
Tel: (972)580-2114
E-mail: eagletter@netbsa.org
Web Site: http://www.nesa.org
To assist the education of an Eagle Scout student.

Title of Award: Zenon C.R. Hansen Leadership Scholarships **Area, Field, or Subject:** General studies. **Level of Education for which Award is Granted:** Undergraduate **Funds Available:** Amount dependent on cost of tuition. **Duration:** One year.

Eligibility Requirements: Applicant must be a full-time Doane College student who is an Eagle Scout; active in the Boy Scouts of America, and planning to remain active in Scouting and leadership activities. **Application Requirements:** Applicants must visit the Doane College website for the details of application. **Additional Information:** Award given by Doane College, Crete, Neb. **Deadline for Receipt:** March 10. **Additional Information:** Financial Aid Office, Doane College 1014 Boswell Avenue Crete, NE 68333, at 800-333-6263. .

1445 ■ NATIONAL EAGLE SCOUT ASSOCIATION

PO Box 152079
Irving, TX 75015-2079
Tel: (972)580-2114
E-mail: eagletter@netbsa.org
Web Site: http://www.nesa.org
To support the education of Eagle Scouts.

Title of Award: Arthur M. and Berdena King Eagle Scout Scholarships **Area, Field, or Subject:** General studies. **Level of Education for which Award is Granted:** High School **Number Awarded:** 3. **Funds Available:** $8000, $4000, and $2000.

Eligibility Requirements: Applicant must be Eagle Scouts currently registered in Scouting and have not reached their 19th birthday. **Application Requirements:** applicants must submit a completed application form together with the Four Generation ancestor chart, and the 500-word essay. **Additional Information:** Awarded by the National Society of the Sons of the American Revolution. **Deadline for Receipt:** Varies by state and chapter. **Additional Information:** Contact the SAR department in their state.

1446 ■ NATIONAL EAGLE SCOUT ASSOCIATION

PO Box 152079
Irving, TX 75015-2079

Tel: (972)580-2114
E-mail: eagletter@netbsa.org
Web Site: http://www.nesa.org
To assist the education of an Eagle Scout student.

Title of Award: Lindenwood University Scouting Scholarships **Area, Field, or Subject:** General studies. **Level of Education for which Award is Granted:** Undergraduate **Number Awarded:** 3. **Funds Available:** $6000-$12,000 per year.

Eligibility Requirements: Applicants must be undergraduate residential students who have been Boy Scouts. **Application Requirements:** Applicants must visit the Lindenwood University website for the details of application. **Additional Information:** Awards given by Lindenwood University, St. Charles, Mo. **Additional Information:** Office of Undergraduate Admissions, Lindenwood University 209 South Kings Highway St. Charles, MO 63301-1695, at 636-949-4949, or admissions@lindenwood.edu.

1447 ■ NATIONAL EAGLE SCOUT ASSOCIATION

PO Box 152079
Irving, TX 75015-2079
Tel: (972)580-2114
E-mail: eagletter@netbsa.org
Web Site: http://www.nesa.org
To assist the education of an Eagle Scout student.

Title of Award: McDaniel College Eagle Scout Scholarships **Area, Field, or Subject:** General studies. **Level of Education for which Award is Granted:** Undergraduate **Funds Available:** $2000.

Eligibility Requirements: Applicant must be enrolled full-time and have a minimum 2.50 cumulative GPA and a minimum SAT-I combined score of 1000. **Application Requirements:** Applicants must visit the McDaniel College website for the details of application. **Additional Information:** Awarded by McDaniel College (formerly Western Maryland College), Westminster, Md. **Deadline for Receipt:** February 1. **Additional Information:** McDaniel College, 2 College Hill Westminster, MD 21157, at 410-848-7000.

1448 ■ NATIONAL EAGLE SCOUT ASSOCIATION

PO Box 152079
Irving, TX 75015-2079
Tel: (972)580-2114
E-mail: eagletter@netbsa.org
Web Site: http://www.nesa.org
To assist the education of a boy and girl scout student.

Title of Award: Newman University Scouting Scholarships **Area, Field, or Subject:** General studies. **Level of Education for which Award is Granted:** Undergraduate **Funds Available:** $1500 per year.

Eligibility Requirements: Applicant must be an Eagle Scout or a Girl Scout (Gold Award winners) with a high school GPA of 2.5 or higher on a 4.0 scale; a first-time freshmen at Newman University; full-time student and maintains a cumulative GPA of at least 2.25; and active in one or more campus organization each year. **Application Requirements:** Applicants must visit the Newman University website for the details of application. **Additional Information:** Awarded by Newman University, Wichita, Kan. **Additional Information:** Newman University, 3100 McCormick Ave. Wichita, KS 67213, at 877-639-6268.

1449 ■ NATIONAL EAGLE SCOUT ASSOCIATION

PO Box 152079
Irving, TX 75015-2079
Tel: (972)580-2114
E-mail: eagletter@netbsa.org
Web Site: http://www.nesa.org
To assist the education of an Eagle Scout student.

Title of Award: Saint Vincent College Eagle Scout Scholarships **Area, Field, or Subject:** General studies. **Level of Education for which Award is Granted:** Undergraduate **Funds Available:** $500. **Duration:** Annual.

Eligibility Requirements: Applicant must be an Eagle Scout student admitted at Saint Vincent College. **Application Requirements:** Applicants must submit a documentation to the admission counselor as part of the admission process. **Additional Information:** Awards given by Saint Vincent College, Latrobe, Penn. **Additional Information:** Saint Vincent College, 300 Fraser Purchase Road Latrobe, PA 15650, at 800-782-5549.

1450 ■ NATIONAL EAGLE SCOUT ASSOCIATION

PO Box 152079
Irving, TX 75015-2079
Tel: (972)580-2114
E-mail: eagletter@netbsa.org
Web Site: http://www.nesa.org
To assist the education of an Eagle Scout student.

Title of Award: University of Louisville Eagle Scout Scholarships **Area, Field, or Subject:** General studies. **Level of Education for which Award is Granted:** Undergraduate **Funds Available:** $2000 to full in-state tuition.

Eligibility Requirements: Applicant must be an incoming freshmen; a resident of Kentucky or Indiana; achieved the rank of Eagle Scout in the Lincoln Heritage Council, Blue Grass Council, Shawnee Trails Council, Dan Beard Council, or Tri-State Area Council; have a minimum high-school GPA of 3.35 on a 4.0 scale and a minimum score of 24 on the ACT or 1090 on the SAT-I. **Application Requirements:** Applicants must visit the University of Louisville website for the details of application. **Additional Information:** Awarded by University of Louisville, Louisville, Ky. **Deadline for Receipt:** January 15. **Additional Information:** Student Financial Aid Office, University of Louisville, Louisville, KY 40292, at 502-852-5511, or finaid@louisville.edu.

1451 ■ NATIONAL EAGLE SCOUT ASSOCIATION

PO Box 152079
Irving, TX 75015-2079
Tel: (972)580-2114
E-mail: eagletter@netbsa.org
Web Site: http://www.nesa.org
To support the education of a student active in Boy Scouting, Varsity Scouting, or Venturing.

Title of Award: Chester M. Vernon Memorial Eagle Scout Scholarships **Area, Field, or Subject:** General studies. **Level of Education for which Award is Granted:** High School **Number Awarded:** 1. **Funds Available:** $1000 per year. **Duration:** Four years.

Eligibility Requirements: Applicant must be currently registered and active in Boy Scouting, Varsity Scouting, or Venturing; have earned the Eagle Scout Award; have earned the Ner Tamid or Etz Chaim religious emblem; active in a synagogue; have demonstrated practical citizenship in the synagogue, school, Scouting unit, and community; have demonstrated financial need; and be enrolled in an accredited high school and in his final year. **Application Requirements:** Applicants must submit a complete application. **Additional Information:** Sponsored by the National Jewish Committee on Scouting. **Deadline for Receipt:** February 28.

1452 ■ NATIONAL EAGLE SCOUT ASSOCIATION

PO Box 152079
Irving, TX 75015-2079
Tel: (972)580-2114
E-mail: eagletter@netbsa.org
Web Site: http://www.nesa.org
To support the education of a student active in Boy Scouting, Varsity Scouting, or Venturing.

Title of Award: Veterans of Foreign Wars Scout of the Year **Area, Field, or Subject:** General studies. **Level of Education for which Award is Granted:** High School **Funds Available:** $5000.

Eligibility Requirements: Applicant must have received the Eagle Scout Award, the Venturing Silver Award, or the Sea Scout Quartermaster Award; have demonstrated practical citizenship in school, Scouting, and the community. **Application Requirements:** Application must be submitted through a single, local VFW post. **Additional Information:** Awarded by The Veterans of Foreign Wars of the United States. **Deadline for Receipt:** March 1. **Additional Information:** Veterans of Foreign Wars, 406 W. 34th St. Kansas City, Missouri 64111 816-756-3390, info@vfw.org.

1453 ■ NATIONAL EAGLE SCOUT ASSOCIATION

PO Box 152079
Irving, TX 75015-2079
Tel: (972)580-2114
E-mail: eagletter@netbsa.org
Web Site: http://www.nesa.org
To support the education of a student active in Boy Scouting, Varsity Scouting, or Venturing.

Title of Award: Frank L. Weil Memorial Eagle Scout Scholarships **Area, Field, or Subject:** General studies. **Level of Education for which Award is Granted:** Undergraduate **Number Awarded:** 1 recipient and 2 runners-up. **Funds Available:** $1000 and $500.

Eligibility Requirements: Applicant must be currently registered and active in Boy Scouting, Varsity Scouting, or Venturing; have earned the Eagle Scout Award; have earned the Ner Tamid or Etz Chaim religious emblem; active in a synagogue; have demonstrated practical citizenship in the synagogue, school, Scouting unit, and community; and be enrolled in an accredited high school and in his final year. **Application Requirements:** Applicants must submit a complete application. **Additional Information:** Sponsored by the National Jewish Committee on Scouting. **Deadline for Receipt:** February 28.

1454 ■ NATIONAL ELECTRICAL MANUFACTURERS REPRESENTATIVES ASSOCIATION

600 White Plains Rd., Ste. 600
Tarrytown, NY 10591-1504
Tel: (914)524-8650
Free: 800-446-3672
Fax: (914)524-8655
E-mail: nemra@nemra.org
Web Site: http://www.nemra.org
To reward the academic excellence of the sons and daughters of NEMRA members and their employees.

Title of Award: NEMRA Educational Scholarship Foundation **Area, Field, or Subject:** General studies. **Level of Education for which Award is Granted:** Undergraduate **Number Awarded:** 18. **Funds Available:** No specific amount.

Eligibility Requirements: Applicants must be children of members of NEMRA (or their employees) who are in good standing as of December 31, and attend, or plan to attend (full-time) an accredited college, university or vocational-technical school. **Application Requirements:** Applicants must submit a completed and signed application form; a current official transcript; a recommendation from an individual who can give an honest assessment of the applicant's academic and personal abilities such as a teacher, pastor or college advisor. Application materials must be placed in a stamped No. 10 business size envelope. Two first class stamps are required. **Additional Information:** Founded in 1985 through a bequest of the late Donald Egan of the Daniel Woodhead Company. **Deadline for Receipt:** January 7.

1455 ■ NATIONAL FEDERATION OF THE BLIND

1800 Johnson St.
Baltimore, MD 21230
Tel: (410)659-9314
Fax: (410)685-5653
Web Site: http://www.nfb.org
To recognize achievement of blind scholars and to create opportunity for all blind people.

Title of Award: Hermoine Grant Calhoun Scholarships **Area, Field, or Subject:** General studies. **Level of Education for which Award is Granted:** Undergraduate **Number Awarded:** 22. **Funds Available:** $3,000.

Eligibility Requirements: All applicants must be legally blind; he/she must be pursuing or planning to pursue a full-time, postsecondary course of study in a degree program at a United States institution; he/she must be participant in NFB national convention and in all scheduled scholarship program activities. **Application Requirements:** Applicant must fill out the application form; he/she must submit two letters of recommendation from individuals that can describe the academic ability, leadership skills, and/or community involvement; copies of transcript of record and a photocopy of score reports for all standardized tests taken for college admission(ACT, SAT or other); applicant must provide a letter of proof of legal blindness from a qualified professional; and an affiliate President's letter. **Deadline for Receipt:** March 31.

1456 ■ NATIONAL FEDERATION OF THE BLIND

1800 Johnson St.
Baltimore, MD 21230
Tel: (410)659-9314
Fax: (410)685-5653
Web Site: http://www.nfb.org

To recognize achievement by blind scholars and create opportunity for all blind people.

Title of Award: Kenneth Jernigan Scholarships **Area, Field, or Subject:** General studies. **Level of Education for which Award is Granted:** Undergraduate **Number Awarded:** 1. **Funds Available:** $12,000.

Eligibility Requirements: All applicants must be legally blind; he/she must be pursuing or planning to pursue a full-time, postsecondary course of study in a Degree Program at a United States institution; he/she must be participant in NFB national convention and in all scheduled scholarship program activities. **Application Requirements:** Applicant must fill out the application form; he/she must submit two letters of recommendation from individuals that can describe the academic ability, leadership skills, and/or community involvement; copies of transcript of record and a photocopy of score reports for all standardized tests taken for college admission (ACT, SAT or other); applicant must provide a letter of proof of legal blindness from a qualified professional; and an affiliate President's letter. **Deadline for Receipt:** March 31.

1457 ■ NATIONAL FEDERATION OF THE BLIND
1800 Johnson St.
Baltimore, MD 21230
Tel: (410)659-9314
Fax: (410)685-5653
Web Site: http://www.nfb.org
To recognize achievement of blind scholars and to create opportunity for all blind people.

Title of Award: Kuchler-Killian Memorial Scholarships **Area, Field, or Subject:** General studies. **Level of Education for which Award is Granted:** Undergraduate **Number Awarded:** 22. **Funds Available:** $3,000.

Eligibility Requirements: All applicants must be legally blind; he/she must be pursuing or planning to pursue a full-time, postsecondary course of study in a degree program at a United States institution; he/she must be participant in NFB national convention and in all scheduled scholarship program activities. **Application Requirements:** Applicant must fill out the application form; he/she must submit two letters of recommendation from individuals that can describe the academic ability, leadership skills, and/or community involvement; copies of transcript of record and a photocopy of score reports for all standardized tests taken for college admission(ACT, SAT or other); applicant must provide a letter of proof of legal blindness from a qualified professional; and an affiliate President's letter. **Deadline for Receipt:** March 31.

1458 ■ NATIONAL FEDERATION OF THE BLIND
1800 Johnson St.
Baltimore, MD 21230
Tel: (410)659-9314
Fax: (410)685-5653
Web Site: http://www.nfb.org
To recognize achievement of blind scholars and to create opportunity for all blind people.

Title of Award: Charles and Melva T. Owen Memorial Scholarships **Area, Field, or Subject:** General studies. **Level of Education for which Award is Granted:** Undergraduate **Number Awarded:** 1. **Funds Available:** $10,000.

Eligibility Requirements: All applicants must be legally blind; he/she must be pursuing or planning to pursue a full-time, postsecondary course of study in a degree program at a United States institution; he/she must be participant in NFB national convention and in all scheduled scholarship program activities. **Application Requirements:** Applicant must fill out the application form; he/she must submit two letters of recommendation from individuals that can describe the academic ability, leadership skills, and/or community involvement; copies of transcript of record and a photocopy of score reports for all standardized tests taken for college admission(ACT, SAT or other); applicant must provide a letter of proof of legal blindness from a qualified professional; and an affiliate President's letter. **Deadline for Receipt:** March 31.

1459 ■ NATIONAL FEDERATION OF THE BLIND
1800 Johnson St.
Baltimore, MD 21230
Tel: (410)659-9314
Fax: (410)685-5653

Web Site: http://www.nfb.org
To recognize achievement of blind scholars and to create opportunity for all blind people.

Title of Award: E.U. Parker Scholarships **Area, Field, or Subject:** General studies. **Level of Education for which Award is Granted:** Undergraduate **Funds Available:** $3,000.

Eligibility Requirements: All applicants must be legally blind; he/she must be pursuing or planning to pursue a full-time, postsecondary course of study in a degree program at a United States institution; he must be participant in NFB national convention and in all scheduled scholarship program activities. **Application Requirements:** Applicant must fill out the application form; he/she must submit two letters of recommendation from individuals that can describe the academic ability, leadership skills, and/or community involvement; copies of transcript of record and a photocopy of score reports for all standardized tests taken for college admission (ACT, SAT or other); applicant must provide a letter of proof of legal blindness from a qualified professional; and an affiliate President's letter. **Deadline for Receipt:** March 31.

1460 ■ NATIONAL FEDERATION OF REPUBLICAN WOMEN
124 N Alfred St.
Alexandria, VA 22314
Tel: (703)548-9688
Fax: (703)548-9836
E-mail: mail@nfrw.org
Web Site: http://www.nfrw.org
To support students with their education.

Title of Award: National Pathfinder Scholarships **Area, Field, or Subject:** General studies. **Level of Education for which Award is Granted:** Graduate, Undergraduate **Number Awarded:** 3. **Funds Available:** $2500. **Duration:** Annual.

Eligibility Requirements: Applicant must be undergraduate sophomore, junior or senior, or student enrolled in a master's degree program. **Application Requirements:** Applicants must submit a completed application form together with three letters of recommendation (include contact numbers of the authors); an official copy of recent college transcript; a 1-page typed essay stating why applicant deserves the scholarship; another 1-page typed essay on career goals; a photograph (optional); and State Federation President Certification. **Additional Information:** Established in 1985 in honor of First Lady Nancy Reagan. **Deadline for Receipt:** June 15.

1461 ■ NATIONAL FOSTER PARENT ASSOCIATION
7512 Stanich Ln., Ste. 6
Gig Harbor, WA 98335
Tel: (253)853-4000
Fax: (253)853-4001
E-mail: info@nfpaonline.org
Web Site: http://www.nfpainc.org
To support foster parents in achieving safety, permanence and well-being for the children and youth in their care.

Title of Award: NFPA Youth Scholarships **Area, Field, or Subject:** General Studies. **Level of Education for which Award is Granted:** Undergraduate **Funds Available:** No specific amount.

Eligibility Requirements: Foster parents must be a member of NFPA. **Application Requirements:** Applicants must submit a completed application form; A minimum of two (2) letters of recommendation from: foster parents, social workers, residential center, principal/teacher/guidance counselor, employer, etc., will be required with each application. A typewritten statement in 300-500 words on "Why I want to further my education and why I should be considered for a National Foster Parent Association Scholarship" will also required. **Deadline for Receipt:** March 31. **Additional Information:** NFPA Scholarship Committee, NFPA at the above address.

1462 ■ NATIONAL FUNERAL DIRECTORS AND MORTICIANS ASSOCIATION
13625 Bishop's Dr.
Brookfield, WI 53005
Tel: (262)789-1880
Free: 800-228-6332
Fax: (262)789-6977
E-mail: nfda@nfda.org

Web Site: http://www.nfda.org
To provide financial support to the students enrolled in.ASUMH.
Title of Award: Arkansas State University Mountain Home Scholarships **Area, Field, or Subject:** General studies. **Level of Education for which Award is Granted:** Undergraduate **Number Awarded:** 2. **Funds Available:** $425. **Duration:** One year.
Eligibility Requirements: Applicant must be enrolled at Arkansas State University Mountain Home; must be a resident of Arkansas; must have a GPA average of 2.5-3.0. **Application Requirements:** Applicant must have three recommendation letters, and for more information regarding the scholarship, applicants are advised to contact the Arkansas State University Mountain Home, 1600 College St., Mountain Home, AR 72653.

1463 ■ NATIONAL FUNERAL DIRECTORS AND MORTICIANS ASSOCIATION
13625 Bishop's Dr.
Brookfield, WI 53005
Tel: (262)789-1880
Free: 800-228-6332
Fax: (262)789-6977
E-mail: nfda@nfda.org
Web Site: http://www.nfda.org
To provide financial assistant to the deserving students in Illinois.
Title of Award: Carl Sandburg College Scholarships **Area, Field, or Subject:** General studies. **Level of Education for which Award is Granted:** Undergraduate **Funds Available:** $500.
Eligibility Requirements: Applicant must be Illinois resident. **Application Requirements:** For further information about the scholarship, applicants are advised to contact the school at: Carl Sandburg College, 2232 Lake Storey Rd., Galesburg, IL 61401-9576. **Additional Information:** Tim Krause.

1464 ■ NATIONAL GROUND WATER ASSOCIATION
601 Dempsey Rd.
Westerville, OH 43081
Tel: (614)898-7791
Free: 800-551-7379
Fax: (614)898-7786
E-mail: ngwa@ngwa.org
Web Site: http://www.ngwa.org
To advance the expertise of all ground water professionals and to further ground water awareness and protection through education and outreach.
Title of Award: Len Assante Scholarship Fund **Area, Field, or Subject:** Water supply industry. **Level of Education for which Award is Granted:** Undergraduate **Funds Available:** No specific amount.
Eligibility Requirements: Applicants must be full-time undergraduate students entering in the field of study that serves, supports, or promotes the ground water industry; must maintain a 2.5 GPA. **Application Requirements:** Applicants must complete the application form. **Deadline for Receipt:** April 1. **Additional Information:** bhowell@ngwa.org.

1465 ■ NATIONAL HEMOPHILIA FOUNDATION
116 W 32nd St., 11th Fl.
New York, NY 10001
Tel: (212)328-3700
Free: 800-424-2631
Fax: (212)328-3777
E-mail: handi@hemophilia.org
Web Site: http://www.hemophilia.org
To encourage aspirations of higher education among individuals with bleeding disorders through providing financial assistance.
Title of Award: Kevin Child Scholarships **Area, Field, or Subject:** General studies. **Level of Education for which Award is Granted:** Undergraduate **Number Awarded:** 1. **Funds Available:** $1,000.
Eligibility Requirements: Applicants must be individuals diagnosed with hemophilia or von Willebrand disease; must be high school seniors with aspirations of attending an institute of higher education or college students already pursuing post secondary education. **Application Requirements:** Applicants must send a complete copy of the application (available from the website) along with a current official transcript of grades and 1 recommendation from an individual not related to the applicant to Renee LaBrew, Department of Finance, Administration & MIS, National Hemophilia Foundation, 116 West 32nd St., 11th Fl., New York, NY 10001-3212. **Deadline for Receipt:** June 27.

1466 ■ NATIONAL HEMOPHILIA FOUNDATION
116 W 32nd St., 11th Fl.
New York, NY 10001
Tel: (212)328-3700
Free: 800-424-2631
Fax: (212)328-3777
E-mail: handi@hemophilia.org
Web Site: http://www.hemophilia.org
To provide educational assistance to people with hemophilia and their families.
Title of Award: Soozie Courter Sharing a Brighter Tomorrow Hemophilia Scholarship Program **Area, Field, or Subject:** General studies. **Level of Education for which Award is Granted:** Graduate, Undergraduate **Number Awarded:** 2 graduate scholarships; 16 college scholarships; 2 vocational scholarships. **Funds Available:** $7,500 (graduate scholarships); $5,000 (college scholarships); $2,500 (vocational scholarships). **Duration:** One year.
Eligibility Requirements: Applicants must have hemophilia A or B; must be a high school senior; must have a graduate equivalency diploma (GED); or be currently enrolled in an accredited junior college, undergraduate, graduate or vocational school. **Application Requirements:** Applicants must visit the website for necessary forms and further instructions. **Deadline for Receipt:** April 4. **Additional Information:** Wyeth/Genetics Institute, Inc. phone: 888-999-2349; website: www.hemophiliavillage.com.

1467 ■ NATIONAL HEMOPHILIA FOUNDATION
116 W 32nd St., 11th Fl.
New York, NY 10001
Tel: (212)328-3700
Free: 800-424-2631
Fax: (212)328-3777
E-mail: handi@hemophilia.org
Web Site: http://www.hemophilia.org
To encourage educational pursuits among students with bleeding disorders by providing financial support.
Title of Award: Eric Delson Memorial Scholarships **Area, Field, or Subject:** General studies. **Level of Education for which Award is Granted:** Graduate, High School, Undergraduate **Number Awarded:** 1 for private high school; 3 for college or trade school. **Funds Available:** $1,500 for private high school; $2,500 for college or trade school. **Duration:** One year.
Eligibility Requirements: Students who are clinically diagnosed with hemophilia or von Willebrand disease are eligible to apply. Applicants must be entering Grades 7 through 12 at private secondary schools or must be high school seniors, high school graduates or equivalent (GED), or post-secondary school students currently enrolled or planning to enroll in a full-time undergraduate or graduate course at an accredited two or four-year college, university or vocational-technical school in the United States. Students must be accepted by the institution during the year for which the scholarship is given and must be enrolled with the designated institution no later than September of the coming year. **Application Requirements:** Applicants must call Caremark request for an application and send it together with a current transcript of grades to: The Eric Delson Memorial Scholarship Program, Citizens' Scholarship Foundation of America, PO Box 297, St. Peter, Minnesota 56802. **Deadline for Receipt:** July 1. **Additional Information:** Caremark: 866-792-2731.

1468 ■ NATIONAL HEMOPHILIA FOUNDATION
116 W 32nd St., 11th Fl.
New York, NY 10001
Tel: (212)328-3700
Free: 800-424-2631
Fax: (212)328-3777
E-mail: handi@hemophilia.org
Web Site: http://www.hemophilia.org
To provide financial assistance to students with hemophilia or a related bleeding disorder.
Title of Award: Eric Dostie Memorial College Scholarships **Area, Field, or Subject:** General studies. **Level of Education for which Award is Granted:** Four Year College, Two Year College, Undergraduate **Number Awarded:** 10. **Funds Available:** $1,000.
Eligibility Requirements: Scholarship is open to students with hemophilia or a related bleeding disorder, or their family members. Ap-

plicants must be citizens of the United States and enrolled full-time in an accredited two or four-year college program. **Application Requirements:** Applicants must submit an essay describing how his or her education will be used to serve humankind and to encourage self-improvement and enrichment. Applicants must request for an application. **Deadline for Receipt:** March 1. **Additional Information:** NuFACTOR, phone: 800-323-6832.

1469 ■ NATIONAL HEMOPHILIA FOUNDATION

116 W 32nd St., 11th Fl.
New York, NY 10001
Tel: (212)328-3700
Free: 800-424-2631
Fax: (212)328-3777
E-mail: handi@hemophilia.org
Web Site: http://www.hemophilia.org
To inspire attainment of higher education among individuals with hemophilia and von Willbrand Disease by providing educational funds.
Title of Award: Education is Power Scholarships **Area, Field, or Subject:** General studies. **Level of Education for which Award is Granted:** Undergraduate **Number Awarded:** 20-25. **Funds Available:** $500-2,500. **Duration:** One year.
Eligibility Requirements: Applicants must be individuals living with hemophilia and von Willebrand Disease; must be entering or attending a community college, junior college, four-year college, university, or vocational school; and must be a United States resident. **Application Requirements:** Applicant must submit the completed application form available from the website; documentation from a physician/nurse of the applicant's bleeding disorder; copy of diploma or graduate equivalency diploma (GED); most recent transcript; proof of admission to the school; proof of school tuition; a separate document outlining the applicant's community involvement and/or volunteer work; an essay (no less than 250 words); and one letter of recommendation or character reference. **Additional Information:** Prior applicants and winners are encouraged to reapply each year. **Deadline for Receipt:** May 1.

1470 ■ NATIONAL HEMOPHILIA FOUNDATION

116 W 32nd St., 11th Fl.
New York, NY 10001
Tel: (212)328-3700
Free: 800-424-2631
Fax: (212)328-3777
E-mail: handi@hemophilia.org
Web Site: http://www.hemophilia.org
To provide academic scholarships for young adults with HIV/AIDS.
Title of Award: Joshua Gomes Memorial Scholarship Fund **Area, Field, or Subject:** General studies. **Level of Education for which Award is Granted:** Graduate, Undergraduate **Number Awarded:** Varies. **Funds Available:** 1,000.
Eligibility Requirements: Applicants must be individuals living with HIV/AIDS; must be accepted or enrolled in a US college or university as a full-time undergraduate or graduate student. **Application Requirements:** Applicants must submit the completed application form available from the website; letter from a doctor certifying that the applicant is HIV positive or has AIDS; official transcripts from high school showing the applicant's cumulative GPA; letter of acceptance from a U.S. college or university; three letters of recommendation; and an attached 500-word essay. Mail all requirements to: The Joshua Gomes Memorial Scholarship Fund, 2700 South Emerson St., Englewood, CO 80113-1737. **Deadline for Receipt:** July 15.

1471 ■ NATIONAL HEMOPHILIA FOUNDATION

116 W 32nd St., 11th Fl.
New York, NY 10001
Tel: (212)328-3700
Free: 800-424-2631
Fax: (212)328-3777
E-mail: handi@hemophilia.org
Web Site: http://www.hemophilia.org
To encourage educational pursuits among women with bleeding disorders through providing financial assistance.
Title of Award: Millie Gonzalez Memorial Scholarships **Area, Field, or Subject:** General studies. **Level of Education for which Award is

Granted: Undergraduate **Number Awarded:** 2. **Funds Available:** $1,000.
Eligibility Requirements: Scholarship is open to women diagnosed with hemophilia or Von Willebrand Disease, and who are entering or attending a college or vocational school. **Application Requirements:** Applicants are encouraged to submit their applications online to: scholarships@factorsupport.com; all the necessary instructions and application forms can be downloaded from the website. **Deadline for Receipt:** April 30. **Additional Information:** Factor Support Network Pharmacy, phone: 877-376-4968, email: scholarships@factorsupport.com.

1472 ■ NATIONAL HEMOPHILIA FOUNDATION

116 W 32nd St., 11th Fl.
New York, NY 10001
Tel: (212)328-3700
Free: 800-424-2631
Fax: (212)328-3777
E-mail: handi@hemophilia.org
Web Site: http://www.hemophilia.org
To provide educational assistance to members of the bleeding disorders community.
Title of Award: Professor Ulla Hedner Scholarships **Area, Field, or Subject:** General studies. **Level of Education for which Award is Granted:** Undergraduate **Number Awarded:** Varies. **Funds Available:** $2,000-$7,000. **Duration:** One year.
Eligibility Requirements: Program is open to high school seniors and college or vocational students under the age of 23. **Application Requirements:** Applicants may call 877NOVO-777 to request for an application. **Deadline for Receipt:** April 30.

1473 ■ NATIONAL HEMOPHILIA FOUNDATION

116 W 32nd St., 11th Fl.
New York, NY 10001
Tel: (212)328-3700
Free: 800-424-2631
Fax: (212)328-3777
E-mail: handi@hemophilia.org
Web Site: http://www.hemophilia.org
To encourage higher learning among individuals with bleeding disorders by providing financial assistance.
Title of Award: Hemophilia Health Services Memorial Scholarship Program **Area, Field, or Subject:** General studies. **Level of Education for which Award is Granted:** Graduate, Undergraduate **Number Awarded:** Varies. **Funds Available:** $1,500.
Eligibility Requirements: Applicant must be a US citizen with hemophilia, VWD or other bleeding disorder. **Application Requirements:** Applicants must visit the website to apply online. **Deadline for Receipt:** May 1. **Additional Information:** Sally Johnson, Special Programs Coordinator, phone: 615-850-5175.

1474 ■ NATIONAL HEMOPHILIA FOUNDATION

116 W 32nd St., 11th Fl.
New York, NY 10001
Tel: (212)328-3700
Free: 800-424-2631
Fax: (212)328-3777
E-mail: handi@hemophilia.org
Web Site: http://www.hemophilia.org
To encourage educational pursuits among men with bleeding disorders through providing financial assistance.
Title of Award: Mike Hylton and Ron Niederman Memorial Scholarships **Area, Field, or Subject:** General studies. **Level of Education for which Award is Granted:** Undergraduate **Number Awarded:** 5. **Funds Available:** $1,000.
Eligibility Requirements: Scholarship is offered to males with hemophilia or Von Willebrand Disease and their immediate family members intending to pursue further learning. **Application Requirements:** Application requirements and instructions are available from the website. **Deadline for Receipt:** April 30. **Additional Information:** Factor Support Network Pharmacy, phone: 877-376-4968, email: scholarships@factorsupport.com.

1475 ■ NATIONAL HEMOPHILIA FOUNDATION

116 W 32nd St., 11th Fl.
New York, NY 10001

Tel: (212)328-3700
Free: 800-424-2631
Fax: (212)328-3777
E-mail: handi@hemophilia.org
Web Site: http://www.hemophilia.org
To help children with hemophilia afford learning assistance.
Title of Award: K-12 Edu-Grants **Area, Field, or Subject:** General studies. **Level of Education for which Award is Granted:** High School **Funds Available:** Up to $500.
Eligibility Requirements: Grant is open to children in Kindergarten through 12th grade. **Application Requirements:** Applicants must submit the completed application form available from the website along with a notarized letter from the tutor outlining the tutoring work done and the fees charged. Copies of receipts indicating payment made to a commercial tutoring center may also be submitted. Forward application forms and supporting documents to: SevenSECURE, PO Box 18648, Louisville, KY 40261. **Additional Information:** SevenSECURE, 877-668-6777.

1476 ■ NATIONAL HEMOPHILIA FOUNDATION
116 W 32nd St., 11th Fl.
New York, NY 10001
Tel: (212)328-3700
Free: 800-424-2631
Fax: (212)328-3777
E-mail: handi@hemophilia.org
Web Site: http://www.hemophilia.org
To inspire educational pursuits among individuals with bleeding disorders by providing financial aid.
Title of Award: Lawrence Madeiros Scholarships **Area, Field, or Subject:** General studies. **Level of Education for which Award is Granted:** Undergraduate **Number Awarded:** Varies. **Funds Available:** $1,000.
Eligibility Requirements: Applicants must be students with an inherited bleeding disorder or other chronic disorder attending an accredited college or university. **Application Requirements:** Applicants must submit the completed application form available from the website along with a copy of current transcript and a statement of recommendation. Forward documents to: The Lawrence Madeiros Scholarship, c/o PO Box 11, Mayfield, NY 12117. **Deadline for Receipt:** June 1.

1477 ■ NATIONAL HEMOPHILIA FOUNDATION
116 W 32nd St., 11th Fl.
New York, NY 10001
Tel: (212)328-3700
Free: 800-424-2631
Fax: (212)328-3777
E-mail: handi@hemophilia.org
Web Site: http://www.hemophilia.org
To expand opportunities for members of the hemophilia community by providing funds for their educational pursuits.
Title of Award: Christopher Pitkin Memorial Scholarships **Area, Field, or Subject:** General studies. **Level of Education for which Award is Granted:** Undergraduate **Funds Available:** $500-1,000.
Eligibility Requirements: All members of the hemophilia and bleeding disorders community, including spouses, siblings and children, are eligible to apply. **Application Requirements:** Applicant must complete application package which includes an application form available from the website; two letters of recommendation from someone who can assess the applicant's academic potentials and knows the applicant in general terms (doctor, nurse, social worker, friend, relative, or community leader). Finalists will be asked to submit transcripts and evidence of enrollment in an educational or vocational institution. **Deadline for Receipt:** July 25.

1478 ■ NATIONAL HEMOPHILIA FOUNDATION
116 W 32nd St., 11th Fl.
New York, NY 10001
Tel: (212)328-3700
Free: 800-424-2631
Fax: (212)328-3777
E-mail: handi@hemophilia.org
Web Site: http://www.hemophilia.org
To assist women with bleeding disorders in their pursuit of post high school studies.

Title of Award: Project Red Flag Academic Scholarships for Women with Bleeding Disorders **Area, Field, or Subject:** General studies. **Level of Education for which Award is Granted:** Undergraduate **Number Awarded:** 2. **Funds Available:** $2,500.
Eligibility Requirements: Applicants must be female residents of the U.S. with a bleeding disorder (includes von Willebrand disease, hemophilia carrier or other clotting factor deficiencies). **Application Requirements:** Applicant may contact Anna DeSimone at adesimone@hemophilia.org for application information and instructions. **Deadline for Receipt:** May 16.

1479 ■ NATIONAL HEMOPHILIA FOUNDATION
116 W 32nd St., 11th Fl.
New York, NY 10001
Tel: (212)328-3700
Free: 800-424-2631
Fax: (212)328-3777
E-mail: handi@hemophilia.org
Web Site: http://www.hemophilia.org
To provide educational assistance to individuals with bleeding disorders.
Title of Award: Salvatore E. Quinci Foundation Scholarships **Area, Field, or Subject:** General studies. **Level of Education for which Award is Granted:** Undergraduate **Number Awarded:** 2. **Funds Available:** $2,000.
Eligibility Requirements: Applicants must be diagnosed with hemophilia or other bleeding disorder, and must be accepted into an accredited university, college or vocational/technical school. **Application Requirements:** Applicants must submit a completed application form, transcripts and letters of recommendation to: Salvatore E. Quinci Foundation, 178 Florence St., Melrose, MA 02176-3710. **Deadline for Receipt:** April 4.

1480 ■ NATIONAL HEMOPHILIA FOUNDATION
116 W 32nd St., 11th Fl.
New York, NY 10001
Tel: (212)328-3700
Free: 800-424-2631
Fax: (212)328-3777
E-mail: handi@hemophilia.org
Web Site: http://www.hemophilia.org
To provide educational assistance to members of the bleeding disorders community.
Title of Award: Rachel Warner Memorial Scholarships **Area, Field, or Subject:** General studies. **Level of Education for which Award is Granted:** Graduate, Undergraduate **Number Awarded:** Varies. **Funds Available:** Varies. **Duration:** One year.
Eligibility Requirements: Program is open to individuals with any bleeding disorder with educational pursuits from high school through graduate school. **Application Requirements:** Applicants may visit the website for application information and instructions. **Deadline for Receipt:** May 1. **Additional Information:** The Committee of Ten Thousand, Phone: 800-488-2688, email: cott-dc@earthlink.net

1481 ■ NATIONAL HISPANIC COALITION OF FEDERAL AVIATION EMPLOYEES
PO Box 23276
Washington, DC 20026-3276
E-mail: nhcfae@nhcfae.org
Web Site: http://www.nhcfae.org
To assist dependents of NHCFAE members, students of minority, and women complete their higher education efforts by recognizing and rewarding academically superior performance and achievements, leadership, and community involvement.
Title of Award: Rene Matos Memorial Scholarships **Area, Field, or Subject:** General Studies. **Level of Education for which Award is Granted:** Undergraduate **Funds Available:** No specific amount.
Eligibility Requirements: Applicants must be accepted to or attending an accredited college, university, or vocational/ trade school at the time the scholarship is awarded. **Application Requirements:** Applicants must submit the following: completed application form; financial need statement; official transcript; letter of recommendation; and a recent photograph. **Additional Information:** NHCFAE Scholarship Selection Committee PO Box 23276 Washington, D.C. 20026-3276.

1482 ■ NATIONAL HONOR SOCIETY

1904 Association Dr.
Reston, VA 20191-1537
Tel: (703)860-0200
Fax: (703)476-5432
Web Site: http://www.nhs.us
To provide educational assistance to NHS members.
Title of Award: NHS National Scholarships **Area, Field, or Subject:** General studies. **Level of Education for which Award is Granted:** Undergraduate **Number Awarded:** 9. **Funds Available:** Total of $200,000.
Eligibility Requirements: Candidate must be a senior student member nominated by an active NHS chapter. **Application Requirements:** Nomination forms will be mailed to all active chapter advisers in early November. **Additional Information:** From among the nine Regional Winners, one National Winner will be identified to receive an additional $10,000 in college scholarship funding. **Deadline for Receipt:** February 1. **Additional Information:** Membership Department, 800-253-7746 x-214, or email at membership@nhs.us.

1483 ■ NATIONAL HOUSING ENDOWMENT

1201 15th St. NW
Washington, DC 20005
Tel: 800-368-5242
Web Site: http://www.nationalhousingendowment.org
To address the need for educating and training construction managers in the residential building industry.
Title of Award: Lee S. Evans/National Housing Endowment Scholarship **Area, Field, or Subject:** Construction. **Level of Education for which Award is Granted:** Graduate, Undergraduate **Funds Available:** Up to $5,000.
Eligibility Requirements: Applicant must be registered as a full-time undergraduate or graduate student for the Fall term; must have at least one full academic year of course work remaining after the scholarship is awarded; must demonstrate interest in obtaining employment in the residential construction industry upon graduation. **Application Requirements:** Applicants must submit a completed application form available at the website; transcript(s) and course requirements; and recommendations. Mail to: The National Housing Endowment, Attn: Lee S. Evans Scholarship, 1201 15th St. NW, Washington, DC 20005-2800. **Deadline for Receipt:** December 7.

1484 ■ NATIONAL HOUSING ENDOWMENT

1201 15th St. NW
Washington, DC 20005
Tel: 800-368-5242
Web Site: http://www.nationalhousingendowment.org
To address the need for educating and training construction managers in the residential building industry.
Title of Award: Herman J. Smith Scholarships **Area, Field, or Subject:** Construction. **Level of Education for which Award is Granted:** Undergraduate **Funds Available:** Up to $2,000. **Duration:** One year.
Eligibility Requirements: Applicant must be registered as a full-time undergraduate or graduate student; must have at least one full academic year of course work remaining after the scholarship is awarded; must be majoring in construction management, mortgage finance, or a construction related field in an accredited 4-year institution; must demonstrate an interest in obtaining employment in the construction industry, mortgage finance, or a construction related field upon graduation. **Application Requirements:** Application package includes application form, transcript and recommendations. Mail to: The National Housing Endowment, Attn: Lee S. Evans Scholarship, 1201 15th St. NW, Washington, DC 20005-2800. **Deadline for Receipt:** May 5.

1485 ■ NATIONAL HUGUENOT SOCIETY

9033 Lyndale Ave., Ste. 108
Bloomington, MN 55420-3535
Tel: (952)885-9776
E-mail: awards@huguenot.netnation.com
Web Site: http://www.huguenot.netnation.com
To coordinate activities of member societies; to promote the principles and virtues of the Huguenots, commemorate Huguenot history, collect and preserve historical data and relics illustrative of Huguenot life, manners, and customs; to provide financial aid for higher education of students who are members of the National Huguenot Society.
Title of Award: National Huguenot Society Scholarships **Area, Field, or Subject:** General studies. **Level of Education for which Award is Granted:** Undergraduate **Funds Available:** $5,000.
Eligibility Requirements: Applicants must be regular memberS of the National Huguenot Society; must be students at an accredited college or graduate school with at least two semesters of history which include at least in part a history of religion; applicants must have completed at least two years of college with a 3.0 GPA on a 4.0 scale. **Application Requirements:** Applicants must complete the application form; attach proof of enrollment at an accredited college or graduate school; attach a transcript of college grades for last two years showing a 3.0 or better GPA; attach proof of membership in the National Huguenot Society. **Additional Information:** Richard Dana Smith, Chairman of Huguenot Scholarship Awards, 647 Brinston Bridge Rd., West Chester, PA 19382.

1486 ■ NATIONAL INDUSTRIAL BELTING ASSOCIATION

N 19 W 24400 Riverwood Dr.
Waukesha, WI 53188
Tel: (262)523-9090
Fax: (262)523-9091
Web Site: http://www.niba.org
To provide financial assistance to an individual pursuing a minimum 2-year course at an accredited college, university or technical school.
Title of Award: Ray Snow Memorial Scholarships **Area, Field, or Subject:** General studies. **Level of Education for which Award is Granted:** Undergraduate **Number Awarded:** 2. **Funds Available:** $4,000.
Eligibility Requirements: Applicants must be children of NIBA Distributor/ Fabricator Member Company employees and must attend a two-year or more accredited college, university or technical school. **Deadline for Receipt:** May 1.

1487 ■ NATIONAL INVESTMENT COMPANY SERVICE ASSOCIATION

2 Mt. Royal Ave.
Marlborough, MA 01752
Tel: (508)485-1500
Fax: (508)485-1560
E-mail: info@nicsa.org
Web Site: http://www.nicsa.org
To financially support dependents of NICSA member company employees in their education.
Title of Award: William T. Blackwell Scholarship Fund **Area, Field, or Subject:** General studies. **Level of Education for which Award is Granted:** Undergraduate **Funds Available:** $2,000-$5,000.
Eligibility Requirements: Applicants must be dependents of full-time employees of NICSA member companies. Applicants must be enrolled, or planning to enroll in a full-time degree seeking course at an accredited four-year college or university. **Application Requirements:** Application form is available from the website. Applicants must prepare a current transcript of grades and an appraisal provided by the school (sent in a sealed envelope). **Additional Information:** The program is administered by Scholarship America. **Deadline for Receipt:** January 15. **Additional Information:** Scholarship America, One Scholarship Way, PO Box 297, Saint Peter, MN 56082. Telephone: 507-931-1682.

1488 ■ NATIONAL ITALIAN AMERICAN FOUNDATION

1860 19th St. NW
Washington, DC 20009
Tel: (202)387-0600
Fax: (202)387-0800
E-mail: information@niaf.org
Web Site: http://www.niaf.org
To financially support the education of Italian American students.
Title of Award: NIAF Scholarships - General Category I **Area, Field, or Subject:** General studies. **Level of Education for which Award is Granted:** Undergraduate **Funds Available:** $2,500-$10,000.
Eligibility Requirements: Applicant must be enrolled in a U.S. accredited institution of higher education for the fall; must have a GPA of at least 3.5 out of 4.0 (or the equivalent); must be a U.S. citizen or a permanent resident alien; and must be an Italian American student who demonstrates

outstanding potential and high academic achievements. **Application Requirements:** Applicants must submit completed student application and Teacher Evaluation Form online, official school transcript and FAFSA Financial Aid Form (optional), submitted by mail. **Deadline for Receipt:** March 7.

1489 ■ NATIONAL JUNIOR ANGUS ASSOCIATION
3201 Frederick Ave.
St. Joseph, MO 64506
Tel: (816)383-5100
Fax: (816)233-9703
E-mail: mjenkins@angusfoundation.org
Web Site: http://www.angusfoundation.org
To support education, youth and research by giving scholarship to young men and women who are active in the angus breed pursuing higher education.
Title of Award: Angus Foundation Scholarships **Area, Field, or Subject:** General studies. **Level of Education for which Award is Granted:** Undergraduate **Funds Available:** $100,000.
Eligibility Requirements: Applicants must be a National Junior Angus Association members and currently a junior, regular or life member of American Angus Association graduating high school senior or must be enrolled in junior college, four-year college/university or other accredited institution of higher education for the fall term, and must have a minimum 2.0 GPA. **Application Requirements:** Applicants must seek application forms available at www.angusfoundation.org. **Deadline for Receipt:** May 1.

1490 ■ NATIONAL LITTLE BRITCHES RODEO ASSOCIATION
5050 Edison Ave., Ste. 105
Colorado Springs, CO 80915
Tel: (719)389-0333
Free: 800-763-3694
Fax: (719)578-1367
Web Site: http://www.nlbra.com
To support student members in their education.
Title of Award: NLBRA/Wrangler Academic Scholarships **Area, Field, or Subject:** General studies. **Level of Education for which Award is Granted:** Undergraduate **Number Awarded:** 6. **Funds Available:** $1,000-$2,000.
Eligibility Requirements: Applicants must be high school seniors; a competing NLBRA member for the previous three years; and will complete their last year of high school prior to the 2008 National Little Britches Finals Rodeo. **Application Requirements:** Applicants must submit a completed application form along with a certified copy of high school transcripts. **Deadline for Receipt:** June 30.

1491 ■ NATIONAL LITTLE BRITCHES RODEO ASSOCIATION
5050 Edison Ave., Ste. 105
Colorado Springs, CO 80915
Tel: (719)389-0333
Free: 800-763-3694
Fax: (719)578-1367
Web Site: http://www.nlbra.com
To support student members in their education.
Title of Award: Rainwater Family Scholarships **Area, Field, or Subject:** General studies. **Level of Education for which Award is Granted:** Undergraduate **Number Awarded:** 4 (2 boys and 2 girls). **Funds Available:** $500.
Eligibility Requirements: Applicant must be a NLBRA member for three years minimum; have a GPA of 3.0 or better; and a NLBRA member in the senior division. **Application Requirements:** Applicants must fill out the entry form and submit it together with an official transcript. **Additional Information:** Established by Warren and Toni Rainwater, in memory of their son, Winn Hal Rainwater, and daughter, Carla Suzanne Rainwater. **Deadline for Receipt:** April 20.

1492 ■ NATIONAL ORGANIZATION OF BLACK LAW ENFORCE-MENT EXECUTIVES
Hubert T. Bell Jr. Office Complex,
4609-F Pinecrest Office Park Dr.
Alexandria, VA 22312-1442
Tel: (703)658-1529

Fax: (703)658-9479
E-mail: jakers@noblenatl.org
Web Site: http://www.noblenational.org
To assist Southern California students in their education.
Title of Award: NOBLE Southern California Chapter Scholarship Program **Area, Field, or Subject:** General studies. **Level of Education for which Award is Granted:** Undergraduate **Number Awarded:** 2. **Funds Available:** $1,000.
Eligibility Requirements: Applicant must be a Southern California resident or student attending a college, university, or academy accredited by the Scholarship Committee. **Application Requirements:** Application forms are available at the website. Applicants must submit a completed application form, a recent photograph, and two letters of recommendation to SCC NOBLE Scholarship Committee. **Deadline for Receipt:** January 12.

1493 ■ NATIONAL PARKING ASSOCIATION
1112 16th St. NW, Ste. 840
Washington, DC 20036
Tel: (202)296-4336
Free: 800-647-PARK
Fax: (202)296-3102
E-mail: info@npapark.org
Web Site: http://www.npapark.org
To provide financial assistance to people with bleeding disorders in their pursuit to obtain higher education degree.
Title of Award: BioRx/Hemophilia of North Carolina Educational Scholarships **Area, Field, or Subject:** General Studies. **Level of Education for which Award is Granted:** Undergraduate **Number Awarded:** 3. **Funds Available:** $2,000.
Eligibility Requirements: Applicant must be caregivers of children affected with bleeding disorders, a person who has been diagnosed with hemophilia, or a sibling of a person diagnosed with hemophilia. **Application Requirements:** Applicants may call or write for application; program instructions are available at the website. **Deadline for Receipt:** May 1. **Additional Information:** BioRx, Phone: 866-442-4679, email cbarnex@biorx.net.

1494 ■ NATIONAL PARKING ASSOCIATION
1112 16th St. NW, Ste. 840
Washington, DC 20036
Tel: (202)296-4336
Free: 800-647-PARK
Fax: (202)296-3102
E-mail: info@npapark.org
Web Site: http://www.npapark.org
To provide assistance and support to individual and families affected by chronic illness and help these students obtain higher education degree.
Title of Award: Beth Carew Memorial Scholarships **Area, Field, or Subject:** General Studies. **Level of Education for which Award is Granted:** Undergraduate **Number Awarded:** 10. **Funds Available:** $2,000. **Duration:** One year.
Eligibility Requirements: Any student with hemophilia, von Willebrand disease, or a related inherited bleeding disorder is eligible to apply for this Scholarship; high school seniors who have been accepted to an accredited college or university may apply; College freshmen, sophomores, and juniors may also apply. **Application Requirements:** Applicants must call, write, or e-mail for application, or download application from the website. **Deadline for Receipt:** April 4. **Additional Information:** Colburn-Keenan Foundation, Inc, phone: 800-966-2431

1495 ■ NATIONAL PARKING ASSOCIATION
1112 16th St. NW, Ste. 840
Washington, DC 20036
Tel: (202)296-4336
Free: 800-647-PARK
Fax: (202)296-3102
E-mail: info@npapark.org
Web Site: http://www.npapark.org
To provide financial assistance to people with bleeding disorders in their pursuit to obtain higher education degree.
Title of Award: Bill McAdam Scholarships **Area, Field, or Subject:** General Studies. **Level of Education for which Award is Granted:** Undergraduate **Number Awarded:** 1. **Funds Available:** $2,000.

Eligibility Requirements: Scholarship is open to a person with hemophilia, VWD or other hereditary bleeding disorder or the person's spouse, partner, child or sibling planning to attend an accredited college or university or certified training program. **Application Requirements:** Applicants may call or write for application. **Deadline for Receipt:** May 15. **Additional Information:** Cathy McAdam Scholarship Fund, 22226 Doxtator, Dearborn, MI 48128 Phone: 313-563-1412, mcmcadam@comcast.net

1496 ■ NATIONAL PARKING ASSOCIATION
1112 16th St. NW, Ste. 840
Washington, DC 20036
Tel: (202)296-4336
Free: 800-647-PARK
Fax: (202)296-3102
E-mail: info@npapark.org
Web Site: http://www.npapark.org
To provide financial aid to support the association's commitment to advance educational opportunities.
Title of Award: Parking Industry Institute Scholarship Program **Area, Field, or Subject:** General studies. **Level of Education for which Award is Granted:** Undergraduate **Funds Available:** $1,000-$3,000. **Duration:** One year.
Eligibility Requirements: Applicants must be undergraduate students enrolled at an accredited two or four year college/university; a child or spouse of a full-time employee of a firm which is a member of the National Parking Association; a full-time or part-time employee of a firm which is a member of the National Parking Association. **Application Requirements:** Applicants must submit a completed application form, and related materials such as transcripts and recommendations to the Trustees of The Parking Industry Institute. **Deadline for Receipt:** March 1.

1497 ■ NATIONAL RECREATION AND PARK ASSOCIATION
22377 Belmont Ridge Rd.
Ashburn, VA 20148
Tel: (703)858-0784
Fax: (703)858-0794
E-mail: info@nrpa.org
Web Site: http://www.nrpa.org
To encourage NRPA Congress and Exposition attendance by members of ethnic minorities; to emphasize the value of involvement in the organization; to develop minority communities to promote the benefits of NRPA.
Title of Award: National Recreation and Park Association Diversity Scholarships **Area, Field, or Subject:** Parks and Recreation. **Level of Education for which Award is Granted:** Undergraduate **Funds Available:** No stated amount. **Duration:** Not stated.
Eligibility Requirements: Applicant must be a person of an ethnic minority; be a professional, citizen or student member of NRPA at the time of application; be currently employed as a professional in parks and recreation agency or a student currently enrolled in a park and recreation degree program. **Application Requirements:** Applicants must submit an application form; two references; and letters of recommendation directly to the National Recreation and Park Association. **Deadline for Receipt:** April 25. **Additional Information:** NRPA Awards Coordinator at the above address.

1498 ■ NATIONAL RECYCLING COALITION
805 15th St. NW, Ste. 425
Washington, DC 20005
Tel: (202)789-1430
Fax: (202)789-1431
E-mail: info@nrc-recycle.org
Web Site: http://www.nrc-recycle.org
To sponsor scholarships for college students.
Title of Award: National Recycling Coalition Congress Scholarships **Area, Field, or Subject:** General studies. **Level of Education for which Award is Granted:** Undergraduate **Number Awarded:** 5. **Funds Available:** No specific amount.
Eligibility Requirements: Applicants must be interested in a professional career and gaining exposure to the recycling field. **Application Requirements:** Applicants should submit the completed application form; must have a letter of recommendation from their school's staff or faculty to the NRC. **Additional Information:** The scholarships are intended as a way

for college students interested in a professional career to gain exposure to the recycling field. They will have the opportunity to attend over 35 conference sessions, workshops and tours, as well as to meet and network with community, state and national recycling leaders. **Deadline for Receipt:** July 25. **Additional Information:** For more information about the scholarship, contact Alec Cooley at alecc@nrc-recycle.org.

1499 ■ NATIONAL ROOFING CONTRACTORS ASSOCIATION
10255 W Higgins Rd., Ste. 600
Rosemont, IL 60018-5607
Tel: (847)299-9070
Fax: (847)299-1183
Web Site: http://www.nrca.net
To provide financial support for students continuing their education and training beyond high school.
Title of Award: Melvin Kruger Endowed Scholarship Program **Area, Field, or Subject:** General studies. **Level of Education for which Award is Granted:** Undergraduate **Funds Available:** $5,000. **Duration:** One year.
Eligibility Requirements: Applicant must be a student who needs financial assistant to continue his/her education. **Application Requirements:** Applicant must visit the NRCA for further instruction and information regarding with the scholarship.

1500 ■ NATIONAL ROOFING CONTRACTORS ASSOCIATION
10255 W Higgins Rd., Ste. 600
Rosemont, IL 60018-5607
Tel: (847)299-9070
Fax: (847)299-1183
Web Site: http://www.nrca.net
To assist employees, immediate family of employees or immediate family of NRCA contractor members, who plan to pursue post-secondary education in college and vocational programs.
Title of Award: Roofing Industry Scholarships **Area, Field, or Subject:** General studies. **Level of Education for which Award is Granted:** Graduate, Undergraduate **Funds Available:** $1,000.
Eligibility Requirements: Applicants must be full-time employees, dependent children or spouse of NRCA contractor members who have a minimum of one year of employment with the company as of the application deadline date. Member companies must have been a contractor member of NRCA for a minimum of one year as of the application deadline date. Applicants must be seniors or graduates who plan to enroll or students who are already enrolled in a full-time undergraduate course of study at an accredited two or four year college, university or vocational technical school. **Application Requirements:** Applicant must complete the application form on the website and mail it along with a current complete official transcript of grades to Scholarship America, One Scholarship Way, PO Box 297, Saint Peter, MN, 56082. **Deadline for Receipt:** January 31.

1501 ■ NATIONAL SOCIETY OF ACCOUNTANTS
1010 N Fairfax St.
Alexandria, VA 22314
Tel: (703)549-6400
Free: 800-966-6679
Fax: (703)549-2984
E-mail: members@nsacct.org
Web Site: http://www.nsacct.org
To assist college students pursuing an accounting major.
Title of Award: National Society of Accountants Scholarship Program **Area, Field, or Subject:** Accounting. **Level of Education for which Award is Granted:** Undergraduate **Number Awarded:** 32. **Funds Available:** $500, $1,000 or $2,000. **Duration:** One academic year.
Eligibility Requirements: Applicant must be a full-time or part-time student majoring in accounting at any U.S. accredited institution; have a "B" (3.0 on a 4.0 scale) or better GPA; be a U.S. or Canadian citizen. **Application Requirements:** Applicants must complete the application form (visit the website) and mail it with a transcript of records. **Additional Information:** Administered by Scholarship Management Services, a department of Scholarship America. **Deadline for Receipt:** March 10. **Additional Information:** Scholarship America, One Scholarship Way, PO Box 297 Saint Peter, MN 56082; Phone: (507)931-1682.

1502 ■ NATIONAL SOCIETY OF ACCOUNTANTS
1010 N Fairfax St.
Alexandria, VA 22314
Tel: (703)549-6400
Free: 800-966-6679
Fax: (703)549-2984
E-mail: members@nsacct.org
Web Site: http://www.nsacct.org
To provide financial assistance to students majoring in accounting.
Title of Award: The Stanley H. Stearman Awards **Area, Field, or Subject:** Accounting. **Level of Education for which Award is Granted:** Undergraduate **Funds Available:** $2,000.
Eligibility Requirements: Applicants must be a dependent or spouse, niece, nephew, son- or daughter-in-law of an active/retired, living or deceased NSA member. **Application Requirements:** Applicants must complete the application form (visit the website) and mail it with a transcript of records. **Additional Information:** The award is to honor retired NSA Executive Vice President Stanley H. Stearman. **Deadline for Receipt:** March 10. **Additional Information:** Scholarship America, One Scholarship Way, PO Box 297 Saint Peter, MN 56082; Phone: (507)931-1682.

1503 ■ NATIONAL SOCIETY OF HIGH SCHOOL SCHOLARS
1936 N Druid Hills Rd.
Atlanta, GA 30319
(866)343-1800
Web Site: http://www.nshss.org
To support members to attain higher education.
Title of Award: Abercrombie and Fitch Global Diversity Scholar Awards **Area, Field, or Subject:** General studies. **Level of Education for which Award is Granted:** High School **Number Awarded:** 10. **Funds Available:** $1000. **Duration:** Annually.
Eligibility Requirements: Applicant must be a NSHSS member. **Application Requirements:** Applicants must submit a completed application form and required materials. **Deadline for Receipt:** April 30.

1504 ■ NATIONAL SOCIETY OF HIGH SCHOOL SCHOLARS
1936 N Druid Hills Rd.
Atlanta, GA 30319
(866)343-1800
Web Site: http://www.nshss.org
To support the education of student members.
Title of Award: Class Nobel Academic Scholarships for Members **Area, Field, or Subject:** General studies. **Level of Education for which Award is Granted:** High School **Funds Available:** $5000. **Duration:** Annually.
Eligibility Requirements: Applicants must be high school student members. **Application Requirements:** Apply online by going to the member log in page. **Deadline for Receipt:** November 30.

1505 ■ NATIONAL SOCIETY OF HIGH SCHOOL SCHOLARS
1936 N Druid Hills Rd.
Atlanta, GA 30319
(866)343-1800
Web Site: http://www.nshss.org
To support members to attain higher education.
Title of Award: Griffith College Scholarships for NSHSS Members **Area, Field, or Subject:** General studies. **Level of Education for which Award is Granted:** High School **Number Awarded:** 5. **Funds Available:** $1000. **Duration:** Annually.
Eligibility Requirements: Applicant must be a NSHSS member. **Application Requirements:** Applicants must submit a completed application form and required materials. **Additional Information:** Sponsored by Griffith College, Dublin. **Deadline for Receipt:** April 30.

1506 ■ NATIONAL SOCIETY OF HIGH SCHOOL SCHOLARS
1936 N Druid Hills Rd.
Atlanta, GA 30319
(866)343-1800
Web Site: http://www.nshss.org
To support members to attain higher education.
Title of Award: Kaplan Test Prep and Admission Scholarships for NSHSS Members **Area, Field, or Subject:** General studies. **Level of Education**

for which **Award is Granted:** High School **Number Awarded:** 2. **Funds Available:** $1000. **Duration:** Annually.
Eligibility Requirements: Applicant must be a NSHSS member. **Application Requirements:** Applicants must submit a completed application form together with the required materials and a stamped, self-addressed postcard. **Additional Information:** Sponsored by Kaplan Test Prep and Admissions. **Deadline for Receipt:** April 30.

1507 ■ NATIONAL SOCIETY OF HIGH SCHOOL SCHOLARS
1936 N Druid Hills Rd.
Atlanta, GA 30319
(866)343-1800
Web Site: http://www.nshss.org
To support the education of student members.
Title of Award: NSHSS Academic Paper Awards **Area, Field, or Subject:** General studies. **Level of Education for which Award is Granted:** High School **Number Awarded:** Depends on the quantity and quality of entries. **Funds Available:** $250. **Duration:** Annually.
Eligibility Requirements: Applicant must be a NSHSS member. **Application Requirements:** Applicants must submit their written high school academic paper (research paper, original essay, or analytical paper) accompanied by the Academic Paper Awards entry form. **Additional Information:** Applicants may submit one paper per year. **Deadline for Receipt:** May 1.

1508 ■ NATIONAL SOCIETY OF HIGH SCHOOL SCHOLARS
1936 N Druid Hills Rd.
Atlanta, GA 30319
(866)343-1800
Web Site: http://www.nshss.org
To support the education of student members.
Title of Award: NSHSS National Scholar Awards **Area, Field, or Subject:** General studies. **Level of Education for which Award is Granted:** High School **Funds Available:** $1000. **Duration:** Annually.
Eligibility Requirements: Applicant must be a high school student member. **Application Requirements:** Apply online by going to the member log in page. **Additional Information:** Award will be given to selected finalist for the Class Nobel Academic Scholarships. **Deadline for Receipt:** November 30.

1509 ■ NATIONAL SOCIETY OF HIGH SCHOOL SCHOLARS
1936 N Druid Hills Rd.
Atlanta, GA 30319
(866)343-1800
Web Site: http://www.nshss.org
To support the education of student members.
Title of Award: Robert P. Sheppard Leadership Awards **Area, Field, or Subject:** General studies. **Level of Education for which Award is Granted:** High School **Funds Available:** $1000. **Duration:** Annually.
Eligibility Requirements: Applicant must be a high school student member. **Application Requirements:** Applicants must submit a completed application form together with the required materials. **Deadline for Receipt:** February 1.

1510 ■ NATIONAL SOCIETY FOR HISTOTECHNOLOGY
10320 Little Patuxent Pkwy., Ste. 804
Columbia, MD 21044
Tel: (443)535-4060
Fax: (443)535-4055
E-mail: histo@nsh.org
Web Site: http://www.nsh.org
To provide educational scholarships and student scholarships to recipients on a reimbursement basis.
Title of Award: Irwin S. Lerner Student Scholarships **Area, Field, or Subject:** General studies. **Level of Education for which Award is Granted:** Undergraduate **Number Awarded:** 4. **Funds Available:** $500. **Duration:** One year.
Eligibility Requirements: Applicants must be students from approved histotechnology schools. **Application Requirements:** Applicants must complete online application and submit with supporting documentation. **Deadline for Receipt:** May 1. **Additional Information:** Award Committee Chair, Jean Mitchell at the above address.

1511 ■ NATIONAL SOCIETY FOR HISTOTECHNOLOGY
10320 Little Patuxent Pkwy., Ste. 804
Columbia, MD 21044
Tel: (443)535-4060
Fax: (443)535-4055
E-mail: histo@nsh.org
Web Site: http://www.nsh.org
To provide educational scholarships and student scholarships to recipients on a reimbursement basis.
Title of Award: Newcomer Supply Student Scholarships **Area, Field, or Subject:** General studies. **Level of Education for which Award is Granted:** Undergraduate **Number Awarded:** 4. **Funds Available:** $500. **Duration:** One year.
Eligibility Requirements: Applicants must be students from approved histotechnology schools. **Application Requirements:** Applicants must complete online application and submit with supporting documentation. **Deadline for Receipt:** May 1. **Additional Information:** Award Committee Chair, Jean Mitchell at the above address.

1512 ■ NATIONAL SOCIETY FOR HISTOTECHNOLOGY
10320 Little Patuxent Pkwy., Ste. 804
Columbia, MD 21044
Tel: (443)535-4060
Fax: (443)535-4055
E-mail: histo@nsh.org
Web Site: http://www.nsh.org
To provide educational scholarships and student scholarships to recipients on a reimbursement basis.
Title of Award: Sakura Finetek Student Scholarships **Area, Field, or Subject:** General studies. **Level of Education for which Award is Granted:** Undergraduate **Number Awarded:** 4. **Funds Available:** $500. **Duration:** One year.
Eligibility Requirements: Applicants must be students from approved histotechnology schools. **Application Requirements:** Applicants must complete online application and submit with supporting documentation. **Deadline for Receipt:** May 1. **Additional Information:** Award Committee Chair, Jean Mitchell at the above address.

1513 ■ NATIONAL SOCIETY FOR HISTOTECHNOLOGY
10320 Little Patuxent Pkwy., Ste. 804
Columbia, MD 21044
Tel: (443)535-4060
Fax: (443)535-4055
E-mail: histo@nsh.org
Web Site: http://www.nsh.org
To provide educational scholarships and student scholarships to recipients on a reimbursement basis.
Title of Award: Sigma Diagnostics Student Scholarships **Area, Field, or Subject:** General studies. **Level of Education for which Award is Granted:** Undergraduate **Number Awarded:** 4. **Funds Available:** $500. **Duration:** One year.
Eligibility Requirements: The applicants must be students from approved histotechnology schools. **Application Requirements:** Applicants must complete online application together with supporting documentation. **Deadline for Receipt:** May 1. **Additional Information:** The Award Committee Chair, Jean Mitchell at the above address.

1514 ■ NATIONAL SPORTING CLAYS ASSOCIATION
5931 Roft Rd.
San Antonio, TX 78253
Tel: (210)688-3371
Free: 800-877-5338
Fax: (210)688-3014
E-mail: nssa@nssa-nsca.com
Web Site: http://www.mynsca.com
To support the education of a student active in sporting clays.
Title of Award: NSSA/NSCA Collegiate Scholarships **Area, Field, or Subject:** General studies. **Level of Education for which Award is Granted:** Undergraduate **Number Awarded:** 1. **Funds Available:** $5000.
Eligibility Requirements: Applicant must be a graduating high school senior; an NSCA member; pursuing a 4-year degree program; and active NSCA registered sporting clays participant. **Application Requirements:** Applicants must submit a completed Scholarship Application; an essay

(maximum of 250 words) describing goals and reasons why deserve the scholarship; a letter of personal recommendation; copy of class rank/high school grades from the school registrar; and a copy of past shooting history and accomplishments. **Deadline for Receipt:** May 31. **Additional Information:** Glynne Moseley.

1515 ■ NATIONAL TECHNICAL HONOR SOCIETY
PO Box 1336
Flat Rock, NC 28731
Tel: (828)698-8011
Fax: (828)698-8564
Web Site: http://www.nths.org
To help students set goals, makes plans, become leaders at work, and prepare for career success.
Title of Award: Leaders at Work Scholarship in Textiles and Apparel **Area, Field, or Subject:** General studies. **Level of Education for which Award is Granted:** Undergraduate **Number Awarded:** 4. **Funds Available:** $500.
Eligibility Requirements: Applicants must be high school seniors; must have been active members of Family, Career, and Community Leaders of America for a minimum of one year; must have paid national and state dues no later than March 1, 2008. **Application Requirements:** Applicant must fill out the on-line application form; must complete the requirements for Outstanding Leader Recognition found on the Career Connection and Leaders at Work CD; must attach recent official high school transcript; a letter of recommendation from the food production and services, or Hospitality, Tourism, and Recreation instructor; and must submit a two-minute videotape (VHS or DVD format) which address the question "How will the leadership skills you have developed through FCCLA help you reach the Family and Consumer Sciences career goal?" and a copy of the chapter affiliation form verifying national dues payment by March 1.

1516 ■ NATIONAL TECHNICAL HONOR SOCIETY
PO Box 1336
Flat Rock, NC 28731
Tel: (828)698-8011
Fax: (828)698-8564
Web Site: http://www.nths.org
To expand leadership potential and develop skills for lifeplanning, goal setting, problem solving, decision making and interpersonal communications.
Title of Award: Beth Middleton Memorial Scholarships **Area, Field, or Subject:** General studies. **Level of Education for which Award is Granted:** Undergraduate **Number Awarded:** 1. **Funds Available:** $400 for tuition, room and/or board.
Eligibility Requirements: Applicant must be a member for a minimum of two years (not necessarily consecutive); a current or former FCCLA state or national officer; he/she must be senior and have a 3.5 GPA activities and have made a significant contribution to a state or national project exemplary of the goals and ideals of FCCLA. **Application Requirements:** Applicant must fill out the on-line application form using a 10pt. Times New Roman font; must attach the most recent official high school transcript of record including the first semester of the senior year including standardized college entrance exam scores(ACT and/or SAT); must provide a copy of the chapter affiliation verifying national dues paid by December 1, 2007; applicants must include recommendations from their local adviser, state adviser, and one other person knowledgeable of student's non-FCCLA activities; **Deadline for Receipt:** December 1.

1517 ■ NATIONAL TECHNICAL HONOR SOCIETY
PO Box 1336
Flat Rock, NC 28731
Tel: (828)698-8011
Fax: (828)698-8564
Web Site: http://www.nths.org
To promote educational excellence; to enhance career opportunities for the NTHS membership.
Title of Award: National Technical Honor Society Scholarships **Area, Field, or Subject:** General studies. **Level of Education for which Award is Granted:** Undergraduate **Funds Available:** $1,000.
Eligibility Requirements: Applicant must be a member who has held the office of the President of the State FCCLA Association; must be a senior and must have taken the ACT or SAT examination; must have applied to a

degree granting institution leading to an associate's or bachelor's degree in any field of study. **Application Requirements:** Applicant must fill out the online application form using the 10pt. Times new Roman font; most recent official high school transcript including the first semester grades of the senior year and standardized college entrance exam scores(ACT and/or SAT); a copy of the chapter affiliation verifying national dues paid by January 1, 2008; applicants must include a letter of recommendation from their local adviser, state adviser, and one other person knowledgeable of student's non-FCCLA activities; all signatures must be included. **Deadline for Receipt:** March 1.

1518 ■ NATIONAL TECHNICAL HONOR SOCIETY

PO Box 1336
Flat Rock, NC 28731
Tel: (828)698-8011
Fax: (828)698-8564
Web Site: http://www.nths.org
To help students set goals, makes plans, become leaders at work, and prepare for career success.
Title of Award: Wiley Publishing Inc. Scholarships **Area, Field, or Subject:** General studies. **Level of Education for which Award is Granted:** Undergraduate **Number Awarded:** 4. **Funds Available:** $1,000.
Eligibility Requirements: Applicants must be students who have outstanding leadership qualities gain through FCCLA membership and other experiences in family, school, and community; applicants must be seniors who have affiliated with national FCCLA by March 1; must have taken the ACT or SAT examination; must have applied to a degree-granting institution leading to an associate's or bachelor's degree in any field of study. **Application Requirements:** Applicant must fill out the online application form; he/she must completed the requirements for Outstanding Leader Recognition found on the Career Connection and Leaders at Work CD; an applicant must submit the completed Outstanding Leader application form; he/she must attach recent official high school transcript; a letter of recommendation from the food production and services, or hospitality, tourism, and recreation instructor; and must submit a two-minute videotape(VHS or DVD format) which addresses the question "How will the leadership skills you have developed through FCCLA help you reach the family and consumer sciences career goal?"; and a copy of the chapter affiliation form verifying national dues payment by May 1.

1519 ■ NATIONAL THROW COACHES ASSOCIATION

PO Box 14114
Palm Desert, CA 92255-4114
Tel: 888-527-6772
Fax: 800-859-4335
E-mail: rlasorsa@dc.rr.com
Web Site: http://www.nationalthrowcoachesassociation.org
To support and encourage children of NTCA members who wish to pursue higher learning.
Title of Award: John O'Connor Memorial Scholarship Fund **Area, Field, or Subject:** General studies. **Level of Education for which Award is Granted:** Undergraduate **Funds Available:** No specific amount.
Eligibility Requirements: Applicants must be children of NTCA members who are presently attending college or will be entering college next fall. **Application Requirements:** Application can be obtained by calling the NTCA at (888) 527-6772.

1520 ■ NATIONAL UNION OF PUBLIC AND GENERAL EMPLOYEES

15 Auriga Dr.
Nepean, ON, Canada K2E 1B7
Tel: (613)228-9800
Fax: (613)228-9801
E-mail: national@nupge.ca
Web Site: http://www.nupge.ca
To provide financial assistance for the post-secondary education of children of NUPGE members.
Title of Award: Tommy Douglas Scholarships **Area, Field, or Subject:** General studies. **Level of Education for which Award is Granted:** Undergraduate **Funds Available:** $1,500.
Eligibility Requirements: Applicants must be children (including foster children) of National Union of Public and General Employees members

who plan to enter the first year of a Canadian public post-secondary education institution. **Application Requirements:** Application forms are available at the website. Applicants must submit an essay and completed application form to: Tommy Douglas Scholarship, National Union of Public and General Employees, 15 Auriga Dr., Nepean, ON K2E 1B7. **Deadline for Receipt:** June 30.

1521 ■ NATIONAL UNION OF PUBLIC AND GENERAL EMPLOYEES

15 Auriga Dr.
Nepean, ON, Canada K2E 1B7
Tel: (613)228-9800
Fax: (613)228-9801
E-mail: national@nupge.ca
Web Site: http://www.nupge.ca
To inspire the educational endeavors of students with disabilities.
Title of Award: Terry Fox Memorial Scholarships **Area, Field, or Subject:** General studies. **Level of Education for which Award is Granted:** Undergraduate **Funds Available:** $1,500.
Eligibility Requirements: Applicants must be disabled children (including foster children) of NAPGE members entering as freshmen in a Canadian public post-secondary educational institution. **Application Requirements:** Application forms are available at the website. Applicants must submit an essay completed application form to: Terry Fox Memorial Scholarship, National Union of Public and General Employees, 15 Auriga Dr., Nepean, ON K2E 1B7. **Deadline for Receipt:** June 30.

1522 ■ NATIONAL UNION OF PUBLIC AND GENERAL EMPLOYEES

15 Auriga Dr.
Nepean, ON, Canada K2E 1B7
Tel: (613)228-9800
Fax: (613)228-9801
E-mail: national@nupge.ca
Web Site: http://www.nupge.ca
To assist Aboriginal Canadian students in their educational endeavors.
Title of Award: Scholarships for Aboriginal Canadians **Area, Field, or Subject:** General studies. **Level of Education for which Award is Granted:** Undergraduate **Funds Available:** $1,500.
Eligibility Requirements: Applicant must be aboriginal Canadian children (including foster children) of National Union of Public and General Employees members entering as freshmen in a Canadian public post-secondary educational institution. **Application Requirements:** Application forms are available at the website. Applicants must submit an essay along with completed application form to: Scholarships for Aboriginal Canadians, National Union of Public and General Employees, 15 Auriga Dr., Nepean, ON K2E 1B7. **Deadline for Receipt:** June 30.

1523 ■ NATIONAL UNION OF PUBLIC AND GENERAL EMPLOYEES

15 Auriga Dr.
Nepean, ON, Canada K2E 1B7
Tel: (613)228-9800
Fax: (613)228-9801
E-mail: national@nupge.ca
Web Site: http://www.nupge.ca
To assist all visible minority students in their education.
Title of Award: Scholarships for Visible Minorities **Area, Field, or Subject:** General studies. **Level of Education for which Award is Granted:** Undergraduate **Funds Available:** $1,500.
Eligibility Requirements: Applicants must be visible minority children (including foster children) of National Union of Public and General Employees members entering as freshmen in a Canadian public post-secondary educational institution. **Application Requirements:** Application forms are available at the website. Applicants must submit an essay along with completed application form to Scholarships for Visible Minorities, National Union of Public and General Employees, 15 Auriga Dr., Nepean, ON K2E 1B7. **Deadline for Receipt:** June 30.

1524 ■ NAVAL INTELLIGENCE PROFESSIONALS

PO Box 11579
Burke, VA 22009-1579
E-mail: navintpro@aol.com
Web Site: http://www.navintpro.org
To provide financial assistance for higher education of NIP members.
Title of Award: Vice Admiral Donald D. Engen Scholarships **Area, Field, or Subject:** General studies. **Level of Education for which Award is Granted:** Undergraduate **Funds Available:** $1,000.

Eligibility Requirements: Applicants must be eligible for college entrance or be enrolled as full-time students in an undergraduate college program or must be active duty enlisted personnel enrolled as full-time students in either an accredited associate or bachelor degree program. Application Requirements: Applicants must submit completed application form along with supporting transcripts and SAT or ACT scores. Deadline for Receipt: April 15.

1525 ■ NAVAL INTELLIGENCE PROFESSIONALS
PO Box 11579
Burke, VA 22009-1579
E-mail: navintpro@aol.com
Web Site: http://www.navintpro.org
To provide financial assistance for the education of NIP members.
Title of Award: Captain Anthony D. Sesow Scholarships Area, Field, or Subject: General studies. Level of Education for which Award is Granted: Undergraduate Funds Available: $1,000.
Eligibility Requirements: Applicants must be eligible for college entrance or be enrolled as full-time students in an undergraduate college program or must be active duty enlisted personnel enrolled as either full-time students in an accredited associate or bachelor degree program. Application Requirements: Applicants must submit completed application form along with supporting transcripts and SAT or ACT scores. Deadline for Receipt: April 15.

1526 ■ NAVAL INTELLIGENCE PROFESSIONALS
PO Box 11579
Burke, VA 22009-1579
E-mail: navintpro@aol.com
Web Site: http://www.navintpro.org
To provide financial assistance for higher education of NIP members.
Title of Award: Commander Dan F. Shanower Scholarships Area, Field, or Subject: General studies. Level of Education for which Award is Granted: Undergraduate Funds Available: $1,000.
Eligibility Requirements: Applicants must be eligible for college entrance or be enrolled as full-time students in an undergraduate college program or must be active duty enlisted personnel enrolled as either full-time students in an accredited associate or bachelor degree program. Application Requirements: Applicants must submit completed application form along with supporting transcripts and SAT or ACT scores. Deadline for Receipt: April 15.

1527 ■ NAVAL RESERVE ASSOCIATION
1619 King St.
Alexandria, VA 22314-2793
Tel: (703)548-5800; (866)672-4968
Fax: (866)683-3647
E-mail: admin@navy-reserve.org
Web Site: http://www.navy-reserve.org
To provide educational assistance for the sons and daughters of members of the Naval Reserve Association.
Title of Award: Naval Reserve Association Scholarships Area, Field, or Subject: General studies. Level of Education for which Award is Granted: Undergraduate Funds Available: No specific amount.
Eligibility Requirements: Applicants must be children of a NRA member in good standing; must be US citizens; must be under 24 years of age; and must be enrolled in or accepted for full-time enrollment at an accredited college, university or a fully-accredited technical school. Application Requirements: Applicants may download an application form available at the NRA web site. Deadline for Receipt: May 1.

1528 ■ NAVY LEAGUE OF THE UNITED STATES
2300 Wilson Blvd., Ste. 200
Arlington, VA 22201-5424
Tel: (703)528-1775
Free: 800-356-5760
Fax: (703)528-2333
E-mail: execdirector@navyleague.org
Web Site: http://www.navyleague.org
To assist in the college/university expenses of the dependents of sea service personnel.
Title of Award: John G. Brokaw Scholarships Area, Field, or Subject: General studies. Level of Education for which Award is Granted: Undergraduate Funds Available: $2,500. Duration: Four years.

Eligibility Requirements: Applicant must be a U.S. citizen; a dependent or direct descendant of an active, reserve, retired or honorably discharged member of the US Navy, Coast Guard, US-Flag Merchant Marine, Marine Corps or US Naval Sea Cadet Corps; completing the final year of high school; and will be entering an accredited college/university. Application Requirements: Applicants must prepare a copy of all applicable transcripts (grade 9-present); two letters of recommendation; copy of SAT/ACT scores; FAFSA information; proof of qualifying sea service duty; a personal statement (one page) on the reasons to be considered for the program; and a list of extracurricular/scholastic activities (maximum of two pages). Deadline for Receipt: March 3.

1529 ■ NAVY LEAGUE OF THE UNITED STATES
2300 Wilson Blvd., Ste. 200
Arlington, VA 22201-5424
Tel: (703)528-1775
Free: 800-356-5760
Fax: (703)528-2333
E-mail: execdirector@navyleague.org
Web Site: http://www.navyleague.org
To assist in the college/university expenses of the dependents of sea service personnel.
Title of Award: Wesley C. Cameron Scholarships Area, Field, or Subject: General studies. Level of Education for which Award is Granted: Undergraduate Funds Available: $2,500. Duration: Four years.
Eligibility Requirements: Applicant must be a U.S. citizen; a dependent or direct descendant of an active, reserve, retired or honorably discharged member of the US Navy, Coast Guard, US-Flag Merchant Marine, Marine Corps or US Naval Sea Cadet Corps; completing the final year of high school; and will be entering an accredited college/university. Application Requirements: Applicants must prepare a copy of all applicable transcripts (grade 9-present); two letters of recommendation; copy of SAT/ACT scores; FAFSA information; proof of qualifying sea service duty; a personal statement (one page) on the reasons to be considered for the program; and a list of extracurricular/scholastic activities (maximum of two pages). Deadline for Receipt: March 3.

1530 ■ NAVY LEAGUE OF THE UNITED STATES
2300 Wilson Blvd., Ste. 200
Arlington, VA 22201-5424
Tel: (703)528-1775
Free: 800-356-5760
Fax: (703)528-2333
E-mail: execdirector@navyleague.org
Web Site: http://www.navyleague.org
To financially assist the dependents of sea service personnel for college/university expenses.
Title of Award: Ann E. Clark Foundation Scholarships Area, Field, or Subject: General studies. Level of Education for which Award is Granted: Undergraduate Funds Available: $2,500. Duration: Four years.
Eligibility Requirements: Applicant must be a U.S. citizen; currently residing in the state of California; a dependent or direct descendant of an active, reserve, retired or honorably discharged member of the US Navy, Coast Guard, US-Flag Merchant Marine, Marine Corps or US Naval Sea Cadet Corps; completing his/her final year of high school and will be entering an accredited college/university. Application Requirements: Applicants must prepare a copy of all applicable transcripts (grade 9-present); two letters of recommendation; copy of SAT/ACT scores; FAFSA information; proof of qualifying sea service duty; a personal statement (one page) on the reasons to be considered for the program; and a list of extracurricular/scholastic activities (maximum of two pages). Deadline for Receipt: March 3.

1531 ■ NAVY LEAGUE OF THE UNITED STATES
2300 Wilson Blvd., Ste. 200
Arlington, VA 22201-5424
Tel: (703)528-1775
Free: 800-356-5760
Fax: (703)528-2333
E-mail: execdirector@navyleague.org
Web Site: http://www.navyleague.org

To assist in the college/university expenses of the dependents of sea service personnel.
Title of Award: Capt. Winifred Quick Collins Scholarships **Area, Field, or Subject:** General studies. **Level of Education for which Award is Granted:** Undergraduate **Funds Available:** $2,500. **Duration:** Four years.
Eligibility Requirements: Applicant must be a U.S. citizen; a dependent or direct descendant of an active, reserve, retired or honorably discharged member of the US Navy, Coast Guard, US-Flag Merchant Marine, Marine Corps or US Naval Sea Cadet Corps; completing the final year of high school; and will be entering an accredited college/university. **Application Requirements:** Applicants must prepare a copy of all applicable transcripts (grade 9-present); two letters of recommendation; copy of SAT/ACT scores; FAFSA information; proof of qualifying sea service duty; a personal statement (one page) on the reasons to be considered for the program; and a list of extracurricular/scholastic activities (maximum of two pages). **Deadline for Receipt:** March 3.

1532 ■ NAVY LEAGUE OF THE UNITED STATES
2300 Wilson Blvd., Ste. 200
Arlington, VA 22201-5424
Tel: (703)528-1775
Free: 800-356-5760
Fax: (703)528-2333
E-mail: execdirector@navyleague.org
Web Site: http://www.navyleague.org
To financially assist the dependents of sea service personnel for college/university expenses.
Title of Award: Gladys Ann Smith Greater Los Angeles Women's Council Scholarships **Area, Field, or Subject:** General studies. **Level of Education for which Award is Granted:** Undergraduate **Funds Available:** $2,500. **Duration:** Four years.
Eligibility Requirements: Applicant must be a U.S. citizen; currently residing in the state of California; a dependent or direct descendant of an active, reserve, retired or honorably discharged member of the US Navy, Coast Guard, US-Flag Merchant Marine, Marine Corps or US Naval Sea Cadet Corps; completing his/her final year of high school and will be entering an accredited college/university. **Application Requirements:** Applicants must prepare a copy of all applicable transcripts (grade 9-present); two letters of recommendation; copy of SAT/ACT scores; FAFSA information; proof of qualifying sea service duty; a personal statement (one page) on the reasons to be considered for the program; and a list of extracurricular/scholastic activities (maximum of two pages). **Deadline for Receipt:** March 3.

1533 ■ NAVY LEAGUE OF THE UNITED STATES
2300 Wilson Blvd., Ste. 200
Arlington, VA 22201-5424
Tel: (703)528-1775
Free: 800-356-5760
Fax: (703)528-2333
E-mail: execdirector@navyleague.org
Web Site: http://www.navyleague.org
To assist in the college/university expenses of the dependents of sea service personnel.
Title of Award: Subic Bay-Cubi Point 1 Scholarships **Area, Field, or Subject:** General studies. **Level of Education for which Award is Granted:** Undergraduate **Funds Available:** $2,500. **Duration:** Four years.
Eligibility Requirements: Applicant must be a U.S. citizen; a dependent or direct descendant of an active, reserve, retired or honorably discharged member of the US Navy, Coast Guard, US-Flag Merchant Marine, Marine Corps or US Naval Sea Cadet Corps; completing the final year of high school; and will be entering an accredited college/university. **Application Requirements:** Applicants must prepare a copy of all applicable transcripts (grade 9-present); two letters of recommendation; copy of SAT/ACT scores; FAFSA information; proof of qualifying sea service duty; a personal statement (one page) on the reasons to be considered for the program; and a list of extracurricular/scholastic activities (maximum of two pages). **Deadline for Receipt:** March 3.

1534 ■ NAVY LEAGUE OF THE UNITED STATES
2300 Wilson Blvd., Ste. 200
Arlington, VA 22201-5424

Tel: (703)528-1775
Free: 800-356-5760
Fax: (703)528-2333
E-mail: execdirector@navyleague.org
Web Site: http://www.navyleague.org
To assist in the college/university expenses of the dependents of sea service personnel.
Title of Award: William A. Sullivan Scholarships **Area, Field, or Subject:** General studies. **Level of Education for which Award is Granted:** Undergraduate **Funds Available:** $2,500. **Duration:** Four years.
Eligibility Requirements: Applicant must be a U.S. citizen; a dependent or direct descendant of an active, reserve, retired or honorably discharged member of the US Navy, Coast Guard, US-Flag Merchant Marine, Marine Corps or US Naval Sea Cadet Corps; completing the final year of high school; and will be entering an accredited college/university. **Application Requirements:** Applicants must prepare a copy of all applicable transcripts (grade 9-present); two letters of recommendation; copy of SAT/ACT scores; FAFSA information; proof of qualifying sea service duty; a personal statement (one page) on the reasons to be considered for the program; and a list of extracurricular/scholastic activities (maximum of two pages). **Deadline for Receipt:** March 3.

1535 ■ NAVY-MARINE CORPS RELIEF SOCIETY
875 N Randolph St., Ste. 225
Arlington, VA 22203-1757
Tel: (703)696-4904
Fax: (703)696-0744
Web Site: http://www.nmcrs.org
To help eligible Navy and Marine Corps families pursue their academic goals by providing education grants and interest-free loans.
Title of Award: Admiral Mike Boorda Scholarship Program **Area, Field, or Subject:** General studies. **Level of Education for which Award is Granted:** Undergraduate **Funds Available:** $500-$2,500. **Duration:** One year.
Eligibility Requirements: Student must be enrolled in either: Marine Enlisted Commissioning Education Program (MECEP), Medical Enlisted Commissioning Program (MECP), or Meritorious Commissioning Program (MCP); must be a high school graduate (or equivalent) and enrolled or accepted as a full-time undergraduate student in a traditional classroom setting at a post-secondary, technical, or vocational institution participating in the U.S. Department of Education's Federal grant and loan program; must have a minimum cumulative GPA of 2.0 on a 4.0 scale; and must possess a current Navy or Marine Corps Military Identification Card. **Application Requirements:** Application instructions and forms are available from the website. **Deadline for Receipt:** May 1. **Additional Information:** NMCRS Education Division, phone: 703-696-4960 or DSN 426-4960, email: education@hq.nmcrs.org.

1536 ■ NAVY-MARINE CORPS RELIEF SOCIETY
875 N Randolph St., Ste. 225
Arlington, VA 22203-1757
Tel: (703)696-4904
Fax: (703)696-0744
Web Site: http://www.nmcrs.org
To provide educational assistance to spouses and children of members of the Society.
Title of Award: Dependents of Deceased Service Members Scholarship Program **Area, Field, or Subject:** General studies. **Level of Education for which Award is Granted:** Undergraduate **Funds Available:** No specific amount. **Duration:** One year.
Eligibility Requirements: Applicants must possess a current military dependent's Uniformed Services Identification and Privilege Card; must have a minimum cumulative GPA of 2.0 on a 4.0 scale; must be the immediate relative of an active duty Sailor or Marine who died as a result of the May 17, 1987 attack on the USS Stark, or the spouse of a service member disabled due to the terrorist attack on the USS STARK; the September 11, 2001 attack on the Pentagon; or the death of a Sailor or Marine due to hostile fire in a theater of combat operation during the Global War on Terrorism (GWOT). **Application Requirements:** Application instructions and forms are available at the website. **Deadline for Receipt:** March 1. **Additional Information:** NMCRS Education Division, phone: 703-696-4960 or DSN 426-4960, email: education@hq.nmcrs.org.

1537 ■ NAVY-MARINE CORPS RELIEF SOCIETY
875 N Randolph St., Ste. 225
Arlington, VA 22203-1757
Tel: (703)696-4904
Fax: (703)696-0744
Web Site: http://www.nmcrs.org
To help eligible Navy and Marine Corps families pursue their academic goals by providing education grants and interest-free loans.
Title of Award: Spouse Tuition Aids Program **Area, Field, or Subject:** General studies. **Level of Education for which Award is Granted:** Graduate, Undergraduate **Funds Available:** Up to 50% of tuition for on-base education programs; up to a maximum of $300 per undergraduate term or $350 per graduate term. Not to exceed $1,500/$1,750 per academic year. **Duration:** One year.
Eligibility Requirements: Program is open only to spouses residing with active duty service members stationed at overseas locations. **Application Requirements:** Application forms and instructions are available from the website. **Additional Information:** Nearest overseas NMCRS location.

1538 ■ NAVY-MARINE CORPS RELIEF SOCIETY
875 N Randolph St., Ste. 225
Arlington, VA 22203-1757
Tel: (703)696-4904
Fax: (703)696-0744
Web Site: http://www.nmcrs.org
To help eligible Navy and Marine Corps families pursue their academic goals by providing education grants and interest-free loans.
Title of Award: USS Tennessee Scholarship Fund **Area, Field, or Subject:** General studies. **Level of Education for which Award is Granted:** Undergraduate **Funds Available:** up to $2,000.
Eligibility Requirements: Program is open to unmarried dependent children of sailors currently serving, or have served, aboard the USS Tennessee. Applicants must possess a current military dependent's Uniformed Services Identification and Privilege Card; must be a high school graduate (or equivalent) and enrolled or accepted as a full-time undergraduate student in a traditional classroom setting at a post-secondary, technical, or vocational institution participating in the U.S. Department of Education's Federal grant and loan program; must have a minimum cumulative GPA of 2.0 (on a 4.0 scale). **Application Requirements:** Application instructions and information are available at the society's website. **Deadline for Receipt:** March 1. **Additional Information:** NMCRS Education Division, phone: 703-696-4960 or DSN 426-4960, email: education@hq.nmcrs.org.

1539 ■ NAZARETH ASSOCIATION
PO Box 224
Nazareth, MI 49074
Tel: (269)342-1191
Fax: (269)381-0343
E-mail: office@nazarethassociation.org
Web Site: http://www.nazarethassociation.org
To provide financial support for eligible undergraduate students of junior or senior status wishing to complete their degree at approved Catholic colleges in Michigan.
Title of Award: The Nazareth Scholarships **Area, Field, or Subject:** General studies. **Level of Education for which Award is Granted:** Undergraduate **Funds Available:** $1,000.
Eligibility Requirements: Applicants must be currently enrolled at an approved Catholic college/university; must be undergraduate junior or senior students; and must have cumulative GPA of 3.0 or better on a 4.0 scale at the conclusion of the present year and be in good standing with their academic institution. **Application Requirements:** Applicants must complete the application form and submit along with transcript of records, a 500-word essay and three letters of recommendation.

1540 ■ NEBRASKA FARM BUREAU
PO Box 80299
Lincoln, NE 68501
Fax: (402)421-4432
Web Site: http://www.nefb.org
To encourage and assist young people between the ages of 18 and 35 to meet their personal goals of higher education.
Title of Award: Nebraska Farm Bureau Young Farmers and Ranchers Greater Horizon Scholarships **Area, Field, or Subject:** General studies.

Level of Education for which Award is Granted: Undergraduate **Funds Available:** $1,000.
Eligibility Requirements: Applicants must be members or family of members of the county of Farm Bureau in Nebraska; must be residents of Nebraska; must have intention of enrolling full-time in a college or university's agricultural field of studies; must demonstrate leadership potential through extracurricular activities and work experiences; and must be 18 to 35 years of age. **Application Requirements:** Applicants must submit the completed application form; three letters of reference; and copy of most recent transcript. **Deadline for Receipt:** March 31.

1541 ■ NEBRASKA HIGH SCHOOL RODEO ASSOCIATION
PO Box 10
Arnold, NE 69120
Tel: (308)848-2664
Fax: (308)848-2544
E-mail: becky.dailey@hotmail.com
Web Site: http://www.hsrodeo-nebraska.com
To assist graduating seniors of Nebraska High School Rodeo Association.
Title of Award: Tom Boots Memorial Scholarships **Area, Field, or Subject:** General studies. **Level of Education for which Award is Granted:** Undergraduate **Funds Available:** $500.
Eligibility Requirements: Applicants must be graduating seniors of Nebraska High School. **Application Requirements:** Applicants must submit a completed application form. **Additional Information:** 404 S Cleveland Ave. PO Box 101, Mullen, NE 69152.

1542 ■ NEBRASKA HIGH SCHOOL RODEO ASSOCIATION
PO Box 10
Arnold, NE 69120
Tel: (308)848-2664
Fax: (308)848-2544
E-mail: becky.dailey@hotmail.com
Web Site: http://www.hsrodeo-nebraska.com
To assist a senior boy or girl in the Nebraska High School Rodeo Association.
Title of Award: Sharon Kreikemeier Memorial Scholarships **Area, Field, or Subject:** General studies. **Level of Education for which Award is Granted:** Undergraduate **Funds Available:** $500.
Eligibility Requirements: Applicants must be enrolled in Nebraska High School. **Application Requirements:** Applicants must complete the application form. **Additional Information:** 1327 D. Rd. West Point, NE 68788.

1543 ■ NEBRASKA HIGH SCHOOL RODEO ASSOCIATION
PO Box 10
Arnold, NE 69120
Tel: (308)848-2664
Fax: (308)848-2544
E-mail: becky.dailey@hotmail.com
Web Site: http://www.hsrodeo-nebraska.com
To assist a graduating senior girl who participates in the Break-A-Way Roping event in the Nebraska State High School.
Title of Award: Brittany Mueller Memorial Scholarships **Area, Field, or Subject:** General studies. **Level of Education for which Award is Granted:** High School **Funds Available:** $500.
Eligibility Requirements: Applicants must be graduating senior girls in Nebraska High School with a 95% GPA. **Application Requirements:** Applicants must submit a cover sheet including name, address and GPA; must submit an at least one page essay stating their career goals, one letter of recommendation and a copy of their grade transcripts. **Deadline for Receipt:** June 1. **Additional Information:** 1600 N Prairie Trace Rd., Sutherland NE 69165.

1544 ■ NEW ENGLAND CLUB MANAGERS ASSOCIATION
300 Arnold Palmer Blvd., Ste. 227
Norton, MA 02766-1365
Tel: (774)430-9050
Fax: (774)430-9051
E-mail: necma@necma.org
Web Site: http://www.necma.org
To support students of hospitality studies and those interested in the club management profession.

Title of Award: David Meador Student Scholarships **Area, Field, or Subject:** General studies. **Level of Education for which Award is Granted:** Undergraduate **Funds Available:** No specific amount.
Eligibility Requirements: Applicants must be full-time students currently working within the club industry, while studying. **Application Requirements:** Applicants must submit a completed and neat application form; a transcript; references; and an essay. **Deadline for Receipt:** September 14.

1545 ■ NEW HAMPSHIRE SNOWMOBILE ASSOCIATION

614 Laconia Rd., Unit 4
Tilton, NH 03276
Tel: (603)273-0220
Fax: (603)273-0218
E-mail: nhsaoffice@nhsa.com
Web Site: http://www.nhsa.com
To assist the education of a dependent of a NHSA member.
Title of Award: New Hampshire Snowmobile Association Scholarships **Area, Field, or Subject:** General studies. **Level of Education for which Award is Granted:** Undergraduate **Number Awarded:** 1. **Funds Available:** $1000.
Eligibility Requirements: Applicant must be a graduating high school senior, accepted at a college, junior college, or vocational school; or a college student already enrolled. **Application Requirements:** Applicants must submit a completed application form along with the required documents. Send materials to Jim Strickland, Chairman, NHSA Scholarship, PO Box 417, Marlow, NH 03456. **Deadline for Receipt:** March 1.

1546 ■ THE NEW YORK TIMES COMPANY FOUNDATION

230 W 41st St., Ste. 1300
New York, NY 10036-7207
Tel: (212)556-1091
Web Site: http://www.nytco.com/company/foundation
To support students who have overcome exceptional hardship to achieve excellence in New York City high schools.
Title of Award: The New York Times College Scholarships **Area, Field, or Subject:** General studies. **Level of Education for which Award is Granted:** Undergraduate **Number Awarded:** 8. **Funds Available:** $7,500. **Duration:** Four years.
Eligibility Requirements: Applicants must be seniors who are attending public, parochial or private high schools in New York City; must have demonstrated academic achievement, commitment to learning-especially in the face of financial and other obstacles, and community service. **Application Requirements:** Applicants may contact The New York Times Company Foundation for the application. **Additional Information:** at the above address.

1547 ■ NON COMMISSIONED OFFICERS ASSOCIATION

PO Box 33790
San Antonio, TX 78265-3790
Tel: (210)653-6161
Free: 800-662-2620
E-mail: execdir@ncoausa.org
Web Site: http://www.ncoausa.org
To assist the children and spouses of NCOA members who wish to pursue their education.
Title of Award: NCOA Scholarships **Area, Field, or Subject:** General studies. **Level of Education for which Award is Granted:** Undergraduate **Number Awarded:** 16. **Funds Available:** $900 (nine children and four spouses), two special awards of $1,000, and one $1,000 from all applications. **Duration:** One year.
Eligibility Requirements: Applicant must be a spouse or child of a NCOA member and must be 25 years old and below (for children of members). **Application Requirements:** Children of NCOA members must submit a completed application form; two letters of recommendation; a handwritten autobiography; personal letter of recommendation; transcripts; copy of ACT/SAT scores; and a composition (maximum of 200 words) about Americanism. Spouses of NCOA members must submit a completed application form; a copy of high school diploma or GED; transcript of completed college courses (if any); a certificate of completion for other training courses; a brief biography; and a letter of intent on: degree course of study, plans for completion of a degree program, and a paragraph about "What a College Degree Means to Me." Mail all docu-

ments in one complete package to: NCOA Scholarship Fund, Inc., PO Box 33610, San Antonio, TX 78265. **Additional Information:** Students must maintain a B average to be considered for renewal. **Deadline for Receipt:** March 31.

1548 ■ NOR' EASTERS SNOWMOBILE CLUB

PO Box 517
Hollis, NH 03049
E-mail: hollisnoreasters@yahoo.com
Web Site: http://www.noreasters.org
To support the education of a student member.
Title of Award: Nor' Easters Scholarships - Four-year Program **Area, Field, or Subject:** General studies. **Level of Education for which Award is Granted:** Undergraduate **Number Awarded:** 1-2. **Funds Available:** $1000. **Duration:** One year.
Eligibility Requirements: Applicant must be a high school senior of exemplary character; a club member; must demonstrate an active interest primarily in the sport of snowmobiling, or secondarily in trail management and maintenance; and must exemplify a commitment to community service. **Application Requirements:** Applicants must submit a completed application form along with the required documents. **Deadline for Receipt:** May 2.

1549 ■ NOR' EASTERS SNOWMOBILE CLUB

PO Box 517
Hollis, NH 03049
E-mail: hollisnoreasters@yahoo.com
Web Site: http://www.noreasters.org
To support the education of a student member.
Title of Award: Nor' Easters Scholarships - Two-year Program **Area, Field, or Subject:** General studies. **Level of Education for which Award is Granted:** Undergraduate **Number Awarded:** 1-2. **Funds Available:** $500. **Duration:** One year.
Eligibility Requirements: Applicant must be a high school senior of exemplary character; a club member; must demonstrate an active interest primarily in the sport of snowmobiling, or secondarily in trail management and maintenance; and must exemplify a commitment to community service. **Application Requirements:** Applicants must submit a completed application form along with the required documents. **Deadline for Receipt:** May 2.

1550 ■ NORTH AMERICAN INTERFRATERNAL FOUNDATION

1750 Royalton Dr.
Carmel, IN 46032-9620
Tel: (317)595-9613
Web Site: http://www.nif-inc.net
To provide funding for individuals with outstanding fraternal leadership who are enrolled in Canadian universities.
Title of Award: James H. McLaughlin Scholarships **Area, Field, or Subject:** General studies. **Level of Education for which Award is Granted:** Undergraduate **Number Awarded:** 1. **Funds Available:** $500.
Eligibility Requirements: Applicants must be undergraduate students who are attending or are agreeable to transfer to a Canadian university; must be a founding member or new member of a Canadian colony or interest group; or must be an IFC or Panhellenic officer at a Canadian University. **Application Requirements:** Applicants must submit a completed application and official transcript from college or university. **Deadline for Receipt:** April.

1551 ■ NORTH AMERICAN INTERFRATERNAL FOUNDATION

1750 Royalton Dr.
Carmel, IN 46032-9620
Tel: (317)595-9613
Web Site: http://www.nif-inc.net
To provide educational funding to undergraduate female students intending to pursue graduate studies.
Title of Award: Mary Louise Roller Panhellenic Scholarships **Area, Field, or Subject:** General studies. **Level of Education for which Award is Granted:** Undergraduate **Number Awarded:** 1. **Funds Available:** $1,500.
Eligibility Requirements: Applicants must be undergraduate women with desire to attend graduate school. **Application Requirements:** Applicants must submit a completed application; official transcript from col-

lege or university; letter of endorsement from Panhellenic Council; letter of endorsement from Panhellenic Advisor; and copy of acceptance letter from graduate school. **Additional Information:** Scholarship is funded by a grant from Alpha Omicron Pi Fraternity in honor of Mary Louise Roller's 33 year tenure on AOPi's Panhellenic Delegation.

1552 ■ NORTH DAKOTA FARMERS UNION
PO Box 2136
Jamestown, ND 58401
Tel: (701)252-2341
Free: 800-366-8331
Fax: (701)252-6584
Web Site: http://www.ndfu.org
To provide scholarship to Farmers Union Torchbearers.
Title of Award: Bergman Scholarships **Area, Field, or Subject:** General studies. **Level of Education for which Award is Granted:** Undergraduate **Number Awarded:** 2. **Funds Available:** $1,000.
Eligibility Requirements: Applicants must be receiving Torchbearer award at the upcoming Farmers Union State Convention; must have at least 2.50 grade point average. **Application Requirements:** Applicants must submit all the required application information. **Deadline for Receipt:** November 17.

1553 ■ NORTH DAKOTA FARMERS UNION
PO Box 2136
Jamestown, ND 58401
Tel: (701)252-2341
Free: 800-366-8331
Fax: (701)252-6584
Web Site: http://www.ndfu.org
To provide financial assistance for deserving students to further their college education.
Title of Award: Farmers Union Marketing and Processing Foundation Stanley Moore Scholarships **Area, Field, or Subject:** General studies. **Level of Education for which Award is Granted:** Undergraduate **Funds Available:** $1,500.
Eligibility Requirements: Applicants must be Farmers Union members and their children in Minnesota, Montana, North Dakota and Wisconsin; must be high school seniors, college students or non-traditional students seeking funding to attend a two- or four-year accredited college or university or technical school for any area of study. **Application Requirements:** Applicants must submit a completed application form; copy of high school/college transcripts; letters of recommendation from a Farmer Union leader and from a teacher or professor; written essay - three pages. **Additional Information:** Scholarship will be awarded with money to be used for tuition and books. **Deadline for Receipt:** June 2.

1554 ■ NORTH DAKOTA FARMERS UNION
PO Box 2136
Jamestown, ND 58401
Tel: (701)252-2341
Free: 800-366-8331
Fax: (701)252-6584
Web Site: http://www.ndfu.org
To provide financial assistance for students who deserve to pursue college but financially constrained.
Title of Award: Stanley Moore Scholarships **Area, Field, or Subject:** General studies. **Level of Education for which Award is Granted:** Undergraduate **Funds Available:** $500. **Duration:** One year.
Eligibility Requirements: Applicants must be Farmers Union members, high school seniors, college students or nontraditional students seeking funding to attend a two- or four-year accredited college, university or technical school for any area of study. **Application Requirements:** Applicants must submit completed application; essay; grade transcripts and letters of recommendation. **Deadline for Receipt:** April 17.

1555 ■ NORTH DAKOTA FARMERS UNION
PO Box 2136
Jamestown, ND 58401
Tel: (701)252-2341
Free: 800-366-8331
Fax: (701)252-6584
Web Site: http://www.ndfu.org

To provide financial assistance to students planning to enroll as freshmen at North Dakota State University.
Title of Award: North Dakota Farmers Union Co-op House Scholarships **Area, Field, or Subject:** General studies. **Level of Education for which Award is Granted:** Undergraduate **Funds Available:** No specific amount.
Eligibility Requirements: Applicants must plan to enroll as freshmen at North Dakota State University; must be Farmers Union members, relatives of past Co-op House members or members of a cooperative; must have at least 2.50 grade point average during the last three years of high school. **Application Requirements:** Applicants must submit all the required application information.

1556 ■ NORTH DAKOTA FARMERS UNION
PO Box 2136
Jamestown, ND 58401
Tel: (701)252-2341
Free: 800-366-8331
Fax: (701)252-6584
Web Site: http://www.ndfu.org
To provide financial to first-year or undergraduate students enrolled in a secondary educational facility.
Title of Award: North Dakota Farmers Union Scholarships **Area, Field, or Subject:** General studies. **Level of Education for which Award is Granted:** Undergraduate **Funds Available:** $500. **Duration:** One year.
Eligibility Requirements: Applicants must be pursuing a career important to rural America, but not limited to agribusiness, farm operation or production agriculture; must be high school seniors and college undergraduates who have at least 2.50 grade point average during the last three years of schooling. **Application Requirements:** Applicants must submit a completed application; financial information; letters of recommendation; and, grade transcript. **Deadline for Receipt:** January 31.

1557 ■ NORTH DAKOTA FARMERS UNION
PO Box 2136
Jamestown, ND 58401
Tel: (701)252-2341
Free: 800-366-8331
Fax: (701)252-6584
Web Site: http://www.ndfu.org
To provide financial assistance for students who deserve to pursue college but are financially constrained.
Title of Award: Hubert K. Seymour Scholarships **Area, Field, or Subject:** General studies. **Level of Education for which Award is Granted:** Undergraduate **Funds Available:** $2,000.
Eligibility Requirements: Applicants must be Farmers' Union members, graduating high school seniors enrolled in an accredited two- or four-year college or university. **Application Requirements:** Applicants must submit a completed application form; copy of high school transcript; two letters of recommendation - one from a Farmers Union leader and one from a school counselor or teacher; an essay, identifying and discussing the significance of rural values in America and on their life. **Deadline for Receipt:** February 15.

1558 ■ NORTHERN ARIZONA NATIVE-AMERICAN FOUNDATION
411 W Cherry Ave.
Flagstaff, AZ 86001
Tel: (928)527-9860
Web Site: http://www.tnanaf.org
To encourage educational pursuits by providing financial assistance for high school seniors.
Title of Award: Northern Arizona Native-American Foundation Scholarships **Area, Field, or Subject:** General studies. **Level of Education for which Award is Granted:** Undergraduate **Funds Available:** $250 up to $2,000. **Duration:** One year.
Eligibility Requirements: Applicants must be freshmen, sophomores, or juniors in high school who are interested in attending a four-year college, community college, art school, or vocational school. **Application Requirements:** Applicants must submit all the required application information.

1559 ■ NORTHWEST MICHIGAN HOME BUILDERS ASSOCIATION
PO Box 171
Cadillac, MI 49601

Tel: (231)775-5256
Fax: (231)775-2134
E-mail: info@nwmhba.com
Web Site: http://www.nwmhba.com
To help build one's business.
Title of Award: R.D. Neuman Memorial Scholarships **Area, Field, or Subject:** Construction. **Level of Education for which Award is Granted:** Undergraduate **Funds Available:** $500-$1,000.
Eligibility Requirements: Applicant must be a resident of Wexford, Missaukee or Oseloa County; must be pursuing a degree in construction, architecture, or engineering or an associate's degree in drafting or building; applicants must have a minimum of 2.5 GPA and be attending school in Michigan. **Application Requirements:** Applicants must submit a written paragraph on goals and aspirations; must submit a list of extracurricular activities/work history. **Deadline for Receipt:** May 1.

1560 ■ NORTHWEST-SHOALS COMMUNITY COLLEGE
PO Box 2545
Muscle Shoals, AL 35662
Tel: (256)331-5200
Free: 800-645-8967
Fax: (256)331-5222
Web Site: http://www.nwscc.edu
To support NW-SCC students in their educational pursuit.
Title of Award: Alabama Power Scholarships **Area, Field, or Subject:** General studies. **Level of Education for which Award is Granted:** Undergraduate **Funds Available:** No specific amount.
Eligibility Requirements: Applicant must be a high school student entering Northwest-Shoals Community College. **Application Requirements:** Applicants must submit a completed application form together with the required materials and information. **Deadline for Receipt:** March 2. **Additional Information:** Northwest Shoals Foundation at 256-331-5240.

1561 ■ NORTHWEST-SHOALS COMMUNITY COLLEGE
PO Box 2545
Muscle Shoals, AL 35662
Tel: (256)331-5200
Free: 800-645-8967
Fax: (256)331-5222
Web Site: http://www.nwscc.edu
To support NW-SCC students in their educational pursuit.
Title of Award: Billy Bowling Memorial Scholarships **Area, Field, or Subject:** General studies. **Level of Education for which Award is Granted:** Undergraduate **Funds Available:** No specific amount.
Eligibility Requirements: Applicant must be a high school student entering Northwest-Shoals Community College. **Application Requirements:** Applicants must submit a completed application form together with the required materials and information. **Deadline for Receipt:** March 2. **Additional Information:** Northwest Shoals Foundation at 256-331-5240.

1562 ■ NORTHWEST-SHOALS COMMUNITY COLLEGE
PO Box 2545
Muscle Shoals, AL 35662
Tel: (256)331-5200
Free: 800-645-8967
Fax: (256)331-5222
Web Site: http://www.nwscc.edu
To support NW-SCC students in their educational pursuit.
Title of Award: Cecil Earl Clapp, Sr. Memorial Scholarships **Area, Field, or Subject:** General studies. **Level of Education for which Award is Granted:** Undergraduate **Funds Available:** No specific amount.
Eligibility Requirements: Applicant must be a high school student entering Northwest-Shoals Community College. **Application Requirements:** Applicants must submit a completed application form together with the required materials and information. **Deadline for Receipt:** March 2. **Additional Information:** Northwest Shoals Foundation at 256-331-5240.

1563 ■ NORTHWEST-SHOALS COMMUNITY COLLEGE
PO Box 2545
Muscle Shoals, AL 35662
Tel: (256)331-5200
Free: 800-645-8967
Fax: (256)331-5222

Web Site: http://www.nwscc.edu
To support NW-SCC students in their educational pursuit.
Title of Award: Marvin E. Daly Memorial Scholarships **Area, Field, or Subject:** General studies. **Level of Education for which Award is Granted:** Undergraduate **Funds Available:** No specific amount.
Eligibility Requirements: Applicant must be a Lauderdale County senior student entering Northwest-Shoals Community College. **Application Requirements:** Applicants must submit a completed application form together with the required materials and information. **Deadline for Receipt:** March 2. **Additional Information:** Northwest Shoals Foundation at 256-331-5240.

1564 ■ NORTHWEST-SHOALS COMMUNITY COLLEGE
PO Box 2545
Muscle Shoals, AL 35662
Tel: (256)331-5200
Free: 800-645-8967
Fax: (256)331-5222
Web Site: http://www.nwscc.edu
To support NW-SCC students in their educational pursuit.
Title of Award: Michael Denton Scholarships **Area, Field, or Subject:** General studies. **Level of Education for which Award is Granted:** Undergraduate **Funds Available:** No specific amount.
Eligibility Requirements: Applicant must be a Colbert Heights High School senior student entering Northwest-Shoals Community College. **Application Requirements:** Applicants must submit a completed application form together with the required materials and information. **Deadline for Receipt:** March 2. **Additional Information:** Northwest Shoals Foundation at 256-331-5240.

1565 ■ NORTHWEST-SHOALS COMMUNITY COLLEGE
PO Box 2545
Muscle Shoals, AL 35662
Tel: (256)331-5200
Free: 800-645-8967
Fax: (256)331-5222
Web Site: http://www.nwscc.edu
To support NW-SCC students with their educational pursuit.
Title of Award: Homajean Grisham Memorial Scholarships **Area, Field, or Subject:** General studies. **Level of Education for which Award is Granted:** Undergraduate **Funds Available:** No specific amount.
Eligibility Requirements: Applicants must be Cherokee High School Senior students entering Northwest-Shoals Community College. **Application Requirements:** Applicants must submit a completed application form together with the required materials and information. **Deadline for Receipt:** March 2. **Additional Information:** Northwest Shoals Foundation at 256-331-5240.

1566 ■ NORTHWEST-SHOALS COMMUNITY COLLEGE
PO Box 2545
Muscle Shoals, AL 35662
Tel: (256)331-5200
Free: 800-645-8967
Fax: (256)331-5222
Web Site: http://www.nwscc.edu
To support NW-SCC students in their educational pursuit.
Title of Award: Howell Heflin Memorial Scholarships **Area, Field, or Subject:** General studies. **Level of Education for which Award is Granted:** Undergraduate **Funds Available:** No specific amount.
Eligibility Requirements: Applicant must be a high school student entering Northwest-Shoals Community College. **Application Requirements:** Applicants must submit a completed application form together with the required materials and information. **Deadline for Receipt:** March 2. **Additional Information:** Northwest Shoals Foundation at 256-331-5240.

1567 ■ NORTHWEST-SHOALS COMMUNITY COLLEGE
PO Box 2545
Muscle Shoals, AL 35662
Tel: (256)331-5200
Free: 800-645-8967
Fax: (256)331-5222
Web Site: http://www.nwscc.edu
To support NW-SCC students in their educational pursuit.

Title of Award: June Hester Memorial Scholarships **Area, Field, or Subject:** General studies. **Level of Education for which Award is Granted:** Undergraduate **Funds Available:** No specific amount. **Eligibility Requirements:** Applicant must be a high school student entering Northwest-Shoals Community College. **Application Requirements:** Applicants must submit a completed application form together with the required materials and information. **Deadline for Receipt:** March 2. **Additional Information:** Northwest Shoals Foundation at 256-331-5240.

1568 ■ NORTHWEST-SHOALS COMMUNITY COLLEGE
PO Box 2545
Muscle Shoals, AL 35662
Tel: (256)331-5200
Free: 800-645-8967
Fax: (256)331-5222
Web Site: http://www.nwscc.edu
To support NW-SCC students in their educational pursuit.
Title of Award: Martha Isabell Memorial Scholarships **Area, Field, or Subject:** General studies. **Level of Education for which Award is Granted:** Undergraduate **Funds Available:** No specific amount. **Eligibility Requirements:** Applicant must be a high school student entering Northwest-Shoals Community College. **Application Requirements:** Applicants must submit a completed application form together with the required materials and information. **Deadline for Receipt:** March 2. **Additional Information:** Northwest Shoals Foundation at 256-331-5240.

1569 ■ NORTHWEST-SHOALS COMMUNITY COLLEGE
PO Box 2545
Muscle Shoals, AL 35662
Tel: (256)331-5200
Free: 800-645-8967
Fax: (256)331-5222
Web Site: http://www.nwscc.edu
To support NW-SCC students in their educational pursuit.
Title of Award: Broughton Isom Memorial Scholarships **Area, Field, or Subject:** General studies. **Level of Education for which Award is Granted:** Undergraduate **Funds Available:** No specific amount. **Eligibility Requirements:** Applicant must be a Phil Campbell High School senior student entering Northwest-Shoals Community College. **Application Requirements:** Applicants must submit a completed application form together with the required materials and information. **Deadline for Receipt:** March 2. **Additional Information:** Northwest Shoals Foundation at 256-331-5240.

1570 ■ NORTHWEST-SHOALS COMMUNITY COLLEGE
PO Box 2545
Muscle Shoals, AL 35662
Tel: (256)331-5200
Free: 800-645-8967
Fax: (256)331-5222
Web Site: http://www.nwscc.edu
To support NW-SCC students in their educational pursuit.
Title of Award: Franklin A. Lentesty Scholarships **Area, Field, or Subject:** General studies. **Level of Education for which Award is Granted:** Undergraduate **Funds Available:** No specific amount. **Eligibility Requirements:** Applicant must be a high school student entering Northwest-Shoals Community College. **Application Requirements:** Applicants must submit a completed application form together with the required materials and information. **Deadline for Receipt:** March 2. **Additional Information:** Northwest Shoals Foundation at 256-331-5240.

1571 ■ NORTHWEST-SHOALS COMMUNITY COLLEGE
PO Box 2545
Muscle Shoals, AL 35662
Tel: (256)331-5200
Free: 800-645-8967
Fax: (256)331-5222
Web Site: http://www.nwscc.edu
To support NW-SCC students with their educational pursuit.
Title of Award: Listerhill Credit Union Scholarships **Area, Field, or Subject:** General studies. **Level of Education for which Award is Granted:** Undergraduate **Funds Available:** No specific amount. **Eligibility Requirements:** Applicant must be Credit Union member entering Northwest-Shoals Community College. **Application Requirements:**

Applicants must submit a completed application form together with the required materials and information. **Deadline for Receipt:** March 2. **Additional Information:** Northwest Shoals Foundation at 256-331-5240.

1572 ■ NORTHWEST-SHOALS COMMUNITY COLLEGE
PO Box 2545
Muscle Shoals, AL 35662
Tel: (256)331-5200
Free: 800-645-8967
Fax: (256)331-5222
Web Site: http://www.nwscc.edu
To support NW-SCC students with their educational pursuit.
Title of Award: David McMeans Memorial Scholarships **Area, Field, or Subject:** General studies. **Level of Education for which Award is Granted:** Undergraduate **Funds Available:** No specific amount. **Eligibility Requirements:** Applicants must be Lauderdale County High School Senior student entering Northwest-Shoals Community College. **Application Requirements:** Applicants must submit a completed application form together with the required materials and information. **Deadline for Receipt:** March 2. **Additional Information:** Northwest Shoa ls Foundation at 256-331-5240.

1573 ■ NORTHWEST-SHOALS COMMUNITY COLLEGE
PO Box 2545
Muscle Shoals, AL 35662
Tel: (256)331-5200
Free: 800-645-8967
Fax: (256)331-5222
Web Site: http://www.nwscc.edu
To support NW-SCC students with their educational pursuit.
Title of Award: Muscle Shoals Kiwanis/Wal-Mart Scholarships **Area, Field, or Subject:** General studies. **Level of Education for which Award is Granted:** Undergraduate **Funds Available:** No specific amount. **Eligibility Requirements:** Applicants must be Muscle Shoals High School Senior students entering Northwest-Shoals Community College. **Application Requirements:** Applicants must submit a completed application form together with the required materials and information. **Deadline for Receipt:** March 2. **Additional Information:** Northwest Shoals Foundation at 256-331-5240.

1574 ■ NORTHWEST-SHOALS COMMUNITY COLLEGE
PO Box 2545
Muscle Shoals, AL 35662
Tel: (256)331-5200
Free: 800-645-8967
Fax: (256)331-5222
Web Site: http://www.nwscc.edu
To support students in their educational pursuit.
Title of Award: Northwest-Shoals Community College Academic Scholarships **Area, Field, or Subject:** General studies. **Level of Education for which Award is Granted:** Undergraduate **Funds Available:** No specific amount. **Duration:** One academic year.
Eligibility Requirements: Applicant must be currently enrolled at Northwest-Shoals Community College with at least 3.0 overall GPA; have completed at least 16 credit hours; have enrolled 12 or more hours each; valid for fall and spring semesters only. **Application Requirements:** Applicants must submit a completed application form along with the required materials and information. **Deadline for Receipt:** March 3. **Additional Information:** Financial Aid Office, at 256-331-5417, or 256-331-6222, email at parrisj@nwscc.edu.

1575 ■ NORTHWEST-SHOALS COMMUNITY COLLEGE
PO Box 2545
Muscle Shoals, AL 35662
Tel: (256)331-5200
Free: 800-645-8967
Fax: (256)331-5222
Web Site: http://www.nwscc.edu
To support NW-SCC students in their educational pursuit.
Title of Award: Northwest-Shoals Community College Athletic Scholarships **Area, Field, or Subject:** General studies. **Level of Education for which Award is Granted:** Undergraduate **Funds Available:** Full tuition, fees, and books.

Eligibility Requirements: Applicant must be an entering full-time fresh-man or a currently enrolled full-time student; must have an overall GPA of 2.0; in basketball, baseball, softball, volleyball, cheerleaders or managers. **Application Requirements:** To qualify, students must file a Northwest-Shoals Community College Application for Admission. Applicants must submit a completed scholarship application form along with the required materials. **Deadline for Receipt:** March 2. **Additional Information:** 256-331-5417/256-331-6232.

1576 ■ NORTHWEST-SHOALS COMMUNITY COLLEGE
PO Box 2545
Muscle Shoals, AL 35662
Tel: (256)331-5200
Free: 800-645-8967
Fax: (256)331-5222
Web Site: http://www.nwscc.edu
To support NW-SCC students in their educational pursuit.
Title of Award: Northwest-Shoals Community College Bank Independent Scholarships **Area, Field, or Subject:** General studies. **Level of Education for which Award is Granted:** Undergraduate **Funds Available:** No specific amount.
Eligibility Requirements: Applicant must be a high school student enter-ing Northwest-Shoals Community College. **Application Requirements:** Applicants must submit a completed application form together with the required materials and information. **Deadline for Receipt:** March 2. **Additional Information:** Northwest Shoals Foundation at 256-331-5240.

1577 ■ NORTHWEST-SHOALS COMMUNITY COLLEGE
PO Box 2545
Muscle Shoals, AL 35662
Tel: (256)331-5200
Free: 800-645-8967
Fax: (256)331-5222
Web Site: http://www.nwscc.edu
To support students with their educational pursuit.
Title of Award: Northwest-Shoals Community College High School Academic Scholarships **Area, Field, or Subject:** General studies. **Level of Education for which Award is Granted:** Undergraduate **Funds Available:** $1500.
Eligibility Requirements: Applicant must be a graduating high school senior; have an overall GPA of 3.25; and enrolled full-time. **Application Requirements:** To qualify, students must file a Northwest-Shoals Com-munity College Application for Admission. Applicants must submit a completed scholarship application form together with the required materi-als and information. **Deadline for Receipt:** March 2. **Additional Informa-tion:** Office of Student Financial Services, at 235-331-5417/256-331-6232.

1578 ■ NORTHWEST-SHOALS COMMUNITY COLLEGE
PO Box 2545
Muscle Shoals, AL 35662
Tel: (256)331-5200
Free: 800-645-8967
Fax: (256)331-5222
Web Site: http://www.nwscc.edu
To support NW-SCC students in their educational pursuit.
Title of Award: Northwest-Shoals Community College Independent Computer Scholarships **Area, Field, or Subject:** General studies. **Level of Education for which Award is Granted:** Undergraduate **Funds Available:** No specific amount.
Eligibility Requirements: Applicant must be a high school student enter-ing Northwest-Shoals Community College. **Application Requirements:** Applicants must submit a completed application form together with the required materials and information. **Deadline for Receipt:** March 2. **Additional Information:** Northwest Shoals Foundation at 256-331-5240.

1579 ■ NORTHWEST-SHOALS COMMUNITY COLLEGE
PO Box 2545
Muscle Shoals, AL 35662
Tel: (256)331-5200
Free: 800-645-8967
Fax: (256)331-5222
Web Site: http://www.nwscc.edu

To support NW-SCC students with their educational pursuit.
Title of Award: Northwest-Shoals Community College Student Activities Scholarships **Area, Field, or Subject:** General studies. **Level of Educa-tion for which Award is Granted:** Undergraduate **Funds Available:** $1500.
Eligibility Requirements: Applicant must be entering full-time freshman or currently enrolled full-time student; have an overall GPA of 2.5; and have successfully completed tryouts, interviews, or have been elected/appointed to positions (SGA President, Vice President or Secretary/Treasurer; Ambassadors; College Bowl). **Application Requirements:** To qualify, students must file a Northwest-Shoals Community College Ap-plication for Admission. Applicants must submit a completed scholarship application form together with the required materials and information. **Deadline for Receipt:** March 2. **Additional Information:** Office of Student Financial Services, at 235-331-5417 or 256-331-6232.

1580 ■ NORTHWEST-SHOALS COMMUNITY COLLEGE
PO Box 2545
Muscle Shoals, AL 35662
Tel: (256)331-5200
Free: 800-645-8967
Fax: (256)331-5222
Web Site: http://www.nwscc.edu
To provide cancer survivor students the opportunity to pursue their educa-tion.
Title of Award: NW-SCC/American Cancer Society College Scholarships **Area, Field, or Subject:** General studies. **Level of Education for which Award is Granted:** Undergraduate **Funds Available:** $1000. **Duration:** One academic year.
Eligibility Requirements: Applicant must be a legal resident of Alabama, Arkansas, Kentucky, Louisiana, Mississippi, Tennessee, or Floyd or Clark counties in Indiana and a United States citizen; have a GPA of 2.5 or equivalent; be 25 years old and below; accepted, without condition, to an accredited two- or four-year university or community college; taking a minimum of 12 hours per semester/full-time student; and has had a diagnosis of cancer before age 21. **Application Requirements:** Ap-plicants must submit a completed application form along with the required materials and information. **Deadline for Receipt:** February. **Additional Information:** American Cancer Society, at 800ACS-2345.

1581 ■ NORTHWEST-SHOALS COMMUNITY COLLEGE
PO Box 2545
Muscle Shoals, AL 35662
Tel: (256)331-5200
Free: 800-645-8967
Fax: (256)331-5222
Web Site: http://www.nwscc.edu
To support students with their educational pursuit.
Title of Award: NW-SCC American Legion Scholarships - Florence/Lauderdale Post No. 11 **Area, Field, or Subject:** General studies. **Level of Education for which Award is Granted:** Undergraduate **Funds Available:** No specific amount.
Eligibility Requirements: Applicant must be an American citizen with no criminal records; a high school graduate or GED equivalent; and a child or grandchild of parent or grandparent who is a member, or a deceased member of the Florence/Lauderdale Post 11 of the American Legion. **Ap-plication Requirements:** Applicants must submit a completed American Legion Scholarship Application along with the required materials and information. **Deadline for Receipt:** March 30. **Additional Information:** American Legion, at 256-764-5122.

1582 ■ NORTHWEST-SHOALS COMMUNITY COLLEGE
PO Box 2545
Muscle Shoals, AL 35662
Tel: (256)331-5200
Free: 800-645-8967
Fax: (256)331-5222
Web Site: http://www.nwscc.edu
To support NW-SCC students in their educational pursuit.
Title of Award: D. Mitchell Self Memorial Scholarships **Area, Field, or Subject:** General studies. **Level of Education for which Award is Granted:** Undergraduate **Funds Available:** No specific amount.
Eligibility Requirements: Applicant must be a high school student enter-ing Northwest-Shoals Community College. **Application Requirements:**

Applicants must submit a completed application form together with the required materials and information. **Deadline for Receipt:** March 2. **Additional Information:** Northwest Shoals Foundation at 256-331-5240.

1583 ■ NORTHWEST-SHOALS COMMUNITY COLLEGE
PO Box 2545
Muscle Shoals, AL 35662
Tel: (256)331-5200
Free: 800-645-8967
Fax: (256)331-5222
Web Site: http://www.nwscc.edu
To support NW-SCC students with their educational pursuit.
Title of Award: Shoals Home Builders Association Scholarships **Area, Field, or Subject:** General studies. **Level of Education for which Award is Granted:** Undergraduate **Funds Available:** No specific amount.
Eligibility Requirements: Applicant must be high school Senior student entering Northwest-Shoals Community College majoring in Building trade. **Application Requirements:** Applicants must submit a completed application form together with the required materials and information. **Deadline for Receipt:** March 2. **Additional Information:** Northwest Shoals Foundation at 256-331-5240.

1584 ■ NORTHWEST-SHOALS COMMUNITY COLLEGE
PO Box 2545
Muscle Shoals, AL 35662
Tel: (256)331-5200
Free: 800-645-8967
Fax: (256)331-5222
Web Site: http://www.nwscc.edu
To support NW-SCC students in their educational pursuit.
Title of Award: Aaron B. Singleton Memorial Scholarships **Area, Field, or Subject:** General studies. **Level of Education for which Award is Granted:** Undergraduate **Funds Available:** No specific amount.
Eligibility Requirements: Applicant must be a Muscle Shoals High School senior student entering Northwest-Shoals Community College. **Application Requirements:** Applicants must submit a completed application form together with the required materials and information. **Deadline for Receipt:** March 2. **Additional Information:** Northwest Shoals Foundation at 256-331-5240.

1585 ■ NORTHWEST-SHOALS COMMUNITY COLLEGE
PO Box 2545
Muscle Shoals, AL 35662
Tel: (256)331-5200
Free: 800-645-8967
Fax: (256)331-5222
Web Site: http://www.nwscc.edu
To support NW-SCC students with their educational pursuit.
Title of Award: Tuscumbia Kiwanis Scholarships **Area, Field, or Subject:** General studies. **Level of Education for which Award is Granted:** Undergraduate **Funds Available:** No specific amount.
Eligibility Requirements: Applicants must be Deshler High School Senior students entering Northwest-Shoals Community College. **Application Requirements:** Applicants must submit a completed application form together with the required materials and information. **Deadline for Receipt:** March 2. **Additional Information:** Northwest Shoals Foundation at 256-331-5240.

1586 ■ NORTHWEST-SHOALS COMMUNITY COLLEGE
PO Box 2545
Muscle Shoals, AL 35662
Tel: (256)331-5200
Free: 800-645-8967
Fax: (256)331-5222
Web Site: http://www.nwscc.edu
To support NW-SCC students with their educational pursuit.
Title of Award: Wayne County Bank Scholarships **Area, Field, or Subject:** General studies. **Level of Education for which Award is Granted:** Undergraduate **Funds Available:** No specific amount.
Eligibility Requirements: Applicants must be Wayne County High School Senior students entering Northwest-Shoals Community College. **Application Requirements:** Applicants must submit a completed applica-

tion form together with the required materials and information. **Deadline for Receipt:** March 2. **Additional Information:** Northwest Shoals Foundation at 256-331-5240.

1587 ■ OCCUPATIONAL PHYSICIANS SCHOLARSHIP FUND
25 NW Point Blvd., Ste. 700
Elk Grove Village, IL 60007-1030
Tel: (847)818-1800
Fax: (847)818-9289
E-mail: opsf@opsf.org
Web Site: http://www.opsf.org
To help alleviate the shortage of properly trained and skilled occupational physicians.
Title of Award: Occupational Physicians Scholarship Fund **Area, Field, or Subject:** Occupational Therapy. **Level of Education for which Award is Granted:** Undergraduate **Funds Available:** No specific amount.
Eligibility Requirements: Applicants must be capable of making a significant contribution in their field and wish to pursue a well-rounded residency education in occupational medicine. **Application Requirements:** Applicants are required to submit the following: a completed OPSF application downloaded from the website; all undergraduate college transcripts; records of previous medical and post-medical school performance; copies of any publications that the applicant has authored; three letters of recommendation, including letters from the directors of any previous training programs; a letter of support from the applicant's current program director, if accepted in an occupational medicine program. **Deadline for Receipt:** November 2. **Additional Information:** Occupational Physicians Scholarship Fund at the above address.

1588 ■ OFFICE PRODUCTS WHOLESALER ASSOCIATION
5024-R Campbell Blvd.
Baltimore, MD 21236-5974
Tel: (410)931-8100
Fax: (410)931-8111
Web Site: http://www.opwa.org
To provide educational assistance to individuals affiliated with the office products industry.
Title of Award: OPWA Educational Scholarships **Area, Field, or Subject:** General studies. **Level of Education for which Award is Granted:** Undergraduate **Funds Available:** $5,000, $2,500 and $1,000.
Eligibility Requirements: Applicant must be an employee, or relative of an employee of an OPWA member company; or a member group or relative of the member group affiliated with the office product industry. **Application Requirements:** Application form is available at the website. Applicant must prepare a transcript of grades and credits; a letter of recommendation from a person employed by a firm in the office products industry (must hold an executive or managerial position) and another from a teacher, professor or other educational professional. **Deadline for Receipt:** March 10.

1589 ■ OKLAHOMA ASSOCIATION FOR THE IMPROVEMENT OF DEVELOPMENTAL EDUCATION
10300 E 81st St. S
Tulsa, OK 74133
Tel: (918)595-8615
E-mail: kdaily@tulsacc.edu
Web Site: http://www.osu-okmulgee.edu
To provide financial assistance to those deserving students.
Title of Award: OKAIDE Scholarships **Area, Field, or Subject:** General Studies. **Level of Education for which Award is Granted:** Undergraduate **Number Awarded:** 2. **Funds Available:** $250. **Duration:** Annually.
Eligibility Requirements: Applicants must be Oklahoma residents of a year or more; must be currently enrolled full-time in an Oklahoma institution of higher education (2 yr. or 4 yr.); during the twelve months prior to application, students must have taken at least one developmental course (0 level), successfully completed all developmental courses taken, and have an overall GPA of 3.3 or higher. **Application Requirements:** Applicants must submit a completed application form and write a one-page statement explaining why they should be considered for this scholarship; a faculty letter of recommendation and two other faculty references with telephone numbers or e-mail address. **Additional Information:** Only complete applications will be considered. **Deadline for Receipt:** October 15. **Additional Information:** Applications should be submitted to: Kathy Daily Tulsa.

1590 ■ OLYMPIA TUMWATER FOUNDATION

PO Box 4098
Tumwater, WA 98501
Tel: (360)943-2550
Fax: (360)943-6755
E-mail: otf@olytumfoundation.org
Web Site: http://www.olytumfoundation.org
To provide support for qualified students.
Title of Award: Olympia Tumwater Foundation Traditional Scholarships
Area, Field, or Subject: General studies. **Level of Education for which Award is Granted:** Undergraduate **Funds Available:** $90,000. **Duration:** One year.
Eligibility Requirements: Applicant must be graduating from a Thurston County high school; must be a Thurston County resident; must be planning to attend a public or private school in Washington State; must have a GPA of 3.0 or better; must show a need for financial aid and academic promise; and must have a strong work ethic and be involved in the community. **Application Requirements:** Applicants are advised to contact Olympia Tumwater Foundation, PO Box 4098, Tumwater, WA 98501 for scholarship information and instructions. **Deadline for Receipt:** March 1.

1591 ■ OLYMPIA TUMWATER FOUNDATION

PO Box 4098
Tumwater, WA 98501
Tel: (360)943-2550
Fax: (360)943-6755
E-mail: otf@olytumfoundation.org
Web Site: http://www.olytumfoundation.org
To provide educational assistance for non-traditional students at South Puget Sound Community College, The Evergreen State College and Saint Martin's University.
Title of Award: Olympia Tumwater Foundation Transitional (non-traditional) Scholarships **Area, Field, or Subject:** General studies. **Level of Education for which Award is Granted:** Undergraduate **Funds Available:** $90,000. **Duration:** One year.
Eligibility Requirements: Applicant must be a resident of Thurston County; must have completed at least 50% of his/her degree or certificate program and have an established plan for completion of the program; and must be in good academic standing. **Application Requirements:** Applicants are advised to contact Olympia Tumwater Foundation, PO Box 4098, Tumwater, WA 98501 for scholarship information and instructions. **Deadline for Receipt:** March 1.

1592 ■ OMAHA EDUCATION ASSOCIATION

4202 S 57th St.
Omaha, NE 68137
Tel: (402)346-0400
Fax: (402)346-8410
Web Site: http://www.omahoea.org
To provide financial assistance to those students who are in need.
Title of Award: Horace Mann Insurance Scholarships **Area, Field, or Subject:** General Studies. **Level of Education for which Award is Granted:** High School **Funds Available:** $30,000.
Eligibility Requirements: Applicants must be high school seniors who are children or legal dependents of U.S. public education employees. **Application Requirements:** Applicants must check the available website for the required materials. **Deadline for Receipt:** February. **Additional Information:** Omaha Education Association at the above address

1593 ■ ONTARIO TRUCKING ASSOCIATION

555 Dixon Rd.
Toronto, ON, Canada M9W 1H8
Tel: (416)249-7401
Fax: (416)245-6152
E-mail: info@ontruck.org
Web Site: http://www.ontruck.org
To educate an individual who demonstrates a commitment to his/her community.
Title of Award: Erb Group Companies Service to Community Scholarships **Area, Field, or Subject:** General studies. **Level of Education for which Award is Granted:** Undergraduate **Funds Available:** No specific amount. **Duration:** One year.
Eligibility Requirements: Applicant must be a first-year postsecondary student enrolled in a recognized college or university, who demonstrates a commitment to his/her community through his/her involvement in community and/or charitable volunteer work. **Application Requirements:** Applicant must submit: an official transcript of record; a curriculum vitae of past volunteer and charity work; a minimum of two reference letters related to applicant's volunteer and charity work; a letter of no more than 500 words that describes why he/she has a strong commitment to community service and details future aspirations relevant to ongoing community service and/or charitable work. Application form and other supporting documents must be sent to OTA Education Foundation, Inc., 555 Dixon Rd., Toronto, ON M9W 1H8. **Deadline for Receipt:** July 15.

1594 ■ ONTARIO TRUCKING ASSOCIATION

555 Dixon Rd.
Toronto, ON, Canada M9W 1H8
Tel: (416)249-7401
Fax: (416)245-6152
E-mail: info@ontruck.org
Web Site: http://www.ontruck.org
To provide scholarship assistance to Ontario students who have demonstrated commitment to academic success and community service, and who have planned to have an affiliation with the trucking industry.
Title of Award: J.O. Goodman Scholarship Awards **Area, Field, or Subject:** General studies. **Level of Education for which Award is Granted:** Undergraduate **Funds Available:** $1,500. **Duration:** One year.
Eligibility Requirements: Applicants must be: outstanding first-year students entering college directly from high school; enrolled in approved programs at approved post-secondary institutions; twenty-five years of age or under. **Application Requirements:** Applicants must submit a written letter of 400 words or less stating why they feel they should be considered for the award; must state their academic and personal accomplishments, contributions to community, extracurricular activities, personal, academic and career goals and other relevant information; must complete the application form available online; must submit the official transcript of marks for the current academic year; must submit the complete Scholarship Sponsorship form; must provide a written essay of 500 words or less that answers, "For the movement of freight, why is trucking considered the most efficient and effective means of transport in North America?". Application form and other supporting documents must be sent to OTA Education Foundation, Inc., 555 Dixon Rd., Toronto, ON M9W 1H8. **Additional Information:** Award is named for Mr. Joe Goodman, who for forty-four years was Senior Staff Executive of the Ontario Trucking Association (OTA). **Deadline for Receipt:** July 15.

1595 ■ ONTARIO TRUCKING ASSOCIATION

555 Dixon Rd.
Toronto, ON, Canada M9W 1H8
Tel: (416)249-7401
Fax: (416)245-6152
E-mail: info@ontruck.org
Web Site: http://www.ontruck.org
To provide scholarship assistance to Ontario students who have demonstrated commitment to academic success and community service, and who have planned to have an affiliation with the trucking industry.
Title of Award: C.V. Hoar Scholarship Awards **Area, Field, or Subject:** General studies. **Level of Education for which Award is Granted:** Undergraduate **Funds Available:** $1,000. **Duration:** One year.
Eligibility Requirements: Applicants must be: outstanding first-year students entering a university directly from high school; enrolled in approved programs at approved post-secondary institutions; twenty-five years of age or under. **Application Requirements:** Applicants must submit a written letter of 400 words or less stating why they feel they should be considered for the award; must state their academic and personal accomplishments, contributions to community, extracurricular activities, personal, academic and career goals and other relevant information; must complete the application form available online. Applicants must submit: the official transcript of marks for the current academic year; complete Scholarship Sponsorship form; an essay of 500 words or less that answers, "For the movement of freight, why is trucking considered the most efficient and effective means of transport in North America?". Application form and other supporting documents must be sent to OTA Education Foundation, Inc., 555 Dixon Rd., Toronto, ON M9W 1H8. **Additional Information:** Award is named for Mr. C.V. (Charles) Hoar, who is one of the founding members of the OTA Education Founda-

tion and who led the Foundation into its current form when he helped establish the J.O. Goodman Awards in 1979 following the retirement of Mr. Goodman as Senior Staff Executive of the Ontario Trucking Association. **Deadline for Receipt:** July 15.

1596 ■ ONTARIO TRUCKING ASSOCIATION
555 Dixon Rd.
Toronto, ON, Canada M9W 1H8
Tel: (416)249-7401
Fax: (416)245-6152
E-mail: info@ontruck.org
Web Site: http://www.ontruck.org
To provide scholarship assistance to Ontario students who have demonstrated commitment to academic success and community service, and who have planned to have an affiliation with the trucking industry.
Title of Award: OTA Education Foundation Scholarships **Area, Field, or Subject:** General studies. **Level of Education for which Award is Granted:** Undergraduate **Funds Available:** 1,000-1,500. **Duration:** One year.
Eligibility Requirements: Applicants must be Ontario students enrolled in approved programs at approved post-secondary institutions; must be twentyfive years of age or under. **Application Requirements:** Applicant must submit: the application form available online; the official transcript of marks for the current academic year; the complete Scholarship Sponsorship form; an essay of 500 words or less that answers, "For the movement of freight, why is trucking considered the most efficient and effective means of transport in North America?". Application form and other supporting documents must be sent to OTA Education Foundation, Inc., 555 Dixon Rd., Toronto, ON M9W 1H8. **Deadline for Receipt:** July 15.

1597 ■ ORANGE COUNTY ASSOCIATION OF EDUCATIONAL OFFICE PROFESSIONALS
550 Blumont St.
Laguna Beach, CA 92651
Tel: (949)497-7700
Fax: (949)497-7710
E-mail: acutler@lagunabeachschools.org
Web Site: http://www.caeop.org/ocaeop.htm
To assist business education students who intend to continue with higher education and pursue a career in business administration or education.
Title of Award: OCAEOP Community Service Scholarship Program **Area, Field, or Subject:** Business administration. **Level of Education for which Award is Granted:** Undergraduate **Funds Available:** $1,000. **Duration:** One year.
Eligibility Requirements: Applicant must have applied for admission to a post-high school accredited institution and plan to enter following the granting of the scholarship, or already be enrolled in an accredited college or university; must be a resident of the State of California; and must intend to continue his/her education in the field of business administration or education. **Application Requirements:** Applicants must submit completed application and biographical information forms; official copy of high school transcript (or university/college transcript for higher education applicants); one-page essay on "Why the applicant is choosing a career in Business or Education"; three letters of recommendation from a language arts or math teacher, principal, counselor or other school administrator describing the candidate's activities, leadership record, character, personality, initiative and home background. **Deadline for Receipt:** March 31.

1598 ■ ORANGE COUNTY COMMUNITY FOUNDATION
30 Corporate Park, Ste. 410
Irvine, CA 92606
Tel: (949)553-4202
Fax: (949)553-4211
E-mail: cmontesano@oc-cf.org
Web Site: http://www.oc-cf.org
to provide scholarship to the students currently pursuing a career in the restaurant/hotel management field.
Title of Award: Frank and Ruth Bila Scholarships **Area, Field, or Subject:** Hotel, institutional, and restaurant management. **Level of Education for which Award is Granted:** Undergraduate **Funds Available:** $5,000.
Eligibility Requirements: Applicant must: be a full-time student and have maintained a GPA greater than or equal to 3.0 for the preceding two years

of high school or college; be a United States citizen; an outstanding student between the ages of 17 and 30 years old. **Application Requirements:** Interested applicant may download an application from the Foundation Web site. In a maximum of 250 words, write abut our academic interests, educational plan, and the way in which your educational plan is appropriate to your situation, abilities and long-term goals. **Deadline for Receipt:** May 4. **Additional Information:** Claudia Montesano, 949-553-4202 ext. 46; cmontesano@oc-cf.org.

1599 ■ ORANGE COUNTY COMMUNITY FOUNDATION
30 Corporate Park, Ste. 410
Irvine, CA 92606
Tel: (949)553-4202
Fax: (949)553-4211
E-mail: cmontesano@oc-cf.org
Web Site: http://www.oc-cf.org
To provide scholarship opportunities to the eligible undergraduate students.
Title of Award: Lee Brennan Memorial Scholarships **Area, Field, or Subject:** General studies. **Level of Education for which Award is Granted:** Undergraduate **Number Awarded:** 1-2. **Funds Available:** $2,000.
Eligibility Requirements: Applicant must: be a graduating senior from Aliso Miguel High School, who is active in athletics or an active participant of a US Diving Southern Pacific Association Diving Team (please make sure to include this information in the application form); be a student who plans to enroll full-time at an accredited college or university and students who enroll in trade schools, for careers such as law enforcement, fire fighting, auto or computer repair, etc.; have at least a C average GPA. **Application Requirements:** Interested applicant may download an application from the Foundation's website. Applicant must also submit a 350-word essay describing the following: How athletics have influenced your life; Your academic plan and ways in which your plan is appropriate to your situation, abilities and long-term goals; Any special circumstances which have impacted or may impact your academic performance, community service or leadership activities. **Deadline for Receipt:** March 15. **Additional Information:** Claudia Montesano, 949-553-4202 ext. 46; cmontesano@oc-cf.org.

1600 ■ ORANGE COUNTY COMMUNITY FOUNDATION
30 Corporate Park, Ste. 410
Irvine, CA 92606
Tel: (949)553-4202
Fax: (949)553-4211
E-mail: cmontesano@oc-cf.org
Web Site: http://www.oc-cf.org
To help local students, with financial difficulties, continue their education.
Title of Award: Case-Swayne Company Scholarships **Area, Field, or Subject:** General studies. **Level of Education for which Award is Granted:** Undergraduate **Number Awarded:** 1-2. **Funds Available:** $800.
Eligibility Requirements: Applicants must: be high school seniors who are graduating from Santa Ana or Corona-Norco School Districts; must be students wishing to enroll full-time at an accredited two- or four-year college, university, or vocational/trade school; must demonstrate outstanding scholastic ability and/or leadership, financial need and determination to graduate from college. **Application Requirements:** Applicants may download an application from the Foundation's website. Applicants must submit an essay with maximum of 250-words. **Deadline for Receipt:** March 15. **Additional Information:** Claudia Montesano, 949-553-4202 ext. 46; cmontesano@oc-cf.org.

1601 ■ ORANGE COUNTY COMMUNITY FOUNDATION
30 Corporate Park, Ste. 410
Irvine, CA 92606
Tel: (949)553-4202
Fax: (949)553-4211
E-mail: cmontesano@oc-cf.org
Web Site: http://www.oc-cf.org
To assist talented and versatile students with first year expenses at the University of California, Berkeley.
Title of Award: Brad Evans Memorial Scholarships **Area, Field, or Subject:** General studies. **Level of Education for which Award is**

Granted: Undergraduate **Number Awarded:** 1. **Funds Available:** $3,000.

Eligibility Requirements: Applicants must: be Orange County high school graduating seniors who are attending school in the Newport Mesa Unified School District; have been accepted to an accredited program at the University of California, Berkeley; have demonstrated record of community service and leadership; have a minimum of 3.0 GPA. **Application Requirements:** Applicants must submit 250 words containing academic interests and educational plan (must be appropriate to situation, abilities and long-term goals). Applicants must completely fill out and sign the attached application. Applicants must submit official transcript of records; 2 letters of recommendation sealed and signed by the writer across the seal. Submit the following to the Foundation in one large envelope: Original plus two copies of your application and essay; Two letters of recommendation, each still sealed; Official Transcript of Grades. **Deadline for Receipt:** April 30. **Additional Information:** Claudia Montesano, 949-553-4202 ext. 46; cmontesano@oc-cf.org.

1602 ■ ORANGE COUNTY COMMUNITY FOUNDATION

30 Corporate Park, Ste. 410
Irvine, CA 92606
Tel: (949)553-4202
Fax: (949)553-4211
E-mail: cmontesano@oc-cf.org
Web Site: http://www.oc-cf.org
To help local youth pursue vocational, technical or advanced education.
Title of Award: MacPherson Scholarships **Area, Field, or Subject:** General studies. **Level of Education for which Award is Granted:** Undergraduate **Funds Available:** $500-$5,000.

Eligibility Requirements: Applicant must: be a high school senior graduating from an Orange County high school or attending an accredited Orange County community college; have a minimum 2.5 GPA; demonstrate financial need; be planning to attend an accredited job training or community college. **Application Requirements:** Interested applicant may download an application from the Foundation's website. Applicant must write at least one page, typed and double-space, answering the following questions: What are your career goals and how do you plan to reach those goals; Describe any classes that you have taken or accomplishments you have achieved that will help you realize your goals; Describe any special circumstances that you have experienced and how they have helped or deterred you from realizing your goals; Where do you picture yourself in five years; Please explain why it is important for you to receive this award. **Deadline for Receipt:** $500-$5,000. **Additional Information:** Claudia Montesano, 949-553-4202 ext. 46; cmontesano@oc-cf.org.

1603 ■ ORANGE COUNTY COMMUNITY FOUNDATION

30 Corporate Park, Ste. 410
Irvine, CA 92606
Tel: (949)553-4202
Fax: (949)553-4211
E-mail: cmontesano@oc-cf.org
Web Site: http://www.oc-cf.org
To assist people who have decided to make a change for the better, through education.
Title of Award: New Opportunities Through Retraining Scholarship Fund **Area, Field, or Subject:** General studies. **Level of Education for which Award is Granted:** Undergraduate **Number Awarded:** 3. **Funds Available:** $1,500.

Eligibility Requirements: Applicant must be: male or female, over the age of 25 years old; interested in improving job and/or educational skills; already applied to, or will apply to, a local junior college, vocational/trade school, or four-year college or university. **Application Requirements:** Applicant must submit an essay answering to the following question with a brief paragraph: Please describe your current financial status; What impact will this scholarship have on your situation; What type of retraining or education do you seek and why; How will retraining and furthering your education assist you in accomplishing your long-term goals. Answers must be typed and double-spaced, with the applicant's full name appearing in the upper right hand corner on all pages that are attached. **Additional Information:** Established in 2001. **Deadline for Receipt:** March 28. **Additional Information:** Claudia Montesano, 949-553-4202 ext. 46; cmontesano@oc-cf.org.

1604 ■ ORANGE COUNTY COMMUNITY FOUNDATION

30 Corporate Park, Ste. 410
Irvine, CA 92606
Tel: (949)553-4202
Fax: (949)553-4211
E-mail: cmontesano@oc-cf.org
Web Site: http://www.oc-cf.org
To award scholarship to the students who are residents of Orange County.
Title of Award: Orange County Centennial Academic Scholarships **Area, Field, or Subject:** Genera studies. **Level of Education for which Award is Granted:** Undergraduate **Number Awarded:** 6. **Funds Available:** $2,500.

Eligibility Requirements: Applicants must: be local high school graduating seniors who are residents of Orange County, California, and who are completing their last three years of high school in the county; be students who are planning to enroll full-time at an accredited college or university; be outstanding students, with a combined math, writing, and critical reading SAT score of at least 2100 and who have also demonstrated a record of community service and leadership in the area. **Application Requirements:** Interested applicants must include in their application a 250 words or less essay. Write about your academic interests and plans and the way in which your plan is appropriate to your situation, abilities and long-term goals. **Deadline for Receipt:** March 15. **Additional Information:** Claudia Montesano, 949-553-4202 ext. 46; cmontesano@oc-cf.org.

1605 ■ ORANGE COUNTY COMMUNITY FOUNDATION

30 Corporate Park, Ste. 410
Irvine, CA 92606
Tel: (949)553-4202
Fax: (949)553-4211
E-mail: cmontesano@oc-cf.org
Web Site: http://www.oc-cf.org
To award scholarship to the students who are residents of Orange County.
Title of Award: Orange County Centennial Certification Scholarships **Area, Field, or Subject:** General studies. **Level of Education for which Award is Granted:** Undergraduate **Funds Available:** No specific amount.

Eligibility Requirements: Applicants must: be local high school graduating seniors who are residents of Orange County, California and who are completing their last three years of high school in the county; be students who are planning to enter the work force after completing a two-year vocational program; have a demonstrated record of community service and leadership in the area. **Application Requirements:** Interested applicants may download an application from the Foundation's website. Applicants must include a 250 words essay in their application. Applicants must write about their academic interest and plans and the way in which their plan is appropriate to their situation, abilities and long-term goals. **Deadline for Receipt:** March 15. **Additional Information:** Claudia Montesano, 949-553-4202 ext. 46; cmontesano@oc-cf.org.

1606 ■ ORANGE COUNTY COMMUNITY FOUNDATION

30 Corporate Park, Ste. 410
Irvine, CA 92606
Tel: (949)553-4202
Fax: (949)553-4211
E-mail: cmontesano@oc-cf.org
Web Site: http://www.oc-cf.org
To assist people who have decided to make a change for the better, through education.
Title of Award: Orange County Tourism Council Scholarships **Area, Field, or Subject:** Travel and tourism. **Level of Education for which Award is Granted:** Undergraduate **Number Awarded:** 2. **Funds Available:** $2,500.

Eligibility Requirements: Applicant must: be male or female age 18 or over; be enrolled or accepted transfer student to California State University, Fullerton; be an Orange County resident; have demonstrated employment in the entertainment/tourism industry, either full-time, part-time or seasonally; Intent to pursue a career in the entertainment/tourism industry; have a minimum of 2.5 GPA. **Application Requirements:** Interested applicants may download an application from the Foundation's website and include a minimum of 200 words essay answering the following questions: Please describe your current financial status; What impact will this scholarship have on your situation; Please explain why you have chosen to have a career in the entertainment/tourism industry; How will retraining and furthering your education assist you in accomplishing your long-term goals. **Deadline for Receipt:** March 31. **Additional Information:** Claudia Montesano, 949-553-4202 ext. 46; cmontesano@oc-cf.org.

1607 ■ ORANGE COUNTY COMMUNITY FOUNDATION

30 Corporate Park, Ste. 410
Irvine, CA 92606
Tel: (949)553-4202
Fax: (949)553-4211
E-mail: cmontesano@oc-cf.org
Web Site: http://www.oc-cf.org
To provide scholarship to the women with high academic ability and significant financial need.
Title of Award: Margaret E. Oser Scholarships for Women **Area, Field, or Subject:** General studies. **Level of Education for which Award is Granted:** Undergraduate **Number Awarded:** 3-4. **Funds Available:** $6,000.
Eligibility Requirements: Applicant must: be enrolled at an accredited Orange County community college at the time of application; have completed at least 12 units of academic work, that are transferable to the California College or university system, within the previous two semesters; have maintained at least a 3.0 GPA in the transferable coursework; have identified a possible educational focus and have obtained a written recommendation from an instructor in that field. If selected for this program, demonstrate ability and intent to earn a bachelor's or advanced degree as a full-time student. **Application Requirements:** Interested applicant may download an application from the Foundation's website. Applicant must also write a maximum of 350 words essay in each of the following: Your academic plans, if you were to receive this stipend through your college graduation; Ways in which your strategy is appropriate to your situation, abilities and long-term goals; a difficult obstacle you have had to overcome in life and how you responded to the challenge. **Deadline for Receipt:** April 15. **Additional Information:** Claudia Montesano, 949-553-4202 ext. 46; cmontesano@oc-cf.org.

1608 ■ ORANGE COUNTY COMMUNITY FOUNDATION

30 Corporate Park, Ste. 410
Irvine, CA 92606
Tel: (949)553-4202
Fax: (949)553-4211
E-mail: cmontesano@oc-cf.org
Web Site: http://www.oc-cf.org
to provide graduating seniors with substantial financial assistance to pursue their undergraduate degree.
Title of Award: Mark P. Tiner Education Scholarships **Area, Field, or Subject:** General studies. **Level of Education for which Award is Granted:** Undergraduate **Funds Available:** $500.
Eligibility Requirements: Applicant must; be Orange County seniors from public and private high schools; have a minimum GPA of at least a 3.75; plan to enroll in a 4-year accredited college or university and fulfill one of the requirements during their senior year of high school; demonstrate financial need. **Application Requirements:** Interested applicant may download an application from the Foundation's website. Applicant must also write a 250-500 word essay, describing your academic goals and plans, describe how your plan is appropriate to your situation, abilities and overall goal. **Deadline for Receipt:** March 15. **Additional Information:** Claudia Montesano, 949-553-4202 ext. 46; cmontesano@oc-cf.org.

1609 ■ ORANGE COUNTY COMMUNITY FOUNDATION

30 Corporate Park, Ste. 410
Irvine, CA 92606
Tel: (949)553-4202
Fax: (949)553-4211
E-mail: cmontesano@oc-cf.org
Web Site: http://www.oc-cf.org
To provide financial assistance to students that graduated from the Whittier Union High School district.
Title of Award: James L. Warner Scholarships **Area, Field, or Subject:** General studies. **Level of Education for which Award is Granted:** Undergraduate **Funds Available:** $1,000-$2,000.
Eligibility Requirements: Students must have attended on the following high schools in the Whittier Union High School: California High School,

Santa Fe High School, Whittier High School, Frontier High School or Pioneer High School. Students must plan to attend on w of the following colleges: Pomona College, Whittier College, University of Southern California; Stanford University or any campus of the University of California system. Students must demonstrate financial need. **Application Requirements:** Interested applicant may download an application from the Foundation's website. A minimum of a one-page, typed, double-spaced essay should address the following: what are your goals in college; Describe your service to your school and community; Explain why you should be awarded this scholarship; How you have benefited from attending high school; Describe any special family or personal circumstance that has affected your achievement in school, work or your participation in school or community service. **Deadline for Receipt:** April 30. **Additional Information:** Claudia Montesano, 949-553-4202 ext. 46; cmontesano@oc-cf.org.

1610 ■ ORANGE COUNTY COMMUNITY FOUNDATION

30 Corporate Park, Ste. 410
Irvine, CA 92606
Tel: (949)553-4202
Fax: (949)553-4211
E-mail: cmontesano@oc-cf.org
Web Site: http://www.oc-cf.org
To award scholarship to the undergraduate student who is an Orange County resident.
Title of Award: Charles H. and Ethel E. Wolfe Scholarships **Area, Field, or Subject:** Genera studies. **Level of Education for which Award is Granted:** Undergraduate **Number Awarded:** 1. **Funds Available:** $2,000.
Eligibility Requirements: Student must: be recommended by the principal of the high school from which the student is graduating; demonstrate high scholastic achievement, financial need, and community involvement; proceed to enroll and study at a non-profit institution of higher learning within the continental United States. **Application Requirements:** Interested applicant may download an application from the Foundation's website. In a maximum of 250 words, write about your academic interests, educational plan, and the way in which your educational plan is appropriate to your situation, abilities and long-term goals. **Deadline for Receipt:** March 15. **Additional Information:** Claudia Montesano, 949-553-4202 ext. 46; cmontesano@oc-cf.org.

1611 ■ ORDER SONS OF ITALY IN AMERICA

219 E St. NE
Washington, DC 20002
Tel: (202)547-2900
Fax: (202)546-8168
Web Site: http://www.osia.org
To provide financial support for education of the US citizens of Italian descent.
Title of Award: Italian Language Scholarships **Area, Field, or Subject:** General studies. **Level of Education for which Award is Granted:** Undergraduate **Funds Available:** $5,000 to $25,000.
Eligibility Requirements: Applicants must be US citizens of Italian descent (at least one Italian or Italian American grandparent) their junior or senior year of undergraduate study for the Fall of 2008 term; majoring or minoring in Italian language studies at an accredited academic institution. **Application Requirements:** Applicants must submit cover sheet; official transcript; test scores; resume outlining extracurricular activities, work, experience, volunteer service and honors, especially as they relate to Italian language, culture and heritage; letters of recommendation; typewritten original essay of 500-700 words in Italian on why learning Italian is important in today's world and plan of how to use the language degree; and the processing fee. **Deadline for Receipt:** February 28.

1612 ■ ORDER SONS OF ITALY IN AMERICA

219 E St. NE
Washington, DC 20002
Tel: (202)547-2900
Fax: (202)546-8168
Web Site: http://www.osia.org
To provide financial support for the education of eligible individuals for the scholarship.
Title of Award: Order Sons of Italy Foundation General Scholarships **Area, Field, or Subject:** General studies. **Level of Education for which**

Award is Granted: Graduate, Undergraduate **Funds Available:** $5,000 to $25,000.

Eligibility Requirements: Applicants must be U.S. citizens of Italian descent enrolled in an undergraduate or graduate program at a four-year, accredited academic institution for the Fall 2008 term. **Application Requirements:** Applicants must submit cover sheet, official transcript, test scores, resume, letters of recommendation, essay, and the processing fee. **Deadline for Receipt:** February 28.

1613 ■ ORDER SONS OF ITALY IN AMERICA

219 E St. NE
Washington, DC 20002
Tel: (202)547-2900
Fax: (202)546-8168
Web Site: http://www.osia.org

To provide financial support to college bound high school senior demonstrating exceptional leadership, deep understanding and respect for the principles of the nation - liberty, freedom and equality.

Title of Award: Henry Salvatori Scholarships **Area, Field, or Subject:** General studies. **Level of Education for which Award is Granted:** Undergraduate **Funds Available:** $5,000 to $25,000.

Eligibility Requirements: Applicants must be U.S. citizens of Italian descent in their senior year of high school and planning to attend a four-year, accredited institution for the Fall 2008 term. **Application Requirements:** Applicants must submit cover sheet, official transcript, test scores, resume, two letters of recommendation from public figures whose careers have demonstrated a commitment to the principles the scholarship embodies, type-written original essay of 750-1,000 words concerning the declaration of independence, the constitution and the bill of rights - discussion of the relevance of these documents to the principles of liberty, freedom and equality in the United States and the processing fee. **Deadline for Receipt:** February 28.

1614 ■ ORGANIZATION OF AMERICAN STATES

1889 F St. NW
Washington, DC 20006
Tel: (202)458-6166
E-mail: scholarships@aos.org
Web Site: http://www.educoas.org

To assist the member states with their domestic efforts in pursuit of integral development goals by supporting human resource development in the priority areas; to promote and support human capacity development and the strengthening of bonds among peoples in the hemisphere by maximizing the number of scholarships awarded in reputable educational institutions in its member states with the resources available.

Title of Award: Organization of American States Academic Scholarships **Area, Field, or Subject:** General studies. **Level of Education for which Award is Granted:** Undergraduate **Funds Available:** No specific amount.

Eligibility Requirements: Applicants must be involved in undergraduate or graduate studies that lead to a degree and/or graduate research at a university or higher learning institution in a member state. **Application Requirements:** Applicants must accomplish application form. **Additional Information:** scholarships@aos.org

1615 ■ ORGANIZATION OF AMERICAN STATES

1889 F St. NW
Washington, DC 20006
Tel: (202)458-6166
E-mail: scholarships@aos.org
Web Site: http://www.educoas.org

To assist the member states with their domestic efforts in pursuit of integral development goals by supporting human resource development in the priority areas; to promote and support human capacity development and the strengthening of bonds among people in the hemisphere by maximizing the number of scholarships awarded in reputable educational institutions in its member states with the resources available.

Title of Award: Organization of American States AOS-Placed Scholarships **Area, Field, or Subject:** General studies. **Level of Education for which Award is Granted:** Undergraduate **Funds Available:** No specific amount.

Eligibility Requirements: Applicants must be enrolled in a university, college, or institution. **Application Requirements:** Applicants must complete the application form. **Additional Information:** scholarships@aos.org

1616 ■ ORGANIZATION OF AMERICAN STATES

1889 F St. NW
Washington, DC 20006
Tel: (202)458-6166
E-mail: scholarships@aos.org
Web Site: http://www.educoas.org

To assist the member states with their domestic efforts in pursuit of integral development goals by supporting human resource development in the priority areas; to promote and support human capacity development and the strengthening of bonds among people in the hemisphere by maximizing the number of scholarships awarded in reputable educational institutions in its member states with the resources available.

Title of Award: Organization of American States Graduate Scholarships **Area, Field, or Subject:** General studies. **Level of Education for which Award is Granted:** Undergraduate **Funds Available:** $30,000.

Eligibility Requirements: Applicants must be enrolled in a master's or doctorate degree program. **Application Requirements:** Applicants must complete the application form. **Additional Information:** scholarships@aos.org

1617 ■ ORGANIZATION OF AMERICAN STATES

1889 F St. NW
Washington, DC 20006
Tel: (202)458-6166
E-mail: scholarships@aos.org
Web Site: http://www.educoas.org

To assist the member states with their domestic efforts in pursuit of integral development goals by supporting human resource development in the priority areas; to promote and support human capacity development and the strengthening of bonds among peoples in the hemisphere by maximizing the number of scholarships awarded in reputable educational institutions in its member states with the resources available.

Title of Award: Organization of American States Self-Placed Scholarships **Area, Field, or Subject:** General studies. **Level of Education for which Award is Granted:** Undergraduate **Funds Available:** No specific amount.

Eligibility Requirements: Applicants must be enrolled in a university, college, or institution. **Application Requirements:** Applicants must complete the application form. **Additional Information:** scholarships@aos.org

1618 ■ ORGANIZATION OF CHINESE AMERICANS

1322 18th St. NW
Washington, DC 20036-1803
Tel: (202)223-5500
Fax: (202)296-0540
E-mail: oca@ocanational.org
Web Site: http://www.ocanatl.org

To provide financial assistance to APA high school seniors entering their first year of college in the upcoming Fall Quarter or Semester.

Title of Award: OCA Scholarships **Area, Field, or Subject:** General studies. **Level of Education for which Award is Granted:** Undergraduate **Funds Available:** No amount mentioned.

Eligibility Requirements: Applicants must be a current APA high school senior entering their first year of college in the upcoming 2008 Fall Semester/Quarter, demonstrate financial need, a permanent resident or U.S. citizen, and have a cumulative Grade Point Average (GPA) of 3.0 or above (on a 4.0 scale). **Application Requirements:** Applicants must submit resume, one page essay, high school transcript, letter of acceptance from college or university, print-out of student aid report (SAR), and financial Aid Award notification (FAN) from college or university. **Deadline for Receipt:** April 18.

1619 ■ OTTAWA CENTRE FOR RESEARCH AND INNOVATION

2625 Queensview Dr., Ste. 200
Ottawa, ON, Canada K2B 8K2
Tel: (613)828-6274
Fax: (613)726-3440
E-mail: worldclass@ocri.ca
Web Site: http://www.ocri.ca

To provide support for Black Canadian students intending to pursue their education.

Title of Award: Black Canadian Scholarships **Area, Field, or Subject:** General studies. **Level of Education for which Award is Granted:** Undergraduate **Funds Available:** $5,000. **Duration:** One year.

Eligibility Requirements: Applicant must be a Black Canadian student graduating from a high school in the city of Ottawa; must be admissible to a recognized Canadian university; must demonstrate a need of financial assistance; must be a Canadian citizen; and must demonstrate leadership in community involvement. **Application Requirements:** Applicants must submit a two-page essay explaining why the scholarship is important to the applicant and how the applicant will satisfy the eligibility criteria; must provide a photocopy of the applicant's latest official transcript of 6 Grade 12 courses with a 75%+average; must have a letter of recommendation from a teacher/guidance counselor in current academic year; must have proof of community service; must have proof of Canadian citizenship; and must have a detailed statement indicating the amount of money expected from various sources. Application form and requirements must be sent to Black Canadian Scholarship Fund, PO Box 8002, Ottawa, ON K1G 5H6. **Deadline for Receipt:** May 31.

1620 ■ OTTAWA CENTRE FOR RESEARCH AND INNOVATION

2625 Queensview Dr., Ste. 200
Ottawa, ON, Canada K2B 8K2
Tel: (613)828-6274
Fax: (613)726-3440
E-mail: worldclass@ocri.ca
Web Site: http://www.ocri.ca
To provide financial assistance for qualified individuals intending to pursue their studies.

Title of Award: George Joseph Cooper Awards **Area, Field, or Subject:** General studies. **Level of Education for which Award is Granted:** Undergraduate **Funds Available:** $1,000. **Duration:** One year.
Eligibility Requirements: Applicant must be a graduating student from a high school in the region of Ottawa; must have applied to a recognized college or university; must be entering a full-time program; and must demonstrate financial need and academic achievements. **Application Requirements:** Applicants must complete the application form, available online; must provide a letter of reference from a teacher/ guidance counselor; and must submit a copy of the latest transcript of record. **Deadline for Receipt:** April 14.

1621 ■ OTTAWA CENTRE FOR RESEARCH AND INNOVATION

2625 Queensview Dr., Ste. 200
Ottawa, ON, Canada K2B 8K2
Tel: (613)828-6274
Fax: (613)726-3440
E-mail: worldclass@ocri.ca
Web Site: http://www.ocri.ca
To provide financial assistance for qualified Ottawa students.

Title of Award: Lord Dundonald Chapter (IODE) Scholarships **Area, Field, or Subject:** General studies. **Level of Education for which Award is Granted:** Undergraduate **Funds Available:** $500. **Duration:** One year.
Eligibility Requirements: Applicant must be a student from a high school in the region of Ottawa; must have applied to a recognized college or university; must be entering a full-time program; and must demonstrate financial need and academic achievements. **Application Requirements:** Applicants must complete the application form, available online; must provide a letter of reference from a teacher/guidance counselor; and must submit a copy of the latest transcript of record. **Deadline for Receipt:** April 14.

1622 ■ OTTAWA CENTRE FOR RESEARCH AND INNOVATION

2625 Queensview Dr., Ste. 200
Ottawa, ON, Canada K2B 8K2
Tel: (613)828-6274
Fax: (613)726-3440
E-mail: worldclass@ocri.ca
Web Site: http://www.ocri.ca
To provide financial support for deserving Ottawa students.

Title of Award: Elizabeth Heath Post-Secondary Awards **Area, Field, or Subject:** General studies. **Level of Education for which Award is Granted:** Undergraduate **Number Awarded:** 2. **Funds Available:** $2,500. **Duration:** One year.
Eligibility Requirements: Applicant must be a graduating student from a high school in the region of Ottawa; must have applied to a recognized college or university; must be entering a full-time program; and must

demonstrate financial need and academic achievements. **Application Requirements:** Applicants must complete the application form, available online; must provide a letter of reference from a teacher/guidance counselor; and must submit a copy of the latest transcript of record. **Deadline for Receipt:** April 14.

1623 ■ OTTAWA CENTRE FOR RESEARCH AND INNOVATION

2625 Queensview Dr., Ste. 200
Ottawa, ON, Canada K2B 8K2
Tel: (613)828-6274
Fax: (613)726-3440
E-mail: worldclass@ocri.ca
Web Site: http://www.ocri.ca
To provide financial assistance for graduating high school students in the Ottawa region.

Title of Award: Elizabeth Heath Technical, Trades Training and Development Awards **Area, Field, or Subject:** General studies. **Level of Education for which Award is Granted:** Undergraduate **Number Awarded:** 3. **Funds Available:** $1,500. **Duration:** One year.
Eligibility Requirements: Applicant must be a student graduating from the apprenticeship Cooperative Education Studies program at a high school in the region of Ottawa; must be pursuing further education or training in an apprenticeship or skilled employment program; must demonstrate a need for financial assistance; and must have demonstrated diligence and determination both "on the job" and at school. **Application Requirements:** Applicants must complete the application form available online; must provide a letter of reference from a teacher/guidance counselor; and must submit a copy of the latest transcript of record. **Deadline for Receipt:** April 14.

1624 ■ OTTAWA CENTRE FOR RESEARCH AND INNOVATION

2625 Queensview Dr., Ste. 200
Ottawa, ON, Canada K2B 8K2
Tel: (613)828-6274
Fax: (613)726-3440
E-mail: worldclass@ocri.ca
Web Site: http://www.ocri.ca
To provide financial assistance to qualified individuals intending to pursue their education.

Title of Award: Barbara Ingram, Janet W. McCarthy and W.J.P. Jack Robertson Memorial Scholarships **Area, Field, or Subject:** General studies. **Level of Education for which Award is Granted:** Undergraduate **Number Awarded:** 2. **Funds Available:** $1,500. **Duration:** One year.
Eligibility Requirements: Applicant must be a graduating student from a high school in the region of Ottawa; must have applied to a recognized college or university; must be entering a full-time program; and must be a person with a physical disability. **Application Requirements:** Applicants must complete the application form, available online; must provide a letter of reference from a teacher/ guidance counselor; and must submit a copy of the latest transcript of record. **Deadline for Receipt:** April 14.

1625 ■ OTTAWA CENTRE FOR RESEARCH AND INNOVATION

2625 Queensview Dr., Ste. 200
Ottawa, ON, Canada K2B 8K2
Tel: (613)828-6274
Fax: (613)726-3440
E-mail: worldclass@ocri.ca
Web Site: http://www.ocri.ca
To provide financial assistance for qualified Ottawa students.

Title of Award: Kildonan Education Awards **Area, Field, or Subject:** General studies. **Level of Education for which Award is Granted:** Undergraduate **Number Awarded:** 3. **Funds Available:** $4,000. **Duration:** One year.
Eligibility Requirements: Applicant must be a graduating student from a high school in the region of Ottawa; must have applied to a recognized college or university; must be entering a full-time program; and must demonstrate both financial need and academic achievements. **Application Requirements:** Applicants must complete the application form, available online; must provide a letter of reference from a teacher/guidance counselor; and must submit a copy of the latest transcript of record. **Deadline for Receipt:** April 14.

1626 ■ OTTAWA CENTRE FOR RESEARCH AND INNOVATION

2625 Queensview Dr., Ste. 200
Ottawa, ON, Canada K2B 8K2

Tel: (613)828-6274
Fax: (613)726-3440
E-mail: worldclass@ocri.ca
Web Site: http://www.ocri.ca
To provide financial assistance for qualified Ottawa students.
Title of Award: Jack Meadows Memorial Awards **Area, Field, or Subject:** General studies. **Level of Education for which Award is Granted:** Undergraduate **Number Awarded:** 6. **Funds Available:** $2,500 (if attending college), $3,000 (if attending university). **Duration:** One year. **Eligibility Requirements:** Applicant must be a graduating student from a high school in the region of Ottawa; must have applied to a recognized college or university; must be entering a full-time program; and must demonstrate financial need and academic achievements. **Application Requirements:** Applicants must complete the application form, available online; must provide a letter of reference from a teacher/guidance counselor; and must submit a copy of the latest transcript of record. **Deadline for Receipt:** April 14.

1627 ■ OUTDOOR POWER EQUIPMENT AFTERMARKET ASSOCIATION

1726 M St. NW, Ste. 1101
Washington, DC 20036
Tel: (202)775-8605
Fax: (202)833-1577
E-mail: opeaa@opeaa.org
Web Site: http://www.opeaa.org
To provide financial assistance for the educational pursuits of employees of OPEEA members and their dependents.
Title of Award: Bill Nelson Scholarship Endowment **Area, Field, or Subject:** General studies. **Level of Education for which Award is Granted:** Undergraduate **Funds Available:** $1,000.
Eligibility Requirements: Applicants must be children, stepchildren, grandchildren and adopted children of employees of OPEEA members; and must be at least senior students in high school. **Application Requirements:** Applicants must fill out application form available in OPEEA website and submit along with sponsor information, essay (in 250 words) describing academic aspirations and two letters of reference.

1628 ■ OUTWARD BOUND

100 Mystery Point Rd.
Garrison, NY 10524
Tel: (845)424-4000
Fax: (845)424-4121
E-mail: info@outwardbound.org
Web Site: http://www.outwardbound.org
To recognize outstanding students who have leadership potential and are in need of financial assistance.
Title of Award: Marmot Leadership Scholarships **Area, Field, or Subject:** Community leadership. **Level of Education for which Award is Granted:** Postgraduate, Professional, Undergraduate **Funds Available:** Funds must be used for tuition only.
Eligibility Requirements: Applicant must be a graduating high school senior (age 17+) or a college/university student (age 23 maximum) who demonstrates leadership potential and financial need. **Application Requirements:** Applicants must submit a complete Marmot Leadership Scholarship Application, Essay Questions, and Financial Application; a $100 application fee; a letter of recommendation that can attest to the applicant's leadership qualities, experience and/or potential; a copy of the applicant's (or parents) most recent 1040 Federal Tax Form, including all schedules. For students under 21 or not self-supporting, both parents' income information is required. Send application to: Email scholarships@outwardbound.org, Subject: OBLS Application: Name
Fax (866)851-7738, Attention: Scholarship Awards Coordinator, Marmot Application; Mail - Scholarship Awards Coordinator, Marmot Application, Outward Bound Wilderness, 910 Jackson St., Golden, CO 80401.
Deadline for Receipt: April 16. **Additional Information:** Scholarship Awards Coordinator toll free number: 888-837-5204, email scholarships@outwardbound.org.

1629 ■ OUTWARD BOUND

100 Mystery Point Rd.
Garrison, NY 10524
Tel: (845)424-4000
Fax: (845)424-4121
E-mail: info@outwardbound.org
Web Site: http://www.outwardbound.org
For students who have demonstrated interest in community service and display potential leadership.
Title of Award: Outward Bound Wilderness Leadership Awards **Area, Field, or Subject:** Community leadership. **Level of Education for which Award is Granted:** High School, Professional **Funds Available:** No specific amount.
Eligibility Requirements: Candidates must be junior high school students; must be identified as candidates by a teacher or a staff. **Application Requirements:** Applicants must submit completed application with answers to essay questions posted in the website. **Additional Information:** Lisa Mattis, lmattis@outwardbound.org.

1630 ■ OWNER-OPERATOR INDEPENDENT DRIVERS ASSOCIATION

1 NW OOIDA Dr.
Grain Valley, MO 64029
Tel: (816)229-5791
Fax: (816)427-4468
E-mail: ooida@ooida.com
Web Site: http://www.ooida.com
To assist the children, grandchildren and legal dependents of OOIDA members in their effort to gain higher education.
Title of Award: Owner-Operator Independent Drivers Association Scholarships **Area, Field, or Subject:** General studies. **Level of Education for which Award is Granted:** Undergraduate **Funds Available:** $1,000. **Duration:** One academic year.
Eligibility Requirements: Applicants must be immediate family members of OOIDA. Scholarships are available for children, grandchildren, and legal dependents of OOIDA members. **Application Requirements:** Applicants must submit a 500-word essay; official certified high school transcript; proof of enrollment from institution of higher education. Application form and guidelines can be obtained from the OOIDA office or can be downloaded from the OOIDA website. **Deadline for Receipt:** February 1.

1631 ■ PAPER STOCK INDUSTRIES

3300 PGA Blvd., Ste. 635
Palm Beach Gardens, FL 33410-2811
Tel: (561)627-9191
E-mail: nktraders@tradersintl.net
Web Site: http://www.paperstockindustries.org
To provide financial assistance to students who wish to continue their education.
Title of Award: Paper Stock Industries/RRF Scholarships **Area, Field, or Subject:** General studies. **Level of Education for which Award is Granted:** Undergraduate **Funds Available:** $1,000.
Eligibility Requirements: Applicant must be a employee, son, daughter or spouse of an individual who has been employed for at least one year in a member firm of a PSI Chapter; must have at least a C+ average in high school and meet all the qualifications for admission to a regionally accredited two-year or four-year post secondary institution. **Application Requirements:** Applicants must submit a completed scholarship application; official transcripts of all high school and/or college grades, SAT, and/or ACT scores; two letters of recommendation; resume of the applicant's personal history; and a one-page short essay entitled "Why College is important to Me." **Deadline for Receipt:** March 15. **Additional Information:** Nini Krever at the above address.

1632 ■ PAPER STOCK INDUSTRIES CHAPTER OF ISRI

3300 PGA Blvd, Ste. 635
Palm Beach Gardens, FL 33410-2811
Tel: (561)627-9191
E-mail: nktraders@tradersintl.net
Web Site: http://www.paperstockindustries.org
To provide financial aid for employees of the Paper Stock Industries Chapter and their immediate families intending to pursue education.
Title of Award: Paper Stock Industries Chapter of ISRI Scholarship Program **Area, Field, or Subject:** General studies. **Level of Education for which Award is Granted:** Undergraduate **Number Awarded:** 4. **Funds Available:** $1,000. **Duration:** One year.
Eligibility Requirements: Applicant must be an employee, or an immediate relative (child or spouse) of an individual who has been employed for

at least one year by a member firm of the PSI Chapter; and must have at least a C+ average in high school. **Application Requirements:** Applicants must submit completed the scholarship application (downloadable from PSI website); official transcript of records (high school and college); standardized test scores: SAT and/or ACT; two letters of recommendation; a personal resume; and a one-page minimum essay on "Why College is Important to Me." Applicants must send an original and two copies of all necessary documents to: Nini Krever c/o Traders International Corp. 3300 PGA Blvd. Ste. 635, Palm Beach Gardens Florida 33410. **Deadline for Receipt:** March 15. **Additional Information:** Nini Krever.

1633 ■ PARKERSBURG AREA COMMUNITY FOUNDATION
501 Avery St.
Parkersburg, WV 26101
Tel: (304)428-4438; (866)428-4438
Fax: (304)428-1200
E-mail: info@pacfwv.com
Web Site: http://www.pacfwv.com
To provide financial assistance for qualified senior high school students from Point Pleasant High School.
Title of Award: Bob Adkins Memorial Scholarships **Area, Field, or Subject:** General studies. **Level of Education for which Award is Granted:** Undergraduate **Funds Available:** $250-$500.
Eligibility Requirements: Applicant must be a graduating senior from Point Pleasant High School; must have a minimum 2.0 GPA; must have financial need for assistance and must have participated in high school athletics (including team participation and/or support services to team, such as manager). **Application Requirements:** Applicants must submit a cover sheet (3 pages) and application form (4 pages); must have a personal essay; must have high school and/or post-secondary transcripts; must provide a letter of recommendation and a signed copy of the page of their or their parent's most recent tax return that indicates adjusted gross income; and must have a Student Aid Report showing estimated family contribution from FAFSA. Application form and other supporting documents must be sent to Our Community's Foundation, P.O Box 1762, Parkersburg, WV 26102. **Deadline for Receipt:** March 20.

1634 ■ PARKERSBURG AREA COMMUNITY FOUNDATION
501 Avery St.
Parkersburg, WV 26101
Tel: (304)428-4438; (866)428-4438
Fax: (304)428-1200
E-mail: info@pacfwv.com
Web Site: http://www.pacfwv.com
To provide financial assistance for qualified students from Parkersburg, Parkersburg South, Parkersburg Catholic, or Williamstown High School.
Title of Award: Ambrose-Ramsey Trust Scholarships **Area, Field, or Subject:** Ministry. **Level of Education for which Award is Granted:** Undergraduate **Funds Available:** $1,000-$3,000.
Eligibility Requirements: Applicant must be a graduate from Parkersburg, Parkersburg South, Parkersburg Catholic, or Williamstown High School with the desire to further their education in the study of the Methodist Ministry. **Application Requirements:** Applicants must submit a cover sheet (3 pages) and application form (4 pages); a personal essay; a high school and/or post-secondary transcript; a letter of recommendation; signed copy of the page of their or their parent's most recent tax return that indicates adjusted gross income; and a Student Aid Report showing estimated family contribution from FAFSA. Application form and other supporting documents must be sent to Our Community's Foundation, P.O Box 1762, Parkersburg, WV 26102. **Deadline for Receipt:** March 20.

1635 ■ PARKERSBURG AREA COMMUNITY FOUNDATION
501 Avery St.
Parkersburg, WV 26101
Tel: (304)428-4438; (866)428-4438
Fax: (304)428-1200
E-mail: info@pacfwv.com
Web Site: http://www.pacfwv.com
To provide financial support for deserving graduate seniors at Parkersburg High School.
Title of Award: Joe Barbarow Memorial Scholarships **Area, Field, or Subject:** General studies. **Level of Education for which Award is Granted:** Undergraduate **Funds Available:** $760.

Eligibility Requirements: Applicant must be a high school graduating senior and must have attended Hamilton Junior High in Wood County. **Application Requirements:** Applicants must submit a cover sheet (3 pages) and application form (4 pages); a personal essay; a high school and/or post-secondary transcript; a letter of recommendation; a signed copy of the page of their or their parent's most recent tax return that indicates adjusted gross income; and a Student Aid Report showing estimated family contribution from FAFSA. Application form and other supporting documents must be sent to Our Community's Foundation, P.O Box 1762, Parkersburg, WV 26102. **Deadline for Receipt:** March 20.

1636 ■ PARKERSBURG AREA COMMUNITY FOUNDATION
501 Avery St.
Parkersburg, WV 26101
Tel: (304)428-4438; (866)428-4438
Fax: (304)428-1200
E-mail: info@pacfwv.com
Web Site: http://www.pacfwv.com
To provide financial assistance for qualified senior high school at Parkersburg High School.
Title of Award: Lewis and Gurry Batten Scholarships **Area, Field, or Subject:** General studies. **Level of Education for which Award is Granted:** Undergraduate **Funds Available:** $600.
Eligibility Requirements: Applicant must be a Parkersburg High School graduating senior; must have a minimum of 2.5 GPA; and must be attending a four-year course in college or university. **Application Requirements:** Applicants must submit a cover sheet (3 pages) and application form (4 pages); a personal essay; a high school and/or post-secondary transcript; a letter of recommendation; a signed copy of the page of their or their parent's most recent tax return that indicates adjusted gross income; and a Student Aid Report showing estimated family contribution from FAFSA. Application form and other supporting documents must be sent to Our Community's Foundation, P.O Box 1762, Parkersburg, WV 26102. **Deadline for Receipt:** March 20.

1637 ■ PARKERSBURG AREA COMMUNITY FOUNDATION
501 Avery St.
Parkersburg, WV 26101
Tel: (304)428-4438; (866)428-4438
Fax: (304)428-1200
E-mail: info@pacfwv.com
Web Site: http://www.pacfwv.com
To provide financial support for qualified students of Wirt County High School.
Title of Award: Chester H. Bruce Memorial Scholarships **Area, Field, or Subject:** Christian education. **Level of Education for which Award is Granted:** Undergraduate **Funds Available:** $750. **Duration:** One year.
Eligibility Requirements: Applicant must be a graduating senior of Wirt County High School; must be pursuing vocational or trade studies or Christian ministry or service; must be enrolled as a full-time student in an undergraduate two-or-four-year program or a vocational program or graduate school; must have a minimum of 2.5 GPA; and must have a strong work ethic. **Application Requirements:** Applicants must submit a cover sheet (3 pages) and application form (4 pages); must have a personal essay; must have a high school and/or post-secondary transcript; must provide a letter of recommendation and a signed copy of the page of their or their parent's most recent tax return that indicates adjusted gross income; and must have a Student Aid Report showing estimated family contribution from FAFSA. Application form and other supporting documents must be sent to Our Community's Foundation, P.O Box 1762, Parkersburg, WV 26102. **Deadline for Receipt:** March 20.

1638 ■ PARKERSBURG AREA COMMUNITY FOUNDATION
501 Avery St.
Parkersburg, WV 26101
Tel: (304)428-4438; (866)428-4438
Fax: (304)428-1200
E-mail: info@pacfwv.com
Web Site: http://www.pacfwv.com
To provide financial assistance for qualified individuals in Wood County.
Title of Award: Bryce-Lietzke Martin Scholarships **Area, Field, or Subject:** General studies. **Level of Education for which Award is Granted:** Undergraduate **Funds Available:** $500-$750.

Eligibility Requirements: Applicant must be a Wood County resident; must have an interest in golf; must have a minimum of 2.5 GPA; and must be accepted or attending a post-secondary education. **Application Requirements:** Applicants must submit a cover sheet (3 pages) and application form (4 pages); must have a personal essay; must have a high school and/or postsecondary transcript; must provide a letter of recommendation and a signed copy of the page of their or their parent's most recent tax return that indicates adjusted gross income; and must have a Student Aid Report showing estimated family contribution, from FAFSA. Application form and other supporting documents must be sent to Our Community's Foundation, P.O Box 1762, Parkersburg, WV 26102. **Deadline for Receipt:** March 20.

1639 ■ PARKERSBURG AREA COMMUNITY FOUNDATION
501 Avery St.
Parkersburg, WV 26101
Tel: (304)428-4438; (866)428-4438
Fax: (304)428-1200
E-mail: info@pacfwv.com
Web Site: http://www.pacfwv.com
To encourage graduating students of Williamstown High School to pursue their education.
Title of Award: Freda Burge Scholarships **Area, Field, or Subject:** General studies. **Level of Education for which Award is Granted:** Undergraduate **Funds Available:** $600.
Eligibility Requirements: Applicant must be a Williamstown High School graduating senior; must be planning to attend West Virginia University-Parkersburg full-time; and must have a minimum of 2.5 GPA. **Application Requirements:** Applicants must submit a cover sheet (3 pages) and application form (4 pages); must have a personal essay; must have a high school and/or post-secondary transcript; must provide a letter of recommendation and a signed copy of the page of their or their parent's most recent tax return that indicates adjusted gross income; and must have a Student Aid Report showing estimated family contribution, from FAFSA. Application form and other supporting documents must be sent to Our Community's Foundation P.O Box 1762, Parkersburg, WV 26102. **Deadline for Receipt:** March 20.

1640 ■ PARKERSBURG AREA COMMUNITY FOUNDATION
501 Avery St.
Parkersburg, WV 26101
Tel: (304)428-4438; (866)428-4438
Fax: (304)428-1200
E-mail: info@pacfwv.com
Web Site: http://www.pacfwv.com
To provide financial assistance for qualified graduating high school students at Parkersburg High School.
Title of Award: Dwight O. Conner and Ellen Conner Lepp Scholarships **Area, Field, or Subject:** General studies. **Level of Education for which Award is Granted:** Undergraduate **Funds Available:** $240.
Eligibility Requirements: Applicant must be a Parkersburg High School graduating senior. **Application Requirements:** Applicants must submit a cover sheet (3 pages) and application form (4 pages); must have a personal essay; must have a high school and/or post-secondary transcript; must provide a letter of recommendation in a signed, copy of the page of their or their parent's most recent tax return that indicates adjusted gross income; and must have a Student Aid Report showing estimated family contribution from FAFSA. Application form and other supporting documents must be sent to Our Community's Foundation, P.O Box 1762, Parkersburg, WV 26102. **Deadline for Receipt:** March 20.

1641 ■ PARKERSBURG AREA COMMUNITY FOUNDATION
501 Avery St.
Parkersburg, WV 26101
Tel: (304)428-4438; (866)428-4438
Fax: (304)428-1200
E-mail: info@pacfwv.com
Web Site: http://www.pacfwv.com
To encourage the graduating students to pursue their education.
Title of Award: Cindy Curry Memorial Scholarships **Area, Field, or Subject:** General studies. **Level of Education for which Award is Granted:** Undergraduate **Funds Available:** $1,000.
Eligibility Requirements: Applicants must be graduating high school seniors from any Wood County high school; must be planning to attend an accredited West Virginia college or university full-time; must have a minimum of 3.0 GPA; and must have a strong motivation to attend school. **Application Requirements:** Applicants must submit a cover sheet (3 pages) and application form (4 pages); must have a personal essay; must have a high school and/or post- secondary transcript; must provide a letter of recommendation and a signed copy of the page of their or their parent's most recent tax return that indicates adjusted gross income; and must have a Student Aid Report, showing estimated family contribution, from FAFSA. Application form and other supporting documents must be sent to Our Community's Foundation, P.O Box 1762, Parkersburg, WV 26102. **Deadline for Receipt:** March 20.

1642 ■ PARKERSBURG AREA COMMUNITY FOUNDATION
501 Avery St.
Parkersburg, WV 26101
Tel: (304)428-4438; (866)428-4438
Fax: (304)428-1200
E-mail: info@pacfwv.com
Web Site: http://www.pacfwv.com
To encourage the graduating seniors of Parkersburg High School to pursue their education in either the state of West Virginia or Ohio.
Title of Award: Lawrence E. Davis Scholarships **Area, Field, or Subject:** General studies. **Level of Education for which Award is Granted:** Undergraduate **Funds Available:** $900.
Eligibility Requirements: Applicants must be graduating seniors from Parkersburg High School who have been admitted to attend an accredited four-year institution of higher education in either the state of West Virginia or Ohio as full-time students, with a minimum 2.5 GPA. **Application Requirements:** Applicants must submit a cover sheet (3 pages) and application form (4 pages); must have a personal essay; must have a high school and/or post-secondary transcript; must provide a letter of recommendation in a signed, copy of the page of their or their parent's most recent tax return that indicates adjusted gross income; and must have a Student Aid Report showing estimated family contribution from FAFSA. Application form and other supporting documents must be sent to Our Community's Foundation, P.O Box 1762, Parkersburg, WV 26102. **Deadline for Receipt:** March 20.

1643 ■ PARKERSBURG AREA COMMUNITY FOUNDATION
501 Avery St.
Parkersburg, WV 26101
Tel: (304)428-4438; (866)428-4438
Fax: (304)428-1200
E-mail: info@pacfwv.com
Web Site: http://www.pacfwv.com
To encourage the graduating students of Doddridge County High School to pursue their education.
Title of Award: Doddridge County Promise Scholarships **Area, Field, or Subject:** General studies. **Level of Education for which Award is Granted:** Undergraduate **Funds Available:** $500-$1,000.
Eligibility Requirements: Applicants must be graduating high school seniors or graduates of Doddridge County High School who have been admitted to the college of their choice; must have a GPA of 3.2 or above, be in the top 20% of the class, ACT of 21 or above or SAT of 1100 or above; must have followed a college-bound curriculum; and must have financial need. **Application Requirements:** Applicants must submit a cover sheet (3 pages) and application form (4 pages); must have a personal essay; must have a high school and/or post-secondary transcript; must provide a letter of recommendation and a signed copy of the page of their or their parent's most recent tax return that indicates adjusted gross income; and must have a Student Aid Report showing estimated family contribution from FAFSA. Application form and other supporting documents must be sent to Our Community's Foundation, P.O Box 1762, Parkersburg, WV 26102. **Deadline for Receipt:** March 20.

1644 ■ PARKERSBURG AREA COMMUNITY FOUNDATION
501 Avery St.
Parkersburg, WV 26101
Tel: (304)428-4438; (866)428-4438
Fax: (304)428-1200
E-mail: info@pacfwv.com
Web Site: http://www.pacfwv.com

To provide financial assistance for qualified graduating seniors at Ravenswood High School.

Title of Award: Deborah Gandee Dudding Memorial Scholarships **Area, Field, or Subject:** General studies. **Level of Education for which Award is Granted:** Undergraduate **Funds Available:** $250-$500.

Eligibility Requirements: Applicant must be a Ravenswood High School graduating senior; must have a minimum of 2.5 GPA. **Application Requirements:** Applicants must submit a cover sheet (3 pages) and application form (4 pages); must have a personal essay; must have high school and/or post-secondary transcripts; must provide a letter of recommendation and a signed copy of the page of their or their parent's most recent tax return that indicates adjusted gross income; and must have a Student Aid Report showing estimated family contribution, from FAFSA. Application form and other supporting documents must be sent to Our Community's Foundation, P.O Box 1762, Parkersburg, WV 26102. **Deadline for Receipt:** March 20.

1645 ■ PARKERSBURG AREA COMMUNITY FOUNDATION
501 Avery St.
Parkersburg, WV 26101
Tel: (304)428-4438; (866)428-4438
Fax: (304)428-1200
E-mail: info@pacfwv.com
Web Site: http://www.pacfwv.com
To encourage graduating seniors at Parkersburg High School to pursue their education.

Title of Award: David Edward Farson Scholarships **Area, Field, or Subject:** General studies. **Level of Education for which Award is Granted:** Undergraduate **Funds Available:** $1,500.

Eligibility Requirements: Applicant must be a Parkersburg High School graduating senior; must be planning to attend Marshall University. **Application Requirements:** Applicants must submit a cover sheet (3 pages) and application form (4 pages); must have a personal essay; must have high school and/or post-secondary transcripts; must provide a letter of recommendation and a signed copy of the page of their or their parent's most recent tax return that indicates adjusted gross income; and must have a Student Aid Report showing estimated family contribution, from FAFSA. Application form and other supporting documents must be sent to Our Community's Foundation, P.O Box 1762, Parkersburg, WV 26102. **Deadline for Receipt:** March 20.

1646 ■ PARKERSBURG AREA COMMUNITY FOUNDATION
501 Avery St.
Parkersburg, WV 26101
Tel: (304)428-4438; (866)428-4438
Fax: (304)428-1200
E-mail: info@pacfwv.com
Web Site: http://www.pacfwv.com
To provide financial assistance for qualified individuals intending to pursue their education.

Title of Award: Fostering Hope Scholarship Fund **Area, Field, or Subject:** General studies. **Level of Education for which Award is Granted:** Undergraduate **Funds Available:** $250-$500.

Eligibility Requirements: Applicants must be students who are actively enrolled, or have been enrolled, in the foster care system; must be WV residents; must be admitted to a course of study at a post-high school educational institution for the upcoming year. **Application Requirements:** Applicants must submit a cover sheet (3 pages) and application form (4 pages); must have a personal essay; must have high school and/or post-secondary transcripts; must provide a letter of recommendation and a signed copy of the page of their or their parent's most recent tax return that indicates adjusted gross income; and must have a Student Aid Report showing estimated family contribution, from FAFSA. Application form and other supporting documents must be sent to Our Community's Foundation, P.O Box 1762, Parkersburg, WV 26102. **Deadline for Receipt:** March 20.

1647 ■ PARKERSBURG AREA COMMUNITY FOUNDATION
501 Avery St.
Parkersburg, WV 26101
Tel: (304)428-4438; (866)428-4438
Fax: (304)428-1200
E-mail: info@pacfwv.com

Web Site: http://www.pacfwv.com
To provide financial assistance for qualified graduating seniors at Parkersburg South High School.

Title of Award: William E. "Bill" Gallagher Scholarships **Area, Field, or Subject:** General studies. **Level of Education for which Award is Granted:** Undergraduate **Funds Available:** $500.

Eligibility Requirements: Applicants must be graduating seniors at Parkersburg South High School who have been admitted to attend Glenville State College in Glenville, WV, or Alderson Broaddus College in Philippi, WV. **Application Requirements:** Applicants must submit a cover sheet (3 pages) and application form (4 pages); must have a personal essay; must have high school and/or post-secondary transcripts; must provide a letter of recommendation and a signed copy of the page of their or their parent's most recent tax return that indicates adjusted gross income; and must have a Student Aid Report, showing estimated family contribution from FAFSA. Application form and other supporting documents must be sent to Our Community's Foundation, P.O Box 1762, Parkersburg, WV 26102. **Deadline for Receipt:** March 20.

1648 ■ PARKERSBURG AREA COMMUNITY FOUNDATION
501 Avery St.
Parkersburg, WV 26101
Tel: (304)428-4438; (866)428-4438
Fax: (304)428-1200
E-mail: info@pacfwv.com
Web Site: http://www.pacfwv.com
To encourage graduating students to pursue their post-secondary education.

Title of Award: Shane Gilbert Memorial Scholarships **Area, Field, or Subject:** General studies. **Level of Education for which Award is Granted:** Undergraduate **Funds Available:** $1,000.

Eligibility Requirements: Applicant must be a Wood County Technical/Caperton Canter graduating senior intending to pursue post-secondary education. **Application Requirements:** Applicants must submit a cover sheet (3 pages) and application form (4 pages); must have a personal essay; must have a high school and/or post-secondary transcript; must provide a letter of recommendation and a signed copy of the page of their or their parent's most recent tax return that indicates adjusted gross income; and must have a Student Aid Report showing estimated family contribution from FAFSA. Application form and other supporting documents must be sent to Our Community's Foundation, P.O Box 1762, Parkersburg, WV 26102. **Deadline for Receipt:** March 20.

1649 ■ PARKERSBURG AREA COMMUNITY FOUNDATION
501 Avery St.
Parkersburg, WV 26101
Tel: (304)428-4438; (866)428-4438
Fax: (304)428-1200
E-mail: info@pacfwv.com
Web Site: http://www.pacfwv.com
To encourage graduating seniors to pursue higher level education.

Title of Award: Russ Grant Memorial Scholarship for Tennis **Area, Field, or Subject:** General studies. **Level of Education for which Award is Granted:** Undergraduate **Funds Available:** $800.

Eligibility Requirements: Applicants must be graduating seniors from Parkersburg High School, Parkersburg South High School or Parkersburg Catholic High School; must have shown evidence of an interest in tennis; must be pursuing higher level education; and must have a minimum of 2.5 GPA. **Application Requirements:** Applicants must submit a cover sheet (3 pages) and application form (4 pages); must have a personal essay; must have a high school and/or post-secondary transcript; must provide a letter of recommendation and a signed copy of the page of their or their parent's most recent tax return that indicates adjusted gross income; and must have a Student Aid Report showing estimated family contribution from FAFSA. Application form and other supporting documents must be sent to Our Community's Foundation, P.O Box 1762, Parkersburg, WV 26102. **Deadline for Receipt:** March 20.

1650 ■ PARKERSBURG AREA COMMUNITY FOUNDATION
501 Avery St.
Parkersburg, WV 26101
Tel: (304)428-4438; (866)428-4438
Fax: (304)428-1200

E-mail: info@pacfwv.com
Web Site: http://www.pacfwv.com
To encourage the graduating students of Ripley High School to pursue their education.
Title of Award: Sarah Gwisdalla Memorial Scholarships **Area, Field, or Subject:** General studies. **Level of Education for which Award is Granted:** Undergraduate **Funds Available:** $250-$500.
Eligibility Requirements: Applicant must be a Ripley High School graduating senior with a minimum of 3.0 GPA. **Application Requirements:** Applicants must submit a cover sheet (3 pages) and application form (4 pages); must have a personal essay; must have a high school and/or post-secondary transcript; must provide a letter of recommendation in a signed, copy of the page of their or their parent's most recent tax return that indicates adjusted gross income; must have a Student Aid Report, showing estimated family contribution from FAFSA. Application form and other supporting documents must be sent to Our Community's Foundation, P.O Box 1762, Parkersburg, WV 26102. **Deadline for Receipt:** March 20.

1651 ■ PARKERSBURG AREA COMMUNITY FOUNDATION
501 Avery St.
Parkersburg, WV 26101
Tel: (304)428-4438; (866)428-4438
Fax: (304)428-1200
E-mail: info@pacfwv.com
Web Site: http://www.pacfwv.com
To encourage the graduate students of Ravenswood High School to pursue their studies.
Title of Award: Nathaniel Hafer Memorial Scholarships **Area, Field, or Subject:** General studies. **Level of Education for which Award is Granted:** Undergraduate **Funds Available:** $250-$500.
Eligibility Requirements: Applicant must be a Ravenswood High School graduating senior; must have a minimum 2.0 GPA. **Application Requirements:** Applicants must submit a cover sheet (3 pages) and application form (4 pages); must have a personal essay; must have a high school and/or post-secondary transcript; must provide a letter of recommendation and a signed copy of the page of their or their parent's most recent tax return that indicates adjusted gross income; and must have a Student Aid Report showing estimated family contribution from FAFSA. Application form and other supporting documents must be sent to Our Community's Foundation, P.O. Box 1762, Parkersburg, WV 26102. **Deadline for Receipt:** March 20.

1652 ■ PARKERSBURG AREA COMMUNITY FOUNDATION
501 Avery St.
Parkersburg, WV 26101
Tel: (304)428-4438; (866)428-4438
Fax: (304)428-1200
E-mail: info@pacfwv.com
Web Site: http://www.pacfwv.com
To provide financial assistance for the residents or graduates of Wirt County.
Title of Award: Clayburn and Garnet R. Hanna Scholarships **Area, Field, or Subject:** General studies. **Level of Education for which Award is Granted:** Undergraduate **Funds Available:** $540.
Eligibility Requirements: Applicant must be a resident of Wirt County or graduate of Wirt County High School; must be planning to attend a post-secondary educational institution full-time. **Application Requirements:** Applicants must submit a cover sheet (3 pages) and application form (4 pages); must have a personal essay; must have a high school and/or post-secondary transcript; must provide a letter of recommendation and a signed copy of the page of their or their parent's most recent tax return that indicates adjusted gross income; and must have a Student Aid Report showing estimated family contribution from FAFSA. Application form and other supporting documents must be sent to Our Community's Foundation, P.O Box 1762, Parkersburg, WV 26102. **Deadline for Receipt:** Maorch 20.

1653 ■ PARKERSBURG AREA COMMUNITY FOUNDATION
501 Avery St.
Parkersburg, WV 26101
Tel: (304)428-4438; (866)428-4438
Fax: (304)428-1200

E-mail: info@pacfwv.com
Web Site: http://www.pacfwv.com
To provide financial assistance for graduating seniors from Ritchie County High School.
Title of Award: H.G. Hardbarger Science and Mathematics Awards **Area, Field, or Subject:** General studies. **Level of Education for which Award is Granted:** Undergraduate **Funds Available:** $670.
Eligibility Requirements: Applicant must be a graduating senior from Ritchie County High School who has demonstrated achievement in the fields of Math/Science. **Application Requirements:** Applicants must submit a cover sheet (3 pages) and application form (4 pages); must have a personal essay; must have high school and/or post-secondary transcripts; must provide a letter of recommendation and a signed copy of the page of their or their parent's most recent tax return that indicates adjusted gross income; and must have a Student Aid Report showing estimated family contribution, from FAFSA. Application form and other supporting documents must be sent to Our Community's Foundation, P.O Box 1762, Parkersburg, WV 26102. **Deadline for Receipt:** March 20.

1654 ■ PARKERSBURG AREA COMMUNITY FOUNDATION
501 Avery St.
Parkersburg, WV 26101
Tel: (304)428-4438; (866)428-4438
Fax: (304)428-1200
E-mail: info@pacfwv.com
Web Site: http://www.pacfwv.com
To provide financial support for qualified graduating female high school students of Wood County, WV.
Title of Award: Ruth Harris Memorial Scholarships **Area, Field, or Subject:** General studies. **Level of Education for which Award is Granted:** Undergraduate **Funds Available:** $1,000.
Eligibility Requirements: Applicant must be a graduating female high school student who is a resident of Wood County, WV, not to be over 20 years of age at first selection and must be planning to attend West Virginia University. **Application Requirements:** Applicants must submit a cover sheet (3 pages) and application form (4 pages); must have a personal essay; must have high school and/or post-secondary transcripts; must provide a letter of recommendation and a signed copy of the page of their or their parent's most recent tax return that indicates adjusted gross income; must have a Student Aid Report, showing estimated family contribution, from FAFSA. Application form and other supporting documents must be sent to Our Community's Foundation, P.O Box 1762, Parkersburg, WV 26102. **Deadline for Receipt:** March 20.

1655 ■ PARKERSBURG AREA COMMUNITY FOUNDATION
501 Avery St.
Parkersburg, WV 26101
Tel: (304)428-4438; (866)428-4438
Fax: (304)428-1200
E-mail: info@pacfwv.com
Web Site: http://www.pacfwv.com
To provide financial assistance for qualified graduating seniors from Parkersburg High School intending to pursue higher education.
Title of Award: Harry C. Hartleben III. Scholarships **Area, Field, or Subject:** General studies. **Level of Education for which Award is Granted:** Undergraduate **Funds Available:** $300.
Eligibility Requirements: Applicant must be a graduating senior from Parkersburg High School who plans to pursue higher education; and must have a minimum 3.0 GPA. **Application Requirements:** Applicants must submit a cover sheet (3 pages) and application form (4 pages); must have a personal essay; must have high school and/or post- secondary transcripts; must provide a letter of recommendation; copy of the page of their or their parent's most recent tax return that indicates adjusted gross income; and must have a Student Aid Report showing estimated family contribution, from FAFSA. Application form and other supporting documents must be sent to Our Community's Foundation, P.O Box 1762, Parkersburg, WV 26102. **Deadline for Receipt:** March 20.

1656 ■ PARKERSBURG AREA COMMUNITY FOUNDATION
501 Avery St.
Parkersburg, WV 26101
Tel: (304)428-4438; (866)428-4438
Fax: (304)428-1200

E-mail: info@pacfwv.com

Web Site: http://www.pacfwv.com

To encourage the graduating students of Ritchie County High School to pursue their education.

Title of Award: Gregory Lynn Haught Citizenship Awards **Area, Field, or Subject:** General studies. **Level of Education for which Award is Granted:** Undergraduate **Funds Available:** $1,000.

Eligibility Requirements: Applicant must be a Ritchie County High School graduating senior. **Application Requirements:** Applicants must submit a cover sheet (3 pages) and application form (4 pages); must have a personal essay; must have a high school and/or postsecondary transcript; must provide a letter of recommendation and a signed copy of the page of their or their parent's most recent tax return that indicates adjusted gross income; and must have a Student Aid Report showing estimated family contribution from FAFSA. Application form and other supporting documents must be sent to Our Community's Foundation, P.O Box 1762, Parkersburg, WV 26102. **Deadline for Receipt:** March 20.

1657 ■ PARKERSBURG AREA COMMUNITY FOUNDATION

501 Avery St.

Parkersburg, WV 26101

Tel: (304)428-4438; (866)428-4438

Fax: (304)428-1200

E-mail: info@pacfwv.com

Web Site: http://www.pacfwv.com

To provide financial support for qualified students intending to attend Marietta College.

Title of Award: Dorcas Edmonson Haught Scholarships **Area, Field, or Subject:** General studies. **Level of Education for which Award is Granted:** Undergraduate **Funds Available:** $250.

Eligibility Requirements: Applicant must be a graduating Parkersburg High School senior who plans to attend Marietta College. **Application Requirements:** Applicants must submit a cover sheet (3 pages) and application form (4 pages); must have a personal essay; must have a high school and/or post-secondary transcript; must provide a letter of recommendation; copy of the page of their or their parent's most recent tax return that indicates adjusted gross income; and a Student Aid Report showing estimated family contribution, from FAFSA. Application form and other supporting documents must be sent to Our Community's Foundation, P.O Box 1762, Parkersburg, WV 26102. **Deadline for Receipt:** March 20.

1658 ■ PARKERSBURG AREA COMMUNITY FOUNDATION

501 Avery St.

Parkersburg, WV 26101

Tel: (304)428-4438; (866)428-4438

Fax: (304)428-1200

E-mail: info@pacfwv.com

Web Site: http://www.pacfwv.com

To encourage graduating students to pursue their education.

Title of Award: Ella Beren Hersch Scholarships **Area, Field, or Subject:** General studies. **Level of Education for which Award is Granted:** Undergraduate **Funds Available:** $1,400.

Eligibility Requirements: Applicants must be a Parkersburg High School graduating senior. **Application Requirements:** Applicants must submit a cover sheet (3 pages) and application form (4 pages); must have a personal essay; must have a high school and/or post-secondary transcript; must provide a letter of recommendation and a signed copy of the page of their or their parent's most recent tax return that indicates adjusted gross income; and must have a Student Aid Report showing estimated family contribution from FAFSA. Application form and other supporting documents must be sent to Our Community's Foundation, P.O Box 1762, Parkersburg, WV 26102. **Deadline for Receipt:** March 20.

1659 ■ PARKERSBURG AREA COMMUNITY FOUNDATION

501 Avery St.

Parkersburg, WV 26101

Tel: (304)428-4438; (866)428-4438

Fax: (304)428-1200

E-mail: info@pacfwv.com

Web Site: http://www.pacfwv.com

To encourage the graduating seniors of Parkersburg South High School to pursue their college degree.

Title of Award: Holly Jackson-Wuller Memorial Scholarships **Area, Field, or Subject:** General studies. **Level of Education for which Award is Granted:** Undergraduate **Funds Available:** $500.

Eligibility Requirements: Applicant must be a graduating senior from Parkersburg South High School planning to attend Marshall University, with minimum 2.5 GPA. **Application Requirements:** Applicants must submit a cover sheet (3 pages) and application form (4 pages); must have a personal essay; must have a high school and/or post-secondary transcript; must provide a letter of recommendation and a signed copy of the page of their or their parent's most recent tax return that indicates adjusted gross income; and must have a Student Aid Report showing estimated family contribution, from FAFSA. Application form and other supporting documents must be sent to Our Community's Foundation, P.O Box 1762, Parkersburg, WV 26102. **Deadline for Receipt:** March 20.

1660 ■ PARKERSBURG AREA COMMUNITY FOUNDATION

501 Avery St.

Parkersburg, WV 26101

Tel: (304)428-4438; (866)428-4438

Fax: (304)428-1200

E-mail: info@pacfwv.com

Web Site: http://www.pacfwv.com

To provide financial support for graduating high school seniors or graduates of Doddridge County High School.

Title of Award: K.A.S.A Memorial Scholarships **Area, Field, or Subject:** General studies. **Level of Education for which Award is Granted:** Undergraduate **Funds Available:** $1,100.

Eligibility Requirements: Applicant must be a graduating high school senior or graduate of Doddridge County High School; must have a minimum GPA of 2.5. **Application Requirements:** Applicants must submit a cover sheet (3 pages) and application form (4 pages); must have a personal essay; must have a high school and/or post-secondary transcript; must provide a letter of recommendation; copy of the page of their or their parent's most recent tax return that indicates adjusted gross income; and a Student Aid Report showing estimated family contribution from FAFSA. Application form and other supporting documents must be sent to Our Community's Foundation, P.O Box 1762, Parkersburg, WV 26102. **Deadline for Receipt:** March 20.

1661 ■ PARKERSBURG AREA COMMUNITY FOUNDATION

501 Avery St.

Parkersburg, WV 26101

Tel: (304)428-4438; (866)428-4438

Fax: (304)428-1200

E-mail: info@pacfwv.com

Web Site: http://www.pacfwv.com

To provide financial assistance for qualified graduating seniors of Ravenswood High School.

Title of Award: Dr. Charles Kelly Memorial Scholarships **Area, Field, or Subject:** General studies. **Level of Education for which Award is Granted:** Undergraduate **Funds Available:** $250-$500.

Eligibility Requirements: Applicant must be a Ravenswood High School graduating senior planning to attend Marshall University. **Application Requirements:** Applicants must submit a cover sheet (3 pages) and application form (4 pages); must have a personal essay; must have a high school and/or post-secondary transcript; must provide a letter of recommendation; copy of the page of their or their parent's most recent tax return that indicates adjusted gross income; and a Student Aid Report showing estimated family contribution from FAFSA. Application form and other supporting documents must be sent to Our Community's Foundation, P.O Box 1762, Parkersburg, WV 26102. **Deadline for Receipt:** March 20.

1662 ■ PARKERSBURG AREA COMMUNITY FOUNDATION

501 Avery St.

Parkersburg, WV 26101

Tel: (304)428-4438; (866)428-4438

Fax: (304)428-1200

E-mail: info@pacfwv.com

Web Site: http://www.pacfwv.com

To assist Ripley High School graduating seniors.

Title of Award: Judge Oliver Kessel Memorial Scholarship-Ripley Rotary **Area, Field, or Subject:** General studies. **Level of Education for which Award is Granted:** Undergraduate **Funds Available:** $500.

Eligibility Requirements: Applicant must be a Ripley High School graduating senior with a minimum GPA of 2.0. **Application Requirements:** Applicants must submit a cover sheet (3 pages) and application form (4 pages); must have a personal essay; must have a high school and/or postsecondary transcript; must provide a letter of recommendation; copy of the page of their or their parent's most recent tax return that indicates adjusted gross income; and a Student Aid Report showing estimated family contribution from FAFSA. Application form and other supporting documents must be sent to Our Community's Foundation, P.O Box 1762, Parkersburg, WV 26102. **Deadline for Receipt:** March 20.

1663 ■ PARKERSBURG AREA COMMUNITY FOUNDATION

501 Avery St.
Parkersburg, WV 26101
Tel: (304)428-4438; (866)428-4438 ·
Fax: (304)428-1200
E-mail: info@pacfwv.com
Web Site: http://www.pacfwv.com
To provide financial assistance for deserving students intending to pursue their education.
Title of Award: Langfitt-Ambrose Trust Fund **Area, Field, or Subject:** General studies. **Level of Education for which Award is Granted:** Undergraduate **Funds Available:** $500-$1,000.
Eligibility Requirements: Applicant must be a graduate from Parkersburg, Parkersburg South, Parkersburg Catholic, or Williamstown High School; must have excelled in the combined fields of Mathematics and English desiring to further their education in those fields. **Application Requirements:** Applicants must submit a cover sheet (3 pages) and application form (4 pages); a personal essay; a high school and/or post-secondary transcript; a letter of recommendation; copy of the page of their or their parent's most recent tax return that indicates adjusted gross income; and a Student Aid Report showing estimated family contribution from FAFSA. Application form and other supporting documents must be sent to Our Community's Foundation, P.O Box 1762, Parkersburg, WV 26102. **Deadline for Receipt:** March 20.

1664 ■ PARKERSBURG AREA COMMUNITY FOUNDATION

501 Avery St.
Parkersburg, WV 26101
Tel: (304)428-4438; (866)428-4438
Fax: (304)428-1200
E-mail: info@pacfwv.com
Web Site: http://www.pacfwv.com
To encourage the graduating seniors of Parkersburg South High School to pursue their college degree.
Title of Award: Megan Nicole Longwell Scholarships **Area, Field, or Subject:** General studies. **Level of Education for which Award is Granted:** Undergraduate **Funds Available:** $1,385.
Eligibility Requirements: Applicants must be Parkersburg South High School graduating seniors who have been admitted to an accredited institution of higher learning as full-time students with a minimum 2.5 GPA. **Application Requirements:** Applicants must submit a cover sheet (3 pages) and application form (4 pages); must have a personal essay; must have a high school and/or post-secondary transcript; must provide a letter of recommendation and a signed copy of the page of their or their parent's most recent tax return that indicates adjusted gross income; and must have a Student Aid Report showing estimated family contribution from FAFSA. Application form and other supporting documents must be sent to Our Community's Foundation, P.O. Box 1762, Parkersburg, WV 26102. **Deadline for Receipt:** March 20.

1665 ■ PARKERSBURG AREA COMMUNITY FOUNDATION

501 Avery St.
Parkersburg, WV 26101
Tel: (304)428-4438; (866)428-4438
Fax: (304)428-1200
E-mail: info@pacfwv.com
Web Site: http://www.pacfwv.com
To assist graduating seniors of Williamstown High School in their educational pursuits.
Title of Award: Dudley Mullins/Cabot Corporation Scholarships **Area, Field, or Subject:** General studies. **Level of Education for which Award is Granted:** Undergraduate **Funds Available:** $1,000.

Eligibility Requirements: Applicant must be a Williamstown graduating senior; must have attended Waverly Elementary School for a minimum of one year and graduated from Waverly Elementary; must have a minimum of 2.0 GPA. **Application Requirements:** Applicants must submit a cover sheet (3 pages) and application form (4 pages); a personal essay; a high school and/or post-secondary transcript; a letter of recommendation; a signed copy of the page of their or their parent's most recent tax return that indicates adjusted gross income; and a Student Aid Report showing estimated family contribution from FAFSA. Application form and other supporting documents must be sent to Our Community's Foundation, P.O Box 1762, Parkersburg, WV 26102. **Deadline for Receipt:** March 20.

1666 ■ PARKERSBURG AREA COMMUNITY FOUNDATION

501 Avery St.
Parkersburg, WV 26101
Tel: (304)428-4438; (866)428-4438
Fax: (304)428-1200
E-mail: info@pacfwv.com
Web Site: http://www.pacfwv.com
To provide financial assistance for graduating seniors of Ritchie County High School intending to pursue their education.
Title of Award: Pennsboro Alumni Scholarship Fund **Area, Field, or Subject:** General studies. **Level of Education for which Award is Granted:** Undergraduate **Funds Available:** $500.
Eligibility Requirements: Applicant must be a Ritchie County High School graduating senior who demonstrates financial need. **Application Requirements:** Applicants must submit a cover sheet (3 pages) and application form (4 pages); a personal essay; a high school and/or post-secondary transcript; a letter of recommendation; a signed copy of the page of their or their parent's most recent tax return that indicates adjusted gross income; and a Student Aid Report showing estimated family contribution from FAFSA. Application form and other supporting documents must be sent to Our Community's Foundation, P.O Box 1762, Parkersburg, WV 26102. **Deadline for Receipt:** March 20.

1667 ■ PARKERSBURG AREA COMMUNITY FOUNDATION

501 Avery St.
Parkersburg, WV 26101
Tel: (304)428-4438; (866)428-4438
Fax: (304)428-1200
E-mail: info@pacfwv.com
Web Site: http://www.pacfwv.com
To assist graduating seniors in their educational pursuits.
Title of Award: Pepsi Wood County Technical/Caperton Center Scholarship Fund **Area, Field, or Subject:** General studies. **Level of Education for which Award is Granted:** Undergraduate **Funds Available:** $900.
Eligibility Requirements: Applicants must be graduating seniors attending Wood County Technical/Caperton Canter who are admitted to a post-secondary education institution. **Application Requirements:** Applicants must submit a cover sheet (3 pages) and application form (4 pages); a personal essay; a high school and/or post-secondary transcript; a letter of recommendation; a signed copy of the page of their or their parent's most recent tax return that indicates adjusted gross income; and a Student Aid Report showing estimated family contribution from FAFSA. Application form and other supporting documents must be sent to Our Community's Foundation, P.O Box 1762, Parkersburg, WV 26102. **Deadline for Receipt:** March 20.

1668 ■ PARKERSBURG AREA COMMUNITY FOUNDATION

501 Avery St.
Parkersburg, WV 26101
Tel: (304)428-4438; (866)428-4438
Fax: (304)428-1200
E-mail: info@pacfwv.com
Web Site: http://www.pacfwv.com
To encourage graduating students to pursue their education.
Title of Award: Herschel Pifer Memorial Scholarships **Area, Field, or Subject:** General studies. **Level of Education for which Award is Granted:** Undergraduate **Funds Available:** $500.
Eligibility Requirements: Applicants must be Ritchie County High School graduating seniors. **Application Requirements:** Applicants must submit a cover sheet (3 pages) and application form (4 pages); must have a personal essay; must have a high school and/or post-secondary

transcript; must provide a letter of recommendation and a signed copy of the page of their or their parent's most recent tax return that indicates adjusted gross income; and must have a Student Aid Report showing estimated family contribution, from FAFSA. Application form and other supporting documents must be sent to Our Community's Foundation, P.O. Box 1762, Parkersburg, WV 26102. **Deadline for Receipt:** March 20.

1669 ■ PARKERSBURG AREA COMMUNITY FOUNDATION
501 Avery St.
Parkersburg, WV 26101
Tel: (304)428-4438; (866)428-4438
Fax: (304)428-1200
E-mail: info@pacfwv.com
Web Site: http://www.pacfwv.com
To encourage graduating students to continue their education.
Title of Award: James H. Roberts Athletic Scholarships **Area, Field, or Subject:** General studies. **Level of Education for which Award is Granted:** Undergraduate **Funds Available:** $1,000.
Eligibility Requirements: Applicant must be a graduating senior from Wirt County High School; must be planning to attend a four-year program of study at a higher education institution in West Virginia; must be a student athlete; and must have a minimum of 2.0 GPA. **Application Requirements:** Applicants must submit a cover sheet (3 pages) and application form (4 pages); a personal essay; a high school and/or post-secondary transcript; a letter of recommendation; a signed copy of the page of their or their parent's most recent tax return that indicates adjusted gross income; and a Student Aid Report showing estimated family contribution from FAFSA. Application form and other supporting documents must be sent to Our Community's Foundation, P.O Box 1762, Parkersburg, WV 26102. **Deadline for Receipt:** March 20.

1670 ■ PARKERSBURG AREA COMMUNITY FOUNDATION
501 Avery St.
Parkersburg, WV 26101
Tel: (304)428-4438; (866)428-4438
Fax: (304)428-1200
E-mail: info@pacfwv.com
Web Site: http://www.pacfwv.com
To encourage graduating students to continue their education.
Title of Award: Thomas Warren Roberts Scholarships **Area, Field, or Subject:** General studies. **Level of Education for which Award is Granted:** Undergraduate **Funds Available:** $650.
Eligibility Requirements: Applicant must be a Belpre High School graduating senior. **Application Requirements:** Applicants must submit a cover sheet (3 pages) and application form (4 pages); a personal essay; a high school and/or post-secondary transcript; a letter of recommendation; a signed copy of the page of their or their parent's most recent tax return that indicates adjusted gross income; and a Student Aid Report showing estimated family contribution from FAFSA. Application form and other supporting documents must be sent to Our Community's Foundation, P.O Box 1762, Parkersburg, WV 26102. **Deadline for Receipt:** March 20.

1671 ■ PARKERSBURG AREA COMMUNITY FOUNDATION
501 Avery St.
Parkersburg, WV 26101
Tel: (304)428-4438; (866)428-4438
Fax: (304)428-1200
E-mail: info@pacfwv.com
Web Site: http://www.pacfwv.com
To provide support for graduating students intending to pursue their education.
Title of Award: James Robinson Memorial Scholarships **Area, Field, or Subject:** General studies. **Level of Education for which Award is Granted:** Undergraduate **Funds Available:** $500.
Eligibility Requirements: Applicant must be a Ripley High School, Jackson County, graduating senior pursuing full-time enrollment or person of any age currently enrolled full-time at WVU Parkersburg Jackson County Center with a minimum of 2.0 GPA. **Application Requirements:** Applicants must submit a cover sheet (3 pages) and application form (4 pages); a personal essay; a high school and/or post-secondary transcript; a letter of recommendation; a signed copy of the page of their or their parent's most recent tax return that indicates adjusted gross income; and a Student Aid Report showing estimated family contribution from FAFSA.

Application form and other supporting documents must be sent to Our Community's Foundation, P.O Box 1762, Parkersburg, WV 26102. **Deadline for Receipt:** March 20.

1672 ■ PARKERSBURG AREA COMMUNITY FOUNDATION
501 Avery St.
Parkersburg, WV 26101
Tel: (304)428-4438; (866)428-4438
Fax: (304)428-1200
E-mail: info@pacfwv.com
Web Site: http://www.pacfwv.com
To encourage graduating students to pursue their education.
Title of Award: Mike Ruben Scholarships **Area, Field, or Subject:** General studies. **Level of Education for which Award is Granted:** Undergraduate **Funds Available:** $250-$500.
Eligibility Requirements: Applicant must be a high school graduating senior. **Application Requirements:** Applicants must submit a cover sheet (3 pages) and application form (4 pages); a personal essay; a high school and/or post-secondary transcript; a letter of recommendation; a signed copy of the page of their or their parent's most recent tax return that indicates adjusted gross income; and a Student Aid Report showing estimated family contribution from FAFSA. Application form and other supporting documents must be sent to Our Community's Foundation, P.O Box 1762, Parkersburg, WV 26102. **Deadline for Receipt:** March 20.

1673 ■ PARKERSBURG AREA COMMUNITY FOUNDATION
501 Avery St.
Parkersburg, WV 26101
Tel: (304)428-4438; (866)428-4438
Fax: (304)428-1200
E-mail: info@pacfwv.com
Web Site: http://www.pacfwv.com
To provide educational assistance to high school graduates or the equivalent who demonstrate academic potential.
Title of Award: Simonton Windows Scholarship Fund **Area, Field, or Subject:** General studies. **Level of Education for which Award is Granted:** Undergraduate **Funds Available:** Amount of the scholarship may vary depending on the type of institution the student is attending and relative cost.
Eligibility Requirements: Applicants must be currently enrolled in undergraduate studies; must have graduated from high school or the equivalent and shall desire to attend a post-secondary educational institution, such as a college, university, technical or trade school, vocational school, business school; and must have a good academic standing with a minimum 2.5 GPA on a 4.0 scale. **Application Requirements:** Applicants must complete the application form, available online; must submit a personal essay, high school and/or post-secondary transcript; must have a copy of the page of their or their parent's most recent tax return that indicates adjusted gross income, a copy of the page from their Student Aid Report from FAFSA that shows their Estimated Family Contribution; must have financial aid award letter from their top-choice post-secondary educational institution. Application form and other supporting documents must be sent to Our Community's Foundation, P.O Box 1762, Parkersburg, WV 26102. **Deadline for Receipt:** April 1.

1674 ■ PARKERSBURG AREA COMMUNITY FOUNDATION
501 Avery St.
Parkersburg, WV 26101
Tel: (304)428-4438; (866)428-4438
Fax: (304)428-1200
E-mail: info@pacfwv.com
Web Site: http://www.pacfwv.com
To encourage graduating seniors to pursue their education.
Title of Award: Bill Six Memorial Scholarship Fund **Area, Field, or Subject:** General studies. **Level of Education for which Award is Granted:** Undergraduate **Funds Available:** $500.
Eligibility Requirements: Applicants must be graduating seniors or previous high school graduates who are permanent residents of Vienna, WV, who have at least a 2.0 GPA. **Application Requirements:** Applicants must submit a cover sheet (3 pages) and application form (4 pages); a personal essay; a high school and/or post-secondary transcript; a letter of recommendation; a signed copy of the page of their or their parent's most recent tax return that indicates adjusted gross income; and

a Student Aid Report showing estimated family contribution from FAFSA. Application form and other supporting documents must be sent to Our Community's Foundation, P.O Box 1762, Parkersburg, WV 26102. **Deadline for Receipt:** March 20.

1675 ■ PARKERSBURG AREA COMMUNITY FOUNDATION

501 Avery St.
Parkersburg, WV 26101
Tel: (304)428-4438; (866)428-4438
Fax: (304)428-1200
E-mail: info@pacfwv.com
Web Site: http://www.pacfwv.com
To encourage graduating students to pursue their education.
Title of Award: C.R. Thomas Scholarships **Area, Field, or Subject:** General studies. **Level of Education for which Award is Granted:** Undergraduate **Funds Available:** $650.
Eligibility Requirements: Applicant must be a graduating senior of Parkersburg High School and must be willing to help the community and others. **Application Requirements:** Applicants must submit a cover sheet (3 pages) and application form (4 pages); a personal essay; a high school and/or post-secondary transcript; a letter of recommendation; a signed copy of the page of their or their parent's most recent tax return that indicates adjusted gross income; and a Student Aid Report showing estimated family contribution from FAFSA. Application form and other supporting documents must be sent to Our Community's Foundation, P.O Box 1762, Parkersburg, WV 26102. **Deadline for Receipt:** March 20.

1676 ■ PARKERSBURG AREA COMMUNITY FOUNDATION

501 Avery St.
Parkersburg, WV 26101
Tel: (304)428-4438; (866)428-4438
Fax: (304)428-1200
E-mail: info@pacfwv.com
Web Site: http://www.pacfwv.com
To encourage graduating seniors of Ritchie County High School to pursue their education.
Title of Award: Wayne-Meador-Elliott Scholarships **Area, Field, or Subject:** General studies. **Level of Education for which Award is Granted:** Undergraduate **Funds Available:** $500.
Eligibility Requirements: Applicant must be a Ritchie County High School graduating senior; must be enrolled as a fulltime student to attend an accredited four-year college or university; and must have a minimum of 3.0 GPA. **Application Requirements:** Applicants must submit a cover sheet (3 pages) and application form (4 pages); a personal essay; a high school and/or post-secondary transcript; a letter of recommendation; a signed copy of the page of their or their parent's most recent tax return that indicates adjusted gross income; and a Student Aid Report showing estimated family contribution from FAFSA. Application form and other supporting documents must be sent to Our Community's Foundation, P.O Box 1762, Parkersburg, WV 26102. **Deadline for Receipt:** March 20.

1677 ■ PENNDELPHIA SCHOLARSHIP FOUNDATION

PO Box 42791
Philadelphia, PA 19101
Tel: (215)576-1216
Web Site: http://www.penndelsf.org
To provide financial assistance to deserving students who want to pursue their studies.
Title of Award: Penndelphia Scholarships Foundation **Area, Field, or Subject:** General studies. **Level of Education for which Award is Granted:** Undergraduate **Funds Available:** $1,000. **Duration:** One year.
Eligibility Requirements: Applicant must be a high school senior, high school graduate or registered as an undergraduate student at an accredited college or post-secondary vocational/technical institution. **Application Requirements:** Applicant must submit: a financial statement and photograph; scholastic record or complete transcript of record; recommendation letter. Application form is available online and must be sent to Penndelphia Scholarship Foundation, PO Box 42791, Philadelphia, PA 19101. **Deadline for Receipt:** April 15.

1678 ■ PENNSYLVANIA LAND SURVEYORS FOUNDATION

2040 Linglestown Rd., Ste. 200
Harrisburg, PA 17110

Tel: (717)540-6811
Fax: (717)540-6815
E-mail: hmorijah@psls.org
Web Site: http://www.psls.org
To promote, improve and encourage the profession and practice of land surveying in the Commonwealth of Pennsylvania by providing financial assistance to those persons intending to pursue or who are currently pursuing an education in surveying with an ultimate goal of becoming practicing Professional Land Surveyors.
Title of Award: Pennsylvania Land Surveyors Foundation Scholarships **Area, Field, or Subject:** Surveying. **Level of Education for which Award is Granted:** Undergraduate **Funds Available:** $20,000.
Eligibility Requirements: Applicants must: be citizens of the United States and be residents of the Commonwealth of Pennsylvania; be enrolled in or accepted in a two-year Surveying Technology Program or a four-year Bachelor of Science Program in Land Surveying; submit copies of SAT scores and high school or college transcripts with completed Transcript Release Form from Guidance Office or Registrar's Office. **Application Requirements:** Application form can be downloaded online. Each portion of the application has a specific point value. Judges will score each section separately. Incomplete applications will not be considered. Forms must be typed or neatly printed. Use of separate paper will be accepted. Points may be lost for poor grammar, incorrect spelling, illegibility, or lack of neatness. Proofread carefully. Applicants must submit a recommendation form to their Guidance Counselor/Advisor. **Deadline for Receipt:** February 1. **Additional Information:** Pennsylvania Land Surveyors' Foundation at the above address.

1679 ■ PENNSYLVANIA LIBRARY ASSOCIATION

220 Cumberland Pkwy., Ste. 10
Mechanicsburg, PA 17055
Tel: (717)766-7663
Free: 800-622-3308
Fax: (717)766-5440
E-mail: glenn@palibraries.org
Web Site: http://www.palibraries.org
To provide opportunities for professional growth, leadership development and continuing education for librarians.
Title of Award: Pennsylvania Library Association Scholarships for MLS Students **Area, Field, or Subject:** Library science. **Level of Education for which Award is Granted:** Undergraduate **Number Awarded:** 3. **Funds Available:** $1,500.
Eligibility Requirements: Applicants must be Pennsylvania residents who are seeking a master's degree in the Library Science field that will earn them professional status; must have completed 12 credit hours toward the degree during the scholarship year. **Application Requirements:** Applicants must submit a completed application form and a verification of enrollment in an ALA accredited graduate program. **Deadline for Receipt:** May 15.

1680 ■ PENNSYLVANIA STATE SYSTEM OF HIGHER EDUCATION FOUNDATION

2986 N 2nd St.
Harrisburg, PA 17110
Tel: (717)720-4086
Fax: (717)720-7082
Web Site: http://www.thepafoundation.org
To provide recognition and financial assistance to low-income, disadvantaged students residing in the city of Philadelphia who attended any of the public high schools or charter schools in the school district of Philadelphia and who wish to enroll in universities of the Pennsylvania State System of Higher Education.
Title of Award: James Hughes Memorial Scholarship Fund **Area, Field, or Subject:** General studies. **Level of Education for which Award is Granted:** Undergraduate **Funds Available:** $1,500. **Duration:** One year.
Eligibility Requirements: Applicants must have graduated from any public high school or charter school in the school district of Philadelphia; must be full-time undergraduate students accepted at a PASSHE university, with priority given to incoming freshmen. **Application Requirements:** Applicants must submit the James Hughes Memorial Scholarship (JHMS) application form; two written references using the letter of reference form (one academic/professional and one personal); current high school transcript; 250-word essay on why they feel they are deserving of

the Hughes scholarship, their desire to achieve academically and how they have overcome adversities in their lives. **Deadline for Receipt:** March 31.

1681 ■ PENNSYLVANIA STATE SYSTEM OF HIGHER EDUCATION FOUNDATION

2986 N 2nd St.
Harrisburg, PA 17110
Tel: (717)720-4086
Fax: (717)720-7082
Web Site: http://www.thepafoundation.org
To provide educational assistance to all the students who are enrolled at PASSHE universities.
Title of Award: Minnie Patton Stayman Scholarships **Area, Field, or Subject:** General studies. **Level of Education for which Award is Granted:** Undergraduate **Funds Available:** $1,000. **Duration:** One year. **Eligibility Requirements:** Applicants must: be residents of Altoona; be full-time undergraduate students who plan to enroll at a Pennsylvania State System of Higher Education university. **Application Requirements:** Applicants must submit all the required application information.

1682 ■ PENSION REAL ESTATE ASSOCIATION

100 Pearl St., 13th Fl.
Hartford, CT 06103
Tel: (860)692-6341
Fax: (860)692-6351
E-mail: membership@prea.org
Web Site: http://www.prea.org
To promote understanding of institutional investment in real estate.
Title of Award: Pension Real Estate Association Scholarships **Area, Field, or Subject:** Real estate. **Level of Education for which Award is Granted:** Undergraduate **Funds Available:** Total amount of $60,000. **Eligibility Requirements:** Applicants must be students studying real estate at the undergraduate and graduate levels. **Application Requirements:** Applicants must submit a completed application form.

1683 ■ PEOPLE TO PEOPLE INTERNATIONAL

911 Main St., Ste. 2110
Kansas City, MO 64105
Tel: (816)531-4701
Fax: (816)561-7502
E-mail: ptpi@ptpi.org
Web Site: http://www.ptpi.org
To encourage youth participation in international activities.
Title of Award: Joyce C. Hall College Scholarships **Area, Field, or Subject:** General Studies. **Level of Education for which Award is Granted:** Undergraduate **Number Awarded:** 5. **Funds Available:** $2,000. Funds must be used to pay tuition first, before books and supplies. **Duration:** One year.
Eligibility Requirements: Applicants must be current members of People to People International with experience in at least one of the many programs offered during the past four years. Applicants must also be full-time college students or high school seniors maintaining a 3.0 grade point average on a 4.0 scale. **Application Requirements:** Applicants must send an application form accompanied by: a statement of the applicant's participation in a People to People International activity, and what that experience meant to increasing his/her understanding of intercultural relations among the peoples of the world; an original essay not more than 1,000 words regarding "Why I believe international friendships are important and how my experiences have improved my understanding of people from other countries/cultures;" Statement of Financial Need Form; three letters of recommendation; transcript. High school seniors must provide proof that they are actively applying to a college or university. **Deadline for Receipt:** October 15.

1684 ■ PHI KAPPA PHI

7576 Goodwood Blvd.
Baton rouge, LA 70806
Tel: (225)388-4917
Free: 800-804-9880
Fax: (225)388-4900
E-mail: info@phikappaphi
Web Site: http://www.phikappaphi.org

To recognize and encourage academic achievement in all disciplines.
Title of Award: Phi Kappa Phi Emerging Scholar Awards **Area, Field, or Subject:** General studies. **Level of Education for which Award is Granted:** Undergraduate **Number Awarded:** 60. **Funds Available:** $250. **Eligibility Requirements:** Applicant must have a cumulative GPA of 3.75 on 4.0 scale and at least earned 30 semester hours as a full-time student during 2007 and spring 2008 academic year at an institution that has an active Phi Kappa Phi chapter. **Application Requirements:** Applicant must answer and submit type-written applications downloadable on the organization's website. **Deadline for Receipt:** July 14.

1685 ■ PHI KAPPA SIGMA

2 Timber Drive
Chester Springs, PA 19425
Tel: (610)469-3282
Fax: (610)469-3286
Web Site: http://www.pks.org
To support student members with their educational pursuits.
Title of Award: Phi Kappa Sigma Need-Based Scholarships **Area, Field, or Subject:** General studies. **Level of Education for which Award is Granted:** Undergraduate **Funds Available:** No specific amount. **Duration:** One academic year.
Eligibility Requirements: Applicant must be an officially registered member of Phi Kappa Sigma Fraternity; with initiation fee having been remitted by the chapter to the Fraternity Headquarters; and must be in undergraduate level. **Application Requirements:** Applicants must submit completed application forms along with the required materials. Official transcript of grades must be forwarded directly by the college registrar. All materials must be submitted to Reynold R. Hagel 6701 Sixth Avenue South Seattle, WA 98108, 206499-2393 or scholarship@pks.org. **Deadline for Receipt:** May 31.

1686 ■ PHI KAPPA SIGMA

2 Timber Drive
Chester Springs, PA 19425
Tel: (610)469-3282
Fax: (610)469-3286
Web Site: http://www.pks.org
To support student members with their educational pursuits.
Title of Award: Phi Kappa Sigma Participation-Based Scholarships **Area, Field, or Subject:** General studies. **Level of Education for which Award is Granted:** Undergraduate **Funds Available:** No specific amount. **Duration:** One academic year.
Eligibility Requirements: Applicant must be an officially registered member of Phi Kappa Sigma Fraternity; with initiation fee having been remitted by the chapter to the Fraternity Headquarters; and must be in undergraduate level. **Application Requirements:** Applicants must submit completed application forms along with the required materials. Official transcript of grades must be forwarded directly by the college registrar. All materials must be submitted to Reynold R. Hagel 6701 Sixth Avenue South Seattle, WA 98108, 206499-2393 or scholarship@pks.org. **Deadline for Receipt:** May 31.

1687 ■ PHI SIGMA PI NATIONAL HONOR FRATERNITY

2119 Ambassador Circle
Lancaster, PA 17603
Tel: (717)299-4710
Fax: (717)390-3054
E-mail: pspoffice@phisigmapi.org
Web Site: http://www.phisigmapi.org
To promote the future academic opportunity of Phi Sigma Pi Brothers.
Title of Award: Richard Cecil Todd and Clauda Pennock Todd Tripod Scholarships **Area, Field, or Subject:** General studies. **Level of Education for which Award is Granted:** Graduate, Undergraduate **Funds Available:** No specific amount.
Eligibility Requirements: Applicant must be undergraduate student pursuing a Bachelor's Degree; or graduating senior entering a graduate school (must provide a proof of enrollment to a graduate program); an active Phi Sigma Pi member; and have a GPA of 3.00. **Application Requirements:** Applicants must submit a completed application form; letters of recommendation; official transcript; and notification from the Financial Aid Office (if applicable). **Additional Information:** All required materials must be typewritten. **Deadline for Receipt:** April 15.

1688 ■ PHILANTHROPIC EDUCATIONAL ORGANIZATION
3700 Grand Ave.
Des Moines, IA 50312
Tel: (515)255-3153
Fax: (515)255-3820
E-mail: glane@peodsm.org
Web Site: http://www.peointernational.org
To provide scholarships for selected women from other countries for study in the United States and Canada.
Title of Award: International Peace Scholarships **Area, Field, or Subject:** General studies. **Level of Education for which Award is Granted:** Undergraduate **Funds Available:** $10,000 (total).
Eligibility Requirements: Applicants must be qualified for admission to full-time graduate study, working toward a graduate degree in the college or university. **Application Requirements:** Applicants must submit completed application form; a copy of confirmation of admission; and a witnessed statement certifying that upon completion of their degree programs they will return to their own country within 60 days. **Deadline for Receipt:** April 1.

1689 ■ PHILANTHROPIC EDUCATIONAL ORGANIZATION
3700 Grand Ave.
Des Moines, IA 50312
Tel: (515)255-3153
Fax: (515)255-3820
E-mail: glane@peodsm.org
Web Site: http://www.peointernational.org
To promote educational opportunities for women who desire higher education and are in need of financial assistance.
Title of Award: PEO Educational Loan Funds **Area, Field, or Subject:** General studies. **Level of Education for which Award is Granted:** Graduate, Undergraduate **Funds Available:** $9,000 (in total).
Eligibility Requirements: Applicants must be recommended by a local chapter of the P.E.O. sisterhood and must be within two years of completing their course of study. Program is also open for applicants who are graduate students in medical or law schools, seniors seeking a bachelor's degree or students enrolled in a hospital professional nurse training program, a non-collegiate, technical program, or vocational program in a college or university. **Application Requirements:** Applicants must submit a cover letter; application form with a packet checklist and instructions; school information form or proof of enrollment; transcript of records; request for permission to obtain credit report; acknowledgement of loan terms; and memo of indebtedness.

1690 ■ THE PHILLIPS FOUNDATION
1 Massachusetts Ave. NW, Ste. 620
Washington, DC 20001
Tel: (202)250-3887
E-mail: jhollingsworth@thephillipsfoundation.org
Web Site: http://www.thephillipsfoundation.org
To assist students in alleviating financial burdens associated with higher education.
Title of Award: Ronald Reagan College Leaders Scholarship Program **Area, Field, or Subject:** General studies. **Level of Education for which Award is Granted:** Undergraduate **Funds Available:** No specific amount.
Eligibility Requirements: Applicants must be U.S. citizens enrolled full-time in good standing at any accredited, four-year degree-granting institution in the United States or its territories. Those attending two-year schools may apply as juniors for a one-time scholarship for the senior year, upon transfer to a four-year institution. **Application Requirements:** Applicants must submit an essay of 500 to 750 words describing their backgrounds, career objectives and scope of participation in leadership activities promoting freedom, American values and constitutional principles.

1691 ■ PHS COMMISSIONED OFFICERS FOUNDATION
8201 Corporate Dr., Ste. 200
Landover, MD 20785
Tel: (301)731-9080
Fax: (301)731-9084
E-mail: info@phscof.org
Web Site: http://www.phscof.org
To provide financial assistance to dependent children or dependent spouses of active duty, retired, or deceased officers of the USPHS Commissioned Corps.
Title of Award: Scholarship for Junior PHS Commissioned Officers **Area, Field, or Subject:** General studies. **Level of Education for which Award is Granted:** Undergraduate **Funds Available:** No specific amount.
Eligibility Requirements: Applicants must be dependent children or spouses of active duty, retired or deceased officers of the USPHS Commissioned Corps; must be current or entering college/vocational students who have a minimum cumulative grade point average of 3.0 (on a 4.0 scale). **Application Requirements:** Applicants must submit all the required application information. **Deadline for Receipt:** June 1.

1692 ■ PIERCE COLLEGE DISTRICT 11
9401 Farwest Dr. SW
Lakewood, WA 98498
Tel: (253)964-6500
Web Site: http://www.pierce.ctc.edu
To support Pierce College students with their education.
Title of Award: Pierce College Foundation Coca-Cola Scholarships **Area, Field, or Subject:** General studies. **Level of Education for which Award is Granted:** Undergraduate **Funds Available:** $1,000.
Eligibility Requirements: Applicants must be U.S. citizens; must have a 2.5 minimum GPA; must be engaged in community service within the previous 12 months or employed full or part-time; must be enrolled in at least two courses. Applicants may not be the children or grandchildren of a Coca-Cola employee. **Application Requirements:** Applicants must submit a completed application form with the required materials to Pierce College Puyallup Attn: Ruth Ann Hatchett 1601 39th Ave SE, Gaspard Building Room No. 108 Puyallup, WA 98374-2222, or to Pierce College Fort Steilacoom Attn: Paula Henson-Williams 9401 Farwest Drive S.W Cascade Building Room No. 325-J Lakewood, WA 98498-1999. **Deadline for Receipt:** May 9.

1693 ■ PIERCE COLLEGE DISTRICT 11
9401 Farwest Dr. SW
Lakewood, WA 98498
Tel: (253)964-6500
Web Site: http://www.pierce.ctc.edu
To render financial assistance for the veterans, children, grandchildren and great-grandchildren of U.S. veterans.
Title of Award: Post 4137 Veterans Foundation Scholarships **Area, Field, or Subject:** General studies. **Level of Education for which Award is Granted:** Undergraduate **Number Awarded:** 1. **Funds Available:** $5,000. **Duration:** One year.
Eligibility Requirements: Applicants must be honorably discharged veterans or, children, grandchildren, or great-grandchildren of an honorably discharged veteran; must be enrolled at or admitted to a private secondary educational institution, or a university, including community colleges. **Application Requirements:** Applicants must complete and submit the application form with the required documents and supporting materials to Post 4137 Veterans Foundation C/O Invicta Law Group, PLLC, 1000 Second Avenue, Suite 3310 Seattle, WA 98115. **Deadline for Receipt:** May 30. **Additional Information:** scholarship@invictalaw.com.

1694 ■ PLUS FOUNDATION
5353 Wayzata Blvd., Ste. 600
Minneapolis, MN 55416
Tel: (952)746-2590
Fax: (952)746-2599
Web Site: http://www.plusfoundation.org
To assist deserving PLUS member students with their college education.
Title of Award: Leo Gilmartin Scholarships **Area, Field, or Subject:** General studies. **Level of Education for which Award is Granted:** High School **Funds Available:** $10,000.
Eligibility Requirements: Applicants must be high school seniors who are children of current PLUS members or children of employees of current PLUS corporate sponsors. **Application Requirements:** Applicants must submit college entrance exam scores; GPA and class rank; essay and letters of recommendation; list of extracurricular and community service activities. **Deadline for Receipt:** March 15.

1695 ■ PLUS FOUNDATION
5353 Wayzata Blvd., Ste. 600
Minneapolis, MN 55416
Tel: (952)746-2590
Fax: (952)746-2599
Web Site: http://www.plusfoundation.org
To assist deserving PLUS member students with their college education.
Title of Award: PLUS Foundation Financial Aid Grants **Area, Field, or Subject:** General studies. **Level of Education for which Award is Granted:** Undergraduate **Funds Available:** $10,000.
Eligibility Requirements: Applicants must be high school seniors who are children of current PLUS members or children of employees of current PLUS corporate sponsors. **Application Requirements:** Applicants must submit the household adjusted gross income; total number in household and number of dependent children attending college; estimated cost of tuition; GPA, class rank, college entrance exams scores. **Deadline for Receipt:** March 15.

1696 ■ POINT FOUNDATION
PO Box 60108
Los Angeles, CA 90060-0108
Tel: (323)933-1234
Fax: (866)33-POINT
E-mail: info@pointfoundation.org
Web Site: http://thepointfoundation.org
To support the LGBT community.
Title of Award: Merle Aronson Point Scholarships **Area, Field, or Subject:** General studies. **Level of Education for which Award is Granted:** Graduate, Undergraduate **Number Awarded:** 1. **Funds Available:** No specific amount.
Eligibility Requirements: Applicant must be LGBT or have a history of leadership in the LGBT community and plan to be a LGBT leader in the future. **Application Requirements:** Applicants must complete the online scholarship application by March 1. If chosen as semi-finalists, students are requested to submit supplemental materials, in one envelope: two to three letters of recommendation; official transcripts; test score verification; and resume. **Additional Information:** Point Foundation will not return submitted supplemental materials. **Deadline for Receipt:** March 1. **Additional Information:** ginger@pointfoundation.org, or 775-782-5659, fax: 775-782-5690.

1697 ■ POINT FOUNDATION
PO Box 60108
Los Angeles, CA 90060-0108
Tel: (323)933-1234
Fax: (866)33-POINT
E-mail: info@pointfoundation.org
Web Site: http://thepointfoundation.org
To support the LGBT community.
Title of Award: Norman Blachford Point Scholarships **Area, Field, or Subject:** General studies. **Level of Education for which Award is Granted:** Graduate, Undergraduate **Funds Available:** No specific amount.
Eligibility Requirements: Applicant must be from the area of San Diego, California; LGBT; or have a history of leadership in the LGBT community and plan to be a LGBT leader in the future. **Application Requirements:** Applicants must complete the online scholarship application by March 1. If chosen as semi-finalist, students are requested to submit supplemental materials, in one envelope: two to three letters of recommendation; official transcripts; test score verification; and resume. **Additional Information:** Point Foundation will not return submitted supplemental materials. **Deadline for Receipt:** March 1. **Additional Information:** ginger@pointfoundation.org, or 775-782-5659, fax: 775-782-5690.

1698 ■ POINT FOUNDATION
PO Box 60108
Los Angeles, CA 90060-0108
Tel: (323)933-1234
Fax: (866)33-POINT
E-mail: info@pointfoundation.org
Web Site: http://thepointfoundation.org
To support the LGBT community.
Title of Award: Carlos Enrique Cisneros Point Scholarships **Area, Field, or Subject:** General studies. **Level of Education for which Award is**

Granted: Graduate, Undergraduate **Funds Available:** No specific amount.
Eligibility Requirements: Applicant must be a LGBT student of distinction attending American University, Washington, DC or have a history of leadership in the LGBT community and plan to be a LGBT leader in the future. **Application Requirements:** Applicants must complete the online scholarship application by March 1. If chosen as semi-finalists, students are requested to submit supplemental materials, in one envelope: two to three letters of recommendation; official transcripts; test score verification; and resume. **Additional Information:** Point Foundation will not return submitted supplemental materials. **Deadline for Receipt:** March 1. **Additional Information:** ginger@pointfoundation.org, or 775-782-5659, fax: 775-782-5690.

1699 ■ POINT FOUNDATION
PO Box 60108
Los Angeles, CA 90060-0108
Tel: (323)933-1234
Fax: (866)33-POINT
E-mail: info@pointfoundation.org
Web Site: http://thepointfoundation.org
To support the LGBT community.
Title of Award: Elsie De Wolfe Point Scholarships **Area, Field, or Subject:** General studies. **Level of Education for which Award is Granted:** Graduate, Undergraduate **Funds Available:** No specific amount.
Eligibility Requirements: Applicant must be LGBT; or have a history of leadership in the LGBT community and plan to be a LGBT leader in the future. **Application Requirements:** Applicants must complete the online scholarship application by March 1. If chosen as semi-finalists, students are requested to submit supplemental materials, in one envelope: two to three letters of recommendation; official transcripts; test score verification; and resume. **Additional Information:** Point Foundation will not return submitted supplemental materials. **Deadline for Receipt:** March 1. **Additional Information:** ginger@pointfoundation.org, or 775-782-5659, fax: 775-782-5690.

1700 ■ POINT FOUNDATION
PO Box 60108
Los Angeles, CA 90060-0108
Tel: (323)933-1234
Fax: (866)33-POINT
E-mail: info@pointfoundation.org
Web Site: http://thepointfoundation.org
To support the LGBT community.
Title of Award: Walter M. Decker Point Scholarships **Area, Field, or Subject:** General studies. **Level of Education for which Award is Granted:** Graduate, Undergraduate **Number Awarded:** one or more. **Funds Available:** No specific amount.
Eligibility Requirements: Applicant must be LGBT; or have a history of leadership in the LGBT community and plan to be a LGBT leader in the future. **Application Requirements:** Applicants must complete the online scholarship application by March 1. If chosen as semi-finalists, students are requested to submit supplemental materials, in one envelope: two to three letters of recommendation; official transcripts; test score verification; and resume. **Additional Information:** Point Foundation will not return submitted supplemental materials. **Deadline for Receipt:** March 1. **Additional Information:** ginger@pointfoundation.org, or 775-782-5659, fax: 775-782-5690.

1701 ■ POINT FOUNDATION
PO Box 60108
Los Angeles, CA 90060-0108
Tel: (323)933-1234
Fax: (866)33-POINT
E-mail: info@pointfoundation.org
Web Site: http://thepointfoundation.org
To support the LGBT community.
Title of Award: Dr. Joan W. Fernandez Point Scholarships **Area, Field, or Subject:** General studies. **Level of Education for which Award is Granted:** Graduate, Undergraduate **Funds Available:** No specific amount.
Eligibility Requirements: Applicant must be lesbian, aspiring to be a theater director and graduate with the MFA degree. **Application Require-**

ments: Applicants must complete the online scholarship application by March 1. If chosen as semi-finalists, students are requested to submit supplemental materials, in one envelope: two to three letters of recommendation; official transcripts; test score verification; and resume. **Additional Information:** Point Foundation will not return submitted supplemental materials. **Deadline for Receipt:** March 1. **Additional Information:** ginger@pointfoundation.org, or 775-782-5659, fax: 775-782-5690.

1702 ■ POINT FOUNDATION
PO Box 60108
Los Angeles, CA 90060-0108
Tel: (323)933-1234
Fax: (866)33-POINT
E-mail: info@pointfoundation.org
Web Site: http://thepointfoundation.org
To support the LGBT community.
Title of Award: David B. Goodstein Point Scholarships **Area, Field, or Subject:** General studies. **Level of Education for which Award is Granted:** Graduate, Undergraduate **Funds Available:** No specific amount.
Eligibility Requirements: Applicant must be LGBT; or have a history of leadership in the LGBT community and plan to be a LGBT leader in the future. **Application Requirements:** Applicants must complete the online scholarship application by March 1. If chosen as semi-finalists, students are requested to submit supplemental materials, in one envelope: two to three letters of recommendation; official transcripts; test score verification; and resume. **Additional Information:** Point Foundation will not return submitted supplemental materials. **Deadline for Receipt:** March 1. **Additional Information:** ginger@pointfoundation.org, or 775-782-5659, fax: 775-782-5690.

1703 ■ POINT FOUNDATION
PO Box 60108
Los Angeles, CA 90060-0108
Tel: (323)933-1234
Fax: (866)33-POINT
E-mail: info@pointfoundation.org
Web Site: http://thepointfoundation.org
To support the LGBT community.
Title of Award: Evelyn W. Harrison Point Scholarships **Area, Field, or Subject:** General studies. **Level of Education for which Award is Granted:** Graduate, Undergraduate **Funds Available:** No specific amount.
Eligibility Requirements: Applicant must be LGBT or have a history of leadership in the LGBT community and plan to be a LGBT leader in the future. **Application Requirements:** Applicants must complete the online scholarship application by March 1. If chosen as semi-finalists, students are requested to submit supplemental materials, in one envelope: two to three letters of recommendation; official transcripts; test score verification; and resume. **Additional Information:** Point Foundation will not return submitted supplemental materials. **Deadline for Receipt:** March 1. **Additional Information:** ginger@pointfoundation.org, or 775-782-5659, fax: 775-782-5690.

1704 ■ POINT FOUNDATION
PO Box 60108
Los Angeles, CA 90060-0108
Tel: (323)933-1234
Fax: (866)33-POINT
E-mail: info@pointfoundation.org
Web Site: http://thepointfoundation.org
To support the LGBT community.
Title of Award: HBO Point Scholarships **Area, Field, or Subject:** General studies. **Level of Education for which Award is Granted:** Graduate, Undergraduate **Funds Available:** No specific amount.
Eligibility Requirements: Applicant must be LGBT or have a history of leadership in the LGBT community and plan to be a LGBT leader in the future and be pursuing a career in the media. **Application Requirements:** Applicants must complete the online scholarship application by March 1. If chosen as semi-finalists, students are requested to submit supplemental materials, in one envelope: two to three letters of recommendation; official transcripts; test score verification; and resume. **Ad-

ditional Information:** Point Foundation will not return submitted supplemental materials. **Deadline for Receipt:** March 1. **Additional Information:** ginger@pointfoundation.org, or 775-782-5659, fax: 775-782-5690.

1705 ■ POINT FOUNDATION
PO Box 60108
Los Angeles, CA 90060-0108
Tel: (323)933-1234
Fax: (866)33-POINT
E-mail: info@pointfoundation.org
Web Site: http://thepointfoundation.org
To support the LGBT community.
Title of Award: Kevin Hummer Point Scholarships **Area, Field, or Subject:** General studies. **Level of Education for which Award is Granted:** Graduate, Undergraduate **Funds Available:** No specific amount.
Eligibility Requirements: Applicant must be LGBT; or have a history of leadership in the LGBT community and plan to be a LGBT leader in the future. **Application Requirements:** Applicants must complete the online scholarship application by March 1. If chosen as semi-finalists, students are requested to submit supplemental materials, in one envelope: two to three letters of recommendation; official transcripts; test score verification; and resume. **Additional Information:** Point Foundation will not return submitted supplemental materials. **Deadline for Receipt:** March 1. **Additional Information:** ginger@pointfoundation.org, or 775-782-5659, fax: 775-782-5690.

1706 ■ POINT FOUNDATION
PO Box 60108
Los Angeles, CA 90060-0108
Tel: (323)933-1234
Fax: (866)33-POINT
E-mail: info@pointfoundation.org
Web Site: http://thepointfoundation.org
To support the LGBT community.
Title of Award: Bryan L. Knapp Point Scholarships **Area, Field, or Subject:** General studies. **Level of Education for which Award is Granted:** Graduate, Undergraduate **Funds Available:** No specific amount.
Eligibility Requirements: Applicant must be an undergraduate LGBT student of distinction from the New York City area attending Cornell University, Ithaca, New York. **Application Requirements:** Applicants must complete the online scholarship application by March 1. If chosen as semi-finalists, students are requested to submit supplemental materials, in one envelope: two to three letters of recommendation; official transcripts; test score verification; and resume. **Additional Information:** Point Foundation will not return submitted supplemental materials. **Deadline for Receipt:** March 1. **Additional Information:** ginger@pointfoundation.org, or 775-782-5659, fax: 775-782-5690.

1707 ■ POINT FOUNDATION
PO Box 60108
Los Angeles, CA 90060-0108
Tel: (323)933-1234
Fax: (866)33-POINT
E-mail: info@pointfoundation.org
Web Site: http://thepointfoundation.org
To support the LGBT community.
Title of Award: Jonathan D. Lewis Point Scholarships **Area, Field, or Subject:** General studies. **Level of Education for which Award is Granted:** Graduate, Undergraduate **Funds Available:** No specific amount.
Eligibility Requirements: Applicant must be LGBT or have a history of leadership in the LGBT community and plan to be a LGBT leader in the future. **Application Requirements:** Applicants must complete the online scholarship application by March 1. If chosen as semi-finalists, students are requested to submit supplemental materials, in one envelope: two to three letters of recommendation; official transcripts; test score verification; and resume. **Additional Information:** Point Foundation will not return submitted supplemental materials. **Deadline for Receipt:** March 1. **Additional Information:** ginger@pointfoundation.org, or 775-782-5659, fax: 775-782-5690.

1708 ■ POINT FOUNDATION

PO Box 60108
Los Angeles, CA 90060-0108
Tel: (323)933-1234
Fax: (866)33-POINT
E-mail: info@pointfoundation.org
Web Site: http://thepointfoundation.org
To support the LGBT community.
Title of Award: Time Warner Point Scholarships **Area, Field, or Subject:**
General studies. **Level of Education for which Award is Granted:**
Graduate, Undergraduate **Funds Available:** No specific amount.
Eligibility Requirements: Applicant must be LGBT or have a history of
leadership in the LGBT community and plan to be a LGBT leader in the
future. **Application Requirements:** Applicants must complete the online
scholarship application by March 1. If chosen as semi-finalists, students
are requested to submit supplemental materials, in one envelope: two to
three letters of recommendation; official transcripts; test score verification;
and resume. **Additional Information:** Point Foundation will not return
submitted supplemental materials. **Deadline for Receipt:** March 1. **Additional Information:** ginger@pointfoundation.org, or 775-782-5659, fax:
775-782-5690.

1709 ■ POLISH FALCONS OF AMERICA

615 Iron City Dr.
Pittsburgh, PA 15205-4397
Tel: (412)922-2244
Free: 800-535-2071
Fax: (412)922-5029
Web Site: http://www.polishfalcons.org
To provide financial support for deserving Falcon members who are aspiring to attend institutions of higher learning.
Title of Award: General Falcon Scholarships **Area, Field, or Subject:**
General studies. **Level of Education for which Award is Granted:**
Undergraduate **Funds Available:** $500.
Eligibility Requirements: Candidates must be graduating high school
seniors or presently enrolled undergraduates intending to pursue further
education as a full time student in an accredited two or four year college,
university or trade school; must have a minimum cumulative GPA of 2.0
out of 4.0; must have taken an active participants in the Polish Falcon
programs. **Application Requirements:** Applicant must complete and sign
the application form available online; must provide a community service
information, essay, and photo; must submit the official transcript,
counselor recommendation, and net information form and letter. **Deadline
for Receipt:** February 1.

1710 ■ POLISH FALCONS OF AMERICA

615 Iron City Dr.
Pittsburgh, PA 15205-4397
Tel: (412)922-2244
Free: 800-535-2071
Fax: (412)922-5029
Web Site: http://www.polishfalcons.org
To provide financial assistance for deserving individuals intending to
pursue their education.
Title of Award: Richard C. Gorecki Scholarships **Area, Field, or Subject:**
General studies. **Level of Education for which Award is Granted:**
Undergraduate **Funds Available:** $15,000.
Eligibility Requirements: Applicant must be a PFA member for six years;
must have a minimum GPA of 3.0 out of 4.0; Applicant must be enrolled
full-time in a four-year college or university, or full-time post-graduate
studies. **Application Requirements:** Applicant must complete the
scholarship application; must have a two part essay (minimum 500 words
for each part); must provide at least three letters of recommendation.
Deadline for Receipt: May 27.

1711 ■ PORTUGUESE AMERICAN LEADERSHIP COUNCIL OF THE UNITED STATES

1316 Pennsylvania Ave. SE, Capitol Hill
Washington, DC 20003
Tel: (202)466-4664
Fax: (202)466-4661
E-mail: palcus@palcus.org
Web Site: http://www.palcus.org

To provide financial support to high school seniors of Portuguese heritage.
Title of Award: Cabrillo Clubs of California Scholarships **Area, Field, or
Subject:** General studies. **Level of Education for which Award is
Granted:** Undergraduate **Funds Available:** $400.
Eligibility Requirements: Applicant must be of Portuguese descent;
must have maintained a 3.50 or better GPA and be a graduating senior
and citizen of the U.S. **Application Requirements:** Applicant must mail
all completed application packets to: Cabrillo Civic Clubs of California,
1455 Willow St., San Diego, CA 92106-2122.

1712 ■ PORTUGUESE AMERICAN LEADERSHIP COUNCIL OF THE UNITED STATES

1316 Pennsylvania Ave. SE, Capitol Hill
Washington, DC 20003
Tel: (202)466-4664
Fax: (202)466-4661
E-mail: palcus@palcus.org
Web Site: http://www.palcus.org
To provide financial assistance to qualified New Jersey students of
Portuguese ancestry, who wants to further their post-secondary school
education and gain greater access to a better way of life.
Title of Award: Portuguese-American Scholarship Foundation **Area,
Field, or Subject:** General studies. **Level of Education for which
Award is Granted:** Undergraduate **Funds Available:** $7,000.
Eligibility Requirements: Applicants must be New Jersey High School
seniors that are Portuguese-born or that have a parent or grandparent
that is Portuguese-born; must be a U.S. citizen or U.S. permanent
residents; must demonstrate financial need; must be a New Jersey high
school senior applying to, or accepted in, a four-year college or university
curriculum leading to a baccalaureate degree; must meet the minimum
PASF academic standards, including a grade point average of B or better.
Application Requirements: Application must be completed and sent to:
Portuguese-American Scholarship Foundation of NJ, Chairperson,
Scholarship Review Board, PO Box 7169, Colonia, NJ 07067. **Deadline
for Receipt:** February 15.

1713 ■ PRIDE FOUNDATION

PO Box 2194, 1122 E Pike St. PMB 1001
Seattle, WA 98112
Tel: (206)323-3318
Free: 800-735-7287
Fax: (206)323-1017
E-mail: prideweb@pridefoundation.org
Web Site: http://www.pridefoundation.org
To provide scholarship to students who have been stigmatized, isolated or
closeted because of sexual identity issues.
Title of Award: Asian and Pacific Islander Queers Sisters Scholarships
Area, Field, or Subject: General studies. **Level of Education for which
Award is Granted:** Undergraduate **Funds Available:** No specific
amount.
Eligibility Requirements: Applicants must be Asian/Pacific Islander
lesbians, bisexual females, or transgender (both MTF and FTM
spectrum). **Application Requirements:** Qualified students are asked to
submit an application to determine eligibility for scholarships. Applicants
may download an application form from the Foundation's website. **Additional Information:** Pride Foundation at the above address.

1714 ■ PRIDE FOUNDATION

PO Box 2194, 1122 E Pike St. PMB 1001
Seattle, WA 98112
Tel: (206)323-3318
Free: 800-735-7287
Fax: (206)323-1017
E-mail: prideweb@pridefoundation.org
Web Site: http://www.pridefoundation.org
To provide scholarship to the students who have been stigmatized,
isolated or closeted because of sexual identity issues.
Title of Award: Barbara Bailey Scholarships **Area, Field, or Subject:**
General studies. **Level of Education for which Award is Granted:**
Undergraduate **Funds Available:** No specific amount.
Eligibility Requirements: Applicant must be a lesbian from the state of
Washington. **Application Requirements:** Qualified students are asked to
submit an application to determine eligibility for scholarships. Applicants

may download an application form from the Foundation's website. **Additional Information:** Pride Foundation at the above address.

1715 ■ PRIDE FOUNDATION
PO Box 2194, 1122 E Pike St. PMB 1001
Seattle, WA 98112
Tel: (206)323-3318
Free: 800-735-7287
Fax: (206)323-1017
E-mail: prideweb@pridefoundation.org
Web Site: http://www.pridefoundation.org
To provide scholarship to the students who have been stigmatized, isolated or closeted because of sexual identity issues.
Title of Award: Bellevue PFLAG Scholarships **Area, Field, or Subject:** General Studies. **Level of Education for which Award is Granted:** Undergraduate **Funds Available:** No specific amount.
Eligibility Requirements: Applicant must be a graduating high school seniors currently attending a greater East King County high school. **Application Requirements:** Qualified students are asked to submit an application to determine eligibility for scholarships. Applicants may download an application form from the Foundation's website. **Additional Information:** Pride Foundation at the above address.

1716 ■ PRIDE FOUNDATION
PO Box 2194, 1122 E Pike St. PMB 1001
Seattle, WA 98112
Tel: (206)323-3318
Free: 800-735-7287
Fax: (206)323-1017
E-mail: prideweb@pridefoundation.org
Web Site: http://www.pridefoundation.org
To provide scholarship to the students who have been stigmatized, isolated or closeted because of sexual identity issues.
Title of Award: Donald O. Coffman Scholarships **Area, Field, or Subject:** General studies. **Level of Education for which Award is Granted:** Undergraduate **Funds Available:** No specific amount.
Eligibility Requirements: Applicant must be a current and future LGBT and straight-ally leaders and role models. **Application Requirements:** Qualified students are asked to submit an application to determine eligibility for scholarships. Applicants may download an application form from the Foundation's website. **Additional Information:** Pride Foundation at the above address.

1717 ■ PRIDE FOUNDATION
PO Box 2194, 1122 E Pike St. PMB 1001
Seattle, WA 98112
Tel: (206)323-3318
Free: 800-735-7287
Fax: (206)323-1017
E-mail: prideweb@pridefoundation.org
Web Site: http://www.pridefoundation.org
To provide scholarship to the students who have been stigmatized, isolated or closeted because of sexual identity issues.
Title of Award: Cole Family Scholarships **Area, Field, or Subject:** General studies. **Level of Education for which Award is Granted:** Undergraduate **Funds Available:** No specific amount.
Eligibility Requirements: Applicant must be a Washington resident under the age of 25 and raised by one or more lesbian or gay parent. **Application Requirements:** Qualified students are asked to submit an application to determine eligibility for scholarships. Applicants may download an application form from the Foundation's website. **Additional Information:** Pride Foundation at the above address.

1718 ■ PRIDE FOUNDATION
PO Box 2194, 1122 E Pike St. PMB 1001
Seattle, WA 98112
Tel: (206)323-3318
Free: 800-735-7287
Fax: (206)323-1017
E-mail: prideweb@pridefoundation.org
Web Site: http://www.pridefoundation.org
To provide scholarship to students who have been stigmatized, isolated or closeted because of sexual identity issues.

Title of Award: Compassionate Care Scholarships **Area, Field, or Subject:** General studies. **Level of Education for which Award is Granted:** Undergraduate **Funds Available:** No specific amount.
Eligibility Requirements: Applicant must be a student committed to offering compassionate support services to those dealing with illness, death, grief or trauma, especially where violent acts such as suicide must be addressed. **Application Requirements:** Qualified students are asked to submit an application to determine eligibility for scholarships. Applicants may download an application form from the Foundation's website. **Additional Information:** Pride Foundation at the above address.

1719 ■ PRIDE FOUNDATION
PO Box 2194, 1122 E Pike St. PMB 1001
Seattle, WA 98112
Tel: (206)323-3318
Free: 800-735-7287
Fax: (206)323-1017
E-mail: prideweb@pridefoundation.org
Web Site: http://www.pridefoundation.org
To provide scholarship to the students who have been stigmatized, isolated or closeted because of sexual identity issues.
Title of Award: Brian M. Day Scholarships **Area, Field, or Subject:** General studies. **Level of Education for which Award is Granted:** Undergraduate **Funds Available:** No specific amount.
Eligibility Requirements: Applicants must be Puget Sound area gay men of color who have significant financial need and demonstrate activism in the gay/lesbian community and their communities of color. **Application Requirements:** Qualified students are asked to submit an application to determine eligibility for scholarships. Applicants may download an application form from the Foundation's website. **Additional Information:** Pride Foundation at the above address.

1720 ■ PRIDE FOUNDATION
PO Box 2194, 1122 E Pike St. PMB 1001
Seattle, WA 98112
Tel: (206)323-3318
Free: 800-735-7287
Fax: (206)323-1017
E-mail: prideweb@pridefoundation.org
Web Site: http://www.pridefoundation.org
To provide scholarship to the students who have been stigmatized, isolated or closeted because of sexual identity issues.
Title of Award: Inland Northwest Business Alliance (INBA) Scholarships **Area, Field, or Subject:** General studies. **Level of Education for which Award is Granted:** Undergraduate **Funds Available:** No specific amount.
Eligibility Requirements: Applicant must be an undergraduate student who is also a resident of Eastern Washington, Idaho, or Montana. **Application Requirements:** Qualified students are asked to submit an application to determine eligibility for scholarships. Applicants may download an application form from the Foundation's website. **Additional Information:** Pride Foundation at the above address.

1721 ■ PRIDE FOUNDATION
PO Box 2194, 1122 E Pike St. PMB 1001
Seattle, WA 98112
Tel: (206)323-3318
Free: 800-735-7287
Fax: (206)323-1017
E-mail: prideweb@pridefoundation.org
Web Site: http://www.pridefoundation.org
To provide scholarship to the students who have been stigmatized, isolated or closeted because of sexual identity issues.
Title of Award: McFarffels Scholarships **Area, Field, or Subject:** General studies. **Level of Education for which Award is Granted:** Undergraduate **Funds Available:** No specific amount.
Eligibility Requirements: Applicant must be a lesbian with financial need entering a field that promotes social change and/or social justice. Preference is given to students who are self-identified lesbian, gay, bisexual or transgender (LGBT). **Application Requirements:** Qualified students are asked to submit an application to determine eligibility for scholarships. Applicants may download an application form from the Foundation's website. **Additional Information:** Pride Foundation at the above address.

1722 ■ PRIDE FOUNDATION
PO Box 2194, 1122 E Pike St. PMB 1001
Seattle, WA 98112
Tel: (206)323-3318
Free: 800-735-7287
Fax: (206)323-1017
E-mail: prideweb@pridefoundation.org
Web Site: http://www.pridefoundation.org
To provide scholarship to the students who have been stigmatized, isolated or closeted because of sexual identity issues. **Title of Award:** Obrzut Ling Scholarships **Area, Field, or Subject:** General studies. **Level of Education for which Award is Granted:** Undergraduate **Funds Available:** No specific amount. **Eligibility Requirements:** Applicant must be a student enrolled or entering a vocational or technical program at an accredited learning institution. Preference is given to students who are self-identified lesbian, gay, bisexual or transgender (LGBT). **Application Requirements:** Qualified students are asked to submit an application to determine eligibility for scholarships. Applicants may download an application form from the Foundation's website. **Additional Information:** Pride Foundation at the above address.

1723 ■ PRIDE FOUNDATION
PO Box 2194, 1122 E Pike St. PMB 1001
Seattle, WA 98112
Tel: (206)323-3318
Free: 800-735-7287
Fax: (206)323-1017
E-mail: prideweb@pridefoundation.org
Web Site: http://www.pridefoundation.org
To provide scholarship to the students who have been stigmatized, isolated or closeted because of sexual identity issues. **Title of Award:** Pride Foundation Regional Scholarships **Area, Field, or Subject:** General studies. **Level of Education for which Award is Granted:** Undergraduate **Funds Available:** No specific amount. **Eligibility Requirements:** Applicant must be a resident of areas outside of King County where Pride Foundation is working to enhance the leadership of the LGBT and straight-ally community: Whatcom/Skagit, Kitsap County, Pierce County, Clark County, Black Hills, Inland Northwest, Southern Idaho and Columbia Basin. **Application Requirements:** Qualified students are asked to submit an application to determine eligibility for scholarships. Applicants may download an application form from the Foundation's website. **Additional Information:** Pride Foundation at the above address.

1724 ■ PRIDE FOUNDATION
PO Box 2194, 1122 E Pike St. PMB 1001
Seattle, WA 98112
Tel: (206)323-3318
Free: 800-735-7287
Fax: (206)323-1017
E-mail: prideweb@pridefoundation.org
Web Site: http://www.pridefoundation.org
To provide scholarship to the students who have been stigmatized, isolated or closeted because of sexual identity issues. **Title of Award:** Richard C. Rolfs Scholarships **Area, Field, or Subject:** General studies. **Level of Education for which Award is Granted:** Undergraduate **Funds Available:** No specific amount. **Eligibility Requirements:** Applicants must be Eastern Washington residents, or undergraduate students attending college in Eastern Washington. **Application Requirements:** Qualified students are asked to submit an application to determine eligibility for scholarships. Applicants may download an application form from the Foundation's website. **Additional Information:** Pride Foundation at the above address.

1725 ■ PRIDE FOUNDATION
PO Box 2194, 1122 E Pike St. PMB 1001
Seattle, WA 98112
Tel: (206)323-3318
Free: 800-735-7287
Fax: (206)323-1017
E-mail: prideweb@pridefoundation.org
Web Site: http://www.pridefoundation.org

To provide scholarship to the students who have been stigmatized, isolated or closeted because of sexual identity issues. **Title of Award:** Rosenberg-Ibarra Scholarships **Area, Field, or Subject:** General studies. **Level of Education for which Award is Granted:** Undergraduate **Funds Available:** No specific amount. **Eligibility Requirements:** Applicant must be a LGBT student who either graduated from a high school in Idaho or will be attending a college or university within the state of Idaho. **Application Requirements:** Qualified students are asked to submit an application to determine eligibility for scholarships. Applicants may download an application form from the Foundation's website. **Additional Information:** Pride Foundation at the above address.

1726 ■ PRIDE FOUNDATION
PO Box 2194, 1122 E Pike St. PMB 1001
Seattle, WA 98112
Tel: (206)323-3318
Free: 800-735-7287
Fax: (206)323-1017
E-mail: prideweb@pridefoundation.org
Web Site: http://www.pridefoundation.org
To provide scholarship to the students who have been stigmatized, isolated or closeted because of sexual identity issues. **Title of Award:** Kathy Spadoni Memorial Scholarships **Area, Field, or Subject:** General studies. **Level of Education for which Award is Granted:** Undergraduate **Funds Available:** No specific amount. **Eligibility Requirements:** Applicant must be a graduating high school senior entering a bachelor's degree program who has demonstrated leadership skills and have a passion for making positive social change. Preference is given to students who are self-identified lesbian, gay, bisexual or transgender (LGBT). **Application Requirements:** Qualified students are asked to submit an application to determine eligibility for scholarships. Applicants may download an application form from the Foundation's website. **Additional Information:** Pride Foundation at the above address.

1727 ■ PRIDE FOUNDATION
PO Box 2194, 1122 E Pike St. PMB 1001
Seattle, WA 98112
Tel: (206)323-3318
Free: 800-735-7287
Fax: (206)323-1017
E-mail: prideweb@pridefoundation.org
Web Site: http://www.pridefoundation.org
To provide scholarship to the students who have been stigmatized, isolated or closeted because of sexual identity issues. **Title of Award:** Phil Sullivan Scholarships **Area, Field, or Subject:** General studies. **Level of Education for which Award is Granted:** Undergraduate **Funds Available:** No specific amount. **Eligibility Requirements:** Applicant must be a student under the age of 21 who demonstrates significant financial need, with preference to those that have been homeless. **Application Requirements:** Qualified students are asked to submit an application to determine eligibility for scholarships. Applicants may download an application form from the Foundation's website. **Additional Information:** Pride Foundation at the above address.

1728 ■ PRIDE FOUNDATION
PO Box 2194, 1122 E Pike St. PMB 1001
Seattle, WA 98112
Tel: (206)323-3318
Free: 800-735-7287
Fax: (206)323-1017
E-mail: prideweb@pridefoundation.org
Web Site: http://www.pridefoundation.org
To provide scholarship to the students who have been stigmatized, isolated or closeted because of sexual identity issues. **Title of Award:** Wells Fargo Scholarships **Area, Field, or Subject:** General studies. **Level of Education for which Award is Granted:** Undergraduate **Funds Available:** No specific amount. **Eligibility Requirements:** Applicant must be a current or future LGBT and straight-ally leaders and role models. **Application Requirements:** Qualified students are asked to submit an application to determine eligibility for scholarships. Applicants may download an application form from the

Foundation's website. **Additional Information:** Pride Foundation at the above address.

1729 ■ PRIDE FOUNDATION
PO Box 2194, 1122 E Pike St. PMB 1001
Seattle, WA 98112
Tel: (206)323-3318
Free: 800-735-7287
Fax: (206)323-1017
E-mail: prideweb@pridefoundation.org
Web Site: http://www.pridefoundation.org
To provide scholarship to the students who have been stigmatized, isolated or closeted because of sexual identity issues.
Title of Award: Whidbey Island Giving Circle Scholarships **Area, Field, or Subject:** General studies. **Level of Education for which Award is Granted:** Undergraduate **Funds Available:** No specific amount.
Eligibility Requirements: Applicant must be a current and future LGBT and straight-ally leaders and role models, with preference given to residents of Whidbey Island. **Application Requirements:** Qualified students are asked to submit an application to determine eligibility for scholarships. Applicants may download an application form from the Foundation's website. **Additional Information:** Pride Foundation at the above address.

1730 ■ PRIDE FOUNDATION
PO Box 2194, 1122 E Pike St. PMB 1001
Seattle, WA 98112
Tel: (206)323-3318
Free: 800-735-7287
Fax: (206)323-1017
E-mail: prideweb@pridefoundation.org
Web Site: http://www.pridefoundation.org
To provide scholarship to the students who have been stigmatized, isolated or closeted because of sexual identity issues.
Title of Award: James and Colin Lee Wozumi Scholarships **Area, Field, or Subject:** General studies. **Level of Education for which Award is Granted:** Undergraduate **Funds Available:** No specific amount.
Eligibility Requirements: Applicant must be an undergraduate student who is goal-oriented, HIV positive, and/or focusing on the treatment and/or eradication of HIV. Preference is given to students who are self-identified lesbian, gay, bisexual or transgender (LGBT). **Application Requirements:** Qualified students are asked to submit an application to determine eligibility for scholarships. Applicants may download an application form from the Foundation's website. **Additional Information:** Pride Foundation at the above address.

1731 ■ PRIDE FOUNDATION
PO Box 2194, 1122 E Pike St. PMB 1001
Seattle, WA 98112
Tel: (206)323-3318
Free: 800-735-7287
Fax: (206)323-1017
E-mail: prideweb@pridefoundation.org
Web Site: http://www.pridefoundation.org
To provide scholarship to the students who have been stigmatized, isolated or closeted because of sexual identity issues.
Title of Award: You Go Girl! Scholarships **Area, Field, or Subject:** General studies. **Level of Education for which Award is Granted:** Undergraduate **Funds Available:** No specific amount.
Eligibility Requirements: Applicants must be lesbians who have completed their sophomore year of college. **Application Requirements:** Qualified students are asked to submit an application to determine eligibility for scholarships. Applicants may download an application form from the Foundation's website. **Additional Information:** Pride Foundation at the above address.

1732 ■ PROFESSIONAL INSTITUTE OF THE PUBLIC SERVICE OF CANADA
250 Tremblay Rd.
Ottawa, ON, Canada K1G 3J8
Tel: (613)228-6310
Fax: (613)228-9048
Web Site: http://www.portal.pipsc.ca

To provide educational assistance for students through three series: The President's Series; The Leader's Series; and The Founders' Series.
Title of Award: Professional Institute of the Public Service of Canada Expanded Scholarships **Area, Field, or Subject:** General studies. **Level of Education for which Award is Granted:** Undergraduate **Funds Available:** $5,000 (President's Series); $3,500 (Leaders' Series); $1,500 (Founders' Series).
Eligibility Requirements: Applicants must be children or grandchildren of regular or retired members in good standing or members who were in good standing at the time of their death. Applicants must be entering their first year of post-secondary education, in a full-time program at an educational institution which is a member of the Association of Universities and Colleges in Canada. **Application Requirements:** Application must include the following: official PIPSC Scholarship Application Form; a copy of the official transcript of marks from the learning institution most recently attended; a statement about why you should receive the scholarship and your future education and career goals; a typed statement about your leadership abilities and community service involvement with supporting evidence; and a 750-1000 word essay on "professionalism". Applicants must submit the application by mail or fax with other supporting documents. **Deadline for Receipt:** July 11.

1733 ■ PUBLIC AGENCY RISK MANAGERS ASSOCIATION
PO Box 6810
San Jose, CA 95150
888-90-PARMA
Fax: 888-412-5913
E-mail: brenda.reisinger@parma.com
Web Site: http://www.parma.com
To promote, develop, and facilitate education and leadership in public agency risk management.
Title of Award: PARMA Scholarships **Area, Field, or Subject:** Management. **Level of Education for which Award is Granted:** Undergraduate **Number Awarded:** 4. **Funds Available:** $500
Eligibility Requirements: Applicant should be an employee of a member public agency pursuing an associate in Risk Management, Risk Management for Public Entities, Associate in Risk Pool Management. **Application Requirements:** An applicant must fill out the application form; attach a written sponsorship statement by a PARMA member agency; must submit of his/her ultimate own goals in the field of risk management; a description of the participation in PARMA including the local Chapter level; and attach any other related experience or information you may wish to submit in support of your scholarship request. **Additional Information:** PARMA Secretary Treasurer PO Box 711894 Santee, CA 92072-1894.

1734 ■ PUBLIC EDUCATION FOUNDATION
3360 W Sahara Ave., Ste. 160
Las Vegas, NV 89102
Tel: (702)799-1042
Fax: (702)799-5247
E-mail: steelej@ccpef.org
Web Site: http://ccpef.org
To assist the education of the dependents of Venetian Resort Hotel Casino Employees.
Title of Award: Adelson Family Scholarships **Area, Field, or Subject:** General studies. **Level of Education for which Award is Granted:** Undergraduate **Number Awarded:** 3. **Funds Available:** $2,500. **Duration:** One year.
Eligibility Requirements: Applicants must be CCSD seniors; must be dependents of a Venetian Resort Hotel Casino employee; must be planning to attend an accredited college/university; must have a minimum 3.5 cumulative GPA; and must demonstrate financial need. **Application Requirements:** Applicants must submit a completed application form together with an essay, two letters of recommendation, transcript and a resume of awards. **Deadline for Receipt:** April 4. **Additional Information:** Shana Venenga at 702-799-1042.

1735 ■ PUBLIC EDUCATION FOUNDATION
3360 W Sahara Ave., Ste. 160
Las Vegas, NV 89102
Tel: (702)799-1042
Fax: (702)799-5247
E-mail: steelej@ccpef.org

Web Site: http://ccpef.org
To promote education in culinary arts.
Title of Award: Alliance of Black Culinarians Scholarships **Area, Field, or Subject:** Culinary arts. **Level of Education for which Award is Granted:** Undergraduate **Number Awarded:** 3. **Funds Available:** $1,000. **Duration:** One year.
Eligibility Requirements: Applicants must be CCSD seniors; must have a minimum 2.5 GPA; and must demonstrate financial need. **Application Requirements:** Applicants must submit a completed application form together with an essay, two letters of recommendation, transcript and a resume. **Deadline for Receipt:** March 31. **Additional Information:** Shana Venenga at 702-799-1042.

1736 ■ PUBLIC EDUCATION FOUNDATION
3360 W Sahara Ave., Ste. 160
Las Vegas, NV 89102
Tel: (702)799-1042
Fax: (702)799-5247
E-mail: steelej@ccpef.org
Web Site: http://ccpef.org
To provide educational opportunities for individuals intending to pursue higher studies.
Title of Award: Susan Ayers Memorial Scholarships **Area, Field, or Subject:** General studies. **Level of Education for which Award is Granted:** Undergraduate **Number Awarded:** 1. **Funds Available:** $500.
Eligibility Requirements: Applicants must be CCSD seniors who have attended the Estes McDoniel Elementary School; must be planning to attend an accredited post-secondary college/university; and must have a minimum 3.0 unweighted cumulative GPA. **Application Requirements:** Applicants must submit a completed application form together with an essay, two letters of recommendation, and transcript. **Deadline for Receipt:** March 7. **Additional Information:** Shana Venenga at 702-799-1042.

1737 ■ PUBLIC EDUCATION FOUNDATION
3360 W Sahara Ave., Ste. 160
Las Vegas, NV 89102
Tel: (702)799-1042
Fax: (702)799-5247
E-mail: steelej@ccpef.org
Web Site: http://ccpef.org
To provide educational opportunities for individuals intending to pursue higher studies.
Title of Award: Blues Ambassador Scholarships **Area, Field, or Subject:** General studies. **Level of Education for which Award is Granted:** Undergraduate **Number Awarded:** 1. **Funds Available:** $10,000 for a four-year program or $5,000 for a two-year program. **Duration:** Four or two years.
Eligibility Requirements: Applicants must be CCSD seniors who have demonstrated an interest and achievement in the arts or shown leadership in encouraging understanding among people of diverse backgrounds; must have a minimum 2.5 cumulative GPA; must be planning to attend an accredited institution of higher learning; and must demonstrate financial need. **Application Requirements:** Applicants must submit a completed application form together with an essay, two letters of recommendation, transcript and a resume of awards. **Deadline for Receipt:** March 7. **Additional Information:** Shana Venenga at 702-799-1042.

1738 ■ PUBLIC EDUCATION FOUNDATION
3360 W Sahara Ave., Ste. 160
Las Vegas, NV 89102
Tel: (702)799-1042
Fax: (702)799-5247
E-mail: steelej@ccpef.org
Web Site: http://ccpef.org
To provide educational opportunities for individuals intending to pursue higher studies.
Title of Award: Agustin Cano Memorial Scholarships **Area, Field, or Subject:** General studies. **Level of Education for which Award is Granted:** Undergraduate **Number Awarded:** 1. **Funds Available:** $500.
Eligibility Requirements: Applicants must be Valley High School seniors planning to attend an accredited college/university as full-time students. **Application Requirements:** Applicants must submit a completed application form together with an essay, two letters of recommendation, and a

resume of awards. **Deadline for Receipt:** March 7. **Additional Information:** Shana Venenga at 702-799-1042.

1739 ■ PUBLIC EDUCATION FOUNDATION
3360 W Sahara Ave., Ste. 160
Las Vegas, NV 89102
Tel: (702)799-1042
Fax: (702)799-5247
E-mail: steelej@ccpef.org
Web Site: http://ccpef.org
To provide educational opportunities for individuals intending to pursue higher studies.
Title of Award: John Caoile Memorial Scholarships **Area, Field, or Subject:** General studies. **Level of Education for which Award is Granted:** Undergraduate **Number Awarded:** 1. **Funds Available:** $1,000.
Eligibility Requirements: Applicants must be Durango High School AFJROTC program seniors planning to attend an accredited post-secondary institution and have excelled in the areas of leadership, community service and extra-curricular activities and must have a minimum 3.0 GPA. **Application Requirements:** Applicants must submit a completed application form together with a letter of recommendation, transcript and a resume of awards. **Deadline for Receipt:** March 7. **Additional Information:** Shana Venenga at 702-799-1042.

1740 ■ PUBLIC EDUCATION FOUNDATION
3360 W Sahara Ave., Ste. 160
Las Vegas, NV 89102
Tel: (702)799-1042
Fax: (702)799-5247
E-mail: steelej@ccpef.org
Web Site: http://ccpef.org
To provide educational opportunities for individuals intending to pursue higher studies.
Title of Award: CCSD School Counselors' Scholarships **Area, Field, or Subject:** General studies. **Level of Education for which Award is Granted:** Undergraduate **Number Awarded:** 1. **Funds Available:** $1,000.
Eligibility Requirements: Applicants must be CCSD seniors who have met and overcome a serious personal challenge or adversity; must have a minimum 2.5 unweighted GPA; and must be planning to attend an accredited post-secondary institution. **Application Requirements:** Applicants must submit a completed application form together with an essay, two letters of recommendation, transcript and a resume of awards. **Deadline for Receipt:** March 7. **Additional Information:** Shana Venenga at 702-799-1042.

1741 ■ PUBLIC EDUCATION FOUNDATION
3360 W Sahara Ave., Ste. 160
Las Vegas, NV 89102
Tel: (702)799-1042
Fax: (702)799-5247
E-mail: steelej@ccpef.org
Web Site: http://ccpef.org
To provide educational opportunities for individuals intending to pursue higher studies.
Title of Award: Cheyenne High School Faculty Memorial Scholarships **Area, Field, or Subject:** General studies. **Level of Education for which Award is Granted:** Undergraduate **Number Awarded:** 2. **Funds Available:** $1000.
Eligibility Requirements: Applicants must be Cheyenne High School seniors planning to attend an accredited post-secondary institution and have a minimum 3.1 unweighted GPA. **Application Requirements:** Applicants must submit a completed application form together with an essay, a resume of awards, and two letters of recommendation. **Deadline for Receipt:** March 7. **Additional Information:** Shana Venenga at 702-799-1042.

1742 ■ PUBLIC EDUCATION FOUNDATION
3360 W Sahara Ave., Ste. 160
Las Vegas, NV 89102
Tel: (702)799-1042
Fax: (702)799-5247

E-mail: steelej@ccpef.org
Web Site: http://ccpef.org
To provide educational opportunities for individuals intending to pursue higher studies.
Title of Award: Corbett-Porter Building Bridges Scholarships **Area, Field, or Subject:** General studies. **Level of Education for which Award is Granted:** Undergraduate **Number Awarded:** 1. **Funds Available:** $1,000.
Eligibility Requirements: Applicants must be CCSD seniors who have worked to create a school environment free of discrimination, harassment and intolerance by building bridges between the gay/lesbian and straight communities; must have a 2.5 minimum GPA; and must be planning to attend an accredited post-secondary institution. **Application Requirements:** Applicants must submit a completed application form together with an essay, two letters of recommendation, transcript, and resume of awards. **Deadline for Receipt:** March 7. **Additional Information:** Shana Venenga at 702-799-1042.

1743 ■ PUBLIC EDUCATION FOUNDATION
3360 W Sahara Ave., Ste. 160
Las Vegas, NV 89102
Tel: (702)799-1042
Fax: (702)799-5247
E-mail: steelej@ccpef.org
Web Site: http://ccpef.org
To provide educational opportunities for individuals intending to pursue higher studies.
Title of Award: Robin M. Daniels Memorial Scholarships **Area, Field, or Subject:** General studies. **Level of Education for which Award is Granted:** Undergraduate **Number Awarded:** 1. **Funds Available:** $1,000.
Eligibility Requirements: Applicants must be CCSD seniors who have met and overcome a serious personal challenge or adversity and plan to attend an accredited post-secondary institution in Nevada. **Application Requirements:** Applicants must submit a completed application form together with an essay, and two letters of recommendation. **Deadline for Receipt:** March 7. **Additional Information:** Shana Venenga at 702-799-1042.

1744 ■ PUBLIC EDUCATION FOUNDATION
3360 W Sahara Ave., Ste. 160
Las Vegas, NV 89102
Tel: (702)799-1042
Fax: (702)799-5247
E-mail: steelej@ccpef.org
Web Site: http://ccpef.org
To provide educational opportunities for individuals intending to pursue higher studies.
Title of Award: Mickey Donnelly Memorial Scholarships **Area, Field, or Subject:** General studies. **Level of Education for which Award is Granted:** Undergraduate **Number Awarded:** 1. **Funds Available:** $500.
Eligibility Requirements: Applicants must be CCSD seniors who have attended Walter Johnson Junior High School for a minimum of one year and are planning to attend an accredited post-secondary institution in Nevada; must have a minimum 2.5 unweighted cumulative GPA. **Application Requirements:** Applicants must submit a completed application form together with an essay, two letters of recommendation, transcript, and resume of awards. **Deadline for Receipt:** March 7. **Additional Information:** Shana Venenga at 702-799-1042.

1745 ■ PUBLIC EDUCATION FOUNDATION
3360 W Sahara Ave., Ste. 160
Las Vegas, NV 89102
Tel: (702)799-1042
Fax: (702)799-5247
E-mail: steelej@ccpef.org
Web Site: http://ccpef.org
To provide educational opportunities for individuals intending to pursue higher studies.
Title of Award: Travis Dunning Memorial Scholarships **Area, Field, or Subject:** General studies. **Level of Education for which Award is Granted:** Undergraduate **Number Awarded:** 1. **Funds Available:** $1,500. **Duration:** One year.

Eligibility Requirements: Applicants must be high school seniors from Green Valley, Coronado, Foothill, Silverado or Liberty planning to attend an accredited four-year college/university and who have a 3.0 weighted or unweighted GPA. **Application Requirements:** Applicants must submit a completed application form together with an essay, two letters of recommendation, transcript, and resume of awards. **Deadline for Receipt:** March 31. **Additional Information:** Shana Venenga at 702-799-1042.

1746 ■ PUBLIC EDUCATION FOUNDATION
3360 W Sahara Ave., Ste. 160
Las Vegas, NV 89102
Tel: (702)799-1042
Fax: (702)799-5247
E-mail: steelej@ccpef.org
Web Site: http://ccpef.org
To promote education in Hotel Management and Food and Beverage.
Title of Award: Epicurean Charitable Foundation Scholarships **Area, Field, or Subject:** Hotel, institutional, and restaurant management. **Level of Education for which Award is Granted:** Undergraduate **Number Awarded:** Up to 8. **Funds Available:** $5,000-$10,000. **Duration:** One year.
Eligibility Requirements: Applicants must be high school seniors in Clark County planning to attend an accredited post-secondary institution; must be planning to obtain a bachelor's degree and major in Hotel Management or Food & Beverage programs; must have demonstrated financial need; and must have a cumulative GPA of 2.75. **Application Requirements:** Applicants must submit a completed application form together with an essay, career goal statement, two letters of recommendation, transcript, and resume of awards. **Deadline for Receipt:** March 7. **Additional Information:** Shana Venenga at 702-799-1042.

1747 ■ PUBLIC EDUCATION FOUNDATION
3360 W Sahara Ave., Ste. 160
Las Vegas, NV 89102
Tel: (702)799-1042
Fax: (702)799-5247
E-mail: steelej@ccpef.org
Web Site: http://ccpef.org
To provide educational opportunities for individuals intending to pursue higher studies.
Title of Award: Evening Mesquite Club Scholarships **Area, Field, or Subject:** General studies. **Level of Education for which Award is Granted:** Undergraduate **Number Awarded:** 1. **Funds Available:** $1,200.
Eligibility Requirements: Applicants must be CCSD female seniors planning to attend an accredited post-secondary institution in Nevada as a full-time student; must have a minimum 3.0 GPA; and must have demonstrated financial need. **Application Requirements:** Applicants must submit a completed application form together with an essay, two letters of recommendation, transcript, and resume of awards. **Deadline for Receipt:** March 7. **Additional Information:** Shana Venenga at 702-799-1042.

1748 ■ PUBLIC EDUCATION FOUNDATION
3360 W Sahara Ave., Ste. 160
Las Vegas, NV 89102
Tel: (702)799-1042
Fax: (702)799-5247
E-mail: steelej@ccpef.org
Web Site: http://ccpef.org
To provide educational opportunities for individuals intending to pursue higher studies.
Title of Award: Gordy Fink Memorial Scholarships **Area, Field, or Subject:** General studies. **Level of Education for which Award is Granted:** Undergraduate **Number Awarded:** 2. **Funds Available:** $1,000.
Eligibility Requirements: Applicants must be Valley High School seniors planning to attend the University of Nevada, Las Vegas as full-time students. **Application Requirements:** Applicants must submit a completed application form together with an essay, two letters of recommendation, transcript, resume of awards, and letter of admission from UNLV. **Deadline for Receipt:** March 7. **Additional Information:** Shana Venenga at 702-799-1042.

1749 ■ PUBLIC EDUCATION FOUNDATION
3360 W Sahara Ave., Ste. 160
Las Vegas, NV 89102
Tel: (702)799-1042
Fax: (702)799-5247
E-mail: steelej@ccpef.org
Web Site: http://ccpef.org
To provide educational opportunities for individuals intending to pursue higher studies.
Title of Award: Veronica Gantt Memorial Scholarships **Area, Field, or Subject:** General studies. **Level of Education for which Award is Granted:** Undergraduate **Number Awarded:** 2. **Funds Available:** $500.
Eligibility Requirements: Applicants must be Del Sol High School seniors active in sports and community; must be planning to attend an accredited college or university; and must have a minimum 3.0 cumulative GPA. **Application Requirements:** Applicants must submit a completed application form together with an essay and a recommendation letter. **Deadline for Receipt:** March 7. **Additional Information:** Shana Venenga at 702-799-1042.

1750 ■ PUBLIC EDUCATION FOUNDATION
3360 W Sahara Ave., Ste. 160
Las Vegas, NV 89102
Tel: (702)799-1042
Fax: (702)799-5247
E-mail: steelej@ccpef.org
Web Site: http://ccpef.org
To provide educational opportunities for individuals intending to pursue higher studies.
Title of Award: Nick Giorgione Hope for Hearts Scholarships **Area, Field, or Subject:** General studies. **Level of Education for which Award is Granted:** Undergraduate **Number Awarded:** 1. **Funds Available:** $1,500.
Eligibility Requirements: Applicants must be CCSD seniors with a minimum 2.8 cumulative GAP, affected by a heart disease. **Application Requirements:** Applicants must submit a completed application form together with an essay, a letter of recommendation, transcript, and a documentation from a school health office or doctor verifying heart condition. **Deadline for Receipt:** March 7. **Additional Information:** Shana Venenga at 702-799-1042.

1751 ■ PUBLIC EDUCATION FOUNDATION
3360 W Sahara Ave., Ste. 160
Las Vegas, NV 89102
Tel: (702)799-1042
Fax: (702)799-5247
E-mail: steelej@ccpef.org
Web Site: http://ccpef.org
To support the education of students having a parent or grandparent participating in the glazing industry.
Title of Award: Glazing Industry Scholarships **Area, Field, or Subject:** General studies. **Level of Education for which Award is Granted:** Undergraduate **Number Awarded:** 6. **Funds Available:** $500.
Eligibility Requirements: Applicants must be High school seniors or post-secondary students in Nevada who are children or grandchildren of individuals actively participating in the glazing industry; must have a desire to achieve excellence through education, planning to attend a post-secondary program; and must have a minimum 2.8 unweighted cumulative GPA. **Application Requirements:** Applicants must submit a completed application form together with an essay, a letter of recommendation, and transcript. **Deadline for Receipt:** March 7. **Additional Information:** Shana Venenga at 702-799-1042.

1752 ■ PUBLIC EDUCATION FOUNDATION
3360 W Sahara Ave., Ste. 160
Las Vegas, NV 89102
Tel: (702)799-1042
Fax: (702)799-5247
E-mail: steelej@ccpef.org
Web Site: http://ccpef.org
To provide educational opportunities for individuals intending to pursue higher studies.
Title of Award: Michael J. Hoggard Memorial Scholarships **Area, Field, or Subject:** General studies. **Level of Education for which Award is**

Granted: Undergraduate **Number Awarded:** 1. **Funds Available:** $1,000.
Eligibility Requirements: Applicants must be Green Valley High School seniors who have been on the school's soccer team for at least two years (including senior year); must be planning to attend an accredited post-secondary college/university; and must have a minimum 3.0 cumulative GPA. **Application Requirements:** Applicants must submit a completed application form with the essay, two letters of recommendation, transcript, and resume of awards. **Deadline for Receipt:** March 7. **Additional Information:** Shana Venenga at 702-799-1042.

1753 ■ PUBLIC EDUCATION FOUNDATION
3360 W Sahara Ave., Ste. 160
Las Vegas, NV 89102
Tel: (702)799-1042
Fax: (702)799-5247
E-mail: steelej@ccpef.org
Web Site: http://ccpef.org
To provide educational opportunities for individuals intending to pursue higher studies.
Title of Award: Knights of Pythias Scholarships **Area, Field, or Subject:** General studies. **Level of Education for which Award is Granted:** Undergraduate **Number Awarded:** 1. **Funds Available:** $1,000.
Eligibility Requirements: Applicants must be CCSD seniors who have demonstrated exemplary participation in community service and planning to attend an accredited post-secondary institution. **Application Requirements:** Applicants must submit a completed application form with the essay, two letters of recommendation, and resume of awards. **Deadline for Receipt:** March 7. **Additional Information:** Shana Venenga at 702-799-1042.

1754 ■ PUBLIC EDUCATION FOUNDATION
3360 W Sahara Ave., Ste. 160
Las Vegas, NV 89102
Tel: (702)799-1042
Fax: (702)799-5247
E-mail: steelej@ccpef.org
Web Site: http://ccpef.org
To provide educational opportunities for individuals intending to pursue higher studies.
Title of Award: Las Vegas Elks Scholarships **Area, Field, or Subject:** General studies. **Level of Education for which Award is Granted:** Undergraduate **Number Awarded:** 5. **Funds Available:** $1,500.
Eligibility Requirements: Applicants must be CCSD seniors planning to attend an accredited college, university or vocational school; must have a GPA which is adequate for entry to the school; must be citizens of the U.S.; and must live at an address in Las Vegas, Nevada. **Application Requirements:** Applicants must submit a completed application form along with the essay, transcript and resume of awards. The essay, resume and reference must not be more than six pages. **Deadline for Receipt:** March 7. **Additional Information:** Shana Venenga at 702-799-1042.

1755 ■ PUBLIC EDUCATION FOUNDATION
3360 W Sahara Ave., Ste. 160
Las Vegas, NV 89102
Tel: (702)799-1042
Fax: (702)799-5247
E-mail: steelej@ccpef.org
Web Site: http://ccpef.org
To provide educational assistance for physically challenged students.
Title of Award: Las Vegas Elks Scholarships for the Physically Challenged **Area, Field, or Subject:** General studies. **Level of Education for which Award is Granted:** Undergraduate **Number Awarded:** 4. **Funds Available:** $5,000.
Eligibility Requirements: Applicants must be CCSD seniors who are physically challenged; must be planning to attend an accredited college, university or vocational school; must have a GPA adequate for entry to the school; must be citizens of the U.S.; and must live at an address in Las Vegas, Nevada. **Application Requirements:** Applicants must submit a completed application form along with an essay, transcript and resume of awards. The essay, resume and reference must not be more than six pages. **Deadline for Receipt:** March 7. **Additional Information:** Shana Venenga at 702-799-1042.

1756 ■ PUBLIC EDUCATION FOUNDATION
3360 W Sahara Ave., Ste. 160
Las Vegas, NV 89102
Tel: (702)799-1042
Fax: (702)799-5247
E-mail: steelej@ccpef.org
Web Site: http://ccpef.org
To provide educational opportunities for individuals intending to pursue higher studies.
Title of Award: Melissa A. Lyles Memorial Scholarships **Area, Field, or Subject:** General studies. **Level of Education for which Award is Granted:** Undergraduate **Number Awarded:** 1. **Funds Available:** $5,000. **Duration:** One academic year.
Eligibility Requirements: Applicants must be CCSD seniors who have demonstrated an academic achievement in a minimum of eleven Honors or Advanced Placement courses; must be planning to attend an accredited college/university; and must have a minimum 4.0 weighted cumulative GPA. **Application Requirements:** Applicants must submit a completed application form along with an essay, transcript and resume of awards. **Deadline for Receipt:** March 7. **Additional Information:** Shana Venenga at 702-799-1042.

1757 ■ PUBLIC EDUCATION FOUNDATION
3360 W Sahara Ave., Ste. 160
Las Vegas, NV 89102
Tel: (702)799-1042
Fax: (702)799-5247
E-mail: steelej@ccpef.org
Web Site: http://ccpef.org
To provide educational opportunities for individuals intending to pursue higher studies.
Title of Award: Nate Mack/Cindi Turner Scholarships **Area, Field, or Subject:** General studies. **Level of Education for which Award is Granted:** Undergraduate **Number Awarded:** 1. **Funds Available:** $500.
Eligibility Requirements: Applicants must be CCSD seniors who attended Nate Mack Elementary School for at least three years; must be planning to attend an accredited college/university; must have a minimum 2.8 cumulative GPA; and must demonstrate financial need. **Application Requirements:** Applicants must submit a completed application form along with an essay, two letters of recommendation, transcript, and resume of awards. **Deadline for Receipt:** March 7. **Additional Information:** Shana Venenga at 702-799-1042.

1758 ■ PUBLIC EDUCATION FOUNDATION
3360 W Sahara Ave., Ste. 160
Las Vegas, NV 89102
Tel: (702)799-1042
Fax: (702)799-5247
E-mail: steelej@ccpef.org
Web Site: http://ccpef.org
To provide educational opportunities for individuals intending to pursue higher studies.
Title of Award: Aaron Matusek Memorial Scholarships **Area, Field, or Subject:** General studies. **Level of Education for which Award is Granted:** Undergraduate **Number Awarded:** 1. **Funds Available:** $800. **Duration:** One year.
Eligibility Requirements: Applicants must be CCSD seniors with a minimum 2.75 cumulative GPA and planning to attend an accredited college/university in Nevada. **Application Requirements:** Applicants must submit a completed application form along with an essay, two letters of recommendation, transcript, and resume of awards. **Deadline for Receipt:** March 7. **Additional Information:** Shana Venenga at 702-799-1042.

1759 ■ PUBLIC EDUCATION FOUNDATION
3360 W Sahara Ave., Ste. 160
Las Vegas, NV 89102
Tel: (702)799-1042
Fax: (702)799-5247
E-mail: steelej@ccpef.org
Web Site: http://ccpef.org
To provide educational opportunities for individuals intending to pursue higher studies.
Title of Award: Ronald McDonald House Charities of Las Vegas Scholarships **Area, Field, or Subject:** General studies. **Level of Education for which Award is Granted:** Undergraduate **Number Awarded:** Varies. **Funds Available:** Varies.
Eligibility Requirements: Applicants must be high school seniors in Clark or Nye County in Nevada; must be eligible to attend an accredited post-secondary educational institute (includes colleges, universities, junior colleges, vocational institutes and trade schools); and must have a minimum 2.5 cumulative GPA-unweighted. **Application Requirements:** Applicants must submit a complete application form together with certified high school transcript; personal statement; letter of recommendation; and a copy of parent's/guardian's IRS Form W2. **Additional Information:** Sponsored by RMHC Charities. **Deadline for Receipt:** march 7.

1760 ■ PUBLIC EDUCATION FOUNDATION
3360 W Sahara Ave., Ste. 160
Las Vegas, NV 89102
Tel: (702)799-1042
Fax: (702)799-5247
E-mail: steelej@ccpef.org
Web Site: http://ccpef.org
To assist the education of African American students.
Title of Award: Nevada Black Police Association Scholarships **Area, Field, or Subject:** General studies. **Level of Education for which Award is Granted:** Undergraduate **Number Awarded:** 4. **Funds Available:** $1,000.
Eligibility Requirements: Applicants must be CCSD African American seniors planning to attend a college/university; must have a 2.5 GPA; and must demonstrate financial need. **Application Requirements:** Applicants must submit a completed application form along with an essay, two letters of recommendation, transcript, resume of awards, and a college letter of admission. **Deadline for Receipt:** March 7. **Additional Information:** Shana Venenga at 702-799-1042.

1761 ■ PUBLIC EDUCATION FOUNDATION
3360 W Sahara Ave., Ste. 160
Las Vegas, NV 89102
Tel: (702)799-1042
Fax: (702)799-5247
E-mail: steelej@ccpef.org
Web Site: http://ccpef.org
To provide educational opportunities for individuals intending to pursue higher studies.
Title of Award: North Las Vegas Firefighters - William J. Harnedy Memorial Scholarships **Area, Field, or Subject:** General studies. **Level of Education for which Award is Granted:** Undergraduate **Number Awarded:** 1. **Funds Available:** $1,000.
Eligibility Requirements: Applicants must be CCSD seniors who have attended a North Las Vegas High School; must be enrolled in the Credit Retrieval Program; must have a minimum cumulative 2.5 GPA; must have demonstrated financial need; and must be planning to attend an accredited post-secondary institution. **Application Requirements:** Applicants must submit a completed application form together with an essay and transcript. **Deadline for Receipt:** March 7. **Additional Information:** Shana Venenga at 702-799-1042.

1762 ■ PUBLIC EDUCATION FOUNDATION
3360 W Sahara Ave., Ste. 160
Las Vegas, NV 89102
Tel: (702)799-1042
Fax: (702)799-5247
E-mail: steelej@ccpef.org
Web Site: http://ccpef.org
To provide educational opportunities for individuals intending to pursue higher studies.
Title of Award: Panther Cafe Scholarships **Area, Field, or Subject:** General studies. **Level of Education for which Award is Granted:** Undergraduate **Number Awarded:** 2. **Funds Available:** $500.
Eligibility Requirements: Applicants must be Palo Verde High School seniors who have participated in a class that is directly associated with the operation of the Panther Cafe and must be planning to attend an accredited post-secondary college or institution. **Application Requirements:** Applicants must submit a completed application form along with an essay, two letters of recommendation, transcript, and resume of awards. **Deadline for Receipt:** March 7. **Additional Information:** Shana Venenga at 702-799-1042.

1763 ■ PUBLIC EDUCATION FOUNDATION
3360 W Sahara Ave., Ste. 160
Las Vegas, NV 89102
Tel: (702)799-1042
Fax: (702)799-5247
E-mail: steelej@ccpef.org
Web Site: http://ccpef.org
To provide educational opportunities for individuals intending to pursue higher studies.
Title of Award: Procida Tile Importers Scholarships **Area, Field, or Subject:** General studies. **Level of Education for which Award is Granted:** Undergraduate **Number Awarded:** Up to 10. **Funds Available:** $1,000. **Duration:** One year.
Eligibility Requirements: Applicants must be CCSD seniors with a minimum 3.5 cumulative GPA and adverse family situations; must be planning to attend the University of Nevada, Las Vegas; and must demonstrate financial need. **Application Requirements:** Applicants must submit a completed application form along with an essay, transcript, resume of awards, and Adult Nominating Form. **Deadline for Receipt:** March 31. **Additional Information:** Shana Venenga at 702-799-1042.

1764 ■ PUBLIC EDUCATION FOUNDATION
3360 W Sahara Ave., Ste. 160
Las Vegas, NV 89102
Tel: (702)799-1042
Fax: (702)799-5247
E-mail: steelej@ccpef.org
Web Site: http://ccpef.org
To provide educational opportunities for individuals intending to pursue higher studies.
Title of Award: Public Education Foundation Opportunity Scholarships **Area, Field, or Subject:** General studies. **Level of Education for which Award is Granted:** Undergraduate **Number Awarded:** 2. **Funds Available:** Full-ride scholarship. **Duration:** Two years.
Eligibility Requirements: Applicants must be CCSD seniors planning to attend an accredited post-secondary institution in Nevada and must maintain a minimum GPA of 3.0. **Application Requirements:** Applicants must submit a completed application form along with an essay, two letters of recommendation, transcript, and resume of awards. **Deadline for Receipt:** March 31. **Additional Information:** Shana Venenga at 702-799-1042.

1765 ■ PUBLIC EDUCATION FOUNDATION
3360 W Sahara Ave., Ste. 160
Las Vegas, NV 89102
Tel: (702)799-1042
Fax: (702)799-5247
E-mail: steelej@ccpef.org
Web Site: http://ccpef.org
To provide educational opportunities for individuals intending to pursue higher studies.
Title of Award: Elizabeth Shafer Memorial Scholarships **Area, Field, or Subject:** Culinary arts. **Level of Education for which Award is Granted:** Undergraduate **Number Awarded:** 1. **Funds Available:** $1,000.
Eligibility Requirements: Applicants must be CCSD seniors pursuing a degree in the culinary field; must have a minimum 2.0 cumulative GPA; and must be U.S. citizens either by birth or naturalization. **Application Requirements:** Applicants must submit a completed application form along with an essay, transcript, resume of awards, and a visible sample of artwork or culinary talents. **Deadline for Receipt:** March 7. **Additional Information:** Shana Venenga at 702-799-1042.

1766 ■ PUBLIC EDUCATION FOUNDATION
3360 W Sahara Ave., Ste. 160
Las Vegas, NV 89102
Tel: (702)799-1042
Fax: (702)799-5247
E-mail: steelej@ccpef.org
Web Site: http://ccpef.org
To provide educational opportunities for individuals intending to pursue higher studies.
Title of Award: Silver Nugget Family Scholarships **Area, Field, or Subject:** General studies. **Level of Education for which Award is**

Granted: Undergraduate **Number Awarded:** 1. **Funds Available:** $3,000.
Eligibility Requirements: Applicants must be CCSD seniors; must be dependents of a Silver Nugget Gaming Team member; and must be planning to attend an accredited college/university. **Application Requirements:** Applicants must submit a completed application together with an essay (400-500 words). **Deadline for Receipt:** March 31. **Additional Information:** Shana Venenga at 702-799-1042.

1767 ■ PUBLIC EDUCATION FOUNDATION
3360 W Sahara Ave., Ste. 160
Las Vegas, NV 89102
Tel: (702)799-1042
Fax: (702)799-5247
E-mail: steelej@ccpef.org
Web Site: http://ccpef.org
To provide educational opportunities for individuals intending to pursue higher studies.
Title of Award: Smith's Personal Best Scholarships **Area, Field, or Subject:** General studies. **Level of Education for which Award is Granted:** Undergraduate **Number Awarded:** 10. **Funds Available:** $1,000.
Eligibility Requirements: Applicants must be CCSD seniors who have met and overcome a serious personal challenge or adversity; must plan to attend an accredited post-secondary institution. **Application Requirements:** Applicants must submit complete application package which include the Applicant's General Information, the Certifications and Authorizations form, the Short Answer Questionnaire and the nomination form completed by an adult who knows the student well - a teacher, counselor, club advisor, employer, etc. **Deadline for Receipt:** March 7. **Additional Information:** Shana Venenga at 702-799-1042.

1768 ■ PUBLIC EDUCATION FOUNDATION
3360 W Sahara Ave., Ste. 160
Las Vegas, NV 89102
Tel: (702)799-1042
Fax: (702)799-5247
E-mail: steelej@ccpef.org
Web Site: http://ccpef.org
To provide educational opportunities for individuals intending to pursue higher studies.
Title of Award: Southern Nevada Sports Hall of Fame Athletic Scholarships **Area, Field, or Subject:** General studies. **Level of Education for which Award is Granted:** Undergraduate **Number Awarded:** 2. **Funds Available:** $2,000.
Eligibility Requirements: Applicants must be CCSD seniors who have participated in athletics for the past four years with a minimum 3.2 unweighted cumulative GPA. **Application Requirements:** Applicants must submit a completed application form along with an essay, two letters of recommendation, transcript, and resume. **Deadline for Receipt:** March 7. **Additional Information:** Shana Venenga at 702-799-1042.

1769 ■ PUBLIC EDUCATION FOUNDATION
3360 W Sahara Ave., Ste. 160
Las Vegas, NV 89102
Tel: (702)799-1042
Fax: (702)799-5247
E-mail: steelej@ccpef.org
Web Site: http://ccpef.org
To provide educational opportunities for individuals intending to pursue higher studies.
Title of Award: Spartan Staff Scholarships **Area, Field, or Subject:** General studies. **Level of Education for which Award is Granted:** Undergraduate **Number Awarded:** 8. **Funds Available:** $500.
Eligibility Requirements: Applicants must be Cimarron-Memorial High School seniors interested in pursuing a degree at an accredited college or university; must have a minimum 3.0 unweighted cumulative GPA; and must demonstrate financial need. **Application Requirements:** Applicants must submit a completed application form along with an essay, two letters of recommendation, transcript, and resume of awards. **Deadline for Receipt:** April. **Additional Information:** Shana Venenga at 702-799-1042.

1770 ■ PUBLIC EDUCATION FOUNDATION
3360 W Sahara Ave., Ste. 160
Las Vegas, NV 89102
Tel: (702)799-1042
Fax: (702)799-5247
E-mail: steelej@ccpef.org
Web Site: http://ccpef.org
To provide educational opportunities for individuals intending to pursue higher studies.
Title of Award: Striving for Success Scholarships **Area, Field, or Subject:** General studies. **Level of Education for which Award is Granted:** Undergraduate **Number Awarded:** 1. **Funds Available:** $500.
Eligibility Requirements: Applicants must be Northeast Region High School special education seniors planning to attend an accredited post-secondary institution. **Application Requirements:** Applicants must submit a completed application form along with an essay, two letters of recommendation, transcript, and resume of awards. **Deadline for Receipt:** March 7. **Additional Information:** Shana Venenga at 702-799-1042.

1771 ■ PUBLIC EDUCATION FOUNDATION
3360 W Sahara Ave., Ste. 160
Las Vegas, NV 89102
Tel: (702)799-1042
Fax: (702)799-5247
E-mail: steelej@ccpef.org
Web Site: http://ccpef.org
To provide educational opportunities for individuals intending to pursue higher studies.
Title of Award: Tall Awareness Scholarships **Area, Field, or Subject:** General studies. **Level of Education for which Award is Granted:** Undergraduate **Number Awarded:** 1. **Funds Available:** $1,000.
Eligibility Requirements: Applicants must be CCSD seniors attending an accredited post-secondary school; must have met the minimum height requirement of 5'10" for female students and 6'2" for male students. **Application Requirements:** Applicants must submit a completed application form along with an essay, a letter of recommendation, and transcript. **Deadline for Receipt:** March 7. **Additional Information:** Shana Venenga at 702-799-1042.

1772 ■ PUBLIC EDUCATION FOUNDATION
3360 W Sahara Ave., Ste. 160
Las Vegas, NV 89102
Tel: (702)799-1042
Fax: (702)799-5247
E-mail: steelej@ccpef.org
Web Site: http://ccpef.org
To support single mothers desiring to advance their education.
Title of Award: Tsutako Curo Scholarships **Area, Field, or Subject:** General studies. **Level of Education for which Award is Granted:** Undergraduate **Number Awarded:** 1. **Funds Available:** $1,500. **Duration:** One year.
Eligibility Requirements: Applicants must be CCSD seniors who are single mothers desiring to advance their education at an accredited post-secondary institution; must have a minimum 2.5 cumulative GPA; and must demonstrate financial need. **Application Requirements:** Applicants must submit a completed application form together with an essay, two letters of recommendation, and transcript. **Deadline for Receipt:** March 7. **Additional Information:** Shana Venenga at 702-799-1042.

1773 ■ PUBLIC EDUCATION FOUNDATION
3360 W Sahara Ave., Ste. 160
Las Vegas, NV 89102
Tel: (702)799-1042
Fax: (702)799-5247
E-mail: steelej@ccpef.org
Web Site: http://ccpef.org
To provide educational opportunities for individuals intending to pursue higher studies.
Title of Award: Williams Foundation Scholarships **Area, Field, or Subject:** General studies. **Level of Education for which Award is Granted:** Undergraduate **Number Awarded:** 5. **Funds Available:** $1,000.

Eligibility Requirements: Applicants must be CCSD seniors planning to attend an accredited post-secondary institution for which they meet entry level requirements. **Application Requirements:** Applicants must submit a completed application form along with an essay, two letters of recommendation, transcript, and resume of awards. **Deadline for Receipt:** March 7. **Additional Information:** Shana Venenga at 702-799-1042.

1774 ■ RAILWAY TIE ASSOCIATION
115 Commerce Dr., Ste. C
Fayetteville, GA 30214
Tel: (770)460-5553
Fax: (770)460-5573
E-mail: ties@rta.org
Web Site: http://www.rta.org
To provide financial support for students attending technical schools, colleges and universities.
Title of Award: John Mabry Forestry Scholarships **Area, Field, or Subject:** General studies. **Level of Education for which Award is Granted:** Undergraduate **Number Awarded:** 2. **Funds Available:** $1,500. **Duration:** One year.
Eligibility Requirements: Applicants must be students in accredited second year technical schools or juniors and seniors attending four-year colleges and universities. **Application Requirements:** Applicants must submit completed application along with personal narrative, one black and white photo, and a copy of transcript. **Deadline for Receipt:** June 30.

1775 ■ JEANNETTE RANKIN FOUNDATION
PO Box 6653
Athens, GA 30604-6653
Tel: (706)208-1211
Fax: (706)548-0202
E-mail: info@rankinfoundation.org
Web Site: http://www.rankinfoundation.org
To financially support the education of a low-income female student who wishes to pursue her educational goals.
Title of Award: Jeannette Rankin Scholarships **Area, Field, or Subject:** General studies. **Level of Education for which Award is Granted:** Undergraduate **Funds Available:** No specific amount.
Eligibility Requirements: Applicant must be female, age 35 or older; a U.S. citizen; enrolled in, or accepted to an accredited school; pursuing a technical or vocational education, an associate's degree, or a first bachelor's degree; and have low-income according to the U.S. Department of Labor's Lower Living Standard. **Application Requirements:** Applicants must submit a completed scholarship application along with a personal statement; two letters of recommendation; and proof of enrollment or acceptance. Applicants are requested to submit two complete sets of the application materials. **Additional Information:** at the above address.

1776 ■ RAYTHEON COMPANY
870 Winter Street
Waltham, MA 02451
Tel: (781)522-3000
Web Site: http://www.raytheon.com
To assist employee's children who plan to continue their education in college.
Title of Award: Raytheon Scholarship Program **Area, Field, or Subject:** General studies. **Level of Education for which Award is Granted:** Undergraduate **Funds Available:** $1,000. **Duration:** One year.
Eligibility Requirements: Applicants must be under the age of 24; dependent children of active employees who work 20 hours or more per week and have at least one year of service with the company by the application deadline; college freshmen, sophomores and juniors who plan to enroll in a full-time undergraduate course of study at an accredited two-year or four-year college or university. **Application Requirements:** Applicants must submit the application and current complete official transcript of grades to Scholarship America. **Deadline for Receipt:** April 30.

1777 ■ REDLANDS COMMUNITY SCHOLARSHIP FOUNDATION
c/o Kathleen Venegas-Boge, Admin. Asst.
PO Box 1683
Redlands, CA 92373

Tel: (909)307-9892
Fax: (909)307-9892
Web Site: http://www.redlandsscholarships.org
To encourage educational pursuits among Redlands Unified School District graduates by providing educational assistance.
Title of Award: Ruth Adams Memorial Scholarships **Area, Field, or Subject:** General studies. **Level of Education for which Award is Granted:** Undergraduate **Number Awarded:** 1. **Funds Available:** $500.
Eligibility Requirements: Applicant must be a female graduating senior who has been accepted at and will be attending the University of Redlands as a full-time student. **Application Requirements:** Applicants must submit: completed application form with the scantron sheet; cover sheet; student activity and community activity sheets; personal essay; and a copy of unofficial transcript (signed by the counselor). **Additional Information:** No electronic submissions of application will be accepted. Submit two printed copies of the application and use a No. 2 pencil on the scantron sheet. **Deadline for Receipt:** February 20.

1778 ■ REDLANDS COMMUNITY SCHOLARSHIP FOUNDATION
c/o Kathleen Venegas-Boge, Admin. Asst.
PO Box 1683
Redlands, CA 92373
Tel: (909)307-9892
Fax: (909)307-9892
Web Site: http://www.redlandsscholarships.org
To encourage educational pursuits among Redlands Unified School District graduates by providing educational assistance.
Title of Award: Patty Ahearn Victoria Elementary Scholarships **Area, Field, or Subject:** General studies. **Level of Education for which Award is Granted:** Undergraduate **Number Awarded:** 1. **Funds Available:** $500.
Eligibility Requirements: Applicant must be a graduating senior; must have a 2.5 GPA or higher; must have attended Victoria Elementary School for at least three years; and must have continued to follow the "Victoria Peace Builder's Pledge." **Application Requirements:** Applicants must submit a completed application form together with the scantron sheet; cover sheet; student activity and community activity sheets; personal essay; and a copy of unofficial transcript (signed by the counselor). **Additional Information:** No electronic submissions of application will be accepted. Submit two printed copies of the application and use a No. 2 pencil on the scantron sheet. **Deadline for Receipt:** February 20.

1779 ■ REDLANDS COMMUNITY SCHOLARSHIP FOUNDATION
c/o Kathleen Venegas-Boge, Admin. Asst.
PO Box 1683
Redlands, CA 92373
Tel: (909)307-9892
Fax: (909)307-9892
Web Site: http://www.redlandsscholarships.org
To encourage educational pursuits among Redlands Unified School District graduates by providing educational assistance.
Title of Award: Robinson G. Allen Athletic Memorial Scholarships **Area, Field, or Subject:** General studies. **Level of Education for which Award is Granted:** Undergraduate **Number Awarded:** 1. **Funds Available:** $500.
Eligibility Requirements: Applicant must be a senior whose athletic prowess has been limited, for the most part, to junior varsity teams and who plans to attend an institution of higher learning on a full-time basis. **Application Requirements:** Applicants must submit a completed application form together with the scantron sheet; cover sheet; student activity and community activity sheets; personal essay; and a copy of unofficial transcript (signed by the counselor). **Additional Information:** No electronic submissions of application will be accepted. Submit two printed copies of the application and use a No. 2 pencil on the scantron sheet. **Deadline for Receipt:** February 20.

1780 ■ REDLANDS COMMUNITY SCHOLARSHIP FOUNDATION
c/o Kathleen Venegas-Boge, Admin. Asst.
PO Box 1683
Redlands, CA 92373
Tel: (909)307-9892
Fax: (909)307-9892
Web Site: http://www.redlandsscholarships.org

To encourage educational pursuits among Redlands Unified School District graduates by providing educational assistance.
Title of Award: William A. Allen Memorial Metal Shop/Auto Body Scholarships **Area, Field, or Subject:** General studies. **Level of Education for which Award is Granted:** Undergraduate **Number Awarded:** 1. **Funds Available:** $300.
Eligibility Requirements: Applicant must be an outstanding metal shop or auto body student who displays dedication, skill and desire to become a true craftsman. Student must demonstrate creativity, show problem solving abilities, and exhibit good social skills. **Application Requirements:** Applicants must submit a completed application form together with the scantron sheet; cover sheet; student activity and community activity sheets; personal essay; and a copy of unofficial transcript (signed by the counselor). **Additional Information:** No electronic submissions of application will be accepted. Submit two printed copies of the application and use a No. 2 pencil on the scantron sheet. **Deadline for Receipt:** February 20.

1781 ■ REDLANDS COMMUNITY SCHOLARSHIP FOUNDATION
c/o Kathleen Venegas-Boge, Admin. Asst.
PO Box 1683
Redlands, CA 92373
Tel: (909)307-9892
Fax: (909)307-9892
Web Site: http://www.redlandsscholarships.org
To encourage educational pursuits among Redlands Unified School District graduates by providing educational assistance.
Title of Award: Cindy Andrews Educational Scholarships **Area, Field, or Subject:** General studies. **Level of Education for which Award is Granted:** Undergraduate **Number Awarded:** 1. **Funds Available:** $300.
Eligibility Requirements: Applicant must be a graduating senior who has been a CSF member for at least 4 semesters and is planning to be a teacher and eventually an administrator in the public school system. **Application Requirements:** Applicants must submit a completed application form together with the scantron sheet; cover sheet; student activity and community activity sheets; personal essay; and a copy of unofficial transcript (signed by the counselor). **Additional Information:** No electronic submissions of application will be accepted. Submit two printed copies of the application and use a No. 2 pencil on the scantron sheet. **Deadline for Receipt:** February 20.

1782 ■ REDLANDS COMMUNITY SCHOLARSHIP FOUNDATION
c/o Kathleen Venegas-Boge, Admin. Asst.
PO Box 1683
Redlands, CA 92373
Tel: (909)307-9892
Fax: (909)307-9892
Web Site: http://www.redlandsscholarships.org
To encourage educational pursuits among Redlands Unified School District graduates by providing educational assistance.
Title of Award: Frank G. Araujo Memorial Scholarships **Area, Field, or Subject:** General studies. **Level of Education for which Award is Granted:** Undergraduate **Number Awarded:** 1. **Funds Available:** $600.
Eligibility Requirements: Applicant must be a student of Mexican-American descent; must have a 3.0 or higher GPA; must demonstrate good citizenship; and must participate in school or community activities. **Application Requirements:** Applicants must submit a completed application form together with the scantron sheet; cover sheet; student activity and community activity sheets; personal essay; and a copy of unofficial transcript (signed by the counselor). **Additional Information:** No electronic submissions of application will be accepted. Submit two printed copies of the application and use a No. 2 pencil on the scantron sheet. **Deadline for Receipt:** February 20.

1783 ■ REDLANDS COMMUNITY SCHOLARSHIP FOUNDATION
c/o Kathleen Venegas-Boge, Admin. Asst.
PO Box 1683
Redlands, CA 92373
Tel: (909)307-9892
Fax: (909)307-9892
Web Site: http://www.redlandsscholarships.org
To encourage educational pursuits among Redlands Unified School District graduates by providing educational assistance.

Title of Award: Connie "Chelo" Armendariz Memorial Scholarships **Area, Field, or Subject:** General studies. **Level of Education for which Award is Granted:** Undergraduate **Number Awarded:** 1. **Funds Available:** $500.
Eligibility Requirements: Applicant must be a graduating senior planning to continue education at a vocational school, junior college, or university. **Application Requirements:** Applicants must submit a completed application form together with the scantron sheet; cover sheet; student activity and community activity sheets; personal essay; and a copy of unofficial transcript (signed by the counselor). **Additional Information:** No electronic submissions of application will be accepted. Submit two printed copies of the application and use a No. 2 pencil on the scantron sheet. **Deadline for Receipt:** February 20.

1784 ■ REDLANDS COMMUNITY SCHOLARSHIP FOUNDATION
c/o Kathleen Venegas-Boge, Admin. Asst.
PO Box 1683
Redlands, CA 92373
Tel: (909)307-9892
Fax: (909)307-9892
Web Site: http://www.redlandsscholarships.org
To encourage educational pursuits among Redlands Unified School District graduates by providing educational assistance.
Title of Award: Baha'i Faith Scholarships for Racial Harmony **Area, Field, or Subject:** General studies. **Level of Education for which Award is Granted:** Undergraduate **Number Awarded:** 1. **Funds Available:** $200.
Eligibility Requirements: Applicant must be a graduating senior who has promoted racial and intercultural harmony on campus. **Application Requirements:** Applicants must submit a completed application form together with the scantron sheet; cover sheet; student activity and community activity sheets; personal essay; and a copy of unofficial transcript (signed by the counselor). **Additional Information:** No electronic submissions of application will be accepted. Submit two printed copies of the application and use a No. 2 pencil on the scantron sheet. **Deadline for Receipt:** February 20.

1785 ■ REDLANDS COMMUNITY SCHOLARSHIP FOUNDATION
c/o Kathleen Venegas-Boge, Admin. Asst.
PO Box 1683
Redlands, CA 92373
Tel: (909)307-9892
Fax: (909)307-9892
Web Site: http://www.redlandsscholarships.org
To encourage educational pursuits among Redlands Unified School District graduates by providing educational assistance.
Title of Award: Timothy Baylink Good Fellowship Awards **Area, Field, or Subject:** General studies. **Level of Education for which Award is Granted:** Undergraduate **Number Awarded:** 1. **Funds Available:** $1,000.
Eligibility Requirements: Applicant must be a graduating senior who possesses some of the attributes of Dr. Timothy Baylink, which include athleticism, sense of adventure, friendliness, free spirit, interest in computers, and commitment to learning. **Application Requirements:** Applicants must submit: a completed application form together with the scantron sheet; cover sheet; student activity and community activity sheets; personal essay; and a copy of unofficial transcript (signed by the counselor). **Additional Information:** No electronic submissions of application will be accepted. Submit two printed copies of the application and use a No. 2 pencil on the scantron sheet. **Deadline for Receipt:** February 20.

1786 ■ REDLANDS COMMUNITY SCHOLARSHIP FOUNDATION
c/o Kathleen Venegas-Boge, Admin. Asst.
PO Box 1683
Redlands, CA 92373
Tel: (909)307-9892
Fax: (909)307-9892
Web Site: http://www.redlandsscholarships.org
To encourage educational pursuits among Redlands Unified School District graduates by providing educational assistance.
Title of Award: Beau Gunn Redlands Baseball For Youth Scholarships **Area, Field, or Subject:** General studies. **Level of Education for which**

Award is Granted: Undergraduate **Number Awarded:** 1. **Funds Available:** $500.
Eligibility Requirements: Applicant must be a senior who has participated in the Redlands Baseball for Youth Program (including score keeping and umpiring) for a minimum of three years and has exemplified good sportsmanship and academic achievement. **Application Requirements:** Applicants must submit a completed application form together with the scantron sheet; cover sheet; student activity and community activity sheets; personal essay; and a copy of unofficial transcript (signed by the counselor). **Additional Information:** No electronic submissions of application will be accepted. Submit two printed copies of the application and use a No. 2 pencil on the scantron sheet. **Deadline for Receipt:** February 20.

1787 ■ REDLANDS COMMUNITY SCHOLARSHIP FOUNDATION
c/o Kathleen Venegas-Boge, Admin. Asst.
PO Box 1683
Redlands, CA 92373
Tel: (909)307-9892
Fax: (909)307-9892
Web Site: http://www.redlandsscholarships.org
To encourage educational pursuits among Redlands Unified School District graduates by providing educational assistance.
Title of Award: Beaver Medical Clinic-Glen Adams Scholarship Awards **Area, Field, or Subject:** General studies. **Level of Education for which Award is Granted:** Undergraduate **Number Awarded:** 1. **Funds Available:** $750.
Eligibility Requirements: Applicant must be a graduating senior seeking a career in the field of medicine and must be outstanding academically, in leadership skills, and in sports participation. **Application Requirements:** Applicants must submit a completed application form together with the scantron sheet; cover sheet; student activity and community activity sheets; personal essay; and a copy of unofficial transcript (signed by the counselor). **Additional Information:** No electronic submissions of application will be accepted. Submit two printed copies of the application and use a No. 2 pencil on the scantron sheet. **Deadline for Receipt:** February 20.

1788 ■ REDLANDS COMMUNITY SCHOLARSHIP FOUNDATION
c/o Kathleen Venegas-Boge, Admin. Asst.
PO Box 1683
Redlands, CA 92373
Tel: (909)307-9892
Fax: (909)307-9892
Web Site: http://www.redlandsscholarships.org
To encourage educational pursuits among Redlands Unified School District graduates by providing educational assistance.
Title of Award: Beaver Medical Clinic-H.E.A.R.T. Scholarship Awards **Area, Field, or Subject:** General studies. **Level of Education for which Award is Granted:** Undergraduate **Number Awarded:** 1. **Funds Available:** $750.
Eligibility Requirements: Applicant must be a graduating senior seeking a career in the field of medicine who participated in the HEART Academy program for three years. **Application Requirements:** Applicants must submit a completed application form together with the scantron sheet; cover sheet; student activity and community activity sheets; personal essay; and a copy of unofficial transcript (signed by the counselor). **Additional Information:** No electronic submissions of application will be accepted. Submit two printed copies of the application and use a No. 2 pencil on the scantron sheet. **Deadline for Receipt:** February 20.

1789 ■ REDLANDS COMMUNITY SCHOLARSHIP FOUNDATION
c/o Kathleen Venegas-Boge, Admin. Asst.
PO Box 1683
Redlands, CA 92373
Tel: (909)307-9892
Fax: (909)307-9892
Web Site: http://www.redlandsscholarships.org
To encourage educational pursuits among Redlands Unified School District graduates by providing educational assistance.
Title of Award: Beaver Medical Clinic-Premed Scholarship Awards **Area, Field, or Subject:** General studies. **Level of Education for which Award is Granted:** Undergraduate **Number Awarded:** 1. **Funds Available:** $4,000.

Eligibility Requirements: Applicant must be a graduating senior seeking a career in the field of medicine. Student must be outstanding both academically and in leadership skills. **Application Requirements:** Applicants must submit a completed application form together with the scantron sheet; cover sheet; student activity and community activity sheets; personal essay; and a copy of unofficial transcript (signed by the counselor). **Additional Information:** No electronic submissions of application will be accepted. Submit two printed copies of the application and use a No. 2 pencil on the scantron sheet. **Deadline for Receipt:** February 20.

1790 ■ REDLANDS COMMUNITY SCHOLARSHIP FOUNDATION
c/o Kathleen Venegas-Boge, Admin. Asst.
PO Box 1683
Redlands, CA 92373
Tel: (909)307-9892
Fax: (909)307-9892
Web Site: http://www.redlandsscholarships.org
To encourage educational pursuits among Redlands Unified School District graduates by providing educational assistance.
Title of Award: Garvin L. Beck Scholarships **Area, Field, or Subject:** General studies. **Level of Education for which Award is Granted:** Undergraduate **Number Awarded:** 1. **Funds Available:** $1000.
Eligibility Requirements: Applicant must be enrolled in a four-year college, junior college or trade school. **Application Requirements:** Applicants must submit a completed application form together with the scantron sheet; cover sheet; student activity and community activity sheets; written documentation of registration at the college or a valid registration to a junior college or trade school; proof of a letter of junior varsity sport during the last two years of high school; a one-page essay; and a copy of unofficial transcript (signed by the counselor). **Additional Information:** No electronic submissions of application will be accepted. Submit two printed copies of the application and use a No. 2 pencil on the scantron sheet. **Deadline for Receipt:** February 20.

1791 ■ REDLANDS COMMUNITY SCHOLARSHIP FOUNDATION
c/o Kathleen Venegas-Boge, Admin. Asst.
PO Box 1683
Redlands, CA 92373
Tel: (909)307-9892
Fax: (909)307-9892
Web Site: http://www.redlandsscholarships.org
To encourage educational pursuits among Redlands Unified School District graduates by providing educational assistance.
Title of Award: Raymond and Donald Beeler Memorial Scholarships **Area, Field, or Subject:** General studies. **Level of Education for which Award is Granted:** Undergraduate **Number Awarded:** 2; 2. **Funds Available:** $500; $1000.
Eligibility Requirements: Applicant must be a student with at least a 3.0 GPA intending to attend a community or four-year college on a full-time basis. **Application Requirements:** Applicants must submit a completed application form together with the scantron sheet; cover sheet; student activity and community activity sheets; personal essay; and a copy of unofficial transcript (signed by the counselor). **Additional Information:** No electronic submissions of application will be accepted. Submit two printed copies of the application and use a No. 2 pencil on the scantron sheet. **Deadline for Receipt:** February 20.

1792 ■ REDLANDS COMMUNITY SCHOLARSHIP FOUNDATION
c/o Kathleen Venegas-Boge, Admin. Asst.
PO Box 1683
Redlands, CA 92373
Tel: (909)307-9892
Fax: (909)307-9892
Web Site: http://www.redlandsscholarships.org
To encourage educational pursuits among Redlands Unified School District graduates by providing educational assistance.
Title of Award: Benchwarmers of Redlands-Jess Mercado Football Scholarships **Area, Field, or Subject:** General studies. **Level of Education for which Award is Granted:** Undergraduate **Number Awarded:** 1. **Funds Available:** $500.
Eligibility Requirements: Applicant must be a three-year member of the Terrier football team who has been a starter for at least one year, exhibits

good citizenship and dedication, and has an eligible GPA. **Application Requirements:** Applicants must submit a completed application form together with the scantron sheet; cover sheet; student activity and community activity sheets; personal essay; and a copy of unofficial transcript (signed by the counselor). **Additional Information:** No electronic submissions of application will be accepted. Submit two printed copies of the application and use a No. 2 pencil on the scantron sheet. **Deadline for Receipt:** February 20.

1793 ■ REDLANDS COMMUNITY SCHOLARSHIP FOUNDATION
c/o Kathleen Venegas-Boge, Admin. Asst.
PO Box 1683
Redlands, CA 92373
Tel: (909)307-9892
Fax: (909)307-9892
Web Site: http://www.redlandsscholarships.org
To encourage educational pursuits among Redlands Unified School District graduates by providing educational assistance.
Title of Award: Barbara Bonnema Memorial Scholarships **Area, Field, or Subject:** General studies. **Level of Education for which Award is Granted:** Undergraduate **Number Awarded:** 2; 1. **Funds Available:** $500; $1000.
Eligibility Requirements: Applicant must be a college-bound graduating senior who will be attending school on a full-time basis. **Application Requirements:** Applicants must submit a completed application form together with the scantron sheet; cover sheet; student activity and community activity sheets; personal essay; and a copy of unofficial transcript (signed by the counselor). **Additional Information:** No electronic submissions of application will be accepted. Submit two printed copies of the application and use a No. 2 pencil on the scantron sheet. **Deadline for Receipt:** February 20.

1794 ■ REDLANDS COMMUNITY SCHOLARSHIP FOUNDATION
c/o Kathleen Venegas-Boge, Admin. Asst.
PO Box 1683
Redlands, CA 92373
Tel: (909)307-9892
Fax: (909)307-9892
Web Site: http://www.redlandsscholarships.org
To encourage educational pursuits among Redlands Unified School District graduates by providing educational assistance.
Title of Award: Boy Scouts of America Troop 3 Scholarships - Art Till/ Nathan E. Smith Memorial Scholarships **Area, Field, or Subject:** General studies. **Level of Education for which Award is Granted:** Undergraduate **Funds Available:** $300.
Eligibility Requirements: Applicant must be a graduating senior with at least a 3.0 GPA; must be planning to attend an accredited college, university, or vocational program; and must have continuous involvement in scouting and community service. **Application Requirements:** Applicants must submit a completed application form together with the scantron sheet; cover sheet; student activity and community activity sheets; personal essay; and a copy of unofficial transcript (signed by the counselor). **Additional Information:** No electronic submissions of application will be accepted. Submit two printed copies of the application and use a No. 2 pencil on the scantron sheet. **Deadline for Receipt:** February 20.

1795 ■ REDLANDS COMMUNITY SCHOLARSHIP FOUNDATION
c/o Kathleen Venegas-Boge, Admin. Asst.
PO Box 1683
Redlands, CA 92373
Tel: (909)307-9892
Fax: (909)307-9892
Web Site: http://www.redlandsscholarships.org
To encourage educational pursuits among Redlands Unified School District graduates by providing educational assistance.
Title of Award: Kathy Bush Memorial Scholarships **Area, Field, or Subject:** General studies. **Level of Education for which Award is Granted:** Undergraduate **Number Awarded:** 1. **Funds Available:** $300.
Eligibility Requirements: Applicant must be a graduating senior who has been outstanding in the field of instrumental music. **Application Requirements:** Applicants must submit a completed application form together with the scantron sheet; cover sheet; student activity and community

activity sheets; personal essay; and a copy of unofficial transcript (signed by the counselor). **Additional Information:** No electronic submissions of application will be accepted. Submit two printed copies of the application and use a No. 2 pencil on the scantron sheet. **Deadline for Receipt:** February 20.

1796 ■ REDLANDS COMMUNITY SCHOLARSHIP FOUNDATION

c/o Kathleen Venegas-Boge, Admin. Asst.
PO Box 1683
Redlands, CA 92373
Tel: (909)307-9892
Fax: (909)307-9892
Web Site: http://www.redlandsscholarships.org
To encourage educational pursuits among Redlands Unified School District graduates by providing educational assistance.
Title of Award: Robert G. Campbell Scholarships **Area, Field, or Subject:** General studies. **Level of Education for which Award is Granted:** Undergraduate **Number Awarded:** 1. **Funds Available:** $1,250 each year. **Duration:** Four years.
Eligibility Requirements: Applicant must be an above-average student who is highly motivated to pursue his/her career. **Application Requirements:** Applicants must submit a completed application form together with the scantron sheet; cover sheet; student activity and community activity sheets; personal essay; and a copy of unofficial transcript (signed by the counselor). **Additional Information:** No electronic submissions of application will be accepted. Submit two printed copies of the application and use a No. 2 pencil on the scantron sheet. **Deadline for Receipt:** February 20.

1797 ■ REDLANDS COMMUNITY SCHOLARSHIP FOUNDATION

c/o Kathleen Venegas-Boge, Admin. Asst.
PO Box 1683
Redlands, CA 92373
Tel: (909)307-9892
Fax: (909)307-9892
Web Site: http://www.redlandsscholarships.org
To encourage educational pursuits among Redlands Unified School District graduates by providing educational assistance.
Title of Award: Cesar E. Chavez Scholarships **Area, Field, or Subject:** General studies. **Level of Education for which Award is Granted:** Undergraduate **Number Awarded:** 1. **Funds Available:** $1,000.
Eligibility Requirements: Applicant must be a graduating senior who is in need of financial assistance in order to attend an institution of higher learning. **Application Requirements:** Applicants must submit a completed application form together with the scantron sheet; cover sheet; student activity and community activity sheets; personal essay; and a copy of unofficial transcript (signed by the counselor). **Additional Information:** No electronic submissions of application will be accepted. Submit two printed copies of the application and use a No. 2 pencil on the scantron sheet. **Deadline for Receipt:** February 20.

1798 ■ REDLANDS COMMUNITY SCHOLARSHIP FOUNDATION

c/o Kathleen Venegas-Boge, Admin. Asst.
PO Box 1683
Redlands, CA 92373
Tel: (909)307-9892
Fax: (909)307-9892
Web Site: http://www.redlandsscholarships.org
To encourage educational pursuits among Redlands Unified School District graduates by providing educational assistance.
Title of Award: Cope Middle School PTSA Scholarships **Area, Field, or Subject:** General studies. **Level of Education for which Award is Granted:** Undergraduate **Number Awarded:** 1. **Funds Available:** $300.
Eligibility Requirements: Applicant must be a graduating senior who attended Cope Middle School for three years. **Application Requirements:** Applicants must submit a completed application form together with the scantron sheet; cover sheet; student activity and community activity sheets; personal essay; and a copy of unofficial transcript (signed by the counselor). **Additional Information:** No electronic submissions of application will be accepted. Submit two printed copies of the application and use a No. 2 pencil on the scantron sheet. **Deadline for Receipt:** February 20.

1799 ■ REDLANDS COMMUNITY SCHOLARSHIP FOUNDATION

c/o Kathleen Venegas-Boge, Admin. Asst.
PO Box 1683
Redlands, CA 92373
Tel: (909)307-9892
Fax: (909)307-9892
Web Site: http://www.redlandsscholarships.org
To encourage educational pursuits among Redlands Unified School District graduates by providing educational assistance.
Title of Award: Crafton Elementary School PTA Scholarships **Area, Field, or Subject:** General studies. **Level of Education for which Award is Granted:** Undergraduate **Number Awarded:** 1. **Funds Available:** $300.
Eligibility Requirements: Applicant must be a graduating senior who attended Crafton Elementary School for at least a year. **Application Requirements:** Applicants must submit a completed application form together with the scantron sheet; cover sheet; student activity and community activity sheets; personal essay; and a copy of unofficial transcript (signed by the counselor). **Additional Information:** No electronic submissions of application will be accepted. Submit two printed copies of the application and use a No. 2 pencil on the scantron sheet. **Deadline for Receipt:** February 20.

1800 ■ REDLANDS COMMUNITY SCHOLARSHIP FOUNDATION

c/o Kathleen Venegas-Boge, Admin. Asst.
PO Box 1683
Redlands, CA 92373
Tel: (909)307-9892
Fax: (909)307-9892
Web Site: http://www.redlandsscholarships.org
To encourage educational pursuits among Redlands Unified School District graduates by providing educational assistance.
Title of Award: Crafton Hills College Foundation Scholarships **Area, Field, or Subject:** General studies. **Level of Education for which Award is Granted:** Undergraduate **Number Awarded:** Varies. **Funds Available:** $500.
Eligibility Requirements: Applicant must be a graduating senior enrolled at Crafton Hills College; must have a minimum 3.0 GPA; and must be attending college on a full-time basis. **Application Requirements:** Applicants must submit a completed application form together with the scantron sheet; cover sheet; student activity and community activity sheets; personal essay; and a copy of unofficial transcript (signed by the counselor). **Additional Information:** No electronic submissions of application will be accepted. Submit two printed copies of the application and use a No. 2 pencil on the scantron sheet. **Deadline for Receipt:** February 20.

1801 ■ REDLANDS COMMUNITY SCHOLARSHIP FOUNDATION

c/o Kathleen Venegas-Boge, Admin. Asst.
PO Box 1683
Redlands, CA 92373
Tel: (909)307-9892
Fax: (909)307-9892
Web Site: http://www.redlandsscholarships.org
To encourage educational pursuits among Redlands Unified School District graduates by providing educational assistance.
Title of Award: Arthur H. Daniels Scholarships **Area, Field, or Subject:** General studies. **Level of Education for which Award is Granted:** Undergraduate **Number Awarded:** 15. **Funds Available:** $300, $500 and $1000.
Eligibility Requirements: Applicant must be a graduating senior demonstrating good citizenship, academic accomplishment, contribution to school and community and the intention to attend a college/university on a full-time basis. **Application Requirements:** Applicants must submit a completed application form together with the scantron sheet; cover sheet; student activity and community activity sheets; personal essay; and a copy of unofficial transcript (signed by the counselor). **Additional Information:** No electronic submissions of application will be accepted. Submit two printed copies of the application and use a No. 2 pencil on the scantron sheet. **Deadline for Receipt:** February 20.

1802 ■ REDLANDS COMMUNITY SCHOLARSHIP FOUNDATION

c/o Kathleen Venegas-Boge, Admin. Asst.
PO Box 1683
Redlands, CA 92373
Tel: (909)307-9892
Fax: (909)307-9892
Web Site: http://www.redlandsscholarships.org
To encourage educational pursuits among Redlands Unified School District graduates by providing educational assistance.
Title of Award: ROP - Dr. Linda Denver Scholarships **Area, Field, or Subject:** General studies. **Level of Education for which Award is Granted:** Undergraduate **Number Awarded:** 1. **Funds Available:** $100.
Eligibility Requirements: Applicant must be a senior who has taken at least one ROP class; must have received a recommendation from a teacher; and must be able to demonstrate in a short essay how his/her ROP class has helped carry out his/her future career plans. **Application Requirements:** Applicants must submit a completed application form together with the scantron sheet; cover sheet; student activity and community activity sheets; personal essay; and a copy of unofficial transcript (signed by the counselor). **Additional Information:** No electronic submissions of application will be accepted. Submit two printed copies of the application and use a No. 2 pencil on the scantron sheet. **Deadline for Receipt:** February 20.

1803 ■ REDLANDS COMMUNITY SCHOLARSHIP FOUNDATION

c/o Kathleen Venegas-Boge, Admin. Asst.
PO Box 1683
Redlands, CA 92373
Tel: (909)307-9892
Fax: (909)307-9892
Web Site: http://www.redlandsscholarships.org
To encourage educational pursuits among Redlands Unified School District graduates by providing educational assistance.
Title of Award: Pat Dermargosian Memorial Scholarships **Area, Field, or Subject:** General studies. **Level of Education for which Award is Granted:** Undergraduate **Number Awarded:** 1. **Funds Available:** No specific amount.
Eligibility Requirements: Applicant must be a graduating senior whose parent has been actively involved in the PTA throughout his/her school years. **Application Requirements:** Applicants must submit a completed application form together with the scantron sheet; cover sheet; student activity and community activity sheets; personal essay; and a copy of unofficial transcript (signed by the counselor). **Additional Information:** No electronic submissions of application will be accepted. Submit two printed copies of the application and use a No. 2 pencil on the scantron sheet. **Deadline for Receipt:** February 20.

1804 ■ REDLANDS COMMUNITY SCHOLARSHIP FOUNDATION

c/o Kathleen Venegas-Boge, Admin. Asst.
PO Box 1683
Redlands, CA 92373
Tel: (909)307-9892
Fax: (909)307-9892
Web Site: http://www.redlandsscholarships.org
To encourage educational pursuits among Redlands Unified School District graduates by providing educational assistance.
Title of Award: James Mackenzie Fallows Scholarships Honoring Gertrude Baccus **Area, Field, or Subject:** General studies. **Level of Education for which Award is Granted:** Undergraduate **Number Awarded:** 1. **Funds Available:** $1,000.
Eligibility Requirements: Applicant must write an essay, article, speech, or some other work of non-fiction designed to explore an idea or explain a situation with the clarity and logic that Mrs. Baccus insisted on from her students. **Application Requirements:** Applicants must submit a completed application form together with the scantron sheet; cover sheet; student activity and community activity sheets; personal essay; and a copy of unofficial transcript (signed by the counselor). **Additional Information:** No electronic submissions of application will be accepted. Submit two printed copies of the application and use a No. 2 pencil on the scantron sheet. **Deadline for Receipt:** February 20.

1805 ■ REDLANDS COMMUNITY SCHOLARSHIP FOUNDATION

c/o Kathleen Venegas-Boge, Admin. Asst.
PO Box 1683
Redlands, CA 92373
Tel: (909)307-9892
Fax: (909)307-9892
Web Site: http://www.redlandsscholarships.org
To encourage educational pursuits among Redlands Unified School District graduates by providing educational assistance.
Title of Award: Arthur and Juna Fisher Memorial Track Scholarships **Area, Field, or Subject:** General studies. **Level of Education for which Award is Granted:** Undergraduate **Number Awarded:** 1. **Funds Available:** $500.
Eligibility Requirements: Applicant must be a graduating senior who has been active in track activities for at least two years and has maintained a 3.0 or better GPA. **Application Requirements:** Applicants must submit a completed form together with the scantron sheet; cover sheet; student activity and community activity sheets; personal essay; and a copy of unofficial transcript (signed by the counselor). **Additional Information:** No electronic submissions of application will be accepted. Submit two printed copies of the application and use a No. 2 pencil on the scantron sheet. **Deadline for Receipt:** February 20.

1806 ■ REDLANDS COMMUNITY SCHOLARSHIP FOUNDATION

c/o Kathleen Venegas-Boge, Admin. Asst.
PO Box 1683
Redlands, CA 92373
Tel: (909)307-9892
Fax: (909)307-9892
Web Site: http://www.redlandsscholarships.org
To encourage educational pursuits among Redlands Unified School District graduates by providing educational assistance.
Title of Award: Franklin Elementary School PTA Scholarships **Area, Field, or Subject:** General studies. **Level of Education for which Award is Granted:** Undergraduate **Number Awarded:** 1. **Funds Available:** $250.
Eligibility Requirements: Applicants must be students who attended Franklin Elementary School and have extensive volunteer service in both school and community. **Application Requirements:** Applicants must submit a completed application form together with the scantron sheet; cover sheet; student activity and community activity sheets; personal essay; and a copy of unofficial transcript (signed by the counselor). **Additional Information:** No electronic submissions of application will be accepted. Submit two printed copies of the application and use a No. 2 pencil on the scantron sheet. **Deadline for Receipt:** February 20.

1807 ■ REDLANDS COMMUNITY SCHOLARSHIP FOUNDATION

c/o Kathleen Venegas-Boge, Admin. Asst.
PO Box 1683
Redlands, CA 92373
Tel: (909)307-9892
Fax: (909)307-9892
Web Site: http://www.redlandsscholarships.org
To encourage educational pursuits among Redlands Unified School District graduates by providing educational assistance.
Title of Award: Gail Garner R.I.S.E. Memorial Scholarships **Area, Field, or Subject:** General studies. **Level of Education for which Award is Granted:** Undergraduate **Number Awarded:** 1. **Funds Available:** $500.
Eligibility Requirements: Applicant must be a student graduating through the Redlands Independent Study Education (R.I.S.E.) program. **Application Requirements:** Applicants must submit a completed application form together with the scantron sheet; cover sheet; student activity and community activity sheets; personal essay; and a copy of unofficial transcript (signed by the counselor). **Additional Information:** No electronic submissions of application will be accepted. Submit two printed copies of the application and use a No. 2 pencil on the scantron sheet. **Deadline for Receipt:** February 20.

1808 ■ REDLANDS COMMUNITY SCHOLARSHIP FOUNDATION

c/o Kathleen Venegas-Boge, Admin. Asst.
PO Box 1683
Redlands, CA 92373
Tel: (909)307-9892

Fax: (909)307-9892
Web Site: http://www.redlandsscholarships.org
To encourage educational pursuits among Redlands Unified School District graduates by providing educational assistance.
Title of Award: Ann and Brad Glassco Scholarships **Area, Field, or Subject:** General studies. **Level of Education for which Award is Granted:** Undergraduate **Number Awarded:** 1. **Funds Available:** $500.
Eligibility Requirements: Applicant must be a student who has performed in at least two acts in the YMCA's Great "Y" Circus in junior or senior year of high school. Student must have a 2.5 GPA or better. **Application Requirements:** Applicants must submit a completed application form together with the scantron sheet; cover sheet; student activity and community activity sheets; personal essay; and a copy of unofficial transcript (signed by the counselor). **Additional Information:** No electronic submissions of application will be accepted. Submit two printed copies of the application and use a No. 2 pencil on the scantron sheet. **Deadline for Receipt:** February 20.

1809 ■ REDLANDS COMMUNITY SCHOLARSHIP FOUNDATION
c/o Kathleen Venegas-Boge, Admin. Asst.
PO Box 1683
Redlands, CA 92373
Tel: (909)307-9892
Fax: (909)307-9892
Web Site: http://www.redlandsscholarships.org
To encourage educational pursuits among Redlands Unified School District graduates by providing educational assistance.
Title of Award: Rachel Graham Memorial Scholarships **Area, Field, or Subject:** General studies. **Level of Education for which Award is Granted:** Undergraduate **Number Awarded:** 8. **Funds Available:** $600.
Eligibility Requirements: Applicant must be a graduating senior attending a four-year college/university on a full-time basis; must have maintained at least a 3.0 GPA; must show good citizenship; and must participate in school and community activities. **Application Requirements:** Applicants must submit a completed application form together with the scantron sheet; cover sheet; student activity and community activity sheets; personal essay; and a copy of unofficial transcript (signed by the counselor). **Additional Information:** No electronic submissions of application will be accepted. Submit two printed copies of the application and use a No. 2 pencil on the scantron sheet. **Deadline for Receipt:** February 20.

1810 ■ REDLANDS COMMUNITY SCHOLARSHIP FOUNDATION
c/o Kathleen Venegas-Boge, Admin. Asst.
PO Box 1683
Redlands, CA 92373
Tel: (909)307-9892
Fax: (909)307-9892
Web Site: http://www.redlandsscholarships.org
To encourage educational pursuits among Redlands Unified School District graduates by providing educational assistance.
Title of Award: Guzkowski Family Scholarships **Area, Field, or Subject:** General studies. **Level of Education for which Award is Granted:** Undergraduate **Number Awarded:** 1. **Funds Available:** $300.
Eligibility Requirements: Applicant must be a graduating senior student. **Application Requirements:** Applicants must submit a completed application form together with the scantron sheet; cover sheet; student activity and community activity sheets; personal essay; and a copy of unofficial transcript (signed by the counselor). **Additional Information:** No electronic submissions of application will be accepted. Submit two printed copies of the application and use a No. 2 pencil on the scantron sheet. **Deadline for Receipt:** February 20.

1811 ■ REDLANDS COMMUNITY SCHOLARSHIP FOUNDATION
c/o Kathleen Venegas-Boge, Admin. Asst.
PO Box 1683
Redlands, CA 92373
Tel: (909)307-9892
Fax: (909)307-9892
Web Site: http://www.redlandsscholarships.org
To encourage educational pursuits among Redlands Unified School District graduates by providing educational assistance.
Title of Award: William T. Hartzell Memorial Scholarships **Area, Field, or Subject:** General studies. **Level of Education for which Award is

Granted: Undergraduate **Number Awarded:** 1. **Funds Available:** $500.
Eligibility Requirements: Applicant must be a graduating senior who maintains at least a 3.5 GPA; must have shown leadership in school activities; must plan to attend a college/university on a full-time basis; and must have attended Redlands area schools for six years or more. **Application Requirements:** Applicants must submit a completed application form together with the scantron sheet; cover sheet; student activity and community activity sheets; personal essay; and a copy of unofficial transcript (signed by the counselor). **Additional Information:** No electronic submissions of application will be accepted. Submit two printed copies of the application and use a No. 2 pencil on the scantron sheet. **Deadline for Receipt:** February 20.

1812 ■ REDLANDS COMMUNITY SCHOLARSHIP FOUNDATION
c/o Kathleen Venegas-Boge, Admin. Asst.
PO Box 1683
Redlands, CA 92373
Tel: (909)307-9892
Fax: (909)307-9892
Web Site: http://www.redlandsscholarships.org
To encourage educational pursuits among Redlands Unified School District graduates by providing educational assistance.
Title of Award: R. Garn Haycock Memorial Scholarships **Area, Field, or Subject:** General studies. **Level of Education for which Award is Granted:** Undergraduate **Number Awarded:** 1. **Funds Available:** $1,000.
Eligibility Requirements: Applicant must be a deserving senior who displays good citizenship, character, and academic potential, has a need for financial assistance and is intending to attend an institution of higher learning on a full-time basis. **Application Requirements:** Applicants must submit a completed application form together with the scantron sheet; cover sheet; student activity and community activity sheets; personal essay; and a copy of unofficial transcript (signed by the counselor). **Additional Information:** No electronic submissions of application will be accepted. Submit two printed copies of the application and use a No. 2 pencil on the scantron sheet. **Deadline for Receipt:** February 20.

1813 ■ REDLANDS COMMUNITY SCHOLARSHIP FOUNDATION
c/o Kathleen Venegas-Boge, Admin. Asst.
PO Box 1683
Redlands, CA 92373
Tel: (909)307-9892
Fax: (909)307-9892
Web Site: http://www.redlandsscholarships.org
To encourage educational pursuits among Redlands Unified School District graduates by providing educational assistance.
Title of Award: Holy Name Of Jesus Parish Scholarships **Area, Field, or Subject:** General studies. **Level of Education for which Award is Granted:** Undergraduate **Number Awarded:** 1. **Funds Available:** $500.
Eligibility Requirements: Applicant must be a graduating senior who is active in parish youth activities; must be above-average in academic standing; must be a registered member of the parish; and must be attending a college/university in the fall. **Application Requirements:** Applicants must submit a completed application form together with the scantron sheet; cover sheet; student activity and community activity sheets; personal essay; and a copy of unofficial transcript (signed by the counselor). **Additional Information:** No electronic submissions of application will be accepted. Submit two printed copies of the application and use a No. 2 pencil on the scantron sheet. **Deadline for Receipt:** February 20.

1814 ■ REDLANDS COMMUNITY SCHOLARSHIP FOUNDATION
c/o Kathleen Venegas-Boge, Admin. Asst.
PO Box 1683
Redlands, CA 92373
Tel: (909)307-9892
Fax: (909)307-9892
Web Site: http://www.redlandsscholarships.org
To encourage educational pursuits among Redlands Unified School District graduates by providing educational assistance.
Title of Award: Eric L. Jacobson Memorial Scholarships **Area, Field, or Subject:** General studies. **Level of Education for which Award is Granted:** Undergraduate **Number Awarded:** 1. **Funds Available:** $1,000.

Eligibility Requirements: Applicant must be a graduating senior who has maintained a 3.0 or higher GPA; must have participated on the speech or debate team for at least two years (one of which must be the senior year); and must be planning to attend a four-year college/university on a full-time basis. **Application Requirements:** Applicants must submit a completed application form together with the scantron sheet; cover sheet; student activity and community activity sheets; personal essay; and a copy of unofficial transcript (signed by the counselor). **Additional Information:** No electronic submissions of application will be accepted. Submit two printed copies of the application and use a No. 2 pencil on the scantron sheet. **Deadline for Receipt:** February 20.

1815 ■ REDLANDS COMMUNITY SCHOLARSHIP FOUNDATION

c/o Kathleen Venegas-Boge, Admin. Asst.
PO Box 1683
Redlands, CA 92373
Tel: (909)307-9892
Fax: (909)307-9892
Web Site: http://www.redlandsscholarships.org
To encourage educational pursuits among Redlands Unified School District graduates by providing educational assistance.
Title of Award: Mike Jensen R.I.S.E. Memorial Scholarships **Area, Field, or Subject:** General studies. **Level of Education for which Award is Granted:** Undergraduate **Number Awarded:** 2. **Funds Available:** $500.
Eligibility Requirements: Applicant must be a graduating senior student.
Application Requirements: Applicants must submit a completed application form together with the scantron sheet; cover sheet; student activity and community activity sheets; personal essay; and a copy of unofficial transcript (signed by the counselor). **Additional Information:** No electronic submissions of application will be accepted. Submit two printed copies of the application and use a No. 2 pencil on the scantron sheet. **Deadline for Receipt:** February 20.

1816 ■ REDLANDS COMMUNITY SCHOLARSHIP FOUNDATION

c/o Kathleen Venegas-Boge, Admin. Asst.
PO Box 1683
Redlands, CA 92373
Tel: (909)307-9892
Fax: (909)307-9892
Web Site: http://www.redlandsscholarships.org
To encourage educational pursuits among Redlands Unified School District graduates by providing educational assistance.
Title of Award: Junior Women of the Contemporary Club Scholarships **Area, Field, or Subject:** General studies. **Level of Education for which Award is Granted:** Undergraduate **Number Awarded:** 1. **Funds Available:** $300.
Eligibility Requirements: Applicant must be a graduating senior who shows financial need, has a respectable GPA, and has a definite goal in mind. **Application Requirements:** Applicants must submit a completed application form together with the scantron sheet; cover sheet; student activity and community activity sheets; personal essay; and a copy of unofficial transcript (signed by the counselor). **Additional Information:** No electronic submissions of application will be accepted. Submit two printed copies of the application and use a No. 2 pencil on the scantron sheet. **Deadline for Receipt:** February 20.

1817 ■ REDLANDS COMMUNITY SCHOLARSHIP FOUNDATION

c/o Kathleen Venegas-Boge, Admin. Asst.
PO Box 1683
Redlands, CA 92373
Tel: (909)307-9892
Fax: (909)307-9892
Web Site: http://www.redlandsscholarships.org
To encourage educational pursuits among Redlands Unified School District graduates by providing educational assistance.
Title of Award: Annette and Ernest Keith Scholarships **Area, Field, or Subject:** General studies. **Level of Education for which Award is Granted:** Undergraduate **Number Awarded:** 5. **Funds Available:** $600.
Eligibility Requirements: Applicant must be a graduating senior belonging to the top ten percent of their class who will be attending a four-year California college/university on a full-time basis. **Application Requirements:** Applicants must submit a completed application form together with the scantron sheet; cover sheet; student activity and community

activity sheets; personal essay; and a copy of unofficial transcript (signed by the counselor). **Additional Information:** No electronic submissions of application will be accepted. Submit two printed copies of the application and use a No. 2 pencil on the scantron sheet. **Deadline for Receipt:** February 20.

1818 ■ REDLANDS COMMUNITY SCHOLARSHIP FOUNDATION

c/o Kathleen Venegas-Boge, Admin. Asst.
PO Box 1683
Redlands, CA 92373
Tel: (909)307-9892
Fax: (909)307-9892
Web Site: http://www.redlandsscholarships.org
To encourage educational pursuits among Redlands Unified School District graduates by providing educational assistance.
Title of Award: Kimberly Elementary School PTA Scholarships **Area, Field, or Subject:** General studies. **Level of Education for which Award is Granted:** Undergraduate **Number Awarded:** 1. **Funds Available:** $300.
Eligibility Requirements: Applicant must be a graduating senior who attended Kimberly Elementary School for a minimum of three years; must be an average or above-average achiever; and must demonstrate good citizenship. **Application Requirements:** Applicants must submit a completed application form together with the scantron sheet; cover sheet; student activity and community activity sheets; personal essay; and a copy of unofficial transcript (signed by the counselor). **Additional Information:** No electronic submissions of application will be accepted. Submit two printed copies of the application and use a No. 2 pencil on the scantron sheet. **Deadline for Receipt:** February 20.

1819 ■ REDLANDS COMMUNITY SCHOLARSHIP FOUNDATION

c/o Kathleen Venegas-Boge, Admin. Asst.
PO Box 1683
Redlands, CA 92373
Tel: (909)307-9892
Fax: (909)307-9892
Web Site: http://www.redlandsscholarships.org
To encourage educational pursuits among Redlands Unified School District graduates by providing educational assistance.
Title of Award: Kingsbury Elementary School PTA Scholarships **Area, Field, or Subject:** General studies. **Level of Education for which Award is Granted:** Undergraduate **Number Awarded:** 1. **Funds Available:** No specific amount.
Eligibility Requirements: Applicant must be a student who attended Kingsbury Elementary School for at least three years; must have a minimum of a "C" average; must have demonstrated good citizenship and leadership; must show financial need; and must demonstrate involvement in extracurricular and community activities. **Application Requirements:** Applicants must submit a completed application form together with the scantron sheet; cover sheet; student activity and community activity sheets; personal essay; and a copy of unofficial transcript (signed by the counselor). **Additional Information:** No electronic submissions of application will be accepted. Submit two printed copies of the application and use a No. 2 pencil on the scantron sheet. **Deadline for Receipt:** February 20.

1820 ■ REDLANDS COMMUNITY SCHOLARSHIP FOUNDATION

c/o Kathleen Venegas-Boge, Admin. Asst.
PO Box 1683
Redlands, CA 92373
Tel: (909)307-9892
Fax: (909)307-9892
Web Site: http://www.redlandsscholarships.org
To encourage educational pursuits among Redlands Unified School District graduates by providing educational assistance.
Title of Award: Jack A. and Louise S. Levine Memorial Scholarships **Area, Field, or Subject:** General studies. **Level of Education for which Award is Granted:** Undergraduate **Number Awarded:** 1. **Funds Available:** $500.
Eligibility Requirements: Applicant must be a graduating senior planning to continue education; must have a 3.0 or higher GPA; must demonstrate good citizenship; and must have participated in school and/or community activities. **Application Requirements:** Applicants must

submit a completed application form together with the scantron sheet; cover sheet; student activity and community activity sheets; personal essay; and a copy of unofficial transcript (signed by the counselor). **Additional Information:** No electronic submissions of application will be accepted. Submit two printed copies of the application and use a No. 2 pencil on the scantron sheet. **Deadline for Receipt:** February 20.

1821 ■ REDLANDS COMMUNITY SCHOLARSHIP FOUNDATION
c/o Kathleen Venegas-Boge, Admin. Asst.
PO Box 1683
Redlands, CA 92373
Tel: (909)307-9892
Fax: (909)307-9892
Web Site: http://www.redlandsscholarships.org
To encourage educational pursuits among Redlands Unified School District graduates by providing educational assistance.
Title of Award: Lugonia Alumni/Harrison Lightfoot Scholarships **Area, Field, or Subject:** General studies. **Level of Education for which Award is Granted:** Undergraduate **Number Awarded:** 1. **Funds Available:** No specific amount.
Eligibility Requirements: Applicant must be a graduating senior who attended Lugonia Elementary School. Student must have extensive community service and/or be involved in school activities; must demonstrate good citizenship; and must have a GPA of 2.5 or higher. **Application Requirements:** Applicants must submit a completed application form together with the scantron sheet; cover sheet; student activity and community activity sheets; personal essay; and a copy of unofficial transcript (signed by the counselor). **Additional Information:** No electronic submissions of application will be accepted. Submit two printed copies of the application and use a No. 2 pencil on the scantron sheet. **Deadline for Receipt:** February 20.

1822 ■ REDLANDS COMMUNITY SCHOLARSHIP FOUNDATION
c/o Kathleen Venegas-Boge, Admin. Asst.
PO Box 1683
Redlands, CA 92373
Tel: (909)307-9892
Fax: (909)307-9892
Web Site: http://www.redlandsscholarships.org
To encourage educational pursuits among Redlands Unified School District graduates by providing educational assistance.
Title of Award: James Mackenzie Fallows Scholarship Honoring William Cunningham **Area, Field, or Subject:** General studies. **Level of Education for which Award is Granted:** Undergraduate **Number Awarded:** 1. **Funds Available:** $1,000.
Eligibility Requirements: Applicant must be a student who shows great promise for public service in his/her career. **Application Requirements:** Applicants must submit a completed application form together with the scantron sheet; cover sheet; student activity and community activity sheets; personal essay; and a copy of unofficial transcript (signed by the counselor). **Additional Information:** No electronic submissions of application will be accepted. Submit two printed copies of the application and use a No. 2 pencil on the scantron sheet. **Deadline for Receipt:** February 20.

1823 ■ REDLANDS COMMUNITY SCHOLARSHIP FOUNDATION
c/o Kathleen Venegas-Boge, Admin. Asst.
PO Box 1683
Redlands, CA 92373
Tel: (909)307-9892
Fax: (909)307-9892
Web Site: http://www.redlandsscholarships.org
To encourage educational pursuits among Redlands Unified School District graduates by providing educational assistance.
Title of Award: Mariposa Elementary School PTA Scholarships **Area, Field, or Subject:** General studies. **Level of Education for which Award is Granted:** Undergraduate **Number Awarded:** 1. **Funds Available:** $300.
Eligibility Requirements: Applicant must be a graduating senior who attended Mariposa Elementary School for at least two years and must have demonstrated serious scholarship, good citizenship, and a desire for further education either in academics or a vocational trade. **Application Requirements:** Applicants must submit a completed application form

together with the scantron sheet; cover sheet; student activity and community activity sheets; personal essay; and a copy of unofficial transcript (signed by the counselor). **Additional Information:** No electronic submissions of application will be accepted. Submit two printed copies of the application and use a No. 2 pencil on the scantron sheet. **Deadline for Receipt:** February 20.

1824 ■ REDLANDS COMMUNITY SCHOLARSHIP FOUNDATION
c/o Kathleen Venegas-Boge, Admin. Asst.
PO Box 1683
Redlands, CA 92373
Tel: (909)307-9892
Fax: (909)307-9892
Web Site: http://www.redlandsscholarships.org
To encourage educational pursuits among Redlands Unified School District graduates by providing educational assistance.
Title of Award: McKinley Elementary School PTA Scholarships **Area, Field, or Subject:** General studies. **Level of Education for which Award is Granted:** Undergraduate **Number Awarded:** 2. **Funds Available:** $300.
Eligibility Requirements: Applicant must be a graduating senior who attended McKinley Elementary School for at least three years and plan to attend a college, university, or vocational school. **Application Requirements:** Applicants must submit a completed application form together with the scantron sheet; cover sheet; student activity and community activity sheets; personal essay; and a copy of unofficial transcript (signed by the counselor). **Additional Information:** No electronic submissions of application will be accepted. Submit two printed copies of the application and use a No. 2 pencil on the scantron sheet. **Deadline for Receipt:** February 20.

1825 ■ REDLANDS COMMUNITY SCHOLARSHIP FOUNDATION
c/o Kathleen Venegas-Boge, Admin. Asst.
PO Box 1683
Redlands, CA 92373
Tel: (909)307-9892
Fax: (909)307-9892
Web Site: http://www.redlandsscholarships.org
To encourage educational pursuits among Redlands Unified School District graduates by providing educational assistance.
Title of Award: Augustine and Sandra Medina Memorial Scholarships **Area, Field, or Subject:** General studies. **Level of Education for which Award is Granted:** Undergraduate **Number Awarded:** 1. **Funds Available:** $350.
Eligibility Requirements: Applicant must be a graduating senior; must have a minimum 2.5 GPA; must be involved in community and/or school activities; must have financial need; and must intend to pursue a two or four-year college degree. **Application Requirements:** Applicants must submit a completed application form together with the scantron sheet; cover sheet; student activity and community activity sheets; personal essay; a copy of unofficial transcript (signed by the counselor); and a short statement regarding a hardship that they experienced and how it impacted their life. **Additional Information:** No electronic submissions of application will be accepted. Submit two printed copies of the application and use a No. 2 pencil on the scantron sheet. **Deadline for Receipt:** February 20.

1826 ■ REDLANDS COMMUNITY SCHOLARSHIP FOUNDATION
c/o Kathleen Venegas-Boge, Admin. Asst.
PO Box 1683
Redlands, CA 92373
Tel: (909)307-9892
Fax: (909)307-9892
Web Site: http://www.redlandsscholarships.org
To encourage educational pursuits among Redlands Unified School District graduates by providing educational assistance.
Title of Award: Dorothy Mitchell Scholarships **Area, Field, or Subject:** General studies. **Level of Education for which Award is Granted:** Undergraduate **Number Awarded:** 1. **Funds Available:** $300.
Eligibility Requirements: Applicant must be a graduating senior planning to enter the teaching profession. **Application Requirements:** Applicants must submit a completed application form together with the scantron sheet; cover sheet; student activity and community activity

sheets; personal essay; and a copy of unofficial transcript (signed by the counselor). **Additional Information:** No electronic submissions of application will be accepted. Submit two printed copies of the application and use a No. 2 pencil on the scantron sheet. **Deadline for Receipt:** February 20.

1827 ■ REDLANDS COMMUNITY SCHOLARSHIP FOUNDATION
c/o Kathleen Venegas-Boge, Admin. Asst.
PO Box 1683
Redlands, CA 92373
Tel: (909)307-9892
Fax: (909)307-9892
Web Site: http://www.redlandsscholarships.org
To encourage educational pursuits among Redlands Unified School District graduates by providing educational assistance.
Title of Award: Moore Middle School PTA Scholarships **Area, Field, or Subject:** General studies. **Level of Education for which Award is Granted:** Undergraduate **Number Awarded:** 1. **Funds Available:** $300. **Eligibility Requirements:** Applicant must be a graduating senior who has attended Moore Middle School for three years and plans to attend college or a trade school. **Application Requirements:** Applicants must submit a completed application form together with the scantron sheet; cover sheet; student activity and community activity sheets; personal essay; and a copy of unofficial transcript (signed by the counselor). **Additional Information:** No electronic submissions of application will be accepted. Submit two printed copies of the application and use a No. 2 pencil on the scantron sheet. **Deadline for Receipt:** February 20.

1828 ■ REDLANDS COMMUNITY SCHOLARSHIP FOUNDATION
c/o Kathleen Venegas-Boge, Admin. Asst.
PO Box 1683
Redlands, CA 92373
Tel: (909)307-9892
Fax: (909)307-9892
Web Site: http://www.redlandsscholarships.org
To encourage educational pursuits among Redlands Unified School District graduates by providing educational assistance.
Title of Award: Harry Munoz Memorial Scholarships **Area, Field, or Subject:** General studies. **Level of Education for which Award is Granted:** Undergraduate **Number Awarded:** 1. **Funds Available:** $1,000.
Eligibility Requirements: Applicant must be a graduate who has demonstrated academic achievement, outstanding citizenship, and a desire to continue his/her education. **Application Requirements:** Applicants must submit a completed application form together with the scantron sheet; cover sheet; student activity and community activity sheets; personal essay; and a copy of unofficial transcript (signed by the counselor). **Additional Information:** No electronic submissions of application will be accepted. Submit two printed copies of the application and use a No. 2 pencil on the scantron sheet. **Deadline for Receipt:** February 20.

1829 ■ REDLANDS COMMUNITY SCHOLARSHIP FOUNDATION
c/o Kathleen Venegas-Boge, Admin. Asst.
PO Box 1683
Redlands, CA 92373
Tel: (909)307-9892
Fax: (909)307-9892
Web Site: http://www.redlandsscholarships.org
To support Redlands Unified School District graduates with their educational pursuit.
Title of Award: Rick Munoz Memorial Scholarships **Area, Field, or Subject:** General studies. **Level of Education for which Award is Granted:** Undergraduate **Number Awarded:** 1. **Funds Available:** $500. **Eligibility Requirements:** Applicant must be a graduating senior who demonstrates high academic achievement, outstanding citizenship, and a desire to continue his/her education. **Application Requirements:** Applicants must submit a completed application form together with the scantron sheet; cover sheet; student activity and community activity sheets; personal essay; a copy of unofficial transcript (signed by the counselor); proof of letter in at least one sport in senior year. **Additional Information:** No electronic submissions of application will be accepted. Submit two printed copies of the application and use a No. 2 pencil on the scantron sheet. **Deadline for Receipt:** February 20.

1830 ■ REDLANDS COMMUNITY SCHOLARSHIP FOUNDATION
c/o Kathleen Venegas-Boge, Admin. Asst.
PO Box 1683
Redlands, CA 92373
Tel: (909)307-9892
Fax: (909)307-9892
Web Site: http://www.redlandsscholarships.org
To encourage educational pursuits among Redlands Unified School District graduates by providing educational assistance.
Title of Award: Jack Nagasaka Memorial Scholarships **Area, Field, or Subject:** General studies. **Level of Education for which Award is Granted:** Undergraduate **Number Awarded:** 2. **Funds Available:** $300. **Eligibility Requirements:** Applicant must be a graduating senior who has outstanding performance in the field of math or science. **Application Requirements:** Applicants must submit a completed application form together with the scantron sheet; cover sheet; student activity and community activity sheets; personal essay; and a copy of unofficial transcript (signed by the counselor). **Additional Information:** No electronic submissions of application will be accepted. Submit two printed copies of the application and use a No. 2 pencil on the scantron sheet. **Deadline for Receipt:** February 20.

1831 ■ REDLANDS COMMUNITY SCHOLARSHIP FOUNDATION
c/o Kathleen Venegas-Boge, Admin. Asst.
PO Box 1683
Redlands, CA 92373
Tel: (909)307-9892
Fax: (909)307-9892
Web Site: http://www.redlandsscholarships.org
To encourage educational pursuits among Redlands Unified School District graduates by providing educational assistance.
Title of Award: Robyn Nance Memorial Scholarships **Area, Field, or Subject:** General studies. **Level of Education for which Award is Granted:** Undergraduate **Number Awarded:** 1. **Funds Available:** $500. **Eligibility Requirements:** Applicant must be a graduating senior active in dramatic arts; must have utilized talents to the utmost; must display a love and enthusiasm for the theatre; and must participate whenever and wherever needed. **Application Requirements:** Applicants must submit a completed application form together with the scantron sheet; cover sheet; student activity and community activity sheets; personal essay; and a copy of unofficial transcript (signed by the counselor). **Additional Information:** No electronic submissions of application will be accepted. Submit two printed copies of the application and use a No. 2 pencil on the scantron sheet. **Deadline for Receipt:** February 20.

1832 ■ REDLANDS COMMUNITY SCHOLARSHIP FOUNDATION
c/o Kathleen Venegas-Boge, Admin. Asst.
PO Box 1683
Redlands, CA 92373
Tel: (909)307-9892
Fax: (909)307-9892
Web Site: http://www.redlandsscholarships.org
To encourage educational pursuits among Redlands Unified School District graduates by providing educational assistance.
Title of Award: Mike Niemeyer Memorial Football Scholarships **Area, Field, or Subject:** General studies. **Level of Education for which Award is Granted:** Undergraduate **Number Awarded:** 1. **Funds Available:** $500. **Eligibility Requirements:** Applicant must be a graduating senior who is a member of the Redlands High School Terrier football team and must demonstrate academic achievement and good citizenship. **Application Requirements:** Applicants must submit a completed application form together with the scantron sheet; cover sheet; student activity and community activity sheets; personal essay; and a copy of unofficial transcript (signed by the counselor). **Additional Information:** No electronic submissions of application will be accepted. Submit two printed copies of the application and use a No. 2 pencil on the scantron sheet. **Deadline for Receipt:** February 20.

1833 ■ REDLANDS COMMUNITY SCHOLARSHIP FOUNDATION
c/o Kathleen Venegas-Boge, Admin. Asst.
PO Box 1683
Redlands, CA 92373

Tel: (909)307-9892
Fax: (909)307-9892
Web Site: http://www.redlandsscholarships.org
To encourage educational pursuits among Redlands Unified School District graduates by providing educational assistance.
Title of Award: Optimist Club Of Redlands - Ralph Maloof Scholarships **Area, Field, or Subject:** General studies. **Level of Education for which Award is Granted:** Undergraduate **Number Awarded:** 1. **Funds Available:** $1,500.
Eligibility Requirements: Applicant must be a graduating male senior who has a minimum 3.0 GPA, a positive attitude, and involvement in service to the community. **Application Requirements:** Applicants must submit a completed application form together with the scantron sheet; cover sheet; student activity and community activity sheets; personal essay; and a copy of unofficial transcript (signed by the counselor). **Additional Information:** No electronic submissions of application will be accepted. Submit two printed copies of the application and use a No. 2 pencil on the scantron sheet. **Deadline for Receipt:** February 20.

1834 ■ REDLANDS COMMUNITY SCHOLARSHIP FOUNDATION
c/o Kathleen Venegas-Boge, Admin. Asst.
PO Box 1683
Redlands, CA 92373
Tel: (909)307-9892
Fax: (909)307-9892
Web Site: http://www.redlandsscholarships.org
To encourage educational pursuits among Redlands Unified School District graduates by providing educational assistance.
Title of Award: Optimist Club of Redlands - Virginia Elliott Scholarships **Area, Field, or Subject:** General studies. **Level of Education for which Award is Granted:** Undergraduate **Number Awarded:** 1. **Funds Available:** $1,500.
Eligibility Requirements: Applicant must be a female graduating senior who has a minimum 3.0 GPA, a positive attitude, and involvement in service to the community. **Application Requirements:** Applicants must submit a completed application form together with the scantron sheet; cover sheet; student activity and community activity sheets; personal essay; and a copy of unofficial transcript (signed by the counselor). **Additional Information:** No electronic submissions of application will be accepted. Submit two printed copies of the application and use a No. 2 pencil on the scantron sheet. **Deadline for Receipt:** February 20.

1835 ■ REDLANDS COMMUNITY SCHOLARSHIP FOUNDATION
c/o Kathleen Venegas-Boge, Admin. Asst.
PO Box 1683
Redlands, CA 92373
Tel: (909)307-9892
Fax: (909)307-9892
Web Site: http://www.redlandsscholarships.org
To encourage educational pursuits among Redlands Unified School District graduates by providing educational assistance.
Title of Award: Marshall Phelps Athletic Memorial Scholarships **Area, Field, or Subject:** General studies. **Level of Education for which Award is Granted:** Undergraduate **Number Awarded:** 1. **Funds Available:** $1,000.
Eligibility Requirements: Applicant must be a graduating male or female with proven athletic ability and interest in a career involving some phase of athletics (sports medicine, coaching, or physical therapy) and is enrolling in a two-year or four-year college program with a minimum 2.0 GPA. **Application Requirements:** Applicants must submit a completed application form together with the scantron sheet; cover sheet; student activity and community activity sheets; personal essay; and a copy of unofficial transcript (signed by the counselor). **Additional Information:** No electronic submissions of application will be accepted. Submit two printed copies of the application and use a No. 2 pencil on the scantron sheet. **Deadline for Receipt:** February 20.

1836 ■ REDLANDS COMMUNITY SCHOLARSHIP FOUNDATION
c/o Kathleen Venegas-Boge, Admin. Asst.
PO Box 1683
Redlands, CA 92373
Tel: (909)307-9892
Fax: (909)307-9892

Web Site: http://www.redlandsscholarships.org
To encourage educational pursuits among Redlands Unified School District graduates by providing educational assistance.
Title of Award: Howard and Mildred Phoenix Scholarships **Area, Field, or Subject:** General studies. **Level of Education for which Award is Granted:** Undergraduate **Number Awarded:** 1. **Funds Available:** $400.
Eligibility Requirements: Applicant must be a graduating senior who has demonstrated good citizenship, academic accomplishment, contribution to school and community; must be planning to further career in a business field; and must have attended Redlands High School for at least three semesters. **Application Requirements:** Applicants must submit a completed application form together with the scantron sheet; cover sheet; student activity and community activity sheets; personal essay; and a copy of unofficial transcript (signed by the counselor). **Additional Information:** No electronic submissions of application will be accepted. Submit two printed copies of the application and use a No. 2 pencil on the scantron sheet. **Deadline for Receipt:** February 20.

1837 ■ REDLANDS COMMUNITY SCHOLARSHIP FOUNDATION
c/o Kathleen Venegas-Boge, Admin. Asst.
PO Box 1683
Redlands, CA 92373
Tel: (909)307-9892
Fax: (909)307-9892
Web Site: http://www.redlandsscholarships.org
To encourage educational pursuits among Redlands Unified School District graduates by providing educational assistance.
Title of Award: Gail Porterfield Memorial Scholarships **Area, Field, or Subject:** General studies. **Level of Education for which Award is Granted:** Undergraduate **Number Awarded:** 1. **Funds Available:** $500.
Eligibility Requirements: Applicant must be a graduating young woman who has a minimum 3.5 GPA; must be planning to enter a medical or scientific field; and must have financial need. **Application Requirements:** Applicants must submit a completed application form together with the scantron sheet; cover sheet; student activity and community activity sheets; personal essay; and a copy of unofficial transcript (signed by the counselor). **Additional Information:** No electronic submissions of application will be accepted. Submit two printed copies of the application and use a No. 2 pencil on the scantron sheet. **Deadline for Receipt:** February 20.

1838 ■ REDLANDS COMMUNITY SCHOLARSHIP FOUNDATION
c/o Kathleen Venegas-Boge, Admin. Asst.
PO Box 1683
Redlands, CA 92373
Tel: (909)307-9892
Fax: (909)307-9892
Web Site: http://www.redlandsscholarships.org
To encourage educational pursuits among Redlands Unified School District graduates by providing educational assistance.
Title of Award: The Power to Continue Learning Scholarships **Area, Field, or Subject:** General studies. **Level of Education for which Award is Granted:** Undergraduate **Number Awarded:** 1. **Funds Available:** $500.
Eligibility Requirements: Applicant must be a graduating young woman; must have a minimum 2.5 GPA; must have participated in at least one school activity; must have demonstrated some type of community service; and must be planning to attend a two-year or four-year college or a vocational program. **Application Requirements:** Applicants must submit a completed application form together with the scantron sheet; cover sheet; student activity and community activity sheets; personal essay; and a copy of unofficial transcript (signed by the counselor). **Additional Information:** No electronic submissions of application will be accepted. Submit two printed copies of the application and use a No. 2 pencil on the scantron sheet. **Deadline for Receipt:** February 20.

1839 ■ REDLANDS COMMUNITY SCHOLARSHIP FOUNDATION
c/o Kathleen Venegas-Boge, Admin. Asst.
PO Box 1683
Redlands, CA 92373
Tel: (909)307-9892
Fax: (909)307-9892
Web Site: http://www.redlandsscholarships.org

To encourage educational pursuits among Redlands Unified School District graduates by providing educational assistance.

Title of Award: Raul Ramirez Memorial Scholarships **Area, Field, or Subject:** General studies. **Level of Education for which Award is Granted:** Undergraduate **Number Awarded:** 1. **Funds Available:** $700.

Eligibility Requirements: Applicant must be a graduating varsity letterman in wrestling, shot put, or track; must show dedication to sports, enthusiasm, an effort to improve, and respect for other athletes and teammates; must have satisfactory grades. **Application Requirements:** Applicants must submit a completed application form together with the scantron sheet; cover sheet; student activity and community activity sheets; personal essay; and a copy of unofficial transcript (signed by the counselor). **Additional Information:** No electronic submissions of application will be accepted. Submit two printed copies of the application and use a No. 2 pencil on the scantron sheet. **Deadline for Receipt:** February 20.

1840 ■ REDLANDS COMMUNITY SCHOLARSHIP FOUNDATION

c/o Kathleen Venegas-Boge, Admin. Asst.
PO Box 1683
Redlands, CA 92373
Tel: (909)307-9892
Fax: (909)307-9892
Web Site: http://www.redlandsscholarships.org

To encourage educational pursuits among Redlands Unified School District graduates by providing educational assistance.

Title of Award: Redlands Area Interfaith Council Scholarships **Area, Field, or Subject:** General studies. **Level of Education for which Award is Granted:** Undergraduate **Number Awarded:** 1. **Funds Available:** $500.

Eligibility Requirements: Applicant must be a graduating student. **Application Requirements:** Applicants must submit a completed application form together with the scantron sheet; cover sheet; student activity and community activity sheets; a 1-page essay explaining "How I can be an agent of peace"; and a copy of unofficial transcript (signed by the counselor). **Additional Information:** No electronic submissions of application will be accepted. Submit two printed copies of the application and use a No. 2 pencil on the scantron sheet. **Deadline for Receipt:** February 20.

1841 ■ REDLANDS COMMUNITY SCHOLARSHIP FOUNDATION

c/o Kathleen Venegas-Boge, Admin. Asst.
PO Box 1683
Redlands, CA 92373
Tel: (909)307-9892
Fax: (909)307-9892
Web Site: http://www.redlandsscholarships.org

To encourage educational pursuits among Redlands Unified School District graduates by providing educational assistance.

Title of Award: Redlands Community Scholarship Foundation Scholarships **Area, Field, or Subject:** General studies. **Level of Education for which Award is Granted:** Undergraduate **Number Awarded:** 15. **Funds Available:** $500.

Eligibility Requirements: Applicant must be a graduating senior student. **Application Requirements:** Applicants must submit a completed application form together with the scantron sheet; cover sheet; student activity and community activity sheets; personal essay; and a copy of unofficial transcript (signed by the counselor). **Additional Information:** No electronic submissions of application will be accepted. Submit two printed copies of the application and use a No. 2 pencil on the scantron sheet. **Deadline for Receipt:** February 20.

1842 ■ REDLANDS COMMUNITY SCHOLARSHIP FOUNDATION

c/o Kathleen Venegas-Boge, Admin. Asst.
PO Box 1683
Redlands, CA 92373
Tel: (909)307-9892
Fax: (909)307-9892
Web Site: http://www.redlandsscholarships.org

To encourage educational pursuits among Redlands Unified School District graduates by providing educational assistance.

Title of Award: Redlands Council PTA - Dorathy Jolley Memorial Scholarships **Area, Field, or Subject:** General studies. **Level of Education for** which **Award is Granted:** Undergraduate **Number Awarded:** 1. **Funds Available:** $300.

Eligibility Requirements: Applicant must be a graduating senior; must have a minimum 3.0 GPA; and must be active in a non-school service group such as church, scouts, or a community service club. **Application Requirements:** Applicants must submit a completed application form together with the scantron sheet; cover sheet; student activity and community activity sheets; personal essay; and a copy of unofficial transcript (signed by the counselor). **Additional Information:** No electronic submissions of application will be accepted. Submit two printed copies of the application and use a No. 2 pencil on the scantron sheet. **Deadline for Receipt:** February 20.

1843 ■ REDLANDS COMMUNITY SCHOLARSHIP FOUNDATION

c/o Kathleen Venegas-Boge, Admin. Asst.
PO Box 1683
Redlands, CA 92373
Tel: (909)307-9892
Fax: (909)307-9892
Web Site: http://www.redlandsscholarships.org

To encourage educational pursuits among Redlands Unified School District graduates by providing educational assistance.

Title of Award: Redlands Footlighters, Inc. - Merle and Peggy Williams Scholarships **Area, Field, or Subject:** General studies. **Level of Education for which Award is Granted:** Undergraduate **Number Awarded:** 1. **Funds Available:** $750.

Eligibility Requirements: Applicant must be a graduating senior who has made major contributions in theatre, either as an actor or as a theatre technician, and intends to continue involvement in theatre activities in the future. **Application Requirements:** Applicants must submit a completed application form together with the scantron sheet; cover sheet; student activity and community activity sheets; personal essay; and a copy of unofficial transcript (signed by the counselor). **Additional Information:** No electronic submissions of application will be accepted. Submit two printed copies of the application and use a No. 2 pencil on the scantron sheet. **Deadline for Receipt:** February 20.

1844 ■ REDLANDS COMMUNITY SCHOLARSHIP FOUNDATION

c/o Kathleen Venegas-Boge, Admin. Asst.
PO Box 1683
Redlands, CA 92373
Tel: (909)307-9892
Fax: (909)307-9892
Web Site: http://www.redlandsscholarships.org

To encourage educational pursuits among Redlands Unified School District graduates by providing educational assistance.

Title of Award: Redlands High School Academic Decathalon Scholarships **Area, Field, or Subject:** General studies. **Level of Education for which Award is Granted:** Undergraduate **Number Awarded:** 3. **Funds Available:** $300.

Eligibility Requirements: Applicant must be an outstanding senior who participated in the Academic Decathlon program. **Application Requirements:** Applicants must submit a completed application form together with the scantron sheet; cover sheet; student activity and community activity sheets; personal essay; and a copy of unofficial transcript (signed by the counselor). **Additional Information:** No electronic submissions of application will be accepted. Submit two printed copies of the application and use a No. 2 pencil on the scantron sheet. **Deadline for Receipt:** February 20.

1845 ■ REDLANDS COMMUNITY SCHOLARSHIP FOUNDATION

c/o Kathleen Venegas-Boge, Admin. Asst.
PO Box 1683
Redlands, CA 92373
Tel: (909)307-9892
Fax: (909)307-9892
Web Site: http://www.redlandsscholarships.org

To encourage educational pursuits among Redlands Unified School District graduates by providing educational assistance.

Title of Award: Redlands High School Boy's Varsity Volleyball Scholarships **Area, Field, or Subject:** General studies. **Level of Education for which Award is Granted:** Undergraduate **Number Awarded:** 1. **Funds Available:** $300.

Eligibility Requirements: Applicant must be a graduating senior who is a member of the Boy's Varsity Volleyball team. **Application Requirements:** Applicants must submit a completed application form together with the scantron sheet; cover sheet; student activity and community activity sheets; personal essay; and a copy of unofficial transcript (signed by the counselor). **Additional Information:** No electronic submissions of application will be accepted. Submit two printed copies of the application and use a No. 2 pencil on the scantron sheet. **Deadline for Receipt:** February 20.

1846 ■ REDLANDS COMMUNITY SCHOLARSHIP FOUNDATION
c/o Kathleen Venegas-Boge, Admin. Asst.
PO Box 1683
Redlands, CA 92373
Tel: (909)307-9892
Fax: (909)307-9892
Web Site: http://www.redlandsscholarships.org
To encourage educational pursuits among Redlands Unified School District graduates by providing educational assistance.
Title of Award: Redlands High School Class of 1957 **Area, Field, or Subject:** General studies. **Level of Education for which Award is Granted:** Undergraduate **Number Awarded:** 1. **Funds Available:** $500.
Eligibility Requirements: Applicant must be a graduating senior; must have a 3.0 or better GPA; must be planning to continue education on a full-time basis at a vocational school, community college, or university; must have good character and citizenship; and must have demonstrated involvement in service to the community. **Application Requirements:** Applicants must submit a completed application form together with the scantron sheet; cover sheet; student activity and community activity sheets; personal essay; and a copy of unofficial transcript (signed by the counselor). **Additional Information:** No electronic submissions of application will be accepted. Submit two printed copies of the application and use a No. 2 pencil on the scantron sheet. **Deadline for Receipt:** February 20.

1847 ■ REDLANDS COMMUNITY SCHOLARSHIP FOUNDATION
c/o Kathleen Venegas-Boge, Admin. Asst.
PO Box 1683
Redlands, CA 92373
Tel: (909)307-9892
Fax: (909)307-9892
Web Site: http://www.redlandsscholarships.org
To encourage educational pursuits among Redlands Unified School District graduates by providing educational assistance.
Title of Award: Redlands High School Girls' Volleyball Boosters Scholarship Awards **Area, Field, or Subject:** General studies. **Level of Education for which Award is Granted:** Undergraduate **Funds Available:** $750.
Eligibility Requirements: Applicant must be a graduating senior volleyball player with good academic standing and citizenship; must be a dedicated team player; and must have positive leadership skills and a positive attitude. **Application Requirements:** Applicants must submit a completed application form together with the scantron sheet; cover sheet; student activity and community activity sheets; personal essay; and a copy of unofficial transcript (signed by the counselor). **Additional Information:** No electronic submissions of application will be accepted. Submit two printed copies of the application and use a No. 2 pencil on the scantron sheet. **Deadline for Receipt:** February 20.

1848 ■ REDLANDS COMMUNITY SCHOLARSHIP FOUNDATION
c/o Kathleen Venegas-Boge, Admin. Asst.
PO Box 1683
Redlands, CA 92373
Tel: (909)307-9892
Fax: (909)307-9892
Web Site: http://www.redlandsscholarships.org
To encourage educational pursuits among Redlands Unified School District graduates by providing educational assistance.
Title of Award: Redlands High School Mock Trial Scholarships **Area, Field, or Subject:** General studies. **Level of Education for which Award is Granted:** Undergraduate **Number Awarded:** 2. **Funds Available:** $300 and $500.
Eligibility Requirements: Applicant must be a graduating senior and a member of the RHS Mock Trial team (either Varsity or Junior Varsity)

whose performances have contributed to a successful program. **Application Requirements:** Applicants must submit a completed application form together with the scantron sheet; cover sheet; student activity and community activity sheets; personal essay; and a copy of unofficial transcript (signed by the counselor). **Additional Information:** No electronic submissions of application will be accepted. Submit two printed copies of the application and use a No. 2 pencil on the scantron sheet. **Deadline for Receipt:** February 20.

1849 ■ REDLANDS COMMUNITY SCHOLARSHIP FOUNDATION
c/o Kathleen Venegas-Boge, Admin. Asst.
PO Box 1683
Redlands, CA 92373
Tel: (909)307-9892
Fax: (909)307-9892
Web Site: http://www.redlandsscholarships.org
To encourage educational pursuits among Redlands Unified School District graduates by providing educational assistance.
Title of Award: Redlands High School-PTSA Scholarships **Area, Field, or Subject:** General studies. **Level of Education for which Award is Granted:** Undergraduate **Funds Available:** $400.
Eligibility Requirements: Applicant must be a graduating senior pursuing a career in a vocational field with a 2.0 or higher GPA; or a graduating senior pursuing a career in a four-year college with a 3.0 or higher GPA. Student must demonstrate good citizenship, a high work capacity, and service to school and/or community. **Application Requirements:** Applicants must submit a completed application form together with the scantron sheet; cover sheet; student activity and community activity sheets; personal essay; and a copy of unofficial transcript (signed by the counselor). **Additional Information:** No electronic submissions of application will be accepted. Submit two printed copies of the application and use a No. 2 pencil on the scantron sheet. **Deadline for Receipt:** February 20.

1850 ■ REDLANDS COMMUNITY SCHOLARSHIP FOUNDATION
c/o Kathleen Venegas-Boge, Admin. Asst.
PO Box 1683
Redlands, CA 92373
Tel: (909)307-9892
Fax: (909)307-9892
Web Site: http://www.redlandsscholarships.org
To encourage educational pursuits among Redlands Unified School District graduates by providing educational assistance.
Title of Award: Redlands High School Soccer Boosters Scholarship Awards **Area, Field, or Subject:** General studies. **Level of Education for which Award is Granted:** Undergraduate **Number Awarded:** 4. **Funds Available:** $350.
Eligibility Requirements: Applicants must be graduating seniors who have participated in a minimum of two seasons in the Redlands High School soccer program, lettered in their senior year; must have demonstrated good citizenship; and must have a minimum 3.3 GPA. **Application Requirements:** Applicants must submit a completed application form together with the scantron sheet; cover sheet; student activity and community activity sheets; personal essay; and a copy of unofficial transcript (signed by the counselor). **Additional Information:** No electronic submissions of application will be accepted. Submit two printed copies of the application and use a No. 2 pencil on the scantron sheet. **Deadline for Receipt:** February 20.

1851 ■ REDLANDS COMMUNITY SCHOLARSHIP FOUNDATION
c/o Kathleen Venegas-Boge, Admin. Asst.
PO Box 1683
Redlands, CA 92373
Tel: (909)307-9892
Fax: (909)307-9892
Web Site: http://www.redlandsscholarships.org
To encourage educational pursuits among Redlands Unified School District graduates by providing educational assistance.
Title of Award: Redlands High School Softball Booster Scholarship Awards **Area, Field, or Subject:** General studies. **Level of Education for which Award is Granted:** Undergraduate **Number Awarded:** 2. **Funds Available:** $250.
Eligibility Requirements: Applicants must be graduating seniors who have earned a varsity letter in senior year and who have a minimum 3.25

weighted GPA. **Application Requirements:** Applicants must submit a completed application form together with the scantron sheet; cover sheet; student activity and community activity sheets; personal essay; and a copy of unofficial transcript (signed by the counselor). **Additional Information:** No electronic submissions of application will be accepted. Submit two printed copies of the application and use a No. 2 pencil on the scantron sheet. **Deadline for Receipt:** February 20.

1852 ■ REDLANDS COMMUNITY SCHOLARSHIP FOUNDATION
c/o Kathleen Venegas-Boge, Admin. Asst.
PO Box 1683
Redlands, CA 92373
Tel: (909)307-9892
Fax: (909)307-9892
Web Site: http://www.redlandsscholarships.org
To encourage educational pursuits among Redlands Unified School District graduates by providing educational assistance.
Title of Award: Redlands High School Speech Boosters Scholarship Awards **Area, Field, or Subject:** General studies. **Level of Education for which Award is Granted:** Undergraduate **Number Awarded:** 6. **Funds Available:** $1,000.
Eligibility Requirements: Applicant must be an outstanding speech team member. **Application Requirements:** Applicants must submit a completed application form together with the scantron sheet; cover sheet; student activity and community activity sheets; personal essay; and a copy of unofficial transcript (signed by the counselor). **Additional Information:** No electronic submissions of application will be accepted. Submit two printed copies of the application and use a No. 2 pencil on the scantron sheet. **Deadline for Receipt:** February 20.

1853 ■ REDLANDS COMMUNITY SCHOLARSHIP FOUNDATION
c/o Kathleen Venegas-Boge, Admin. Asst.
PO Box 1683
Redlands, CA 92373
Tel: (909)307-9892
Fax: (909)307-9892
Web Site: http://www.redlandsscholarships.org
To encourage educational pursuits among Redlands Unified School District graduates by providing educational assistance.
Title of Award: Redlands High School Spiritleaders Scholarships **Area, Field, or Subject:** General studies. **Level of Education for which Award is Granted:** Undergraduate **Funds Available:** $300.
Eligibility Requirements: Applicant must be a graduating senior who has been in Spiritleaders for a minimum of two years. **Application Requirements:** Applicants must submit a completed application form together with the scantron sheet; cover sheet; student activity and community activity sheets; personal essay; and a copy of unofficial transcript (signed by the counselor). **Additional Information:** No electronic submissions of application will be accepted. Submit two printed copies of the application and use a No. 2 pencil on the scantron sheet. **Deadline for Receipt:** February 20.

1854 ■ REDLANDS COMMUNITY SCHOLARSHIP FOUNDATION
c/o Kathleen Venegas-Boge, Admin. Asst.
PO Box 1683
Redlands, CA 92373
Tel: (909)307-9892
Fax: (909)307-9892
Web Site: http://www.redlandsscholarships.org
To encourage educational pursuits among Redlands Unified School District graduates by providing educational assistance.
Title of Award: Redlands High School Terrier Band Boosters Club Scholarships **Area, Field, or Subject:** General studies. **Level of Education for which Award is Granted:** Undergraduate **Funds Available:** $250.
Eligibility Requirements: Applicant must be a graduating senior who participated in the Redlands High School instrumental music program and plans to continue with instrumental music in some capacity (not necessarily majoring in music). **Application Requirements:** Applicants must submit a completed application form together with the scantron sheet; cover sheet; student activity and community activity sheets; personal essay; and a copy of unofficial transcript (signed by the counselor). **Additional Information:** No electronic submissions of application will be ac-

cepted. Submit two printed copies of the application and use a No. 2 pencil on the scantron sheet. **Deadline for Receipt:** February 20.

1855 ■ REDLANDS COMMUNITY SCHOLARSHIP FOUNDATION
c/o Kathleen Venegas-Boge, Admin. Asst.
PO Box 1683
Redlands, CA 92373
Tel: (909)307-9892
Fax: (909)307-9892
Web Site: http://www.redlandsscholarships.org
To encourage educational pursuits among Redlands Unified School District graduates by providing educational assistance.
Title of Award: Redlands High School Vocal Music Boosters Scholarship Awards **Area, Field, or Subject:** General studies. **Level of Education for which Award is Granted:** Undergraduate **Number Awarded:** 2. **Funds Available:** $500 and $400.
Eligibility Requirements: Applicant must be a graduating senior who has participated in the Redlands High School choral program and plans to continue with music in some capacity. **Application Requirements:** Applicants must submit a completed application form together with the scantron sheet; cover sheet; student activity and community activity sheets; personal essay; and a copy of unofficial transcript (signed by the counselor). **Additional Information:** No electronic submissions of application will be accepted. Submit two printed copies of the application and use a No. 2 pencil on the scantron sheet. **Deadline for Receipt:** February 20.

1856 ■ REDLANDS COMMUNITY SCHOLARSHIP FOUNDATION
c/o Kathleen Venegas-Boge, Admin. Asst.
PO Box 1683
Redlands, CA 92373
Tel: (909)307-9892
Fax: (909)307-9892
Web Site: http://www.redlandsscholarships.org
To encourage educational pursuits among Redlands Unified School District graduates by providing educational assistance.
Title of Award: Redlands Morning Kiwanis Club Foundation Scholarships **Area, Field, or Subject:** General studies. **Level of Education for which Award is Granted:** Undergraduate **Number Awarded:** 1. **Funds Available:** $2,000.
Eligibility Requirements: Applicant must be a graduating senior; must have at least a 3.0 GPA; and must be planning to attend an accredited college, university, or vocational program. **Application Requirements:** Applicants must submit a completed application form together with the scantron sheet; cover sheet; student activity and community activity sheets; a 1-page essay on "What I feel is the importance of volunteerism, and how community service will/may affect my future."; and a copy of unofficial transcript (signed by the counselor). **Additional Information:** No electronic submissions of application will be accepted. Submit two printed copies of the application and use a No. 2 pencil on the scantron sheet. **Deadline for Receipt:** February 20.

1857 ■ REDLANDS COMMUNITY SCHOLARSHIP FOUNDATION
c/o Kathleen Venegas-Boge, Admin. Asst.
PO Box 1683
Redlands, CA 92373
Tel: (909)307-9892
Fax: (909)307-9892
Web Site: http://www.redlandsscholarships.org
To encourage educational pursuits among Redlands Unified School District graduates by providing educational assistance.
Title of Award: Redlands Noon Kiwanis Club Foundation Scholarships **Area, Field, or Subject:** General studies. **Level of Education for which Award is Granted:** Undergraduate **Number Awarded:** 3. **Funds Available:** $5,000. **Duration:** Four years.
Eligibility Requirements: Applicant must be a graduating senior with good citizenship, extracurricular activity involvement, and demonstrated leadership abilities. **Application Requirements:** Applicants must submit a completed application form together with the scantron sheet; cover sheet; student activity and community activity sheets; personal essay; and a copy of unofficial transcript (signed by the counselor). **Additional Information:** No electronic submissions of application will be accepted. Submit two printed copies of the application and use a No. 2 pencil on the scantron sheet. **Deadline for Receipt:** February 20.

1858 ■ REDLANDS COMMUNITY SCHOLARSHIP FOUNDATION
c/o Kathleen Venegas-Boge, Admin. Asst.
PO Box 1683
Redlands, CA 92373
Tel: (909)307-9892
Fax: (909)307-9892
Web Site: http://www.redlandsscholarships.org
To encourage educational pursuits among Redlands Unified School District graduates by providing educational assistance.
Title of Award: Redlands Noon Kiwanis Club - Martin and Dorothy Munz Scholarships **Area, Field, or Subject:** General studies. **Level of Education for which Award is Granted:** Undergraduate **Number Awarded:** 1. **Funds Available:** $1,250.
Eligibility Requirements: Applicant must be a graduating senior; must be a COMPACT student for at least his/her senior year; must have a 3.0 GPA in all subjects; must have an interest or aptitude for education or a business career; must be involved in community service such as scouting, church, etc.; must be involved in extracurricular school activities; must be highly motivated to obtain a four-year college degree; and must demonstrate a financial need. **Application Requirements:** Applicants must submit a completed application form together with the scantron sheet; cover sheet; student activity and community activity sheets; personal essay; and a copy of unofficial transcript (signed by the counselor). **Additional Information:** No electronic submissions of application will be accepted. Submit two printed copies of the application and use a No. 2 pencil on the scantron sheet. **Deadline for Receipt:** February 20.

1859 ■ REDLANDS COMMUNITY SCHOLARSHIP FOUNDATION
c/o Kathleen Venegas-Boge, Admin. Asst.
PO Box 1683
Redlands, CA 92373
Tel: (909)307-9892
Fax: (909)307-9892
Web Site: http://www.redlandsscholarships.org
To encourage educational pursuits among Redlands Unified School District graduates by providing educational assistance.
Title of Award: Redlands Rotary Club - Donald C. Anderson Scholarships **Area, Field, or Subject:** General studies. **Level of Education for which Award is Granted:** Undergraduate **Number Awarded:** 1. **Funds Available:** $2000.
Eligibility Requirements: Applicant must be a graduating senior demonstrating high academic achievement, outstanding citizenship, and service to school and community. **Application Requirements:** Applicants must submit a completed application form together with the scantron sheet; cover sheet; student activity and community activity sheets; personal essay; and a copy of unofficial transcript (signed by the counselor). **Additional Information:** No electronic submissions of application will be accepted. Submit two printed copies of the application and use a No. 2 pencil on the scantron sheet. **Deadline for Receipt:** February 20.

1860 ■ REDLANDS COMMUNITY SCHOLARSHIP FOUNDATION
c/o Kathleen Venegas-Boge, Admin. Asst.
PO Box 1683
Redlands, CA 92373
Tel: (909)307-9892
Fax: (909)307-9892
Web Site: http://www.redlandsscholarships.org
To encourage educational pursuits among Redlands Unified School District graduates by providing educational assistance.
Title of Award: Redlands Rotary Club - Ernest L. Cronemeyer Memorial Scholarships **Area, Field, or Subject:** General studies. **Level of Education for which Award is Granted:** Undergraduate **Number Awarded:** 1. **Funds Available:** $4,000.
Eligibility Requirements: Applicant must be a graduating senior with high academic achievement, outstanding citizenship, and service to school and community. **Application Requirements:** Applicants must submit a completed application form together with the scantron sheet; cover sheet; student activity and community activity sheets; personal essay; and a copy of unofficial transcript (signed by the counselor). **Additional Information:** No electronic submissions of application will be accepted. Submit two printed copies of the application and use a No. 2 pencil on the scantron sheet. **Deadline for Receipt:** February 20.

1861 ■ REDLANDS COMMUNITY SCHOLARSHIP FOUNDATION
c/o Kathleen Venegas-Boge, Admin. Asst.
PO Box 1683
Redlands, CA 92373
Tel: (909)307-9892
Fax: (909)307-9892
Web Site: http://www.redlandsscholarships.org
To encourage educational pursuits among Redlands Unified School District graduates by providing educational assistance.
Title of Award: Redlands Rotary Club Foundation Discretionary Scholarships **Area, Field, or Subject:** General studies. **Level of Education for which Award is Granted:** Undergraduate **Number Awarded:** 2. **Funds Available:** $1,000.
Eligibility Requirements: Applicant must be a graduating senior who has demonstrated high academic achievement, outstanding citizenship, and service to school and community. **Application Requirements:** Applicants must submit a completed application form together with the scantron sheet; cover sheet; student activity and community activity sheets; personal essay; and a copy of unofficial transcript (signed by the counselor). **Additional Information:** No electronic submissions of application will be accepted. Submit two printed copies of the application and use a No. 2 pencil on the scantron sheet. **Deadline for Receipt:** February 20.

1862 ■ REDLANDS COMMUNITY SCHOLARSHIP FOUNDATION
c/o Kathleen Venegas-Boge, Admin. Asst.
PO Box 1683
Redlands, CA 92373
Tel: (909)307-9892
Fax: (909)307-9892
Web Site: http://www.redlandsscholarships.org
To encourage educational pursuits among Redlands Unified School District graduates by providing educational assistance.
Title of Award: Redlands Teachers Association Scholarships **Area, Field, or Subject:** General studies. **Level of Education for which Award is Granted:** Undergraduate **Funds Available:** $500.
Eligibility Requirements: Applicant must be a graduating senior; must have a minimum 3.0 GPA or better; must be active in school and community; must have demonstrated outstanding citizenship; must be enrolled in college; and must make a presentation to the Sunrise Rotary Club. **Application Requirements:** Applicants must submit a completed application form together with the scantron sheet; cover sheet; student activity and community activity sheets; personal essay; and a copy of unofficial transcript (signed by the counselor). **Additional Information:** No electronic submissions of application will be accepted. Submit two printed copies of the application and use a No. 2 pencil on the scantron sheet. **Deadline for Receipt:** February 20.

1863 ■ REDLANDS COMMUNITY SCHOLARSHIP FOUNDATION
c/o Kathleen Venegas-Boge, Admin. Asst.
PO Box 1683
Redlands, CA 92373
Tel: (909)307-9892
Fax: (909)307-9892
Web Site: http://www.redlandsscholarships.org
To encourage educational pursuits among Redlands Unified School District graduates by providing educational assistance.
Title of Award: ROP - Ambassadors Scholarships **Area, Field, or Subject:** General studies. **Level of Education for which Award is Granted:** Undergraduate **Funds Available:** $250.
Eligibility Requirements: Applicant must be a senior who participates in the ROP Ambassador program and submits and presents before a panel of judges a marketing concept that helps to promote ROP and its programs. **Application Requirements:** Applicants must submit a completed application form together with the scantron sheet; cover sheet; student activity and community activity sheets; personal essay; and a copy of unofficial transcript (signed by the counselor). **Additional Information:** No electronic submissions of application will be accepted. Submit two printed copies of the application and use a No. 2 pencil on the scantron sheet. **Deadline for Receipt:** February 20.

1864 ■ REDLANDS COMMUNITY SCHOLARSHIP FOUNDATION
c/o Kathleen Venegas-Boge, Admin. Asst.
PO Box 1683
Redlands, CA 92373
Tel: (909)307-9892
Fax: (909)307-9892
Web Site: http://www.redlandsscholarships.org
To encourage educational pursuits among Redlands Unified School District graduates by providing educational assistance.
Title of Award: ROP - Bob Bruce Memorial Scholarships **Area, Field, or Subject:** General studies. **Level of Education for which Award is Granted:** Undergraduate **Funds Available:** $200.
Eligibility Requirements: Applicant must be a graduating senior who has done outstanding work in an ROP class. **Application Requirements:** Applicants must submit a completed application form together with the scantron sheet; cover sheet; student activity and community activity sheets; personal essay; and a copy of unofficial transcript (signed by the counselor). **Additional Information:** No electronic submissions of application will be accepted. Submit two printed copies of the application and use a No. 2 pencil on the scantron sheet. **Deadline for Receipt:** February 20.

1865 ■ REDLANDS COMMUNITY SCHOLARSHIP FOUNDATION
c/o Kathleen Venegas-Boge, Admin. Asst.
PO Box 1683
Redlands, CA 92373
Tel: (909)307-9892
Fax: (909)307-9892
Web Site: http://www.redlandsscholarships.org
To encourage educational pursuits among Redlands Unified School District graduates by providing educational assistance.
Title of Award: Michael A. Russo Memorial Scholarships **Area, Field, or Subject:** General studies. **Level of Education for which Award is Granted:** Undergraduate **Number Awarded:** 1. **Funds Available:** $1,000.
Eligibility Requirements: Applicant must be a graduating senior pursuing a career in a medical or medically-allied profession or career. **Application Requirements:** Applicants must submit a completed application form together with the scantron sheet; cover sheet; student activity and community activity sheets; personal essay; and a copy of unofficial transcript (signed by the counselor). **Additional Information:** No electronic submissions of application will be accepted. Submit two printed copies of the application and use a No. 2 pencil on the scantron sheet. **Deadline for Receipt:** February 20.

1866 ■ REDLANDS COMMUNITY SCHOLARSHIP FOUNDATION
c/o Kathleen Venegas-Boge, Admin. Asst.
PO Box 1683
Redlands, CA 92373
Tel: (909)307-9892
Fax: (909)307-9892
Web Site: http://www.redlandsscholarships.org
To encourage educational pursuits among Redlands Unified School District graduates by providing educational assistance.
Title of Award: Schoolsfirst Federal Credit Union Scholarships **Area, Field, or Subject:** General studies. **Level of Education for which Award is Granted:** Undergraduate **Funds Available:** No specific amount.
Eligibility Requirements: Applicants must be high school seniors. **Application Requirements:** Applicants must submit a completed application form together with the scantron sheet; cover sheet; student activity and community activity sheets; personal essay; and a copy of unofficial transcript (signed by the counselor). **Additional Information:** No electronic submissions of application will be accepted. Submit two printed copies of the application and use a No. 2 pencil on the scantron sheet. **Deadline for Receipt:** February 20.

1867 ■ REDLANDS COMMUNITY SCHOLARSHIP FOUNDATION
c/o Kathleen Venegas-Boge, Admin. Asst.
PO Box 1683
Redlands, CA 92373
Tel: (909)307-9892
Fax: (909)307-9892

Web Site: http://www.redlandsscholarships.org
To encourage educational pursuits among Redlands Unified School District graduates by providing educational assistance.
Title of Award: Felix R. Sepulveda Memorial Scholarships - Northside Booster Club **Area, Field, or Subject:** General studies. **Level of Education for which Award is Granted:** Undergraduate **Number Awarded:** 1. **Funds Available:** $500.
Eligibility Requirements: Applicant must be a graduating male or female who has maintained at least a 2.5 GPA and participated in at least one sport. **Application Requirements:** Applicants must submit a completed application form together with the scantron sheet; cover sheet; student activity and community activity sheets; personal essay; and a copy of unofficial transcript (signed by the counselor). **Additional Information:** No electronic submissions of application will be accepted. Submit two printed copies of the application and use a No. 2 pencil on the scantron sheet. **Deadline for Receipt:** February 20.

1868 ■ REDLANDS COMMUNITY SCHOLARSHIP FOUNDATION
c/o Kathleen Venegas-Boge, Admin. Asst.
PO Box 1683
Redlands, CA 92373
Tel: (909)307-9892
Fax: (909)307-9892
Web Site: http://www.redlandsscholarships.org
To encourage educational pursuits among Redlands Unified School District graduates by providing educational assistance.
Title of Award: Shervin Tehranchi Wrestling Scholarships **Area, Field, or Subject:** General studies. **Level of Education for which Award is Granted:** Undergraduate **Number Awarded:** 1. **Funds Available:** $300.
Eligibility Requirements: Applicant must be a graduating senior; must have been a member of the wrestling team for at least two years; must have a minimum 2.7 GPA; and must demonstrate good citizenship. **Application Requirements:** Applicants must submit completed application form together with the scantron sheet; cover sheet; student activity and community activity sheets; personal essay; and a copy of unofficial transcript (signed by the counselor). **Additional Information:** No electronic submissions of application will be accepted. Submit two printed copies of the application and use a No. 2 pencil on the scantron sheet. **Deadline for Receipt:** February 20.

1869 ■ REDLANDS COMMUNITY SCHOLARSHIP FOUNDATION
c/o Kathleen Venegas-Boge, Admin. Asst.
PO Box 1683
Redlands, CA 92373
Tel: (909)307-9892
Fax: (909)307-9892
Web Site: http://www.redlandsscholarships.org
To encourage educational pursuits among Redlands Unified School District graduates by providing educational assistance.
Title of Award: Rajadi Sjarif Memorial Scholarships **Area, Field, or Subject:** General studies. **Level of Education for which Award is Granted:** Undergraduate **Number Awarded:** 1. **Funds Available:** $300.
Eligibility Requirements: Applicant must be an ELL student with a GPA of 3.0 or higher. **Application Requirements:** Applicants must submit a completed application form together with the scantron sheet; cover sheet; student activity and community activity sheets; personal essay; and a copy of unofficial transcript (signed by the counselor). **Additional Information:** No electronic submissions of application will be accepted. Submit two printed copies of the application and use a No. 2 pencil on the scantron sheet. **Deadline for Receipt:** February 20.

1870 ■ REDLANDS COMMUNITY SCHOLARSHIP FOUNDATION
c/o Kathleen Venegas-Boge, Admin. Asst.
PO Box 1683
Redlands, CA 92373
Tel: (909)307-9892
Fax: (909)307-9892
Web Site: http://www.redlandsscholarships.org
To encourage educational pursuits among Redlands Unified School District graduates by providing educational assistance.
Title of Award: Smiley Elementary School PTA - Beverly Roberts Memorial Scholarships **Area, Field, or Subject:** General studies. **Level of Education for which Award is Granted:** Undergraduate **Number Awarded:** 1. **Funds Available:** $500.

Eligibility Requirements: Applicant must be a graduating senior in the upper half of the senior class who attended Smiley Elementary School and is a well-rounded student. **Application Requirements:** Applicants must submit a completed application form together with the scantron sheet; cover sheet; student activity and community activity sheets; personal essay; and a copy of unofficial transcript (signed by the counselor). **Additional Information:** No electronic submissions of application will be accepted. Submit two printed copies of the application and use a No. 2 pencil on the scantron sheet. **Deadline for Receipt:** February 20.

1871 ■ REDLANDS COMMUNITY SCHOLARSHIP FOUNDATION
c/o Kathleen Venegas-Boge, Admin. Asst.
PO Box 1683
Redlands, CA 92373
Tel: (909)307-9892
Fax: (909)307-9892
Web Site: http://www.redlandsscholarships.org
To encourage educational pursuits among Redlands Unified School District graduates by providing educational assistance.
Title of Award: Redlands Evening Lions Club - Barbara Westen Scholarships **Area, Field, or Subject:** General studies. **Level of Education for which Award is Granted:** Undergraduate **Number Awarded:** 1. **Funds Available:** $350.
Eligibility Requirements: Applicant must be a graduating senior student who has demonstrated scholastic ability and financial need. **Application Requirements:** Applicants must submit a completed application form together with the scantron sheet; cover sheet; student activity and community activity sheets; personal essay; and a copy of unofficial transcript (signed by the counselor). **Additional Information:** No electronic submissions of application will be accepted. Submit two printed copies of the application and use a No. 2 pencil on the scantron sheet. **Deadline for Receipt:** February 20.

1872 ■ RESERVE OFFICERS ASSOCIATION OF THE UNITED STATES
1 Constitution Ave. NE
Washington, DC 20002-5618
Tel: (202)479-2200
Free: 800-809-9448
Fax: (202)547-1641
E-mail: info@roa.org
Web Site: http://www.roa.org
To assist in the educational pursuits of members of ROA, ROAL, and their dependents.
Title of Award: Henry J. Reilly Memorial Scholarships - For Freshmen in College **Area, Field, or Subject:** General studies. **Level of Education for which Award is Granted:** Undergraduate **Funds Available:** $500.
Eligibility Requirements: Applicants must be dependents of an active or associate ROA or ROAL member; must be 21 years old or below; must be accepted for full-time undergraduate study at a regional accredited four-year U.S. college/university; must be in the top 1/4th of the graduating class; and must have a GPA of 3.3 or higher (on a 4.0 scale). **Application Requirements:** Application materials are available at the website. Applicants must complete the application form and submit together with an official high school transcript; recent official college transcript; test score verification; and a 500-word essay on their career goals. All materials must be submitted in one envelope at one time only. **Deadline for Receipt:** April 10. **Additional Information:** Ms. Betsy Allen, 800-809-9448 x-756, or scholarship@roa.org.

1873 ■ RESERVE OFFICERS ASSOCIATION OF THE UNITED STATES
1 Constitution Ave. NE
Washington, DC 20002-5618
Tel: (202)479-2200
Free: 800-809-9448
Fax: (202)547-1641
E-mail: info@roa.org
Web Site: http://www.roa.org
To assist in the educational pursuits of members of ROA, ROAL, and their dependents.
Title of Award: Henry J. Reilly Memorial Scholarships - For Graduating High School Seniors **Area, Field, or Subject:** General studies. **Level of

Education for which Award is Granted: Undergraduate **Funds Available:** $500.
Eligibility Requirements: Applicants must be dependents of an active or associate ROA or ROAL member; must be 21 years old or below; must be accepted for full-time undergraduate study at a regional accredited four-year U.S. college/university; must be in the top 1/4th of the graduating class; and must have a GPA of 3.3 and above on a 4.0 scale. **Application Requirements:** Application materials are available at the website. Applicants must submit completed application along with an official high school transcript; copy of acceptance letter; test scores; Verification and Assessment Report and Academic and Personal Assessment Report; an essay on the applicant's career goals (500 words). All materials must be submitted in one envelope at one time only. **Deadline for Receipt:** April 10. **Additional Information:** Ms. Betsy Allen, 800-809-9448 x-756, or scholarship@roa.org.

1874 ■ RESERVE OFFICERS ASSOCIATION OF THE UNITED STATES
1 Constitution Ave. NE
Washington, DC 20002-5618
Tel: (202)479-2200
Free: 800-809-9448
Fax: (202)547-1641
E-mail: info@roa.org
Web Site: http://www.roa.org
To assist in the educational pursuits of members of ROA, ROAL, and their dependents.
Title of Award: Henry J. Reilly Memorial Scholarships - For Sophomores and Juniors in College **Area, Field, or Subject:** General studies. **Level of Education for which Award is Granted:** Undergraduate **Funds Available:** $500.
Eligibility Requirements: Applicants must be dependents of an active or associate ROA or ROAL member; must be 26 years old or below; must be accepted for full-time undergraduate study at a regional accredited four-year U.S. college/university; must have a GPA of 3.3 or higher on a 4.0 scale; and must have evidence of acceptance (for community college students transferring to a four-year college/university). **Application Requirements:** Application materials are available at the website. Applicants must complete the application form and submit together with an official high school transcript; recent official college transcript; test score verification; and a 500-word essay on their career goals. All materials must be submitted in one envelope at one time only. **Deadline for Receipt:** April 10. **Additional Information:** Ms. Betsy Allen, 800-809-9448 x-756, or scholarship@roa.org.

1875 ■ RETAIL PACKAGING ASSOCIATION
PO Box 17656
Covington, KY 41017
Tel: (859)341-9623
Fax: (859)341-6211
E-mail: info@retailpackaging.org
Web Site: http://www.retailpackaging.org
To provide educational assistance to dependents of members of the association.
Title of Award: RPA Scholarships **Area, Field, or Subject:** General studies. **Level of Education for which Award is Granted:** Undergraduate **Number Awarded:** 2. **Funds Available:** $1,000. **Duration:** One year.
Eligibility Requirements: Applicants must be high school seniors or college freshmen, sophomores and juniors who are dependents of a fulltime RPA member. **Application Requirements:** Applicants are advised to visit the website for the online application process. **Deadline for Receipt:** May 15.

1876 ■ RETIRED LEAGUE POSTMASTERS OF THE NATIONAL LEAGUE OF POSTMASTERS
One Beltway Center
5904 Richmond Highway, Ste. 500
Alexandria, VA 22303-1864
Tel: (703)329-4550
Fax: (703)329-0466
E-mail: information@postmasters.org
Web Site: http://www.postmasters.org

To provide financial assistance for the education of children or grandchildren of an active Postmasters or retired postmasters, who are members of the National League of Postmasters. **Title of Award:** Retired League Postmasters Scholarship Program **Area, Field, or Subject:** General studies. **Level of Education for which Award is Granted:** Undergraduate **Funds Available:** No specific amount.

Eligibility Requirements: Applicants must be high school graduates accepted as first year students, for fall admission to an accredited college, university or trade school; must have a 3.0 GPA over all or a 3.0 average for the last full year of high school. **Application Requirements:** Applicants must submit transcript of grades covering the most recent year of school and list of awards or community service during previous school terms. **Deadline for Receipt:** June 30.

1877 ■ RHODE ISLAND FOUNDATION
One Union Sta.
Providence, RI 02903
Tel: (401)274-4564
Fax: (401)331-8085
Web Site: http://www.rifoundation.org/matriarch/default.asp
To provide financial assistance to descendants of members of the Franklin Lodge of Freemasons in Wesley, RI.
Title of Award: Edward Leon Duhamel Freemasons Scholarships **Area, Field, or Subject:** General studies. **Level of Education for which Award is Granted:** Undergraduate **Funds Available:** $500-$1,000. **Duration:** One year.

Eligibility Requirements: Applicants must be descendants of a member of Franklin Lodge in Wesley, Rhode Island, or descendants of other Freemansons who are RI residents; must be able to demonstrate scholastic achievement and good citizenship; and must be enrolled in an accredited post-secondary institution. **Application Requirements:** Applicants must complete the application form, available online; must submit a financial aid award letter, recent official transcript, essay, and a copy of their final student aid report. Application form and other supporting documents must be sent to Libby Monahan, Duhamel Scholarship, Rhode Island Foundation, One Union Station, Providence, RI 02903. **Deadline for Receipt:** May 19.

1878 ■ RHODE ISLAND FOUNDATION
One Union Sta.
Providence, RI 02903
Tel: (401)274-4564
Fax: (401)331-8085
Web Site: http://www.rifoundation.org/matriarch/default.asp
To provide support for females living in Washington County who need financial assistance in order to pursue education or job training.
Title of Award: GFWC Women's Club of South County Scholarships **Area, Field, or Subject:** General studies. **Level of Education for which Award is Granted:** Undergraduate **Number Awarded:** 2. **Funds Available:** $1,000. **Duration:** One year.

Eligibility Requirements: Applicants must be able to demonstrate financial need; must be a resident of Washington County; must be a female, age 25 or older; and must be enrolled or registered in an educational or job skills training program and working toward their first degree or certificate. **Application Requirements:** Applicants must complete the application form available online; must submit a financial aid award letter, a copy of final Student Aid Report, one essay, recent official transcript, and letter of recommendation. Application forms and other supporting documents must be sent to Libby Monahan, GFWC Women's Club of South County Scholarship, Rhode Island Foundation, One Union Station, Providence, RI 02903. **Deadline for Receipt:** June 2.

1879 ■ RHODE ISLAND FOUNDATION
One Union Sta.
Providence, RI 02903
Tel: (401)274-4564
Fax: (401)331-8085
Web Site: http://www.rifoundation.org/matriarch/default.asp
To provide financial assistance for promising students with a distinguished record of public services.
Title of Award: Rhode Island Association of Former Legislators Scholarships **Area, Field, or Subject:** General studies. **Level of Education for**

which **Award is Granted:** Undergraduate **Funds Available:** $1,500. **Duration:** One year.

Eligibility Requirements: Applicant must be a graduating high school senior and resident of Rhode Island; must have a history of substantial voluntary involvement in community service; must have been accepted into an accredited post-secondary institution; must be able to demonstrate financial need. **Application Requirements:** Applicants must complete the application form, available online; must submit a copy of financial aid award letter, most recent official high school transcript, one letter of recommendation, one essay, and a copy of their final Student Aid Report. Application forms and other supporting documents must be sent to Libby Monahan, GFWC Women's Club of South County Scholarship, Rhode Island Foundation, One Union Station, Providence, RI 02903. **Deadline for Receipt:** June 4.

1880 ■ RHODE ISLAND FOUNDATION
One Union Sta.
Providence, RI 02903
Tel: (401)274-4564
Fax: (401)331-8085
Web Site: http://www.rifoundation.org/matriarch/default.asp
To provide support for individuals intending to pursue their education or job training.
Title of Award: Rhode Island Commission on Women/Freda H. Goldman Education Awards **Area, Field, or Subject:** General studies. **Level of Education for which Award is Granted:** Undergraduate **Funds Available:** No specific amount. **Duration:** One year.

Eligibility Requirements: Applicants must be enrolled or registered in an educational or job skills training program; must be Rhode Island residents; and must be able to demonstrate financial need. **Application Requirements:** Applicants must complete the application form, available online; must have their financial aid award letter, a copy of their final Student Aid Report, one essay, most recent official academic transcript, letter of recommendation, and resume. Application forms and other supporting documents must be sent to Libby Monahan, GFWC Women's Club of South County Scholarship, Rhode Island Foundation, One Union Station, Providence, RI 02903. **Deadline for Receipt:** June 12.

1881 ■ RHODE ISLAND FOUNDATION
One Union Sta.
Providence, RI 02903
Tel: (401)274-4564
Fax: (401)331-8085
Web Site: http://www.rifoundation.org/matriarch/default.asp
To encourage older students to return to undergraduate school for further education.
Title of Award: Lily and Catello Sorrentino Memorial Scholarships **Area, Field, or Subject:** General studies. **Level of Education for which Award is Granted:** Undergraduate **Funds Available:** $350-$1,000. **Duration:** One year.

Eligibility Requirements: Applicant must be a Rhode Island resident who is at least 45 years of age; must be attending any degree-conferring, non-parochial educational college or university within Rhode Island towards an undergraduate degree; must be able to demonstrate financial need; must not have any relationship with the Sorrentino family or the Rhode Island Foundation that can be construed in any way as influencing the fund's recommendation. **Application Requirements:** Applicants must complete the application form, available online; must have a copy of their financial aid award letter, official transcript, one essay, copy of their final student aid report, and two letters of recommendation. Application form and other supporting documents must be sent to Libby Monahan Sorrentino Scholarships, Rhode Island Foundation, 1 Union Station, Providence, RI 02903. **Deadline for Receipt:** May 15.

1882 ■ RHODE ISLAND FOUNDATION
One Union Sta.
Providence, RI 02903
Tel: (401)274-4564
Fax: (401)331-8085
Web Site: http://www.rifoundation.org/matriarch/default.asp
To assist single parents in the pursuit of education beyond high school.
Title of Award: Bruce and Marjorie Sundlun Scholarships **Area, Field, or Subject:** General studies. **Level of Education for which Award is**

Granted: Undergraduate **Number Awarded:** 3-5. **Funds Available:** $1,000. **Duration:** One year.
Eligibility Requirements: Applicants must be single parents, either male or female, who are currently enrolled in a Rhode Island institution of higher learning or continuing education; must be Rhode Island residents and able to demonstrate financial need. **Application Requirements:** Applicants must complete the application form, available online; must submit a copy of their financial aid award letter, and a recent official transcript; must prepare one essay; must have a copy of their final Student Aid Report and letter of recommendation. Application forms and other supporting documents must be sent to Libby Monahan, GFWC Women's Club of South County Scholarship, Rhode Island Foundation, One Union Station, Providence, RI 02903. **Deadline for Receipt:** June 13.

1883 ■ JACKIE ROBINSON FOUNDATION
1 Hudson Sq.
75 Varick St., 2nd Fl.
New York, NY 10013-1917
Tel: (212)290-8600
Fax: (212)290-8081
E-mail: general@jackierobinson.org
Web Site: http://www.jackierobinson.org
To financially support minority students in attaining higher educational pursuits.
Title of Award: Jackie Robinson Scholarships **Area, Field, or Subject:** General studies. **Level of Education for which Award is Granted:** Undergraduate **Funds Available:** $7,500. **Duration:** Four years.
Eligibility Requirements: Applicant must be a minority high school student showing leadership potential and demonstrating financial need to attend an accredited 4-year college or university. **Application Requirements:** Applicants must submit a letter of recommendation, official transcript (with raised seal), and SAT or ACT scores. **Deadline for Receipt:** March 31.

1884 ■ ROOFING INDUSTRY ALLIANCE FOR PROGRESS
10255 W Higgins Rd., Ste. 600
Rosemont, IL 60018-5607
Tel: (847)299-9070
Fax: (847)299-1183
E-mail: bjudson@roofingindustryalliance.net
Web Site: http://www.nrca.net/rp/related/nrf
To provide financial support to immediate families of NRCA members to be able to attend college or vocational programs.
Title of Award: Roofing Industry Alliance for Progress Scholarships **Area, Field, or Subject:** General studies. **Level of Education for which Award is Granted:** Graduate, Undergraduate **Funds Available:** $1000. **Duration:** One year.
Eligibility Requirements: Applicant must be dependents of full-time employees or spouses of NRCA contractor members or companies that have been NRCA members for at least one year; high school seniors or graduates or undergraduates enrolled full-time in a course of study in an accredited two- or four-year college/university or vocational school; relatives of Alliance trustees or officers are not eligible. **Application Requirements:** Applicant must send a completed application form together with a transcript. **Deadline for Receipt:** January 31. **Additional Information:** The Roofing Industry Alliance for Progress Scholarship Program, Scholarship America, One Scholarship Way, P.O. Box 297, Saint Peter, MN 56082, Telephone: (507)931-1682, ext. 629

1885 ■ ROOTHBERT FUND
475 Riverside Dr., Rm. 252
New York, NY 10115
Tel: (212)870-3116
E-mail: mail@roothbertfund.org
Web Site: http://www.roothbertfund.org
To provide financial assistance to people motivated by spiritual values.
Title of Award: Roothbert Fund Scholarships **Area, Field, or Subject:** General studies. **Level of Education for which Award is Granted:** Undergraduate **Funds Available:** $2,000-$3,000.
Eligibility Requirements: Scholarship is open to all people in the United States regardless of sex, age, color, nationality or religious background. **Application Requirements:** Applicants must submit all the application information.

1886 ■ THE ROTARY FOUNDATION
1560 Sherman Ave.
Evanston, IL 60201
Tel: (847)866-3000
Fax: (847)328-8554
E-mail: jennifer.deters@rotary.org
Web Site: http://www.rotary.org
To further international understanding and friendly relations among people of different countries and geographical areas.
Title of Award: The Rotary Foundation Ambassadorial Scholarships **Area, Field, or Subject:** General studies. **Level of Education for which Award is Granted:** Undergraduate **Funds Available:** No specific amount.
Eligibility Requirements: Applicants must be currently enrolled in a university, college, or institution. **Application Requirements:** Applicants must complete the application form; applicants must provide an essay including a brief autobiography, work experience, and volunteer activities; a detailed statement of intent (not more than three pages); a list of principal interests and activities (not more than one page); applicants must submit a transcript of records. **Deadline for Receipt:** March 1; August 15.

1887 ■ ROWAN BUSINESS ALLIANCE
PO Box 1907
Salisbury, NC 28145-1907
Tel: (704)636-3629
Fax: (704)633-4970
Web Site: http://www.rowanalliance.com
To help young people further their education.
Title of Award: Julian C. Johnston Memorial Scholarships **Area, Field, or Subject:** General Studies. **Level of Education for which Award is Granted:** Undergraduate **Funds Available:** No specific amount.
Eligibility Requirements: Applicants must have demonstrated leadership in school and volunteer community activities or work experience, awards or honors; must have a minimum of 3.0 GPA; must have a minimum SAT score of 910 or ACT composite score of 19; must be of good character. **Application Requirements:** Applicant must submit the following: signed and dated official scholarship award application form; activity sheet; an original letter (no photocopies) from the student, addressed to the RBA Selection Committee, stating why and where he or she intends to further their education and what he or she plans to do upon graduation. Applicant must also submit school transcripts, including SAT and/or ACT scores, class rank, grade point average (and weighted average if available); a written summary to the selection committee of how student plans to pay for his or her total college education; and a photograph. **Additional Information:** JCJ Scholarships are not solely chosen on academic scores or need. Personal interviews are required. **Deadline for Receipt:** March 16.

1888 ■ ROYAL BANK OF CANADA
260 Adelaide St. E
Toronto, ON, Canada M5A 1N1
(866)363-1722
E-mail: 4edu@sympatico.ca
Web Site: http://www.rbcroyalbank.com
To provide scholarship assistance to qualified individuals who wants to pursue their studies.
Title of Award: RBC Royal Bank Scholarships for New Canadians **Area, Field, or Subject:** General studies. **Level of Education for which Award is Granted:** Undergraduate **Number Awarded:** 12. **Funds Available:** $2,000. **Duration:** One year.
Eligibility Requirements: Applicants must be Canadian citizens or permanent residents of Canada; must be in graduating year in Canadian high school or CEGEP; intends to enroll or enter in an accredited Canadian college or university as full-time students; must have achieved at least a 70% average in their previous year of study. **Application Requirements:** Applicants must complete the application form available online; must provide basic contact details, including their email address, phone number, mailing address, and must provide information about their citizenship status, place of birth and year of arrival in Canada; must provide information about their current school, grade average, extracurricular activities and future educational plans. **Deadline for Receipt:** June 8.

1889 ■ ROYAL CANADIAN GOLF ASSOCIATION
1333 Dorval Dr., Ste. 1
Oakville, ON, Canada L6M 4X7
Tel: (905)849-9700
Fax: (905)845-7040
E-mail: ssimmons@rcga.org
Web Site: http://www.rcga.org
To support young golfers who wish to pursue their studies.
Title of Award: Suzanne Beauregard Scholarships **Area, Field, or Subject:** General studies. **Level of Education for which Award is Granted:** Undergraduate **Funds Available:** $1,000. **Duration:** One year.
Eligibility Requirements: Applicants must have completed at least one full year in a post-secondary degree program and show a minimum average of 70%; must be a full-time student at a university, college or CEGEP; must demonstrate a record of athletic and academic excellence; must be a member in good standing of Golf Quebec; must demonstrate regular participation in community and or extracurricular activities. **Application Requirements:** Application forms are available online and must be sent to RCGA, 1333 Dorval Dr., Ste. 1, Oakville, ON L6M 4X7. **Deadline for Receipt:** June 30.

1890 ■ ROYAL CANADIAN GOLF ASSOCIATION
1333 Dorval Dr., Ste. 1
Oakville, ON, Canada L6M 4X7
Tel: (905)849-9700
Fax: (905)845-7040
E-mail: ssimmons@rcga.org
Web Site: http://www.rcga.org
To provide financial assistance to young Canadian men and women.
Title of Award: Canadian Seniors Golf Association Scholarships **Area, Field, or Subject:** General studies. **Level of Education for which Award is Granted:** Undergraduate **Number Awarded:** 4. **Funds Available:** $3,000. **Duration:** One year.
Eligibility Requirements: Applicants must be Canadian men and women who elect to obtain an education and participate in the golf program at a RCGA Foundation-recognized university in Canada; must have successfully completed at least one full year in a post-secondary degree program and show a minimum average of 70% in each year of the program; must have experience in competitive golf at a regional, provincial or national level; must have been accepted at and plan to attend an RCGA Foundation recognized college or university, and must have been named or be becoming named to the institution's golf team. **Application Requirements:** Application forms are available online and must be sent to RCGA, 1333 Dorval Dr., Ste. 1, Oakville, ON L6M 4X7. **Deadline for Receipt:** June 30.

1891 ■ ROYAL CANADIAN GOLF ASSOCIATION
1333 Dorval Dr., Ste. 1
Oakville, ON, Canada L6M 4X7
Tel: (905)849-9700
Fax: (905)845-7040
E-mail: ssimmons@rcga.org
Web Site: http://www.rcga.org
To assist promising Nova Scotia Atlantic Canada men and women to obtain a degree and participate in the golf program at a university.
Title of Award: Connor/Spafford Scholarships **Area, Field, or Subject:** General studies. **Level of Education for which Award is Granted:** Undergraduate **Number Awarded:** 2. **Funds Available:** $5,000. **Duration:** One year.
Eligibility Requirements: Applicants must be a Canadian citizen or a resident in Atlantic Canada; must have successfully completed at least one full year in a postsecondary degree program and have maintained a minimum average of 70%; must have been accepted at a university or college and have been named or will be named to the institution's golf team; must have experience in competitive golf at a regional, provincial or natural level. **Application Requirements:** Application forms are available online and must be sent to RCGA, 1333 Dorval Dr., Ste. 1, Oakville, ON L6M 4X7. **Deadline for Receipt:** June 30.

1892 ■ ROYAL CANADIAN GOLF ASSOCIATION
1333 Dorval Dr., Ste. 1
Oakville, ON, Canada L6M 4X7
Tel: (905)849-9700

Fax: (905)845-7040
E-mail: ssimmons@rcga.org
Web Site: http://www.rcga.org
To provide financial assistance to Canadian women.
Title of Award: Mary Ellen Driscoll Scholarships **Area, Field, or Subject:** General studies. **Level of Education for which Award is Granted:** Undergraduate **Funds Available:** $1,000. **Duration:** One year.
Eligibility Requirements: Applicant must be a female Canadian citizen or a resident in New Brunswick; must have successfully completed at least one full year in a post-secondary degree program at a recognized educational institution; must have been accepted at a university or college and have been named or will be named to the institution's golf team; must have experience in competitive golf at the regional, provincial or national level. **Application Requirements:** Application forms are available online and must be sent to RCGA, 1333 Dorval Dr., Ste. 1, Oakville, ON L6M 4X7. **Deadline for Receipt:** June 30.

1893 ■ ROYAL CANADIAN GOLF ASSOCIATION
1333 Dorval Dr., Ste. 1
Oakville, ON, Canada L6M 4X7
Tel: (905)849-9700
Fax: (905)845-7040
E-mail: ssimmons@rcga.org
Web Site: http://www.rcga.org
To assist promising students towards an undergraduate degree in turfgrass management.
Title of Award: Nu-Gro Corporation Turfgrass Scholarships (Undergraduate) **Area, Field, or Subject:** Turfgrass management. **Level of Education for which Award is Granted:** Undergraduate **Funds Available:** $5,000. **Duration:** One year.
Eligibility Requirements: Applicant must be a student of turfgrass agronomy or turfgrass management; must have completed at least one full year in a postsecondary degree/diploma program at a recognized institution and show a minimum average of 75%; must have experience in the game of golf and a desire to pursue a career in the golf industry; must have participated in community and/or extracurricular activities. **Application Requirements:** Application forms are available online and must be sent to RCGA, 1333 Dorval Dr., Ste. 1, Oakville, ON L6M 4X7. **Deadline for Receipt:** June 30.

1894 ■ ROYAL CANADIAN GOLF ASSOCIATION
1333 Dorval Dr., Ste. 1
Oakville, ON, Canada L6M 4X7
Tel: (905)849-9700
Fax: (905)845-7040
E-mail: ssimmons@rcga.org
Web Site: http://www.rcga.org
To support the Canadian female golfers attending Canadian universities and colleges recognized by the RCGA Foundation.
Title of Award: Marlene Streit Golf Scholarships **Area, Field, or Subject:** General studies. **Level of Education for which Award is Granted:** Undergraduate **Number Awarded:** 2. **Funds Available:** $3,500. **Duration:** One year.
Eligibility Requirements: Applicants must be Canadian female golfers; must have a minimum of 70% in the last two years of high school/CEGEP and have graduated (minimum grade 12). Applicant musts also complete at least one full year in a post-secondary degree program and show a minimum average of 70%; must have experience in competitive golf at a regional, provincial or national level; must have been accepted at an RCGA Foundation recognized college or university, and have been named or will be named to the institution's golf team; must be Canadian citizens or landed immigrants. **Application Requirements:** Application forms are available online and must be sent to RCGA, 1333 Dorval Dr., Ste. 1, Oakville, ON L6M 4X7. **Deadline for Receipt:** June 30.

1895 ■ RURAL TELEPHONE COMPANY
892 W Madison Ave.
Glenns Ferry, ID 83623
Tel: (208)366-2614; 888-366-7821
Fax: (208)366-2615
Web Site: http://www.rtci.net
To provide fund for the education of high school senior whose parents or legal guardian is a subscriber to any of the following Rural Telephone Company services.

Title of Award: Rural Telephone Company Scholarships **Area, Field, or Subject:** General studies. **Level of Education for which Award is Granted:** Undergraduate **Number Awarded:** 7. **Funds Available:** $250, $500 and $1,000.

Eligibility Requirements: Applicants must be high school seniors whose parents or legal guardians are subscribers to any of the following Rural Telephone Company services: Cable, Telephone, Cellular PCS, Wireless Internet or Satellite Internet. **Application Requirements:** Applicants must submit completed scholarship application. **Deadline for Receipt:** May 8. **Additional Information:** susan.case@ruraltelephone.com.

1896 ■ RUSSIAN BROTHERHOOD ORGANIZATION OF THE USA
1733 Spring Garden St.
Philadelphia, PA 19130
Tel: (215)563-2537
Free: 800-726-8721
E-mail: info@rbo.org
Web Site: http://www.rbo.org
To support the education of a student member.

Title of Award: Saints Cyril and Methodius Scholarships **Area, Field, or Subject:** General studies. **Level of Education for which Award is Granted:** Undergraduate **Funds Available:** Depends on the financial need of the student's family. **Duration:** Annually.

Eligibility Requirements: Applicant must be a high school graduate or prep school; hold a Russian Brotherhood Organization life insurance certificate of not less than $3000; and a member of the society in good standing. **Application Requirements:** Applicants must submit a completed application form and send it to SS. Cyril and Methodius Scholarships.

1897 ■ SACHS FOUNDATION
90 S Cascade Ave., Ste. 1410
Colorado Springs, CO 80903
Tel: (719)633-2353
Web Site: http://www.sachsfoundation.org
To provide educational assistance to deserving Colorado black students.

Title of Award: SACHS Foundation Undergraduate Scholarships for Colorado Black Students **Area, Field, or Subject:** General studies. **Level of Education for which Award is Granted:** High School **Funds Available:** $4,000. **Duration:** One year.

Eligibility Requirements: Applicants must be African-American students who are residents of Colorado for a minimum of 5 years; current high school seniors, or those who have graduated not more than 3 years prior to the application and did not or are not currently attending college. **Application Requirements:** Applicants must submit the completed application form; SACHS Foundation financial statement; copy of parents' most recent completed federal tax return including W-2(s), (IRS Form 1040); certified copy of high school grade transcript; three current letters of recommendation from persons not related to them; recent small photograph; and the copy of Colorado enrollment form, which indicates racial category. **Deadline for Receipt:** March 1.

1898 ■ SAFE SCHOOLS COALITION
1002 E Seneca St.
Seattle, WA 98122-4203
Tel: (206)957-1621
Fax: (206)325-2689
Web Site: http://www.safeschoolscoalition.org
To provide financial assistance for students who have a commitment or involvement in AIDS awareness.

Title of Award: AIDS Awareness Scholarships **Area, Field, or Subject:** General studies. **Level of Education for which Award is Granted:** Undergraduate **Funds Available:** No specific amount.

Eligibility Requirements: Applicants must be enrolled at Golden Gate University. **Application Requirements:** Applicants must check the available website for the required materials. **Deadline for Receipt:** April. **Additional Information:** Golden Gate University Financial Aid Office at 536 Mission Street San Francisco, CA 94105 Phone: 1-415-442-7270 Fax: 1-415-442-7807.

1899 ■ SAFE SCHOOLS COALITION
1002 E Seneca St.
Seattle, WA 98122-4203

Tel: (206)957-1621
Fax: (206)325-2689
Web Site: http://www.safeschoolscoalition.org
To provide financial assistance for LGBT undergraduate students.

Title of Award: Albuquerque Lesbian and Gay Chamber of Commerce Scholarships **Area, Field, or Subject:** General studies. **Level of Education for which Award is Granted:** Undergraduate **Number Awarded:** 6. **Funds Available:** $1,000. **Duration:** One year.

Eligibility Requirements: Applicants must be gay or lesbian undergraduate students at the University of New Mexico or the Technical Vocation Institute of Albuquerque and residents of New Mexico for at least one year. **Application Requirements:** Applicants must check the available website for more information. **Deadline for Receipt:** May 15. **Additional Information:** Albuquerque Lesbian & Gay Chamber of Commerce Scholarships PO Box 27207 Albuquerque, NM 87125 Phone: 505-243-6767.

1900 ■ SAFE SCHOOLS COALITION
1002 E Seneca St.
Seattle, WA 98122-4203
Tel: (206)957-1621
Fax: (206)325-2689
Web Site: http://www.safeschoolscoalition.org
To provide financial assistance for students demonstrating service to or achievement in the gay-lesbian community.

Title of Award: Allen (Dan) Memorial Scholarships **Area, Field, or Subject:** General studies. **Level of Education for which Award is Granted:** Undergraduate **Funds Available:** $600.

Eligibility Requirements: Applicants must be enrolled at City College of San Francisco (CA) and have a GPA of 2.5 or better. **Deadline for Receipt:** October 31 for Fall semester and April 1 for Spring semester. **Additional Information:** Safe Schools Coalition at the above address.

1901 ■ SAFE SCHOOLS COALITION
1002 E Seneca St.
Seattle, WA 98122-4203
Tel: (206)957-1621
Fax: (206)325-2689
Web Site: http://www.safeschoolscoalition.org
To support transgendered students by helping them financially by awarding scholarships to transgendered students for the innovative use of technology in their schoolwork.

Title of Award: Apple Scholars **Area, Field, or Subject:** General studies. **Level of Education for which Award is Granted:** Undergraduate **Number Awarded:** 10. **Funds Available:** $2,000.

Eligibility Requirements: Applicants must be high school seniors. **Application Requirements:** Applicants must check the available website for the required materials. **Additional Information:** Recipients will also receive a MacBook Pro and iPod nano. **Deadline for Receipt:** May 30. **Additional Information:** Safe Schools Coalition at the above address.

1902 ■ SAFE SCHOOLS COALITION
1002 E Seneca St.
Seattle, WA 98122-4203
Tel: (206)957-1621
Fax: (206)325-2689
Web Site: http://www.safeschoolscoalition.org
To provide financial support for gay students.

Title of Award: Asian/Pacific Gays and Friends Scholarships **Area, Field, or Subject:** General studies. **Level of Education for which Award is Granted:** Undergraduate **Funds Available:** $1,000.

Eligibility Requirements: Applicants must be male Asian/Pacific Islanders involved in gay community leadership/activities in Southern California (counties of Los Angeles, Orange, Riverside, San Bernardino, Ventura). **Application Requirements:** Applicants must check the available website for the required materials. **Deadline for Receipt:** September 15. **Additional Information:** The Fund for Lesbian and Gay Scholarships PO Box 48320 Los Angeles, CA 90048. Phone: 1-213-650-5752.

1903 ■ SAFE SCHOOLS COALITION
1002 E Seneca St.
Seattle, WA 98122-4203
Tel: (206)957-1621

Fax: (206)325-2689
Web Site: http://www.safeschoolscoalition.org
To provide financial assistance to students demonstrating service to or achievement in the gay, lesbian, bisexual or transgender community.
Title of Award: BIGALA (Bisexual Gay and Lesbian Alliance) Scholarships **Area, Field, or Subject:** General studies. **Level of Education for which Award is Granted:** Undergraduate **Funds Available:** $200 per year.
Eligibility Requirements: Applicants must be enrolled at City College of San Francisco and have a GPA of 3.0 or better. **Application Requirements:** Applicants must check the available website for the required materials. **Additional Information:** Safe Schools Coalition at the above address.

1904 ■ SAFE SCHOOLS COALITION
1002 E Seneca St.
Seattle, WA 98122-4203
Tel: (206)957-1621
Fax: (206)325-2689
Web Site: http://www.safeschoolscoalition.org
To encourage and reward involvement and activism by members of the LGBT community at Duke University.
Title of Award: Carolina's Gay & Lesbian Scholarships **Area, Field, or Subject:** General studies. **Level of Education for which Award is Granted:** Undergraduate **Funds Available:** No specific amount.
Eligibility Requirements: Applicants must be gay, lesbian, bisexual and transgender students from North or South Carolina who are attending Duke University. **Application Requirements:** Applicants must check the available website for the required materials.

1905 ■ SAFE SCHOOLS COALITION
1002 E Seneca St.
Seattle, WA 98122-4203
Tel: (206)957-1621
Fax: (206)325-2689
Web Site: http://www.safeschoolscoalition.org
To provide financial assistance for lesbian, gay, bisexual and transgender (LGBT) Asian and Pacific Islanders (API) who are in the process of applying to or are currently attending a post-secondary institution.
Title of Award: George Choy Memorial/Gay Asian Pacific Alliance (GAPA) Scholarships **Area, Field, or Subject:** General studies. **Level of Education for which Award is Granted:** Undergraduate **Funds Available:** No specific amount.
Eligibility Requirements: Applicants must be an Asian/Pacific Islander graduating from a Bay Area high school (counties of Alameda, Contra Costa, Marin, San Francisco, San Mateo, Santa Clara, Napa, Sonoma and Solano) with a GPA of 3.0 or better. **Application Requirements:** Applicants must check the contact information for inquiries. **Deadline for Receipt:** June 15. **Additional Information:** The Horizons Foundation 870 Market Street, Suite 1155 San Francisco, CA 94102 Phone: 1-415-398-2333.

1906 ■ SAFE SCHOOLS COALITION
1002 E Seneca St.
Seattle, WA 98122-4203
Tel: (206)957-1621
Fax: (206)325-2689
Web Site: http://www.safeschoolscoalition.org
To provide financial support for those who are in need.
Title of Award: College of Marin Gay and Lesbian Student Scholarships **Area, Field, or Subject:** General studies. **Level of Education for which Award is Granted:** Undergraduate **Funds Available:** $250 per year.
Eligibility Requirements: Applicant must be a gay or lesbian student enrolled at the College of Marin. **Application Requirements:** Applicants must check the contact information for inquiries. **Deadline for Receipt:** March. **Additional Information:** College of Marin Foundation Development Office at PO Box 446 Kentfield, CA 94914 Phone: 1-415-485-9382.

1907 ■ SAFE SCHOOLS COALITION
1002 E Seneca St.
Seattle, WA 98122-4203
Tel: (206)957-1621
Fax: (206)325-2689

Web Site: http://www.safeschoolscoalition.org
To sponsor scholarships for deaf lesbian, gay, bisexual, transgender, intersex or queer students who are out about their sexual orientation/identity.
Title of Award: Deaf Queer Youth Scholarships **Area, Field, or Subject:** General studies. **Level of Education for which Award is Granted:** Undergraduate **Funds Available:** $500.
Eligibility Requirements: Applicants must be currently enrolled in high school or college; must be under the age of 25; and must have a minimum 2.5 GPA. US Citizenship is required. **Application Requirements:** Applicants must check the available website for the required materials. **Deadline for Receipt:** July 15. **Additional Information:** Safe Schools Coalition at the above address.

1908 ■ SAFE SCHOOLS COALITION
1002 E Seneca St.
Seattle, WA 98122-4203
Tel: (206)957-1621
Fax: (206)325-2689
Web Site: http://www.safeschoolscoalition.org
To provide financial support for gay, lesbian, bisexual and transgendered students who are in need.
Title of Award: Lee Dubin Scholarship Fund **Area, Field, or Subject:** General studies. **Level of Education for which Award is Granted:** Undergraduate **Number Awarded:** 3-5. **Funds Available:** $1,000.
Eligibility Requirements: Applicants must be children of lesbian, gay, bisexual and transgendered parents and guardians who have worked to affect change in the LGBT community and the community at large. **Application Requirements:** Applicants must check the available website for more information. **Deadline for Receipt:** April 15.

1909 ■ SAFE SCHOOLS COALITION
1002 E Seneca St.
Seattle, WA 98122-4203
Tel: (206)957-1621
Fax: (206)325-2689
Web Site: http://www.safeschoolscoalition.org
To provide financial assistance for graduating high school seniors from Northern and Central California who have promoted understanding of and equality for the lesbian, gay, bisexual, transgender community.
Title of Award: eQuality Scholarships **Area, Field, or Subject:** General studies. **Level of Education for which Award is Granted:** Undergraduate **Funds Available:** $1,500.
Eligibility Requirements: Applicants must be LGBT students. **Application Requirements:** Applicants must check the available website for the required materials.

1910 ■ SAFE SCHOOLS COALITION
1002 E Seneca St.
Seattle, WA 98122-4203
Tel: (206)957-1621
Fax: (206)325-2689
Web Site: http://www.safeschoolscoalition.org
To provide financial assistance for high school seniors who have worked to reduce homophobia and increase awareness and tolerance of gay and lesbian issues.
Title of Award: First Friday Breakfast Club Scholarships **Area, Field, or Subject:** General studies. **Level of Education for which Award is Granted:** Undergraduate **Number Awarded:** 1. **Funds Available:** Maximum of $3,000.
Eligibility Requirements: Applicants must be high school seniors. **Application Requirements:** Applicants must check the available website for the required materials. **Deadline for Receipt:** March 31. **Additional Information:** Safe Schools Coalition at the above address.

1911 ■ SAFE SCHOOLS COALITION
1002 E Seneca St.
Seattle, WA 98122-4203
Tel: (206)957-1621
Fax: (206)325-2689
Web Site: http://www.safeschoolscoalition.org
To provide financial assistance for LGBT students.
Title of Award: Gay and Lesbian Business Association of Santa Barbara Scholarships **Area, Field, or Subject:** General studies. **Level of Educa-

tion for which Award is Granted: Undergraduate **Funds Available:** Varies.

Eligibility Requirements: Applicants must show financial need, academic achievement, community involvement and extracurricular activities. **Application Requirements:** Applicants must check the available website for the required materials. **Deadline for Receipt:** July 1. **Additional Information:** Gay and Lesbian Business Association of Santa Barbara PO Box 90907 Santa Barbara, CA 93190.

1912 ■ SAFE SCHOOLS COALITION

1002 E Seneca St.
Seattle, WA 98122-4203
Tel: (206)957-1621
Fax: (206)325-2689
Web Site: http://www.safeschoolscoalition.org
To provide financial assistance for LGBT students.
Title of Award: Gill Foundation Scholarships (Colorado) **Area, Field, or Subject:** General studies. **Level of Education for which Award is Granted:** Undergraduate **Funds Available:** $2,000. **Duration:** One year.
Eligibility Requirements: Applicants must be gay, lesbian, bisexual or transgendered students attending Colorado colleges. **Application Requirements:** Applicants must check the available website for the required materials. **Additional Information:** For more inquiries just contact your college's financial aid office or Dean of students office.

1913 ■ SAFE SCHOOLS COALITION

1002 E Seneca St.
Seattle, WA 98122-4203
Tel: (206)957-1621
Fax: (206)325-2689
Web Site: http://www.safeschoolscoalition.org
To provide financial support for gay, lesbian, bisexual or transgendered students.
Title of Award: GLSEN Connecticut Chapter Scholarships **Area, Field, or Subject:** General studies. **Level of Education for which Award is Granted:** Undergraduate **Funds Available:** $500.
Eligibility Requirements: Applicant must be a Connecticut resident between 16 and 21 years old. **Application Requirements:** Applicants must check the available website for the required materials. **Deadline for Receipt:** April 15. **Additional Information:** Ronnie Kim G. H. Robertson School 227 Cross Street Coventry, CT 06238.

1914 ■ SAFE SCHOOLS COALITION

1002 E Seneca St.
Seattle, WA 98122-4203
Tel: (206)957-1621
Fax: (206)325-2689
Web Site: http://www.safeschoolscoalition.org
To provide financial assistance for gay, lesbian, bisexual and transgender youth who contribute to the community by improving the environment for GLBT youth.
Title of Award: Bobby Griffith Memorial Scholarships **Area, Field, or Subject:** General studies. **Level of Education for which Award is Granted:** Undergraduate **Funds Available:** No specific amount.
Eligibility Requirements: Applicants must be residents of Contra Costa County and must be graduating seniors. **Application Requirements:** Applicants must check the available website for the required materials. **Additional Information:** Gay, Lesbian and Straight Education Network San Francisco Bay Area Chapter (formerly BANGLE) PO Box 30482 Walnut Creek, CA 94598.

1915 ■ SAFE SCHOOLS COALITION

1002 E Seneca St.
Seattle, WA 98122-4203
Tel: (206)957-1621
Fax: (206)325-2689
Web Site: http://www.safeschoolscoalition.org
To provide financial assistance for students who have been diagnosed with cancer or AIDS or students with physical disabilities.
Title of Award: Jaye Haddad Memorial Fund **Area, Field, or Subject:** General Studies. **Level of Education for which Award is Granted:** Undergraduate **Funds Available:** No specific amount.
Eligibility Requirements: Must be enrolled at UCSD as an undergraduate student. **Application Requirements:** Applicants must check the avail-

able website for the required materials. **Deadline for Receipt:** November 30. **Additional Information:** Safe Schools Coalition at the above address.

1916 ■ SAFE SCHOOLS COALITION

1002 E Seneca St.
Seattle, WA 98122-4203
Tel: (206)957-1621
Fax: (206)325-2689
Web Site: http://www.safeschoolscoalition.org
To provide financial assistance for gay, lesbian, bisexual and transgendered students.
Title of Award: Peter Kaufman Memorial Scholarships **Area, Field, or Subject:** General studies. **Level of Education for which Award is Granted:** Undergraduate **Funds Available:** $1,000. **Duration:** 1 year.
Eligibility Requirements: Program is open to gay, lesbian, bisexual or transgender high school seniors who have worked with the GLBT community. **Application Requirements:** Applicants must check the available website for the required materials. **Additional Information:** Kathy J. Gill, Director Gay & Lesbian Education Commission Los Angeles Unified School District, Room 242 450 N. Grand Avenue Los Angeles, CA 90012 Phone: 1-213-625-6392.

1917 ■ SAFE SCHOOLS COALITION

1002 E Seneca St.
Seattle, WA 98122-4203
Tel: (206)957-1621
Fax: (206)325-2689
Web Site: http://www.safeschoolscoalition.org
To provide financial support for students who are in need.
Title of Award: Bill Kidder Fund Awards **Area, Field, or Subject:** General studies. **Level of Education for which Award is Granted:** Undergraduate **Funds Available:** $1,500.
Eligibility Requirements: Applicants must be enrolled as an undergraduate or graduate student at UNH and demonstrate service to the lesbian, gay, bisexual and transgendered community. **Application Requirements:** Applicants must check the available website for the required materials. **Deadline for Receipt:** April.

1918 ■ SAFE SCHOOLS COALITION

1002 E Seneca St.
Seattle, WA 98122-4203
Tel: (206)957-1621
Fax: (206)325-2689
Web Site: http://www.safeschoolscoalition.org
To provide financial assistance for students showing academic excellence and service to the lesbian, gay and bisexual community, regardless of sexual orientation.
Title of Award: Lambda Alumni (UCLA Lesbian & Gay Alumni Association) Scholarships Program **Area, Field, or Subject:** General studies. **Level of Education for which Award is Granted:** Undergraduate **Funds Available:** $1,000 per year.
Eligibility Requirements: Applicants must demonstrate financial need and be enrolled at UCLA. **Application Requirements:** Applicants must check the available website for the required materials. **Deadline for Receipt:** March. **Additional Information:** UCLA Lambda Alumni Association at PO Box 24075 Los Angeles, CA 90024.

1919 ■ SAFE SCHOOLS COALITION

1002 E Seneca St.
Seattle, WA 98122-4203
Tel: (206)957-1621
Fax: (206)325-2689
Web Site: http://www.safeschoolscoalition.org
To encourage gay men to obtain additional education, aspire to positions in which they contribute to society, be open about their sexual preference and act as role models for other gay men with similar potential.
Title of Award: Jonathan Lax Scholarship Fund for Gay Men **Area, Field, or Subject:** General studies. **Level of Education for which Award is Granted:** Undergraduate **Funds Available:** $20,000 for 1 scholar and $5,000 for multiple scholars.
Eligibility Requirements: Applicants must be gay students. **Application Requirements:** Applicants must check the available website for the required materials.

1920 ■ SAFE SCHOOLS COALITION
1002 E Seneca St.
Seattle, WA 98122-4203
Tel: (206)957-1621
Fax: (206)325-2689
Web Site: http://www.safeschoolscoalition.org
To provide financial assistance for lesbian, gay, bisexual and transgender high school seniors.
Title of Award: LEAGUE Foundation Scholarships **Area, Field, or Subject:** General studies. **Level of Education for which Award is Granted:** Undergraduate **Funds Available:** No specific amount.
Eligibility Requirements: Applicants must be lesbian, gay, bisexual and transgender high school seniors; must have a minimum of 3.0 GPA; and must be actively and substantially involved in community service. **Application Requirements:** Applicants must check the available website for the required materials. **Additional Information:** Scholarships include the Matthew Shepard Memorial Scholarship (name used with permission of the Shepard family), named for the Wyoming college student murdered in 1998 for his sexual orientation, and the Laurel Hester Memorial Scholarship. **Deadline for Receipt:** April.

1921 ■ SAFE SCHOOLS COALITION
1002 E Seneca St.
Seattle, WA 98122-4203
Tel: (206)957-1621
Fax: (206)325-2689
Web Site: http://www.safeschoolscoalition.org
To provide financial assistance for lesbians in New Mexico pursuing higher education.
Title of Award: Lesbians for Change Scholarships **Area, Field, or Subject:** General studies. **Level of Education for which Award is Granted:** Undergraduate **Number Awarded:** 2. **Funds Available:** $500.
Eligibility Requirements: Applicants must be residents of New Mexico involved politically in the lesbian community. **Application Requirements:** Applicants must check the available website for the required materials. **Deadline for Receipt:** June. **Additional Information:** Lesbians for Change PO Box 27664 Albuquerque, NM 87125 Phone: 1-505-292-2219 (Sonia Bettez).

1922 ■ SAFE SCHOOLS COALITION
1002 E Seneca St.
Seattle, WA 98122-4203
Tel: (206)957-1621
Fax: (206)325-2689
Web Site: http://www.safeschoolscoalition.org
To provide scholarships for gay, bisexual and transgender students and allies who have made significant contributions to society by "living out loud" and supporting the LGBT community.
Title of Award: Live Out Loud Annual Scholarships **Area, Field, or Subject:** General studies. **Level of Education for which Award is Granted:** Undergraduate **Number Awarded:** 3. **Funds Available:** $2,500.
Eligibility Requirements: Applicants must be graduating high school seniors and students who deferred attending an educational institution for one year following graduation. **Application Requirements:** Applicants must check the available contact information for inquiries. **Deadline for Receipt:** March 31.

1923 ■ SAFE SCHOOLS COALITION
1002 E Seneca St.
Seattle, WA 98122-4203
Tel: (206)957-1621
Fax: (206)325-2689
Web Site: http://www.safeschoolscoalition.org
To recognize out lesbians, gay, bisexual and transgender students of color who are making significant contributions to their communities by supporting them financially.
Title of Award: Audre Lord Scholarships **Area, Field, or Subject:** General studies. **Level of Education for which Award is Granted:** Graduate, Undergraduate **Funds Available:** $1,000.
Eligibility Requirements: Applicants must be gay and lesbian undergraduate and graduate students of African descent. **Application Requirements:** Applicants must check the contact information for inquiries. **Additional Information:** Zami is Atlanta's premiere organization for lesbians of African descent, and the award's emphasis is on service to the lesbian community. **Deadline for Receipt:** May 15.

1924 ■ SAFE SCHOOLS COALITION
1002 E Seneca St.
Seattle, WA 98122-4203
Tel: (206)957-1621
Fax: (206)325-2689
Web Site: http://www.safeschoolscoalition.org
To provide financial assistance for gay and lesbian undergraduate and graduate students who help enhance the greater society's perception of gay and lesbian people.
Title of Award: Markowski-Leach Scholarships Fund **Area, Field, or Subject:** General studies. **Level of Education for which Award is Granted:** Graduate, Undergraduate **Funds Available:** $1,250. **Duration:** 2 years.
Eligibility Requirements: Applicant must be enrolled as an undergraduate or graduate student at San Francisco State University, the University of California at Berkeley or Stanford University, with a GPA of 2.5 or better. **Application Requirements:** Applicants must check the available website for the required materials. **Deadline for Receipt:** April.

1925 ■ SAFE SCHOOLS COALITION
1002 E Seneca St.
Seattle, WA 98122-4203
Tel: (206)957-1621
Fax: (206)325-2689
Web Site: http://www.safeschoolscoalition.org
To provide recognition and financial assistance for outstanding undergraduate students enrolled or planning to enroll at Penn State University who have demonstrated need for funds to meet their necessary college expenses and who advocate for or contribute to the lesbian, gay, bisexual, transgender (LGBT) community.
Title of Award: Barry H. Marshal Scholarships **Area, Field, or Subject:** General studies. **Level of Education for which Award is Granted:** Undergraduate **Funds Available:** No specific amount.
Eligibility Requirements: Applicants must be undergraduate students at Penn State University. **Application Requirements:** Applicants must check the available website for the required materials.

1926 ■ SAFE SCHOOLS COALITION
1002 E Seneca St.
Seattle, WA 98122-4203
Tel: (206)957-1621
Fax: (206)325-2689
Web Site: http://www.safeschoolscoalition.org
To recognize students who have made a contribution to the gay and lesbian community.
Title of Award: Michael L. Marx and Donald K. Marshall Scholarships **Area, Field, or Subject:** General studies. **Level of Education for which Award is Granted:** Undergraduate **Funds Available:** $1,000.
Eligibility Requirements: Applicants must be enrolled at UCSD at the sophomore, junior, or senior level. **Application Requirements:** Applicants must check the available website for the required materials. **Deadline for Receipt:** February. **Additional Information:** University of California, San Diego Scholarship Office 0013 La Jolla, CA 92093-0013 Phone: 1-619-534-3263.

1927 ■ SAFE SCHOOLS COALITION
1002 E Seneca St.
Seattle, WA 98122-4203
Tel: (206)957-1621
Fax: (206)325-2689
Web Site: http://www.safeschoolscoalition.org
To help San Diego area students achieve their goals of vocational, technical or professional careers.
Title of Award: Harvey Milk/Tom Homann Gay and Lesbian Student Scholarships **Area, Field, or Subject:** General studies. **Level of Education for which Award is Granted:** Undergraduate **Funds Available:** $250-$1,000.
Eligibility Requirements: Program is open to lesbian, gay, bisexual or transgender residents of San Diego County. **Application Requirements:**

Applicants must check the available website for the required materials. **Deadline for Receipt:** June. **Additional Information:** The Harvey Milk/Tom Homann Gay and Lesbian Student Scholarship c/o The Imperial Court de San Diego, Inc. PO Box 33915 San Diego, CA 92163 Phone: 1-619-692-1967 Fax: 1-619-295-7829.

1928 ■ SAFE SCHOOLS COALITION
1002 E Seneca St.
Seattle, WA 98122-4203
Tel: (206)957-1621
Fax: (206)325-2689
Web Site: http://www.safeschoolscoalition.org
To recognize outstanding gay, lesbian, bisexual and transgender youth and friends and to support their continuing education.
Title of Award: Minnesota GLBT Educational Fund **Area, Field, or Subject:** General studies. **Level of Education for which Award is Granted:** Undergraduate **Funds Available:** $1,000-$2,000.
Eligibility Requirements: Applicants must be residents of Minnesota or residents from elsewhere who are attending (or planning to attend) a Minnesota educational institution. **Application Requirements:** Applicants must check the available website for the required materials. **Additional Information:** Awards Committee Minnesota GLBT Educational Fund 1409 Willow St, Suite 305 Minneapolis, MN 55403-3251 Phone: 1-612-870-1806 Fax: 1-612-871-6587.

1929 ■ SAFE SCHOOLS COALITION
1002 E Seneca St.
Seattle, WA 98122-4203
Tel: (206)957-1621
Fax: (206)325-2689
Web Site: http://www.safeschoolscoalition.org
To provide financial assistance for students pursuing higher education from diverse cultural, ethnic, educational and special needs backgrounds.
Title of Award: NYNEX Diversity Scholarship Awards **Area, Field, or Subject:** General studies. **Level of Education for which Award is Granted:** Undergraduate **Funds Available:** $2,500.
Eligibility Requirements: Applicants must reside in the NYNEX service territory. **Application Requirements:** Applicants must check the available website for the required materials. **Additional Information:** For more information, call 1-800-537-4180.

1930 ■ SAFE SCHOOLS COALITION
1002 E Seneca St.
Seattle, WA 98122-4203
Tel: (206)957-1621
Fax: (206)325-2689
Web Site: http://www.safeschoolscoalition.org
To provide financial assistance for a gay, lesbian, bisexual or transgender individual intending to pursue their college education.
Title of Award: Sheldon Oppenheim Memorial Scholarships **Area, Field, or Subject:** General studies. **Level of Education for which Award is Granted:** Undergraduate **Funds Available:** $250-$500.
Eligibility Requirements: Applicants must be identified as GLBT; must register as a matriculated student; and must register for at least 6 credits in a degree or certificate program at RCC. **Application Requirements:** Applicants must submit the following: an essay describing any obstacles they may have overcome, their educational goals; any community service, or special circumstances; two letters of recommendation are optional. **Deadline for Receipt:** June.

1931 ■ SAFE SCHOOLS COALITION
1002 E Seneca St.
Seattle, WA 98122-4203
Tel: (206)957-1621
Fax: (206)325-2689
Web Site: http://www.safeschoolscoalition.org
To provide financial support for students who have dedicated time and energy to the GLBT community and toward GLBT and HIV/AIDS issues.
Title of Award: OSU Gay, Lesbian, Bisexual and Transgender Alumni Society (PFLAG Scholarships) **Area, Field, or Subject:** General studies. **Level of Education for which Award is Granted:** Undergraduate **Funds Available:** No specific amount.
Eligibility Requirements: Applicants should have a minimum GPA of 2.0. **Application Requirements:** Applicants must complete and submit the

application form, accompanied by a letter of recommendation. **Deadline for Receipt:** February. **Additional Information:** Safe Schools Coalition at the above address

1932 ■ SAFE SCHOOLS COALITION
1002 E Seneca St.
Seattle, WA 98122-4203
Tel: (206)957-1621
Fax: (206)325-2689
Web Site: http://www.safeschoolscoalition.org
To provide financial assistance for a student who is making or has made significant contributions to the LGBT community.
Title of Award: Dr. Connell Persico Scholarships **Area, Field, or Subject:** General studies. **Level of Education for which Award is Granted:** Undergraduate **Funds Available:** $2,500.
Eligibility Requirements: Applicants must be students who made significant contributions to the lesbian, gay, bisexual and transgender community. **Application Requirements:** Applicants must check the available website for the required materials. **Additional Information:** Safe Schools Coalition at the above address.

1933 ■ SAFE SCHOOLS COALITION
1002 E Seneca St.
Seattle, WA 98122-4203
Tel: (206)957-1621
Fax: (206)325-2689
Web Site: http://www.safeschoolscoalition.org
To provide financial assistance for LGBT students who are in need.
Title of Award: PFLAG/HATCH Youth Scholarship Foundation **Area, Field, or Subject:** General studies. **Level of Education for which Award is Granted:** Undergraduate **Funds Available:** $2,000 for over 2 years and $10,000 for over 4 years.
Eligibility Requirements: Applicants must be Houston area students or students from outside the Houston area who will attend Houston colleges. **Application Requirements:** Applicants must check the available website for the required materials. **Deadline for Receipt:** May 1. **Additional Information:** PFLAG/HATCH Youth Scholarship Foundation P.O. Box 667010 Houston, TX 77266-7010 Phone: 1-713-467-3524.

1934 ■ SAFE SCHOOLS COALITION
1002 E Seneca St.
Seattle, WA 98122-4203
Tel: (206)957-1621
Fax: (206)325-2689
Web Site: http://www.safeschoolscoalition.org
To provide financial support and hope for meritorious undergraduate, graduate and postgraduate students who are marginalized because of their sexual orientation or gender identity.
Title of Award: Point Foundation Scholarships **Area, Field, or Subject:** General studies. **Level of Education for which Award is Granted:** Graduate, Postgraduate, Undergraduate **Funds Available:** $5,000-$28,000.
Eligibility Requirements: Applicants must be LGBT students with a 3.5 GPA. **Application Requirements:** Applicants must check the available contact information for more inquiries. **Deadline for Receipt:** March 1. **Additional Information:** The Point Foundation PO Box 11210 Chicago, IL 60611 Phone: 1-866-33-POINT (1-866-337-6468) Fax: 1-866-39-POINT (1-866-397-6468).

1935 ■ SAFE SCHOOLS COALITION
1002 E Seneca St.
Seattle, WA 98122-4203
Tel: (206)957-1621
Fax: (206)325-2689
Web Site: http://www.safeschoolscoalition.org
To complement successful academic experiences by providing financial support for student leadership and involvement in the LGBT community at Puget Sound.
Title of Award: Puget Sound LGBT Leadership Scholarships Fund **Area, Field, or Subject:** General studies. **Level of Education for which Award is Granted:** Undergraduate **Funds Available:** $2,000.
Eligibility Requirements: Applicants who identify themselves as lesbian, gay, bisexual, transgender or allies are welcome and eligible for this

award. **Application Requirements:** Applicants must check the available website for the required materials. **Deadline for Receipt:** April.

1936 ■ SAFE SCHOOLS COALITION
1002 E Seneca St.
Seattle, WA 98122-4203
Tel: (206)957-1621
Fax: (206)325-2689
Web Site: http://www.safeschoolscoalition.org
To provide scholarships for individuals who are able to do academic work at the university level and who are part of the progressive movement on the campus and in the community.
Title of Award: Davis Putter Scholarships Fund **Area, Field, or Subject:** General studies. **Level of Education for which Award is Granted:** Undergraduate **Funds Available:** Maximum of $8,000 and may be considerably smaller depending on the applicant's circumstances and the amount of funding available.
Eligibility Requirements: Applicants must be students actively working for peace and justice; must be enrolled in an accredited school and receiving college credit for the time period covered by their grants; and must be living in the United States and planning to enroll in school in the U.S. in order to apply. **Application Requirements:** Applicants must submit a completed application form with a short personal statement, transcripts, letters of support from two people able to evaluate the applicant's current political work, an official financial statement (i.e., FAFSA or SAR), and a passport-like photograph suitable for reproduction. **Deadline for Receipt:** April. **Additional Information:** Safe Schools Coalition at the above address.

1937 ■ SAFE SCHOOLS COALITION
1002 E Seneca St.
Seattle, WA 98122-4203
Tel: (206)957-1621
Fax: (206)325-2689
Web Site: http://www.safeschoolscoalition.org
To provide financial assistance for gay and lesbian high school seniors from Iowa planning to attend an Iowa Board of Regions university (Iowa State, University of Iowa or the University of Northern Iowa).
Title of Award: Matthew Shepard Scholarships **Area, Field, or Subject:** General studies. **Level of Education for which Award is Granted:** Undergraduate **Funds Available:** No specific amount.
Eligibility Requirements: Applicants must be gay and lesbian high school seniors planning to be admitted in an Iowa Board of Regions University. **Application Requirements:** Applicants must check the available website for the required materials. **Deadline for Receipt:** March 31. **Additional Information:** Safe Schools Coalition at the above address.

1938 ■ SAFE SCHOOLS COALITION
1002 E Seneca St.
Seattle, WA 98122-4203
Tel: (206)957-1621
Fax: (206)325-2689
Web Site: http://www.safeschoolscoalition.org
To provide financial assistance for gay and lesbian students or students who have provided service to or worked on behalf of gay and lesbian issues.
Title of Award: Wiggsy Sivertsen Scholarships **Area, Field, or Subject:** General studies. **Level of Education for which Award is Granted:** Undergraduate **Funds Available:** $750.
Eligibility Requirements: Applicants must be enrolled at San Jose State University and demonstrate financial need. **Application Requirements:** Applicants must check the available website for the required materials. **Additional Information:** Dr. Jill Steinberg SJSU Counseling Center Phone: 408-924-5910.

1939 ■ SAFE SCHOOLS COALITION
1002 E Seneca St.
Seattle, WA 98122-4203
Tel: (206)957-1621
Fax: (206)325-2689
Web Site: http://www.safeschoolscoalition.org
To provide financial assistance for self-identified lesbian, gay, bisexual or transgender (LGBT) student-athletes who have enhanced the perception of the LGBT community through contributions and involvement in one or more sports.

Title of Award: Team DC Student-Athlete Scholarships **Area, Field, or Subject:** General studies. **Level of Education for which Award is Granted:** Undergraduate **Funds Available:** $1,500.
Eligibility Requirements: Applicants must be high school seniors in the Washington DC metropolitan area who will be attending an accredited two-year or four-year college or university in the United States with demonstrated academic and athletic excellence as well as potential to serve as a positive LGBT role model. **Application Requirements:** Applicants must check the available contact information for inquiries about the requirements. **Deadline for Receipt:** April 1.

1940 ■ SAFE SCHOOLS COALITION
1002 E Seneca St.
Seattle, WA 98122-4203
Tel: (206)957-1621
Fax: (206)325-2689
Web Site: http://www.safeschoolscoalition.org
To provide financial assistance for children of gay and lesbian families.
Title of Award: Joseph Towner Fund for Gay and Lesbian Families **Area, Field, or Subject:** General studies. **Level of Education for which Award is Granted:** Undergraduate **Funds Available:** There is a maximum award of $500 per term; $1,000 per academic year; With a lifetime maximum of $4,000.
Eligibility Requirements: Applicant must be a postsecondary student with at least one gay or lesbian parent residing in the Bay Area (counties of Alameda, Contra Costa, Marin, San Francisco, San Mateo, Santa Clara, Napa, Sonoma and Solano); must be 25 years old or younger and have a GPA of 2.5 or better. **Application Requirements:** Applicants must check the available contact information for inquiries. **Deadline for Receipt:** June 15. **Additional Information:** The Horizons Foundation 870 Market Street, Suite 1155 San Francisco, CA 94102 Phone: 1-415-398-2333.

1941 ■ SAFE SCHOOLS COALITION
1002 E Seneca St.
Seattle, WA 98122-4203
Tel: (206)957-1621
Fax: (206)325-2689
Web Site: http://www.safeschoolscoalition.org
To provide financial assistance for deserving high school students to further their educational goals.
Title of Award: United Teachers Los Angeles Stonewall Scholarship Fund **Area, Field, or Subject:** General studies. **Level of Education for which Award is Granted:** Undergraduate **Funds Available:** The scholarship amount varies, but is generally $250 to $500.
Eligibility Requirements: Applicants must be students of the Los Angeles Unified School District (LAUSD) or enrolled in a high school completion program. **Application Requirements:** Applicants must check the contact information for inquiries. **Deadline for Receipt:** April. **Additional Information:** Judith Bruner at 3303 Wilshire Blvd., 10th floor Los Angeles, CA 90010 Phone: 1-800-556-8852 or 1-213-487-5560.

1942 ■ SAFE SCHOOLS COALITION
1002 E Seneca St.
Seattle, WA 98122-4203
Tel: (206)957-1621
Fax: (206)325-2689
Web Site: http://www.safeschoolscoalition.org
To provide financial assistance for students with good academic achievement.
Title of Award: University of California LGBT Alumni (UCGALA) scholarships **Area, Field, or Subject:** General studies. **Level of Education for which Award is Granted:** Undergraduate **Funds Available:** No specific amount.
Eligibility Requirements: Applicants must be LGBT alumni at the University of California. **Application Requirements:** Applicants must check the available website for the required materials. **Additional Information:** University of California, Berkeley, Alumni House Berkeley, CA 94720-7450 Phone: 1-510-643-2315.

1943 ■ SAFE SCHOOLS COALITION
1002 E Seneca St.
Seattle, WA 98122-4203

Tel: (206)957-1621
Fax: (206)325-2689
Web Site: http://www.safeschoolscoalition.org
To provide financial assistance for UCI lesbian, gay and bisexual students who contribute in improving the campus environment for other lesbian, gay and bisexual students.
Title of Award: Bruce Wade Memorial Scholarships for Lesbian, Gay and Bisexual **Area, Field, or Subject:** General studies. **Level of Education for which Award is Granted:** Undergraduate **Number Awarded:** 2. **Funds Available:** $1,200.
Eligibility Requirements: Applicants must be enrolled as undergraduate or graduate students at UCI and demonstrate service to the lesbian, gay and bisexual campus community. **Application Requirements:** Applicants must check the available website for the required materials. **Deadline for Receipt:** April. **Additional Information:** Pat Walsh; UCI Lesbian, Gay, Bisexual Resource Center at University of California, Irvine 106 Gateway Commons Irvine, CA 92697 Phone: 1-714-824-3277.

1944 ■ SAFE SCHOOLS COALITION
1002 E Seneca St.
Seattle, WA 98122-4203
Tel: (206)957-1621
Fax: (206)325-2689
Web Site: http://www.safeschoolscoalition.org
To provide financial assistance for LGBT students who are in need.
Title of Award: White Rose Scholarships **Area, Field, or Subject:** General studies. **Level of Education for which Award is Granted:** Undergraduate **Funds Available:** No specific amount.
Eligibility Requirements: Applicants must demonstrate financial need and must have earned a cumulative of 3.0 GPA. **Application Requirements:** Applicants must check the contact information for inquiries. **Deadline for Receipt:** January 15. **Additional Information:** For more information, visit the web site of the Imperial Court of the Rocky Mountain Empire, or write to White Rose Scholarship Foundation, Attn: Scholarship Selection Committee, PO Box 100811, Denver, CO 80250-0811.

1945 ■ SAFE SCHOOLS COALITION
1002 E Seneca St.
Seattle, WA 98122-4203
Tel: (206)957-1621
Fax: (206)325-2689
Web Site: http://www.safeschoolscoalition.org
To provide financial assistance for those who are in need.
Title of Award: Tim Wolfred Scholarships **Area, Field, or Subject:** General studies. **Level of Education for which Award is Granted:** Undergraduate **Funds Available:** $50 based on need.
Eligibility Requirements: Applicants must be students who are taking at least one class in the Gay, Lesbian and Bisexual Studies Department at City College of San Francisco. **Application Requirements:** Applicants must check the available website for the required materials. **Additional Information:** Elaine Mannon, Coordinator, Scholarship Office at City College of San Francisco Batmale Hall, Room 366 50 Phelan Avenue, Box L230 San Francisco, CA 94112 Phone: 1-415-239-3339.

1946 ■ SAINT ANDREW'S SOCIETY OF THE STATE OF NEW YORK
150 E 55 St., Ste. 3
New York, NY 10022
Tel: (212)223-4248
Fax: (212)223-0748
E-mail: office@standrewsny.org
Web Site: http://www.standrewsny.org
To promote cultural interchange and goodwill between Scotland and the United States.
Title of Award: Saint Andrews Scholarships **Area, Field, or Subject:** General studies. **Level of Education for which Award is Granted:** Undergraduate **Funds Available:** $20,000.
Eligibility Requirements: Applicants must be senior undergraduate students who will obtain a Bachelor's degree from an accredited college or university and who can demonstrate the significance of studying in Scotland; must reside or attend school within 250 miles of New York State. **Application Requirements:** Applicants must submit application and letters of reference from appropriate professors.

1947 ■ SAINT PAUL UNIVERSITY CANADA
223 Main St.
Ottawa, ON, Canada K1S 1C4
Tel: (613)236-1393
Free: 800-637-6859
E-mail: info@ustpaul.ca
Web Site: http://www.ustpaul.ca
To provide educational assistance for the students of Saint Paul University.
Title of Award: Saint Paul University Excellence Scholarships **Area, Field, or Subject:** General studies. **Level of Education for which Award is Granted:** Undergraduate **Number Awarded:** 8. **Funds Available:** $1,000.
Eligibility Requirements: Program is open to all students in Saint Paul University. **Application Requirements:** Applicants must submit a request for scholarships to a national council. **Deadline for Receipt:** May 1 and September 30. **Additional Information:** Saint Paul University at the above address.

1948 ■ SAINT PAUL UNIVERSITY CANADA
223 Main St.
Ottawa, ON, Canada K1S 1C4
Tel: (613)236-1393
Free: 800-637-6859
E-mail: info@ustpaul.ca
Web Site: http://www.ustpaul.ca
To provide educational assistance for all students in Saint Paul University.
Title of Award: Saint Paul University Financial Aid Brasseries **Area, Field, or Subject:** General studies. **Level of Education for which Award is Granted:** Undergraduate **Funds Available:** No specific amount.
Eligibility Requirements: Applicants must be full-time students enrolled in a program of 1st, 2nd and 3rd cycles of Saint Paul University. Bursaries are offered to Canadian citizens, permanent residents and foreign students alike. **Application Requirements:** Applicants may get an application form six weeks before the deadline at the Scholarships Office or at the Saint Paul University website. **Deadline for Receipt:** May 1. **Additional Information:** Saint Paul University Scholarships Office, room 150-A, Guigues Hall.

1949 ■ SALLIE MAE FUND
12061 Bluemont Way
Reston, VA 20190
Tel: (703)533-4834
Web Site: http://www.salliemaefund.org
To assist African-American students with financial need.
Title of Award: American Dream Scholarship Program **Area, Field, or Subject:** General studies. **Level of Education for which Award is Granted:** Undergraduate **Funds Available:** $500-$5,000.
Eligibility Requirements: Applicant must be a U.S. citizen; with a GPA of 2.5 on a 4.0 scale; meet the criteria of Pell Grant eligibility; must be enrolled full-time at an accredited, undergraduate institution. **Application Requirements:** Applicants must apply online at www.salliemaefund.org. **Additional Information:** In partnership with the United Negro College Fund. **Deadline for Receipt:** April 15.

1950 ■ SALLIE MAE FUND
12061 Bluemont Way
Reston, VA 20190
Tel: (703)533-4834
Web Site: http://www.salliemaefund.org
To help finance first in the family Hispanic American students pursue their college education.
Title of Award: First in My Family Scholarship Program **Area, Field, or Subject:** General studies. **Level of Education for which Award is Granted:** Undergraduate **Funds Available:** $500-$5,000.
Eligibility Requirements: Applicants must be U.S. citizen Hispanic Americans; have a GPA of 3.0 on a 4.0 scale; must be enrolled as full-time undergraduates at accredited institutions. **Application Requirements:** Applicants must mail an official transcript; proof of family income and citizenship status. Submit online: a letter of recommendation; resume; an essay. A Financial Aid Verification is needed for applicants chosen as finalists. **Additional Information:** In partnership with the Hispanic College

Fund. **Deadline for Receipt:** April 15. **Additional Information:** Hispanic College Fund 1301 K St. NW, Ste. 450-A West Washington, DC 20005, Telephone: 800-644-4223.

1951 ■ SALLIE MAE FUND
12061 Bluemont Way
Reston, VA 20190
Tel: (703)533-4834
Web Site: http://www.salliemaefund.org
To assist in the financial needs of children of the victims of the September 11, 2001 terrorist attack.

Title of Award: The Sallie Mae 911 Education Fund **Area, Field, or Subject:** General studies. **Level of Education for which Award is Granted:** Undergraduate **Funds Available:** $2,500. **Duration:** One school year.

Eligibility Requirements: Applicant must be a dependent of a September 11, 2001 victim; must be enrolled full-time and having a satisfactory academic process at: a Public two years, or a Private/Proprietary two years, or a Public or Public four years. **Application Requirements:** Applicants must complete an application form available at the website (www.salliemaefund.org) and submit to the Financial Aid Director of the applicant's school. Mail completed applications to: The Sallie Mae 911 Educational Fund Scholarship Program c/o The Community foundation for the National Capital Region 1201 15th St. NW, Ste. 420 Washington, DC 20005. **Deadline for Receipt:** May 15.

1952 ■ SALLIE MAE FUND
12061 Bluemont Way
Reston, VA 20190
Tel: (703)533-4834
Web Site: http://www.salliemaefund.org
To support students with more than $1,000 short of financial need.

Title of Award: Unmet Need Scholarships **Area, Field, or Subject:** General studies. **Level of Education for which Award is Granted:** Undergraduate **Funds Available:** $1,000-$3,800.

Eligibility Requirements: Applicant must be a U.S. citizen; must have a $30,000 or less family adjusted gross income; have a GPA of 2.5 on a 4.0 scale or minimum 42 GED average test score; a high school senior or graduate or a student enrolled as a full-time undergraduate in an accredited post secondary institution; must demonstrate unmet financial need of at least $1,000 after the financial aid award package has been determined. **Application Requirements:** Applicants must complete an application form available at the website www.salliemaefund.org and mail it together with: current, complete transcript of grades (Official transcript of grades; or unofficial transcript that includes that student and school's name; or Student-generated online transcript that includes that student name, school name, grade and credit hours earned for each course, and term in which each course was taken; or GED test score results); Student Aid Report (SAR) or Institutional Student Information Report (ISIR) (Complete SAR Print Summary from the FAFSA website; or student copy of the complete SAR; or school's complete ISIR). The application and all documents must be mailed in one envelope to: Scholarship America The Sallie Mae Fund Unmet Need Scholarship Program One Scholarship Way, PO Box 297 Saint Peter, MN 56082. **Deadline for Receipt:** May 31. **Additional Information:** 507-931-1682.

1953 ■ SALLIE MAE FUND
12061 Bluemont Way
Reston, VA 20190
Tel: (703)533-4834
Web Site: http://www.salliemaefund.org
To focus on the importance of developing good writing skills.

Title of Award: Writers of Passage Scholarship Program **Area, Field, or Subject:** General studies. **Level of Education for which Award is Granted:** Undergraduate **Funds Available:** $5,000 for the recipient and $20,000 grant to the winner's university.

Eligibility Requirements: Applicant must be an enrolled full-time undergraduate at a Historically Black College or University (HBCU) or Predominantly Black College (PBI); must demonstrate financial need as defined by the applicant's college or university; have a minimum GPA of 2.5 on a 4.0 scale; must have filed the Free Application for Federal Student Aid (FAFSA) at www.fafsa.ed.gov. **Application Requirements:** Applicants must complete and submit the application form available at the

website www.nafeo.org/home.php; Certification and Authorization Form; "Writers of Passage" essay; transcripts (college transcripts for students who have completed one or more semesters of post-secondary education); copy of complete academic year Student Aid report (SAR). All documents must be in an envelope and mailed to: The "Writers of Passage" Essay Competition National Association for Equal Opportunity in Higher Education (NAFEO) 209 Third Street, SE Washington, DC 20003. **Additional Information:** In partnership with the National Association for Equal Opportunity in Higher Education (NAFEO). **Deadline for Receipt:** February 1. **Additional Information:** Rachel Cooke (202)552-3300 email: rcooke@nafeo.org.

1954 ■ THE SAN DIEGO FOUNDATION
2508 Historic Decatur Rd., Ste. 200
San Diego, CA 92106
Tel: (619)235-2300
Fax: (619)239-1710
E-mail: info@sdfoundation.org
Web Site: http://www.sdfoundation.org
To support the education of students from California.

Title of Award: 92109 Community Fund-Mark and Karla Stuart Family Scholarships **Area, Field, or Subject:** General studies. **Level of Education for which Award is Granted:** Undergraduate **Number Awarded:** To be determined. **Funds Available:** No specific amount.

Eligibility Requirements: Applicant must be a resident of San Diego County (military personnel and dependents are exempt); must be a citizen or legal resident of the United States; must attend an accredited two-year college, four-year university or licensed trade and vocational school in the U.S.; must be a full-time student (unless otherwise noted); must have a measure of academic and civic achievement; must be of good moral and personal character; must be a graduate from Mission Bay High School, San Diego, CA; have a minimum 3.0 GPA on a 4.0 scale; and committed in serving the community through involvement in community service, church or extra-curricular activities. **Application Requirements:** Applicants must submit a completed Common Scholarship Application together with personal statement; two letters of recommendation on official letterhead (written within the last six months); official transcript in an official and sealed envelope; and a copy of 2006 or most recent tax form (Form 1040-pages 1 & 2; Form 1040A-pages 1 & 2; Form 1040EZ-page 1). **Deadline for Receipt:** January 28. **Additional Information:** Arzo Mansury, Dir. Scholarships at 619-814-1343, or scholarships@sdfoundation.org.

1955 ■ THE SAN DIEGO FOUNDATION
2508 Historic Decatur Rd., Ste. 200
San Diego, CA 92106
Tel: (619)235-2300
Fax: (619)239-1710
E-mail: info@sdfoundation.org
Web Site: http://www.sdfoundation.org
To support the education of students from California.

Title of Award: After-the-Fires Scholarships **Area, Field, or Subject:** General studies. **Level of Education for which Award is Granted:** Undergraduate **Number Awarded:** To be determined. **Funds Available:** $500-$2500.

Eligibility Requirements: Applicant must be a resident of San Diego County (military personnel and dependents are exempt); a citizen or legal resident of the United States; attend an accredited two-year college, four-year university or licensed trade and vocational school in the U.S.; a full-time student (unless otherwise noted); have a measure of academic and civic achievement; be of good moral and personal character; have a minimum 2.50 GPA on a 4.0 scale; demonstrated financial need; and lost homes and/or source of income in the 2007 wildfires. **Application Requirements:** Applicants must submit a completed Common Scholarship Application together with personal statement; two letters of recommendation on official letterhead (written within the last six months); official transcript in an official and sealed envelope; copy of most recent tax form (Form 1040-pages 1 & 2; Form 1040A-pages 1 & 2; Form 1040EZ-page 1); and a formal documentation or a letter on official letterhead from FEMA (insurance company), or high school/college guidance counselor/principal indicating the loss of home in the 2007 wildfires and/or a letter from employer indicating loss of income. **Deadline for Receipt:** January 28. **Additional Information:** Arzo Mansury, Dir. Scholarships at 619-814-1343, or scholarships@sdfoundation.org

1956 ■ THE SAN DIEGO FOUNDATION
2508 Historic Decatur Rd., Ste. 200
San Diego, CA 92106
Tel: (619)235-2300
Fax: (619)239-1710
E-mail: info@sdfoundation.org
Web Site: http://www.sdfoundation.org
To support the education of students from California.
Title of Award: ARREOLA/CBSPM Scholarships **Area, Field, or Subject:** General studies. **Level of Education for which Award is Granted:** Undergraduate **Number Awarded:** 2. **Funds Available:** $1,000.
Eligibility Requirements: Applicant must be a graduating senior from Montgomery and Southwest high schools in the Sweetwater Union High School District; have a minimum 3.25 GPA on a 4.0 scale; planning to attend an accredited two-year college, four-year university, or licensed trade/vocational school in the U.S.; have demonstrated financial need and strong commitment to contribute to the community as demonstrated by the involvement in extra-curricular/church activities, or work/volunteer experience. **Application Requirements:** Applicants must submit a completed Common Scholarship Application together with personal statement; two letters of recommendation on official letterhead (written within the last six months); official transcript in an official and sealed envelope; and a copy of most recent tax form (Form 1040-pages 1 & 2; Form 1040Apages 1 & 2; Form 1040EZ-page 1). **Deadline for Receipt:** January 28. **Additional Information:** Arzo Mansury, Dir. Scholarships at 619-814-1343, or scholarships@sdfoundation.org.

1957 ■ THE SAN DIEGO FOUNDATION
2508 Historic Decatur Rd., Ste. 200
San Diego, CA 92106
Tel: (619)235-2300
Fax: (619)239-1710
E-mail: info@sdfoundation.org
Web Site: http://www.sdfoundation.org
To support the education of students from California.
Title of Award: William and Lucille Ash Scholarships **Area, Field, or Subject:** General studies. **Level of Education for which Award is Granted:** Undergraduate **Number Awarded:** 3. **Funds Available:** $1,000-$5,000.
Eligibility Requirements: Applicant must be an adult re-entry student; have a minimum 3.0 GPA on a 4.0 scale; demonstrated financial need; planning to attend an accredited two-year college, four-year university, or licensed trade/vocational school in the state of California; and employed (minimum part-time) and involved in serving the community as demonstrated by involvement in extra-curricular activities, community/church service, or work experience. **Application Requirements:** Applicants must submit a completed Common Scholarship Application together with personal statement; two letters of recommendation on official letterhead (written within the last six months); official transcript in an official and sealed envelope; a copy of most recent tax form (Form 1040-pages 1 & 2; Form 1040A-pages 1 & 2; Form 1040EZ-page 1); a letter from the applicant's workplace supervisor, on official letterhead, verifying employment, either part-time or full-time (letter must title, job responsibilities, and the length of time have been employed). If the applicant have been in the foster care system, include a letter of recommendation from social worker indicating that the applicant have been in foster care. **Deadline for Receipt:** January 28. **Additional Information:** Arzo Mansury, Dir. Scholarships at 619-814-1343, or scholarships@sdfoundation.org.

1958 ■ THE SAN DIEGO FOUNDATION
2508 Historic Decatur Rd., Ste. 200
San Diego, CA 92106
Tel: (619)235-2300
Fax: (619)239-1710
E-mail: info@sdfoundation.org
Web Site: http://www.sdfoundation.org
To support the education of students from California.
Title of Award: Frank H. Ault Scholarships **Area, Field, or Subject:** Accounting. **Level of Education for which Award is Granted:** Undergraduate **Number Awarded:** 6. **Funds Available:** $1,500 each.
Eligibility Requirements: Applicant must be a graduating high school student or junior college student; planning to major in accounting or finance at an accredited four-year university; or a current college student (sophomore, junior, or senior year) have declared a major in finance or accounting. Students must minimum 3.0 GPA on a 4.0 scale; and have participated in extra-curricular or community service activities. **Application Requirements:** Applicants must submit a completed Common Scholarship Application together with personal statement; two letters of recommendation on official letterhead (written within the last six months); official transcript in an official and sealed envelope; and copy of most recent tax form (Form 1040-pages 1 & 2; Form 1040A-pages 1 & 2; Form 1040EZ-page 1). **Deadline for Receipt:** January 28. **Additional Information:** Arzo Mansury, Dir. Scholarships at 619-814-1343, or scholarships@sdfoundation.org.

1959 ■ THE SAN DIEGO FOUNDATION
2508 Historic Decatur Rd., Ste. 200
San Diego, CA 92106
Tel: (619)235-2300
Fax: (619)239-1710
E-mail: info@sdfoundation.org
Web Site: http://www.sdfoundation.org
To support the education of students from California.
Title of Award: Ballard Family Foundation Scholarships **Area, Field, or Subject:** General studies. **Level of Education for which Award is Granted:** Undergraduate **Number Awarded:** 4. **Funds Available:** $1000. **Duration:** One year.
Eligibility Requirements: Applicant must be a student between the ages of 17-25; have been in foster care; have demonstrated financial need; have a minimum high school GPA of 2.50 on a 4.0 scale or a 2.75 college GPA on a 4.0 scale; and be attending an accredited four-year university, two-year college or licensed trade/vocational school in the U.S. **Application Requirements:** Applicants must submit a completed Common Scholarship Application together with personal statement; two letters of recommendation on official letterhead (written within the last six months); official transcript in an official and sealed envelope; and a letter of recommendation from the applicant's social worker indicating the applicant is or has been in foster care. **Deadline for Receipt:** January 28. **Additional Information:** Arzo Mansury, Dir. Scholarships at 619-814-1343, or scholarships@sdfoundation.org.

1960 ■ THE SAN DIEGO FOUNDATION
2508 Historic Decatur Rd., Ste. 200
San Diego, CA 92106
Tel: (619)235-2300
Fax: (619)239-1710
E-mail: info@sdfoundation.org
Web Site: http://www.sdfoundation.org
To support the education of students from California.
Title of Award: Ray and Mary Bell Memorial Scholarships **Area, Field, or Subject:** General studies. **Level of Education for which Award is Granted:** Undergraduate **Number Awarded:** 1. **Funds Available:** $1,000.
Eligibility Requirements: Applicant must be a graduating high school senior from Fallbrook High School in Fallbrook, CA; will attend an accredited two-year college or four-year university in the U.S; have a minimum 3.0 GPA on a 4.0 scale; and have a commitment to serving the community through involvement in community service, church or extra-curricular activities. **Application Requirements:** Applicants must submit a completed Common Scholarship Application together with personal statement; two letters of recommendation on official letterhead (written within the last six months); official transcript in an official and sealed envelope; and a copy of most recent tax form (Form 1040-pages 1 & 2; Form 1040A-pages 1 & 2; Form 1040EZ-page 1); and an essay (maximum one page, typed, double-spaced) describing the world the applicant came from. **Deadline for Receipt:** January 28. **Additional Information:** Arzo Mansury, Dir. Scholarships at 619-814-1343, or scholarships@sdfoundation.org.

1961 ■ THE SAN DIEGO FOUNDATION
2508 Historic Decatur Rd., Ste. 200
San Diego, CA 92106
Tel: (619)235-2300
Fax: (619)239-1710
E-mail: info@sdfoundation.org

Web Site: http://www.sdfoundation.org
To support the education of students from California.

Title of Award: James R. and Geraldine F. Bertelsen Scholarships **Area, Field, or Subject:** General studies. **Level of Education for which Award is Granted:** Undergraduate **Number Awarded:** 3. **Funds Available:** Minimum of $5,000.

Eligibility Requirements: Applicant must be a practicing Roman Catholic who is: a graduating high school senior who has applied to, been accepted by, and will attend a four-year Roman Catholic college/university in the U.S.; or a student currently enrolled at a Catholic college/university in the U.S. Student must be resident of Carlsbad, CA for a minimum of one full year and be enrolling in or currently be enrolled in a course of instruction that will enable to obtain an undergraduate degree within four years. Student in senior year of college, who will graduate early and not complete a full academic year, are not eligible. **Application Requirements:** Applicants must submit a completed Common Scholarship Application together with personal statement; two letters of recommendation on official letterhead (written within the last six months); official transcript in an official and sealed envelope; copy of 2006 or most recent taxes (Form 1040-pages 1 & 2; Form 1040A-pages 1 & 2; Form 1040EZ -page 1); a letter of recommendation on official letterhead from the applicant's parish priest, deacon or other church official who can verify the applicant is a practicing Catholic; and a form verifying Carlsbad residency for each period of 2006 and 2007, or 2007 and 2008 (utility bills, insurance forms, etc.). **Deadline for Receipt:** January 28. **Additional Information:** Arzo Mansury, Dir. Scholarships at 619-814-1343, or scholarships@sdfoundation.org.

1962 ■ THE SAN DIEGO FOUNDATION
2508 Historic Decatur Rd., Ste. 200
San Diego, CA 92106
Tel: (619)235-2300
Fax: (619)239-1710
E-mail: info@sdfoundation.org
Web Site: http://www.sdfoundation.org
To support the education of students from California.

Title of Award: Dorothy M. Bolyard Memorial Scholarships **Area, Field, or Subject:** General studies. **Level of Education for which Award is Granted:** Undergraduate **Number Awarded:** 5. **Funds Available:** $1,000.

Eligibility Requirements: Applicant must be a San Diego resident (age 25 years and older); pursuing a degree at an accredited two-year college or four-year university in San Diego County; have a minimum 3.0 GPA on a 4.0 scale; and demonstrated financial need. **Application Requirements:** Applicants must submit a completed Common Scholarship Application together with personal statement; two letters of recommendation on official letterhead (written within the last six months); official transcript in an official and sealed envelope; and copy of most recent tax form (Form 1040-pages 1 & 2; Form 1040A-pages 1 & 2; Form 1040EZ-page 1). **Deadline for Receipt:** January 28. **Additional Information:** Arzo Mansury, Dir. Scholarships at 619-814-1343, or scholarships@sdfoundation.org.

1963 ■ THE SAN DIEGO FOUNDATION
2508 Historic Decatur Rd., Ste. 200
San Diego, CA 92106
Tel: (619)235-2300
Fax: (619)239-1710
E-mail: info@sdfoundation.org
Web Site: http://www.sdfoundation.org
To support the education of students from California.

Title of Award: Breslauer Family Scholarships **Area, Field, or Subject:** General studies. **Level of Education for which Award is Granted:** Undergraduate **Number Awarded:** 4. **Funds Available:** $500-$750.

Eligibility Requirements: Applicant must be a graduating senior from San Diego High School in downtown San Diego; have a minimum 3.0 GPA on a 4.0 scale; demonstrated financial needs; planning to attend an accredited four-year university in the U.S. **Application Requirements:** Applicants must submit a completed Common Scholarship Application together with personal statement; two letters of recommendation on official letterhead (written within the last six months); official transcript in an official and sealed envelope; and copy of 2006 or most recent tax form (Form 1040-pages 1 & 2; Form 1040A-pages 1 & 2; Form 1040EZ-page

1). **Deadline for Receipt:** January 28. **Additional Information:** Arzo Mansury, Dir. Scholarships at 619-814-1343, or scholarships@sdfoundation.org.

1964 ■ THE SAN DIEGO FOUNDATION
2508 Historic Decatur Rd., Ste. 200
San Diego, CA 92106
Tel: (619)235-2300
Fax: (619)239-1710
E-mail: info@sdfoundation.org
Web Site: http://www.sdfoundation.org
To support the education of students from California.

Title of Award: Louise A. Broderick San Diego County Scholarships **Area, Field, or Subject:** General studies. **Level of Education for which Award is Granted:** Undergraduate **Number Awarded:** 2. **Funds Available:** $2,000.

Eligibility Requirements: Applicant must be a single parent with dependent children who are re-entering college or are already in college. Applicants must have a minimum 2.0 GPA on a 4.0 scale; demonstrated financial need; and plan to attend a two-year community college, four-year university, or trade and vocational school. **Application Requirements:** Applicants must submit a completed Common Scholarship Application together with personal statement; two letters of recommendation on official letterhead (written within the last six months); official transcript in an official and sealed envelope; and a copy of most recent tax form (Form 1040-pages 1 & 2; Form 1040A-pages 1 & 2; Form 1040EZ-page 1). **Deadline for Receipt:** January 28. **Additional Information:** Arzo Mansury, Dir. Scholarships at 619-814-1343, or scholarships@sdfoundation.org.

1965 ■ THE SAN DIEGO FOUNDATION
2508 Historic Decatur Rd., Ste. 200
San Diego, CA 92106
Tel: (619)235-2300
Fax: (619)239-1710
E-mail: info@sdfoundation.org
Web Site: http://www.sdfoundation.org
To support the education of students from California.

Title of Award: Cheerful Giver Scholarships **Area, Field, or Subject:** General studies. **Level of Education for which Award is Granted:** Undergraduate **Funds Available:** No specific amount.

Eligibility Requirements: Applicant must be a graduating high school senior, a child of a single parent; or a child of parents who serve the community (pastor, church staff, teacher/educator, police officer, firefighter, military, etc.). Students must have a minimum 2.0 GPA and plan to attend an accredited four-year university in the U.S. **Application Requirements:** Applicants must submit a completed Scholarship Application together with a typed personal statement (maximum of two pages); a copy of transcripts; and a copy of most recent tax form (Form 1040-pages 1 & 2; Form 1040A-pages 1 & 2; Form 1040EZpage 1). **Deadline for Receipt:** March 10. **Additional Information:** scholarships@sdfoundation.org.

1966 ■ THE SAN DIEGO FOUNDATION
2508 Historic Decatur Rd., Ste. 200
San Diego, CA 92106
Tel: (619)235-2300
Fax: (619)239-1710
E-mail: info@sdfoundation.org
Web Site: http://www.sdfoundation.org
To support the education of students from California.

Title of Award: The Club at Morningside Scholarships **Area, Field, or Subject:** General studies. **Level of Education for which Award is Granted:** Undergraduate **Funds Available:** No specific amount.

Eligibility Requirements: Applicant must be a graduating high school senior, student already in college, or planning to attend an accredited two-year college, four-year university, graduate school, or licensed trade/vocational school in the U.S. High school senior and student currently enrolled in school must have a cumulative GPA of 2.50 or higher on a 4.0 scale. **Application Requirements:** Applicants must submit a completed Scholarship Application together with a typed personal statement (maximum of two pages); two letters or recommendation on official letterhead; official transcripts in a sealed envelope; a copy of most recent tax form (Form 1040-pages 1 & 2; Form 1040A-pages 1 & 2; Form 1040EZ-page 1); and a letter verifying the applicants or applicant's parent(s) are employed by The Club at Morningside. **Deadline for Receipt:** January 28. **Additional Information:** Arzo Mansury, Dir. Scholarships at 619-814-1343, or scholarships@sdfoundation.org.

1967 ■ THE SAN DIEGO FOUNDATION

2508 Historic Decatur Rd., Ste. 200
San Diego, CA 92106
Tel: (619)235-2300
Fax: (619)239-1710
E-mail: info@sdfoundation.org
Web Site: http://www.sdfoundation.org
To support the education of students from California.
Title of Award: Madison and Edith Cooper Scholarships **Area, Field, or Subject:** General studies. **Level of Education for which Award is Granted:** Undergraduate **Number Awarded:** 10. **Funds Available:** $1,000.
Eligibility Requirements: Applicant must be young adult in San Diego County (to age 24); have been in the foster care system; planning to attend an accredited two-year college, four-year university, or licensed trade/vocational school in the U.S.; have a minimum 2.50 GPA on a 4.0 scale; demonstrated financial need; and involved in serving the community through extra-curricular activities, community service, or work experience. **Application Requirements:** Applicants must submit a completed Common Scholarship Application together with personal statement; two letters of recommendation on official letterhead (written within the last six months); official transcript in an official and sealed envelope; a copy of most recent tax form (Form 1040-pages 1 & 2; Form 1040A-pages 1 & 2; Form 1040EZ-page 1); and a letter of recommendation on official letterhead from a social worker indicating that the applicant have been in foster care. **Deadline for Receipt:** January 28. **Additional Information:** Arzo Mansury, Dir. Scholarships at 619-814-1343, or scholarships@sdfoundation.org.

1968 ■ THE SAN DIEGO FOUNDATION

2508 Historic Decatur Rd., Ste. 200
San Diego, CA 92106
Tel: (619)235-2300
Fax: (619)239-1710
E-mail: info@sdfoundation.org
Web Site: http://www.sdfoundation.org
To support the education of students from California.
Title of Award: Crawford Scholarships **Area, Field, or Subject:** General studies. **Level of Education for which Award is Granted:** Undergraduate **Number Awarded:** 12. **Funds Available:** $4,000 each.
Eligibility Requirements: Applicant must be a graduating senior from the Crawford Educational Complex; have a minimum 2.50 GPA on a 4.0 scale; planning to attend an accredited two-year college or four-year university in the U.S.; have demonstrated financial need; and engaged in the community through involvement in extra-curricular/church/volunteer activities or work experience. **Application Requirements:** Applicants must submit a completed Common Scholarship Application together with personal statement; two letters of recommendation on official letterhead (written within the last six months); official transcript in an official and sealed envelope; and copy of 2006 or most recent tax form (Form 1040-pages 1 & 2; Form 1040A-pages 1 & 2; Form 1040EZ-page 1). **Deadline for Receipt:** January 28. **Additional Information:** Arzo Mansury, Dir. Scholarships at 619-814-1343, or scholarships@sdfoundation.org.

1969 ■ THE SAN DIEGO FOUNDATION

2508 Historic Decatur Rd., Ste. 200
San Diego, CA 92106
Tel: (619)235-2300
Fax: (619)239-1710
E-mail: info@sdfoundation.org
Web Site: http://www.sdfoundation.org
To support the education of students from California.
Title of Award: Daddy Longlegs Scholarships **Area, Field, or Subject:** General studies. **Level of Education for which Award is Granted:** Undergraduate **Number Awarded:** 4. **Funds Available:** $500-$2,000.
Eligibility Requirements: Applicant must be a young adult in San Diego County (to age 25) who have been in foster care; planning to attend an accredited two-year college, four-year university, or licensed trade/

vocational school in the U.S.; have a minimum 2.0 GPA on a 4.0 scale; and demonstrated financial need. **Application Requirements:** Applicants must submit a completed Common Scholarship Application together with personal statement; two letters of recommendation on official letterhead (written within the last six months); official transcript in an official and sealed envelope; copy of most recent tax form (Form 1040-pages 1 & 2; Form 1040A-pages 1 & 2; Form 1040EZ-page 1); and a letter of recommendation on official letterhead from the applicant's social worker indicating he/she is currently or has been in the foster care system. **Deadline for Receipt:** January 28. **Additional Information:** Arzo Mansury, Dir. Scholarships at 619-814-1343, or scholarships@sdfoundation.org.

1970 ■ THE SAN DIEGO FOUNDATION

2508 Historic Decatur Rd., Ste. 200
San Diego, CA 92106
Tel: (619)235-2300
Fax: (619)239-1710
E-mail: info@sdfoundation.org
Web Site: http://www.sdfoundation.org
To support the education of students from California.
Title of Award: Davis Family Scholarships **Area, Field, or Subject:** General studies. **Level of Education for which Award is Granted:** Undergraduate **Number Awarded:** 3. **Funds Available:** $1,000.
Eligibility Requirements: Applicant must be a graduating Latino high school senior from a San Diego County public school; planning to attend an accredited four-year public university in the state of California; have demonstrated financial need; and have an unweighted GPA between 3.00 to 3.50 GPA on a 4.0 scale. **Application Requirements:** Applicants must submit a completed Common Scholarship Application together with personal statement; two letters of recommendation on official letterhead (written within the last six months); official transcript in an official and sealed envelope; and copy of 2006 or most recent tax (Form 1040-pages 1 & 2; Form 1040A-pages 1 & 2; Form 1040EZ-page 1). **Deadline for Receipt:** January 28. **Additional Information:** Arzo Mansury, Dir. Scholarships at 619-814-1343, or scholarships@sdfoundation.org.

1971 ■ THE SAN DIEGO FOUNDATION

2508 Historic Decatur Rd., Ste. 200
San Diego, CA 92106
Tel: (619)235-2300
Fax: (619)239-1710
E-mail: info@sdfoundation.org
Web Site: http://www.sdfoundation.org
To support the education of students from California.
Title of Award: Ruth DeMoss Scholarships **Area, Field, or Subject:** General studies. **Level of Education for which Award is Granted:** Undergraduate **Number Awarded:** 1. **Funds Available:** $1,000.
Eligibility Requirements: Applicant must be an African-American, Native American, or Latino student currently attending an accredited two-year college in San Diego County and will transfer to a four-year university in San Diego County. Student must have a minimum 2.50 GPA on a 4.0 scale; have demonstrated financial need, and a commitment to the community as shown by leadership and volunteer activities. **Application Requirements:** Applicants must submit a completed Common Scholarship Application together with personal statement; two letters of recommendation on official letterhead (written within the last six months); official transcript in an official and sealed envelope; a copy of most recent tax form (Form 1040-pages 1 & 2; Form 1040A-pages 1 & 2; Form 1040EZ-page 1); and a letter of acceptance on official letterhead from the four-year university in San Diego County to which he/she will be transferring upon receipt of this scholarship. **Deadline for Receipt:** January 28. **Additional Information:** Arzo Mansury, Dir. Scholarships at 619-814-1343, or scholarships@sdfoundation.org.

1972 ■ THE SAN DIEGO FOUNDATION

2508 Historic Decatur Rd., Ste. 200
San Diego, CA 92106
Tel: (619)235-2300
Fax: (619)239-1710
E-mail: info@sdfoundation.org
Web Site: http://www.sdfoundation.org
To support the education of students from California.
Title of Award: Herman H. Derksen Scholarships **Area, Field, or Subject:** General studies. **Level of Education for which Award is**

Granted: Undergraduate **Number Awarded:** 4. **Funds Available:** $2,000.

Eligibility Requirements: Applicant must be a San Diego resident pursuing a trade or vocation; will attend an accredited two-year college or licensed trade/vocational school in San Diego County; have a minimum 2.0 GPA on a 4.0 scale; and demonstrated financial need. **Application Requirements:** Applicants must submit a completed Common Scholarship Application together with personal statement; two letters of recommendation on official letterhead (written within the last six months); official transcript in an official and sealed envelope; copy of most recent tax form (Form 1040-pages 1 & 2; Form 1040A-pages 1 & 2; Form 1040EZ-page 1); and an essay (maximum one page, typed, double spaced) detailing applicant's reasons for, and interest in, pursuing a vocational education. **Deadline for Receipt:** January 28. **Additional Information:** Arzo Mansury, Dir. Scholarships at 619-814-1343, or scholarships@sdfoundation.org.

1973 ■ THE SAN DIEGO FOUNDATION

2508 Historic Decatur Rd., Ste. 200
San Diego, CA 92106
Tel: (619)235-2300
Fax: (619)239-1710
E-mail: info@sdfoundation.org
Web Site: http://www.sdfoundation.org
To support the education of students from California.
Title of Award: Hans H. and Margaret B. Doe Scholarships **Area, Field, or Subject:** General studies. **Level of Education for which Award is Granted:** Graduate, Undergraduate **Funds Available:** Covers the entire cost of college.
Eligibility Requirements: Applicant must be a biological, adopted or stepchild of an employee at the Vista Irrigation District. Student may attend a trade/vocational school, two-year college, four-year university or graduate school, including medical and law. **Application Requirements:** Applicants must contact The San Diego Foundation for obtaining the application form and guidelines. **Deadline for Receipt:** March 10. **Additional Information:** 619-814-1343 or scholarships@sdfoundation.org.

1974 ■ THE SAN DIEGO FOUNDATION

2508 Historic Decatur Rd., Ste. 200
San Diego, CA 92106
Tel: (619)235-2300
Fax: (619)239-1710
E-mail: info@sdfoundation.org
Web Site: http://www.sdfoundation.org
To support the education of students from California.
Title of Award: Dokmo Family Scholarships **Area, Field, or Subject:** General studies. **Level of Education for which Award is Granted:** Undergraduate **Number Awarded:** 5. **Funds Available:** $1,000 each.
Eligibility Requirements: Applicant must be a graduating senior attending a high school in the Poway Unified School District; planning to attend an accredited two-year college or four-year university in San Diego County; have an unweighted GPA of 2.50 on a 4.0 scale; have demonstrated financial need; and actively involved in serving the community through involvement in extra-curricular activities, community and church service, or work experience. **Application Requirements:** Applicants must submit a completed Common Scholarship Application together with personal statement; two letters of recommendation on official letterhead (written within the last six months); official transcript in an official and sealed envelope; copy of most recent tax form (Form 1040-pages 1 & 2; Form 1040A-pages 1 & 2; Form 1040EZ -page 1); and a form verifying residency in Rancho Bernardo or Poway from for each period of 2004, 2005, 2006 and 2007, or 2005, 2006, 2007 and 2008 (phone/utility bills or property tax information). **Deadline for Receipt:** January 28. **Additional Information:** Arzo Mansury, Dir. Scholarships at 619-814-1343, or scholarships@sdfoundation.org.

1975 ■ THE SAN DIEGO FOUNDATION

2508 Historic Decatur Rd., Ste. 200
San Diego, CA 92106
Tel: (619)235-2300
Fax: (619)239-1710
E-mail: info@sdfoundation.org
Web Site: http://www.sdfoundation.org

To support the education of students from California.
Title of Award: Drinkwater Family Scholarships **Area, Field, or Subject:** General studies. **Level of Education for which Award is Granted:** Undergraduate **Number Awarded:** 4. **Funds Available:** $1,000.
Eligibility Requirements: Applicant must be a graduating high school senior; the first in the family to attend an accredited four-year university in the U.S.; have a minimum unweighted GPA of 3.25 on a 4.0 scale; demonstrated financial need; and actively involved in serving the community as shown by participation in extra-curricular, church activities, or community service. **Application Requirements:** Applicants must submit a completed Common Scholarship Application together with personal statement; two letters of recommendation on official letterhead (written within the last six months); official transcript in an official and sealed envelope; copy of 2006 or most recent tax form (Form 1040-pages 1 & 2; Form 1040A-pages 1 & 2; Form 1040EZ -page 1); and a letter of recommendation from the applicant's high school counselor indicating he/she is the first person in his/her family to attend college. **Deadline for Receipt:** January 28. **Additional Information:** Arzo Mansury, Dir. Scholarships at 619-814-1343, or scholarships@sdfoundation.org.

1976 ■ THE SAN DIEGO FOUNDATION

2508 Historic Decatur Rd., Ste. 200
San Diego, CA 92106
Tel: (619)235-2300
Fax: (619)239-1710
E-mail: info@sdfoundation.org
Web Site: http://www.sdfoundation.org
To support the education of students from California.
Title of Award: Leslie Jane Hahn Memorial Scholarships **Area, Field, or Subject:** General studies. **Level of Education for which Award is Granted:** Undergraduate **Number Awarded:** 1. **Funds Available:** $3,000.
Eligibility Requirements: Applicant must be a graduating high school senior girl from a public school; attending an accredited four-year college/university in the U.S.; have at least a 3.75 GPA on a 4.0 scale; demonstrated financial need; and have a history of active involvement in athletics, other extracurricular activities, community service or work experience. **Application Requirements:** Applicants must submit a completed Common Scholarship Application together with personal statement; two letters of recommendation on official letterhead (written within the last six months); official transcript in an official and sealed envelope; and a copy of most recent tax form (Form 1040-pages 1 & 2; Form 1040A-pages 1 & 2; Form 1040EZ-page 1). **Deadline for Receipt:** January 28. **Additional Information:** Arzo Mansury, Dir. Scholarships at 619-814-1343, or scholarships@sdfoundation.org.

1977 ■ THE SAN DIEGO FOUNDATION

2508 Historic Decatur Rd., Ste. 200
San Diego, CA 92106
Tel: (619)235-2300
Fax: (619)239-1710
E-mail: info@sdfoundation.org
Web Site: http://www.sdfoundation.org
To support the education of students from California.
Title of Award: Doris Hendren Memorial Scholarships **Area, Field, or Subject:** Liberal arts. **Level of Education for which Award is Granted:** Undergraduate **Number Awarded:** 5. **Funds Available:** $1,000.
Eligibility Requirements: Applicant must be a student attending an accredited two-year college or four-year university in San Diego County; pursuing a degree in a field of liberal arts; have a minimum 3.0 GPA on a 4.0 scale; demonstrated financial need; have commitment to the San Diego community through work experience, community, church, or school activities. **Application Requirements:** Applicants must submit a completed Common Scholarship Application together with personal statement; two letters of recommendation on official letterhead (written within the last six months); official transcript in an official and sealed envelope; and copy of most recent tax form (Form 1040-pages 1 & 2; Form 1040A-pages 1 & 2; Form 1040EZ-page 1). **Deadline for Receipt:** January 28. **Additional Information:** Arzo Mansury, Dir. Scholarships at 619-814-1343, or scholarships@sdfoundation.org.

1978 ■ THE SAN DIEGO FOUNDATION

2508 Historic Decatur Rd., Ste. 200
San Diego, CA 92106

Tel: (619)235-2300
Fax: (619)239-1710
E-mail: info@sdfoundation.org
Web Site: http://www.sdfoundation.org
To support the education of students from California.
Title of Award: Albert W. and Mildred Hubbard Scholarships **Area, Field, or Subject:** General studies. **Level of Education for which Award is Granted:** Undergraduate **Number Awarded:** 8. **Funds Available:** May be the actual amount of tuition charged by the respective college/university, but no more than the actual amount of tuition charged by the University of California system.
Eligibility Requirements: Applicant must be a graduating senior attending high school in Escondido or Valley Center; a resident of Escondido or Valley Center already in college; or a student currently attending the San Pasqual Academy in Escondido, CA. Applicant must have a minimum 2.50 GPA on a 4.0 scale; a resident of Escondido, CA or Valley Center, CA for the past four years (excluding students attending San Pasqual Academy); have demonstrated financial need; and plan to attend an accredited two-year college or four-year university in the U.S. **Application Requirements:** Applicants must submit a completed Common Scholarship Application together with personal statement; two letters of recommendation on official letterhead (written within the last six months); official transcript in an official and sealed envelope; copy of most recent tax form (Form 1040-pages 1 & 2; Form 1040A-pages 1 & 2; Form 1040EZ-page 1); and any form verifying residency in Escondido or Valley Center for each period of 2004, 2005, 2006, and 2007, or 2005, 2006, 2007 and 2008 (i.e. bank statements, utility bills, insurance forms, etc.). **Deadline for Receipt:** January 28. **Additional Information:** Arzo Mansury, Dir. Scholarships at 619-814-1343, or scholarships@sdfoundation.org.

1979 ■ THE SAN DIEGO FOUNDATION
2508 Historic Decatur Rd., Ste. 200
San Diego, CA 92106
Tel: (619)235-2300
Fax: (619)239-1710
E-mail: info@sdfoundation.org
Web Site: http://www.sdfoundation.org
To support the education of students from California.
Title of Award: Ruth E. Jenkins Scholarships **Area, Field, or Subject:** General studies. **Level of Education for which Award is Granted:** Undergraduate **Number Awarded:** 1. **Funds Available:** $1,000.
Eligibility Requirements: Applicant must be a graduating African-American high school senior from San Diego County attending an accredited four-year university in the U.S. Student must have a 3.0 GPA on a 4.0 scale; have demonstrated financial need; and be involved in serving the communities through extra-curricular activities, work, church, or community service. **Application Requirements:** Applicants must submit a completed Common Scholarship Application together with personal statement; two letters of recommendation on official letterhead (written within the last six months); official transcript in an official and sealed envelope; and a copy of most recent tax form (Form 1040-pages 1 & 2; Form 1040A-pages 1 & 2; Form 1040EZ-page 1). **Deadline for Receipt:** January 28. **Additional Information:** Arzo Mansury, Dir. Scholarships at 619-814-1343, or scholarships@sdfoundation.org.

1980 ■ THE SAN DIEGO FOUNDATION
2508 Historic Decatur Rd., Ste. 200
San Diego, CA 92106
Tel: (619)235-2300
Fax: (619)239-1710
E-mail: info@sdfoundation.org
Web Site: http://www.sdfoundation.org
To support the education of students from California.
Title of Award: Napoleon A. Jones, III Memorial Scholarships **Area, Field, or Subject:** General studies. **Level of Education for which Award is Granted:** Undergraduate **Number Awarded:** 1. **Funds Available:** $2,000-$3,000.
Eligibility Requirements: Applicant must be a graduating high school senior residing within the zip codes of 92113, 92114, and 92115; or a graduating senior attending one of the following public high schools: Crawford, Hoover, Lincoln, Morse, San Diego High (located in downtown San Diego), and School for the Creative and Performing Arts. Student must have a minimum 3.0 GPA on a 4.0 scale; planning to attend an ac-

credited four-year university in the U.S.; have financial need; and engaged in serving the community as demonstrated by involvement in extra-curricular, work, church, or volunteer activities. **Application Requirements:** Applicants must submit a completed Common Scholarship Application together with personal statement; two letters of recommendation on official letterhead (written within the last six months); official transcript in an official and sealed envelope; and a copy of most recent tax form (Form 1040-pages 1 & 2; Form 1040A-pages 1 & 2; Form 1040EZ-page 1). **Deadline for Receipt:** January 28. **Additional Information:** Arzo Mansury, Dir. Scholarships at 619-814-1343, or scholarships@sdfoundation.org.

1981 ■ THE SAN DIEGO FOUNDATION
2508 Historic Decatur Rd., Ste. 200
San Diego, CA 92106
Tel: (619)235-2300
Fax: (619)239-1710
E-mail: info@sdfoundation.org
Web Site: http://www.sdfoundation.org
To support the education of students from California.
Title of Award: Kawano Family Scholarships **Area, Field, or Subject:** General studies. **Level of Education for which Award is Granted:** Undergraduate **Number Awarded:** 1-2. **Funds Available:** $1,000-$2,000.
Eligibility Requirements: Applicant must be a student from San Diego County who have arthritis or have an immediate family member affected by arthritis, which impacts the applicant on a daily basis. Student must have a minimum 3.0 GPA on a 4.0 scale; demonstrated financial need; and planning to attend, or attending an accredited four-year university in the U.S. **Application Requirements:** Applicants must submit a completed Common Scholarship Application together with personal statement; two letters of recommendation on official letterhead (written within the last six months); official transcript in an official and sealed envelope; and a copy of most recent tax form (Form 1040-pages 1 & 2; Form 1040A-pages 1 & 2; Form 1040EZ-page 1); and an essay (maximum of two pagess, typed, double-spaced) clearly addressing who has arthritis and how life has been affected by it. **Deadline for Receipt:** January 28. **Additional Information:** Arzo Mansury, Dir. Scholarships at 619-814-1343, or scholarships@sdfoundation.org.

1982 ■ THE SAN DIEGO FOUNDATION
2508 Historic Decatur Rd., Ste. 200
San Diego, CA 92106
Tel: (619)235-2300
Fax: (619)239-1710
E-mail: info@sdfoundation.org
Web Site: http://www.sdfoundation.org
To support the education of students from California.
Title of Award: Kiwanis Club of Escondido Scholarships I **Area, Field, or Subject:** General studies. **Level of Education for which Award is Granted:** Undergraduate **Number Awarded:** 2. **Funds Available:** $1,000.
Eligibility Requirements: Applicant must be a graduating high school senior in the Escondido High School District; planning to attend an accredited four-year university in the U.S.; have a minimum 3.0 GPA on a 4.0 scale; an active member of a Key Club (sponsored by an Escondido Kiwanis Club); have demonstrated financial need; and be actively involved in serving the community through involvement in extra-curricular activities, community service, sports, or work experience. **Application Requirements:** Applicants must submit a completed Common Scholarship Application together with personal statement; two letters of recommendation on official letterhead (written within the last six months); official transcript in an official and sealed envelope; a copy of most recent tax form (Form 1040-pages 1 & 2; Form 1040A-pages 1 & 2; Form 1040EZ-page 1); and a letter of recommendation from the applicant's Key Club Advisor indicating the student's degree of involvement. **Deadline for Receipt:** January 28. **Additional Information:** Arzo Mansury, Dir. Scholarships at 619-814-1343, or scholarships@sdfoundation.org.

1983 ■ THE SAN DIEGO FOUNDATION
2508 Historic Decatur Rd., Ste. 200
San Diego, CA 92106
Tel: (619)235-2300
Fax: (619)239-1710

E-mail: info@sdfoundation.org
Web Site: http://www.sdfoundation.org
To support the education of students from California.
Title of Award: Kiwanis Club of Escondido Scholarships II **Area, Field, or Subject:** General studies. **Level of Education for which Award is Granted:** Undergraduate **Number Awarded:** 2. **Funds Available:** $1,000.
Eligibility Requirements: Applicant must be a graduating high school senior in the Escondido High School District; planning to attend a two-year college or licensed trade/vocational school in the U.S.; have a minimum 2.0 GPA on a 4.0 scale; active member of a Key Club (sponsored by an Escondido Kiwanis·Club); have demonstrated financial need; and actively involved in serving the community through involvement in extra-curricular activities, community service, sports, or work experience. **Application Requirements:** Applicants must submit a completed Common Scholarship Application together with personal statement; two letters of recommendation on official letterhead (written within the last six months); official transcript in an official and sealed envelope; a copy of most recent tax form (Form 1040-pages 1 & 2; Form 1040A-pages 1 & 2; Form 1040EZ-page 1); and a letter of recommendation from the applicant's Key Club Advisor indicating the student's degree of involvement. **Deadline for Receipt:** January 28. **Additional Information:** Arzo Mansury, Dir. Scholarships at 619-814-1343, or scholarships@sdfoundation.org.

1984 ■ THE SAN DIEGO FOUNDATION

2508 Historic Decatur Rd., Ste. 200
San Diego, CA 92106
Tel: (619)235-2300
Fax: (619)239-1710
E-mail: info@sdfoundation.org
Web Site: http://www.sdfoundation.org
To support the education of students from California.
Title of Award: Judith Keller Marx Krumholz Scholarships **Area, Field, or Subject:** General studies. **Level of Education for which Award is Granted:** Undergraduate **Number Awarded:** 5. **Funds Available:** $500.
Eligibility Requirements: Applicant must be a student attending San Diego City College who have completed one full academic semester; have a minimum 2.50 GPA on a 4.0 scale; demonstrated financial need; and attending San Diego City College. **Application Requirements:** Applicants must submit a completed Common Scholarship Application together with personal statement; two letters of recommendation on official letterhead (written within the last six months); official transcript in an official and sealed envelope; and a copy of most recent tax form (Form 1040-pages 1 & 2; Form 1040A-pages 1 & 2; Form 1040EZ-page 1). **Deadline for Receipt:** January 28. **Additional Information:** Arzo Mansury, Dir. Scholarships at 619-814-1343, or scholarships@sdfoundation.org.

1985 ■ THE SAN DIEGO FOUNDATION

2508 Historic Decatur Rd., Ste. 200
San Diego, CA 92106
Tel: (619)235-2300
Fax: (619)239-1710
E-mail: info@sdfoundation.org
Web Site: http://www.sdfoundation.org
To support the education of students from California.
Title of Award: Joseph C. Larson Entrepreneurial Scholarships **Area, Field, or Subject:** General studies. **Level of Education for which Award is Granted:** Undergraduate **Number Awarded:** 3. **Funds Available:** $2,500.
Eligibility Requirements: Applicant must be a graduating high school senior who will attend an accredited four-year university; or a student who have successfully completed at least one full academic year towards undergraduate degree at an accredited four-year university in the U.S. Student must have a minimum 3.0 GPA on a 4.0 scale. **Application Requirements:** Applicants must submit a completed Common Scholarship Application together with personal statement; two letters of recommendation on official letterhead (written within the last six months); official transcript in an official and sealed envelope; copy of most recent tax form (Form 1040-pages 1 & 2; Form 1040A-pages 1 & 2; Form 1040EZ-page 1); and an essay (maximum two pages, typed, double-spaced) explaining the applicant's plan in using education in furthering entrepreneurial goals.

Deadline for Receipt: January 28. **Additional Information:** Arzo Mansury, Dir. Scholarships at 619-814-1343, or scholarships@sdfoundation.org.

1986 ■ THE SAN DIEGO FOUNDATION

2508 Historic Decatur Rd., Ste. 200
San Diego, CA 92106
Tel: (619)235-2300
Fax: (619)239-1710
E-mail: info@sdfoundation.org
Web Site: http://www.sdfoundation.org
To support the education of students from California.
Title of Award: Patrick Ledden Honorary Scholarships **Area, Field, or Subject:** General studies. **Level of Education for which Award is Granted:** Undergraduate **Number Awarded:** 4. **Funds Available:** $3,000.
Eligibility Requirements: Applicant must be a graduating senior at The Preuss School, UCSD; have a minimum 3.50 GPA on a 4.0 scale; and planning to attend a public or private four-year university in the state of California. **Application Requirements:** Applicants must submit a completed Common Scholarship Application together with personal statement; two letters of recommendation on official letterhead (written within the last six months); official transcript in an official and sealed envelope; a copy of most recent tax form (Form 1040-pages 1 & 2; Form 1040A-pages 1 & 2; Form 1040EZ -page 1); and an essay (maximum one page, typed, double-spaced) answering "What have you learned from your experience at The Preuss School, UCSD that you feel will best benefit you in college?". **Deadline for Receipt:** January 28. **Additional Information:** Arzo Mansury, Dir. Scholarships at 619-814-1343, or scholarships@sdfoundation.org.

1987 ■ THE SAN DIEGO FOUNDATION

2508 Historic Decatur Rd., Ste. 200
San Diego, CA 92106
Tel: (619)235-2300
Fax: (619)239-1710
E-mail: info@sdfoundation.org
Web Site: http://www.sdfoundation.org
To support the education of students from California.
Title of Award: Ken Lee Memorial Scholarships **Area, Field, or Subject:** General studies. **Level of Education for which Award is Granted:** Undergraduate **Number Awarded:** One scholarship to each high school in Chula Vista that submits at least three applications. **Funds Available:** $1,000.
Eligibility Requirements: Applicant must be a graduating senior; a resident of Chula Vista, CA; attending a public or private Chula Vista high school; have a minimum 3.50 GPA on a 4.0 scale; planning to attend an accredited four-year university in the U.S.; have demonstrated commitment to the Chula Vista community through involvement in extra-curricular activities, community service, sports, or work experience. **Application Requirements:** Applicants must submit a completed Common Scholarship Application together with personal statement; two letters of recommendation on official letterhead (written within the last six months); official transcript in an official and sealed envelope; and a copy of most recent tax form (Form 1040-pages 1 & 2; Form 1040A-pages 1 & 2; Form 1040EZ-page 1); and a form verifying residency in Chula Vista for each period of 2004, 2005, 2006 and 2007 or 2005, 2006, 2007 and 2008 must be submitted (phone/utility bills or property tax information). **Deadline for Receipt:** January 28. **Additional Information:** Arzo Mansury, Dir. Scholarships at 619-814-1343, or scholarships@sdfoundation.org.

1988 ■ THE SAN DIEGO FOUNDATION

2508 Historic Decatur Rd., Ste. 200
San Diego, CA 92106
Tel: (619)235-2300
Fax: (619)239-1710
E-mail: info@sdfoundation.org
Web Site: http://www.sdfoundation.org
To support the education of students from California.
Title of Award: Lehman Family Scholarships **Area, Field, or Subject:** General studies. **Level of Education for which Award is Granted:** Undergraduate **Number Awarded:** 4. **Funds Available:** $1,500.
Eligibility Requirements: Applicant must be a graduating senior from Lincoln, Morse, or San Diego (downtown San Diego) high Schools; have

a minimum 3.00 GPA on a 4.0 scale; planning to attend an accredited four-year university in the U.S; have financial need; and have demonstrated commitment to the through involvement in extra-curricular activities, work or volunteer experience, or church activities. **Application Requirements:** Applicants must submit a completed Common Scholarship Application together with personal statement; two letters of recommendation on official letterhead (written within the last six months); official transcript in an official and sealed envelope; and a copy of most recent tax form (Form 1040-pages 1 & 2; Form 1040A-pages 1 & 2; Form 1040EZ-page 1). **Deadline for Receipt:** January 28. **Additional Information:** Arzo Mansury, Dir. Scholarships at 619-814-1343, or scholarships@sdfoundation.org.

1989 ■ THE SAN DIEGO FOUNDATION
2508 Historic Decatur Rd., Ste. 200
San Diego, CA 92106
Tel: (619)235-2300
Fax: (619)239-1710
E-mail: info@sdfoundation.org
Web Site: http://www.sdfoundation.org
To support the education of students from California.
Title of Award: The Lemon Grove Education Foundation Scholarships **Area, Field, or Subject:** General studies. **Level of Education for which Award is Granted:** Undergraduate **Number Awarded:** 3. **Funds Available:** $1,000.
Eligibility Requirements: Applicant must be a graduating high school senior or adult (ages 18 or over); reside within the boundaries of the Lemon Grove School District; have a minimum 2.0 GPA on a 4.0 scale; attending a four-year public university, two-year community college, licensed trade/vocational school, or regional occupational program in San Diego County. **Application Requirements:** Applicants must submit a completed Common Scholarship Application together with personal statement; two letters of recommendation on official letterhead (written within the last six months); official transcript in an official and sealed envelope; copy of most recent tax form (Form 1040-pages 1 & 2; Form 1040A-pages 1 & 2; Form 1040EZ-page 1); and a form verifying residency within the boundaries of the Lemon Grove School District for each period of 2005 and 2006, or 2006 and 2007 (phone/utility bills, property tax forms, etc.) **Deadline for Receipt:** January 28. **Additional Information:** Arzo Mansury, Dir. Scholarships at 619-814-1343, or scholarships@sdfoundation.org.

1990 ■ THE SAN DIEGO FOUNDATION
2508 Historic Decatur Rd., Ste. 200
San Diego, CA 92106
Tel: (619)235-2300
Fax: (619)239-1710
E-mail: info@sdfoundation.org
Web Site: http://www.sdfoundation.org
To support the education of students from California.
Title of Award: MKC Scholarships **Area, Field, or Subject:** General studies. **Level of Education for which Award is Granted:** Undergraduate **Number Awarded:** Varies. **Funds Available:** $1,000-$3,000.
Eligibility Requirements: Applicant must be a graduating senior or a student who have already graduated from The Preuss School, UCSD. Student must have financial need; planning to attend an accredited two-year college or four-year university in the U.S.; have a minimum 3.0 GPA on a 4.0 scale; and involved in the community through participation in extra-curricular or religious activities or volunteer or work experience. **Application Requirements:** Applicants must submit a completed Common Scholarship Application together with personal statement; two letters of recommendation on official letterhead (written within the last six months); official transcript in an official and sealed envelope; a copy of most recent tax form (Form 1040-pages 1 & 2; Form 1040A-pages 1 & 2; Form 1040EZ-page 1); an essay (one page, typed, double-spaced) answering "What would you say to a student thinking of entering The Preuss School, UCSD, and what has been the most important aspect of your experience while attending?"; (for students who have already graduated and are currently attending a college or university) a copy of high school transcript from The Preuss School, UCSD. **Deadline for Receipt:** January 28. **Additional Information:** Arzo Mansury, Dir. Scholarships at 619-814-1343, or scholarships@sdfoundation.org.

1991 ■ THE SAN DIEGO FOUNDATION
2508 Historic Decatur Rd., Ste. 200
San Diego, CA 92106
Tel: (619)235-2300
Fax: (619)239-1710
E-mail: info@sdfoundation.org
Web Site: http://www.sdfoundation.org
To support the education of students from California.
Title of Award: Native American Charter High Schools After-the-Fires Scholarships **Area, Field, or Subject:** General studies. **Level of Education for which Award is Granted:** Undergraduate **Number Awarded:** To be determined. **Funds Available:** To be determined.
Eligibility Requirements: Applicant must be a graduating high school senior enrolled in a Tribal Charter High School in San Diego County whose family was financially impacted by the 2007 wildfires. Student must have a minimum 2.0 GPA on a 4.0 scale and planning to attend an accredited two-year college, four-year university, or licensed trade/vocational school in the U.S. **Application Requirements:** Applicants must submit a completed Common Scholarship Application together with personal statement; two letters of recommendation on official letterhead (written within the last six months); official transcript in an official and sealed envelope; a copy of most recent tax form (Form 1040-pages 1 & 2; Form 1040A-pages 1 & 2; Form 1040EZ-page 1); and a formal documentation or a letter on official letterhead from FEMA (insurance company), or high school guidance counselor/principal indicating the loss of home in the 2007 wildfires and/or letter from parents' or parent's employer(s) indicating loss of income. **Deadline for Receipt:** January 28. **Additional Information:** Arzo Mansury, Dir. Scholarships at 619-814-1343, or scholarships@sdfoundation.org.

1992 ■ THE SAN DIEGO FOUNDATION
2508 Historic Decatur Rd., Ste. 200
San Diego, CA 92106
Tel: (619)235-2300
Fax: (619)239-1710
E-mail: info@sdfoundation.org
Web Site: http://www.sdfoundation.org
To support the education of students from California.
Title of Award: Pearman Family Scholarships **Area, Field, or Subject:** General studies. **Level of Education for which Award is Granted:** Undergraduate **Number Awarded:** 1. **Funds Available:** $750.
Eligibility Requirements: Applicant must be a graduating African-American high school senior from San Diego County; have a minimum 3.0 GPA on a 4.0 scale; planning to attend an accredited four-year university in the U.S.; and have demonstrated financial need. **Application Requirements:** Applicants must submit a completed Common Scholarship Application together with personal statement; two letters of recommendation on official letterhead (written within the last six months); official transcript in an official and sealed envelope; and a copy of most recent tax form (Form 1040-pages 1 & 2; Form 1040A-pages 1 & 2; Form 1040EZ-page 1). **Deadline for Receipt:** January 28. **Additional Information:** Arzo Mansury, Dir. Scholarships at 619-814-1343, or scholarships@sdfoundation.org.

1993 ■ THE SAN DIEGO FOUNDATION
2508 Historic Decatur Rd., Ste. 200
San Diego, CA 92106
Tel: (619)235-2300
Fax: (619)239-1710
E-mail: info@sdfoundation.org
Web Site: http://www.sdfoundation.org
To support the education of students from California.
Title of Award: Pollard-Bailey Scholarships **Area, Field, or Subject:** General studies. **Level of Education for which Award is Granted:** Undergraduate **Number Awarded:** 5. **Funds Available:** $1,000.
Eligibility Requirements: Applicant must be a graduating high school senior who will attend Grossmont or Cuyamaca Community College; must have a minimum 2.50 GPA on a 4.0 scale; demonstrated financial need; and engaged in serving the community through involvement in extra-curricular activities/church/volunteer activities or work experience. **Application Requirements:** Applicants must submit a completed Common Scholarship Application together with personal statement; two letters of recommendation on official letterhead (written within the last six months);

official transcript in an official and sealed envelope; and a copy of most recent tax form (Form 1040-pages 1 & 2; Form 1040A-pages 1 & 2; Form 1040EZ-page 1). **Deadline for Receipt:** January 28. **Additional Information:** Arzo Mansury, Dir. Scholarships at 619-814-1343, or scholarships@sdfoundation.org.

1994 ■ THE SAN DIEGO FOUNDATION
2508 Historic Decatur Rd., Ste. 200
San Diego, CA 92106
Tel: (619)235-2300
Fax: (619)239-1710
E-mail: info@sdfoundation.org
Web Site: http://www.sdfoundation.org
To support the education of students from California.

Title of Award: Port with No Borders Scholarships **Area, Field, or Subject:** General studies. **Level of Education for which Award is Granted:** Undergraduate **Number Awarded:** 6. **Funds Available:** $2,000.
Eligibility Requirements: Applicants must be San Diego Port tenants, sub-tenants, or Port of San Diego employees or their children who are residents of San Diego County. Applicants must be graduating high school seniors, or currently enrolled college students; having a minimum 2.50 GPA on a 4.0 scale; working towards their undergraduate degree; have a demonstrated financial need; and plan to attend an accredited two-year college or four-year university in the U.S. **Application Requirements:** Applicants must submit a completed Common Scholarship Application together with personal statement; two letters of recommendation on official letterhead (written within the last six months); official transcript in an official and sealed envelope; a copy of 2006 or most recent tax form (Form 1040-pages 1 & 2; Form 1040A-pages 1 & 2; Form 1040EZ-page 1); a letter from the employer on official letterhead verifying the applicant is an employee of a tenant or sub-tenant of the Port of San Diego or his/her parent is employed by a tenant or sub-tenant of the Port of San Diego; and an essay (maximum one page, typed, double-spaced) addressing how the applicant's studies could lead to a career related to the business and operations of a port. **Deadline for Receipt:** January 28. **Additional Information:** Arzo Mansury, Dir. Scholarships at 619-814-1343, or scholarships@sdfoundation.org.

1995 ■ THE SAN DIEGO FOUNDATION
2508 Historic Decatur Rd., Ste. 200
San Diego, CA 92106
Tel: (619)235-2300
Fax: (619)239-1710
E-mail: info@sdfoundation.org
Web Site: http://www.sdfoundation.org
To support the education of students from California.

Title of Award: Qualcomm San Diego Science, Technology, Engineering and Mathematics Scholarships **Area, Field, or Subject:** General studies. **Level of Education for which Award is Granted:** Undergraduate **Number Awarded:** 5. **Funds Available:** $2,500.
Eligibility Requirements: Applicant must be a graduating high school senior; or a student currently attending a local community college and transferring to either the University of California, San Diego, San Diego State University or California State University, San Marcos. Student must have a minimum of 3.50 GPA on a 4.0 scale and demonstrated financial need. **Application Requirements:** Applicants must submit a completed Common Scholarship Application together with personal statement; two letters of recommendation on official letterhead (written within the last six months); official transcript in an official and sealed envelope; and a copy of most recent tax form (Form 1040-pages 1 & 2; Form 1040A-pages 1 & 2; Form 1040EZ-page 1). **Deadline for Receipt:** January 28. **Additional Information:** Arzo Mansury, Dir. Scholarships at 619-814-1343, or scholarships@sdfoundation.org.

1996 ■ THE SAN DIEGO FOUNDATION
2508 Historic Decatur Rd., Ste. 200
San Diego, CA 92106
Tel: (619)235-2300
Fax: (619)239-1710
E-mail: info@sdfoundation.org
Web Site: http://www.sdfoundation.org
To support the education of students from California.

Title of Award: Rancho Bernardo/Smith Scholarships **Area, Field, or Subject:** General studies. **Level of Education for which Award is Granted:** Undergraduate **Number Awarded:** 2. **Funds Available:** $1,000.
Eligibility Requirements: Applicant must be a graduating high school senior from Rancho Bernardo; will attend an accredited, public four-year university in the state of California; must have a minimum 3.50 GPA on a 4.0 scale; and demonstrated commitment to the Rancho Bernardo community through involvement in extra-curricular activities, community service, sports, or work experience. **Application Requirements:** Applicants must submit a completed Common Scholarship Application together with personal statement; two letters of recommendation on official letterhead (written within the last six months); official transcript in an official and sealed envelope; a copy of most recent tax form (Form 1040-pages 1 & 2; Form 1040A-pages 1 & 2; Form 1040EZ-page 1); and a form verifying residency in Rancho Bernardo for at least one year for each period of 2006-2007 or 2007-2008 (bank statements, utility bills, insurance forms, etc.). **Deadline for Receipt:** January 28. **Additional Information:** Arzo Mansury, Dir. Scholarships at 619-814-1343, or scholarships@sdfoundation.org.

1997 ■ THE SAN DIEGO FOUNDATION
2508 Historic Decatur Rd., Ste. 200
San Diego, CA 92106
Tel: (619)235-2300
Fax: (619)239-1710
E-mail: info@sdfoundation.org
Web Site: http://www.sdfoundation.org
To support the education of students from California.

Title of Award: The Remington Club Scholarships **Area, Field, or Subject:** General studies. **Level of Education for which Award is Granted:** Undergraduate **Number Awarded:** To be determined. **Funds Available:** $1,000-$4,000.
Eligibility Requirements: Applicants must be employees, and the children of employees at The Remington Club. Applicants must have a minimum 2.50 GPA on a 4.0 scale; planning to attend an accredited two-year college, four-year university, or licensed trade/vocational school in the U.S.; have a commitment to the community as demonstrated through involvement in extra-curricular activities, community service, sports, or work experience; may be graduating high school seniors, students already in school, or adults re-entering school. Employees must be employed at The Remington Club for a minimum of six consecutive months. **Application Requirements:** Applicants must submit a completed Common Scholarship Application together with personal statement; two letters of recommendation on official letterhead (written within the last six months); official transcript in an official and sealed envelope; a copy of most recent tax form (Form 1040-pages 1 & 2; Form 1040A-pages 1 & 2; Form 1040EZ -page 1); and a letter from The Remington Club (on official letterhead and signed by personnel in Human Resources or an immediate supervisor) indicating how long the employee has been employed at The Remington Club, the position he/she holds and, if applicable, the name of the son/daughter who is applying for the scholarship.. **Deadline for Receipt:** January 28. **Additional Information:** Arzo Mansury, Dir. Scholarships at 619-814-1343, or scholarships@sdfoundation.org.

1998 ■ THE SAN DIEGO FOUNDATION
2508 Historic Decatur Rd., Ste. 200
San Diego, CA 92106
Tel: (619)235-2300
Fax: (619)239-1710
E-mail: info@sdfoundation.org
Web Site: http://www.sdfoundation.org
To support the education of students from California.

Title of Award: The Rotary Club of Rancho Bernardo Sunrise Abraxas Student Scholarships **Area, Field, or Subject:** General studies. **Level of Education for which Award is Granted:** Undergraduate **Number Awarded:** To be determined. **Funds Available:** To be determined.
Eligibility Requirements: Applicant must be graduating high school senior of Abraxas High School in Poway, CA; have a minimum 2.50 GPA on a 4.0 scale; and planning to attend an accredited two-year college, four-year university or licensed trade/vocational school in the U.S. **Application Requirements:** Applicants must submit a completed Common Scholarship Application together with personal statement; two letters of

recommendation on official letterhead (written within the last six months); official transcript in an official and sealed envelope; a copy of most recent tax form (Form 1040-pages 1 & 2; Form 1040A-pages 1 & 2; Form 1040EZ -page 1); and a letter of recommendation from an administrator or teacher from Abraxas High School. **Deadline for Receipt:** January 28. **Additional Information:** Arzo Mansury, Dir. Scholarships at 619-814-1343, or scholarships@sdfoundation.org.

1999 ■ THE SAN DIEGO FOUNDATION
2508 Historic Decatur Rd., Ste. 200
San Diego, CA 92106
Tel: (619)235-2300
Fax: (619)239-1710
E-mail: info@sdfoundation.org
Web Site: http://www.sdfoundation.org
To support the education of students from California.
Title of Award: Rubinstein Family Scholarships **Area, Field, or Subject:** General studies. **Level of Education for which Award is Granted:** Undergraduate **Number Awarded:** 1. **Funds Available:** $1,000.
Eligibility Requirements: Applicant must be a graduating high school senior; or a student enrolled at an institution of higher education who have been diagnosed with a chronic illness (e.g. Crohn's & Colitis, Diabetes, Asthma, etc.). Student must have a minimum 3.0 GPA on a 4.0 scale; and planning to attend an accredited two-year college or four-year university in the U.S. **Application Requirements:** Applicants must submit a completed Common Scholarship Application together with personal statement; two letters of recommendation on official letterhead (written within the last six months); official transcript in an official and sealed envelope; a copy of most recent tax form (Form 1040-pages 1 & 2; Form 1040A-pages 1 & 2; Form 1040EZ-page 1); and a one page essay on how the applicant has coped with their chronic illness. **Deadline for Receipt:** January 28. **Additional Information:** Arzo Mansury, Dir. Scholarships at 619-814-1343, or scholarships@sdfoundation.org.

2000 ■ THE SAN DIEGO FOUNDATION
2508 Historic Decatur Rd., Ste. 200
San Diego, CA 92106
Tel: (619)235-2300
Fax: (619)239-1710
E-mail: info@sdfoundation.org
Web Site: http://www.sdfoundation.org
To support the education of students from California.
Title of Award: San Diego City College Study Abroad Scholarships **Area, Field, or Subject:** General studies. **Level of Education for which Award is Granted:** Undergraduate **Number Awarded:** 2 for Italy and 2 for Spain. **Funds Available:** $500-$1,000.
Eligibility Requirements: Applicant must be a student enrolled in at least 6 units (online courses are not applicable) at San Diego City College, have completed a minimum of 12 college level units; have a cumulative GPA of 2.50 or higher on a 4.0 scale; must have no previous study abroad experience; a citizen or permanent resident of the U.S.; and have a demonstrated financial need. **Application Requirements:** Applicants must submit a completed scholarship application form, along with a typed personal statement (maximum of two pages); a copy of transcripts; and a copy of most recent tax form(s) used to complete financial information (Form 1040-pages 1 & 2; Form 1040A-pages 1 & 2: Form 1040EZ-page 1). **Deadline for Receipt:** September 15. **Additional Information:** 619-814-1343 or scholarships@sdfoundation.org.

2001 ■ THE SAN DIEGO FOUNDATION
2508 Historic Decatur Rd., Ste. 200
San Diego, CA 92106
Tel: (619)235-2300
Fax: (619)239-1710
E-mail: info@sdfoundation.org
Web Site: http://www.sdfoundation.org
To support the education of students from California.
Title of Award: The San Diego Foundation Community Scholarship II **Area, Field, or Subject:** General studies. **Level of Education for which Award is Granted:** Undergraduate **Number Awarded:** 10-20. **Funds Available:** $500-$1,000.
Eligibility Requirements: Applicant must be graduating high school senior; have a minimum 2.50 GPA on a 4.0 scale; and will attend an ac-

credited two-year college in San Diego County. **Application Requirements:** Applicants must submit a completed Common Scholarship Application together with personal statement; two letters of recommendation on official letterhead (written within the last six months); official transcript in an official and sealed envelope; and a copy of most recent tax form (Form 1040-pages 1 & 2; Form 1040A-pages 1 & 2; Form 1040EZ-page 1). **Deadline for Receipt:** January 28. **Additional Information:** Arzo Mansury, Dir. Scholarships at 619-814-1343, or scholarships@sdfoundation.org.

2002 ■ THE SAN DIEGO FOUNDATION
2508 Historic Decatur Rd., Ste. 200
San Diego, CA 92106
Tel: (619)235-2300
Fax: (619)239-1710
E-mail: info@sdfoundation.org
Web Site: http://www.sdfoundation.org
To support the education of students from California.
Title of Award: The San Diego Foundation Community Scholarships I **Area, Field, or Subject:** General studies. **Level of Education for which Award is Granted:** Undergraduate **Number Awarded:** 5. **Funds Available:** $1,000.
Eligibility Requirements: Applicant must be a senior graduating from a San Diego County continuation high school; must have a minimum 2.0 GPA on a 4.0 scale; and will attend an accredited two-year college, four-year university, or licensed trade/vocational school in the U.S. **Application Requirements:** Applicants must submit a completed Common Scholarship Application together with personal statement; two letters of recommendation on official letterhead (written within the last six months); official transcript in an official and sealed envelope; and a copy of most recent tax form (Form 1040-pages 1 & 2; Form 1040A-pages 1 & 2; Form 1040EZ-page 1). **Deadline for Receipt:** January 28. **Additional Information:** Arzo Mansury, Dir. Scholarships at 619-814-1343, or scholarships@sdfoundation.org.

2003 ■ THE SAN DIEGO FOUNDATION
2508 Historic Decatur Rd., Ste. 200
San Diego, CA 92106
Tel: (619)235-2300
Fax: (619)239-1710
E-mail: info@sdfoundation.org
Web Site: http://www.sdfoundation.org
To support the education of students from California.
Title of Award: San Diego National Bank Scholarships **Area, Field, or Subject:** General studies. **Level of Education for which Award is Granted:** Undergraduate **Number Awarded:** 5. **Funds Available:** $500-$2,500.
Eligibility Requirements: Applicant must be adult with low and moderate income levels less than or equal to 80% of the prevailing San Diego County Metropolitan Statistical Area HUD median income level (currently $34,700); 21 years of age or over with a high school diploma or GED; have financial need; working towards undergraduate degree; planning to attend an accredited two-year college, four-year university, or licensed trade/vocational school in San Diego County; and committed to the community as demonstrated by participation in community, church or school activities. **Application Requirements:** Applicants must submit a completed Common Scholarship Application together with personal statement; two letters of recommendation on official letterhead (written within the last six months); official transcript in an official and sealed envelope; and a copy of most recent tax form (Form 1040-pages 1 & 2; Form 1040A-pages 1 & 2; Form 1040EZ-page 1). **Deadline for Receipt:** January 28. **Additional Information:** Arzo Mansury, Dir. Scholarships at 619-814-1343, or scholarships@sdfoundation.org.

2004 ■ THE SAN DIEGO FOUNDATION
2508 Historic Decatur Rd., Ste. 200
San Diego, CA 92106
Tel: (619)235-2300
Fax: (619)239-1710
E-mail: info@sdfoundation.org
Web Site: http://www.sdfoundation.org
To support the education of students from California.
Title of Award: San Diego Pathways to College Scholarships **Area, Field, or Subject:** General studies. **Level of Education for which**

Award is Granted: Undergraduate **Number Awarded:** To be determined. **Funds Available:** To be determined.

Eligibility Requirements: Applicant must be graduating high school senior attending a four-year university in the state of California; have a minimum 3.0 GPA on a 4.0 scale; demonstrated financial need; and actively involved in extra-curricular activities, community service, religious activities, work experience, or athletics. **Application Requirements:** Applicants must submit a completed Common Scholarship Application together with personal statement; two letters of recommendation on official letterhead (written within the last six months); official transcript in an official and sealed envelope; and a copy of 2006 or most recent tax form (Form 1040-pages 1 & 2; Form 1040A-pages 1 & 2; Form 1040EZ-page 1). **Deadline for Receipt:** January 28. **Additional Information:** Arzo Mansury, Dir. Scholarships at 619-814-1343, or scholarships@sdfoundation.org.

2005 ■ THE SAN DIEGO FOUNDATION
2508 Historic Decatur Rd., Ste. 200
San Diego, CA 92106
Tel: (619)235-2300
Fax: (619)239-1710
E-mail: info@sdfoundation.org
Web Site: http://www.sdfoundation.org
To support the education of students from California.

Title of Award: San Pasqual Academy Scholarships **Area, Field, or Subject:** General studies. **Level of Education for which Award is Granted:** Undergraduate **Number Awarded:** 5. **Funds Available:** $1,000.

Eligibility Requirements: Applicant must be graduating high school senior at San Pasqual Academy; must have a minimum 2.50 GPA on a 4.0 scale; and planning to attend an accredited two-year college, four-year university, or licensed trade/vocational school in the U.S. **Application Requirements:** Applicants must submit a completed Common Scholarship Application together with personal statement; two letters of recommendation on official letterhead (written within the last six months); official transcript in an official and sealed envelope; a copy of most recent tax form (Form 1040-pages 1 & 2; Form 1040A-pages 1 & 2; Form 1040EZ-page 1); and a letter of recommendation on official letterhead from the staff or faculty at San Pasqual Academy indicating the student is enrolled at the school. **Deadline for Receipt:** January 28. **Additional Information:** Arzo Mansury, Dir. Scholarships at 619-814-1343, or scholarships@sdfoundation.org.

2006 ■ THE SAN DIEGO FOUNDATION
2508 Historic Decatur Rd., Ste. 200
San Diego, CA 92106
Tel: (619)235-2300
Fax: (619)239-1710
E-mail: info@sdfoundation.org
Web Site: http://www.sdfoundation.org
To support the education of students from California.

Title of Award: Malini E. Sathyadev Memorial Scholarships **Area, Field, or Subject:** General studies. **Level of Education for which Award is Granted:** Undergraduate **Number Awarded:** 3. **Funds Available:** $1,500.

Eligibility Requirements: Applicant must be a graduating high school senior from Horizon High School and Cathedral Catholic High School; have a minimum 3.50 GPA on a 4.0 scale; attending an accredited four-year university in the U.S.; and involved in serving the community as demonstrated by involvement in community service and extra-curricular activities such as sports and music. **Application Requirements:** Applicants must submit a completed Common Scholarship Application together with personal statement; two letters of recommendation on official letterhead (written within the last six months); official transcript in an official and sealed envelope; a copy of most recent tax form (Form 1040-pages 1 & 2; Form 1040A-pages 1 & 2; Form 1040EZ-page 1); and an essay (one page, typed, double-spaced) on the role that Jesus Christ plays in the applicant's life. **Deadline for Receipt:** January 28. **Additional Information:** Arzo Mansury, Dir. Scholarships at 619-814-1343, or scholarships@sdfoundation.org.

2007 ■ THE SAN DIEGO FOUNDATION
2508 Historic Decatur Rd., Ste. 200
San Diego, CA 92106

Tel: (619)235-2300
Fax: (619)239-1710
E-mail: info@sdfoundation.org
Web Site: http://www.sdfoundation.org
To support the education of students from California.

Title of Award: Harvey L. Simmons Memorial Scholarships **Area, Field, or Subject:** General studies. **Level of Education for which Award is Granted:** Undergraduate **Number Awarded:** 2. **Funds Available:** $500.

Eligibility Requirements: Applicant must be a graduating high school senior; will attend an accredited two-year college or four-year university in the U.S.; have a minimum 3.0 GPA on a 4.0 scale; have demonstrated financial need; and committed to serving the community through involvement in community service, church or extra-curricular activities. **Application Requirements:** Applicants must submit a completed Common Scholarship Application together with personal statement; two letters of recommendation on official letterhead (written within the last six months); official transcript in an official and sealed envelope; copy of 2006 or most recent tax form (Form 1040-pages 1 & 2; Form 1040A-pages 1 & 2; Form 1040EZ-page 1); and a letter of recommendation on letterhead from the applicant's coach detailing the sport(s) played, level and years of participation, and achievements. **Deadline for Receipt:** January 28. **Additional Information:** Arzo Mansury, Dir. Scholarships at 619-814-1343, or scholarships@sdfoundation.org.

2008 ■ THE SAN DIEGO FOUNDATION
2508 Historic Decatur Rd., Ste. 200
San Diego, CA 92106
Tel: (619)235-2300
Fax: (619)239-1710
E-mail: info@sdfoundation.org
Web Site: http://www.sdfoundation.org
To support the education of students from California.

Title of Award: Gwen Stefani After-the-Fires Scholarships **Area, Field, or Subject:** General studies. **Level of Education for which Award is Granted:** Undergraduate **Number Awarded:** To be determined. **Funds Available:** To be determined.

Eligibility Requirements: Applicant must be a graduating high school senior or a current college student who lost homes and/or source of income in the 2007 wildfires. Student must have a minimum 2.50 GPA on a 4.0 scale; have demonstrated financial need; and plan to attend or currently attending an accredited two-year college or four-year university in the U.S. **Application Requirements:** Applicants must submit a completed Common Scholarship Application together with personal statement; two letters of recommendation on official letterhead (written within the last six months); official transcript in an official and sealed envelope; copy of most recent tax form (Form 1040-pages 1 & 2; Form 1040A-pages 1 & 2; Form 1040EZ-page 1); and a formal documentation or a letter on official letterhead from FEMA (insurance company), or high school/college guidance counselor/principal indicating the loss of home in the 2007 wildfires and/or a letter from the applicant's employer indicating loss of income. **Deadline for Receipt:** January 28. **Additional Information:** Arzo Mansury, Dir. Scholarships at 619-814-1343, or scholarships@sdfoundation.org.

2009 ■ THE SAN DIEGO FOUNDATION
2508 Historic Decatur Rd., Ste. 200
San Diego, CA 92106
Tel: (619)235-2300
Fax: (619)239-1710
E-mail: info@sdfoundation.org
Web Site: http://www.sdfoundation.org
To support the education of students from California.

Title of Award: Step Up Scholarships **Area, Field, or Subject:** General studies. **Level of Education for which Award is Granted:** Undergraduate **Number Awarded:** 1. **Funds Available:** $2,000.

Eligibility Requirements: Applicant must be a resident of San Diego County pursuing a teaching credential at a four-year university in San Diego County; must have a minimum 3.20 GPA on a 4.0 scale; a U.S. citizen and resident of California. **Application Requirements:** Applicants must submit a completed Common Scholarship Application together with personal statement; two letters of recommendation on official letterhead (written within the last six months); official transcript in an official and sealed envelope; and a copy of most recent tax form (Form 1040-pages 1

& 2; Form 1040A-pages 1 & 2; Form 1040EZ-page 1). **Deadline for Receipt:** January 28. **Additional Information:** Arzo Mansury, Dir. Scholarships at 619-814-1343, or scholarships@sdfoundation.org.

2010 ■ THE SAN DIEGO FOUNDATION

2508 Historic Decatur Rd., Ste. 200
San Diego, CA 92106
Tel: (619)235-2300
Fax: (619)239-1710
E-mail: info@sdfoundation.org
Web Site: http://www.sdfoundation.org
To support the education of students from California.

Title of Award: Raymond A. Tice Scholarships I **Area, Field, or Subject:** General studies. **Level of Education for which Award is Granted:** Undergraduate **Number Awarded:** 15. **Funds Available:** $1,000-$2,500.
Eligibility Requirements: Applicant must be a graduating high school senior; attending an accredited two-year college or four-year university in San Diego County; have a minimum 2.25 to 3.50 GPA on a 4.0 scale and demonstrated financial need; actively involved in serving the community as demonstrated by involvement in extra-curricular activities, community/church service, or work experience. **Application Requirements:** Applicants must submit a completed Common Scholarship Application together with personal statement; two letters of recommendation on official letterhead (written within the last six months); official transcript in an official and sealed envelope; and a copy of most recent tax form (Form 1040-pages 1 & 2; Form 1040A-pages 1 & 2; Form 1040EZ-page 1). **Deadline for Receipt:** January 28. **Additional Information:** Arzo Mansury, Dir. Scholarships at 619-814-1343, or scholarships@sdfoundation.org.

2011 ■ THE SAN DIEGO FOUNDATION

2508 Historic Decatur Rd., Ste. 200
San Diego, CA 92106
Tel: (619)235-2300
Fax: (619)239-1710
E-mail: info@sdfoundation.org
Web Site: http://www.sdfoundation.org
To support the education of students from California.

Title of Award: Raymond A. Tice Scholarships II **Area, Field, or Subject:** General studies. **Level of Education for which Award is Granted:** Undergraduate **Number Awarded:** 15. **Funds Available:** $1,000-$2,500.
Eligibility Requirements: Applicant must be a student attending an accredited two-year college or four-year university in San Diego County who will continue college education in San Diego. Student must have a minimum 2.75 to 3.75 GPA on a 4.0 scale; demonstrated financial need; involved in serving the community as demonstrated by involvement in extra-curricular activities, community/church service, or work experience. **Application Requirements:** Applicants must submit a completed Common Scholarship Application together with personal statement; two letters of recommendation on official letterhead (written within the last six months); official transcript in an official and sealed envelope; and a copy of most recent tax form (Form 1040-pages 1 & 2; Form 1040A-pages 1 & 2; Form 1040EZ-page 1). **Deadline for Receipt:** January 28. **Additional Information:** Arzo Mansury, Dir. Scholarships at 619-814-1343, or scholarships@sdfoundation.org.

2012 ■ THE SAN DIEGO FOUNDATION

2508 Historic Decatur Rd., Ste. 200
San Diego, CA 92106
Tel: (619)235-2300
Fax: (619)239-1710
E-mail: info@sdfoundation.org
Web Site: http://www.sdfoundation.org
To support the education of students from California.

Title of Award: USA Freestyle Martial Arts Scholarships **Area, Field, or Subject:** General studies. **Level of Education for which Award is Granted:** Undergraduate **Number Awarded:** 2. **Funds Available:** $1,000-3,000.
Eligibility Requirements: Applicant must be a student currently attending or have attended USA Freestyle Martial Arts for at least two years; must have a minimum 2.50 GPA on a 4.0 scale; and either be graduating high school senior or current college student planning to attend an accredited two-year college, four-year university, or licensed trade/

vocational school in the U.S. **Application Requirements:** Applicants must submit a completed Common Scholarship Application together with personal statement; two letters of recommendation on official letterhead (written within the last six months); official transcript in an official and sealed envelope; a copy of most recent tax form (Form 1040-pages 1 & 2; Form 1040A-pages 1 & 2; Form 1040EZ-page 1); essay (maximum one page, typed, double-spaced) addressing "How you anticipate utilizing the skills you have learned from the study of Martial Arts to inspire a caring world"; and a letter on official letterhead from USA Freestyle Martial Arts verifying the applicant is/was a student at the school. **Deadline for Receipt:** January 28. **Additional Information:** Arzo Mansury, Dir. Scholarships at 619-814-1343, or scholarships@sdfoundation.org.

2013 ■ THE SAN DIEGO FOUNDATION

2508 Historic Decatur Rd., Ste. 200
San Diego, CA 92106
Tel: (619)235-2300
Fax: (619)239-1710
E-mail: info@sdfoundation.org
Web Site: http://www.sdfoundation.org
To support the education of students from California.

Title of Award: Weissbuch Family Scholarships **Area, Field, or Subject:** General studies. **Level of Education for which Award is Granted:** Undergraduate **Number Awarded:** 2. **Funds Available:** $1,500.
Eligibility Requirements: Applicant must be a student enrolled at the University of California, San Diego (UCSD); be in freshman, sophomore or junior year; and have a minimum 2.50 GPA on a 4.0 scale. Student must be employed part-time and have a demonstrated financial need. Applicants must be a resident of San Diego County for a minimum of four years. **Application Requirements:** Applicants must submit a completed Common Scholarship Application together with personal statement; two letters of recommendation on official letterhead (written within the last six months); official transcript in an official and sealed envelope; a copy of most recent tax form (Form 1040-pages 1 & 2; Form 1040A-pages 1 & 2; Form 1040EZ-page 1); a form verifying residency in San Diego County for at least four years for each period of 2004, 2005, 2006 and 2007, or 2005, 2006, 2007 and 2008 (bank statements, utility bills, insurance forms, high school transcripts, etc.); and a letter from current employer on official letterhead verifying employment. **Deadline for Receipt:** January 28. **Additional Information:** Arzo Mansury, Dir. Scholarships at 619-814-1343, or scholarships@sdfoundation.org.

2014 ■ THE SAN DIEGO FOUNDATION

2508 Historic Decatur Rd., Ste. 200
San Diego, CA 92106
Tel: (619)235-2300
Fax: (619)239-1710
E-mail: info@sdfoundation.org
Web Site: http://www.sdfoundation.org
To support the education of students from California.

Title of Award: Randy Williams Scholarships **Area, Field, or Subject:** General studies. **Level of Education for which Award is Granted:** Undergraduate **Number Awarded:** 1. **Funds Available:** $1,000.
Eligibility Requirements: Applicant must be a graduating high school senior; have participated in high school and/or club competitive swimming programs; planning to attend an accredited two-year college, four-year university or licensed trade/vocational school in the U.S.; and have a minimum 2.50 GPA on a 4.0 scale. **Application Requirements:** Applicants must submit a completed Common Scholarship Application together with personal statement; two letters of recommendation on official letterhead (written within the last six months); official transcript in an official and sealed envelope; a copy of most recent tax form (Form 1040-pages 1 & 2; Form 1040A-pages 1 & 2; Form 1040EZ -page 1); a letter of recommendation on official letterhead from the applicant's swim coach; and an essay (maximum one page, typed, double-spaced) describing the benefits enjoyed from being involved in competitive swimming and emphasizing how to utilize the skills learned in swimming in reaching the applicant's goals. **Deadline for Receipt:** January 28. **Additional Information:** Arzo Mansury, Dir. Scholarships at 619-814-1343, or scholarships@sdfoundation.org.

2015 ■ SASKATCHEWAN TRUCKING ASSOCIATION

1335 Wallace St.
Regina, SK, Canada S4N 3Z5

Tel: (306)569-9696
Free: 800-563-7623
Fax: (306)569-1008
Web Site: http://www.sasktrucking.com
To provide support to the employees and children of employees of association members.
Title of Award: Saskatchewan Trucking Association Scholarships **Area, Field, or Subject:** General studies. **Level of Education for which Award is Granted:** Undergraduate **Number Awarded:** 7. **Funds Available:** $5,000. **Duration:** One year.
Eligibility Requirements: Applicant must be a grade 12 graduate who is an employee or a child of an employee, a carrier or associate trade member of the association; must be a student returning to post-secondary education after an absence of more than five years. **Application Requirements:** Applicants must submit a transcript of record and the application form and must send it to Scholarship Applications, c/o Saskatchewan Trucking Association, 1335 Wallace St., Regina, Saskatchewan S4N 3Z5. **Deadline for Receipt:** June 30.

2016 ■ SCHOLARSHIP FOUNDATION OF SANTA BARBARA

PO Box 3620
Santa Barbara, CA 93130
Tel: (805)687-6065
Fax: (805)687-6031
E-mail: info@sbscholarship.org
Web Site: http://www.sbscholarship.org
To provide assistance to deserving students for continuing their education.
Title of Award: South Coast Area High School Senior Honors Scholarship Program **Area, Field, or Subject:** General studies. **Level of Education for which Award is Granted:** High School **Funds Available:** No specific amount.
Eligibility Requirements: Applicants must be graduating high school seniors who have attended at least four of the six secondary grade school years in Southern Santa Barbara County (Goleta, Santa Barbara, Carpinteria). **Application Requirements:** Applicants must submit completed application form; personal statement/essay; academic transcript; academic recommendation letter; and employer/supervisor recommendation letter in order to qualify for an interview. **Deadline for Receipt:** November 15.

2017 ■ SEASPACE INCORPORATION

PO Box 3753
Houston, TX 77253-3753
Tel: (713)467-6675
E-mail: seaspace@seaspace.org
Web Site: http://www.seaspace.org
To support marine-related courses of study.
Title of Award: Seaspace Scholarships **Area, Field, or Subject:** General studies. **Level of Education for which Award is Granted:** Postgraduate, Undergraduate **Funds Available:** No specific amount.
Eligibility Requirements: Applicants must be undergraduate students entering their junior or senior year and graduate students with an overall GPA of at least 3.3 on a 4.0 scale; must be enrolled or accepted full-time in an accredited U.S. college or university. **Application Requirements:** Applicants must submit a completed application form. **Additional Information:** Jesse Cancelmo at jesse@cancelmophoto.com.

2018 ■ SHORELINE COMMUNITY COLLEGE FOUNDATION

16101 Greenwood Ave. N, Ste. 1005
Shoreline, WA 98133-5696
Tel: (206)546-4755
Fax: (206)546-5826
E-mail: rmanchester@shoreline.edu
Web Site: http://www.shoreline.edu
To increase access and success of Shoreline Community College students.
Title of Award: Ina Knutsen Scholarships **Area, Field, or Subject:** General studies. **Level of Education for which Award is Granted:** Undergraduate **Funds Available:** No specific amount.
Eligibility Requirements: Applicants must be full-time or part-time students at the Shoreline/Lake Forest Park area who are enrolling at SCC. **Application Requirements:** Applicants must complete the application form.

2019 ■ SHORELINE COMMUNITY COLLEGE FOUNDATION

16101 Greenwood Ave. N, Ste. 1005
Shoreline, WA 98133-5696
Tel: (206)546-4755
Fax: (206)546-5826
E-mail: rmanchester@shoreline.edu
Web Site: http://www.shoreline.edu
To increase access and success of Shoreline Community College students.
Title of Award: Ron LaFreniere Business Scholarships **Area, Field, or Subject:** Business Administration. **Level of Education for which Award is Granted:** Undergraduate **Funds Available:** No specific amount.
Eligibility Requirements: Applicants must be part-time or full-time students who are currently enrolled at Shoreline Community College. **Application Requirements:** Applicants must complete the application form.

2020 ■ SHORELINE COMMUNITY COLLEGE FOUNDATION

16101 Greenwood Ave. N, Ste. 1005
Shoreline, WA 98133-5696
Tel: (206)546-4755
Fax: (206)546-5826
E-mail: rmanchester@shoreline.edu
Web Site: http://www.shoreline.edu
To increase access and success of Shoreline Community College students.
Title of Award: Shoreline Community College Academic Excellence Scholarships for Graduating High School Seniors **Area, Field, or Subject:** General studies. **Level of Education for which Award is Granted:** Undergraduate **Funds Available:** No specific amount.
Eligibility Requirements: Applicants must be graduating high school seniors in the Shoreline/Lake Forest Park area who are enrolling at SCC; must have demonstrated strong academic performance. **Application Requirements:** Applicants must complete the application form.

2021 ■ SHORELINE COMMUNITY COLLEGE FOUNDATION

16101 Greenwood Ave. N, Ste. 1005
Shoreline, WA 98133-5696
Tel: (206)546-4755
Fax: (206)546-5826
E-mail: rmanchester@shoreline.edu
Web Site: http://www.shoreline.edu
To increase access and success of Shoreline Community College students.
Title of Award: Shoreline Community College Academic Improvement Scholarships for Graduating High School Seniors **Area, Field, or Subject:** General studies. **Level of Education for which Award is Granted:** Undergraduate **Funds Available:** No specific amount.
Eligibility Requirements: Applicants must be graduating high school seniors in the Shoreline/Lake Forest Park area who are enrolling at SCC; must have demonstrated strong academic improvement in the last three semesters. **Application Requirements:** Applicants must complete the application form.

2022 ■ SHORELINE COMMUNITY COLLEGE FOUNDATION

16101 Greenwood Ave. N, Ste. 1005
Shoreline, WA 98133-5696
Tel: (206)546-4755
Fax: (206)546-5826
E-mail: rmanchester@shoreline.edu
Web Site: http://www.shoreline.edu
To increase access and success of Shoreline Community College students.
Title of Award: Shoreline Community College Continuing Students Scholarships **Area, Field, or Subject:** General studies. **Level of Education for which Award is Granted:** Undergraduate **Funds Available:** No specific amount.
Eligibility Requirements: Applicants must be part-time or full-time students who are currently enrolled at Shoreline Community College. **Application Requirements:** Applicants must complete the application form.

2023 ■ SHORELINE COMMUNITY COLLEGE FOUNDATION

16101 Greenwood Ave. N, Ste. 1005
Shoreline, WA 98133-5696

Tel: (206)546-4755
Fax: (206)546-5826
E-mail: rmanchester@shoreline.edu
Web Site: http://www.shoreline.edu
To increase access and success of Shoreline Community College students.

Title of Award: Shoreline Community College Part-Time Students Scholarships **Area, Field, or Subject:** General studies. **Level of Education for which Award is Granted:** Undergraduate **Funds Available:** No specific amount.

Eligibility Requirements: Applicants must be part-time students who are currently enrolled at Shoreline Community College. **Application Requirements:** Applicants must complete the application form.

2024 ■ SHORELINE COMMUNITY COLLEGE FOUNDATION
16101 Greenwood Ave. N, Ste. 1005
Shoreline, WA 98133-5696
Tel: (206)546-4755
Fax: (206)546-5826
E-mail: rmanchester@shoreline.edu
Web Site: http://www.shoreline.edu
To increase access and success of Shoreline Community College students.

Title of Award: Elizabeth Thomas Scholarships **Area, Field, or Subject:** General studies. **Level of Education for which Award is Granted:** Undergraduate **Funds Available:** No specific amount.

Eligibility Requirements: Applicants must be full-time or part-time students at the Shoreline/Lake Forest Park area who are enrolling at SCC. **Application Requirements:** Applicants must complete the application form.

2025 ■ SICKLE CELL DISEASE ASSOCIATION OF AMERICA
31 East Baltimore St., Ste. 800
Baltimore, MD 21202
Tel: (410)528-1555
Free: 800-421-8453
Fax: (410)528-1495
E-mail: scdaa@sicklecelldisease.org
Web Site: http://www.sicklecelldisease.org
To promote educational pursuits of individuals with sickle cell disease.

Title of Award: Kermit B. Nash Academic Scholarships **Area, Field, or Subject:** General studies. **Level of Education for which Award is Granted:** Undergraduate **Number Awarded:** 1. **Funds Available:** $5,000 per academic year. **Duration:** 4 years.

Eligibility Requirements: Applicants must be individuals with sickle cell disease (individuals with sickle cell trait are not eligible); and must be graduating high school seniors. **Application Requirements:** Applicants must submit an application form; transcripts; physician's certification of sickle cell status; and an essay. **Deadline for Receipt:** May. **Additional Information:** Mr. Manning, 800-421-8453 or lmanning@sicklecelldisease. org.

2026 ■ SIERRA STUDENT COALITION
600 14th St. NW, Ste. 750
Washington, DC 20005
888-564-6772
Fax: (202)637-0410
E-mail: sierra.student@sierraclub.org
Web Site: http://www.ssc.org
To provide financial support and to advocate for fairness, equity and strong communities.

Title of Award: Drum Major Institute Scholars **Area, Field, or Subject:** General studies. **Level of Education for which Award is Granted:** Undergraduate **Funds Available:** No specific amount.

Eligibility Requirements: Applicants must be sophomore and junior college students and must be 18 years old. **Application Requirements:** Applicants must check the available website for the required materials. **Additional Information:** DMI Scholars is a "Public Policy 101" for young people who want to shape the direction of our country. **Additional Information:** Sierra Student Coalition at the above address.

2027 ■ SIERRA STUDENT COALITION
600 14th St. NW, Ste. 750
Washington, DC 20005

888-564-6772
Fax: (202)637-0410
E-mail: sierra.student@sierraclub.org
Web Site: http://www.ssc.org
To provide financial assistance for deserving students and to offer career building skills and educational opportunities for participants as well as the opportunity to use these skills to build awareness about international sustainable development issues on their campuses and in their communities.

Title of Award: NWF's Women for Sustainable Development (WSD) Scholarships **Area, Field, or Subject:** General studies. **Level of Education for which Award is Granted:** Undergraduate **Funds Available:** No specific amount.

Eligibility Requirements: Applicants must be females enrolled in undergraduate schools in the U.S. and Mexico. **Application Requirements:** Applicants must check the available website for the required materials.

2028 ■ SIERRA STUDENT COALITION
600 14th St. NW, Ste. 750
Washington, DC 20005
888-564-6772
Fax: (202)637-0410
E-mail: sierra.student@sierraclub.org
Web Site: http://www.ssc.org
To support talented student organizers to implement the "Building Environmental Campus Community" (BECC) project during the upcoming fall semester on selected campuses nationwide and to conduct a hard-hitting campaign for clean energy on campus.

Title of Award: SSC-Building Environmental Campus Community (BECC) Fellowships **Area, Field, or Subject:** General studies. **Level of Education for which Award is Granted:** Undergraduate **Funds Available:** $1,500.

Eligibility Requirements: Applicants must meet the following criteria: currently enrolled full-time in a college or university; president or leader of an environmental group; demonstrated leadership and recruitment skills; willing and able to use the Sierra Student Coalition name for environmental group, or indicate affiliation with the SSC in campaign materials, media outreach, meetings, and events; and commitment to the BECC model of face-to-face outreach and contact to get students on campus involved in energy issues. **Application Requirements:** Applicants must check the available website for the required materials. **Additional Information:** Sierra Student Coalition at the above address.

2029 ■ SIERRA STUDENT COALITION
600 14th St. NW, Ste. 750
Washington, DC 20005
888-564-6772
Fax: (202)637-0410
E-mail: sierra.student@sierraclub.org
Web Site: http://www.ssc.org
To provide financial support, technical support and media assistance while a student implements a self-designed blueprint for social justice.

Title of Award: Young People For (YP4) Scholarships **Area, Field, or Subject:** General studies. **Level of Education for which Award is Granted:** Undergraduate **Number Awarded:** 200. **Funds Available:** No specific amount.

Eligibility Requirements: Applicants must be undergraduate students at two and four-year institutions. **Application Requirements:** Applicants must check the available website for the required materials. **Additional Information:** Sierra Student Coalition at the above address.

2030 ■ SIGMA KAPPA FOUNDATION
8733 Founder Rd.
Indianapolis, IN 46268
Tel: (317)872-3275
E-mail: alewis@sigmakappa.org
Web Site: http://www.sigmakappafoundation.org
To encourage and support the scholastic development of the collegiate and alumnae sisters of the foundation.

Title of Award: Beta Nu/Caryl Cordis D'hondt Scholarships **Area, Field, or Subject:** General studies. **Level of Education for which Award is Granted:** Undergraduate **Number Awarded:** 1. **Funds Available:** $500.

Eligibility Requirements: Applicants must be a initiated members in good standing (scholastic, financial, membership) of Beta Nu Chapter (Bradley University); must be in need of financial assistance; must be involved in Sigma Kappa and the Bradley University campus. **Application Requirements:** Application forms are available online. Applicant must submit the transcript and recommendation letter through online. **Deadline for Receipt:** March 1.

2031 ■ SIGMA KAPPA FOUNDATION
8733 Founder Rd.
Indianapolis, IN 46268
Tel: (317)872-3275
E-mail: alewis@sigmakappa.org
Web Site: http://www.sigmakappafoundation.org
To encourage and support the scholastic development of the collegiate and alumnae sisters of the foundation.
Title of Award: Beta Omega Scholarships **Area, Field, or Subject:** General studies. **Level of Education for which Award is Granted:** Undergraduate **Number Awarded:** 1. **Funds Available:** $1,000.
Eligibility Requirements: Applicants must be initiated, active members in good standing of Beta Omega Chapter (University of Nebraska, Omaha); must be a junior or senior class status (mid-year graduating seniors are eligible); must have a minimum cumulative GPA: 3.0; must be in need of financial assistance. **Application Requirements:** Application forms are available online. Applicant must submit the transcript and recommendation letter through online. **Deadline for Receipt:** March 1.

2032 ■ SIGMA KAPPA FOUNDATION
8733 Founder Rd.
Indianapolis, IN 46268
Tel: (317)872-3275
E-mail: alewis@sigmakappa.org
Web Site: http://www.sigmakappafoundation.org
To encourage and support the scholastic development of the collegiate and alumnae sisters of the foundation.
Title of Award: Beta Sigma Scholarships **Area, Field, or Subject:** General studies. **Level of Education for which Award is Granted:** Undergraduate **Number Awarded:** 1. **Funds Available:** $500.
Eligibility Requirements: Applicants must be an active, initiated members in good standing of Beta Sigma Chapter (Purdue University); must be a sophomore, junior, or senior class status (mid-year graduating seniors are eligible); must have a minimum cumulative GPA: 2.5; must be in need of financial assistance; must be Residing in the chapter house; must demonstrate leadership in their chapter and on campus. **Application Requirements:** Application forms are available online. Applicant must submit the transcript and recommendation letter through online. **Deadline for Receipt:** March 1.

2033 ■ SIGMA KAPPA FOUNDATION
8733 Founder Rd.
Indianapolis, IN 46268
Tel: (317)872-3275
E-mail: alewis@sigmakappa.org
Web Site: http://www.sigmakappafoundation.org
To encourage and support the scholastic development of the collegiate and alumnae sisters of the foundation.
Title of Award: Walta Wilkinson Carmichael Scholarships **Area, Field, or Subject:** General studies. **Level of Education for which Award is Granted:** Undergraduate **Number Awarded:** 1. **Funds Available:** $500.
Eligibility Requirements: Applicant must be a alumnae members in good standing, enrolled in a graduate program, who have demonstrated participation in collegiate chapter activities from their beginning year and continuing through the senior year of membership; must have a minimum undergraduate GPA: 3.0. **Application Requirements:** Application forms are available online. Applicant must submit the transcript and recommendation letter through online. **Deadline for Receipt:** March 1.

2034 ■ SIGMA KAPPA FOUNDATION
8733 Founder Rd.
Indianapolis, IN 46268
Tel: (317)872-3275
E-mail: alewis@sigmakappa.org
Web Site: http://www.sigmakappafoundation.org

To encourage and support the scholastic development of the collegiate and alumnae sisters of the foundation.
Title of Award: Christine Kerr Cawthorne Scholarships **Area, Field, or Subject:** General studies. **Level of Education for which Award is Granted:** Undergraduate **Number Awarded:** 1. **Funds Available:** $1,000.
Eligibility Requirements: Applicants must be initiated collegiate members in good standing of Alpha Chi Chapter (Georgetown College); must be a matriculated rising sophomore at the time the application is completed, and therefore a matriculated junior in the academic year for which the scholarship is issued; must have a minimum cumulative GPA: 3.0. **Application Requirements:** Application forms are available online. Applicant must submit the transcript and recommendation letter through online. **Deadline for Receipt:** March 1.

2035 ■ SIGMA KAPPA FOUNDATION
8733 Founder Rd.
Indianapolis, IN 46268
Tel: (317)872-3275
E-mail: alewis@sigmakappa.org
Web Site: http://www.sigmakappafoundation.org
To encourage and support the scholastic development of the collegiate and alumnae sisters of the foundation.
Title of Award: Delta Chi Alumnae Memorial Scholarships **Area, Field, or Subject:** General studies. **Level of Education for which Award is Granted:** Undergraduate **Number Awarded:** 1. **Funds Available:** $400.
Eligibility Requirements: Applicants must be a initiated members of Delta Chi Chapter (University of Central Oklahoma); must be a junior or senior class status; must have a minimum cumulative GPA: 3.25; must be currently enrolled in 12 hours or more. **Application Requirements:** Application forms are available online. Applicant must submit the transcript and recommendation letter through online. **Deadline for Receipt:** March 1.

2036 ■ SIGMA KAPPA FOUNDATION
8733 Founder Rd.
Indianapolis, IN 46268
Tel: (317)872-3275
E-mail: alewis@sigmakappa.org
Web Site: http://www.sigmakappafoundation.org
To encourage and support the scholastic development of the collegiate and alumnae sisters of the foundation.
Title of Award: Wilma Sackett Dressel Scholarships **Area, Field, or Subject:** General studies. **Level of Education for which Award is Granted:** Undergraduate **Number Awarded:** 1. **Funds Available:** $500.
Eligibility Requirements: Applicant must be a initiated member in good standing of Alpha Tau Chapter (Michigan State University); must demonstrate financial need. **Application Requirements:** Application forms are available online. Applicant must submit the transcript and recommendation letter through online. **Deadline for Receipt:** March 1.

2037 ■ SIGMA KAPPA FOUNDATION
8733 Founder Rd.
Indianapolis, IN 46268
Tel: (317)872-3275
E-mail: alewis@sigmakappa.org
Web Site: http://www.sigmakappafoundation.org
To encourage and support the scholastic development of the collegiate and alumnae sisters of the foundation.
Title of Award: Epsilon Epsilon Scholarships **Area, Field, or Subject:** General studies. **Level of Education for which Award is Granted:** Undergraduate **Number Awarded:** 1. **Funds Available:** $500.
Eligibility Requirements: Applicant must be a initiated member in good standing of Epsilon Epsilon Chapter (University of Georgia); must be a junior or senior class status; must have a minimum cumulative GPA 3.00. **Application Requirements:** Application forms are available online. Applicant must submit the transcript and recommendation letter through online. **Deadline for Receipt:** March 1.

2038 ■ SIGMA KAPPA FOUNDATION
8733 Founder Rd.
Indianapolis, IN 46268
Tel: (317)872-3275

E-mail: alewis@sigmakappa.org
Web Site: http://www.sigmakappafoundation.org
To encourage and support the scholastic development of the collegiate and alumnae sisters of the foundation.
Title of Award: Epsilon Tau Scholarships **Area, Field, or Subject:** General studies. **Level of Education for which Award is Granted:** Undergraduate **Number Awarded:** 1. **Funds Available:** $500.
Eligibility Requirements: Applicant must be a initiated member in good standing (scholastic, financial, membership) of Epsilon Tau Chapter (California State University at Fullerton); must demonstrate financial need and involvement in Sigma Kappa, campus, and the community. **Application Requirements:** Application forms are available online. Applicant must submit the transcript and recommendation letter through online. **Deadline for Receipt:** March 1.

2039 ■ SIGMA KAPPA FOUNDATION
8733 Founder Rd.
Indianapolis, IN 46268
Tel: (317)872-3275
E-mail: alewis@sigmakappa.org
Web Site: http://www.sigmakappafoundation.org
To encourage and support the scholastic development of the collegiate and alumnae sisters of the foundation.
Title of Award: Marian Johnson Frutiger Scholarships **Area, Field, or Subject:** General studies. **Level of Education for which Award is Granted:** Undergraduate **Number Awarded:** 3. **Funds Available:** $1,000.
Eligibility Requirements: Candidates must be a initiated member in good financial standing of the foundation; must have a minimum cumulative GPA: 3.0; must exemplifies the ideals and standards of Sigma Kappa; must exhibits outstanding sisterhood and must demonstrate leadership in the Greek system. **Application Requirements:** Application forms are available online. Applicant must submit the transcript and recommendation letter through online. **Deadline for Receipt:** March 1.

2040 ■ SIGMA KAPPA FOUNDATION
8733 Founder Rd.
Indianapolis, IN 46268
Tel: (317)872-3275
E-mail: alewis@sigmakappa.org
Web Site: http://www.sigmakappafoundation.org
To encourage and support the scholastic development of the collegiate and alumnae sisters of the foundation.
Title of Award: Gamma Iota Scholarships - Gamma Tau **Area, Field, or Subject:** General studies. **Level of Education for which Award is Granted:** Undergraduate **Number Awarded:** 1. **Funds Available:** $500.
Eligibility Requirements: Applicants must be a initiated members attending Kappa Eta (Texas Christian University), Zeta Nu (University of Texas at San Antonio), Gamma Tau (Midwestern State), or Zeta Kappa (Angelo State); must have a minimum cumulative GPA: 3.0; must held or currently hold a Sorority position; must demonstrate involvement in campus and community activities; must be in need of financial assistance. **Application Requirements:** Application forms are available online. Applicant must submit the transcript and recommendation letter through online. **Deadline for Receipt:** March 1.

2041 ■ SIGMA KAPPA FOUNDATION
8733 Founder Rd.
Indianapolis, IN 46268
Tel: (317)872-3275
E-mail: alewis@sigmakappa.org
Web Site: http://www.sigmakappafoundation.org
To encourage and support the scholastic development of the collegiate and alumnae sisters of the foundation.
Title of Award: Gamma Iota Scholarships - Kappa Eta **Area, Field, or Subject:** General studies. **Level of Education for which Award is Granted:** Undergraduate **Number Awarded:** 1. **Funds Available:** $500.
Eligibility Requirements: Applicants must be a initiated members attending Kappa Eta (Texas Christian University), Zeta Nu (University of Texas at San Antonio), Gamma Tau (Midwestern State), or Zeta Kappa (Angelo State); must have a minimum cumulative GPA: 3.0; must have held or currently hold a Sorority position; must demonstrate involvement in campus and community activities; must be in need of financial as-

sistance. **Application Requirements:** Application forms are available online. Applicant must submit the transcript and recommendation letter through online. **Deadline for Receipt:** March 1.

2042 ■ SIGMA KAPPA FOUNDATION
8733 Founder Rd.
Indianapolis, IN 46268
Tel: (317)872-3275
E-mail: alewis@sigmakappa.org
Web Site: http://www.sigmakappafoundation.org
To encourage and support the scholastic development of the collegiate and alumnae sisters of the foundation.
Title of Award: Gamma Iota Scholarships - Zeta Kappa **Area, Field, or Subject:** General studies. **Level of Education for which Award is Granted:** Undergraduate **Number Awarded:** 1. **Funds Available:** $500.
Eligibility Requirements: Applicants must be a initiated members attending Kappa Eta (Texas Christian University), Zeta Nu (University of Texas at San Antonio), Gamma Tau (Midwestern State), or Zeta Kappa (Angelo State); must have a minimum cumulative GPA: 3.0; must have held or currently hold a Sorority position; must demonstrate involvement in campus and community activities; must be in need of financial assistance. **Application Requirements:** Application forms are available online. Applicant must submit the transcript and recommendation letter through online. **Deadline for Receipt:** March 1.

2043 ■ SIGMA KAPPA FOUNDATION
8733 Founder Rd.
Indianapolis, IN 46268
Tel: (317)872-3275
E-mail: alewis@sigmakappa.org
Web Site: http://www.sigmakappafoundation.org
To encourage and support the scholastic development of the collegiate and alumnae sisters of the foundation.
Title of Award: Gamma Iota Scholarships - Zeta Nu **Area, Field, or Subject:** General studies. **Level of Education for which Award is Granted:** Undergraduate **Number Awarded:** 1. **Funds Available:** $500.
Eligibility Requirements: Applicant must be a initiated members attending Kappa Eta (Texas Christian University), Zeta Nu (University of Texas at San Antonio), Gamma Tau (Midwestern State), or Zeta Kappa (Angelo State); must have a minimum cumulative GPA: 3.0; must have held or currently hold a Sorority position; must have demonstrate involvement in campus and community activities; must be in need of financial assistance. **Application Requirements:** Application forms are available online. Applicant must submit the transcript and recommendation letter through online. **Deadline for Receipt:** March 1.

2044 ■ SIGMA KAPPA FOUNDATION
8733 Founder Rd.
Indianapolis, IN 46268
Tel: (317)872-3275
E-mail: alewis@sigmakappa.org
Web Site: http://www.sigmakappafoundation.org
To encourage and support the scholastic development of the collegiate and alumnae sisters of the foundation.
Title of Award: Lucile Cheever Graubart/Lambda Scholarships **Area, Field, or Subject:** General studies. **Level of Education for which Award is Granted:** Undergraduate **Number Awarded:** 2. **Funds Available:** $750.
Eligibility Requirements: Applicants must be a initiated members of Lambda Chapter (University of California, Berkeley) in good standing; must be in need of financial assistance. **Application Requirements:** Application forms are available online. Applicant must submit the transcript and recommendation letter through online. **Deadline for Receipt:** March 1.

2045 ■ SIGMA KAPPA FOUNDATION
8733 Founder Rd.
Indianapolis, IN 46268
Tel: (317)872-3275
E-mail: alewis@sigmakappa.org
Web Site: http://www.sigmakappafoundation.org
To encourage and support the scholastic development of the collegiate and alumnae sisters of the foundation.

Title of Award: Elise Reed Jenkins Memorial Scholarships - Gamma Lambda **Area, Field, or Subject:** General studies. **Level of Education for which Award is Granted:** Undergraduate **Number Awarded:** 1. **Funds Available:** $500.
Eligibility Requirements: Applicants must be an undergraduate member of either Alpha Delta Chapter (University of Tennessee, Knoxville), Gamma Lambda Chapter (East Tennessee State University), or Gamma Psi Chapter (Tennessee Wesleyan); must be a loyal members of Sigma Kappa for at least two, and preferably three years; must have a minimum cumulative GPA of: 3.0. **Application Requirements:** Application forms are available online. Applicant must submit the transcript and recommendation letter through online. **Deadline for Receipt:** March 1.

2046 ■ SIGMA KAPPA FOUNDATION
8733 Founder Rd.
Indianapolis, IN 46268
Tel: (317)872-3275
E-mail: alewis@sigmakappa.org
Web Site: http://www.sigmakappafoundation.org
To encourage and support the scholastic development of the collegiate and alumnae sisters of the foundation.
Title of Award: Elise Reed Jenkins Memorial Scholarships - Gamma Psi **Area, Field, or Subject:** General studies. **Level of Education for which Award is Granted:** Undergraduate **Number Awarded:** 1. **Funds Available:** $500.
Eligibility Requirements: Applicants must be an undergraduate member of either Alpha Delta Chapter (University of Tennessee, Knoxville), Gamma Lambda Chapter (East Tennessee State University), or Gamma Psi Chapter (Tennessee Wesleyan); must be loyal members of Sigma Kappa for at least two, and preferably three years; must have a minimum cumulative GPA of: 3.0. **Application Requirements:** Application forms are available online. Applicant must submit the transcript and recommendation letter through online. **Deadline for Receipt:** March 1.

2047 ■ SIGMA KAPPA FOUNDATION
8733 Founder Rd.
Indianapolis, IN 46268
Tel: (317)872-3275
E-mail: alewis@sigmakappa.org
Web Site: http://www.sigmakappafoundation.org
To encourage and support the scholastic development of the collegiate and alumnae sisters of the foundation.
Title of Award: Kappa Zeta Scholarships **Area, Field, or Subject:** General studies. **Level of Education for which Award is Granted:** Undergraduate **Number Awarded:** 1. **Funds Available:** $750.
Eligibility Requirements: Applicants must be a initiated members of Kappa Zeta Chapter (Elon University) in good standing; must demonstrate outstanding leadership and service to the chapter, Panhellenic, and the University; must have a minimum cumulative GPA: 3.4. **Application Requirements:** Application forms are available online. Applicant must submit the transcript and recommendation letter through online. **Deadline for Receipt:** March 1.

2048 ■ SIGMA KAPPA FOUNDATION
8733 Founder Rd.
Indianapolis, IN 46268
Tel: (317)872-3275
E-mail: alewis@sigmakappa.org
Web Site: http://www.sigmakappafoundation.org
To encourage and support the scholastic development of the collegiate and alumnae sisters of the foundation.
Title of Award: Joan Reagin McNeill Scholarships - Alpha Theta **Area, Field, or Subject:** General studies. **Level of Education for which Award is Granted:** Undergraduate **Number Awarded:** 1. **Funds Available:** $500.
Eligibility Requirements: Applicants must be an active sophomore, junior, or senior members of Alpha Theta Chapter (University of Louisville) or Theta Phi Chapter (University of Tennessee, Chattanooga) in good standing with at least one year remaining for completion of an undergraduate degree; must have a minimum cumulative GPA: 3.25. **Application Requirements:** Application forms are available online. Applicant must submit the transcript and recommendation letter through online. **Deadline for Receipt:** March 1.

2049 ■ SIGMA KAPPA FOUNDATION
8733 Founder Rd.
Indianapolis, IN 46268
Tel: (317)872-3275
E-mail: alewis@sigmakappa.org
Web Site: http://www.sigmakappafoundation.org
To encourage and support the scholastic development of the collegiate and alumnae sisters of the foundation.
Title of Award: Joan Reagin McNeill Scholarships - Theta Phi **Area, Field, or Subject:** General studies. **Level of Education for which Award is Granted:** Undergraduate **Number Awarded:** 1. **Funds Available:** $500.
Eligibility Requirements: Applicants must be a active sophomore, junior, or senior members of Alpha Theta Chapter (University of Louisville) or Theta Phi Chapter (University of Tennessee, Chattanooga) in good standing with at least one year remaining for completion of an undergraduate degree; must have a minimum cumulative GPA: 3.25. **Application Requirements:** Application forms are available online. Applicant must submit the transcript and recommendation letter through online. **Deadline for Receipt:** March 1.

2050 ■ SIGMA KAPPA FOUNDATION
8733 Founder Rd.
Indianapolis, IN 46268
Tel: (317)872-3275
E-mail: alewis@sigmakappa.org
Web Site: http://www.sigmakappafoundation.org
To encourage and support the scholastic development of the collegiate and alumnae sisters of the foundation.
Title of Award: Evelyn S. Nish Scholarships **Area, Field, or Subject:** General studies. **Level of Education for which Award is Granted:** Undergraduate **Number Awarded:** 1. **Funds Available:** $1,000.
Eligibility Requirements: Applicants must be initiated, active members in good standing of the Theta Chapter (University of Illinois); must be a junior or senior student enrolled during the academic year that the scholarship is granted; must have a minimum cumulative GPA: 3.0. **Application Requirements:** Application forms are available online. Applicant must submit the transcript and recommendation letter through online. **Deadline for Receipt:** March 1.

2051 ■ SIGMA KAPPA FOUNDATION
8733 Founder Rd.
Indianapolis, IN 46268
Tel: (317)872-3275
E-mail: alewis@sigmakappa.org
Web Site: http://www.sigmakappafoundation.org
To encourage and support the scholastic development of the collegiate and alumnae sisters of the foundation.
Title of Award: Mary Turnbull Schacht Memorial Scholarships **Area, Field, or Subject:** General studies. **Level of Education for which Award is Granted:** Undergraduate **Number Awarded:** 1. **Funds Available:** $500.
Eligibility Requirements: Applicants must be initiated, active members in good standing of the Lambda Chapter (University of California, Berkeley); must demonstrate outstanding leadership and service provided to the chapter, panhellenic and the University of California, Berkeley; must have a minimum cumulative GPA: 3.0. **Application Requirements:** Application forms are available online. Applicant must submit the transcript and recommendation letter through online. **Deadline for Receipt:** March 1.

2052 ■ SIGMA KAPPA FOUNDATION
8733 Founder Rd.
Indianapolis, IN 46268
Tel: (317)872-3275
E-mail: alewis@sigmakappa.org
Web Site: http://www.sigmakappafoundation.org
To encourage and support the scholastic development of the collegiate and alumnae sisters of the foundation.
Title of Award: Sigma Kappa Foundation Alumnae Continuing Education Scholarships **Area, Field, or Subject:** General studies. **Level of Education for which Award is Granted:** Undergraduate **Number Awarded:** 5. **Funds Available:** $1,000.

Eligibility Requirements: Applicant must be a alumnae currently possessing an undergraduate degree from a four-year institution and having been accepted/enrolled in an advanced degree program; must have a minimum cumulative GPA: 3.0. **Application Requirements:** Application forms are available online. Applicant must submit the transcript and recommendation letter through online. **Deadline for Receipt:** March 1.

2053 ■ SIGMA KAPPA FOUNDATION
8733 Founder Rd.
Indianapolis, IN 46268
Tel: (317)872-3275
E-mail: alewis@sigmakappa.org
Web Site: http://www.sigmakappafoundation.org
To encourage and support the scholastic development of the collegiate and alumnae sisters of the foundation.
Title of Award: Sigma Kappa Foundation Founders' Scholarships **Area, Field, or Subject:** General studies. **Level of Education for which Award is Granted:** Undergraduate **Number Awarded:** 5. **Funds Available:** $1,000.
Eligibility Requirements: Applicants should be active, initiated, continuing members in good standing; must have a minimum cumulative GPA: 3.0; must demonstrate a leadership role on campus (student government, chapter officer, Panhellenic officer). **Application Requirements:** Application forms are available online. Applicant must submit the transcript and recommendation letter through online. **Deadline for Receipt:** March 1.

2054 ■ SIGMA KAPPA FOUNDATION
8733 Founder Rd.
Indianapolis, IN 46268
Tel: (317)872-3275
E-mail: alewis@sigmakappa.org
Web Site: http://www.sigmakappafoundation.org
To encourage and support the scholastic development of the collegiate and alumnae sisters of the foundation.
Title of Award: Sigma Kappa Foundation Michigan Scholarships **Area, Field, or Subject:** General studies. **Level of Education for which Award is Granted:** Undergraduate **Number Awarded:** 1. **Funds Available:** $250.
Eligibility Requirements: Applicant must be a Michigan resident as defined by the university of attendance; must be initiated in Sigma Kappa, currently active, and in good standing with the chapter at a College or University in Michigan; must have at least two semesters of undergraduate study remaining at the time of the award; must have a minimum GPA: 2.5 and in good standing with the university of enrollment. Applicant may not have received the scholarship previously. **Application Requirements:** Application forms are available online. Applicant must submit the transcript and recommendation letter through online. **Deadline for Receipt:** March 1.

2055 ■ SIGMA KAPPA FOUNDATION
8733 Founder Rd.
Indianapolis, IN 46268
Tel: (317)872-3275
E-mail: alewis@sigmakappa.org
Web Site: http://www.sigmakappafoundation.org
To encourage and support the scholastic development of the collegiate and alumnae sisters of the foundation.
Title of Award: Elin J. Stene/Xi Scholarships **Area, Field, or Subject:** General studies. **Level of Education for which Award is Granted:** Undergraduate **Number Awarded:** 2. **Funds Available:** $1,000.
Eligibility Requirements: Applicants must be initiated, active members in good standing of Xi Chapter (University of Kansas); must be a junior or senior class status (mid-year graduating seniors are eligible); must have a minimum cumulative GPA: 3.0; must be in need of financial assistance. **Application Requirements:** Application forms are available online. Applicant must submit the transcript and recommendation letter through online. **Deadline for Receipt:** March 1.

2056 ■ SIGMA KAPPA FOUNDATION
8733 Founder Rd.
Indianapolis, IN 46268
Tel: (317)872-3275
E-mail: alewis@sigmakappa.org

Web Site: http://www.sigmakappafoundation.org
To encourage and support the scholastic development of the collegiate and alumnae sisters of the foundation.
Title of Award: Lorraine E. Swain Scholarships **Area, Field, or Subject:** General studies. **Level of Education for which Award is Granted:** Undergraduate **Number Awarded:** 1. **Funds Available:** $500.
Eligibility Requirements: Applicant must initiated in Sigma Kappa, currently active, and in good standing with the chapter at a College or University in Colorado. **Application Requirements:** Application forms are available online. Applicant must submit the transcript and recommendation letter through online. **Deadline for Receipt:** March 1.

2057 ■ SIGMA KAPPA FOUNDATION
8733 Founder Rd.
Indianapolis, IN 46268
Tel: (317)872-3275
E-mail: alewis@sigmakappa.org
Web Site: http://www.sigmakappafoundation.org
To encourage and support the scholastic development of the collegiate and alumnae sisters of the foundation.
Title of Award: Theta/Caryl Cordis D'hondt Scholarships **Area, Field, or Subject:** General studies. **Level of Education for which Award is Granted:** Undergraduate **Number Awarded:** 1. **Funds Available:** $500.
Eligibility Requirements: Applicants must be initiated, active members in good standing with Theta Tau Chapter (Kansas State University); must be a junior or senior class status (mid-year graduating seniors are also eligible); must have a minimum cumulative GPA: 3.0; must be in need of financial assistance. **Application Requirements:** Application forms are available online. Applicant must submit the transcript and recommendation letter through online. **Deadline for Receipt:** March 1.

2058 ■ SIGMA KAPPA FOUNDATION
8733 Founder Rd.
Indianapolis, IN 46268
Tel: (317)872-3275
E-mail: alewis@sigmakappa.org
Web Site: http://www.sigmakappafoundation.org
To encourage and support the scholastic development of the collegiate and alumnae sisters of the foundation.
Title of Award: Theta Tau Scholarships **Area, Field, or Subject:** General studies. **Level of Education for which Award is Granted:** Undergraduate **Number Awarded:** 1. **Funds Available:** $1,000.
Eligibility Requirements: Applicant must be initiated, active members in good standing with Theta Tau Chapter (Kansas State University); must be a junior or senior class status (mid-year graduating seniors are also eligible); must have a minimum cumulative GPA: 3.0; must be in need of financial assistance. **Application Requirements:** Application forms are available online. Applicant must submit the transcript and recommendation letter through online. **Deadline for Receipt:** March 1.

2059 ■ SIGMA KAPPA FOUNDATION
8733 Founder Rd.
Indianapolis, IN 46268
Tel: (317)872-3275
E-mail: alewis@sigmakappa.org
Web Site: http://www.sigmakappafoundation.org
To encourage and support the scholastic development of the collegiate and alumnae sisters of the foundation.
Title of Award: Barber Owen Thomas Scholarships **Area, Field, or Subject:** General studies. **Level of Education for which Award is Granted:** Undergraduate **Number Awarded:** 1. **Funds Available:** $500.
Eligibility Requirements: Applicant must be an active members in good standing of the Beta Sigma Chapter (Purdue University); must be a junior or senior in class status (mid-year graduating seniors are also eligible); must have a minimum cumulative GPA: 2.5; must be in need of financial assistance; must be residing in the chapter house. **Application Requirements:** Application forms are available online. Applicant must submit the transcript and recommendation letter through online. **Deadline for Receipt:** March 1.

2060 ■ SIGMA KAPPA FOUNDATION
8733 Founder Rd.
Indianapolis, IN 46268

Tel: (317)872-3275
E-mail: alewis@sigmakappa.org
Web Site: http://www.sigmakappafoundation.org
To encourage and support the scholastic development of the collegiate and alumnae sisters of the foundation.
Title of Award: Irma E. Voigt Memorial Scholarships **Area, Field, or Subject:** General studies. **Level of Education for which Award is Granted:** Undergraduate **Number Awarded:** 1. **Funds Available:** $500.
Eligibility Requirements: Applicants must be a initiated members of Beta Upsilon Chapter (Ohio University) in good standing; must be a junior class status, currently enrolled in 12 or more hours; must have a minimum cumulative GPA: 3.0; must be actively involved in her chapter, on campus, and in the community. **Application Requirements:** Application forms are available online. Applicant must submit the transcript and recommendation letter through online. **Deadline for Receipt:** March 1.

2061 ■ SIGMA KAPPA FOUNDATION
8733 Founder Rd.
Indianapolis, IN 46268
Tel: (317)872-3275
E-mail: alewis@sigmakappa.org
Web Site: http://www.sigmakappafoundation.org
To encourage and support the scholastic development of the collegiate and alumnae sisters of the foundation.
Title of Award: Alice Hersey Wick Scholarships **Area, Field, or Subject:** General studies. **Level of Education for which Award is Granted:** Undergraduate **Number Awarded:** 1. **Funds Available:** $500.
Eligibility Requirements: Applicant must be initiated collegiate members in good standing; must have a minimum cumulative GPA of 3.0. **Application Requirements:** Application forms are available online. Applicant must submit the transcript and recommendation letter through online. **Deadline for Receipt:** March 1.

2062 ■ SIGMA KAPPA FOUNDATION
8733 Founder Rd.
Indianapolis, IN 46268
Tel: (317)872-3275
E-mail: alewis@sigmakappa.org
Web Site: http://www.sigmakappafoundation.org
To encourage and support the scholastic development of the collegiate and alumnae sisters of the foundation.
Title of Award: Andrea Will Memorial Scholarships **Area, Field, or Subject:** General studies. **Level of Education for which Award is Granted:** Undergraduate **Number Awarded:** 1. **Funds Available:** $500.
Eligibility Requirements: Applicants must be a new initiates in good standing of Gamma Mu Chapter, matriculating at Eastern Illinois University; must have a minimum cumulative GPA: 3.0; must demonstrate involvement in co-curricular activities, and evidence of leadership qualities and experience. **Application Requirements:** Application forms are available online. Applicant must submit the transcript and recommendation letter through online. **Deadline for Receipt:** March 1.

2063 ■ SILICON VALLEY COMMUNITY FOUNDATION
2240 W El Camino Real Ste. 300
Mountain View, CA 94040-1498
Tel: (650)450-5400
Fax: (650)450-5401
Web Site: http://www.siliconvalleycf.org
To support high school graduates of high academic achievement who would be unable to pursue higher education without financial assistance.
Title of Award: Hazel Reed Baumeister Scholarship Program **Area, Field, or Subject:** General Studies. **Level of Education for which Award is Granted:** Undergraduate **Number Awarded:** 15. **Funds Available:** maximum award amount: $5,000.
Eligibility Requirements: Applicants must be current graduating seniors or graduates of a public or private high school in San Mateo County or Santa Clara County; must be United States citizens; must have demonstrated financial hardship; must have earned a minimum cumulative grade point average of 3.3. **Application Requirements:** Applicants must check the available website for the required materials. **Deadline for Receipt:** March 5. **Additional Information:** Silicon Valley Community Foundation at the above address

2064 ■ SILICON VALLEY COMMUNITY FOUNDATION
2240 W El Camino Real Ste. 300
Mountain View, CA 94040-1498
Tel: (650)450-5400
Fax: (650)450-5401
Web Site: http://www.siliconvalleycf.org
To enable high school graduates to pursue courses of study they would otherwise be unable to follow due to limited financial means.
Title of Award: Crain Educational Grants Program **Area, Field, or Subject:** General Studies. **Level of Education for which Award is Granted:** Undergraduate **Number Awarded:** 10. **Funds Available:** Maximum award amount: $5,000.
Eligibility Requirements: Applicants must be current graduating seniors or graduates of a public or private high school in San Mateo County or Santa Clara County; must be United States citizens; must have demonstrated financial hardship; must have a minimum cumulative grade point average of 3.3. **Application Requirements:** Applicants must check the available website to download the application form online. **Deadline for Receipt:** March 5. **Additional Information:** Silicon Valley Community Foundation at the above address

2065 ■ SILICON VALLEY COMMUNITY FOUNDATION
2240 W El Camino Real Ste. 300
Mountain View, CA 94040-1498
Tel: (650)450-5400
Fax: (650)450-5401
Web Site: http://www.siliconvalleycf.org
To provide financial support to those students who are in need.
Title of Award: Curry Award for Girls and Young Women **Area, Field, or Subject:** General Studies. **Level of Education for which Award is Granted:** Undergraduate **Number Awarded:** 10. **Funds Available:** $1,000 per award.
Eligibility Requirements: Applicants must be current residents of San Mateo County; must be United States citizens or legal residents; must be young women 16 to 26 years old. **Application Requirements:** Applicants must check the available website for the required materials. **Deadline for Receipt:** March 5. **Additional Information:** Silicon Valley Community Foundation at the above address

2066 ■ SILICON VALLEY COMMUNITY FOUNDATION
2240 W El Camino Real Ste. 300
Mountain View, CA 94040-1498
Tel: (650)450-5400
Fax: (650)450-5401
Web Site: http://www.siliconvalleycf.org
To help promising high school and junior college students pursue higher education at an accredited two- or four-year college or vocational school.
Title of Award: Eustace-Kwan Family Foundation Scholarships **Area, Field, or Subject:** General Studies. **Level of Education for which Award is Granted:** Undergraduate **Number Awarded:** 12. **Funds Available:** Maximum award amount: $2,500.
Eligibility Requirements: Applicants must be current residents of San Mateo County or Northern Santa Clara County; must be current graduating high school seniors planning to attend an accredited two- or four-year college or vocational school or current community college students planning to transfer to a four-year college; must be United States citizens or legal residents; must have a cumulative grade point average of 3.5 on a 4.0 scale; must have demonstrated community involvement. **Application Requirements:** Applicants must check the available website for more information. **Deadline for Receipt:** March 5. **Additional Information:** Silicon Valley Community Foundation at the above address

2067 ■ SILICON VALLEY COMMUNITY FOUNDATION
2240 W El Camino Real Ste. 300
Mountain View, CA 94040-1498
Tel: (650)450-5400
Fax: (650)450-5401
Web Site: http://www.siliconvalleycf.org
To provide financial assistance to those students who are in need.
Title of Award: Dr. Mary Finegold Scholarships **Area, Field, or Subject:** Science. **Level of Education for which Award is Granted:** Undergraduate **Number Awarded:** 1. **Funds Available:** $3,000.
Eligibility Requirements: Applicants must be senior females graduating from a public or private high school in San Mateo or Northern Santa Clara

County; must be United States citizens; must intend to complete a four-year degree in the sciences; must have a minimum cumulative grade point average of 3.0 on a 4.0 scale; must have demonstrated financial hardship; must be active in athletics. **Application Requirements:** Applicants must check the available website for the required materials. **Deadline for Receipt:** March 5. **Additional Information:** Silicon Valley Community Foundation at the above address

2068 ■ SILICON VALLEY COMMUNITY FOUNDATION
2240 W El Camino Real Ste. 300
Mountain View, CA 94040-1498
Tel: (650)450-5400
Fax: (650)450-5401
Web Site: http://www.siliconvalleycf.org
To provide financial assistance to those students who are in need.
Title of Award: Bobette Bibo Gugliotta Memorial Scholarships for Creative Writing **Area, Field, or Subject:** General Studies. **Level of Education for which Award is Granted:** Undergraduate **Funds Available:** $2,000 for undergraduate; $1,000 for graduating high school seniors.
Eligibility Requirements: Applicants must be current graduating seniors or graduates of a public or private high school in San Mateo County or Northern Santa Clara County; must be accepted to or awaiting acceptance to a two- or four- year college or university; must be United States citizens. **Application Requirements:** Applicants must check the available website for the required materials. **Deadline for Receipt:** March 5. **Additional Information:** Silicon Valley Community Foundation at the above address

2069 ■ SILICON VALLEY COMMUNITY FOUNDATION
2240 W El Camino Real Ste. 300
Mountain View, CA 94040-1498
Tel: (650)450-5400
Fax: (650)450-5401
Web Site: http://www.siliconvalleycf.org
To support current community college students who wish to transfer to a four-year institution.
Title of Award: Kumin Scholars Program **Area, Field, or Subject:** General Studies. **Level of Education for which Award is Granted:** Undergraduate **Number Awarded:** 15. **Funds Available:** Maximum award amount: $18,000. **Duration:** Over 6 years.
Eligibility Requirements: Applicants must be United States citizens or legal residents; must be enrolled part-time or full-time in a community college; must have completed at least 20 graded semester or quarter units; must have earned a minimum GPA of 2.5. **Application Requirements:** Applicants must check the available website for the required materials. **Deadline for Receipt:** June 25. **Additional Information:** Silicon Valley Community Foundation at the above address

2070 ■ SILICON VALLEY COMMUNITY FOUNDATION
2240 W El Camino Real Ste. 300
Mountain View, CA 94040-1498
Tel: (650)450-5400
Fax: (650)450-5401
Web Site: http://www.siliconvalleycf.org
To broaden the educational opportunities of students who, by virtue of their academic and extracurricular achievement, demonstrate a passion for science and technology that extends beyond the classroom.
Title of Award: Rambus Scholarship Fund **Area, Field, or Subject:** General Studies. **Level of Education for which Award is Granted:** Undergraduate **Number Awarded:** 8. **Funds Available:** Maximum award amount: $10,000.
Eligibility Requirements: Applicants must be graduating students from high schools located in either Mountain View or Los Altos, California, and planning to attend a four year college/university. Applicants must have a minimum of 3.0 GPA (on a 4.0 scale) for grades 10-12. **Application Requirements:** Applicants must check the available website for the required materials. **Additional Information:** For more information and application visit: http://www.rambus.com/scholarship

2071 ■ SILICON VALLEY COMMUNITY FOUNDATION
2240 W El Camino Real Ste. 300
Mountain View, CA 94040-1498

Tel: (650)450-5400
Fax: (650)450-5401
Web Site: http://www.siliconvalleycf.org
To provide financial assistance to those students who are in need.
Title of Award: Ruppert Educational Grant Program **Area, Field, or Subject:** General Studies. **Level of Education for which Award is Granted:** Undergraduate **Number Awarded:** 30. **Funds Available:** $2,000.
Eligibility Requirements: Applicants must be United States citizens; must be current graduating seniors attending high schools in San Mateo County or Northern Santa Clara County (Daly City through Mountain View). Applicants must demonstrate: financial hardship; evidence of partial self-support (e.g., savings from summer jobs, part-time work, etc.); community involvement; academic promise and GPA improvement during high school years. **Application Requirements:** Applicants must check the available website for the required materials. **Deadline for Receipt:** March 5. **Additional Information:** Silicon Valley Community Foundation at the above address

2072 ■ SILICON VALLEY COMMUNITY FOUNDATION
2240 W El Camino Real Ste. 300
Mountain View, CA 94040-1498
Tel: (650)450-5400
Fax: (650)450-5401
Web Site: http://www.siliconvalleycf.org
To provide financial assistance to those students who are in need.
Title of Award: Sand Hill Scholars Program **Area, Field, or Subject:** General Studies. **Level of Education for which Award is Granted:** Undergraduate **Number Awarded:** 5. **Funds Available:** $4,000. **Duration:** 4 years.
Eligibility Requirements: Applicants must be eighth-grade graduates of the Ravenswood City School District; must be current graduating seniors attending a high school in San Mateo County or Northern Santa Clara County. **Application Requirements:** Applicants must check the available website for the required materials. **Deadline for Receipt:** March 5. **Additional Information:** Silicon Valley Community Foundation at the above address

2073 ■ SIMON YOUTH FOUNDATION
225 W Washington St.
Indianapolis, IN 46204
Tel: (317)636-1600
Free: 800-509-3676
Fax: (317)263-2371
E-mail: syf@simon.com
Web Site: http://www.syf.org
To provide scholarships to the promising at-risk students enrolled in Education Resource Centers across the country.
Title of Award: Education Resource Center (ERC) Scholarships **Area, Field, or Subject:** General studies. **Level of Education for which Award is Granted:** Undergraduate **Funds Available:** $1,500-$2,500.
Eligibility Requirements: Applicants for the SYF Education Resource Center Scholarship Program must be graduating ERC students who plan to enroll in a full-time undergraduate course of study at an accredited two- or four-year college, university, or vocational/technical school. **Application Requirements:** Applicants must submit their application together with other required documents to the Foundation. **Additional Information:** SYF at the above address.

2074 ■ SIMON YOUTH FOUNDATION
225 W Washington St.
Indianapolis, IN 46204
Tel: (317)636-1600
Free: 800-509-3676
Fax: (317)263-2371
E-mail: syf@simon.com
Web Site: http://www.syf.org
To provide scholarships to the promising students in communities that host Simon properties.
Title of Award: Simon Youth Foundation Community Scholarships **Area, Field, or Subject:** General studies. **Level of Education for which Award is Granted:** Undergraduate **Funds Available:** $1,500.
Eligibility Requirements: Scholarship is available to students who plan to enroll in a full-time undergraduate course of study at an accredited two-

or four-year college, university, or vocational/technical school. **Application Requirements:** Applicants may submit an application and other required documents to the Foundation. **Additional Information:** SYF at the above address.

2075 ■ DW SIMPSON GLOBAL ACTUARIAL RECRUITMENT

1800 W Larchmont Ave.
Chicago, IL 60613
Tel: (312)867-2300
Free: 800-837-8338
Fax: (312)951-8386
E-mail: actuaries@dwsimpson.com
Web Site: http://www.actuaryjobs.com
To provide financial support for deserving students who are pursuing study in actuarial science.
Title of Award: DW Simpson Actuarial Science Scholarship Program **Area, Field, or Subject:** Actuarial science. **Level of Education for which Award is Granted:** Undergraduate **Funds Available:** $1,000. **Duration:** One year.
Eligibility Requirements: Applicants must be entering their senior year of undergraduate study in actuarial science, have maintained a GPA of 3.2 or higher in their major and an overall GPA of 3.0 or better and have passed at least 1 actuarial examination, and be eligible to work in the United States. **Application Requirements:** Applicants must complete the application form available online at the DW Simpsons Global Actuarial Recruitment. **Deadline for Receipt:** April 30 for the Fall scholarship; October 31 for the Spring scholarship.

2076 ■ SINFONIA EDUCATIONAL FOUNDATION

10600 Old State Rd.
Evansville, IN 47711-1399
Tel: 800-473-2649
Fax: (812)867-0633
E-mail: foundationinfo@sinfonia.org
Web Site: http://www.sinfonia.org
To provide educational assistance for American college students.
Title of Award: Delta Iota Alumni Scholarships **Area, Field, or Subject:** General studies. **Level of Education for which Award is Granted:** Undergraduate **Number Awarded:** 1. **Funds Available:** $500.
Eligibility Requirements: Applicants must have been college students for at least two semesters; must be in good standing; must maintain good standing status during the academic year of scholarship. **Application Requirements:** Applicants must submit typed or computer-generated application with 2-4 page essay on the topic: How Sinfonians take active roles in building of better men in society; two letters of support, one from a Sinfonian and one from a non-Sinfonian, that address evidence of the applicant's integrity, ethics, initiative and overall devotion to the Object of Phi Mu Alpha Sinfonia Fraternity; composite style coat and tie photo for promotional purposes only; name and address of hometown newspaper for promotional purposes. **Deadline for Receipt:** February 1.

2077 ■ SINFONIA EDUCATIONAL FOUNDATION

10600 Old State Rd.
Evansville, IN 47711-1399
Tel: 800-473-2649
Fax: (812)867-0633
E-mail: foundationinfo@sinfonia.org
Web Site: http://www.sinfonia.org
To provide educational assistance for American college students.
Title of Award: W. Eldridge and Emily Lowe Scholarships **Area, Field, or Subject:** General studies. **Level of Education for which Award is Granted:** Undergraduate **Number Awarded:** 1. **Funds Available:** $1,000.
Eligibility Requirements: Applicants must have been college students for at least two semesters; must be in good standing; must maintain good standing status during the academic year of scholarship. **Application Requirements:** Applicants must submit typed or computer-generated application with 2-4 page essay on the topic: How Sinfonians take active roles in building of better men in society; two letters of support, one from a Sinfonian and one from a non-Sinfonian, that address evidence of the applicant's integrity, ethics, initiative and overall devotion to the Object of Phi Mu Alpha Sinfonia Fraternity; composite style coat and tie photo for promotional purposes only; name and address of hometown newspaper for promotional purposes. **Deadline for Receipt:** February 1.

2078 ■ SINFONIA EDUCATIONAL FOUNDATION

10600 Old State Rd.
Evansville, IN 47711-1399
Tel: 800-473-2649
Fax: (812)867-0633
E-mail: foundationinfo@sinfonia.org
Web Site: http://www.sinfonia.org
To provide educational assistance for American college students.
Title of Award: James H. Patrenos Memorial Scholarships **Area, Field, or Subject:** General studies. **Level of Education for which Award is Granted:** Undergraduate **Number Awarded:** 1. **Funds Available:** $1,000.
Eligibility Requirements: Applicants must have attended college for at least two semesters; must be in good standing; must maintain good standing status during the academic year of scholarship. **Application Requirements:** Applicants must submit typed or computer-generated application with 2-4 page essay on the topic: How Sinfonians take active roles in building of better men in society; two letters of support, one from a Sinfonian and one from a non-Sinfonian, that address evidence of the applicant's integrity, ethics, initiative and overall devotion to the Object of Phi Mu Alpha Sinfonia Fraternity; composite style coat and tie photo for promotional purposes only; name and address of hometown newspaper for promotional purposes. **Deadline for Receipt:** February 1.

2079 ■ SNOWMOBILE ASSOCIATION OF MASSACHUSETTS

PO Box 386
Conway, MA 01341
Tel: (413)369-8092
Fax: (413)369-0203
E-mail: webmaster@sledmass.com
Web Site: http://www.sledmass.com
To develop and maintain an expanding interconnected snowmobile trail system, allowing snowmobile enthusiasts to travel from Worcester County.
Title of Award: Snowmobile Association of Massachusetts Scholarships **Area, Field, or Subject:** Transportation. **Level of Education for which Award is Granted:** Undergraduate **Number Awarded:** 2. **Funds Available:** $2,500.
Eligibility Requirements: Applicants must be high school seniors or college students. **Application Requirements:** Applicants must submit a completed application form; an official high school or college transcript; recommendations in writing by at lest two teachers; recommendations in writing by one or two friends, employers, or clergy; proof of acceptance at the listed college, university or vocational school; a written essay about snowmobiling in the state. All required documents must be provided in five copies. **Deadline for Receipt:** March 25.

2080 ■ SOCIETY OF ALLIED WEIGHT ENGINEERS

PO Box 60024, Terminal Annex
Los Angeles, CA 90060
Tel: (562)596-2873
Fax: (562)596-2874
Web Site: http://www.sawe.org
To provide financial assistance for the education of the dependents of SAWE members.
Title of Award: SAWE Scholarships **Area, Field, or Subject:** General studies. **Level of Education for which Award is Granted:** Undergraduate **Number Awarded:** 5. **Funds Available:** $1000. **Duration:** One year.
Eligibility Requirements: Applicants must be children or grandchildren of SAWE members; must be aged 25 or below; and must full-time undergraduate students. **Application Requirements:** Application forms are available at the website. Applicants must submit completed application form and send together with a complete transcript of grades. **Deadline for Receipt:** April. **Additional Information:** Ginny Miller, Scholarship Management Services, Telephone: (507)931-1682, Tollfree: (800)537-4180.

2081 ■ SOCIETY FOR HUMAN RESOURCE MANAGEMENT

1800 Duke St.
Alexandria, VA 22314
Tel: (703)548-3440
Free: 800-283-SHRM
Fax: (703)535-6490

Web Site: http://www.shrm.org

To encourage interest and education in the field of human resources.
Title of Award: SHRM Foundation Regional Academic Scholarships
Area, Field, or Subject: Personnel administration/human resources.
Level of Education for which Award is Granted: Graduate, Undergraduate **Number Awarded:** 8. **Funds Available:** $1,375.
Eligibility Requirements: Applicants must be working full-time in the field of human resources or pursuing graduate college degree in a Human Resource related field in an accredited institution of higher learning (full-time, part-time, online and distance learning programs are acceptable). Previous applicants and past scholarship recipients are eligible to re-apply. **Application Requirements:** Applicants must return the signed application form with a letter of acceptance from the college and two letters of reference. **Deadline for Receipt:** July 15.

2082 ■ SOCIETY OF GEORGIA ARCHIVISTS
PO Box 133085
Atlanta, GA 30333
Tel: (404)651-2477
Fax: (404)651-4314
E-mail: vicepresident@soga.org
Web Site: http://www.soga.org
To enhance archival education.
Title of Award: Brenda S. Bank Educational Workshop Scholarships
Area, Field, or Subject: General studies. **Level of Education for which Award is Granted:** Undergraduate **Funds Available:** No specific amount.
Eligibility Requirements: Eligible applicants are those who are engaged in compensated or volunteer archival work at any level in an institution in the state of Georgia, SGA members employed outside the state of Georgia, graduate students preparing for a career in archives at a college or university in Georgia or SGA students studying outside of Georgia. **Application Requirements:** Applicants must submit: completed application form; a cover letter; letter of recommendation; resume; 500-word or less essay discussing how scholarship will enhance their overall professional development and/or what they hope to bring back to their current and/or anticipated work from the experience. **Deadline for Receipt:** May 19. **Additional Information:** PO Box 1027 Savannah, GA 31402.

2083 ■ SOCIETY OF GEORGIA ARCHIVISTS
PO Box 133085
Atlanta, GA 30333
Tel: (404)651-2477
Fax: (404)651-4314
E-mail: vicepresident@soga.org
Web Site: http://www.soga.org
To enhance archival education.
Title of Award: Anthony R. Dees Educational Workshop Scholarships
Area, Field, or Subject: General studies. **Level of Education for which Award is Granted:** Undergraduate **Funds Available:** No specific amount.
Eligibility Requirements: Eligible applicants are those who are engaged in compensated or volunteer archival work at any level in an institution in the state of Georgia, SGA members employed outside the state of Georgia, graduate students preparing for a career in archives at a college or university in Georgia or SGA students studying outside of Georgia. **Application Requirements:** Applicants must submit: completed application form; a cover letter; letter of recommendation; resume; a 500-word or less essay discussing how scholarship will enhance their overall professional development and/or what they hope to bring back to their current and/or anticipated work from the experience. **Additional Information:** PO Box 1027 Savannah, GA 31402.

2084 ■ SOCIETY OF GEORGIA ARCHIVISTS
PO Box 133085
Atlanta, GA 30333
Tel: (404)651-2477
Fax: (404)651-4314
E-mail: vicepresident@soga.org
Web Site: http://www.soga.org
To enhance archival education, membership and participation in the profession.
Title of Award: Larry Gulley Scholarships **Area, Field, or Subject:** General studies. **Level of Education for which Award is Granted:**

Undergraduate **Funds Available:** No specific amount.
Eligibility Requirements: Eligible applicants are those who are engaged in compensated or volunteer archival work at any level in an institution in the state of Georgia, SGA members employed outside the state of Georgia, graduate students preparing for a career in archives at a college or university in Georgia or SGA students studying outside of Georgia. **Application Requirements:** Applicants must submit: completed application form; a cover letter; letter of recommendation; resume; a 500-word or less essay discussing how scholarship will enhance their overall professional development and/or what they hope to bring back to their current and/or anticipated work from the experience. **Deadline for Receipt:** February 15. **Additional Information:** PO Box 1027 Savannah, GA 31402.

2085 ■ SOCIETY FOR JUDGMENT AND DECISION MAKING
PO Box 3061110
Tallahassee, FL 32306-1110
E-mail: bfennema@cob.fsu.edu
Web Site: http://www.sjdm.org
To encourage outstanding work by new researchers.
Title of Award: Einhorn New Investigator Awards **Area, Field, or Subject:** General studies. **Level of Education for which Award is Granted:** Undergraduate **Funds Available:** No specific amount.
Eligibility Requirements: Applicants must be individuals who have not yet completed their PhD. **Application Requirements:** Applicants must submit four copies of a journal-style manuscript on any topic related to judgment and decision making accompanied by: (1) four copies of a summary or extended abstract of the paper, not to exceed four pages in length and (2) a cover letter that includes the name of the investigator's graduate advisor and the date that the Ph.D. was awarded (if applicable). In the case of co-authored papers, if the authors are all new investigators they can be considered jointly; otherwise, the new investigator(s) must be the primary author(s) and should be the primary source of ideas. **Deadline for Receipt:** July 1. **Additional Information:** Craig R. M. McKenzie, 9500 Gilman Dr. MC 0109, University of California, San Diego La Jolla, CA, 92093-0109, USA.

2086 ■ SOCIETY OF LOUISIANA CERTIFIED PUBLIC ACCOUNTANTS
2400 Veterans Blvd., Ste. 500
Kenner, LA 70062
Tel: (504)464-1040
Free: 800-288-5272
E-mail: ghazel@lcpa.org
Web Site: http://www.lcpa.org
To further develop the accounting education and the accounting profession.
Title of Award: Society of Louisiana Certified Public Accountants Scholarships **Area, Field, or Subject:** Accounting. **Level of Education for which Award is Granted:** Undergraduate **Funds Available:** No specific amount.
Eligibility Requirements: Applicants must have 2.5 academic grade point average; must be Louisiana domiciled; must be enrolled in an accounting program in a Louisiana four year college or university; and must be an at least fifth semester student. **Application Requirements:** Applicants must complete the application form and submit an official college transcript and essay. **Deadline for Receipt:** June 7.

2087 ■ SOCIETY OF MARINE PORT ENGINEERS
111 Broad St.
PO Box 369
Eatontown, NJ 07724
Tel: (732)389-2009
Fax: (732)389-2264
E-mail: dmoore@smpe.org
Web Site: http://www.smpe.org
To assist members of SMPE and their families in pursuing higher studies.
Title of Award: Society of Marine Port Engineers Scholarship Loans
Area, Field, or Subject: General Studies. **Level of Education for which Award is Granted:** Undergraduate **Funds Available:** No specific amount. **Duration:** Annual.
Eligibility Requirements: Program is open to children of SMPE members with a minimum of three years membership; and must be attending or accepted as full-time students in the next regular term of

indicated institutions of higher education. **Application Requirements:** Application forms and instructions are available at the SMPE website. **Deadline for Receipt:** July 15.

2088 ■ SOCIETY OF NUCLEAR MEDICINE
1850 Samuel Morse Dr.
Reston, VA 20190
Tel: (703)708-9000
Fax: (703)708-9015
Web Site: http://www.snm.org
To support students pursuing a Bachelor's degree completion program related to their nuclear medicine career.
Title of Award: SNMTS Bachelor's Degree Completion Scholarships **Area, Field, or Subject:** General studies. **Level of Education for which Award is Granted:** Undergraduate **Funds Available:** $5,000.
Eligibility Requirements: Applicants must demonstrate financial need; hold a certificate or associate's degree in nuclear medicine technology; currently enrolled in a bachelor's level program to advance their career in nuclear medicine; have a minimum cumulative GPA of 2.5 or better (on 4.0 scale) or B average in the program's core curriculum, and member of the SNMTS. **Application Requirements:** Applicants must submit a completed application, which includes applicant's statement and recommenders' signature; official transcripts of all formal education (high school transcripts are not necessary if transcripts of college level work are submitted); a letter of recommendation from an educational or professional reference; an official transcript or letter from the institution's registrar's office verifying the applicant's enrollment or acceptance in the Bachelor's degree program. **Deadline for Receipt:** May 30.

2089 ■ SOCIETY FOR RANGE MANAGEMENT
10030 W 27th Ave.
Wheat Ridge, CO 80215-6601
Tel: (303)986-3309
Fax: (303)986-3892
E-mail: info@rangelands.org
Web Site: http://www.rangelands.org
To financially assist students with their education.
Title of Award: Masonic-Range Science Scholarships **Area, Field, or Subject:** Science. **Level of Education for which Award is Granted:** Undergraduate **Funds Available:** Varies each year. **Duration:** Maximum of 8 semesters.
Eligibility Requirements: Applicant must be a high school senior, or college freshman or sophomore planning to major in/currently majoring in range science or a closely related field; and must be sponsored by a member of the Society for Range Management (SRM), the National Association of Conservation Districts (NACD), or the Soil and Water Conservation Society (SWCS). **Application Requirements:** Applicants must submit a completed application form together with a copy of high school and college transcripts; official copy of SAT and ACT scores; two letters of references. Send materials to Paul Loeffler Texas General Land Office 500 West Ave H, Suite 101, Box 2 Alpine, TX 79830-6008. **Deadline for Receipt:** January 15. **Additional Information:** vtrujillo@rangelands.org.

2090 ■ SOCIETY FOR THE SCIENTIFIC STUDY OF SEXUALITY
PO Box 416
Allentown, PA 18105-0416
Tel: (610)530-2483
Fax: (610)530-2485
E-mail: thesociety@sexscience.org
Web Site: http://www.sexscience.org
To advance knowledge of sexuality; to advance the quality and quantity of the knowledge base in sexual science; to foster the recognition of sexual science within the scientific community, public policy makers, and the general public; to communicate the implications of sexual science.
Title of Award: Society for the Scientific Study of Sexuality Student Research Grants **Area, Field, or Subject:** Sexuality. **Level of Education for which Award is Granted:** Undergraduate **Number Awarded:** 2. **Funds Available:** $1,000.
Eligibility Requirements: Applicants must be students who are doing human sexuality research. **Application Requirements:** Applicants must obtain IRB approval for the project; applicants must prepare a 150-word abstract of the proposed research; prepare a short biographical sketch

suitable for the use of the society's newsletter; applicants must prepare a ten-page, double-spaced abstract of the proposed research and bibliography in MS Word; applicants must prepare a proposed budget for the project. **Additional Information:** mlpeters@sexscience.org.

2091 ■ SOKOL USA
PO Box 189
East Orange, NJ 07019-0189
Tel: (973)676-0280; 888-253-0362
Fax: (973)676-3348
E-mail: sokolusahqs@aol.com
Web Site: http://www.Sokolusa.org
To support Sokol USA student members in furthering their education.
Title of Award: Milan Getting Scholarships **Area, Field, or Subject:** General studies. **Level of Education for which Award is Granted:** Undergraduate **Funds Available:** $500. **Duration:** Four years.
Eligibility Requirements: Applicant must be a Sokol USA member; furthering education in a four-year college or university. **Application Requirements:** Applicants must request scholarship application at the Sokol USA Headquarters. **Deadline for Receipt:** March 1.

2092 ■ SOLID WASTE ASSOCIATION OF NORTH AMERICA
1100 Wayne Ave., Ste. 700
Silver Spring, MD 20910
Tel: 800-467-9262
Fax: (301)589-7068
Web Site: http://www.swana.org
To promote education and professional development by providing financial aid.
Title of Award: Grant H. Flint International Scholarships - Category I **Area, Field, or Subject:** General Studies. **Level of Education for which Award is Granted:** Undergraduate **Number Awarded:** 3. **Funds Available:** $2,000.
Eligibility Requirements: Applicants must be sons, daughters, grandsons or granddaughters of members (sponsors) and in good standing at the time of recommendation, selection and award; graduating high school seniors or graduate equivalent certified candidates who have been accepted for enrollment in a junior college, a four-year college, or a university (any program). **Application Requirements:** Applicants may visit SWANA website for scholarship forms and instructions. **Deadline for Receipt:** May 1. **Additional Information:** Kathy Callaghan, Staff Administrator, at the above address tel 240-494-2248, email: kcallaghan@swana.org.

2093 ■ SONS OF CONFEDERATE VETERANS
PO Box 59
Columbia, TN 38402
Tel: 800-380-1896
Fax: (931)831-6712
Web Site: http://www.scv.org
To encourage educational pursuits by providing educational assistance.
Title of Award: Stand Watie Scholarships **Area, Field, or Subject:** General studies. **Level of Education for which Award is Granted:** Undergraduate **Funds Available:** $1,000. **Duration:** One year.
Eligibility Requirements: Applicants must be members of: Sons of Confederate Veterans, Children of the Confederacy, or United Daughters of the Confederacy; must be students in an accredited junior college or 4-year college or university. **Application Requirements:** Application package includes a personal letter of application, proof of membership in one of the organizations named, a complete personal data, three letters of recommendation. Send complete application package to: Stand Watie Scholarship Fund, Chairman Michael Hann Hayes, 4335 Hwy. 63, Malcolm, IA 50157. **Additional Information:** phone: 641-528-4409; iowa_rebel@yahoo.com.

2094 ■ SONS OF UNION VETERANS OF THE CIVIL WAR
PO Box 1865
Harrisburg, PA 17105
Tel: (717)232-7000
Web Site: http://www.suvcw.org
To inspire higher learning by providing educational opportunities.
Title of Award: SUVCW Scholarships **Area, Field, or Subject:** General studies. **Level of Education for which Award is Granted:** Undergraduate **Number Awarded:** 2. **Funds Available:** $1,000. **Duration:** One year.

Eligibility Requirements: Male applicants must be current members or Associate of Sons of Union Veterans of the Civil War; female applicants must be the daughters or granddaughters of a current member or Associate of Sons of Union Veterans of the Civil War and must be current members of at least one of the following organizations: Woman's Relief Corps, Ladies of the Grand Army of the Republic, Daughters of Union Veterans of the Civil War 1861-1865, or Auxiliary to the Sons of Union Veterans of the Civil War; must rank in the upper one-fourth of high school graduating class, preferably in the upper one-tenth; must have a record of performance in activities both in school and in the community; must have a sound interest and positive attitude toward college work. **Application Requirements:** Applicants can download forms from the website. **Deadline for Receipt:** March 31.

2095 ■ SOUTH CAROLINA ASSOCIATION FOR FINANCIAL PROFESSIONALS

301 University Ridge, Ste. 600
Greenville, SC 29601
Tel: (864)467-7210
E-mail: jkintigh@greenvillecounty.org
Web Site: http://www.scafponline.org
To provide a forum for the exchange of ideas and discussion of legislative, regulatory, and banking issues and developments and the opportunity to network with other Treasury Management professionals; to award an academic scholarship to an outstanding undergraduate student pursuing a degree in business in the areas including, but not limited to, accounting, economics, finance, business administration and management.
Title of Award: South Carolina Association for Financial Professionals College Education Scholarships **Area, Field, or Subject:** Finance. **Level of Education for which Award is Granted:** Undergraduate **Number Awarded:** 2-5. **Funds Available:** $1,000.
Eligibility Requirements: Applicants must be South Carolina residents; must be U.S. citizens or legal permanent residents; must earn a cumulative 3.0 GPA on a 4.0 scale and a GPA in their major area of 3.5 on a 4.0 scale; must be enrolled as degree-seeking students at eligible South Carolina public or independent (private) institutions; must not be current recipients of a full-tuition scholarship. **Application Requirements:** Applicants must complete the application form; must submit a one page summary of academic achievement including the applicant's GPA (overall and major area) and a list of all relevant courses in the Treasury Management field; must submit a letter of recommendation from their major field faculty member; must provide a three-to-five page, double-spaced discussion of the Treasury Management field.

2096 ■ SOUTH CENTRAL POWER COMPANY

PO Box 250
Lancaster, OH 43130
Tel: (740)653-4422
Free: 800-282-5064
Fax: (740)681-4488
E-mail: feedback@scp.utilities.com
Web Site: http://www.southcentralpower.com
To help high school seniors pursuing their education at a college, vocational or technical school.
Title of Award: South Central Power Scholarships **Area, Field, or Subject:** General studies. **Level of Education for which Award is Granted:** Undergraduate **Number Awarded:** 6. **Funds Available:** $400-$2,500.
Eligibility Requirements: Applicants must be graduating seniors who have basic credits for entering college or a proper vocational or technical school; have current career GPA of at least 3.6 on a 4.0 scale and a combined ACT score of at least 22; must be accepted or will be accepted at an accredited college or proper vocational or technical school; and must live at the South Central Power account location. Parents/guardians of the students must be members/consumers of South Central Power Company. Applicants who have received a full tuition scholarship to the school of their choice are not qualified. **Application Requirements:** Each high school in South Central Power Company's service area will nominate one boy and one girl to represent the school in the contest. Nominated students must submit a completed official scholarship application form (must be typed), together with the complete high school grade transcript. **Deadline for Receipt:** March 7. **Additional Information:** Rita Tate, Office Services Support Specialist, at 740-653-4422 x-6167, or 800-282-5064 x-6167.

2097 ■ SOUTH CENTRAL POWER COMPANY

PO Box 250
Lancaster, OH 43130
Tel: (740)653-4422
Free: 800-282-5064
Fax: (740)681-4488
E-mail: feedback@scp.utilities.com
Web Site: http://www.southcentralpower.com
To help high school seniors pursuing their education at a college, vocational or technical school.
Title of Award: Touchstone Special Achievement Scholarships **Area, Field, or Subject:** General studies. **Level of Education for which Award is Granted:** Undergraduate **Number Awarded:** 2 first place, and 2 second place. **Funds Available:** $750 and $1,500.
Eligibility Requirements: Applicants must be graduating high school senior students whose parents or guardians are electric members of an Ohio rural electric cooperative. **Application Requirements:** Applicants must submit a completed scholarship application to Ohio Rural Electric Cooperative (OREC). **Additional Information:** Rita Tate, Office Services Support Specialist, at 740-653-4422 x-6167, or 800-282-5064 x-6167.

2098 ■ SOUTH JERSEY GOLF ASSOCIATION

10 Bennington Dr.
Medford, NJ 08055
Tel: (609)953-6873
E-mail: golfoffice@sjgolf.org
Web Site: http://www.sjgolf.org
To provide support for deserving high school seniors intending to pursue their education.
Title of Award: South Jersey Golf Association Scholarships **Area, Field, or Subject:** General studies. **Level of Education for which Award is Granted:** Undergraduate **Funds Available:** $500-$750. **Duration:** One year.
Eligibility Requirements: Applicant must be a graduating high school senior of Atlantic, Burlington, Camden, Cape May, Cumberland, Gloucester, Ocean or Salem County high schools; must have plans to enroll as a full-time undergraduate student at an accredited college or university within the United States. **Application Requirements:** Applicants must have a copy of their college/university letter of acceptance or waitlist deferral; must provide a copy of their transcript which must include midyear grades through the fall semester of senior year; must provide a copy of their SATI or ACT Score Reports; must have a typed essay, three letters of recommendation, completed resume, and a senior yearbook photograph. Application form and requirements must be sent to 3 Southern Dr., Tinton Falls, NJ 07724. **Deadline for Receipt:** April 30.

2099 ■ SOUTH KENTUCKY RURAL ELECTRIC COOPERATIVE CORPORATION

PO Box 910
Somerset, KY 42502
Tel: (606)678-4121
Free: 800-264-5112
Fax: (606)679-8279
Web Site: http://www.skrecc.com
To provide financial assistance for students to continue college education.
Title of Award: Sam J. Hord Memorial Scholarships **Area, Field, or Subject:** General studies. **Level of Education for which Award is Granted:** Undergraduate **Funds Available:** No specific amount.
Eligibility Requirements: Applicants must be students who are members of South Kentucky Rural Electric Cooperative, or whose parents are members. **Application Requirements:** Applicants must submit a completed scholarship application; copy of grade transcript; copy of most recent family federal tax return; and, ACT, SAT or COMPASS results. **Deadline for Receipt:** March 1.

2100 ■ SOUTH KENTUCKY RURAL ELECTRIC COOPERATIVE CORPORATION

PO Box 910
Somerset, KY 42502
Tel: (606)678-4121
Free: 800-264-5112
Fax: (606)679-8279
Web Site: http://www.skrecc.com

To provide financial assistance for high school seniors to continue college education.

Title of Award: South Kentucky RECC High School Senior Scholarships **Area, Field, or Subject:** General studies. **Level of Education for which Award is Granted:** Undergraduate **Funds Available:** $1,000. **Duration:** Two years.

Eligibility Requirements: Applicants must be full-time high school seniors whose principal residence has an active account with South Kentucky RECC. **Application Requirements:** Applicants must submit a completed application form along with an essay about how Rural Electrification has affected their lives, their home communities and their local economy. **Additional Information:** Scholarship is paid directly to the accredited educational institution of the student's choice upon enrollment.

2101 ■ SOUTH KENTUCKY RURAL ELECTRIC COOPERATIVE CORPORATION

PO Box 910
Somerset, KY 42502
Tel: (606)678-4121
Free: 800-264-5112
Fax: (606)679-8279
Web Site: http://www.skrecc.com

To provide financial assistance for Kentucky students to continue college education.

Title of Award: Woman In Rural Electrification Scholarships **Area, Field, or Subject:** General studies. **Level of Education for which Award is Granted:** Undergraduate **Funds Available:** $1,000.

Eligibility Requirements: Applicants must be students whose immediate family is served by a Kentucky rural electric cooperative, such as South Kentucky RECC; must be full-time juniors or seniors with at least 60 hours of credits at a Kentucky college or university by the start of the fall term. **Application Requirements:** Applicants must contact their local South Kentucky RECC office or call the toll-free number found in the cooperative's website, for further information.

2102 ■ SOUTHEASTERN LIBRARY ASSOCIATION

PO Box 950
Rex, GA 30273
Tel: (770)961-3520
Fax: (770)961-3712
Web Site: http://selaonline.org

To recruit beginning professional librarians who have potential for leadership and have made a commitment to service in the libraries of the Southeastern United States; to provide financial assistance towards the completion of their graduate degree in library science from an institution accredited by the American Library Association.

Title of Award: The Ginny Frankenthaler Memorial Scholarship **Area, Field, or Subject:** Science. **Level of Education for which Award is Granted:** Undergraduate **Funds Available:** $1,000.

Eligibility Requirements: Applicants must be completing their senior year at an accredited college or university or be graduates of such an institution; must be accepted as students in a degree program accredited by the American Library Association; must be ready to begin the program of study no later than the fall term of the year in which the scholarship is awarded; must indicate their intention to complete the degree requirements within three years; must maintain a "B" GPA throughout the program and must agree to work within one year following the graduation from library school. **Application Requirements:** Applicants must submit an official application form, three letters of acceptance from a library school accredited by the American Library Association, three letters of reference sent directly by the references, and an official transcript of all academic works. **Deadline for Receipt:** May 1.

2103 ■ SOUTHERN SCHOLARSHIP FOUNDATION

322 Stadium Dr.
Tallahassee, FL 32304
Tel: (850)222-3833
Free: 800-253-2769
Fax: (850)222-6750
Web Site: http://www.southernscholarship.org

To support students attending the four major universities in Florida.

Title of Award: Southern Scholarship Foundation Scholarships **Area, Field, or Subject:** General studies. **Level of Education for which**

Award is Granted: Undergraduate **Funds Available:** No specific amount.

Eligibility Requirements: Applicant must be attending one of the four major universities in Florida (Florida A&M University, Florida Gulf Coast University, Florida State University, and the University of Florida); demonstrate financial need (submit the FAFSA); and have at least a 3.00 GPA. **Application Requirements:** Applicants must submit a completed scholarship application form, recent photograph, an acceptance letter, a list of honors and activities, transcript, three letters of recommendation, the essay, financial information, and resume. **Deadline for Receipt:** March and November.

2104 ■ SOUTHWEST FLORIDA COMMUNITY FOUNDATION

8260 College Pkwy., Ste. 101
Fort Myers, FL 33919
Tel: (239)274-5900
Fax: (239)274-5930
Web Site: http://www.floridacommunity.com

To provide to a two-year regionally accredited college or university to a Lee County high school senior who can demonstrate financial need.

Title of Award: Judge Isaac Anderson, Jr. Scholarships **Area, Field, or Subject:** General studies. **Level of Education for which Award is Granted:** Undergraduate **Funds Available:** $1,000.

Eligibility Requirements: Applicant must be a graduate from public or private high school in Lee County; must have financial need; must maintain a GPA of 3.0 or higher; must demonstrate strong ties to the community through extracurricular activities, religious endeavors or community service; and must plan to attend a two-or-four year regionally accredited college or university. **Application Requirements:** Applicants must complete the application forms available online and must have a letter of interest, transcript and letter of recommendation. **Deadline for Receipt:** March 26. **Additional Information:** Kathryn Clinton at kcintron@floridacommunity.com.

2105 ■ SOUTHWEST FLORIDA COMMUNITY FOUNDATION

8260 College Pkwy., Ste. 101
Fort Myers, FL 33919
Tel: (239)274-5900
Fax: (239)274-5930
Web Site: http://www.floridacommunity.com

To fund books and tuition for students pursuing either of the following educational paths: (1) certification to teach the deaf and blind; (2) seminary or pre-seminary school to study church, Christian music or Christian education.

Title of Award: Lewis B. Barber Memorial Scholarships **Area, Field, or Subject:** Christian education; Church occupations. **Level of Education for which Award is Granted:** Undergraduate **Funds Available:** $1,200.

Eligibility Requirements: Applicants must graduate from public or private high school in Charlotte, Collier, Glades, Hendry or Lee County; must maintain satisfactory grades; must acknowledge and express Jesus Christ as Lord and Savior; and must demonstrate financial need. **Application Requirements:** Application forms are available online. Applicants must submit a letter of interest, transcript, and letter of recommendation. **Deadline for Receipt:** February 15.

2106 ■ SOUTHWEST FLORIDA COMMUNITY FOUNDATION

8260 College Pkwy., Ste. 101
Fort Myers, FL 33919
Tel: (239)274-5900
Fax: (239)274-5930
Web Site: http://www.floridacommunity.com

To fund tuition for high school students intending to pursue vocational or technical studies.

Title of Award: James Bilder Scholarships **Area, Field, or Subject:** General studies. **Level of Education for which Award is Granted:** Undergraduate **Funds Available:** $1,000.

Eligibility Requirements: Applicants must have graduated from public high school in Lee County; must pursue 2-year degree at community college or technical certification at certified technical school; and must demonstrate financial need. **Application Requirements:** Applicants must submit a letter of interest, transcript, and letter of recommendation. **Deadline for Receipt:** February 15.

2107 ■ SOUTHWEST FLORIDA COMMUNITY FOUNDATION
8260 College Pkwy., Ste. 101
Fort Myers, FL 33919
Tel: (239)274-5900
Fax: (239)274-5930
Web Site: http://www.floridacommunity.com
To fund scholarships for a North Fort Myers High School male or female student athlete.
Title of Award: Jordan ABDO/Michael Bluett Memorial Scholarships **Area, Field, or Subject:** General studies. **Level of Education for which Award is Granted:** Undergraduate **Funds Available:** $1,000. **Duration:** One year.
Eligibility Requirements: Applicants must have graduated from North Fort Myers High School; must be student athletes with a GPA of at least 3.5. **Application Requirements:** Applicants must complete the application form available online and submit a letter of interest, transcript, and letter of recommendation. **Deadline for Receipt:** February 15.

2108 ■ SOUTHWEST FLORIDA COMMUNITY FOUNDATION
8260 College Pkwy., Ste. 101
Fort Myers, FL 33919
Tel: (239)274-5900
Fax: (239)274-5930
Web Site: http://www.floridacommunity.com
To fund tuition for college-bound students of one or more immigrant parents.
Title of Award: Carl E. Brooks Scholarships **Area, Field, or Subject:** General studies. **Level of Education for which Award is Granted:** Undergraduate **Number Awarded:** 2. **Funds Available:** $2,000. **Duration:** One year.
Eligibility Requirements: Applicants must have graduated from public or private high school in Charlotte, Collier, Glades, Hendry or Lee County. **Application Requirements:** Applicants must provide proof of parent's immigrant status and must submit a letter of interest, transcript, and letter of recommendation. **Deadline for Receipt:** February 15.

2109 ■ SOUTHWEST FLORIDA COMMUNITY FOUNDATION
8260 College Pkwy., Ste. 101
Fort Myers, FL 33919
Tel: (239)274-5900
Fax: (239)274-5930
Web Site: http://www.floridacommunity.com
To fund education of students with physical disability intending to pursue higher education in a college, university or technical school.
Title of Award: John and Ruth Childe Scholarships **Area, Field, or Subject:** General studies. **Level of Education for which Award is Granted:** Undergraduate **Funds Available:** No specific amount. **Duration:** One year.
Eligibility Requirements: Applicants must be graduates from a public or private high school in Lee county; must have a disability; and must have good academic standing. **Application Requirements:** Applicants must complete application form, available online and must have a letter of interest, transcript and letter of recommendation. Application form and other supporting documents must be sent to Southwest Florida, Community Foundation, 8260 College Pkwy., Ste. 101, Fort Myers, FL 33919. **Deadline for Receipt:** February 15.

2110 ■ SOUTHWEST FLORIDA COMMUNITY FOUNDATION
8260 College Pkwy., Ste. 101
Fort Myers, FL 33919
Tel: (239)274-5900
Fax: (239)274-5930
Web Site: http://www.floridacommunity.com
To provide financial assistance for qualified dependents of Sanibel City employees to attend a college or university.
Title of Award: City of Sanibel Employee Dependent Scholarships **Area, Field, or Subject:** General studies. **Level of Education for which Award is Granted:** Undergraduate **Funds Available:** $1,000. **Duration:** One year.
Eligibility Requirements: Applicant must be a dependent of a Sanibel City Employee (includes City Clerk's office, finance, legal, legislative, planning, police, building, natural resources, public works, management information systems, utility, recreation, and administrative services); must

demonstrate financial need and academic achievement. **Application Requirements:** Applicants must complete the application form, available online; must have a student letter of interest, financial need documentation, transcript, and two letters of recommendation. Application form and other supporting documents must be sent to Community Foundation of Sanibel-Captiva, 8260 College Pkwy., Ste. 101, Fort Myers, FL 33919. **Deadline for Receipt:** February 15. **Additional Information:** Kathryn Cintron at the above address.

2111 ■ SOUTHWEST FLORIDA COMMUNITY FOUNDATION
8260 College Pkwy., Ste. 101
Fort Myers, FL 33919
Tel: (239)274-5900
Fax: (239)274-5930
Web Site: http://www.floridacommunity.com
To fund a Dunbar High School graduating student of African-American descent in pursuing a bachelor's degree at an accredited college.
Title of Award: Dunbar Heritage Scholarships **Area, Field, or Subject:** General studies. **Level of Education for which Award is Granted:** Undergraduate **Funds Available:** Amount of scholarship is determined each year by the Selection Committee. **Duration:** One year.
Eligibility Requirements: Applicant must be a graduating member of Dunbar High School; must be of African-American descent; must have financial need; must have a GPA of 2.5 or higher; and must enter college within the year following high school graduation. **Application Requirements:** Applicants must submit a letter of interest, transcript, and letter of recommendation. Application forms are available online. **Deadline for Receipt:** February 15.

2112 ■ SOUTHWEST FLORIDA COMMUNITY FOUNDATION
8260 College Pkwy., Ste. 101
Fort Myers, FL 33919
Tel: (239)274-5900
Fax: (239)274-5930
Web Site: http://www.floridacommunity.com
To fund post-high school educational opportunities at the college, community college, or technical school level for males and females with a physical disability and who use a wheelchair.
Title of Award: Anne M. Fassett Scholarships **Area, Field, or Subject:** General studies. **Level of Education for which Award is Granted:** Undergraduate **Funds Available:** Scholarship award amount is determined by committee. **Duration:** One year.
Eligibility Requirements: Applicants must have graduated from a public or private high school in Charlotte, Collier, Glades, Hendry or Lee County; must be currently enrolled or planning to attend a Florida state college, community college or technical school; must have a physical disability and use a wheelchair; and must demonstrate financial need. **Application Requirements:** Application forms are available online. Applicants must submit a letter of recommendation, letter of interest, financial need documentation, and transcript. **Deadline for Receipt:** March 20.

2113 ■ SOUTHWEST FLORIDA COMMUNITY FOUNDATION
8260 College Pkwy., Ste. 101
Fort Myers, FL 33919
Tel: (239)274-5900
Fax: (239)274-5930
Web Site: http://www.floridacommunity.com
To fund Lee County females who are enrolled in accredited programs of study at either 2-year or 4-year accredited institutions.
Title of Award: American Association of University Women-Mary Sue Gottcent Memorial Scholarships **Area, Field, or Subject:** General studies. **Level of Education for which Award is Granted:** Undergraduate **Funds Available:** $1,000.
Eligibility Requirements: Applicants must be residents of Lee County who demonstrate financial need. **Application Requirements:** Application forms are available online. Applicants must submit a personal statement essay, proof of financial need, high school/college transcript, and three letters of recommendation. **Deadline for Receipt:** March 20. **Additional Information:** Kathryn Cintron at the above address.

2114 ■ SOUTHWEST FLORIDA COMMUNITY FOUNDATION
8260 College Pkwy., Ste. 101
Fort Myers, FL 33919

Tel: (239)274-5900
Fax: (239)274-5930
Web Site: http://www.floridacommunity.com
To fund tuition for college-bound seniors from Lee County high schools.
Title of Award: Francis Harris Gresham Scholarships **Area, Field, or Subject:** General studies. **Level of Education for which Award is Granted:** Undergraduate **Funds Available:** $1,000. **Duration:** One year. **Eligibility Requirements:** Applicants must have graduated from a public or private high school in Lee County. **Application Requirements:** Applicants must submit a letter of interest, transcript, and letter of recommendation. Application forms are available online. **Deadline for Receipt:** February 15.

2115 ■ SOUTHWEST FLORIDA COMMUNITY FOUNDATION
8260 College Pkwy., Ste. 101
Fort Myers, FL 33919
Tel: (239)274-5900
Fax: (239)274-5930
Web Site: http://www.floridacommunity.com
To fund books and tuition for college-bound male baseball players.
Title of Award: Matt Harmon Memorial Scholarships **Area, Field, or Subject:** General studies. **Level of Education for which Award is Granted:** Undergraduate **Funds Available:** $500. **Duration:** One year. **Eligibility Requirements:** Applicants must be graduates of a public school in Lee County; must be male; must demonstrate financial need; and must have played baseball in high school. **Application Requirements:** Applicants must submit a letter of interest, transcript, and letter of recommendation. Application forms are available online. **Deadline for Receipt:** February 15.

2116 ■ SOUTHWEST FLORIDA COMMUNITY FOUNDATION
8260 College Pkwy., Ste. 101
Fort Myers, FL 33919
Tel: (239)274-5900
Fax: (239)274-5930
Web Site: http://www.floridacommunity.com
To fund scholarships for students who have completed 60 hours of college and plan to attend one of named colleges.
Title of Award: Chip Johnson Scholarships **Area, Field, or Subject:** General studies. **Level of Education for which Award is Granted:** Undergraduate **Number Awarded:** 7. **Funds Available:** $1,200. **Duration:** One year. **Eligibility Requirements:** Applicants must have completed 60 semester hours of college and plan to continue study toward a 4-year degree at Barry University, FGCU, Nova, Edison College or International College, or a regionally-accredited college in the 5-county area; must have a GPA of 3.5 or above and an outstanding record of academic achievement; must have lived in the 5-county area served by the Community Foundation (Charlotte, Collier, Glades, Hendry and Lee); and must have demonstrated leadership, community service and service to school. **Application Requirements:** Applicants must complete the application forms available online; must submit a letter of recommendation from college instructor and letter of interest; must have a transcript of record. **Deadline for Receipt:** March 20.

2117 ■ SOUTHWEST FLORIDA COMMUNITY FOUNDATION
8260 College Pkwy., Ste. 101
Fort Myers, FL 33919
Tel: (239)274-5900
Fax: (239)274-5930
Web Site: http://www.floridacommunity.com
To fund a scholarship for college or vocational school for a student who was an active member of 4-H or a FFA Organization for two consecutive years and has attended a Moore Haven, Clewiston, or LaBelle high school.
Title of Award: Doc Keen Memorial Scholarships **Area, Field, or Subject:** General studies. **Level of Education for which Award is Granted:** Undergraduate **Funds Available:** $1,000. **Duration:** One year. **Eligibility Requirements:** Applicant must be a graduate from a Moore Haven, Clewinston or LaBelle high school; must pursue higher education; must maintain satisfactory grades; and must have been an active member of 4-H or a FFA Organization for two consecutive years. **Application Requirements:** Application forms are available online. Applicants must

submit a letter of interest, transcript, list of 4-H or FFA activities, and letter of recommendation. **Deadline for Receipt:** February 15.

2118 ■ SOUTHWEST FLORIDA COMMUNITY FOUNDATION
8260 College Pkwy., Ste. 101
Fort Myers, FL 33919
Tel: (239)274-5900
Fax: (239)274-5930
Web Site: http://www.floridacommunity.com
To fund tuition for high school graduates with a "B" average of 3.03.7.
Title of Award: Isabel Mayer Kirkpatrick Scholarships **Area, Field, or Subject:** General studies. **Level of Education for which Award is Granted:** Undergraduate **Funds Available:** $1,000. **Duration:** one year. **Eligibility Requirements:** Applicants must graduate from public or private high school in Lee County; must be well-rounded in terms of education, community service, sports and leadership activities; and must have a GPA of 3.0-3.7 (anything higher will disqualify the student). **Application Requirements:** Applicants must submit a letter of interest, transcript, and letter of recommendation. Application forms are available online. **Deadline for Receipt:** February 15.

2119 ■ SOUTHWEST FLORIDA COMMUNITY FOUNDATION
8260 College Pkwy., Ste. 101
Fort Myers, FL 33919
Tel: (239)274-5900
Fax: (239)274-5930
Web Site: http://www.floridacommunity.com
To fund high school and undergraduate/graduate students who are pursuing a career in finance or accounting.
Title of Award: Robert A. Kleckner Scholarships **Area, Field, or Subject:** Finance; Accounting. **Level of Education for which Award is Granted:** Undergraduate **Funds Available:** $1,200. **Eligibility Requirements:** Applicants must be residents of Charlotte, Glades, Hendry or Lee County pursuing a degree in finance or accounting. **Application Requirements:** Application forms are available online. Applicants must submit a letter of interest, high school/college transcript, and letter of recommendation. **Deadline for Receipt:** February 15.

2120 ■ SOUTHWEST FLORIDA COMMUNITY FOUNDATION
8260 College Pkwy., Ste. 101
Fort Myers, FL 33919
Tel: (239)274-5900
Fax: (239)274-5930
Web Site: http://www.floridacommunity.com
To fund books, tuition and/or course fees for Bonita Spring residents to attend a college or technical school.
Title of Award: Love of Bonita Empowerment Scholarships **Area, Field, or Subject:** General studies. **Level of Education for which Award is Granted:** Undergraduate **Funds Available:** $1,000. **Duration:** One year. **Eligibility Requirements:** Applicant must be a resident of Bonita Spring and must demonstrate financial need. **Application Requirements:** Applicants must submit a letter of interest, financial need documentation, transcript, and letter of recommendation. Applicants must submit the application forms and other supporting documents to Kathryn Cintron, Donor Services, Bonita Spring Community Foundation, 8260 College Pkwy., Ste. 101, Fort Myers, FL 33919. **Deadline for Receipt:** February 15.

2121 ■ SOUTHWEST FLORIDA COMMUNITY FOUNDATION
8260 College Pkwy., Ste. 101
Fort Myers, FL 33919
Tel: (239)274-5900
Fax: (239)274-5930
Web Site: http://www.floridacommunity.com
To provide financial assistance for qualified high school seniors who will be attending the University of Florida.
Title of Award: Judge William J. Nelson Scholarships **Area, Field, or Subject:** General studies. **Level of Education for which Award is Granted:** Undergraduate **Funds Available:** $1,000. **Duration:** One year. **Eligibility Requirements:** Applicant must be a resident of Charlotte, Collier, Glades, Hendry or Lee County; must have overcome adversity in some way; and must attend the University of Florida. **Application Requirements:** Applicants must submit a letter of interest, transcript, and letter of recommendation. Application forms are available online. **Deadline for Receipt:** February 15.

2122 ■ SOUTHWEST FLORIDA COMMUNITY FOUNDATION
8260 College Pkwy., Ste. 101
Fort Myers, FL 33919
Tel: (239)274-5900
Fax: (239)274-5930
Web Site: http://www.floridacommunity.com
To fund tuition for economically-disadvantaged students to attend college or technical school.
Title of Award: Robert B. and Dorothy Pence Scholarships **Area, Field, or Subject:** General studies. **Level of Education for which Award is Granted:** Undergraduate **Funds Available:** $1,000. **Duration:** One year.
Eligibility Requirements: Applicants must have graduated from a public or private high school in Lee County and must be an industrious student with good moral character and document financial need. **Application Requirements:** Applicants must submit a letter of interest, transcript, and letter of recommendation. Application forms are available online: **Deadline for Receipt:** February 15.

2123 ■ SOUTHWEST FLORIDA COMMUNITY FOUNDATION
8260 College Pkwy., Ste. 101
Fort Myers, FL 33919
Tel: (239)274-5900
Fax: (239)274-5930
Web Site: http://www.floridacommunity.com
To provide funding support for students pursuing a career in accounting.
Title of Award: Chet and Jannett Perry Scholarships **Area, Field, or Subject:** Accounting. **Level of Education for which Award is Granted:** Undergraduate **Funds Available:** $1,000. **Duration:** One year.
Eligibility Requirements: Applicant must be graduating from a public or private high school in Charlotte, Hendry, Glades or Lee County; must pursue a degree in accounting; and must enter college within a year following high school graduation. **Application Requirements:** Applicants must submit a letter of interest, transcript, and letter of recommendation. Application forms are available online. **Deadline for Receipt:** February 15.

2124 ■ SOUTHWEST FLORIDA COMMUNITY FOUNDATION
8260 College Pkwy., Ste. 101
Fort Myers, FL 33919
Tel: (239)274-5900
Fax: (239)274-5930
Web Site: http://www.floridacommunity.com
To fund a student who has displayed high levels of excellence in academic and/or athletics and who has lost a parent due to an illness or sudden death and to help qualified students to pay for education in a college, university or technical school.
Title of Award: Rockin' Christmas Fund Scholarships **Area, Field, or Subject:** General studies. **Level of Education for which Award is Granted:** Undergraduate **Funds Available:** No specific amount. **Duration:** One year.
Eligibility Requirements: Applicants must have graduated from a public or private high school in Lee or Collier to receive the award which will be based upon satisfactory evidence of matriculation to a college, university or technical school; must provide evidence of a academic athletic achievement from any coach at school or from any league participated in, if not at school; and must demonstrate financial need. Applicants do not have to have played high school sports but rather must demonstrate that athletics are a part of their life. **Application Requirements:** Applicants must provide a letter from guidance counselors of the high school signed by the counselor on how the student qualifies under the loss of parent criteria; must submit a letter of interest, transcript, and letter of recommendation. Application forms are available online. **Deadline for Receipt:** February 15.

2125 ■ SOUTHWEST FLORIDA COMMUNITY FOUNDATION
8260 College Pkwy., Ste. 101
Fort Myers, FL 33919
Tel: (239)274-5900
Fax: (239)274-5930
Web Site: http://www.floridacommunity.com
To provide tuition for high school graduates' post-secondary educational opportunities, including trade/technical school, undergraduate work, post-graduate work, and professional education.

Title of Award: Robert C. and Margaret A. Schikora Scholarships **Area, Field, or Subject:** General studies. **Level of Education for which Award is Granted:** Undergraduate **Funds Available:** $1,000. **Duration:** One year.
Eligibility Requirements: Applicants must graduate from public or private high school in Lee County with documented "B" average; must be well-rounded in terms of education, community service, sports and leadership activities; and must demonstrate financial need. **Application Requirements:** Applicants must submit a letter of interest, transcript, and letter of recommendation. Application forms are available online. **Deadline for Receipt:** February 15.

2126 ■ SOUTHWEST FLORIDA COMMUNITY FOUNDATION
8260 College Pkwy., Ste. 101
Fort Myers, FL 33919
Tel: (239)274-5900
Fax: (239)274-5930
Web Site: http://www.floridacommunity.com
To fund books, laboratory fees, or any expenses related to student's academic costs.
Title of Award: Southwest Florida Community Foundation College Assistance Scholarships **Area, Field, or Subject:** General studies. **Level of Education for which Award is Granted:** Undergraduate **Funds Available:** $500. **Duration:** One year.
Eligibility Requirements: Applicants must reside in Charlotte, Lee, Glades, Hendry or Collier County and must demonstrate financial need. **Application Requirements:** Applicants must submit a letter of interest, transcript, and financial need documentation. **Deadline for Receipt:** February 15.

2127 ■ SOUTHWEST FLORIDA COMMUNITY FOUNDATION
8260 College Pkwy., Ste. 101
Fort Myers, FL 33919
Tel: (239)274-5900
Fax: (239)274-5930
Web Site: http://www.floridacommunity.com
To provide financial funds for qualified high school students who are dependents of law enforcement officers.
Title of Award: SWFL Deputy Sheriffs Association Fund Scholarships **Area, Field, or Subject:** General studies. **Level of Education for which Award is Granted:** Undergraduate **Funds Available:** No specific amount. **Duration:** One year.
Eligibility Requirements: Applicant must be a graduate from high school in Charlotte, Collier, Lee, Hendry or Glades Counties; must be a dependent of a law enforcement officer in the above counties; and must list name of law enforcement officer. **Application Requirements:** Applicants must complete the application form, available online, and submit a letter of interest, transcript, and letter of recommendation. **Deadline for Receipt:** February 15.

2128 ■ SOUTHWEST FLORIDA COMMUNITY FOUNDATION
8260 College Pkwy., Ste. 101
Fort Myers, FL 33919
Tel: (239)274-5900
Fax: (239)274-5930
Web Site: http://www.floridacommunity.com
To provide tuition for high school graduates who played competitive golf in their senior year and at least one other year during high school.
Title of Award: SWFL Professional Golfers Association Scholarships **Area, Field, or Subject:** General studies. **Level of Education for which Award is Granted:** Undergraduate **Funds Available:** $1,000. **Duration:** One year.
Eligibility Requirements: Applicants must have graduated from a public or private high school in Charlotte, Lee or Collier County; must have played competitive golf in their senior year and at least one other year during high school; and must have academic achievement and show evidence of community service and outside activities. **Application Requirements:** Applicants must submit a letter of interest, transcript, and letter of recommendation. Application forms are available online. **Deadline for Receipt:** February 15.

2129 ■ SPECIALIZED CARRIERS AND RIGGING ASSOCIATION
2750 Prosperity Ave., Ste. 620
Fairfax, VA 22031-4312

Tel: (703)698-0291
Fax: (703)698-0297
E-mail: info@scranet.org
Web Site: http://www.scranet.org
To support a research by technical/vocational college students.
Title of Award: SC and R Foundation Grant Program **Area, Field, or Subject:** Transportation. **Level of Education for which Award is Granted:** Undergraduate **Funds Available:** $1500.
Eligibility Requirements: Applicants must have at least one term of undergraduate study remaining or have applied to technical/vocational college; must have study leading to an associate degree in the field of specialized carriers and rigging industry; an employees or a relative of an employees of SC and RA Member Company. **Application Requirements:** Applicants must complete the application form together with two letters of recommendation (one letter from an academic advisor or employer); official transcripts; recent photograph; and contact information.
Additional Information: Scholarship Subcommittee, rpage@scranet.org.

2130 ■ SPECIALIZED CARRIERS AND RIGGING ASSOCIATION

2750 Prosperity Ave., Ste. 620
Fairfax, VA 22031-4312
Tel: (703)698-0291
Fax: (703)698-0297
E-mail: info@scranet.org
Web Site: http://www.scranet.org
To provides career opportunities and scholarship to its members.
Title of Award: SC and R Foundation Scholarships **Area, Field, or Subject:** Transportation. **Level of Education for which Award is Granted:** Undergraduate **Number Awarded:** 1. **Funds Available:** $3000.
Duration: One year.
Eligibility Requirements: Applicants must have at least one term of undergraduate study remaining or have applied to a college/university; must have study leading to bachelor degree in fields related to specialized carriers and rigging industry; must be employees or relatives of employees of SC and RA Member Company. **Application Requirements:** Applicants must complete the application form together with two letters of recommendation (one letter from an academic advisor or employer); official transcripts; recent photograph; and contact information.
Additional Information: Scholarship Subcommittee, rpage@scranet.org.

2131 ■ SPINA BIFIDA ASSOCIATION OF AMERICA

4590 MacArthur Blvd. NW
Washington, DC 20007
Tel: (202)944-3285
Free: 800-621-3141
Fax: (202)944-3295
E-mail: sbaa@sbaa.org
Web Site: http://www.sbaa.org
To assist persons born with Spina Bifida to achieve their full potential through higher education.
Title of Award: SBA Four-Year Scholarships Program **Area, Field, or Subject:** General studies. **Level of Education for which Award is Granted:** Undergraduate **Number Awarded:** 1. **Funds Available:** $5000.
Duration: 4 years.
Eligibility Requirements: Applicants must have Spina Bifida (present a physician's statement of disability); must be high school seniors; enrolled in, or accepted by a college or university; must demonstrate financial need. **Application Requirements:** Scholarship application forms are available at the website. Applicants must file a completed application together with the physician's statement of disability (includes the physician's address and phone number); official school transcript; test scores (SAT, ACT, GRE); acceptance letter by school or college; three recommendation letters, two from faculty members; personal statement about educational goals (3 pages) and send to: SBA, Attn: Scholarship Committee 4590 MacArthur Boulevard, NW Ste. 250, Washington, DC 20007-4226. **Additional Information:** Immediate family members of SBA Board, Scholarship Committee and Staff are not eligible for the awards.
Deadline for Receipt: March 7. **Additional Information:** Tanya Coogan, tcoogan@sbaa.org.

2132 ■ SPINA BIFIDA ASSOCIATION OF AMERICA

4590 MacArthur Blvd. NW
Washington, DC 20007

Tel: (202)944-3285
Free: 800-621-3141
Fax: (202)944-3295
E-mail: sbaa@sbaa.org
Web Site: http://www.sbaa.org
To assist persons born with Spina Bifida to achieve their full potential through higher education.
Title of Award: SBA One-Year Scholarships Program **Area, Field, or Subject:** General studies. **Level of Education for which Award is Granted:** Undergraduate **Number Awarded:** 5. **Funds Available:** $2000.
Duration: One academic year.
Eligibility Requirements: Applicants must have Spina Bifida (present a physician's statement of disability); must be high school graduates or possess a General Education Development (GED) test; must be enrolled in a four year university, junior college, approved trade, vocational, or business school. **Application Requirements:** Scholarship application forms are available at the website. Applicants must file a completed application together with the physician's statement of disability (includes the physician's address and phone number); official school transcript; test scores (SAT, ACT, GRE); acceptance letter by school or college; three recommendation letters, two from faculty members; personal statement about educational goals (3 pages) and send to: SBA, Attn: Scholarship Committee 4590 MacArthur Boulevard, NW, Ste. 250, Washington, DC 20007-4226. **Additional Information:** Immediate family members of SBA Board, Scholarship Committee and Staff are not eligible for the awards.
Deadline for Receipt: March 7. **Additional Information:** Tanya Coogan, tcoogan@sbaa.org.

2133 ■ STARK COMMUNITY FOUNDATION

400 Market Ave. N, Ste. 200
Canton, OH 44702-2107
Tel: (330)454-3426
Fax: (330)454-5855
Web Site: http://www.starkcommunityfoundation.org
To provide scholarship assistance to qualified individuals who want to pursue their studies.
Title of Award: Wayne D. Ackerman Family Scholarship Fund **Area, Field, or Subject:** General studies. **Level of Education for which Award is Granted:** Undergraduate **Funds Available:** No specific amount. **Duration:** One year.
Eligibility Requirements: Applicants must be senior students attending high school in Stark County, OH; must be enrolled as full-time students; must have GPA of at least 3.0 on 4.0 scale; must demonstrate outstanding involvement both in academics and extracurricular activities; must have been accepted into a four-year college or university. **Application Requirements:** Application forms are available online and must be sent to Stark Community Foundation, 400 Market Ave. N, Ste. 200, Canton, OH 44702. **Deadline for Receipt:** May 1.

2134 ■ STARK COMMUNITY FOUNDATION

400 Market Ave. N, Ste. 200
Canton, OH 44702-2107
Tel: (330)454-3426
Fax: (330)454-5855
Web Site: http://www.starkcommunityfoundation.org
To provide scholarship assistance to qualified individuals who want to pursue their studies.
Title of Award: Harry D. Callahan Educational Trust **Area, Field, or Subject:** General studies. **Level of Education for which Award is Granted:** Undergraduate **Funds Available:** No specific amount.
Eligibility Requirements: Applicants must be students residing in Stark County who are pursuing a two-year or four-year college degree at an accredited school within approximately 150 miles of Canton; must have participation in athletics, government and other extracurricular and community activities; and must demonstrate leadership qualities. **Application Requirements:** Applicants must submit completed application form and other supporting documents to Catholic Youth Council, 1330 Park Ave., NW, Canton, OH 44708. **Deadline for Receipt:** April 30. **Additional Information:** Kris Baum.

2135 ■ STARK COMMUNITY FOUNDATION

400 Market Ave. N, Ste. 200
Canton, OH 44702-2107

Tel: (330)454-3426
Fax: (330)454-5855
Web Site: http://www.starkcommunityfoundation.org
To provide scholarship assistance to qualified individuals who want to pursue their studies.
Title of Award: George H. and Anna Casper Fund **Area, Field, or Subject:** General studies. **Level of Education for which Award is Granted:** Undergraduate **Funds Available:** No specific amount. **Duration:** One year.
Eligibility Requirements: Applicants must be students residing in Stark County; must be attending college full or part-time; must demonstrate financial need and academic excellence. **Application Requirements:** Applicants must complete and submit the application form and requirements to Robert Martelet, Sec., 836 Market Ave. N, Canton, OH 44702. **Deadline for Receipt:** May 20.

2136 ■ STARK COMMUNITY FOUNDATION
400 Market Ave. N, Ste. 200
Canton, OH 44702-2107
Tel: (330)454-3426
Fax: (330)454-5855
Web Site: http://www.starkcommunityfoundation.org
To provide scholarship assistance to qualified individuals who want to pursue their studies.
Title of Award: Julio C. Diaz Memorial Scholarship Fund **Area, Field, or Subject:** General studies. **Level of Education for which Award is Granted:** Undergraduate **Funds Available:** No specific amount.
Eligibility Requirements: Applicants must be attending or who have been accepted at St. Thomas Aquinas High School; must have GPA of at least 3.0 on a 4.0 scale. **Application Requirements:** Applicants must have and completed the application form and two letters of recommendation from the following: teacher, school administrators, or guidance counselors. Application form and requirements must be sent to St. Thomas Aquinas High School, Victoria Frustaci/Business Office, 2121 Reno Dr., Louisville, OH 44641. **Deadline for Receipt:** May 1.

2137 ■ STARK COMMUNITY FOUNDATION
400 Market Ave. N, Ste. 200
Canton, OH 44702-2107
Tel: (330)454-3426
Fax: (330)454-5855
Web Site: http://www.starkcommunityfoundation.org
To provide scholarship assistance to qualified individuals who want to pursue their studies.
Title of Award: Rob Digiacomo Scholarship Fund **Area, Field, or Subject:** General studies. **Level of Education for which Award is Granted:** Undergraduate **Number Awarded:** 1. **Funds Available:** $600.
Eligibility Requirements: Applicants must be graduating seniors residing at the Lake Local School District; must demonstrate commitment to excellence in academic and athletic accomplishments; must have exceptional moral and personal characteristics; must have leadership skills; and must demonstrate devotion to family. **Application Requirements:** Applicants must complete the application form available online and must be sent to Edmond J. DiGiacomo and Sandra E. DiGiacomo, 755 Oneida Trail, Hartville, OH 44632. **Deadline for Receipt:** April 15.

2138 ■ STARK COMMUNITY FOUNDATION
400 Market Ave. N, Ste. 200
Canton, OH 44702-2107
Tel: (330)454-3426
Fax: (330)454-5855
Web Site: http://www.starkcommunityfoundation.org
To provide scholarship assistance to qualified individuals who want to pursue their studies.
Title of Award: Emergency Medicine Physicians Scholarship Fund for Non-Physician Employee Dependents **Area, Field, or Subject:** General studies. **Level of Education for which Award is Granted:** Undergraduate **Number Awarded:** 2. **Funds Available:** $2,500-$5,000. **Duration:** One year.
Eligibility Requirements: Applicants must be dependent children of non-physician employees of Emergency Medicine Physicians, Inc. who are pursuing or applying for college level studies. **Application Requirements:** Applicants must submit two letters of recommendation and an

educational or professional essay; must complete the application form together with the application requirements to EMP Scholarship Program, Emergency Medicine Physicians 4535 Dressler Rd. NW, Canton, OH 44718. **Deadline for Receipt:** August 10.

2139 ■ STARK COMMUNITY FOUNDATION
400 Market Ave. N, Ste. 200
Canton, OH 44702-2107
Tel: (330)454-3426
Fax: (330)454-5855
Web Site: http://www.starkcommunityfoundation.org
To provide scholarship assistance to qualified individuals who want to pursue their studies.
Title of Award: Jack B. Fisher Scholarship Fund **Area, Field, or Subject:** Fisheries sciences/management. **Level of Education for which Award is Granted:** Undergraduate **Number Awarded:** 4. **Funds Available:** $250. **Duration:** One year.
Eligibility Requirements: Applicants must be graduate of a Stark County High school and current employees of Fisher Foods in good standing (If employed during high school, a minimum of one year of employment is required. If employed after graduation from high school, a minimum of 2 years of employment is required); must have above average accomplishment in high school; must demonstrate good moral and personal characteristics. **Application Requirements:** Applicants must submit a recommendation letter from a store manager, and application form to Fisher Foods Marketing, Inc. 4855 Frank Rd. NW N, Canton, OH 44720. **Deadline for Receipt:** July 23.

2140 ■ STARK COMMUNITY FOUNDATION
400 Market Ave. N, Ste. 200
Canton, OH 44702-2107
Tel: (330)454-3426
Fax: (330)454-5855
Web Site: http://www.starkcommunityfoundation.org
To provide scholarship assistance to qualified individuals who want to pursue their studies.
Title of Award: Alice J. Foit Scholarships **Area, Field, or Subject:** General Studies. **Level of Education for which Award is Granted:** Undergraduate **Funds Available:** No specific amount. **Duration:** One year.
Eligibility Requirements: Applicants must be high school graduates or seniors residing in Carroll County, German Township, Harrison County, OH; must be enrolled as full time students; must have achieved high school cumulative GPA of at least 2.5 on a 4.0 scale, and if attending college a cumulative GPA of at least 2.0 on a 4.0 scale; must have demonstrated involvement, both in extracurricular activities or community and religious activities; must have been accepted into a two or four year college on university program leading to a degree; must intend to live in or work in either Carroll or Harrison County, OH for a minimum of two year after completion of their education. **Application Requirements:** Applicants must complete and submit the application form and requirements to Richard Lee Rumbaugh, 63 E Main St., Carrollton, OH 44615. **Deadline for Receipt:** November.

2141 ■ STARK COMMUNITY FOUNDATION
400 Market Ave. N, Ste. 200
Canton, OH 44702-2107
Tel: (330)454-3426
Fax: (330)454-5855
Web Site: http://www.starkcommunityfoundation.org
To provide scholarship assistance to qualified individuals who want to pursue their studies.
Title of Award: David A. and Pamela A. Gault Charitable Fund **Area, Field, or Subject:** General studies. **Level of Education for which Award is Granted:** Undergraduate **Number Awarded:** 2. **Funds Available:** No specific amount. **Duration:** One year.
Eligibility Requirements: Applicants must be graduates of Stark County High School with residency in Stark County for a minimum of 5 years; must be enrolled at Otterbein College or Walsh University, pursuing a graduate or undergraduate degree in business; must have a minimum of 2.5 GPA on a 4.0 scale. **Application Requirements:** Applicants must have a recommendation letter by Otterbein College or Walsh University. Application forms are available online and must be sent to Stark Com-

munity Foundation, 400 market Ave. N, Canton, OH 44702. **Deadline for Receipt:** April 1.

2142 ■ STARK COMMUNITY FOUNDATION

400 Market Ave. N, Ste. 200
Canton, OH 44702-2107
Tel: (330)454-3426
Fax: (330)454-5855
Web Site: http://www.starkcommunityfoundation.org
To provide scholarship assistance to qualified individuals who want to pursue their studies.
Title of Award: James H. and Shirley L. Green Scholarship Fund **Area, Field, or Subject:** General studies. **Level of Education for which Award is Granted:** Undergraduate **Funds Available:** No specific amount.
Eligibility Requirements: Applicants must be seniors attending Canton South High School, Canton, OH; must have been accepted into a two-year or four-year college or university; must demonstrate financial need. **Application Requirements:** Application forms are available online and must be sent to Barbara Tscholl, Canton South High School, 600 Faircrest St. SE, Canton OH 44707. **Deadline for Receipt:** April 1.

2143 ■ STARK COMMUNITY FOUNDATION

400 Market Ave. N, Ste. 200
Canton, OH 44702-2107
Tel: (330)454-3426
Fax: (330)454-5855
Web Site: http://www.starkcommunityfoundation.org
To provide scholarship assistance to qualified individuals who want to pursue their studies.
Title of Award: Dr. James H. Heckaman Memorial Scholarship Fund **Area, Field, or Subject:** General studies. **Level of Education for which Award is Granted:** Undergraduate **Funds Available:** No specific amount.
Eligibility Requirements: Applicants must be Hoover High School graduating seniors; must have above average accomplishment in high school; must have demonstrated financial need; must be planning to a four-year degree program in any field of study; must demonstrate good moral and personal characteristics. **Application Requirements:** Application forms are available online and must be sent to Barbara Tarantino, Dir. of Guidance, Hoover Canton, OH 44720.

2144 ■ STARK COMMUNITY FOUNDATION

400 Market Ave. N, Ste. 200
Canton, OH 44702-2107
Tel: (330)454-3426
Fax: (330)454-5855
Web Site: http://www.starkcommunityfoundation.org
To provide scholarship assistance to qualified individuals who want to pursue their studies.
Title of Award: Minnie Hopkins Memorial Scholarship Fund of Lathrop/Compton School **Area, Field, or Subject:** General studies. **Level of Education for which Award is Granted:** Undergraduate **Funds Available:** No specific amount.
Eligibility Requirements: Applicants must have graduated from Lathrop/Compton School and attended Lathrop/Compton for at least three years; must have graduated from Stark County public high school and been accepted into a college, university, or technical school; must have leadership skills; must have academic ability and achievement; must have initiative and motivation; must demonstrate financial need. **Application Requirements:** Applicants must provide statement about his/ her family background. Application form and requirements must be sent to Stark Community Foundation, 400 Market Ave. N, Ste. 200, Canton, OH 44702. **Deadline for Receipt:** April 15.

2145 ■ STARK COMMUNITY FOUNDATION

400 Market Ave. N, Ste. 200
Canton, OH 44702-2107
Tel: (330)454-3426
Fax: (330)454-5855
Web Site: http://www.starkcommunityfoundation.org
To provide scholarship assistance to qualified individuals who want to pursue their studies.

Title of Award: Jackson High School Alumni Scholarship Fund **Area, Field, or Subject:** General studies. **Level of Education for which Award is Granted:** Undergraduate **Funds Available:** No specific amount. **Duration:** One year.
Eligibility Requirements: Applicants must be graduating seniors at Jackson High School or Jackson High School graduates who are currently enrolled as full-time college students; must have minimum GPA of 2.5 or above. **Application Requirements:** Application forms are available online and must be sent to Mr. Dan Headland, 5585 Stoney Ridge Rd., Canton, OH 44718. **Deadline for Receipt:** April.

2146 ■ STARK COMMUNITY FOUNDATION

400 Market Ave. N, Ste. 200
Canton, OH 44702-2107
Tel: (330)454-3426
Fax: (330)454-5855
Web Site: http://www.starkcommunityfoundation.org
To provide scholarship assistance to qualified individuals who want to pursue their studies.
Title of Award: Junior Achievement of East Central Ohio, Inc. Scholarship Fund **Area, Field, or Subject:** General studies. **Level of Education for which Award is Granted:** Undergraduate **Funds Available:** No specific amount.
Eligibility Requirements: Applicants must be high school seniors who have participated in Junior Achievement of Stark County. **Application Requirements:** Applicants must complete and submit the application form and other supporting documents to Jody L. Levitt, JA of East Central Ohio, Inc., 4353 Executive Circle NW, Canton, OH 44718. **Deadline for Receipt:** March 1.

2147 ■ STARK COMMUNITY FOUNDATION

400 Market Ave. N, Ste. 200
Canton, OH 44702-2107
Tel: (330)454-3426
Fax: (330)454-5855
Web Site: http://www.starkcommunityfoundation.org
To provide scholarship assistance to qualified individuals who want to pursue their studies.
Title of Award: David A. Kaiser Memorial Scholarship Fund **Area, Field, or Subject:** General studies. **Level of Education for which Award is Granted:** Undergraduate **Funds Available:** $3,000. **Duration:** One year.
Eligibility Requirements: Applicants must be fulltime students in high school in the Canton City School District; must be accepted into an accredited college or university; must be planning to pursue a four-year degree. **Application Requirements:** Application forms are available online at www.starkcommunityfoundation.org or for more information applicants are advice to contact the foundation at Stark Community Foundation, 400 Market Ave. N, Ste. 200, Canton, OH 44702. **Deadline for Receipt:** March 15.

2148 ■ STARK COMMUNITY FOUNDATION

400 Market Ave. N, Ste. 200
Canton, OH 44702-2107
Tel: (330)454-3426
Fax: (330)454-5855
Web Site: http://www.starkcommunityfoundation.org
To assist qualified individuals who want to pursue their studies.
Title of Award: Jay C. and B. Nadine Leggett Charitable Scholarship Fund **Area, Field, or Subject:** General studies. **Level of Education for which Award is Granted:** Undergraduate **Funds Available:** No specific amount. **Duration:** One year.
Eligibility Requirements: Applicants must be graduates of Conotton Valley High School or high school seniors who applied to and have been accepted by college, university, or recognized educational institution of higher learning, or presently enrolled in college. **Application Requirements:** Applicants must be complete and submit the application form and requirements to Judson Lada, Guidance Counselor, Conotton Valley High School, 7205 Cumberland Rd. SW, Bowerston, OH 44695. **Deadline for Receipt:** April 1.

2149 ■ STARK COMMUNITY FOUNDATION

400 Market Ave. N, Ste. 200
Canton, OH 44702-2107

Tel: (330)454-3426
Fax: (330)454-5855
Web Site: http://www.starkcommunityfoundation.org
To provide scholarship assistance to qualified individuals who want to pursue their studies.
Title of Award: Lillian Grace Mahan Scholarship Fund **Area, Field, or Subject:** Library and archival sciences. **Level of Education for which Award is Granted:** Undergraduate **Number Awarded:** 8. **Funds Available:** $4,895. **Duration:** One year.
Eligibility Requirements: Applicants must be graduate or undergraduate students of library science who are residents of Stark County; must have an outstanding academic performance and aptitude and/or are in need of financial assistance to pursue a degree in library science; must have demonstrated academic performance record and other activities. **Application Requirements:** Application forms are available online and must be sent to Canton Student Loan Foundation, 4974 Higbee Ave. NW, Canton, OH 44718. **Deadline for Receipt:** April 1.

2150 ■ STARK COMMUNITY FOUNDATION
400 Market Ave. N, Ste. 200
Canton, OH 44702-2107
Tel: (330)454-3426
Fax: (330)454-5855
Web Site: http://www.starkcommunityfoundation.org
To provide scholarship assistance to qualified individuals who want to pursue their studies.
Title of Award: Markley Family Scholarship Fund **Area, Field, or Subject:** General studies. **Level of Education for which Award is Granted:** Undergraduate **Funds Available:** No specific amount. **Duration:** One year.
Eligibility Requirements: Applicants must be full time undergraduate students of Walsh University, North Canton, OH. **Application Requirements:** Applicants must complete and submit the application form to Assistant Director of Financial Aid, Walsh University, 2020 Easton NW, North Canton, OH 44720. **Deadline for Receipt:** April 1.

2151 ■ STARK COMMUNITY FOUNDATION
400 Market Ave. N, Ste. 200
Canton, OH 44702-2107
Tel: (330)454-3426
Fax: (330)454-5855
Web Site: http://www.starkcommunityfoundation.org
To provide scholarship assistance to qualified individuals who want to pursue their studies.
Title of Award: Bill McCarthy Scout Scholarship Fund **Area, Field, or Subject:** General studies. **Level of Education for which Award is Granted:** Undergraduate **Funds Available:** No specific amount. **Duration:** One year.
Eligibility Requirements: Applicants must be male students who are or have been Boy Scouts; having belonged to a troop in the Tuslaw District; and who have attained at least the rank of a First Class Scout; and who ranks at least among the highest ten boys in his graduating class in high school. **Application Requirements:** Applicants must complete and submit the application requirements to Mr. Andy McGeee, Tuslaw High School Guidance Counselor, 1847 Manchester NW, Massillon, OH 44647. **Deadline for Receipt:** April 1.

2152 ■ STARK COMMUNITY FOUNDATION
400 Market Ave. N, Ste. 200
Canton, OH 44702-2107
Tel: (330)454-3426
Fax: (330)454-5855
Web Site: http://www.starkcommunityfoundation.org
To provide scholarship assistance to qualified individuals who want to pursue their studies.
Title of Award: Harry Mestel Memorial Accounting Scholarship Fund **Area, Field, or Subject:** Accounting. **Level of Education for which Award is Granted:** Undergraduate **Funds Available:** No specific amount.
Eligibility Requirements: Applicants must be accounting students enrolled in an Ohio college or university in their final year, in pursuit of a Bachelor of Science in Accounting Degree, whose permanent address is in Stark County; must demonstrate financial need; must demonstrate

involvement in community activities; must have achieved a cumulative GPA of at least 3.0 on a 4.0 scale. **Application Requirements:** Applicants must complete and submit the application form and requirements to Stark Community Foundation, 400 Market Ave. N, Canton, OH 44702. **Deadline for Receipt:** May 1.

2153 ■ STARK COMMUNITY FOUNDATION
400 Market Ave. N, Ste. 200
Canton, OH 44702-2107
Tel: (330)454-3426
Fax: (330)454-5855
Web Site: http://www.starkcommunityfoundation.org
To provide scholarship assistance to qualified individuals who want to pursue their studies.
Title of Award: Notre Dame Club of Canton Scholarships **Area, Field, or Subject:** General studies. **Level of Education for which Award is Granted:** Undergraduate **Funds Available:** No specific amount. **Duration:** One year.
Eligibility Requirements: Applicants must be students who have attended Stork County or Tuscarawas County, Ohio High School, Dalton High School, or Orville High School in Wayne County, Ohio, or Central Kidron Christian School in Kidron, OH; must have GPA of at least 3.0 on a 4.0 scale while in high school; must demonstrate outstanding involvement both in academics and extracurricular activities; must have been accepted to attend the University of Notre Dame, Notre Dame, Indiana. **Application Requirements:** Applicants must complete and submit the application form to Stark Community Foundation, 400 Market Ave. N, Ste. 200, Canton, OH 44702. **Deadline for Receipt:** June 15.

2154 ■ STARK COMMUNITY FOUNDATION
400 Market Ave. N, Ste. 200
Canton, OH 44702-2107
Tel: (330)454-3426
Fax: (330)454-5855
Web Site: http://www.starkcommunityfoundation.org
To provide scholarship assistance to qualified individuals who want to pursue their studies.
Title of Award: O'Jays Scholarship Fund **Area, Field, or Subject:** General studies. **Level of Education for which Award is Granted:** Undergraduate **Funds Available:** No specific amount. **Duration:** One year.
Eligibility Requirements: Applicants must be seniors attending high school in Stark County who will graduate the year the scholarship is awarded, or residents of Stark County who have previously attained high school diploma or Graduate Equivalency Diploma; must be accepted by or presently attending a two-year college or university, nursing school, or other post high school vocational educational program; must have cumulative GPA of 2.5 on a 4.0 scale; must demonstrate extracurricular activities or community activities; must demonstrate financial need. **Application Requirements:** Applicants must complete and submit the application form to Stark Community Foundation, 400 Market Ave. N, Ste. 200, Canton, OH 44702. **Deadline for Receipt:** April 30.

2155 ■ STARK COMMUNITY FOUNDATION
400 Market Ave. N, Ste. 200
Canton, OH 44702-2107
Tel: (330)454-3426
Fax: (330)454-5855
Web Site: http://www.starkcommunityfoundation.org
To provide scholarship assistance to qualified individuals who want to pursue their studies.
Title of Award: Perry Township School Memorial Scholarship Fund **Area, Field, or Subject:** General studies. **Level of Education for which Award is Granted:** Undergraduate **Funds Available:** No specific amount. **Duration:** One year.
Eligibility Requirements: Applicants must be high school graduates or high school seniors who have permanent residency in Perry Township, Carroll County, OH or who have permanent residency on the date they began their post high school education; must have been accepted at and planning to enroll, or are currently enrolled, at an accredited college, university, or technical school with at least a two year course of study to pursue further education; must have good moral and personal characteristics; must demonstrate involvement in community and religious activi-

ties; must demonstrate financial need. **Application Requirements:** Applicants must submit completed application form and are advice to contact Carrollton High School Guidance Office. **Deadline for Receipt:** March 14.

2156 ■ STARK COMMUNITY FOUNDATION
400 Market Ave. N, Ste. 200
Canton, OH 44702-2107
Tel: (330)454-3426
Fax: (330)454-5855
Web Site: http://www.starkcommunityfoundation.org
To provide scholarship assistance to qualified individuals who want to pursue their studies.
Title of Award: August M. Rocco Scholarship Fund **Area, Field, or Subject:** General studies. **Level of Education for which Award is Granted:** Undergraduate **Funds Available:** No specific amount. **Duration:** One year.
Eligibility Requirements: Applicants must be male or female graduates of Canton Central Catholic High School or St. Thomas Aquinas High School and of the Catholic faith; must be accepted to attend college at University of Notre Dame, South Bend, IN; must have good scholastic record and character traits. **Application Requirements:** Applicants must complete and submit the application form and other supporting documents to Stark Community Foundation, 400 Market Ave. N, Canton, OH 44702. **Deadline for Receipt:** June 5.

2157 ■ STARK COMMUNITY FOUNDATION
400 Market Ave. N, Ste. 200
Canton, OH 44702-2107
Tel: (330)454-3426
Fax: (330)454-5855
Web Site: http://www.starkcommunityfoundation.org
To provide scholarship assistance to qualified individuals who want to pursue their studies.
Title of Award: Don and Madalyn Sickafoose Educational Trust **Area, Field, or Subject:** General studies. **Level of Education for which Award is Granted:** Undergraduate **Funds Available:** No specific amount.
Eligibility Requirements: Applicants must be students living in Southeastern Stark County, Northwestern Carroll County and Northern Tuscarawas County which would include the following district: Brown Local, Canton Local, Osnaburg Local, Fairless Local, Sandy Valley, Tusky Valley and Carrollton Exempted Village. **Application Requirements:** Applicants must complete and submit the application form and requirements to Stark Community Foundation, 400 Market Ave. N, Ste. 200, Canton, OH 44702. **Deadline for Receipt:** May 15.

2158 ■ STARK COMMUNITY FOUNDATION
400 Market Ave. N, Ste. 200
Canton, OH 44702-2107
Tel: (330)454-3426
Fax: (330)454-5855
Web Site: http://www.starkcommunityfoundation.org
To provide scholarship assistance to qualified individuals who want to pursue their studies.
Title of Award: R. Skeeles Memorial Scholarship Fund **Area, Field, or Subject:** General studies. **Level of Education for which Award is Granted:** Undergraduate **Funds Available:** No specific amount. **Duration:** One year.
Eligibility Requirements: Applicants must have attended Worley School for at least four years; must have good academic accomplishment in high school; must have good moral and personal characteristic. **Application Requirements:** Applicants must complete and submit the application form and requirements to Worley School PTA President, 424 21st St. NW, Canton, OH 44709. **Deadline for Receipt:** April 1.

2159 ■ STARK COMMUNITY FOUNDATION
400 Market Ave. N, Ste. 200
Canton, OH 44702-2107
Tel: (330)454-3426
Fax: (330)454-5855
Web Site: http://www.starkcommunityfoundation.org
To provide scholarship assistance to qualified individuals who want to pursue their studies.

Title of Award: Jeffery Tyler Sweitzer Wrestling Memorial Scholarship Fund **Area, Field, or Subject:** General studies. **Level of Education for which Award is Granted:** Undergraduate **Funds Available:** No specific amount. **Duration:** One year.
Eligibility Requirements: Applicants must be male residents of Stark County, OH; must have achieved passing GPA on a 4.0 scale; must be graduating students from Hoover High School, North Canton, OH, have participated in the wrestling program; must be students attending West Liberty College, Wheeling, WV; must be students graduating from any Stark County area high school who have participated in a wrestling program. **Application Requirements:** Applicants must submit completed application form and requirements to Canton Hoover High School Wrestling Booster Club.

2160 ■ STARK COMMUNITY FOUNDATION
400 Market Ave. N, Ste. 200
Canton, OH 44702-2107
Tel: (330)454-3426
Fax: (330)454-5855
Web Site: http://www.starkcommunityfoundation.org
To provide scholarship assistance to qualified individuals who want to pursue their studies.
Title of Award: Timothy S. Sweterlitsch Memorial Scholarship Fund **Area, Field, or Subject:** General studies. **Level of Education for which Award is Granted:** Undergraduate **Number Awarded:** 2. **Funds Available:** $6,000. **Duration:** One year.
Eligibility Requirements: Applicants must be graduates of Washington High School, Massillon, OH; must have an academic accomplishment; must have good moral and personal characteristics. **Application Requirements:** Applicants must complete and submit the application form and other supporting documents to Mr. Frank Sweterlitsch, 802 Deerfield Lane NE, Massillon, OH 44646. **Deadline for Receipt:** April 15.

2161 ■ STARK COMMUNITY FOUNDATION
400 Market Ave. N, Ste. 200
Canton, OH 44702-2107
Tel: (330)454-3426
Fax: (330)454-5855
Web Site: http://www.starkcommunityfoundation.org
To provide scholarship assistance to qualified individuals who want to pursue their studies.
Title of Award: Tim Triner Letter Carriers Scholarship Fund **Area, Field, or Subject:** General studies. **Level of Education for which Award is Granted:** Undergraduate **Funds Available:** No specific amount.
Eligibility Requirements: Applicants must be seniors enrolled as full-time students; must have scholastic achievements; must be children or legal wards of Donor's active, retired or deceased members of Branch No. 238, National Association of Letter; must have a proof of acceptance into a post-secondary college, university or technical training program. **Application Requirements:** Applicants must complete and submit the application form and requirements to Scholarship Chairman, Branch No. 238 NALC, P.O Box 20248, Canton, OH 44701-0248. **Deadline for Receipt:** May 31.

2162 ■ STARK COMMUNITY FOUNDATION
400 Market Ave. N, Ste. 200
Canton, OH 44702-2107
Tel: (330)454-3426
Fax: (330)454-5855
Web Site: http://www.starkcommunityfoundation.org
To provide scholarship assistance to qualified individuals who want to pursue their studies.
Title of Award: Norman J. Tschantz/Walter C. Deuble Scholarships **Area, Field, or Subject:** General studies. **Level of Education for which Award is Granted:** Undergraduate **Funds Available:** No specific amount. **Duration:** One year.
Eligibility Requirements: Applicants must have served at least one year as a caddy at Congress Lake Country Club; must have academic achievement in high school, college, or trade school; must have extracurricular activities. **Application Requirements:** Applicants must submit completed application form and are advised to contact Congress Lake Pro Shop at 330877-0576.

2163 ■ STARK COMMUNITY FOUNDATION
400 Market Ave. N, Ste. 200
Canton, OH 44702-2107
Tel: (330)454-3426
Fax: (330)454-5855
Web Site: http://www.starkcommunityfoundation.org
To provide scholarship assistance to qualified individuals who want to pursue their studies.
Title of Award: Ira G. Turpin Scholar Fund **Area, Field, or Subject:** General studies. **Level of Education for which Award is Granted:** Undergraduate **Funds Available:** No specific amount.
Eligibility Requirements: Applicants must be students attending Stark Country schools. **Application Requirements:** Application forms are available online and must be sent to: Judge David E. Stucki, Stark County Family Court, 110 Central Plaza S, Ste. 601, Canton, OH 447021414.

2164 ■ STARK COMMUNITY FOUNDATION
400 Market Ave. N, Ste. 200
Canton, OH 44702-2107
Tel: (330)454-3426
Fax: (330)454-5855
Web Site: http://www.starkcommunityfoundation.org
To provide scholarship assistance to qualified individuals who want to pursue their studies.
Title of Award: John R. and Joan F. Warren Scholarship Fund **Area, Field, or Subject:** General studies. **Level of Education for which Award is Granted:** Undergraduate **Funds Available:** $500-$1,000. **Duration:** One year.
Eligibility Requirements: Applicants must be students planning to enroll or are presently enrolled at Grove City College. **Application Requirements:** Applicants must complete and submit the application form and requirements to Financial Aid Office, 100Campus Dr., Grove City, PA 16127. **Deadline for Receipt:** April 15.

2165 ■ STARK COMMUNITY FOUNDATION
400 Market Ave. N, Ste. 200
Canton, OH 44702-2107
Tel: (330)454-3426
Fax: (330)454-5855
Web Site: http://www.starkcommunityfoundation.org
To provide scholarship assistance to qualified individuals who want to pursue their studies.
Title of Award: Lester and Eleanor Webster Charitable Trust Fund **Area, Field, or Subject:** General studies. **Level of Education for which Award is Granted:** Undergraduate **Funds Available:** No specific amount. **Duration:** One year.
Eligibility Requirements: Applicants must be students residing in Stark County who are pursuing a two-year or four-year college degree at an accredited school within the State of Ohio and who have attained sophomore status in college at time of award. **Application Requirements:** Applicants must complete and submit the application form and requirements to Stark Community Foundation, 400 Market Ave. N, Ste. 200, Canton, OH 44702. **Deadline for Receipt:** June 1.

2166 ■ STEUBEN COUNTY COMMUNITY FOUNDATION
1701 N Wayne St.
Angola, IN 46703
Tel: (260)665-6656
Fax: (260)665-8420
Web Site: http://www.steubenfoundation.org
To provide financial support to outstanding students.
Title of Award: Clifford V. Abbott Memorial Scholarships **Area, Field, or Subject:** General Studies. **Level of Education for which Award is Granted:** Undergraduate **Funds Available:** No specific amount.
Eligibility Requirements: Applicants must be residents of Steuben County; must be graduating seniors from Fremont High School. **Application Requirements:** Applicants must check the website for the application process online. **Deadline for Receipt:** March 15. **Additional Information:** Steuben County Community Foundation at the above address.

2167 ■ STEUBEN COUNTY COMMUNITY FOUNDATION
1701 N Wayne St.
Angola, IN 46703

Tel: (260)665-6656
Fax: (260)665-8420
Web Site: http://www.steubenfoundation.org
To provide financial support to those graduating students of Fremont High School.
Title of Award: Richard L. Baker Memorial Scholarships **Area, Field, or Subject:** General Studies. **Level of Education for which Award is Granted:** Undergraduate **Funds Available:** No specific amount.
Eligibility Requirements: Applicants must be graduating seniors from Fremont High School; must be residing within the Fremont Community School District; must be admitted to a college or university as full-time students; must receive Academic Honors from Fremont High School. **Application Requirements:** Applicants must submit a completed application form; a 250-word essay; and high school transcripts. **Deadline for Receipt:** March 15. **Additional Information:** Steuben County Community Foundation at the above address.

2168 ■ STEUBEN COUNTY COMMUNITY FOUNDATION
1701 N Wayne St.
Angola, IN 46703
Tel: (260)665-6656
Fax: (260)665-8420
Web Site: http://www.steubenfoundation.org
To provide financial assistance to those students who are in need.
Title of Award: Verna Curry Boyer Scholarships **Area, Field, or Subject:** General Studies. **Level of Education for which Award is Granted:** Undergraduate **Funds Available:** No specific amount.
Eligibility Requirements: Applicants must be graduates of any Steuben County High School, including Prairie Heights, Fremont, Hamilton or MSD of Steuben County. **Application Requirements:** Applicants must check the website for the application process online. **Deadline for Receipt:** March 15. **Additional Information:** Steuben County Community Foundation at the above address.

2169 ■ STEUBEN COUNTY COMMUNITY FOUNDATION
1701 N Wayne St.
Angola, IN 46703
Tel: (260)665-6656
Fax: (260)665-8420
Web Site: http://www.steubenfoundation.org
To provide financial support to those students who are in need.
Title of Award: Builders Association of Northeast Indiana (BANI) Scholarships **Area, Field, or Subject:** General Studies. **Level of Education for which Award is Granted:** Undergraduate **Funds Available:** No specific amount.
Eligibility Requirements: Applicants must be graduating seniors attending a high school and residing in Steuben County. **Application Requirements:** Applicants must check the website for the application process online. **Deadline for Receipt:** March 15. **Additional Information:** Steuben County Community Foundation at the above address.

2170 ■ STEUBEN COUNTY COMMUNITY FOUNDATION
1701 N Wayne St.
Angola, IN 46703
Tel: (260)665-6656
Fax: (260)665-8420
Web Site: http://www.steubenfoundation.org
To provide financial assistance to those deserving students.
Title of Award: Ellen Eberhardt Memorial Scholarships **Area, Field, or Subject:** General Studies. **Level of Education for which Award is Granted:** Undergraduate **Funds Available:** No specific amount.
Eligibility Requirements: Applicants must be residents of Steuben County; must be graduating seniors from a Steuben County High School; must be entering a four-year college or university with the intent to pursue a career in environmental education, biology, earth science or elementary education; must demonstrate financial need. **Application Requirements:** Applicants must check the website for the application process and required materials. **Deadline for Receipt:** March 15. **Additional Information:** Steuben County Community Foundation at the above address.

2171 ■ STEUBEN COUNTY COMMUNITY FOUNDATION
1701 N Wayne St.
Angola, IN 46703

Tel: (260)665-6656
Fax: (260)665-8420
Web Site: http://www.steubenfoundation.org
To provide financial assistance to deserving students.
Title of Award: Farmers State Bank Scholarships **Area, Field, or Subject:** General Studies. **Level of Education for which Award is Granted:** Undergraduate **Funds Available:** No specific amount.
Eligibility Requirements: Applicants must be residents of Steuben County; must be seniors at Angola High School, Fremont High School or Hamilton High School planning to enroll in a full-time undergraduate course at an accredited two or four-year college, university, or vocational-technical school in the fall following graduation; must have a documented GPA at the time of application between 2.5 and 3.5 on a scale of 4.0. **Application Requirements:** Applicants must check the website for the application process online. **Deadline for Receipt:** March 15. **Additional Information:** Steuben County Community Foundation at the above address.

2172 ■ STEUBEN COUNTY COMMUNITY FOUNDATION
1701 N Wayne St.
Angola, IN 46703
Tel: (260)665-6656
Fax: (260)665-8420
Web Site: http://www.steubenfoundation.org
To provide financial support to those graduating students from Angola High School, Fremont, Hamilton or Prairie Heights High School.
Title of Award: H. Pauline Hand Memorial Scholarships **Area, Field, or Subject:** General Studies. **Level of Education for which Award is Granted:** Undergraduate **Funds Available:** No specific amount.
Eligibility Requirements: Applicants must be residents of Steuben County; must be full-time students at any accredited college or university. **Application Requirements:** Applicants must check the website for the application process and required materials. **Deadline for Receipt:** March 15. **Additional Information:** Steuben County Community Foundation at the above address.

2173 ■ STEUBEN COUNTY COMMUNITY FOUNDATION
1701 N Wayne St.
Angola, IN 46703
Tel: (260)665-6656
Fax: (260)665-8420
Web Site: http://www.steubenfoundation.org
To provide financial assistance to those students who are in need.
Title of Award: Dale Hughes, Jr. Memorial Scholarships **Area, Field, or Subject:** General Studies. **Level of Education for which Award is Granted:** Undergraduate **Funds Available:** No specific amount.
Eligibility Requirements: Applicants must be residents of Steuben County; must be graduating from Prairie Heights High School; must be continuing their education through an accredited program at any institution of higher education. **Application Requirements:** Applicants must check the website for the application process and required materials. **Deadline for Receipt:** March 15. **Additional Information:** Steuben County Community Foundation at the above address.

2174 ■ STEUBEN COUNTY COMMUNITY FOUNDATION
1701 N Wayne St.
Angola, IN 46703
Tel: (260)665-6656
Fax: (260)665-8420
Web Site: http://www.steubenfoundation.org
To provide financial support to those students who are in need.
Title of Award: Sylvia E. Jackson Scholarships **Area, Field, or Subject:** General Studies. **Level of Education for which Award is Granted:** Undergraduate **Funds Available:** No specific amount.
Eligibility Requirements: Applicants must be residents of Steuben County and must be enrolled as seniors in Angola High School on or before October 1 of their senior year; must attend an accredited school within the boundaries of the United States. **Application Requirements:** Applicants must check the website for the application process and required materials. **Deadline for Receipt:** March 15. **Additional Information:** Steuben County Community Foundation at the above address.

2175 ■ STEUBEN COUNTY COMMUNITY FOUNDATION
1701 N Wayne St.
Angola, IN 46703

Tel: (260)665-6656
Fax: (260)665-8420
Web Site: http://www.steubenfoundation.org
To provide financial assistance to students having difficulty financing their education.
Title of Award: Las Limas Community Scholarships **Area, Field, or Subject:** General Studies. **Level of Education for which Award is Granted:** Undergraduate **Funds Available:** No specific amount.
Eligibility Requirements: Applicants must be residents of Steuben, Lagrange or Dekalb counties in Indiana; must be enrolled in an Indiana state accredited school of higher education, trade school, certificate or degree program. **Application Requirements:** Applicants must check the website for the application process and required materials. **Deadline for Receipt:** March 15. **Additional Information:** Steuben County Community Foundation at the above address.

2176 ■ STEUBEN COUNTY COMMUNITY FOUNDATION
1701 N Wayne St.
Angola, IN 46703
Tel: (260)665-6656
Fax: (260)665-8420
Web Site: http://www.steubenfoundation.org
To develop the youth into productive and responsible adults by supporting them financially for their studies.
Title of Award: Paul and Inger Friend 4-H Scholarships **Area, Field, or Subject:** General Studies. **Level of Education for which Award is Granted:** Undergraduate **Funds Available:** No specific amount.
Eligibility Requirements: Applicants must have graduated from Angola, Hamilton, Fremont or Prairie Heights High School; must have completed at least 7 years in the 4-H program (minimum of 5 years in Steuben County, Indiana). **Application Requirements:** Applicants must check the website for the application process and required materials. **Deadline for Receipt:** March 15. **Additional Information:** Steuben County Community Foundation at the above address.

2177 ■ STEUBEN COUNTY COMMUNITY FOUNDATION
1701 N Wayne St.
Angola, IN 46703
Tel: (260)665-6656
Fax: (260)665-8420
Web Site: http://www.steubenfoundation.org
To provide financial assistance to those students who are in need.
Title of Award: Dr. J. Glenn Radcliffe Memorial Scholarships **Area, Field, or Subject:** General Studies. **Level of Education for which Award is Granted:** Undergraduate **Number Awarded:** Minimum of 3 persons. **Funds Available:** No specific amount.
Eligibility Requirements: Applicants must be residents of Steuben County; must be graduating high school seniors; must be attending TSU to receive a baccalaureate degree; must have a cumulative of 3.5 GPA. **Application Requirements:** Applicants must check the website for the application process and required materials. **Deadline for Receipt:** March 15. **Additional Information:** Steuben County Community Foundation at the above address.

2178 ■ STEUBEN COUNTY COMMUNITY FOUNDATION
1701 N Wayne St.
Angola, IN 46703
Tel: (260)665-6656
Fax: (260)665-8420
Web Site: http://www.steubenfoundation.org
To provide financial assistance to those students who are in need.
Title of Award: Nettie and Edward Shelah Scholarships **Area, Field, or Subject:** General Studies. **Level of Education for which Award is Granted:** Undergraduate **Funds Available:** No specific amount.
Eligibility Requirements: Applicants must be Hamilton High School graduating seniors; must be enrolled in an accredited Indiana College or University. **Application Requirements:** Applicants must check the website for the application process and required materials. **Deadline for Receipt:** March 15. **Additional Information:** Steuben County Community Foundation at the above address.

2179 ■ STICKLER INVOLVED PEOPLE
15 Angelina Dr.
Augusta, KS 67010

Tel: (316)259-5194
E-mail: sip@sticklers.org
Web Site: http://www.sticklers.org
To assist deserving college-bound adults afflicted with Stickler Syndrome to pursue their dreams and education goals.
Title of Award: Dr. Gunnar B. Stickler Scholarships **Area, Field, or Subject:** General studies. **Level of Education for which Award is Granted:** Undergraduate **Number Awarded:** 1. **Funds Available:** $500. **Duration:** One year.
Eligibility Requirements: Applicants must be graduating students who have a minimum GPA of 3.0 on a 4.0 scale or equivalent from any American high school students who plan to enter any accredited public or private community, junior, or four-year college or university or vocational-technical school. **Application Requirements:** Applicants must fill out the application form. **Deadline for Receipt:** June 15.

2180 ■ STONEWALL COMMUNITY FOUNDATION
119 W 24th St., 7th F.
New York, NY 10011
Tel: (212)367-1155
Fax: (212)367-1157
E-mail: stonewall@stonewallfoundation.org
Web Site: http://www.stonewallfoundation.org
To provide emerging gay and lesbian athletes with a reliable pool of resources (both monetary and community-based) to help them reach their potential and realize their dreams.
Title of Award: The Gene and John Athletic Scholarships **Area, Field, or Subject:** Athletics. **Level of Education for which Award is Granted:** Undergraduate **Funds Available:** $2,500-$5,000.
Eligibility Requirements: Applicants must be LGBT athlete students who are looking to continue their education while pursuing athletes. **Application Requirements:** Applicants must submit a completed application form. **Deadline for Receipt:** July 31. **Additional Information:** stonewall@stonewallfoundation.org.

2181 ■ STONEWALL COMMUNITY FOUNDATION
119 W 24th St., 7th F.
New York, NY 10011
Tel: (212)367-1155
Fax: (212)367-1157
E-mail: stonewall@stonewallfoundation.org
Web Site: http://www.stonewallfoundation.org
To encourage and supports LGBT students in their quest for higher education.
Title of Award: Traub-Dicker Rainbow Scholarships **Area, Field, or Subject:** General studies. **Level of Education for which Award is Granted:** Undergraduate **Number Awarded:** 3. **Funds Available:** $3,000.
Eligibility Requirements: Applicants must be lesbians who are graduating high school seniors; must plan to attend a recognized college or university or be currently enrolled. **Application Requirements:** Applicants must submit a completed application form, three essays, transcript of records and two letters of reference. **Deadline for Receipt:** April 15. **Additional Information:** stonewall@stonewallfoundation.org.

2182 ■ STRAIGHTFORWARD MEDIA
508 7th St., Ste 202
Rapid City, SD 57701
Tel: (605)348-3042
Fax: (605)348-3043
E-mail: info@straightforwardmedia.com
Web Site: http://www.straightforwardmedia.com
To financially assist students in their educational pursuits.
Title of Award: Dale E. Fridell Memorial Scholarships **Area, Field, or Subject:** General studies. **Level of Education for which Award is Granted:** Undergraduate **Funds Available:** $1000.
Eligibility Requirements: Applicant must be a student currently enrolled or planning to enroll in a university, college, trade school, technical institute, vocational training or other post-secondary education program. **Application Requirements:** Applicants must complete the Online Scholarship Application. **Additional Information:** Awards are given four times a year. **Deadline for Receipt:** January, April, July, October.

2183 ■ STRAIGHTFORWARD MEDIA
508 7th St., Ste 202
Rapid City, SD 57701
Tel: (605)348-3042
Fax: (605)348-3043
E-mail: info@straightforwardmedia.com
Web Site: http://www.straightforwardmedia.com
To financially assist students in their educational pursuits.
Title of Award: Mesothelioma Memorial Scholarships **Area, Field, or Subject:** General studies. **Level of Education for which Award is Granted:** Undergraduate **Funds Available:** $500.
Eligibility Requirements: Applicant must be a student currently enrolled or planning to enroll in a university, college, trade school, technical institute, vocational training or other post-secondary education program. **Application Requirements:** Applicants must complete scholarship application online. **Additional Information:** Awards are given four times a year, every three months.

2184 ■ STRAIGHTFORWARD MEDIA
508 7th St., Ste 202
Rapid City, SD 57701
Tel: (605)348-3042
Fax: (605)348-3043
E-mail: info@straightforwardmedia.com
Web Site: http://www.straightforwardmedia.com
To financially assist students in their educational pursuits.
Title of Award: StraightForward Media's Liberal Arts Scholarships **Area, Field, or Subject:** Liberal arts. **Level of Education for which Award is Granted:** Undergraduate **Number Awarded:** 1. **Funds Available:** $500.
Eligibility Requirements: Applicant must be a liberal arts student. **Application Requirements:** Applicants must complete scholarship application online.

2185 ■ STRAIGHTFORWARD MEDIA
508 7th St., Ste 202
Rapid City, SD 57701
Tel: (605)348-3042
Fax: (605)348-3043
E-mail: info@straightforwardmedia.com
Web Site: http://www.straightforwardmedia.com
To financially assist students in their educational pursuits.
Title of Award: StraightForward Media's Minority Scholarships **Area, Field, or Subject:** General studies. **Level of Education for which Award is Granted:** Undergraduate **Number Awarded:** 4. **Funds Available:** $500.
Eligibility Requirements: Applicant must be a minority student. **Application Requirements:** Applicants must complete scholarship application online. **Additional Information:** Awards are given four times a year. **Deadline for Receipt:** March, June, September, December.

2186 ■ STRAIGHTFORWARD MEDIA
508 7th St., Ste 202
Rapid City, SD 57701
Tel: (605)348-3042
Fax: (605)348-3043
E-mail: info@straightforwardmedia.com
Web Site: http://www.straightforwardmedia.com
To financially assist students in their educational pursuits.
Title of Award: StraightForward Media's Science Scholarships **Area, Field, or Subject:** Science. **Level of Education for which Award is Granted:** Undergraduate **Number Awarded:** 4. **Funds Available:** $500.
Eligibility Requirements: Applicant must be a student pursuing a degree in a science-related field. **Application Requirements:** Applicants must complete scholarship application online. **Additional Information:** Awards are given four times a year.

2187 ■ FRASER STRYKER
500 Energy Plaza, 409 S 17th St.
Omaha, NE 68102-2663
Tel: (402)341-6000
Fax: (402)341-8290
E-mail: sbruckner@fraserstryker.com
Web Site: http://www.fraserstryker.com

To provide financial assistance in the form of college tuition and provide paid internships to students.
Title of Award: Fraser Stryker Diversity Scholarships **Area, Field, or Subject:** General studies. **Level of Education for which Award is Granted:** Undergraduate **Funds Available:** $2,500.
Eligibility Requirements: Applicants must be of African-American, Asian, Latino or Native-American origins who are graduating seniors at any of the public or private high schools in the greater Omaha area; must have been accepted to an accredited college or university located in the united States; must be college students who have received Fraser Diversity Scholarships in prior years. **Application Requirements:** Applicants must submit a completed application form and evidence of enrollment. **Additional Information:** 402-341-6000.

2188 ■ SUN COUNTRY AMATEUR GOLF ASSOCIATION
1440 Rio Rancho Blvd.
Rio Rancho, NM 87124
Tel: (505)897-0864
Free: 800-346-5319
Fax: (505)897-3494
E-mail: mwilliams@newmexicogolf.org
Web Site: http://www.newmexicogolf.org
To provide financial support to those deserving students.
Title of Award: Sun Country Amateur Golf Association Scholarships **Area, Field, or Subject:** General Studies. **Level of Education for which Award is Granted:** Undergraduate **Funds Available:** No specific amount.
Eligibility Requirements: Applicants must have completed their junior year in high school or at least one year in college; have achieved 3.0 or higher cumulative grade point average; and must have connection to golf. **Application Requirements:** Applicants must check the available website for the required materials. **Additional Information:** For more information please contact: Barbara Saia at (505) 897-0864.

2189 ■ SUNSHINE LADY FOUNDATION
4900 Randall Pkwy., Ste. H
Wilmington, NC 28403
Tel: (910)397-0023; (866)255-7742
Fax: (910)397-0023
E-mail: nancy@sunshinelady.org
Web Site: http://www.sunshinelady.org
To help support the battered woman to overcome barriers to their education, which is necessary for their becoming employable and financially stable.
Title of Award: Change Your World Scholarships **Area, Field, or Subject:** General studies. **Level of Education for which Award is Granted:** Undergraduate **Funds Available:** No specific amount.
Eligibility Requirements: Applicants must be direct survivors of domestic violence or partner abuse. Applicants must be citizens or legal residents of the United States. Applicants must be officially accepted to an accredited university or institution in the United States. Applicants must be 17 to 25 years old. Applicants must maintain a 3.0 GPA and a full-time enrollment status. **Application Requirements:** Applicants must complete the application form and provide evidence of enrollment. **Deadline for Receipt:** July 1.

2190 ■ SUNSHINE LADY FOUNDATION
4900 Randall Pkwy., Ste. H
Wilmington, NC 28403
Tel: (910)397-0023; (866)255-7742
Fax: (910)397-0023
E-mail: nancy@sunshinelady.org
Web Site: http://www.sunshinelady.org
To help survivors of domestic violence obtain an education that will in turn offer them the chance to secure employment, personal independence and self-sufficiency. To help battered women overcome barriers to the education necessary for their becoming employable and financially stable. To help single mothers with young children who have the greatest financial challenges to gain work so they can support their families.
Title of Award: Women's Independence Scholarship Programs **Area, Field, or Subject:** General studies. **Level of Education for which Award is Granted:** Undergraduate **Funds Available:** No specific amount.

Eligibility Requirements: Applicants must be direct survivors of domestic violence or partner abuse. Applicants must be citizens or legal residents of the United States. Applicants must be officially accepted into an accredited course of study at a United States institution. **Application Requirements:** Applicants must complete the application form and provide the necessary documents such as transcripts. **Additional Information:** nancy@sunshinelady.org

2191 ■ SUPREME COUNCIL, ANCIENT ACCEPTED SCOTTISH RITE OF FREE-MASONRY
PO Box 519
Lexington, MA 02420-0519
Tel: (781)862-4410
Fax: (781)863-1833
E-mail: info@supremecouncil.org
Web Site: http://www.supremecouncil.org
To support the continuing education of young men and women from Scottish Rite families and Masonic-related youth groups.
Title of Award: Abbott Scholarships **Area, Field, or Subject:** General studies. **Level of Education for which Award is Granted:** Undergraduate **Funds Available:** No specific amount.
Eligibility Requirements: Applicant must be currently enrolled at an accredited college or university; have a GPA of 2.75; a child or grandchild of a Scottish Rite Mason in the Northern Masonic Jurisdiction; or a member of a youth organization sponsored by the Masonic fraternity in the Northern Masonic Jurisdiction; or a graduate of one of the 32nd degree Masonic Learning Centers for Children in the Northern Masonic Jurisdiction. **Application Requirements:** Applicants must submit a completed application form together with a copy of current college transcript; a letter of recommendation; and current FAFSA form. Mail applications to the Valley providing for their eligibility. **Additional Information:** Named after Leon M. Abbott, Sovereign Grand Commander from 1921-1932.

2192 ■ SURFACE OFFICER SPOUSES
PO Box 9902
Norfolk, VA 23505-9902
Web Site: http://www.surfaceofficerspousesnorfolk.com
To provide financial assistance for academically qualified dependents of current and former members of the Naval Surface Forces, Atlantic.
Title of Award: Anchor Scholarship Foundation **Area, Field, or Subject:** General studies. **Level of Education for which Award is Granted:** Undergraduate **Funds Available:** $500.
Eligibility Requirements: Applicants must attend an accredited, four-year college or university in the United States and intend to work toward their first bachelor's degree on a full time basis; must be high school seniors or college students in an accredited school or equivalent educational institution; must be dependent children or spouses whose service member meets the following requirements: a) sponsor is active duty or retired US Navy; b) sponsor has served a minimum of six years in a unit under the administrative control of Commander, Naval Surface Force, US Atlantic Fleet or US Pacific Fleet. **Application Requirements:** Applicants must submit all the needed materials for the scholarship.

2193 ■ SWISS BENEVOLENT SOCIETY OF NEW YORK
500 Fifth Ave., Rm. 1800
New York, NY 10110
Tel: (212)246-0655
Fax: (212)246-1366
E-mail: info@sbsny.com
Web Site: http://www.sbsny.org
To provide financial support to college seniors or graduate students who have demonstrated sustained academic excellence in a demanding study program.
Title of Award: Sonia S. Maguire Outstanding Scholastic Achievement Awards **Area, Field, or Subject:** General studies. **Level of Education for which Award is Granted:** Graduate, Undergraduate **Funds Available:** No specific amount.
Eligibility Requirements: Applicants or one of their parents must be Swiss nationals; must be domiciled in New York, New Jersey, Connecticut, Pennsylvania or Delaware; must demonstrate the need for financial support; must be in good academic standing and show aptitude in their chosen fields of study. **Application Requirements:** Application forms can be downloaded at the SBSNY web site. Applicants must submit

the following required documents: general and scholastic pages of application packet; official transcripts of all high school, college and graduate grades when applying for the first time, official updates thereafter; SAT or GRE results when applying for the first time; proof of Swiss citizenship of applicant or one parent when applying for the first time; proof of U.S. citizenship or visa status when applying for the first time; two letters of recommendation from professors in the applicant's major area of study, on official letterhead. **Deadline for Receipt:** January 31. **Additional Information:** SBSNY at the above address.

2194 ■ SWISS BENEVOLENT SOCIETY OF NEW YORK

500 Fifth Ave., Rm. 1800
New York, NY 10110
Tel: (212)246-0655
Fax: (212)246-1366
E-mail: info@sbsny.org
Web Site: http://www.sbsny.org
To provide partial financial support for U.S. residents at the junior, senior or graduate college level who have been accepted to study at a Swiss University or Federal Institute of Technology.
Title of Award: Medicus Student Exchange **Area, Field, or Subject:** General studies. **Level of Education for which Award is Granted:** Graduate, Undergraduate **Funds Available:** No specific amount.
Eligibility Requirements: Applicants must be residents of the United States and must be in good academic standing and show aptitude in their chosen fields of study. **Application Requirements:** Application forms can be downloaded at the SBSNY web site. Applicants must submit the following required documents: general and scholastic pages of application packet; official transcripts of all high school, college and graduate grades when applying for the first time, official updates thereafter; SAT or GRE results when applying for the first time; proof of Swiss citizenship of applicant or one parent when applying for the first time; proof of U.S. citizenship or visa status when applying for the first time; letter of acceptance from Swiss University or Federal Institute of Technology or Technical College; two letters of recommendation from professors in the applicant's major area of study, on official letterhead; proof of proficiency in the language of instruction; statement of sufficient total funding. For studies in the U.S.: official transcript of records of at least one year of study in the U.S.; transcripts of education in Switzerland; letter of recommendation from a professor in the applicant's major area of study, on official letterhead. **Deadline for Receipt:** January 31. **Additional Information:** SBSNY at the above address.

2195 ■ SWISS BENEVOLENT SOCIETY OF NEW YORK

500 Fifth Ave., Rm. 1800
New York, NY 10110
Tel: (212)246-0655
Fax: (212)246-1366
E-mail: info@sbsny.com
Web Site: http://www.sbsny.org
To provide financial support to post-secondary school level students for vocational, undergraduate or graduate academic studies at an accredited school.
Title of Award: Pellegrini Scholarships **Area, Field, or Subject:** General studies. **Level of Education for which Award is Granted:** Graduate, Undergraduate **Funds Available:** No specific amount.
Eligibility Requirements: Applicants or one of their parents must be Swiss nationals; must be domiciled in New York, New Jersey, Connecticut, Pennsylvania or Delaware; must demonstrate the need for financial support; must be in good academic standing and show aptitude in their chosen fields of study. **Application Requirements:** Application forms can be downloaded at the SBSNY web site. Applicants must submit the following required documents: general and scholastic pages of application packet; official transcripts of all high school, college and graduate grades when applying for the first time, official updates thereafter; SAT or GRE results when applying for the first time; proof of Swiss citizenship of applicant or one parent when applying of the first time; proof of U.S. citizenship or visa status when applying for the first time; financial pages of application packet, including all requested information, unless applying for merit portion only; signed copy of all pages and schedules of Federal Income Tax returns, and of W-2 forms of applicant and supporting party and/or spouse, where applicable; proof of cost for tuition and room and board, copy of bursar's bill (high school applicants provide figures of

anticipated cost); letter of reference from a high school principal or a guidance counselor, or from a professor in the applicant's major area of study, on official letterhead. **Deadline for Receipt:** January 31. **Additional Information:** SBSNY at the above address.

2196 ■ TAIWANESE AMERICAN CITIZENS LEAGUE

3001 Walnut Grove Ave., No. 7
Rosemead, CA 91770
Tel: (626)202-0170
E-mail: tacl@tacl.org
Web Site: http://www.tacl.org
To recognize high school seniors with leadership qualities as well as a public service and to encourage them to pursue higher education.
Title of Award: Taiwanese American Community Scholarships **Area, Field, or Subject:** General studies. **Level of Education for which Award is Granted:** Undergraduate **Funds Available:** $500.
Eligibility Requirements: Applicants should be college bound senior graduating class from one of the ten high schools: Irvine High School, Northwood High School, Canyon High School, University High School, Woodbridge High School, Villa Park High School, Laguna High School, Aliso Niguel High School, Troy High School and Fountain Valley High School. **Application Requirements:** Applicant may download an application form from the website. Applicant must submit a one-page biography that includes activities and volunteer work during your high school years; A typed essay of no more than 1000 words, on the topic: "Indicate a person who has as a significant influence on you and describe that influence"; One recommendation letter form on of your school teachers or counselors; A copy of your official high school transcript. **Deadline for Receipt:** April 18. **Additional Information:** TACL at the above address.

2197 ■ TALL CLUBS INTERNATIONAL

PO Box 441
Portland, OR 97207
Tel: 888-468-2552
E-mail: admin@tall.org
Web Site: http://www.tall.org
To promote tall awareness among tall men and women, and in the community.
Title of Award: Tall Clubs International Student Scholarships **Area, Field, or Subject:** General studies. **Level of Education for which Award is Granted:** Undergraduate **Funds Available:** $1,000.
Eligibility Requirements: Applicant must be under 21 years of age and attending their first year of college in the following fall. The recipient must also meet the TCI height requirement minimums of 5'10 for women and 6'2 for men. **Application Requirements:** To a club meeting simply select a known student as a candidate for a TCI scholarship award. TCI has forms that are downloadable by any Club member in the Member Services Console pertaining to student scholarship.

2198 ■ TANANA VALLEY CAMPUS

604 Barnette St.
Fairbanks, AK 99701
Tel: (907)455-2800; 877-882-8827
Web Site: http://www.tvc.uaf.edu
To encourage students to pursue their career in emergency service program.
Title of Award: William C. Leary Memorial Emergency Services Scholarships **Area, Field, or Subject:** Emergency and disaster services. **Level of Education for which Award is Granted:** Undergraduate **Funds Available:** $500. **Duration:** One year.
Eligibility Requirements: Applicants must be students enrolled in emergency service program. **Application Requirements:** Scholarship applications are available at uaonline.alaska.edu (to access the scholarship application, you must choose "Login to secure area" if they have a UA ID or apply for admission for the new students).

2199 ■ TANANA VALLEY CAMPUS

604 Barnette St.
Fairbanks, AK 99701
Tel: (907)455-2800; 877-882-8827
Web Site: http://www.tvc.uaf.edu
To provide financial support for deserving individuals intending to pursue their educational goals.

Title of Award: Ruth Lister Scholarships **Area, Field, or Subject:** General studies. **Level of Education for which Award is Granted:** Undergraduate **Funds Available:** $2,000. **Duration:** One year. **Eligibility Requirements:** Applicants must be residents of Alaska; must be enrolled in a vocational program. **Application Requirements:** Scholarship applications are available online at uaonline.alaska.edu (to access the scholarship application, applicant must choose "Login to secured area" if they have a UA ID or apply for admission for the new students).

2200 ■ TANANA VALLEY CAMPUS
604 Barnette St.
Fairbanks, AK 99701
Tel: (907)455-2800; 877-882-8827
Web Site: http://www.tvc.uaf.edu
To provide support for deserving students intending to pursue their study in culinary arts.
Title of Award: Tanana Valley Campus Culinary Arts Scholarships **Area, Field, or Subject:** Culinary arts. **Level of Education for which Award is Granted:** Undergraduate **Funds Available:** Varies. **Duration:** One year. **Eligibility Requirements:** Applicants must be students intending to pursue a career in culinary arts in Alaska. **Application Requirements:** Applicants are advised to contact the Culinary Arts at 455-2902 for further information about the application requirements and procedure.

2201 ■ TELECOMMUNICATIONS ASSOCIATION OF MICHIGAN
600 W Shiawassee St.
Lansing, MI 48933
Tel: (517)482-4166
Fax: (517)482-3548
Web Site: http://telecommich.org
To elevate the technical and business competence of young people by providing them with assistance to acquire meaningful and marketable skills; to provide educational incentive to deserving students who will ultimately provide leadership for the professions in business, education and public service.
Title of Award: Telecommunications Association of Michigan Scholarship Fund **Area, Field, or Subject:** General Studies. **Level of Education for which Award is Granted:** Undergraduate **Funds Available:** No specific amount.
Eligibility Requirements: Applicants must be member of a non-Michigan high school or enrolled in an accredited, degree-granting, non-Michigan college or university. **Application Requirements:** Applicants must check the available website for the required materials. **Additional Information:** Telecommunications Association of Michigan Foundation, Inc. at the above address

2202 ■ TELLURIDE ASSOCIATION
217 West Ave.
Ithaca, NY 14850
Tel: (607)273-5011
Fax: (607)272-2667
E-mail: ithaca_info@tellurideassociation.org
Web Site: http://www.tellurideassociation.org
To provide a unique educational opportunity to students from all social and financial backgrounds.
Title of Award: Telluride Association Summer Program Scholarships **Area, Field, or Subject:** General studies. **Level of Education for which Award is Granted:** High School **Funds Available:** Covers all cost for the Telluride Association Summer Program (except travel cost). May also offer $500 as stipend to replace summer work earnings for students who would otherwise be unable to attend the program.
Eligibility Requirements: Applicant must be a junior high school; must be nominated by a teacher, counselor, and other educators. **Application Requirements:** Teachers, educators, or counselors can nominate up to five candidates. TASP Nomination Form is available at the website. **Deadline for Receipt:** December 3. **Additional Information:** Ellen Baer, Administrative Director: ellen.baer@tellurideassociation.org

2203 ■ TEXAS ASSOCIATION OF DEVELOPING COLLEGES
1140 Empire Central, Ste. 550
Dallas, TX 75247
Tel: (214)630-2511

Fax: (214)631-2030
E-mail: info@txadc.org
Web Site: http://www.txadc.org
To strategically plan, organize and direct cooperative opportunities and programs for its members and serve as administrator of educational and community programs.
Title of Award: The Urban Scholarships Fund **Area, Field, or Subject:** General studies. **Level of Education for which Award is Granted:** Undergraduate **Funds Available:** $700 for community college; $2,000 for private four-year college students.
Eligibility Requirements: Applicants must be U.S. citizens; must be full-time undergraduate students in good standing or graduating high school students. **Application Requirements:** Applicants must submit a completed application form and a copy of high school or college transcript.

2204 ■ TEXAS SCOTTISH RITE HOSPITAL FOR CHILDREN
2222 Welborn St.
Dallas, TX 75219
Tel: (214)559-5000
Free: 800-421-1121
Fax: (214)559-7428
E-mail: tsrhpress@tsrh.org
Web Site: http://www.tsrhc.org
To provide educational assistance for former patients of Texas Scottish Rite Hospital for Children.
Title of Award: Legacy Scholarship Program **Area, Field, or Subject:** General studies. **Level of Education for which Award is Granted:** Undergraduate **Funds Available:** No specific amount.
Eligibility Requirements: Applicants must be present or former patients of TSRHC; must have applied and been accepted to an undergraduate program in a university, junior college or approved technical training program. **Application Requirements:** Applicants must submit all the required application information. **Deadline for Receipt:** March 10.

2205 ■ TEXAS STATE UNIVERSITY - SAN MARCOS DEVELOPMENT FOUNDATION
601 University Dr., JCK 960
San Marcos, TX 78666
Tel: (512)245-3860
Fax: (512)245-4929
Web Site: http://www.developmentfoundation.com
To provide financial assistance to students who want to pursue accounting in college.
Title of Award: Max Godwin Endowed Scholarships **Area, Field, or Subject:** Accounting. **Level of Education for which Award is Granted:** Undergraduate **Funds Available:** $500.
Eligibility Requirements: Applicants must be enrolled full-time (12 hours or more) in the undergraduate accounting program, in good standing with the San Marcos Accounting Club; must have at least one semester remaining before graduation and a 2.50 overall GPA; must have completed Principles of Financial Accounting and Principles of Managerial Accounting with at least a "B". **Application Requirements:** Applicants must submit all the required application information.

2206 ■ TEXAS TELEPHONE ASSOCIATION
1001 Congress Ave., Ste. 450
Austin, TX 78701
Tel: (512)472-1183
Fax: (512)472-1293
E-mail: braddenton@tta.org
Web Site: http://www.tta.org
To provide financial assistance to those students with financial hardship.
Title of Award: Texas Telephone Association Foundation Scholarships **Area, Field, or Subject:** General Studies. **Level of Education for which Award is Granted:** Undergraduate **Funds Available:** $1,500.
Eligibility Requirements: Applicants must be U.S citizens; must have earned a cumulative GPA of 3.0 or higher; must plan to attend a Texas college or university. **Application Requirements:** Applicants must submit completed application, postmarked before March 14. Application must include a current transcript; a letter of acceptance from a Texas college or university; a copy of student's SAR (Student Aid Report). **Additional Information:** Special consideration will be given to students who will be

pursuing a college degree in fields of study relevant to telecommunications (math, business, engineering, and computer science). **Additional Information:** Texas Telephone Association Foundation at the above address

2207 ■ TEXTILE CARE ALLIED TRADES ASSOCIATION
271 Rte. 46 W No. D203
Fairfield, NJ 07004
Tel: (973)244-1790
Fax: (973)244-4455
E-mail: info@tcata.org
Web Site: http://www.tcata.org
To provide financial support for students interested in pursuing a degree at any accredited U.S. college or university on a full-time basis.
Title of Award: TCATA College Scholarship Program **Area, Field, or Subject:** General studies. **Level of Education for which Award is Granted:** Undergraduate **Funds Available:** $1,000.
Eligibility Requirements: Applicant must be a full-time employee, or a son or daughter of a full-time employee, of a member company in good standing of the Textile Care Allied Trades Association for three years. **Application Requirements:** Applicants must complete an application form and provide a copy of Scholarship Aptitude Text (SAT) or American College Test (ACT) scores; transcripts of all high school grades and any college grades if applicable; a letter from their high school principal - or other highest official equivalent - describing their leadership qualities, extracurricular activities and other relevant information; and a letter describing past personal accomplishments, immediate goals and future academic and career objectives. **Deadline for Receipt:** April 1.

2208 ■ THANKSUSA
1390 Chain Bridge Rd., No. 260
McLean, VA 22101
888-849-8720
Web Site: http://www.thanksusa.org
To support the dependents and spouses of active duty U.S. military service personnel with their educational pursuits.
Title of Award: ThanksUSA Scholarships **Area, Field, or Subject:** General studies. **Level of Education for which Award is Granted:** Undergraduate **Number Awarded:** 500. **Funds Available:** $3,000.
Eligibility Requirements: Applicants must be dependent children, age 24 and under, or spouses of active-duty U.S. military service personnel; planning to enroll full-time in an accredited two-year or four-year college, university, vocational school or technical school; have at least a 2.5 cumulative GPA on a 4.0 scale, or its equivalent, on relevant academic record (high-school record for incoming freshmen or post-secondary school record for those already enrolled in a college, university or vocational/technical school). **Application Requirements:** Applicants must submit a completed application along with transcripts and evidence of active military duty to verify eligibility. Copies of military I.D. are not acceptable. Mail application to ThanksUSA Scholarship Program, Scholarship America, c/o Shellee Hintz, One Scholarship Way, PO Box 297, St. Peter, MN 56082. **Deadline for Receipt:** May 15. **Additional Information:** Scholarship Management Services at 507-931-0408, or shintz@scholarshipamerica.org.

2209 ■ THUNDER BAY COMMUNITY FOUNDATION
PO Box 20120
Thunder Bay, ON, Canada P7E 6P2
Tel: (807)475-7279
E-mail: tbcf@tbaytel.net
Web Site: http://www.tbcf.org
To provide scholarship assistance to qualified graduating students from Hammarskjold, Hillcrest and St. Ignatius High Schools.
Title of Award: Helen L. Dewar Scholarships **Area, Field, or Subject:** General studies. **Level of Education for which Award is Granted:** Undergraduate **Number Awarded:** 3. **Funds Available:** No specific amount. **Duration:** One year.
Eligibility Requirements: Applicant must be from Hammerskfold High School, Hillcrest High School, or St. Ignatius High School; must have a minimum overall average of 80% in grade 12 credits; must be seeking full-time admission to a Canadian university that is accredited by the Association of Universities and Colleges of Canada. **Application Requirements:** Applicant must submit: completed application form (available online); three reference letters (one from a school source, one from extracurricular source, and one from the nominating committee/individual sponsoring their application for the scholarship); must submit all required documents to the Thunder Bay Community Foundation. **Deadline for Receipt:** April 15.

2210 ■ THUNDER BAY COMMUNITY FOUNDATION
PO Box 20120
Thunder Bay, ON, Canada P7E 6P2
Tel: (807)475-7279
E-mail: tbcf@tbaytel.net
Web Site: http://www.tbcf.org
To provide scholarship assistance to qualified graduating students from Dennis Franklin Cromarty, Geraldton Composite, La Verendrye, Lake Superior, Manitouwadge, Marathon, and Nipigon-Red Rock District High Schools.
Title of Award: Joshua Dyke Family Scholarships **Area, Field, or Subject:** General studies. **Level of Education for which Award is Granted:** Undergraduate **Number Awarded:** 3. **Funds Available:** No specific amount. **Duration:** One year.
Eligibility Requirements: Applicants must be from Sir Winston Churchill C&VI, St. Patrick High School or Westgate C&VI; must be in their graduating year of secondary school; must have a minimum overall average of 80% in grade 12 credits; must be seeking full-time admission to a Canadian university that is accredited by the Association of Universities and Colleges of Canada. **Application Requirements:** Applicants must submit: completed application form (available online); three reference letters (one from a school source, one from extracurricular source, and one from the nominating committee/individual sponsoring their application for the scholarship); must submit all required documents to the Thunder Bay Community Foundation. **Deadline for Receipt:** April 15.

2211 ■ THUNDER BAY COMMUNITY FOUNDATION
PO Box 20120
Thunder Bay, ON, Canada P7E 6P2
Tel: (807)475-7279
E-mail: tbcf@tbaytel.net
Web Site: http://www.tbcf.org
To provide scholarship assistance to graduating students who meet the requirements set out by Marathon Pulp Inc.
Title of Award: Marathon Pulp Inc. Education Achievement Scholarships **Area, Field, or Subject:** General studies. **Level of Education for which Award is Granted:** Undergraduate **Funds Available:** $6,000. **Duration:** One year.
Eligibility Requirements: Applicant must have completed the last year of secondary school less than 12 months prior; must have obtained an average of 75% in the last two years of schooling; must be seeking admission on a full-time basis to a university that is a member or affiliated to a member of the Association of University and Colleges of Canada. **Application Requirements:** Information and application forms are available at Marathon High School Student Services or may be obtained by written request to the Thunder Bay Community Foundation. Application and other supporting documents must be sent to the Thunder Bay Community Foundation. **Deadline for Receipt:** April 30.

2212 ■ THUNDER BAY COMMUNITY FOUNDATION
PO Box 20120
Thunder Bay, ON, Canada P7E 6P2
Tel: (807)475-7279
E-mail: tbcf@tbaytel.net
Web Site: http://www.tbcf.org
To provide scholarship assistance to qualified graduating students from Dennis Franklin Cromarty, Geraldton Composite, La Verendrye, Lake Superior, Manitouwadge, Marathon, and Nipigon-Red Rock District High School.
Title of Award: Geraldine Ruth Rogers Scholarships **Area, Field, or Subject:** General studies. **Level of Education for which Award is Granted:** Undergraduate **Number Awarded:** 5. **Funds Available:** No specific amount. **Duration:** One year.
Eligibility Requirements: Applicants must be from Dennis Franklin Cromarty High School, Geraldton Composite High School, Ecole secondaire catholique de la Verendrye, Lake Superior High School, Manitouwadge High School, Marathon High School or Nipigon-Red Rock

District High School; must be in their graduating year of secondary school; must have a minimum overall average of 80% in Grade 12 credits; must be seeking full-time admission to a Canadian university that accredited by the Association of Universities and Colleges of Canada. **Application Requirements:** Applicants must submit: completed application form (available online); three reference letters (one from a school source, one from extracurricular source, and one from the nominating committee/individual sponsoring their application for the scholarship); must submit all required documents to the Thunder Bay Community Foundation. **Deadline for Receipt:** April 15.

2213 ■ THUNDER BAY COMMUNITY FOUNDATION
PO Box 20120
Thunder Bay, ON, Canada P7E 6P2
Tel: (807)475-7279
E-mail: tbcf@tbaytel.net
Web Site: http://www.tbcf.org
To provide scholarship assistance to qualified graduating students at Hammarskjold High School who excel in science.
Title of Award: Ross A. Wilson Science Scholarships **Area, Field, or Subject:** Science. **Level of Education for which Award is Granted:** Undergraduate **Number Awarded:** 3. **Funds Available:** No specific amount. **Duration:** One year.
Eligibility Requirements: Applicant must be: from Hammarskjold High School; pursuing a university degree and career in the sciences; in their graduating year of secondary school. Applicant must have a minimum overall average of 80% in Grade 12 credits; must be seeking full-time admission to a Canadian university that is accredited by the Association of Universities and Colleges of Canada. **Application Requirements:** Applicant must submit: completed application form (available online); three reference letters (one from a school source, one from extracurricular source, and one from the nominating committee/individual sponsoring their application for the scholarship); must submit all required documents to the Thunder Bay Community Foundation. **Deadline for Receipt:** April 15.

2214 ■ TIDEWATER BUILDERS ASSOCIATION
2117 Smith Ave.
Chesapeake, VA 23320-2515
Tel: (757)420-2434
Fax: (757)424-5954
E-mail: cpfieffer@tbaonline.org
Web Site: http://www.tbaonline.org
To improve climate for quality housing for all incomes; to promote the growth and development of the shelter industry; to promote excellence and professionalism among members through educational and networking opportunities; to support and enhance the community through charitable projects.
Title of Award: Tidewater Builders Association Scholarships **Area, Field, or Subject:** General studies. **Level of Education for which Award is Granted:** Undergraduate **Funds Available:** No specific amount.
Eligibility Requirements: Applicants must be local high school seniors residing in the TBA service area; must be U.S. citizens; must attend an accredited four-year undergraduate degree program as a full-time student during the four-year period of continual and uninterrupted studies. **Application Requirements:** Applicants must complete the application form. **Deadline for Receipt:** March 21. **Additional Information:** mhearring@tbaonline.org.

2215 ■ TOYOTA MOTOR SALES
19001 S Western Ave. Dept. WC11
Torrance, CA 90501
800-331-4331
Fax: (310)468-7814
Web Site: http://www.toyota.com
To provide financial support to those students who are in need.
Title of Award: Toyota Community Scholars **Area, Field, or Subject:** General studies. **Level of Education for which Award is Granted:** Undergraduate **Number Awarded:** 100. **Funds Available:** $10,000; $20,000.
Eligibility Requirements: Applicants must be high school seniors; must be in good academic standing; must have leadership skills and commitment to community service. **Application Requirements:** Applicants must

see their high school guidance counselors or administration office for an application. **Additional Information:** High School Guidance Counselor: For more information, please contact: Educational Testing Service P. O. Box 6730 Princeton, NJ 08541 at 609-771-7878; 609-771-7750; (f) or email: srp-csr@ets.org.

2216 ■ TRANSPORT WORKERS UNION OF AMERICA
1700 Broadway
New York, NY 10019
Tel: (212)259-4900
Fax: (212)265-4537
Web Site: http://www.twu.org
To provide professional legal, education, research and public relations services to the local and divisions.
Title of Award: Michael J. Quill Scholarships **Area, Field, or Subject:** General studies. **Level of Education for which Award is Granted:** Undergraduate **Number Awarded:** 15. **Funds Available:** $1,200.
Eligibility Requirements: Applicants must be senior high school students of son, daughter, dependent brothers and sisters of present, retired, or deceased TWU members who will enter an accredited college of their own choice. **Application Requirements:** Applicants must fill out the coupon on the back page of the January, February, or March TWU Express. **Deadline for Receipt:** May 1. **Additional Information:** Transport Worker's Union of America at the above address.

2217 ■ TRANSPORTATION ASSOCIATION OF CANADA
2323 St., Laurent Blvd.
Ottawa, ON, Canada K1G 4J8
Tel: (613)736-1350
Fax: (613)736-1395
E-mail: secretariat@tac-act.ca
Web Site: http://www.tac-atc.ca
To recognize the importance of education in the transportation field.
Title of Award: TAC Foundation-3M Canada Company **Area, Field, or Subject:** Transportation. **Level of Education for which Award is Granted:** Postgraduate, Undergraduate **Funds Available:** $5,000. **Duration:** One year.
Eligibility Requirements: Applicants must be Canadian citizens or landed immigrants. **Application Requirements:** Applicant must complete the application form available online; must provide academic references and relevant employment information; must have an electronic version of their transcript of record. Application form and requirements must be sent to the TAC Foundation. **Deadline for Receipt:** March 3.

2218 ■ TRANSPORTATION ASSOCIATION OF CANADA
2323 St., Laurent Blvd.
Ottawa, ON, Canada K1G 4J8
Tel: (613)736-1350
Fax: (613)736-1395
E-mail: secretariat@tac-act.ca
Web Site: http://www.tac-atc.ca
To encourage students to acquire the full range of technical skills required for contributing to the development of superior transportation solutions.
Title of Award: TAC Foundation-BA Group Scholarships **Area, Field, or Subject:** Transportation. **Level of Education for which Award is Granted:** Postgraduate, Undergraduate **Funds Available:** $5,000. **Duration:** One year.
Eligibility Requirements: Applicants must be Canadian citizens or landed immigrants. **Application Requirements:** Applicant must complete the application form available online; must provide academic references and relevant employment information; must have an electronic version of their transcript of record. Application form and requirements must be sent to the TAC Foundation. **Deadline for Receipt:** March 3.

2219 ■ TRANSPORTATION ASSOCIATION OF CANADA
2323 St., Laurent Blvd.
Ottawa, ON, Canada K1G 4J8
Tel: (613)736-1350
Fax: (613)736-1395
E-mail: secretariat@tac-act.ca
Web Site: http://www.tac-atc.ca
To recognize the importance of education in the transportation field.
Title of Award: TAC Foundation-Cement Association of Canada Scholarships **Area, Field, or Subject:** Transportation. **Level of Education for**

which Award is Granted: Postgraduate, Undergraduate **Funds Available:** $5,000. **Duration:** One year.
Eligibility Requirements: Applicants must be Canadian citizens or landed immigrants. **Application Requirements:** Applicant must complete the application form available online; must provide academic references and relevant employment information; must have an electronic version of their transcript of record. Application form and requirements must be sent to the TAC Foundation. **Deadline for Receipt:** March 3.

2220 ■ TRANSPORTATION ASSOCIATION OF CANADA

2323 St., Laurent Blvd.
Ottawa, ON, Canada K1G 4J8
Tel: (613)736-1350
Fax: (613)736-1395
E-mail: secretariat@tac-act.ca
Web Site: http://www.tac-atc.ca
To recognize the importance of education in the transportation field.
Title of Award: TAC Foundation-Delcan Corporation Scholarships **Area, Field, or Subject:** Transportation. **Level of Education for which Award is Granted:** Postgraduate, Undergraduate **Funds Available:** $5,000. **Duration:** One year.
Eligibility Requirements: Applicants must be Canadian citizens or landed immigrants. **Application Requirements:** Applicant must complete the application form available online; must provide academic references and relevant employment information; must have an electronic version of their transcript of record. Application form and requirements must be sent to the TAC Foundation. **Deadline for Receipt:** March 3.

2221 ■ TRANSPORTATION ASSOCIATION OF CANADA

2323 St., Laurent Blvd.
Ottawa, ON, Canada K1G 4J8
Tel: (613)736-1350
Fax: (613)736-1395
E-mail: secretariat@tac-act.ca
Web Site: http://www.tac-atc.ca
To provide support and encouragement to those interested in pursuing a career in transportation planning or transportation engineering.
Title of Award: TAC Foundation-Dillon Consulting Scholarships **Area, Field, or Subject:** Transportation. **Level of Education for which Award is Granted:** Undergraduate **Funds Available:** $5,000. **Duration:** One year.
Eligibility Requirements: Applicant must be entering third or fourth year studies; must intend to pursue a career in some aspect of the transportation field and meet the conditions of the scholarships; must have achieved an overall B level or equivalent average mark in their previous academic year. **Application Requirements:** Applicant must complete the application form (available online); must provide academic references and relevant employment information; must have an electronic version of their transcript of record. Application form and requirements must be sent to the TAC Foundation. **Deadline for Receipt:** March 3.

2222 ■ TRANSPORTATION ASSOCIATION OF CANADA

2323 St., Laurent Blvd.
Ottawa, ON, Canada K1G 4J8
Tel: (613)736-1350
Fax: (613)736-1395
E-mail: secretariat@tac-act.ca
Web Site: http://www.tac-atc.ca
To provide scholarship to graduate and postgraduate students who are doing research in transportation infrastructure and systems.
Title of Award: TAC Foundation-EBA Engineering Consultants Ltd. Scholarships **Area, Field, or Subject:** Transportation. **Level of Education for which Award is Granted:** Postgraduate, Undergraduate **Funds Available:** $5,000. **Duration:** One year.
Eligibility Requirements: Applicants must be Canadian citizens or landed immigrants. **Application Requirements:** Applicant must complete the application form available online; must provide academic references and relevant employment information; must have an electronic version of their transcript of record. Application form and requirements must be sent to the TAC Foundation. **Deadline for Receipt:** March 3.

2223 ■ TRANSPORTATION ASSOCIATION OF CANADA

2323 St., Laurent Blvd.
Ottawa, ON, Canada K1G 4J8

Tel: (613)736-1350
Fax: (613)736-1395
E-mail: secretariat@tac-act.ca
Web Site: http://www.tac-atc.ca
To provide scholarship to graduate and postgraduate students who are pursuing a degree in transportation.
Title of Award: TAC Foundation-IBI Group Scholarships **Area, Field, or Subject:** Transportation. **Level of Education for which Award is Granted:** Postgraduate, Undergraduate **Funds Available:** $5,000. **Duration:** One year.
Eligibility Requirements: Applicants must be Canadian citizens or landed immigrants. **Application Requirements:** Applicant must complete the application form (available online); must provide academic references and relevant employment information; must have an electronic version of their transcript of record. Application form and requirements must be sent to the TAC Foundation. **Deadline for Receipt:** March 3.

2224 ■ TRANSPORTATION ASSOCIATION OF CANADA

2323 St., Laurent Blvd.
Ottawa, ON, Canada K1G 4J8
Tel: (613)736-1350
Fax: (613)736-1395
E-mail: secretariat@tac-act.ca
Web Site: http://www.tac-atc.ca
To recognize the importance of education in the transportation field.
Title of Award: TAC Foundation-McCormick Rankin Corporation Scholarships **Area, Field, or Subject:** Transportation. **Level of Education for which Award is Granted:** Undergraduate **Funds Available:** $5,000. **Duration:** One year.
Eligibility Requirements: Applicant must be entering third or fourth year studies; must intend to pursue a career in some aspect of the transportation field and meet the conditions of the scholarships; must have achieved an overall B level or equivalent average mark in their previous academic year. **Application Requirements:** Applicant must complete the application form available online; must provide academic references and relevant employment information; must have an electronic version of their transcript of record. Application form and requirements must be sent to the TAC Foundation. **Deadline for Receipt:** March 3.

2225 ■ TRANSPORTATION ASSOCIATION OF CANADA

2323 St., Laurent Blvd.
Ottawa, ON, Canada K1G 4J8
Tel: (613)736-1350
Fax: (613)736-1395
E-mail: secretariat@tac-act.ca
Web Site: http://www.tac-atc.ca
To recognize the importance of education in the transportation field.
Title of Award: TAC Foundation-MMM Group Limited Scholarships **Area, Field, or Subject:** Transportation. **Level of Education for which Award is Granted:** Postgraduate, Undergraduate **Funds Available:** $5,000. **Duration:** One year.
Eligibility Requirements: Applicants must be Canadian citizens or landed immigrants. **Application Requirements:** Applicant must complete the application form (available online); must provide academic references and relevant employment information; must have an electronic version of their transcript of record. Application form and requirements must be sent to the TAC Foundation. **Deadline for Receipt:** March 3.

2226 ■ TRANSPORTATION ASSOCIATION OF CANADA

2323 St., Laurent Blvd.
Ottawa, ON, Canada K1G 4J8
Tel: (613)736-1350
Fax: (613)736-1395
E-mail: secretariat@tac-act.ca
Web Site: http://www.tac-atc.ca
To recognize the importance of education in the transportation field.
Title of Award: TAC Foundation-Municipalities Scholarships **Area, Field, or Subject:** Transportation. **Level of Education for which Award is Granted:** Postgraduate, Undergraduate **Funds Available:** $3,000. **Duration:** One year.
Eligibility Requirements: Applicants must be Canadian citizens or landed immigrants. **Application Requirements:** Applicant must complete the application form (available online); must provide academic references

and relevant employment information; must have an electronic version of their transcript of record. Application form and requirements must be sent to the TAC Foundation. **Deadline for Receipt:** March 3.

2227 ■ TRANSPORTATION ASSOCIATION OF CANADA
2323 St., Laurent Blvd.
Ottawa, ON, Canada K1G 4J8
Tel: (613)736-1350
Fax: (613)736-1395
E-mail: secretariat@tac-act.ca
Web Site: http://www.tac-atc.ca
To recognize the importance of education in the transportation field.
Title of Award: TAC Foundation-Provinces and Territories Scholarships **Area, Field, or Subject:** Transportation. **Level of Education for which Award is Granted:** Postgraduate, Undergraduate **Funds Available:** $5,000. **Duration:** One year.
Eligibility Requirements: Applicants must be Canadian citizens or landed immigrants. **Application Requirements:** Applicant must complete the application form (available online); must provide academic references and relevant employment information; must have an electronic version of their transcript of record. Application form and requirements must be sent to the TAC Foundation. **Deadline for Receipt:** March 3.

2228 ■ TRANSPORTATION ASSOCIATION OF CANADA
2323 St., Laurent Blvd.
Ottawa, ON, Canada K1G 4J8
Tel: (613)736-1350
Fax: (613)736-1395
E-mail: secretariat@tac-act.ca
Web Site: http://www.tac-atc.ca
To recognize the importance of education in the transportation field.
Title of Award: TAC Foundation Scholarships **Area, Field, or Subject:** Transportation. **Level of Education for which Award is Granted:** Postgraduate, Undergraduate **Funds Available:** $5,000. **Duration:** One year.
Eligibility Requirements: Applicants must be Canadian citizens or landed immigrants. **Application Requirements:** Applicant must complete the application form available online; must provide academic references and relevant employment information; must have an electronic version of their transcript of record. Application form and requirements must be sent to the TAC Foundation. **Deadline for Receipt:** March 3.

2229 ■ TRANSPORTATION ASSOCIATION OF CANADA
2323 St., Laurent Blvd.
Ottawa, ON, Canada K1G 4J8
Tel: (613)736-1350
Fax: (613)736-1395
E-mail: secretariat@tac-act.ca
Web Site: http://www.tac-atc.ca
To provide scholarship to the individuals working towards a career in the transportation industry as engineers, planners, program mangers or other technical specialties.
Title of Award: TAC Foundation-UMA Engineering Ltd. Scholarships **Area, Field, or Subject:** Transportation. **Level of Education for which Award is Granted:** Undergraduate **Funds Available:** $5,000. **Duration:** One year.
Eligibility Requirements: Applicant must be entering third or fourth year studies; must intend to pursue a career in some aspect of the transportation field and meet the conditions of the scholarships; must have achieved an overall B level or equivalent average mark in their previous academic year. **Application Requirements:** Applicant must complete the application form available online; must provide academic references and relevant employment information; must have an electronic version of their transcript of record. Application form and requirements must be sent to the TAC Foundation. **Deadline for Receipt:** March 3.

2230 ■ TRANSPORTATION CLUBS INTERNATIONAL
PO Box 2223
Ocean Shores, WA 98569
Tel: 877-858-8627; (187)78588628
E-mail: info@transportationclubsinternational.com
Web Site: http://www.transportationclubsinternational.com

To create, stimulate, and perpetuate discussion of topics relating to local and national transportation issues; to promote member clubs, companies, and individuals the importance of transportation and transportation logistics; to promote the general welfare of member clubs and their membership; to provide an international forum for local transportation and logistics organizations; to stimulate and perpetuate dialogue among its members on subjects of national and international transportation importance; and to promote education in the transportation industry.
Title of Award: Ginger and Fred Deines Canada Scholarships **Area, Field, or Subject:** Transportation; Logistics; Traffic Management. **Level of Education for which Award is Granted:** Undergraduate **Funds Available:** $2,000.
Eligibility Requirements: Applicants must be enrolled in an educational program in an accredited institution of higher learning in a vocational or degree program in the fields of Transportation, Logistics or Traffic Management or related fields intending to prepare for a career in these areas. They must be of Canadian nationality and enrolled in a school in Canada or the U.S. **Application Requirements:** Applicants must submit a certified copy of the college/university transcript; three letters of recommendation; a small, current photograph to be used for publication; an essay of not more than 200-words, explaining why you have chosen transportation or an allied field as a career path; and outline of the objectives. **Deadline for Receipt:** May 31. **Additional Information:** Transportation Clubs International Scholarships Attn: Bill Blair, Zimmer Worldwide Logistics at 15710 JFK Blvd., Houston, Texas 77032; bblair@zimmerworlwide.com

2231 ■ TRANSPORTATION CLUBS INTERNATIONAL
PO Box 2223
Ocean Shores, WA 98569
Tel: 877-858-8627; (187)78588628
E-mail: info@transportationclubsinternational.com
Web Site: http://www.transportationclubsinternational.com
To create, stimulate, and perpetuate discussion of topics relating to local and national transportation issues; to promote member clubs, companies, and individuals the importance of transportation and transportation logistics; to promote the general welfare of member clubs and their membership; to provide an international forum for local transportation and logistics organizations; to stimulate and perpetuate dialogue among its members on subjects of national and international transportation importance; and to promote education in the transportation industry.
Title of Award: Ginger and Fred Deines Mexico Scholarships **Area, Field, or Subject:** Transportation; Logistics; Traffic Management. **Level of Education for which Award is Granted:** Undergraduate **Funds Available:** $2,000.
Eligibility Requirements: Applicants must be enrolled in an educational program in an accredited institution of higher learning in a vocational or degree program in the fields of Transportation, Logistics or Traffic Management or related fields intending to prepare for a career in these areas. They must be of Mexican nationality and enrolled in a school in Mexico or the U.S. **Application Requirements:** Applicants must submit a certified copy of the college/university transcript; three letters of recommendation; a small, current photograph to be used for publication; an essay of not more than 200 words explaining why you have chosen transportation or an allied field as a career path; and outline of the objectives. **Deadline for Receipt:** May 31. **Additional Information:** Transportation Clubs International Scholarships Attn: Bill Blair, Zimmer Worldwide Logistics at 15710 JFK Blvd., Houston, Texas 77032; bblair@zimmerworlwide.com

2232 ■ TRANSPORTATION CLUBS INTERNATIONAL
PO Box 2223
Ocean Shores, WA 98569
Tel: 877-858-8627; (187)78588628
E-mail: info@transportationclubsinternational.com
Web Site: http://www.transportationclubsinternational.com
To create, stimulate, and perpetuate discussion of topics relating to local and national transportation issues; to promote member clubs, companies, and individuals the importance of transportation and transportation logistics; to promote the general welfare of member clubs and their membership; to provide an international forum for local transportation and logistics organizations; to stimulate and perpetuate dialogue among its members on subjects of national and international transportation importance; and to promote education in the transportation industry.

Title of Award: Hooper Memorial Scholarships **Area, Field, or Subject:** Transportation; Logistics; Traffic Management. **Level of Education for which Award is Granted:** Undergraduate **Funds Available:** $2,000.
Eligibility Requirements: Applicants must be enrolled in an educational program in an accredited institution of higher learning in a vocational or degree program in the fields of Transportation, Logistics or Traffic Management or related fields intending to prepare for a career in these areas. **Application Requirements:** Applicants must submit a certified copy of the college/university transcript; three letters of recommendation; a small, current photograph to be use for publication; an essay of not more than 200-words, explaining why you have chosen transportation or an allied field as a career path; and outline of the objectives. **Deadline for Receipt:** May 31. **Additional Information:** Transportation Clubs International Scholarships Attn: Bill Blair, Zimmer Worldwide Logistics at 15710 JFK Blvd., Houston, Texas 77032; bblair@zimmerworlwide.com

2233 ■ TRANSPORTATION CLUBS INTERNATIONAL
PO Box 2223
Ocean Shores, WA 98569
Tel: 877-858-8627; (187)78588628
E-mail: info@transporationclubsinternational.com
Web Site: http://www.transportationclubsinternational.com
To create, stimulate, and perpetuate discussion of topics relating to local and national transportation issues; to promote member clubs, companies, and individuals the importance of transportation and transportation logistics; to promote the general welfare of member clubs and their membership; to provide an international forum for local transportation and logistics organizations; to stimulate and perpetuate dialogue among its members on subjects of national and international transportation importance; and to promote education in the transportation industry.
Title of Award: Denny Lydic Scholarships **Area, Field, or Subject:** Transportation; Logistics; Traffic Management. **Level of Education for which Award is Granted:** Undergraduate **Funds Available:** $1,000.
Eligibility Requirements: Applicants must be enrolled in an educational program in an accredited institution of higher learning in a vocational or degree program in the fields of Transportation, Logistics or Traffic Management or related fields intending to prepare for a career in these areas. **Application Requirements:** Applicants must submit a certified copy of the college/university transcript; three letters of recommendation; a small, current photograph to be used for publication; an essay not more than 200-words explaining why you have chosen transportation or an allied field as a career path; and outline of the objectives. **Deadline for Receipt:** May 31. **Additional Information:** Transportation Clubs International Scholarships Attn: Bill Blair, Zimmer Worldwide Logistics at 15710 JFK Blvd., Houston, Texas 77032; bblair@zimmerworlwide.com

2234 ■ TRANSPORTATION CLUBS INTERNATIONAL
PO Box 2223
Ocean Shores, WA 98569
Tel: 877-858-8627; (187)78588628
E-mail: info@transporationclubsinternational.com
Web Site: http://www.transportationclubsinternational.com
To create, stimulate, and perpetuate discussion of topics relating to local and national transportation issues; to promote member clubs, companies, and individuals the importance of transportation and transportation logistics; to promote the general welfare of member clubs and their membership; to provide an international forum for local transportation and logistics organizations; To stimulate and perpetuate dialogue among members on subjects of national and international transportation importance; and to promote education in the transportation industry.
Title of Award: Texas Transportation Scholarships **Area, Field, or Subject:** Transportation; Logistics; Traffic Management. **Level of Education for which Award is Granted:** Undergraduate **Funds Available:** $1,500.
Eligibility Requirements: Applicants must be enrolled in an educational program in an accredited institution of higher learning in a vocational or degree program in the fields of Transportation, Logistics or Traffic Management or related fields intending to prepare for a career in these areas. **Application Requirements:** Applicants must submit a certified copy of the college/university transcript; three letters of recommendation; a small, current photograph to be used for publication; an essay of not more than 200-words explaining why you have chosen transportation or an allied field as a career path; and outline of the objectives. **Deadline for

Receipt: May 31. **Additional Information:** Transportation Clubs International Scholarships Attn: Bill Blair, Zimmer Worldwide Logistics at 15710 JFK Blvd., Houston, Texas 77032; bblair@zimmerworlwide.com

2235 ■ TRANSPORTATION CLUBS INTERNATIONAL
PO Box 2223
Ocean Shores, WA 98569
Tel: 877-858-8627; (187)78588628
E-mail: info@transportationclubsinternational.com
Web Site: http://www.transportationclubsinternational.com
To create, stimulate, and perpetuate discussion of topics relating to local and national transportation issues; to promote member clubs, companies, and individuals the importance of transportation and transportation logistics; to promote the general welfare of member clubs and their membership; to provide an international forum for local transportation and logistics organizations; To stimulate and perpetuate dialogue among its members on subjects of national and international transportation importance; and to promote education in the transportation industry.
Title of Award: Alice Glaisyer Warfield Scholarships **Area, Field, or Subject:** Transportation; Logistics; Traffic Management. **Level of Education for which Award is Granted:** Undergraduate **Funds Available:** $1,500.
Eligibility Requirements: Applicants must be enrolled in an educational program in an accredited institution of higher learning in a vocational or degree program in the fields of Transportation, Logistics or Traffic Management or related fields intending to prepare for a career in these areas. **Application Requirements:** Applicants must submit a certified copy of the college/university transcript; three letters of recommendation; a small, current photograph to be used for publication; an essay of not more than 200 words explaining why you have chosen transportation or an allied field as a career path; and outline of the objectives. **Deadline for Receipt:** May 31. **Additional Information:** Transportation Clubs International Scholarships Attn: Bill Blair, Zimmer Worldwide Logistics at 15710 JFK Blvd., Houston, Texas 77032; bblair@zimmerworlwide.com

2236 ■ TRUCK RENTING AND LEASING ASSOCIATION
675 N Washington St., Ste. 410
Alexandria, VA 22314
Tel: (703)299-9120
Fax: (703)299-9115
E-mail: pvroom@trala.com
Web Site: http://www.trala.org
To provide financial assistance for the education of the dependents of TRALA members.
Title of Award: TRALA Scholarships Program **Area, Field, or Subject:** General studies. **Level of Education for which Award is Granted:** Undergraduate **Number Awarded:** 2. **Funds Available:** $5000. **Duration:** One year.
Eligibility Requirements: Applicant must be a high school senior; a dependent of a full-time employee of TRALA member companies; and have a GPA of 3.0 or higher in a 4.0 scale. **Application Requirements:** Application form is available at the website. Applicants must submit a completed application form together with a current transcript of grades to: TRALA Scholarship Fund, Scholarship America, One Scholarship Way PO Box 297 St. Peter, MN 56082. **Deadline for Receipt:** = January 15. **Additional Information:** Scholarship America, Telephone: (507)931-1682 Fax: (507)931-9168.

2237 ■ TRUCKLOAD CARRIERS ASSOCIATION
555 E Braddock Rd.
Alexandria, VA 22314
Tel: (703)838-1950
Fax: (703)838-6610
E-mail: tca@truckload.org
Web Site: http://www.truckload.org
To provide financial assistance for the education of TCA members.
Title of Award: Truckload Carriers Association Scholarships **Area, Field, or Subject:** General studies. **Level of Education for which Award is Granted:** Undergraduate **Funds Available:** $2,000 up to $5,000.
Eligibility Requirements: Applicants must be a college junior or senior in good standing, who is a child, grandchild or spouse of an employee of a trucking company, or the child, grandchild or spouse of an independent contractor or an independent contractor affiliated with a trucking company

and attending an accredited four-year college or university. **Application Requirements:** Applicants must send their complete application, official complete transcript of all college courses and grades, course schedule including tuition and fees for upcoming term. **Deadline for Receipt:** May 16.

2238 ■ TURKISH COALITION OF AMERICA
1025 Connecticut Ave. NW, Ste. 1000
Washington, DC 20036
Tel: (202)370-1399
Fax: (202)370-1398
E-mail: info@turkishcoalitionofamerica.org
Web Site: http://www.turkishcoalition.org
To foster friendship, understanding and cooperation between the United States and Turkey and to explore the historical and cultural links between Turkey and Bosnia Herzegovina.
Title of Award: TCA-BAACBH Scholarships **Area, Field, or Subject:** General studies. **Level of Education for which Award is Granted:** Undergraduate **Funds Available:** No specific amount.
Eligibility Requirements: Applicants must be Bosnian-American students. **Application Requirements:** Applicants must check the available website for more information. **Additional Information:** Turkish Coalition of America at the above address.

2239 ■ TURKISH COALITION OF AMERICA
1025 Connecticut Ave. NW, Ste. 1000
Washington, DC 20036
Tel: (202)370-1399
Fax: (202)370-1398
E-mail: info@turkishcoalitionofamerica.org
Web Site: http://www.turkishcoalition.org
To foster friendship, understanding and cooperation between the United States and Turkey and to explore the historical and cultural links between Turkey and Macedonia.
Title of Award: TCA-UMD Scholarships **Area, Field, or Subject:** General studies. **Level of Education for which Award is Granted:** Undergraduate **Number Awarded:** 10. **Funds Available:** $2,000.
Eligibility Requirements: Applicants must be full time Macedonian-American undergraduates. **Application Requirements:** Applicants must check the available website for the required materials. **Additional Information:** Turkish Coalition of America at the above address.

2240 ■ UNITARIAN UNIVERSALIST ASSOCIATION OF CONGREGATIONS
25 Beacon St.
Boston, MA 02108
Tel: (617)742-2100
E-mail: info@uua.org
Web Site: http://www.uua.org
To defray undergraduate college expenses of the children of Unitarian Universalist Ministers.
Title of Award: Children of Unitarian Universalist Ministers College Scholarships **Area, Field, or Subject:** General studies. **Level of Education for which Award is Granted:** Undergraduate **Funds Available:** No specific amount.
Eligibility Requirements: Applicant must be college undergraduate and a dependent of a Unitarian Universalist Minister. **Application Requirements:** Applicants must complete the online Application process and submit a proof of college enrollment to the UUA Office of Church Staff Finances. **Deadline for Receipt:** September 30.

2241 ■ UNITARIAN UNIVERSALIST ASSOCIATION OF CONGREGATIONS
25 Beacon St.
Boston, MA 02108
Tel: (617)742-2100
E-mail: info@uua.org
Web Site: http://www.uua.org
To support the education of a UU woman with education.
Title of Award: Alice Schulman Simmons Scholarships for UU Women **Area, Field, or Subject:** General studies. **Level of Education for which Award is Granted:** Undergraduate **Number Awarded:** 2. **Funds Available:** $25,000.

Eligibility Requirements: Applicant must be a Unitarian Universalist Women attending Simmons College in Boston. **Application Requirements:** Applicants must apply and submit the Information Profile for Endowed Scholarships through the Office of Student Financial Services at Simmons College. **Additional Information:** Stewardship and Development Office, at 617-948-4655.

2242 ■ UNITED FOODS AND COMMERCIAL WORKERS INTERNATIONAL UNION
1775 K St., NW
Washington, DC 20006
Tel: (202)223-3111
Free: 800-551-4010
Web Site: http://www.ufcw.org
To financially support UFCW members and their unmarried dependents with their educational pursuit.
Title of Award: UFCW Scholarships **Area, Field, or Subject:** General studies. **Level of Education for which Award is Granted:** Undergraduate **Funds Available:** $2,000. **Duration:** One year.
Eligibility Requirements: Applicants must be UFCW members or their unmarried dependents under age of 20. **Application Requirements:** Applicants must complete the UFCW Scholarship Application online or request by writing to the UFCW International Union, Attn: Scholarship Program. **Deadline for Receipt:** March 15. **Additional Information:** scholarship@ufcw.org.

2243 ■ UNITED METHODIST YOUTH ORGANIZATION
PO Box 340003
Nashville, TN 37203
Tel: (615)340-7079; 877-899-2780
E-mail: youngpeople@gbod.org
Web Site: http://www.gbod.org/youngpeople
To aid United Methodist students who are continuing their self-development through higher education.
Title of Award: David W. Self Scholarships **Area, Field, or Subject:** Church occupations. **Level of Education for which Award is Granted:** Undergraduate **Funds Available:** Up to $1000. **Duration:** One year.
Eligibility Requirements: Applicant must be U.S. citizen or permanent resident; a racial/ethnic minority youth active in local United Methodist Church for at least one year; graduating high school senior entering first year of undergraduate study; admitted to a full-time degree program in an accredited college or university; maintaining at least "C" average in high school; pursuing a church-related career; and established financial need. **Application Requirements:** Applicants must submit a completed application form. **Deadline for Receipt:** June 1.

2244 ■ UNITED METHODIST YOUTH ORGANIZATION
PO Box 340003
Nashville, TN 37203
Tel: (615)340-7079; 877-899-2780
E-mail: youngpeople@gbod.org
Web Site: http://www.gbod.org/youngpeople
To aid United Methodist students continuing their self-development through higher education.
Title of Award: Richard S. Smith Scholarships **Area, Field, or Subject:** Church occupations. **Level of Education for which Award is Granted:** Undergraduate **Funds Available:** Up to $1000. **Duration:** One year.
Eligibility Requirements: Applicant must be U.S. citizen or permanent resident; a racial/ethnic minority youth active in local United Methodist Church for at least one year; graduating high school senior entering first year of undergraduate study; admitted to a full-time degree program in an accredited college or university; maintaining at least "C" average in high school; pursuing a church-related career; and established financial need. **Application Requirements:** Applicants must submit a completed application form. **Deadline for Receipt:** June 1.

2245 ■ UNITED SOUTH AND EASTERN TRIBES
711 Stewarts Ferry Pike, Ste. 100
Nashville, TN 37214
Tel: (615)872-7900
Fax: (615)872-7417
E-mail: mcook@usetinc.org
Web Site: http://www.usetinc.org

To provide financial assistance to Indian students in the USET service area.

Title of Award: United South and Eastern Tribes Scholarship Fund **Area, Field, or Subject:** General studies. **Level of Education for which Award is Granted:** Undergraduate **Funds Available:** $500.

Eligibility Requirements: Applicants must be Indian students who are enrolled members of one of twenty-four USET member tribes. **Application Requirements:** Applicants must complete the application found on the website of USET. **Deadline for Receipt:** April 30.

2246 ■ U.S. AIR FORCE ROTC

551 E Maxwell Blvd.
Maxwell AFB, AL 36112-5917
Tel: (334)953-6167
Fax: (866)423-7682
Web Site: http://www.afrotc.com

To meet officer production requirements and enhance enrollment at HBCUs.

Title of Award: Air Force ROTC Enhanced HBCU Scholarships **Area, Field, or Subject:** General studies. **Level of Education for which Award is Granted:** Undergraduate **Funds Available:** Tuition capped at $15,000; Books at $900. per year.

Eligibility Requirements: Applicants must be enrolled at the following colleges/universities: Jackson State University; Tuskegee University; Alabama State University; Howard University; North Carolina A&T State University; Fayetteville State University; Tennessee State University. **Application Requirements:** Applicants may start the application process for the scholarship program by contacting the Air Force ROTC detachment at the school that they wish to enroll in.

2247 ■ U.S. AIR FORCE ROTC

551 E Maxwell Blvd.
Maxwell AFB, AL 36112-5917
Tel: (334)953-6167
Fax: (866)423-7682
Web Site: http://www.afrotc.com

To meet officer production requirements and enhance enrollment at HSIs.

Title of Award: Hispanic Serving Institution Scholarships **Area, Field, or Subject:** General studies. **Level of Education for which Award is Granted:** Undergraduate **Funds Available:** Tuition capped at $15,000; Books at $900 per year. **Duration:** 2-3 years.

Eligibility Requirements: Applicants must be students enrolled as HSIs (Hispanic Serving Institution), including those schools which host an Air force ROTC detachment and those which are crosstowns of another school that hosts a detachment. **Application Requirements:** Applicants may start the application process for the scholarship program by contacting the Air Force ROTC detachment at the school that they wish to attend.

2248 ■ U.S. AIR FORCE ROTC

551 E Maxwell Blvd.
Maxwell AFB, AL 36112-5917
Tel: (334)953-6167
Fax: (866)423-7682
Web Site: http://www.afrotc.com

To meet officer production requirements and enhance enrollment at HBCUs.

Title of Award: Historically Black College or University Scholarships **Area, Field, or Subject:** General studies. **Level of Education for which Award is Granted:** Undergraduate **Funds Available:** Tuition capped at $15,000; Books at $900. **Duration:** 2-3 years.

Eligibility Requirements: Applicants must be enrolled at an HBCU (Historically Black College or University), including those schools which host an Air Force ROTC detachment and those which are crosstowns of another school that hosts a detachment. **Application Requirements:** Applications for the HBCU Scholarship are processed and approved at the detachment level. Applicant must contact the detachment serving the school, and the school will work to nominate the applicant for the appropriate scholarship program. Applications are accepted at any time each year.

2249 ■ U.S. AIR FORCE ROTC

551 E Maxwell Blvd.
Maxwell AFB, AL 36112-5917
Tel: (334)953-6167

Fax: (866)423-7682
Web Site: http://www.afrotc.com

To meet officer production requirements and enhance enrollment at HSIs.

Title of Award: U.S. Air Force ROTC Enhanced HSI Scholarship **Area, Field, or Subject:** General studies. **Level of Education for which Award is Granted:** Undergraduate **Funds Available:** Tuition capped at $15,000; Books at $900. per year.

Eligibility Requirements: Applicants must be enrolled at the following colleges/universities: California State University; New Mexico State University; University of New Mexico; University of Puerto Rico- Rio Piedras; University of Puerto Rico-Mayaguez; University of Texas - San Antonio. **Application Requirements:** Applicants may start the application process for the scholarship program by contacting the Air Force ROTC detachment at the school that they wish to enroll in. at the above address.

2250 ■ U.S. AIR FORCE ROTC

551 E Maxwell Blvd.
Maxwell AFB, AL 36112-5917
Tel: (334)953-6167
Fax: (866)423-7682
Web Site: http://www.afrotc.com

To provide financial assistance to high school seniors.

Title of Award: U.S. Air Force ROTC High School Scholarships **Area, Field, or Subject:** General studies. **Level of Education for which Award is Granted:** Undergraduate **Funds Available:** Type 1-$900; Type 2-$15,000: Type 7-$9,000.

Eligibility Requirements: Applicants must be United States citizens or able to obtain citizenship by the last day of the first term of the freshman year for 4-year offers, or the first term of the sophomore year for 3-year offers; must be a high school graduate or have an equivalent certificate; must be 17-31 years old prior to scholarship activation; and must not be enrolled full-time at a college or a university except for joint high school college programs. **Application Requirements:** Applicants must submit their application online and include the following forms: Counselor Certification, Personal Statement, Physical Fitness Assessment, and resume. Applicants must have their high school transcripts with raised seal or signature as well as their SAT or ACT scores. **Deadline for Receipt:** December 1.

2251 ■ U.S. AIR FORCE ROTC

551 E Maxwell Blvd.
Maxwell AFB, AL 36112-5917
Tel: (334)953-6167
Fax: (866)423-7682
Web Site: http://www.afrotc.com

To provide scholarships to college freshmen and sophomores in any major.

Title of Award: U.S. Air Force ROTC In-College Scholarships **Area, Field, or Subject:** General studies. **Level of Education for which Award is Granted:** Undergraduate **Funds Available:** Type 2-$15,000; Type 3-$9,000; Type 6-$3,000. **Duration:** 2-3 years.

Eligibility Requirements: Applicants must be United States citizens by the end of the projected term of activation; must pass the Air Force Officer Qualifying Test; must meet the Air Force ROTC weight and body fat standards; must pass the Air Force ROTC Physical Fitness Test; have at least a 2.5 cumulative college grade point average; pass a physical examination; must not be a contracted scholarship recipient; and must meet the age, moral and other scholarship eligibility requirements for Air force ROTC. **Application Requirements:** Applicants must fill out the application request form online.

2252 ■ UNITED STATES ARMY WARRANT OFFICERS ASSOCIATION

462 Herndon Pkwy., Ste. 207
Herndon, VA 20170-5235
Tel: (703)742-7727
Free: 800-587-2962
Fax: (703)742-7728
Web Site: http://www.penfed.org/usawoa

To give financial awards to deserving candidates.

Title of Award: USAWOASF/Grantham University On-Line Scholarships **Area, Field, or Subject:** General studies. **Level of Education for which Award is Granted:** Graduate, Undergraduate **Funds Available:** No specific amount.

Eligibility Requirements: Applicant must be a member, or a spouse of a member of the association, or their dependents under 23 years of age (high school seniors and above); planning to attend full-time or continue education at an accredited American college or university or a vocational technical institution; and has a GPA of 3.0 or higher on a 4.0 scale. **Application Requirements:** Application form is available at the website. Applicant must submit a complete application packet consisting of: the application form; an essay (800-100 words, include word count) on educational goals; circumstances which may effect the applicant's school attendance; list of extracurricular activities; recommendation letter (from instructor, faculty advisor, etc.); National Test Scores, SAT, ACT, etc.; transcript of grades; and a 4x6 photograph (view head and shoulders). **Deadline for Receipt:** May 1.

2253 ■ UNITED STATES ARMY WARRANT OFFICERS ASSOCIATION
462 Herndon Pkwy., Ste. 207
Herndon, VA 20170-5235
Tel: (703)742-7727
Free: 800-587-2962
Fax: (703)742-7728
Web Site: http://www.penfed.org/usawoa
To give financial awards to deserving candidates.
Title of Award: USAWOASF Regular Scholarships **Area, Field, or Subject:** General studies. **Level of Education for which Award is Granted:** Undergraduate **Funds Available:** $1000.
Eligibility Requirements: Applicant must be a spouse or dependent of a USAWOA member, 23 years old and below; must be planning to attend full-time or continue education at an accredited American college or university, or a vocational technical institution; and has a GPA of 3.0 or higher on a 4.0 scale. **Application Requirements:** Application form is available at the website. Applicant must submit a complete application packet consisting of: the application form (typewritten format); an essay (800-100 words, include word count) on educational goals; circumstances which may effect the applicant's school attendance; list of extracurricular activities; a recommendation letter (from instructor, faculty advisor, etc.); National Test Scores, SAT, ACT, etc.; and a 4x6 photograph (view head and shoulders). **Deadline for Receipt:** May 1.

2254 ■ UNITED STATES GOLF ASSOCIATION
PO Box 708
Far Hills, NJ 07931
Tel: (908)234-2300
Fax: (908)234-9687
E-mail: koconnor@usga.org
Web Site: http://www.usga.org
To provide opportunity for participants to think critically about leadership skills and become more engaged and invested citizens in their respective communities.
Title of Award: United States Golf Association Scholarship Program **Area, Field, or Subject:** Athletics. **Level of Education for which Award is Granted:** Undergraduate **Funds Available:** No specific amount.
Eligibility Requirements: Applicants must be 15 to 19 years old; must be "Honor Roll" students or maintain a strong GPA; must play or be qualified to play at a varsity level; must demonstrate leadership, must have an active involvement in community activities/service and have proven ability in an event of size and magnitude. **Application Requirements:** Applicants must submit a completed application form. **Deadline for Receipt:** May 5. **Additional Information:** mkeys@usgagrants.org.

2255 ■ UNITED STATES HUNTER JUMPER ASSOCIATION
4047 Iron Works Pky.
Lexington, KY 40511
Tel: (859)225-2055
Fax: (859)258-9033
E-mail: sdotson@ushja.org
Web Site: http://www.ushja.org
To recognize athlete students by supporting them financially.
Title of Award: USHJA Athletic Scholarships **Area, Field, or Subject:** General Studies. **Level of Education for which Award is Granted:** Undergraduate **Funds Available:** No specific amount.
Eligibility Requirements: Applicants must be full-time undergraduate students attending Midway College who will participate in one of the fol-

lowing sports: Equestrian, Tennis, Basketball, Softball or Soccer. **Application Requirements:** Applicants must check the available website for details. **Additional Information:** United States Hunter Jumper Association at the above address

2256 ■ UNITED STATES HUNTER JUMPER ASSOCIATION
4047 Iron Works Pky.
Lexington, KY 40511
Tel: (859)225-2055
Fax: (859)258-9033
E-mail: sdotson@ushja.org
Web Site: http://www.ushja.org
To provide financial support to those students who are in need.
Title of Award: USHJA General Scholarships **Area, Field, or Subject:** General Studies. **Level of Education for which Award is Granted:** Undergraduate **Number Awarded:** 4. **Funds Available:** $5,000.
Eligibility Requirements: Applicants must be graduating high school seniors or current undergraduate students who are pursuing postsecondary studies. **Application Requirements:** Applicants must check the available website for the required materials. **Deadline for Receipt:** April 30. **Additional Information:** For more information, please visit: http://www.asha.net

2257 ■ UNITED STATES MARINE CORPS DRILL INSTRUCTORS ASSOCIATION
PO Box 5401
Parris Island, SC 29905
Tel: (912)632-4557
Fax: (912)632-4557
Web Site: http://www.usmcdiassn.com
To support the members' children to pursue their careers.
Title of Award: L.D. "Crow" Crawford Scholarships **Area, Field, or Subject:** General studies. **Level of Education for which Award is Granted:** Undergraduate **Number Awarded:** 2. **Funds Available:** $500. **Duration:** One year.
Eligibility Requirements: Applicant must be a members' dependent child under 21 years of age; must be pursuing undergraduate work; must maintain a "B" grade point average. **Application Requirements:** Applicant must have the letter from college or university stating that the applicant are accepted to attend their institutions; must have a transcript from the last school attended; must have a 500 word or less essay about the applicant's educational goals (new applicant only). Scholarship applications are available through National Headquarters. **Deadline for Receipt:** July 31.

2258 ■ U.S. PAN ASIAN AMERICAN CHAMBER OF COMMERCE
1329 18th St., NW
Washington, DC 20036
Tel: (202)296-5221
Free: 800-696-7818
Fax: (202)296-5225
E-mail: info@uspaacc.com
Web Site: http://www.uspaacc.com
To provide financial assistance to Asian American high school seniors who have demonstrated scholastic achievement and financial need and will pursue post-secondary education at an accredited educational institution in the United States.
Title of Award: Paul Shearman Allen and Associate Scholarships **Area, Field, or Subject:** General studies. **Level of Education for which Award is Granted:** Undergraduate **Funds Available:** $5,000.
Eligibility Requirements: Applicants must be: at least 16 years of age at the time of application; of Asian Pacific Island heritage; citizens or permanent residents of the United States; beginning full-time study at an accredited post-secondary educational institution in the United States; must have a 3.3 grade point average. **Application Requirements:** Applicants must submit: completed online application with photo attached on the top right hand corner; short biography; essay; transcript; household tax return (signed by taxpayers); recommendations; additional attachments; post-secondary institution information. **Deadline for Receipt:** February 22.

2259 ■ U.S. PAN ASIAN AMERICAN CHAMBER OF COMMERCE
1329 18th St., NW
Washington, DC 20036

Tel: (202)296-5221
Free: 800-696-7818
Fax: (202)296-5225
E-mail: info@uspaacc.com
Web Site: http://www.uspaacc.com

To provide financial assistance to Asian American high school seniors who have demonstrated scholastic achievement and financial need and will pursue post-secondary education at an accredited educational institution in the United States.

Title of Award: Asian American Scholarships **Area, Field, or Subject:** General studies. **Level of Education for which Award is Granted:** Undergraduate **Funds Available:** $5,000.
Eligibility Requirements: Applicants must be: at least 16 years of age at the time of application; of Asian Pacific Island heritage; citizens or permanent residents of the United States; beginning full-time study at an accredited post-secondary educational institution in the United States; must have a 3.3 grade point average or higher. **Application Requirements:** Applicants must submit: completed online application with photo attached on the top right hand corner; short biography; essay; transcript; household tax return; recommendations; additional attachments; and post-secondary institution information. **Deadline for Receipt:** February 22.

2260 ■ U.S. PAN ASIAN AMERICAN CHAMBER OF COMMERCE

1329 18th St., NW
Washington, DC 20036
Tel: (202)296-5221
Free: 800-696-7818
Fax: (202)296-5225
E-mail: info@uspaacc.com
Web Site: http://www.uspaacc.com

To provide financial assistance to Asian American high school seniors who have demonstrated scholastic achievement and financial need and will pursue post-secondary education at an accredited educational institution in the United States.

Title of Award: Darden Restaurants Scholarships **Area, Field, or Subject:** General studies. **Level of Education for which Award is Granted:** Undergraduate **Funds Available:** $5,000.
Eligibility Requirements: Applicants must be: at least 16 years of age at the time of application; of Asian Pacific Island heritage; citizens or permanent residents of the United States; beginning full-time study at an accredited post-secondary educational institution in the United States; must have a GPA of 3.3 or higher. **Application Requirements:** Applicants must submit: completed online application with photo attached on the top right hand corner; short biography; essay; transcript; household tax return (signed by taxpayers); recommendations; additional attachments; post-secondary institution information. **Deadline for Receipt:** February 22.

2261 ■ U.S. PAN ASIAN AMERICAN CHAMBER OF COMMERCE

1329 18th St., NW
Washington, DC 20036
Tel: (202)296-5221
Free: 800-696-7818
Fax: (202)296-5225
E-mail: info@uspaacc.com
Web Site: http://www.uspaacc.com

To provide financial assistance to Asian American high school seniors who have demonstrated scholastic achievement and financial need and will pursue post-secondary education at an accredited educational institution in the United States.

Title of Award: Home Depot Scholarships **Area, Field, or Subject:** General studies. **Level of Education for which Award is Granted:** Undergraduate **Funds Available:** $5,000.
Eligibility Requirements: Applicants must be: at least 16 years of age at the time of application; of Asian Pacific Island heritage; citizens or permanent residents of the United States; beginning full-time study at an accredited post-secondary educational institution in the United States; must have a GPA of 3.3 or higher. **Application Requirements:** Applicants must submit: completed online application with photo attached on the top right hand corner; short biography; essay; transcript; household tax return (signed by taxpayers); recommendations; additional attachments; post-secondary institution information. **Deadline for Receipt:** February 22.

2262 ■ U.S. PAN ASIAN AMERICAN CHAMBER OF COMMERCE

1329 18th St., NW
Washington, DC 20036
Tel: (202)296-5221
Free: 800-696-7818
Fax: (202)296-5225
E-mail: info@uspaacc.com
Web Site: http://www.uspaacc.com

To provide financial assistance to a student with strong character, who has persevered and prevailed over adversity, and who will pursue post-secondary education at an accredited educational institution in the United States.

Title of Award: Bruce Lee Scholarships **Area, Field, or Subject:** General studies. **Level of Education for which Award is Granted:** Undergraduate **Funds Available:** $5,000.
Eligibility Requirements: Applicants must be: at least 16 years of age at the time of application; of Asian Pacific Island heritage; citizens or permanent residents of the United States; beginning full-time study at an accredited post-secondary educational institution in the United States; must have a GPA of 3.0 or higher. **Application Requirements:** Applicants must submit: completed online application with photo attached on the top right hand corner; short biography; essay; transcript; household tax return (signed by taxpayers); recommendations; additional attachments; post-secondary institution information. **Deadline for Receipt:** February 22.

2263 ■ U.S. PAN ASIAN AMERICAN CHAMBER OF COMMERCE

1329 18th St., NW
Washington, DC 20036
Tel: (202)296-5221
Free: 800-696-7818
Fax: (202)296-5225
E-mail: info@uspaacc.com
Web Site: http://www.uspaacc.com

To encourage the students to travel back to the land of their birth or heritage during summer break and share the experience with the greater USPAAC community.

Title of Award: LeePapa and Associates Scholarship for Travel **Area, Field, or Subject:** General studies. **Level of Education for which Award is Granted:** Graduate, Undergraduate **Funds Available:** $5,000.
Eligibility Requirements: Applicants must be of Asian Pacific Island heritage; must be citizens of United States; must be undergraduate or graduate students, with minimum of 3.3 grade point average at an accredited post-secondary educational institution in the United States. **Application Requirements:** Applicants must submit: downloaded application for the award; photo; additional attachment describing extracurricular activities, academic honors, and community service activities; 100-word biography; essay of 500 words on I Need This Scholarship (typed, double-spaced and signed by the applicants and their academic guidance counselors); transcripts from undergrad or post-grad school; copy of most recent household tax return signed by taxpayers; two letters of recommendation from those listed as references in the application. **Deadline for Receipt:** March 17.

2264 ■ U.S. PAN ASIAN AMERICAN CHAMBER OF COMMERCE

1329 18th St., NW
Washington, DC 20036
Tel: (202)296-5221
Free: 800-696-7818
Fax: (202)296-5225
E-mail: info@uspaacc.com
Web Site: http://www.uspaacc.com

To provide financial assistance to female Asian American high school seniors who will be pursuing post-secondary education at an accredited educational institution in the United States.

Title of Award: Ruth Mu-Lan and James S.C. Chao Scholarship **Area, Field, or Subject:** General studies. **Level of Education for which Award is Granted:** Undergraduate **Funds Available:** $3,000.
Eligibility Requirements: Applicants must be: females and at least 16 years of age at the of application; of Asian Pacific Island heritage; citizens or permanent residents of the United States; beginning full-time study at an accredited post-secondary educational institution in the United States; must have a GPA of 3.5 or higher. **Application Requirements:** Ap-

plicants must submit: completed online application with photo attached on the top right hand corner; short biography; essay; transcript; household tax return (signed by taxpayers); recommendations; additional attachments; post-secondary institution information. **Deadline for Receipt:** February 22.

2265 ■ U.S. PAN ASIAN AMERICAN CHAMBER OF COMMERCE
1329 18th St., NW
Washington, DC 20036
Tel: (202)296-5221
Free: 800-696-7818
Fax: (202)296-5225
E-mail: info@uspaacc.com
Web Site: http://www.uspaacc.com
To provide financial assistance to Asian American high school seniors who have demonstrated scholastic achievement and financial need and will pursue post-secondary education at an accredited educational institution in the United States.
Title of Award: Pepsico Scholarships **Area, Field, or Subject:** General studies. **Level of Education for which Award is Granted:** Undergraduate **Funds Available:** $5,000.
Eligibility Requirements: Applicants must be: at least 16 years of age at the time of application; of Asian Pacific Island heritage; citizens or permanent residents of the United States; beginning full-time study at an accredited post-secondary educational institution in the United States; must have a GPA of 3.3 or higher. **Application Requirements:** Applicants must submit: completed online application with photo attached on the top right hand corner; short biography; essay; transcript; household tax return (signed by taxpayers); recommendations; additional attachments; post-secondary institution information. **Deadline for Receipt:** February 22.

2266 ■ U.S. PAN ASIAN AMERICAN CHAMBER OF COMMERCE
1329 18th St., NW
Washington, DC 20036
Tel: (202)296-5221
Free: 800-696-7818
Fax: (202)296-5225
E-mail: info@uspaacc.com
Web Site: http://www.uspaacc.com
To provide financial assistance to Asian American high school seniors who have demonstrated scholastic achievement and financial need and will pursue post-secondary education at an accredited educational institution in the United States.
Title of Award: Philip Morris USA Scholarships **Area, Field, or Subject:** General studies. **Level of Education for which Award is Granted:** Undergraduate **Funds Available:** $5,000.
Eligibility Requirements: Applicants must be: at least 16 years of age at the time of application; of Asian Pacific Island heritage; citizens or permanent residents of the United States; beginning full-time study at an accredited post-secondary educational institution in the United States; must have a GPA of 3.3 or higher. **Application Requirements:** Applicants must submit: completed online application with photo attached on the top right hand corner; short biography; essay; transcript; household tax return (signed by taxpayers); recommendations; additional attachments; post-secondary institution information. **Deadline for Receipt:** February 22.

2267 ■ U.S. PAN ASIAN AMERICAN CHAMBER OF COMMERCE
1329 18th St., NW
Washington, DC 20036
Tel: (202)296-5221
Free: 800-696-7818
Fax: (202)296-5225
E-mail: info@uspaacc.com
Web Site: http://www.uspaacc.com
To provide financial assistance to Asian American high school seniors who have demonstrated scholastic achievement and financial need and will pursue post-secondary education at an accredited educational institution in the United States.
Title of Award: Ken and Pam Pong Scholarships **Area, Field, or Subject:** General studies. **Level of Education for which Award is Granted:** Undergraduate **Funds Available:** $2,000.

Eligibility Requirements: Applicants must be: at least 16 years of age at the time of application; of Asian Pacific Island heritage; citizens or permanent residents of the United States; beginning full-time study at an accredited post-secondary educational institution in the United States; must have a 3.3 GPA or higher. **Application Requirements:** Applicants must submit: completed online application with photo attached on the top right hand corner; short biography; essay; transcript; household tax return (signed by taxpayers); recommendations; additional attachments; post-secondary institution information. **Deadline for Receipt:** February 22.

2268 ■ U.S. PAN ASIAN AMERICAN CHAMBER OF COMMERCE
1329 18th St., NW
Washington, DC 20036
Tel: (202)296-5221
Free: 800-696-7818
Fax: (202)296-5225
E-mail: info@uspaacc.com
Web Site: http://www.uspaacc.com
To provide financial assistance to Asian American high school seniors who have demonstrated scholastic achievement and financial need and will pursue post-secondary education at an accredited educational institution in the United States.
Title of Award: Drs. Poh Shien and Judy Young Scholarships **Area, Field, or Subject:** General studies. **Level of Education for which Award is Granted:** Undergraduate **Funds Available:** $4,000.
Eligibility Requirements: Applicants must be: at least 16 years of age at the time of application; of Asian Pacific Island heritage; citizens or permanent residents of the United States; beginning full-time study at an accredited post-secondary educational institution in the United States; must have a GPA of 3.3 or higher. **Application Requirements:** Applicants must submit: completed online application with photo attached on the top right hand corner; short biography; essay; transcript; household tax return (signed by taxpayers); recommendations; additional attachments; post-secondary institution information. **Deadline for Receipt:** February 22.

2269 ■ U.S. PAN ASIAN AMERICAN CHAMBER OF COMMERCE
1329 18th St., NW
Washington, DC 20036
Tel: (202)296-5221
Free: 800-696-7818
Fax: (202)296-5225
E-mail: info@uspaacc.com
Web Site: http://www.uspaacc.com
To provide financial assistance to Asian American high school seniors who have demonstrated scholastic achievement and financial need and will pursue post-secondary education at an accredited educational institution in the United States.
Title of Award: Telamon Scholarships **Area, Field, or Subject:** General studies. **Level of Education for which Award is Granted:** Undergraduate **Funds Available:** $2,000.
Eligibility Requirements: Applicants must be: at least 16 years of age at the time of application; of Asian Pacific Island heritage; citizens or permanent residents of the United States; beginning full-time study at an accredited post-secondary educational institution in the United States; must have a GPA of 3.3 or higher. **Application Requirements:** Applicants must submit: completed online application with photo attached on the top right hand corner; short biography; essay; transcript; household tax return (signed by taxpayers); recommendations; additional attachments; post-secondary institution information. **Deadline for Receipt:** February 22.

2270 ■ U.S. PAN ASIAN AMERICAN CHAMBER OF COMMERCE
1329 18th St., NW
Washington, DC 20036
Tel: (202)296-5221
Free: 800-696-7818
Fax: (202)296-5225
E-mail: info@uspaacc.com
Web Site: http://www.uspaacc.com
To provide financial assistance to Asian American high school seniors who have demonstrated scholastic achievement and financial need and will pursue post-secondary education at an accredited educational institution in the United States.

Title of Award: U.S. Pan Asian American Chamber of Commerce CBS Scholarships **Area, Field, or Subject:** General studies. **Level of Education for which Award is Granted:** Undergraduate **Funds Available:** $5,000.

Eligibility Requirements: Applicants must be: at least 16 years of age at the time of application; of Asian Pacific Island heritage; citizens or permanent residents of the United States; beginning full-time study at an accredited post-secondary educational institution in the United States; must have a GPA of 3.3 or higher. **Application Requirements:** Applicants must submit: completed online application with photo attached on the top right hand corner; short biography; essay; transcript; household tax return (signed by taxpayers); recommendations; additional attachments; post-secondary institution information. **Deadline for Receipt:** February 22.

2271 ■ U.S. PAN ASIAN AMERICAN CHAMBER OF COMMERCE

1329 18th St., NW
Washington, DC 20036
Tel: (202)296-5221
Free: 800-696-7818
Fax: (202)296-5225
E-mail: info@uspaacc.com
Web Site: http://www.uspaacc.com
To provide financial assistance to Asian American high school seniors who have demonstrated scholastic achievement and financial need and will pursue post-secondary education at an accredited educational institution in the United States.
Title of Award: U.S. Pan Asian American Chamber of Commerce McDonald's Scholarships **Area, Field, or Subject:** General studies. **Level of Education for which Award is Granted:** Undergraduate **Funds Available:** $3,000.

Eligibility Requirements: Applicants must be: at least 16 years of age at the time of application; of Asian Pacific Island heritage; citizens or permanent residents of the United States; beginning full-time study at an accredited post-secondary educational institution in the United States; must have a GPA 3.3 GPA or higher. **Application Requirements:** Applicants must submit completed online application with photo attached on the top right hand corner; short biography; essay; transcript; household tax return (signed by taxpayers); recommendations; additional attachments; post-secondary institution information. **Deadline for Receipt:** February 22.

2272 ■ U.S. PAN ASIAN AMERICAN CHAMBER OF COMMERCE

1329 18th St., NW
Washington, DC 20036
Tel: (202)296-5221
Free: 800-696-7818
Fax: (202)296-5225
E-mail: info@uspaacc.com
Web Site: http://www.uspaacc.com
To provide financial assistance to Asian American high school seniors who have demonstrated scholastic achievement and financial need and will pursue post-secondary education at an accredited educational institution in the United States.
Title of Award: U.S. Pan Asian American Chamber of Commerce UPS Scholarships **Area, Field, or Subject:** General studies. **Level of Education for which Award is Granted:** Undergraduate **Funds Available:** $5,000.

Eligibility Requirements: Applicants must be: at least 16 years of age at the time of application; of Asian Pacific Island heritage; citizens or permanent residents of the United States; beginning full-time study at an accredited post-secondary educational institution in the United States; must have a GPA of 3.3 or higher. **Application Requirements:** Applicants must submit: completed online application with photo attached on the top right hand corner; short biography; essay; transcript; household tax return (signed by taxpayers); recommendations; additional attachments; post-secondary institution information. **Deadline for Receipt:** February 22.

2273 ■ UNITED STATES TOUR OPERATORS ASSOCIATION

275 Madisn Ave., Ste. 2014
New York, NY 10016
Tel: (212)599-6599

Fax: (212)599-6744
E-mail: information@ustoa.com
Web Site: http://www.ustoa.com
To educate the travel industry; to foster professionalism within the tour operator industry; to facilitate and develop travel on a worldwide basis.
Title of Award: United States Tour Operators Association Scholarships **Area, Field, or Subject:** Travel and Tourism. **Level of Education for which Award is Granted:** Undergraduate **Funds Available:** $2,500.

Eligibility Requirements: Applicants must be students enrolled at an accredited four-year college or university in the United States or Canada; must have a degree emphasis in travel or be in a tourism-related program with a 3.0 GPA. **Application Requirements:** Applicants must submit a completed application form; a typed resume; an official copy of transcript sent from the school detailing courses completed, academic standing and GPA; and one letter of recommendation from a tourism professor. **Deadline for Receipt:** April 1.

2274 ■ U.S.-UKRAINE FOUNDATION

1701 K St. NW Ste. 903
Washington, DC 20006
Tel: (202)223-2228
Fax: (202)223-1224
E-mail: info@usukraine.org
Web Site: http://www.usukraine.org
To offer full scholarships on a need-blind basis.
Title of Award: European College of Liberal Arts (ECLA) Scholarships **Area, Field, or Subject:** General Studies. **Level of Education for which Award is Granted:** Undergraduate **Funds Available:** No specific amount.

Eligibility Requirements: Applicants must study German while attending ECLA; must have earned 30 credit hours in a full year program and 8 credits in the summer program; should be between ages 18-24 with the right background and interests, proficient academic performance and good values. **Application Requirements:** Applicants must check the available website for more information. **Additional Information:** For more information about ECLA and the scholarship program, see www.ecla.de. For other questions, please email Dick Shriver at rhsusa@yahoo.com.

2275 ■ U.S.-UKRAINE FOUNDATION

1701 K St. NW Ste. 903
Washington, DC 20006
Tel: (202)223-2228
Fax: (202)223-1224
E-mail: info@usukraine.org
Web Site: http://www.usukraine.org
To provide scholarships to those deserving undergraduate international students.
Title of Award: University of Maryland International Student Scholarships **Area, Field, or Subject:** General Studies. **Level of Education for which Award is Granted:** Undergraduate **Funds Available:** No specific amount.

Eligibility Requirements: Applicants must be undergraduate international students; must have demonstrated a strong record of academic achievement and proficient English skills. **Application Requirements:** Applicants must check the available website for more information. **Deadline for Receipt:** June 1. **Additional Information:** For more information just contact the Office of International Admissions at 410-704-6069 or visit their website for complete details: www.towson.edu/intladm

2276 ■ U.S.-UKRAINE FOUNDATION

1701 K St. NW Ste. 903
Washington, DC 20006
Tel: (202)223-2228
Fax: (202)223-1224
E-mail: info@usukraine.org
Web Site: http://www.usukraine.org
To provide financial support to talented high school students in Ukraine.
Title of Award: USA/USA-Ukramerazha Scholarships **Area, Field, or Subject:** General Studies. **Level of Education for which Award is Granted:** Undergraduate **Funds Available:** No specific amount.

Eligibility Requirements: Applicants must be talented high school students in Ukraine heading to preparatory schools and colleges in the U.S., Canada or the United Kingdom. **Application Requirements:** Applicants must check the available website for more information. **Additional Information:** USA/USA Program services help selected students understand the requirements and procedures of Western educational institutions by offering advisory workshops and scholarships for entrance exams. **Additional Information:** U.S.Ukraine Foundation at the above address.

2277 ■ UNIVERSITY OF ALASKA ANCHORAGE
3211 Providence Dr.
Anchorage, AK 99508
Tel: (907)786-1800
Web Site: http://www.uaa.alaska.edu
To provide financial assistance for tuition and other related educational expenses to a UAA student who is enrolled full-time or parttime with a declared major in accounting.
Title of Award: Lenore & George Hedla Accounting Scholarships **Area, Field, or Subject:** Accounting. **Level of Education for which Award is Granted:** Undergraduate **Funds Available:** No specific amount.
Eligibility Requirements: Applicants must demonstrate motivation, academic and leadership potential; must be in good academic standing with a minimum cumulative GPA of 2.0; must be formally admitted to an undergraduate accounting degreeseeking program at the UAA; must plan on enrolling at least full-time or part-time at the UAA; may be a U.S. citizen, non-U.S. citizen, Alaska resident, or out-of-state resident; must be enrolled in the semester for which the award is made. **Application Requirements:** Applicants must complete the electronic scholarship application available online at www.uaa.alaska.edu/scholarships/hedla.cfm. **Deadline for Receipt:** February 15.

2278 ■ UNIVERSITY OF ALASKA ANCHORAGE
3211 Providence Dr.
Anchorage, AK 99508
Tel: (907)786-1800
Web Site: http://www.uaa.alaska.edu
To encourage undergraduate students in the United States and Canada by providing a unique opportunity for academic exchange.
Title of Award: Killam Fellowships Program **Area, Field, or Subject:** General studies. **Level of Education for which Award is Granted:** Undergraduate **Funds Available:** $10,000. **Duration:** One academic year.
Eligibility Requirements: Applicant must be a citizen of Canada or the United States; must be a full-time undergraduate student in good standing at a degree-granting institution in Canada or the United States; must meet the eligibility requirements of their home university; must be fluent in English; must have a superior academic record; must complete all the steps of the application process prior to the published deadlines, and, in the case of the direct exchange applicants; must be nominated by his/her university to receive a Killam Fellowship. **Application Requirements:** Applications and instructions can be obtained online at www.killamfellowships.com. **Deadline for Receipt:** January 31.

2279 ■ UNIVERSITY OF ALASKA ANCHORAGE
3211 Providence Dr.
Anchorage, AK 99508
Tel: (907)786-1800
Web Site: http://www.uaa.alaska.edu
To provide financial assistance for tuition and other related educational expenses to a University of Alaska Anchorage student who is enrolled in at least nine credits with a declared major in accounting, and to encourage non-traditional students to pursue academic endeavors.
Title of Award: UAA Accounting Club Scholarships **Area, Field, or Subject:** Accounting. **Level of Education for which Award is Granted:** Undergraduate **Funds Available:** $500. **Duration:** One year.
Eligibility Requirements: Applicants must demonstrate motivation, academic and leadership potential; must be in good academic standing with a minimum cumulative GPA of 3.0; must be formally admitted to an undergraduate Accounting degree-seeking program at the UAA; must plan on enrolling at least nine credits at the UAA; must demonstrate an involvement in extracurricular activities, with specific involvement in the UAA Accounting Club; must be junior or senior standing and have completed a 300-level accounting course or be enrolled in a 300-level accounting course during the semester of the award; may be a U.S. citizen, non-U.S. citizen, Alaska resident, or out-of-state resident; must be

enrolled in the semester for which the award is made. **Application Requirements:** Applicants must complete the electronic scholarship application available online. **Deadline for Receipt:** February 15.

2280 ■ UNIVERSITY OF ALASKA ANCHORAGE
3211 Providence Dr.
Anchorage, AK 99508
Tel: (907)786-1800
Web Site: http://www.uaa.alaska.edu
To provide financial assistance to students who want to pursue their education at UAA.
Title of Award: UAA Alumni Association Scholarships **Area, Field, or Subject:** General studies. **Level of Education for which Award is Granted:** Undergraduate **Number Awarded:** 6. **Funds Available:** $1,000. **Duration:** One academic year.
Eligibility Requirements: Applicants must demonstrate motivation, academic, and leadership potential; must be in good academic standing with a minimum cumulative GPA of 2.5 for undergraduates and 3.0 for graduates; must be formally admitted to a degree- or certificate-seeking program within one of the following UAA schools/ colleges: College of Business, College of Business and Public Policy, College of Arts and Sciences, College of Health and Social Welfare, Community & Technical College, School of Engineering, and the College of Education; must plan on enrolling full-time (12 credits for undergraduates, 9 credits for graduates) at UAA; must be an incoming or continuing student at UAA; may be a U.S citizen, non-U.S citizen, Alaska resident, or out-ofstate resident. **Application Requirements:** Application forms are available online. **Deadline for Receipt:** February 15.

2281 ■ UNIVERSITY OF ALASKA ANCHORAGE
3211 Providence Dr.
Anchorage, AK 99508
Tel: (907)786-1800
Web Site: http://www.uaa.alaska.edu
To provide financial assistance for tuition and other educational expenses to full-time students who are formally admitted to the Accounting degree program at the UAA.
Title of Award: UAA Melissa J. Wolf Scholarships **Area, Field, or Subject:** Accounting. **Level of Education for which Award is Granted:** Undergraduate **Funds Available:** No specific amount.
Eligibility Requirements: Applicants must demonstrate motivation, academic and leadership potential; must be in good academic standing with a minimum cumulative grade point average of 2.0; must be formally admitted to an Accounting degree at the UAA; must plan on enrolling full-time (twelve credits) at the UAA; may be a U.S. citizen, non-U.S. citizen, Alaska resident, or out-of-state resident; must be enrolled in the semester for which the award is made. **Application Requirements:** Applicants must complete the electronic scholarship application online. **Deadline for Receipt:** February 15.

2282 ■ UNIVERSITY OF ALASKA FAIRBANKS ALUMNI ASSOCIATION
PO Box 750126
Fairbanks, AK 99775
Tel: (907)474-7081
Free: 800-770-ALUM
E-mail: fvalum@uaf.edu
Web Site: http://www.uaf.edu/alumni
To support students with their educational pursuit.
Title of Award: Jim Doogan Memorial Scholarships **Area, Field, or Subject:** General studies. **Level of Education for which Award is Granted:** Undergraduate **Funds Available:** No specific amount.
Eligibility Requirements: Applicant must be a sophomore student or above. **Application Requirements:** Applicants may apply using the Supplement for Scholarship Application. **Additional Information:** Established in memory of Jim Doogan, a supporter of UAF and an active member of the UAF Alumni Association. **Deadline for Receipt:** February 15. **Additional Information:** Scholarship Coordinator, 907-474-5372.

2283 ■ UNIVERSITY OF ALASKA FAIRBANKS ALUMNI ASSOCIATION
PO Box 750126
Fairbanks, AK 99775

Tel: (907)474-7081
Free: 800-770-ALUM
E-mail: fvalum@uaf.edu
Web Site: http://www.uaf.edu/alumni
To support students in their educational pursuits.
Title of Award: Fairbanks Chapter Legacy Scholarships **Area, Field, or Subject:** General studies. **Level of Education for which Award is Granted:** Undergraduate **Funds Available:** No specific amount. **Eligibility Requirements:** Applicant must be a sophomore student or above. **Application Requirements:** Applicants may apply using the Supplement for Scholarship Application. **Deadline for Receipt:** February 15. **Additional Information:** Scholarship Coordinator, 907-474-5372.

2284 ■ UNIVERSITY OF ALASKA FAIRBANKS ALUMNI ASSOCIATION
PO Box 750126
Fairbanks, AK 99775
Tel: (907)474-7081
Free: 800-770-ALUM
E-mail: fvalum@uaf.edu
Web Site: http://www.uaf.edu/alumni
To support students with their educational pursuit.
Title of Award: Jay Hammond Memorial Scholarships **Area, Field, or Subject:** General studies. **Level of Education for which Award is Granted:** Undergraduate **Funds Available:** No specific amount. **Eligibility Requirements:** Applicant must exhibit leadership and desire to make a difference in Alaska. **Application Requirements:** Applicants may apply using the Supplement for Scholarship Application. **Additional Information:** The scholarship is named after Jay Hammond, former governor. **Deadline for Receipt:** February 15. **Additional Information:** Scholarship Coordinator, 907-474-5372.

2285 ■ UNIVERSITY OF ALASKA FAIRBANKS ALUMNI ASSOCIATION
PO Box 750126
Fairbanks, AK 99775
Tel: (907)474-7081
Free: 800-770-ALUM
E-mail: fvalum@uaf.edu
Web Site: http://www.uaf.edu/alumni
To support students with their educational pursuit.
Title of Award: Audrey Loftus Memorial Scholarships **Area, Field, or Subject:** General studies. **Level of Education for which Award is Granted:** Undergraduate **Funds Available:** No specific amount. **Eligibility Requirements:** Applicants must be freshmen or transfer students, demonstrated experience in and future commitment to extracurricular/ community activities; and have a GPA of 3.0 and above. **Application Requirements:** Applicants may apply using the Supplement for Scholarship Application. **Additional Information:** Established in memory of Adrey Loftus, founding director of the UAFAA. **Deadline for Receipt:** February 15. **Additional Information:** Scholarship Coordinator, 907-474-5372.

2286 ■ UNIVERSITY OF ALASKA FAIRBANKS ALUMNI ASSOCIATION
PO Box 750126
Fairbanks, AK 99775
Tel: (907)474-7081
Free: 800-770-ALUM
E-mail: fvalum@uaf.edu
Web Site: http://www.uaf.edu/alumni
To support the education of a dependent of an alumni.
Title of Award: UAF Alumni Association Scholarships **Area, Field, or Subject:** General studies. **Level of Education for which Award is Granted:** Undergraduate **Funds Available:** No specific amount. **Eligibility Requirements:** Applicants must be undergraduate sophomores, juniors and seniors; dependents of active alumni association members; and have a GPA of 2.5-3.5 range. **Application Requirements:** Applicants may apply using the Supplement for Scholarship Application. **Additional Information:** Recipients are expected to be involved in the alumni development after graduation. Previous awardees may re-apply. **Deadline for Receipt:** February 15. **Additional Information:** Scholarship Coordinator, 907-474-5372.

2287 ■ UNIVERSITY OF LOUISVILLE ALUMNI ASSOCIATION
Malcolm B. Chancey Center
Alumni Office
Louisville, KY 40292
Tel: (502)852-6186
Free: 800-813-8635
Fax: (502)852-6920
E-mail: jimmy.ford@louisville.edu
Web Site: http://www.alumni.louisville.edu
To financially support students in their educational pursuit.
Title of Award: Beth K. Fields Scholarships **Area, Field, or Subject:** General studies. **Level of Education for which Award is Granted:** Undergraduate **Funds Available:** No specific amount. **Eligibility Requirements:** Applicant must be 25 years old and below; have a minimum of 12 semester hours college credit; have a 3.0 GPA; be a full-time student; and must be supporting at least one dependent. **Application Requirements:** Applicants must submit a completed application form together with a copy of official transcripts; a 300-word essay; and two letters of recommendations. **Deadline for Receipt:** March 15. **Additional Information:** Amanda Thompson, 502-852-4956 or ajthom01@gwise.louisville.edu.

2288 ■ UNIVERSITY OF LOUISVILLE ALUMNI ASSOCIATION
Malcolm B. Chancey Center
Alumni Office
Louisville, KY 40292
Tel: (502)852-6186
Free: 800-813-8635
Fax: (502)852-6920
E-mail: jimmy.ford@louisville.edu
Web Site: http://www.alumni.louisville.edu
To support direct descendants of an individuals who served in the Navy V-12 program or the Naval ROTC program at UofL.
Title of Award: Raymond A. Kent-Navy V-12/ROTC **Area, Field, or Subject:** General studies. **Level of Education for which Award is Granted:** Undergraduate **Funds Available:** No specific amount. **Eligibility Requirements:** Applicant must be a direct descendant an individual who served the Navy V-12 program or the Naval ROTC program. **Application Requirements:** Applicants must submit a completed application form together with a copy of official transcripts; a 300-word essay; and two letters of recommendations. **Deadline for Receipt:** March 15. **Additional Information:** Amanda Thompson, 502-852-4956 or ajthom01@gwise.louisville.edu.

2289 ■ UNIVERSITY OF LOUISVILLE ALUMNI ASSOCIATION
Malcolm B. Chancey Center
Alumni Office
Louisville, KY 40292
Tel: (502)852-6186
Free: 800-813-8635
Fax: (502)852-6920
E-mail: jimmy.ford@louisville.edu
Web Site: http://www.alumni.louisville.edu
To support students in their educational pursuits.
Title of Award: Kentucky Alumni Club Scholarships - Capital Region Alumni Club **Area, Field, or Subject:** General studies. **Level of Education for which Award is Granted:** Undergraduate **Number Awarded:** 1. **Funds Available:** $500 for the first year. **Duration:** Four years. **Eligibility Requirements:** Applicant must reside in the state of Kentucky specifically in Anderson, Franklin, Henry, Owen, Mercer, Shelby, and Spencer counties; and must maintain a GPA of 3.0. **Application Requirements:** Applicant must complete the application with an essay; official copies of transcripts; test scores; and two letters of recommendation (one from a teacher) submitted to the Scholarship Committee. **Deadline for Receipt:** March 15. **Additional Information:** 502-852-6186.

2290 ■ UNIVERSITY OF LOUISVILLE ALUMNI ASSOCIATION
Malcolm B. Chancey Center
Alumni Office
Louisville, KY 40292
Tel: (502)852-6186
Free: 800-813-8635
Fax: (502)852-6920

E-mail: jimmy.ford@louisville.edu
Web Site: http://www.alumni.louisville.edu
To support students in their educational pursuits.
Title of Award: Kentucky Alumni Club Scholarships - Central Kentucky Alumni Club **Area, Field, or Subject:** General studies. **Level of Education for which Award is Granted:** Undergraduate **Funds Available:** Full tuition. **Duration:** One academic year.
Eligibility Requirements: Applicant must reside in the state of Kentucky specifically in Fayette, Jessamine, Woodford, Clark, Bourbon, Scott, Harrison and Madison counties. **Application Requirements:** Applicant must complete the application with an essay; official copies of transcripts; test scores; and two letters of recommendation (one from a teacher) submitted to Paul W. Graf, 3367 Ridgecane Rd. Lexington, KY 40513. **Deadline for Receipt:** April 15.

2291 ■ UNIVERSITY OF LOUISVILLE ALUMNI ASSOCIATION
Malcolm B. Chancey Center
Alumni Office
Louisville, KY 40292
Tel: (502)852-6186
Free: 800-813-8635
Fax: (502)852-6920
E-mail: jimmy.ford@louisville.edu
Web Site: http://www.alumni.louisville.edu
To support students in their educational pursuits.
Title of Award: Kentucky Alumni Club Scholarships - Lake Cumberland Alumni Club **Area, Field, or Subject:** General studies. **Level of Education for which Award is Granted:** Undergraduate **Number Awarded:** 1. **Funds Available:** $500. **Duration:** One academic year.
Eligibility Requirements: Applicant must reside in the state of Kentucky specifically in Adair, Casey, Clinton, Cumberland, Laurel, McCreary, Pulaski, Rockcastle, Russell and Wayne counties; must be admitted to University of Louisville; have a GPA of 3.5 or above and an ACT/SAT equivalent of 24 or higher. **Application Requirements:** Applicant must complete the application with an essay; official copies of transcripts; test scores; and two letters of recommendation (one from a teacher) submitted to Dr. Sonya Jones, PO Box 289 Somerset, KY 42502. **Deadline for Receipt:** April 1. **Additional Information:** Susan Hughes, 606-348-4086 or shugdes@wayne.k12.ky.us.

2292 ■ UNIVERSITY OF LOUISVILLE ALUMNI ASSOCIATION
Malcolm B. Chancey Center
Alumni Office
Louisville, KY 40292
Tel: (502)852-6186
Free: 800-813-8635
Fax: (502)852-6920
E-mail: jimmy.ford@louisville.edu
Web Site: http://www.alumni.louisville.edu
To support students in their educational pursuits.
Title of Award: Kentucky Alumni Club Scholarships - Northern Kentucky Alumni Club **Area, Field, or Subject:** General studies. **Level of Education for which Award is Granted:** Undergraduate **Number Awarded:** 1. **Funds Available:** $500.
Eligibility Requirements: Applicant must reside in the state of Kentucky specifically in Boone, Kenton, Campbelle, Grant, Carroll, Pendleton, and Gallatin counties or in Hamilton County in Ohio; must maintain a GPA of 3.0; and an ACT/SAT equivalent of 20 or above. **Application Requirements:** Applicant must complete the application with an essay; official copies of transcripts; test scores; and two letters of recommendation (one from a teacher) submitted to Kathleen Annear Carnes, 332 Forest Hill Dr., Lexington, KY 40509-1970.

2293 ■ UNIVERSITY OF LOUISVILLE ALUMNI ASSOCIATION
Malcolm B. Chancey Center
Alumni Office
Louisville, KY 40292
Tel: (502)852-6186
Free: 800-813-8635
Fax: (502)852-6920
E-mail: jimmy.ford@louisville.edu
Web Site: http://www.alumni.louisville.edu
To support students in their educational pursuits.

Title of Award: Outstanding Undergraduate Scholarships (SOAR) **Area, Field, or Subject:** General studies. **Level of Education for which Award is Granted:** Undergraduate **Number Awarded:** 1. **Funds Available:** $1,000.
Eligibility Requirements: Applicant must be registered full-time for the semester. **Application Requirements:** Applicants must submit a completed application form together with a copy of official transcripts; a 300-word essay; and two letters of recommendations. **Deadline for Receipt:** March 15. **Additional Information:** Amanda Thompson, 502-852-4956 or ajthom01@gwise.louisville.edu.

2294 ■ UNIVERSITY OF LOUISVILLE ALUMNI ASSOCIATION
Malcolm B. Chancey Center
Alumni Office
Louisville, KY 40292
Tel: (502)852-6186
Free: 800-813-8635
Fax: (502)852-6920
E-mail: jimmy.ford@louisville.edu
Web Site: http://www.alumni.louisville.edu
To support the children and grandchildren of UofL alumni.
Title of Award: Rodney Williams Legacy Scholarships **Area, Field, or Subject:** General studies. **Level of Education for which Award is Granted:** Undergraduate **Funds Available:** No specific amount.
Eligibility Requirements: Applicant must be related to a UofL graduate; incoming freshman or transfer student; have a 3.0 GPA; and must be a full-time student for the semester. **Application Requirements:** Applicants must submit a completed application form together with a copy of official transcripts; a 300-word essay; and two letters of recommendations. **Deadline for Receipt:** March 15. **Additional Information:** Amanda Thompson, 502-852-4956 or ajthom01@gwise.louisville.edu.

2295 ■ UNIVERSITY OF MINNESOTA
240 Williamson Hall
231 Pillsbury Dr. SE
Minneapolis, MN 55455-0213
Tel: (612)625-2008
Free: 800-752-1000
Fax: (612)626-1693
Web Site: http://www1.umn.edu/twincities
To provide support for qualified individuals intending to pursue an educational career.
Title of Award: Carol E. Macpherson Memorial Scholarship and Alumnae Society Scholarships **Area, Field, or Subject:** General studies. **Level of Education for which Award is Granted:** Graduate, Undergraduate **Funds Available:** $1,000-$4,000. **Duration:** One year.
Eligibility Requirements: Applicant must be a female student who has had a five-year or longer break in their postsecondary education; must demonstrate financial need; must have a admission or pending admission to an undergraduate or graduate/professional degree or credit certificate program at any University of Minnesota campus; must meet half-time enrollment status minimum; must provide academic transcripts of all college/post-secondary enrollment; must have a good academic standing at the University of Minnesota; must submit a support letters from two references who have known the applicants and their educational goals. **Application Requirements:** Applicant must submit the complete application, including their personal statement and a copy of their Student Aid Report; must have a transcript of all college/post-secondary enrollment; must have two Applicant Appraisal Forms (to be sent directly from references or attached to application in a sealed envelope signed by the writer across the seal). **Deadline for Receipt:** April 30.

2296 ■ UNIVERSITY OF MINNESOTA
240 Williamson Hall
231 Pillsbury Dr. SE
Minneapolis, MN 55455-0213
Tel: (612)625-2008
Free: 800-752-1000
Fax: (612)626-1693
Web Site: http://www1.umn.edu/twincities
To help the students in University of Minnesota to pursue their education.
Title of Award: University of Minnesota Women Student Travel Grants **Area, Field, or Subject:** General studies. **Level of Education for which Award is Granted:** Graduate, Undergraduate **Funds Available:** $100-$300.

Eligibility Requirements: Applicant must be a University of Minnesota, Twin Cities undergraduate or graduate student in good standing with his/her college; must have a cumulative GPA of 3.00. **Application Requirements:** Application forms are available in the website. Applicant must attach conference program information and proof of registration; must provide the student-issued University transcript, and information about other sources of funding. Application form and other application materials must be sent to: Office for University Women, 185 Klaeber Court, 320 16th Ave., SE, Minneapolis, MN 55455. **Deadline for Receipt:** August 1 and December 1.

2297 ■ UNIVERSITY OF NEW HAMPSHIRE

Office of Admission
4 Garrison Ave.
Durham, NH 03824
Tel: (603)862-1360
Fax: (603)862-0077
E-mail: admission@unh.edu
Web Site: http://www.unh.edu
To provide financial assistance to students who want to continue their education at UNH.
Title of Award: UNH Alumni Association Legacy Scholarships **Area, Field, or Subject:** General studies. **Level of Education for which Award is Granted:** Undergraduate **Funds Available:** $3,000. **Duration:** One year.
Eligibility Requirements: Applicants must be enrolled or accepted as full-time students in a four-year degree program at UNH, Durham campus; must possess leadership potential as demonstrated through involvement in academic, co-curricular and/or work activities; must have a relative who is an alumnus/a of the University of Hampshire who must have been a dues-paying member at the time of his or her death; and must have a cumulative GPA of 3.2. **Application Requirements:** Applicants must complete the application form available online; and must have a letter of recommendation from a high school teacher, guidance counselor or UNH faculty member. **Deadline for Receipt:** March 31.

2298 ■ UNIVERSITY OF NEW HAMPSHIRE

Office of Admission
4 Garrison Ave.
Durham, NH 03824
Tel: (603)862-1360
Fax: (603)862-0077
E-mail: admission@unh.edu
Web Site: http://www.unh.edu
To provide financial assistance to students who want to continue their education at UNH.
Title of Award: UNH Parent's Association Endowment Scholarship Fund **Area, Field, or Subject:** General studies. **Level of Education for which Award is Granted:** Undergraduate **Funds Available:** $5,000-$9,000. **Duration:** One year.
Eligibility Requirements: Applicants must demonstrate academic achievement; must be of good character; must have a minimum cumulative GPA of 2.8; must be involved in community service projects or in the university community; and must be making financial contributions to their education through employment. **Application Requirements:** Applicants must submit a University Community and/or Community Service verification letter; an employment verification Letter; a background information statement (maximum of 1 page double spaced); and must have a faculty recommendation. Application forms are available online and must be sent to University of New Hampshire Parent's Association.

2299 ■ UNIVERSITY OF NORTH CAROLINA SCHOOL OF JOURNALISM AND MASS COMMUNICATION

University of North Carolina, Carol Hall CB 3365
Chapel Hill, NC 27599-3365
Tel: (919)962-1204
Fax: (919)962-0620
E-mail: jomc@unc.edu
Web Site: http://www.jomc.unc.edu
To educate journalists.
Title of Award: Molly McKay Scholarships **Area, Field, or Subject:** Religion. **Level of Education for which Award is Granted:** Undergraduate **Funds Available:** $1,000.

Eligibility Requirements: Applicants must be students interested in religion. **Application Requirements:** Applicants must complete the application form.

2300 ■ UNIVERSITY OF OREGON

1217 University of Oregon
Eugene, OR 97403
Tel: (541)346-1000
Free: 800-232-3825
Fax: (541)346-5815
E-mail: stl@uoregon.edu
Web Site: http://www.uoregon.edu
To provide financial support for undergraduate students with financial need.
Title of Award: Oregon Community Credit Union Scholarships **Area, Field, or Subject:** General studies. **Level of Education for which Award is Granted:** Undergraduate **Funds Available:** $4,800. **Duration:** One year.
Eligibility Requirements: Applicants must be students from Oregon who demonstrate academic excellence and contribute to the community in which they live. Applicants must have graduated from high school in one of the following Oregon counties: Benton, Columbia, Lane, Linn, Marion, Multnumah, Polk, Washington or Yamhill; and must have a high school GPA of 3.50 or higher. **Application Requirements:** Applicants must submit an extra-curricular activities listing, one short statement, and one essay as part of the University of Oregon Scholarship Application. **Deadline for Receipt:** January 15.

2301 ■ UNIVERSITY OF OREGON

1217 University of Oregon
Eugene, OR 97403
Tel: (541)346-1000
Free: 800-232-3825
Fax: (541)346-5815
E-mail: stl@uoregon.edu
Web Site: http://www.uoregon.edu
To encourage qualified individuals to pursue their studies in the University of Oregon.
Title of Award: University of Oregon Dean's Scholarships **Area, Field, or Subject:** General studies. **Level of Education for which Award is Granted:** Undergraduate **Funds Available:** $500-$6,000. **Duration:** One year.
Eligibility Requirements: Applicants must be entering freshmen; must have a minimum cumulative high school GPA of 3.6; must meet all current UO freshman admission requirements; must have not attended another college after graduation from high school. **Application Requirements:** Applicants must submit the UO Undergraduate Admission Application available online to the Office of Admission. **Deadline for Receipt:** January 15.

2302 ■ UNIVERSITY OF OREGON

1217 University of Oregon
Eugene, OR 97403
Tel: (541)346-1000
Free: 800-232-3825
Fax: (541)346-5815
E-mail: stl@uoregon.edu
Web Site: http://www.uoregon.edu
To encourage the undergraduate and graduate students to enhance their educational experience by sharing diverse cultural experiences.
Title of Award: University of Oregon Diversity-Building Scholarships **Area, Field, or Subject:** General studies. **Level of Education for which Award is Granted:** Graduate, Undergraduate **Funds Available:** No specific amount. **Duration:** One year.
Eligibility Requirements: Applicants must be U.S citizens or permanent residents; must be currently enrolled as UO students in good academic standing; must meet the DBS minimum GPA requirements; must have a minimum cumulative GPA of 3.0 for freshmen, and 2.50 for other applicants. **Application Requirements:** Application forms are available online. Applicants must submit a personal statement, letter of recommendation and official transcripts. Application form and other supporting materials must be submitted to the Office of Student Financial Aid & Scholarships. **Deadline for Receipt:** January 15.

2303 ■ UNIVERSITY OF OREGON
1217 University of Oregon
Eugene, OR 97403
Tel: (541)346-1000
Free: 800-232-3825
Fax: (541)346-5815
E-mail: stl@uoregon.edu
Web Site: http://www.uoregon.edu
To support qualified individuals who wish to pursue their education.
Title of Award: University of Oregon General University Scholarships **Area, Field, or Subject:** General studies. **Level of Education for which Award is Granted:** Undergraduate **Funds Available:** $1,000-$2,700. **Duration:** One year.
Eligibility Requirements: Applicants must have a minimum GPA of 3.50.
Application Requirements: Applicants must complete the Scholarship Application Form and submit high school transcripts as well as SAT or ACT scores. **Deadline for Receipt:** January 15.

2304 ■ UNIVERSITY OF OREGON
1217 University of Oregon
Eugene, OR 97403
Tel: (541)346-1000
Free: 800-232-3825
Fax: (541)346-5815
E-mail: stl@uoregon.edu
Web Site: http://www.uoregon.edu
To provide financial support to the state's brightest students.
Title of Award: University of Oregon Presidential Scholarships **Area, Field, or Subject:** General studies. **Level of Education for which Award is Granted:** Undergraduate **Funds Available:** $6,500. **Duration:** One year.
Eligibility Requirements: Applicants must be Oregon residents; must be entering freshmen; must have a minimum GPA of 3.5. **Application Requirements:** Applicants must complete the Scholarship Application forms available online; and must submit official high school transcripts and SAT or ACT scores to the Office of Admissions. **Deadline for Receipt:** January 15.

2305 ■ UNIVERSITY OF TORONTO
315 Bloor St. W
Toronto, ON, Canada M5S 1A3
Tel: (416)978-2011
E-mail: information.commonsats@utoronto.ca
Web Site: http://www.utoronto.ca
To support students with their educational pursuits.
Title of Award: Al Mercury Scholarships **Area, Field, or Subject:** General studies. **Level of Education for which Award is Granted:** Undergraduate **Funds Available:** Approximately $700.
Eligibility Requirements: Applicant must be a UofT student demonstrated community involvement, academic excellence, integrity and an appreciation and interest in music. **Application Requirements:** Applicants must submit a completed application form along with the required materials and information. **Deadline for Receipt:** March 28.

2306 ■ UNIVERSITY OF TORONTO
315 Bloor St. W
Toronto, ON, Canada M5S 1A3
Tel: (416)978-2011
E-mail: information.commonsats@utoronto.ca
Web Site: http://www.utoronto.ca
To support students with their educational pursuits.
Title of Award: Leon C. Bynoe Memorial Scholarships **Area, Field, or Subject:** General studies. **Level of Education for which Award is Granted:** Undergraduate **Funds Available:** Approximately $1300.
Eligibility Requirements: Applicant must be a student of U of T; an undergraduate student enrolled in an undergraduate degree program; and must demonstrate outstanding service to the Afro-Canadian community. **Application Requirements:** Applicants must submit a completed Leon C. Bynoe Memorial Scholarships application form along with the required materials and information. **Deadline for Receipt:** November 30.

2307 ■ UNIVERSITY OF TORONTO
315 Bloor St. W
Toronto, ON, Canada M5S 1A3

Tel: (416)978-2011
E-mail: information.commonsats@utoronto.ca
Web Site: http://www.utoronto.ca
To support students with their educational pursuits.
Title of Award: Canadian Federation of University Women Etobicoke Bursary **Area, Field, or Subject:** General studies. **Level of Education for which Award is Granted:** Graduate, Undergraduate **Number Awarded:** 1 first year undergraduate student; 1 second or higher year undergraduate student; and 1 graduate student. **Funds Available:** $1000 and $650.
Eligibility Requirements: Applicant must be a female undergraduate or graduate student of U of T; a resident of Etobicoke; and in need of financial assistance for education. **Application Requirements:** Applicants must submit a completed Canadian Federation of University Women Etobicoke Bursary application form along with the required materials and information. **Deadline for Receipt:** October 31.

2308 ■ UNIVERSITY OF TORONTO
315 Bloor St. W
Toronto, ON, Canada M5S 1A3
Tel: (416)978-2011
E-mail: information.commonsats@utoronto.ca
Web Site: http://www.utoronto.ca
To support students with their educational pursuits.
Title of Award: Canadian Macedonian Federation Scholarships **Area, Field, or Subject:** General studies. **Level of Education for which Award is Granted:** Undergraduate **Funds Available:** Approximately $250.
Eligibility Requirements: Applicants must be a student of U of T in second, third or fourth year of any degree program with a minimum GPA of 3.5; a member of the Canadian Macedonian Federation, or have made a major commitment to any of its member service organizations through community service, contribution of a minimum of one year. **Application Requirements:** Applicants must submit a letter outlining the qualifications; attach a transcript of results, with a list of involvement or contribution to the Canadian Macedonian Federation or its member service organizations; and a proof of membership in the Federation (if applicable). **Deadline for Receipt:** March 28.

2309 ■ UNIVERSITY OF TORONTO
315 Bloor St. W
Toronto, ON, Canada M5S 1A3
Tel: (416)978-2011
E-mail: information.commonsats@utoronto.ca
Web Site: http://www.utoronto.ca
To support students with their educational pursuits.
Title of Award: Irving J. Hoffman Memorial Scholarships **Area, Field, or Subject:** General studies. **Level of Education for which Award is Granted:** Undergraduate **Funds Available:** Approximately $500.
Eligibility Requirements: Applicant must be a physically handicapped student, enrolled on either a full-time or part-time basis, demonstrates superior academic achievement; have completed at least five university level courses, or the equivalent. Students registered in OISE are not qualified. **Application Requirements:** Applicants must submit a completed application form along with the required materials and information. **Deadline for Receipt:** March 28.

2310 ■ UNIVERSITY OF TORONTO
315 Bloor St. W
Toronto, ON, Canada M5S 1A3
Tel: (416)978-2011
E-mail: information.commonsats@utoronto.ca
Web Site: http://www.utoronto.ca
To support students with their educational pursuits.
Title of Award: Hosinec Family Scholarships **Area, Field, or Subject:** General studies. **Level of Education for which Award is Granted:** Graduate, Undergraduate **Number Awarded:** 5. **Funds Available:** $3000.
Eligibility Requirements: Applicant must be undergraduate or graduate student of the U of T. **Application Requirements:** Applicants must submit a completed application form and required materials and information. **Additional Information:** Funded by the Hosinec Family Endowment Fund. **Deadline for Receipt:** November 30.

2311 ■ UNIVERSITY OF TORONTO

315 Bloor St. W
Toronto, ON, Canada M5S 1A3
Tel: (416)978-2011
E-mail: information.commonsats@utoronto.ca
Web Site: http://www.utoronto.ca
To support students with their educational pursuits.
Title of Award: Khaki University and Y.M.C.A. Memorial Scholarships
Area, Field, or Subject: General studies. **Level of Education for which Award is Granted:** Undergraduate **Funds Available:** Variable.
Eligibility Requirements: Applicant must be enrolled in the second or higher year of an undergraduate course proceeding to a degree; have at least first class honours standing. **Application Requirements:** Applicants must submit a completed application form along with the required materials and information. **Deadline for Receipt:** November 30.

2312 ■ UNIVERSITY OF TORONTO

315 Bloor St. W
Toronto, ON, Canada M5S 1A3
Tel: (416)978-2011
E-mail: information.commonsats@utoronto.ca
Web Site: http://www.utoronto.ca
To support students with their educational pursuits.
Title of Award: Lo Family Scholarships **Area, Field, or Subject:** General studies. **Level of Education for which Award is Granted:** Undergraduate **Funds Available:** No specific amount.
Eligibility Requirements: Applicant must be a Canadian citizen, permanent resident or protected person (recognized convention refugee) and will be enrolled full-time; an active leader, respected and considered to be well-rounded citizen in school and community, and have demonstrated financial need. **Application Requirements:** Applicants must submit an online UTAPS application and a letter outlining community activity and demonstrated leadership skills; and a letter of support from school. **Deadline for Receipt:** January.

2313 ■ UNIVERSITY OF TORONTO

315 Bloor St. W
Toronto, ON, Canada M5S 1A3
Tel: (416)978-2011
E-mail: information.commonsats@utoronto.ca
Web Site: http://www.utoronto.ca
To support students with their educational pursuits.
Title of Award: John Macara, Barrister of Goderich, Scholarships **Area, Field, or Subject:** General studies. **Level of Education for which Award is Granted:** Undergraduate **Funds Available:** No specific amount.
Eligibility Requirements: Applicant must be a Canadian citizen, permanent resident or protected person (recognized convention refugee) and will be enrolled full-time. **Application Requirements:** Applicants must submit an online UTAPS application and a letter explaining how they are related to the late Mrs. Glasgow. **Deadline for Receipt:** January.

2314 ■ UNIVERSITY OF TORONTO

315 Bloor St. W
Toronto, ON, Canada M5S 1A3
Tel: (416)978-2011
E-mail: information.commonsats@utoronto.ca
Web Site: http://www.utoronto.ca
To support students with their educational pursuits.
Title of Award: Ontario Hockey Association War Memorial Scholarships
Area, Field, or Subject: General studies. **Level of Education for which Award is Granted:** Undergraduate **Funds Available:** No specific award.
Eligibility Requirements: Applicant must be a Canadian citizen, permanent resident or protected person (recognized convention refugee) and will be enrolled full-time; and a descendent of one who has served with the Canadian forces. **Application Requirements:** Applicants must submit an online UTAPS application and the proof of service. **Deadline for Receipt:** January.

2315 ■ UNIVERSITY OF TORONTO

315 Bloor St. W
Toronto, ON, Canada M5S 1A3
Tel: (416)978-2011
E-mail: information.commonsats@utoronto.ca
Web Site: http://www.utoronto.ca
To support students with their educational pursuits.
Title of Award: University of Toronto SAC Undergraduate Grants **Area, Field, or Subject:** General studies. **Level of Education for which Award is Granted:** Undergraduate **Funds Available:** $1300.
Eligibility Requirements: Applicant must be a UofT full-time undergraduate student maintaining a minimum academic standing of "C". **Application Requirements:** Applicants must submit a completed application form together with the required materials and information. **Deadline for Receipt:** November 30.

2316 ■ UNIVERSITY OF TORONTO

315 Bloor St. W
Toronto, ON, Canada M5S 1A3
Tel: (416)978-2011
E-mail: information.commonsats@utoronto.ca
Web Site: http://www.utoronto.ca
To support students with their educational pursuits.
Title of Award: Frank M. Waddell Scholarships **Area, Field, or Subject:** General studies. **Level of Education for which Award is Granted:** Graduate, Undergraduate **Number Awarded:** 1. **Funds Available:** $5000.
Eligibility Requirements: Applicant must be a U of T student coming from Brant County, Ontario; and have a minimum average of B-. **Application Requirements:** Applicant must submit a letter outlining how the applicant meet the "Brant County" criteria. **Deadline for Receipt:** April 25.

2317 ■ UNIVERSITY OF VIRGINIA

PO Box 400160
Charlottesville, VA 22904-4160
Tel: (434)924-0311
Web Site: http://www.virginia.edu
To support students at the University of Virginia with their educational pursuits.
Title of Award: Bayly-Tiffany Scholarships **Area, Field, or Subject:** General studies. **Level of Education for which Award is Granted:** Undergraduate **Funds Available:** No specific amount.
Eligibility Requirements: Applicants must be students of the University of Virginia and residents of Accomack or Northampton counties in Virginia. **Application Requirements:** Students do not need to complete a separate application form but are considered automatically when admitted. **Additional Information:** Student Financial Services, 434-982-6000/866-391-0063, or at faid@virginia.edu.

2318 ■ UNIVERSITY OF VIRGINIA

PO Box 400160
Charlottesville, VA 22904-4160
Tel: (434)924-0311
Web Site: http://www.virginia.edu
To support students at the University of Virginia with their educational pursuits.
Title of Award: V. Thomas Forehand, Jr. Scholarships **Area, Field, or Subject:** General studies. **Level of Education for which Award is Granted:** Undergraduate **Funds Available:** No specific amount.
Eligibility Requirements: Applicants must be University of Virginia undergraduate students from the city of Chesapeake, and attended Oscar F. Smith High School, Norfolk Academy, or Nansemond-Suffolk Academy. **Application Requirements:** Students do not need to complete a separate application form but are considered automatically when admitted. **Additional Information:** Student Financial Services, 434-982-6000, 866-391-0063, or at faid@virginia.edu.

2319 ■ UNIVERSITY OF VIRGINIA

PO Box 400160
Charlottesville, VA 22904-4160
Tel: (434)924-0311
Web Site: http://www.virginia.edu
To support students at the University of Virginia with their educational pursuits.
Title of Award: Kaprielian Memorial Scholarships **Area, Field, or Subject:** General studies. **Level of Education for which Award is Granted:** Undergraduate **Funds Available:** No specific amount.

Eligibility Requirements: Applicants must be University of Virginia students; U.S. citizens or registered permanent residents of Armenian descent. **Application Requirements:** Students do not need to complete a separate application form but are considered automatically when admitted. **Additional Information:** Student Financial Services, 434-982-6000, 866-391-0063, or at faid@virginia.edu.

2320 ■ UNIVERSITY OF VIRGINIA
PO Box 400160
Charlottesville, VA 22904-4160
Tel: (434)924-0311
Web Site: http://www.virginia.edu
To support students at the University of Virginia with their educational pursuits.
Title of Award: John Allen Love Scholarships **Area, Field, or Subject:** General studies. **Level of Education for which Award is Granted:** Graduate, Undergraduate **Funds Available:** No specific amount.
Eligibility Requirements: Applicants must be University of Virginia undergraduate or graduate students residing in Missouri. **Application Requirements:** Students do not need to complete a separate application form but are considered automatically when admitted. **Additional Information:** Student Financial Services, 434-982-6000/866-391-0063, or at faid@virginia.edu.

2321 ■ UNIVERSITY OF VIRGINIA
PO Box 400160
Charlottesville, VA 22904-4160
Tel: (434)924-0311
Web Site: http://www.virginia.edu
To support students at the University of Virginia with their educational pursuits.
Title of Award: Margaret E. Phillips Scholarships **Area, Field, or Subject:** General studies. **Level of Education for which Award is Granted:** Undergraduate **Funds Available:** No specific amount.
Eligibility Requirements: Applicants must be University of Virginia students preparing for and proposing to becoming a minister of the Protestant Episcopal Church in America. **Application Requirements:** Students do not need to complete a separate application form but are considered automatically when admitted. **Additional Information:** Student Financial Services, 434-982-6000/866-391-0063, or at faid@virginia.edu.

2322 ■ UNIVERSITY OF VIRGINIA
PO Box 400160
Charlottesville, VA 22904-4160
Tel: (434)924-0311
Web Site: http://www.virginia.edu
To support students at the University of Virginia with their educational pursuits.
Title of Award: Charles Fred Wonson Scholarships **Area, Field, or Subject:** General studies. **Level of Education for which Award is Granted:** Undergraduate **Funds Available:** No specific amount.
Eligibility Requirements: Applicants must be graduates of Robert E. Lee High School in Staunton, Virginia. **Application Requirements:** Students do not need to complete a separate application form but are considered automatically when admitted. **Additional Information:** Student Financial Services, 434-982-6000/866-391-0063, or at faid@virginia.edu.

2323 ■ UNIVERSITY OF WISCONSIN-MADISON
432 N Murray St.
Madison, WI 53706-1496
Tel: (608)262-3060
Fax: (608)262-9068
E-mail: askbucky@uwmad.wisc.edu
Web Site: http://www.wisc.edu
To support Wisconsin students in their education.
Title of Award: Victor Albright Scholarships-Dane County **Area, Field, or Subject:** General studies. **Level of Education for which Award is Granted:** Undergraduate **Number Awarded:** Varies. **Funds Available:** $100.
Eligibility Requirements: Applicants must be graduates of a Dane County public high school. **Application Requirements:** Students must be nominated by their high school principals or guidance counselors.

2324 ■ UNIVERSITY OF WISCONSIN-MADISON
432 N Murray St.
Madison, WI 53706-1496
Tel: (608)262-3060
Fax: (608)262-9068
E-mail: askbucky@uwmad.wisc.edu
Web Site: http://www.wisc.edu
To support Wisconsin students in their education.
Title of Award: Victor Albright Scholarships **Area, Field, or Subject:** General studies. **Level of Education for which Award is Granted:** Undergraduate **Number Awarded:** 2. **Funds Available:** $500-$1,000. **Duration:** One academic year.
Eligibility Requirements: Applicants must be graduates of public high schools within Wisconsin counties (excluding Dane). **Application Requirements:** Students must be nominated by their high school principals or guidance counselors.

2325 ■ UNIVERSITY OF WISCONSIN-MADISON
432 N Murray St.
Madison, WI 53706-1496
Tel: (608)262-3060
Fax: (608)262-9068
E-mail: askbucky@uwmad.wisc.edu
Web Site: http://www.wisc.edu
To support students in their education.
Title of Award: Bascom Hill Society Scholarships **Area, Field, or Subject:** General studies. **Level of Education for which Award is Granted:** Undergraduate **Number Awarded:** 1. **Funds Available:** No amount specified. **Duration:** One year.
Eligibility Requirements: Applicants must be full-time juniors or seniors with outstanding volunteer contributions to the university and/or their community while maintaining a solid academic record; must have a cumulative GPA of at least a 3.2. Wisconsin and Minnesota residents must have an unmet need of at least $1,000 and out-of-state students must have an unmet need of at least $5,000. **Application Requirements:** Applicants must contact the Office of Undergraduate Academic Awards for more information. **Deadline for Receipt:** End of March. **Additional Information:** Office of Undergraduate Academic Awards, Julie Stubbs, at 608-890-0370, or stubbs@wisc.edu.

2326 ■ UNIVERSITY OF WISCONSIN-MADISON
432 N Murray St.
Madison, WI 53706-1496
Tel: (608)262-3060
Fax: (608)262-9068
E-mail: askbucky@uwmad.wisc.edu
Web Site: http://www.wisc.edu
To provide financial assistance to students who wish to pursue their education.
Title of Award: Evjue Foundation, Inc./Capital Times Scholarships **Area, Field, or Subject:** General studies. **Level of Education for which Award is Granted:** Undergraduate **Number Awarded:** Varies. **Funds Available:** No amount specified.
Eligibility Requirements: Applicant must be a dependent of a regular full-time employee of The Capital Times. **Application Requirements:** Applicants must contact the Evjue Foundation for more information about the scholarship. **Deadline for Receipt:** February. **Additional Information:** The Evjue Foundation, Inc., at 608-252-6401.

2327 ■ UNIVERSITY OF WISCONSIN-MADISON
432 N Murray St.
Madison, WI 53706-1496
Tel: (608)262-3060
Fax: (608)262-9068
E-mail: askbucky@uwmad.wisc.edu
Web Site: http://www.wisc.edu
To financial assistance to students who wish to pursue their education.
Title of Award: Edward R. and Hazel N. Felber Scholarships **Area, Field, or Subject:** General studies. **Level of Education for which Award is Granted:** Undergraduate **Number Awarded:** Varies. **Funds Available:** $2,000. **Duration:** One year.
Eligibility Requirements: Applicant must be a dependent of a Madison Gas and Electric (MG&E) employee. **Application Requirements:** Applicants must contact MG&E at 608252-7392 to request for an application. **Deadline for Receipt:** May 1.

2328 ■ UNIVERSITY OF WISCONSIN-MADISON
432 N Murray St.
Madison, WI 53706-1496
Tel: (608)262-3060
Fax: (608)262-9068
E-mail: askbucky@uwmad.wisc.edu
Web Site: http://www.wisc.edu
To support UW-Madison students in their education.
Title of Award: Gay, Lesbian, Bisexual, Transgender Alumni Council Scholarships **Area, Field, or Subject:** General studies. **Level of Education for which Award is Granted:** Undergraduate **Number Awarded:** Varies. **Funds Available:** Up to $2,000.
Eligibility Requirements: Applicants must be committed to the gay, lesbian, bisexual, and transgender community, and maintaining an outstanding academic achievement. **Application Requirements:** Applicants must contact the Wisconsin Alumni Association for information about the program. **Deadline for Receipt:** spring. **Additional Information:** Wisconsin Alumni Association, at 608-262-2551, or glbtac@uwalumni.com, visit the website www.uwalumni.com/glbtac.

2329 ■ UNIVERSITY OF WISCONSIN-MADISON
432 N Murray St.
Madison, WI 53706-1496
Tel: (608)262-3060
Fax: (608)262-9068
E-mail: askbucky@uwmad.wisc.edu
Web Site: http://www.wisc.edu
To support students in their education.
Title of Award: James Jesinski Scholarships **Area, Field, or Subject:** General studies. **Level of Education for which Award is Granted:** Undergraduate **Number Awarded:** 2. **Funds Available:** $2,000.
Eligibility Requirements: Applicant must be a dependent of a member of Wisconsin Teamsters Union Locals 43, 56, 75, 200, 344, 354, 446, 563, 579, 662, 695, or 1081. Applicants must also be affiliated with Teamsters Joint Council 39. **Application Requirements:** Applicants must apply for UW-Madison financial aid by March 1. **Deadline for Receipt:** March 31. **Additional Information:** Office of Student Financial Services, Scholarship Section, at 608-262-9996, or finaid@finaid.wisc.edu.

2330 ■ UNIVERSITY OF WISCONSIN-MADISON
432 N Murray St.
Madison, WI 53706-1496
Tel: (608)262-3060
Fax: (608)262-9068
E-mail: askbucky@uwmad.wisc.edu
Web Site: http://www.wisc.edu
To support UW-Madison students in their education.
Title of Award: Kemper K. Knapp Scholarships **Area, Field, or Subject:** General studies. **Level of Education for which Award is Granted:** Undergraduate **Number Awarded:** Varies. **Funds Available:** Up to $5,000.
Eligibility Requirements: Student must be Wisconsin residents entering UW-Madison as freshmen. **Application Requirements:** Students do not need to complete a separate application form but are considered automatically when admitted. **Deadline for Receipt:** Varies. **Additional Information:** Office of Student Financial Services, Scholarship Section, at 608-262-9996, or finaid@finaid.wisc.edu.

2331 ■ UNIVERSITY OF WISCONSIN-MADISON
432 N Murray St.
Madison, WI 53706-1496
Tel: (608)262-3060
Fax: (608)262-9068
E-mail: askbucky@uwmad.wisc.edu
Web Site: http://www.wisc.edu
To support UW-Madison students in their education.
Title of Award: Lawton Minority Retention Grants **Area, Field, or Subject:** General studies. **Level of Education for which Award is Granted:** Undergraduate **Number Awarded:** Varies. **Funds Available:** Up to $2,500.
Eligibility Requirements: Applicants must be underrepresented students of color; must be Wisconsin or Minnesota residents; and must be sophomore, junior, or senior students. **Application Requirements:** Ap-

plicants must file an application at FAFSA in order to be considered. In addition, applicants must contact the Minority and Disadvantaged Coordinator in the UW-Madison school or college where they are enrolled. **Deadline for Receipt:** July 15.

2332 ■ UNIVERSITY OF WISCONSIN-MADISON
432 N Murray St.
Madison, WI 53706-1496
Tel: (608)262-3060
Fax: (608)262-9068
E-mail: askbucky@uwmad.wisc.edu
Web Site: http://www.wisc.edu
To support UW-Madison students in their education.
Title of Award: McBurney Disability Scholarships **Area, Field, or Subject:** General studies. **Level of Education for which Award is Granted:** Undergraduate **Number Awarded:** Up to 20. **Funds Available:** $500-$2,500.
Eligibility Requirements: Applicants must have a documented disability (physical, psychological, sensory, or learning) as verified by the McBurney Disability Resource Center. **Application Requirements:** Applicants must submit a completed McBurney Scholarship Application along with two letters of recommendation and a current transcript. **Deadline for Receipt:** April 15.

2333 ■ UNIVERSITY OF WISCONSIN-MADISON
432 N Murray St.
Madison, WI 53706-1496
Tel: (608)262-3060
Fax: (608)262-9068
E-mail: askbucky@uwmad.wisc.edu
Web Site: http://www.wisc.edu
To support students in their education.
Title of Award: Charles S. Pearce Scholarships **Area, Field, or Subject:** General studies. **Level of Education for which Award is Granted:** Undergraduate **Number Awarded:** 1. **Funds Available:** Wisconsin resident tuition.
Eligibility Requirements: Applicants must be admitted and enrolled at the university, and must be winners of the JSEHS research competition. **Application Requirements:** Students must contact the Engineering Learning Center. **Deadline for Receipt:** December. **Additional Information:** Engineering Learning Center, Sandy Courter, at 608-265-9767, or courter@engr.wisc.edu.

2334 ■ UNIVERSITY OF WISCONSIN-MADISON
432 N Murray St.
Madison, WI 53706-1496
Tel: (608)262-3060
Fax: (608)262-9068
E-mail: askbucky@uwmad.wisc.edu
Web Site: http://www.wisc.edu
To support UW-Madison students in their education.
Title of Award: Powers-Knapp Scholarships **Area, Field, or Subject:** General studies. **Level of Education for which Award is Granted:** Undergraduate **Number Awarded:** Up to 60. **Funds Available:** Wisconsin resident tuition for Wisconsin and Minnesota residents. Non-residents receive the difference between resident and non-resident tuition.
Eligibility Requirements: Applicants must be incoming freshmen, underrepresented, students of color with an outstanding academic achievement. **Application Requirements:** Contact the Chancellor's Scholarships Program for more information. **Deadline for Receipt:** February 1. **Additional Information:** 608-262-9315.

2335 ■ UNIVERSITY OF WISCONSIN-MADISON
432 N Murray St.
Madison, WI 53706-1496
Tel: (608)262-3060
Fax: (608)262-9068
E-mail: askbucky@uwmad.wisc.edu
Web Site: http://www.wisc.edu
To support Wisconsin students in their education.
Title of Award: University of Wisconsin-Madison Academic Excellence Scholarships **Area, Field, or Subject:** General studies. **Level of Education for which Award is Granted:** Undergraduate **Number Awarded:** 1-6 per high school. **Funds Available:** $2,250. **Duration:** One academic year.

Eligibility Requirements: Applicants must be incoming freshmen; must be Wisconsin residents with the highest GPA in high school class; enrolled as first-year students at a post-secondary institution in Wisconsin. **Application Requirements:** Applicants must contact their high school guidance counselor for information about the scholarship. **Deadline for Receipt:** February 15.

2336 ■ UNIVERSITY OF WISCONSIN-MADISON
432 N Murray St.
Madison, WI 53706-1496
Tel: (608)262-3060
Fax: (608)262-9068
E-mail: askbucky@uwmad.wisc.edu
Web Site: http://www.wisc.edu
To support UW-Madison students in their education.

Title of Award: University of Wisconsin-Madison African American Alumni Scholarships **Area, Field, or Subject:** General studies. **Level of Education for which Award is Granted:** Undergraduate **Number Awarded:** 1-2. **Funds Available:** Varies.
Eligibility Requirements: Applicants must be African American full-time students. **Application Requirements:** Applicants must contact Wisconsin Alumni Association for the application materials and procedures. **Deadline for Receipt:** June 1. **Additional Information:** Wisconsin Alumni Association at 608-262-2551, or waa@uwalumni.com.

2337 ■ UNIVERSITY OF WISCONSIN-MADISON
432 N Murray St.
Madison, WI 53706-1496
Tel: (608)262-3060
Fax: (608)262-9068
E-mail: askbucky@uwmad.wisc.edu
Web Site: http://www.wisc.edu
To support UW-Madison students in their education.

Title of Award: University of Wisconsin-Madison American Indian Alumni Scholarships **Area, Field, or Subject:** General studies. **Level of Education for which Award is Granted:** Undergraduate **Number Awarded:** Varies. **Funds Available:** No specific amount.
Eligibility Requirements: Applicants must be American Indian full-time students. **Application Requirements:** Applicants must file the FAFSA. **Deadline for Receipt:** July 1. **Additional Information:** Wisconsin Alumni Association at 608-262-2551, or waa@uwalumni.com.

2338 ■ UNIVERSITY OF WISCONSIN-MADISON
432 N Murray St.
Madison, WI 53706-1496
Tel: (608)262-3060
Fax: (608)262-9068
E-mail: askbucky@uwmad.wisc.edu
Web Site: http://www.wisc.edu
To support UW-Madison students in their education.

Title of Award: University of Wisconsin-Madison Chancellor's Scholarships **Area, Field, or Subject:** General studies. **Level of Education for which Award is Granted:** Undergraduate **Number Awarded:** Up to 40. **Funds Available:** Full tuition and an annual book stipend of $800.
Eligibility Requirements: Applicants must be incoming freshmen, underrepresented, students of color with outstanding academic achievements. **Application Requirements:** Contact the Chancellor's Scholarships Program for more information. **Deadline for Receipt:** February 1. **Additional Information:** 608-262-9315.

2339 ■ UNIVERSITY OF WISCONSIN-MADISON
432 N Murray St.
Madison, WI 53706-1496
Tel: (608)262-3060
Fax: (608)262-9068
E-mail: askbucky@uwmad.wisc.edu
Web Site: http://www.wisc.edu
To support UW-Madison students in their education.

Title of Award: University of Wisconsin-Madison Hispanic/Latino Alumni Scholarships **Area, Field, or Subject:** General studies. **Level of Education for which Award is Granted:** Undergraduate **Number Awarded:** 1-2. **Funds Available:** Varies.
Eligibility Requirements: Applicants must be Hispanic or Latino full-time students. **Application Requirements:** Applicants must contact the

Wisconsin Alumni Association for information about the program. **Deadline for Receipt:** June 1. **Additional Information:** Wisconsin Alumni Association, at 608-262-2551, or glbtac@uwalumni.com, visit the website www.uwalumni.com/glbtac.

2340 ■ UNIVERSITY OF WISCONSIN-MADISON
432 N Murray St.
Madison, WI 53706-1496
Tel: (608)262-3060
Fax: (608)262-9068
E-mail: askbucky@uwmad.wisc.edu
Web Site: http://www.wisc.edu
To support UW-Madison students in their education.

Title of Award: University of Wisconsin-Madison National Merit Scholarships **Area, Field, or Subject:** General studies. **Level of Education for which Award is Granted:** Undergraduate **Number Awarded:** 5. **Funds Available:** $750-$2,000.
Eligibility Requirements: Applicants must be entering UW-Madison as freshman; and must have taken the Preliminary SAT/National Merit Scholarship Qualifying Test (PSAT/NMSQT) during the spring semester of the sophomore year or the fall semester of the junior year. **Application Requirements:** Students must file a FAFSA to be considered. **Additional Information:** Office of Student Financial Services, Scholarship Section, at 608-262-9996, or finaid@finaid.wisc.edu.

2341 ■ UNIVERSITY OF WISCONSIN-MADISON
432 N Murray St.
Madison, WI 53706-1496
Tel: (608)262-3060
Fax: (608)262-9068
E-mail: askbucky@uwmad.wisc.edu
Web Site: http://www.wisc.edu
To support students in their education.

Title of Award: University of Wisconsin-Madison Single Parent and Adult Scholarships **Area, Field, or Subject:** General studies. **Level of Education for which Award is Granted:** Undergraduate **Number Awarded:** Varies. **Funds Available:** $1,000-$2,000.
Eligibility Requirements: Applicants must be single parents or adults enrolled in at least 9 credit units; must be in good academic standing; must be U.S. citizens or permanent residents; must show proof of financial need; and must demonstrate probability for academic success. **Application Requirements:** Applicants must contact the Adult and Student Services Center for more information. **Deadline for Receipt:** March 1.

2342 ■ UNIVERSITY OF WISCONSIN-MADISON
432 N Murray St.
Madison, WI 53706-1496
Tel: (608)262-3060
Fax: (608)262-9068
E-mail: askbucky@uwmad.wisc.edu
Web Site: http://www.wisc.edu
To support UW-Madison students in their education.

Title of Award: Vilas Equity Scholarships **Area, Field, or Subject:** General studies. **Level of Education for which Award is Granted:** Undergraduate **Number Awarded:** Varies. **Funds Available:** $400.
Eligibility Requirements: Applicants must be entering UW-Madison as freshmen. **Application Requirements:** Students are considered automatically when admitted. **Additional Information:** Office of Student Financial Services, Scholarship Section, at 608-262-9996, or finaid@finaid.wisc.edu.

2343 ■ UNIVERSITY OF WISCONSIN-MADISON
432 N Murray St.
Madison, WI 53706-1496
Tel: (608)262-3060
Fax: (608)262-9068
E-mail: askbucky@uwmad.wisc.edu
Web Site: http://www.wisc.edu
To support UW-Madison students in their education.

Title of Award: William F. Vilas Scholarships **Area, Field, or Subject:** General studies. **Level of Education for which Award is Granted:** Undergraduate **Number Awarded:** Varies. **Funds Available:** $400.

Eligibility Requirements: Students must be entering UW-Madison as freshmen; and must have a strong academic performance based on class rank and GPA. **Application Requirements:** Students do not need to complete a separate application form but are considered automatically when admitted. **Additional Information:** Office of Student Financial Services, Scholarship Section, at 608-262-9996, or finaid@finaid.wisc. edu.

2344 ■ UNIVERSITY OF WISCONSIN-MADISON
432 N Murray St.
Madison, WI 53706-1496
Tel: (608)262-3060
Fax: (608)262-9068
E-mail: askbucky@uwmad.wisc.edu
Web Site: http://www.wisc.edu
To support Wisconsin students in their education.
Title of Award: Wisconsin High School Scholarships **Area, Field, or Subject:** General studies. **Level of Education for which Award is Granted:** Undergraduate **Number Awarded:** Varies. **Funds Available:** No specific amount.
Eligibility Requirements: Applicants must be graduates of participating Wisconsin high schools. **Application Requirements:** Applicants must contact their high school guidance councilors for more information.

2345 ■ URBAN AND LAND INSTITUTE
1025 Thomas Jefferson St. NW, Ste. 500
Washington, DC 20007
Tel: (202)624-7000
Free: 800-321-5011
Fax: (202)624-7140
E-mail: customerservice@uli.org
Web Site: http://www.uli.org
To promote interdisciplinary education and to encourage excellence in real estate-related studies.
Title of Award: Kenneth M. Good Graduate Students Fellowship Program **Area, Field, or Subject:** Real Estate. **Level of Education for which Award is Granted:** Undergraduate **Number Awarded:** 8. **Funds Available:** $5,000.
Eligibility Requirements: Applicants must be graduating students who are studying real estate, real estate development, or related subjects at a major North American university. **Application Requirements:** Applicants must submit evidence that they are currently attending a real estate degree program.

2346 ■ URBAN LEAGUE OF METROPOLITAN DENVER
5900 E 39th Ave.
Denver, CO 80207
Tel: (303)388-5861
E-mail: adminassistant@denverurbanleague.org
Web Site: http://www.denverurbanleague.org
To promote the life changing benefits of education and honor individuals who have shown desire to improve their lives and the lives of those around them through education.
Title of Award: University of Phoenix First Chance Scholarship Fund **Area, Field, or Subject:** General studies. **Level of Education for which Award is Granted:** Undergraduate **Funds Available:** No specific amount.
Eligibility Requirements: Applicants must meet one of the following criteria: must be legal residents of the United States; have a valid visa that does not prohibit educational studies; have been granted temporary protection status along with approved Notice of Action issued by Citizen Immigration Services and verified through CIS Form g-845; or have been granted asylum along with the approved Notice of Action issued by the Citizen Immigration Services; are not receiving 100% tuition reimbursement; are not employees or family members of Apollo Group, Inc. University of Phoenix, Western International University, Institute for Professional Development or any other subsidiary of Apollo Group Inc. **Application Requirements:** Applicants must submit the following: a complete, signed application, together with all supporting documentation, if any, by the deadline date listed below. The completion of the application form does not create an obligation to award a scholarship to applicant. Submit a complete questionnaire. High importance will be placed on the applicant's desire to advance in their education, with an emphasis on

furthering their careers, and their impact in the community for which they reside. To be considered the essay must meet the following requirements: Each of the four questions should be answered in complete sentences and paragraph format with approximately 4-7 sentences, Double spaced, 12 point font 8 x 11 paper, and pages must be paper-clipped together (no staples). **Deadline for Receipt:** June 29. **Additional Information:** Urban League of Metropolitan Denver Inc. at the above address.

2347 ■ USDA ANIMAL AND PLANT HEALTH INSPECTION SERVICE
USDA, APHIS, Human Resources/Employment
4700 River Rd., Unit 106
Riverdale, MD 20737
Tel: (301)734-5596
Web Site: http://www.aphis.usda.gov
To provide financial assistance to academically qualified students who are enrolled in college-level programs related to agriculture or the biological sciences.
Title of Award: PPQ William F. Helms Student Scholarships **Area, Field, or Subject:** General studies. **Level of Education for which Award is Granted:** Undergraduate **Funds Available:** No specific amount.
Eligibility Requirements: Applicants must be: United States citizens; enrolled in an accredited college or university within the U.S.; sophomores or juniors in good academic standing (must maintain an at least 2.5 grade point average); enrolled in programs related to agriculture or the biological sciences; must agree to work for the agency during school breaks (both summer and holiday periods) a minimum of 640 hours prior to completion of studies. **Application Requirements:** Applicants must submit completed application which contains an Optional Application for Federal Employment (OF-612) or resume; a personal letter that describes their interests, goals and chosen career plans, explains how they envision their ability will contribute to the PPQ mission, outlines why they should be selected for this program over other candidates, and lists the permanent addresses at which they can be contacted all year. Applicants must also submit transcripts of their college work to date; three letters of recommendation from people not related to them; documentation of service, if they have served in the U.S. Armed Forces. **Deadline for Receipt:** March 1.

2348 ■ USTA TENNIS AND EDUCATION FOUNDATION
70 W Road Oak Ln.
White Plains, NY 10604
Tel: (914)696-7223
E-mail: eliezer@usta.com
Web Site: http://www.usta.com
To provide scholarships to deserving youngsters who have participated in the United States Tennis Association.
Title of Award: Marian Wood Baird Scholarships **Area, Field, or Subject:** General studies. **Level of Education for which Award is Granted:** Undergraduate **Funds Available:** $15,000.
Eligibility Requirements: Applicants must have a strong involvement in extracurricular activities, course work and community service; must exhibit Financial Need; must be involved in an organized community tennis program such as USTA School Tennis, NJTL, USTA Team Tennis, etc.; must be entering first year of undergraduate work as a full-time student in a four-year college/university program; must have a minimum of 3.0 GPA on a 4.0 scale. **Application Requirements:** Applicants must submit in one envelope the following required forms and supporting documents: A typed or clearly printed application signed by the applicant and parent or guardian; A typed or clearly printed endorsement from a faculty member from the applicant's high school and from a coach/program director; A typed endorsement from an individual of the applicant's choice; An official high school transcript; ACT/SAT examination scores; The applicant's official financial aid form; and a current photograph of the applicant. **Deadline for Receipt:** February 8.

2349 ■ USTA TENNIS AND EDUCATION FOUNDATION
70 W Road Oak Ln.
White Plains, NY 10604
Tel: (914)696-7223
E-mail: eliezer@usta.com
Web Site: http://www.usta.com
To provide scholarships to qualified high school seniors.
Title of Award: Dwight F. Davis Memorial Scholarships **Area, Field, or Subject:** General studies. **Level of Education for which Award is**

Granted: Undergraduate **Number Awarded:** 2. **Funds Available:** $7,500. **Duration:** Four years.

Eligibility Requirements: Applicants must be high school seniors with strong involvement in extracurricular activities, course work and community service; must exhibit financial need; must be actively involved in an organized community tennis program such as USTA School Tennis, NJTL, USTA Team Tennis, etc.; must be entering the first year of undergraduate work as a full-time student in a four-year college/university program. **Application Requirements:** Applicants must submit in one envelope the following required forms and supporting documents: A typed or clearly printed application signed by the applicant and parent or guardian; a typed or clearly printed endorsement from a faculty member from the applicant's high school and from a coach/program director; a typed endorsement from an individual of the applicant's choice; an official high school transcript; ACT/SAT examination scores; applicant's official financial aid form; and a current photograph. **Deadline for Receipt:** February 8.

2350 ■ USTA TENNIS AND EDUCATION FOUNDATION

70 W Road Oak Ln.
White Plains, NY 10604
Tel: (914)696-7223
E-mail: eliezer@usta.com
Web Site: http://www.usta.com
To provide scholarships to qualified high school seniors.

Title of Award: Eve Kraft Education and College Scholarships **Area, Field, or Subject:** General studies. **Level of Education for which Award is Granted:** Undergraduate **Funds Available:** $2,500.

Eligibility Requirements: Applicants must be high school seniors with strong involvement in extracurricular activities, course work and community service; must exhibit financial need; must be actively involved in an organized community tennis program such as USTA School Tennis, NJTL, USTA Team Tennis, etc.; must be entering the first year of undergraduate work as a full-time student in a four-year college/university program. **Application Requirements:** Applicants must submit in one envelope the following required forms and supporting documents: A typed or clearly printed application signed by the applicant and parent or guardian; a typed or clearly printed endorsement from a faculty member from the applicant's high school and from a coach/program director; a typed endorsement from an individual of the applicant's choice; an official high school transcript; ACT/SAT examination scores; applicant's official financial aid form; and a current photograph. **Additional Information:** The scholarship is partially supported by Robert Kraft and family. **Deadline for Receipt:** February 8.

2351 ■ USTA TENNIS AND EDUCATION FOUNDATION

70 W Road Oak Ln.
White Plains, NY 10604
Tel: (914)696-7223
E-mail: eliezer@usta.com
Web Site: http://www.usta.com
To provide scholarship to high school seniors of ethnically diverse heritage.

Title of Award: Dwight Mosley Scholarships **Area, Field, or Subject:** General studies. **Level of Education for which Award is Granted:** Undergraduate **Number Awarded:** 2. **Funds Available:** $10,000. **Duration:** Four years.

Eligibility Requirements: Applicants must be high school seniors with strong involvement in extracurricular activities, course work and community service; must exhibit financial need; must be actively involved in an organized community tennis program such as USTA School Tennis, NJTL, USTA Team Tennis, etc.; must be entering the first year of undergraduate work as a full-time student in a four-year college/university program. **Application Requirements:** Applicants must submit in one envelope the following required forms and supporting documents: A typed or clearly printed application signed by the applicant and parent or guardian; a typed or clearly printed endorsement from a faculty member from the applicant's high school and from a coach/program director; a typed endorsement from an individual of the applicant's choice; an official high school transcript; ACT/SAT examination scores; applicant's official financial aid form; and a current photograph. **Deadline for Receipt:** February 8.

2352 ■ USTA TENNIS AND EDUCATION FOUNDATION

70 W Road Oak Ln.
White Plains, NY 10604
Tel: (914)696-7223
E-mail: eliezer@usta.com
Web Site: http://www.usta.com
To provide scholarships to qualified high schools.

Title of Award: USTA Tennis and Education Foundation College Education Scholarships **Area, Field, or Subject:** General Studies. **Level of Education for which Award is Granted:** Undergraduate **Funds Available:** $6,000. **Duration:** Four years.

Eligibility Requirements: Applicants must be high school seniors with strong involvement in extracurricular activities, course work and community service; must exhibit financial need; must be actively involved in an organized community tennis program such as USTA School Tennis, NJTL, USTA Team Tennis, etc.; must be entering the first year of undergraduate work as a full-time student in a four-year college/university program. **Application Requirements:** Applicants must submit in one envelope the following required forms and supporting documents: A typed or clearly printed application signed by the applicant and parent or guardian; a typed or clearly printed endorsement from a faculty member from the applicant's high school and from a coach/program director; a typed endorsement from an individual of the applicant's choice; an official high school transcript; ACT/SAT examination scores; applicant's official financial aid form; and a current photograph. **Deadline for Receipt:** February 8.

2353 ■ USTA TENNIS AND EDUCATION FOUNDATION

70 W Road Oak Ln.
White Plains, NY 10604
Tel: (914)696-7223
E-mail: eliezer@usta.com
Web Site: http://www.usta.com
To provide a one-time award to assist students in purchasing textbooks or supplies.

Title of Award: USTA Tennis and Education Foundation College Textbook Scholarships **Area, Field, or Subject:** General studies. **Level of Education for which Award is Granted:** Undergraduate **Funds Available:** $1,000.

Eligibility Requirements: Applicants must be high school seniors with strong involvement in extracurricular activities, course work and community service; must exhibit financial need; must be actively involved in an organized community tennis program such as USTA School Tennis, NJTL, USTA Team Tennis, etc.; must be entering the first year of undergraduate work as a full-time student in a four-year college/university program. **Application Requirements:** Applicants must submit in one envelope the following required forms and supporting documents: A typed or clearly printed application signed by the applicant and parent or guardian; a typed or clearly printed endorsement from a faculty member from the applicant's high school and from a coach/program director; a typed endorsement from an individual of the applicant's choice; an official high school transcript; ACT/SAT examination scores; applicant's official financial aid form; and a current photograph. **Deadline for Receipt:** February 8.

2354 ■ UTILITY WORKERS UNION OF AMERICA

815 16th St. NW
Washington, DC 20006
Tel: (202)974-8200
Fax: (202)974-8201
E-mail: webmaster@uwua.net
Web Site: http://www.uwua.net
To identify and honor exceptionally able high school students; to provide a system of services for corporations, foundations, and other organizations that wish to sponsor college undergraduate scholarships for outstanding students who interest them.

Title of Award: Utility Workers Union of America Scholarship Program **Area, Field, or Subject:** General studies. **Level of Education for which Award is Granted:** Undergraduate **Funds Available:** $500-$2,000. **Duration:** 4 years.

Eligibility Requirements: Applicants must be high school students who are sons and daughters of active members of UWUA; must be a U.S. citizen and have a permanent residence in the United States. **Application**

Requirements: Applicants must fill out the application form; must take the PSAT/NMSQT; must obtain a copy of the Official Student Guide to the PSAT/NMSQT from the high school counselor and make arrangements with the school to take the PSAT/NMSQT. **Deadline for Receipt:** December 31.

2355 ■ VIETNAM VETERANS OF AMERICA
8605 Cameron St., Ste. 400
Silver Spring, MD 20910
Tel: (301)585-4000; (180)0882-1316
Fax: (301)585-0519
E-mail: jrowan@vva.org
Web Site: http://www.vva.org
To provide support and assistance to veterans in securing earned benefits from the Department of Veterans Affairs.
Title of Award: Mike Nash Memorial Scholarships **Area, Field, or Subject:** General studies. **Level of Education for which Award is Granted:** Undergraduate **Number Awarded:** 1. **Funds Available:** No amount specified.
Eligibility Requirements: Applicants must be dependent children, grandchildren, orphans, and widows of deceased Vietnam Veterans. **Application Requirements:** Applicants must submit a completed application form; a high school or college transcript; photocopy of SAT, ACT, or other acknowledged testing source results; a letter of acceptance from a college, university or post-secondary training institution; a copy of form DD-214 and death certificate from the related Vietnam era veteran, if the veteran is deceased. Applicants must provide a statement describing financial need; include a copy of the applicant's parent and the applicant's most current personal income tax form; two letters of reference from current or former teachers, academic advisors, employers, or ministers attesting the applicant's character; and a letter in the applicant's own words, expressing current educational goals and objectives, individual accomplishments and any other personal information that may assist in the selection process. **Deadline for Receipt:** May 31.

2356 ■ VIETNAMESE AMERICAN SCHOLARSHIP FOUNDATION
PO Box 429
Stafford, TX 77497
E-mail: scholarships@vietscholarships.org
Web Site: http://www.vietscholarships.org
To provide financial assistance to students of Vietnamese descent from the Greater Houston area for pursuing further education.
Title of Award: Danny T. Le Memorial Scholarships **Area, Field, or Subject:** General studies. **Level of Education for which Award is Granted:** High School, Undergraduate **Funds Available:** $1,250.
Eligibility Requirements: Applicants must be of Vietnamese descent; must be graduated or graduating from a high school in the Greater Houston Area and pursuing degree at an accredited 4-year college or university. **Application Requirements:** Applicants must download and complete the application form and submit it with their resume, an essay and a letter of recommendation. **Deadline for Receipt:** May 5.

2357 ■ VIETNAMESE AMERICAN SCHOLARSHIP FOUNDATION
PO Box 429
Stafford, TX 77497
E-mail: scholarships@vietscholarships.org
Web Site: http://www.vietscholarships.org
To provide financial assistance to outstanding graduating high school seniors attending college in the upcoming fall semester.
Title of Award: Le Hoang Nguyen (LHN) College Scholarships **Area, Field, or Subject:** General studies. **Level of Education for which Award is Granted:** High School **Number Awarded:** 1. **Funds Available:** $500. **Duration:** One year.
Eligibility Requirements: Applicants must be Vietnamese descendants and residents of the state of Texas; must be graduating high school seniors with a GPA of 3.0 or higher; must be ranked in the top 10% of graduating high school class; must attend the first semester at an accredited college or university immediately following notification of the scholarship award. **Application Requirements:** Applicants must complete the online application; upload resume and essays with online application and submit recommendation online. **Deadline for Receipt:** May 5.

2358 ■ VIETNAMESE AMERICAN SCHOLARSHIP FOUNDATION
PO Box 429
Stafford, TX 77497
E-mail: scholarships@vietscholarships.org
Web Site: http://www.vietscholarships.org
To provide financial assistance to high school senior students for furthering their education.
Title of Award: The Thuy Nguyen Scholarships **Area, Field, or Subject:** General studies. **Level of Education for which Award is Granted:** High School **Funds Available:** No specific amount.
Eligibility Requirements: Applicants must be graduating high school seniors from Houston or the surrounding area; must have a cumulative GPA of 3.5 or higher; must be descendants of at least one Vietnamese parent; and must have a family annual income of less than $50,000. **Application Requirements:** Applicants must complete online application form; upload resume and essay with online application and submit recommendation online. **Deadline for Receipt:** May 5.

2359 ■ VIETNAMESE AMERICAN SCHOLARSHIP FOUNDATION
PO Box 429
Stafford, TX 77497
E-mail: scholarships@vietscholarships.org
Web Site: http://www.vietscholarships.org
To provide financial assistance to graduating high school seniors of Vietnamese descent wishing to pursue further education.
Title of Award: Vera Tran Memorial Scholarships **Area, Field, or Subject:** General studies. **Level of Education for which Award is Granted:** Undergraduate **Funds Available:** $2,000.
Eligibility Requirements: Applicants must be of Vietnamese descent, graduating high school seniors from Houston or the surrounding area who are planning to pursue an education at an accredited 4-year college or university. **Application Requirements:** Applicants must complete the online application and submit it with their resume; must also send one transcript and recommendation. **Deadline for Receipt:** May 5.

2360 ■ VIRGINIA FOUNDATION FOR INDEPENDENT COLLEGES
8010 Ridge Rd., Ste. B
Richmond, VA 23229-7288
Tel: (804)288-6609
Free: 800-230-6757
Fax: (804)282-4635
E-mail: info@vfic.org
Web Site: http://www.vfic.org
To provide financial assistance for students who are current juniors of VFIC institutions.
Title of Award: Witt Mares Scholarships **Area, Field, or Subject:** Accounting. **Level of Education for which Award is Granted:** Undergraduate **Funds Available:** $2,500.
Eligibility Requirements: Applicants must be full-time students at one of the five pre-selected private colleges/universities associated with the Virginia Foundation for Independent Colleges: Lynchburg College, Shenandoah University, Marymount University, Virginia Wesleyan College, Randolph-Macon College; must have a cumulative grade point average of at least a 3.0 on a 4.0 scale; be a junior at the time of application; be an accounting major, or have a related major or minor with coursework which includes completion of the Introductory Accounting sequence (sophomore year) and planning to complete the Intermediate Accounting sequence in their junior year; must be citizens of the United States of America. **Application Requirements:** Applicants must submit all the required application information. **Deadline for Receipt:** November 1.

2361 ■ VIRGINIA TECH MULTICULTURAL PROGRAMS AND SERVICES
150 Squires Student Center
Blacksburg, VA 24061
Tel: (540)231-8584
Fax: (540)231-0945
E-mail: mps@vt.edu
Web Site: http://www.mps.vt.edu
To create a career opportunities in media industry for minority youth that focuses on scholastic achievement, direct work experience and professional development.
Title of Award: Emma L. Bowen Foundation Scholarships for Minority Interests in Media work/study Program **Area, Field, or Subject:** General

studies. **Level of Education for which Award is Granted:** Undergraduate **Funds Available:** No specific amount.
Eligibility Requirements: Applicant must be African American, Hispanic, Asian or Native American rising high school senior, graduating high school senior or college freshman; must have a cumulative GPA of at least 3.0 and interest in pursuing a career in media industry; must be planning to attend a four-year accredited college or university; must be a U.S. citizen or a legal resident of United States and can speak and write English fluently. **Application Requirements:** Applicants must submit an official transcript, at least two educational references from teachers and advisors and a 500 to 1,000 word essay; must submit an original and two copies of application in an envelope. **Deadline for Receipt:** May 9.

2362 ■ VIRGINIA TECH MULTICULTURAL PROGRAMS AND SERVICES
150 Squires Student Center
Blacksburg, VA 24061
Tel: (540)231-8584
Fax: (540)231-0945
E-mail: mps@vt.edu
Web Site: http://www.mps.vt.edu
To assist Virginia Tech in creating a welcoming environment that affirms and celebrates the diversity of its community particularly those from underrepresented and historically marginalized populations.
Title of Award: Brown and Caldwell Minority Scholarships **Area, Field, or Subject:** General studies. **Level of Education for which Award is Granted:** Undergraduate **Funds Available:** $3,000.
Eligibility Requirements: Applicants must be full-time minority students in their junior year of study; must have a minimum 3.0 GPA and must be majoring in engineering and science-related studies; must be U.S. citizens or permanent residents; must be able to commit to an eight-week summer internship. **Application Requirements:** Applicants must submit a 250 word essay stating the reasons of choosing environmental disciplines as major. **Deadline for Receipt:** May 1.

2363 ■ EARL WARREN LEGAL TRAINING PROGRAM
99 Hudson St., Ste. 1600
New York, NY 10013
Tel: (212)965-2200
Web Site: http://www.naacpldf.org
To provide students financial assistance in entering college.
Title of Award: Herbert Lehman Education Scholarships **Area, Field, or Subject:** General studies. **Level of Education for which Award is Granted:** Undergraduate **Funds Available:** $ 2000. **Duration:** One Academic year.
Eligibility Requirements: Applicants must be students entering four-year college as a full-time student for the first time; a U.S. citizens; be of excellent character with recommendations from teachers, community representatives or employers; have exceptional leadership potential with an ability to work well in diverse settings. **Application Requirements:** Applications must be requested by writing to The Herbert Lehman Education Fund; application materials must be typed or neatly printed in ink and they must conform to program guidelines. **Additional Information:** Named after the former Governor and United States Senator from New York State; **Deadline for Receipt:** April 30.

2364 ■ THE WASHINGTON GROUP
720 Park Blvd.
PO Box 73
Boise, ID 83729
Tel: (208)386-5000
E-mail: membership@washingtongroup.org
Web Site: http://www.wgint.com
To encourage active participation in Ukrainian community.
Title of Award: Alberta Ukrainian Centennial Commemorative Scholarships **Area, Field, or Subject:** General studies. **Level of Education for which Award is Granted:** Undergraduate **Funds Available:** No specific amount.
Eligibility Requirements: Applicants must be graduate students intending to study in Alberta or Canadian graduate students from Alberta intending to study in Ukraine. **Application Requirements:** Applicants must fill out the application and supporting materials. **Deadline for Receipt:** February 1. **Additional Information:** Alberta Heritage Scholarship Fund

at 9940 106th Street, Edmonton, Alberta, T5K 2V1, Canada; 1403-427-5538; 1403-422-4516.

2365 ■ THE WASHINGTON GROUP
720 Park Blvd.
PO Box 73
Boise, ID 83729
Tel: (208)386-5000
E-mail: membership@washingtongroup.org
Web Site: http://www.wgint.com
To encourage active participation in Ukrainian community.
Title of Award: Canada-Ukraine Parliamentary Program (CUPP) Internship Scholarships **Area, Field, or Subject:** General studies. **Level of Education for which Award is Granted:** Undergraduate **Funds Available:** No specific amount.
Eligibility Requirements: Program is open for individuals seeking scholarships for a three-month internship for Ukrainian undergraduates with a Member of Parliament of the House of Commons in Ottawa, Canada. This internship is open only to citizens of Ukraine. Proficiency in English or French as well as in Ukrainian is a requirement. **Application Requirements:** Application is available online. **Deadline for Receipt:** February 1. **Additional Information:** Ukrainian Studies Foundation, 620 Spadina Avenue, Toronto, Ontario, Canada M5S 2H4; 416-234-9114; cupp@infoukes.com.

2366 ■ THE WASHINGTON GROUP
720 Park Blvd.
PO Box 73
Boise, ID 83729
Tel: (208)386-5000
E-mail: membership@washingtongroup.org
Web Site: http://www.wgint.com
To encourage active participation in Ukrainian community.
Title of Award: Eugene & Elinor Kotur Scholarship Trust Fund **Area, Field, or Subject:** General studies. **Level of Education for which Award is Granted:** Undergraduate **Funds Available:** $1,000.
Eligibility Requirements: Applicants must be enrolled in the sophomore or higher year or graduate school of about thirty leading colleges and universities in the USA listed on the application form. Applicants may have to be members of the Ukrainian Fraternal Association for two years. **Application Requirements:** Applicants must write for application. **Additional Information:** Ukrainian Fraternal Association Scholarship Program, PO Box 350, Scranton, PA 18501-0350; 1717-342-0937.

2367 ■ WASHINGTON HIGHER EDUCATION COORDINATING BOARD
PO Box 43430
Olympia, WA 98504-3430
Tel: (360)753-7800
E-mail: info@hecb.wa.gov
Web Site: http://www.hecb.wa.gov
To help financially needy students with close social and cultural ties to a Native American community to pursue undergraduate and graduate studies.
Title of Award: American Indian Endowed Scholarships **Area, Field, or Subject:** General studies. **Level of Education for which Award is Granted:** Graduate, Undergraduate **Number Awarded:** 15. **Funds Available:** $500-$2000.
Eligibility Requirements: Applicant must have demonstrated financial need based on a completed FAFSA; a Washington state resident; enrolled full-time as an undergraduate or graduate student in an eligible program; and not pursuing a degree in theology. **Application Requirements:** Applicants must submit an American Indian Endowed Scholarship application form together with the required materials and information. **Additional Information:** Students can use the scholarships at public colleges and universities and accredited independent colleges, universities, and career schools in Washington. **Deadline for Receipt:** February 1.

2368 ■ WASHINGTON HIGHER EDUCATION COORDINATING BOARD
PO Box 43430
Olympia, WA 98504-3430
Tel: (360)753-7800

E-mail: info@hecb.wa.gov
Web Site: http://www.hecb.wa.gov
To provide hope and incentive for students and families who otherwise might not consider college as an option because of its cost.
Title of Award: Washington College Bound Scholarships **Area, Field, or Subject:** General studies. **Level of Education for which Award is Granted:** Undergraduate **Funds Available:** Covers the cost of college tuition, fees and books. **Duration:** Four years.
Eligibility Requirements: Applicants must be seventh-grade students from families eligible for free or reduced-priced lunches who sign the pledge. Their family income must remain at 65 percent or less of the state's median income by the time of high school graduation. **Application Requirements:** The online application and brochure are being finalized. Materials will be sent to all middle schools, including a link to the online application.

2369 ■ WASHINGTON HIGHER EDUCATION COORDINATING BOARD
PO Box 43430
Olympia, WA 98504-3430
Tel: (360)753-7800
E-mail: info@hecb.wa.gov
Web Site: http://www.hecb.wa.gov
To encourage financially needy students to complete a bachelor's degree.
Title of Award: Washington Higher Education Coordinating Board Educational Opportunity Grants **Area, Field, or Subject:** General studies. **Level of Education for which Award is Granted:** Undergraduate **Funds Available:** $5000.
Eligibility Requirements: Applicants must have place bound circumstances (having personal barriers which unable the student to continue education); a Washington resident; have at least junior standing before the first term of enrollment at an eligible four-year college; have financial need; and a junior or senior transfer student (student cannot receive EOG to continue at the current college). **Application Requirements:** Applicants must submit a completed application form along with the required materials and information. **Deadline for Receipt:** October 1; February 1; April 1; and June 1.

2370 ■ WASHINGTON HIGHER EDUCATION COORDINATING BOARD
PO Box 43430
Olympia, WA 98504-3430
Tel: (360)753-7800
E-mail: info@hecb.wa.gov
Web Site: http://www.hecb.wa.gov
To help state's lowest-income undergraduate students pursue degrees, hone skills, or retrain for new careers.
Title of Award: Washington Higher Education Coordinating Board State Need Grants **Area, Field, or Subject:** General studies. **Level of Education for which Award is Granted:** Undergraduate **Funds Available:** Amounts vary by the type of school the applicant's attending.
Eligibility Requirements: Applicant must have a family income of equal to or less than 70 percent of the state median; a Washington State resident; enrolled as an undergraduate student in an eligible program, at a minimum of 3 credits; pursuing a certificate, bachelor's degree, or first associate degree; and not pursuing a degree in theology. **Application Requirements:** Applicants must file a FAFSA (Free Application for Federal Student Aid) to be considered.

2371 ■ WASHINGTON METROPOLITAN SCHOLARS
110 Maryland Ave. NE, Ste. 502
Washington, DC 20002
Tel: (202)544-8301
Fax: (202)318-0761
E-mail: geoff@wmscholars.org
Web Site: http://www.wmscholars.org
To assist students with their college admission, scholarship seminars, college counseling, academic support and retention services, internships and career development workshops.
Title of Award: Washington Metropolitan Scholarships **Area, Field, or Subject:** General studies. **Level of Education for which Award is Granted:** Undergraduate **Funds Available:** Maximum amount of $5,000.
Eligibility Requirements: Applicants must be African American; must have at least a cumulative GPA of 3.5 on a 4.0 scale, or is in the top twenty-five percent of his or her senior class; must be a citizen or a legal permanent resident of the United States, and resides in the Washington metropolitan area; must be a prospective graduating senior from an accredited public, private, or parochial school in the metropolitan area; must also be entering an accredited college or university as a full-time, degree-seeking freshmen in the upcoming year; must demonstrate leadership abilities through participation in community service, extracurricular or other activities; must exhibit financial need. **Application Requirements:** Applicants must fill out the online application form; submit an official recommendation from a teacher or counselor who has personal knowledge of the student's abilities and must be signed by the principal; submit an official transcript of records. **Deadline for Receipt:** November 3. **Additional Information:** geoff@wmscholars.org.

2372 ■ WASHINGTON SCHOLARSHIP FUND
1100 17th St. NW, Ste. 330
Washington, DC 20036
Tel: (202)222-0535
Fax: (202)222-0543
E-mail: scholarships@washingtonscholarshipfund.org
Web Site: http://www.washingtonscholarshipfund.org
To increase educational opportunities for low-income students and families in Washington, D.C.
Title of Award: D.C. Opportunity Scholarship Program **Area, Field, or Subject:** General studies. **Level of Education for which Award is Granted:** Undergraduate **Funds Available:** $7,500.
Eligibility Requirements: Applicants must be living in Washington, D.C.; must currently be attending a public school; must be five years old or entering kindergarten; must have a household income at or below 185 percent of poverty. **Application Requirements:** Applicants must submit a report card or other school document from the school year showing the child's name, current grade, and school name; applicants must submit a birth certificate for any child who will be entering kindergarten. **Additional Information:** scholarships@washingtonscholarshipfund.org.

2373 ■ WASHINGTON SCHOLARSHIP FUND
1100 17th St. NW, Ste. 330
Washington, DC 20036
Tel: (202)222-0535
Fax: (202)222-0543
E-mail: scholarships@washingtonscholarshipfund.org
Web Site: http://www.washingtonscholarshipfund.org
To increase educational opportunities for low-income students and families in Washington, D.C.
Title of Award: Washington Scholarship Fund Signature Scholarships Program **Area, Field, or Subject:** General studies. **Level of Education for which Award is Granted:** Undergraduate **Funds Available:** $3,000.
Eligibility Requirements: Applicants must be living in Washington, D.C.; must currently be attending a public school; must be five years old or entering kindergarten; must have a household income at or below 270 percent of poverty. **Application Requirements:** Applicants must submit a report card or other school document from the school year showing the child's name, current grade, and school name; applicants must submit a birth certificate for any child who will be entering kindergarten. **Additional Information:** scholarships@washingtonscholarshipfund.org.

2374 ■ WATER AND SEWER DISTRIBUTORS OF AMERICA
100 North 20th St., 4th floor
Philadelphia, PA 19103-1443
Tel: (215)564-3484
Fax: (215)963-9785
E-mail: wasda@fernley.com
Web Site: http://www.wasda.com
To promote the waterworks/wastewater products distribution industry; to improve the image of WASDA and the industry.
Title of Award: Matt Stager Memorial Scholarship Fund **Area, Field, or Subject:** General studies. **Level of Education for which Award is Granted:** Undergraduate **Funds Available:** No specific amount. **Duration:** 4 years.
Eligibility Requirements: Applicant must have been employed by a company which was or is a regular Member of WASDA; must have an office in Canada, United States, or Puerto Rico; must have knowledge in distribution selling in waterworks, and sewer or storm drainage pipes. **Ap-**

plication Requirements: Applicants must prepare a one-page detailed narrative description of the academic plans for the future and the career goals; must attach two letters of recommendation from teachers who are not related or members of the Matt Stager Scholarship Section Committee who have knowledge in academic achievements and who are able to comment on the academic motivation and character; must have a WASDA member contact verify parent's employment; have the Counselor fill out the counselor's report; submit the required scores and forward all requirements to the WASDA Headquarters. **Deadline for Receipt:** April 1.

2375 ■ WATSON-BROWN FOUNDATION

310 Tom Watson Way
Thomson, GA 30824
Tel: (706)595-8886
Fax: (706)595-3948
Web Site: http://www.watson-brown.org
To assist Georgia and South Carolina students with their educational pursuits.

Title of Award: Watson-Brown Scholarships **Area, Field, or Subject:** General studies. **Level of Education for which Award is Granted:** Undergraduate **Number Awarded:** Approximately 200. **Funds Available:** $3,000 and $5,000.

Eligibility Requirements: Applicants must be students from Georgia or South Carolina; must be high school seniors or current undergraduate students. **Application Requirements:** Applicants must complete the online scholarship application and submit supporting documents (essay, financial need statement, letters of recommendation, high school/college transcript, IRS Form 1040 or 1040 EZ) which must be mailed separately. **Deadline for Receipt:** February 15. **Additional Information:** Sarah Katherine McNeil, Director of Scholarships and Alumni Relations, at skmcneil@watson-brown.org.

2376 ■ WEST VIRGINIA COAL ASSOCIATION

PO Box 3923
Charleston, WV 25309
Tel: (304)342-4153
Fax: (304)342-7651
E-mail: braney@wvcoal.com
Web Site: http://www.wvcoal.com
To provide a strong and dependable infrastructure for the continued mining of West Virginia coal.

Title of Award: Friends of Coal Scholarships **Area, Field, or Subject:** General studies. **Level of Education for which Award is Granted:** Undergraduate **Funds Available:** $2,500.

Eligibility Requirements: Applicants must be high school honor graduates; must have high GPA's in high school; must be living in West Virginia. **Application Requirements:** Applicants must submit a filled-out application form.

2377 ■ WEST VIRGINIA CONGRESS OF PARENTS AND TEACHERS

PO Box 3557
Parkersburg, WV 26103
Tel: (304)420-9576
Fax: (304)420-9577
E-mail: wv_office@pta.org
Web Site: http://www.wvpta.net
To support the education of WV students.

Title of Award: West Virginia PTA Scholarships **Area, Field, or Subject:** General studies. **Level of Education for which Award is Granted:** Undergraduate **Funds Available:** $500.

Eligibility Requirements: Applicants must be high school seniors in a WV school; and have at least a 2.0 grade point average. **Application Requirements:** Applicant's must submit the completed application form with supporting documents. One original, and four copies must be submitted to the Scholarship Committee. **Deadline for Receipt:** February 15.

2378 ■ WEST VIRGINIA HOSPITALITY AND TRAVEL ASSOCIATION

PO Box 2391
Charleston, WV 25328
Tel: (304)342-6511
E-mail: sharonhrowe@charter.net
Web Site: http://www.wvhta.com
To complete the educational pathway already underway in West Virginia.

Title of Award: Peter Meyer Memorial Scholarships **Area, Field, or Subject:** Travel and tourism. **Level of Education for which Award is Granted:** Undergraduate **Funds Available:** $500.

Eligibility Requirements: Applicants must be high school seniors who plan to enroll in a hospitality degree program. **Application Requirements:** Applicants must submit a typed or neatly printed application; an official transcript from high school attended; proof of hospitality and travel-related work experience with a minimum of 250 hours verified by copies of paycheck stubs or letters from employer stipulating number of hours worked; one letter of recommendation on letterhead from a current/previous employer; and acceptance letter from the post-secondary institution. **Deadline for Receipt:** May 31. **Additional Information:** edfdn@wvhta.com

2379 ■ WEST VIRGINIA HOSPITALITY AND TRAVEL ASSOCIATION

PO Box 2391
Charleston, WV 25328
Tel: (304)342-6511
E-mail: sharonhrowe@charter.net
Web Site: http://www.wvhta.com
To complete the educational pathway already underway in West Virginia.

Title of Award: West Virginia Educational Foundation Hospitality Business Alliance Scholarships **Area, Field, or Subject:** Travel and tourism. **Level of Education for which Award is Granted:** Undergraduate **Funds Available:** $1,000.

Eligibility Requirements: Applicants must be prostart and lodging management program high school senior students who plan to enroll in a hospitality degree program. Applicants must be West Virginia residents and may be planning to attend out-of-state schools. **Application Requirements:** Applicants must submit a completed application form.

2380 ■ WEST VIRGINIA HOSPITALITY AND TRAVEL ASSOCIATION

PO Box 2391
Charleston, WV 25328
Tel: (304)342-6511
E-mail: sharonhrowe@charter.net
Web Site: http://www.wvhta.com
To complete the educational pathway already underway in West Virginia.

Title of Award: West Virginia Hospitality and Travel Association General Scholarships **Area, Field, or Subject:** Travel and tourism. **Level of Education for which Award is Granted:** Undergraduate **Funds Available:** $1,000.

Eligibility Requirements: Applicants must be graduating seniors in a West Virginia High School; must have a minimum grade point of average of 2.75 on a 4.0 scale; must have performed a minimum of 250 hours of hospitality and travel industry related work experience; must have applied to a hospitality, travel, or recreation management program in a post-secondary institution, either full-time or substantial part-time with the intent to enroll in a minimum of 2 terms. **Application Requirements:** Applicants must submit a typed or neatly printed application; an official transcript from high school attended; proof of hospitality and travel-related work experience with a minimum of 250 hours verified by copies of paycheck stubs or letters from employer stipulating number of hours worked; one letter of recommendation on letterhead from a current/previous employer; and acceptance letter from the post-secondary institution. **Deadline for Receipt:** May 31. **Additional Information:** edfdn@wvhta.com.

2381 ■ WESTERN GOLF ASSOCIATION

1 Briar Rd.
Golf, IL 60029
Tel: (847)724-4600
Fax: (847)724-7133
E-mail: evansscholars@wgaesf.com
Web Site: http://www.westerngolfassociation.com
To help caddies to pursue education.

Title of Award: Chuck Evans Scholarships **Area, Field, or Subject:** General studies. **Level of Education for which Award is Granted:** Undergraduate **Funds Available:** Full-tuition.

Eligibility Requirements: Applicant must be caddies nominated by their club and have caddied, successfully and regularly, for a minimum of two years and also expected to caddie or work at their sponsoring club during the summer prior to the application; have completed junior year of high school with above B average in college preparatory courses and are required to take the ACT; have clearly establish their need for financial assistance; and have an outstanding character. **Application Requirements:** Caddies must be nominated by their respective clubs.

2382 ■ WILLAMETTE UNIVERSITY
900 State St.
Salem, OR 97301
Tel: (503)370-6300
Web Site: http://www.willamette.edu
To provide financial support to individuals who wish to pursue their studies.
Title of Award: Melvin Henderson-Rubio Scholarships **Area, Field, or Subject:** General studies. **Level of Education for which Award is Granted:** Undergraduate **Funds Available:** $5,000. **Duration:** One year.
Eligibility Requirements: Applicants must be student enrolling from a home address in the greater Los Angeles area. **Application Requirements:** For more information about the scholarship, applicants must contact the Office of Financial Aid. **Deadline for Receipt:** January 1.

2383 ■ WILLAMETTE UNIVERSITY
900 State St.
Salem, OR 97301
Tel: (503)370-6300
Web Site: http://www.willamette.edu
To provide financial support to individuals who wish to pursue their studies.
Title of Award: Mary Stuart Rogers Scholarships **Area, Field, or Subject:** General studies. **Level of Education for which Award is Granted:** Undergraduate **Number Awarded:** 14. **Funds Available:** $4,000. **Duration:** One year.
Eligibility Requirements: Applicants must have a 3.0 GPA to be considered. **Application Requirements:** For more information about the scholarship, applicants must contact the Office of Financial Aid. **Deadline for Receipt:** January 1.

2384 ■ JOHN G. WILLIAMS FOUNDATION
PO Box 1229
Camp Hill, PA 17001-1229
Tel: (717)763-1333
Fax: (717)763-1336
E-mail: amgrpmld@aol.com
Web Site: http://www.jgwfoundation.org
To provide financial assistance to Pennsylvania residents for their pursuit of college, post-graduate, and/or professional education opportunities, in courses and at educational institutions that they select and that are acceptable to the Board of Trustees.
Title of Award: John G. Williams Scholarships Fund **Area, Field, or Subject:** General studies. **Level of Education for which Award is Granted:** Undergraduate **Funds Available:** No specific amount.
Eligibility Requirements: Applicants must be a resident of Pennsylvania. Applicants must be high school graduates and enrolled full-time. Applicants must have and maintain at all times a minimum GPA of 3.0 or its equivalent. **Application Requirements:** Applicants must complete the standard financial need and financial aid form. Applicants must submit a transcript of grades for the most recent academic year. Applicants must provide evidence of acceptance and attendance by college or graduate school and two character recommendations. **Deadline for Receipt:** June 15.

2385 ■ WINSTON-SALEM FOUNDATION
860 W Fifth St.
Winston-Salem, NC 27101-2506
Tel: (336)725-2382
Fax: (336)727-0581
E-mail: info@wsfoundation.org
Web Site: http://www.wsfoundation.org
To assist graduating high school seniors and adults in their studies.
Title of Award: William H. Andrews/HAWS Scholarships **Area, Field, or Subject:** General studies. **Level of Education for which Award is Granted:** Undergraduate **Funds Available:** No specific amount.
Eligibility Requirements: Applicants must be graduating high school seniors or adults wishing to continue in post-secondary education; must

be residents living in a property owned or managed by HAWS. **Application Requirements:** Applicants may download an application form at WSF website or send request to Scholarship coordinator. **Deadline for Receipt:** March 15. **Additional Information:** Michelle Greene, 336-399-3579.

2386 ■ WINSTON-SALEM FOUNDATION
860 W Fifth St.
Winston-Salem, NC 27101-2506
Tel: (336)725-2382
Fax: (336)727-0581
E-mail: info@wsfoundation.org
Web Site: http://www.wsfoundation.org
To graduating high school seniors from Stokes County public high schools.
Title of Award: Chester Arzell and Helen Miller Montgomery Scholarships **Area, Field, or Subject:** General studies. **Level of Education for which Award is Granted:** Undergraduate **Funds Available:** $1,000.
Eligibility Requirements: Applicants must have a minimum, cumulative, unweighted GPA of 2.0; participate in community service; demonstrate good character; participate in extracurricular activities; demonstrate financial need. **Application Requirements:** Scholarship applications are available online or in the guidance offices of the three Stokes county high schools. **Deadline for Receipt:** April 1. **Additional Information:** WSF Student Aid Department, 336-714-3445.

2387 ■ WINSTON-SALEM FOUNDATION
860 W Fifth St.
Winston-Salem, NC 27101-2506
Tel: (336)725-2382
Fax: (336)727-0581
E-mail: info@wsfoundation.org
Web Site: http://www.wsfoundation.org
To assist graduating high school students of Forsyth County.
Title of Award: F.A. and Charlotte Blount Scholarships **Area, Field, or Subject:** General studies. **Level of Education for which Award is Granted:** Undergraduate **Funds Available:** $750. **Duration:** One year.
Eligibility Requirements: Applicants must be graduating Forsyth County high school students who will pursue a baccalaureate degree at an accredited college or university. **Application Requirements:** Applicants must submit a completed application form; grade transcript through first semester of the 12th grade; and one recommendation. **Deadline for Receipt:** March 31. **Additional Information:** Winston-Salem Foundation at the above address.

2388 ■ WINSTON-SALEM FOUNDATION
860 W Fifth St.
Winston-Salem, NC 27101-2506
Tel: (336)725-2382
Fax: (336)727-0581
E-mail: info@wsfoundation.org
Web Site: http://www.wsfoundation.org
To assist graduating high school seniors who have attended the Winston-Salem/Forsyth County Schools' Career Center.
Title of Award: Tien Bui Memorial Scholarships **Area, Field, or Subject:** General studies. **Level of Education for which Award is Granted:** Undergraduate **Funds Available:** No specific amount.
Eligibility Requirements: Applicants must: demonstrate a minimum cumulative GPA of 3.5; must have strong SAT scores and challenging academic course selection as a graduating high school senior; must demonstrate financial need (award not restricted to lowest family income); have attended the Winston-Salem/Forsyth County Schools' Career Center during their high school and successfully completed either advanced placement in Math or Science. **Application Requirements:** Scholarship applications are available online. Applicants must complete the Tien Bui Memorial Scholarship application; must submit grade transcript through 1st semester of 12th grade; and submit letter of acceptance from NCSU that specifies enrollment in the College of Engineering. **Deadline for Receipt:** March 31. **Additional Information:** Foundation's Student Aid Department, 336-714-3445.

2389 ■ WINSTON-SALEM FOUNDATION
860 W Fifth St.
Winston-Salem, NC 27101-2506

Tel: (336)725-2382
Fax: (336)727-0581
E-mail: info@wsfoundation.org
Web Site: http://www.wsfoundation.org
To provide college scholarships to worthy graduating high school seniors at Mt. Tabor High School.
Title of Award: Andrew Blake Clark Memorial Scholarships **Area, Field, or Subject:** General studies. **Level of Education for which Award is Granted:** Undergraduate **Funds Available:** $1,000.
Eligibility Requirements: Applicants must be gradauting seniors at Mt. Tabor High School. **Application Requirements:** Students interested in being considered for the scholarship award should submit the following to Stan Huck in the Mt. Tabor Guidance Office: transcript of high school courses through 1st semester 12th grade; high school resume; personal statement describing accomplishments and future plans. **Deadline for Receipt:** April 4. **Additional Information:** WSF Student Aid Department, 336-714-3445.

2390 ■ WINSTON-SALEM FOUNDATION
860 W Fifth St.
Winston-Salem, NC 27101-2506
Tel: (336)725-2382
Fax: (336)727-0581
E-mail: info@wsfoundation.org
Web Site: http://www.wsfoundation.org
To provide a college scholarship to a worthy graduating high school senior from a Forsyth County high school.
Title of Award: Elmer and Rosa Lee Collins Scholarships **Area, Field, or Subject:** General studies. **Level of Education for which Award is Granted:** Undergraduate **Funds Available:** $2,500. **Duration:** One year.
Eligibility Requirements: Applicants must demonstrate character and purpose as evidenced in school, community, church, and work activities; academic success by achieving a minimum, unweighted, cumulative GPA of 3.5 with strong course selection; financial need (however, the scholarship is not restricted to lower family incomes); and must be US citizens. **Application Requirements:** Eligible high school seniors may complete an application online. Applicants are responsible for submitting the completed application and all supplemental items to the Foundation. Supplemental items include: grade transcript through the 1st semester of the 12th grade; one recommendation from a teacher, guidance couselor, coach, principal, employer, clergy, or other community leader who has supervised, counseled or coached applicant in some capacity. **Deadline for Receipt:** March 31. **Additional Information:** WSF Student Aid Department, 336-714-3445.

2391 ■ WINSTON-SALEM FOUNDATION
860 W Fifth St.
Winston-Salem, NC 27101-2506
Tel: (336)725-2382
Fax: (336)727-0581
E-mail: info@wsfoundation.org
Web Site: http://www.wsfoundation.org
To award scholarships to worthy graduating high school seniors form North, South, and West Stokes High Schools who will attend an accredited two or four-year college or university.
Title of Award: Lloyd E. and Rachel S. Collins Scholarships **Area, Field, or Subject:** General studies. **Level of Education for which Award is Granted:** Undergraduate **Funds Available:** $1,000.
Eligibility Requirements: Applicants must demonstrate academic achievement, participate in community service, demonstrate good character, participate in extracurricular activities, demonstrate financial need. **Application Requirements:** Applications for the scholarship are available in the guidance offices of the three Stokes County high schools. **Additional Information:** Established in 1991. **Deadline for Receipt:** April 1. **Additional Information:** WSF Student Aid Department, 336-714-3445.

2392 ■ WINSTON-SALEM FOUNDATION
860 W Fifth St.
Winston-Salem, NC 27101-2506
Tel: (336)725-2382
Fax: (336)727-0581
E-mail: info@wsfoundation.org

Web Site: http://www.wsfoundation.org
To award scholarship to a graduating high school senior from Forbush High School.
Title of Award: D.C. Cornelius Memorial Scholarships **Area, Field, or Subject:** General studies. **Level of Education for which Award is Granted:** Undergraduate **Funds Available:** $1,000.
Eligibility Requirements: Applicants must demonstrate, character, leadership, compassion for all people and dedication to service of community and school. Applicants must have a minimum GPA of 2.8. Demonstration of financial need is preferred. Applicants must be a US citizen. **Application Requirements:** Scholarship applications will be available in the guidance office at Forbush High School and also online. Students must complete the application in its entirety; include grade transcripts with the application at time of submittal; and include recommendations with the application. **Deadline for Receipt:** April 15. **Additional Information:** WSF Student Aid Department, 336-714-3445.

2393 ■ WINSTON-SALEM FOUNDATION
860 W Fifth St.
Winston-Salem, NC 27101-2506
Tel: (336)725-2382
Fax: (336)727-0581
E-mail: info@wsfoundation.org
Web Site: http://www.wsfoundation.org
To provide financial aid for needy students.
Title of Award: Serena D. Dalton Scholarships **Area, Field, or Subject:** General studies. **Level of Education for which Award is Granted:** Undergraduate **Funds Available:** No specific amount.
Eligibility Requirements: Applicants must have adjusted gross income within the table guidelines (table is based on up to 330% above the federal poverty level); be a resident of Forsyth County; must have achieved a current cumulative GPA of at least 2.0; must be enrolled a minimum of six credit hours/semester during the academic year in a program leading to a first time two or four year degree, certificate, or diploma from an accredited institution which participates in the federal student aid program; must be a US citizen. **Application Requirements:** The following items are required to complete the application process: Submittal of completed application and signed signature page; Signed copy of parents'/guardians'/family's previous year's 1040, 1040A, or 1040EZ income tax return (for dependent students); Signed copy of applicant's previous year's tax return; Official high school grade transcript through at least 1st semester of the 12th grade or year-end college grade transcript, whichever is the most recent (request from the school's Registrar and forward to the Foundation); Copy of the Student Aid Report if applicant has applied for federal aid; Copy of the financial aid award letter. Please submit the application on-line and follow with additional items as soon as you receive them. **Deadline for Receipt:** March 31. **Additional Information:** WSF Student Aid Department, 336-714-3445.

2394 ■ WINSTON-SALEM FOUNDATION
860 W Fifth St.
Winston-Salem, NC 27101-2506
Tel: (336)725-2382
Fax: (336)727-0581
E-mail: info@wsfoundation.org
Web Site: http://www.wsfoundation.org
To provide travel and college scholarships to high school juniors and seniors.
Title of Award: Dean Prim Scholarships **Area, Field, or Subject:** General studies. **Level of Education for which Award is Granted:** Undergraduate **Funds Available:** $500.
Eligibility Requirements: Qualified candidates must be: at least 16 years of age; a high school junior or high school senior; must demonstrate excellence in schoolwork as evidenced by course selection and grades (minimum unweighted GPA of 3.0); must participate in extracurricular school activities, community and/or church activities, and school or community athletics; must demonstrate good character and show interest in and concern for being an active member of society; must be committed to traveling and studying in China and have the full support of parent(s) to participate. The scholarship is available to students regardless of race, sex, national, origin, or religion. **Application Requirements:** The Prim scholarship application is on The Winston-Salem Foundation's web site. It is the student's responsibility to make sure that, along with submittal for

the electronic application completed in its entirety, all supplemental materials are in the office of The Winston-Salem Foundation by the deadline. Supplemental materials include: a grade transcript, through 10th grade for juniors and 11th grade for seniors; two recommendations as described in the application; a recent photograph (include student's name on back of photo); **Deadline for Receipt:** October 31. **Additional Information:** WSF Student Aid Department, 336-714-3445.

2395 ■ WINSTON-SALEM FOUNDATION

860 W Fifth St.
Winston-Salem, NC 27101-2506
Tel: (336)725-2382
Fax: (336)727-0581
E-mail: info@wsfoundation.org
Web Site: http://www.wsfoundation.org
to provide scholarships to worthy high school seniors graduating from either North Stokes or South Stokes High schools.
Title of Award: Wade and Marcelene Duncan Scholarships **Area, Field, or Subject:** General studies. **Level of Education for which Award is Granted:** Undergraduate **Funds Available:** $250.
Eligibility Requirements: Applicant must be a graduating senior from either North Stokes or South Stokes High School who will attend an accredited four-year educational institution. Applicants must demonstrate leadership, participate in community service, participate in athletics and be generally well-rounded. **Application Requirements:** Applications and all required materials must be delivered to your high school guidance office. Students should contact the guidance office at North Stokes High School or South Stokes High School to request applications. Applications are also available online. **Deadline for Receipt:** March 31. **Additional Information:** North Stokes High School, 336-593-8134; South Stokes High School, 336-994-2995.

2396 ■ WINSTON-SALEM FOUNDATION

860 W Fifth St.
Winston-Salem, NC 27101-2506
Tel: (336)725-2382
Fax: (336)727-0581
E-mail: info@wsfoundation.org
Web Site: http://www.wsfoundation.org
To give priority consideration to those students who will attend Davidson College or Wake Forest University.
Title of Award: Gaddy Student Scholarships **Area, Field, or Subject:** General studies. **Level of Education for which Award is Granted:** Undergraduate **Funds Available:** $1,000. **Duration:** Four consecutive years of undergraduate study.
Eligibility Requirements: This renewable scholarship seeks to identify those students: who are graduating high school seniors from R.J. Reynolds High School; who demonstrate academic promise; who are US citizens; who have participated as athletes or in support positions in high school athletics (broad consideration); who have financial need (broad consideration given - not restricted to lower family incomes). **Application Requirements:** Students must provide the following: A completed application; grade transcript through 1st semester, 12th grade; one recommendation as described in the application guidelines. Schedule an interview, if so advised. **Additional Information:** Established in 1997. **Deadline for Receipt:** March 31. **Additional Information:** WSF Student Aid Department, 336-714-3445.

2397 ■ WINSTON-SALEM FOUNDATION

860 W Fifth St.
Winston-Salem, NC 27101-2506
Tel: (336)725-2382
Fax: (336)727-0581
E-mail: info@wsfoundation.org
Web Site: http://www.wsfoundation.org
To provide scholarships to the graduating high school seniors from accredited public, private, or parochial schools, who will attend accredited higher education institutions seeking undergraduate degrees.
Title of Award: John L. Gilmer Educational Grants **Area, Field, or Subject:** General studies. **Level of Education for which Award is Granted:** Undergraduate **Funds Available:** $1,000.
Eligibility Requirements: Applicants must be Forsyth County residents; be graduating high school seniors; have achieved a minimum, unweighted

cumulative GPA of 3.0; have a family adjusted gross income not exceeding $80,000. **Application Requirements:** Eligible high school seniors may complete an application online. Applicants are responsible for submitting the completed application and all supplemental items, except the family federal tax return, to the Foundation by March 31. The family federal tax return must be submitted by April 15. Supplemental items include: Grade transcript through the 1st semester of the 12th grade; Family federal tax return from last year; An interview if so advised. Those recipients completing an undergraduate degree in three years will forfeit the fourth year's scholarship. **Deadline for Receipt:** March 31. **Additional Information:** WSF Student Aid Department, 336-714-3445.

2398 ■ WINSTON-SALEM FOUNDATION

860 W Fifth St.
Winston-Salem, NC 27101-2506
Tel: (336)725-2382
Fax: (336)727-0581
E-mail: info@wsfoundation.org
Web Site: http://www.wsfoundation.org
To provide scholarships to the graduating high school seniors from accredited public, private, or parochial schools, who will attend accredited higher education institutions seeking undergraduate degrees.
Title of Award: John L. Gilmer Merit Based Scholarships **Area, Field, or Subject:** General studies. **Level of Education for which Award is Granted:** Undergraduate **Funds Available:** No specific amount.
Eligibility Requirements: Applicants must be Forsyth County residents; graduating high school seniors; must have achieved a minimum, unweighted cumulative GPA of 3.5. **Application Requirements:** Eligible high school seniors may complete an application online. Applicants are responsible for submitting the completed application and all supplemental items to the Foundation. Supplemental items include: Grade transcript through the 1st semester of the 12th grade; One recommendation from a teacher, guidance counselor, coach, principal, employer, clergy, or other community leader who has supervised, counseled or coached applicant in some capacity; An interview if so advised. Those recipients completing an undergraduate degree in three years will forfeit the fourth year's scholarship. **Deadline for Receipt:** March 31. **Additional Information:** WSF Student Aid Department, 336-714-3445.

2399 ■ WINSTON-SALEM FOUNDATION

860 W Fifth St.
Winston-Salem, NC 27101-2506
Tel: (336)725-2382
Fax: (336)727-0581
E-mail: info@wsfoundation.org
Web Site: http://www.wsfoundation.org
To award worthy graduating high school seniors in Forsyth County.
Title of Award: L. Gordon, Jr. and June D. Pfefferkorn Scholarships **Area, Field, or Subject:** General studies. **Level of Education for which Award is Granted:** Undergraduate **Funds Available:** No specific amount.
Eligibility Requirements: Applicants must: attend an accredited four-year college or university in North Carolina; be a resident of Forsyth County; have achieved a current cumulative, unweighted GPA of at least 3.5; demonstrate significant promise in leadership, community service, and school service; be US citizens; demonstrate financial need, (award not restricted to lowest family incomes); be graduating high school seniors. **Application Requirements:** The following items are required to complete the application process: submittal of completed application and signed signature page; signed copy of parents'/guardians'/ family's previous year's 1040, 1040A, 1040EZ income tax return; signed copy of applicant's previous year's tax return; official high school grade transcript through at least 1st semester of the 12th grade; one recommendation from a teacher, guidance, coach, principal, employer, clergy, or other community leader who has supervised, counseled or coached applicant in some capacity. **Deadline for Receipt:** March 31. **Additional Information:** WSF Student Aid Department, 336-714-3445.

2400 ■ WINSTON-SALEM FOUNDATION

860 W Fifth St.
Winston-Salem, NC 27101-2506
Tel: (336)725-2382
Fax: (336)727-0581

E-mail: info@wsfoundation.org
Web Site: http://www.wsfoundation.org
To provide financial support for a graduating high school senior from Forsyth County who will attend Forsyth Technical Community College.
Title of Award: Jimmy Johnson Memorial Scholarships **Area, Field, or Subject:** Construction. **Level of Education for which Award is Granted:** Undergraduate **Funds Available:** No specific amount.
Eligibility Requirements: This fund seeks to identify those high school seniors who: demonstrate significant promise in academics and involvement in community service; have a minimum, unweighted high school GPA of 3.0; demonstrate financial need (preferred, but not restricted to lowest family incomes); are enrolled full-time at Forsyth Technical Community College in a construction or a house-build related program. Applicants must be US citizens; Forsyth County residents; graduating high school seniors. **Application Requirements:** Applications are available online. First time applicants must complete the application in its entirety and provide the following supplemental items as they are obtained by the applicant: parent/guardian's tax return from previous year; applicant's tax return from previous year; official high school grade transcript through the first semester of the 12th grade; resume; one recommendation; copy of Student Aid Report if applicant applied for federal aid; copy of Financial Aid Award Notice. **Deadline for Receipt:** March 31. **Additional Information:** WSF Student Aid Department, 336-714-3445.

2401 ■ WINSTON-SALEM FOUNDATION
860 W Fifth St.
Winston-Salem, NC 27101-2506
Tel: (336)725-2382
Fax: (336)727-0581
E-mail: info@wsfoundation.org
Web Site: http://www.wsfoundation.org
To provide educational aid for college to qualified traditional and nontraditional age applicants from charitable funds established by generous supporters of the community.
Title of Award: Stella B. Johnson Scholarships **Area, Field, or Subject:** General studies. **Level of Education for which Award is Granted:** Undergraduate **Funds Available:** No specific amount.
Eligibility Requirements: Applicants must: have a family adjusted gross income within the table guidelines (table is based on up to 330% above the federal poverty level); be residents of Forsyth County; have achieved a current cumulative grade point average of at least 2.0; must be enrolled a minimum of six credit hours/semester during the academic year in a program leading to a first time two or four year degree, certificate, or diploma from an accredited institution which participates in the federal student aid program; must be US citizens. **Application Requirements:** The following items are required to complete the application process: submittal of completed application and signed signature page; signed copy of parents'/guardians'/family's previous year's 1040, 1040A, or 1040EZ income tax return (for dependent students); signed copy of applicant's previous year's tax return; official high school grade transcript through at least 1st semester of the 12th grade or year-end college grade transcript, whichever is the most recent (request from the school's Registrar and forward to the Foundation); copy of the Student Aid Report if applicant has applied for federal aid; copy of the financial aid award letter; interview if so advised. Please submit the application on-line **Deadline for Receipt:** March 31. **Additional Information:** WSF Student Aid Department, 336-714-3445.

2402 ■ WINSTON-SALEM FOUNDATION
860 W Fifth St.
Winston-Salem, NC 27101-2506
Tel: (336)725-2382
Fax: (336)727-0581
E-mail: info@wsfoundation.org
Web Site: http://www.wsfoundation.org
To provide educational scholarships for residents of Forsyth County to attend Wake Forest University.
Title of Award: L.D. and Elsie Long Memorial Scholarships **Area, Field, or Subject:** General studies. **Level of Education for which Award is Granted:** Undergraduate **Funds Available:** No specific amount.
Eligibility Requirements: Applicant must have a family adjusted gross income within the table guidelines (table is based on up to 330% above the federal poverty level); be a resident of Forsyth County; have achieved

a current cumulative GPA of at least 2.0; must be enrolled a minimum of six credits hours/semester during the academic year in a program leading to a graduate degree from Wake Forest University. **Application Requirements:** The following items are required to complete the application process: submittal of completed application and signed signature page; signed copy of applicant's previous year's tax return; official high school grade transcript through at least 1st semester of the 12th grade or year-end college grade transcript, whichever is the most recent (request from the school's Registrar and forward to the Foundation); copy of the Student Aid Report (SAR) if applicant has applied for federal aid; copy of the financial award letter; interview if so advised. **Deadline for Receipt:** March 31. **Additional Information:** WSF Student Aid Department, 336-714-3445.

2403 ■ WINSTON-SALEM FOUNDATION
860 W Fifth St.
Winston-Salem, NC 27101-2506
Tel: (336)725-2382
Fax: (336)727-0581
E-mail: info@wsfoundation.org
Web Site: http://www.wsfoundation.org
To award worthy graduating high school senior who attended Millennium Charter Academy in Mount Airy, North Carolina in grades six through eight.
Title of Award: Millennium Charter Academy College Scholarships **Area, Field, or Subject:** General studies. **Level of Education for which Award is Granted:** Undergraduate **Funds Available:** No specific amount.
Eligibility Requirements: Applicants must be graduating seniors pursuing a bachelor's degree at a college or university; have attended Millennium Charter Academy for at least three years; exemplify noteworthy academic success, strong moral character and a keen sense of community. **Application Requirements:** The following items must be submitted to the Millennium Charter Academic Scholarship Committee: a grade transcript with class rank, as well as weighted and unweighted GPA; one educational reference and two non-family character references; records of leadership and extra-curricular school and community activities; a 100-300 word typed essay that describes applicant's personal and professional goals. **Deadline for Receipt:** February 28. **Additional Information:** Kirby R. McCrary, Headmaster Millennium Charter Academy 500 Old Springs Road Mt. Airy, N.C. 27030.

2404 ■ WINSTON-SALEM FOUNDATION
860 W Fifth St.
Winston-Salem, NC 27101-2506
Tel: (336)725-2382
Fax: (336)727-0581
E-mail: info@wsfoundation.org
Web Site: http://www.wsfoundation.org
To provide merit-based scholarships for worthy students attending Forsyth Technical Community College.
Title of Award: N.W. Mitchell-Piedmont Federal Savings and Loans Endowed Scholarships **Area, Field, or Subject:** General studies. **Level of Education for which Award is Granted:** Undergraduate **Number Awarded:** 2. **Funds Available:** $1,000.
Eligibility Requirements: The renewable scholarship seeks to identify those students who: demonstrate academic success; are residents of Forsyth, Davie, Davidson, Stokes, Surry, Watauge, or Yadkin counties; are first semester students enrolled in a minimum of 12 course hours per semester; are US citizens or eligible noncitizens (as verified by the Student Aid Report); show interest and concern for being an active member of society. **Application Requirements:** Students should complete the application in its entirety and submit it by the deadline. In addition, the following supplemental items must also be submitted by the deadline: official year-end grade transcript; one recommendation; and student aid report. **Deadline for Receipt:** July 31. **Additional Information:** WSF Student Aid Department, 336-714-3445.

2405 ■ WINSTON-SALEM FOUNDATION
860 W Fifth St.
Winston-Salem, NC 27101-2506
Tel: (336)725-2382
Fax: (336)727-0581

E-mail: info@wsfoundation.org
Web Site: http://www.wsfoundation.org
To help deserving adult women achieve their educational goals.
Title of Award: Alice Conger Patterson Scholarships **Area, Field, or Subject:** General studies. **Level of Education for which Award is Granted:** Undergraduate **Funds Available:** No specific amount.
Eligibility Requirements: Scholarship seeks to identify those: who demonstrate financial need; who are female students, twenty-three years of age or older; who have earned a high school diploma or equivalent certificate (GED, home school completion, adult high school diploma); who are applying to or are currently enrolled in a four-year college or university in the Piedmont Triad of North Carolina in pursuit of an undergraduate degree. Preference will be given to students at Salem College who demonstrate a strong purpose in pursuing a liberal arts degree.
Application Requirements: Scholarship applications will be available online. Students must submit: completed application and signed signature page; copy of federal tax return for previous year; copy of the financial aid award letter for upcoming year; grade transcripts with class ranking in high school and transcripts for all college or university work to date; one recommendation. **Deadline for Receipt:** March 31. **Additional Information:** WSF Student Aid Department, 336-714-3445.

2406 ■ WINSTON-SALEM FOUNDATION
860 W Fifth St.
Winston-Salem, NC 27101-2506
Tel: (336)725-2382
Fax: (336)727-0581
E-mail: info@wsfoundation.org
Web Site: http://www.wsfoundation.org
To provide college scholarships for worthy Forsyth County residents.
Title of Award: William H. and Lena M. Petree Scholarships **Area, Field, or Subject:** General studies. **Level of Education for which Award is Granted:** Undergraduate **Funds Available:** No specific amount.
Eligibility Requirements: Applicants must be graduating high-school seniors; demonstrate academic promise during high-school; have a minimum, cumulative, unweighted GPA of 3.5 through 1st semester, 12th grade; demonstrate a willingness for self-help during high school; demonstrate leadership, school service, and community service during high school; demonstrate financial need for upcoming college expenses (award not restricted to lowest family incomes); be US citizens. **Application Requirements:** Application may be downloaded from the Foundation's web site. In addition to completing the application, students must: submit one recommendation; submit a grade transcript through first semester, 12th grade; be present for an interview. **Deadline for Receipt:** March 31. **Additional Information:** WSF Student Aid Department, 336-714-3445.

2407 ■ WINSTON-SALEM FOUNDATION
860 W Fifth St.
Winston-Salem, NC 27101-2506
Tel: (336)725-2382
Fax: (336)727-0581
E-mail: info@wsfoundation.org
Web Site: http://www.wsfoundation.org
To provide scholarships for Forsyth County residents seeking nursing degrees at Forsyth Technical Community College.
Title of Award: Pfafftown Jaycees/Lynn Canada Memorial Scholarships **Area, Field, or Subject:** General studies. **Level of Education for which Award is Granted:** Undergraduate **Funds Available:** No specific amount.
Eligibility Requirements: Applicants must be enrolled on a full-time basis in the pursuit of a first associate or a first baccalaureate degree; provide a copy of letter of admission into the nursing program at FTCC (ineligible until accepted into nursing program); maintain an unweighted high school or college cumulative GPA of 2.5; not exceed annual adjusted gross family income of $80,000; be US citizens. **Application Requirements:** Eligible applicants may obtain a scholarship application from The Winston-Salem Foundation's website. In addition to the completed/signed application, the applicants is responsible for providing the following required supplemental items: signed copy of parent/guardian's federal income tax return; signed copy of student's federal income tax return, if applicable; applicant's official high school (as of 1st semester, 12th grade) or official college grade transcript (as of academic year-end); copy of

Student Aid Report and financial aid notice if student applied for federal aid. **Deadline for Receipt:** March 31. **Additional Information:** Edna Barker, 336-714-3445.

2408 ■ WINSTON-SALEM FOUNDATION
860 W Fifth St.
Winston-Salem, NC 27101-2506
Tel: (336)725-2382
Fax: (336)727-0581
E-mail: info@wsfoundation.org
Web Site: http://www.wsfoundation.org
To provide an award to a graduating high school senior in Forsyth County N.C.
Title of Award: John S. and Jacqueline P. Rider Scholarships **Area, Field, or Subject:** General studies. **Level of Education for which Award is Granted:** Undergraduate **Funds Available:** $500.
Eligibility Requirements: Applicants must: demonstrate financial need (not restricted to lower family incomes); be a resident of Forsyth County; have achieved a current cumulative grade point average of at least 3.5; must be enrolled full-time in a program leading to a two or four year degree, certificate, or diploma from an accredited institution which participates in the federal student aid program; be a graduating high school senior. **Application Requirements:** The following items are required to complete the application process: submittal of completed application and signed signature page; signed copy of parent's/guardians'/family's previous year's 1040, 1040A, or 1040EZ income tax return; signed copy of applicant's previous year's tax return; official high school grade transcript through at least 1st semester of the 12th grade (request from the school's registrar and forward to the Foundation); one recommendation from a teacher, guidance counselor, coach, principal, employer, clergy, or other community leader who has supervised, counseled or coached applicant in some capacity. **Deadline for Receipt:** March 31. **Additional Information:** WSF Student Aid Department, 336-714-3445.

2409 ■ WINSTON-SALEM FOUNDATION
860 W Fifth St.
Winston-Salem, NC 27101-2506
Tel: (336)725-2382
Fax: (336)727-0581
E-mail: info@wsfoundation.org
Web Site: http://www.wsfoundation.org
To provide financial assistance for college tuition, fees and room and board for worthy graduating high school seniors in Forsyth County.
Title of Award: Ray and Pearly Sams Scholarships **Area, Field, or Subject:** General studies. **Level of Education for which Award is Granted:** Undergraduate **Funds Available:** $2,500.
Eligibility Requirements: This fund seeks to identify the well-rounded graduating high-school senior who: has achieved excellence in school work as evidence by course selection and grades (minimum cumulative unweighted GPA of 3.5 on a 4.0 scale, or equivalent) through 1st semester of the 12th grade; has participated in school service clubs and/or other school activities; has participated in non-school community service activities; demonstrates good moral character; demonstrates evidence of financial need, although award is not restricted to lower incomes; is a United States citizen. **Application Requirements:** High school seniors may complete and submit the application online. The application and the following items must be received in the foundation's office by the deadline: official grade transcript through the 1st semester of the 12 grade; one recommendation from a teacher, guidance counselor, coach, principal, employer, clergy, or other community leader who has supervised, counseled or coached applicant in some capacity; an interview with the Foundation's Director of Student Aid, if so advised **Deadline for Receipt:** May 1. **Additional Information:** WSF Student Aid Department, 336-714-3445.

2410 ■ WINSTON-SALEM FOUNDATION
860 W Fifth St.
Winston-Salem, NC 27101-2506
Tel: (336)725-2382
Fax: (336)727-0581
E-mail: info@wsfoundation.org
Web Site: http://www.wsfoundation.org

To provide an award to a graduating high school student from a Forsyth County school who displays the traits of athletic excellence, academic achievement, leadership, and social responsibility.

Title of Award: Bruce Shelton Scholarships **Area, Field, or Subject:** General studies. **Level of Education for which Award is Granted:** Undergraduate **Funds Available:** $1,000.

Eligibility Requirements: The renewable scholarship seeks to identify students who exhibit the following qualities in equal measure: athletic excellence the student must have excelled in at least one varsity sport; social responsibility - the student must have participated in at least one extra-curricular or community activity; academic success - the student must have a minimum, unweighted high school cumulative grade point average of at least 3.0, as of the 1st semester of the 12th grade and be ranked in the top 25% of the senior class; leadership - the student must possess qualities that exhibit a willingness to "go the extra mile". Recipients receiving renewal awards must maintain a minimum cumulative GPA of 2.5 and full time enrollment of at least 12 hours each semester at accredited four-year institutions. Official grade transcripts must be submitted each summer by July 1 for verification of acceptable academic pace and GPA. Recipients should request grade transcripts from the Registrar for themselves and forward to the Foundation. **Application Requirements:** Students should complete the application in its entirety and submit it by the deadline. In addition, the following supplemental items must be submitted: a grade transcript through the first semester of the 12th grade; one recommendation as described in the application. **Deadline for Receipt:** March 31. **Additional Information:** WSF Student Aid Department, 336-714-3445.

2411 ■ WINSTON-SALEM FOUNDATION
860 W Fifth St.
Winston-Salem, NC 27101-2506
Tel: (336)725-2382
Fax: (336)727-0581
E-mail: info@wsfoundation.org
Web Site: http://www.wsfoundation.org

To award worthy students from the counties of Forsyth, Wikes, Surry, Yahkin, and Davie who plan to attend an accredited two or four year college or university, preferably in North Carolina.

Title of Award: Tom Shown Scholarships **Area, Field, or Subject:** General studies. **Level of Education for which Award is Granted:** Undergraduate **Funds Available:** $1,000-$2,000.

Eligibility Requirements: Applicants must: demonstrate financial need (award not restricted to lower incomes); have a cumulative, minimum high school or college GPA of 2.7; must be employed a minimum of 20 hours, monthly (including college work study); be US citizens. **Application Requirements:** The General Financial Aid Application should be completed for this scholarship and is available online. Applicants are responsible for submitting the completed application and all supplemental items. Supplemental items include: Parent/guardian's tax return (for dependent students); applicant's tax return; official high school grade transcript through at least the first semester of the 12th grade or year-end college grade transcript; a copy of your Student Aid Report and financial aid notice if student applied for federal aid; an interview at The Winston-Salem Foundation. **Deadline for Receipt:** July 31. **Additional Information:** WSF Student Aid Department, 336-714-3445.

2412 ■ WINSTON-SALEM FOUNDATION
860 W Fifth St.
Winston-Salem, NC 27101-2506
Tel: (336)725-2382
Fax: (336)727-0581
E-mail: info@wsfoundation.org
Web Site: http://www.wsfoundation.org

To provide educational aid to qualified traditional and non-traditional age applicants from charitable funds established by generous supporters of the community.

Title of Award: Stultz Scholarships **Area, Field, or Subject:** General studies. **Level of Education for which Award is Granted:** Undergraduate **Funds Available:** No specific amount.

Eligibility Requirements: Applicant must: have a family adjusted gross income within the table guidelines (table is based on up to 330% above the federal poverty level); be a resident of Forsyth County; have achieved a current cumulative grade point of at least 2.0; be enrolled a minimum of six credit hours/semester during the academic year, in a program leading to a first time two or four year degree, certificate, or diploma from an accredited institution which participates in the federal student aid program; be a US citizen. **Application Requirements:** The following items are required to complete the application process: submittal of completed application and signed signature page; signed copy of parent's/guardians'/family's previous year's 1040, 1040A, or 1040EZ income tax return; signed copy of applicant's previous year's tax return; official high school grade transcript through at least 1st semester of the 12th grade or year-end college grade transcript, whichever is the most recent, (request from the school's Registrar and forward to the Foundation); copy of the Student Aid Report (SAR) and financial aid award letter if applicant has applied for federal aid; interview if so advised. **Deadline for Receipt:** July 31. **Additional Information:** WSF Student Aid Department, 336-714-3445.

2413 ■ WINSTON-SALEM FOUNDATION
860 W Fifth St.
Winston-Salem, NC 27101-2506
Tel: (336)725-2382
Fax: (336)727-0581
E-mail: info@wsfoundation.org
Web Site: http://www.wsfoundation.org

To support worthy graduating high school seniors from a Forsyth County High School and admitted to a four year accredited college or university.

Title of Award: Jeff Turner-Forsyth Audubon Society Scholarships **Area, Field, or Subject:** General studies. **Level of Education for which Award is Granted:** Undergraduate **Funds Available:** $500.

Eligibility Requirements: Applicants must demonstrate character, leadership, and solid academic skills (minimum unweighted GPA of 3.0). Demonstration of financial need will be considered but is not required. US citizenship is required. **Application Requirements:** Scholarship Applications will be available online. Student must: complete the Winston-Salem Foundation application in its entirety, including an attached listing of student activities as well as personal statement; provide grade transcript through 1st semester of 12th grade with the application, at time of submittal; include at least one letter of reference (3 maximum) which addresses the applicant's character as well as environmental interest/experiences. **Additional Information:** Established in May of 2005. **Deadline for Receipt:** April 30. **Additional Information:** WSF Student Aid Department, 336-714-3445.

2414 ■ WINSTON-SALEM FOUNDATION
860 W Fifth St.
Winston-Salem, NC 27101-2506
Tel: (336)725-2382
Fax: (336)727-0581
E-mail: info@wsfoundation.org
Web Site: http://www.wsfoundation.org

To award merit-based scholarships to worthy graduating high school seniors in Forsyth County who intend to pursue baccalaureate degrees at accredited universities and colleges.

Title of Award: Nell and Spencer Waggoner Scholarships **Area, Field, or Subject:** General studies. **Level of Education for which Award is Granted:** Undergraduate **Funds Available:** No specific amount.

Eligibility Requirements: Preference is given to students who: demonstrate evidence of excellence through course selection and academic achievement with a minimum cumulative GPA of 3.0 (D's are undesirable in any coursework in grades 9-12); outstanding community and school leadership; demonstrate community service and/or school service and concern for being a contributing member of society (work experience recognized for those who have less community involvement due to work obligations). The scholarships are for four consecutive years, provided requirements for renewal are met. Renewing recipients must provide an official academic year-end grade transcript to the Foundation each year. Students must request grade transcripts for themselves from the college registrar and then forward the transcript to the Foundation. **Application Requirements:** In addition to a completed application, the following items are required: a high school grade transcript through at least the first semester of the 12th grade; an interview if so advised; one recommendation. **Deadline for Receipt:** March 31. **Additional Information:** WSF Student Aid Department, 336-714-3445.

2415 ■ WINSTON-SALEM FOUNDATION

860 W Fifth St.
Winston-Salem, NC 27101-2506
Tel: (336)725-2382
Fax: (336)727-0581
E-mail: info@wsfoundation.org
Web Site: http://www.wsfoundation.org
To provide college scholarships to graduating high school seniors at Mt. Tabor High School who will attend the University of North Carolina at Chapel Hill.
Title of Award: Edward Kent Welch Memorial Scholarships **Area, Field, or Subject:** General studies. **Level of Education for which Award is Granted:** Undergraduate **Funds Available:** $1,500.
Eligibility Requirements: Students must: have academic promise; evidence of strong moral character; have a genuine concern for others; have school and/or community leadership. The scholarship is available to students regardless of race, sex, national origin, religion, or handicap. **Application Requirements:** The Mt. Tabor Guidance Office will select the recipient of this award from its pool of students admitted by and planning to attend UNC-Chapel Hill. **Additional Information:** WSF Student Aid Department, 336-714-3445.

2416 ■ WINSTON-SALEM FOUNDATION

860 W Fifth St.
Winston-Salem, NC 27101-2506
Tel: (336)725-2382
Fax: (336)727-0581
E-mail: info@wsfoundation.org
Web Site: http://www.wsfoundation.org
To award worthy graduating high school seniors who plan to attend the University of North Carolina at Chapel Hill.
Title of Award: Elizabeth T. Williams Scholarships **Area, Field, or Subject:** General studies. **Level of Education for which Award is Granted:** Undergraduate **Funds Available:** No specific amount.
Eligibility Requirements: This fund seeks to identify the well-rounded individual who: has achieved academic success (minimum, cumulative, unweighted GPA of 3.0 on a 4.0 scale, or equivalent through first semester, 12th grade with appropriate course selection); has participated in student service clubs and/or other school activities; has participated in non-school community service activities; has participated directly in athletics or in support positions for athletics; may or may not have part-time work experience; demonstrates good moral character; shows evidence of financial need (not restricted to lowest incomes); and is a United States citizen. **Application Requirements:** Applications may be submitted by accessing the Foundation's web site. Applicants are responsible for submitting the application and getting the supplemental items to The Winston-Salem Foundation on or before the deadline. The application packet will contain the following components: the completed application; grade transcript; two recommendations; list of student activities. **Deadline for Receipt:** March 31. **Additional Information:** WSF Student Aid Department, 336-714-3445.

2417 ■ WINSTON-SALEM FOUNDATION

860 W Fifth St.
Winston-Salem, NC 27101-2506
Tel: (336)725-2382
Fax: (336)727-0581
E-mail: info@wsfoundation.org
Web Site: http://www.wsfoundation.org
To provide scholarships to a graduating high school senior who will pursue a bachelor's degree at the University of North Carolina-Greensboro.
Title of Award: Edwin H. and Louise N. Williamson Endowed Scholarships **Area, Field, or Subject:** General studies. **Level of Education for which Award is Granted:** Undergraduate **Funds Available:** $1,500.
Eligibility Requirements: This scholarship seeks to identify those students who: demonstrate a minimum, cumulative, unweighted GPA of 3.0; have a financial need, however, the scholarship is not restricted to lowest family incomes; will attend the University of North Carolina-Greensboro; are graduating from a Forsyth County high school. **Application Requirements:** Scholarship applications are available online. Students must: complete application in its entirety; provide grade transcript through the 1st semester of 12th grade; provide one recom-

mendation, as described in the application; attend an interview, if so advised. **Deadline for Receipt:** February 15. **Additional Information:** WSF Student Aid Department, 336-714-3445.

2418 ■ WOMEN'S ARMY CORPS VETERANS ASSOCIATION

PO Box 5577
Fort McClellan, AL 36205-5577
Tel: (256)820-6824
E-mail: info@armywomen.org
Web Site: http://www.armywomen.org
To provide educational assistance to relatives of Army Service Women.
Title of Award: Women's Army Corps Veterans Association Scholarships **Area, Field, or Subject:** General studies. **Level of Education for which Award is Granted:** Undergraduate **Funds Available:** $1,500. **Duration:** One year.
Eligibility Requirements: Program is open to relatives of Army Service Women. **Application Requirements:** Applicants must submit the completed application form available from the website, an official 7-semester high school transcript, three letters of recommendation (one of which must be written by a teacher, counselor or principal); biographical sketch; and documentation of sponsor's military service. Forward materials to: Women's Army Corps Veteran's Association, Women's Army Corps Veterans Scholarship, PO Box 5577, Fort McClellan, Alabama 36205-5577.

2419 ■ WOMEN'S BUSINESS ENTERPRISE NATIONAL COUNCIL

1120 Connecticut Ave. NW, Ste. 1000
Washington, DC 20036
Tel: (202)872-5515
Fax: (202)872-5505
E-mail: ldenny@wbenc.org
Web Site: http://www.wbenc.org
To provide financial assistance and opportunities for women to attend an executive level course.
Title of Award: Dorothy B. Brothers Executive Scholarship Program **Area, Field, or Subject:** General Studies. **Level of Education for which Award is Granted:** High School **Funds Available:** $4,500.
Eligibility Requirements: Applicants must be currently certified as a woman business enterprise by WBENC; must have at least three-to-five years experience running a business; must employ at least three full-time employees; must maintain a minimum annual sales volume of $500,000 (the range is $500,000-$50,000); must not have previously attended a comparable executive management program (TUK-WBENC Executive Program). **Application Requirements:** Applicants must fill out the application form and submit an essay stating the applicant's career goals related to business. **Deadline for Receipt:** April 30.

2420 ■ WOMEN'S MISSIONARY COUNCIL OF THE CHRISTIAN METHODIST EPISCOPAL CHURCH

11321 South Aberdeen
Chicago, IL 60643
Tel: (773)264-2273
Fax: (773)264-2274
E-mail: hamb@sbcglobal.ne
Web Site: http://www.cme-church.org/Missionary_Council
To emphasizes the importance of educational training beyond the high school level.
Title of Award: The Helena B. Cobb Annual Scholarships **Area, Field, or Subject:** General studies. **Level of Education for which Award is Granted:** Undergraduate **Funds Available:** $100. **Duration:** Annually.
Eligibility Requirements: Applicant must be a member of the Christian Methodist Episcopal Church; a high school graduate; and enrolled in a college, university, or vocational-technical school. **Application Requirements:** Applicants must submit a completed application form. **Additional Information:** The program was named for the first Vice President of the Council, Helena B. Cobb. **Deadline for Receipt:** December 31.

2421 ■ WOMEN'S MISSIONARY COUNCIL OF THE CHRISTIAN METHODIST EPISCOPAL CHURCH

11321 South Aberdeen
Chicago, IL 60643
Tel: (773)264-2273
Fax: (773)264-2274

E-mail: hamb@sbcglobal.ne
Web Site: http://www.cme-church.org/Missionary_Council
To emphasizes the importance of educational training beyond the high school level.
Title of Award: The Helena B. Cobb Four-Year Higher Education Grants **Area, Field, or Subject:** General studies. **Level of Education for which Award is Granted:** Undergraduate **Number Awarded:** 10. **Funds Available:** $1000-$4000. **Duration:** Quadrennial.
Eligibility Requirements: Applicant must be a member of the Christian Methodist Episcopal Church; a high school graduate; and enrolled in a college, university, or vocational-technical school. **Application Requirements:** Applicants must submit a completed application form. **Additional Information:** The program was named for the first Vice President of the Council, Helena B. Cobb. **Deadline for Receipt:** December 31.

2422 ■ WOMEN'S OVERSEAS AND SERVICE LEAGUE
PO Box 7124
Washington, DC 20044-7124
E-mail: carolhabgood@sbcglobal.net
Web Site: http://www.wosl.org
To assist women who have served overseas in or with the Armed Forces.
Title of Award: Women's Overseas and Service League Scholarships for Women **Area, Field, or Subject:** General studies. **Level of Education for which Award is Granted:** Undergraduate **Funds Available:** $500-$1,000.00. **Duration:** Entire length of undergraduate study.
Eligibility Requirements: Applicants must be women who are committed to the advancement in military or other public service careers; must have demonstrated such commitment through life experiences; have successfully completed a minimum of 12 semester(18 quarter) hours of study in any institution of higher Education with a minimum of 2.5 grade point average; must be admitted for study in an institution of higher learning program leading to an academic degree (Associate Degree or higher). The program must be professional or technical in nature; must agree to enroll for a minimum of six semester(nine quarter) hours of study each academic period; and she must agree to maintain academic standards. **Application Requirements:** Applicants must fill out the application form; must include all needed documents such as resume, transcripts, essays and references. **Deadline for Receipt:** March 1.

2423 ■ WOMEN'S TRANSPORTATION SEMINAR
1701 K St. NW, Ste. 800
Washington, DC 20006
Tel: (202)955-5085
Fax: (202)955-5088
E-mail: membership@wtsinternational.org
Web Site: http://www.wtsinternational.org
To introduce cultural and organizational changes aimed at motivating the public transit work force.
Title of Award: Sharon D. Banks Undergraduate Memorial Scholarships **Area, Field, or Subject:** Transportation; Finance; Logistics. **Level of Education for which Award is Granted:** Undergraduate **Funds Available:** $3,000.
Eligibility Requirements: Applicants must be women pursuing undergraduate studies in transportation engineering, planning, finance or logistics, or related fields. Applicants must have at least a GPA of 3.0 or higher. **Application Requirements:** Applicants must fill out the scholarship application form **Deadline for Receipt:** May 15.

2424 ■ WOMEN'S TRANSPORTATION SEMINAR
1701 K St. NW, Ste. 800
Washington, DC 20006
Tel: (202)955-5085
Fax: (202)955-5088
E-mail: membership@wtsinternational.org
Web Site: http://www.wtsinternational.org
To provide financial assistance to women who wish to further their careers as leaders in the transportation industry.
Title of Award: Anne Koby Legacy Scholarships **Area, Field, or Subject:** Transportation; Finance; Logistics. **Level of Education for which Award is Granted:** Undergraduate **Funds Available:** $3,000.
Eligibility Requirements: Applicants must be women pursuing undergraduate studies in transportation engineering, planning, finance or logistics, or related fields; and must have a GPA of at least 3.0 or higher.

Application Requirements: Applicants must fill out the scholarship application form and submit them to local WTS Chapters. **Deadline for Receipt:** May 15.

2425 ■ WOMEN'S TRANSPORTATION SEMINAR
1701 K St. NW, Ste. 800
Washington, DC 20006
Tel: (202)955-5085
Fax: (202)955-5088
E-mail: membership@wtsinternational.org
Web Site: http://www.wtsinternational.org
To introduce cultural and organizational changes aimed at motivating the public transit work force.
Title of Award: Helen M. Overly Memorial Scholarships **Area, Field, or Subject:** Transportation; Finance; Logistics. **Level of Education for which Award is Granted:** Undergraduate **Funds Available:** $6,000.
Eligibility Requirements: Applicants must be women pursuing undergraduate studies in transportation engineering, planning, finance or logistics, or related fields. Applicants must have at least a GPA of 3.0 or higher. **Application Requirements:** Applicants must fill out the scholarship application form **Deadline for Receipt:** May 15.

2426 ■ WORKING AGAINST CANCER
PO Box 70233
Pasadena, CA 91107
Tel: (626)914-2914
E-mail: contactus@workingagainstcancer.org
Web Site: http://www.workingagainstcancer.org
To assist young adult cancer survivors (ages 30 yrs and under) by providing awards toward academic and vocational education.
Title of Award: Survival Scholarship Program **Area, Field, or Subject:** General Studies. **Level of Education for which Award is Granted:** Undergraduate **Number Awarded:** 3. **Funds Available:** $500 (2) and $1,000 (1).
Eligibility Requirements: Applicants must be cancer survivors or recently diagnosed with cancer. **Application Requirements:** Applicants must check the available website for other requirements. **Additional Information:** Working Against Cancer at the above address

2427 ■ WORLDWIDE ASSURANCE FOR EMPLOYEES OF PUBLIC AGENCIES
7651 Leesburg Pike
Falls Church, VA 22043
Tel: (703)790-8010
Free: 800-368-3484
E-mail: info@waepa.org
Web Site: http://www.waepa.org
To assist policy holders' children who plan to continue education in college or vocational school programs.
Title of Award: WAEPA Scholarship Program **Area, Field, or Subject:** General studies. **Level of Education for which Award is Granted:** Undergraduate **Number Awarded:** 50. **Funds Available:** $1,000 to $4,000. **Duration:** One year.
Eligibility Requirements: Applicants must be children, under the age of 23, of WAEPA life insurance policy holders; must be high school seniors or graduates who plan to enroll or are already enrolled full-time in an accredited two-year or four-year college, university or vocational-technical school; must have a minimum grade point average of 3.0 on a 4.0 scale or its equivalent. **Application Requirements:** Applicants must complete the application and mail it along with a current and complete transcript of grades to Scholarship America. **Deadline for Receipt:** February 1. **Additional Information:** WAEPA Scholarship Program; Scholarship America; One Scholarship Way, PO Box 297, Saint Peter, MN 56082; Telephone: 507-931-1682.

2428 ■ XAVIER UNIVERSITY
3800 Victory Pky.
Cincinnati, OH 45207
Tel: (513)745-3000
Free: 800-344-GOXU
Web Site: http://www.xavier.edu
To financially support students with their education.
Title of Award: Edgecliff Alumni Awards **Area, Field, or Subject:** General studies. **Level of Education for which Award is Granted:** Undergraduate **Funds Available:** Begins at $500.

Eligibility Requirements: Applicants must be the children, grandchildren, nieces or nephews of a Edgecliff College alumni. **Application Requirements:** Applicants admitted at the Xavier University are automatically considered. **Deadline for Receipt:** February 1.

2429 ■ XAVIER UNIVERSITY
3800 Victory Pky.
Cincinnati, OH 45207
Tel: (513)745-3000
Free: 800-344-GOXU
Web Site: http://www.xavier.edu
To financially support students with their education.
Title of Award: James E. Hoff, S.J. Scholars **Area, Field, or Subject:** General studies. **Level of Education for which Award is Granted:** Undergraduate **Funds Available:** Varies.
Eligibility Requirements: Applicants must be the children, grandchildren, nieces or nephews of a Edgecliff College alumni; must demonstrate exceptional leadership, vision, courage, service and compassion in academic and personal life. **Application Requirements:** Applicants admitted at the Xavier University are automatically considered. **Additional Information:** Award may be given to an Edgecliff alumni award recipient. **Deadline for Receipt:** February 1.

2430 ■ XAVIER UNIVERSITY
3800 Victory Pky.
Cincinnati, OH 45207
Tel: (513)745-3000
Free: 800-344-GOXU
Web Site: http://www.xavier.edu
To financially support students with their education.
Title of Award: Indiana Alumni Scholarships **Area, Field, or Subject:** General studies. **Level of Education for which Award is Granted:** Undergraduate **Number Awarded:** 2. **Funds Available:** $2000. **Duration:** One year.
Eligibility Requirements: Applicant must be an incoming freshmen from Indiana. **Application Requirements:** Applicants must apply for financial aid by completing the FAFSA. **Deadline for Receipt:** FAFSA deadline: February 15; Application deadline: March 1.

2431 ■ XAVIER UNIVERSITY
3800 Victory Pky.
Cincinnati, OH 45207
Tel: (513)745-3000
Free: 800-344-GOXU
Web Site: http://www.xavier.edu
To financially support students with their education.
Title of Award: Ohio War Orphan Scholarships **Area, Field, or Subject:** General studies. **Level of Education for which Award is Granted:** Undergraduate **Funds Available:** $660. **Duration:** One academic year.
Eligibility Requirements: Applicant must be student with a parent who served at least 90 days of active duty during wartime and is disabled or deceased as a result of service. **Application Requirements:** Applications available from high school guidance counselors or veterans offices.

2432 ■ XAVIER UNIVERSITY
3800 Victory Pky.
Cincinnati, OH 45207
Tel: (513)745-3000
Free: 800-344-GOXU
Web Site: http://www.xavier.edu
To financially support students with their education.
Title of Award: Miguel Pro Scholarships **Area, Field, or Subject:** General studies. **Level of Education for which Award is Granted:** Undergraduate **Funds Available:** Up to full-tuition.
Eligibility Requirements: Applicant must be a Hispanic/Latino first-year student with excellent academic achievement. **Application Requirements:** Applicants admitted at the Xavier University are automatically considered. **Additional Information:** Selected students will be interviewed on the campus. The scholarship is named in honor of Miguel Pro, S.J., a Mexican priest who was martyred by the Mexican government in 1927 for his practice and teaching of the Catholic faith. **Deadline for Receipt:** December 1.

2433 ■ XAVIER UNIVERSITY
3800 Victory Pky.
Cincinnati, OH 45207
Tel: (513)745-3000
Free: 800-344-GOXU
Web Site: http://www.xavier.edu
To financially support students with their education.
Title of Award: Trustee, Schawe, Presidential and Honor Scholarships **Area, Field, or Subject:** General studies. **Level of Education for which Award is Granted:** Undergraduate **Funds Available:** $8000-$12,000.
Eligibility Requirements: Applicant must be an incoming first-year student with excellent academic achievement (rank at least in the top 25 percent of high school class, have appropriately high grades, and have a minimum SAT of 1130, 25 ACT). **Application Requirements:** Applicants admitted at the Xavier University are automatically considered.

2434 ■ XAVIER UNIVERSITY
3800 Victory Pky.
Cincinnati, OH 45207
Tel: (513)745-3000
Free: 800-344-GOXU
Web Site: http://www.xavier.edu
To financially support students with their education.
Title of Award: Francis X. Weninger Scholarships **Area, Field, or Subject:** General studies. **Level of Education for which Award is Granted:** Undergraduate **Funds Available:** Up to full-tuition. **Duration:** Four year.
Eligibility Requirements: Applicant must be an African American first-year student with excellent academic achievement. **Application Requirements:** Applicants admitted at the Xavier University are automatically considered. **Additional Information:** Selected students will be interviewed on the campus. The Scholarship is named in honor of Francis Xavier Weninger, S.J., founder of St. Ann Parish in 1865. **Deadline for Receipt:** December 1.

2435 ■ XAVIER UNIVERSITY
3800 Victory Pky.
Cincinnati, OH 45207
Tel: (513)745-3000
Free: 800-344-GOXU
Web Site: http://www.xavier.edu
To financially support students with their education.
Title of Award: St. Francis Xavier Scholarships **Area, Field, or Subject:** General studies. **Level of Education for which Award is Granted:** Undergraduate **Number Awarded:** 10. **Funds Available:** Full-tuition. **Duration:** Four years.
Eligibility Requirements: Applicant must be an incoming first-year student with exceptional academic achievement and outstanding leadership involvement in the community or school. **Application Requirements:** Applicants admitted at the Xavier University are automatically considered. **Additional Information:** Selected students will be interviewed in the campus. **Deadline for Receipt:** December 1.

2436 ■ XAVIER UNIVERSITY
3800 Victory Pky.
Cincinnati, OH 45207
Tel: (513)745-3000
Free: 800-344-GOXU
Web Site: http://www.xavier.edu
To financially support students with their education.
Title of Award: Xavier Service Fellowships **Area, Field, or Subject:** General studies. **Level of Education for which Award is Granted:** Undergraduate **Number Awarded:** 5. **Funds Available:** Full tuition, room and board. **Duration:** Four years.
Eligibility Requirements: Applicant must be incoming first-year student who have demonstrated high academic achievement, outstanding service to community, school, or church, and leadership in encouraging others to serve. **Application Requirements:** Applicants admitted at the Xavier University are automatically considered. **Additional Information:** Selected students will be interviewed on the campus. **Deadline for Receipt:** December 1.

2437 ■ XAVIER UNIVERSITY
3800 Victory Pky.
Cincinnati, OH 45207

Tel: (513)745-3000
Free: 800-344-GOXU
Web Site: http://www.xavier.edu
To financially support students with their education.
Title of Award: Xavier University Chancellor Scholarships **Area, Field, or Subject:** General studies. **Level of Education for which Award is Granted:** Undergraduate **Number Awarded:** 15. **Funds Available:** $15,000. **Duration:** Four years.
Eligibility Requirements: Applicant must be an incoming first-year student with excellent academic achievement. **Application Requirements:** Applicants admitted at the Xavier University are automatically considered. **Additional Information:** Selected students will be interviewed in the campus. Named in honor of Xavier's late Chancellor James E. Hoff, S.J. **Deadline for Receipt:** December 1.

2438 ■ XAVIER UNIVERSITY
3800 Victory Pky.
Cincinnati, OH 45207
Tel: (513)745-3000
Free: 800-344-GOXU
Web Site: http://www.xavier.edu
To financially support students with their education.
Title of Award: Xavier University Legacy Scholarships **Area, Field, or Subject:** General studies. **Level of Education for which Award is Granted:** Undergraduate **Number Awarded:** 2. **Funds Available:** $3000.
Eligibility Requirements: Applicants must be full-time undergraduate student who are children or grandchildren of Xavier alumni. **Application Requirements:** Applicants must submit a completed Legacy Scholarship Application along with the requires supporting materials. **Deadline for Receipt:** March 21.

2439 ■ YOUTH FOR UNDERSTANDING
6400 Goldsboro Rd., Ste. 100
Bethesda, MD 20817
Tel: (240)235-2100; (866)4YFU-USA
Fax: (240)235-2104
E-mail: admission@yfu.org
Web Site: http://www.yfu-usa.org
To provide deserving individuals with the best international exchange experience.
Title of Award: Youth for Understanding Scholarships **Area, Field, or Subject:** Travel and tourism. **Level of Education for which Award is Granted:** Undergraduate **Funds Available:** No specific amount. **Duration:** One year.

Eligibility Requirements: Applicants must be between the ages of 15 and 18 and have maintained a minimum 3.0 GPA for a year or semester program or 2.0 GPA for a summer program, and be in good health. **Application Requirements:** Applicant must file an application online at the website of YFU.

2440 ■ ZETA PHI BETA SORORITY
1734 New Hampshire Ave. NW
Washington, DC 20009
Tel: (202)387-3103
Fax: (202)232-4593
E-mail: ihq@zphib1920.org
Web Site: http://www.zphib1920.org
To support students in pursuit of higher education.
Title of Award: Deborah Partridge Wolfe International Fellowships **Area, Field, or Subject:** General studies. **Level of Education for which Award is Granted:** Graduate, Undergraduate **Funds Available:** $500-$1000.
Eligibility Requirements: Applicant must be a full-time graduate or undergraduate U.S. student studying abroad; or full-time graduate or undergraduate foreign student studying in the U.S. **Application Requirements:** Applicants must submit a completed application forms along with the required materials. **Deadline for Receipt:** February 1.

2441 ■ ZETA PHI BETA SORORITY
1734 New Hampshire Ave. NW
Washington, DC 20009
Tel: (202)387-3103
Fax: (202)232-4593
E-mail: ihq@zphib1920.org
Web Site: http://www.zphib1920.org
To support students for the pursuit of higher education.
Title of Award: Zeta Phi Beta Sorority General Undergraduate Scholarships **Area, Field, or Subject:** General studies. **Level of Education for which Award is Granted:** Undergraduate **Number Awarded:** 1. **Funds Available:** $500-$1000. **Duration:** One academic year.
Eligibility Requirements: Applicant must be a full-time undergraduate freshman, sophomore, junior, senior or graduating high school planning to enter college. **Application Requirements:** Applicants must submit completed application form along with the required materials. **Deadline for Receipt:** February 1.

General

2442 ■ FIRST COMMUNITY FOUNDATION OF PENNSYLVANIA, WILLIAMSPORT-LYCOMING
330 Pine St., Suite 401
Williamsport, PA 17701
Tel: (570)321-1500; (866)901-2372
Fax: (570)321-6434
E-mail: fcfpa@fcfpa.org
Web Site: http://www.wlfoundation.org
To provide financial assistance for South Williamsport Area High School seniors.
Title of Award: Jane Salanky-Onzik Scholarship Fund **Area, Field, or Subject:** Spanish studies. **Level of Education for which Award is Granted:** Undergraduate **Funds Available:** No specific amount.
Eligibility Requirements: Applicants must be high school seniors who have been accepted into a full-time undergraduate program at an institution of higher education (preferably in Pennsylvania) to study secondary education (preferably to teach Spanish) or to study Spanish in preparation for a career that would utilize the Spanish language. Applicants must have exhibited good citizenship and community involvement, must have unmet financial need and must not have been the recipient of other major scholarship awards. **Application Requirements:** Applicant must submit an application to the Guidance Counselor's office. **Additional Information:** Verna Correll, Guidance Counselor, s Williamsport Jr./Sr. High School, 700 Percy St., S Williamsport, PA 17702; 570-326-2684; vcorrell@mounties.k12.pa.us.

2443 ■ NATIONAL IRANIAN AMERICAN COUNCIL
1411 K St. NW, Ste. 600
Washington, DC 20005
Tel: (202)386-6325
Fax: (202)386-6409
Web Site: http://www.niacouncil.org
To provide scholarships to students of Iranian descent.
Title of Award: The Iranian-American Scholarship Fund **Area, Field, or Subject:** Ethnic. **Level of Education for which Award is Granted:** Undergraduate **Funds Available:** $1,000-$3,000.
Eligibility Requirements: Applicants must be of Iranian heritage; Undergraduate (sophomore or above); Graduate (Masters Program or equivalent); GPA 3.5 or above. **Application Requirements:** Applicants may download an application form at Iranian-American Scholarship Fund website. Applicant must submit the completed application and all supporting documents. **Deadline for Receipt:** April 1. **Additional Information:** Iranian-American Scholarship Fund; PO Box 500835, San Diego, CA 92150.

2444 ■ NATIONAL IRANIAN AMERICAN COUNCIL
1411 K St. NW, Ste. 600
Washington, DC 20005
Tel: (202)386-6325
Fax: (202)386-6409
Web Site: http://www.niacouncil.org
To provide scholarships to students who are of Iranian descent.
Title of Award: Iranian Association of Boston's IAB Scholarships **Area, Field, or Subject:** Ethnic. **Level of Education for which Award is Granted:** Undergraduate **Funds Available:** $3,000.
Eligibility Requirements: The applicant must not be a relative or close relation of any members of the Scholarship Committee; must have legal immigration status; must be of Iranian descent or have active interest in Iranian culture and heritage; The applicant must be a full-time student of an accredited New England graduate or undergraduate institution in any of the following states: ME, VT, NH, MA, CT, or RI. **Application Requirements:** Applicant may download an application form at the NIAC website. Applicant must complete and submit the application and other requirements. **Deadline for Receipt:** February 1. **Additional Information:** NIAC at the above address.

2445 ■ NATIONAL IRANIAN AMERICAN COUNCIL
1411 K St. NW, Ste. 600
Washington, DC 20005
Tel: (202)386-6325
Fax: (202)386-6409
Web Site: http://www.niacouncil.org
To provide scholarships to students of Iranian descent.
Title of Award: Iranian Federated Women's Club Scholarships **Area, Field, or Subject:** Ethnic. **Level of Education for which Award is Granted:** Undergraduate **Funds Available:** $10,000.
Eligibility Requirements: Open to all students of Iranian descent attending an undergraduate and graduate course. **Application Requirements:** Applicant may download an application form at the Iranian Federated Women's Club website. Applicant must submit the complete application form and a personal essay describing himself/herself, his/her goals, and his/her qualifications for this scholarship. Applicant must also submit the following: two letters of reference; parent's tax return (for each tax return you must include IRS Form 4506); official transcript. **Deadline for Receipt:** July 21. **Additional Information:** ifwc@aol.com.

2446 ■ NATIONAL IRANIAN AMERICAN COUNCIL
1411 K St. NW, Ste. 600
Washington, DC 20005
Tel: (202)386-6325
Fax: (202)386-6409
Web Site: http://www.niacouncil.org
To provide scholarships to students of Iranian descent.
Title of Award: Momeni Foundation Scholarships **Area, Field, or Subject:** Ethnic. **Level of Education for which Award is Granted:** Undergraduate **Funds Available:** $500-$1,000.
Eligibility Requirements: Applicants must be college students and graduating high school seniors of Iranian descent of any citizenry, anywhere in the world. **Application Requirements:** Applicants must submit a resume or list of extra curricular activities, community leadership or voluntarism, membership in clubs or organizations and any other evidence of outstanding achievement; must submit a short narrative describing goals and plans and motivation towards such. **Deadline for Receipt:** June 30. **Additional Information:** Momeni Foundation 12720 SW Allen Blvd., Beaverton, OR 97005 USA; 503-349-4939.

African Studies

2447 ■ BLUES HEAVEN FOUNDATION

2120 S Michigan Ave.
Chicago, IL 60616
Tel: (312)808-1286
Fax: (312)808-0273
E-mail: info@bluesheaven.com
Web Site: http://www.bluesheaven.com
To provide financial assistance to students in Chicago.
Title of Award: Muddy Waters Scholarships **Area, Field, or Subject:** Music education, music, African-American studies, folklore, performing arts, journalism, radio and television. **Level of Education for which Award is Granted:** Undergraduate **Funds Available:** NO specific amount.
Eligibility Requirements: Applicant must have a full-time enrollment status in a Chicago area college or university; must be in at least their first year of undergraduate studies or graduate program. **Application Requirements:** Application form are available in the website address; must be sent to: Blues Heaven Foundation Inc., 2120 S Michigan Ave., Chicago, IL 60616. **Deadline for Receipt:** April 30.

American Studies

2448 ■ AMERICAN SOCIETY FOR LEGAL HISTORY

University of Minnesota School of Law
326 Mondale Hall
229-19th Ave. S
Minneapolis, MN 55455
Fax: (612)625-2011
E-mail: gallanis@umn.edu
Web Site: http://www.h-net.msu.edu/~law/ASLH/aslh.htm
To support research and writing in American legal history.
Title of Award: Cromwell Fellowships **Area, Field, or Subject:** American History. **Level of Education for which Award is Granted:** Undergraduate **Number Awarded:** 3-5. **Funds Available:** $5,000.
Eligibility Requirements: Applicants must be currently enrolled in an institution, college, or university. **Application Requirements:** Applicants must complete the application form.

2449 ■ ASSOCIATION ON AMERICAN INDIAN AFFAIRS

966 Hungerford Dr., Ste. 12-B
Rockville, MD 20850
Tel: (240)314-7155
Fax: (240)314-7159
E-mail: general.aaia@verizon.net
Web Site: http://indian-affairs.org
To provide financial assistance for helping native people for higher education.
Title of Award: Adolph Van Pelt Special Fund for Indians Scholarships **Area, Field, or Subject:** American Indian studies. **Level of Education for which Award is Granted:** Undergraduate **Funds Available:** $1,500.
Eligibility Requirements: Applicants must be students from any curriculum. **Application Requirements:** Students are eligible to apply on a yearly basis. **Deadline for Receipt:** July 1.

2450 ■ HARTFORD FOUNDATION FOR PUBLIC GIVING

10 Columbus Blvd., 8th Flr.
Hartford, CT 06106
Tel: (860)548-1888
Fax: (860)524-8346
E-mail: hfpg@hfpg.org
Web Site: http://www.hfpg.org
To provide financial assistance to students entering or enrolled as undergraduate or graduate at a four-year college or university or summer program in Poland.
Title of Award: Tadeusz Sendzimir Scholarships **Area, Field, or Subject:** Polish studies; American history. **Level of Education for which Award is Granted:** Undergraduate **Number Awarded:** 1-5. **Funds Available:** $1,000-$5,000.
Eligibility Requirements: Applicants must be Connecticut residents; studying Polish/Slavic Language, history or culture in the US or Poland.

Preference to students of Polish descent. **Application Requirements:** Applicants may obtain application materials from Connecticut Community Foundation, 43 Field St., Waterbury, CT 06702. **Deadline for Receipt:** March 1. **Additional Information:** Tallitha Richardson-Selby, Program/ Scholarship Associate; 203-756-3054; info@conncf.org.

2451 ■ NATIONAL SOCIETY, DAUGHTERS OF THE AMERICAN REVOLUTION

1776 D St. NW
Washington, DC 20006-5303
Tel: (202)628-1776
Web Site: http://www.dar.org
To promote the study of American history among students.
Title of Award: American History Scholarships **Area, Field, or Subject:** American history. **Level of Education for which Award is Granted:** Undergraduate **Funds Available:** $2,000. **Duration:** One year.
Eligibility Requirements: Applicants must be graduating students who want to pursue an undergraduate degree with a concentrated study of a minimum of 24 credit hours in American History and American Government. **Application Requirements:** Applicants must obtain a letter of sponsorship from their local DAR chapter. Application forms and other supporting documents must be completed correctly and submitted in one package. **Deadline for Receipt:** February 15.

2452 ■ MORRIS K. UDALL FOUNDATION

130 S Scott Ave.
Tucson, AZ 85701-1922
Tel: (520)901-8500
Fax: (520)670-5530
E-mail: info@udall.gov
Web Site: http://www.udall.gov
To provide scholarship assistance for qualified individuals.
Title of Award: Morris K. Udall Scholarships **Area, Field, or Subject:** Environmental technology; Native American studies. **Level of Education for which Award is Granted:** Undergraduate **Funds Available:** No specific amount. **Duration:** One year.
Eligibility Requirements: Applicant must be a student who has demonstrated commitment to a career related to the environment; or must be a Native American or Alaska Native student who has demonstrated commitment to a career related to tribal public policy or Native health care; must be a sophomore or junior level college student; must have a college GPA of at least 3.0 or the equivalent; and must be a U.S citizen, U.S national, or U.S permanent resident. **Application Requirements:** Applicants must complete and sign Udall Scholarship Application and submit along with an 800-word essay (signed and dated), a current official college transcript and transcripts for other colleges attended, and three letters of recommendation. **Deadline for Receipt:** March 4.

Armenian Studies

2453 ■ ARMENIAN STUDENTS' ASSOCIATION OF AMERICA

333 Atlantic Ave.
Warwick, RI 02888
Tel: (401)461-6114
E-mail: asa@asainc.org
Web Site: http://www.asainc.org
To provide financial assistance to those who are in need.
Title of Award: Karekin DerAvedision Memorial Endowment Fund **Area, Field, or Subject:** Armenian Studies. **Level of Education for which Award is Granted:** Undergraduate **Funds Available:** Maximum of $8,000.
Eligibility Requirements: Applicants must be graduate students in Armenian Studies who has been accepted for admission to UCLA. **Application Requirements:** Applicants must check the available website for the required materials. **Deadline for Receipt:** December 15. **Additional Information:** UCLA Graduate Division Special; Fellowship Office 1252 Murphy Hall Box 951419 Los Angeles, CA 90095-1419 Tel: (310) 825-3521

2454 ■ ARMENIAN STUDENTS' ASSOCIATION OF AMERICA

333 Atlantic Ave.
Warwick, RI 02888

Tel: (401)461-6114
E-mail: asa@asainc.org
Web Site: http://www.asainc.org
To provide financial assistance to those students who are in need.
Title of Award: Garikian Scholarship Fund **Area, Field, or Subject:** Armenian Studies; Sociology; Psychology; Political Science; Middle Eastern History; Journalism; Education; Music. **Level of Education for which Award is Granted:** Undergraduate **Funds Available:** $750-$1,000.
Eligibility Requirements: Applicants must have completed their first academic year in college or university in California; must be pursuing one of the above field of studies. **Application Requirements:** Applicants must apply to the Executive Board for application forms and return them, completed, before the deadline. **Deadline for Receipt:** August 31. **Additional Information:** Berj S. Baghdoyan c/o Western Prelacy at 4401 Russell Avenue, Los Angeles, CA 90027.

2455 ■ ARMENIAN STUDENTS' ASSOCIATION OF AMERICA
333 Atlantic Ave.
Warwick, RI 02888
Tel: (401)461-6114
E-mail: asa@asainc.org
Web Site: http://www.asainc.org
To provide financial assistance to those students who are in need.
Title of Award: Knights of Vartan, Fresno Lodge No. 9 Scholarships **Area, Field, or Subject:** Armenian Studies. **Level of Education for which Award is Granted:** Undergraduate **Number Awarded:** 2. **Funds Available:** $750, one for an entering freshman and one for a continuing student at C.S.U.F. **Duration:** One year.
Eligibility Requirements: Applicants must be new or continuing full-time students (12 units per semester) at Fresno State and maintain a 3.0 GPA or higher. **Application Requirements:** Applicants must check the available website for the required materials. **Deadline for Receipt:** November 1. **Additional Information:** Ms. Linda Tamura; Scholarship Coordinator; Tel: 209-278-6572

East European Studies

2456 ■ CANADIAN INSTITUTE OF UKRAINIAN STUDIES
4-50 Athabasca Hall
Edmonton, AB, Canada T6G 2E8
Tel: (780)492-2972
Fax: (780)492-4967
E-mail: cius@ualberta.ca
Web Site: http://www.ualberta.ca/CIUS
To help students pursue their final year of study in the faculty of Arts or Education.
Title of Award: Leo J. Krysa Family Undergraduate Scholarships **Area, Field, or Subject:** Ukrainian studies. **Level of Education for which Award is Granted:** Undergraduate **Funds Available:** $3,500.
Eligibility Requirements: Candidates must be Canadian citizens or permanent residents of Canada at the time of application; must be students in the faculty of Arts and Education about to enter their final year of study in pursuit of an undergraduate degree. **Application Requirements:** Applicants must submit an official transcript of records. Application form is available from the Canadian Institute of Ukrainian Studies, 450 Athabasca Hall, University of Alberta, Edmonton, AB, CAN T6G 2E8. **Deadline for Receipt:** March 1.

2457 ■ CANADIAN INSTITUTE OF UKRAINIAN STUDIES
4-50 Athabasca Hall
Edmonton, AB, Canada T6G 2E8
Tel: (780)492-2972
Fax: (780)492-4967
E-mail: cius@ualberta.ca
Web Site: http://www.ualberta.ca/CIUS
To support students who wish to pursue their final year of study in the faculty of Education.
Title of Award: Ukrainian Canadian Professional and Business Club Scholarships in Education **Area, Field, or Subject:** Ukrainian studies. **Level of Education for which Award is Granted:** Undergraduate **Funds Available:** $800.

Eligibility Requirements: Applicant must be a full-time undergraduate student completing the third or fourth year in the faculty of Education at the University of Alberta; must have taken one course in language acquisition or teaching and one senior course in Ukrainian language or literature; must have both academic standing and demonstrated involvement in the Ukrainian community. **Application Requirements:** Applicants must submit an official transcript of records. Application form is available from the Canadian Institute of Ukrainian Studies, 450 Athabasca Hall, University of Alberta, Edmonton, AB, CAN T6G 2E8. **Deadline for Receipt:** March 1.

European Studies

2458 ■ ALBERTA LEARNING INFORMATION SERVICE - ALBERTA SCHOLARSHIP PROGRAM
Box 28000 Sta. Main
Edmonton, AB, Canada T5J 4R4
Tel: (780)427-8640
Fax: (780)427-1288
E-mail: scholarship@gov.ab.ca
Web Site: http://www.alis.alberta.ca
To assist Albertans in pursuing post-secondary studies taught in French.
Title of Award: Fellowships for Full-time Studies in French **Area, Field, or Subject:** French studies. **Level of Education for which Award is Granted:** Undergraduate **Funds Available:** $500-$1,000.
Eligibility Requirements: Applicants must be Alberta residents, Canadian citizens or landed immigrants enrolled full-time in a post-secondary program. In addition, applicants must be enrolled in a minimum of three courses per semester which have French as the language of instruction. **Application Requirements:** Applicants may obtain an application form from the Students Awards Office at Alberta post-secondary institutions that offer programs taught in French and from Alberta Scholarship Programs. Applicants must include proof of Canadian citizenship: either a photocopy of Canadian birth certificate, passport or immigration papers. College applicants must include a transcript. **Deadline for Receipt:** November 15. **Additional Information:** Alberta Scholarship Programs at the above address.

2459 ■ AMERICAN SWEDISH INSTITUTE
2600 Pk. Ave.
Minneapolis, MN 55407-1090
Tel: (612)871-4907
Fax: (612)871-8682
Web Site: http://www.americanswedishinst.org
To promote the study of Swedish heritage.
Title of Award: Lilly Lorenzen Scholarships **Area, Field, or Subject:** Swedish studies. **Level of Education for which Award is Granted:** Undergraduate **Funds Available:** $2,500.
Eligibility Requirements: Applicants must be Minnesota residents and have knowledge of the Swedish language. **Application Requirements:** Applicants must submit a complete application form and a transcript or a statement of professional and community achievement. **Additional Information:** Established in memory of Lilly Lorenzen, an instructor in Swedish University of Minnesota and the American Swedish Institute, and author of the book "Of Swedish Ways". **Deadline for Receipt:** May 1.

2460 ■ AMERICAN SWEDISH INSTITUTE
2600 Pk. Ave.
Minneapolis, MN 55407-1090
Tel: (612)871-4907
Fax: (612)871-8682
Web Site: http://www.americanswedishinst.org
To promote study at the American Swedish Institute.
Title of Award: Malmberg Fellowships **Area, Field, or Subject:** Swedish studies. **Level of Education for which Award is Granted:** Undergraduate **Funds Available:** $4,000.
Eligibility Requirements: Applicants must be students aged 21 years old and above; Sweden residents are also qualified. For organizational applicants, the project manager is identified as the applicant. **Application Requirements:** Applicant must send a study proposal. **Deadline for Receipt:** November.

2461 ■ AMERICAN SWEDISH INSTITUTE
2600 Pk. Ave.
Minneapolis, MN 55407-1090

Tel: (612)871-4907
Fax: (612)871-8682
Web Site: http://www.americanswedishinst.org
To provide financial assistance to individuals to study in Sweden.
Title of Award: Malmberg Scholarships **Area, Field, or Subject:** Swedish studies. **Level of Education for which Award is Granted:** Undergraduate **Funds Available:** $10,000. **Duration:** Nine months.
Eligibility Requirements: Applicants must be U.S. citizens; enrolled in a degree-granting program in college/university; or in a study or research that requires or can be enhanced by study in Sweden; have knowledge in Swedish language. **Application Requirements:** Applicants must submit an application form and a letter of invitation or affiliation from the Swedish institution/organization; a project summary; transcript (optional if out of school for 3 years); resume; and two letters of recommendation. **Deadline for Receipt:** November 15.

2462 ■ CLAN ROSS ASSOCIATION OF THE UNITED STATES
1867 Via Acorde
Camarillo, CA 93010
Tel: (805)389-4338
Web Site: http://www.clanrossassociation.org/USA.htm
To enhance the knowledge of the youth about Scottish culture.
Title of Award: Clan Ross Foundation Scholarships **Area, Field, or Subject:** Scottish studies. **Level of Education for which Award is Granted:** Undergraduate **Number Awarded:** 2. **Funds Available:** $ 1,000 each. **Duration:** One year.
Eligibility Requirements: Applicants must be current members of Clan Ross Association of the United States, Inc. for at least a year. Applicants who are also related with the current members of the Association are also welcome to apply. Families or members of the Clan Ross Scholarship Committee are disqualified for the scholarships. **Application Requirements:** Applicants must write or call the Clan Ross Association for complete information of the Clan Ross Association of the United States, Inc. **Deadline for Receipt:** March 1. **Additional Information:** Virgil Bumann.

2463 ■ GERMAN ACADEMIC EXCHANGE SERVICE
871 United Nations Plz.
New York, NY 10017
Tel: (212)758-3223
Fax: (212)755-5780
E-mail: daadny@daad.org
Web Site: http://www.daad.org
To encourage research and promote the study of cultural, political, historical, economic, and social aspects of modern and contemporary German affairs from an inter and multidisciplinary perspective.
Title of Award: German Studies Research Grant **Area, Field, or Subject:** German studies. **Level of Education for which Award is Granted:** Undergraduate **Funds Available:** $1,500-$2,500.
Eligibility Requirements: Applicant must be a undergraduates with at least junior standing pursuing a German Studies track or minor may be nominated for the grant by their department and/or program chair; must be citizens of the U.S. enrolled full time at the university that nominates them; must be younger than 32 at the start of the grant period. **Application Requirements:** Applicant must submit a completed DAAD application form, resume, detailed description of the research project or the pre dissertation proposal, including a research plan and itinerary, budget statement, list of German language and German Studies courses taken, two letters of recommendation, including one from the professor supervising the German Studies curriculum or the research project, DAAD language evaluation form signed by a German Department faculty member, official transcript of records. **Deadline for Receipt:** May 1 and November 1.

2464 ■ GERMAN ACADEMIC EXCHANGE SERVICE
871 United Nations Plz.
New York, NY 10017
Tel: (212)758-3223
Fax: (212)755-5780
E-mail: daadny@daad.org
Web Site: http://www.daad.org
To attend a broad range of summer courses at German universities which focus mainly on literary, cultural, political and economic aspects of modern and contemporary Germany.

Title of Award: University Summer Course Grants **Area, Field, or Subject:** German studies. **Level of Education for which Award is Granted:** Undergraduate **Funds Available:** 770 Euros.
Eligibility Requirements: Applicant must be a full-time student in a Canadian or US colleges or universities in any field of study; must at least reached Junior standing or third year (10 full-course credits for Canadians) at the time of application; must be younger than 32 at the start of the grant period. **Application Requirements:** Applicant must submit a completed DAAD application form, autobiographical essay in German, a detailed statement (in English) of approximately 500 words explaining why the applicant wants to attend a university summer course, recommendation letter written by a professor in the applicant's major field of study but the recommendation should not be from the same professor who evaluates the language proficiency, complete, official transcripts of all post-secondary studies, DAAD language evaluation form (Sprachzeugnis) signed by any member of German Department at the applicant's institution or by an official of a Goethe Institute, **Deadline for Receipt:** January 31.

2465 ■ THE GERMAN SOCIETY OF PENNSYLVANIA
611 Spring Garden St.
Philadelphia, PA 19123
Tel: (215)627-2332
Fax: (215)627-5297
E-mail: info@germansociety.org
Web Site: http://www.germansociety.org
To provide financial assistance for undergraduate students majoring in German language and literature.
Title of Award: German Society Scholarships **Area, Field, or Subject:** Foreign languages; German studies. **Level of Education for which Award is Granted:** Undergraduate **Funds Available:** $2500.
Eligibility Requirements: Applicant must be a resident of the Greater Delaware Valley; and a high school senior intending to major in German, or a German major (Double majors are also eligible). **Application Requirements:** Applicants must submit a completed application form; a German writing sample (up to one typewritten page); recent transcript; and two letters of reference. **Deadline for Receipt:** March 17.

2466 ■ HARTFORD FOUNDATION FOR PUBLIC GIVING
10 Columbus Blvd., 8th Flr.
Hartford, CT 06106
Tel: (860)548-1888
Fax: (860)524-8346
E-mail: hfpg@hfpg.org
Web Site: http://www.hfpg.org
To provide educational assistance for graduating high school seniors who live in or are attending school in Greater Hartford.
Title of Award: Alliance Francaise of Hartford Harpin/Rohinsky Scholarships **Area, Field, or Subject:** French studies. **Level of Education for which Award is Granted:** Undergraduate **Number Awarded:** 1. **Funds Available:** $3,000.
Eligibility Requirements: Applicants must be entering a four-year college or university (full-time enrollment); must pursue French studies in college; must have a financial need; must rank top third of their class; and must be active volunteers in school, community, or other extracurricular activities. **Application Requirements:** Applicants must download and fill out the online application and attach the following requirements: letter of recommendation from your guidance counselor or a from your teacher; official high school transcript, including SAT or ACT scores; copy of the essay you submitted with your college application (if you did not have to submit one, write a brief essay (no more than 2 pages) regarding your future goals); copy of pages 1 and 2 of your parents' most recent completed federal tax form 1040; and mail everything to Hartford Foundation College Scholarship Program. **Deadline for Receipt:** February 6. **Additional Information:** Hartford Foundation College Scholarship Program, Scholarship Management Services, Scholarship America, One Scholarship Way, PO Box 297, St. Peter, MN 56082.800-537-4180.

2467 ■ NATIONAL ITALIAN AMERICAN FOUNDATION
1860 19th St. NW
Washington, DC 20009
Tel: (202)387-0600
Fax: (202)387-0800

E-mail: information@niaf.org
Web Site: http://www.niaf.org
To promote the study of Italian American studies or a related field.
Title of Award: NIAF Scholarships - General Category II **Area, Field, or Subject:** Italian studies. **Level of Education for which Award is Granted:** Undergraduate **Funds Available:** $2,500-$10,000.
Eligibility Requirements: Applicant must be enrolled in an U.S. accredited institution of higher education for the fall; must have a GPA of at least 3.5 out of 4.0 (or the equivalent); must be a U.S. citizen or a permanent resident alien; and must be from any ethnic background majoring or minoring in Italian language, Italian studies, Italian American studies or a related field who demonstrate outstanding potential and high academic achievements. **Application Requirements:** Applicants must submit completed student application and Teacher Evaluation Form online; and submit official school transcript and FAFSA Financial Aid Form (optional) by mail. **Deadline for Receipt:** March 7.

Jewish Studies

2468 ■ HARTFORD FOUNDATION FOR PUBLIC GIVING
10 Columbus Blvd., 8th Flr.
Hartford, CT 06106
Tel: (860)548-1888
Fax: (860)524-8346
E-mail: hfpg@hfpg.org
Web Site: http://www.hfpg.org
To provide scholarship to the Jewish high school senior or college student.
Title of Award: Hebrew Ladies Sheltering Home Scholarships **Area, Field, or Subject:** Jewish studies. **Level of Education for which Award is Granted:** Undergraduate **Number Awarded:** 1-3. **Funds Available:** $1,000-$3,000.
Eligibility Requirements: Applicants must: be a resident of Greater Hartford; pursuing Jewish studies; have a requisite academic ability. **Application Requirements:** Applicants may obtain application from Jewish Community Foundation of Greater Hartford. **Deadline for Receipt:** April 15. **Additional Information:** Michael Elfenbaum, 333 Bloomfield Ave. Ste. D, West Hartford, CT06117. Phone: 860-523-7460 Fax: 860-231-0576; melbenbaum@jchartford.org.

2469 ■ NATIONAL WOMEN'S STUDIES ASSOCIATION
7100 Baltimore Ave., Ste. 502
College Park, MD 20740
Tel: (301)403-0407
E-mail: nsaoffice@nwsa.org
Web Site: http://www.nwsa.org
To encourage the participation in NWSA of individuals whose presence enrich the diversity of and increase participation by underrepresented constituencies in the NWSA.
Title of Award: Jewish Caucus Scholarships **Area, Field, or Subject:** Jewish studies. **Level of Education for which Award is Granted:** Undergraduate **Funds Available:** $1,000. **Duration:** June 1.
Eligibility Requirements: Applicants must be graduate students who are enrolled for the current academic year and who have a special interest in the lives, work and culture of Jewish women. **Application Requirements:** Applicants must complete the application form including name and contact information; dissertation/thesis title; two-to-three page abstract of the work; and two letters of recommendation. The Scholarship Review Committee would like applicants to attach a statement of no more than five pages addressing the following: demonstrate your preparation for conducting research in Jewish Women's Studies (please include a one-page abstract of your thesis or dissertation proposal); how have your activities demonstrated your interest in Jewish life and feminist life on campus or in your community; and what additional information about you, such as your background and other influences, might shed light on how you understand the relationship of feminism and Judaism. **Deadline for Receipt:** March 1.

Latin American Studies

2470 ■ NATIONAL ASSOCIATION FOR CHICANA AND CHICANO STUDIES
PO Box 720052
San Jose, CA 95172-0052

Tel: (408)924-5310
Fax: (408)924-5700
E-mail: naccs@naccs.org
Web Site: http://www.naccs.org
To support students in their educational journey.
Title of Award: Leonor R. Guerrero Memorial Scholarships **Level of Education for which Award is Granted:** Undergraduate **Funds Available:** $1,000. **Duration:** One year.
Eligibility Requirements: Applicants must be a Chicana/Latino Decent. A part-time or full-time student. **Application Requirements:** Applicants must send personal information. Applicants must also answer the 500 word essay questions online, and send to LRG Memorial Scholarship. **Deadline for Receipt:** May 4. **Additional Information:** LRG Memorial Scholarship, attn: Lourdes R. Guerrero, MSW 10423 Montgomery Ave., Granada Hills, CA 91344

2471 ■ ORGANIZATION OF AMERICAN STATES
1889 F St. NW
Washington, DC 20006
Tel: (202)458-6166
E-mail: scholarships@aos.org
Web Site: http://www.educoas.org
To help finance higher educational pursuits in the United States.
Title of Award: Leo S. Rowe Pan American Fund **Area, Field, or Subject:** Latin American Studies; Arts; Science. **Level of Education for which Award is Granted:** Undergraduate **Funds Available:** $15,000 (in total).
Eligibility Requirements: Applicants must be undergraduate or graduate students from Latin American or Caribbean AOS member countries who are studying or have been admitted for studies in the United States to a program leading to a university degree in an institution of higher learning accredited by the corresponding regional or national council; or must be students and professionals who are either currently pursuing or wish to pursue advanced studies, research, or technical activities in the arts or sciences in institution in the United States; must able to demonstrate, to the Committee's satisfaction their need for assistance, the usefulness of their studies, and ability to successfully complete them; must be nationals of Latin American or Carribbean member State of the AOS; must have a grade point average of at least 3.0 or "B" from their current or most recent academic institution; and must agree to return to their origin after completion of their studies. **Application Requirements:** Applicants must submit original, duly sealed, stamped, or notarized transcript of grades; diplomas; and foreign student advisor form.

Near and Middle East Studies

2472 ■ ARMENIAN STUDENTS' ASSOCIATION OF AMERICA
333 Atlantic Ave.
Warwick, RI 02888
Tel: (401)461-6114
E-mail: asa@asainc.org
Web Site: http://www.asainc.org
To provide financial assistance to those students who are in need.
Title of Award: Garikian Scholarship Fund **Area, Field, or Subject:** Armenian Studies; Sociology; Psychology; Political Science; Middle Eastern History; Journalism; Education; Music. **Level of Education for which Award is Granted:** Undergraduate **Funds Available:** $750-$1,000.
Eligibility Requirements: Applicants must have completed their first academic year in college or university in California; must be pursuing one of the above field of studies. **Application Requirements:** Applicants must apply to the Executive Board for application forms and return them, completed, before the deadline. **Deadline for Receipt:** August 31. **Additional Information:** Berj S. Baghdoyan c/o Western Prelacy at 4401 Russell Avenue, Los Angeles, CA 90027.

Polish Studies

2473 ■ AMERICAN INSTITUTE OF POLISH CULTURE
1440 79th St. Causeway, Ste. 117
Miami, FL 33141

Tel: (305)864-2349
Fax: (305)865-5150
E-mail: info@ampolinstitute.org
Web Site: http://www.ampolinstitute.org
To provide financial support American students of Polish descent who wish to continue their education after high school.
Title of Award: Harriet Irsay Scholarships **Area, Field, or Subject:** Communications; Education; Media arts; History; International affairs and relations; Journalism; Liberal arts; Polish studies; Public relations. **Level of Education for which Award is Granted:** Graduate, Undergraduate **Number Awarded:** 10-15. **Funds Available:** $1,000.
Eligibility Requirements: Applicants must be of Polish heritage; an American citizen or permanent resident; full-time graduate or undergraduate students in the field of communication, education, film, history, International Relation, journalism, liberal arts, polish studies, public relations; or graduate student in business programs with a thesis related to Poland, or graduate students with a thesis with Polish subject. **Application Requirements:** Applicants must submit a completed application form; school transcripts; resume; essay (200-400 words) about "Why should I receive the scholarship"; an article about Poland (maximum of 700 words); and 3 signed recommendation letters on a letterhead stationary from teachers or other person knowledgeable about the applicant's academic background. A non-refundable $10 processing fee (check or money order) must also be included. **Deadline for Receipt:** April 20.

2474 ■ HARTFORD FOUNDATION FOR PUBLIC GIVING

10 Columbus Blvd., 8th Flr.
Hartford, CT 06106
Tel: (860)548-1888
Fax: (860)524-8346
E-mail: hfpg@hfpg.org
Web Site: http://www.hfpg.org
To provide financial assistance to students entering or enrolled as undergraduate or graduate at a four-year college or university or summer program in Poland.
Title of Award: Tadeusz Sendzimir Scholarships **Area, Field, or Subject:** Polish studies; American history. **Level of Education for which Award is Granted:** Undergraduate **Number Awarded:** 1-5. **Funds Available:** $1,000-$5,000.
Eligibility Requirements: Applicants must be Connecticut residents; studying Polish/Slavic Language, history or culture in the US or Poland. Preference to students of Polish descent. **Application Requirements:** Applicants may obtain application materials from Connecticut Community Foundation, 43 Field St., Waterburry, CT 06702. **Deadline for Receipt:** March 1. **Additional Information:** Tallitha Richardson-Selby, Program/Scholarship Associate; 203-756-3054; info@conncf.org.

2475 ■ KOSCIUSZKO FOUNDATION

15 E 65th St.
New York, NY 10065
Tel: (212)734-2130
Fax: (212)628-4552
E-mail: info@thekf.org
Web Site: http://www.kosciuszkofoundation.org
To support American students of Polish descent for full-time graduate studies in the United States.
Title of Award: Kosciuszko Foundation Tuition Scholarships **Area, Field, or Subject:** Polish studies. **Level of Education for which Award is Granted:** Undergraduate **Funds Available:** $1,000 to $7,000. **Duration:** One academic year.
Eligibility Requirements: Applicant must be a United States citizen or permanent resident of Polish descent who are beginning or continuing graduate studies in the academic year; must have a minimum GPA of 3.0 **Application Requirements:** Applicant must complete the Tuition Scholarship application form and Financial Information page (application may be obtained from the Kosciuszko Foundation); must submit a personal statement about their academic goals, career goals, and the major they are pursuing and area of specialization; must have two passport photos for publication purposes; must have the official transcript; must prepare two confidential letters of academic reference from professors/teachers submitted on letterhead; must provide proof of Polish ancestry. **Deadline for Receipt:** January 15.

2476 ■ KOSCIUSZKO FOUNDATION

15 E 65th St.
New York, NY 10065
Tel: (212)734-2130
Fax: (212)628-4552
E-mail: info@thekf.org
Web Site: http://www.kosciuszkofoundation.org
To support the deserving students to continue their Polish language studies.
Title of Award: Kosciuszko Foundation Year Abroad Scholarships **Area, Field, or Subject:** Polish studies. **Level of Education for which Award is Granted:** Undergraduate **Funds Available:** Scholarship includes acceptance to the program, a tuition waiver and a stipend for housing and living expenses. **Duration:** One academic year.
Eligibility Requirements: Applicant must be a United States citizen and permanent resident of Polish descent who are undergraduate sophomore, junior, senior or graduate student; must have a minimum GPA of 3.0. **Application Requirements:** Applicant must complete the Polish Ministry of National Education application entitled Bureau for Academic Recognition and International Exchange; must attach copies of transcripts of records; must submit two letters of recommendation from professors and must have two passport size photos with printed name on the reverse. **Deadline for Receipt:** January 15.

2477 ■ KOSCIUSZKO FOUNDATION

15 E 65th St.
New York, NY 10065
Tel: (212)734-2130
Fax: (212)628-4552
E-mail: info@thekf.org
Web Site: http://www.kosciuszkofoundation.org
To support the qualified residents of Massachusetts to pursue their education.
Title of Award: Massachusetts Federation of Polish Women's Clubs Scholarships **Area, Field, or Subject:** Polish studies. **Level of Education for which Award is Granted:** Undergraduate **Funds Available:** $1,250. **Duration:** One academic year.
Eligibility Requirements: Applicant must be a United States citizen of Polish descent or Polish citizens with permanent residency status in the United States residing in Massachusetts who will engage in second, third or fourth year of undergraduate studies during academic year; must have a minimum GPA of 3.0. **Application Requirements:** Applicant must complete the scholarship application form and financial information page; must submit a personal statement about their academic goals, career goals and specialization; must have a two passport size photos for publication purposes; must submit a official transcripts; must have two confidential letters of academic reference from professor and teachers; must provide proof of Polish ancestry. **Deadline for Receipt:** January 15.

2478 ■ KOSCIUSZKO FOUNDATION

15 E 65th St.
New York, NY 10065
Tel: (212)734-2130
Fax: (212)628-4552
E-mail: info@thekf.org
Web Site: http://www.kosciuszkofoundation.org
To provide financial assistance to qualified students in the United States.
Title of Award: Polish American Club of North Jersey Scholarships **Area, Field, or Subject:** Polish studies. **Level of Education for which Award is Granted:** Undergraduate **Funds Available:** $500-$2,000. **Duration:** One academic year.
Eligibility Requirements: Applicant must be a United States citizen of Polish descent or Polish citizens with permanent residency status in the U.S who are active members of the Polish American Club of North Jersey; must have a minimum GPA of 3.0; must be children or grandchildren of club members. **Application Requirements:** Applicant must complete the scholarship application form and financial information page; must have a personal statement about their academic goals, career goals and specialization; must have two passport photos for publication purposes; must submit an official transcript; must prepare a two confidential letters of academic reference from professor and teachers; must provide a proof of Polish ancestry. **Deadline for Receipt:** January 15.

2479 ■ KOSCIUSZKO FOUNDATION

15 E 65th St.
New York, NY 10065
Tel: (212)734-2130
Fax: (212)628-4552
E-mail: info@thekf.org
Web Site: http://www.kosciuszkofoundation.org
To provide financial assistance to all qualified students wanting to pursue their studies in United States.

Title of Award: Polish National Alliance of Brooklyn, USA Scholarships **Area, Field, or Subject:** Polish studies. **Level of Education for which Award is Granted:** Undergraduate **Funds Available:** $2,000. **Duration:** One academic year.

Eligibility Requirements: Applicants must be a United States citizen of Polish descent or Polish citizens with permanent residency status in the U.S. who are members in good standing of the Polish National Alliance of Brooklyn, USA and the Polish National Alliance of the United States of North America; must have a minimum GPA of 3.0. **Application Requirements:** Applicant must complete the scholarship application form and financial information page; must submit a personal statement about their academic goals, career goals and the major expect to pursue; must have a two passport photos for publication purposes; must have two confidential letters of academic reference; must have a official transcript of record; must have two letters of academic reference from professor and teachers; must provide a proof of Polish ancestry. **Deadline for Receipt:** January 15.

2480 ■ KOSCIUSZKO FOUNDATION

15 E 65th St.
New York, NY 10065
Tel: (212)734-2130
Fax: (212)628-4552
E-mail: info@thekf.org
Web Site: http://www.kosciuszkofoundation.org
To support the young women of Polish ancestry in their education.

Title of Award: Dr. Marie E. Zakrzewski Medical Scholarships **Area, Field, or Subject:** Polish studies. **Level of Education for which Award is Granted:** Undergraduate **Funds Available:** $3,500. **Duration:** One academic year.

Eligibility Requirements: Applicant must be a U.S. citizen of Polish descent or Polish citizens with permanent residency status in United States who are entering first, second or third year of M.D. studies in academic year; must have a minimum GPA of 3.0; must be a female **Application Requirements:** Applicant must submit a personal statement about the academic goals, career goals and area of specialization; must have a two passport sized photos for publication purposes; must have an official transcript and two confidential letters of academic reference from professors and teachers; must provide a proof of Polish ancestry. **Deadline for Receipt:** January 15.

2481 ■ POLISH FALCONS OF AMERICA

615 Iron City Dr.
Pittsburgh, PA 15205-4397
Tel: (412)922-2244
Free: 800-535-2071
Fax: (412)922-5029
Web Site: http://www.polishfalcons.org
To provide financial support for deserving Falcon members aspiring to attend institutions of higher learning.

Title of Award: Falcon Achievement Scholarships **Area, Field, or Subject:** Polish studies. **Level of Education for which Award is Granted:** Undergraduate **Funds Available:** $1,000.

Eligibility Requirements: Candidates must be graduating high school seniors or presently enrolled undergraduates intending to pursue further education as a full time student in an accredited two or four year college, university or trade school; must have a minimum cumulative GPA of 2.0 out of 4.0. **Application Requirements:** Applicant must complete and sign the application form available online; must provide a community service information, essay, and photo; must submit the official transcript, counselor recommendation, and net information form and letter. **Deadline for Receipt:** February 1.

South Asian Studies

2482 ■ JAPAN FOUNDATION, NEW YORK

152 W 7th St., 17th Fl.
New York, NY 10019
Tel: (212)489-0299
Fax: (212)489-0409
E-mail: info@jfny.org
Web Site: http://www.jfny.org
To provide opportunities for outstanding scholars in Japanese Studies to conduct research in Japan.

Title of Award: Japan Foundation, New York Research Fellowship Program **Area, Field, or Subject:** Japanese studies. **Level of Education for which Award is Granted:** Undergraduate **Funds Available:** No specific amount. **Duration:** 2-12 months.

Eligibility Requirements: Applicants must be scholars/researchers from the U.S. holding academic positions in a research institution and must have substantial experience in research, teaching, and writing in their respective fields of study. **Application Requirements:** Applicants who have U.S. citizenship or permanent residency should complete the application materials and submit them to the Japan Foundation New York Office. Applications should be sent directly (by mail only) to the JFNY office. U.S. citizenship holders should use a different form, which is available in the nearest Japan Foundation office or Japanese diplomatic mission. Multiple applications will make all applications invalid. Other guidelines and procedures are available in the JFNY website. **Deadline for Receipt:** November 1.

2483 ■ UNIVERSITY OF TORONTO

315 Bloor St. W
Toronto, ON, Canada M5S 1A3
Tel: (416)978-2011
E-mail: information.commonsats@utoronto.ca
Web Site: http://www.utoronto.ca
To support students with their educational pursuits.

Title of Award: Mary Jane Hendrie Memorial Scholarships **Area, Field, or Subject:** Japanese studies. **Level of Education for which Award is Granted:** Graduate, Undergraduate **Funds Available:** Approximately $3500.

Eligibility Requirements: Applicant must be a senior undergraduate or graduate student of U of T; interested in relations between Japan and Canada with studies in business, law, economics, international relations, or political science. **Application Requirements:** Applicants must submit a completed application form along with the required materials and information. **Additional Information:** Faculty members can nominate a student by writing a letter to the Scholarship Selection Committee describing the student's qualifications for the award. **Deadline for Receipt:** March 28.

Southeast Asian Studies

2484 ■ GAMEWARDEN OF VIETNAM ASSOCIATION

PO Box 701786
San Antonio, TX 78270
(186)6220-7477
E-mail: jwoody@texas.net
Web Site: http://www.tf116.org
To discuss military history, military news, and othe rtopics of concern or interest about Vietnam.

Title of Award: Gamewarden Scholarship program **Area, Field, or Subject:** Vietnamese studies. **Level of Education for which Award is Granted:** High School, Undergraduate **Number Awarded:** 3. **Funds Available:** $500.

Eligibility Requirements: Applicant must be 16-21 years old, full-time student; high school student may be considered; must be U.S. citizen; must be needing the assistance; must be the son, daughter or grandchild of a member of Game wardens; an applicant must be receiving an education from a four year or two year college, university or vocational school. **Application Requirements:** an applicant must fill out the application form and send to Game warden of Vietnam Association Office. **Deadline for Receipt:** April 1.

2485 ■ PBR FORCES VETERANS ASSOCIATION
6097 Davon St.
Jacksonville, FL 32244-3178
Tel: (419)281-4711
Web Site: http://www.pbr-fva.org
To assist the direct descendants of members.
Title of Award: James Elliott Williams Scholarship Fund **Area, Field, or Subject:** Army. **Level of Education for which Award is Granted:** Undergraduate **Funds Available:** Varies depending on available funds.
Eligibility Requirements: Candidates must be a direct descent of an active Vietnam Veteran member of PBR Forces Veterans Association; must be enrolled in a two or four-year accredited college/technical school. **Application Requirements:** Applicants must fill out the application form; form must be printed using blue or black ink; and application must be countersigned by the Sponsor.

Western European Studies

2486 ■ LATIN AMERICAN EDUCATIONAL FOUNDATION
561 Santa Fe Dr.
Denver, CO 80204
Tel: (303)446-0526
E-mail: info@laef.org
Web Site: http://www.laef.org
To award funds to qualified students who have demonstrated a commitment to the Hispanic community.
Title of Award: Latin American Educational Foundation Scholarships **Area, Field, or Subject:** Hispanic American studies. **Level of Education for which Award is Granted:** Undergraduate **Funds Available:** No specific amount.
Eligibility Requirements: Applicants must be Colorado residents with Hispanic heritage and/or are actively involved in the Hispanic community; must be accepted in an accredited college, university or vocational school; must at least have a 3.0 cumulative grade point average. Recipients will be required to fulfill 10 hours of community service during the year of funding. **Application Requirements:** Applicants must submit completed application form available in the LAEF website; most recent federal income tax returns; a list of community service and extracurricular activities for the previous 2 years including leadership positions held; a one-page essay to include the applicant's interests and career goals; how you anticipate achieving your goals and what has motivated you to pursue higher education; two letters of recommendation on official letterhead (the first letter must come from an educator and the other must come from a community service organization, employer, clergy or coach). Letters should discuss your academic achievements and community service as well as your potential for future success. Qualities such as maturity, motivation, self-confidence, leadership and commitment should be addressed. **Deadline for Receipt:** March 1.

2487 ■ LEAGUE OF LATIN AMERICAN CITIZENS
2000 L St. NW, Ste. 610
Washington, DC 20036
Tel: (202)833-6310
Fax: (202)833-6135
E-mail: RosaRosales@LULAC.org
Web Site: http://www.lulac.org
To provide high quality educational opportunities to the Hispanic community.
Title of Award: LULAC GE Scholarships **Area, Field, or Subject:** Hispanic American Studies. **Level of Education for which Award is Granted:** Undergraduate **Funds Available:** $2,500. **Duration:** One semester.
Eligibility Requirements: Applicant must be a U.S. citizen or legal resident; Must have applied to or be enrolled in a college, university, or graduate school, including 2-year colleges, or vocational schools that lead to an associate's degree; must not be related to a scholarship committee member, the Council President, or an individual contributor to the local funds of the Council. **Application Requirements:** Applicants should mail their application directly to the nearest LULAC Council.

2488 ■ LEAGUE OF LATIN AMERICAN CITIZENS
2000 L St. NW, Ste. 610
Washington, DC 20036

Tel: (202)833-6310
Fax: (202)833-6135
E-mail: RosaRosales@LULAC.org
Web Site: http://www.lulac.org
To provide high quality educational opportunities to the Hispanic community.
Title of Award: LULAC GM Scholarships **Area, Field, or Subject:** Hispanic American Studies. **Level of Education for which Award is Granted:** Graduate, High School, Undergraduate **Funds Available:** No specific amount.
Eligibility Requirements: Applicant must be an American citizen or legal resident; Must have applied to or be enrolled in a college, university, or graduate school, including 2-year colleges, or vocational schools that lead to an associate's degree; must not be related to a scholarship committee member, the Council President, or an individual contributor to the local funds of the Council. **Application Requirements:** Applicants should be mailed directly their application to the nearest LULAC Council. **Additional Information:** LULAC GM Scholarship is managed by the LULAC national Educational Service Centers. General Motors Corporation founded in 1908, is best known as the world' largest full-vehicle manufacturer. **Deadline for Receipt:** December 14. **Additional Information:** LULAC at the above address.

2489 ■ LEAGUE OF LATIN AMERICAN CITIZENS
2000 L St. NW, Ste. 610
Washington, DC 20036
Tel: (202)833-6310
Fax: (202)833-6135
E-mail: RosaRosales@LULAC.org
Web Site: http://www.lulac.org
To provide high quality educational opportunities to the Hispanic community.
Title of Award: LULAC National Scholarship Fund **Area, Field, or Subject:** Hispanic American Studies. **Level of Education for which Award is Granted:** Graduate, High School, Undergraduate **Funds Available:** No specific amount.
Eligibility Requirements: Applicant must be a US citizen or legal resident; Must have applied to or be enrolled in a college, university, or graduate school, including 2-year colleges, or vocational schools that lead to an associate's degree; must not be related to a scholarship committee member, the Council President, or an individual contributor to the local funds of the Council. **Application Requirements:** Applicants should be mailed directly their application to the nearest LULAC Council. **Deadline for Receipt:** January 15. **Additional Information:** LULAC at the above address.

2490 ■ LEAGUE OF LATIN AMERICAN CITIZENS
2000 L St. NW, Ste. 610
Washington, DC 20036
Tel: (202)833-6310
Fax: (202)833-6135
E-mail: RosaRosales@LULAC.org
Web Site: http://www.lulac.org
To provide high quality educational opportunities to the students.
Title of Award: Pepsi Escribe tu Futuro Scholarships **Area, Field, or Subject:** Hispanic American studies. **Level of Education for which Award is Granted:** Undergraduate **Funds Available:** $500-$2,000.
Eligibility Requirements: Applicants must be a U.S. citizen; Must have applied to or be enrolled in a college, university, including 2-year colleges, or vocational schools that lead to an associate's degree. **Application Requirements:** Applications are available on the LNESC website and from participating LULAC Council; Students must complete the entire application. It should be mailed with a current complete official high school or college transcript of grade to the LULAC National Educational Service Centers (LNESC) national office. **Additional Information:** The Pepsi Escribe tu Futuro Scholarship is funded by the Pepsi-Cola Company, to help young Latinos in their pursuit towards a college education to help improve their future and career opportunities. **Deadline for Receipt:** February 28. **Additional Information:** www.yourworldyourpepsi.com.

Women's Studies

2491 ■ CENTER FOR THE EDUCATION OF WOMEN
330 E Liberty St.
Ann Arbor, MI 48103
Tel: (734)764-6005
Fax: (734)998-6203
E-mail: contactCEW@umich.edu
Web Site: http://www.umich.edu/~cew
To promote every woman's career, leadership, education, growth and development, healing and wellbeing.
Title of Award: Student Research Grants **Area, Field, or Subject:** Women's studies. **Level of Education for which Award is Granted:** Undergraduate **Funds Available:** $750.
Eligibility Requirements: Applicants must be undergraduate students.
Application Requirements: Applicants must send an applications which includes the applicant's name, address, contact number, email address, and student ID number; proposal (2 pages) accompanied with project budget; a statement of support from an advisor; a curriculum vitae; and proof of IRB approval for the project (if relevant). Submit application packets to: Dr. Jean Waltman, Center for the Education of Women 330 E Liberty St., Ann Arbor, MI 48104-2289. **Additional Information:** Jean Waltman, jwaltman@umich.edu.

2492 ■ STEUBEN COUNTY COMMUNITY FOUNDATION
1701 N Wayne St.
Angola, IN 46703
Tel: (260)665-6656
Fax: (260)665-8420
Web Site: http://www.steubenfoundation.org
To provide financial support to those students who will be entering a four-year college or university with intent of pursuing a Bachelor's Degree.
Title of Award: Tara Lynne Arnold Scholarships **Area, Field, or Subject:** Psychology; Women's Studies. **Level of Education for which Award is Granted:** Undergraduate **Funds Available:** No specific amount.
Eligibility Requirements: Applicants must attend or have attended Angola High School; must be in good academic standing. **Application Requirements:** Applicants must check the website for the application process online and required materials. **Deadline for Receipt:** March 15.

2493 ■ UNIVERSITY OF TORONTO
315 Bloor St. W
Toronto, ON, Canada M5S 1A3
Tel: (416)978-2011
E-mail: information.commonsats@utoronto.ca
Web Site: http://www.utoronto.ca
To support students with their educational pursuits.
Title of Award: City of Toronto Women's Studies Scholarships **Area, Field, or Subject:** Women's studies. **Level of Education for which Award is Granted:** Graduate, Undergraduate **Number Awarded:** 1 undergraduate; and 1 graduate student. **Funds Available:** Undergraduate - $5000; Graduate scholarship valued at the balance of the annual income.
Eligibility Requirements: Applicants must be undergraduate or graduate students in Women's Studies. **Application Requirements:** Applicants must submit a completed application form along with the required materials and information. **Deadline for Receipt:** Undergraduate: June 30; Graduate: November 1.

General

2494 ■ APPRAISAL INSTITUTE EDUCATION TRUST
550 W Van Buren St., Ste. 1000
Chicago, IL 60607
Tel: (312)335-4100
Fax: (312)335-4400
E-mail: information@appraisalinstitute.org
Web Site: http://www.appraisalinstitute.org
To help finance the education endeavors of individuals concentrating in real estate appraisal, land economics, real estate or allied fields.
Title of Award: Appraisal Institute Education Trust Scholarships **Area, Field, or Subject:** Real estate; Land economics. **Level of Education for which Award is Granted:** Graduate, Undergraduate **Funds Available:** $2,000 Undergraduate; $3,000 Graduate.
Eligibility Requirements: Applicants must be U.S. citizens, enrolled full-time for the academic year beginning August through June in a University or Community College in the U.S. majoring in real estate appraisal, land economics, real estate or allied fields. **Application Requirements:** Applicants must submit a completed application together with letters of recommendation from the college Dean and two individuals, a signed statement regarding general activities and intellectual interests in college, official copies of all collegiate records and proposed student program. Graduate student applicants must have served, or is about to serve, an internship with an appraiser or the appraisal department of a corporation (letter from employer required). **Deadline for Receipt:** March 15. **Additional Information:** Olivia Carreon at the above address.

2495 ■ ARKANSAS ENVIRONMENTAL FEDERATION
1400 W Markham St., Ste. 302
Little Rock, AR 72201
Tel: (501)374-0263
Fax: (501)374-8752
Web Site: http://www.environmentark.org
To provide financial assistance for selected students from Arkansas universities.
Title of Award: Randall Matthis for Environmental Studies Scholarships **Area, Field, or Subject:** Environmental science; Health education; Natural resources. **Level of Education for which Award is Granted:** Graduate, Undergraduate **Funds Available:** $2,500. **Duration:** One year.
Eligibility Requirements: Applicants must be U.S. citizens residing in Arkansas and must be undergraduate or graduate students with at least 2.8 cumulative GPA based on 4.0 system. **Application Requirements:** Applicants must submit a completed application form along with current official transcript(s) and letters. **Deadline for Receipt:** April 11.

2496 ■ ARKANSAS ENVIRONMENTAL FEDERATION
1400 W Markham St., Ste. 302
Little Rock, AR 72201
Tel: (501)374-0263
Fax: (501)374-8752
Web Site: http://www.environmentark.org
To provide financial assistance for selected students from Arkansas universities.
Title of Award: Larry Wilson for Environmental Studies Scholarships **Area, Field, or Subject:** Environmental science. **Level of Education for**

which **Award is Granted:** Graduate, Undergraduate **Funds Available:** No specific amount.
Eligibility Requirements: Applicants must be U.S. citizens residing in Arkansas; must be full-time undergraduate or graduate students at the time of application and in the year scholarship is awarded; must have a minimum of 2.8 cumulative grade point average based of 4.0 scale; and must be nominated by a faculty member. **Application Requirements:** Applicants must submit a completed application form along with current official transcript(s) and letters. **Deadline for Receipt:** April 11.

2497 ■ ARKANSAS PUBLIC HEALTH ASSOCIATION
4815 W Marketing St., Slot 52
Little Rock, AR 72205
Tel: (501)661-2392
E-mail: catherine.tapp@arkansas.gov
Web Site: http://www.arkpublichealth.org
To support Arkansas students.
Title of Award: Arkansas Society of Professional Sanitarians Scholarships **Area, Field, or Subject:** Environmental technology. **Level of Education for which Award is Granted:** Undergraduate **Funds Available:** $250-$500. **Duration:** One year.
Eligibility Requirements: Applicant must be Arkansas resident; must be enrolled, or have plans to enroll, in an environmental field; must be a sophomore student; must have at least a 2.5 GPA; must demonstrate financial need. **Application Requirements:** Application forms are available online. Application form must be sent to Rebecca Wright, Scholarship Chairman, 1195 N Charley's Loop, Camden, AR 71701. **Deadline for Receipt:** April 11.

2498 ■ ENERGY AND MINERAL LAW FOUNDATION
340 S Broadway, Ste. 101
Lexington, KY 40508
Tel: (859)231-0271
Fax: (859)226-0485
E-mail: eml@aol.com
Web Site: http://www.blairchiropractic.com
To provide educational assistance to encourage the study of energy, environmental, natural resources, and mineral law.
Title of Award: EMLF Law Student Scholarships **Area, Field, or Subject:** Environmental science, Natural resources, Mineralogy, Energy-related areas. **Level of Education for which Award is Granted:** Undergraduate **Funds Available:** $1,000-$3,000.
Eligibility Requirements: Applicants must be law school students for the current academic year and must demonstrate an interest in the study of natural resources, energy or mineral law. **Deadline for Receipt:** April 11.

2499 ■ FLORIDA ATLANTIC PLANNING SOCIETY
777 Galdes Rd.
Boca Raton, FL 33431
Tel: (561)297-3000
E-mail: marketing@fau.edu
Web Site: http://www.fau.edu
To foster increased interest among African-American undergraduates in urban planning as a graduate field of study and as a professional career.
Title of Award: The Robert A Catlin/David W. Long Memorial Scholarship **Area, Field, or Subject:** Environmental science. **Level of Education for**

which Award is Granted: Undergraduate **Funds Available:** $2,500. **Eligibility Requirements:** Applicants must be African-Americans who are entering juniors or seniors; must be majoring in urban planning or related fields; must have a minimum of 3.0 GPA and must be full-time enrolled students. **Application Requirements:** Applicants must submit a completed application form, personal statement, two letters of recommendation, one sealed official academic transcript for each college or university attended and a self-addressed, stamped postcard for notification of the receipt of a complete application form. **Deadline for Receipt:** October 30.

2500 ■ GRAND HAVEN AREA COMMUNITY FOUNDATION
1 S. Harbor Dr.
Grand Haven, MI 49417
Tel: (616)842-6378
Fax: (616)842-9518
E-mail: bpost@ghacf.org
Web Site: http://www.ghacf.org
To assist an upperclassman or graduate student majoring in environmental science field.

Title of Award: Marjorie M. Hendricks Environmental Education Scholarships Fund **Area, Field, or Subject:** Environmental science. **Level of Education for which Award is Granted:** Undergraduate **Funds Available:** No specific amount.
Eligibility Requirements: Applicants must be upperclassmen or graduate students majoring in an environmental science field who plan to attend Aquinas College or Grand Valley State University. **Application Requirements:** Applicants must submit: completed application form; current high school or college transcript; Student Aid Report (SAR) from the Free Application for Federal Student Aid (FAFSA), unless applying for scholarships that do not consider financial need; and letter of recommendation. **Deadline for Receipt:** March 7. **Additional Information:** 616-842-6378.

2501 ■ GRAND HAVEN AREA COMMUNITY FOUNDATION
1 S. Harbor Dr.
Grand Haven, MI 49417
Tel: (616)842-6378
Fax: (616)842-9518
E-mail: bpost@ghacf.org
Web Site: http://www.ghacf.org
To improve and enhance the quality of life in the Tri-Cities area by serving as a leader, catalyst and resource for philanthropy; to strive for community improvement through strategic grantmaking in such fields as arts, education, health, environment, youth, social services and other human needs.
Title of Award: Miller G. Sherwood Family Scholarship Fund **Area, Field, or Subject:** Environmental science. **Level of Education for which Award is Granted:** Undergraduate **Funds Available:** No specific amount.
Eligibility Requirements: Applicants must be graduating seniors of Grand Haven or Spring Lake High School who plan to pursue an education in the areas of environment or social services. **Application Requirements:** Applicants must submit: completed application form; current high school or college transcript, Student Aid Report (SAR) from the Free Application for Federal Student Aid (FAFSA), unless applying for scholarships that do not consider financial need; and letter of recommendation. **Deadline for Receipt:** March 7. **Additional Information:** 616-842-6378.

2502 ■ HAMILTON INDUSTRIAL ENVIRONMENTAL ASSOCIATION
PO Box 35545
Hamilton, ON, Canada L8H 7S6
Tel: (905)561-4432
E-mail: info@hiea.org
Web Site: http://www.hiea.org
To provide financial assistance to those students who are in need.
Title of Award: Hamilton Industrial Environmental Association Bursaries-Mohawk College **Area, Field, or Subject:** Engineering Technology; Environmental Technology. **Level of Education for which Award is Granted:** Undergraduate **Funds Available:** No specific amount.
Eligibility Requirements: Applicants must be 2nd year students in their final semester; must have been raised in Hamilton or graduated from Hamilton High School. **Application Requirements:** Applicants must check the available website for more information. **Additional Information:** Hamilton Industrial Environmental Association at the above address.

2503 ■ HISPANIC SCHOLARSHIP FUND
55 Second St., Ste. 1500
San Francisco, CA 94105
877-473-4636
Fax: (415)808-2302
E-mail: info@hsf.net
Web Site: http://www.hsf.net
To provide financial assistance to those who are studying engineering.
Title of Award: Marathon Oil Corporation College Scholarship Program **Area, Field, or Subject:** Chemical engineering; Civil engineering; Electrical engineering; Mechanical engineering; Petroleum engineering; Geology; Geophysics; Accounting; Marketing and distribution; Land management; Transportation; Logistics; Engineering, Petroleum **Level of Education for which Award is Granted:** Graduate, Undergraduate **Funds Available:** $20,000. **Duration:** Two academic years.
Eligibility Requirements: Applicant must be of Hispanic American, African American, Asian Pacific Islander American or American Indian/Alaskan Native heritage; U.S. citizen or legal permanent resident with a valid Social Security Number and a permanent resident card or passport stamped I-551; have a minimum 3.0 GPA on a 4.0 scale; a sophomore majoring in chemical engineering, civil engineering, electrical engineering, mechanical engineering, petroleum engineering, geology, geophysics, accounting, marketing, global procurement or supply chain management, environmental health & safety, energy management or petroleum land management, transportation & logistics or geotechnical engineering; or a senior pursuing a Masters degree in geology or geophysics; must participate in a possible paid summer internship opportunity in Marathon Oil Corporation; must apply for federal financing aid using the Free Application for Federal Student Aid (FAFSA) at www.fafsa.ed.gov. **Application Requirements:** Applications must be submitted using the HSF online application system. **Additional Information:** Scholars will be paired with a Marathon Oil Corporation employee as a professional mentor. **Deadline for Receipt:** November 1. **Additional Information:** scholar1@hsf.net.

2504 ■ ISLAND RESOURCES FOUNDATION
1718 "P" St. NW, Ste. T-4
Washington, DC 20036
Tel: (202)265-9712
Fax: (202)232-0748
E-mail: bpotter@irf.org
Web Site: http://www.irf.org
To support studies and activities that address environmental concerns that transcend the boundaries of any single island or island state.
Title of Award: Judith A. Towle Environmental Studies Fund **Area, Field, or Subject:** Environmental science. **Level of Education for which Award is Granted:** Undergraduate **Funds Available:** $70,000.
Eligibility Requirements: Applicant must be a graduate student or resident of, or a not-for-profit institution based in, the U.S. or British Virgin Islands or in the Federation of St. Kitts and Nevis. **Application Requirements:** Applicants must submit complete application form.

2505 ■ LEWIS-CLARK STATE COLLEGE
500 8th Ave.
Lewiston, ID 83501
Tel: (208)792-5272
Web Site: http://www.lcsc.edu
To provide financial assistance to students who are majoring in these fields: Accounting, Biology, Business, Communications, Computer Science, Economics, Environmental Science, Engineering, Mathematics, Natural Resources, Political Science, Statistics.
Title of Award: Avista Corporation Minds in Motion Scholarships **Area, Field, or Subject:** Accounting; Biology; Business; Communications; Computer and Information Sciences; Economics; Environmental Science; Engineering; Mathematics; Natural Resources; Political Science; Statistics. **Level of Education for which Award is Granted:** Undergraduate **Number Awarded:** 2. **Funds Available:** No specific Amount.
Eligibility Requirements: Applicants must be full-time students attending LCSC and must have a cumulative GPA of 2.5. **Application Requirements:** Applicants must submit general application. **Deadline for Receipt:** March 1.

2506 ■ LOUISIANA ENVIRONMENTAL HEALTH ASSOCIATION
PO Box 2661
Baton Rouge, LA 70821

Tel: (225)219-3242
Fax: (225)219-3310
E-mail: james.miller@la.gov
Web Site: http://www.leha.net
To encourage an outstanding undergraduate student to pursue their education.
Title of Award: Frank L. Dautriel Memorial Scholarships (Undergraduate) **Area, Field, or Subject:** Environmental science; Environmental technology; Public health. **Level of Education for which Award is Granted:** Undergraduate **Funds Available:** $1,000. **Duration:** One year.
Eligibility Requirements: Applicant must be enrolled as a full-time student in an environmental health, environmental science, environmental engineering, or public health related degree program at an accredited university; must be a Louisiana resident; must have maintained an overall 2.75 or higher on a 4.0 point rating system and have a record of good conduct supported by official transcript; must demonstrate a need for a scholarship. **Application Requirements:** Application forms are available online and must be sent to Louisiana Environmental Health Association, PO Box 2661, Baton Rouge, LA 70821. **Deadline for Receipt:** October 31.

2507 ■ NATIONAL ASSOCIATION OF STATE LAND RECLAMATIONISTS
Coal Research Center
Southern Illinois University
Carbondale, IL 62901-4623
Tel: (618)536-5521
Fax: (618)453-7346
E-mail: aharrington@crc.siu.edu
Web Site: http://www.crc.siu.edu/naslr/home.htm
To provide deserving individuals with a financial grant that will cover costs associated with education and research regarding mined land reclamation.
Title of Award: Mined Land Reclamation Educational Grant Program **Area, Field, or Subject:** Land management. **Level of Education for which Award is Granted:** Undergraduate **Funds Available:** $1,000.
Eligibility Requirements: Applicants must be enrolled as full-time juniors, seniors or graduate students in an accredited college or university in the United States with course works like special studies, and/or research in the area of mined land reclamation or closely related fields.
Application Requirements: Applicants must submit completed application form and all required materials. **Deadline for Receipt:** August 15.

2508 ■ NATIONAL ENVIRONMENTAL HEALTH ASSOCIATION
720 S Colorado Blvd., Ste. 1000-N
Denver, CO 80246
Tel: (303)756-9090
Fax: (303)691-9490
E-mail: staff@neha.org
Web Site: http://www.neha.org
To encourage and support early commitment by students to a career in environmental health.
Title of Award: National Environmental Health Association Scholarship Fund **Area, Field, or Subject:** Environmental science. **Level of Education for which Award is Granted:** Graduate, Undergraduate **Funds Available:** No specific amount. **Duration:** One year.
Eligibility Requirements: Applicants must be enrolled in an undergraduate or graduate program of studies in environmental health sciences and/or public health. **Application Requirements:** Applicants must complete the official application form (no faxes, copies or email submissions will be accepted); must provide an official copy of academic transcript; submit two faculty letters of recommendation from the school in which they are currently enrolled; and submit a letter of recommendation from an active NEHA member (three letters of recommendation must be received for an application to be considered). **Deadline for Receipt:** February 1. **Additional Information:** Nelson E. Fabian at the above address.

2509 ■ NEW YORK WATER ENVIRONMENT ASSOCIATION
525 Plum St., Ste. 102
Syracuse, NY 13204
Tel: (315)422-7811
Fax: (315)422-3851

E-mail: mail@nywea.org
Web Site: http://www.nywea.org
To help lead the way toward existing state and national clean water programs.
Title of Award: New York Water Environment Association Scholarships **Area, Field, or Subject:** Environmental science. **Level of Education for which Award is Granted:** Undergraduate **Funds Available:** $1,500.
Eligibility Requirements: Applicants must be students enrolled at a college or university where there is a NYWEA student chapter or high school students who will be enrolled in an environmentally related program in a four year college or university. **Application Requirements:** Applicants must complete the application form; must submit a requested essay; official school transcript; and a minimum of two letters of recommendation, from which one must come from a teacher and the other from someone not related to the applicant. **Deadline for Receipt:** January 22.

2510 ■ NORTH CAROLINA AMERICAN WATER WORKS ASSOCIATION
3701 National Dr., Ste. 205
Raleigh, NC 27612
Tel: (919)784-9030
Fax: (919)784-9032
E-mail: sshoaf@ci.burlington.nc.us
Web Site: http://www.ncsafewater.org
To encourage interest in environmental education.
Title of Award: Carol Bond College Scholarships **Area, Field, or Subject:** Environmental science. **Level of Education for which Award is Granted:** Undergraduate **Funds Available:** $1,000.
Eligibility Requirements: Applicants must be future or current community college students; must be either high school seniors accepted for enrollment or current community college students enrolled at a North Carolina community college; must be pursuing a degree in Environmental Sciences or Water Resources Management concentrations; must be U.S. citizens. **Application Requirements:** Applicants must submit: an official application form; one copy of an official, sealed transcript of all university education; two letters of recommendation from professors, employers, or academic advisors; a 500-750 word typed or legibly written essay that discusses why theyu should be a scholarship recipient; proof of U.S. citizenship. **Deadline for Receipt:** June 1.

2511 ■ NORTH CAROLINA AMERICAN WATER WORKS ASSOCIATION
3701 National Dr., Ste. 205
Raleigh, NC 27612
Tel: (919)784-9030
Fax: (919)784-9032
E-mail: sshoaf@ci.burlington.nc.us
Web Site: http://www.ncsafewater.org
To encourage interest in environmental education.
Title of Award: Carol Bond University Scholarships **Area, Field, or Subject:** Environmental science. **Level of Education for which Award is Granted:** Undergraduate **Funds Available:** $1,000.
Eligibility Requirements: Program is open to four-year university students pursuing a bachelor's degree in either Environmental Sciences or Environmental Engineering. Applicants must have a minimum overall 2.75 GPA and must be U.S. citizens. **Application Requirements:** Applicants must submit: an official application form; a copy of an official, sealed transcript of all university education; two letters of recommendation from professors, employers, or academic advisors; a 500-750 word typed or legibly written essay that discusses why they should be a scholarship recipient; proof of U.S. citizenship. **Deadline for Receipt:** April 1.

2512 ■ PUBLIC EDUCATION FOUNDATION
3360 W Sahara Ave., Ste. 160
Las Vegas, NV 89102
Tel: (702)799-1042
Fax: (702)799-5247
E-mail: steelej@ccpef.org
Web Site: http://ccpef.org
To promote education in the area of environmental studies/sciences.
Title of Award: Republic Services Environmental Studies Scholarships **Area, Field, or Subject:** Environmental science. **Level of Education for which Award is Granted:** Undergraduate **Number Awarded:** 1. **Funds Available:** $1,500.

Eligibility Requirements: Applicants must be CCSD seniors planning to major in Environmental Studies/Sciences at a four-year institution with a minimum 3.5 cumulative GPA. **Application Requirements:** Applicants must submit a completed application form along with the essay, a letter of recommendation, and resume. **Deadline for Receipt:** March 31. **Additional Information:** Shana Venenga at 702-799-1042.

2513 ■ SHORELINE COMMUNITY COLLEGE FOUNDATION
16101 Greenwood Ave. N, Ste. 1005
Shoreline, WA 98133-5696
Tel: (206)546-4755
Fax: (206)546-5826
E-mail: rmanchester@shoreline.edu
Web Site: http://www.shoreline.edu
To increase access and success of Shoreline Community College students.
Title of Award: Eric Niemitalo Scholarships in Earth and Environmental Science **Area, Field, or Subject:** Environmental Science. **Level of Education for which Award is Granted:** Undergraduate **Funds Available:** No specific amount.
Eligibility Requirements: Applicants must be full-time or part-time students at the Shoreline/Lake Forest Park area who are enrolling at SCC. **Application Requirements:** Applicants must complete the application form.

2514 ■ SOLID WASTE ASSOCIATION OF NORTH AMERICA
1100 Wayne Ave., Ste. 700
Silver Spring, MD 20910
Tel: 800-467-9262
Fax: (301)589-7068
Web Site: http://www.swana.org
To promote education and professional development by providing financial aid.
Title of Award: Grant H. Flint International Scholarships - Category II **Area, Field, or Subject:** Environmental Science; Engineering. **Level of Education for which Award is Granted:** Undergraduate **Number Awarded:** 1. **Funds Available:** $2,000. **Duration:** Annual.
Eligibility Requirements: Applicants can be SWANA student members who are currently enrolled full-time students and/or entering their junior or senior undergraduate year; must be pursuing a degree in environmental science, engineering, or other suitable major related to solid waste management. **Application Requirements:** Application forms and instructions are available at SWANA website. **Deadline for Receipt:** May 1. **Additional Information:** Kathy Callaghan, Staff Administrator, at the above address tel 240-494-2248, email: kcallaghan@swana.org.

2515 ■ SOUTHWEST FLORIDA COMMUNITY FOUNDATION
8260 College Pkwy., Ste. 101
Fort Myers, FL 33919
Tel: (239)274-5900
Fax: (239)274-5930
Web Site: http://www.floridacommunity.com
To provide financial assistance for qualified students in Florida.
Title of Award: Charles and Margaret Foster Scholarships **Area, Field, or Subject:** Environmental technology; Music. **Level of Education for which Award is Granted:** Undergraduate **Number Awarded:** 2. **Funds Available:** $300. **Duration:** One year.
Eligibility Requirements: Applicant must be a resident of Lee County and must be studying environmental studies or environmental education at the University of Florida or studying music at Florida State University. **Application Requirements:** Applicants must have the application form, available online, and must submit a transcript, letter of interest and letter of recommendation. **Deadline for Receipt:** February 15.

2516 ■ MORRIS K. UDALL FOUNDATION
130 S Scott Ave.
Tucson, AZ 85701-1922
Tel: (520)901-8500
Fax: (520)670-5530
E-mail: info@udall.gov
Web Site: http://www.udall.gov
To provide scholarship assistance for qualified individuals.
Title of Award: Morris K. Udall Scholarships **Area, Field, or Subject:** Environmental technology; Native American studies. **Level of Education**

for which **Award is Granted:** Undergraduate **Funds Available:** No specific amount. **Duration:** One year.
Eligibility Requirements: Applicant must be a student who has demonstrated commitment to a career related to the environment; or must be a Native American or Alaska Native student who has demonstrated commitment to a career related to tribal public policy or Native health care; must be a sophomore or junior level college student; must have a college GPA of at least 3.0 or the equivalent; and must be a U.S citizen, U.S national, or U.S permanent resident. **Application Requirements:** Applicants must complete and sign Udall Scholarship Application and submit along with an 800-word essay (signed and dated), a current official college transcript and transcripts for other colleges attended, and three letters of recommendation. **Deadline for Receipt:** March 4.

2517 ■ UNIVERSITY OF CALIFORNIA, BERKELEY
301B Campbell Hall No. 2922
Berkeley, CA 94720-2922
Tel: (510)643-6929
E-mail: scholarships@learning.berkeley.edu
Web Site: http://www.berkeley.edu
To provide financial support for outstanding sophomore and junior students.
Title of Award: Udall Scholarships **Area, Field, or Subject:** Environmental science, Health care services. **Level of Education for which Award is Granted:** Undergraduate **Funds Available:** $5,000 for educational expenses. UC Berkeley selection committee will select the university's nominee based on the application materials and criteria.
Eligibility Requirements: Applicant must be a student who studies the environmental and related fields; must be a Native American or Alaska Native in fields related to health care or tribal public policy; Applicant must be a full-time sophomore or junior students; must be a U.S. citizen or resident alien; must have a minimum of 3.0 GPA. **Application Requirements:** Applicant must complete the application form; must have a 800-word essay discussing a significant public speech, legislative act, or public policy statement by Congressman Udall and its relationship to the applicant's interest or coursework; must have a three letters of recommendation from: (1) a faculty member who can discuss the applicant's potential; (2) a faculty member in the applicant's of study; (3) another individual who can attest to the applicant's capabilities; must have the official college transcripts. **Deadline for Receipt:** February 20.

2518 ■ UNIVERSITY OF TORONTO
315 Bloor St. W
Toronto, ON, Canada M5S 1A3
Tel: (416)978-2011
E-mail: information.commonsats@utoronto.ca
Web Site: http://www.utoronto.ca
To support students with their educational pursuits.
Title of Award: J.P. Bickell Mining Scholarships **Area, Field, or Subject:** Geology; Geophysics; Earth sciences; Mining; Environmental science. **Level of Education for which Award is Granted:** Undergraduate **Funds Available:** Approximately $2000.
Eligibility Requirements: Applicant must be a student of U of T; an undergraduate student in second or higher years studying mining (including the geological and geophysical fields as well as environmental sciences, geological sciences, earth science programs and mining engineering); have a minimum GPA of B or better and have demonstrated interest in the mining industry or field. **Application Requirements:** Applicants must submit a letter of application together with a letter outlining the interest in the mining industry. **Deadline for Receipt:** October 31.

2519 ■ THE WASHINGTON GROUP
720 Park Blvd.
PO Box 73
Boise, ID 83729
Tel: (208)386-5000
E-mail: membership@washingtongroup.org
Web Site: http://www.wgint.com
To encourage active participation in Ukrainian community.
Title of Award: Chopivsky Fellowships **Area, Field, or Subject:** Forestry; Environmental Studies; Economics. **Level of Education for which Award is Granted:** Undergraduate **Number Awarded:** 2. **Funds Available:** No specific amount.

Eligibility Requirements: Applicants must be Ukrainian citizens and must be first admitted to the appropriate faculties at Yale; must be in graduate degree program leading to master's degree at the Yale School of Management at the Yale School of Forestry and Environmental Studies, and in the Departments of International Relations, International Economics, and Developmental Studies. **Application Requirements:** Applicants must fill out the application form and supporting materials. **Deadline for Receipt:** January 1. **Additional Information:** PO Box 208206, New Haven, CT 06520-8606; 1203-432-3423; 12034325963.

2520 ■ WASHINGTON STATE LAKE PROTECTION ASSOCIATION
PO Box 4245
Seattle, WA 98194
Tel: (206)263-6242
E-mail: info@walpa.org
Web Site: http://www.walpa.org
To support undergraduate and graduate students in their pursuit of degrees specializing in the fields of Environmental Science.
Title of Award: WALPA Lake Scholarships **Area, Field, or Subject:** Environmental Science. **Level of Education for which Award is Granted:** Graduate, Undergraduate **Number Awarded:** 2. **Funds Available:** $750-$1,000.
Eligibility Requirements: Applicants must be enrolled as part or full time undergraduate or graduate students in an accredited college or university in Washington or Idaho and be completing course work or research related to biology, hydrology, ecology and management or restoration of lakes and watersheds in Washington and Idaho. **Application Requirements:** Applicants must check the available website for the required materials. **Additional Information:** Washington State Lake Protection Association at the above address.

Conservation

2521 ■ BAT CONSERVATION INTERNATIONAL
PO Box 162603
Austin, TX 78716
Tel: (512)327-9721
Free: 800-538-2287
Fax: (512)327-9724
E-mail: bathouses@batcon.org
Web Site: http://www.batcon.org
To teach people the value of bats; to protect and conserve critical bat habitats; to advance scientific knowledge through research.
Title of Award: Bat Conservation International Student Research Scholarships **Area, Field, or Subject:** Environmental conservation. **Level of Education for which Award is Granted:** Undergraduate **Number Awarded:** 1. **Funds Available:** $1,000-$5,000.
Eligibility Requirements: Applicant must be enrolled in any college or university. **Application Requirements:** Applicant must apply online or send documents as attachments to grant@batcon.org; he/she must submit a proposal, budget, and curriculum vitae. **Deadline for Receipt:** December15. **Additional Information:** grant@batcon.org.

2522 ■ MICHIGAN WATER ENVIRONMENT ASSOCIATION
PO Box 397
Bath, MI 48808
Tel: (517)641-7377
Fax: (517)641-7388
E-mail: mwea@mi-wea.org
Web Site: http://www.mi-wea.org
To educate and inform policy makers and the general public; to promote scientifically-sound environmental practices and regulation; to promote and advance the water quality profession; to promote public and ecological health by preserving and enhancing Michigan's water environment.
Title of Award: Antenore C. "Buth" Davanzo Scholarships **Area, Field, or Subject:** Environmental Conservation. **Level of Education for which Award is Granted:** Undergraduate **Funds Available:** $500.
Eligibility Requirements: Applicants must be attending a Michigan college or university; must be part-time students and pursuing a course of study leading to a career in Wastewater Treatment or some aspect of the water environment field; must be entering the second year of a two or four-year program in the year following receipt of the award or be in a

graduate level course of study; must have at least a 2.5 GPA on a 4.0 scale; must be organization members at the time of the presentation of the award. **Application Requirements:** Applicants must submit a paper of between 500 and 600 words reflecting on their career interests and objectives and how they envision using their education to enhance water quality; must submit a current copy of their college or university transcript; resume with all full and part-time employment, education history and extracurricular activities; a letter of recommendation from their academic advisor or other appropriate official attesting to their course of study and other aspects of their application. **Deadline for Receipt:** March 15. **Additional Information:** 810-231-1200.

2523 ■ MICHIGAN WATER ENVIRONMENT ASSOCIATION
PO Box 397
Bath, MI 48808
Tel: (517)641-7377
Fax: (517)641-7388
E-mail: mwea@mi-wea.org
Web Site: http://www.mi-wea.org
To educate and inform policy makers and the general public; to promote scientifically-sound environmental practices and regulation; to promote and advance the water quality profession; to promote public and ecological health by preserving and enhancing Michigan's water environment.
Title of Award: John P. Hennessy Scholarships **Area, Field, or Subject:** Environmental Conservation. **Level of Education for which Award is Granted:** Undergraduate **Funds Available:** $1,000.
Eligibility Requirements: Applicants must be attending a Michigan college or university; must be full-time students and pursuing a course of study leading to a career in Wastewater Treatment or some aspect of the water environment field; must be entering the second year of a two- or four-year program the year following receipt of the award, or be in a graduate level course of study; must have an at least 2.5 GPA on a 4.0 scale; must be organization members at the time of the presentation of the award. **Application Requirements:** Applicants must submit a paper of between 500 and 600 words reflecting on their career interests and objectives and how they envision using their education to enhance water quality; must submit a current copy of their college or university transcript; resume with all full and part-time employment, education history and extracurricular activities; a letter of recommendation from their academic advisor or other appropriate official attesting to their course of study and other aspects of their application. **Deadline for Receipt:** March 15. **Additional Information:** 810-231-1200.

2524 ■ MICHIGAN WATER ENVIRONMENT ASSOCIATION
PO Box 397
Bath, MI 48808
Tel: (517)641-7377
Fax: (517)641-7388
E-mail: mwea@mi-wea.org
Web Site: http://www.mi-wea.org
To educate and inform policy makers and the general public; to promote scientifically-sound environmental practices and regulation; to promote and advance the water quality profession; to promote public and ecological health by preserving and enhancing Michigan's water environment.
Title of Award: Jack H. Wagner Scholarships **Area, Field, or Subject:** Environmental Conservation. **Level of Education for which Award is Granted:** Undergraduate **Funds Available:** $1,000.
Eligibility Requirements: Applicants must be enrolled full-time and pursuing a course of study leading to a career in Wastewater Treatment or some other aspect of the water environment and/or environmental engineering field; must be entering the third or fourth year of their undergraduate program or be in a graduate level course of study. Applicant must have an at least 2.5 GPA on a 4.0 scale; must be organization member at the time of the presentation of the award. **Application Requirements:** Applicants must submit: a paper of between 500 and 600 words reflecting on their career interests and objectives and how they envision using their education to enhance water quality; a current copy of their college or university transcript; a resume with all full and part-time employment, education history and extracurricular activities; letter of recommendation from their academic advisor or other appropriate official attesting to their course of study and other aspects of their application. **Deadline for Receipt:** March 15. **Additional Information:** 810-231-1200.

2525 ■ VOLUNTARY PROTECTION PROGRAMS PARTICIPANTS' ASSOCIATION
7600-E Leesburg Pike, Ste. 440
Falls Church, VA 22043-2004
Tel: (703)761-1146
Fax: (703)761-1148
E-mail: administrator@vpppa.org
Web Site: http://www.vpppa.org
To encourage students' active participation in occupational safety, health and/or environmental outreach programs in their schools, community and/or workplace.
Title of Award: Delta/VPPPA Safety, Health and Environmental Scholarships **Area, Field, or Subject:** Environmental conservation; Occupational safety and health. **Level of Education for which Award is Granted:** Undergraduate **Funds Available:** No specific amount.
Eligibility Requirements: Applicants must be students who are enrolled or enrolling in a college or university (graduate or undergraduate level) or a vocational school pursuing a degree in the environmental, occupational safety and/or health field; they must be either employed at a VPPPA Full, Corporate or Associate member company or the child or grandchild of an employee; and must have had or have at least a 2.5 GPA on a scale of 4.0. **Application Requirements:** Applicants must submit a completed application form and supporting documents to: VPPPA, Inc., Attn: Awards Committee, 7600-E Leesburg Pike, Ste. 440, Falls Church, VA 22043-2004; or fax to: (703) 761-1148, Attn: Awards Committee. **Additional Information:** The scholarship supports Delta's "Force for Global Good" initiative that focuses on Breast Cancer Awareness, The Red Cross, Habitat for Humanity and environmental responsibility. **Deadline for Receipt:** May 1.

2526 ■ VOLUNTARY PROTECTION PROGRAMS PARTICIPANTS' ASSOCIATION
7600-E Leesburg Pike, Ste. 440
Falls Church, VA 22043-2004
Tel: (703)761-1146
Fax: (703)761-1148
E-mail: administrator@vpppa.org
Web Site: http://www.vpppa.org
To recognize an employee at a VPPPA full member site who has made significant contributions to the VPP program at his or her site.
Title of Award: VPPPA William Sullivan Scholarships **Area, Field, or Subject:** Environmental conservation; Occupational safety and health. **Level of Education for which Award is Granted:** Graduate, Undergraduate **Funds Available:** No specific amount. **Duration:** Annual.
Eligibility Requirements: Applicants must be a current employee at a VPP site (the site must be a VPPPA full member in good standing); must demonstrate their contributions to the VPP site; must be pursuing a degree (undergraduate or graduate) either part-time or full-time; and must have at least a 2.5 GPA on a scale of 4.0. **Application Requirements:** Applicants must submit a completed application form, an official transcript and a reference letter relating to your VPP involvement at your site from a site VPP coordinator, operations manager, site EHS staff, OSHA, Regional VPPPA Chapter Chairperson, and others. Forward to: VPPPA, Inc., Attn: Awards Committee, 7600-E Leesburg Pike, Ste. 440, Falls Church, VA 22043-2004; or fax to: (703) 761-1148, Attn: Awards Committee. **Deadline for Receipt:** May 1.

2527 ■ VOLUNTARY PROTECTION PROGRAMS PARTICIPANTS' ASSOCIATION
7600-E Leesburg Pike, Ste. 440
Falls Church, VA 22043-2004
Tel: (703)761-1146
Fax: (703)761-1148
E-mail: administrator@vpppa.org
Web Site: http://www.vpppa.org
To encourage careers in the areas of safety, health and environment by providing educational support.
Title of Award: VPPPA June Brothers Scholarships **Area, Field, or Subject:** Environmental conservation; Occupational safety and health. **Level of Education for which Award is Granted:** Graduate, Undergraduate **Number Awarded:** Varies. **Funds Available:** No specific amount. **Duration:** Annual.
Eligibility Requirements: Applicants must be students who either work at a current VPP site or the children/grandchildren of an employee of a VPP site (the site must be a VPPPA full member in good standing); must be pursuing a degree (undergraduate or graduate) in the environmental, safety and health areas (either part-time or full-time); must have at least a 2.5 GPA on a scale of 4.0. **Application Requirements:** Applicants must submit completed application form available in the website; a typewritten biography of at least 300 words describing interests and accomplishments or current resume; copy of current transcript; reference letters from the VPPPA site employee and from high school teacher, university's department head, professor or supervisor at current job. Forward all requirements to: VPPPA, Inc., Attn: Awards Committee, 7600-E Leesburg Pike, Ste. 440, Falls Church, VA 22043-2004; or fax to: (703) 761-1148, Attn: Awards Committee. **Deadline for Receipt:** May 1.

2528 ■ VOLUNTARY PROTECTION PROGRAMS PARTICIPANTS' ASSOCIATION
7600-E Leesburg Pike, Ste. 440
Falls Church, VA 22043-2004
Tel: (703)761-1146
Fax: (703)761-1148
E-mail: administrator@vpppa.org
Web Site: http://www.vpppa.org
To encourage careers in the areas of safety, health and environment by providing educational support.
Title of Award: VPPPA Stephen Brown Scholarships **Area, Field, or Subject:** Environmental conservation; Occupational safety and health. **Level of Education for which Award is Granted:** Graduate, Undergraduate **Number Awarded:** 1. **Funds Available:** No specific amount. **Duration:** Annual.
Eligibility Requirements: Applicants must be students who either work at a current VPP site or the children/grandchildren of an employee of a VPP site (the site must be a VPPPA full member in good standing); must be pursuing a degree (undergraduate or graduate) in the environmental, safety and health areas (either part-time or full-time); must have at least a 2.5 GPA on a scale of 4.0. **Application Requirements:** Applicants must submit completed application form available in the website; a typewritten biography of at least 300 words describing interests and accomplishments; copy of current transcript; reference letters from the VPPPA site employee and from high school teacher, university's department head, professor or supervisor at current job. Forward all requirements to: VPPPA, Inc., Attn: Awards Committee, 7600-E Leesburg Pike, Ste. 440, Falls Church, VA 22043-2004; or fax to: (703) 761-1148, Attn: Awards Committee. **Deadline for Receipt:** May 1.

Ecology

2529 ■ BEN MEADOWS
PO Box 5277
Janesville, WI 53547-5277
800-241-6401
Fax: (608)743-8007
E-mail: mail@benmeadows.com
Web Site: http://www.benmeadows.com
To provide fund for students enrolled in a natural resource program.
Title of Award: Ben Meadows Natural Resource Scholarships - Academic Achievement Scholarships **Area, Field, or Subject:** Forestry; Environmental science; Natural resources; Wildlife conservation, management, and science; Fisheries sciences/management. **Level of Education for which Award is Granted:** Undergraduate **Number Awarded:** 1. **Funds Available:** $2,500.
Eligibility Requirements: Applicant must be a junior or senior student enrolled in a natural resource program working toward a bachelor of arts or science degree, which includes, but not limited to, agro forestry, urban forestry, environmental studies, natural resource management, natural resource recreation, wildlife management, wood science and fisheries management. Student must have a GPA of 3.2 or higher on a 4.0 scale. **Application Requirements:** Applicants must complete the online scholarship application and must provide a letter of recommendation from educational superior (professor, teacher, advisor), and attach official copies of transcripts reflecting the GPA. **Deadline for Receipt:** June 30.

2530 ■ BEN MEADOWS
PO Box 5277
Janesville, WI 53547-5277

800-241-6401
Fax: (608)743-8007
E-mail: mail@benmeadows.com
Web Site: http://www.benmeadows.com
To provide fund for students enrolled in a natural resource program.
Title of Award: Ben Meadows Natural Resource Scholarships - Leadership Scholarships **Area, Field, or Subject:** Forestry; Environmental science; Natural resources; Wildlife conservation, management, and science; Fisheries sciences/management. **Level of Education for which Award is Granted:** Undergraduate **Number Awarded:** 1. **Funds Available:** $2,500.
Eligibility Requirements: Applicant must be a junior or senior student enrolled in a natural resource program working toward a bachelor of arts or science degree, which includes, but not limited to, agro forestry, urban forestry, environmental studies, natural resource management, natural resource recreation, wildlife management, wood science and fisheries management. Student must have a GPA of 2.5 or higher on a 4.0 scale.
Application Requirements: Applicants must complete the online scholarship application and must provide a letter of recommendation from educational superior (professor, teacher, advisor), and attach official copies of transcripts reflecting the GPA. **Deadline for Receipt:** June 30.

2531 ■ CALIFORNIA WATERFOWL ASSOCIATION
4630 Northgate Blvd., Ste. 150
Sacramento, CA 95834
Tel: (916)648-1406
Fax: (916)648-1665
E-mail: cwa@calwaterfowl.org
Web Site: http://www.calwaterfowl.org
To provide field experience a training in the tools, methods, concepts of waterfowl, wetlands research and management.
Title of Award: Dennis Raveling Scholarships **Area, Field, or Subject:** Wildlife conservation, management and sciences; Zoology; Botany; Ecology. **Level of Education for which Award is Granted:** Undergraduate **Number Awarded:** 2. **Funds Available:** $2,000 for first place; $1,000 for 2nd place.
Eligibility Requirements: Applicants must be students with a desire to pursue a career in waterfowl or wetlands ecology. **Application Requirements:** Applicants must submit a "one-page" proposal summary description on an original research or management project; must submit a detailed proposal if required or "one-page" statement explaining the course of study for which they need to support. **Deadline for Receipt:** October 31. **Additional Information:** Nocole Berset at the above address.

2532 ■ THE COMMUNITY FOUNDATION OF MIDDLE TENNESSEE
3833 Cleghorn Ave., Ste. 400
Nashville, TN 37215-2519
Tel: (615)321-4939; 888-540-5200
E-mail: mail@cfmt.org
Web Site: http://www.cfmt.org
To help students in planning their postsecondary education.
Title of Award: Maude Keisling/Cumberland County Extension Homemakers Scholarships **Area, Field, or Subject:** Ecology; Education; Social work. **Level of Education for which Award is Granted:** Undergraduate **Funds Available:** No specific amount.
Eligibility Requirements: Applicants must be residents of Cumberland County, Tennessee for a period of four years or more. Applicants must be graduating high school seniors, GED graduates, or current college undergraduates with a GPA of 2.5 or better. Applicants must pursue a field of study such as, but not limited to, human ecology, family and consumer science, education, and social services. **Application Requirements:** Applicants must complete the application form. Applicants must submit two applicant appraisals; transcript of grades; student essay describing educational plans and how these will help in career goals. Applicants must submit one recent photograph. **Deadline for Receipt:** March 15. **Additional Information:** pcole@cfmt.org

2533 ■ FUR TAKERS OF AMERICA
853 E 1000 N Rd.
Onarga, IL 60955
Tel: (217)394-2577
E-mail: krumui@illicom.net

Web Site: http://www.furtakersofamerica.com
To promote interest in the accumulation and dissemination of knowledge concerning the trapping of fur bearing animals among persons interested therein.
Title of Award: Charles Dobbins FTA Scholarships **Area, Field, or Subject:** Agricultural Science; Biology; Wildlife Conservation and management. **Level of Education for which Award is Granted:** Undergraduate **Funds Available:** $250.
Eligibility Requirements: Applicants must be members of FTA or their immediate relatives; must be majoring in agriculture, biology, wildlife management or related courses in an accredited two-year or four-year college, university, or vocational/technical school. **Application Requirements:** Applicants must provide proof of high school graduation or pending graduation; official documents indicating that they have been accepted in an institution as first year students, or registration of classes if applicants are already in school. Applicants must also submit an essay that discusses career goals and how the scholarship would help to achieve these goals. **Deadline for Receipt:** June 1. **Additional Information:** Carol Krumwiede at the above address.

2534 ■ MATANUSKA-SUSITNA COLLEGE
PO Box 2889
Palmer, AK 99645
Tel: (907)745-9774
Fax: (907)745-9711
E-mail: info@matsu.alaska.edu
Web Site: http://www.matsu.alaska.edu
To provide financial support for deserving students in Alaska intending to pursue an education in any campus of the University of Alaska.
Title of Award: Alaska Support Industry Alliance Scholarships **Area, Field, or Subject:** Resource management, Biology, Wildlife conservation, management, and science, Petroleum engineering. **Level of Education for which Award is Granted:** Undergraduate **Funds Available:** $500.
Eligibility Requirements: Applicants must be full-time students and Alaska residents who have at least 3.0 GPA majoring in a field that will support the industry growth in Alaska and at the same time showing concern for the environment and how industry is developed. **Application Requirements:** Applicants must complete the application forms available in the website; must attach a personal essay, two letters of recommendation, and their current transcripts. **Deadline for Receipt:** February 15.

2535 ■ MATANUSKA-SUSITNA COLLEGE
PO Box 2889
Palmer, AK 99645
Tel: (907)745-9774
Fax: (907)745-9711
E-mail: info@matsu.alaska.edu
Web Site: http://www.matsu.alaska.edu
To provide support to deserving students in Alaska who want to pursue an education in any campus of the University of Alaska.
Title of Award: Lyle Carlson Wildlife Management Scholarships **Area, Field, or Subject:** Wildlife conservation, management, and science. **Level of Education for which Award is Granted:** Undergraduate **Funds Available:** $500.
Eligibility Requirements: Applicant must be a student majoring in wildlife management, wildlife biology or another closely related major and have a minimum GPA of 3.0. **Application Requirements:** Applicant must complete the application forms available at the website; must attach a personal essay, two letters of recommendation, and current transcripts. **Deadline for Receipt:** February 15.

2536 ■ MATANUSKA-SUSITNA COLLEGE
PO Box 2889
Palmer, AK 99645
Tel: (907)745-9774
Fax: (907)745-9711
E-mail: info@matsu.alaska.edu
Web Site: http://www.matsu.alaska.edu
To provide support to deserving students in Alaska who want to pursue an education in any campus of the University of Alaska.
Title of Award: Dr. Orrin J. Rongstad Wildlife Management Scholarships **Area, Field, or Subject:** Wildlife conservation, management, and science. **Level of Education for which Award is Granted:** Undergraduate **Funds Available:** $500.

2537 ■ ENVIRONMENTAL STUDIES ■ ECOLOGY

Scholarships, Fellowships, Grants & Loans

Eligibility Requirements: Applicants must be full-time students majoring in wildlife management and be in good academic standing. **Application Requirements:** Applicant must complete the application forms available at the website; must attach a personal essay, two letters of recommendation, and current transcripts. **Deadline for Receipt:** February 15.

2537 ■ MATANUSKA-SUSITNA COLLEGE
PO Box 2889
Palmer, AK 99645
Tel: (907)745-9774
Fax: (907)745-9711
E-mail: info@matsu.alaska.edu
Web Site: http://www.matsu.alaska.edu
To provide support to deserving students in Alaska who want to pursue an education in any campus of the University of Alaska.
Title of Award: Russian/Central Asian Student Scholarships **Area, Field, or Subject:** General studies. **Level of Education for which Award is Granted:** Undergraduate **Funds Available:** $500.
Eligibility Requirements: Applicants must be residents of Russia, Central Asia or the former Soviet Union, Kazakhstan, Uzbekistan, Turkmenistan, or Kyrgyzstan. **Application Requirements:** Applicant must complete the application forms available at the website; must attach

a personal essay, two letters of recommendation, and current transcripts. **Deadline for Receipt:** February 15.

2538 ■ UNIVERSITY OF WISCONSIN-MADISON
432 N Murray St.
Madison, WI 53706-1496
Tel: (608)262-3060
Fax: (608)262-9068
E-mail: askbucky@uwmad.wisc.edu
Web Site: http://www.wisc.edu
To support UW-Madison students in their education.
Title of Award: Human Ecology Continuing Undergraduate Student Scholarships **Area, Field, or Subject:** Ecology. **Level of Education for which Award is Granted:** Undergraduate **Number Awarded:** Up to 35. **Funds Available:** $2,000.
Eligibility Requirements: Applicants must be UW-Madison sophomores, juniors, or seniors enrolled in the School of Human Ecology. **Application Requirements:** Applicants must submit the School of Human Ecology Continuing Undergraduate Student Scholarship Application, along with three letters of recommendation, official transcripts, and a resume. **Deadline for Receipt:** February 15. **Additional Information:** School of Human Ecology, Office of Student Academic Affairs, at 608-262-2608.

The College Blue Book, 36th Edition

General

2539 ■ ALBERTA LEARNING INFORMATION SERVICE - ALBERTA SCHOLARSHIP PROGRAM
Box 28000 Sta. Main
Edmonton, AB, Canada T5J 4R4
Tel: (780)427-8640
Fax: (780)427-1288
E-mail: scholarship@gov.ab.ca
Web Site: http://www.alis.alberta.ca
To recognize student's leadership and community service.
Title of Award: Lois Hole Humanities and Social Sciences Scholarship **Area, Field, or Subject:** Humanities; Social sciences. **Level of Education for which Award is Granted:** Undergraduate **Funds Available:** $5,000.
Eligibility Requirements: Applicants must be students enrolled full-time in the second or subsequent year of post-secondary study in the Faculty of Humanities or the Faculty of Social Sciences, at the University of Alberta, the University of Calgary, the University of Lethbridge, or Athabasca University. **Application Requirements:** Applicants may contact the Student Awards Office at participating educational institutions for other application requirements. **Deadline for Receipt:** October 15 for University of Alberta and Athabasca University; November 15 for University Lethbridge and the University of Calgary. **Additional Information:** Alberta Scholarship Programs at the above address.

2540 ■ AMBUCS RESOURCE CENTER
PO Box 5127
High Point, NC 27262
800-838-1845
Fax: (336)852-6830
E-mail: janiceb@ambucs.org
Web Site: http://www.ambucs.org
To ensure that a new generation of therapists will continue to enhance the lives of people with disabilities.
Title of Award: AMBUCS Scholarships for Therapists Program **Area, Field, or Subject:** Physical therapy; Occupational therapy; Speech and language pathology/audiology. **Level of Education for which Award is Granted:** Graduate, Undergraduate **Funds Available:** $500-$1,500.
Eligibility Requirements: Applicant must be a citizen of the United States; with documented financial need; with good scholastic standing; be accepted at the junior or senior undergraduate, or graduate level in a program which qualifies the applicant for clinical practice in occupational therapy, physical therapy, speech and language pathology and hearing audiology; express an intent to enter clinical practice in chosen field of therapy in the United States upon completion of course of study for which aid is requested. **Application Requirements:** Applicants should complete online application and must submit most current IRS form 1040, narrative statement and enrollment certification. **Deadline for Receipt:** Mid-January until April 15 annually.

2541 ■ AMERICAN ASSOCIATION FOR THE ADVANCEMENT OF SCIENCE
1200 New York Ave. NW
Washington, DC 20005
Tel: (202)326-6400
E-mail: webmaster@aaas.org
Web Site: http://www.aaas.org
To increase public understanding of science and technology.
Title of Award: AAAS Mass Media Science and Engineering Fellowships **Area, Field, or Subject:** Media Art; Science Technologies; Engineering. **Level of Education for which Award is Granted:** Graduate, Postgraduate, Undergraduate **Funds Available:** $450.
Eligibility Requirements: Applicants must be undergraduates in their senior year; must be graduate or post-graduate students. **Application Requirements:** Applicants must fill out the application form. Applicants must submit a copy of resume including honors, awards and relevant activities; one brief sample of their writing (two-to-three pages on any subjects written in terms appropriate for the general public); journal articles; three letters of recommendation; transcript of the undergraduate and graduate work. **Deadline for Receipt:** January 15.

2542 ■ AMERICAN RESEARCH INSTITUTE IN TURKEY
3260 S St.
Philadelphia, PA 19104-6324
Tel: (215)898-3474
Fax: (215)898-0657
E-mail: leinwand@sas.upenn.edu
Web Site: http://www.ccat.sas.upenn.edu
To expand the number of Americans studying and mastering critical need foreign languages.
Title of Award: Critical Language Scholarships for Intensive Summer Institutes **Area, Field, or Subject:** Business; Engineering; Science; Social Sciences; Humanities. **Level of Education for which Award is Granted:** Graduate, Undergraduate **Funds Available:** no stated amount.
Eligibility Requirements: Applicants must be U.S. citizens; must be currently enrolled in a degree-granting program at the undergraduate or graduate level; must have graduated from an undergraduate or graduate program no more than two-years ago; undergraduate students must have completed at least one year of general college course-work by program start date (one year is defined as two semesters or three quarters); or students in all disciplines including business, engineering, science, the social sciences and humanities are encourage to apply. **Application Requirements:** Applicants must submit completed application form; transcript of records; and letters of recommendation. **Deadline for Receipt:** January 25.

2543 ■ ASSOCIATION FOR APPLIED AND THERAPEUTIC HUMOR
65 Enterprise
Aliso Viejo, CA 92656
Tel: (949)715-2284
Fax: (949)715-6931
E-mail: staff@aath.org
Web Site: http://www.aath.org
To help cultivate the next generation of AATH members.
Title of Award: The Dave Family "Humor Studies" Scholarships **Area, Field, or Subject:** Therapy. **Level of Education for which Award is Granted:** Undergraduate **Funds Available:** $500.
Eligibility Requirements: Applicants must be college students pursuing humor/laughter studies with an interest in entering the field of applied or

therapeutic humor. **Application Requirements:** Applicants must submit three essays (up to 250 words each) answering these questions: How do you plan to apply our Humor/Laughter education in the field after college?; Why do you feel you are most deserving of this conference scholarship?; How has humor/laughter helped you in a difficult situation? **Deadline for Receipt:** October 15. **Additional Information:** Association for Applied Therapeutic Humor; email at staff@aath.org.

2544 ■ ASSOCIATION FOR APPLIED AND THERAPEUTIC HUMOR

65 Enterprise
Aliso Viejo, CA 92656
Tel: (949)715-2284
Fax: (949)715-6931
E-mail: staff@aath.org
Web Site: http://www.aath.org
To honor the work, dedication, commitment and contribution to AATH and the field of therapeutic humor.
Title of Award: Patty Wooten Scholarships **Area, Field, or Subject:** Therapy. **Level of Education for which Award is Granted:** Undergraduate **Funds Available:** No amount specified.
Eligibility Requirements: Program is open to nurses (R.N., L.P.N., L.V.N. or C.N.A). **Application Requirements:** Applicants must submit an essay (not to exceed 250 words) describing how humor helped them in work-related situations. **Deadline for Receipt:** October 15.

2545 ■ ASSOCIATION FOR WOMEN IN SPORTS MEDIA

3899 N Front St.
Harrisburg, PA 17110
Tel: (717)903-3086
E-mail: president@awsmonline.org
Web Site: http://www.awsmonline.org
To assist female college students interested in sports media careers through paid internships with employers.
Title of Award: Association for Women in Sports Media Internship Program **Area, Field, or Subject:** Media arts. **Level of Education for which Award is Granted:** Graduate, Undergraduate **Funds Available:** $1,000.
Eligibility Requirements: Applicants must be full-time female students seeking an undergraduate or graduate degree. **Application Requirements:** Applicants must submit the completed application form or a typewritten page containing the information required on the form; one-page essay of 750 words or less, describing the most memorable experience in sports and sports media; one-page resume highlighting journalism experience; three references with contact information; one letter of recommendation from a professor, advisor, editor, producer or other supervisor who is familiar with their work; maximum of five samples of their work: clips, editing examples, headlines, layout, press releases, video or audio tapes. Limit recordings to 10 minutes or less. $15 application fee must be paid by check or money order.

2546 ■ BULLETIN OF THE ATOMIC SCIENTISTS

77 W Washington St., Ste. 2120
Chicago, IL 60602
Tel: (312)364-9715
Fax: (312)364-9715
E-mail: kbenedict@thebulletin.org
Web Site: http://www.thebulletin.org/index.htm
To provide financial support to undergraduate students pursuing a project relating to interaction of science, global security, and public policy.
Title of Award: Rieser Fellowships **Area, Field, or Subject:** Peace studies; National security. **Level of Education for which Award is Granted:** Undergraduate **Number Awarded:** 3-5. **Funds Available:** $2500 $5000. **Duration:** One year.
Eligibility Requirements: Applicant must be undergraduate student at a U.S. college/university. **Application Requirements:** Applicant must send an application form (available at the website); resume; proposal (800-1000 words); official letters confirming internships, acceptance to conference; an essay (one-page, single-spaced) explaining how the fellowship would be benefit to the applicant; project budget; and two letters of recommendation. **Deadline for Receipt:** December. **Additional Information:** Rieser Fellowship rieser@thebulletin.org.

2547 ■ COMMUNITY FOUNDATION OF NORTHERN ILLINOIS

946 N 2nd St.
Rockford, IL 61107

Tel: (815)962-2110
Fax: (815)962-2116
Web Site: http://www.cfnil.org
To serve the four county area (Boone, Ogle, Stephenson and Winnebago) through philanthropy; to provide leadership in meeting charitable needs and to be a responsible steward to the Foundation's donors and of the Foundation's endowment.
Title of Award: Helen R. Finley-Loescher Scholarships **Area, Field, or Subject:** Arts. **Level of Education for which Award is Granted:** Undergraduate **Funds Available:** No specific amount.
Eligibility Requirements: Applicants must be Freeport High School students demonstrating academic achievement, self-motivation and an interest in the arts; must have exhibited artistic talent through participation in the high school arts curriculum; must have plans to pursue education in fine arts. **Application Requirements:** Applicants must contact a Freeport High school Art Department Instructor for an application form. **Deadline for Receipt:** March 1. **Additional Information:** jpatterson@cfnil.org.

2548 ■ DELTA ZETA SORORITY

202 E Church St.
Oxford, OH 45056
Tel: (513)523-7597
Web Site: http://www.deltazeta.org
To provide financial assistance to all qualified undergraduate students.
Title of Award: Houston/Nancy Holliman Scholarships **Area, Field, or Subject:** Speech and language pathology/audiology; Hearing and deafness; Allied health. **Level of Education for which Award is Granted:** Undergraduate **Funds Available:** $1,000-$2,500. **Duration:** One academic year.
Eligibility Requirements: Applicant must be a junior or senior active, continuing member majoring in hearing and speech, audiology or an allied field; must have an academic achievements (maintaining a 3.0 average), campus honors and activities, and service to Delta Zeta. **Application Requirements:** Scholarship applications are available on the website and must be completed properly. Applicant must have the FAFSA reply form. **Deadline for Receipt:** February 15.

2549 ■ EDUCATIONAL AUDIOLOGY ASSOCIATION

3030 W 81st Ave.
Westminster, CO 80031-4111
Tel: 800-460-7322
E-mail: eaa@imigroup.org
Web Site: http://www.edaud.org
To promote educational audiology.
Title of Award: Noel D. Matkin Awards **Area, Field, or Subject:** Speech and language pathology/audiology. **Level of Education for which Award is Granted:** Undergraduate **Number Awarded:** Varies. **Duration:** Annually.
Eligibility Requirements: Applicant must be a member of EAA. **Application Requirements:** Members are encouraged to submit proposals for these awards. The proposals should be typed, double spaced, and should include the requested information on the pdf rule. The proposals should include section headings in your proposal and number pages. **Deadline for Receipt:** February 1. **Additional Information:** EAA Headquarters, 11166 Huron Street, Suite 27, Denver, Colorado 870234.

2550 ■ FLORIDA ASSOCIATION FOR MEDIA IN EDUCATION

2563 Capital Medical Blvd.
Tallahassee, FL 32308
Tel: (850)531-8351
Fax: (850)531-8344
E-mail: info@floridamedia.org
Web Site: http://www.floridamedia.org
To help every student in Florida be involved in and have open access to a quality school library media program, administered by a highly competent, certified library media specialist.
Title of Award: Sandy Ulm Scholarships **Area, Field, or Subject:** Media Arts. **Level of Education for which Award is Granted:** Undergraduate **Funds Available:** $1,000.
Eligibility Requirements: Applicants must be students studying to be school library media specialists. **Application Requirements:** Applicants must submit a completed application form and submit a copy of the transcript of all college credits for the graduate program in which they are

currently enrolled, two letters of recommendation (one must come from a professor) and a notarized statement (found in application).

2551 ■ HARTFORD FOUNDATION FOR PUBLIC GIVING
10 Columbus Blvd., 8th Flr.
Hartford, CT 06106
Tel: (860)548-1888
Fax: (860)524-8346
E-mail: hfpg@hfpg.org
Web Site: http://www.hfpg.org
To provide scholarship to the students enrolled in an accredited school of Occupational or Physical Therapy.
Title of Award: Hartford Foundation for Public Giving Occupational Therapy Scholarships **Area, Field, or Subject:** Art therapy; Music therapy; Physical therapy. **Level of Education for which Award is Granted:** Undergraduate **Funds Available:** $500.
Eligibility Requirements: Applicants must: be a US citizen; be enrolled in an Occupational (including art and music) or Physical Therapy; have a letter of sponsorship form local DAR chapter. **Application Requirements:** For Connecticut residents, to obtain application materials, send a self-addressed stamped envelope to: National Society Daughters of American Revolution, 215 Loomis St., North Granby, CT 06060. **Deadline for Receipt:** February 15 or August 15. **Additional Information:** Mrs. Michael L. Stewart, CT State Chairperson, NSDAR Scholarship Committee. L2stew@yahoo.com; 860-653-4203.

2552 ■ HELLENIC UNIVERSITY CLUB OF PHILADELPHIA
PO Box 42199
Philadelphia, PA 19101-2199
Tel: (215)483-7440
E-mail: hucphila@yahoo.com
Web Site: http://www.hucphila.org
To provide scholarships for students with outstanding academic qualifications and financial need.
Title of Award: Hellenic University Club of Philadelphia Founders Scholarships **Area, Field, or Subject:** Greek studies. **Level of Education for which Award is Granted:** Undergraduate **Funds Available:** $3,000.
Eligibility Requirements: Applicants must be of Greek descent; must be U.S. citizens; and must be undergraduate students who have declared majors in Greek studies. **Application Requirements:** Application form can be obtained from the HUCPhila website. Applicants must complete the application form and mail to Scholarship Chairman. Applicants must also provide one letter of recommendation and scholastic transcripts. **Deadline for Receipt:** April 21. **Additional Information:** Scholarship Chairman at the above address.

2553 ■ HISPANIC SCHOLARSHIP FUND
55 Second St., Ste. 1500
San Francisco, CA 94105
877-473-4636
Fax: (415)808-2302
E-mail: info@hsf.net
Web Site: http://www.hsf.net
To support outstanding Community College Transfer Students.
Title of Award: HSF/Nissan Community College Transfer Scholarship Program **Area, Field, or Subject:** Business; Engineering; Communications; Media arts. **Level of Education for which Award is Granted:** Undergraduate **Funds Available:** $2,500.
Eligibility Requirements: Applicant must be of Hispanic heritage; U.S. citizen or legal permanent resident with a valid permanent resident card or passport stamped I-551; currently enrolled part-time or full-time at a community college; planning to transfer and enroll full-time in a degree-seeking program at a four-year U.S. accredited institution; must reside or transfer to a four-year institution in Atlanta, Georgia; Chicago Illinois; Greater Dallas/Forth Worth, Texas; Jackson/Canton, Mississippi; Los Angeles, California; Nashville, Tennessee; Northern California; New York City/New Jersey; be pursuing a degree in Business, Engineering, Communications or Media Arts; have a minimum GPA of 3.0 on a 4.0 scale; must apply for federal financing aid using the Free Application for Federal Student Aid (FAFSA) at www.fafsa.ed.gov. **Application Requirements:** Applications must be submitted using the HSF online application system. **Additional Information:** In partnership with Nissan North America, Inc. **Deadline for Receipt:** March 15. **Additional Information:** cctransfer@hsf.net.

2554 ■ JAPANESE AMERICAN CITIZENS LEAGUE
1765 Sutter St.
San Francisco, CA 94115
Tel: (415)921-5225
Fax: (415)921-4671
E-mail: jacl@jacl.org
Web Site: http://www.jacl.org
To provide financial assistance for deserving students intending to pursue their studies.
Title of Award: Gongoro Nakamura Memorial Scholarships **Area, Field, or Subject:** Speech, Debate, and Forensics. **Level of Education for which Award is Granted:** Undergraduate **Funds Available:** $60,000. **Duration:** One year.
Eligibility Requirements: Applicant must be an active National JACL member at either an individual or Student/ Youth level; must be planning to attend full-time at a college, university, trade school, business school, or any other institution of higher learning within the United States at the undergraduate or graduate school level. Entering freshman applicants must be a high school senior. **Application Requirements:** Application forms are available online at www.jacl.org/join.html. **Deadline for Receipt:** March 1 (entering freshman) and April 1 (all applications excluding entering freshman).

2555 ■ JEWISH VOCATIONAL SERVICE
216 W Jackson Blvd., Ste. 700
Chicago, IL 60606
Tel: (312)673-3400
Fax: (312)553-5544
E-mail: jvs@jvschicago.org
Web Site: http://www.jvschicago.org
To support the education of a Jewish college or graduate student.
Title of Award: Jewish Federation Academic Scholarships **Area, Field, or Subject:** Medicine; Education; Social work; Arts; Public health; Urban affairs/design/planning; Law. **Level of Education for which Award is Granted:** Graduate, Undergraduate **Funds Available:** More than $500,000 each year.
Eligibility Requirements: Applicant must be Jewish; be born or raised in either: Cook County, Chicago metropolitan area, or Northwest Indiana; or have one continuous year of full-time employment in Cook County or Chicago metropolitan area prior to starting professional education; must intend to remain in the Chicago metropolitan area after completing school; must be entering as a full-time student in an accredited professional graduate program or entering as junior or senior undergraduate student at an accredited professional education program; and must be demonstrating career promise in a helping profession. **Application Requirements:** Applicants must submit a completed Application Data Form; Career Statement Form; Budget Worksheet; and Academic Budget form as an attachment to jvsscholarship@jvschicago.org. In addition, applicants must send by mail a Legal Domicility Form; two letter of reference form; IRS Forms; parents' or spouse's IRS; documentation of tuition cost; Release of Information form; and official transcripts. **Deadline for Receipt:** February 15. **Additional Information:** 312-673-3457.

2556 ■ MANUFACTURING JEWELERS AND ASSOCIATION OF AMERICA
45 Royal Little Dr.
Providence, RI 02904
Tel: (401)274-3840
Free: 800-444-6572
Fax: (401)274-0265
E-mail: info@mjsa.org
Web Site: http://www.mjsa.org
To financially support students enrolled in jewelry-related field.
Title of Award: MJSA Education Foundation Scholarship Fund **Area, Field, or Subject:** Design. **Level of Education for which Award is Granted:** Undergraduate **Funds Available:** $250-$2,000.
Eligibility Requirements: Applicant must be a U.S. citizen; must be enrolled in a jewelry program; pursuing a career in the jewelry industry; and with demonstrated financial need. **Application Requirements:** Applicant must complete the application form available at the website; must submit a copy of financial aid award letter; official transcript; an essay; and a letter of recommendation. Forward completed application and supporting documents in one envelope to: Libby Monahan MJSA Scholarship

The Rhode Island Foundation One Union Station Providence, RI 02903. **Deadline for Receipt:** June 1.

2557 ■ NATIONAL ORGANIZATION FOR HUMAN SERVICES
90 Madison St., Ste. 206
Denver, CO 80206
Tel: (303)320-5430
Fax: (303)322-1455
Web Site: http://www.nationalhumanservices.org
To support the education of a student in a human service program.
Title of Award: David C. Maloney Scholarship Program **Area, Field, or Subject:** Humanities; Human relation. **Level of Education for which Award is Granted:** Undergraduate **Funds Available:** No specific amount.
Eligibility Requirements: Applicant must be an Associate, Baccalaureate, or Master's student member of NOHS; have a GPA of 3.0 and above on a 4.0 scale; enrolled in a Human Services studies program. **Application Requirements:** Applicants must submit an official transcript (sent by the university in a sealed envelope); a resume; an essay (500-words) about the applicant's commitment to the field of helping and quality of Human Service Education; copy of current NOHS membership card; and two reference letters. Send applications as email attachments to Linda Wark, PhD, LMFT, Chair, Professional Development Committee at warkl@ipfw.edu. **Deadline for Receipt:** May 1.

2558 ■ NORTHWEST-SHOALS COMMUNITY COLLEGE
PO Box 2545
Muscle Shoals, AL 35662
Tel: (256)331-5200
Free: 800-645-8967
Fax: (256)331-5222
Web Site: http://www.nwscc.edu
To support NW-SCC students with their educational pursuit.
Title of Award: Northwest-Shoals Community College Fine Arts Scholarships - Art **Area, Field, or Subject:** Arts. **Level of Education for which Award is Granted:** Undergraduate **Funds Available:** No specific amount.
Eligibility Requirements: Applicant must be entering full-time freshman or currently enrolled full-time student; and have an overall GPA of 2.5. **Application Requirements:** To qualify, students must file a Northwest-Shoals Community College Application for Admission. Applicants must submit a completed scholarship application form together with the portfolio. **Deadline for Receipt:** March 2. **Additional Information:** 256-331-6394/256-331-5494.

2559 ■ NORTHWEST-SHOALS COMMUNITY COLLEGE
PO Box 2545
Muscle Shoals, AL 35662
Tel: (256)331-5200
Free: 800-645-8967
Fax: (256)331-5222
Web Site: http://www.nwscc.edu
To support NW-SCC students with their educational pursuit.
Title of Award: Northwest-Shoals Community College Fine Arts Scholarships - Drama **Area, Field, or Subject:** Drama criticism. **Level of Education for which Award is Granted:** Undergraduate **Funds Available:** No specific amount.
Eligibility Requirements: Applicant must be entering full-time freshman or currently enrolled full-time student; and have an overall GPA of 2.5. **Application Requirements:** To qualify, students must file a Northwest-Shoals Community College Application for Admission. Applicants must submit a completed scholarship application form along with the required materials. **Deadline for Receipt:** March 2. **Additional Information:** 256-331-6233.

2560 ■ ORGANIZATION OF AMERICAN STATES
1889 F St. NW
Washington, DC 20006
Tel: (202)458-6166
E-mail: scholarships@aos.org
Web Site: http://www.educoas.org
To help finance higher educational pursuits in the United States.
Title of Award: Leo S. Rowe Pan American Fund **Area, Field, or Subject:** Latin American Studies; Arts; Science. **Level of Education for**

which **Award is Granted:** Undergraduate **Funds Available:** $15,000 (in total).
Eligibility Requirements: Applicants must be undergraduate or graduate students from Latin American or Caribbean AOS member countries who are studying or have been admitted for studies in the United States to a program leading to a university degree in an institution of higher learning accredited by the corresponding regional or national council; or must be students and professionals who are either currently pursuing or wish to pursue advanced studies, research, or technical activities in the arts or sciences in institution in the United States; must able to demonstrate, to the Committee's satisfaction their need for assistance, the usefulness of their studies, and ability to successfully complete them; must be nationals of Latin American or Carribbean member State of the AOS; must have a grade point average of at least 3.0 or "B" from their current or most recent academic institution; and must agree to return to their origin after completion of their studies. **Application Requirements:** Applicants must submit original, duly sealed, stamped, or notarized transcript of grades; diplomas; and foreign student advisor form.

2561 ■ PRESCOTT FINE ARTS ASSOCIATION
208 N Marina St.
Prescott, AZ 86301
Tel: (928)541-0209
E-mail: pfaadirector@qwestoffice.net
Web Site: http://www.pfaa.net
To recognize and support the talented young people of Yavapai County.
Title of Award: Prescott Fine Arts Association Scholarship Program **Area, Field, or Subject:** Fine Arts. **Level of Education for which Award is Granted:** Undergraduate **Number Awarded:** 7. **Funds Available:** $500.
Eligibility Requirements: Applicants must be high school students who reside in Yavapai County. **Application Requirements:** Applicants must complete the application form.

2562 ■ PUBLIC EDUCATION FOUNDATION
3360 W Sahara Ave., Ste. 160
Las Vegas, NV 89102
Tel: (702)799-1042
Fax: (702)799-5247
E-mail: steelej@ccpef.org
Web Site: http://ccpef.org
To promote education in arts and business.
Title of Award: Silver Nugget Gaming Ambassadors Scholarships **Area, Field, or Subject:** Arts; Business. **Level of Education for which Award is Granted:** Undergraduate **Number Awarded:** 1. **Funds Available:** $3,000.
Eligibility Requirements: Applicants must be CCSD seniors who attended Rancho High School, Desert Pines High School, Community College East or Area Technical Trade Center; must have demonstrated an interest in the arts and business; and must have shown leadership skills. **Application Requirements:** Applicants must submit a completed application form together with an essay (400-500 words). **Deadline for Receipt:** March 31. **Additional Information:** Shana Venenga at 702-799-1042.

2563 ■ RHODE ISLAND FOUNDATION
One Union Sta.
Providence, RI 02903
Tel: (401)274-4564
Fax: (401)331-8085
Web Site: http://www.rifoundation.org/matriarch/default.asp
To provide financial assistance for qualified individuals pursuing graduate education toward a master's or doctorate in order to pursue a teaching career in the arts.
Title of Award: Antonio Cirino Memorial Art Education Fellowships **Area, Field, or Subject:** Arts. **Level of Education for which Award is Granted:** Undergraduate **Number Awarded:** 16. **Funds Available:** $74,500.
Eligibility Requirements: Applicant must be a Rhode Island resident; must be an artist pursuing graduate education toward a master's or doctorate in order to pursue a teaching career in the arts; must demonstrate financial need; and must have lived in Rhode Island for at least five years prior to applying for the award. **Application Requirements:** Application forms are available online and must be submit to www.callforentry.org. **Deadline for Receipt:** May 23.

2564 ■ THE SAN DIEGO FOUNDATION
2508 Historic Decatur Rd., Ste. 200
San Diego, CA 92106
Tel: (619)235-2300
Fax: (619)239-1710
E-mail: info@sdfoundation.org
Web Site: http://www.sdfoundation.org
To support the education of students from California.
Title of Award: Anneka McMillan Creative Arts Scholarships **Area, Field, or Subject:** Creative arts. **Level of Education for which Award is Granted:** Undergraduate **Number Awarded:** 1-2. **Funds Available:** $1,000.
Eligibility Requirements: Applicant must be a student from San Diego County who is continuing training or pursuing a career or degree in a creative arts (creative writing, photography, art, drama, music, or dance); have a minimum 2.50 GPA on a 4.0 scale; demonstrated financial need; and planning to attend an accredited educational institution or arts academy in the U.S. **Application Requirements:** Applicants must submit a completed Common Scholarship Application together with personal statement; two letters of recommendation on official letterhead (written within the last six months); official transcript in an official and sealed envelope; copy of most recent tax form (Form 1040-pages 1 & 2; Form 1040A-pages 1 & 2; Form 1040EZ -page 1); and copies of creative arts materials (portfolio with illustrations, a video, an audio recording, etc.) which demonstrates achievements. Materials will not be returned. **Deadline for Receipt:** January 28. **Additional Information:** Arzo Mansury, Dir. Scholarships at 619-814-1343, or scholarships@sdfoundation.org

2565 ■ THE SAN DIEGO FOUNDATION
2508 Historic Decatur Rd., Ste. 200
San Diego, CA 92106
Tel: (619)235-2300
Fax: (619)239-1710
E-mail: info@sdfoundation.org
Web Site: http://www.sdfoundation.org
To support the education of students from California.
Title of Award: The UCSD Black Alumni Scholarship for Arts and Humanities **Area, Field, or Subject:** Humanities; Arts. **Level of Education for which Award is Granted:** Undergraduate **Number Awarded:** 5. **Funds Available:** $1,000-$2,500.
Eligibility Requirements: Applicant must be an African-American student currently attending the University of California, San Diego (UCSD); or prospective African-American student enrolling at UCSD. Student must be majoring in the arts or humanities. High school student must have a 3.0 GPA on a 4.0 scale while current UCSD students must maintain at least a 2.75 GPA on a 4.0 scale. **Application Requirements:** Applicants must submit a completed Common Scholarship Application together with personal statement; two letters of recommendation on official letterhead (written within the last six months); official transcript in an official and sealed envelope; and a copy of most recent tax form (Form 1040-pages 1 & 2; Form 1040A-pages 1 & 2; Form 1040EZ-page 1). **Deadline for Receipt:** January 28. **Additional Information:** Arzo Mansury, Dir. Scholarships at 619-814-1343, or scholarships@sdfoundation.org.

2566 ■ THE SAN DIEGO FOUNDATION
2508 Historic Decatur Rd., Ste. 200
San Diego, CA 92106
Tel: (619)235-2300
Fax: (619)239-1710
E-mail: info@sdfoundation.org
Web Site: http://www.sdfoundation.org
To support the education of students from California.
Title of Award: The UCSD Black Alumni Scholarships for Engineering, Mathematics and Science **Area, Field, or Subject:** Humanities; Arts. **Level of Education for which Award is Granted:** Undergraduate **Number Awarded:** 5. **Funds Available:** $1,000-$2,500.
Eligibility Requirements: Applicant must be an African-American student currently attending the University of California, San Diego (UCSD); or prospective African-American student who will be enrolling at UCSD. Students must be majoring in the arts or humanities. High school students must have a 3.0 GPA on a 4.0 scale while current UCSD

students must have maintained at least a 2.75 GPA on a 4.0 scale. **Application Requirements:** Applicants must submit a completed Common Scholarship Application together with personal statement; two letters of recommendation on official letterhead (written within the last six months); official transcript in an official and sealed envelope; and a copy of most recent tax form (Form 1040-pages 1 & 2; Form 1040A-pages 1 & 2; Form 1040EZ-page 1). **Deadline for Receipt:** January 28. **Additional Information:** Arzo Mansury, Dir. Scholarships at 619-814-1343, or scholarships@sdfoundation.org.

2567 ■ SCHOLARSHIP FOUNDATION OF SANTA BARBARA
PO Box 3620
Santa Barbara, CA 93130
Tel: (805)687-6065
Fax: (805)687-6031
E-mail: info@sbscholarship.org
Web Site: http://www.sbscholarship.org
To provide financial assistance to students who are planning to major in Art or an art-related major at college.
Title of Award: Scholarship Foundation of Santa Barbara Art Scholarship Program **Area, Field, or Subject:** Arts. **Level of Education for which Award is Granted:** High School **Funds Available:** No specific amount.
Eligibility Requirements: Applicants must be graduating high school seniors who have attended at least four of the six secondary grade school years in Southern Santa Barbara County, comprised of Goleta, Santa Barbara, and Carpinteria; must be planning to major in Art or an art-related field in college. **Application Requirements:** Applicants must submit all the required application information. **Deadline for Receipt:** November 15.

2568 ■ SCROLLSAW ASSOCIATION OF THE WORLD
116 E Lynn St.
Botkins, OH 45306
Tel: (937)693-3309
Web Site: http://www.saw-online.com
To promote activities within Local Chapter that will enhance the groups scrolling knowledge.
Title of Award: Patrick Spielman Memorial Scholarship Program **Area, Field, or Subject:** Arts. **Level of Education for which Award is Granted:** Undergraduate **Number Awarded:** 2. **Funds Available:** $1,000 **Duration:** 1 year.
Eligibility Requirements: Applicant must be undergraduate or a senior high school student; he/she is at least 24 age and under enrolled in a full time undergraduate course study at an accredited two or four year college, university, or vocational-technical school. **Application Requirements:** Applicant must request an application form to be sent by writing the SAW Office. **Deadline for Receipt:** March 15.

2569 ■ SOCIETY FOR HUMAN RESOURCE MANAGEMENT
1800 Duke St.
Alexandria, VA 22314
Tel: (703)548-3440
Free: 800-283-SHRM
Fax: (703)535-6490
Web Site: http://www.shrm.org
To provide educational fund for pursuing college degree in human resources or a related field.
Title of Award: Barbara Sanchez Scholarships **Area, Field, or Subject:** Personnel administration/human resources; Media arts. **Level of Education for which Award is Granted:** Undergraduate **Number Awarded:** 5. **Funds Available:** $1500.
Eligibility Requirements: Applicants must be SHRM members; must be working full-time in human resources media field. **Application Requirements:** Applicants must return the signed application form with a letter of acceptance from the college and two letters of reference. **Additional Information:** The scholarship was created to honor the late Barbara Sanchez, an HR Director at Newsday and dedicated member of the Media Human Resources Association board of directors. **Deadline for Receipt:** July 15.

2570 ■ STRAIGHTFORWARD MEDIA
508 7th St., Ste 202
Rapid City, SD 57701

Tel: (605)348-3042
Fax: (605)348-3043
E-mail: info@straightforwardmedia.com
Web Site: http://www.straightforwardmedia.com
To financially assist students in their educational pursuits.
Title of Award: StraightForward Media's Art School Scholarships **Area, Field, or Subject:** Arts. **Level of Education for which Award is Granted:** Undergraduate **Funds Available:** $500.
Eligibility Requirements: Applicant must be an art student. **Application Requirements:** Applicants must complete scholarship application online.
Additional Information: Awards are given four times a year. **Deadline for Receipt:** November, February, May, August.

2571 ■ STRAIGHTFORWARD MEDIA

508 7th St., Ste 202
Rapid City, SD 57701
Tel: (605)348-3042
Fax: (605)348-3043
E-mail: info@straightforwardmedia.com
Web Site: http://www.straightforwardmedia.com
To financially assist students in their educational pursuits.
Title of Award: StraightForward Media's Media and Communications Scholarships **Area, Field, or Subject:** Media arts; Communications. **Level of Education for which Award is Granted:** Undergraduate **Number Awarded:** 4. **Funds Available:** $500.
Eligibility Requirements: Applicant must be a student majoring in communications or media. **Application Requirements:** Applicants must complete scholarship application online. **Additional Information:** Awards are given four times a year. **Deadline for Receipt:** March, June, September, December.

2572 ■ UNIVERSITY OF CALIFORNIA, BERKELEY

301B Campbell Hall No. 2922
Berkeley, CA 94720-2922
Tel: (510)643-6929
E-mail: scholarships@learning.berkeley.edu
Web Site: http://www.berkeley.edu
To encourage a junior student to continue studies in the arts, humanities, or social sciences.
Title of Award: Beinecke Brothers Memorial Scholarships **Area, Field, or Subject:** Arts, Humanities, Social sciences. **Level of Education for which Award is Granted:** Undergraduate **Funds Available:** $34,000.
Eligibility Requirements: Applciant must be a junior student; must be a U.S citizen or U.S national from American Samoa or the Commonwealth of Northern Mariana Islands; must have a superior intellectual ability (typically a minimum 3.5 GPA); must have a financial need. **Application Requirements:** Applicant must complete a application form (available online); must have a current resume; must provide a 1000-word personal statement describing background, interests, career goals, and plan for graduate study; must have a official copies of all college transcripts; must have three letters of recommendation from faculty members. **Deadline for Receipt:** February 15.

2573 ■ UNIVERSITY FILM AND VIDEO ASSOCIATION

PO Box 1777
Edwardsville, IL 62026
(866)647-8382
E-mail: ufvahome@aol.com
Web Site: http://www.ufva.org
To support a student research project.
Title of Award: UFVA Carole Fielding Student Grants **Area, Field, or Subject:** Video; Media arts. **Level of Education for which Award is Granted:** Graduate, Undergraduate **Funds Available:** No specific amount.
Eligibility Requirements: Applicants must be an undergraduate or graduate student (a faculty member who is also a member of the association must sponsor the applicant). **Application Requirements:** Applicants must submit six stapled copies of the application form as cover sheet (available at the website); a one-page description of the project; a one-page resume; a statement by the sponsoring UFVA member; and a one-page budget statement to: Professor Robert Johnson Jr., UFVA Carole Fielding Students Grants Chairman, Framingham State College, 100 State St., Framingham, MA 01701-9101. **Deadline for Receipt:** December 15. **Additional Information:** Professor Robert Johnson, Jr.

2574 ■ UNIVERSITY OF TORONTO

315 Bloor St. W
Toronto, ON, Canada M5S 1A3
Tel: (416)978-2011
E-mail: information.commonsats@utoronto.ca
Web Site: http://www.utoronto.ca
To support students with their educational pursuits.
Title of Award: John H. Moss Scholarships **Area, Field, or Subject:** Arts; Science. **Level of Education for which Award is Granted:** Undergraduate **Funds Available:** Up to $16,650.
Eligibility Requirements: Applicant must be a U of T student having a minimum GPA of 3.3 (B+); demonstrates outstanding academic and extra-curricular leadership; in the graduating year in Arts and Science at the University of Toronto (St. George, Mississauga and Scarborough campuses) and intending to pursue a second degree or studies at the graduate level. **Application Requirements:** Applicants must submit a completed application form together with the required materials and information. **Deadline for Receipt:** November 26.

2575 ■ WOMEN IN DEFENSE

2111 Wilson Blvd., Ste. 400
Arlington, VA 22201-3061
Tel: (703)247-2552
Fax: (703)522-1885
E-mail: wid@ndia.org
Web Site: http://wid.ndia.org
To provide financial assistance to further educational objectives of women either employed or planning careers in defense or national security areas.
Title of Award: Women In Defense HORIZONS Scholarships **Area, Field, or Subject:** National security; Military history; Government; Engineering; Computer and information sciences; Physics; Mathematics and mathematical sciences; Business; Law; International affairs and relations; Political science; Economics. **Level of Education for which Award is Granted:** Graduate, Undergraduate **Funds Available:** No specific amount.
Eligibility Requirements: Applicant must be currently enrolled at an accredited university/college, either full-time or part-time; must have junior, senior or graduate status; demonstrate interest in pursuing a career related to national security or defense; demonstrate financial need; have a minimum GPA of 3.25. Applicant must be a female citizen of the United States. **Application Requirements:** Applicants must submit a completed scholarship application form with the essays, recommendations, and transcripts. **Additional Information:** Established in 1988. **Deadline for Receipt:** July 1.

2576 ■ XAVIER UNIVERSITY

3800 Victory Pky.
Cincinnati, OH 45207
Tel: (513)745-3000
Free: 800-344-GOXU
Web Site: http://www.xavier.edu
To financially support students with their education.
Title of Award: Edgecliff McAuley Art Scholarships **Area, Field, or Subject:** Arts. **Level of Education for which Award is Granted:** Undergraduate **Number Awarded:** 3. **Funds Available:** 1 Full-tuition, and 2 half-tuition.
Eligibility Requirements: Applicant must be an incoming first year student with good academic achievement and outstanding artistic talent, and have declared a major in the Arts. **Application Requirements:** Students admitted at the Xavier University are automatically considered. Applicants must submit a Portfolio (minimum of eight or maximum of twelve examples of applicant's best work). Portfolios must be clearly labeled with the applicant's name, home phone number, school, and must include an inventory list and a one page personal resume. All pieces must be matted (white mats are mandatory) unless in slide/digital format. All work must be original. **Deadline for Receipt:** December 1. **Additional Information:** 513-745-3811.

2577 ■ XAVIER UNIVERSITY

3800 Victory Pky.
Cincinnati, OH 45207
Tel: (513)745-3000
Free: 800-344-GOXU

Web Site: http://www.xavier.edu
To financially support students with their education.
Title of Award: Xavier University Honors Bachelor of Arts Scholarships **Area, Field, or Subject:** Arts. **Level of Education for which Award is Granted:** Undergraduate **Funds Available:** One-quarter tuition.
Eligibility Requirements: Applicant must be a student enrolled in the honor bachelor of arts program. **Application Requirements:** Applicants admitted at the Xavier University are automatically considered.

Archaeology

2578 ■ ARCHAEOLOGICAL INSTITUTE OF AMERICA
656 Beacon St., 6th Fl.
Boston, MA 02215-2006
Tel: (617)353-9361
Fax: (617)353-6550
E-mail: aia@aia.bu.edu
Web Site: http://www.archaeological.org
To help students pay their expenses associated with participation on an archaeological excavation or survey project.
Title of Award: Jane C. Waldbaum Archaeological Field School Scholarships **Area, Field, or Subject:** Archeology. **Level of Education for which Award is Granted:** Undergraduate **Funds Available:** $1,000.
Eligibility Requirements: Applicant must be a junior and senior undergraduate student and first-year graduate student currently enrolled at a college or university in the U.S or Canada; must be at least 18 years old and have not previously participated in an archaeological excavation. **Application Requirements:** Applicant must complete the online application form; must submit two copies of transcript, brief cover letter (300 words or less) in the applicant's own words, outline of anticipated expenses associated with participation on the project and a statement from the applicant indicating any other financial resources available to help cover expenses and two references for letters of recommendation from professors or academic advisors at the applicant's college or university. **Deadline for Receipt:** March 15.

Architecture

2579 ■ AMERICAN ARCHITECTURAL FOUNDATION
1799 New York Ave. NW
Washington, DC 20006
Tel: (202)626-7318
Fax: (202)626-7420
E-mail: info@archfoundation.org
Web Site: http://www.archfoundation.org
To encourage and support foreign travel undertaken to further educational goals.
Title of Award: The RTKL Traveling Fellowships **Area, Field, or Subject:** Architecture. **Level of Education for which Award is Granted:** Undergraduate **Number Awarded:** 1. **Funds Available:** $2,500. **Duration:** One year.
Eligibility Requirements: Applicants must be students planning independent foreign travel outside the United States and those who have been selected to participate in established school travel programs. Students must be in the second-to-last year of a BArch or MArch program when applying and complete the travel prior to graduation. Those undertaking independent travel must be accepted in an advanced degree program. **Application Requirements:** Applicants must submit a completed official application form; an 800-word proposal describing the objective for the trip and the relationship to his/her education goals; an official transcript from each college attended; three references in support of the proposal; an itinerary; an estimated budget; a list of previous scholarships and architectural awards. **Deadline for Receipt:** February 15.

2580 ■ AMERICAN INSTITUTE OF STEEL CONSTRUCTION
1 E Wacker Dr., Ste. 700
Chicago, IL 60601-1802
Tel: (312)670-5408
Fax: (312)670-5403

Web Site: http://www.aisc.org
To encourage greater interest in structural steel design.
Title of Award: AISC/Carolina Steel Scholarships **Area, Field, or Subject:** Civil engineering; Architectural engineering. **Level of Education for which Award is Granted:** Undergraduate **Number Awarded:** 1. **Funds Available:** $3,000. **Duration:** One year.
Eligibility Requirements: Applicants must be full-time civil or architectural engineering students of U.S. Citizenship entering their 3rd or 4th year of study from a university in Alabama, North Carolina, South Carolina and Virginia. **Application Requirements:** Applicants must submit an official transcript; a reference and optional letter of reference; a short essay on overall career objective and an original sample steel design analysis/design solution with calculations. **Deadline for Receipt:** April 9. **Additional Information:** Fromy Rosenburg at the above address.

2581 ■ AMERICAN INSTITUTE OF STEEL CONSTRUCTION
1 E Wacker Dr., Ste. 700
Chicago, IL 60601-1802
Tel: (312)670-5408
Fax: (312)670-5403
Web Site: http://www.aisc.org
To provide financial assistance to those studying civil engineering.
Title of Award: AISC/Fred R. Havens Fellowships **Area, Field, or Subject:** Civil engineering; Architectural engineering. **Level of Education for which Award is Granted:** Graduate, Undergraduate **Number Awarded:** 1. **Funds Available:** $5,000.
Eligibility Requirements: Applicants must be U.S. citizens studying civil or architectural engineering full-time at universities in Missouri, Kansas or at MIT. Applicants must be graduate or undergraduate students who have completed one steel design course. **Application Requirements:** Undergraduate applicants must submit an official transcript; a reference and optional letter of reference; a two-page essay on his/her interest in steel structures and an original sample steel design analysis/design solution with calculations. In addition to the mentioned requirements, graduate students applying must submit an official transcript; a reference and optional letter of reference; and a one-page detailed answers to the following: (a) Demonstrate concentration on steel related course work and/or thesis with a strong steel orientation, or (b) Demonstrate proposed course work and proposed thesis concentration in structural steel. **Deadline for Receipt:** April 9. **Additional Information:** Fromy Rosenberg at the above address.

2582 ■ AMERICAN INSTITUTE OF STEEL CONSTRUCTION
1 E Wacker Dr., Ste. 700
Chicago, IL 60601-1802
Tel: (312)670-5408
Fax: (312)670-5403
Web Site: http://www.aisc.org
To encourage greater interest in structural steel design.
Title of Award: AISC/Southern Association of Steel Fabricators Scholarships **Area, Field, or Subject:** Civil engineering; Architectural engineering. **Level of Education for which Award is Granted:** Undergraduate **Number Awarded:** 1. **Funds Available:** $2,500. **Duration:** One year.
Eligibility Requirements: Applicants must be full-time civil or architectural engineering students who are U.S. Citizens entering their 3rd or 4th year of study with an interest in structural steel from a university in Alabama, Arkansas, Florida, Georgia, Kentucky, Louisiana, Mississippi and Tennessee. **Application Requirements:** Applicants must submit an official transcript; a reference and optional letter of reference; and a short essay on overall career objective. **Deadline for Receipt:** April 9. **Additional Information:** Fromy Rosenberg at the above address.

2583 ■ AMERICAN SOCIETY OF LANDSCAPE ARCHITECTS
636 Eye St. NW
Washington, DC 20001-3736
Tel: (202)898-2444; 888-999-2752
Fax: (202)898-1185
E-mail: dsaunders@asla.org
Web Site: http://www.asla.org
To aid outstanding students who would not otherwise have an opportunity to continue a professional degree program in the area of landscape architecture due to unmet financial need; to increase the interest and participation of economically disadvantaged and underrepresented

populations in the study of landscape architecture through a more diverse population; to enrich the profession of landscape architecture through a more diverse population.
Title of Award: American Society of Landscape Architects Council of Fellow Scholarships **Area, Field, or Subject:** Landscape architecture and design. **Level of Education for which Award is Granted:** Undergraduate **Number Awarded:** 2. **Funds Available:** $4,000.
Eligibility Requirements: Applicants must be permanent U.S. citizens or permanent resident aliens who are third, fourth, or fifth year undergraduates at Landscape Architecture Accreditation Board accredited programs of landscape architecture. **Application Requirements:** Applicants must submit a 300-word essay about how the applicant envisions himself or herself contributing to the profession of landscape architecture; two letters of recommendation specifically addressing the quality of applicant's performance as a student of landscape architecture and promise as a professional (one letter of recommendation must come from a faculty member and the other one must be sent by a non-academic member); and a student aid report. **Deadline for Receipt:** February 15.

2584 ■ AMERICAN SOCIETY OF LANDSCAPE ARCHITECTS
636 Eye St. NW
Washington, DC 20001-3736
Tel: (202)898-2444; 888-999-2752
Fax: (202)898-1185
E-mail: dsaunders@asla.org
Web Site: http://www.asla.org
To assist undergraduate or graduate students enrolled in programs in landscape architecture and ornamental horticulture in California.
Title of Award: Class Fund Ornamental Horticulture Scholarship Program **Area, Field, or Subject:** Landscape architecture; Horticulture. **Level of Education for which Award is Granted:** Undergraduate **Number Awarded:** 1. **Funds Available:** $3,000.
Eligibility Requirements: Applicants must be undergraduate or graduate students in financial need who show promise and commitment to the profession; must be continuing their studies in landscape architecture or ornamental horticulture. **Application Requirements:** Applicants must submit a 300-word statement on the profession; 100-word statement indicating intended use of funds; two letters of recommendation from the faculty; and one confidential letter of recommendation from the department head. **Deadline for Receipt:** February 15.

2585 ■ AMERICAN SOCIETY OF LANDSCAPE ARCHITECTS
636 Eye St. NW
Washington, DC 20001-3736
Tel: (202)898-2444; 888-999-2752
Fax: (202)898-1185
E-mail: dsaunders@asla.org
Web Site: http://www.asla.org
To recognize an outstanding architect student.
Title of Award: Edith H. Henderson Scholarships **Area, Field, or Subject:** Landscape architecture and design. **Level of Education for which Award is Granted:** Undergraduate **Funds Available:** $1,000.
Eligibility Requirements: Applicants must be students pursuing a program in landscape architecture. **Application Requirements:** Applicants must submit a typewritten essay review of Mrs. Henderson's book entitled "Edith Henderson's Home Landscape Companion" (200-400 words maximum). **Deadline for Receipt:** April 1. **Additional Information:** rfigura@lafoundation.org.

2586 ■ AMERICAN SOCIETY OF LANDSCAPE ARCHITECTS
636 Eye St. NW
Washington, DC 20001-3736
Tel: (202)898-2444; 888-999-2752
Fax: (202)898-1185
E-mail: dsaunders@asla.org
Web Site: http://www.asla.org
To recognize an outstanding architect student and to emphasize the importance of 24-hour lighting in landscape designs.
Title of Award: William J. Locklin Scholarships **Area, Field, or Subject:** Landscape architecture and design. **Level of Education for which Award is Granted:** Undergraduate **Funds Available:** $1,000.
Eligibility Requirements: Applicants must be students pursuing a program in lighting design or landscape architectural students focusing on lighting design in studio projects. **Application Requirements:** Applicants must submit a typed, double-spaced 300-word essay highlighting the design project, the overall effect to be obtained, rationale for choice of lamp and placement of fixture, and anticipated results; visual samples (schematics/renderings/sketchers or other plans) reduced 81/2"X11"; and one letter of recommendation relevant to the proposed project and applicant, preferably from a current professor. **Deadline for Receipt:** April 1. **Additional Information:** rfigura@lafoundation.org.

2587 ■ AMERICAN SOCIETY OF LANDSCAPE ARCHITECTS
636 Eye St. NW
Washington, DC 20001-3736
Tel: (202)898-2444; 888-999-2752
Fax: (202)898-1185
E-mail: dsaunders@asla.org
Web Site: http://www.asla.org
To give an undergraduate student the opportunity to follow Mr. Page's example of directing profession in the area of landscape architecture and design by answering the challenges of tomorrow.
Title of Award: Raymond E. Page Scholarships **Area, Field, or Subject:** Landscape architecture and design. **Level of Education for which Award is Granted:** Undergraduate **Funds Available:** $1,000.
Eligibility Requirements: Applicants must be currently enrolled in an institution or university. **Application Requirements:** Applicants must submit a double-spaced, two-page essay describing the applicant's need for financial assistance and how the award is to be used; a letter of recommendation from a current professor who is familiar with the applicant's character and goals in pursuing an education in landscape architecture; three copies of application; and a cover sheet. **Deadline for Receipt:** April 1. **Additional Information:** rfigura@lafoundation.org.

2588 ■ AMERICAN SOCIETY OF LANDSCAPE ARCHITECTS
636 Eye St. NW
Washington, DC 20001-3736
Tel: (202)898-2444; 888-999-2752
Fax: (202)898-1185
E-mail: dsaunders@asla.org
Web Site: http://www.asla.org
To bring young creative individuals into careers in the area of landscape architecture and design who may not otherwise have the financial ability to cover all the costs of their educational program.
Title of Award: Rae L. Price Scholarships **Area, Field, or Subject:** Landscape architecture and design. **Level of Education for which Award is Granted:** Undergraduate **Funds Available:** $5,000.
Eligibility Requirements: Applicants must be U.S. citizens who are undergraduate students in the final two years of study in LAAB accredited schools; must demonstrate financial need; and must have a minimum "B" GPA. **Application Requirements:** Applicants must submit a 500-word essay describing the applicant's aspirations, ability to surmount obstacles, high level of drive, and need for financial assistance; two letters of recommendations from current professors familiar with the applicant's character and goals in pursuing an education in landscape architecture. **Deadline for Receipt:** February 15.

2589 ■ AMERICAN SOCIETY OF LANDSCAPE ARCHITECTS
636 Eye St. NW
Washington, DC 20001-3736
Tel: (202)898-2444; 888-999-2752
Fax: (202)898-1185
E-mail: dsaunders@asla.org
Web Site: http://www.asla.org
To recognize an outstanding architect student.
Title of Award: Rain Bird Scholarships **Area, Field, or Subject:** Landscape architecture and design. **Level of Education for which Award is Granted:** Undergraduate **Funds Available:** $1,000.
Eligibility Requirements: Applicants must be undergraduate students majoring in landscape architecture. **Application Requirements:** Applicants must submit a typed, double-spaced 300 word-essay stating career goals and explaining how he/she will contribute to the advancement of landscape architecture. **Deadline for Receipt:** April 1. **Additional Information:** rfigura@lafoundation.org.

2590 ■ AMERICAN SOCIETY OF LANDSCAPE ARCHITECTS
636 Eye St. NW
Washington, DC 20001-3736

Tel: (202)898-2444; 888-999-2752
Fax: (202)898-1185
E-mail: dsaunders@asla.org
Web Site: http://www.asla.org
To recognize an outstanding architect student.
Title of Award: Harriet Barnhart Wimmer Scholarships **Area, Field, or Subject:** Landscape architecture and design. **Level of Education for which Award is Granted:** Undergraduate **Funds Available:** $1,000.
Eligibility Requirements: Applicants must be females entering their final year of undergraduate landscape studies who have demonstrated excellence in design ability and sensitivity to the environment. **Application Requirements:** Applicants must submit a typed, double-spaced autobiography and statement of personal and professional goals with a maximum of 500-words; one letter of recommendation regarding student's design abilities and attitude from a design instructor; graphic samples of work from three different projects, comprising a total of six 8X10 black and white or color photos; brief written descriptions of design intent for each graphic; and financial aid forms. **Deadline for Receipt:** April 1. **Additional Information:** rfigura@lafoundation.org.

2591 ■ AMERICAN SOCIETY OF LANDSCAPE ARCHITECTS

636 Eye St. NW
Washington, DC 20001-3736
Tel: (202)898-2444; 888-999-2752
Fax: (202)898-1185
E-mail: dsaunders@asla.org
Web Site: http://www.asla.org
To recognize an outstanding architect student.
Title of Award: David T. Woolsey Scholarships **Area, Field, or Subject:** Landscape architecture and design. **Level of Education for which Award is Granted:** Undergraduate **Funds Available:** $1,000.
Eligibility Requirements: Applicants must be third, fourth, or fifth year undergraduate or graduate students of landscape architecture who are permanent residents of Hawaii. **Application Requirements:** Applicants must submit a typed, double-spaced autobiography and statement of personal and professional goals with a maximum of 500-words; a design work; three 8X10 color and/or black and white photographs; two letters of recommendation including one from a design instructor; and proof of Hawaii residency. **Deadline for Receipt:** April 1. **Additional Information:** rfigura@lafoundation.org.

2592 ■ ARCHITECTURAL PRECAST ASSOCIATION

6710 Winkler Rd., Ste. 8
Fort Myers, FL 33919
Tel: (239)454-6989
Fax: (239)454-6787
E-mail: info@archprecast.org
Web Site: http://www.archprecast.org
To provide financial assistance to those studying architectural.
Title of Award: Tom Cory Memorial Scholarships **Area, Field, or Subject:** Architecture. **Level of Education for which Award is Granted:** Undergraduate **Funds Available:** $1,500.
Eligibility Requirements: Applicants must have a cumulative GPA of 3.0 or higher; must have at least two semesters of school left to complete from date of award; must be involved in activities related to the architectural field. **Application Requirements:** Applicants must send a completed application form; transcript of two years college through the last grading period to the date of application; letter of recommendation from a faculty member of the collage; written description of the applicant's career plans after graduation; an essay explaining why the applicant chose the architectural field. **Deadline for Receipt:** March 1.

2593 ■ ASSOCIATION OF INDEPENDENT COLLEGES AND UNIVERSITIES OF PENNSYLVANIA

101 N Front St.
Harrisburg, PA 17101-1405
Tel: (717)232-8649
Fax: (717)233-8574
E-mail: duck@aicup.org
Web Site: http://www.aicup.org
To promote the engineering and information technology profession to individuals from groups historically underrepresented in engineering.
Title of Award: Michael Baker Corporation Scholarship Program **Area, Field, or Subject:** Civil engineering; Architectural engineering. **Level of**

Education for which Award is Granted: Undergraduate **Number Awarded:** 1. **Funds Available:** $2,500.
Eligibility Requirements: Applicant must be: full-time undergraduate students majoring in Civil, Environmental or Architectural Engineering only; enrolled as juniors in the fall; maintaining a minimum GPA of 3.0; women and/or members of the following minority groups: American Indians or Alaska Natives, Asians, Black or African Americans, Hispanics or Latinos, Native Hawaiians or Other Pacific Islanders. Student must be accepted at, or currently attending, one of 84 member colleges and universities of the Association of Independent Colleges and Universities of Pennsylvania. **Application Requirements:** Application forms are available at the Financial Aid office. Applicant must submit complete application to Mary Maronic, Foundation Associate, Association of Independent Colleges and Universities of Pennsylvania. A complete application consists of a completed, signed application form, a copy of the student's transcript, a resume and an essay; the candidate may submit a letter of recommendation. **Deadline for Receipt:** April 29. **Additional Information:** Mary Maronic, 717-232-8649 ext. 232; maronic@aicup.org.

2594 ■ ASSOCIATION OF INDEPENDENT COLLEGES AND UNIVERSITIES OF PENNSYLVANIA

101 N Front St.
Harrisburg, PA 17101-1405
Tel: (717)232-8649
Fax: (717)233-8574
E-mail: duck@aicup.org
Web Site: http://www.aicup.org
To promote the engineering and information technology profession to individuals from groups historically underrepresented in engineering.
Title of Award: HDR Engineering, Inc. Scholarship for Diversity in Engineering **Area, Field, or Subject:** Civil engineering; Architectural engineering; Engineering, Geological. **Level of Education for which Award is Granted:** Undergraduate **Funds Available:** $2,500.
Eligibility Requirements: Applicants must: be full-time undergraduate students majoring only in civil engineering, structural engineering or geotechnical engineering; be enrolled as juniors in fall; have a minimum GPA of 3.0; be women and/or members of one of the following minority groups: American Indian or Alaska Native, Asian, Black or African American, Hispanic or Latino, Native Hawaiian or Other Pacific Islander. Applicants must be accepted at, or currently attending, one of 84 member colleges and universities of the Association of Independent Colleges and Universities of Pennsylvania. **Application Requirements:** Application forms are available at the Financial Aid office. Applicant must submit complete application materials to Mary Maronic, Foundation Associate, Association of Independent Colleges and Universities of Pennsylvania. A complete application consists of a completed, signed application form, a copy of the student's transcript, a resume and an essay; the candidate may submit a letter of recommendation. **Deadline for Receipt:** April 29. **Additional Information:** Mary Maronic, 717-232-8649 ext. 232; maronic@aicup.org.

2595 ■ ASSOCIATION FOR WOMEN IN ARCHITECTURE

22815 Frampton Ave.
Torrance, CA 90501-5034
Tel: (310)534-8466
Fax: (310)257-6885
E-mail: president@awa-la.org
Web Site: http://www.awa-la.org
To advance and support the positions of women in architecture and allied fields.
Title of Award: Association for Women in Architecture Scholarships **Area, Field, or Subject:** Architecture. **Level of Education for which Award is Granted:** Undergraduate **Number Awarded:** 5. **Funds Available:** $1,000.
Eligibility Requirements: Applicants must be residents of California or attending a California school; must be enrolled in one of the qualifying majors for the current school term; must have completed a minimum of 18 units in their major by the application due date. **Application Requirements:** Applicants must complete the application form; must submit an official transcript of records from each college and university attended, two sealed letters of recommendation with signature over the seal from an instructor who has taught in their major; must submit a typewritten personal statement stating the reasons for studying the chosen field and

career objectives; must submit a portfolio in "11x17" format showing one-to-three projects from their school work and self-addressed stamped envelope, standard business size. **Deadline for Receipt:** April 15.

2596 ■ CALIFORNIA LANDSCAPE CONTRACTORS ASSOCIATION
1491 River Park Dr., Ste. 100
Sacramento, CA 95815
Tel: (916)830-2780
Fax: (916)830-2788
E-mail: web_admin@clca.org
Web Site: http://www.clca.org
To serve and protect the interest of members, promote professionalism and advance public awareness of the landscape industry.
Title of Award: California Landscape Contractors Association Scholarships **Area, Field, or Subject:** Landscape architecture and design. **Level of Education for which Award is Granted:** Undergraduate **Funds Available:** No specific amount.
Eligibility Requirements: Applicants must be students attending an accredited California community college or state university, majoring in ornamental horticulture and taking a minimum of six units. **Application Requirements:** Applicants must submit typed, printed and completed application form, personal reference letters and resume. **Deadline for Receipt:** April 1.

2597 ■ COMMUNITY FOUNDATION OF PRINCE EDWARD ISLAND
119-121 Quenn St., Ste. 105
Charlottetown, PE, Canada C1A 1Z4
Tel: (902)892-3440
Free: 800-566-7307
Fax: (902)892-0880
E-mail: foundation@cfpei.ca
Web Site: http://www.cfpei.ca
To provide financial assistance to qualified individuals who want to pursue their education.
Title of Award: Architects Association of PEI Scholarships **Area, Field, or Subject:** Architecture. **Level of Education for which Award is Granted:** Undergraduate **Funds Available:** No specific amount.
Eligibility Requirements: Applicant must be a Prince Edward Island student who graduated from a PEI High School and has been accepted into a recognized architectural program. **Application Requirements:** Applicant must complete the application form available online; must submit an official transcript of marks, copy of letter of acceptance from the university, an essay, two reference letters, and portfolio of work. Application form and other supporting documents must be sent to Community Foundation of Prince Edward Island, 119-121 Queen St. Ste. 105, Charlottetown, PE C1A 4B3. **Deadline for Receipt:** May 30.

2598 ■ EDIS COMPANY
PO Box 2697
Wilmington, DE 19805
Tel: (302)421-5700
Fax: (302)421-5715
Web Site: http://www.ediscompany.com
To recognize members of the community who played a part in the growth of EDiS.
Title of Award: Gen III Scholarships **Area, Field, or Subject:** Architecture; Engineering; Business. **Level of Education for which Award is Granted:** Undergraduate **Number Awarded:** 2. **Funds Available:** $1,000 renewable. **Duration:** One year.
Eligibility Requirements: Applicant must be a resident within the community in which EDiS is currently working; must not be any employee of an EDiS Company or a relative of an employee of an EDiS Company; must be pursuing either an Associate's degree or Bachelor's degree; field of study is limited to business or construction-related degrees; and must have a cumulative GPA of 2.5 or greater for renewal. **Application Requirements:** Applicants must submit a completed scholarship application together with official transcript (from current institution), and a copy of best SAT score. **Deadline for Receipt:** May 2. **Additional Information:** Ms. Cyndi Slothour.

2599 ■ HARTFORD FOUNDATION FOR PUBLIC GIVING
10 Columbus Blvd., 8th Flr.
Hartford, CT 06106

Tel: (860)548-1888
Fax: (860)524-8346
E-mail: hfpg@hfpg.org
Web Site: http://www.hfpg.org
To provide scholarship for graduating high school seniors, undergraduate, or graduate students.
Title of Award: Connecticut Building Congress Scholarships **Area, Field, or Subject:** Engineering; Architecture. **Level of Education for which Award is Granted:** Undergraduate **Funds Available:** $500-$2,000.
Eligibility Requirements: Applicants must be attending two or four-year college or university; must demonstrate financial need, academic excellence and community service; must be residents of Connecticut. **Application Requirements:** Applicants may obtain application materials from Connecticut Bldg. Congress Scholarship Fund, Inc. 10 Westgate Rd. Columbia, CT 06237. Phone: 2032281387
Fax: 203228-2296. info@cbc-ct.org. **Deadline for Receipt:** March 15.

2600 ■ HARTFORD FOUNDATION FOR PUBLIC GIVING
10 Columbus Blvd., 8th Flr.
Hartford, CT 06106
Tel: (860)548-1888
Fax: (860)524-8346
E-mail: hfpg@hfpg.org
Web Site: http://www.hfpg.org
To provide scholarship to the students attending five-year accredited colleges or universities offering Architecture.
Title of Award: Charles Dubose Scholarships **Area, Field, or Subject:** Architecture. **Level of Education for which Award is Granted:** Undergraduate **Number Awarded:** 1-2. **Funds Available:** $5,000-$10,000.
Eligibility Requirements: Applicants must: completed a two years of Bachelor in Architecture Program; be a Connecticut connection; demonstrated financial need and academic excellence. **Application Requirements:** Applicants may obtain application materials from Connecticut Architecture Foundation, 87 Willow St., New Haven, CT 06511. Phone: 203865-2195
Fax: 203562-5378. www.aiact.org. **Deadline for Receipt:** April 15.

2601 ■ HELLENIC UNIVERSITY CLUB OF PHILADELPHIA
PO Box 42199
Philadelphia, PA 19101-2199
Tel: (215)483-7440
E-mail: hucphila@yahoo.com
Web Site: http://www.hucphila.org
To provide financial assistance for qualified students pursuing a degree in the fields of Architecture and/or Engineering.
Title of Award: Dimitri J. Ververelli Memorial Scholarships **Area, Field, or Subject:** Architecture; Engineering. **Level of Education for which Award is Granted:** Undergraduate **Funds Available:** $2,000.
Eligibility Requirements: Applicants must be of Greek descent; must be U.S. citizens; and must be pursuing a degree in the fields of Architecture and/or Engineering. **Application Requirements:** Application form can be obtained from the HUCPhila website. Applicants must complete the application form and mail to Scholarship Chairman. Applicants must also provide one letter of recommendation and scholastic transcripts. **Deadline for Receipt:** April 21. **Additional Information:** Scholarship Chairman at the above address.

2602 ■ HISPANIC SCHOLARSHIP FUND
55 Second St., Ste. 1500
San Francisco, CA 94105
877-473-4636
Fax: (415)808-2302
E-mail: info@hsf.net
Web Site: http://www.hsf.net
To provide financial resources to assist outstanding Latino high school graduates.
Title of Award: Toyota High School Scholarship Program **Area, Field, or Subject:** Accounting; Actuarial science; Advertising; Architecture; Automotive technology; Bioengineering; Business; Chemical engineering; Civil engineering; Engineering, Computer; Electronics; Computer and information sciences; Construction; Drafting; Economics; Education; Education, Bilingual and cross-cultural; Education, Early childhood;

Education, Special; Counseling/Guidance; Electrical engineering; Engineering; Environmental design; Environmental science; Geology; Educational administration; Education-Curricula; Personnel administration/human resources; Industrial design; Engineering, Industrial; Information science and technology; Management; Marketing and distribution; International trade; Manufacturing; Mechanical engineering; Engineering, Nuclear; Public administration; Public relations; Transportation. **Level of Education for which Award is Granted:** Undergraduate **Funds Available:** $5,000.

Eligibility Requirements: Applicant must be of Hispanic heritage; U.S. citizen or legal permanent resident with a valid permanent resident card or passport stamped I-551; have a minimum GPA of 3.0 on a 4.0 scale or equivalent; must apply for federal financing aid using the Free Application for Federal Student Aid (FAFSA) at www.fafsa.ed.gov; enrolling as full-time freshman at: Arizona State University; Central Missouri University; Colorado State University, Pueblo; Cornell University; Ferris State; Florida International University; Harvard University; Indiana University; Massachusetts Institute of Technology; New York University; Northwestern University; Pennsylvania Tech College; Pittsburg State University; Southern Illinois University; Stanford University; Texas A&M University; University of Arizona; University of California, Berkeley; University of California, Davis; University of California, Los Angeles; University of California, San Diego; University of Florida; University of Houston; University of Illinois at Chicago; University of Illinois at Urbana-Champaign; University of Michigan; University of New Mexico; University of Pennsylvania; University of Southern California; University of Texas at Austin; University of Texas at El Paso; University of Texas at San Antonio; University of Texas, Pan American; or Weber State University. Applicants must pursue a degree in: Accounting; Actuarial Science; Advertising; Architecture; Automotive Technology; Bio-Engineering; Business; Chemical Engineering; Civil Engineering; Computer Electronics; Computer Engineering; Computer Information Systems (CIS); Computer Programming; Computer Science; Construction; Drafting/CAD; Economics; Education Admin./Leadership; Education/Teaching; Education: Bilingual; Education: Early Childhood/ Elementary; Education: Special; Educational Counseling; Electrical Engineering; Engineering; Environmental Design/ Landscaping; Environmental Management/Science; Environmental/ Geological Engineering; Human Resource Management; Industrial Design; Industrial Engineering; Information Technology (IT); International Business; Management; Management Information Systems (MIS); Manufacturing Engineering; Marketing; Materials/ Manufacturing; Mechanical Engineering; Network Administration; Non-Profit Management; Nuclear Engineering; Office Administration; Public Administration; Public Relations; Supply Chain Management; or Transportation. **Application Requirements:** Applications must be submitted using the HSF online application system. **Additional Information:** In partnership with Toyota Motor Sales, USA. **Deadline for Receipt:** July 16. **Additional Information:** highschool@hsf.net.

2603 ■ INTERNATIONAL ASSOCIATION OF LIGHTING DESIGNERS
The Merchandise Mart, Ste. 9-104
Chicago, IL 60654
Tel: (312)527-3677
Fax: (312)527-3680
E-mail: iald@iald.org
Web Site: http://www.iald.org
To promote education in architectural lighting design.

Title of Award: IALD Scholarship Programs **Area, Field, or Subject:** Architecture; Lighting science. **Level of Education for which Award is Granted:** Graduate, Undergraduate **Number Awarded:** One year. **Funds Available:** $500 $5000.

Eligibility Requirements: Applicant must be a graduate or undergraduate student studying in the field of architectural lighting design. **Application Requirements:** Applicants must complete an application form (available at the website) attach a copy of official transcript; resume; two letters of recommendation; statement of personal experience with lighting, reasons for studying lighting or why deserve the scholarship (maximum of 2 pages); and examples of work in 8.5x11 format (maximum of 10 images). Send the application and attachments to: Scholarship Chairman, International Association of lighting Designers, Merchandise Mart, Suite 9-104 200 World Trade Center Chicago, IL 60654. **Deadline for Receipt:** February 15.

2604 ■ INTERNATIONAL FURNISHINGS AND DESIGN ASSOCIATION
150 S Warner Rd., Ste. 156
King of Prussia, PA 19406
Tel: (610)535-6422
Fax: (610)535-6423
E-mail: info@ifda.com
Web Site: http://www.ifdaef.org
To foster educational and philanthropic activities which will benefit individuals and institutions; to promote, develop or enhance the furnishings and design industries and the practice of the professions.

Title of Award: IFDA Educational Foundation **Area, Field, or Subject:** Architectural Lighting Design. **Level of Education for which Award is Granted:** Undergraduate **Funds Available:** No. 1500.

Eligibility Requirements: Applicant must be attending the college education majoring in lighting designs. **Application Requirements:** An applicant must submit an official transcript of records verifying an students enrollment and GPA; a letter of recommendation from a design educator; four copies of an essay describing personal long and short term goals, award and achievements in no more than 300-400 words; four copies of two digital photos of students own original work preferably in color or in one page; Ruth Clark Furniture design Scholarship requires five different original furniture designs; and recommendation from IFDA member. **Deadline for Receipt:** March 31.

2605 ■ LANDSCAPE ARCHITECTURE FOUNDATION
818 18th St. NW, Ste. 810
Washington, DC 20006
Tel: (202)331-7070
Fax: (202)331-7079
E-mail: scholarships@lafoundation.org
Web Site: http://www.lafoundation.org
To aid outstanding students who would not otherwise have an opportunity to continue a professional degree program due to unmet financial need, to increase the interest and participation of economically disadvantaged and under-represented populations in the study of landscape architecture and to enrich the profession of landscape architecture.

Title of Award: ASLA Council of Fellows Scholarships **Area, Field, or Subject:** Landscape architecture and design. **Level of Education for which Award is Granted:** Undergraduate **Number Awarded:** 2. **Funds Available:** $4,000. **Duration:** One year.

Eligibility Requirements: Applicants must be permanent U.S. citizens or permanent resident aliens who are third-, fourth-, or fifth-year undergraduates at Landscape Architecture Accreditation Board (LAAB) accredited programs of landscape architecture. Applicants seeking special consideration for the diversity scholarship should indicate and identify their association with a specific ethnic or cultural group. **Application Requirements:** Applicants must submit an entry form, a photo (head shot with a plain background; 300 ppi, size 4 x 6 inches in .jpg format) and a personal profile (two page maximum including education, extracurricular activities and financial information); a 300-word essay about how the applicant envisions herself/himself contributing to the profession of landscape architecture; two letters of recommendation addressing the quality of performance as a student of landscape architecture and the promise as a professional. One letter of recommendation must come from a faculty member; the other letter may be sent by a non-academic member of ASLA or another faculty member; a Student Aid Report (SAR) as proof of unmet financial need. All application materials (with the exception of reference letters) must be sent through email as a single document. Each document must be formatted as follows: create one-inch minimum margins; include page number and surname/document name/ award name on all pages of all documents prepared by applicant. **Additional Information:** Established by the ASLA Council of Fellows in 2004. **Deadline for Receipt:** February 15.

2606 ■ LANDSCAPE ARCHITECTURE FOUNDATION
818 18th St. NW, Ste. 810
Washington, DC 20006
Tel: (202)331-7070
Fax: (202)331-7079
E-mail: scholarships@lafoundation.org
Web Site: http://www.lafoundation.org

To assist undergraduate or graduate students enrolled in programs in landscape architecture and ornamental horticulture in California.
Title of Award: CLASS Fund Irrigation Scholarship Program **Area, Field, or Subject:** Landscape architecture and design. **Level of Education for which Award is Granted:** Graduate, Undergraduate **Number Awarded:** 1. **Funds Available:** $1,500.
Eligibility Requirements: Applicants must be undergraduate or graduate students with financial need. Applicants must be continuing their studies in landscape architecture or ornamental horticulture. Student must be enrolled in the irrigation curriculum at Cal Poly Pomona. **Application Requirements:** Applicants must submit a 300-word (maximum) statement on the profession; a 100-word (maximum) statement indicating intended use of funds; two letters of recommendation from the faculty; and one confidential letter of recommendation from the department head. **Additional Information:** Students applying for multiple CLASS (California Landscape Architectural Student Scholarship) Fund Scholarships must submit a separate application for each scholarship. **Deadline for Receipt:** February 15.

2607 ■ LANDSCAPE ARCHITECTURE FOUNDATION

818 18th St. NW, Ste. 810
Washington, DC 20006
Tel: (202)331-7070
Fax: (202)331-7079
E-mail: scholarships@lafoundation.org
Web Site: http://www.lafoundation.org
To assist undergraduate or graduate students enrolled in programs in landscape architecture and ornamental horticulture in California.
Title of Award: CLASS Fund Landscape Architecture Scholarship Program **Area, Field, or Subject:** Landscape architecture and design. **Level of Education for which Award is Granted:** Graduate, Undergraduate **Number Awarded:** 4. **Funds Available:** $1,000.
Eligibility Requirements: Applicants must be continuing their studies in landscape architecture or ornamental horticulture. Applicants must be enrolled at the University of California-Berkeley, or University of California-Los Angeles. **Application Requirements:** Applicants must submit a 300-word statement on the profession; a 100-word statement indicating intended use of funds; two letters of recommendation from the faculty; and one confidential letter of recommendation from the department head. **Additional Information:** Students applying for multiple CLASS (California Landscape Architectural Student Scholarship) Fund Scholarships must submit a separate application for each scholarship. **Deadline for Receipt:** February 15.

2608 ■ LANDSCAPE ARCHITECTURE FOUNDATION

818 18th St. NW, Ste. 810
Washington, DC 20006
Tel: (202)331-7070
Fax: (202)331-7079
E-mail: scholarships@lafoundation.org
Web Site: http://www.lafoundation.org
To assist undergraduate or graduate students enrolled in programs in landscape architecture and ornamental horticulture in California.
Title of Award: CLASS Fund University Scholarship Program **Area, Field, or Subject:** Landscape architecture and design. **Level of Education for which Award is Granted:** Graduate, Undergraduate **Number Awarded:** maximum of two (2) students at Cal Poly Pomona; one (1) student at Cal Poly San Luis Obispo; one (1) student at Cal Poly (faculty decision); maximum of two (2) students at the University of California, Davis. **Funds Available:** $2,000.
Eligibility Requirements: Applicants must be undergraduate or graduate students in financial need who show promise and commitment to the profession. Applicants must be continuing their studies in landscape architecture or ornamental horticulture. **Application Requirements:** Applicants must submit a 300-word (maximum) statement on the profession; a 100-word (maximum) statement indicating intended use of funds; two letters of recommendation from the faculty; and one confidential letter of recommendation from the department head. **Additional Information:** Students applying for multiple CLASS (California Landscape Architectural Student Scholarship) Fund Scholarships must submit a separate application for each scholarship. **Deadline for Receipt:** February 15.

2609 ■ LANDSCAPE ARCHITECTURE FOUNDATION

818 18th St. NW, Ste. 810
Washington, DC 20006
Tel: (202)331-7070
Fax: (202)331-7079
E-mail: scholarships@lafoundation.org
Web Site: http://www.lafoundation.org
To provide funds for educational or professional development purposes.
Title of Award: Hawaii Chapter/David T. Woolsey Scholarships **Area, Field, or Subject:** Landscape architecture and design. **Level of Education for which Award is Granted:** Graduate, Undergraduate **Number Awarded:** 1. **Funds Available:** $2,000.
Eligibility Requirements: Applicants must be third-, fourth-, or fifth-year undergraduate or graduate students of landscape architecture at Landscape Architecture Accreditation Board (LAAB) accredited programs. Applicants must also be permanent residents of Hawaii. **Application Requirements:** Applicants must submit an entry form, a photo (head shot with a plain background; 300 ppi, size 4 x 6 inches in extracurricular activities and financial information); a typed, 500-word maximum double-spaced autobiography and statement of personal and professional goals; three 8 1/2 x 11 work samples in either design instructor and proof of Hawaii residency. All application materials (with the exception of reference letters) must be sent through email as a single document. Each document must be formatted as follows: create one-inch minimum margins; include page number and surname/document name/award name on all pages of all documents prepared by applicant. **Deadline for Receipt:** February 15.

2610 ■ LANDSCAPE ARCHITECTURE FOUNDATION

818 18th St. NW, Ste. 810
Washington, DC 20006
Tel: (202)331-7070
Fax: (202)331-7079
E-mail: scholarships@lafoundation.org
Web Site: http://www.lafoundation.org
To recognize a student who has high potential in the design of play environments.
Title of Award: Steven G. King Play Environments Scholarships **Area, Field, or Subject:** Landscape architecture and design. **Level of Education for which Award is Granted:** Undergraduate **Number Awarded:** 1. **Funds Available:** $5,000.
Eligibility Requirements: Applicants must be landscape architecture students with an interest and aptitude in the design of play environments. Candidates must be enrolled in graduate or the final two years of undergraduate study in LAAB accredited schools. **Application Requirements:** Applicants must submit an entry form, a photo (head shot with a plain background; 300 ppi, size 4 x 6 inches in extracurricular activities and financial information); a 300 to 500-word essay describing the applicant's views of the significant social and educational value of play and the value of integrating playgrounds into play and recreation environments; a plan and details of a play environment of the applicant's design in either .jpg or PDF format; two letters of recommendation from current professors familiar with the applicant's demonstrated interest in park and playground planning, creativity and openness to innovation. All application materials (with the exception of reference letters) must be sent through email as a single document. Each document must be formatted as follows: create one-inch minimum margins; include page number and surname/document name/award name on all pages of all documents prepared by applicant. **Deadline for Receipt:** February 15.

2611 ■ LANDSCAPE ARCHITECTURE FOUNDATION

818 18th St. NW, Ste. 810
Washington, DC 20006
Tel: (202)331-7070
Fax: (202)331-7079
E-mail: scholarships@lafoundation.org
Web Site: http://www.lafoundation.org
To honor excellence in design for people.
Title of Award: Landscape Forms Design for People Scholarships **Area, Field, or Subject:** Landscape architecture and design. **Level of Education for which Award is Granted:** Undergraduate **Number Awarded:** 1. **Funds Available:** $3,000.
Eligibility Requirements: Applicants must be landscape architecture students who will be starting their final year of full-time undergraduate

study in an LAAB-accredited program. Applicants must show a proven contribution to the design of public spaces that integrates landscape design and the use of amenities to promote social interaction. **Application Requirements:** Applicants must submit an entry form, a photo (head shot with a plain background; 300 ppi, size 4 x 6 inches in .jpg format) and a personal profile (two-page maximum including education, extracurricular activities and financial information); a 300-word maximum essay describing the qualities essential to the creation of great and successful public spaces; three 8 1/2 x 11 academic or internship work samples in either .jpg or PDF format; two letters of recommendation from current professors and/or internship employers. All application materials (with the exception of reference letters) must be sent through email as a single document. Each document must be formatted as follows: create one-inch minimum margins; include page number and surname/document name/award name on all pages of all documents prepared by applicant. **Deadline for Receipt:** February 15.

2612 ∎ LANDSCAPE ARCHITECTURE FOUNDATION

818 18th St. NW, Ste. 810
Washington, DC 20006
Tel: (202)331-7070
Fax: (202)331-7079
E-mail: scholarships@lafoundation.org
Web Site: http://www.lafoundation.org
To assist students with outstanding academic record and unmet financial need.

Title of Award: Courtland Paul Scholarships **Area, Field, or Subject:** Landscape architecture and design. **Level of Education for which Award is Granted:** Undergraduate **Number Awarded:** 1. **Funds Available:** $5,000. Funds must be used for tuition and books within the school year of the award. **Duration:** One school year.

Eligibility Requirements: Applicants must be United States citizens who are undergraduate students in the final two years of study in Landscape Architecture Accreditation Board accredited schools. Applicants must demonstrate financial need and have a minimum grade point average of C. **Application Requirements:** Applicants must submit an entry form, a photo (head shot with a plain background; 300 ppi, size 4 x 6 inches in .jpg format) and a personal profile (two page maximum including education, extracurricular activities and financial information); 500-word maximum essay describing the applicant's aspirations, ability to surmount obstacles, high level of drive and need for financial assistance; two letters of recommendation from current professors familiar with the applicant's character and goals in pursuing an education in landscape architecture. All application materials (with the exception of reference letters) must be sent through email as a single document. Each document must be formatted as follows: create one-inch minimum margins; include page number and surname/document name/ award name on all pages of all documents prepared by applicant. **Additional Information:** The scholarship is given in honor of Courtland P. Paul. **Deadline for Receipt:** February 15.

2613 ∎ LANDSCAPE ARCHITECTURE FOUNDATION

818 18th St. NW, Ste. 810
Washington, DC 20006
Tel: (202)331-7070
Fax: (202)331-7079
E-mail: scholarships@lafoundation.org
Web Site: http://www.lafoundation.org
To assist individuals into may not otherwise have the financial ability to cover all the costs of their educational program.

Title of Award: Peridian International, Inc./Rae L. Price, FASLA Scholarships **Area, Field, or Subject:** Landscape architecture and design. **Level of Education for which Award is Granted:** Undergraduate **Number Awarded:** 1. **Funds Available:** $5,000. Use of funds is restricted to tuition, books and program required supplies within the school year of the award. **Duration:** One year.

Eligibility Requirements: Applicants must be United States citizens; students in the final two years of study in Landscape Architecture at the University of California at Los Angeles Extension Program, or in the case of UCLA's termination of the program, other California accredited schools of programs in Landscape Architecture. Applicants must demonstrate financial need and a minimum grade point average of B. **Application Requirements:** Applicants must submit an entry form, a photo (head shot with a plain background; 300 ppi, size 4 x 6 inches in .jpg format) and a

personal profile (two pages including education, extracurricular activities and financial information); a 500-word essay describing the applicant's aspirations, ability to surmount obstacles, high level of drive and need for financial assistance; two letters of recommendation from current professors familiar with the applicant's character and goals in pursuing an education in landscape architecture. All application materials (with the exception of reference letters) must be sent through email as a single document. Each document must be formatted as follows: create one-inch minimum margins; include page number and surname/document name/ award name on all pages of all documents prepared by applicant. **Additional Information:** The use of funds is restricted to tuition, books and program required supplies within the school year of the award. **Deadline for Receipt:** February 15.

2614 ∎ LANDSCAPE ARCHITECTURE FOUNDATION

818 18th St. NW, Ste. 810
Washington, DC 20006
Tel: (202)331-7070
Fax: (202)331-7079
E-mail: scholarships@lafoundation.org
Web Site: http://www.lafoundation.org
To recognize an outstanding landscape architecture, horticulture or irrigation science student.

Title of Award: Rain Bird Intelligent Use of Water Scholarships **Area, Field, or Subject:** Landscape architecture and design; Horticulture. **Level of Education for which Award is Granted:** Undergraduate **Number Awarded:** 1. **Funds Available:** $2,500.

Eligibility Requirements: Applicants must be students in the final two years of undergraduate study (third-, fourth-, or fifth-year students) who have demonstrated commitment to these professions through participation in extracurricular activities and exemplary scholastic achievements. **Application Requirements:** Applicants must submit an entry form, a photo (head shot with a plain background; 300 ppi, size 4 x 6 inches in extracurricular activities and financial information); a cover letter; a typed, double-spaced 300-word essay stating career goals and explaining how the applicant will contribute to the advancement of the profession of landscape architecture, horticulture or irrigation science. All application materials (with the exception of reference letters) must be sent through email as a single document. Each document must be formatted as follows: create one-inch minimum margins; include page number and surname/document name/award name on all pages of all documents prepared by applicant. **Deadline for Receipt:** February 15.

2615 ∎ MATANUSKA-SUSITNA COLLEGE

PO Box 2889
Palmer, AK 99645
Tel: (907)745-9774
Fax: (907)745-9711
E-mail: info@matsu.alaska.edu
Web Site: http://www.matsu.alaska.edu
To provide an incentive for Alaska's middle and high school students to achieve academic excellence, and to encourage the top high school graduates from every community in Alaska to attend the University of Alaska.

Title of Award: Snodgrass Scholarships **Area, Field, or Subject:** Accounting; Engineering, Architectural; Computer and information sciences; Fires and fire prevention; Heating, air conditioning, and refrigeration; Business administration; Telecommunications systems. **Level of Education for which Award is Granted:** Undergraduate **Funds Available:** $500-$2,000. **Duration:** One academic year.

Eligibility Requirements: Applicant must be admitted to the given Matanuska-Susitna College degree programs; must be a continuing student at Matanuska-Susitna College who has earned at least 20 credit hours; must have a cumulative GPA of 3.0 or higher; must exhibit good moral character and conduct; must be registered for eight or more credit hours. **Application Requirements:** Applicants must complete the MSC scholarship application and attach a resume showing their work experience; must compose an essay of 500 words or less describing their educational and career goals and how they plan to attain them; must have two letters of recommendation, written within the last two years. Application form and other supporting documents must be sent to Snodgrass Scholarships, Matanuska-Susitna College, Student Service, FSM 102, Palmer, AK 99645. **Deadline for Receipt:** May 31.

2616 ■ MICHIGAN NURSERY AND LANDSCAPE ASSOCIATION

2149 Commons Pkwy.
Okemos, MI 48864
Tel: (517)381-0437
Free: 800-879-6652
Fax: (517)381-0638
E-mail: stonebridge@aol.com
Web Site: http://www.mnla.org
To further education of individuals pursuing careers in the Green Industry.
Title of Award: Michigan Nursery and Landscape Association Scholarships **Area, Field, or Subject:** Landscape architecture and design. **Level of Education for which Award is Granted:** Undergraduate **Funds Available:** No specific amount.
Eligibility Requirements: Applicants must be students pursuing a degree in the area of landscaping. **Application Requirements:** Applicants must submit a completed application form, a cover letter, resume, two letters of recommendation and photos/information on industry work completed. **Deadline for Receipt:** November 1.

2617 ■ NATIONAL FEDERATION OF THE BLIND

1800 Johnson St.
Baltimore, MD 21230
Tel: (410)659-9314
Fax: (410)685-5653
Web Site: http://www.nfb.org
To recognize achievement of blind scholars and to create opportunity for all blind people.
Title of Award: Howard B. Rickard Scholarships **Area, Field, or Subject:** Law; Medicine; Engineering; Architecture; Natural Science. **Level of Education for which Award is Granted:** Undergraduate **Funds Available:** $3,000.
Eligibility Requirements: All applicants must be legally blind; he/she must be pursuing or planning to study in the field of law, medicine, engineering, architecture or the natural science; he/she must be participant in NFB national convention and in all scheduled scholarship program activities. **Application Requirements:** Applicant must fill out the application form; he/she must submit two letters of recommendation from individuals that can describe the academic ability, leadership skills, and/or community involvement; copies of transcript of record and a photocopy of score reports for all standardized tests taken for college admission (ACT, SAT or other); an applicant must provide a letter of proof of legal blindness from a qualified professional; and an affiliate President's letter. **Deadline for Receipt:** March 31.

2618 ■ NORTH CAROLINA NURSERY AND LANDSCAPE ASSOCIATION

968 Trinity Rd.
Raleigh, NC 27607
Tel: (919)816-9119
Fax: (919)816-9118
E-mail: rgelvin@ncan.com
Web Site: http://www.ncnla.com
To identify and reward horticulture students who exemplify scholastic aptitude, positive attitude and industry potential.
Title of Award: Certified Landscape Technician Scholarships **Area, Field, or Subject:** Landscape technology. **Level of Education for which Award is Granted:** Undergraduate **Funds Available:** $250.
Eligibility Requirements: Applicants must be full-time students enrolled in a horticulture curriculum and interested in becoming CLT-certified. **Application Requirements:** Applicants must complete the application form. **Deadline for Receipt:** April 24. **Additional Information:** 919-816-9119.

2619 ■ PUBLIC EDUCATION FOUNDATION

3360 W Sahara Ave., Ste. 160
Las Vegas, NV 89102
Tel: (702)799-1042
Fax: (702)799-5247
E-mail: steelej@ccpef.org
Web Site: http://ccpef.org
To promote education in architecture.
Title of Award: JMA Architecture Studios Scholarships **Area, Field, or Subject:** Architecture. **Level of Education for which Award is Granted:** Undergraduate **Number Awarded:** 1. **Funds Available:** $3,500.
Eligibility Requirements: Applicants must be CCSD seniors interested in pursuing a career in architecture; must be planning to attend a university with an accredited School of Architecture; must demonstrate financial need; and must have a minimum 3.0 unweighted cumulative GPA. **Application Requirements:** Applicants must submit a completed application form along with a work sample, two letters of recommendation, transcript, resume of awards, and a college/university admission acceptance letter. **Deadline for Receipt:** March 7. **Additional Information:** Shana Venenga at 702-799-1042.

2620 ■ PUBLIC EDUCATION FOUNDATION

3360 W Sahara Ave., Ste. 160
Las Vegas, NV 89102
Tel: (702)799-1042
Fax: (702)799-5247
E-mail: steelej@ccpef.org
Web Site: http://ccpef.org
To provide educational opportunities for individuals intending to pursue higher studies.
Title of Award: Pardee Community Building Scholarships **Area, Field, or Subject:** Business; Civil engineering; Architecture; Construction. **Level of Education for which Award is Granted:** Undergraduate **Number Awarded:** 10. **Funds Available:** $1,500. **Duration:** One year.
Eligibility Requirements: Applicants must be CCSD seniors who have demonstrated an interest in home building and community development; must be planning to attend a Nevada accredited college or university; must be pursuing studies in areas of business, civil engineering, architecture or landscape architecture and construction management; and must have a minimum 2.8 cumulative GPA. **Application Requirements:** Applicants must submit a completed application form along with an essay, two letters of recommendation, transcript, and resume of awards. **Deadline for Receipt:** March 7. **Additional Information:** Shana Venenga at 702-799-1042.

2621 ■ REDLANDS COMMUNITY SCHOLARSHIP FOUNDATION

c/o Kathleen Venegas-Boge, Admin. Asst.
PO Box 1683
Redlands, CA 92373
Tel: (909)307-9892
Fax: (909)307-9892
Web Site: http://www.redlandsscholarships.org
To encourage educational pursuits among Redlands Unified School District graduates by providing educational assistance.
Title of Award: PCH Architects/Steven J. Lehnhof Memorial Architectural Scholarships **Area, Field, or Subject:** Architecture; Architectural engineering. **Level of Education for which Award is Granted:** Undergraduate **Number Awarded:** 1. **Funds Available:** $1000.
Eligibility Requirements: Applicant must be a graduating senior who will be majoring in architecture or architectural engineering at an accredited college/university. **Application Requirements:** Applicants must submit a completed application form together with the scantron sheet; cover sheet; student activity and community activity sheets; personal essay; and a copy of unofficial transcript (signed by the counselor). **Additional Information:** No electronic submissions of application will be accepted. Submit two printed copies of the application and use a No. 2 pencil on the scantron sheet. **Deadline for Receipt:** February 20.

2622 ■ THE SAN DIEGO FOUNDATION

2508 Historic Decatur Rd., Ste. 200
San Diego, CA 92106
Tel: (619)235-2300
Fax: (619)239-1710
E-mail: info@sdfoundation.org
Web Site: http://www.sdfoundation.org
To support the education of students from California.
Title of Award: Stuart L. Noderer Memorial Scholarships **Area, Field, or Subject:** Science; Engineering; Architecture. **Level of Education for which Award is Granted:** Undergraduate **Number Awarded:** 2. **Funds Available:** $1,000.
Eligibility Requirements: Applicant must be graduating senior from Mission Bay High School; planning to attend an accredited four-year university in the U.S.; have a minimum 3.50 GPA on a 4.0 scale; and will major in science, engineering or architecture. **Application Require-**

ments: Applicants must submit a completed Common Scholarship Application together with personal statement; two letters of recommendation on official letterhead (written within the last six months); official transcript in an official and sealed envelope; and a copy of 2006 or most recent tax form (Form 1040-pages 1 & 2; Form 1040Apages 1 & 2; Form 1040EZ-page 1). **Deadline for Receipt:** January 28. **Additional Information:** Arzo Mansury, Dir. Scholarships at 619-814-1343, or scholarships@ sdfoundation.org.

2623 ■ SILICON VALLEY COMMUNITY FOUNDATION

2240 W El Camino Real Ste. 300
Mountain View, CA 94040-1498
Tel: (650)450-5400
Fax: (650)450-5401
Web Site: http://www.siliconvalleycf.org
To provide financial support to those students who are in need.
Title of Award: Leo and Trinidad Sanchez Scholarships **Area, Field, or Subject:** Architecture. **Level of Education for which Award is Granted:** Undergraduate **Number Awarded:** 1. **Funds Available:** Maximum award amount: $4,500.
Eligibility Requirements: Applicants must be Hispanic/American (with at least one parent of Hispanic or Hispanic/American heritage); must be residents of Santa Clara or Santa Cruz County; must be seniors in high school or students at West Valley College enrolled in a program leading to a degree in architecture, or students in any architectural school. **Application Requirements:** Applicants must check the available website for more information regarding this award. **Additional Information:** Silicon Valley Community Foundation at the above address

2624 ■ SOUTHWEST FLORIDA COMMUNITY FOUNDATION

8260 College Pkwy., Ste. 101
Fort Myers, FL 33919
Tel: (239)274-5900
Fax: (239)274-5930
Web Site: http://www.floridacommunity.com
To fund a student who will attend: FGCU, university of Florida/Gainesville, Florida State University/Tallahassee, Flagler College, Stetson University/Deland, University of Miami, University of Tampa, or Embry Riddle Aeronautical University/Daytona Beach.
Title of Award: D&A Florida Scholarships **Area, Field, or Subject:** Architecture; Business; Engineering; International affairs and relations; Journalism; Computer and information sciences; Law; Literature; Medicine; Physics; Chemistry; Political science. **Level of Education for which Award is Granted:** Undergraduate **Funds Available:** $10,000. **Duration:** One year.
Eligibility Requirements: Applicants must have graduated from a public or private high school in Charlotte, Glades, Hendry or Lee County; must pursue a degree in Architecture, Business, Engineering, International affairs and relations, Journalism, Computer and information sciences, Law, Literature, Medicine, Physics, Chemistry, or Political science. **Application Requirements:** Application forms are available online. Applicants must submit a letter of interest and letter of recommendation, a transcript and financial need documentation. **Deadline for Receipt:** February 15.

2625 ■ SOUTHWEST FLORIDA COMMUNITY FOUNDATION

8260 College Pkwy., Ste. 101
Fort Myers, FL 33919
Tel: (239)274-5900
Fax: (239)274-5930
Web Site: http://www.floridacommunity.com
To fund students pursuing degrees or advanced degrees in medicine, law, dentistry, teaching (math and science), ministry, engineering, accounting, architecture and computer science.
Title of Award: John M. and Mary A. Shanley Memorial Scholarships **Area, Field, or Subject:** Medicine; Law; Dentistry; Teaching; Ministry; Engineering; Accounting; Agriculture; Economic aspects; Architecture; Computer and information sciences. **Level of Education for which Award is Granted:** Undergraduate **Funds Available:** $5,000. **Duration:** One year.
Eligibility Requirements: Applicant must be a resident of Charlotte, Hendry or Lee County. **Application Requirements:** Application forms are available online. Applicants must submit a letter of interest, letter of recommendation and transcript. **Deadline for Receipt:** February 15.

2626 ■ WINSTON-SALEM FOUNDATION

860 W Fifth St.
Winston-Salem, NC 27101-2506
Tel: (336)725-2382
Fax: (336)727-0581
E-mail: info@wsfoundation.org
Web Site: http://www.wsfoundation.org
To provide financial support for educational opportunities to legal residents of North Carolina who will attend a two and/or four year college and have been accepted into the Horticulture Technology or Landscape Architecture curriculums at Forsyth Technical Community College or other accredited post-secondary schools in North Carolina.
Title of Award: Garden Club Council of Winston-Salem and Forsyth County Council **Area, Field, or Subject:** Horticulture; Landscape architecture and design. **Level of Education for which Award is Granted:** Undergraduate **Funds Available:** No specific amount.
Eligibility Requirements: Applicants must demonstrate academic potential; financial need; full-time attendance (minimum of 12 credit hours/semester); pursuit of undergraduate associate or baccalaureate degree (first-time degrees preferred); must be US citizens. The scholarship is renewable for a second consecutive year if student maintains a cumulative college GPA of 2.0, continues full-time enrollment and continues in horticulture or landscape architecture; otherwise, scholarship is forfeited. Available to traditional and non-traditional age students. **Application Requirements:** Application must be completed and submitted with all required materials to the Student Aid Department at The Winston-Salem Foundation. Supplemental materials listed on the last page of the application include previous year's federal tax return for student and parent, if student is a dependent; academic year-end grade transcript; Federal Student Aid Report; federal award notice and interview with student aid staff. **Deadline for Receipt:** March 31. **Additional Information:** Edna Barker, 336-714-3445; Kay Dillon, 336-714-3446.

Classical Studies

2627 ■ THE AMERICAN CLASSICAL LEAGUE

Miami University
Oxford, OH 45056
Tel: (513)529-7741
Fax: (513)529-7742
E-mail: info@aclclassics.org
Web Site: http://www.aclclassics.org
To encourage teaching profession of classics by providing educational fund for deserving teacher and undergraduate or graduate member of the American Classical League.
Title of Award: Glenn Knudsvig Memorial Scholarships **Area, Field, or Subject:** Classical studies. **Level of Education for which Award is Granted:** Graduate, Undergraduate **Funds Available:** $1,000 covering expenses on registration, room, board on campus and travel for Annual ACL Institute.
Eligibility Requirements: Applicant must be a current JCL sponsor who attended the most recent NJCL convention; teacher of Latin, Greek or Classics with less than five years classroom experience and has never attended an ACL Institute; graduate student who plans to teach K-12 Latin, Greek or Classics; teacher whose students participated in the 2007 National Latin Exam and has never attended an ACL Institute. **Application Requirements:** Application form and instructions are available at the website. **Deadline for Receipt:** January 15.

2628 ■ THE AMERICAN CLASSICAL LEAGUE

Miami University
Oxford, OH 45056
Tel: (513)529-7741
Fax: (513)529-7742
E-mail: info@aclclassics.org
Web Site: http://www.aclclassics.org
To provide educational fund for deserving teachers, undergraduate or graduate members of the American Classical League as they pursue careers in teaching classics.
Title of Award: Arthur Patch McKinlay Scholarships **Area, Field, or Subject:** Classical studies. **Level of Education for which Award is Granted:** Graduate, Undergraduate **Funds Available:** $1,500 covering expenses on registration, room, board on campus and the cost of transportation.

Eligibility Requirements: Applicant must be an ACL member for the preceding three years and planning to teach classics at elementary through secondary level for the school year 2008-2009. **Application Requirements:** Application form and instructions are available at the website. **Deadline for Receipt:** January 15.

2629 ■ THE AMERICAN CLASSICAL LEAGUE
Miami University
Oxford, OH 45056
Tel: (513)529-7741
Fax: (513)529-7742
E-mail: info@aclclassics.org
Web Site: http://www.aclclassics.org
To provide educational fund for deserving teachers, undergraduate or graduate members of the American Classical League.
Title of Award: Ed Phinney Commemorative Scholarships **Area, Field, or Subject:** Classical studies. **Level of Education for which Award is Granted:** Graduate, Undergraduate **Funds Available:** $1,000 covering expenses on registration, room, board on campus and the cost of transportation.
Eligibility Requirements: Applicant must be a current member of The American Classical League; must also have been an ACL member for year prior to applying (if applying to attend ACL Institute for the first time, only current ACL membership required.) **Application Requirements:** Application form and instructions are available at the website. **Deadline for Receipt:** January 15.

2630 ■ MATANUSKA-SUSITNA COLLEGE
PO Box 2889
Palmer, AK 99645
Tel: (907)745-9774
Fax: (907)745-9711
E-mail: info@matsu.alaska.edu
Web Site: http://www.matsu.alaska.edu
To provide support to deserving students in Alaska who want to pursue an education in any campus of the University of Alaska.
Title of Award: Clair Shirey Scholarships **Area, Field, or Subject:** Classical studies. **Level of Education for which Award is Granted:** Undergraduate **Funds Available:** $500.
Eligibility Requirements: Applicants must be music majors with a demonstrated interest or emphasis in classical/liturgical organ. **Application Requirements:** Applicant must complete the application forms available at the website; must attach a personal essay, two letters of recommendation, and current transcripts. **Deadline for Receipt:** February 15.

2631 ■ XAVIER UNIVERSITY
3800 Victory Pky.
Cincinnati, OH 45207
Tel: (513)745-3000
Free: 800-344-GOXU
Web Site: http://www.xavier.edu
To financially support students with their education.
Title of Award: Xavier University Departmental Scholarships **Area, Field, or Subject:** Chemistry; Classical studies; History; Mathematics and mathematical sciences; Modern languages; Physics. **Level of Education for which Award is Granted:** Undergraduate **Funds Available:** $2500.
Eligibility Requirements: Applicant must top the score in either of the six departmental exams (chemistry, classics (Latin), history, mathematics, modern languages (French, German or Spanish) and physics). Student must major in the area for which the scholarship is awarded. **Application Requirements:** Participants will take an exam in the appropriate subject area and have an opportunity to speak with faculty and learn more about the department.

Creative Arts

2632 ■ ADVERTISING PRODUCTION CLUB OF NEW YORK
428 E State St.
Long Beach, NY 11561
Tel: (212)671-2975
Fax: (718)228-8202
E-mail: admin@apc-ny.org

Web Site: http://www.apc-ny.org
To provide financial assistance to students pursuing a full-time graphic arts/communications degree.
Title of Award: Advertising Production Club Scholarship Awards **Area, Field, or Subject:** Graphic art and design; Communications. **Level of Education for which Award is Granted:** Graduate, Undergraduate **Number Awarded:** 4. **Funds Available:** $500. Funds are applied to tuition expenses. **Duration:** One year.
Eligibility Requirements: Applicant must be a resident of New York City metro area attending a graphic arts/communications degree program full-time in any college in the New York City metro area. **Application Requirements:** Guidelines and application forms are available from the Advertising Production Club office or can be downloaded from the APC website. Applicants must submit a completed hard copy application with the APC office together with registration receipt for the new semester, college transcript and acceptance letter. **Deadline for Receipt:** October 15.

2633 ■ ADVERTISING PRODUCTION CLUB OF NEW YORK
428 E State St.
Long Beach, NY 11561
Tel: (212)671-2975
Fax: (718)228-8202
E-mail: admin@apc-ny.org
Web Site: http://www.apc-ny.org
To provide financial assistance to those studying graphic arts and communications.
Title of Award: APC High School Scholarships **Area, Field, or Subject:** Graphic art and design; Communications. **Level of Education for which Award is Granted:** Undergraduate **Number Awarded:** 2. **Funds Available:** $250. Funds are applied to tuition expenses. **Duration:** One year.
Eligibility Requirements: Applicants must present a positive identification and confirmation by the high school principal; graduate high school with at least a B average; be duly accepted as a full-time, matriculated student in an accredited graphic arts or communications program at a college in the United States. **Application Requirements:** Guidelines and application forms are available from the Advertising Production Club office or can be downloaded from the APC website. Applicants must submit a completed hard copy application with the APC office together with registration receipt for the new semester, college transcript and acceptance letter. **Deadline for Receipt:** October 15.

2634 ■ ADVERTISING PRODUCTION CLUB OF NEW YORK
428 E State St.
Long Beach, NY 11561
Tel: (212)671-2975
Fax: (718)228-8202
E-mail: admin@apc-ny.org
Web Site: http://www.apc-ny.org
To provide financial assistance to students pursuing graphic communications careers.
Title of Award: PGSF-GATF Scholarships **Area, Field, or Subject:** Graphic art and design; Communications. **Level of Education for which Award is Granted:** Graduate, Undergraduate **Number Awarded:** 2. **Funds Available:** $500. Funds are applied to tuition expenses. **Duration:** One year.
Eligibility Requirements: Applicant must be a resident of New York City metro area attending a graphic arts/communications degree program full-time in an accredited college in the U.S. **Application Requirements:** Guidelines and application forms are available from the Advertising Production Club office or can be downloaded from the APC website. Applicants must submit a completed hard copy application with the APC office together with registration receipt for the new semester, college transcript and acceptance letter. **Deadline for Receipt:** October 15.

2635 ■ ALBERTA LEARNING INFORMATION SERVICE - ALBERTA SCHOLARSHIP PROGRAM
Box 28000 Sta. Main
Edmonton, AB, Canada T5J 4R4
Tel: (780)427-8640
Fax: (780)427-1288
E-mail: scholarship@gov.ab.ca
Web Site: http://www.alis.alberta.ca

To recognize and reward the academic and leadership accomplishments of three students graduating from Sexsmith Secondary School who are entering post-secondary studies.

Title of Award: Dr. Robert and Anna Shaw Scholarships **Area, Field, or Subject:** Agriculture; Engineering; Art industries and trade; Fine arts. **Level of Education for which Award is Granted:** Undergraduate **Funds Available:** $500.

Eligibility Requirements: Applicants must be Alberta residents and plan to enroll full-time in a post-secondary program related to agriculture, engineering/trades or fine arts. **Application Requirements:** Applicants may obtain application form from Alberta Scholarship Programs and from the Counseling Office at Sexsmith Secondary School. **Deadline for Receipt:** June 1. **Additional Information:** Alberta Scholarship Programs at the above address.

2636 ■ AMERICAN SOCIETY OF COMPOSERS, AUTHORS AND PUBLISHERS (ASCAP) FOUNDATION

1 Lincoln Plaza
New York, NY 10023-7142
Tel: (212)621-6219
E-mail: concertmusic@ascap.com
Web Site: http://www.ascapfoundation.org

To award scholarship to qualified college-level students.

Title of Award: David Rose Scholarships **Area, Field, or Subject:** Filmmaking; Music. **Level of Education for which Award is Granted:** Undergraduate **Funds Available:** No specific amount. **Duration:** One year.

Eligibility Requirements: Applicant must be a college-level student working toward a career in scoring for film and/or television who is participating in ASCAP's Film and Television Scoring Workshop. **Application Requirements:** The ASCAP Foundation does not accept applications for this scholarship. Interested students should consult their school's financial aid office for application information.

2637 ■ ART INSTITUTE OF COLORADO

1200 Lincoln St.
Denver, CO 80203-2172
Tel: (303)837-0825
Free: 800-275-2420
E-mail: aicadm@aii.edu
Web Site: http://www.artinstitutes.edu/denver

To provide higher education programs leading to professional opportunities in the fields of art and design, culinary arts, and technology that prepare graduates for job entry and career advancement.

Title of Award: Art Institute of Colorado Scholarships **Area, Field, or Subject:** Art. **Level of Education for which Award is Granted:** Undergraduate **Number Awarded:** 1. **Funds Available:** $7,000.

Eligibility Requirements: Applicants must be high school seniors from the Sixth Congressional District who enter their work in The Artistic Discovery Art Program. **Application Requirements:** Applicants must complete the application form.

2638 ■ ART INSTITUTE OF COLORADO

1200 Lincoln St.
Denver, CO 80203-2172
Tel: (303)837-0825
Free: 800-275-2420
E-mail: aicadm@aii.edu
Web Site: http://www.artinstitutes.edu/denver

To provide higher education programs leading to professional opportunities in the fields of art and design, culinary arts, and technology which prepare graduates for job entry and career advancement.

Title of Award: Art Institute's Best Teen Chef in America Culinary Scholarships **Area, Field, or Subject:** Art. **Level of Education for which Award is Granted:** Undergraduate **Number Awarded:** 1. **Funds Available:** Maximum amount of $30,000.

Eligibility Requirements: Applicants must be high school seniors. **Application Requirements:** Applicants must complete the application form. Applicants must submit a notebook that includes the menu and detailed recipes and directions from each course. Applicants must submit a paragraph stating their reason for wanting to be a culinary professional; and a current high school transcript. **Deadline for Receipt:** February 14.

2639 ■ ART INSTITUTE OF COLORADO

1200 Lincoln St.
Denver, CO 80203-2172
Tel: (303)837-0825
Free: 800-275-2420
E-mail: aicadm@aii.edu
Web Site: http://www.artinstitutes.edu/denver

To provide higher education programs leading to professional opportunities in the fields of art and design, culinary arts, and technology which prepare graduates for job entry and career advancement.

Title of Award: James Beard Foundation/Art Institute of Colorado Scholarships **Area, Field, or Subject:** Art. **Level of Education for which Award is Granted:** Undergraduate **Number Awarded:** 2. **Funds Available:** Maximum amount of $1,500.

Eligibility Requirements: Applicants must be freshmen high school students. Applicants must have a 3.0 GPA. **Application Requirements:** Applicants must complete the application form and must submit a transcript of records. **Additional Information:** 212-675-4984.

2640 ■ ART INSTITUTE OF COLORADO

1200 Lincoln St.
Denver, CO 80203-2172
Tel: (303)837-0825
Free: 800-275-2420
E-mail: aicadm@aii.edu
Web Site: http://www.artinstitutes.edu/denver

To provide higher education programs leading to professional opportunities in the fields of art and design, culinary arts, and technology which prepare graduates for job entry and career advancement.

Title of Award: Colorado PROSTART/Art Institute of Colorado Art Scholarships for High School Seniors **Area, Field, or Subject:** Art. **Level of Education for which Award is Granted:** Undergraduate **Funds Available:** Maximum amount of $14,490. **Duration:** 2 years.

Eligibility Requirements: Applicants must be senior high school students. **Application Requirements:** Applicants must complete the application form and must submit a transcript of records.

2641 ■ ART INSTITUTE OF COLORADO

1200 Lincoln St.
Denver, CO 80203-2172
Tel: (303)837-0825
Free: 800-275-2420
E-mail: aicadm@aii.edu
Web Site: http://www.artinstitutes.edu/denver

To provide higher education programs leading to professional opportunities in the fields of art and design, culinary arts, and technology, to prepare graduates for job entry and career advancement.

Title of Award: Colorado Springs Pikes Peak Region School District Young Peoples Art Show Scholarships **Area, Field, or Subject:** Art. **Level of Education for which Award is Granted:** Undergraduate **Number Awarded:** 1. **Funds Available:** $4,416.

Eligibility Requirements: Applicants must be high school seniors selected as winners through this art show. **Application Requirements:** Applicants must complete the application form.

2642 ■ ART INSTITUTE OF COLORADO

1200 Lincoln St.
Denver, CO 80203-2172
Tel: (303)837-0825
Free: 800-275-2420
E-mail: aicadm@aii.edu
Web Site: http://www.artinstitutes.edu/denver

To provide higher education programs leading to professional opportunities in the fields of art and design, culinary arts, and technology which prepare graduates for job entry and career advancement.

Title of Award: Denver Public School Art Award/Scholarships for High School Seniors **Area, Field, or Subject:** Art. **Level of Education for which Award is Granted:** Undergraduate **Funds Available:** Maximum amount of $13,248.

Eligibility Requirements: Applicants must be senior high school students in Denver public schools. **Application Requirements:** Applicants must complete the application form and submit a transcript of records.

2643 ■ ART INSTITUTE OF COLORADO

1200 Lincoln St.
Denver, CO 80203-2172
Tel: (303)837-0825
Free: 800-275-2420
E-mail: aicadm@aii.edu
Web Site: http://www.artinstitutes.edu/denver
To provide higher education programs leading to professional opportunities in the fields of art and design, culinary arts, and technology which prepare graduates for job entry and career advancement.
Title of Award: Douglas County Art Awards Scholarship for High School Seniors **Area, Field, or Subject:** Art. **Level of Education for which Award is Granted:** Undergraduate **Number Awarded:** 2. **Funds Available:** Maximum amount of $13,248.
Eligibility Requirements: Applicants must be senior high school students in Denver public schools. **Application Requirements:** Applicants must complete the application form and must submit a transcript of record.

2644 ■ ART INSTITUTE OF COLORADO

1200 Lincoln St.
Denver, CO 80203-2172
Tel: (303)837-0825
Free: 800-275-2420
E-mail: aicadm@aii.edu
Web Site: http://www.artinstitutes.edu/denver
To provide higher education programs leading to professional opportunities in the fields of art and design, culinary arts, and technology which prepare graduates for job entry and career advancement.
Title of Award: Jefferson County Art Awards Scholarship for High school Seniors **Area, Field, or Subject:** Art. **Level of Education for which Award is Granted:** Undergraduate **Funds Available:** Maximum amount of $13,248.
Eligibility Requirements: Applicants must be high school students. **Application Requirements:** Applicants must complete the application form and must submit a transcript of records.

2645 ■ ART INSTITUTE OF COLORADO

1200 Lincoln St.
Denver, CO 80203-2172
Tel: (303)837-0825
Free: 800-275-2420
E-mail: aicadm@aii.edu
Web Site: http://www.artinstitutes.edu/denver
To provide higher education programs leading to professional opportunities in the fields of art and design, culinary arts, and technology, to prepare graduates for job entry and career advancement.
Title of Award: Wyoming Art Symposium Scholarships **Area, Field, or Subject:** Art. **Level of Education for which Award is Granted:** Undergraduate **Funds Available:** Maximum amount of $13,248.
Eligibility Requirements: Applicants must be high school senior students in Wyoming high schools. **Application Requirements:** Applicants must complete the application form and must submit a transcript of records.

2646 ■ BARRIENTOS SCHOLARSHIP FOUNDATION

PO Box 7173
Omaha, NE 68107
Tel: (402)215-5106
E-mail: info@barrientosscholarship.org
Web Site: http://www.barrientosscholarship.org
To provide financial assistance to qualified students who want to pursue their studies.
Title of Award: Artistic Scholarship Awards **Area, Field, or Subject:** Music; Visual arts; Theater arts; Dance. **Level of Education for which Award is Granted:** Undergraduate **Number Awarded:** No specific amount. **Funds Available:** $250-$500. **Duration:** One year.
Eligibility Requirements: Applicants must be students pursuing higher education and career goals that focus on one or more of the arts - music, visual arts, theater, or dance; must be of Latino heritage; must be high school graduating seniors, currently enrolled in college, or adults ready to pursue college; must plan to enroll in at least two classes and attend an accredited community college, university, or technical or vocational school in the state of Nebraska or surrounding greater Omaha Metropolitan area; must have a minimum of 2.5 GPA. **Application Requirements:** Applicants must complete the application form available online; must have a personal essay with a minimum of two pages; must submit letters of recommendation and official high school or college transcript. Application form and requirements must be sent to Barrientos Scholarship Foundation, P.O Box 7173, Omaha, NE 68107. **Deadline for Receipt:** May 15.

2647 ■ BLACK BUSINESS AND PROFESSIONAL ASSOCIATION

675 King St. W, Ste. 210
Toronto, ON, Canada M5V 1M9
Tel: (416)504-4097
Fax: (416)504-7343
E-mail: bbpa@bellnet.ca
Web Site: http://www.bbpa.org
To provide support for Black Canadian students.
Title of Award: Guntley-Lorimer Science and Arts Scholarships **Area, Field, or Subject:** Science; Art. **Level of Education for which Award is Granted:** Undergraduate **Number Awarded:** 4. **Funds Available:** $2,000-$3,000. **Duration:** One year.
Eligibility Requirements: Applicant must be a Canadian citizen or a permanent resident; must be 17 to 30 years of age; and must be enrolled in a full-time degree (graduate or undergraduate), diploma or certificate program at a Canadian college or university for the academic year. **Application Requirements:** Applicants must complete the application form and submit along with a letter describing the reasons why they would be worthy recipients of a BBPA National Scholarship; a completed financial information schedule stating their budget for the coming year including information on their expected sources of funding, family income and related information; and a letter of reference from the two individuals named in their application (must be a teacher from their high school, college or university, and an individual who is familiar with their community service). Application form and requirements must be sent to The Board of Trustees, BBPA National Scholarship Fund, 675 King St., W, Ste. 210, Toronto, ON M5V 1M9. **Deadline for Receipt:** May 30.

2648 ■ BLACK THEATRE NETWORK

2609 Douglas Road SE, Ste. 109
Washington, DC 20020-6540
Tel: (202)274-5667
E-mail: lreese@udc.edu
Web Site: http://www.blacktheatrenetwork.org
To encourage research and scholarship in black theatre.
Title of Award: S. Randolph Edmonds Young Scholars Competition **Area, Field, or Subject:** Theatre arts. **Level of Education for which Award is Granted:** Graduate, Undergraduate **Funds Available:** $250.
Eligibility Requirements: Applicant must be a college/university undergraduate or graduate working on a paper concerned with an aspect of the Black Theatre in either the United States or throughout the world. **Application Requirements:** Applicants must submit their papers. Papers must typed double-spaced, and in MLA format with a works cited page. If applicable, also include endnotes that demonstrate awareness of formal methods of documentation. Papers should be approximately 10 pages in length, not including endnotes. **Deadline for Receipt:** May 12. **Additional Information:** Koritha Mitchell; mitchell.717@osu.edu; 543 Denney Hall, 164 West 17th Avenue, Columbus, Ohio 43210.

2649 ■ CAMDEN COUNTY COLLEGE

200 N Broadway
Camden, NJ 08102-1185
Tel: (856)338-1817
Web Site: http://www.camdencc.edu
To provide opportunity to qualified students to pursue an education at CCC.
Title of Award: Diane Basilone-Engle Memorial Scholarships **Area, Field, or Subject:** Theater arts; Secretarial sciences; Veterinary science and medicine; Education. **Level of Education for which Award is Granted:** Undergraduate **Funds Available:** No specific amount. **Duration:** One academic year.
Eligibility Requirements: Applicants must be students who want to continue their degree or certificate in theater, secretariat science, veterinary science or education. **Application Requirements:** Applicants must submit one recommendation from a faculty member or administrator

at Camden County College. Application forms are available online and must be sent to Camden County College Foundation, PO Box 200, College Dr., Blackwood, NJ 08012. **Deadline for Receipt:** February 18.

2650 ■ THE COMMUNITY FOUNDATION OF MIDDLE TENNESSEE
3833 Cleghorn Ave., Ste. 400
Nashville, TN 37215-2519
Tel: (615)321-4939; 888-540-5200
E-mail: mail@cfmt.org
Web Site: http://www.cfmt.org
To help students in planning their postsecondary education.
Title of Award: Fine Arts and Music Scholarships **Area, Field, or Subject:** Fine arts; Music. **Level of Education for which Award is Granted:** Undergraduate **Funds Available:** No specific amount.
Eligibility Requirements: Applicants must be rising sophomores, juniors and seniors in college, and graduate students at an accredited college, university, or institute full-time or part-time (6 or more credits). **Application Requirements:** Applicants must complete the application form. Applicants must submit two applicant appraisals; transcript of grades; student essay describing educational plans and how these will help in career goals. Applicants must submit one recent photograph. **Deadline for Receipt:** March 15. **Additional Information:** pcole@cfmt.org

2651 ■ THE COMMUNITY FOUNDATION OF MIDDLE TENNESSEE
3833 Cleghorn Ave., Ste. 400
Nashville, TN 37215-2519
Tel: (615)321-4939; 888-540-5200
E-mail: mail@cfmt.org
Web Site: http://www.cfmt.org
To help students in planning their postsecondary education. To help graduates of Christ the King School of Nashville, Tennessee who have a desire to attend either Father Ryan High School or St. Cecilia Academy, both in Nashville, Tennessee.
Title of Award: Regina Higdon Scholarships **Area, Field, or Subject:** Art. **Level of Education for which Award is Granted:** Undergraduate **Funds Available:** No specific amount.
Eligibility Requirements: Applicants must be graduating eighth graders of Christ the King School and/or former graduates of Christ the King School attending Father Ryan High School or St. Cecilia Academy. Applicants must have at least a 2.5 GPA or equivalent. Applicants must exhibit a love for the arts. **Application Requirements:** Applicants must complete the application form. Applicants must submit two applicant appraisals; transcript of grades; student essay describing educational plans and how these will help in career goals. Applicants must submit one recent photograph. **Deadline for Receipt:** March 15. **Additional Information:** pcole@cfmt.org

2652 ■ THE COMMUNITY FOUNDATION OF MIDDLE TENNESSEE
3833 Cleghorn Ave., Ste. 400
Nashville, TN 37215-2519
Tel: (615)321-4939; 888-540-5200
E-mail: mail@cfmt.org
Web Site: http://www.cfmt.org
To help students in planning their postsecondary education.
Title of Award: Eloise Pitts O'More Scholarships **Area, Field, or Subject:** Interior Design. **Level of Education for which Award is Granted:** Undergraduate **Funds Available:** No specific amount.
Eligibility Requirements: Applicants must be interior design students who are currently pursuing a degree in interior design at O'More College of Design. Applicants must be classified as juniors or higher and have a GPA of 3.0 or higher at the time of application. Applicants must be actively participating members of either the American Society of Interior Design and/or International Design Association's student chapters. **Application Requirements:** Applicants must complete the application form. Applicants must submit two applicant appraisals; transcript of grades; student essay describing educational plans and how these will help in career goals. Applicants must submit one recent photograph. **Deadline for Receipt:** March 15. **Additional Information:** pcole@cfmt.org

2653 ■ COMMUNITY FOUNDATION OF NORTHERN ILLINOIS
946 N 2nd St.
Rockford, IL 61107
Tel: (815)962-2110

Fax: (815)962-2116
Web Site: http://www.cfnil.org
To serve the four county area (Boone, Ogle, Stephenson and Winnebago) through philanthropy; to provide leadership in meeting charitable needs and to be a responsible steward to the Foundation's donors and of the Foundation's endowment.
Title of Award: William R. Durham/Theater Scholarship **Area, Field, or Subject:** Theater Arts. **Level of Education for which Award is Granted:** Undergraduate **Funds Available:** No specific amount.
Eligibility Requirements: Applicants must be high school graduates or graduating seniors with a permanent address within Winnebago or Boone county with a GPA of at least 3.0 on a 4.0 scale; must plan to attend an accredited four-year college or university to obtain an M.A. or B.A.; must intend to teach theater or work professionally as a performer or technician in theater. **Application Requirements:** Applicants must submit a completed application form, verification form, an official transcript in a sealed envelope and two letters of recommendation. **Deadline for Receipt:** March 1. **Additional Information:** jpatterson@cfnil.org.

2654 ■ COMMUNITY FOUNDATION OF PRINCE EDWARD ISLAND
119-121 Quenn St., Ste. 105
Charlottetown, PE, Canada C1A 1Z4
Tel: (902)892-3440
Free: 800-566-7307
Fax: (902)892-0880
E-mail: foundation@cfpei.ca
Web Site: http://www.cfpei.ca
To provide financial assistance to qualified individuals who want to pursue their education.
Title of Award: Joan Auld Scholarships **Area, Field, or Subject:** Art; Crafts; Design. **Level of Education for which Award is Granted:** Undergraduate **Funds Available:** $200. **Duration:** One year.
Eligibility Requirements: Applicant must be a Canadian citizen; must have been a resident of P.E.I for at least the 6 months prior to application; must be undertaking full-time studies in a craft-related field at a recognized institution of applied art, craft and design; must demonstrate high school graduation or equivalence. **Application Requirements:** Applicants must complete the application form available online; must provide an outline of the proposed course of study and the name of the institution where they will attend the class; must submit a essay about their background, interest, aims, and ambitions; must submit a letter of reference and portfolio demonstrating previous work, samples of craft-related work, sketches, video or pictures; must include written verification of acceptance. Application form and other supporting documents must be sent to Joan Auld Scholarship Fund c/o The Community Foundation of Prince Edward Island, 119- 121 Queen St. Charlottetown, PE C1A 4B3. **Deadline for Receipt:** May 30.

2655 ■ DELTA DELTA DELTA
PO Box 5987
Arlington, TX 76005-5987
Tel: (817)633-8001
Fax: (817)652-0212
E-mail: info@trideltaeo.org
Web Site: http://www.tridelta.org
To provide financial assistance to qualified undergraduate students.
Title of Award: Margaret M. Alkek Scholarship **Area, Field, or Subject:** Education, Music, Theater arts. **Level of Education for which Award is Granted:** Undergraduate **Funds Available:** $500-$1,500. **Duration:** One academic year.
Eligibility Requirements: Applicant must be a Theta Xi chapter member at the University of Southern California; must have academic achievement at the collegiate level; must be an initiated sophomore or junior members. **Application Requirements:** Application forms are available on the website. Applicant must provide a personal statement about their educational and vocational goals; must have a recommendation letter from a faculty member; must have an official transcript from each undergraduate institution. Application materials must be sent to: Delta Delta Delta, PO Box 5987, Arlington, TX 76005. **Deadline for Receipt:** March 15.

2656 ■ DELTA ZETA SORORITY
202 E Church St.
Oxford, OH 45056

Tel: (513)523-7597
Web Site: http://www.deltazeta.org
To provide financial assistance to all qualified undergraduate students.
Title of Award: Edith Head Scholarships **Area, Field, or Subject:** Fashion design. **Level of Education for which Award is Granted:** Undergraduate **Funds Available:** $1,000-$2,500. **Duration:** One academic year.
Eligibility Requirements: Applicant must be an initiated, active, continuing member of Delta Zeta pursuing a course study leading to a career in design, production, and merchandising of textile and apparel products, and/or costume design; must be a junior or senior student, graduate level, or a professional school which offers fashion merchandising, textiles, and clothing or costume design; must have at least a 3.0 average. **Application Requirements:** Scholarship applications are available on the website and must be completed properly. Applicant must have the FAFSA reply form. **Deadline for Receipt:** February 15.

2657 ■ ENTERTAINMENT SOFTWARE ASSOCIATION
575 7th St. NW, Ste. 300
Washington, DC 20004
Tel: (202)223-2400
E-mail: esa@theesa.com
Web Site: http://www.theesa.com
To assist women and minority students who plan to continue their education in fields supporting Video Game Development.
Title of Award: ESA Foundation Computer and Video Game Scholarship Program **Area, Field, or Subject:** Graphic Arts and Design; Computer and Information Sciences. **Level of Education for which Award is Granted:** Undergraduate **Number Awarded:** 15. **Funds Available:** $3,000.
Eligibility Requirements: Applicants must be enrolled full time study in an accredited four year colleges and universities. **Application Requirements:** Applicants must complete online application form. Applicants must provide proof that he/she is currently enrolled in a college, university, or institution. **Deadline for Receipt:** April 15.

2658 ■ EQUITY FOUNDATION
P.O Box 5696
Portland, OR 97228
Tel: (503)231-5759
E-mail: info@equityfoundation.org
Web Site: http://www.equityfoundation.org
To encourage and facilitate post-secondary education in the arts for people who are gay, lesbian, bisexual or transgender (GLBT).
Title of Award: Gregori Jakovina Endowment Scholarships **Area, Field, or Subject:** Arts. **Level of Education for which Award is Granted:** Undergraduate **Funds Available:** No specific amount.
Eligibility Requirements: Applicants must be Oregon or Clark County Washington residents who demonstrate financial need. **Application Requirements:** Applicants must check the application process online. **Deadline for Receipt:** August 31. **Additional Information:** Equity Foundation at the above address

2659 ■ EQUITY FOUNDATION
P.O Box 5696
Portland, OR 97228
Tel: (503)231-5759
E-mail: info@equityfoundation.org
Web Site: http://www.equityfoundation.org
To encourage students whom, regardless of sexual orientation or gender identity, have authored material based, in large part, on GLBT themes, to develop their creative writing skills.
Title of Award: Armistead Maupin Creative Writing Scholarship Fund **Area, Field, or Subject:** Creative Writing; Liberal Arts. **Level of Education for which Award is Granted:** Undergraduate **Funds Available:** No specific amount.
Eligibility Requirements: Applicants must be entering or pursuing post-secondary education in the liberal arts, literary arts or creative writing, at accredited colleges and universities in the Northwest of the continental United States (Oregon, Washington, Idaho), who are in need of financial assistance. **Application Requirements:** Applicants must check the application process online. **Deadline for Receipt:** June 30. **Additional Information:** Equity Foundation at the above address

2660 ■ EQUITY FOUNDATION
P.O Box 5696
Portland, OR 97228
Tel: (503)231-5759
E-mail: info@equityfoundation.org
Web Site: http://www.equityfoundation.org
To provide financial assistance to those who are in need.
Title of Award: Larry McDonald Scholarships **Area, Field, or Subject:** Arts; Humanities. **Level of Education for which Award is Granted:** Undergraduate **Funds Available:** No specific amount.
Eligibility Requirements: Applicants must be adults in mid-life who are gay, lesbian, bisexual, or transgender who seek to make a significant change in their lives or vocations by taking classes in the arts or humanities. **Application Requirements:** Applicants must check the application process online. **Deadline for Receipt:** August 31. **Additional Information:** Equity Foundation at the above address

2661 ■ FINE ARTS ASSOCIATION
38660 mentor Ave.
Willoughby, OH 44094
Tel: (440)951-7500
Fax: (440)975-4590
E-mail: jflemming-gifford@fineartsassociation.org
Web Site: http://www.fineartsassociation.org
To ensure that the opportunity for art education is available to all who deserve it and to create customized educational arts experiences in music, dance, drama, visual arts and music therapy.
Title of Award: Fine Arts Association Minority Scholarships **Area, Field, or Subject:** Fine arts. **Level of Education for which Award is Granted:** Undergraduate **Funds Available:** No specific amount.
Eligibility Requirements: Students applying must be residents of Lake County who are members of a minority population as defined by the Ohio Arts Council. **Application Requirements:** Applicants must complete the application form with parents/guardians if they are dependents. Forms are available at the FAA Customer Service Center and are also available for download at the website. First time applicants must include a copy of the first page of their most recent IRS 1040 form. **Additional Information:** Peter Grossetti, Director of Development at 440-951-7500.

2662 ■ FINE ARTS ASSOCIATION
38660 mentor Ave.
Willoughby, OH 44094
Tel: (440)951-7500
Fax: (440)975-4590
E-mail: jflemming-gifford@fineartsassociation.org
Web Site: http://www.fineartsassociation.org
To ensure that the opportunity for art education is available to all who deserve it and to create customized educational arts experiences in music, dance, drama, visual arts and music therapy.
Title of Award: Fine Arts Association United Way Scholarships **Area, Field, or Subject:** Fine Arts. **Level of Education for which Award is Granted:** Undergraduate **Funds Available:** No specific amount.
Eligibility Requirements: Applicants must be students residing in Lake County and must have total family income not exceeding $18,400 annually, unless there are extenuating financial circumstances. **Application Requirements:** Applicants must complete the application form with parents/guardians if they are dependents. Forms are available at the FAA Customer Service Center and are also available for download at the website. First time applicants must include a copy of the first page of their most recent IRS 1040 form. **Additional Information:** Peter Grossetti, Director of Development at 440-951-7500.

2663 ■ FINE ARTS ASSOCIATION
38660 mentor Ave.
Willoughby, OH 44094
Tel: (440)951-7500
Fax: (440)975-4590
E-mail: jflemming-gifford@fineartsassociation.org
Web Site: http://www.fineartsassociation.org
To ensure that the opportunity for art education is available to all who deserve it and to create customized educational arts experiences in music, dance, drama, visual arts and music therapy.
Title of Award: Gwen Yarnell Theatre Scholarships **Area, Field, or Subject:** Fine arts; Theater arts. **Level of Education for which Award is Granted:** Undergraduate **Funds Available:** No specific amount.

Eligibility Requirements: Program is open to new and returning Fine Arts students intending to study theatre. **Application Requirements:** Forms can be requested by calling the association's Customer Service Center. **Additional Information:** Peter Grossetti, Director of Development at 440-951-7500.

2664 ■ FIRST COMMUNITY FOUNDATION OF PENNSYLVANIA, WILLIAMSPORT-LYCOMING

330 Pine St., Suite 401
Williamsport, PA 17701
Tel: (570)321-1500; (866)901-2372
Fax: (570)321-6434
E-mail: fcfpa@fcfpa.org
Web Site: http://www.wlfoundation.org
To provide scholarship for Montoursville Area High School seniors who will be attending Yale College.
Title of Award: Eleanor M. Wolfson Memorial Scholarship Fund **Area, Field, or Subject:** Creative writing. **Level of Education for which Award is Granted:** Undergraduate **Funds Available:** No specific amount.
Eligibility Requirements: Students must be graduating seniors at Montoursville Area High School. If there are no graduating students planning to attend Yale College, a graduating student with an outstanding academic record and a demonstrated talent in creative writing will be considered. **Application Requirements:** Applicants may contact and request an application from the Montoursville Area High School. **Additional Information:** Ronda Albert, Montoursville Area High School, 100 N Arch St, Montoursville, PA 17754; 570-368-3509; ralbert@montoursville.k12.pa.us.

2665 ■ FOUNDATION FOR THE CAROLINAS

217 S Tryon St.
Charlotte, NC 28202
Tel: (704)973-4500
Free: 800-973-7244
Web Site: http://www.fftc.org
To assist students who are enrolled in the associate degree in Graphic Arts Management Program at Central Piedmont Community College.
Title of Award: Cadmus Communications Corporation Graphics Scholarship Endowment Fund **Area, Field, or Subject:** Graphic art and design. **Level of Education for which Award is Granted:** Undergraduate **Funds Available:** No specific amount. **Duration:** One year.
Eligibility Requirements: Applicants must have completed at least two semesters of the CPCC Graphic Arts and Imaging Technology Program with 3.0 minimum cumulative grade point average on 4.0 scale. **Application Requirements:** Applicants must submit all the required application information and materials. **Additional Information:** CPCC Graphic Arts and Imaging Technology Program; 704-330-4437.

2666 ■ FOUNDATION FOR ENHANCING COMMUNITIES

200 N Third St., PO Box 678
Harrisburg, PA 17108-0678
Tel: (717)236-5040
Fax: (717)231-4463
E-mail: dawn@tfec.org
Web Site: http://www.ghf.org
To award scholarship to a student from either Central Dauphin High School or Central Dauphin East High School.
Title of Award: Adrienne Zoe Fedok Art and Music Scholarships **Area, Field, or Subject:** Art; Music. **Level of Education for which Award is Granted:** Undergraduate **Funds Available:** $1,000.
Eligibility Requirements: Applicant must be from either Central Dauphin High School or Central Dauphin East High School entering his or her freshman year in post-secondary education in the field of Art and Music. **Application Requirements:** The application and the required attachments must be completed and postmarked on or before the deadline. Required attachments include: completed application; high school transcript including GPA; SAT scores; FAFSA Student Aid Report Form (Financial Aid Form); two letters of recommendation (one from a faculty member in the art or music department); a list of extra-curricular activities demonstrating leadership and community service; and personal essay on the applicant's educational and career goals. **Deadline for Receipt:** April 3. **Additional Information:** Dawn Morris, Program Officer; 717-236-5040; dawn@tfec.org.

2667 ■ FOUNDATION FOR ENHANCING COMMUNITIES

200 N Third St., PO Box 678
Harrisburg, PA 17108-0678
Tel: (717)236-5040
Fax: (717)231-4463
E-mail: dawn@tfec.org
Web Site: http://www.ghf.org
To assist students with their college tuition expenses.
Title of Award: Henry and Janet Guareillo Scholarship Fund **Area, Field, or Subject:** Music; Theater arts. **Level of Education for which Award is Granted:** Undergraduate **Funds Available:** No specific amount.
Eligibility Requirements: Program is open to graduating seniors who have studied at Cumberland Valley School of Music for four consecutive years; must have been accepted into a college or conservatory to pursue a degree in music or the theater arts; must have demonstrated ability to become successful candidates in their chosen field; and must demonstrate financial need. Other factors will include performance history, teacher recommendations, if the candidate studied more than one instrument at CVSM or was a Merit Scholarship Award winner. **Application Requirements:** Applicants must complete and submit the application and the attachments on or before the deadline. Application can be obtained online. **Deadline for Receipt:** April 20. **Additional Information:** Dawn Morris, Program Officer; 717-236-5040; dawn@tfec.org.

2668 ■ GRAND HAVEN AREA COMMUNITY FOUNDATION

1 S. Harbor Dr.
Grand Haven, MI 49417
Tel: (616)842-6378
Fax: (616)842-9518
E-mail: bpost@ghacf.org
Web Site: http://www.ghacf.org
To improve and enhance the quality of life in the Tri-Cities area by serving as a leader, catalyst and resource for philanthropy; to strive for community improvement through strategic grantmaking in such fields as arts, education, health, environment, youth, social services and other human needs.
Title of Award: Marvin R. and Pearl E. Patterson Family Scholarships Fund **Area, Field, or Subject:** Fine Arts. **Level of Education for which Award is Granted:** Undergraduate **Funds Available:** No specific amount.
Eligibility Requirements: Applicants must be students who will be graduating or graduated from a Tri-Cities area public high school; must have at least 3.0 GPA and plan to attend any two-year or four-year college or university to study graphic arts or fine arts. **Application Requirements:** Applicants must submit: completed application form; current high school or college transcript; Student Aid Report (SAR) from the Free Application for Federal Student Aid (FAFSA), unless applying for scholarships that do not consider financial need; and letter of recommendation. **Deadline for Receipt:** March 7. **Additional Information:** 616-842-6378.

2669 ■ GRAND RAPIDS COMMUNITY FOUNDATION

161 Ottawa Ave. NW
Ste. 209-C Waters Bldg.
Grand Rapids, MI 49503
Tel: (616)454-1751
Fax: (616)454-6455
E-mail: grfound@grfoundation.org
Web Site: http://www.grfoundation.org
To provide financial assistance to deserving students.
Title of Award: Paul Collins Scholarships **Area, Field, or Subject:** Applied Arts; Fine Arts. **Level of Education for which Award is Granted:** Undergraduate **Funds Available:** No specific amount.
Eligibility Requirements: Applicants must be undergraduate level students studying Fine or Applied Arts at Aquinas, Calvin, GVSU, GRCC or Kendall. Applicants must be residents of Kent County. Applicants must have a minimum of 2.5 GPA, financial need and demonstrate artistic talent. **Application Requirements:** Applicants must check the available website for more information. **Additional Information:** Grand Rapids Community Foundation at the above address

2670 ■ GRAND RAPIDS COMMUNITY FOUNDATION

161 Ottawa Ave. NW
Ste. 209-C Waters Bldg.
Grand Rapids, MI 49503

Tel: (616)454-1751
Fax: (616)454-6455
E-mail: grfound@grfoundation.org
Web Site: http://www.grfoundation.org
To provide financial assistance to those students who are in need.
Title of Award: Mathilda & Carolyn Gallmeyer Scholarships **Area, Field, or Subject:** Fine Arts. **Level of Education for which Award is Granted:** Undergraduate **Funds Available:** No specific amount.
Eligibility Requirements: Applicants must be Kent County residents. Applicants must be pursuing Painting or Fine arts. Applicants must demonstrate artistic talent, financial need and a minimum of 2.75 GPA. **Application Requirements:** Applicants must check the available website for the required materials. **Additional Information:** Grand Rapids Community Foundation at the above address

2671 ■ HANDWEAVERS GUILD OF AMERICA

1255 Boford Hwy., Ste. 211
Suwanee, GA 30024
Tel: (678)730-0010
Fax: (678)730-0836
E-mail: hga@weavespindye.org
Web Site: http://www.weavespindye.org
To provide students in fiber arts programs the opportunity to assist internationally known instructors and to participate in the Convergence experience.
Title of Award: Convergence Assistantship Grants **Area, Field, or Subject:** Art. **Level of Education for which Award is Granted:** Undergraduate **Funds Available:** No specific amount.
Eligibility Requirements: Applicant must be currently enrolled in an accredited academic program and available to attend a Training Class Saturday at the Convention Center. **Application Requirements:** Awardee must submit a Letter of Nomination from the Professor; must provide the Convergence complete registration form and personal statement. Application documents must be sent to: HGA, 1255 Boford Hwy., Ste. 211, Suwanee, GA 30024. **Deadline for Receipt:** April 3.

2672 ■ HANDWEAVERS GUILD OF AMERICA

1255 Boford Hwy., Ste. 211
Suwanee, GA 30024
Tel: (678)730-0010
Fax: (678)730-0836
E-mail: hga@weavespindye.org
Web Site: http://www.weavespindye.org
To further the education in the field of fiber arts, including training for research, textile history, and conservation.
Title of Award: HGA and Dendel Scholarships **Area, Field, or Subject:** Art. **Level of Education for which Award is Granted:** Undergraduate **Funds Available:** Amounts of the awards are based on income from the scholarship funds. **Duration:** One year.
Eligibility Requirements: Applicant must be enrolled in accredited undergraduate or graduate programs in the United States and Canada. **Application Requirements:** Application forms are available on the website. Applicant must have the following: Transcript (a copy of the transcript must accompany the application), and slide description sheet. Application and other required materials must be sent to: HGA Scholarship Chair, Handweavers Guild of America, Inc., 1255 Buford Hwy., Ste. 211 Suwanee, GA 30024. **Deadline for Receipt:** March 15.

2673 ■ HILLEL MONTREAL

3460 Stanley St.
Montreal, QC, Canada H3A 1R8
Tel: (514)845-9171
Fax: (514)345-6418
E-mail: romy@hillel.ca
Web Site: http://montreal.hillel.ca
To improve the quality and diversity of Hillel Montreal.
Title of Award: Hadar J. Chemtob Scholarship **Area, Field, or Subject:** Fashion design. **Level of Education for which Award is Granted:** Undergraduate **Funds Available:** No specific amount.
Eligibility Requirements: Applicants must be Jewish students pursuing a career in fashion. **Application Requirements:** Applicants must submit a letter stating the objectives and reasons for request; proof of Quebec residency; letter of acceptance for fashion studies program; transcript of grades; two letters of recommendation from teachers and Social Insurance Number. **Deadline for Receipt:** May 30.

2674 ■ HISPANIC ASSOCIATION OF COLLEGES AND UNIVERSITIES

8415 Datapoint Dr., Ste. 400
San Antonio, TX 78229
Tel: (210)698-3805
Fax: (210)692-0823
E-mail: hacu@hacu.net
Web Site: http://www.hacu.net
To promote the development of member colleges and universities; to improve access to and the quality of post-secondary educational opportunities for Hispanic students; and to meet the needs of business, industry and government through the development and sharing of resources, information and expertise.
Title of Award: GAP, Inc. Scholarships Award **Area, Field, or Subject:** Management; Fashion Design. **Level of Education for which Award is Granted:** Undergraduate **Funds Available:** $1,000.
Eligibility Requirements: Applicants must be full-time or part-time, undergraduate and graduate students attending four year institutions; must possess a minimum cumulative GPA of 3.0. **Application Requirements:** Applicants must fill out the application form and must provide any documents showing that they are currently enrolled or accepted by a college, university, or institution. **Deadline for Receipt:** May 23.

2675 ■ HISPANIC SCHOLARSHIP FUND

55 Second St., Ste. 1500
San Francisco, CA 94105
877-473-4636
Fax: (415)808-2302
E-mail: info@hsf.net
Web Site: http://www.hsf.net
To provide financial assistance to students of Hispanic heritage.
Title of Award: HSF/Wal-Mart Stores Inc. Scholarship Program **Area, Field, or Subject:** Marketing and distribution; Accounting; Business; Finance; Management; Computer and information sciences; Information science and technology; Civil engineering; Construction; Electrical engineering; Geology; Engineering, Industrial; Fashion design; Law; **Level of Education for which Award is Granted:** Graduate, Undergraduate **Funds Available:** $2,500.
Eligibility Requirements: Applicant must be of Hispanic heritage; U.S. citizen or legal permanent resident with a valid permanent resident card or passport stamped I-551; enrolled as sophomore, junior, senior undergraduate or First or Second year Master student in a full-time degree-seeking program at an accredited U.S. institution in the U.S., Puerto Rico, U.S. Virgin Islands or Guam; have a minimum 3.0 GPA on a 4.0 scale or 4.00 on a 5.00 scale; must apply for Federal Financing Aid; pursuing his/her first undergraduate or graduate degree. Undergraduate students must be majoring in: Marketing, Accounting, Business, Finance, Management, Computer Science, Computer Programming, Information Technology (IT), Civil Engineering, Construction, Electrical Engineering, Environmental/Geological Engineering, Industrial Engineering, and Fashion. Master's students must be majoring in: Business, Finance, Marketing, Civil Engineering, Construction, Electrical Engineering, Environmental/Geological Engineering and Law. **Application Requirements:** Applications must be submitted using the HSF online application system. **Additional Information:** In partnership with Wal-Mart Stores, Inc. **Deadline for Receipt:** March 15. **Additional Information:** scholar1@hsf.net.

2676 ■ HISPANIC SCHOLARSHIP FUND

55 Second St., Ste. 1500
San Francisco, CA 94105
877-473-4636
Fax: (415)808-2302
E-mail: info@hsf.net
Web Site: http://www.hsf.net
To provide financial assistance to creative arts-related undergraduate and graduate students beginning or completing an art project.
Title of Award: McNamara Family Creative Arts Project Grants **Area, Field, or Subject:** Art; Media arts; Broadcasting; Filmmaking; Performing arts; Communications; Writing. **Level of Education for which Award is Granted:** Graduate, Undergraduate **Funds Available:** $5,000-$20,000.

Eligibility Requirements: Applicant must be of Hispanic heritage; U.S. citizen or legal permanent resident with a valid permanent resident card or passport stamped I-551; enrolled full-time undergraduate or graduate student in a degree-seeking program at a U.S. accredited institution in the U.S., Puerto Rico or U.S. Virgin Islands in the upcoming academic year; pursuing a major in Arts, including but not limited to media, film, performing arts, communications or writing; have a minimum 3.0 GPA on a 4.0 scale; must apply for federal financing aid using the Free Application for Federal Student Aid (FAFSA) at www.fafsa.ed.gov. **Application Requirements:** Applications must be submitted using the HSF online application system. **Additional Information:** In partnership with the McNamara Family Foundation. **Deadline for Receipt:** March 15. **Additional Information:** scholar1@hsf.net.

2677 ■ HUMAN RACE THEATRE COMPANY

126 N Main St., Ste. 300
Dayton, OH 45402-1710
Tel: (937)461-3823
Fax: (937)461-7223
E-mail: contact@humanracetheatre.org
Web Site: http://www.humanracetheatre.org
To support singers/actors in the greater Dayton area who are training for a career in musical theatre.

Title of Award: Stephen Schwartz Musical Theatre Scholarships **Area, Field, or Subject:** Theater arts. **Level of Education for which Award is Granted:** Undergraduate **Number Awarded:** 2. **Funds Available:** $1,500 for high school senior; $3,500 for a college student.
Eligibility Requirements: Applicants must have a permanent address in Montgomery County or one of seven contiguous counties (Preble, Darke, Miami, Clark, Greene, Warren or Butler); must be currently enrolled at a college in one of the eight counties previously listed. High school senior applicants must be currently applying or accepted into a college program and have plans to train in musical theatre. College student must be currently training for a career in musical theatre. **Application Requirements:** Applicants may contact the Executive Director of The Human Race Theatre Company for more information about the scholarship. **Additional Information:** Established in honor of musical theatre legend Stephen Schwartz. **Additional Information:** Kevin Moore, Executive Director, at 937-461-3823 x3115, or email kevin@humanracetheatre.org.

2678 ■ INDIANA STATE ALUMNI ASSOCIATION

200 N 7th St.
Terre Haute, IN 47809-9989
800-GO-TO-ISU
Web Site: http://www.indstate.edu/alum/alum_assoc.htm
To support educational pursuit of students.

Title of Award: Academic Promise Scholarships **Area, Field, or Subject:** Art; Science. **Level of Education for which Award is Granted:** Undergraduate **Funds Available:** $2000. **Duration:** One year.
Eligibility Requirements: Applicant must hold an associate of arts, science, or applied science at any Ivy Tech campus or at Vincennes University; have a minimum GPA of 3.0. **Application Requirements:** Student must indicate in the admission application the specific Ivy Tech campus attended. **Deadline for Receipt:** Must be admitted before June 1 (fall semester) or December 1 (spring semester). **Additional Information:** admissions@indstate.edu.

2679 ■ INDIANA STATE ALUMNI ASSOCIATION

200 N 7th St.
Terre Haute, IN 47809-9989
800-GO-TO-ISU
Web Site: http://www.indstate.edu/alum/alum_assoc.htm
To support educational pursuit of students.

Title of Award: Indiana State Alumni Association Creative and Performing Arts Award **Area, Field, or Subject:** Art; Music; English language and literature; Theater arts. **Level of Education for which Award is Granted:** Undergraduate **Funds Available:** $2000. **Duration:** One year.
Eligibility Requirements: Applicant must be entering college as freshmen at the Indiana State University; majoring or have a minor in Art, Music, English, Physical Education (Dance), Theater. **Application Requirements:** Applicant must submit an application form; portfolio review; must audition at the departments; and will be interview. Contact the department where the applicant is majoring. **Deadline for Receipt:**

Must be admitted before February 1. **Additional Information:** Art: 812-237-3697; Music: 812-237-27771; English: 812-237-3163; Physical Education: 812-237-2520; Theater: 812-237-3331.

2680 ■ INDIANA STATE ALUMNI ASSOCIATION

200 N 7th St.
Terre Haute, IN 47809-9989
800-GO-TO-ISU
Web Site: http://www.indstate.edu/alum/alum_assoc.htm
To support educational pursuit of students.

Title of Award: Phi Theta Kappa Scholarships **Area, Field, or Subject:** Art; Science. **Level of Education for which Award is Granted:** Undergraduate **Funds Available:** $4000. **Duration:** One year.
Eligibility Requirements: Applicant must hold an associate of arts, science, or applied science; have a minimum GPA of 3.5; and a member of Phi Theta Kappa National Honor Society. **Application Requirements:** Student must be admitted to the Indiana State University and will be automatically qualified for the scholarship. In addition, student must provide a documentation of honor society membership and a letter of recommendation together with the admission application. **Deadline for Receipt:** Must be admitted before June 1 (fall semester) or December 1 (spring semester). **Additional Information:** admissions@indstate.edu.

2681 ■ INTERNATIONAL FOODSERVICE EDITORIAL COUNCIL

PO Box 491
Hyde Park, NY 12538
Tel: (845)229-6973
Fax: (845)229-6993
E-mail: info@ifeconline.com
Web Site: http://www.ifec-is-us.com
To increase awareness and understanding of the career opportunities available in the field of food service communications and to encourage entry of qualified professionals in the field.

Title of Award: International Foodservice Editorial Council Scholarships **Area, Field, or Subject:** Culinary arts; Communications; Food service careers; Food science and technology; Photography; Hotel, institutional, and restaurant management; Nutrition; Dietetics; Journalism; Public relations; Graphic art and design. **Level of Education for which Award is Granted:** Graduate, Undergraduate **Number Awarded:** Varies. **Funds Available:** $3,750.
Eligibility Requirements: Applicants must be full-time students in a U.S. accredited post-secondary educational institution working towards an associate's, bachelor's or master's degree. **Application Requirements:** Applicants must submit a complete application together with academic transcript and two letters of recommendation. Application requirements must be typewritten and submitted using U.S. Postal Service's Return Receipt Service. **Deadline for Receipt:** March 15.

2682 ■ INTERNATIONAL FURNISHINGS AND DESIGN ASSOCIATION

150 S Warner Rd., Ste. 156
King of Prussia, PA 19406
Tel: (610)535-6422
Fax: (610)535-6423
E-mail: info@ifda.com
Web Site: http://www.ifdaef.org
to promote, develop, or enhance the furnishings and design industries and the practice of these professions.

Title of Award: IFDA Part-time Student Scholarships **Area, Field, or Subject:** Part-time students. **Level of Education for which Award is Granted:** Undergraduate **Duration:** Entire length of undergraduate study.
Eligibility Requirements: All applicants must have completed four courses in interior design or related field; he/she must be enrolled as a part-time student and be currently enrolled in at least two courses. **Application Requirements:** Applicant must submit a certified, sealed transcript of course work that verifies enrollment with GPA. It may be sent by the school or college; a separate letter of recommendation from a professor or instructor on official school stationery; four copies of 300-400 word essay explaining long and short-term goals, achievements, awards or accomplishments; four digital copies of two photos of the student's original work preferably on one-page and in color; four copies of completed application form. **Deadline for Receipt:** March 31. **Additional Information:** Earline Clark feldman tapis2@bellsouth.org

2683 ■ INTERNATIONAL FURNISHINGS AND DESIGN ASSOCIATION

150 S Warner Rd., Ste. 156
King of Prussia, PA 19406
Tel: (610)535-6422
Fax: (610)535-6423
E-mail: info@ifda.com
Web Site: http://www.ifdaef.org
To promote, develop, or enhance the furnishings and design industries and the practice of these professions.

Title of Award: Charles D. Mayo Student Scholarships **Area, Field, or Subject:** Interior design. **Level of Education for which Award is Granted:** Undergraduate **Number Awarded:** 1. **Funds Available:** $1,000. **Duration:** Entire length of undergraduate study.

Eligibility Requirements: All applicants must completed their four design courses in post secondary education at the time of application and must be majoring in interior design or a closely related field. **Application Requirements:** All applicants must have completed four design courses in post secondary education at the time of application and are majoring in interior design or a closely related field; an applicant must submit a certified, sealed transcript of course work that verifies full-time status with GPA. It may be sent by the school or college; a separate letter of recommendation from a professor or instructor on official school stationery; four copies of a 300-400 word essay explaining long and short-term goals, achievements, awards and accomplishments; four copies of two digital photos of student's original work preferably on one-page and in color; four copies of the completed application form. **Deadline for Receipt:** March 31. **Additional Information:** Earline Clark Feldman 080403tapis2@bellsouth.net

2684 ■ JAMAICAN CANADIAN ASSOCIATION

995 Arrow Rd.
Toronto, ON, Canada M9M 2Z5
Tel: (416)746-5772
Fax: (416)746-7035
E-mail: info@jcassoc.org
Web Site: http://www.jcassoc.org
To provide financial assistance to students from the Caribbean/ African community, who are pursuing postsecondary studies in Ontario universities/colleges.

Title of Award: Anne-Marie Bonner Scholarships **Area, Field, or Subject:** Art. **Level of Education for which Award is Granted:** Undergraduate **Funds Available:** $1,000. **Duration:** One year.

Eligibility Requirements: Applicants must be in the first year of study in an arts or Caribbean studies program; must be Canadian citizens or landed immigrants of Caribbean/African background; must be enrolled as full-time first-year students at an Ontario university/college or other postsecondary institution; must demonstrate remarkable academic performance or progress in high school; must demonstrate involvement and leadership in campus and/or community activities; must demonstrate financial need. **Application Requirements:** Application forms are available online and must be sent to The Jamaican Canadian Association Center, 995 Arrow Rd., Toronto M9M 2Z5. **Additional Information:** Scholarship is sponsored by Anne-Marie Bonner, Jamaica's Consular General to Toronto. **Deadline for Receipt:** July 25.

2685 ■ JUNIOR ACHIEVEMENT

One Education Way
Colorado Springs, CO 80906
Tel: (719)540-8000; 888-4JA-ALUM
Fax: (719)540-6299
E-mail: newmedia@ja.org
Web Site: http://www.ja.org
To allow educational advancements by providing financial assistance.

Title of Award: Walt Disney Company Foundation Scholarships **Area, Field, or Subject:** Business administration; Fine arts. **Level of Education for which Award is Granted:** Undergraduate **Number Awarded:** 1. **Funds Available:** Covers full-tuition plus $200 cash per year for incidental fees. **Duration:** Four years.

Eligibility Requirements: Program is open to exceptional high school seniors who are graduating before June 30. Applicants must have excellent academic and extra-curricular credentials; and must be pursuing a major in either business administration or fine arts. **Application Require-**

ments: Applicants must submit a completed application form along with other supporting materials. **Additional Information:** The scholarship is sponsored by The Walt Disney Company Foundation. **Deadline for Receipt:** February 1. **Additional Information:** scholarships@ja.org.

2686 ■ LEWIS-CLARK STATE COLLEGE

500 8th Ave.
Lewiston, ID 83501
Tel: (208)792-5272
Web Site: http://www.lcsc.edu
To inspire educational pursuits among less capable individuals by providing financial assistance.

Title of Award: Lewis-Clark State College Presidential Technical Out-of-State Scholarships **Area, Field, or Subject:** Chemistry; Computer Science; Engineering; Information Systems Analysis; Industrial Electronics; Biology; Earth Information Systems; Radiology; Heating/Air Conditioning; Automated Manufacturing Technology; Mathematics; Printing Technology; Graphic Arts or Web Development. **Level of Education for which Award is Granted:** Undergraduate **Funds Available:** No specific amount.

Eligibility Requirements: Applicants must be new non-resident high school or transfer students who have at least 14 transferable semester credits. **Application Requirements:** Applicants must accomplish a general application available in the website. **Deadline for Receipt:** March 1 for Fall enrollment or November 1 for Spring enrollment.

2687 ■ MATANUSKA-SUSITNA COLLEGE

PO Box 2889
Palmer, AK 99645
Tel: (907)745-9774
Fax: (907)745-9711
E-mail: info@matsu.alaska.edu
Web Site: http://www.matsu.alaska.edu
To provide support to deserving students in Alaska who want to pursue an education in any campus of the University of Alaska.

Title of Award: Donald Wills Jacobs Scholarships **Area, Field, or Subject:** Fine arts. **Level of Education for which Award is Granted:** Undergraduate **Funds Available:** $500.

Eligibility Requirements: Applicant must be a full-time junior or senior student enrolled in a Bachelor of Fine Arts program at the University of Alaska. **Application Requirements:** Applicant must complete the application forms available at the website; must attach a personal essay, two letters of recommendation, and current transcripts. **Deadline for Receipt:** February 15.

2688 ■ MEDIA ACTION NETWORK FOR ASIAN AMERICANS

PO Box 11105
Burbank, CA 91510
Tel: (213)486-4433; 888-90-MANAA
E-mail: manaaletters@yahoo.com
Web Site: http://www.manaa.org
To promote education in filmmaking and in television production.

Title of Award: MANAA Media Scholarships **Area, Field, or Subject:** Filmmaking; Television. **Level of Education for which Award is Granted:** Graduate, Undergraduate **Number Awarded:** 1. **Funds Available:** $1000.

Eligibility Requirements: Applicants must be graduate or undergraduate students pursuing careers as filmmakers and in television production (not broadcast journalism). **Application Requirements:** Applicants must submit a copy of all official transcripts; copy of completed financial aid documents; two letters of recommendation; a double-spaced essay (maximum of 1,000 words); and a work sample consisting of a short film or screenplay (optional). Send applications to MANAA Scholarship, P.O. Box 11105, Burbank, CA 91510. Do not send applications via certified or registered mail. **Additional Information:** The scholarship was formed in 1992. **Deadline for Receipt:** May 9.

2689 ■ MILL CREEK BUSINESS ASSOCIATION

13300 Bothell-Everett Hwy.
Mill Creek, WA 98012
Tel: (425)673-6200
E-mail: info@millcreekbiz.com
Web Site: http://www.millcreekbiz.com

To encourage and assist local high school students in their pursuit of higher learning in Business or Fine Arts.
Title of Award: Mill Creek Business Association Scholarships **Area, Field, or Subject:** Business; Fine Arts. **Level of Education for which Award is Granted:** Undergraduate **Funds Available:** No specific amount.
Eligibility Requirements: Applicants must live in Mill Creek and/or attend school at Jacksonville High school or Archbishop Murphy High School; must be senior students in good standing at the time of application; must be accepted to attend a full-time accredited college, university or Fine Arts school; must be planning an academic course of study in the field of business/fine arts and/or plan to pursue a career in business or fine arts.
Application Requirements: Applicants must complete the application form; must submit two letters of reference and recommendation from teachers, advisors, and/or local business people; a copy of the letter of acceptance from their institution; must provide a 200 word, typed essay stating their academic and career plans. **Deadline for Receipt:** May 1.
Additional Information: 13300 Bothell-Everett Hwy., Mill Creek, WA 98012.

2690 ■ MONTANA BROADCASTERS ASSOCIATION

HC 70, Box 90
Bonner, MT 59823
Tel: (406)244-4622
Fax: (406)244-5518
E-mail: mba@mtbroadcasters.org
Web Site: http://www.mtbroadcasters.org
To promote the values of local, free over-the-air broadcasting to the business community, governmental bodies and the general public in Montana; and to support the Montana broadcasting industry by providing services, information, continuing education, recruitment and a strong unified voice.
Title of Award: Montana Broadcasters Association Directors' Scholarships **Area, Field, or Subject:** Broadcasting; Theater Arts. **Level of Education for which Award is Granted:** Undergraduate **Funds Available:** No specific amount.
Eligibility Requirements: Applicants must be students majoring in media and theater arts. **Application Requirements:** Applicants must submit a completed application form.

2691 ■ NATIONAL GOVERNMENT PUBLISHING ASSOCIATION

207 Third Ave.
Hattiesburg, MS 39401
Tel: (601)582-3330
Fax: (601)582-3354
E-mail: info@govpublishing.org
Web Site: http://www.govpublishing.org
To promote education in the printing and graphic communications industry.
Title of Award: Don Bailey Scholarships **Area, Field, or Subject:** Printing trades and industries; Graphic art and design. **Level of Education for which Award is Granted:** Undergraduate **Funds Available:** $1,000-$50,000 per academic year. **Duration:** Four years.
Eligibility Requirements: Applicants must be pursuing a career in graphic communications, printing technology, printing management or publishing; must be a high school senior or high school graduate; must be enrolled in a two or four year accredited graphic or printing program at a technical school, college/university in the United States; a full-time student maintaining a cumulative GPA of 3.0 or higher. **Application Requirements:** Applicant must submit a completed application form; a copy of SAT scores; an official transcript; a photocopy of the intended course of study. **Additional Information:** In honor of Donald L. Bailey Sr. **Deadline for Receipt:** March 1 for high school and April 1 for college students.

2692 ■ NATIONAL IRANIAN AMERICAN COUNCIL

1411 K St. NW, Ste. 600
Washington, DC 20005
Tel: (202)386-6325
Fax: (202)386-6409
Web Site: http://www.niacouncil.org
To promote and facilitate the appreciation of Iranian-American artists.
Title of Award: Iranian Artist Scholarships **Area, Field, or Subject:** Fine arts. **Level of Education for which Award is Granted:** Undergraduate **Funds Available:** $1,000.

Eligibility Requirements: Applicants must be Iranian or Iranian-American artists living and studying fine arts in the United States. Applicant must be between the ages of 18 and 30. **Application Requirements:** Interested applicants must submit the following: a current resume; ten (10) slides labeled with title, size and medium (CD-ROM and video accepted); articles/reviews about applicant's work or exhibitions; an artist statement about his/her work (500-1000 words); a self-addressed stamped envelope. **Deadline for Receipt:** June 1. **Additional Information:** EP-Scholarship, 11118 Lakespray Way, Reston, VA 20191; 202-607-0754.

2693 ■ NATIONAL SCULPTURE SOCIETY

237 Park Ave., Ground Fl.
New York, NY 10017
E-mail: info@nationalsculpture.org
Web Site: http://www.nationalsculpture.org
To provide financial assistance to those studying figurative or representational sculpture.
Title of Award: National Sculpture Society Scholarships **Area, Field, or Subject:** Sculpture. **Level of Education for which Award is Granted:** Undergraduate **Funds Available:** $2,000.
Eligibility Requirements: Applicant must be enrolled in a sculpture school. **Application Requirements:** Applicants must submit a letter of application including a brief biography and the background in sculpture; two letters of recommendation; 8-10 images of work on CD with at least three works shown; and a proof of financial need. Submit all materials to: Scholarship National Sculpture Society, 237 Park Ave., Ground Fl. New York, NY 10017. **Additional Information:** Applicants must also provide a self-addressed stamped envelope for the return of the materials. **Deadline for Receipt:** May 31.

2694 ■ ORANGE COUNTY COMMUNITY FOUNDATION

30 Corporate Park, Ste. 410
Irvine, CA 92606
Tel: (949)553-4202
Fax: (949)553-4211
E-mail: cmontesano@oc-cf.org
Web Site: http://www.oc-cf.org
To award scholarship to the students who are residents of Orange County.
Title of Award: Orange County Centennial Arts Scholarships **Area, Field, or Subject:** Performing arts; Visual Arts; Theater arts; Music. **Level of Education for which Award is Granted:** Undergraduate **Number Awarded:** 3. **Funds Available:** $2,000.
Eligibility Requirements: Applicants must: be local high school graduating seniors who are residents of Orange County, California, and who are completing their last three years of high school in the county; be students who are planning to enroll full-time at an accredited college or university and majoring in the arts. Example of acceptable majors include: dance, voice, opera, theater arts, musical theater, visual arts and music; demonstrated record of community service and leadership. particular attention will be given to training, honors and achievements in the arts. **Application Requirements:** Applicants must include a 250-word essay in their application. Applicants must write about their interests and plans and the way in which their plan is appropriate to their situation, abilities and long-term goals. **Deadline for Receipt:** March 15. **Additional Information:** Claudia Montesano, 949-553-4202 ext. 46; cmontesano@oc-cf.org.

2695 ■ PALOS FINE ARTS ASSOCIATION

8901 W 123rd St.
Palos Park, IL 60464
Tel: (708)671-3755
E-mail: info@palosfinearts.com
Web Site: http://www.palosfinearts.com
To further interest in and study of arts.
Title of Award: Palos Fine Arts Association Scholarships **Area, Field, or Subject:** Fine Arts. **Level of Education for which Award is Granted:** Undergraduate **Number Awarded:** 2. **Funds Available:** $500.
Eligibility Requirements: Applicants must be junior or senior high school students residing within the boundaries of high school districts 230 or 218; must attend Stagg, Sandburg, Andrew, Shepard, Chicago Christian, Marist, McCauly, Sacred Heart or be home-schooled. **Application Requirements:** Applicants must submit: a completed application form; release form; art materials in the form of CD, tape, slides, audio or

manuscript; a 1,000 word essay including a brief self-history, goals, when and where the class or workshops will be held and reasons for interest in attending the class.

2696 ■ PHI UPSILON OMICRON
PO Box 329
Fairmont, WV 26555
Tel: (304)368-0612
E-mail: info@phiu.org
Web Site: http://www.phiu.org
To promote education in advance family and consumer sciences and related areas.
Title of Award: S. Penny Chappell Scholarships **Area, Field, or Subject:** Fashion design; Textile science. **Level of Education for which Award is Granted:** Undergraduate **Funds Available:** No specific amount.
Eligibility Requirements: Applicant must be a Phi U member; pursuing a baccalaureate degree in fashion design and construction, textile design and development and/or textile preservation. **Application Requirements:** Applicants must submit an application; transcripts; recommendations. Application documents must be assembled in order, clipped together with a paper clip and placed in a 10" x 13" envelope. Enclose a self-addressed stamped postcard. **Additional Information:** Applicants may apply for more than one fellowship. **Deadline for Receipt:** February 1.

2697 ■ PHI UPSILON OMICRON
PO Box 329
Fairmont, WV 26555
Tel: (304)368-0612
E-mail: info@phiu.org
Web Site: http://www.phiu.org
To promote education in advance family and consumer sciences and related areas.
Title of Award: Sutherland/Purdy Scholarships **Area, Field, or Subject:** Fashion design; Textile science. **Level of Education for which Award is Granted:** Undergraduate **Funds Available:** No specific amount.
Eligibility Requirements: Applicant must be a Phi U member; pursuing a baccalaureate degree in clothing and textiles or a related area such as apparel design or fashion merchandising; have held a leadership position in her/his Phi U chapter; and have earned at least a 3.0 out of 4.0 overall point average. **Application Requirements:** Applicants must submit an application; transcripts; recommendations. Application documents must be assembled in order, clipped together with a paper clip and placed in a 10" x 13" envelope. Enclose a self-addressed stamped postcard. **Additional Information:** Applicants may apply for more than one fellowship. **Deadline for Receipt:** February 1.

2698 ■ POINT FOUNDATION
PO Box 60108
Los Angeles, CA 90060-0108
Tel: (323)933-1234
Fax: (866)33-POINT
E-mail: info@pointfoundation.org
Web Site: http://thepointfoundation.org
To support the LGBT community.
Title of Award: Casey Sakir Point Scholarships **Area, Field, or Subject:** Fashion design; Arts. **Level of Education for which Award is Granted:** Graduate, Undergraduate **Funds Available:** No specific amount.
Eligibility Requirements: Applicant must be LGBT; or have a history of leadership in the LGBT community and plan to be a LGBT leader in the future, and planning a future in the fields of design, fashion or the arts. **Application Requirements:** Applicants must complete the online scholarship application by March 1. If chosen as semi-finalists, students are requested to submit supplemental materials, in one envelope: two to three letters of recommendation; official transcripts; test score verification; and resume. **Additional Information:** Point Foundation will not return submitted supplemental materials. **Deadline for Receipt:** March 1. **Additional Information:** ginger@pointfoundation.org, or 775-782-5659, fax: 775-782-5690.

2699 ■ PRIDE FOUNDATION
PO Box 2194, 1122 E Pike St. PMB 1001
Seattle, WA 98112
Tel: (206)323-3318

Free: 800-735-7287
Fax: (206)323-1017
E-mail: prideweb@pridefoundation.org
Web Site: http://www.pridefoundation.org
To provide scholarship to the students who have been stigmatized, isolated or closeted because of sexual identity issues.
Title of Award: Paul Arnold Memorial Scholarships **Area, Field, or Subject:** Interior design; Fashion design; Graphic art and design. **Level of Education for which Award is Granted:** Undergraduate **Funds Available:** No specific amount.
Eligibility Requirements: Applicants must be young men and women studying interior, fashion, graphic design. **Application Requirements:** Qualified students are asked to submit an application to determine eligibility for scholarships. Applicants may download an application form from the Foundation's website. **Additional Information:** Pride Foundation at the above address.

2700 ■ PRIDE FOUNDATION
PO Box 2194, 1122 E Pike St. PMB 1001
Seattle, WA 98112
Tel: (206)323-3318
Free: 800-735-7287
Fax: (206)323-1017
E-mail: prideweb@pridefoundation.org
Web Site: http://www.pridefoundation.org
To provide scholarship to the students who have been stigmatized, isolated or closeted because of sexual identity issues.
Title of Award: Charly Baker and Heath Merriwether Memorial Scholarships **Area, Field, or Subject:** Theater arts. **Level of Education for which Award is Granted:** Undergraduate **Funds Available:** No specific amount.
Eligibility Requirements: Applicant must be a student under the age of 25 who graduated from any West Seattle high school or are studying theater art. **Application Requirements:** Qualified students are asked to submit an application to determine eligibility for scholarships. Applicants may download an application form from the Foundation's website. **Additional Information:** Pride Foundation at the above address.

2701 ■ PRIDE FOUNDATION
PO Box 2194, 1122 E Pike St. PMB 1001
Seattle, WA 98112
Tel: (206)323-3318
Free: 800-735-7287
Fax: (206)323-1017
E-mail: prideweb@pridefoundation.org
Web Site: http://www.pridefoundation.org
To provide scholarship to the students who have been stigmatized, isolated or closeted because of sexual identity issues.
Title of Award: Patricia Van Kirk Scholarships **Area, Field, or Subject:** Theater arts; Visual arts. **Level of Education for which Award is Granted:** Undergraduate **Funds Available:** No specific amount.
Eligibility Requirements: Applicant must be a lesbian studying theater or visual arts. Preference is given to students who are self-identified lesbian, gay, bisexual or transgender (LGBT). **Application Requirements:** Qualified students are asked to submit an application to determine eligibility for scholarships. Applicants may download an application form from the Foundation's website. **Additional Information:** Pride Foundation at the above address.

2702 ■ PUBLIC EDUCATION FOUNDATION
3360 W Sahara Ave., Ste. 160
Las Vegas, NV 89102
Tel: (702)799-1042
Fax: (702)799-5247
E-mail: steelej@ccpef.org
Web Site: http://ccpef.org
To provide educational opportunities for individuals intending to pursue higher studies.
Title of Award: Palo Verde High School Faculty Follies Scholarships **Area, Field, or Subject:** Theater arts. **Level of Education for which Award is Granted:** Undergraduate **Number Awarded:** 1. **Funds Available:** $500.
Eligibility Requirements: Applicants must be Palo Verde High School seniors who have completed six semesters of theater classes; must be

planning to attend an accredited college/university; and must have a minimum 2.5 cumulative GPA. **Application Requirements:** Applicants must submit a completed application form along with an essay, transcript, resume of awards, and Leadership, Activities and Achievement Information. **Deadline for Receipt:** March 7. **Additional Information:** Shana Venenga at 702-799-1042.

2703 ■ REDLANDS COMMUNITY SCHOLARSHIP FOUNDATION
c/o Kathleen Venegas-Boge, Admin. Asst.
PO Box 1683
Redlands, CA 92373
Tel: (909)307-9892
Fax: (909)307-9892
Web Site: http://www.redlandsscholarships.org
To encourage educational pursuits among Redlands Unified School District graduates by providing educational assistance.
Title of Award: David Beltran Memorial Scholarships **Area, Field, or Subject:** Theater arts. **Level of Education for which Award is Granted:** Undergraduate **Number Awarded:** 2. **Funds Available:** $500.
Eligibility Requirements: Applicant must be a college-bound graduating senior planning to major in drama, theater arts or thespian studies. **Application Requirements:** Applicants must submit a completed application form together with the scantron sheet; cover sheet; student activity and community activity sheets; personal essay; and a copy of unofficial transcript (signed by the counselor). **Additional Information:** No electronic submissions of application will be accepted. Submit two printed copies of the application and use a No. 2 pencil on the scantron sheet. **Deadline for Receipt:** February 20.

2704 ■ THE SAN DIEGO FOUNDATION
2508 Historic Decatur Rd., Ste. 200
San Diego, CA 92106
Tel: (619)235-2300
Fax: (619)239-1710
E-mail: info@sdfoundation.org
Web Site: http://www.sdfoundation.org
To support the education of students from California.
Title of Award: California Association of Family and Consumer Sciences (CAFCS)-San Diego Chapter Scholarships **Area, Field, or Subject:** Food science and technology; Diabetes; Nutrition; Food service careers; Home Economics; Fashion design; Textile science; Housing; Management. **Level of Education for which Award is Granted:** Graduate, Undergraduate **Number Awarded:** To be determined. **Funds Available:** To be determined.
Eligibility Requirements: Applicant must be a graduating high school senior, current college student, or graduate student majoring in Food Sciences; Dietetics; Nutrition; Food Services; Hospitality; Human, Child and Family Development; Apparel, Fashion and Textile Services; Housing and Interiors; Consumer Economics; Management and Resources; or Family and Consumer Science Education. Student must have a minimum 2.50 GPA on a 4.0 scale; planning to attend an accredited two-year college, four-year university, or licensed trade-vocational school in the U.S. Undergraduate student must be enrolled in school full-time (12 units per semester or 9 per quarter). Graduate student may be enrolled full-time or part-time with awards allocated appropriately based upon enrollment units. **Application Requirements:** Applicants must submit a completed Common Scholarship Application together with personal statement; two letters of recommendation on official letterhead (written within the last six months); official transcript in an official and sealed envelope; copy of 2006 or most recent tax form (Form 1040-pages 1 & 2; Form 1040A-pages 1 & 2; Form 1040EZ -page 1); and a letter of recommendation on official letterhead from an instructor or professional indicating the applicant's interest in pursing one of the above listed fields. **Deadline for Receipt:** January 28. **Additional Information:** Arzo Mansury, Dir. Scholarships at 619-814-1343, or scholarships@sdfoundation.org.

2705 ■ SHORELINE COMMUNITY COLLEGE FOUNDATION
16101 Greenwood Ave. N, Ste. 1005
Shoreline, WA 98133-5696
Tel: (206)546-4755
Fax: (206)546-5826
E-mail: rmanchester@shoreline.edu
Web Site: http://www.shoreline.edu

To increase access and success of Shoreline Community College students; to attract, encourage and assist talented students enrolled in Fine Arts programs at SCC.
Title of Award: Beta Sigma Phi-VCT Scholarships **Area, Field, or Subject:** Fine Arts. **Level of Education for which Award is Granted:** Undergraduate **Funds Available:** No specific amount.
Eligibility Requirements: Applicants must be full-time or part-time students at the Shoreline/Lake Forest Park area who are enrolling at SCC; applicants must have demonstrated strong academic improvement in the last three semesters. **Application Requirements:** Applicants must complete the application form.

2706 ■ SOUTHEASTERN THEATRE CONFERENCE
PO Box 9868
Greensboro, NC 27429
Tel: (336)272-3645
Fax: (336)272-8810
E-mail: setc@setc.org
Web Site: http://www.setc.org
To provide services and educational programs for those individuals and organizations engaged in theatre in the southeast.
Title of Award: Leighton M. Ballew Directing Scholarships **Area, Field, or Subject:** Theatre arts. **Level of Education for which Award is Granted:** Undergraduate **Funds Available:** $3,300.
Eligibility Requirements: Applicants must have completed their undergraduate work at an accredited institution within the SETC region; and be entering graduate school in any region for the time or be currently enrolled in a graduate directing program in a college or university in any region. **Application Requirements:** the following information should be provided by all applicants: Personal letter outlining plans and objectives for graduate work or internship; A complete resume, including work in stage management or play direction; Names, addresses, and telephone numbers of three references who have had agreed, at the request of the award committee, to write letters recommending the applicant; Complete undergraduate and graduate transcripts; Letter of acceptance by an accredited graduate program in directing. **Deadline for Receipt:** January 15. **Additional Information:** Marc Powers, University of South Florida, University of Theatre and Dance, 4202 E. Fowler Ave., TAR 230 Tampa, FL 33620; mpowers@arts.usf.edu.

2707 ■ SOUTHEASTERN THEATRE CONFERENCE
PO Box 9868
Greensboro, NC 27429
Tel: (336)272-3645
Fax: (336)272-8810
E-mail: setc@setc.org
Web Site: http://www.setc.org
To provide services and educational programs for those individuals and organizations engaged in theatre in the southeast.
Title of Award: Polly Holliday Scholarships **Area, Field, or Subject:** Theatre arts. **Level of Education for which Award is Granted:** Undergraduate **Funds Available:** $1,000.
Eligibility Requirements: Any high school senior in the southeastern Theatre Conference Region who is planning to attend a college or university with the intent of majoring in theatre arts. **Application Requirements:** Applicants must provide the following: An official transcript, along with verification of class rank and available SAT or ACT scores from the high school guidance counselor or principal; Three completed recommendation forms, with one being from the nominee's high school principal; The students completed nominee resume form. **Deadline for Receipt:** January 15. **Additional Information:** Roy Hudson 3541 Oakdale Drive, Birmingham, AL 35223; rhudson@jefcoed.com.

2708 ■ SOUTHEASTERN THEATRE CONFERENCE
PO Box 9868
Greensboro, NC 27429
Tel: (336)272-3645
Fax: (336)272-8810
E-mail: setc@setc.org
Web Site: http://www.setc.org
To provide services and educational programs for those individuals and organizations engaged in theatre in the southeast.
Title of Award: Southeastern Theatre Conference Secondary School Scholarships **Area, Field, or Subject:** Theatre arts. **Level of Education**

for which Award is Granted: Undergraduate **Funds Available:** $2,100. **Eligibility Requirements:** Any high school senior in the southeastern theatre conference region who is planning to attend a college or university in the SETC region with the intent of majoring in Theatre Arts. **Application Requirements:** Applicant must provide the following: An official transcript, along with verification of class rank and available SAT or ACT scores from the high-school guidance counselor or principal; Three completed recommendation forms, with one being from the nominee's high-school principal; The student's completed nominee resume form. **Deadline for Receipt:** January 15. **Additional Information:** SETC at the above address.

2709 ■ SOUTHWEST FLORIDA COMMUNITY FOUNDATION

8260 College Pkwy., Ste. 101
Fort Myers, FL 33919
Tel: (239)274-5900
Fax: (239)274-5930
Web Site: http://www.floridacommunity.com
To fund tuition for graduating seniors pursuing higher education in the fine or performing arts.
Title of Award: George E. Judd Scholarships **Area, Field, or Subject:** Fine arts; Performing arts. **Level of Education for which Award is Granted:** Undergraduate **Funds Available:** $1,000. **Duration:** One year. **Eligibility Requirements:** Applicants must graduate from public or private high school in Lee County and must pursue a degree in the fine or performing arts. **Application Requirements:** Applicants must submit a letter of interest, transcript, and letter of recommendation. Application forms are available online. **Deadline for Receipt:** February 15.

2710 ■ SOUTHWEST FLORIDA COMMUNITY FOUNDATION

8260 College Pkwy., Ste. 101
Fort Myers, FL 33919
Tel: (239)274-5900
Fax: (239)274-5930
Web Site: http://www.floridacommunity.com
To fund tuition for high school seniors who plan to study the arts in an accredited school.
Title of Award: David G. Robinson Arts Scholarships **Area, Field, or Subject:** Arts. **Level of Education for which Award is Granted:** Undergraduate **Funds Available:** $1,000. **Duration:** One year. **Eligibility Requirements:** Applicants must graduate from a public school in Lee County; must be an industrious student with good moral character; must document financial need; and must show leadership and community service. **Application Requirements:** Applicants must submit a letter of interest, transcript, and letter of recommendation. Application forms are available online. **Deadline for Receipt:** February 15.

2711 ■ STEUBEN COUNTY COMMUNITY FOUNDATION

1701 N Wayne St.
Angola, IN 46703
Tel: (260)665-6656
Fax: (260)665-8420
Web Site: http://www.steubenfoundation.org
To provide financial assistance to those students who are in need.
Title of Award: Ed Haas Memorial Scholarships **Area, Field, or Subject:** Education; Humanities; Arts. **Level of Education for which Award is Granted:** Undergraduate **Funds Available:** No specific amount. **Eligibility Requirements:** Applicants must be residents of Steuben County; must be graduating seniors from Angola High School; must be pursuing degree in the field of Education, Humanities or Arts. **Application Requirements:** Applicants must submit any supporting statements from former teachers or supervisors of any paid or volunteer work in your chosen field will be considered; copy of school transcripts; an essay answering the questions "why do you want to pursue a career in Education, Humanities or the Arts?" and "what influenced your decision?" Applicants must check the website for the application process and required materials. **Deadline for Receipt:** March 15. **Additional Information:** Steuben County Community Foundation at the above address.

2712 ■ TAG AND LABEL MANUFACTURERS INSTITUTE

40 Shuman Blvd., Ste. 295
Naperville, IL 60563
Tel: (630)357-9222

Free: 800-533-8564
Fax: (630)357-0192
E-mail: office@tlmi.com
Web Site: http://www.tlmi.com
To promote education in the flexographic industry.
Title of Award: TLMI Scholarships - Four-Year Colleges **Area, Field, or Subject:** Management; Marketing and distribution; Graphic art and design. **Level of Education for which Award is Granted:** Undergraduate **Number Awarded:** 6. **Funds Available:** $5,000. **Eligibility Requirements:** Applicant must be a second or third year full-time college student pursuing a career in the tag and table manufacturing industry; majoring in management, sales/ marketing, graphic arts, graphic design, or production; and must maintain a 3.00 or higher GPA. **Application Requirements:** Applicants must fill out the application online; must prepare a personal statement (one page) on personal information, work experiences, family financial report, career and educational goals and reasons why they deserve the award; a school transcript; three references; and samples of work (not mandatory). **Deadline for Receipt:** January 1-March 31. **Additional Information:** Karen Planzat.

2713 ■ UNITARIAN UNIVERSALIST ASSOCIATION OF CONGREGATIONS

25 Beacon St.
Boston, MA 02108
Tel: (617)742-2100
E-mail: info@uua.org
Web Site: http://www.uua.org
To support Unitarian Universalist students with their educational pursuit.
Title of Award: Pauly D'Orlando Memorial Art Scholarships **Area, Field, or Subject:** Fine arts. **Level of Education for which Award is Granted:** Graduate, Undergraduate **Number Awarded:** Varies. **Funds Available:** Varies. **Duration:** One academic year. **Eligibility Requirements:** Applicant must be a Unitarian Universalist graduate or undergraduate student pursuing a career in fine arts. Performing arts majors are not eligible. **Application Requirements:** Applicants must submit a completed application form along with the supporting documentation. **Additional Information:** Funded by a trust set up by the First Unitarian Church of New Orleans. **Deadline for Receipt:** February 15.

2714 ■ UNITARIAN UNIVERSALIST ASSOCIATION OF CONGREGATIONS

25 Beacon St.
Boston, MA 02108
Tel: (617)742-2100
E-mail: info@uua.org
Web Site: http://www.uua.org
To support Unitarian Universalist students with their educational pursuit.
Title of Award: Marion Barr Stanfield Art Scholarships **Area, Field, or Subject:** Fine arts. **Level of Education for which Award is Granted:** Graduate, Undergraduate **Number Awarded:** Varies. **Funds Available:** Varies. **Duration:** One academic year. **Eligibility Requirements:** Applicant must be a Unitarian Universalist graduate or undergraduate student pursuing a career in fine arts. Performing arts majors are not eligible. **Application Requirements:** Applicants must submit a completed application form along with the supporting documentation. **Deadline for Receipt:** February 15.

2715 ■ U.S.-UKRAINE FOUNDATION

1701 K St. NW Ste. 903
Washington, DC 20006
Tel: (202)223-2228
Fax: (202)223-1224
E-mail: info@usukraine.org
Web Site: http://www.usukraine.org
To support the education of Art students from the Academy of Fine Arts in Kyiv.
Title of Award: Mychajlo Dmytrenko Fine Arts Foundation Scholarships **Area, Field, or Subject:** Fine Arts. **Level of Education for which Award is Granted:** Undergraduate **Funds Available:** No specific amount. **Eligibility Requirements:** Applicants must be art students at the academy of Fine Arts in Kyiv. **Application Requirements:** Applicants must submit a completed application form. **Additional Information:** 1425

La Perla Long Beach CA 90815 USA and look for Mark Dmytrenko, President or call at Tel: 877-813-4591
Fax: 562-986-5770 Email: foundation@dmytrenko.org

2716 ■ UNIVERSITY OF ALASKA ANCHORAGE

3211 Providence Dr.
Anchorage, AK 99508
Tel: (907)786-1800
Web Site: http://www.uaa.alaska.edu
To provide financial assistance for tuition and other related educational expenses to a full-time student attending the University of Alaska Anchorage who are junior-standing art majors.
Title of Award: UAA Emi Chance Memorial Scholarships **Area, Field, or Subject:** Art. **Level of Education for which Award is Granted:** Undergraduate **Funds Available:** No specific amount.
Eligibility Requirements: Applicants must demonstrate motivation, talent, academic, and leadership potential; must have demonstrated a commitment to his/her community; must be in good academic standing with a minimum cumulative GPA of 3.0; must be a full-time student (12 credits) at the University of Alaska Anchorage; must be formally admitted to an art degree-seeking program at the University of Alaska Anchorage; must be a drawing and/or painting major with a junior class standing; must submit one drawing and/or painting with application; may be a U.S. citizen, non-U.S. citizen, Alaska resident, or out-of-state resident; must be enrolled in the semester for which the award is made. **Application Requirements:** Applicants must submit one drawing and/or painting to the UAA Office of Student Financial Assistance. Application forms are available online and must be sent to UAA Office of Student Financial Assistance, EMI Chance Memorial Scholarships, PO Box 141608, AK 99514-1608. **Deadline for Receipt:** February 15.

2717 ■ UNIVERSITY OF ALASKA ANCHORAGE

3211 Providence Dr.
Anchorage, AK 99508
Tel: (907)786-1800
Web Site: http://www.uaa.alaska.edu
To provide financial assistance for tuition and other educational expenses to students who are formally admitted to a degree-seeking program within the College of Arts & Sciences at the University of Alaska Anchorage.
Title of Award: UAA Jack & Martha Roderick Scholarships **Area, Field, or Subject:** Art; Science. **Level of Education for which Award is Granted:** Graduate, Undergraduate **Number Awarded:** 2. **Funds Available:** $500-$1,000. **Duration:** One academic year.
Eligibility Requirements: Applicants must be in good academic standing with a minimum cumulative GPA of 2.0 for undergraduates and 3.0 for graduates; must be formally admitted to an undergraduate, graduate, and/or certificate degree-seeking program within the College of Arts & Science at the University of Alaska Anchorage; must plan on enrolling at least part-time (six credits for undergraduate or five for graduate) at the University of the Alaska Anchorage; may be a U.S citizen, non-U.S citizen, Alaska resident, or out-of-state resident; must be able to demonstrate financial need; must be enrolled in the semester for which the award is made. **Application Requirements:** Application forms are available at www.uaa.alaska.edu/scholarships/jack.cfm. **Deadline for Receipt:** February 15.

2718 ■ UNIVERSITY OF ALASKA ANCHORAGE

3211 Providence Dr.
Anchorage, AK 99508
Tel: (907)786-1800
Web Site: http://www.uaa.alaska.edu
To provide financial assistance for tuition and other educational expenses to full-time junior or senior students who are formally admitted into a Bachelor of Arts or Bachelor of Fine Arts program in the area of sculpture and/or performance art at the University of Alaska Anchorage.
Title of Award: UAA Ken Gray Endowment Scholarships **Area, Field, or Subject:** Performing arts, Sculpture. **Level of Education for which Award is Granted:** Undergraduate **Funds Available:** $500-$800.
Eligibility Requirements: Applicants must exhibit an innovative, experimental, and conceptual direction in his/her artwork that stretches the limits of traditional sculpture; must demonstrate motivation, academic and leadership potential; must be in good academic standing with a minimum cumulative GPA of 3.25 and a cumulative GPA of 3.5 in the area

of concentration; must formally be admitted to a Bachelor of Arts or Bachelor of Fine Arts at the University of Alaska Anchorage; must plan on enrolling full-time at the University of Alaska Anchorage; must submit a portfolio of work consisting of twenty slides, three letters of reference from practitioners in the sculpture area and/or faculty, and a two-page artist's statement reflecting the criteria for selection; must be enrolled in the semester for which the award is made; may be a U.S. citizen, non-U.S. citizen, Alaska resident, or out-of-state resident. **Application Requirements:** Applicants must submit a portfolio of work consisting of 20 slides; must have three letters of reference from practitioners in the sculpture area and/or UAA faculty; must have a two-page artist's statement reflecting the criteria for selection. Application materials must be sent to UAA Office of Student Financial Assistance, Ken Gray Scholarships, PO Box 141608, Anchorage, AK 99514-1608. **Deadline for Receipt:** February 15.

2719 ■ UNIVERSITY OF ALASKA ANCHORAGE

3211 Providence Dr.
Anchorage, AK 99508
Tel: (907)786-1800
Web Site: http://www.uaa.alaska.edu
To provide financial assistance for tuition and other related educational expenses to full-time students at the University of Alaska Anchorage with a declared major in art or journalism & public communications.
Title of Award: UAA Kimura Scholarship Fund (Photography Scholarships) **Area, Field, or Subject:** Art; Journalism; Photography. **Level of Education for which Award is Granted:** Undergraduate **Number Awarded:** 2. **Funds Available:** No specific amount.
Eligibility Requirements: Applicant must be a full-time student attending the University of Alaska Anchorage with a declared major in art or with a declared major in journalism & public communication with an emphasis in photography; must be in their junior year and has completed at least nine credits in studio photography classes at the 200 level or above; must be in good academic standing with at least a 3.0 GPA. **Application Requirements:** Applicants must submit a proof of their photography work. Application documents and other supporting documents must submit to UAA Office of Student Financial Assistance, Kimura Scholarships, PO Box 141608, Anchorage, AK 99514. **Deadline for Receipt:** February 15.

2720 ■ UNIVERSITY OF ALASKA ANCHORAGE

3211 Providence Dr.
Anchorage, AK 99508
Tel: (907)786-1800
Web Site: http://www.uaa.alaska.edu
To provide financial assistance for tuition and other related educational expenses to full-time students at the University of Alaska Anchorage with a declared major in art or journalism & public communications.
Title of Award: UAA Kimura Scholarship Funds (Illustration Scholarships) **Area, Field, or Subject:** Art; Journalism; Illustrators and illustrations. **Level of Education for which Award is Granted:** Undergraduate **Number Awarded:** 2. **Funds Available:** No specific amount.
Eligibility Requirements: Applicants must be a full-time student (12 credits per semester) attending the University of Alaska Anchorage with a declared major in art with an emphasis in illustration; must be in their junior year and have completed at least nine credits in illustration classes at the 200 level or above; must be in good academic standing with at least a 3.0 GPA. **Application Requirements:** Applicants must submit a proof of their photography work. Application documents and other supporting documents must submit to UAA Office of Student Financial Assistance, Kimura Scholarships, PO Box 141608, Anchorage, AK 99514. **Deadline for Receipt:** February 15.

2721 ■ UNIVERSITY OF ALASKA ANCHORAGE

3211 Providence Dr.
Anchorage, AK 99508
Tel: (907)786-1800
Web Site: http://www.uaa.alaska.edu
To provide financial assistance for tuition and other educational expenses to full-time students who are formally admitted to a degreeseeking program at the University of Alaska Anchorage and who have a demonstrated talent in art.
Title of Award: UAA Muriel Hannah Scholarships in Art **Area, Field, or Subject:** Art. **Level of Education for which Award is Granted:** Undergraduate **Funds Available:** $500-$1,000.

Eligibility Requirements: Applicants must demonstrate motivation, academic and leadership potential; must be in good academic standing with a minimum cumulative GPA of 2.0 for undergraduate and 3.0 for graduate; must be formally admitted to an undergraduate, graduate, certificate, and/or vocational degree-seeking program at the University of Alaska Anchorage; must plan on enrolling full-time (12 credits) for undergraduate and (nine credits) for graduate at the University of Alaska Anchorage; must be able to demonstrate a talent in art; must be enrolled in the semester for which the award is made; must be an incoming or continuing student at the University of Alaska Anchorage; must be a U.S. citizen, non-U.S. citizen, Alaska resident, or out-of-state resident. **Application Requirements:** Applicants must provide ten (10) slides of artwork to demonstrate their talent in art. Application forms are available at the website and must be sent to UAA Office of Student Financial Assistance, PO Box 141608, Anchorage, AK 99514-1608. **Deadline for Receipt:** February 15.

2722 ■ UNIVERSITY OF ALASKA ANCHORAGE

3211 Providence Dr.
Anchorage, AK 99508
Tel: (907)786-1800
Web Site: http://www.uaa.alaska.edu
To provide an annual scholarship to art majors at the University of Alaska Anchorage.
Title of Award: UAA Paul G. Landis Scholarships **Area, Field, or Subject:** Art. **Level of Education for which Award is Granted:** Undergraduate **Funds Available:** $1,000. **Duration:** One year.
Eligibility Requirements: Applicants must demonstrate motivation, talent, academic, and leadership potential; must be in good academic standing with a minimum cumulative GPA of 2.0; must be attending at least part-time (6 credits); must be formally admitted to an art degree-seeking program at the University of Alaska Anchorage; must submit one drawing and/ or painting; may be a U.S citizen, non-U.S citizen, Alaska resident, or out-of-state resident; must be enrolled in the semester for which the award is made. **Application Requirements:** Applicant must submit ten (10) visual examples of their art work in slides or digital imagery using CD ROM/DVD formats; must submit a brief statement (125 words max) indicating the conceptual and formal direction pertinent to the student's current body of work. **Deadline for Receipt:** February 15.

2723 ■ UNIVERSITY OF OREGON

1217 University of Oregon
Eugene, OR 97403
Tel: (541)346-1000
Free: 800-232-3825
Fax: (541)346-5815
E-mail: stl@uoregon.edu
Web Site: http://www.uoregon.edu
To provide financial support to students who desire to further their education without financial burden.
Title of Award: Robert W. and Bernice Ingalls Staton Scholarships **Area, Field, or Subject:** Humanities; Fine arts; Education; Music. **Level of Education for which Award is Granted:** Undergraduate **Funds Available:** $5,000. **Duration:** One year.
Eligibility Requirements: Applicants must be Oregon residents and must have an extraordinary financial need. **Application Requirements:** Applicants must submit the Admission application available online to the Office of Admission. **Deadline for Receipt:** January 15.

2724 ■ WOMEN'S JEWELRY ASSOCIATION

7000 W Southwest Hwy.
Chicago Ridge, IL 60415
Tel: (708)361-6000
Fax: (708)361-6166
E-mail: info@womensjewelry.org
Web Site: http://www.womensjewelry.org
To provide educational financial assistance for students in the international jewelry, watch and related industries.
Title of Award: Women's Jewelry Association Scholarships **Area, Field, or Subject:** Fashion design; Design. **Level of Education for which Award is Granted:** Undergraduate **Funds Available:** A total amount of $25,000 is available.
Eligibility Requirements: Applicants must be students enrolled in fine jewelry and watch design courses in the United States. **Application**

Requirements: Applicants must submit a completed application form to the WJA Scholarship Committee. **Additional Information:** Lisa Slovis, Student Scholarship Committee Chair.

2725 ■ YOUNG MENSWEAR ASSOCIATION

36 W 20th St., 3rd Fl.
New York, NY 10011
Tel: (212)594-6422
E-mail: hharrison@ymafashionscholarshipfund.org
Web Site: http://the-yma.com
To promote education in the fashion industry.
Title of Award: YMA Fashion Scholarships **Area, Field, or Subject:** Fashion design; Business. **Level of Education for which Award is Granted:** Undergraduate **Funds Available:** No specific amount.
Eligibility Requirements: Applicant must be a full-time junior or senior student with a GPA of 3.0 or above in a 4.0 GPA system. **Application Requirements:** Educators can nominate up to eight applicants per school. Nominated applicants must submit all the student records and transcript; and an essay. For Design students, submit a portfolio (at least 2 designs/projects) not to exceed 8 1/2"x 11" folder size. For Business students, submit a project about merchandising, marketing or finance not to exceed 8 1/2"x 11" folder size. Application form is to be sent electronically to hharrison@ymafashionscholarshipfund.org; a box per school containing all other materials of the applicants must be sent to: The YMA Fashion Scholarship Fund, 36 West 20th St., 3rd Fl., New York, NY 10011. **Deadline for Receipt:** January 15.

Fine Arts

2726 ■ LEWIS-CLARK STATE COLLEGE

500 8th Ave.
Lewiston, ID 83501
Tel: (208)792-5272
Web Site: http://www.lcsc.edu
To inspire educational pursuits among less capable individuals by providing financial assistance.
Title of Award: Lewis-Clark State College Presidential Technical Out-of-State Scholarships **Area, Field, or Subject:** Chemistry; Computer Science; Engineering; Information Systems Analysis; Industrial Electronics; Biology; Earth Information Systems; Radiology; Heating/Air Conditioning; Automated Manufacturing Technology; Mathematics; Printing Technology; Graphic Arts or Web Development. **Level of Education for which Award is Granted:** Undergraduate **Funds Available:** No specific amount.
Eligibility Requirements: Applicants must be new non-resident high school or transfer students who have at least 14 transferable semester credits. **Application Requirements:** Applicants must accomplish a general application available in the website. **Deadline for Receipt:** March 1 for Fall enrollment or November 1 for Spring enrollment.

Language and Literature

2727 ■ AMERICAN INSTITUTE OF POLISH CULTURE

1440 79th St. Causeway, Ste. 117
Miami, FL 33141
Tel: (305)864-2349
Fax: (305)865-5150
E-mail: info@ampolinstitute.org
Web Site: http://www.ampolinstitute.org
To provide financial support American students of Polish descent who wish to continue their education after high school.
Title of Award: Harriet Irsay Scholarships **Area, Field, or Subject:** Communications; Education; Media arts; History; International affairs and relations; Journalism; Liberal arts; Polish studies; Public relations. **Level of Education for which Award is Granted:** Graduate, Undergraduate **Number Awarded:** 10-15. **Funds Available:** $1,000.
Eligibility Requirements: Applicants must be of Polish heritage; an American citizen or permanent resident; full-time graduate or undergraduate students in the field of communication, education, film, history, International Relation, journalism, liberal arts, polish studies, public relations; or graduate student in business programs with a thesis related to

Poland, or graduate students with a thesis with Polish subject. **Application Requirements:** Applicants must submit a completed application form; school transcripts; resume; essay (200-400 words) about "Why should I receive the scholarship"; an article about Poland (maximum of 700 words); and 3 signed recommendation letters on a letterhead stationary from teachers or other person knowledgeable about the applicant's academic background. A non-refundable $10 processing fee (check or money order) must also be included. **Deadline for Receipt:** April 20.

2728 ■ AMERICAN QUARTER HORSE YOUTH ASSOCIATION

PO Box 200
Amarillo, TX 79168
Tel: (806)376-4811
Web Site: http://www.aqha.com/youth.html
To develop and educate the future professionals.
Title of Award: American Quarter Horse Foundation Scholarships **Area, Field, or Subject:** Education; Nursing; Journalism; Veterinary science and medicine. **Level of Education for which Award is Granted:** Undergraduate **Funds Available:** No specific amount.
Eligibility Requirements: An applicant must be enrolled in college specializing degree programs such as education, nursing, journalism, veterinary and racing. **Application Requirements:** Applicant must fill out the application form and submit proof that he/she is currently enrolled in a college or university. **Deadline for Receipt:** not stated. **Additional Information:** 806-378-5000.

2729 ■ AMERICAN RADIO RELAY LEAGUE (ARRL) FOUNDATION

225 Main St.
Newington, CT 06111
Tel: (860)594-0200
Fax: (860)594-0259
E-mail: foundation@arrl.org
Web Site: http://www.arrlf.org
To support the education of students holding a valid FCC-granted Amateur Radio license for post-secondary education.
Title of Award: PHD ARA Scholarships **Area, Field, or Subject:** Radio and television; Journalism; Computer and information sciences; Electronics. **Level of Education for which Award is Granted:** Undergraduate **Number Awarded:** 1. **Funds Available:** $500.
Eligibility Requirements: Applicant must hold an FCC amateur radio license; be a resident of ARRL Midwest Division (IA, KS, MO, NE); with course sof study in journalism, computer science or electronic engineering; and be the child of a deceased radio amateur. **Application Requirements:** Applicants must submit a completed scholarship application form along with a recent high school (or equivalent) or college transcript. **Deadline for Receipt:** February 1.

2730 ■ ARAB AMERICAN INSTITUTE

1600 K St. NW, Ste. 601
Washington, DC 20006
Tel: (202)429-9210
Fax: (202)429-9214
E-mail: aai@aaiusa.org
Web Site: http://www.aaiusa.org
To provide scholarship opportunity to the American students who are Arab descent.
Title of Award: Al Muammar Scholarships for Journalism **Area, Field, or Subject:** Journalism. **Level of Education for which Award is Granted:** Undergraduate **Funds Available:** $5,000.
Eligibility Requirements: Applicants must: be Arab American, college students who are majoring in journalism, as well as college seniors who have been accepted to a graduate journalism school; be a UC citizen or permanent resident of Arab descent; be a full-time student at an accredited college or university in the United States; have current GPA of 3.3 or higher. **Application Requirements:** Applicant may download an application from the Foundation's website. Applicant must also include an official transcript and letter of recommendation (one letter must be from the professor in the applicant's journalism program and second would be ideally be from a leader in an Arab American community organization with which the applicant has had a relationship). Applicant must send five copies of the following items, collated into five complete packets, each with one copy of each item, in the following order: Completed application form; Unofficial transcript; Resume; Short Essay; Work samples. **Deadline for**

Receipt: March 3. **Additional Information:** Al Muammar Scholarship Administrator, Arab American Institute Foundation, 1600 K St. NW Ste. 600 Washington, DC 20006.

2731 ■ ARAB AMERICAN INSTITUTE

1600 K St. NW, Ste. 601
Washington, DC 20006
Tel: (202)429-9210
Fax: (202)429-9214
E-mail: aai@aaiusa.org
Web Site: http://www.aaiusa.org
To promote academic excellence and to provide an opportunity for outstanding student to reach their fullest potential.
Title of Award: Ameen Rihani Scholarship Program **Area, Field, or Subject:** Literature; Philosophy; Political science. **Level of Education for which Award is Granted:** Undergraduate **Funds Available:** $1,500.
Eligibility Requirements: Individual must: be a Lebanese or other Arab Descent; be a citizen or legal permanent residents of the United States; have attained a cumulative GPA of 3.25 on a 4.0 scale; enter a college or university as a full-time, degree-seeking freshman in the fall of the year; have demonstrated leadership abilities through participation in community service, extracurricular or other activities. **Application Requirements:** Teachers, counselors, and principals are invited to nominate students with outstanding academic qualifications, particularly those who would promote success in the fields of literature, philosophy, or political science. **Deadline for Receipt:** May 31. **Additional Information:** Ameen Rihani Scholarship Program, The Ameen Rihani Organization, 1010 Wayne Ave. Ste 420 Silver Spring, MD 20910.

2732 ■ ARMENIAN RELIEF SOCIETY - EASTERN UNITED STATES

80 Bigelow Avenue, Ste. 200
Watertown, MA 02472
Tel: (617)926-3801
Fax: (617)924-7238
E-mail: arseastus@aol.com
Web Site: http://www.arseastus.com
To encourage educational pursuits among undergraduate students of Armenian descent.
Title of Award: ARS Undergraduate Scholarships **Area, Field, or Subject:** Law; History; Political science; Journalism; Government; Economics; Business administration; Medicine; Public service. **Level of Education for which Award is Granted:** Four Year College, Two Year College, Undergraduate **Funds Available:** No specific amount. **Duration:** One year.
Eligibility Requirements: Applicants must be of Armenian descent; must be undergraduate students who have completed at least one semester at an accredited four-year college or university in the United States or must be enrolled in a two-year college and are transferring to a four-year college or university as a full-time student in the Fall. **Application Requirements:** Application must include financial aid forms, recent official transcript, two letters of recommendation and tuition costs. Forward materials to: Scholarship Committee, Armenian Relief Society of Eastern USA, Inc., 80 Bigelow Ave., Ste. 200, Watertown, MA 02472. **Deadline for Receipt:** April 1.

2733 ■ ARMENIAN STUDENTS' ASSOCIATION OF AMERICA

333 Atlantic Ave.
Warwick, RI 02888
Tel: (401)461-6114
E-mail: asa@asainc.org
Web Site: http://www.asainc.org
To provide financial assistance to those students who are in need.
Title of Award: Garikian Scholarship Fund **Area, Field, or Subject:** Armenian Studies; Sociology; Psychology; Political Science; Middle Eastern History; Journalism; Education; Music. **Level of Education for which Award is Granted:** Undergraduate **Funds Available:** $750-$1,000.
Eligibility Requirements: Applicants must have completed their first academic year in college or university in California; must be pursuing one of the above field of studies. **Application Requirements:** Applicants must apply to the Executive Board for application forms and return them, completed, before the deadline. **Deadline for Receipt:** August 31. **Additional Information:** Berj S. Baghdoyan c/o Western Prelacy at 4401 Russell Avenue, Los Angeles, CA 90027.

2734 ■ ASIAN AMERICAN JOURNALISTS ASSOCIATION

1182 Market St., Ste. 320
San Francisco, CA 94102
Tel: (415)346-2051
Fax: (415)346-6343
E-mail: national@aaja.org
Web Site: http://www.aaja.org
To provide financial assistance to students majoring in broadcast or online journalism.
Title of Award: AAJA/CNN Scholar Program **Area, Field, or Subject:** Journalism; Broadcasting. **Level of Education for which Award is Granted:** Graduate, Undergraduate **Number Awarded:** 4. **Funds Available:** $25,000. **Duration:** Four years.
Eligibility Requirements: Applicants must be graduating high school senior, undergraduate or graduate student enrolled full time with at least 12 credit units for each semester; must be currently taking or planning to take journalism courses. **Application Requirements:** Applicants must submit the completed application form; a resume; an official transcript; two letters of recommendation; a short essay, not exceeding 500 words, on the topic: "Describe any involvement or interest that you have in the Asian American community. If you were awarded an AAJA scholarship, propose how you would contribute to the field of journalism and/or media issues involving the Asian American and Pacific Islander community." **Deadline for Receipt:** March 28. **Additional Information:** Nao Vang; AAJA Student Programs Coordinator; 415-346-2051; programs@aaja.org.

2735 ■ ASIAN AMERICAN JOURNALISTS ASSOCIATION

1182 Market St., Ste. 320
San Francisco, CA 94102
Tel: (415)346-2051
Fax: (415)346-6343
E-mail: national@aaja.org
Web Site: http://www.aaja.org
To assist students who are interested in pursuing a career in print, broadcast, or photojournalism.
Title of Award: AAJA/COX Foundation Scholarships **Area, Field, or Subject:** Journalism; Broadcasting; Photography, Journalistic. **Level of Education for which Award is Granted:** Graduate, Undergraduate **Number Awarded:** 1. **Funds Available:** $1,250.
Eligibility Requirements: Applicants must be graduating high school senior, undergraduate or graduate student enrolled full time with at least 12 credit units for each semester; must be currently taking or planning to take journalism courses. **Application Requirements:** Applicants must submit the completed application form; a resume; an official transcript; two letters of recommendation; a short essay, not exceeding 500 words, on the topic: "Describe any involvement or interest that you have in the Asian American community. If you were awarded an AAJA scholarship, propose how you would contribute to the field of journalism and/or media issues involving the Asian American and Pacific Islander community." **Deadline for Receipt:** March 28. **Additional Information:** Nao Vang; AAJA Student Programs Coordinator; 415-346-2051; programs@aaja.org.

2736 ■ ASIAN AMERICAN JOURNALISTS ASSOCIATION

1182 Market St., Ste. 320
San Francisco, CA 94102
Tel: (415)346-2051
Fax: (415)346-6343
E-mail: national@aaja.org
Web Site: http://www.aaja.org
To provide educational funds to students pursuing a career in print journalism.
Title of Award: AAJA/S.I. Newhouse Foundation Scholarships **Area, Field, or Subject:** Journalism. **Level of Education for which Award is Granted:** Graduate, Undergraduate **Funds Available:** $5,000.
Eligibility Requirements: Applicants must be graduating high school senior, undergraduate or graduate student enrolled full time with at least 12 credit units for each semester; must be currently taking or planning to take journalism courses. **Application Requirements:** Applicants must submit the completed application form; a resume; an official transcript; two letters of recommendation; a short essay, not exceeding 500 words, on the topic: "Describe any involvement or interest that you have in the Asian American community. If you were awarded an AAJA scholarship, propose how you would contribute to the field of journalism and/or media issues

involving the Asian American and Pacific Islander community." **Deadline for Receipt:** March 28. **Additional Information:** Nao Vang; AAJA Student Programs Coordinator; 415-346-2051; programs@aaja.org.

2737 ■ ASSOCIATION OF ELECTRONIC JOURNALISTS

4121 Plank Rd., Ste. 512
Fredericksburg, VA 22407
Tel: (202)659-6510
Fax: (202)223-4007
E-mail: barbarac@rtnda.org
Web Site: http://www.rtnda.org
To help RTNDF members embody and uphold the standards of ethical journalism. To promote leadership in the newsroom.
Title of Award: Association of Electronic Journalists President's Scholarships **Area, Field, or Subject:** Journalism. **Level of Education for which Award is Granted:** Undergraduate **Number Awarded:** 2. **Funds Available:** $2,500.
Eligibility Requirements: Applicants must be currently enrolled as college sophomores, juniors, and seniors in good standing. **Application Requirements:** Applicant must complete the application form and provide evidence proving that he/she is currently enrolled. Applicants must submit one to three examples showing journalistic skills, totaling 15 minutes of editing and producing, and a list of colleagues; a one-page statement explaining why applicant seeks a career in electronic journalism; and a letter of reference from the dean or faculty sponsor. **Additional Information:** stacey@rtnda.org; 202-467-5205.

2738 ■ ASSOCIATION OF ELECTRONIC JOURNALISTS

4121 Plank Rd., Ste. 512
Fredericksburg, VA 22407
Tel: (202)659-6510
Fax: (202)223-4007
E-mail: barbarac@rtnda.org
Web Site: http://www.rtnda.org
To recognize a promising minority journalist in radio or television news.
Title of Award: N.S. Beinstock Fellowships **Area, Field, or Subject:** Journalism. **Level of Education for which Award is Granted:** Undergraduate **Funds Available:** $2,500.
Eligibility Requirements: Applicants must be journalism students or senior broadcast news and mid-career professionals. **Application Requirements:** Applicants must complete the application form. Applicants must submit a resume; a cover letter with the reasons for seeking a fellowship and how the award will be used; a letter of recommendation from the news manager; a sample of the best work relevant to the fellowship, not exceeding 15 minutes on audio (cassette or CD) or video (VHS or DVD), and accompanied by scripts. International applications must include a full English translation. **Deadline for Receipt:** May 12. **Additional Information:** 202-467-5205; staceys@rtnda.org.

2739 ■ ASSOCIATION OF ELECTRONIC JOURNALISTS

4121 Plank Rd., Ste. 512
Fredericksburg, VA 22407
Tel: (202)659-6510
Fax: (202)223-4007
E-mail: barbarac@rtnda.org
Web Site: http://www.rtnda.org
To help RTNDF members embody and uphold the standards of ethical journalism; to promote leadership in the newsroom.
Title of Award: Ed Bradley Scholarships **Area, Field, or Subject:** Journalism. **Level of Education for which Award is Granted:** Undergraduate **Funds Available:** $10,000.
Eligibility Requirements: Applicants must be enrolled in radio and television news. Applicants must be full-time college students with at least one full year of college remaining whose career objective is to enter into the electronic journalism field. **Application Requirements:** Applicant must complete the application form and provide evidence proving that he/she is currently enrolled. Applicants must submit one to three examples showing their journalistic skills, totaling 15 minutes of editing and producing, and a list of colleagues; a one-page statement explaining why they seek a career in electronic journalism; a letter of reference from the dean or faculty sponsor. **Additional Information:** stacey@rtnda.org; 202-467-5205.

2740 ■ ASSOCIATION OF ELECTRONIC JOURNALISTS
4121 Plank Rd., Ste. 512
Fredericksburg, VA 22407
Tel: (202)659-6510
Fax: (202)223-4007
E-mail: barbarac@rtnda.org
Web Site: http://www.rtnda.org
To send journalists of color to leadership and management training programs.
Title of Award: Broadcast News Management Fellowships **Area, Field, or Subject:** Journalism. **Level of Education for which Award is Granted:** Undergraduate **Funds Available:** No specific amount.
Eligibility Requirements: Applicants must be senior broadcast news and mid-career professionals. **Application Requirements:** Applicants must submit an application form. Applicant must submit a letter of recommendation from his or her supervisor. **Additional Information:** melaniel@rtnda.org; 202-467-5218.

2741 ■ ASSOCIATION OF ELECTRONIC JOURNALISTS
4121 Plank Rd., Ste. 512
Fredericksburg, VA 22407
Tel: (202)659-6510
Fax: (202)223-4007
E-mail: barbarac@rtnda.org
Web Site: http://www.rtnda.org
To honor women journalists in television news.
Title of Award: Michelle Clark Fellowships **Area, Field, or Subject:** Journalism. **Level of Education for which Award is Granted:** Undergraduate **Funds Available:** $1,000.
Eligibility Requirements: Applicants must be journalism students or senior broadcast news and midcareer professionals. **Application Requirements:** Applicants must complete the application form. Applicants must submit a resume; a cover letter with the reasons for seeking a fellowship and how the award will be used; a letter of recommendation from the news manager; a sample of the best work relevant to the fellowship, not exceeding 15 minutes on audio (cassette or CD) or video (VHS or DVD) and accompanied by scripts. International applications must include a full English translation. **Deadline for Receipt:** May 12. **Additional Information:** 202-467-5205; staceys@rtnda.org.

2742 ■ ASSOCIATION OF ELECTRONIC JOURNALISTS
4121 Plank Rd., Ste. 512
Fredericksburg, VA 22407
Tel: (202)659-6510
Fax: (202)223-4007
E-mail: barbarac@rtnda.org
Web Site: http://www.rtnda.org
To help RTNDF members embody and uphold the standards of ethical journalism. To promote leadership in the newsroom.
Title of Award: George Foreman Tribute to Lyndon B. Johnson Scholarships **Area, Field, or Subject:** Journalism. **Level of Education for which Award is Granted:** Undergraduate **Funds Available:** $6,000.
Eligibility Requirements: Applicants must be journalism students at the University of Texas-Austin. **Application Requirements:** Applicant must complete the application form and provide evidence proving that he/she is currently enrolled. Applicants must submit a copy of their FAFSA Student Aid Report (SAR). Applicants must submit one to three examples showing journalistic skills, totaling 15 minutes of editing and producing, and a list of colleagues; a one-page statement explaining why applicant seeks a career in electronic journalism; and a letter of reference from the dean or faculty sponsor. **Additional Information:** stacey@rtnda.org; 202-467-5205.

2743 ■ ASSOCIATION OF ELECTRONIC JOURNALISTS
4121 Plank Rd., Ste. 512
Fredericksburg, VA 22407
Tel: (202)659-6510
Fax: (202)223-4007
E-mail: barbarac@rtnda.org
Web Site: http://www.rtnda.org
To help RTNDF members embody and uphold the standards of ethical journalism. To promote leadership in the newsroom.
Title of Award: Ken Kashiwara Scholarships **Area, Field, or Subject:** Journalism. **Level of Education for which Award is Granted:** Undergraduate **Funds Available:** $2,500.

Eligibility Requirements: Applicants must be enrolled in radio and television news. Applicants must be full-time college students whose career objective is to enter the electronic journalism field. Applicants must have at least one full year of college remaining. **Application Requirements:** Applicant must complete the application form and provide evidence proving that he/she is currently enrolled. Applicants must submit one to three examples showing journalistic skills, totaling 15 minutes of editing and producing, and a list of colleagues; a one-page statement explaining why applicant seeks a career in electronic journalism; a letter of reference from the dean or faculty sponsor . **Additional Information:** stacey@rtnda.org; 202-467-5205.

2744 ■ ASSOCIATION OF ELECTRONIC JOURNALISTS
4121 Plank Rd., Ste. 512
Fredericksburg, VA 22407
Tel: (202)659-6510
Fax: (202)223-4007
E-mail: barbarac@rtnda.org
Web Site: http://www.rtnda.org
To recognize excellence in health or medical television and radio reporting.
Title of Award: Jacque I. Minnotte Health Reporting Fellowships **Area, Field, or Subject:** Journalism. **Level of Education for which Award is Granted:** Undergraduate **Funds Available:** $2,000.
Eligibility Requirements: Applicants must be journalism students or senior broadcast news and mid-career professionals. **Application Requirements:** Applicants must complete the application form. Applicants must submit a resume; a cover letter with the reasons for seeking a fellowship and how the award will be used; a letter of recommendation from the news manager; a sample of the best work relevant to the fellowship, not exceeding 15 minutes on audio (cassette or CD) or video (VHS or DVD) and accompanied by scripts. International applications must include a full English translation. **Deadline for Receipt:** May 12. **Additional Information:** 202-467-5205; staceys@rtnda.org.

2745 ■ ASSOCIATION OF ELECTRONIC JOURNALISTS
4121 Plank Rd., Ste. 512
Fredericksburg, VA 22407
Tel: (202)659-6510
Fax: (202)223-4007
E-mail: barbarac@rtnda.org
Web Site: http://www.rtnda.org
To help RTNDF members embody and uphold the standards of ethical journalism. To promote leadership in the newsroom.
Title of Award: Lou and Carole Prato Sports Reporting Scholarships **Area, Field, or Subject:** Journalism. **Level of Education for which Award is Granted:** Undergraduate **Funds Available:** $1,000.
Eligibility Requirements: Applicants must be students pursuing a career as a sports reporter in television or radio. **Application Requirements:** Applicant must complete the application form and provide evidence proving that he/she is currently enrolled. Applicants must submit one to three examples showing journalistic skills, totaling 15 minutes of editing and producing, and a list of colleagues; a one-page statement explaining why applicant seeks a career in electronic journalism; and a letter of reference from the dean or faculty sponsor. **Additional Information:** stacey@rtnda.org; 202-467-5205.

2746 ■ ASSOCIATION OF ELECTRONIC JOURNALISTS
4121 Plank Rd., Ste. 512
Fredericksburg, VA 22407
Tel: (202)659-6510
Fax: (202)223-4007
E-mail: barbarac@rtnda.org
Web Site: http://www.rtnda.org
To help RTNDF members embody and uphold the standards of ethical journalism. To promote leadership in the newsroom.
Title of Award: Nike Reynolds Journalism Scholarships **Area, Field, or Subject:** Journalism. **Level of Education for which Award is Granted:** Undergraduate **Funds Available:** $1,000.
Eligibility Requirements: Applicants must be currently enrolled in journalism school and have good writing abilities, excellent grades, and a dedication to the news business. Applicants must have strong interest in pursuing electronic journalism. Applicants must have demonstrated

financial need. **Application Requirements:** Applicant must complete the application form and provide evidence proving that he/she is currently enrolled. Applicants must submit a copy of their FAFSA Student Aid Report (SAR). Applicants must submit one to three examples showing journalistic skills, totaling 15 minutes of editing and producing, and a list of colleagues; a one-page statement explaining why applicant seeks a career in electronic journalism; and a letter of reference from the dean or faculty sponsor. **Additional Information:** stacey@rtnda.org; 202-467-5205.

2747 ■ ASSOCIATION OF ELECTRONIC JOURNALISTS
4121 Plank Rd., Ste. 512
Fredericksburg, VA 22407
Tel: (202)659-6510
Fax: (202)223-4007
E-mail: barbarac@rtnda.org
Web Site: http://www.rtnda.org
To help RTNDF members embody and uphold the standards of ethical journalism. To promote leadership in the newsroom. To encourage and help minority students overcome hurdles along their career path.
Title of Award: Carole Simpson Scholarships **Area, Field, or Subject:** Journalism. **Level of Education for which Award is Granted:** Undergraduate **Funds Available:** $2,000.
Eligibility Requirements: Applicants must be enrolled in radio and television news; applicants must be full-time college students whose career objective is to enter the electronic journalism field and who have at least one full year of college remaining. **Application Requirements:** Applicant must complete the application form and provide evidence proving that he/she is currently enrolled. Applicants must submit one to three examples showing journalistic skills, totaling 15 minutes of editing and producing, and a list of colleagues; a one-page statement explaining why applicant seeks a career in electronic journalism; and a letter of reference from the dean or faculty sponsor. **Additional Information:** stacey@rtnda.org; 202-467-5205.

2748 ■ ASSOCIATION OF ELECTRONIC JOURNALISTS
4121 Plank Rd., Ste. 512
Fredericksburg, VA 22407
Tel: (202)659-6510
Fax: (202)223-4007
E-mail: barbarac@rtnda.org
Web Site: http://www.rtnda.org
To help RTNDF members embody and uphold the standards of ethical journalism. To promote leadership in the newsroom.
Title of Award: Pete Wilson Journalism Scholarships **Area, Field, or Subject:** Journalism. **Level of Education for which Award is Granted:** Undergraduate **Funds Available:** $4,000.
Eligibility Requirements: Applicants must be full-time undergraduate or graduate students who plan to work in the electronic journalism field in the San Francisco Bay area. **Application Requirements:** Applicant must complete the application form and provide evidence proving that he/she is currently enrolled. Applicants must submit one to three examples showing journalistic skills, totaling 15 minutes of editing and producing, and a list of colleagues; a one-page statement explaining why applicant seeks a career in electronic journalism; and a letter of reference from the dean or faculty sponsor. **Additional Information:** stacey@rtnda.org; 202-467-5205.

2749 ■ BLUES HEAVEN FOUNDATION
2120 S Michigan Ave.
Chicago, IL 60616
Tel: (312)808-1286
Fax: (312)808-0273
E-mail: info@bluesheaven.com
Web Site: http://www.bluesheaven.com
To provide financial assistance to students in Chicago.
Title of Award: Muddy Waters Scholarships **Area, Field, or Subject:** Music education, music, African-American studies, folklore, performing arts, journalism, radio and television. **Level of Education for which Award is Granted:** Undergraduate **Funds Available:** NO specific amount.
Eligibility Requirements: Applicant must have a full-time enrollment status in a Chicago area college or university; must be in at least their first year of undergraduate studies or graduate program. **Application Requirements:** Application form are available in the website address; must be sent to: Blues Heaven Foundation Inc., 2120 S Michigan Ave., Chicago, IL 60616. **Deadline for Receipt:** April 30.

2750 ■ BOWLING WRITERS ASSOCIATION OF AMERICA
8501 N Manor Ln.
Fox Point, WI 53217
Tel: (414)351-6085
E-mail: sjames2652@wi.rr.com
Web Site: http://www.bowlingwriters.com
To provide financial support for students pursuing a career in communications that involve the sport of bowling.
Title of Award: Chuck Pezzano Scholarships **Area, Field, or Subject:** Communication; Sports writing. **Level of Education for which Award is Granted:** Undergraduate **Funds Available:** $1000.
Eligibility Requirements: Applicants must have a minimum of 2.5 GPA; must be a high school or vocational school senior or college student. **Application Requirements:** Applicant must send application form (available at the website); transcript; at least one reference letter; and any other information to support your application. **Additional Information:** Established in honor of Chuck Pezzano a BWAA, American Bowling Congress and Professional Bowlers Association Hall of Fame journalist. **Deadline for Receipt:** May 15. **Additional Information:** Steve James, Executive Director

2751 ■ CANADIAN ASSOCIATION OF BROADCASTERS
PO Box 627, Sta. B
Ottawa, ON, Canada K1P 1A4
Tel: (613)233-4035
Fax: (613)233-6961
E-mail: cab@cab-acr.ca
Web Site: http://www.cab-acr.ca
To provide financial assistance to deserving students enrolled in a broadcast journalism course.
Title of Award: Jim Allard Broadcast Journalism Scholarships **Area, Field, or Subject:** Journalism. **Level of Education for which Award is Granted:** Undergraduate **Funds Available:** $2,500. **Duration:** One year.
Eligibility Requirements: Applicants must be aspiring broadcasters enrolled in broadcast journalism courses at a Canadian college or university. **Application Requirements:** Applicant must provide a 500-word essay outlining why they are interested in broadcast journalism, career goals, and how the scholarship can help them to attain their goal; must submit a signed recommendation from the course director. **Additional Information:** Established in 1963 by the Canadian Association of Broadcasters, in memory of T.J. Allard, its long-time executive vicepresident. **Deadline for Receipt:** June 30.

2752 ■ THE COMMUNITY FOUNDATION OF MIDDLE TENNESSEE
3833 Cleghorn Ave., Ste. 400
Nashville, TN 37215-2519
Tel: (615)321-4939; 888-540-5200
E-mail: mail@cfmt.org
Web Site: http://www.cfmt.org
To help students in planning their postsecondary education.
Title of Award: Drue Smith/Society of Professional Journalists Scholarships **Area, Field, or Subject:** Journalism. **Level of Education for which Award is Granted:** Undergraduate **Funds Available:** No specific amount.
Eligibility Requirements: Applicants must be college juniors, seniors or graduate students who have graduated from high school in Middle Tennessee and have chosen journalism or broadcast news for a career, or mid-career working journalists who seek training to develop professionally or further their careers. **Application Requirements:** Applicants must complete the application form. Applicants must submit two applicant appraisals; transcript of grades; student essay describing educational plans and how these will help in career goals. Applicants must submit one recent photograph. **Deadline for Receipt:** March 15. **Additional Information:** pcole@cfmt.org

2753 ■ COMMUNITY FOUNDATION FOR SOUTHEAST MICHIGAN
333 West Fort St., Ste. 2010
Detroit, MI 48226-3134

Tel: (313)961-6675
Fax: (313)961-2886
E-mail: cfsem@cfsem.org
Web Site: http://www.cfsem.org
To provide financial assistance to graduating seniors from North Farmington High School who demonstrate leadership, good grades and male varsity athlete who will enter college majoring liberal studies, especially History and English.
Title of Award: Dick Depaolis Memorial Scholarships **Area, Field, or Subject:** History; English language and literature. **Level of Education for which Award is Granted:** Undergraduate **Funds Available:** $500.
Eligibility Requirements: Applicants must be members of the graduating class at North Farmington High School; must demonstrate exemplary desire, ability and have a GPA of 3.0 or higher; must be male athletes demonstrating leadership, academic discipline and good sportsmanship on and off the field; must be playing varsity sports (football preferred); have applied or been accepted as full-time students in an accredited educational institution in the United States with a major in liberal studies, especially History and English. **Application Requirements:** Applicants must use a computer, typewriter or print neatly in blue or black ink in completing the application form. **Deadline for Receipt:** April 2.

2754 ■ COUNCIL FOR THE ADVANCEMENT OF SCIENCE WRITING
PO Box 910
Hedgesville, WV 25427
Tel: (304)754-5077
Web Site: http://www.casw.org
To provide financial support to students who want to pursue a career in science writing.
Title of Award: Taylor/Blakeslee University Fellowships **Area, Field, or Subject:** Journalism. **Level of Education for which Award is Granted:** Undergraduate **Funds Available:** $2,000.
Eligibility Requirements: Applicant must be a enrolled in U.S graduate-level science writing program; must be a U.S citizen. **Application Requirements:** Applicant must complete the application form and must have resume, samples of writing, and a statement (not to exceed 500 words). Application form and other supporting materials must be sent to: CASW Rennie Taylor/Alton Blakeslee Fellowship Program at PO Box 910, Hedgesville, WV 25427. **Deadline for Receipt:** July 1.

2755 ■ DADE COMMUNITY FOUNDATION, INC.
200 S Biscayne Blvd., Ste. 505
Miami, FL 33131-2343
Tel: (305)371-2711
Fax: (305)371-5342
Web Site: http://www.dadecommunityfoundation.org
To help talented South Florida students for aspiring a career in journalism, broadcast or mass communications.
Title of Award: Leo Suarez Journalism Scholarships **Area, Field, or Subject:** Journalism; Broadcasting; Communications. **Level of Education for which Award is Granted:** Undergraduate **Funds Available:** $1,000. **Duration:** One year.
Eligibility Requirements: Applicants must be high school seniors in Miami-Dade or Broward public school; must have minimum of 3.0 grade point average; must intend to major in journalism, broadcast or mass communications in undergraduate studies at four year university and/or two year college. **Application Requirements:** Applicants must submit the completed application form together with the three writing samples that have been published and letter of recommendation from the journalism sponsor or English professor at their high school. **Deadline for Receipt:** March 21.

2756 ■ DELTA DELTA DELTA
PO Box 5987
Arlington, TX 76005-5987
Tel: (817)633-8001
Fax: (817)652-0212
E-mail: info@trideltaeo.org
Web Site: http://www.tridelta.org
To provide financial assistance to qualified undergraduate students.
Title of Award: Virginia Nicklas Scholarships **Area, Field, or Subject:** Literature, Science, Arts. **Level of Education for which Award is Granted:** Undergraduate **Funds Available:** $500-$1,500. **Duration:** One academic year.

Eligibility Requirements: Applicant must be an Iota chapter member at the University of Michigan; must be a permanent resident outside of Michigan; must live in Iota chapter house; must be currently enrolled in Literature, Science, and Arts. **Application Requirements:** Application forms are available on the website. Applicant must provide a personal statement about educational and vocational goals; must have a recommendation letter from a faculty member; must have an official transcript from each undergraduate institution. Application materials must be sent to: Delta Delta Delta, PO Box 5987, Arlington, TX 76005. **Deadline for Receipt:** March 15.

2757 ■ ALLISON E. FISHER MEMORIAL FUND
PO Box 43402
Baltimore, MD 21236
Tel: (410)679-0595
E-mail: fishers@verizon.net
Web Site: http://www.allisonfisherfund.org
To provide financial assistance to students who are attending an accredited four-year university.
Title of Award: Allison E. Fisher Scholarships **Area, Field, or Subject:** Journalism; Photography; Radio and television. **Level of Education for which Award is Granted:** Undergraduate **Funds Available:** $2,500.
Eligibility Requirements: Applicants must be any foreign or U.S. students who are majoring in journalism-print, photography or radio and television or planning a career in one of those fields; must be currently attending accredited four-year university; must have cumulative grade point average of 3.0 and be enrolled in undergraduate or graduate school during the award year. **Application Requirements:** Applicants must submit all the required application information.

2758 ■ FLORIDA OUTDOOR WRITERS ASSOCIATION
24 NW, 33rd Court, Ste. A
Gainesville, FL 32607
Tel: (352)392-2801
E-mail: info@fowa.org
Web Site: http://www.fowa.org
To motivate and encourage young people to enter outdoor communications career fields.
Title of Award: Florida Outdoor Writers Association Scholarships **Area, Field, or Subject:** Communications; Journalism. **Level of Education for which Award is Granted:** Undergraduate **Funds Available:** $500-$1,000.
Eligibility Requirements: Applicants must be students at Florida Colleges and universities, or must be students whose applications are endorsed by a FOWA member or a faculty advisor. **Application Requirements:** Applicants must submit a completed application form; must submit an essay, 500-1,000-words, that expresses their appreciation for the outdoor experience; an up-to-date resume; a letter of endorsement from a FOWA member or faculty advisor. **Deadline for Receipt:** August 31.

2759 ■ FOUNDATION FOR THE CAROLINAS
217 S Tryon St.
Charlotte, NC 28202
Tel: (704)973-4500
Free: 800-973-7244
Web Site: http://www.fftc.org
To assist graduating seniors at East Mecklenburg High School in Charlotte, NC who demonstrate interest in foreign languages and/or journalism.
Title of Award: Pete and Ellen Bensley Memorial Scholarship Fund **Area, Field, or Subject:** Foreign languages; Journalism. **Level of Education for which Award is Granted:** Undergraduate **Funds Available:** Amount not specified.
Eligibility Requirements: Applicants must be legal residents of Mecklenburg County and graduating seniors at East Mecklenburg High School who are planning to major in foreign languages and/or journalism. **Application Requirements:** Applicants must submit all the required materials and complete application information. **Additional Information:** The Scholarship Coordinator at East Mecklenburg High School, 980-343-6430.

2760 ■ GEORGIA PRESS EDUCATIONAL FOUNDATION
3066 Mercer University Dr., Ste. 200
Atlanta, GA 30341-4137

Tel: (770)454-6776
Fax: (770)454-6778
E-mail: mail@gapress.org
Web Site: http://www.gapress.org
To provide scholarship for outstanding students majoring in print journalism at a Georgia college or university.
Title of Award: Durwood McAlister Scholarships **Area, Field, or Subject:** Journalism. **Level of Education for which Award is Granted:** Undergraduate **Funds Available:** No specific amount.
Eligibility Requirements: Applicants must be enrolled full-time taking up journalism. **Application Requirements:** Scholarship application can be obtained from the GPEF website. The following documents must be enclosed in your application: most recent grade transcript; anticipated budget; school photograph; copy of SAT scores; parents'/your tax return; and recommendations of high school counselor, principal, college professor, or Georgia Press Association member. **Additional Information:** The McAlister Scholarship is named in honor of Durwood McAlister, former editor of The Atlanta Journal. **Deadline for Receipt:** February 1. **Additional Information:** Georgia Press Educational Foundation at the above address.

2761 ■ GEORGIA PRESS EDUCATIONAL FOUNDATION

3066 Mercer University Dr., Ste. 200
Atlanta, GA 30341-4137
Tel: (770)454-6776
Fax: (770)454-6778
E-mail: mail@gapress.org
Web Site: http://www.gapress.org
To provide scholarships for outstanding print journalism students.
Title of Award: Morris Newspaper Corp. Scholarships **Area, Field, or Subject:** Journalism. **Level of Education for which Award is Granted:** Undergraduate **Funds Available:** No specific amount.
Eligibility Requirements: Applicants must be enrolled full-time taking up journalism. **Application Requirements:** Applications are submitted through newspapers in the Morris Newspaper Corporation chain. **Additional Information:** Established in 1987 by Charles Morris. **Deadline for Receipt:** February 1. **Additional Information:** Georgia Press Educational Foundation at the above address.

2762 ■ GEORGIA PRESS EDUCATIONAL FOUNDATION

3066 Mercer University Dr., Ste. 200
Atlanta, GA 30341-4137
Tel: (770)454-6776
Fax: (770)454-6778
E-mail: mail@gapress.org
Web Site: http://www.gapress.org
To award scholarships to Georgia residents attending Georgia colleges and universities.
Title of Award: William C. Rogers Scholarships **Area, Field, or Subject:** Journalism. **Level of Education for which Award is Granted:** Undergraduate **Funds Available:** No specific amount.
Eligibility Requirements: Applicant must be a junior or senior majoring in the news-editorial sequence at the Grady College of Journalism and Mass Communication at the University of Georgia. **Application Requirements:** Scholarship application can be obtained from the GPEF website. The following documents must be enclosed in your application: most recent grade transcript; anticipated budget; school photograph; copy of SAT scores; parents'/your tax return; and recommendations of high school counselor, principal, college professor, or Georgia Press Association member. **Additional Information:** The Rogers Scholarship is named in honor of William C. Rogers, Publisher of The Blade, Sawinsboro, and a past president of the Georgia Press Association. **Deadline for Receipt:** February 1. **Additional Information:** Georgia Press Educational Foundation at the above address.

2763 ■ GEORGIA PRESS EDUCATIONAL FOUNDATION

3066 Mercer University Dr., Ste. 200
Atlanta, GA 30341-4137
Tel: (770)454-6776
Fax: (770)454-6778
E-mail: mail@gapress.org
Web Site: http://www.gapress.org

To award scholarships to Georgia residents attending Georgia colleges and universities.
Title of Award: Kirk Sutlive Scholarships **Area, Field, or Subject:** Journalism. **Level of Education for which Award is Granted:** Undergraduate **Funds Available:** No specific amount.
Eligibility Requirements: Applicant must be a junior or senior majoring in either the news-editorial or public relations sequence at the Henry W. Grady College of Journalism and Mass Communication at the University of Georgia. **Application Requirements:** Scholarship application can be obtained from the GPEF website. The following documents must be enclosed in your application: most recent grade transcript; anticipated budget; school photograph; copy of SAT scores; parents'/your tax return; and recommendations of high school counselor, principal, college professor, or Georgia Press Association member. **Deadline for Receipt:** February 1. **Additional Information:** Georgia Press Educational Foundation at the above address.

2764 ■ GERMAN ACADEMIC EXCHANGE SERVICE

871 United Nations Plz.
New York, NY 10017
Tel: (212)758-3223
Fax: (212)755-5780
E-mail: daadny@daad.org
Web Site: http://www.daad.org
To place strong emphasis on intercultural exchange and the transmission of cultural values; to provide outstanding young journalism students the opportunity to immerse themselves in the society, culture, values, and political attitudes in Germany.
Title of Award: InternXchange **Area, Field, or Subject:** Journalism. **Level of Education for which Award is Granted:** Undergraduate **Funds Available:** 600 Euros. **Duration:** 11-weeks program.
Eligibility Requirements: Applicants should be journalism or majoring journalism-related field student in the U.S.; undergraduate, graduate, and graduating seniors; must have German language proficiency at least equal to the advanced intermediate level; has interest in Germany and Germany affairs. **Application Requirements:** Applicant must Complete the online form with signature with two copies; submit resume in English, statement of motivation in English, two pages, double spaced, one-page journalistic writing sample or broadcast transcript, two letters of recommendation from professors in major field of study, official academic transcripts, DAAD German Language Evaluation Certificate **Deadline for Receipt:** February 15. **Additional Information:** Laura Montgomery at montgomery@daad.org.

2765 ■ KEITH GILMORE FOUNDATION

5160 Skyline Way NE
Calgary, AB, Canada T2E 6V1
Tel: (403)274-1734
E-mail: kgf@keithgilmorefoundation.com
Web Site: http://www.keithgilmorefoundation.com
To provide scholarships for deserving individuals.
Title of Award: Keith Gilmore Foundation - Undergraduate Scholarships **Area, Field, or Subject:** Agriculture, Economic aspects; Medicine, Veterinary; Journalism; Communications. **Level of Education for which Award is Granted:** Undergraduate **Number Awarded:** 4. **Funds Available:** $1,500. **Duration:** One year.
Eligibility Requirements: Applicant must be an individual enrolled in an undergraduate degree program in agriculture, veterinary medicine, journalism and/or communications at a recognized university, leading to a career in the field of agriculture. **Application Requirements:** Application forms are available online at www.keithgilmorefoundation.com. Completed application must be sent to Keith Gilmore Foundation, 5160 Skyline Way NE, Calgary, AB T2E 6V1. **Deadline for Receipt:** July 1.

2766 ■ HARTFORD FOUNDATION FOR PUBLIC GIVING

10 Columbus Blvd., 8th Flr.
Hartford, CT 06106
Tel: (860)548-1888
Fax: (860)524-8346
E-mail: hfpg@hfpg.org
Web Site: http://www.hfpg.org
To provide financial assistance to students planning a career in Journalism.

Title of Award: Deedee Segel - Hartford Courant Internships **Area, Field, or Subject:** Journalism; Communication. **Level of Education for which Award is Granted:** Undergraduate **Funds Available:** No specific amount.
Eligibility Requirements: Applicants must be college students majoring in Journalism or Communication. **Application Requirements:** Applicants may obtain application materials from The Hartford Courant and include the following requirements: resume with cover letter; application; eight published writings samples; reporting experience; college grades; references. **Deadline for Receipt:** January 1. **Additional Information:** Lynne DeLucia, Asst. Managing Ed., State/Metro, 285 Broad St., Hartford, CT 06115.

2767 ■ HISPANIC SCHOLARSHIP FUND
55 Second St., Ste. 1500
San Francisco, CA 94105
877-473-4636
Fax: (415)808-2302
E-mail: info@hsf.net
Web Site: http://www.hsf.net
To provide financial assistance to creative arts-related undergraduate and graduate students beginning or completing an art project.
Title of Award: McNamara Family Creative Arts Project Grants **Area, Field, or Subject:** Art; Media arts; Broadcasting; Filmmaking; Performing arts; Communications; Writing. **Level of Education for which Award is Granted:** Graduate, Undergraduate **Funds Available:** $5,000-$20,000.
Eligibility Requirements: Applicant must be of Hispanic heritage; U.S. citizen or legal permanent resident with a valid permanent resident card or passport stamped I-551; enrolled full-time undergraduate or graduate student in a degree-seeking program at a U.S. accredited institution in the U.S., Puerto Rico or U.S. Virgin Islands in the upcoming academic year; pursuing a major in Arts, including but not limited to media, film, performing arts, communications or writing; have a minimum 3.0 GPA on a 4.0 scale; must apply for federal financing aid using the Free Application for Federal Student Aid (FAFSA) at www.fafsa.ed.gov. **Application Requirements:** Applications must be submitted using the HSF online application system. **Additional Information:** In partnership with the McNamara Family Foundation. **Deadline for Receipt:** March 15. **Additional Information:** scholar1@hsf.net.

2768 ■ IDAHO COMMUNITY FOUNDATION
210 W State St.
Boise, ID 83702
Tel: (208)342-3535
Free: 800-657-5357
Fax: (208)342-3577
E-mail: info@idcomfdn.org
Web Site: http://www.idcomfdn.org
To encourage and promote the attainment of higher education goals for students who have demonstrated an aptitude for and an interest in writing.
Title of Award: Jim Poore Memorial Scholarship **Area, Field, or Subject:** Writing. **Level of Education for which Award is Granted:** Undergraduate **Funds Available:** $1,000.
Eligibility Requirements: Applicants must be graduating seniors from public or private school of Ada, Adams, Boise, Canyon, Elmore, Gem, Payette, Valley, Washington or a high school serving the Marsing, Homedale, Bruneau or Riggins communities. **Application Requirements:** Applicants must submit a completed application form. **Deadline for Receipt:** April 15.

2769 ■ INDIANA STATE ALUMNI ASSOCIATION
200 N 7th St.
Terre Haute, IN 47809-9989
800-GO-TO-ISU
Web Site: http://www.indstate.edu/alum/alum_assoc.htm
To support educational pursuit of students.
Title of Award: Indiana State Alumni Association Creative and Performing Arts Award **Area, Field, or Subject:** Art; Music; English language and literature; Theater arts. **Level of Education for which Award is Granted:** Undergraduate **Funds Available:** $2000. **Duration:** One year.
Eligibility Requirements: Applicant must be entering college as freshmen at the Indiana State University; majoring or have a minor in Art, Music, English, Physical Education (Dance), Theater. **Application**

Requirements: Applicant must submit an application form; portfolio review; must audition at the departments; and will be interview. Contact the department where the applicant is majoring. **Deadline for Receipt:** Must be admitted before February 1. **Additional Information:** Art: 812-237-3697; Music: 812-237-27771; English: 812-237-3163; Physical Education: 812-237-2520; Theater: 812-237-3331.

2770 ■ INTER AMERICAN PRESS ASSOCIATION
Jules Dubois Bldg.
1801 SW 3rd Ave.
Miami, FL 33129
Tel: (305)634-2465
Fax: (305)635-2272
E-mail: info@sipiapa.org
Web Site: http://www.sipiapa.com
To defend and promote the right of the peoples of the Americas to be fully and freely informed through an independent press.
Title of Award: Inter American Press Association Scholarships **Area, Field, or Subject:** Journalism. **Level of Education for which Award is Granted:** Undergraduate **Funds Available:** $20,000.
Eligibility Requirements: Applicants must be journalists or journalism seniors or graduates between 21 to 35 years of age with a good command of the language they are to use; must have completed their degree before beginning the scholarship year; must take a minimum of three university courses; and must participate in the Scholarship Fund's Reporting Program. **Application Requirements:** Applicants must complete the application form and submit along with an autobiography; transcripts of the university studies; three letters of recommendation; and proof of certification. **Deadline for Receipt:** December 31. **Additional Information:** zchirinos@sipiapa.org

2771 ■ INTERNATIONAL FOODSERVICE EDITORIAL COUNCIL
PO Box 491
Hyde Park, NY 12538
Tel: (845)229-6973
Fax: (845)229-6993
E-mail: info@ifeconline.com
Web Site: http://www.ifec-is-us.com
To increase awareness and understanding of the career opportunities available in the field of food service communications and to encourage entry of qualified professionals in the field.
Title of Award: International Foodservice Editorial Council Scholarships **Area, Field, or Subject:** Culinary arts; Communications; Food service careers; Food science and technology; Photography; Hotel, institutional, and restaurant management; Nutrition; Dietetics; Journalism; Public relations; Graphic art and design. **Level of Education for which Award is Granted:** Graduate, Undergraduate **Number Awarded:** Varies. **Funds Available:** $3,750.
Eligibility Requirements: Applicants must be full-time students in a U.S. accredited post-secondary educational institution working towards an associate's, bachelor's or master's degree. **Application Requirements:** Applicants must submit a complete application together with academic transcript and two letters of recommendation. Application requirements must be typewritten and submitted using U.S. Postal Service's Return Receipt Service. **Deadline for Receipt:** March 15.

2772 ■ IOWA NEWSPAPER ASSOCIATION
319 E. 5th St.
Des Moines, IA 50309
Tel: (515)244-2145
Fax: (515)244-4855
E-mail: ina@inanews.com
Web Site: http://www.inanews.com
To champion the quality and future of Iowa's newspaper enterprises and the communities they serve.
Title of Award: INF Scholarships **Area, Field, or Subject:** Journalism. **Level of Education for which Award is Granted:** Undergraduate **Number Awarded:** 2. **Funds Available:** $1,000.
Eligibility Requirements: Applicants must be Iowa college students preparing for a career in the newspaper industry. High school seniors and students currently enrolled at a college or university are encouraged to apply. **Application Requirements:** Applicants must attach two letters of reference including one from a teacher or guidance counselor; must at-

tach a one-page statement about self, educational and career goals; two samples of writing or other examples of works which attest to the applicant's abilities. Samples should be printed on or affixed to 8.5" x 11" sheets of white copy paper. **Additional Information:** info@inanews.com.

2773 ■ IOWA NEWSPAPER ASSOCIATION
319 E. 5th St.
Des Moines, IA 50309
Tel: (515)244-2145
Fax: (515)244-4855
E-mail: ina@inanews.com
Web Site: http://www.inanews.com
To champion the quality and future of Iowa's newspaper enterprises and the communities they serve.
Title of Award: Iowa Journalism Institute Scholarships **Area, Field, or Subject:** Journalism; Communication. **Level of Education for which Award is Granted:** Undergraduate **Funds Available:** No specific amount.
Eligibility Requirements: Applicants must be students studying journalism, communications, mass communications, photojournalism, graphic design, marketing or public relations at a college or university in Iowa, Illinois, or Wisconsin. **Application Requirements:** Applicants must attach two letters of reference including one from a teacher or guidance counselor; must attach a one-page statement about self, educational and career goals; two samples of writings or other examples of work which attest to the abilities of applicants in their intended career field. These samples should be printed on or affixed to 8.5" x 11" sheets of white copy paper. **Additional Information:** info@inanews.com.

2774 ■ IOWA NEWSPAPER ASSOCIATION
319 E. 5th St.
Des Moines, IA 50309
Tel: (515)244-2145
Fax: (515)244-4855
E-mail: ina@inanews.com
Web Site: http://www.inanews.com
To champion the quality and future of Iowa's newspaper enterprises and the communities they serve.
Title of Award: Carter Pitts Scholarships **Area, Field, or Subject:** Journalism. **Level of Education for which Award is Granted:** Undergraduate **Funds Available:** $500.
Eligibility Requirements: Applicants must be Iowa college students preparing for a career in the newspaper industry. High school seniors and students currently enrolled at a college or university are encouraged to apply. **Application Requirements:** Applicants must attach two letters of reference including one from teacher or guidance counselor; must attach a one-page statement about self, educational and career goals; two samples of writings or other examples of work that attest to their abilities in the journalism field. Samples should be printed on or affixed to 8.5" x 11" sheets of white copy paper. **Additional Information:** info@inanews.com.

2775 ■ JAPANESE AMERICAN CITIZENS LEAGUE
1765 Sutter St.
San Francisco, CA 94115
Tel: (415)921-5225
Fax: (415)921-4671
E-mail: jacl@jacl.org
Web Site: http://www.jacl.org
To provide financial assistance for qualified individuals.
Title of Award: Kyutaro & Yasuo Abiko Memorial Scholarships **Area, Field, or Subject:** Journalism; Agricultural economics. **Level of Education for which Award is Granted:** Undergraduate **Funds Available:** $60,000. **Duration:** One year.
Eligibility Requirements: Applicant must be an active National JACL member at either an individual or student/youth level; must be planning to attend full-time at a college, university, trade school, business school, or any other institution of higher learning within the United States at the undergraduate or graduate school level. Entering freshman applicant must be a high school senior. **Application Requirements:** Application forms are available online at www.jacl.org/join.html. **Deadline for Receipt:** March 1 (entering freshman) and April 1 (all applications excluding entering freshman).

2776 ■ JOURNALISM EDUCATION ASSOCIATION
103 Kedzie Hall
Kansas State University
Manhattan, KS 66506-1505
Tel: (785)532-5532; (866)532-5532
Fax: (785)532-5563
E-mail: jea@spub.ksu.edu
Web Site: http://www.jea.org
To recognize some of the top high school journalists in the country.
Title of Award: Sister Rita Jeanne Scholarships **Area, Field, or Subject:** Journalism. **Level of Education for which Award is Granted:** Undergraduate **Number Awarded:** 7. **Funds Available:** $5,000. **Duration:** One academic year.
Eligibility Requirements: Applicants must be graduating high school seniors who plan to study journalism or mass communications in college and pursue a journalism or mass communications career; must have at least a 3.0 GPA on a 4.0 scale with at least two years in high school journalism; must be a student of a JEA member adviser. **Application Requirements:** Applicants must submit a portfolio which includes: an official entry form; a self-analytical evaluation of "journalistic life" using the most creative form; photo of the applicant that shows journalism (for example: interviewing, taking a photograph, etc.); official copy of transcript; 3 or 4 letters of recommendation from an adviser, people who see the applicant's leadership and journalistic abilities, and practitioners that the applicants have worked with. Applicants must also include samples of their work. **Deadline for Receipt:** February 15.

2777 ■ LEWIS-CLARK STATE COLLEGE
500 8th Ave.
Lewiston, ID 83501
Tel: (208)792-5272
Web Site: http://www.lcsc.edu
To inspire educational pursuits among less capable individuals by providing financial assistance.
Title of Award: Susan P. Schroeder Memorial Scholarships **Area, Field, or Subject:** Natural Sciences; English Language and Literature. **Level of Education for which Award is Granted:** Undergraduate **Funds Available:** No specific amount.
Eligibility Requirements: Applicants must be graduates of Idaho high school; must be majoring in Natural Sciences or English; and must have a cumulative 3.0 GPA. **Application Requirements:** Applicants must accomplish a general application available at the website. **Deadline for Receipt:** March 1.

2778 ■ LIN TELEVISION CORPORATION
300 Wavy St.
Portsmouth, VA 23704
Tel: (757)673-5314
Fax: (757)673-5300
E-mail: rosetta.rolan@lintv.com
Web Site: http://www.lintv.com
To help educate and train outstanding minority candidates who seek to enter the television broadcast field.
Title of Award: LIN Television Corporation Minority Scholarships and Training Program **Area, Field, or Subject:** Broadcasting; Journalism. **Level of Education for which Award is Granted:** Undergraduate **Funds Available:** $20,000. **Duration:** One year.
Eligibility Requirements: Applicants must be citizens of the United States and of non-white origin; must be sophomores or have completed sufficient semester hours or similar educational units to be within two years of receiving an undergraduate bachelor's degree; must have a minimum of 3.0 cumulative GPA and with declared major in journalism, broadcast journalism, business or marketing at an accredited university or college. **Application Requirements:** Applicants must submit completed application form; list of organizations and activities in which they have held leadership position where nature of involvement must be briefly described; three references, up to two faculty members (university or secondary) and one or two other references that will recommend their work; list of personal achievements and honors; description of career goals in 50 words or less; and, short essay about themselves (up to 500 words, double-spaced). **Deadline for Receipt:** March 15.

2779 ■ MATANUSKA-SUSITNA COLLEGE
PO Box 2889
Palmer, AK 99645
Tel: (907)745-9774
Fax: (907)745-9711
E-mail: info@matsu.alaska.edu
Web Site: http://www.matsu.alaska.edu
To provide support to deserving students in Alaska who want to pursue an education in any campus of the University of Alaska.
Title of Award: Alaska Press Club Scholarships **Area, Field, or Subject:** Journalism. **Level of Education for which Award is Granted:** Undergraduate **Funds Available:** $500.
Eligibility Requirements: Applicant must be a junior, senior or graduate journalism student with a minimum GPA of 2.0. **Application Requirements:** Applicant must complete the application forms available at the website; must attach a personal essay, two letters of recommendation, and current transcripts. **Deadline for Receipt:** February 15.

2780 ■ MATANUSKA-SUSITNA COLLEGE
PO Box 2889
Palmer, AK 99645
Tel: (907)745-9774
Fax: (907)745-9711
E-mail: info@matsu.alaska.edu
Web Site: http://www.matsu.alaska.edu
To provide support to deserving students in Alaska who want to pursue an education in any campus of the University of Alaska.
Title of Award: Ward Sims Memorial Scholarships **Area, Field, or Subject:** Journalism. **Level of Education for which Award is Granted:** Undergraduate **Funds Available:** $1,000.
Eligibility Requirements: Applicants must be full-time junior or senior students enrolled in the Journalism program with a minimum GPA of 2.0. **Application Requirements:** Applicant must complete the application forms available at the website; must attach a personal essay, two letters of recommendation, and current transcripts. **Deadline for Receipt:** February 15.

2781 ■ NATIONAL BUSINESS AVIATION ASSOCIATION
1200 18th St. NW, Ste. 400
Washington, DC 20036-9000
Tel: (202)783-9000
Fax: (202)331-8364
E-mail: info@nbaa.org
Web Site: http://www.nbaa.org
To benefit a student intending to pursue a career in journalism, preferably with an aviation focus.
Title of Award: David E. Ewald Journalism Scholarships **Area, Field, or Subject:** Aviation; Journalism. **Level of Education for which Award is Granted:** Undergraduate **Funds Available:** $1,000.
Eligibility Requirements: Applicants must be either enrolled or accepted for enrollment in an accredited college or university program in journalism or a related area and must be U.S. citizens. **Application Requirements:** Applicants must submit a completed application form; an official transcript of record; a proof of enrollment or acceptance, prior to the distribution of award; a 500-1,000-word, typed, double-spaced essay describing the applicant's interest in and goals for a career in journalism; two letters of recommendation from either a faculty member or other individual who is familiar with the applicant's capabilities; and a current resume. **Deadline for Receipt:** August 15. **Additional Information:** Jay Evans at the above address.

2782 ■ NATIONAL COLLEGIATE ATHLETIC ASSOCIATION
PO Box 6222
Indianapolis, IN 46206-6222
Tel: (317)917-6222
Fax: (317)917-6888
E-mail: pmr@ncaa.org
Web Site: http://www2.ncaa.org
To foster freedom of speech and press while promoting quality sports journalism education at the collegiate level.
Title of Award: Freedom Forum-NCAA Sports-Journalism Scholarships **Area, Field, or Subject:** Sports writing; Journalism. **Level of Education for which Award is Granted:** Undergraduate **Number Awarded:** 8. **Funds Available:** $3000. **Duration:** One academic year.

Eligibility Requirements: Applicant must be a junior college student with career goals in sports journalism, majors in journalism, or experience in campus sports journalism. **Application Requirements:** Applicants must submit a completed application form along with official grade transcripts; three published journalism samples relative to sports; at least one letter of recommendation; and the essay. **Additional Information:** In cooperation with The Freedom Forum. **Deadline for Receipt:** December 14. **Additional Information:** Suzy Hays, at 317-917-6477.

2783 ■ NATIONAL IRANIAN AMERICAN COUNCIL
1411 K St. NW, Ste. 600
Washington, DC 20005
Tel: (202)386-6325
Fax: (202)386-6409
Web Site: http://www.niacouncil.org
To provide outstanding Iranian-American college students with internships in political and media organizations.
Title of Award: National Iranian American Council Fellowships **Area, Field, or Subject:** Political science; Economics; International affairs and relations; Journalism. **Level of Education for which Award is Granted:** Graduate, Undergraduate **Funds Available:** Travel expenses covered to and from DC; $500 monthly stipend; $700 monthly towards rent.
Eligibility Requirements: Applicant must be a college junior, senior, and graduate student who is a U.S. citizen or a legal permanent resident of Iranian descent. **Application Requirements:** Applicant must submit the following requirements: a completed application form; three letters of recommendation (two academic and one from an employment supervisor); resume; current college transcript; a 500-word essay answering the question: "How has being Iranian-American influenced your decision to pursue a career in public service or journalism?" **Deadline for Receipt:** February 15. **Additional Information:** NIAC at the above address.

2784 ■ NEW JERSEY PRESS FOUNDATION
840 Bear Tavern Rd., Ste. 305
West Trenton, NJ 08628-1019
Tel: (609)406-0600
Fax: (609)406-0300
E-mail: jjobrien@njpa.org
Web Site: http://www.njpa.org
To promote journalism careers and newspaper readership among New Jersey residents.
Title of Award: Richard Drukker Memorial Scholarships **Area, Field, or Subject:** Journalism. **Level of Education for which Award is Granted:** Undergraduate **Funds Available:** $2,000.
Eligibility Requirements: Applicants must be journalism minors and staff members of the Montclarion. **Application Requirements:** Applicants must complete the application form and submit an academic transcript for all college work completed; three samples of journalistic writing that has appeared in any newspaper or was done for class assignments; a statement of interest in a newspaper career, written as an autobiographical sketch describing their journalistic skills and achievements (not more than 500 words); and a statement of financial or family circumstances. **Deadline for Receipt:** February 28.

2785 ■ NEW JERSEY PRESS FOUNDATION
840 Bear Tavern Rd., Ste. 305
West Trenton, NJ 08628-1019
Tel: (609)406-0600
Fax: (609)406-0300
E-mail: jjobrien@njpa.org
Web Site: http://www.njpa.org
To promote journalism career and newspaper readership among New Jersey residents.
Title of Award: Bernard Kilgore Memorial Scholarships **Area, Field, or Subject:** Journalism. **Level of Education for which Award is Granted:** Undergraduate **Funds Available:** $5,000.
Eligibility Requirements: Applicants must be graduating high school seniors. Applicants must be planning to study journalism in college and to pursue a journalism career; must have at least a 3.0 GPA on a 4.0 scale and have participated in high school journalism for at least two years. **Application Requirements:** Applicants must submit an official entry form; a self-analytical evaluation of the journalistic life using a creative form; and one action photo of themselves in a journalistic role; and an official copy

of their transcript. Applicants should secure three to four letters of recommendation from advisers, teachers familiar with their leadership and journalistic abilities, or practitioners with whom they have worked. **Deadline for Receipt:** February 15.

2786 ■ NEW JERSEY PRESS FOUNDATION
840 Bear Tavern Rd., Ste. 305
West Trenton, NJ 08628-1019
Tel: (609)406-0600
Fax: (609)406-0300
E-mail: jjobrien@njpa.org
Web Site: http://www.njpa.org
To promote journalism careers and newspaper readership among New Jersey residents.
Title of Award: Isaac Roth Newspaper Carrier Scholarships Program **Area, Field, or Subject:** Journalism. **Level of Education for which Award is Granted:** Undergraduate **Funds Available:** $2,000.
Eligibility Requirements: Applicants must be adult carriers who are currently enrolled as full-time college students and plan to continue as full-time students. **Application Requirements:** Applicants must complete the application form. Applicants must submit an essay of 150 words; a copy of thier transcript; and up to five letters of recommendation from the carrier's route customers. **Deadline for Receipt:** April 30.

2787 ■ NEW YORK FINANCIAL WRITERS ASSOCIATION
PO Box 338
Ridgewood, NJ 07451-0338
Tel: (201)612-0100
Fax: (201)612-9915
E-mail: info@nyfwa.org
Web Site: http://www.nyfwa.org
To provide financial assistance to those studying business, finance, and journalism.
Title of Award: New York Financial Writers' Associations Scholarships **Area, Field, or Subject:** Business; Finance; Journalism. **Level of Education for which Award is Granted:** Graduate, Undergraduate **Funds Available:** No specific amount.
Eligibility Requirements: Undergraduate or graduate journalism students in the Metropolitan New York area who are seriously interested in pursuing a career in business and financial journalism. **Application Requirements:** Applicants must send an application form together with an essay explaining why the applicant is pursuing a career in business and financial journalism, current resume, list of other scholarships received and samples of financial writings and clippings created. If an application form is unavailable, applicants may submit a cover letter with the requirements listed. **Deadline for Receipt:** April 15. **Additional Information:** NYFWS Scholarship Committee at the above address.

2788 ■ NEW YORK WOMEN IN COMMUNICATIONS FOUNDATION
355 Lexington Ave., 15th Fl.
New York, NY 10017-6603
Tel: (212)297-2133
Fax: (212)370-9047
Web Site: http://www.nywici.org
To provide financial assistance for the education of the residents of NY, NJ, CT, or PA.
Title of Award: New York Women in Communications, Inc. Foundation Scholarships **Area, Field, or Subject:** Advertising; Broadcasting; Communications; Media arts; Journalism; Marketing and distribution; Media arts; Public relations. **Level of Education for which Award is Granted:** Graduate, Undergraduate **Funds Available:** No specific amount. **Duration:** One year.
Eligibility Requirements: Applicants must be high school seniors, or college undergraduate or graduate students who are permanent residents of NY, NJ, CT or PA majoring or declaring a major in a communications-related field, including but not limited to advertising, broadcasting, communications, English, film, journalism, marketing, new media, or public relations. Applicants must have an overall GPA of 3.2 or better (or the high school equivalent). **Application Requirements:** Applicants must submit completed application form and all other required application information and materials. **Deadline for Receipt:** January 30.

2789 ■ NEWSWOMEN'S CLUB OF NEW YORK
15 Gramercy Park S
New York, NY 10003

Tel: (212)777-1610
Web Site: http://www.newswomensclubnewyork.com
To provide financial assistance to aspiring journalists to pursue their careers.
Title of Award: Anne O'Hare McCormick Scholarship Fund **Area, Field, or Subject:** Journalism. **Level of Education for which Award is Granted:** Undergraduate **Number Awarded:** 2. **Funds Available:** $5,000.
Eligibility Requirements: Applicants must be journalists attending Columbia University's Graduate School of Journalism; must be citizens of the United States and have financial need. **Application Requirements:** Application form must be print or type clearly. Applicant must submit the list of job-related experience, with dates of employment; must have a brief statement of financial resources, including needs for tuition and living expenses during the academic year; must have two letters of recommendation that focus on the applicants qualifications for the field of journalism; must prepare an autobiographical essay mentioning family, educational background, journalistic experience and goals; must have one or two examples of the applicant's writing. Application and other documents must be sent to: Anne O'Hare McCormick Journalism Scholarship Fund, Newswomen's Club of New York, 15 Gramercy Park S, 2nd Flr., New York, NY 10003. **Deadline for Receipt:** June 1.

2790 ■ OHIO NEWSPAPER ASSOCIATION
1335 Dublin Rd., Ste. 216-B
Columbus, OH 43215
Tel: (614)486-6677
Fax: (614)486-4940
Web Site: http://www.ohionews.org
To provide educational assistance for students from Northern Ohio.
Title of Award: Harold K. Douhhit Regional Scholarships **Area, Field, or Subject:** Journalism. **Level of Education for which Award is Granted:** Undergraduate **Funds Available:** $1,500.
Eligibility Requirements: Applicants must have graduated from a high school in Cuyahog, Lorain, Huron, Erie, Wood, Geauga, Sandusky, Ottawa or Lucas county; must be enrolled as sophomores, juniors or seniors at an Ohio college or university; must have a minimum grade point average of 3.0 (B); and must clearly demonstrate ability to write. **Application Requirements:** Applicants must submit completed application form typed or printed legibly by the applicant; official university or college transcript; an autobiography of 750 to 1,000 words describing academic and career interests, awards, extracurricular activities and any journalism-related activities; and two letters of recommendation from college or university faculty members familiar with the student's work and career interests, with special emphasis on the student's financial need. Students are encouraged to provide writing samples or articles that have been published. **Deadline for Receipt:** March 31. **Additional Information:** Ohio Newspaper Foundation at the above address.

2791 ■ OHIO NEWSPAPER ASSOCIATION
1335 Dublin Rd., Ste. 216-B
Columbus, OH 43215
Tel: (614)486-6677
Fax: (614)486-4940
Web Site: http://www.ohionews.org
To provide educational assistance for minority high school seniors in Ohio intending to pursue a newspaper journalism career.
Title of Award: Ohio Newspaper Association Minority Scholarships **Area, Field, or Subject:** Journalism. **Level of Education for which Award is Granted:** Undergraduate **Funds Available:** $1,500.
Eligibility Requirements: Applicants must be graduating seniors at an Ohio high school; must be enrolled as college freshmen at an Ohio college or university; must have a minimum high school grade point average of 2.5 (C+); must clearly demonstrate ability to write; and must be African American, Hispanic, Asian American or American Indian. **Application Requirements:** Applicants must submit completed application form typed or printed legibly by the applicant; an autobiography of 750 to 1,000 words describing academic and career interest, awards, extracurricular activities and any journalism-related activities; and two letters of recommendation from high school faculty members familiar with the student's work and career interests. Students may provide additional information such as samples or articles that have been published. **Deadline for Receipt:** March 31. **Additional Information:** Ohio Newspaper Foundation at the above address.

2792 ■ OHIO NEWSPAPER ASSOCIATION

1335 Dublin Rd., Ste. 216-B
Columbus, OH 43215
Tel: (614)486-6677
Fax: (614)486-4940
Web Site: http://www.ohionews.org
To provide educational assistance for students demonstrating a career commitment to newspaper journalism.
Title of Award: Ohio Newspaper Association University Journalism Scholarships **Area, Field, or Subject:** Journalism. **Level of Education for which Award is Granted:** Undergraduate **Funds Available:** $1,500.
Eligibility Requirements: Applicants must be enrolled as sophomores, juniors or seniors at an Ohio college or university; must have a minimum grade point average of 2.5 (C+); and must clearly demonstrate ability to write. **Application Requirements:** Applicants must submit completed application form typed or printed legibly by the applicant; official college or university transcript; an autobiography of 750 to 1,000 words describing academic and career interests, awards, extracurricular activities and any journalism-related activities (emphasis should be given to newspaper or print journalism); two letters of recommendation from college or university faculty members familiar with the student's work and career interests; and writing samples or articles that have been published. **Deadline for Receipt:** March 31. **Additional Information:** Ohio News Foundation at the above address.

2793 ■ OHIO NEWSPAPER ASSOCIATION

1335 Dublin Rd., Ste. 216-B
Columbus, OH 43215
Tel: (614)486-6677
Fax: (614)486-4940
Web Site: http://www.ohionews.org
To provide educational assistance for students in an Ohio college or university.
Title of Award: Ohio Newspaper Association Women's Scholarships **Area, Field, or Subject:** Journalism. **Level of Education for which Award is Granted:** Undergraduate **Funds Available:** $1,500.
Eligibility Requirements: Applicants must be enrolled as juniors or seniors at an Ohio college or university. **Application Requirements:** Applicants must submit completed application form together with official college or university transcript; two letters of recommendation; three to four news clippings; and statements answering the three application questions. **Deadline for Receipt:** March 31. **Additional Information:** Ohio Newspaper Foundation at the above address.

2794 ■ ORANGE COUNTY COMMUNITY FOUNDATION

30 Corporate Park, Ste. 410
Irvine, CA 92606
Tel: (949)553-4202
Fax: (949)553-4211
E-mail: cmontesano@oc-cf.org
Web Site: http://www.oc-cf.org
To provide scholarship to the students interested in pursuing a career in journalism.
Title of Award: D.R. Segal Memorial Scholarships for Journalistic Excellence **Area, Field, or Subject:** Journalism. **Level of Education for which Award is Granted:** Undergraduate **Number Awarded:** 4. **Funds Available:** $2,000.
Eligibility Requirements: Applicants must be Orange County high school graduating seniors or current college students wishing to pursue a career in journalism. **Application Requirements:** Interested applicant may download an application from the Foundation's website. As an attachment to your application, write about your father and how he has influenced your life. The essay should be a maximum of one page, typed and double-spaced. **Deadline for Receipt:** March 28. **Additional Information:** Claudia Montesano, 949-553-4202 ext. 46; cmontesano@oc-cf.org.

2795 ■ OUTDOOR WRITERS ASSOCIATION OF AMERICA

121 Hickory St., Ste. 1
Missoula, MT 59801
Tel: (406)728-7434
Fax: (406)728-7445
E-mail: krhoades@owaa.org

Web Site: http://www.owaa.org
To provide educational services to members.
Title of Award: Bodie McDowell Scholarships **Area, Field, or Subject:** Writing. **Level of Education for which Award is Granted:** Graduate, Undergraduate **Funds Available:** $1,000 to $4,000. **Duration:** One year.
Eligibility Requirements: Applicant must be an undergraduate or graduate students from any discipline and all schools; must have a career goal in outdoor communications. **Application Requirements:** Applicant must submit a completed application, letter of recommendation from school, transcript, example of outdoor communication work, a one to two page statement of career goals, and optional letters of recommendation from others familiar with applicant's work. **Deadline for Receipt:** March 1. **Additional Information:** Kevin Rhoades at krhoades@owaa.org.

2796 ■ PARKERSBURG AREA COMMUNITY FOUNDATION

501 Avery St.
Parkersburg, WV 26101
Tel: (304)428-4438; (866)428-4438
Fax: (304)428-1200
E-mail: info@pacfwv.com
Web Site: http://www.pacfwv.com
To provide financial assistance for qualified graduating students from Wood County.
Title of Award: Harold Knopp Scholarships **Area, Field, or Subject:** Journalism. **Level of Education for which Award is Granted:** Undergraduate **Funds Available:** $450.
Eligibility Requirements: Applicant must be a graduating senior from Wood County; must have excelled in journalism in high school; and must be planning to pursue a career in journalism. **Application Requirements:** Applicants must submit a cover sheet (3 pages) and application form (4 pages); must have a personal essay; must have a high school and/or post-secondary transcript; must provide a letter of recommendation; copy of the page of their or their parent's most recent tax return that indicates adjusted gross income; and a Student Aid Report showing estimated family contribution from FAFSA. Application form and other supporting documents must be sent to Our Community's Foundation, P.O Box 1762, Parkersburg, WV 26102. **Deadline for Receipt:** March 20.

2797 ■ PARKERSBURG AREA COMMUNITY FOUNDATION

501 Avery St.
Parkersburg, WV 26101
Tel: (304)428-4438; (866)428-4438
Fax: (304)428-1200
E-mail: info@pacfwv.com
Web Site: http://www.pacfwv.com
To provide financial support for qualified individuals intending to pursue their education.
Title of Award: Glenn Wilson Broadcast Journalism Scholarships **Area, Field, or Subject:** Journalism; Communications; Marketing and distribution. **Level of Education for which Award is Granted:** Undergraduate **Funds Available:** $560.
Eligibility Requirements: Applicants must be current or previous Wood or Pleasant County, WV, or Washington County, OH, high school students; must be studying broadcast journalism, journalism, communications or marketing; and must have a minimum 2.5 GPA. **Application Requirements:** Applicants must submit a cover sheet (3 pages) and application form (4 pages); a personal essay; a high school and/or post-secondary transcript; a letter of recommendation; a signed copy of the page of their or their parent's most recent tax return that indicates adjusted gross income; and a Student Aid Report showing estimated family contribution from FAFSA. Application form and other supporting documents must be sent to Our Community's Foundation, P.O Box 1762, Parkersburg, WV 26102. **Deadline for Receipt:** March 20.

2798 ■ PUBLIC EDUCATION FOUNDATION

3360 W Sahara Ave., Ste. 160
Las Vegas, NV 89102
Tel: (702)799-1042
Fax: (702)799-5247
E-mail: steelej@ccpef.org
Web Site: http://ccpef.org
To promote education in communication.
Title of Award: Harvey N. Dondero Communication and Journalism Excellence Scholarships **Area, Field, or Subject:** Journalism; Com-

munications. **Level of Education for which Award is Granted:** Undergraduate **Number Awarded:** 1. **Funds Available:** $1,200.
Eligibility Requirements: Applicants must be CCSD seniors planning to attend an accredited post-secondary institution pursuing a degree in journalism or communications. **Application Requirements:** Applicants must submit a completed application form together with an essay, transcript, and a recommendation written by a journalism or English teacher. **Deadline for Receipt:** March 31. **Additional Information:** Shana Venenga at 702-799-1042.

2799 ■ PUBLIC EDUCATION FOUNDATION
3360 W Sahara Ave., Ste. 160
Las Vegas, NV 89102
Tel: (702)799-1042
Fax: (702)799-5247
E-mail: steelej@ccpef.org
Web Site: http://ccpef.org
To promote education in photography and journalism.
Title of Award: Don English Memorial Scholarships **Area, Field, or Subject:** Photography; Journalism. **Level of Education for which Award is Granted:** Undergraduate **Number Awarded:** 1. **Funds Available:** $4,100.
Eligibility Requirements: Applicants must be CCSD seniors planning to attend an accredited college, university, or institute as full-time students in the field of photography, media arts, or journalism; must have a minimum 3.0 cumulative GPA. **Application Requirements:** Applicants must submit a completed application form together with an essay, two letters of recommendation, transcript, and resume of awards. **Deadline for Receipt:** March 7. **Additional Information:** Shana Venenga at 702-799-1042.

2800 ■ PUBLIC RELATIONS SOCIETY OF AMERICA
33 Maiden Ln., 11th Fl.
New York, NY 10038-5150
Tel: (212)460-1474
Fax: (212)995-0757
E-mail: prssa@prsa.org
Web Site: http://www.prssa.org
To provide educational assistance for qualified students intending to pursue a career in the field of public relations.
Title of Award: Stephen D. Pisinski Memorial Scholarships **Area, Field, or Subject:** Public relations; Journalism; Communications. **Level of Education for which Award is Granted:** Undergraduate **Funds Available:** $1,500.
Eligibility Requirements: Applicants must be majoring in journalism, communications, or public relations; must be junior or senior level only; must have at least a 3.3 overall GPA on a 4.0 system; must be members of the Public Relations Student Society of America, and leadership positions are a plus. **Application Requirements:** Applicants must submit a resume including any academic honors, special projects, activities and/or work experience or training; an official transcript of all college studies, including grades of the preceding semester; an essay of 1,000 words or less stating your career goals; two strong writing samples; and two letters of academic and/or professional recommendations. Application form and other required items must be sent to PRSSA Headquarters by Stephen D. Pininski Memorial Scholarship, Public Relations Student Society of America, 33 Maiden Ln., 11th Fl., New York, NY 10038. **Deadline for Receipt:** June 2.

2801 ■ QUILL AND SCROLL SOCIETY
100 Adler Journalism Bldg.
Iowa City, IA 52242
Tel: (319)335-3457
Fax: (319)335-3989
E-mail: quill-scroll@uiowa.edu
Web Site: http://www.uiowa.edu
To provide financial assistance to well-qualified individuals to attend any college or university that offers a major in journalism.
Title of Award: Edward J. Nell Memorial Scholarships in Journalism **Area, Field, or Subject:** Journalism. **Level of Education for which Award is Granted:** Undergraduate **Funds Available:** $500 to $1,500.
Eligibility Requirements: Applicant must be a student in freshman year.
Application Requirements: Applicant must submit three separate forms (Form I - Principal or Counselor, Form II - Student and Form III - Journal-

ism Adviser) together with the supporting material (official transcript, applicant's letter regarding journalistic experience, and five selections of student's published work and letters of endorsement from principal, counselor and/or adviser). **Deadline for Receipt:** May 10.

2802 ■ SAFE SCHOOLS COALITION
1002 E Seneca St.
Seattle, WA 98122-4203
Tel: (206)957-1621
Fax: (206)325-2689
Web Site: http://www.safeschoolscoalition.org
To sponsor scholarships for gay, lesbian, bisexual and transgendered students pursuing a degree in journalism and communications at an accredited four-year college or university.
Title of Award: Messenger-Anderson Journalism Scholarships and Internships Program **Area, Field, or Subject:** Journalism; Communications. **Level of Education for which Award is Granted:** Undergraduate **Funds Available:** $5,000 for the first year and $2,500 for the second and third years.
Eligibility Requirements: Applicants must be high school seniors or current undergraduate students with a cumulative 2.8 GPA or better. **Application Requirements:** Applicants may check the available contact information for inquiries. **Additional Information:** The award is sponsored by the National Gay and Lesbian Task Force (NGLTF). Winners are required to participate in the Messenger-Anderson Scholarship Intern Program at NGLTF offices in Washington, DC, or New York City during the summer. **Deadline for Receipt:** February.

2803 ■ SAFE SCHOOLS COALITION
1002 E Seneca St.
Seattle, WA 98122-4203
Tel: (206)957-1621
Fax: (206)325-2689
Web Site: http://www.safeschoolscoalition.org
To provide scholarships and awards for LGBT students interested in journalism.
Title of Award: National Lesbian and Gay Journalists Association (NLGJA) Scholarships **Area, Field, or Subject:** Journalism. **Level of Education for which Award is Granted:** Undergraduate **Funds Available:** $5,000 for Leroy F. Aarons Scholarships; $1,000 for Bob Ross Scholarships.
Eligibility Requirements: Applicants must be LGBT journalism students. **Application Requirements:** Applicants must check the available website for more scholarship information. **Deadline for Receipt:** February; July. **Additional Information:** Safe Schools Coalition at the above address

2804 ■ THE SAN DIEGO FOUNDATION
2508 Historic Decatur Rd., Ste. 200
San Diego, CA 92106
Tel: (619)235-2300
Fax: (619)239-1710
E-mail: info@sdfoundation.org
Web Site: http://www.sdfoundation.org
To support the education of students from California.
Title of Award: Steve Petix Journalism Scholarship **Area, Field, or Subject:** Journalism. **Level of Education for which Award is Granted:** Undergraduate **Number Awarded:** 2. **Funds Available:** $1,000.
Eligibility Requirements: Applicant must be graduating senior attending schools in the Grossmont Union High School District interested in pursuing a career in journalism or related writing career; have a minimum 2.50 GPA on a 4.0 scale; and planning to attend an accredited two-year college or four-year university in the U.S. **Application Requirements:** Applicants must submit a completed Common Scholarship Application together with personal statement; two letters of recommendation on official letterhead (written within the last six months); official transcript in an official and sealed envelope; and a copy of most recent tax form (Form 1040-pages 1 & 2; Form 1040A-pages 1 & 2; Form 1040EZ-page 1). **Deadline for Receipt:** January 28. **Additional Information:** Arzo Mansury, Dir. Scholarships at 619-814-1343, or scholarships@sdfoundation.org.

2805 ■ SIGMA KAPPA FOUNDATION
8733 Founder Rd.
Indianapolis, IN 46268

Tel: (317)872-3275
E-mail: alewis@sigmakappa.org
Web Site: http://www.sigmakappafoundation.org
To encourage and support the scholastic development of the collegiate and alumnae sisters of the foundation.
Title of Award: Frances Warren Baker Memorial Scholarships **Area, Field, or Subject:** Journalism, Communications. **Level of Education for which Award is Granted:** Undergraduate **Number Awarded:** 1. **Funds Available:** $500.
Eligibility Requirements: Applicant must be a member in good standing enrolled in an undergraduate program in the fields of journalism or communication (print media); must have a minimum cumulative GPA: 3.0. **Application Requirements:** Application forms are available online. Applicant must submit the transcript and recommendation letter through online. **Deadline for Receipt:** March 1.

2806 ■ SOCIETY OF PROFESSIONAL JOURNALISTS
Eugene S. Pulliam National Journalism Center
3909 N Meridian St.
Indianapolis, IN 46208
Tel: (317)927-8000
Fax: (317)920-4789
E-mail: tharper@spj.org
Web Site: http://www.spj.org
To encourage the free practice of journalism and stimulate high standards of ethical behavior.
Title of Award: Fred Archibald Communications Internships **Area, Field, or Subject:** Journalism. **Level of Education for which Award is Granted:** Undergraduate **Funds Available:** $400 per week. **Duration:** 10 weeks.
Eligibility Requirements: Applicants must be juniors or seniors pursuing a degree in journalism, marketing, communications or public relations at a college or university, or a recent college graduate; must be willing to relocate to Indianapolis for ten weeks if not a resident; must have writing and/or reporting experience; Should be able to manage multiple tasks, remain organized and meet deadlines; must have decision making, problem solving, and research skills; must possess ability to express ideas and opinions with willingness to take initiative and work cooperatively with others; must have proficient computer skills; must have strong work ethics and a positive attitude. **Application Requirements:** Applicants must submit a completed application form and attach a cover letter, current resume, three to five writing samples and a one-page essay detailing their future goals and objectives. **Additional Information:** bking@apj.org

2807 ■ SOCIETY OF PROFESSIONAL JOURNALISTS
Eugene S. Pulliam National Journalism Center
3909 N Meridian St.
Indianapolis, IN 46208
Tel: (317)927-8000
Fax: (317)920-4789
E-mail: tharper@spj.org
Web Site: http://www.spj.org
To encourage the free practice of journalism and stimulate high standards of ethical behavior.
Title of Award: Pulliam/Kilgore Freedom of Information Internships **Area, Field, or Subject:** Journalism. **Level of Education for which Award is Granted:** Undergraduate **Funds Available:** $400 per week.
Eligibility Requirements: Applicants must be journalism students who are entering or just completing their senior year, graduate journalism students, or law students with a journalism background. **Application Requirements:** Applicant must submit a completed application form along with resume and one-page essay that illustrates their understanding of Freedom of Information issues and what they expect to gain from the internship (not more than five writings). **Deadline for Receipt:** January 5. **Additional Information:** quill@spj.org.

2808 ■ SOCIETY OF PROFESSIONAL JOURNALISTS
Eugene S. Pulliam National Journalism Center
3909 N Meridian St.
Indianapolis, IN 46208
Tel: (317)927-8000
Fax: (317)920-4789

E-mail: tharper@spj.org
Web Site: http://www.spj.org
To encourage the free practice of journalism and stimulate high standards of ethical behavior.
Title of Award: The Working Press Internships **Area, Field, or Subject:** Journalism. **Level of Education for which Award is Granted:** Undergraduate **Number Awarded:** 12. **Funds Available:** $400 per week.
Eligibility Requirements: Applicants must be student writers, photographers, and designers. **Application Requirements:** Applicant must submit two copies of the following: completed application form; a resume; three clips, lay-outs or published photos. **Deadline for Receipt:** April 19. **Additional Information:** jskeel@spj.org

2809 ■ SOUTH ASIAN JOURNALISTS ASSOCIATION
c/o Sreenath Sreenivasan
Columbia Graduate School of Journalism
2950 Broadway
New York, NY 10027
Tel: (212)854-0191
E-mail: saja@columbia.edu
Web Site: http://www.saja.org
To provide educational fund to students pursuing journalism as a career.
Title of Award: SAJA Journalism Scholarships **Area, Field, or Subject:** Journalism. **Level of Education for which Award is Granted:** Undergraduate **Number Awarded:** 5. **Funds Available:** $1000 for high school senior about to enter college; $1500 for undergraduate college student (four-year or community college); $2000 for graduate-level students; $2000 for undergraduate or graduate student in broadcast or journalism.
Eligibility Requirements: Applicants must be South Asian descents; a high school seniors; must be enrolled or current students in an accredited college or university (two-year or four year) in the United States or Canada and/or entering a graduate-level program in the United States or Canada. **Application Requirements:** Applicants must fill out online application form available at the website. **Deadline for Receipt:** February 15.

2810 ■ SOUTH CAROLINA SCHOLASTIC PRESS ASSOCIATION
University of South Carolina
College of Mass Communications and Information Studies
Columbia, SC 29208
Tel: (803)777-6284
Fax: (803)777-4103
E-mail: flowersk@mailbox.sc.edu
Web Site: http://www.sc.edu
To provide financial assistance to those students who are in need.
Title of Award: McClatchy Scholarships **Area, Field, or Subject:** Journalism. **Level of Education for which Award is Granted:** Undergraduate **Funds Available:** No specific amount.
Eligibility Requirements: Applicants must be minority students pursuing print journalism careers in the School of Journalism and Mass Communications. **Application Requirements:** Applicants must check the available website for more information. **Additional Information:** South Carolina Scholastic Press Association at the above address.

2811 ■ SOUTH CAROLINA SCHOLASTIC PRESS ASSOCIATION
University of South Carolina
College of Mass Communications and Information Studies
Columbia, SC 29208
Tel: (803)777-6284
Fax: (803)777-4103
E-mail: flowersk@mailbox.sc.edu
Web Site: http://www.sc.edu
To provide financial support to deserving students.
Title of Award: SCSPA Scholarships **Area, Field, or Subject:** Journalism. **Level of Education for which Award is Granted:** Undergraduate **Funds Available:** No specific amount.
Eligibility Requirements: Applicants must be graduating seniors who have been admitted and plan to attend the USC School of Journalism and Mass Communications. **Application Requirements:** Applicants must check the available website for the required materials. **Additional Information:** South Carolina Scholastic Press Association at the above address.

2812 ■ SOUTH CAROLINA SCHOLASTIC PRESS ASSOCIATION

University of South Carolina
College of Mass Communications and Information Studies
Columbia, SC 29208
Tel: (803)777-6284
Fax: (803)777-4103
E-mail: flowersk@mailbox.sc.edu
Web Site: http://www.sc.edu
To provide financial assistance to deserving students.
Title of Award: SCSPA Yearbook Scholarships **Area, Field, or Subject:** Journalism. **Level of Education for which Award is Granted:** Undergraduate **Funds Available:** No specific amount.
Eligibility Requirements: Applicants must be graduating high school seniors who have shown academic excellence and plan to attend the University of South Carolina main campus in Columbia. **Application Requirements:** Applicants must check the available website for more information. **Additional Information:** South Carolina Scholastic Press Association at the above address.

2813 ■ SOUTHWEST FLORIDA COMMUNITY FOUNDATION

8260 College Pkwy., Ste. 101
Fort Myers, FL 33919
Tel: (239)274-5900
Fax: (239)274-5930
Web Site: http://www.floridacommunity.com
To fund a student who will attend: FGCU, university of Florida/Gainesville, Florida State University/Tallahassee, Flagler College, Stetson University/Deland, University of Miami, University of Tampa, or Embry Riddle Aeronautical University/Daytona Beach.
Title of Award: D&A Florida Scholarships **Area, Field, or Subject:** Architecture; Business; Engineering; International affairs and relations; Journalism; Computer and information sciences; Law; Literature; Medicine; Physics; Chemistry; Political science. **Level of Education for which Award is Granted:** Undergraduate **Funds Available:** $10,000. **Duration:** One year.
Eligibility Requirements: Applicants must have graduated from a public or private high school in Charlotte, Glades, Hendry or Lee County; must pursue a degree in Architecture, Business, Engineering, International affairs and relations, Journalism, Computer and information sciences, Law, Literature, Medicine, Physics, Chemistry, or Political science. **Application Requirements:** Application forms are available online. Applicants must submit a letter of interest and letter of recommendation, a transcript and financial need documentation. **Deadline for Receipt:** February 15.

2814 ■ SOUTHWEST FLORIDA COMMUNITY FOUNDATION

8260 College Pkwy., Ste. 101
Fort Myers, FL 33919
Tel: (239)274-5900
Fax: (239)274-5930
Web Site: http://www.floridacommunity.com
To fund high school or undergraduate/graduate students planning to study at a 4-year accredited college in the area of Communications or Journalism.
Title of Award: Paul B. & Aline Flynn Scholarships **Area, Field, or Subject:** Communications; Journalism. **Level of Education for which Award is Granted:** Undergraduate **Funds Available:** No specific amount. **Duration:** One year.
Eligibility Requirements: Applicants must have graduated from a public or private high school in Charlotte, Collier, Glades, Hendry or Lee County; must pursue a degree in Communications, English or Journalism; and must maintain satisfactory grades. **Application Requirements:** Application forms are available online. Applicants must submit a student letter of interest, high school/college transcript, and letter of recommendation. **Deadline for Receipt:** February 15.

2815 ■ STARK COMMUNITY FOUNDATION

400 Market Ave. N, Ste. 200
Canton, OH 44702-2107
Tel: (330)454-3426
Fax: (330)454-5855
Web Site: http://www.starkcommunityfoundation.org
To provide scholarship assistance to qualified individuals who want to pursue their studies.
Title of Award: Velma Shotwell Griffin Memorial Scholarship Fund **Area, Field, or Subject:** History; Writing; Music. **Level of Education for which**
Award is Granted: Undergraduate **Number Awarded:** 1. **Funds Available:** $1,000. **Duration:** One year.
Eligibility Requirements: Applicants must be graduates of Conotton Valley High School or Carrollton High School; must be planning to enroll, or currently enrolled, at an accredited college or university to pursue further education in the following fields: (1) History; (2) Writing, not limited to, English Journalism, Language Arts, Communications and programs in Mass Media; (3) Music, not limited to vocal music, instrumental music, music history, music education, and music performance; (4) Any other program or field of study approved by the selection committee. **Application Requirements:** Applicants must submit completed application form and are advised to contact Carrollton High School Guidance Office, Connotton Valley High School Guidance Office. **Deadline for Receipt:** April 28.

2816 ■ UNITED METHODIST COMMUNICATIONS

PO Box 320
Nashville, TN 37202-0320
Tel: (615)742-5400
E-mail: umcom@umcom.org
Web Site: http://www.umcom.org
To provide financial assistance to students who intend to pursue a career in religion journalism for communications.
Title of Award: Leonard M. Perryman Communications Scholarships for Ethnic Minority Students **Area, Field, or Subject:** Religion; Journalism; Communications. **Level of Education for which Award is Granted:** Undergraduate **Funds Available:** $2,500.
Eligibility Requirements: Applicants must be undergraduate United Methodist students, who intend to pursue a career in religion journalism for study at an accredited U.S. college or university. **Application Requirements:** Applicants must submit all the required application information. **Deadline for Receipt:** March 15.

2817 ■ UNIVERSITY OF ALASKA ANCHORAGE

3211 Providence Dr.
Anchorage, AK 99508
Tel: (907)786-1800
Web Site: http://www.uaa.alaska.edu
To provide financial assistance for tuition and other educational expenses to full-time students who are formally admitted to a journalism, engineering, or education degree-seeking program at the University of Alaska Anchorage.
Title of Award: Sturgulewski Family Scholarships **Area, Field, or Subject:** Journalism; Engineering; Education. **Level of Education for which Award is Granted:** Graduate, Undergraduate **Funds Available:** $500.
Eligibility Requirements: Applicants must demonstrate motivation, academic and leadership potential; must be in good academic standing with a minimum cumulative GPA of 2.0 for undergraduates and 3.0 for graduates; must be formally admitted to a journalism, engineering, or education undergraduate, graduate, certificate, and/or vocational degree-seeking program at the University of Alaska Anchorage; must have plan on enrolling full-time (12 credits for undergraduates and 9 for graduates) at the University of Alaska Anchorage; may be an incoming or continuing student at the University of Alaska Anchorage; may be a U.S citizen, non-US citizen, Alaska resident, or out-of-state resident; must be enrolled in the semester for which the award is made. **Application Requirements:** Applicants must complete the electronic scholarship application available online at www.uaa.alaska.edu/scholarships/sturgulewski_family.cfm. **Deadline for Receipt:** February 15.

2818 ■ UNIVERSITY OF ALASKA ANCHORAGE

3211 Providence Dr.
Anchorage, AK 99508
Tel: (907)786-1800
Web Site: http://www.uaa.alaska.edu
To provide financial assistance for tuition and other educational expenses to minority students who are formally admitted to the journalism degree-seeking program at the University of Alaska Anchorage.
Title of Award: UAA Anchorage Daily News Minority Journalism Scholarships **Area, Field, or Subject:** Journalism. **Level of Education for which Award is Granted:** Undergraduate **Funds Available:** $500-$1,000. **Duration:** One year.

Eligibility Requirements: Applicants must demonstrate motivation, academic and leadership potential; must be in good academic standing with a minimum cumulative GPA of 2.0; must be formally admitted to a journalism degreeseeking program at the University of Alaska Anchorage; must plan on enrolling full-time (12 credits for undergraduates) at the University of Alaska Anchorage; may be an incoming or continuing student at the University of Alaska Anchorage; must be enrolled in the semester for which the award is made. **Application Requirements:** Applicants must complete the electronic scholarship application available online at www.uaa.alaska.edu/scholarships/adn.cfm. **Deadline for Receipt:** February 15.

2819 ■ UNIVERSITY OF ALASKA ANCHORAGE
3211 Providence Dr.
Anchorage, AK 99508
Tel: (907)786-1800
Web Site: http://www.uaa.alaska.edu
To provide financial assistance to University of Alaska Anchorage students who are formally admitted to the journalism & public communication degree-seeking program.
Title of Award: UAA Elaine Atwood Scholarships **Area, Field, or Subject:** Journalism; Public affairs. **Level of Education for which Award is Granted:** Undergraduate **Funds Available:** $2,500-5,000. **Duration:** One year.
Eligibility Requirements: Applicants must demonstrate motivation, academic and leadership potential; must be in good academic standing with a minimum cumulative GPA of 3.0; must be formally admitted to the Journalism and Public Communication degree program at UAA; must plan on enrolling full-time (12 credits) at the University of Alaska Anchorage; may be an incoming or continuing student at the University of Alaska Anchorage; must be an Alaska resident who will pursue a career in Alaska. **Application Requirements:** Applicants must complete the electronics scholarship application available online at www.uaa.alaska.edu/scholarships/elaine.cfm. **Deadline for Receipt:** February 15.

2820 ■ UNIVERSITY OF ALASKA ANCHORAGE
3211 Providence Dr.
Anchorage, AK 99508
Tel: (907)786-1800
Web Site: http://www.uaa.alaska.edu
To provide financial assistance for tuition and other educational expenses to full-time students who are formally admitted to a journalism & public communications degree-seeking program at the University of Alaska Anchorage and who are in financial need.
Title of Award: UAA GCI, Inc. Scholarships **Area, Field, or Subject:** Journalism; Public affairs. **Level of Education for which Award is Granted:** Undergraduate **Funds Available:** No specific amount.
Eligibility Requirements: Applicants must demonstrate motivation, academic and leadership potential; must be in good academic standing with a minimum cumulative GPA of 3.0; must be formally admitted to a journalism & public communications degree-seeking program at the University of Alaska Anchorage; must plan on enrolling full-time (12 credits) at the University of Alaska Anchorage; must be able to demonstrate financial need; must be enrolled in the semester for which the award is made; may be an incoming or continuing student at the University of Alaska Anchorage; may be a U.S citizen, non-U.S citizen, Alaska resident, or out-of-state resident. **Application Requirements:** Applicants must complete the electronic scholarship application available online at www.uaa.alaska.edu/scholarships/sturgulewski_family.cfm. **Deadline for Receipt:** February 15.

2821 ■ UNIVERSITY OF ALASKA ANCHORAGE
3211 Providence Dr.
Anchorage, AK 99508
Tel: (907)786-1800
Web Site: http://www.uaa.alaska.edu
To provide financial assistance for tuition and other related educational expenses to full-time students at the University of Alaska Anchorage with a declared major in art or journalism & public communications.
Title of Award: UAA Kimura Scholarship Fund (Photography Scholarships) **Area, Field, or Subject:** Art; Journalism; Photography. **Level of Education for which Award is Granted:** Undergraduate **Number Awarded:** 2. **Funds Available:** No specific amount.

Eligibility Requirements: Applicant must be a full-time student attending the University of Alaska Anchorage with a declared major in art or with a declared major in journalism & public communication with an emphasis in photography; must be in their junior year and has completed at least nine credits in studio photography classes at the 200 level or above; must be in good academic standing with at least a 3.0 GPA. **Application Requirements:** Applicants must submit a proof of their photography work. Application documents and other supporting documents must submit to UAA Office of Student Financial Assistance, Kimura Scholarships, PO Box 141608, Anchorage, AK 99514. **Deadline for Receipt:** February 15.

2822 ■ UNIVERSITY OF NORTH CAROLINA SCHOOL OF JOURNALISM AND MASS COMMUNICATION
University of North Carolina, Carol Hall CB 3365
Chapel Hill, NC 27599-3365
Tel: (919)962-1204
Fax: (919)962-0620
E-mail: jomc@unc.edu
Web Site: http://www.jomc.unc.edu
To educate journalists; to recognize students who demonstrate outstanding journalistic talent and a strong commitment to improving the community through honest and accurate work.
Title of Award: Floyd S. Alford Jr. Scholarships **Area, Field, or Subject:** Journalism. **Level of Education for which Award is Granted:** Undergraduate **Funds Available:** $500.
Eligibility Requirements: Applicants must be undergraduate students majoring in journalism. **Application Requirements:** Applicants must complete the application form.

2823 ■ UNIVERSITY OF NORTH CAROLINA SCHOOL OF JOURNALISM AND MASS COMMUNICATION
University of North Carolina, Carol Hall CB 3365
Chapel Hill, NC 27599-3365
Tel: (919)962-1204
Fax: (919)962-0620
E-mail: jomc@unc.edu
Web Site: http://www.jomc.unc.edu
To educate journalists.
Title of Award: Peggy Allen Community Newspaper Internships **Area, Field, or Subject:** Journalism; Communication. **Level of Education for which Award is Granted:** Undergraduate **Funds Available:** $5,000.
Eligibility Requirements: Applicants must be enrolled or plan to enroll in university and have an at least 2.9 GPA. **Application Requirements:** Applicants must complete the application form. **Deadline for Receipt:** February 1. **Additional Information:** PO Box 1080, Chapel Hill, NC 27514-1080.

2824 ■ UNIVERSITY OF NORTH CAROLINA SCHOOL OF JOURNALISM AND MASS COMMUNICATION
University of North Carolina, Carol Hall CB 3365
Chapel Hill, NC 27599-3365
Tel: (919)962-1204
Fax: (919)962-0620
E-mail: jomc@unc.edu
Web Site: http://www.jomc.unc.edu
To educate journalists.
Title of Award: Phillip Alston Scholarships **Area, Field, or Subject:** Journalism; Communications. **Level of Education for which Award is Granted:** Undergraduate **Funds Available:** $500.
Eligibility Requirements: Applicants must be undergraduate students in university. **Application Requirements:** Applicants must complete the application form.

2825 ■ UNIVERSITY OF NORTH CAROLINA SCHOOL OF JOURNALISM AND MASS COMMUNICATION
University of North Carolina, Carol Hall CB 3365
Chapel Hill, NC 27599-3365
Tel: (919)962-1204
Fax: (919)962-0620
E-mail: jomc@unc.edu
Web Site: http://www.jomc.unc.edu
To provide financial assistance to news-editorial journalism and community journalism students.
Title of Award: Jim Batten Community Newspaper Internships **Area, Field, or Subject:** Journalism; Communication. **Level of Education for**

which Award is Granted: Undergraduate **Funds Available:** $5,000. **Eligibility Requirements:** Applicants must be enrolled or plan to enroll in university and have at least 2.9 GPA. **Application Requirements:** Applicants must submit a completed application form. Applicants must contact the school's director of graduate studies for other application requirements. **Deadline for Receipt:** February 1. **Additional Information:** PO Box 1080, Chapel Hill, NC 27514-1080.

2826 ■ UNIVERSITY OF NORTH CAROLINA SCHOOL OF JOURNALISM AND MASS COMMUNICATION
University of North Carolina, Carol Hall CB 3365
Chapel Hill, NC 27599-3365
Tel: (919)962-1204
Fax: (919)962-0620
E-mail: jomc@unc.edu
Web Site: http://www.jomc.unc.edu
To educate journalists.
Title of Award: Tom Bost Scholarships **Area, Field, or Subject:** Journalism; Communications. **Level of Education for which Award is Granted:** Undergraduate **Funds Available:** $500.
Eligibility Requirements: Applicants must be undergraduate students in university. **Application Requirements:** Applicants must complete the application form.

2827 ■ UNIVERSITY OF NORTH CAROLINA SCHOOL OF JOURNALISM AND MASS COMMUNICATION
University of North Carolina, Carol Hall CB 3365
Chapel Hill, NC 27599-3365
Tel: (919)962-1204
Fax: (919)962-0620
E-mail: jomc@unc.edu
Web Site: http://www.jomc.unc.edu
To educate journalists.
Title of Award: Rick Brewer Scholarships **Area, Field, or Subject:** Broadcasting; Journalism; Public relations. **Level of Education for which Award is Granted:** Undergraduate **Funds Available:** $1,000.
Eligibility Requirements: Applicants must be undergraduate students with a keen interest in pursuing a career in sports journalism, broadcasting, or public relations. **Application Requirements:** Applicants must complete the application form.

2828 ■ UNIVERSITY OF NORTH CAROLINA SCHOOL OF JOURNALISM AND MASS COMMUNICATION
University of North Carolina, Carol Hall CB 3365
Chapel Hill, NC 27599-3365
Tel: (919)962-1204
Fax: (919)962-0620
E-mail: jomc@unc.edu
Web Site: http://www.jomc.unc.edu
To provide educational assistance for journalists intending to achieve better communication skills.
Title of Award: Ardis Cohoon Scholarships **Area, Field, or Subject:** Communications; Journalism. **Level of Education for which Award is Granted:** Undergraduate **Funds Available:** $500.
Eligibility Requirements: Applicants must be currently enrolled or plan to enroll in university with at least a 2.9 GPA. **Application Requirements:** Applicants must complete the application package.

2829 ■ UNIVERSITY OF NORTH CAROLINA SCHOOL OF JOURNALISM AND MASS COMMUNICATION
University of North Carolina, Carol Hall CB 3365
Chapel Hill, NC 27599-3365
Tel: (919)962-1204
Fax: (919)962-0620
E-mail: jomc@unc.edu
Web Site: http://www.jomc.unc.edu
To educate journalists.
Title of Award: Kathryn M. Cronin Scholarships **Area, Field, or Subject:** Journalism; Communications. **Level of Education for which Award is Granted:** Undergraduate **Funds Available:** $3,000.
Eligibility Requirements: Applicants must be enrolled or plan to enroll in university and have an at least 2.9 GPA. **Application Requirements:** Applicants must complete the application form; see Professor Tom Linden. **Deadline for Receipt:** March 1. **Additional Information:** PO Box 1080, Chapel Hill, NC 27514-1080.

2830 ■ UNIVERSITY OF NORTH CAROLINA SCHOOL OF JOURNALISM AND MASS COMMUNICATION
University of North Carolina, Carol Hall CB 3365
Chapel Hill, NC 27599-3365
Tel: (919)962-1204
Fax: (919)962-0620
E-mail: jomc@unc.edu
Web Site: http://www.jomc.unc.edu
To educate journalists.
Title of Award: James Davis Scholarships **Area, Field, or Subject:** Journalism; Communication. **Level of Education for which Award is Granted:** Undergraduate **Funds Available:** $4,000.
Eligibility Requirements: Applicants must be enrolled or plan to enroll in university and have an at least 2.9 GPA; Applicants must be studying North Carolina history, and North Carolina natives. **Application Requirements:** Applicants must complete the application form. **Deadline for Receipt:** February 1. **Additional Information:** PO Box 1080, Chapel Hill, NC 27514-1080.

2831 ■ UNIVERSITY OF NORTH CAROLINA SCHOOL OF JOURNALISM AND MASS COMMUNICATION
University of North Carolina, Carol Hall CB 3365
Chapel Hill, NC 27599-3365
Tel: (919)962-1204
Fax: (919)962-0620
E-mail: jomc@unc.edu
Web Site: http://www.jomc.unc.edu
To provide financial assistance to journalism students.
Title of Award: Vivian Edmonds Scholarships **Area, Field, or Subject:** Journalism; Communication. **Level of Education for which Award is Granted:** Undergraduate **Funds Available:** $1,000.
Eligibility Requirements: Applicants must be sophomore students and must have a minimum of 2.9 GPA. **Application Requirements:** Applicants must submit a completed application form. **Deadline for Receipt:** February 1. **Additional Information:** PO Box 1080, Chapel Hill, NC 27514-1080.

2832 ■ UNIVERSITY OF NORTH CAROLINA SCHOOL OF JOURNALISM AND MASS COMMUNICATION
University of North Carolina, Carol Hall CB 3365
Chapel Hill, NC 27599-3365
Tel: (919)962-1204
Fax: (919)962-0620
E-mail: jomc@unc.edu
Web Site: http://www.jomc.unc.edu
To educate journalists.
Title of Award: Reese Felts Scholarships **Area, Field, or Subject:** Communication; Journalism. **Level of Education for which Award is Granted:** Undergraduate **Funds Available:** $2,500.
Eligibility Requirements: Applicants must be currently enrolled or plan to enroll in university. **Application Requirements:** Applicants must complete the application form.

2833 ■ UNIVERSITY OF NORTH CAROLINA SCHOOL OF JOURNALISM AND MASS COMMUNICATION
University of North Carolina, Carol Hall CB 3365
Chapel Hill, NC 27599-3365
Tel: (919)962-1204
Fax: (919)962-0620
E-mail: jomc@unc.edu
Web Site: http://www.jomc.unc.edu
To educate journalists.
Title of Award: Ameel J. Fisher Scholarships **Area, Field, or Subject:** Journalism; Communication. **Level of Education for which Award is Granted:** Undergraduate **Funds Available:** $4,000.
Eligibility Requirements: Applicants must be enrolled or plan to enroll in university and have an at least 2.9 GPA. **Application Requirements:** Applicants must complete the application form. **Deadline for Receipt:** February 1. **Additional Information:** PO Box 1080, Chapel Hill, NC 27514-1080.

2834 ■ UNIVERSITY OF NORTH CAROLINA SCHOOL OF JOURNALISM AND MASS COMMUNICATION
University of North Carolina, Carol Hall CB 3365
Chapel Hill, NC 27599-3365

Tel: (919)962-1204
Fax: (919)962-0620
E-mail: jomc@unc.edu
Web Site: http://www.jomc.unc.edu
To educate journalists.

Title of Award: Kays Gary Scholarships **Area, Field, or Subject:** Communications; Journalism. **Level of Education for which Award is Granted:** Undergraduate **Funds Available:** $500.
Eligibility Requirements: Applicants must be currently enrolled or plan to enroll in university and have an at least 2.9 GPA. **Application Requirements:** Applicants must complete the application form.

2835 ■ UNIVERSITY OF NORTH CAROLINA SCHOOL OF JOURNALISM AND MASS COMMUNICATION
University of North Carolina, Carol Hall CB 3365
Chapel Hill, NC 27599-3365
Tel: (919)962-1204
Fax: (919)962-0620
E-mail: jomc@unc.edu
Web Site: http://www.jomc.unc.edu
To educate journalists.

Title of Award: Joy Gibson Scholarships **Area, Field, or Subject:** Journalism; Communications. **Level of Education for which Award is Granted:** Undergraduate **Funds Available:** $500.
Eligibility Requirements: Applicants must be undergraduate students in university. **Application Requirements:** Applicants must complete the application form.

2836 ■ UNIVERSITY OF NORTH CAROLINA SCHOOL OF JOURNALISM AND MASS COMMUNICATION
University of North Carolina, Carol Hall CB 3365
Chapel Hill, NC 27599-3365
Tel: (919)962-1204
Fax: (919)962-0620
E-mail: jomc@unc.edu
Web Site: http://www.jomc.unc.edu
To educate journalists.

Title of Award: L.C. Gifford Distinguished Journalism Scholarships **Area, Field, or Subject:** Communication; Journalism. **Level of Education for which Award is Granted:** Undergraduate **Funds Available:** $2,000.
Eligibility Requirements: Applicants must be journalism students from the University of North Carolina Chapel Hill. **Application Requirements:** Applicants must complete the application form.

2837 ■ UNIVERSITY OF NORTH CAROLINA SCHOOL OF JOURNALISM AND MASS COMMUNICATION
University of North Carolina, Carol Hall CB 3365
Chapel Hill, NC 27599-3365
Tel: (919)962-1204
Fax: (919)962-0620
E-mail: jomc@unc.edu
Web Site: http://www.jomc.unc.edu
To educate journalists.

Title of Award: Charles Hauser Scholarships **Area, Field, or Subject:** Communications; Journalism. **Level of Education for which Award is Granted:** Undergraduate **Funds Available:** $500.
Eligibility Requirements: Applicants must be currently enrolled or plan to enroll in university and have an at least 2.9 GPA. **Application Requirements:** Applicants must complete the application form.

2838 ■ UNIVERSITY OF NORTH CAROLINA SCHOOL OF JOURNALISM AND MASS COMMUNICATION
University of North Carolina, Carol Hall CB 3365
Chapel Hill, NC 27599-3365
Tel: (919)962-1204
Fax: (919)962-0620
E-mail: jomc@unc.edu
Web Site: http://www.jomc.unc.edu
To educate journalists.

Title of Award: Paul Green Houston Scholarships **Area, Field, or Subject:** Communication; Journalism. **Level of Education for which Award is Granted:** Undergraduate **Funds Available:** $1,500.
Eligibility Requirements: Applicants must be students majoring in news editorial journalism. **Application Requirements:** Applicants must complete the application form.

2839 ■ UNIVERSITY OF NORTH CAROLINA SCHOOL OF JOURNALISM AND MASS COMMUNICATION
University of North Carolina, Carol Hall CB 3365
Chapel Hill, NC 27599-3365
Tel: (919)962-1204
Fax: (919)962-0620
E-mail: jomc@unc.edu
Web Site: http://www.jomc.unc.edu
To provide financial assistance to journalism students.

Title of Award: James F. Hurley III Bicentennial Merit Scholarships **Area, Field, or Subject:** Journalism; Communication. **Level of Education for which Award is Granted:** Undergraduate **Funds Available:** $7,250.
Eligibility Requirements: Applicants must be enrolled or plan to enroll in university and have an at least 2.9 GPA. **Application Requirements:** Applicants must submit a completed application form. Applicants must contact the school's director of graduate studies for other application requirements. **Deadline for Receipt:** February 1. **Additional Information:** PO Box 1080, Chapel Hill, NC 27514-1080.

2840 ■ UNIVERSITY OF NORTH CAROLINA SCHOOL OF JOURNALISM AND MASS COMMUNICATION
University of North Carolina, Carol Hall CB 3365
Chapel Hill, NC 27599-3365
Tel: (919)962-1204
Fax: (919)962-0620
E-mail: jomc@unc.edu
Web Site: http://www.jomc.unc.edu
To educate journalists; to help defray expenses associated with travel to foreign countries for courses.

Title of Award: Fred Hutchison Travel Scholarships **Area, Field, or Subject:** Journalism; Communication. **Level of Education for which Award is Granted:** Undergraduate **Funds Available:** No specific amount.
Eligibility Requirements: Applicants must be students who are currently enrolled or plan to enroll in university. **Application Requirements:** Applicants must complete the application form; see Professor Tom Linden. **Deadline for Receipt:** March 1. **Additional Information:** jyopp@email.unc.edu.

2841 ■ UNIVERSITY OF NORTH CAROLINA SCHOOL OF JOURNALISM AND MASS COMMUNICATION
University of North Carolina, Carol Hall CB 3365
Chapel Hill, NC 27599-3365
Tel: (919)962-1204
Fax: (919)962-0620
E-mail: jomc@unc.edu
Web Site: http://www.jomc.unc.edu
To educate journalists; to support undergraduate students in traveling to a European country to learn about it's politics, culture, and mass media by working there.

Title of Award: Edward Jackson International Scholarships **Area, Field, or Subject:** Communication; Journalism. **Level of Education for which Award is Granted:** Undergraduate **Funds Available:** $2,500.
Eligibility Requirements: Applicants must be news editorial undergraduate students, preferably from North Carolina. **Application Requirements:** Applicants must complete the application form. **Deadline for Receipt:** February 1.

2842 ■ UNIVERSITY OF NORTH CAROLINA SCHOOL OF JOURNALISM AND MASS COMMUNICATION
University of North Carolina, Carol Hall CB 3365
Chapel Hill, NC 27599-3365
Tel: (919)962-1204
Fax: (919)962-0620
E-mail: jomc@unc.edu
Web Site: http://www.jomc.unc.edu
To educate journalists.

Title of Award: Gene Jackson Scholarships **Area, Field, or Subject:** Communication; Journalism. **Level of Education for which Award is Granted:** Undergraduate **Funds Available:** $1,250.
Eligibility Requirements: Applicants must be graduate students of the school whve had a distinguished career in newspaper and worked in the University of North Carolina Chapel Hill Development Office. **Application Requirements:** Applicants must complete the application form.

2843 ■ UNIVERSITY OF NORTH CAROLINA SCHOOL OF JOURNALISM AND MASS COMMUNICATION
University of North Carolina, Carol Hall CB 3365
Chapel Hill, NC 27599-3365
Tel: (919)962-1204
Fax: (919)962-0620
E-mail: jomc@unc.edu
Web Site: http://www.jomc.unc.edu
To provide educational assistance for journalists to help them achieve effective communication in the fields of science and medicine.
Title of Award: Peter Lars Jacobson Scholarships **Area, Field, or Subject:** Journalism; Communications. **Level of Education for which Award is Granted:** Undergraduate **Funds Available:** $500.
Eligibility Requirements: Applicants must be journalism and mass communication students who are able to write the best medical story. **Application Requirements:** Applicants must submit completed application form; applicants must submit a story or stories with name, address, telephone number and class year to Professor Tom Linden. **Deadline for Receipt:** February 1.

2844 ■ UNIVERSITY OF NORTH CAROLINA SCHOOL OF JOURNALISM AND MASS COMMUNICATION
University of North Carolina, Carol Hall CB 3365
Chapel Hill, NC 27599-3365
Tel: (919)962-1204
Fax: (919)962-0620
E-mail: jomc@unc.edu
Web Site: http://www.jomc.unc.edu
To educate journalists.
Title of Award: Glenn Keever Scholarships **Area, Field, or Subject:** Communication; Journalism. **Level of Education for which Award is Granted:** Undergraduate **Funds Available:** $2,500.
Eligibility Requirements: Applicants must be undergraduate students, preferably in North Carolina. **Application Requirements:** Applicants must complete the application form.

2845 ■ UNIVERSITY OF NORTH CAROLINA SCHOOL OF JOURNALISM AND MASS COMMUNICATION
University of North Carolina, Carol Hall CB 3365
Chapel Hill, NC 27599-3365
Tel: (919)962-1204
Fax: (919)962-0620
E-mail: jomc@unc.edu
Web Site: http://www.jomc.unc.edu
To educate journalists.
Title of Award: Raleigh Mann Scholarships **Area, Field, or Subject:** Journalism; Communications. **Level of Education for which Award is Granted:** Undergraduate **Funds Available:** $500.
Eligibility Requirements: Applicants must be undergraduate students in university. **Application Requirements:** Applicants must complete the application package.

2846 ■ UNIVERSITY OF NORTH CAROLINA SCHOOL OF JOURNALISM AND MASS COMMUNICATION
University of North Carolina, Carol Hall CB 3365
Chapel Hill, NC 27599-3365
Tel: (919)962-1204
Fax: (919)962-0620
E-mail: jomc@unc.edu
Web Site: http://www.jomc.unc.edu
To educate journalists.
Title of Award: C.A. "Pete" McKnight Scholarships **Area, Field, or Subject:** Journalism. **Level of Education for which Award is Granted:** Undergraduate **Funds Available:** $2,500.
Eligibility Requirements: Applicants must be currently enrolled or plan to enroll in university. **Application Requirements:** Applicants must complete the application form.

2847 ■ UNIVERSITY OF NORTH CAROLINA SCHOOL OF JOURNALISM AND MASS COMMUNICATION
University of North Carolina, Carol Hall CB 3365
Chapel Hill, NC 27599-3365
Tel: (919)962-1204

Fax: (919)962-0620
E-mail: jomc@unc.edu
Web Site: http://www.jomc.unc.edu
To educate journalists.
Title of Award: Edward Heywood Megson Scholarships **Area, Field, or Subject:** Journalism; Communications. **Level of Education for which Award is Granted:** Undergraduate **Funds Available:** $750.
Eligibility Requirements: Applicants must be graduates of University of North Carolina- Chapel Hill. **Application Requirements:** Applicants must complete the application form.

2848 ■ UNIVERSITY OF NORTH CAROLINA SCHOOL OF JOURNALISM AND MASS COMMUNICATION
University of North Carolina, Carol Hall CB 3365
Chapel Hill, NC 27599-3365
Tel: (919)962-1204
Fax: (919)962-0620
E-mail: jomc@unc.edu
Web Site: http://www.jomc.unc.edu
To provide financial assistance to minority and disadvantaged students.
Title of Award: Quincy Sharpe Mills Scholarships **Area, Field, or Subject:** Journalism; Communication. **Level of Education for which Award is Granted:** Undergraduate **Funds Available:** $3,000.
Eligibility Requirements: Applicants must be currently enrolled in or planning to attend university and must have a minimum of 2.9 GPA. **Application Requirements:** Applicants must submit a completed application form. **Deadline for Receipt:** February 1. **Additional Information:** PO Box 1080, Chapel Hill, NC 27514-1080.

2849 ■ UNIVERSITY OF NORTH CAROLINA SCHOOL OF JOURNALISM AND MASS COMMUNICATION
University of North Carolina, Carol Hall CB 3365
Chapel Hill, NC 27599-3365
Tel: (919)962-1204
Fax: (919)962-0620
E-mail: jomc@unc.edu
Web Site: http://www.jomc.unc.edu
To provide financial assistance to journalism students.
Title of Award: Alexander Morisey Scholarships **Area, Field, or Subject:** Journalism; Communication. **Level of Education for which Award is Granted:** Undergraduate **Funds Available:** $1,000.
Eligibility Requirements: Applicants must be first year students and must have a minimum of 2.9 GPA. **Application Requirements:** Applicants must submit a completed application form. **Deadline for Receipt:** February 1. **Additional Information:** PO Box 1080, Chapel Hill, NC 27514-1080.

2850 ■ UNIVERSITY OF NORTH CAROLINA SCHOOL OF JOURNALISM AND MASS COMMUNICATION
University of North Carolina, Carol Hall CB 3365
Chapel Hill, NC 27599-3365
Tel: (919)962-1204
Fax: (919)962-0620
E-mail: jomc@unc.edu
Web Site: http://www.jomc.unc.edu
To provide financial assistance to journalism students.
Title of Award: Robert Pittman Scholarships **Area, Field, or Subject:** Journalism; Communication. **Level of Education for which Award is Granted:** Undergraduate **Funds Available:** $7,000.
Eligibility Requirements: Applicants must be enrolled or plan to enroll in university and have at least 2.9 GPA; applicants must have an internship at St. Petersburg Times. **Application Requirements:** Applicants must submit a completed application form. Applicants must contact the School's Director of graduate studies for other application requirements. **Deadline for Receipt:** February 1. **Additional Information:** PO Box 1080, Chapel Hill, NC 27514-1080.

2851 ■ UNIVERSITY OF NORTH CAROLINA SCHOOL OF JOURNALISM AND MASS COMMUNICATION
University of North Carolina, Carol Hall CB 3365
Chapel Hill, NC 27599-3365
Tel: (919)962-1204
Fax: (919)962-0620

E-mail: jomc@unc.edu
Web Site: http://www.jomc.unc.edu
To provide financial assistance to Latino students studying newspaper journalism.

Title of Award: Erwin Potts Scholarships **Area, Field, or Subject:** Journalism; Communication. **Level of Education for which Award is Granted:** Undergraduate **Funds Available:** $2,000.

Eligibility Requirements: Applicants must be currently enrolled or plan to attend in university and must have a minimum of 2.9 GPA. **Application Requirements:** Applicants must submit a completed application form. **Deadline for Receipt:** February 1. **Additional Information:** PO Box 1080, Chapel Hill, NC 27514-1080.

2852 ■ UNIVERSITY OF NORTH CAROLINA SCHOOL OF JOURNALISM AND MASS COMMUNICATION

University of North Carolina, Carol Hall CB 3365
Chapel Hill, NC 27599-3365
Tel: (919)962-1204
Fax: (919)962-0620
E-mail: jomc@unc.edu
Web Site: http://www.jomc.unc.edu
To provide financial assistance to journalism students.

Title of Award: Peter DeWitt Pruden and Phyliss Harrill Pruden Scholarships **Area, Field, or Subject:** Journalism; Communication. **Level of Education for which Award is Granted:** Undergraduate **Funds Available:** $10,000.

Eligibility Requirements: Applicants must be enrolled or plan to enroll in a university in North Carolina, Tennessee, or Virginia and have an at least 2.9 GPA. **Application Requirements:** Applicants must submit a completed application form. Applicants must contact the school's director of graduate studies for other application requirements. **Deadline for Receipt:** February 1. **Additional Information:** PO Box 1080, Chapel Hill, NC 27514-1080.

2853 ■ UNIVERSITY OF NORTH CAROLINA SCHOOL OF JOURNALISM AND MASS COMMUNICATION

University of North Carolina, Carol Hall CB 3365
Chapel Hill, NC 27599-3365
Tel: (919)962-1204
Fax: (919)962-0620
E-mail: jomc@unc.edu
Web Site: http://www.jomc.unc.edu
To educate journalists.

Title of Award: Bob Quincy Scholarships **Area, Field, or Subject:** Communication; Journalism. **Level of Education for which Award is Granted:** Undergraduate **Funds Available:** $2,500.

Eligibility Requirements: Applicants must be currently enrolled or plan to enroll in university. **Application Requirements:** Applicants must complete the application form.

2854 ■ UNIVERSITY OF NORTH CAROLINA SCHOOL OF JOURNALISM AND MASS COMMUNICATION

University of North Carolina, Carol Hall CB 3365
Chapel Hill, NC 27599-3365
Tel: (919)962-1204
Fax: (919)962-0620
E-mail: jomc@unc.edu
Web Site: http://www.jomc.unc.edu
To educate journalists.

Title of Award: Marjorie Usher Regan Scholarships **Area, Field, or Subject:** Communication; Journalism. **Level of Education for which Award is Granted:** Undergraduate **Funds Available:** $2,000.

Eligibility Requirements: Applicants must be women with a career interest in print journalism. **Application Requirements:** Applicants must complete the application form.

2855 ■ UNIVERSITY OF NORTH CAROLINA SCHOOL OF JOURNALISM AND MASS COMMUNICATION

University of North Carolina, Carol Hall CB 3365
Chapel Hill, NC 27599-3365
Tel: (919)962-1204
Fax: (919)962-0620
E-mail: jomc@unc.edu

Web Site: http://www.jomc.unc.edu
To educate journalists so that they can communicate effectively.

Title of Award: Eugene L. Roberts Jr. Prize **Area, Field, or Subject:** Journalism. **Level of Education for which Award is Granted:** Undergraduate **Funds Available:** $5,500.

Eligibility Requirements: Applicants must be undergraduate students interested in print journalism who propose the best idea for a Gene Roberts-type story; applicants must be returning to the School for at least one semester, when he or she will research and write the story in JOMC 296. The course is "Independent Study" supervised by a faculty member for three credits. **Application Requirements:** Applicants must complete the application form. **Deadline for Receipt:** February 1.

2856 ■ UNIVERSITY OF NORTH CAROLINA SCHOOL OF JOURNALISM AND MASS COMMUNICATION

University of North Carolina, Carol Hall CB 3365
Chapel Hill, NC 27599-3365
Tel: (919)962-1204
Fax: (919)962-0620
E-mail: jomc@unc.edu
Web Site: http://www.jomc.unc.edu
To educate journalists.

Title of Award: A.C. Snow Scholarships **Area, Field, or Subject:** Journalism. **Level of Education for which Award is Granted:** Undergraduate **Funds Available:** $750.

Eligibility Requirements: Applicants must be news editorial students with an interest in grammar. **Application Requirements:** Applicants must complete the application form.

2857 ■ UNIVERSITY OF NORTH CAROLINA SCHOOL OF JOURNALISM AND MASS COMMUNICATION

University of North Carolina, Carol Hall CB 3365
Chapel Hill, NC 27599-3365
Tel: (919)962-1204
Fax: (919)962-0620
E-mail: jomc@unc.edu
Web Site: http://www.jomc.unc.edu
To provide financial assistance to journalism students.

Title of Award: Tucker Family Scholarships **Area, Field, or Subject:** Journalism; Communication. **Level of Education for which Award is Granted:** Undergraduate **Funds Available:** $5,000.

Eligibility Requirements: Applicants must be enrolled or plan to enroll in university and have at least 2.9 GPA. **Application Requirements:** Applicants must submit a completed application form. **Deadline for Receipt:** February 1. **Additional Information:** PO Box 1080, Chapel Hill, NC 27514-1080.

2858 ■ UNIVERSITY OF NORTH CAROLINA SCHOOL OF JOURNALISM AND MASS COMMUNICATION

University of North Carolina, Carol Hall CB 3365
Chapel Hill, NC 27599-3365
Tel: (919)962-1204
Fax: (919)962-0620
E-mail: jomc@unc.edu
Web Site: http://www.jomc.unc.edu
To educate journalists.

Title of Award: David Julian Wichard Scholarships **Area, Field, or Subject:** Communication; Journalism. **Level of Education for which Award is Granted:** Undergraduate **Funds Available:** $2,000.

Eligibility Requirements: Applicants must be currently enrolled or planning to enroll in university; applicants must be residents of North Carolina. **Application Requirements:** Applicants must complete the application form.

2859 ■ UNIVERSITY OF NORTH CAROLINA SCHOOL OF JOURNALISM AND MASS COMMUNICATION

University of North Carolina, Carol Hall CB 3365
Chapel Hill, NC 27599-3365
Tel: (919)962-1204
Fax: (919)962-0620
E-mail: jomc@unc.edu
Web Site: http://www.jomc.unc.edu
To provide financial assistance to news-editorial graduate students.

Title of Award: Tom Wicker Scholarships **Area, Field, or Subject:** Journalism; Communication. **Level of Education for which Award is

Granted: Undergraduate **Funds Available:** $1,000.
Eligibility Requirements: Applicants must be enrolled or plan to enroll in university and have an at least 2.9 GPA. **Application Requirements:** Applicants must submit a completed application form. Applicants must contact the school's director of graduate studies for other application requirements. **Deadline for Receipt:** February 1. **Additional Information:** PO Box 1080, Chapel Hill, NC 27514-1080.

2860 ■ UNIVERSITY OF NORTH CAROLINA SCHOOL OF JOURNALISM AND MASS COMMUNICATION
University of North Carolina, Carol Hall CB 3365
Chapel Hill, NC 27599-3365
Tel: (919)962-1204
Fax: (919)962-0620
E-mail: jomc@unc.edu
Web Site: http://www.jomc.unc.edu
To provide financial assistance to journalism students.
Title of Award: WTVD Endowment Scholarships **Area, Field, or Subject:** Journalism; Communication. **Level of Education for which Award is Granted:** Undergraduate **Funds Available:** $1,000.
Eligibility Requirements: Applicants must be enrolled or plan to enroll in university and have at least 2.9 GPA. **Application Requirements:** Applicants must submit a completed application form. **Deadline for Receipt:** February 1. **Additional Information:** PO Box 1080, Chapel Hill, NC 27514-1080.

2861 ■ UNIVERSITY OF WISCONSIN-MADISON
432 N Murray St.
Madison, WI 53706-1496
Tel: (608)262-3060
Fax: (608)262-9068
E-mail: askbucky@uwmad.wisc.edu
Web Site: http://www.wisc.edu
To support UW-Madison students in their education.
Title of Award: Wisconsin-Madison Journalism Scholarships **Area, Field, or Subject:** Journalism. **Level of Education for which Award is Granted:** Undergraduate **Number Awarded:** Varies. **Funds Available:** $500-$1,500.
Eligibility Requirements: Applicants must be UW-Madison junior or senior journalism students who demonstrated academic merit and have gained professional experience. **Application Requirements:** Applicants must complete the electronic application available online. **Deadline for Receipt:** Varies. **Additional Information:** School of Journalism, Placement Office, at 608-263-4858, or salkin@facstaff.wisc.edu.

2862 ■ WHITE HOUSE CORRESPONDENTS' ASSOCIATION
600 New Hampshire Ave.
Washington, DC 20037
Tel: (202)266-7453
Fax: (202)266-7454
Web Site: http://www.whca.net
To provide financial assistance to promising journalism students.
Title of Award: The Frank Cormier Scholarships **Area, Field, or Subject:** Journalism. **Level of Education for which Award is Granted:** Undergraduate **Funds Available:** $24,000. **Duration:** Four years of undergraduate study.
Eligibility Requirements: Applicants must be undergraduate journalism students at Phillip Merrill College of Journalism at the University of Maryland. **Additional Information:** Established in 1991, in 1994 it was named in honor of Frank Cormier, legendary White House correspondent for The Associated Press.

2863 ■ WINSTON-SALEM FOUNDATION
860 W Fifth St.
Winston-Salem, NC 27101-2506
Tel: (336)725-2382
Fax: (336)727-0581
E-mail: info@wsfoundation.org
Web Site: http://www.wsfoundation.org
To provide a merit scholarship to high school senior planning to pursue a career in journalism.
Title of Award: Denise Franklin Journalism Scholarships **Area, Field, or Subject:** Journalism. **Level of Education for which Award is Granted:** Undergraduate **Funds Available:** $500.

Eligibility Requirements: Students must have a minimum, unweighted, grade point average of 3.0. Applicants should have a minimum of two years involvement in a journalism project or involvement in two different types of journalistic media. Students of color with a strong academic record and desire to pursue a career in journalism are encouraged to apply. Applicant must be a US citizen. **Application Requirements:** Applicants must complete and submit an application online at the Foundation's Web site. In addition to submittal of the application, applicants must also provide the following to be considered: Provide a letter of recommendation from a current journalism instructor; Submit up to three samples of journalism work such as published newspaper articles, audio or videotapes, a website or a photo essay (samples will not be returned); High school grade transcript through first semester, 12th grade. **Additional Information:** Established in 2004. **Deadline for Receipt:** March 31. **Additional Information:** Edna Barker, 336-714-3445; Kay Dillon, 336-714-3446.

2864 ■ XAVIER UNIVERSITY
3800 Victory Pky.
Cincinnati, OH 45207
Tel: (513)745-3000
Free: 800-344-GOXU
Web Site: http://www.xavier.edu
To financially support students with their education.
Title of Award: Xavier University Departmental Scholarships **Area, Field, or Subject:** Chemistry; Classical studies; History; Mathematics and mathematical sciences; Modern languages; Physics. **Level of Education for which Award is Granted:** Undergraduate **Funds Available:** $2500.
Eligibility Requirements: Applicant must top the score in either of the six departmental exams (chemistry, classics (Latin), history, mathematics, modern languages (French, German or Spanish) and physics). Student must major in the area for which the scholarship is awarded. **Application Requirements:** Participants will take an exam in the appropriate subject area and have an opportunity to speak with faculty and learn more about the department.

Music

2865 ■ BARRIENTOS SCHOLARSHIP FOUNDATION
PO Box 7173
Omaha, NE 68107
Tel: (402)215-5106
E-mail: info@barrientosscholarship.org
Web Site: http://www.barrientosscholarship.org
To provide financial assistance to qualified students who want to pursue their studies.
Title of Award: Artistic Scholarship Awards **Area, Field, or Subject:** Music; Visual arts; Theater arts; Dance. **Level of Education for which Award is Granted:** Undergraduate **Number Awarded:** No specific amount. **Funds Available:** $250-$500. **Duration:** One year.
Eligibility Requirements: Applicants must be students pursuing higher education and career goals that focus on one or more of the arts - music, visual arts, theater, or dance; must be of Latino heritage; must be high school graduating seniors, currently enrolled in college, or adults ready to pursue college; must plan to enroll in at least two classes and attend an accredited community college, university, or technical or vocational school in the state of Nebraska or surrounding greater Omaha Metropolitan area; must have a minimum of 2.5 GPA. **Application Requirements:** Applicants must complete the application form available online; must have a personal essay with a minimum of two pages; must submit letters of recommendation and official high school or college transcript. Application form and requirements must be sent to Barrientos Scholarship Foundation, P.O Box 7173, Omaha, NE 68107. **Deadline for Receipt:** May 15.

2866 ■ DULUTH SUPERIOR AREA COMMUNITY FOUNDATION
324 W Superior St., Ste. 212
Duluth, MN 55802
Tel: (218)726-0232
Fax: (218)726-0257
E-mail: info@communityfoundation.com
Web Site: http://www.dsacommunityfoundation.com

To provide financial assistance for art students.
Title of Award: William E. Barto Scholarships **Area, Field, or Subject:** Arts; Visual arts. **Level of Education for which Award is Granted:** Undergraduate **Number Awarded:** 1. **Funds Available:** $2,000. **Duration:** One year.
Eligibility Requirements: Applicants must be graduating seniors of public and private high schools in Duluth and Superior; must be planning to major in arts or visual arts; must rank in the upper 25% of their class. **Application Requirements:** Applicants must submit all the required application information. **Additional Information:** Scholarship may be accepted in addition to other awards, provided that the combined amount does not exceed the full amount of tuition, books, fees and room and board charges. **Deadline for Receipt:** January 15.

2867 ■ FIRST COMMUNITY FOUNDATION OF PENNSYLVANIA, WILLIAMSPORT-LYCOMING
330 Pine St., Suite 401
Williamsport, PA 17701
Tel: (570)321-1500; (866)901-2372
Fax: (570)321-6434
E-mail: fcfpa@fcfpa.org
Web Site: http://www.wlfoundation.org
To provide financial assistance for Danville Area High School seniors who have been accepted into a full-time undergraduate program.
Title of Award: Jane Hood Memorial Fund **Area, Field, or Subject:** Visual arts; Mathematics and mathematical science; Science; Engineering. **Level of Education for which Award is Granted:** Undergraduate **Funds Available:** No specific amount.
Eligibility Requirements: Applicants must be accepted in a full-time undergraduate program at an institution of higher education to study graphic-visual arts, math and/or science (including engineering). Applicants must have exhibited good citizenship and community involvement. **Application Requirements:** Applicants may request an application to the Guidance Counselor of Danville Area School District. **Additional Information:** Gary Grozier, Guidance Counselor of Danville Area School District, 600 Walnut St., Danville, PA 17821; 570-271-3268 ext. 2006; ggrozier@danville.k12.pa.us.

2868 ■ FOUNDATION FOR THE CAROLINAS
217 S Tryon St.
Charlotte, NC 28202
Tel: (704)973-4500
Free: 800-973-7244
Web Site: http://www.fftc.org
To provide financial assistance for Richmond County, NC students with demonstrated talent and career interests in the visual arts.
Title of Award: Sally Cole Visual Arts Scholarship Fund **Area, Field, or Subject:** Visual arts. **Level of Education for which Award is Granted:** Undergraduate **Funds Available:** $7,500. **Duration:** One year.
Eligibility Requirements: Applicants must be planning to attend an accredited two-year or four-year postsecondary institution with a degree program in visual arts; must be high school seniors in good academic standing scheduled to graduate in the spring of the current school year; must have an expressed and demonstrated interest in the visual and/or studio arts which primarily includes, but are not limited to, painting, drawing, sculpture, illustration and ceramics; must be legal residents of Richmond County, NC. **Application Requirements:** Applicants must submit completed application form; official copy of high school transcript(s), including SAT/ACT scores if taken; three recommendation forms, two of which must come from individuals able to evaluate the applicants' aptitude and career potential in the visual arts; one to two pages type-written statement expressing a) applicants' reasons for applying for the scholarship, b) applicants' interest in the arts, c) applicants' educational and career goals in the field of visual arts; and samples (3-5 labeled color slides) of applicants' original artwork. **Deadline for Receipt:** March 1.

2869 ■ ORANGE COUNTY COMMUNITY FOUNDATION
30 Corporate Park, Ste. 410
Irvine, CA 92606
Tel: (949)553-4202
Fax: (949)553-4211
E-mail: cmontesano@oc-cf.org

Web Site: http://www.oc-cf.org
To award scholarship to the students who are residents of Orange County.
Title of Award: Orange County Centennial Arts Scholarships **Area, Field, or Subject:** Performing arts; Visual Arts; Theater arts; Music. **Level of Education for which Award is Granted:** Undergraduate **Number Awarded:** 3. **Funds Available:** $2,000.
Eligibility Requirements: Applicants must: be local high school graduating seniors who are residents of Orange County, California, and who are completing their last three years of high school in the county; be students who are planning to enroll full-time at an accredited college or university and majoring in the arts. Example of acceptable majors include: dance, voice, opera, theater arts, musical theater, visual arts and music; demonstrated record of community service and leadership. particular attention will be given to training, honors and achievements in the arts. **Application Requirements:** Applicants must include a 250-word essay in their application. Applicants must write about their interests and plans and the way in which their plan is appropriate to their situation, abilities and long-term goals. **Deadline for Receipt:** March 15. **Additional Information:** Claudia Montesano, 949-553-4202 ext. 46; cmontesano@oc-cf.org.

2870 ■ PRIDE FOUNDATION
PO Box 2194, 1122 E Pike St. PMB 1001
Seattle, WA 98112
Tel: (206)323-3318
Free: 800-735-7287
Fax: (206)323-1017
E-mail: prideweb@pridefoundation.org
Web Site: http://www.pridefoundation.org
To provide scholarship to the students who have been stigmatized, isolated or closeted because of sexual identity issues.
Title of Award: Bill Bendiner and Doug Morgenson Scholarships **Area, Field, or Subject:** Human relations; Health sciences; Visual arts. **Level of Education for which Award is Granted:** Undergraduate **Funds Available:** No specific amount.
Eligibility Requirements: Applicant must be pursing a career in human services, health sciences or visual arts. **Application Requirements:** Qualified students are asked to submit an application to determine eligibility for scholarships. Applicants may download an application form from the Foundation's website. **Additional Information:** Pride Foundation at the above address.

2871 ■ PRIDE FOUNDATION
PO Box 2194, 1122 E Pike St. PMB 1001
Seattle, WA 98112
Tel: (206)323-3318
Free: 800-735-7287
Fax: (206)323-1017
E-mail: prideweb@pridefoundation.org
Web Site: http://www.pridefoundation.org
To provide scholarship to the students who have been stigmatized, isolated or closeted because of sexual identity issues.
Title of Award: Jack D. Motteler Scholarships **Area, Field, or Subject:** Visual arts. **Level of Education for which Award is Granted:** Undergraduate **Funds Available:** No specific amount.
Eligibility Requirements: Applicant must be an undergraduate student in the visual arts. **Application Requirements:** Qualified students are asked to submit an application to determine eligibility for scholarships. Applicants may download an application form from the Foundation's website. **Additional Information:** Pride Foundation at the above address.

2872 ■ PRIDE FOUNDATION
PO Box 2194, 1122 E Pike St. PMB 1001
Seattle, WA 98112
Tel: (206)323-3318
Free: 800-735-7287
Fax: (206)323-1017
E-mail: prideweb@pridefoundation.org
Web Site: http://www.pridefoundation.org
To provide scholarship to the students who have been stigmatized, isolated or closeted because of sexual identity issues.
Title of Award: Ric Ulrich and Chuck Pischke Scholarships **Area, Field, or Subject:** Visual arts. **Level of Education for which Award is Granted:** Undergraduate **Funds Available:** No specific amount.

Eligibility Requirements: Candidate must intend to study in visual arts and design. Preference is given to students who are self-identified lesbian, gay, bisexual or transgender (LGBT). **Application Requirements:** Qualified students are asked to submit an application to determine eligibility for scholarships. Applicants may download an application form from the Foundation's website. **Additional Information:** Pride Foundation at the above address.

2873 ■ PRIDE FOUNDATION
PO Box 2194, 1122 E Pike St. PMB 1001
Seattle, WA 98112
Tel: (206)323-3318
Free: 800-735-7287
Fax: (206)323-1017
E-mail: prideweb@pridefoundation.org
Web Site: http://www.pridefoundation.org
To provide scholarship to the students who have been stigmatized, isolated or closeted because of sexual identity issues.
Title of Award: Patricia Van Kirk Scholarships **Area, Field, or Subject:** Theater arts; Visual arts. **Level of Education for which Award is Granted:** Undergraduate **Funds Available:** No specific amount.
Eligibility Requirements: Applicant must be a lesbian studying theater or visual arts. Preference is given to students who are self-identified lesbian, gay, bisexual or transgender (LGBT). **Application Requirements:** Qualified students are asked to submit an application to determine eligibility for scholarships. Applicants may download an application form from the Foundation's website. **Additional Information:** Pride Foundation at the above address.

2874 ■ RHODE ISLAND FOUNDATION
One Union Sta.
Providence, RI 02903
Tel: (401)274-4564
Fax: (401)331-8085
Web Site: http://www.rifoundation.org/matriarch/default.asp
To provide support for deserving visual art or music major students intending to pursue their education.
Title of Award: Constant Memorial Scholarship for Aquidneck Island Resident **Area, Field, or Subject:** Visual arts; Education, Music. **Level of Education for which Award is Granted:** Undergraduate **Number Awarded:** 2. **Funds Available:** $2,000-$5,000. **Duration:** One year.
Eligibility Requirements: Applicants must be Aquidneck Island residents for at least three years; must demonstrate a serious interest in visual arts and/or music; must have a proof of enrollment in an arts or music major at an accredited institution of higher education; and must be able to demonstrate financial need. **Application Requirements:** Applicants must complete the application form, available online; must have a copy of their financial aid award letter; must submit a recent official college transcript; three proofs of Rhode Island residency; one essay; copy of their final Student Aid Report; one letter of recommendation; and a sample of work done within the last 12 months. Application forms and other supporting documents must be sent to Libby Monahan, GFWC Women's Club of South County Scholarship, Rhode Island Foundation, One Union Station, Providence, RI 02903. **Deadline for Receipt:** June 9.

2875 ■ ROYAL BANK OF CANADA
260 Adelaide St. E
Toronto, ON, Canada M5A 1N1
(866)363-1722
E-mail: 4edu@sympatico.ca
Web Site: http://www.rbcroyalbank.com
To provide scholarship assistance to qualified individuals who want to pursue their studies.
Title of Award: RBC Royal Bank Scholarships for Undergraduates **Area, Field, or Subject:** Business; Science; Visual arts. **Level of Education for which Award is Granted:** Undergraduate **Number Awarded:** 9. **Funds Available:** Gold: $5,000; Silver: $3,000; Bronze: $2,000. **Duration:** One year.
Eligibility Requirements: Applicants must be Canadian citizens or permanent residents; must be enrolled as full-time students in an accredited Canadian college or university; must be entering their second through final program year; must have minimum cumulative GPA equivalent to 70% average. **Application Requirements:** Applicants must

provide basic contact details, including their email address, phone numbers, mailing address, and must provide information about their college or university, program of study, and cumulative GPA. **Deadline for Receipt:** June 9.

2876 ■ SAFE SCHOOLS COALITION
1002 E Seneca St.
Seattle, WA 98122-4203
Tel: (206)957-1621
Fax: (206)325-2689
Web Site: http://www.safeschoolscoalition.org
To provide financial assistance for gay, lesbian, bisexual and transgender students pursuing higher education.
Title of Award: Pride Foundation Scholarships **Area, Field, or Subject:** Business Administration; Computer Science; Political Science; Visual arts. **Level of Education for which Award is Granted:** Undergraduate **Funds Available:** Range from $500 to $10,000.
Eligibility Requirements: Applicants must be gay, lesbian, bisexual and transgendered students in these fields of studies. **Application Requirements:** Applicants must check the available website for the required materials. **Deadline for Receipt:** January.

2877 ■ STARK COMMUNITY FOUNDATION
400 Market Ave. N, Ste. 200
Canton, OH 44702-2107
Tel: (330)454-3426
Fax: (330)454-5855
Web Site: http://www.starkcommunityfoundation.org
To provide scholarship assistance to qualified individuals who want to pursue their studies.
Title of Award: Manzer-Keener-Wefler Scholarships **Area, Field, or Subject:** Photography; Visual arts. **Level of Education for which Award is Granted:** Undergraduate **Funds Available:** No specific amount.
Eligibility Requirements: Applicants must have been accepted by, or are currently attending, a two-year or four-year college or university or art institute within the United States; that their chosen field of study is in the field of or related to photography or visual arts; either seniors attending a high school in Stark County, OH, or counties contiguous to Stark, who will graduate the year the scholarship is awarded or college undergraduate students originally from Stark County, OH, or counties contiguous to Stark, who are currently attending a two-year or four-year college or university or art institute full time or non-traditional college students originally from Stark County, OH, or counties contiguous to Stark, who are currently attending a two-year or four-year college or university or art institute part-time; and first time applicants must have a minimum GPA of at least 2.5 on a 4.0. **Application Requirements:** Applicants must submit a two letters of recommendation letter. Application from and other supporting documents must be sent to Stark Community Foundation, 400 Market Ave. N, Ste. 200, Canton, OH 44702. **Deadline for Receipt:** May 1.

2878 ■ VESALIUS TRUST
20751 W Chartwell Dr.
Kildeer, IL 60047
Tel: (847)540-8671
Fax: (847)540-8681
E-mail: vesaliustrust@aol.com
Web Site: http://www.vesaliustrust.org
To support students enrolled in medical illustration programs.
Title of Award: Vesalius Trust Student Scholarships **Area, Field, or Subject:** Visual arts. **Level of Education for which Award is Granted:** Undergraduate **Funds Available:** No specific amount.
Eligibility Requirements: Applicants must be enrolled in a medical illustration program and must have completed one year of the curriculum. **Application Requirements:** Applicants must submit an application form; a resume; graduate project description; budget and timeline; transcripts; preceptor form and faculty advisor form. **Deadline for Receipt:** November 9. **Additional Information:** Wendy Hiller Gee, VT Student Grants and Scholarships, 650-244-4320 or wendy.hillergee@krames.com.

Performing Arts

2879 ■ ALABAMA COMMISSION ON HIGHER EDUCATION
PO Box 302000
Montgomery, AL 36130-2000

Tel: (334)242-1998
Fax: (334)242-0268
Web Site: http://www.ache.alabama.gov
To support the education of Alabama students.
Title of Award: ACHE Junior and Community College Performing Arts Scholarships **Area, Field, or Subject:** Performing arts. **Level of Education for which Award is Granted:** Undergraduate **Funds Available:** Not to exceed total tuition and books. **Duration:** Once academic year.
Eligibility Requirements: Applicant must be full-time student enrolled in public junior and community colleges in Alabama. **Application Requirements:** Applications must contact the financial aid office at any public junior or community college in Alabama. Competitive auditions will also be scheduled as part of the application process.

2880 ■ AMERICAN ASSOCIATION FOR HEALTH EDUCATION
1900 Association Dr.
Reston, VA 20191-1598
Tel: (703)476-3400
Free: 800-213-7193
Web Site: http://www.aahperd.org/aahe
To support members with their educational pursuit.
Title of Award: Ruth Abernathy Presidential Scholarships **Area, Field, or Subject:** Health education; Physical education. **Level of Education for which Award is Granted:** Graduate, Undergraduate **Number Awarded:** Three undergraduates; Two graduate students. **Funds Available:** $1000-$1500; and a three-year AAHPERD membership.
Eligibility Requirements: Applicant must be undergraduate or graduate student members majoring in a field related to one or more of the disciplines represented by AAHPERD and its associations; and have a cumulative GPA of 3.5. **Application Requirements:** Applicants must submit a completed application from together with the required materials. Application materials should be submitted by U.S. mail (fax copies will not be accepted). **Deadline for Receipt:** October 15. **Additional Information:** Deb Callis at dcallis@aahperd.org.

2881 ■ AMERICAN MUSICOLOGICAL SOCIETY
6010 College Station
Brunswick, ME 04011-8451
Tel: (207)798-4243; 877-679-7648
Fax: (207)798-4254
E-mail: ams@ams-net.org
Web Site: http://www.ams-net.org
To provide financial assistance for full-time studies.
Title of Award: Alvin H. Johnson AMS Dissertation Fellowships **Area, Field, or Subject:** Music. **Level of Education for which Award is Granted:** Undergraduate **Number Awarded:** 50. **Funds Available:** $19,000.
Eligibility Requirements: Applicants must be anyone eligibly registered in good standing for a doctorate at a North American university and must have completed all formal degree requirements except the dissertation at the time of full application. **Application Requirements:** Applicants can apply and submit applications online via the AMS website. **Deadline for Receipt:** January 15.

2882 ■ AMERICAN SOCIETY OF COMPOSERS, AUTHORS AND PUBLISHERS (ASCAP) FOUNDATION
1 Lincoln Plaza
New York, NY 10023-7142
Tel: (212)621-6219
E-mail: concertmusic@ascap.com
Web Site: http://www.ascapfoundation.org
To award scholarship to students in their junior year.
Title of Award: Louis Armstrong Scholarships **Area, Field, or Subject:** Music. **Level of Education for which Award is Granted:** High School **Funds Available:** No specific amount.
Eligibility Requirements: Applicant must be a junior-year student and enrolled full-time at Mt. Vernon High School. **Application Requirements:** The ASCAP Foundation does not accept applications for this scholarship. Interested students should consult their financial aid office for application information. **Additional Information:** Mt. Vermon High School, Guidance and Career Center, 703-619-3244 or ASCAP Foundation at the above address.

2883 ■ AMERICAN SOCIETY OF COMPOSERS, AUTHORS AND PUBLISHERS (ASCAP) FOUNDATION
1 Lincoln Plaza
New York, NY 10023-7142
Tel: (212)621-6219
E-mail: concertmusic@ascap.com
Web Site: http://www.ascapfoundation.org
To provide scholarship to young composers, aged 18 or under, to be used for music study at an accredited college or music conservatory.
Title of Award: Charlotte V. Bergen Scholarships **Area, Field, or Subject:** Music. **Level of Education for which Award is Granted:** Undergraduate **Funds Available:** No specific amount.
Eligibility Requirements: Applicants must be citizens or permanent residents of the United States, or enrolled students with Students Visas. **Application Requirements:** Applicants must submit a completed application form, one reproduction of a manuscript or score, biographical information including music studies, background and experience and a list of compositions. Completed Application materials must be postmarked on or before the deadline. **Deadline for Receipt:** March 1.

2884 ■ AMERICAN SOCIETY OF COMPOSERS, AUTHORS AND PUBLISHERS (ASCAP) FOUNDATION
1 Lincoln Plaza
New York, NY 10023-7142
Tel: (212)621-6219
E-mail: concertmusic@ascap.com
Web Site: http://www.ascapfoundation.org
To award scholarships annually to African-American college or university students.
Title of Award: Cherry Lane Foundation/Music Alive! Scholarships **Area, Field, or Subject:** Music. **Level of Education for which Award is Granted:** Undergraduate **Funds Available:** No specific amount. **Duration:** Annual.
Eligibility Requirements: Applicant must be an African-American college or university student majoring in music. Applicants must demonstrate musical talent and proficiency in the areas of arranging, producing, conducting, performing. **Application Requirements:** The ASCAP Foundation does not accept applications for this scholarship. Interested students should consult their school's financial aid office for application information.

2885 ■ AMERICAN SOCIETY OF COMPOSERS, AUTHORS AND PUBLISHERS (ASCAP) FOUNDATION
1 Lincoln Plaza
New York, NY 10023-7142
Tel: (212)621-6219
E-mail: concertmusic@ascap.com
Web Site: http://www.ascapfoundation.org
To award scholarship to qualified college-level students.
Title of Award: David Rose Scholarships **Area, Field, or Subject:** Filmmaking; Music. **Level of Education for which Award is Granted:** Undergraduate **Funds Available:** No specific amount. **Duration:** One year.
Eligibility Requirements: Applicant must be a college-level student working toward a career in scoring for film and/or television who is participating in ASCAP's Film and Television Scoring Workshop. **Application Requirements:** The ASCAP Foundation does not accept applications for this scholarship. Interested students should consult their school's financial aid office for application information.

2886 ■ AMERICAN SOCIETY OF COMPOSERS, AUTHORS AND PUBLISHERS (ASCAP) FOUNDATION
1 Lincoln Plaza
New York, NY 10023-7142
Tel: (212)621-6219
E-mail: concertmusic@ascap.com
Web Site: http://www.ascapfoundation.org
To provide scholarship to the music composition students at the Manhattan School of Music.
Title of Award: Fran Morgenstern Davis Scholarships **Area, Field, or Subject:** Music. **Level of Education for which Award is Granted:** Undergraduate **Number Awarded:** 2. **Funds Available:** No specific amount.
Eligibility Requirements: Applicants must be full-time undergraduate music composition students at the Manhattan School of Music who

demonstrate the potential to produce creative and original work and who also demonstrate financial need. **Application Requirements:** Applicants must submit an application together with other required documents to the Manhattan School of Music.

2887 ■ AMERICAN SOCIETY OF COMPOSERS, AUTHORS AND PUBLISHERS (ASCAP) FOUNDATION

1 Lincoln Plaza
New York, NY 10023-7142
Tel: (212)621-6219
E-mail: concertmusic@ascap.com
Web Site: http://www.ascapfoundation.org
To provide young music students with an opportunity to attend a summer music camp which they would otherwise not be able to afford.
Title of Award: John Denver Music Scholarships **Area, Field, or Subject:** Music. **Level of Education for which Award is Granted:** Undergraduate **Number Awarded:** 3. **Funds Available:** No specific amount.
Eligibility Requirements: Applicants must be students, aged 10-16, who demonstrate both musical promise and financial need. **Application Requirements:** Applicants must submit an application to the Perry-Mansfield School in Steamboat Springs, Colorado. **Additional Information:** Perry-Mansfield School in Steamboat Springs, Colorado Free: 800-430-ARTS; p-m@cmn.ne.

2888 ■ AMERICAN SOCIETY OF COMPOSERS, AUTHORS AND PUBLISHERS (ASCAP) FOUNDATION

1 Lincoln Plaza
New York, NY 10023-7142
Tel: (212)621-6219
E-mail: concertmusic@ascap.com
Web Site: http://www.ascapfoundation.org
To award scholarships to composition students for scores written for dance, film/video or theater.
Title of Award: Louis Dreyfus Warner-Chappell City College Scholarships **Area, Field, or Subject:** Music. **Level of Education for which Award is Granted:** Undergraduate **Funds Available:** No specific amount.
Eligibility Requirements: Applicants must be students enrolled in either a B.A. or B.F.A. program at the City College/City University of New York. **Application Requirements:** The ASCAP Foundation does not accept applications for this scholarship. Interested students should consult their school's financial aid office for application information.

2889 ■ AMERICAN SOCIETY OF COMPOSERS, AUTHORS AND PUBLISHERS (ASCAP) FOUNDATION

1 Lincoln Plaza
New York, NY 10023-7142
Tel: (212)621-6219
E-mail: concertmusic@ascap.com
Web Site: http://www.ascapfoundation.org
To provide assistance to young aspiring songwriters, musicians and vocalists.
Title of Award: Leiber and Stoller Music Scholarships **Area, Field, or Subject:** Music. **Level of Education for which Award is Granted:** Undergraduate **Number Awarded:** 2. **Funds Available:** No specific amount.
Eligibility Requirements: Applicants must be incoming freshmen at Berklee College of Music. **Application Requirements:** Interested students should consult their financial aid office for application information.

2890 ■ AMERICAN SOCIETY OF COMPOSERS, AUTHORS AND PUBLISHERS (ASCAP) FOUNDATION

1 Lincoln Plaza
New York, NY 10023-7142
Tel: (212)621-6219
E-mail: concertmusic@ascap.com
Web Site: http://www.ascapfoundation.org
To present scholarships to aspiring Latino songwriters.
Title of Award: Rudy Perez Songwriting Scholarships **Area, Field, or Subject:** Music. **Level of Education for which Award is Granted:** Undergraduate **Funds Available:** No specific amount.
Eligibility Requirements: Applicant must be an aspiring Latino songwriter who demonstrates potential to produce creative and original

work and also demonstrates financial need. **Application Requirements:** The ASCAP Foundation does not accept applications for this scholarship. Interested students should consult their school's financial aid office for application information.

2891 ■ ARMENIAN STUDENTS' ASSOCIATION OF AMERICA

333 Atlantic Ave.
Warwick, RI 02888
Tel: (401)461-6114
E-mail: asa@asainc.org
Web Site: http://www.asainc.org
To provide financial assistance to those students who are in need.
Title of Award: Garikian Scholarship Fund **Area, Field, or Subject:** Armenian Studies; Sociology; Psychology; Political Science; Middle Eastern History; Journalism; Education; Music. **Level of Education for which Award is Granted:** Undergraduate **Funds Available:** $750-$1,000.
Eligibility Requirements: Applicants must have completed their first academic year in college or university in California; must be pursuing one of the above field of studies. **Application Requirements:** Applicants must apply to the Executive Board for application forms and return them, completed, before the deadline. **Deadline for Receipt:** August 31. **Additional Information:** Berj S. Baghdoyan c/o Western Prelacy at 4401 Russell Avenue, Los Angeles, CA 90027.

2892 ■ BARRIENTOS SCHOLARSHIP FOUNDATION

PO Box 7173
Omaha, NE 68107
Tel: (402)215-5106
E-mail: info@barrientosscholarship.org
Web Site: http://www.barrientosscholarship.org
To provide financial assistance to qualified students who want to pursue their studies.
Title of Award: Artistic Scholarship Awards **Area, Field, or Subject:** Music; Visual arts; Theater arts; Dance. **Level of Education for which Award is Granted:** Undergraduate **Number Awarded:** No specific amount. **Funds Available:** $250-$500. **Duration:** One year.
Eligibility Requirements: Applicants must be students pursuing higher education and career goals that focus on one or more of the arts - music, visual arts, theater, or dance; must be of Latino heritage; must be high school graduating seniors, currently enrolled in college, or adults ready to pursue college; must plan to enroll in at least two classes and attend an accredited community college, university, or technical or vocational school in the state of Nebraska or surrounding greater Omaha Metropolitan area; must have a minimum of 2.5 GPA. **Application Requirements:** Applicants must complete the application form available online; must have a personal essay with a minimum of two pages; must submit letters of recommendation and official high school or college transcript. Application form and requirements must be sent to Barrientos Scholarship Foundation, P.O Box 7173, Omaha, NE 68107. **Deadline for Receipt:** May 15.

2893 ■ BLUES HEAVEN FOUNDATION

2120 S Michigan Ave.
Chicago, IL 60616
Tel: (312)808-1286
Fax: (312)808-0273
E-mail: info@bluesheaven.com
Web Site: http://www.bluesheaven.com
To provide financial assistance to students in Chicago.
Title of Award: Muddy Waters Scholarships **Area, Field, or Subject:** Music education, music, African-American studies, folklore, performing arts, journalism, radio and television. **Level of Education for which Award is Granted:** Undergraduate **Funds Available:** NO specific amount.
Eligibility Requirements: Applicant must have a full-time enrollment status in a Chicago area college or university; must be in at least their first year of undergraduate studies or graduate program. **Application Requirements:** Application form are available in the website address; must be sent to: Blues Heaven Foundation Inc., 2120 S Michigan Ave., Chicago, IL 60616. **Deadline for Receipt:** April 30.

2894 ■ CASCADE BLUES ASSOCIATION

PO Box 14493
Portland, OR 97293-0493

Tel: (503)223-1850
Fax: (503)223-1850
E-mail: cbastaff@cascadeblues.org
Web Site: http://www.cascadeblues.org
To encourage anyone to pursue an undergraduate degree at a local college.
Title of Award: Christopher Mesi Music Scholarships **Area, Field, or Subject:** Music. **Level of Education for which Award is Granted:** Undergraduate **Funds Available:** $500.
Eligibility Requirements: Applicants must be high school senior or college music students; must have a GPA of 2.5 or better. **Application Requirements:** Applicants must submit a transcript of records, two letters of recommendation from which one must come from music teacher and one must come from a counselor, employer or teacher. **Deadline for Receipt:** July 15.

2895 ■ CENTRAL TEXAS BLUEGRASS ASSOCIATION

PO Box 9816
Austin, TX 78766-9816
Tel: (512)261-9440
E-mail: ctba@centraltexasbluegrass.org
Web Site: http://www.centraltexasbluegrass.org
To further the enjoyment of bluegrass music through teaching, sharing and playing; to promote bluegrass music in Central Texas.
Title of Award: Willa Beach-Porter Music Scholarships **Area, Field, or Subject:** Music. **Level of Education for which Award is Granted:** Undergraduate **Funds Available:** No specific amount.
Eligibility Requirements: Applicants must be 12 years of age or over. **Application Requirements:** Applicants must complete an application form. **Deadline for Receipt:** May 15. **Additional Information:** 512-261-9440.

2896 ■ CHOPIN FOUNDATION OF THE UNITED STATES

1440 79th St. Causeway, Ste. 117
Miami, FL 33141
Tel: (305)868-0624
Fax: (305)865-5150
E-mail: info@chopin.org
Web Site: http://www.chopin.org
To support pianists studying music.
Title of Award: Chopin Foundation of the United States Scholarships **Area, Field, or Subject:** Music, Piano. **Level of Education for which Award is Granted:** Undergraduate **Funds Available:** No specific amount.
Eligibility Requirements: Applicant must be American pianists (citizens or legal residents); not younger than 14 and not older than 17 years; studying in the field of music, majoring in piano, and enrolled at the secondary or undergraduate school level as a full-time student. **Application Requirements:** Applicants must submit a statement of career goals; a minimum of two references from piano teachers or performers; a video tape of 20-30 minutes of Chopin's works and registration fee of $25. **Deadline for Receipt:** February.

2897 ■ CHORISTERS GUILD

2834 W Kingsley Rd.
Garland, TX 75041-2498
Tel: (972)271-1521
Free: 800-246-7478
Fax: (972)840-3113
E-mail: membership@mailcg.org
Web Site: http://www.choristerguild.org
To provide financial aid to full time students preparing for church music ministry.
Title of Award: Ruth K. Jacobs Memorial Scholarship Fund **Area, Field, or Subject:** Music. **Level of Education for which Award is Granted:** Graduate, Undergraduate **Funds Available:** No amount mentioned.
Eligibility Requirements: Applicant must be a junior, senior or graduate student majoring in music, who holds choral music with children and youth as a primary interest; have an official transcript sent from all past and current institutions in which enrolled; demonstrate talent and leadership ability and demonstrate promise of future usefulness in church music; and show the need for financial aid. **Application Requirements:** Applicant must submit applications for the Ruth Jacobs Memorial Scholarship must

be submitted prior to February 1 of each year; recipients will be notified by June 1; scholarship funding will be payable to the school and will be dispensed upon receipt of verification of enrollment, full-time status and chosen major; applicant may reapply using application provided for renewal request. Renewing scholarship funding amounts may vary from stated scholarship at the discretion of the Memorial Scholarship Committee. **Deadline for Receipt:** March 1.

2898 ■ CIVIC MUSIC ASSOCIATION OF MILWAUKEE

3195 S Superior St., Ste. 209
Milwaukee, WI 53207
Tel: (414)483-3223
Fax: (414)483-3356
E-mail: info@civicmusicmilwaukee.org
Web Site: http://www.civicmusicmilwaukee.org
To provide music education and performance opportunities with an emphasis on youth in the greater Milwaukee area.
Title of Award: John D. Anello Sr. and Albert A. Silverman Memorial Scholarships **Area, Field, or Subject:** Music, vocal. **Level of Education for which Award is Granted:** Undergraduate **Number Awarded:** 3. **Funds Available:** $1,000; $500.
Eligibility Requirements: Applicants must be full-time high school or college Wisconsin music students, ages 14-22 and must have one Italian parent or grandparent. **Application Requirements:** Applicants must submit a complete application form; must pass the audition process; must attach a 250-word brief description including the musical study they plan to focus on and why and a brief biography that includes school involvement, honors, awards, and any other accomplishments. **Deadline for Receipt:** December 15. **Additional Information:** 3195 S. Superior St., Ste. 209 Milwaukee, WI 53207.

2899 ■ CIVIC MUSIC ASSOCIATION OF MILWAUKEE

3195 S Superior St., Ste. 209
Milwaukee, WI 53207
Tel: (414)483-3223
Fax: (414)483-3356
E-mail: info@civicmusicmilwaukee.org
Web Site: http://www.civicmusicmilwaukee.org
To encourage one or more students who have demonstrated exceptional musical potential but are not presently taking private lessons.
Title of Award: Norbert J. Beihoff Scholarships **Area, Field, or Subject:** Music. **Level of Education for which Award is Granted:** Undergraduate **Funds Available:** No specific amount.
Eligibility Requirements: Applicants must be fourth to seventh grade band and orchestra students who have not yet had the opportunity for private study. **Application Requirements:** Applicants must undergo an audition and must prepare an essay about his or her experiences in school music activities. **Deadline for Receipt:** December 15. **Additional Information:** civicmusiccma@aol.com

2900 ■ CIVIC MUSIC ASSOCIATION OF MILWAUKEE

3195 S Superior St., Ste. 209
Milwaukee, WI 53207
Tel: (414)483-3223
Fax: (414)483-3356
E-mail: info@civicmusicmilwaukee.org
Web Site: http://www.civicmusicmilwaukee.org
To provide music education and performance opportunities with an emphasis on youth in the greater Milwaukee area.
Title of Award: Elizabeth W. Boyce Scholarships **Area, Field, or Subject:** Music, vocal. **Level of Education for which Award is Granted:** Undergraduate **Funds Available:** $2,000.
Eligibility Requirements: Applicants must be high school sophomores, juniors, and seniors in Milwaukee Metropolitan Area High School in Milwaukee. **Application Requirements:** Applicants must submit a completed application form; 250-words including the musical study they to focus on and why and a brief biography that includes school involvement, honors, awards, and other accomplishments. **Deadline for Receipt:** December 15. **Additional Information:** 3195 S. Superior St., Ste. 209 Milwaukee, WI 53207.

2901 ■ CIVIC MUSIC ASSOCIATION OF MILWAUKEE

3195 S Superior St., Ste. 209
Milwaukee, WI 53207

Tel: (414)483-3223
Fax: (414)483-3356
E-mail: info@civicmusicmilwaukee.org
Web Site: http://www.civicmusicmilwaukee.org
To provide music education and performance opportunities with an emphasis on youth in the greater Milwaukee area.
Title of Award: Harold A. Levin Scholarships **Area, Field, or Subject:** Music. **Level of Education for which Award is Granted:** Undergraduate **Funds Available:** Varies.
Eligibility Requirements: Applicants must be college students majoring in music who graduated from a Milwaukee area high school or who currently attend a Milwaukee area college, who are under 30 years of age. **Application Requirements:** Applicants must submit three copies of a CD, or high quality cassette tape containing not more than 15 minutes of music, including at least two contrasting periods and styles, and recorded within the last 12 months. **Deadline for Receipt:** October 1. **Additional Information:** civicmusiccma@aol.com.

2902 ■ CIVIC MUSIC ASSOCIATION OF MILWAUKEE
3195 S Superior St., Ste. 209
Milwaukee, WI 53207
Tel: (414)483-3223
Fax: (414)483-3356
E-mail: info@civicmusicmilwaukee.org
Web Site: http://www.civicmusicmilwaukee.org
To provide music education and performance opportunities with an emphasis on youth in the greater Milwaukee area.
Title of Award: Donald and Idabelle Mohr Scholarships **Area, Field, or Subject:** Music education. **Level of Education for which Award is Granted:** Undergraduate **Funds Available:** $500.
Eligibility Requirements: Applicants must be graduating seniors pursuing further education in a musical field, including music education, music therapy, theory-composition, performance and musicology. **Application Requirements:** Applicants must submit a completed application form; must pass the audition process; must attach a 250-word brief description including the musical study they plan to focus on and why and a brief biography that includes school involvement, honors, awards, and any other accomplishments. **Deadline for Receipt:** December 15. **Additional Information:** 3195 S. Superior St., Ste. 209 Milwaukee, WI 53207.

2903 ■ COASTAL BEND COMMUNITY FOUNDATION
600 Leopard St., Ste. 1716
Corpus Christi, TX 78473
Tel: (361)882-9745
Fax: (361)882-2865
Web Site: http://www.cbcfoundation.org
To provide financial assistance to high school seniors or graduates of a Coastal Bend high school in furthering their college education.
Title of Award: Cecil E. Burney Scholarships **Area, Field, or Subject:** Liberal arts; History; Political science; Music; Education. **Level of Education for which Award is Granted:** High School, Undergraduate **Funds Available:** $2,000.
Eligibility Requirements: Applicants must be high school seniors or graduates of a Coastal Bend high school pursuing a liberal arts degree majoring in history, political science, music or education; have a high school GPA of 90 percent or higher; maintain a college 3.0 GPA or higher and at least 12 hours per semester. **Application Requirements:** Applicants must submit all the required application information. **Deadline for Receipt:** March 14.

2904 ■ COMMUNITY FOUNDATION FOR GREATER NEW HAVEN
70 Audubon St.
New Haven, CT 06510-9755
Tel: (203)777-2386
Fax: (203)787-6584
E-mail: contactus@cfgnh.org
Web Site: http://www.cfgnh.org
To create positive and sustainable change in Greater New Haven by increasing the amount of and enhancing the impact of community philanthropy.
Title of Award: Curtis M. Saulsbury Scholarship Fund **Area, Field, or Subject:** Music. **Level of Education for which Award is Granted:** Undergraduate **Funds Available:** No specific amount.

Eligibility Requirements: Applicants must be graduating from secondary school in the region serviced by the community foundation. **Application Requirements:** Applicants must complete the application form and attach a personal essay; academic verification; letter of recommendation; and Parent/Guardian IRS Form. **Deadline for Receipt:** March 21. **Additional Information:** 203-777-7097; 203-787-6584.

2905 ■ THE COMMUNITY FOUNDATION OF MIDDLE TENNESSEE
3833 Cleghorn Ave., Ste. 400
Nashville, TN 37215-2519
Tel: (615)321-4939; 888-540-5200
E-mail: mail@cfmt.org
Web Site: http://www.cfmt.org
To help students in planning their postsecondary education.
Title of Award: Belmont University Commercial Music Scholarships **Area, Field, or Subject:** Music. **Level of Education for which Award is Granted:** Undergraduate **Funds Available:** No specific amount.
Eligibility Requirements: Applicants must be high school seniors, college freshmen, sophomores, or juniors accepted to or attending Belmont University in Nashville, Tennessee as commercial music majors. **Application Requirements:** Applicants must complete the application form. Applicants must submit two applicant appraisals; transcript of grades; student essay describing their educational plans and how these will help in career goals. Applicants must submit one recent photograph. **Deadline for Receipt:** March 15. **Additional Information:** pcole@cfmt.org

2906 ■ THE COMMUNITY FOUNDATION OF MIDDLE TENNESSEE
3833 Cleghorn Ave., Ste. 400
Nashville, TN 37215-2519
Tel: (615)321-4939; 888-540-5200
E-mail: mail@cfmt.org
Web Site: http://www.cfmt.org
To help students in planning their postsecondary education.
Title of Award: Fine Arts and Music Scholarships **Area, Field, or Subject:** Fine arts; Music. **Level of Education for which Award is Granted:** Undergraduate **Funds Available:** No specific amount.
Eligibility Requirements: Applicants must be rising sophomores, juniors and seniors in college, and graduate students at an accredited college, university, or institute full-time or part-time (6 or more credits). **Application Requirements:** Applicants must complete the application form. Applicants must submit two applicant appraisals; transcript of grades; student essay describing educational plans and how these will help in career goals. Applicants must submit one recent photograph. **Deadline for Receipt:** March 15. **Additional Information:** pcole@cfmt.org

2907 ■ THE COMMUNITY FOUNDATION OF MIDDLE TENNESSEE
3833 Cleghorn Ave., Ste. 400
Nashville, TN 37215-2519
Tel: (615)321-4939; 888-540-5200
E-mail: mail@cfmt.org
Web Site: http://www.cfmt.org
To help students in planning their postsecondary education.
Title of Award: John W. Work III Memorial Foundation Scholarships **Area, Field, or Subject:** Music. **Level of Education for which Award is Granted:** Undergraduate **Funds Available:** No specific amount.
Eligibility Requirements: Applicants must be undergraduate juniors, seniors, or graduate students pursuing a degree in music at an accredited university, college or institute. Applicants must have a B average and demonstrate potential for excellence in music. Special preference will be given to African Americans. **Application Requirements:** Applicants must complete the application form. Applicants must submit two applicant appraisals; transcript of grades; student essay describing educational plans and how these will help in career goals. Applicants must submit one recent photograph. **Deadline for Receipt:** March 15. **Additional Information:** pcole@cfmt.org

2908 ■ COMMUNITY FOUNDATION OF NORTHERN ILLINOIS
946 N 2nd St.
Rockford, IL 61107
Tel: (815)962-2110
Fax: (815)962-2116
Web Site: http://www.cfnil.org

To serve the four county area (Boone, Ogle, Stephenson and Winnebago) through philanthropy; to provide leadership in meeting charitable needs and to be a responsible steward to the Foundation's donors and of the Foundation's endowment; to encourage and support other students who are actively involved in extracurricular activities.
Title of Award: Mark A. Reid Memorial Scholarship Grant **Area, Field, or Subject:** Drama. **Level of Education for which Award is Granted:** Undergraduate **Funds Available:** No specific amount.
Eligibility Requirements: Applicants must be graduating seniors at Oregon High School who actively participate in music or drama. **Application Requirements:** Applicants must contact Mitch Lauer for more information. **Additional Information:** 732-6241.

2909 ■ COMMUNITY FOUNDATION OF NORTHERN ILLINOIS
946 N 2nd St.
Rockford, IL 61107
Tel: (815)962-2110
Fax: (815)962-2116
Web Site: http://www.cfnil.org
To serve the four county area (Boone, Ogle, Stephenson and Winnebago) through philanthropy; to provide leadership in meeting charitable needs and to be a responsible steward to the Foundation's donors and of the Foundation's endowment.
Title of Award: Gary S. Wilmer RAMI Music Scholarship **Area, Field, or Subject:** Music. **Level of Education for which Award is Granted:** Undergraduate **Funds Available:** No specific amount.
Eligibility Requirements: Applicants must be graduating senior students from Boone or Winnebago County who have a GPA of at least 2.5; must have plans to pursue a degree in music performance, education or composition and be actively involved in school or community musical groups; must be nominated by a music teacher. **Application Requirements:** Applicants must submit a completed application form, verification form, an official transcript in a sealed envelope, two letters of recommendation and a five minute or less performance tape or C.D. **Deadline for Receipt:** March 1. **Additional Information:** jpatterson@cfnil.org.

2910 ■ DELTA DELTA DELTA
PO Box 5987
Arlington, TX 76005-5987
Tel: (817)633-8001
Fax: (817)652-0212
E-mail: info@trideltaeo.org
Web Site: http://www.tridelta.org
To provide financial assistance to qualified undergraduate students.
Title of Award: Margaret M. Alkek Scholarship **Area, Field, or Subject:** Education, Music, Theater arts. **Level of Education for which Award is Granted:** Undergraduate **Funds Available:** $500-$1,500. **Duration:** One academic year.
Eligibility Requirements: Applicant must be a Theta Xi chapter member at the University of Southern California; must have academic achievement at the collegiate level; must be an initiated sophomore or junior members. **Application Requirements:** Application forms are available on the website. Applicant must provide a personal statement about their educational and vocational goals; must have a recommendation letter from a faculty member; must have an official transcript from each undergraduate institution. Application materials must be sent to: Delta Delta Delta, PO Box 5987, Arlington, TX 76005. **Deadline for Receipt:** March 15.

2911 ■ FIRST COMMUNITY FOUNDATION OF PENNSYLVANIA, WILLIAMSPORT-LYCOMING
330 Pine St., Suite 401
Williamsport, PA 17701
Tel: (570)321-1500; (866)901-2372
Fax: (570)321-6434
E-mail: fcfpa@fcfpa.org
Web Site: http://www.wlfoundation.org
To provide financial assistance for Lycoming County high school seniors graduating from public or private schools with a demonstrated interest in music who plan to attend a qualified institution of higher education in a music-related field of study.
Title of Award: Albert and Alice Nacinovich Music Scholarships **Area, Field, or Subject:** Music. **Level of Education for which Award is Granted:** Undergraduate **Funds Available:** $1,000.

Eligibility Requirements: Applicants must be graduating high school seniors from any Lycoming County high school, public or private (secular or Christian), or as part of a qualified home-schooling arrangement within Lycoming County; must have been accepted to a qualified institution of higher education with the intention of pursuing further education or a career in music in a degree-granting program in music education or a music-related field of study; and must have a demonstrated interest in music, which may include participation in band, chorus, music theory and composition, and performance service at school, church, or community. **Application Requirements:** Applicants will be required to complete an application, provide copies of transcripts, and attach a 500-word of essay or less outlining his or her interest in music and how a scholarship award will help to advance his or her goals within a musical field or discipline. A recording of the applicant's work must also be submitted with completed application and essay. **Deadline for Receipt:** May 1. **Additional Information:** Candy Bower, Manager of Program and Scholarship Services, candyb@fcfpa.org.

2912 ■ FIRST COMMUNITY FOUNDATION OF PENNSYLVANIA, WILLIAMSPORT-LYCOMING
330 Pine St., Suite 401
Williamsport, PA 17701
Tel: (570)321-1500; (866)901-2372
Fax: (570)321-6434
E-mail: fcfpa@fcfpa.org
Web Site: http://www.wlfoundation.org
To provide scholarship for Montoursville Area High School seniors who will be attending Yale College.
Title of Award: Wendy Y. Wolfson Memorial Scholarship Fund **Area, Field, or Subject:** Music; Drama criticism. **Level of Education for which Award is Granted:** Undergraduate **Funds Available:** No specific amount.
Eligibility Requirements: Students must be graduating seniors of Montoursville Area High School. If there are no graduating students planning to attend Yale College, graduating students with an outstanding academic record and a demonstrated talent in music or drama will be considered. **Application Requirements:** Applicants may contact and request an application from the Montoursville Area High School. **Additional Information:** Ronda Albert, Montoursville Area High School, 100 N Arch St, Montoursville, PA 17754; 570-368-3509; ralbert@montoursville.k12.pa.us.

2913 ■ FOUNDATION FOR ENHANCING COMMUNITIES
200 N Third St., PO Box 678
Harrisburg, PA 17108-0678
Tel: (717)236-5040
Fax: (717)231-4463
E-mail: dawn@tfec.org
Web Site: http://www.ghf.org
To provide educational assistance for deserving music students in the areas of classical music composition, teaching, and/or performance.
Title of Award: Lou Drane Fund **Area, Field, or Subject:** Classical music. **Level of Education for which Award is Granted:** Undergraduate **Funds Available:** No specific amount.
Eligibility Requirements: Applicant must have a serious interest in classical music and display unusual ability and/or creativity; must apply for financial aid from the school he/she plans to attend; must attend an accredited post-secondary institution of higher learning or have been accepted and plan to attend same; be a citizen of the United States and must maintain a permanent residence on one of the following counties in central Pennsylvania: Adams, Cumberland; Dauphin, Franklin, Fulton, Juniata, Lancaster, Lebanon, Montour, Northumberland, Perry, Snyder or York. **Application Requirements:** Applicants must attach FAFSA Student Aid Report and a letter detailing applicant's financial need. Applicants must submit, along with the application, an example of their ability, in one of the following fields: Composition or composition-teaching - a CD not to exceed 20 minutes in length - and a written music score - of two separate works of you own composition. Identify yourself, your instrument and title at the beginning of the tape. Label the recording with this information also. Audition recordings of original compositions must be of live performances. MIDI and other electronic performances are not accepted; For applications in Performance or performance-teaching submit a CD, not to exceed 20 minutes in length, of two separate works reflecting a variety of style.

Identify yourself, your instrument and title at the beginning of the recording. Label the tape with this information also. All instruments with the exception of piano and classical guitar must be accompanied, but avoid lengthy introductions by accompaniment. **Deadline for Receipt:** January 31. **Additional Information:** Dawn Morris, Program Officer; 717-236-5040; dawn@tfec.org.

2914 ■ FOUNDATION FOR ENHANCING COMMUNITIES

200 N Third St., PO Box 678
Harrisburg, PA 17108-0678
Tel: (717)236-5040
Fax: (717)231-4463
E-mail: dawn@tfec.org
Web Site: http://www.ghf.org
To award scholarship to a student from either Central Dauphin High School or Central Dauphin East High School.
Title of Award: Adrienne Zoe Fedok Art and Music Scholarships **Area, Field, or Subject:** Art; Music. **Level of Education for which Award is Granted:** Undergraduate **Funds Available:** $1,000.
Eligibility Requirements: Applicant must be from either Central Dauphin High School or Central Dauphin East High School entering his or her freshman year in post-secondary education in the field of Art and Music. **Application Requirements:** The application and the required attachments must be completed and postmarked on or before the deadline. Required attachments include: completed application; high school transcript including GPA; SAT scores; FAFSA Student Aid Report Form (Financial Aid Form); two letters of recommendation (one from a faculty member in the art or music department); a list of extra-curricular activities demonstrating leadership and community service; and personal essay on the applicant's educational and career goals. **Deadline for Receipt:** April 3. **Additional Information:** Dawn Morris, Program Officer; 717-236-5040; dawn@tfec.org.

2915 ■ FOUNDATION FOR ENHANCING COMMUNITIES

200 N Third St., PO Box 678
Harrisburg, PA 17108-0678
Tel: (717)236-5040
Fax: (717)231-4463
E-mail: dawn@tfec.org
Web Site: http://www.ghf.org
To assist students with their college tuition expenses.
Title of Award: Henry and Janet Guareillo Scholarship Fund **Area, Field, or Subject:** Music; Theater arts. **Level of Education for which Award is Granted:** Undergraduate **Funds Available:** No specific amount.
Eligibility Requirements: Program is open to graduating seniors who have studied at Cumberland Valley School of Music for four consecutive years; must have been accepted into a college or conservatory to pursue a degree in music or the theater arts; must have demonstrated ability to become successful candidates in their chosen field; and must demonstrate financial need. Other factors will include performance history, teacher recommendations, if the candidate studied more than one instrument at CVSM or was a Merit Scholarship Award winner. **Application Requirements:** Applicants must complete and submit the application and the attachments on or before the deadline. Application can be obtained online. **Deadline for Receipt:** April 20. **Additional Information:** Dawn Morris, Program Officer; 717-236-5040; dawn@tfec.org.

2916 ■ FOUNDATION FOR ENHANCING COMMUNITIES

200 N Third St., PO Box 678
Harrisburg, PA 17108-0678
Tel: (717)236-5040
Fax: (717)231-4463
E-mail: dawn@tfec.org
Web Site: http://www.ghf.org
To assist needy students of classical music in the fields of composition, teaching and performance.
Title of Award: Joseph L. and Vivian E. Steele Music Scholarship Fund **Area, Field, or Subject:** Music. **Level of Education for which Award is Granted:** Undergraduate **Funds Available:** No specific amount.
Eligibility Requirements: Applicant must have a serious interest in classical music and display unusual ability and/or creativity; must apply for financial aid from the school he/she plans to attend; must attend an accredited post-secondary institution of higher learning or have been ac-

cepted and plan to attend same; must be a citizen of the United States and must maintain permanent residence in one of the following counties in central Pennsylvania: Adams, Cumberland, Dauphin, Franklin, Fulton, Juniata, Lancaster, Lebanon, Montour, Northumberland, Perry, Snyder or York. **Application Requirements:** Each applicant is required to submit the attached application on or before the deadline. Submit, along with the application, an example of your ability, in one of the following fields: Composition or composition-teaching - a CD not to exceed 20 minutes in length and a written music score for two separate works of your own composition. Identify yourself, your instrument and title at the beginning of the tape. Label the tape with this information also; Performance or performance-teaching - a CD, not to exceed 20 minutes in length, of two separate works reflecting a variety of style. identify yourself, your instrument and title at the beginning of the recording. **Deadline for Receipt:** January 31. **Additional Information:** Dawn Morris, Program Officer at the above address.

2917 ■ GRAND RAPIDS COMMUNITY FOUNDATION

161 Ottawa Ave. NW
Ste. 209-C Waters Bldg.
Grand Rapids, MI 49503
Tel: (616)454-1751
Fax: (616)454-6455
E-mail: grfound@grfoundation.org
Web Site: http://www.grfoundation.org
To recognize those students with talent in musical instruments by supporting them financially.
Title of Award: Llewellyn L. Cayvan String Instrument Scholarships **Area, Field, or Subject:** Music. **Level of Education for which Award is Granted:** Undergraduate **Funds Available:** No specific amount.
Eligibility Requirements: Applicants must be undergraduate or graduate level students studying the violin, viola, violoncello, or the bass violin. No residency or financial need requirements. **Application Requirements:** Applicants must check the available website for the application process and other requirements. **Additional Information:** Grand Rapids Community Foundation at the above address

2918 ■ GRAND RAPIDS COMMUNITY FOUNDATION

161 Ottawa Ave. NW
Ste. 209-C Waters Bldg.
Grand Rapids, MI 49503
Tel: (616)454-1751
Fax: (616)454-6455
E-mail: grfound@grfoundation.org
Web Site: http://www.grfoundation.org
To provide financial assistance to deserving students.
Title of Award: Guy D. & Mary Edith Halladay Music Scholarships **Area, Field, or Subject:** Music. **Level of Education for which Award is Granted:** Graduate, Undergraduate **Funds Available:** No specific amount.
Eligibility Requirements: Applicants must be residents of Kent County who are majoring in Music at any college or university in the U.S. Applicants must have financial need. Applicants must have a cumulative GPA of 3.0. **Application Requirements:** Applicants must check the available website for the required materials. **Additional Information:** Grand Rapids Community Foundation at the above address

2919 ■ HARTFORD FOUNDATION FOR PUBLIC GIVING

10 Columbus Blvd., 8th Flr.
Hartford, CT 06106
Tel: (860)548-1888
Fax: (860)524-8346
E-mail: hfpg@hfpg.org
Web Site: http://www.hfpg.org
To provide scholarship for students currently attending Duke Ellington School of Performing Arts in Washington, DC.
Title of Award: Nellie Love Butcher Scholarships **Area, Field, or Subject:** Music, Piano. **Level of Education for which Award is Granted:** Undergraduate **Number Awarded:** 1. **Funds Available:** No specific amount.
Eligibility Requirements: Applicants must be studying piano or voice with a minimum 3.0 GPA. **Application Requirements:** Application materials (for Connecticut residents) may be obtained by sending a self-

addressed stamped envelope to NSDAR Scholarship Committee, 215 Loomis Rd. N Granby, CT 06060. **Deadline for Receipt:** April 15. **Additional Information:** Mrs. Michael L. Stewart, CT State Chairperson. 860-653-4203. L2stew@yahoo.com.

2920 ■ HARTFORD FOUNDATION FOR PUBLIC GIVING

10 Columbus Blvd., 8th Flr.
Hartford, CT 06106
Tel: (860)548-1888
Fax: (860)524-8346
E-mail: hfpg@hfpg.org
Web Site: http://www.hfpg.org
To provide scholarship to the graduating high school senior.
Title of Award: Hartford Jazz Society Scholarships **Area, Field, or Subject:** Music, Jazz. **Level of Education for which Award is Granted:** Undergraduate **Number Awarded:** 2-3. **Funds Available:** $3,000.
Eligibility Requirements: Applicants must: be a Connecticut Capitol Region resident; be attending a four-year college or university; be a Music major with interest in jazz. **Application Requirements:** Applicants must complete the General Scholarship Application and include the following requirements: a cassette tape of applicant both reading and improvising; two letters of reference, at least one form a music teacher or school music director and submit to Hartford Jazz Society, Inc., Chairperson, Scholarship Committee, 116 Cottage Grove Rd., Bloomfield, CT 06002. Phone: 860242-6688

Fax: 860243-8871. hartjazzsocinc@aol.com. **Deadline for Receipt:** May 1.

2921 ■ HISPANIC SCHOLARSHIP FUND

55 Second St., Ste. 1500
San Francisco, CA 94105
877-473-4636
Fax: (415)808-2302
E-mail: info@hsf.net
Web Site: http://www.hsf.net
To provide financial assistance to creative arts-related undergraduate and graduate students beginning or completing an art project.
Title of Award: McNamara Family Creative Arts Project Grants **Area, Field, or Subject:** Art; Media arts; Broadcasting; Filmmaking; Performing arts; Communications; Writing. **Level of Education for which Award is Granted:** Graduate, Undergraduate **Funds Available:** $5,000-$20,000.
Eligibility Requirements: Applicant must be of Hispanic heritage; U.S. citizen or legal permanent resident with a valid permanent resident card or passport stamped I-551; enrolled full-time undergraduate or graduate student in a degree-seeking program at a U.S. accredited institution in the U.S., Puerto Rico or U.S. Virgin Islands in the upcoming academic year; pursuing a major in Arts, including but not limited to media, film, performing arts, communications or writing; have a minimum 3.0 GPA on a 4.0 scale; must apply for federal financing aid using the Free Application for Federal Student Aid (FAFSA) at www.fafsa.ed.gov. **Application Requirements:** Applications must be submitted using the HSF online application system. **Additional Information:** In partnership with the McNamara Family Foundation. **Deadline for Receipt:** March 15. **Additional Information:** scholar1@hsf.net.

2922 ■ INDIANA STATE ALUMNI ASSOCIATION

200 N 7th St.
Terre Haute, IN 47809-9989
800-GO-TO-ISU
Web Site: http://www.indstate.edu/alum/alum_assoc.htm
To support educational pursuit of students.
Title of Award: Indiana State Alumni Association Creative and Performing Arts Award **Area, Field, or Subject:** Art; Music; English language and literature; Theater arts. **Level of Education for which Award is Granted:** Undergraduate **Funds Available:** $2000. **Duration:** One year.
Eligibility Requirements: Applicant must be entering college as freshmen at the Indiana State University; majoring or have a minor in Art, Music, English, Physical Education (Dance), Theater. **Application Requirements:** Applicant must submit an application form; portfolio review; must audition at the departments; and will be interview. Contact the department where the applicant is majoring. **Deadline for Receipt:** Must be admitted before February 1. **Additional Information:** Art: 812-237-3697; Music: 812-237-27771; English: 812-237-3163; Physical Education: 812-237-2520; Theater: 812-237-3331.

2923 ■ INTERNATIONAL HORN SOCIETY

PO Box 630158
Lanai City, HI 96763-0158
Tel: (808)565-7273
Fax: (808)565-7273
E-mail: exec-secretary@hornsociety.org
Web Site: http://www.hornsociety.org
To provide opportunities for full-time students attending the IHS international symposium to receive a lesson from a world renowned artist or teacher.
Title of Award: Paul Mansur Scholarships **Area, Field, or Subject:** Music. **Level of Education for which Award is Granted:** Undergraduate **Number Awarded:** 2. **Funds Available:** No amount mentioned.
Eligibility Requirements: Applicants must be full-time students 18 years or younger and 19-26 years old at the time of the symposium. **Application Requirements:** Applicants must submit applications to the IHS Executive Secretary, either on paper or by email; proof of full-time public or private school, conservatory, or university enrollment; and essay on the subject of how attending and receiving a lesson during the symposium will enhance his/her education. **Deadline for Receipt:** May 1. **Additional Information:** Heidi Vogel, IHS Executive Secretary at the above address.

2924 ■ THE LIBERACE MUSEUM AND FOUNDATION

1775 E Tropicana Ave.
Las Vegas, NV 89119-6529
Tel: (702)798-5595
E-mail: info@liberace.org
Web Site: http://www.liberace.org
To help talented students pursue careers in the arts by providing financial assistance for them.
Title of Award: Liberace Scholarship Fund **Area, Field, or Subject:** Arts. **Level of Education for which Award is Granted:** Undergraduate **Funds Available:** No specific amount.
Eligibility Requirements: Applicants must be from accredited institutions of higher learning offering degrees in either the creative or performing arts and local arts organizations. **Application Requirements:** Applicants must use and sign the official foundation application form; must answer all application questions; supplemental sheets to the application must be attached; and attach a copy of school year calendar for next year.

2925 ■ GLENN MILLER BIRTHPLACE SOCIETY

PO Box 61
Clarinda, IA 51632
Tel: (712)542-2461
E-mail: gmbs@heartland.net
Web Site: http://www.glennmiller.org
To seek out and assist promising young talents in any field of applied music who may be musical leaders of tomorrow.
Title of Award: Glenn Miller Scholarships **Area, Field, or Subject:** Music. **Level of Education for which Award is Granted:** Undergraduate **Funds Available:** $1,000 to $4,000.
Eligibility Requirements: Applicants must be graduating high school seniors or first year college students intending to make music a central part of their future life and high school seniors, unless they have been previous first place winners. **Application Requirements:** Applicants must submit an audition CD or tape and completed application. **Deadline for Receipt:** March 15.

2926 ■ NAMM, THE INTERNATIONAL MUSIC PRODUCTS ASSOCIATION

5790 Armada Dr.
Carlsbad, CA 92008
Tel: (760)438-8001
Free: 800-767-6266
Fax: (760)438-7327
E-mail: info@namm.com
Web Site: http://www.namm.org
To enhance education and careers in the music product industry.
Title of Award: William R. Gard Memorial Scholarships **Area, Field, or Subject:** Music; Music education. **Level of Education for which Award is Granted:** Undergraduate **Funds Available:** $2,000 per academic year. **Duration:** Scholarship may be renewed for up to three additional years.
Eligibility Requirements: Applicants must be a member of NAMM Member firm; have completed 400 hours of employment at the NAMM

Member firm; and enrolled full-time college student. **Application Requirements:** Application form is available at the website. Applicants must prepare reference letters; grade transcripts; awards and community involvement; and photograph. Forward completed application form and other required materials to: NAMM, International Music Products Association, William R. Gard Memorial Scholarship, 5790 Armanda Drive, Carlsbad, CA 92008. **Deadline for Receipt:** March 31. **Additional Information:** NAMM Professional Development Department, 800-767-6266/760-438-8007 or gard@namm.org.

2927 ■ NATIONAL ASSOCIATION OF PASTORAL MUSICIANS
962 Wayne Ave., Ste. 210
Silver Spring, MD 20910-4461
Tel: (240)247-3000
Fax: (240)247-3001
Web Site: http://www.npm.org
To assist with the cost of education formation for pastoral musicians.
Title of Award: National Association of Pastoral Musicians Academic Scholarships **Area, Field, or Subject:** Music. **Level of Education for which Award is Granted:** Graduate, Undergraduate **Funds Available:** $34,000.
Eligibility Requirements: Applicants must be NPM members; part-time or full-time in an undergraduate or graduate degree program of studies related to the field of pastoral music during the 2008-2009 school year; and must intend to work at least two years in the field of pastoral music following graduation/program completion. **Application Requirements:** Applicants must submit letter or short essay containing the following information: name and contact information including address, home and work phone, and email; definition of the term "pastoral musician"; description of talents; previous experience as pastoral musician; educational background, educational program enrolled; recording (cassette or CD format) demonstrating solo performance skills or those of an ensemble under applicants' direction; two letters of recommendation, including one written by pastor; and completed financial need statement. **Deadline for Receipt:** March 7.

2928 ■ NATIONAL ASSOCIATION OF PASTORAL MUSICIANS
962 Wayne Ave., Ste. 210
Silver Spring, MD 20910-4461
Tel: (240)247-3000
Fax: (240)247-3001
Web Site: http://www.npm.org
To assist pastoral musicians with limited financial resources in taking advantage of opportunities for continuing formation at NPM conventions and institutes.
Title of Award: NPM Program Scholarships **Area, Field, or Subject:** Music. **Level of Education for which Award is Granted:** Undergraduate **Funds Available:** No amount mentioned.
Eligibility Requirements: Applicants must be NPM members and should be from economically disadvantaged parishes. **Application Requirements:** Applicants must submit completed NPM Program Scholarship Application and the NPM Program Scholarship Applicant's letter; and parish recommendation completed by your pastor or pastoral administrator.

2929 ■ NEW JERSEY PERFORMING ARTS CENTER
36 Park Place
Newark, NJ 07102
Tel: (973)642-8989; 888-466-5722
E-mail: ticketservices@njpac.org
Web Site: http://www.njpac.org
To motivate talented young artists seeking an outlet for musical expression.
Title of Award: Jeffrey Carollo Music Scholarships **Area, Field, or Subject:** Music. **Level of Education for which Award is Granted:** Undergraduate **Funds Available:** No specific amount.
Eligibility Requirements: Applicants must be enrolled in the music program at the Newark Community School of the Arts. **Application Requirements:** Applicants must submit a completed application form. **Additional Information:** 973-353-8009.

2930 ■ NEW JERSEY PERFORMING ARTS CENTER
36 Park Place
Newark, NJ 07102

Tel: (973)642-8989; 888-466-5722
E-mail: ticketservices@njpac.org
Web Site: http://www.njpac.org
To provide higher education opportunities for the young people of Newark; to provide an opportunity to gain practical experience at the New Jersey Performing Arts Center through internships.
Title of Award: Star-Ledger Scholarships for the Performing Arts **Area, Field, or Subject:** Performing Arts. **Level of Education for which Award is Granted:** Undergraduate **Funds Available:** No specific amount.
Eligibility Requirements: Applicants must be high school seniors who wish to realize their potential by attending college but who may not be able to attend because of financial limitations. **Application Requirements:** Applicants must submit a completed application form.

2931 ■ NORTHWEST-SHOALS COMMUNITY COLLEGE
PO Box 2545
Muscle Shoals, AL 35662
Tel: (256)331-5200
Free: 800-645-8967
Fax: (256)331-5222
Web Site: http://www.nwscc.edu
To support NW-SCC students with their educational pursuit.
Title of Award: Northwest-Shoals Community College Fine Arts Scholarships - Music **Area, Field, or Subject:** Music. **Level of Education for which Award is Granted:** Undergraduate **Funds Available:** No specific amount.
Eligibility Requirements: Applicant must be entering full-time freshman or currently enrolled full-time student; and have an overall GPA of 2.5. **Application Requirements:** To qualify, students must file a Northwest-Shoals Community College Application for Admission. Applicants must submit a completed scholarship application form together with the required materials. **Deadline for Receipt:** March 2. **Additional Information:** 256-331-6299 or 256-331-5332.

2932 ■ ORANGE COUNTY COMMUNITY FOUNDATION
30 Corporate Park, Ste. 410
Irvine, CA 92606
Tel: (949)553-4202
Fax: (949)553-4211
E-mail: cmontesano@oc-cf.org
Web Site: http://www.oc-cf.org
To award scholarship to the students who are residents of Orange County.
Title of Award: Orange County Centennial Arts Scholarships **Area, Field, or Subject:** Performing arts; Visual Arts; Theater arts; Music. **Level of Education for which Award is Granted:** Undergraduate **Number Awarded:** 3. **Funds Available:** $2,000.
Eligibility Requirements: Applicants must: be local high school graduating seniors who are residents of Orange County, California, and who are completing their last three years of high school in the county; be students who are planning to enroll full-time at an accredited college or university and majoring in the arts. Example of acceptable majors include: dance, voice, opera, theater arts, musical theater, visual arts and music; demonstrated record of community service and leadership. particular attention will be given to training, honors and achievements in the arts. **Application Requirements:** Applicants must include a 250-word essay in their application. Applicants must write about their interests and plans and the way in which their plan is appropriate to their situation, abilities and long-term goals. **Deadline for Receipt:** March 15. **Additional Information:** Claudia Montesano, 949-553-4202 ext. 46; cmontesano@oc-cf.org.

2933 ■ PARKERSBURG AREA COMMUNITY FOUNDATION
501 Avery St.
Parkersburg, WV 26101
Tel: (304)428-4438; (866)428-4438
Fax: (304)428-1200
E-mail: info@pacfwv.com
Web Site: http://www.pacfwv.com
To provide financial assistance for qualified high school seniors from Parkersburg High School.
Title of Award: Martin K. Alsup Scholarships **Area, Field, or Subject:** Music. **Level of Education for which Award is Granted:** Undergraduate **Funds Available:** $1,200.
Eligibility Requirements: Applicant must be a graduating senior from Parkersburg High School; must have a strong commitment to the field of

instrumental music and music-related activities as demonstrated by participation in orchestra or the Big Red Band. **Application Requirements:** Applicants must submit a cover sheet (3 pages) and application form (4 pages); must have a personal essay; must have high school and/or post- secondary transcripts; must provide a letter of recommendation; copy of the page of their or their parent's most recent tax return that indicates adjusted gross income; and must have a Student Aid Report, showing estimated family contribution, from FAFSA. Application form and other supporting documents must be sent to Our Community's Foundation, P.O Box 1762, Parkersburg, WV 26102. **Deadline for Receipt:** March 20.

2934 ■ PARKERSBURG AREA COMMUNITY FOUNDATION
501 Avery St.
Parkersburg, WV 26101
Tel: (304)428-4438; (866)428-4438
Fax: (304)428-1200
E-mail: info@pacfwv.com
Web Site: http://www.pacfwv.com
To assist graduating students in their educational pursuits.
Title of Award: William R. Pfalzgraf Scholarships **Area, Field, or Subject:** Law; Education, English as a second language; Music. **Level of Education for which Award is Granted:** Undergraduate **Funds Available:** $760.
Eligibility Requirements: Applicant must be a Parkersburg High School graduating senior with a minimum of 3.0 GPA. **Application Requirements:** Applicants must submit a cover sheet (3 pages) and application form (4 pages); a personal essay; a high school and/or post-secondary transcript; a letter of recommendation; a signed copy of the page of their or their parent's most recent tax return that indicates adjusted gross income; and a Student Aid Report showing estimated family contribution from FAFSA. Application form and other supporting documents must be sent to Our Community's Foundation, P.O Box 1762, Parkersburg, WV 26102. **Deadline for Receipt:** March 20.

2935 ■ PARKERSBURG AREA COMMUNITY FOUNDATION
501 Avery St.
Parkersburg, WV 26101
Tel: (304)428-4438; (866)428-4438
Fax: (304)428-1200
E-mail: info@pacfwv.com
Web Site: http://www.pacfwv.com
To encourage graduating students to pursue their education.
Title of Award: S. Byrl Ross Memorial Scholarship Fund **Area, Field, or Subject:** Music. **Level of Education for which Award is Granted:** Undergraduate **Funds Available:** $1,150.
Eligibility Requirements: Applicant must be a graduating senior of Wood or Ritchie Counties pursuing a major in music or a music-related field at a post-secondary educational institution. **Application Requirements:** Applicants must submit a cover sheet (3 pages) and application form (4 pages); a personal essay; a high school and/or post-secondary transcript; a letter of recommendation; a signed copy of the page of their or their parent's most recent tax return that indicates adjusted gross income; and a Student Aid Report showing estimated family contribution from FAFSA. Application form and other supporting documents must be sent to Our Community's Foundation, P.O Box 1762, Parkersburg, WV 26102. **Deadline for Receipt:** March 20.

2936 ■ PRIDE FOUNDATION
PO Box 2194, 1122 E Pike St. PMB 1001
Seattle, WA 98112
Tel: (206)323-3318
Free: 800-735-7287
Fax: (206)323-1017
E-mail: prideweb@pridefoundation.org
Web Site: http://www.pridefoundation.org
To provide scholarship to the students who have been stigmatized, isolated or closeted because of sexual identity issues.
Title of Award: Deloris Carter Hampton Scholarships **Area, Field, or Subject:** Education; Dance. **Level of Education for which Award is Granted:** Undergraduate **Funds Available:** No specific amount.
Eligibility Requirements: Applicants must be women of color who have a demonstrated history of activism and/or leadership in the LGBT com-

munity and are pursuing a degree in education, women's health, or dance. **Application Requirements:** Qualified students are asked to submit an application to determine eligibility for scholarships. Applicants may download an application form from the Foundation's website. **Additional Information:** Pride Foundation at the above address.

2937 ■ PRIDE FOUNDATION
PO Box 2194, 1122 E Pike St. PMB 1001
Seattle, WA 98112
Tel: (206)323-3318
Free: 800-735-7287
Fax: (206)323-1017
E-mail: prideweb@pridefoundation.org
Web Site: http://www.pridefoundation.org
To provide scholarship to the students who have been stigmatized, isolated or closeted because of sexual identity issues.
Title of Award: Dennis Coleman Choral Conducting Scholarships **Area, Field, or Subject:** Music. **Level of Education for which Award is Granted:** Undergraduate **Funds Available:** No specific amount.
Eligibility Requirements: Applicant must be a LGBT student studying choral conducting or music with preference given to those committed to creating social change through music. **Application Requirements:** Qualified students are asked to submit an application to determine eligibility for scholarships. Applicants may download an application form from the Foundation's website. **Additional Information:** Pride Foundation at the above address.

2938 ■ REDLANDS COMMUNITY SCHOLARSHIP FOUNDATION
c/o Kathleen Venegas-Boge, Admin. Asst.
PO Box 1683
Redlands, CA 92373
Tel: (909)307-9892
Fax: (909)307-9892
Web Site: http://www.redlandsscholarships.org
To encourage educational pursuits among Redlands Unified School District graduates by providing educational assistance.
Title of Award: Contemporary Club Scholarships **Area, Field, or Subject:** Music. **Level of Education for which Award is Granted:** Undergraduate **Number Awarded:** 1. **Funds Available:** $500.
Eligibility Requirements: Applicant must be a graduating senior intending to continue his/her studies in music. **Application Requirements:** Applicants must submit a completed application form together with the scantron sheet; cover sheet; student activity and community activity sheets; personal essay; and a copy of unofficial transcript (signed by the counselor). **Additional Information:** No electronic submissions of application will be accepted. Submit two printed copies of the application and use a No. 2 pencil on the scantron sheet. **Deadline for Receipt:** February 20.

2939 ■ REDLANDS COMMUNITY SCHOLARSHIP FOUNDATION
c/o Kathleen Venegas-Boge, Admin. Asst.
PO Box 1683
Redlands, CA 92373
Tel: (909)307-9892
Fax: (909)307-9892
Web Site: http://www.redlandsscholarships.org
To encourage educational pursuits among Redlands Unified School District graduates by providing educational assistance.
Title of Award: Redlands High School Drama Boosters Award **Area, Field, or Subject:** Performing arts. **Level of Education for which Award is Granted:** Undergraduate **Number Awarded:** 1. **Funds Available:** $200.
Eligibility Requirements: Applicant must be a graduating senior pursuing a performing arts degree in college. **Application Requirements:** Applicants must submit: a completed application form together with the scantron sheet; cover sheet; student activity and community activity sheets; personal essay; and a copy of unofficial transcript (signed by the counselor). **Additional Information:** No electronic submissions of application will be accepted. Submit two printed copies of the application and use a No. 2 pencil on the scantron sheet. **Deadline for Receipt:** February 20.

2940 ■ RHODE ISLAND FOUNDATION
One Union Sta.
Providence, RI 02903

Tel: (401)274-4564
Fax: (401)331-8085
Web Site: http://www.rifoundation.org/matriarch/default.asp
To provide financial assistance for promising music students to pursue their career.
Title of Award: Bach Organ and Keyboard Music Scholarships **Area, Field, or Subject:** Education, Music. **Level of Education for which Award is Granted:** Undergraduate **Funds Available:** $1,000. **Duration:** One year.
Eligibility Requirements: Applicant must be a Rhode Island resident enrolled in college as a music major; must be a church organist and an American Guild of Organists member; and must demonstrate financial need. **Application Requirements:** Applicants must complete the application form, available online; must submit one essay, recent high school or college transcript (music majors); must have a copy of their final Student Aid Report, financial aid award letter, and one recommendation from their organ/keyboard teacher or church official. Application forms and other supporting documents must be sent to Libby Monahan, GFWC Women's Club of South County Scholarship, Rhode Island Foundation, One Union Station, Providence, RI 02903. **Deadline for Receipt:** June 9.

2941 ■ RHODE ISLAND FOUNDATION
One Union Sta.
Providence, RI 02903
Tel: (401)274-4564
Fax: (401)331-8085
Web Site: http://www.rifoundation.org/matriarch/default.asp
To provide support for deserving visual art or music major students intending to pursue their education.
Title of Award: Constant Memorial Scholarship for Aquidneck Island Resident **Area, Field, or Subject:** Visual arts; Education, Music. **Level of Education for which Award is Granted:** Undergraduate **Number Awarded:** 2. **Funds Available:** $2,000-$5,000. **Duration:** One year.
Eligibility Requirements: Applicants must be Aquidneck Island residents for at least three years; must demonstrate a serious interest in visual arts and/or music; must have a proof of enrollment in an arts or music major at an accredited institution of higher education; and must be able to demonstrate financial need. **Application Requirements:** Applicants must complete the application form, available online; must have a copy of their financial aid award letter; must submit a recent official college transcript; three proofs of Rhode Island residency; one essay; copy of their final Student Aid Report; one letter of recommendation; and a sample of work done within the last 12 months. Application forms and other supporting documents must be sent to Libby Monahan, GFWC Women's Club of South County Scholarship, Rhode Island Foundation, One Union Station, Providence, RI 02903. **Deadline for Receipt:** June 9.

2942 ■ THE SAN DIEGO FOUNDATION
2508 Historic Decatur Rd., Ste. 200
San Diego, CA 92106
Tel: (619)235-2300
Fax: (619)239-1710
E-mail: info@sdfoundation.org
Web Site: http://www.sdfoundation.org
To support the education of students from California.
Title of Award: Barta-Lehman Musical Scholarships **Area, Field, or Subject:** Music. **Level of Education for which Award is Granted:** Undergraduate **Number Awarded:** 4. **Funds Available:** $2,000.
Eligibility Requirements: Applicant must be a graduating high school senior, or current undergraduate or graduate college student; must be a serious and talented musician; planning to pursue a career in music and/or play professionally (string instruments preferred); have a minimum 3.0 GPA on a 4.0 scale; and planning to attend an accredited four-year university or music academy in the U.S. **Application Requirements:** Applicants must submit a completed Common Scholarship Application together with personal statement; two letters of recommendation on official letterhead (written within the last six months); official transcript in an official and sealed envelope; copy of most recent tax form (Form 1040-pages 1 & 2; Form 1040A-pages 1 & 2; Form 1040EZ -page 1); a letter of recommendation on letterhead must come from a music teacher indicating level of talent and seriousness about pursuing music as a career; and a CD or video of the applicant's music. **Deadline for Receipt:** January 28. **Additional Information:** Arzo Mansury, Dir. Scholarships at 619-814-1343, or scholarships@sdfoundation.org.

2943 ■ SANTA BARBARA DANCE ALLIANCE
PO Box 22256
Santa Barbara, CA 93121
Tel: (805)966-6950
Fax: (805)966-6950
E-mail: dance@sbdancealliance.org
Web Site: http://www.sbdancealliance.org
To provide financial support to talented students.
Title of Award: Dance Education Scholarship Program **Area, Field, or Subject:** Dance. **Level of Education for which Award is Granted:** High School **Funds Available:** No specific amount.
Eligibility Requirements: Applicants must be students ages 8-16 years old; must have talent, dedication and financial need. Applicants may dance in any form; must have studied for at least 2 years, and be recommended by their instructors or studios. **Application Requirements:** Applicants must submit a completed application form. **Deadline for Receipt:** May 9. **Additional Information:** Santa Barbara Dance Alliance at the above address.

2944 ■ SCREEN ACTORS GUILD
5757 Wilshire Blvd.
Los Angeles, CA 90036
Tel: (323)549-6708
E-mail: saginfo@sag.org
Web Site: http://www.sagfoundation.org
To assist students in their chosen field.
Title of Award: The John L. Dales Scholarship Fund **Area, Field, or Subject:** Performing Arts. **Level of Education for which Award is Granted:** Undergraduate **Funds Available:** No specific amount.
Eligibility Requirements: The scholarship applies only to accredited and licensed universities, colleges, junior colleges, adult specialty schools or trade/vocational schools. **Application Requirements:** Applicant shall submit a transcript of all high school, college and university course and evaluations, SAT scores, and any other relevant information; Applicant shall submit the Confidential Financial Aid Form for applicant and a copy of their most recent Federal Income Tax Returns for applicant and parent; If either applicant or parents are incorporated, the Corporate Tax Return must be submitted. All submitted tax returns must be complete; Applicant shall submit an essay of 350 to 750 words on one of the topics provided with the application; and a two personal letters of recommendation. **Deadline for Receipt:** March 15. **Additional Information:** Davidson Lloyd, Administrative Director, 323-549-6649, dlloyd@sag.org.

2945 ■ SOUTHWEST FLORIDA COMMUNITY FOUNDATION
8260 College Pkwy., Ste. 101
Fort Myers, FL 33919
Tel: (239)274-5900
Fax: (239)274-5930
Web Site: http://www.floridacommunity.com
To provide financial assistance for qualified students in Florida.
Title of Award: Charles and Margaret Foster Scholarships **Area, Field, or Subject:** Environmental technology; Music. **Level of Education for which Award is Granted:** Undergraduate **Number Awarded:** 2. **Funds Available:** $300. **Duration:** One year.
Eligibility Requirements: Applicant must be a resident of Lee County and must be studying environmental studies or environmental education at the University of Florida or studying music at Florida State University. **Application Requirements:** Applicants must have the application form, available online, and must submit a transcript, letter of interest and letter of recommendation. **Deadline for Receipt:** February 15.

2946 ■ SOUTHWEST FLORIDA COMMUNITY FOUNDATION
8260 College Pkwy., Ste. 101
Fort Myers, FL 33919
Tel: (239)274-5900
Fax: (239)274-5930
Web Site: http://www.floridacommunity.com
To fund tuition for graduating seniors pursuing higher education in the fine or performing arts.
Title of Award: George E. Judd Scholarships **Area, Field, or Subject:** Fine arts; Performing arts. **Level of Education for which Award is Granted:** Undergraduate **Funds Available:** $1,000. **Duration:** One year.
Eligibility Requirements: Applicants must graduate from public or private high school in Lee County and must pursue a degree in the fine or

performing arts. **Application Requirements:** Applicants must submit a letter of interest, transcript, and letter of recommendation. Application forms are available online. **Deadline for Receipt:** February 15.

2947 ■ STARK COMMUNITY FOUNDATION

400 Market Ave. N, Ste. 200
Canton, OH 44702-2107
Tel: (330)454-3426
Fax: (330)454-5855
Web Site: http://www.starkcommunityfoundation.org
To provide scholarship assistance to qualified individuals who want to pursue their studies.
Title of Award: American Guild of Organists, Canton Chapter Charitable Fund **Area, Field, or Subject:** Music. **Level of Education for which Award is Granted:** Undergraduate **Funds Available:** No specific amount.
Eligibility Requirements: Applicants must be students residing in Stark County, without regard to gender, race, color, creed or nationality who are pursuing a four-year bachelor degree program at an accredited college or university in music with a major in instrument; must show an evidence of competent technique and musicianship. **Application Requirements:** Application forms are available online. Applicants must submit a letters of reference and a submitted tape and/or audition including one Bach work or movement, one French work or movement, and a third work of applicant's choice. Application form and requirements must be sent to Mr. Greg L. Hollinger, Treas. at 9264 Shipton Circle NW, North Canton, OH 44720. **Deadline for Receipt:** April 15.

2948 ■ STARK COMMUNITY FOUNDATION

400 Market Ave. N, Ste. 200
Canton, OH 44702-2107
Tel: (330)454-3426
Fax: (330)454-5855
Web Site: http://www.starkcommunityfoundation.org
To provide scholarship assistance to qualified applicants from Stark County, Ohio.
Title of Award: Ruth M. Cogan Scholarship Fund **Area, Field, or Subject:** Music. **Level of Education for which Award is Granted:** Undergraduate **Funds Available:** Amount of award will be determined by the Selection committee.
Eligibility Requirements: Applicants must be high school students and present college students with an interest in studying music, have an inner feeling for music and whose lives have reflected the spiritual qualities, depth, understanding and love. **Application Requirements:** Applicants must complete the application form available online and must be sent to Stark Community Foundation, 400 Market Ave. N, Ste. 200, Canton, OH 44702. **Deadline for Receipt:** April 15.

2949 ■ STARK COMMUNITY FOUNDATION

400 Market Ave. N, Ste. 200
Canton, OH 44702-2107
Tel: (330)454-3426
Fax: (330)454-5855
Web Site: http://www.starkcommunityfoundation.org
To provide scholarship assistance to qualified individuals who want to pursue their studies.
Title of Award: Velma Shotwell Griffin Memorial Scholarship Fund **Area, Field, or Subject:** History; Writing; Music. **Level of Education for which Award is Granted:** Undergraduate **Number Awarded:** 1. **Funds Available:** $1,000. **Duration:** One year.
Eligibility Requirements: Applicants must be graduates of Conotton Valley High School or Carrollton High School; must be planning to enroll, or currently enrolled, at an accredited college or university to pursue further education in the following fields: (1) History; (2) Writing, not limited to, English Journalism, Language Arts, Communications and programs in Mass Media; (3) Music, not limited to vocal music, instrumental music, music history, music education, and music performance; (4) Any other program or field of study approved by the selection committee. **Application Requirements:** Applicants must submit completed application form and are advised to contact Carrollton High School Guidance Office, Connotton Valley High School Guidance Office. **Deadline for Receipt:** April 28.

2950 ■ TEXAS MUSIC EDUCATORS ASSOCIATION

7900 Centre Park
Austin, TX 78754
Tel: (512)452-0710
Fax: (512)451-9213
E-mail: rfloyd@tmea.org
Web Site: http://www.tmea.org
To provide professional growth opportunities; to encourage interaction among music education professionals; to foster public support for music in school; to offer quality musical experiences for students; to cultivate universal appreciation and lifetime involvement in music; to develop and maintain productive working relationships with other professional organizations.
Title of Award: Bill Cormack Scholarships **Area, Field, or Subject:** Music. **Level of Education for which Award is Granted:** Undergraduate **Funds Available:** $2,500. **Duration:** 5 years.
Eligibility Requirements: Applicants must be entering freshmen in a Texas college or university; must major in a music degree program leading to Texas teacher-certification with music as the primary teaching field. **Application Requirements:** Applicant must submit: completed application form; a high school transcript; a one-to-two page essay that describes his/her reasons for becoming a teacher, commitment to music education and future career goals; three-to-five evaluations from individuals who can assess the applicant's potential for success in an undergraduate music education program and as a music educator, music skills and abilities, work ethic and other personal qualities; must submit a verification from student's advisor that the applicant will teach within the semester indicated on the application. **Deadline for Receipt:** November 15. **Additional Information:** Kay Vanlandingham at the above address.

2951 ■ TEXAS MUSIC EDUCATORS ASSOCIATION

7900 Centre Park
Austin, TX 78754
Tel: (512)452-0710
Fax: (512)451-9213
E-mail: rfloyd@tmea.org
Web Site: http://www.tmea.org
To provide professional growth opportunities; to encourage interaction among music education professionals; to foster public support for music in school; to offer quality musical experiences for students; to cultivate universal appreciation and lifetime involvement in music; to develop and maintain productive working relationships with other professional organizations.
Title of Award: Texas Music Educators Association Past-Presidents Memorial Scholarships **Area, Field, or Subject:** Music. **Level of Education for which Award is Granted:** Undergraduate **Funds Available:** $2,000. **Duration:** 5 years.
Eligibility Requirements: Applicants must be entering freshmen at a Texas college or university; must major in a music degree program leading to Texas teacher-certification with music as the primary teaching field. **Application Requirements:** Applicants must submit: completed application form; high school transcript; a one-to-two-page essay that describes his or her reasons for becoming a teacher, commitment to music education and future career goals; three-to-five evaluations from individuals who can assess the applicant's potential for success in an undergraduate music education program and as a music educator, music skills and abilities, work ethic and other personal qualities; must submit a verification by student's advisor that the applicant will teach within the semester indicated on the application. **Deadline for Receipt:** November 15. **Additional Information:** Kay Vanlandingham at the above address.

2952 ■ TURKISH COALITION OF AMERICA

1025 Connecticut Ave. NW, Ste. 1000
Washington, DC 20036
Tel: (202)370-1399
Fax: (202)370-1398
E-mail: info@turkishcoalitionofamerica.org
Web Site: http://www.turkishcoalition.org
To provide financial support for deserving students of Turkish descent pursuing undergraduate or graduate studies in music.
Title of Award: Ahmet Ertegun Memorial Scholarships **Area, Field, or Subject:** Music. **Level of Education for which Award is Granted:** Graduate, Undergraduate **Funds Available:** No specific amount.

Eligibility Requirements: Applicants must be music students at Juilliard School in New York City. **Application Requirements:** Applicants must check the available website for the required materials. **Additional Information:** One of the seminal figures in the history of popular music, Ahmet Ertegun was also a prominent philanthropist dedicated to enhancing relations and cultural understanding between the United States and his native country, Turkey.

2953 ■ UNIVERSITY OF ALASKA ANCHORAGE
3211 Providence Dr.
Anchorage, AK 99508
Tel: (907)786-1800
Web Site: http://www.uaa.alaska.edu
To provide financial assistance for tuition and other related educational expenses to full-time students of the University of Alaska Anchorage who are formally admitted to an undergraduate engineering or music degree-seeking program.
Title of Award: Alaska Community Foundation Sven E. & Lorraine Eriksson Scholarships **Area, Field, or Subject:** Engineering; Music. **Level of Education for which Award is Granted:** Undergraduate **Funds Available:** No specific amount. **Duration:** One academic year.
Eligibility Requirements: Applicant must demonstrate motivation, academic and leadership potential; must be an Alaskan resident who has graduated from an Alaskan high school; must be a United States citizen; must be an incoming college freshman must have a minimum high school GPA of 2.5; must have a minimum cumulative grade point average of 3.0 from college and have had a 2.5 GPA from high school; must be formally admitted to an undergraduate engineering or music degree-seeking program at the University of Alaska Anchorage; must demonstrate financial need; must be an incoming or continuing student at the University of Alaska Anchorage. **Application Requirements:** Applicants must complete the application form available online. **Deadline for Receipt:** February 15.

2954 ■ UNIVERSITY OF ALASKA ANCHORAGE
3211 Providence Dr.
Anchorage, AK 99508
Tel: (907)786-1800
Web Site: http://www.uaa.alaska.edu
To provide financial assistance for tuition and other educational expenses to students who are formally admitted to a music degree-seeking program at the University of Alaska Anchorage.
Title of Award: UAA Brown Schoenheit Memorial Scholarships **Area, Field, or Subject:** Music. **Level of Education for which Award is Granted:** Undergraduate **Funds Available:** No specific amount.
Eligibility Requirements: Applicants must demonstrate motivation, academic and leadership potential, and musical ability; must be in good academic standing with a minimum cumulative GPA of 2.0; must be formally admitted to a music degree-seeking program at the University of Alaska Anchorage by the start of the semester for which the award is to be made; must be a Music major with emphasis in an orchestral instrument; must plan on enrolling at least half-time (6 credits) at the University of Alaska Anchorage for the semester in which the award is made; may be an incoming or continuing student at the University of Alaska Anchorage; may be a U.S. citizen, non-U.S. citizen, Alaska resident, or out-of-state resident. **Application Requirements:** Applicants must complete the electronic scholarship application available online at www.uaa.alaska.edu/scholarships/brown.cfm. **Deadline for Receipt:** February 15.

2955 ■ UNIVERSITY OF ALASKA ANCHORAGE
3211 Providence Dr.
Anchorage, AK 99508
Tel: (907)786-1800
Web Site: http://www.uaa.alaska.edu
To provide financial assistance for tuition and other educational expenses to full-time students who are formally admitted to a music degree-seeking program at the University of Alaska Anchorage.
Title of Award: UAA Edward Rollin Clinton Memorial for Music **Area, Field, or Subject:** Music. **Level of Education for which Award is Granted:** Undergraduate **Funds Available:** $1,000.
Eligibility Requirements: Applicant must be in good academic standing with a minimum cumulative GPA of 3.0; must be formally admitted to a music degree-seeking program at the University of Alaska Anchorage;

must plan on enrolling at least full-time (12 credits) at the University of Alaska Anchorage; may be an incoming or continuing student at the University of Alaska Anchorage; may be a U.S citizen, non-U.S citizen, Alaska resident, or out-of-state resident. **Application Requirements:** Applicants must submit a compact disc recording which must include a minimum of two (2) selections from the standard classical repertoire. Application form and other supporting documents must be sent to UAA Office of Student Financial Assistance, Edward Rollin Clinton Scholarship, PO Box 141608, Anchorage, AK 99514. **Deadline for Receipt:** February 15.

2956 ■ UNIVERSITY OF ALASKA ANCHORAGE
3211 Providence Dr.
Anchorage, AK 99508
Tel: (907)786-1800
Web Site: http://www.uaa.alaska.edu
To provide financial assistance for tuition and other education related expenses to a full-time University of Alaska Anchorage student who has shown a proven interest in the performing arts.
Title of Award: UAA Friends of the Performing Arts Scholarships **Area, Field, or Subject:** Performing arts. **Level of Education for which Award is Granted:** Undergraduate **Funds Available:** $750. **Duration:** One year.
Eligibility Requirements: Applicants must demonstrate motivation, academic and leadership potential; must be in good academic standing in an undergraduate performing arts degree-seeking program at the University of Alaska Anchorage; must plan on enrolling full-time (12 credits) at the University of Alaska Anchorage; must show proven interest in the performing arts; may be an incoming or continuing student at the University of Alaska Anchorage; may be a U.S. citizen, non-U.S. citizen, Alaska resident, or out-of-state resident; must be enrolled in the semester for which the award is made. **Application Requirements:** Applicants must complete the scholarship application available online at www.uaa.alaska.edu/scholarships/friends_arts.cfm. **Deadline for Receipt:** February 15.

2957 ■ UNIVERSITY OF ALASKA ANCHORAGE
3211 Providence Dr.
Anchorage, AK 99508
Tel: (907)786-1800
Web Site: http://www.uaa.alaska.edu
To provide financial assistance for tuition and other educational expenses to full-time junior or senior students who are formally admitted into a Bachelor of Arts or Bachelor of Fine Arts program in the area of sculpture and/or performance art at the University of Alaska Anchorage.
Title of Award: UAA Ken Gray Endowment Scholarships **Area, Field, or Subject:** Performing arts, Sculpture. **Level of Education for which Award is Granted:** Undergraduate **Funds Available:** $500-$800.
Eligibility Requirements: Applicants must exhibit an innovative, experimental, and conceptual direction in his/her artwork that stretches the limits of traditional sculpture; must demonstrate motivation, academic and leadership potential; must be in good academic standing with a minimum cumulative GPA of 3.25 and a cumulative GPA of 3.5 in the area of concentration; must formally be admitted to a Bachelor of Arts or Bachelor of Fine Arts at the University of Alaska Anchorage; must plan on enrolling full-time at the University of Alaska Anchorage; must submit a portfolio of work consisting of twenty slides, three letters of reference from practitioners in the sculpture area and/or faculty, and a two-page artist's statement reflecting the criteria for selection; must be enrolled in the semester for which the award is made; may be a U.S. citizen, non-U.S. citizen, Alaska resident, or out-of-state resident. **Application Requirements:** Applicants must submit a portfolio of work consisting of 20 slides; must have three letters of reference from practitioners in the sculpture area and/or UAA faculty; must have a two-page artist's statement reflecting the criteria for selection. Application materials must be sent to UAA Office of Student Financial Assistance, Ken Gray Scholarships, PO Box 141608, Anchorage, AK 99514-1608. **Deadline for Receipt:** February 15.

2958 ■ UNIVERSITY OF OREGON
1217 University of Oregon
Eugene, OR 97403
Tel: (541)346-1000
Free: 800-232-3825
Fax: (541)346-5815
E-mail: stl@uoregon.edu

Web Site: http://www.uoregon.edu
To provide financial support to students who desire to further their education without financial burden.
Title of Award: Robert W. and Bernice Ingalls Staton Scholarships **Area, Field, or Subject:** Humanities; Fine arts; Education; Music. **Level of Education for which Award is Granted:** Undergraduate **Funds Available:** $5,000. **Duration:** One year.
Eligibility Requirements: Applicants must be Oregon residents and must have an extraordinary financial need. **Application Requirements:** Applicants must submit the Admission application available online to the Office of Admission. **Deadline for Receipt:** January 15.

2959 ■ UNIVERSITY OF TORONTO
315 Bloor St. W
Toronto, ON, Canada M5S 1A3
Tel: (416)978-2011
E-mail: information.commonsats@utoronto.ca
Web Site: http://www.utoronto.ca
To support students with their educational pursuits.
Title of Award: In-course Scholarships - Chinese Dance Workshop Scholarships **Area, Field, or Subject:** Dance. **Level of Education for which Award is Granted:** Undergraduate **Funds Available:** Approximately $2400.
Eligibility Requirements: Applicant must be a student of U of T and have attended a recognized dance institute for at least three years. **Application Requirements:** Applicants must submit a letter of application verifying at least three years of attendance at a recognized dance institute along with a transcript of marks. **Deadline for Receipt:** October 31.

2960 ■ UNIVERSITY OF WISCONSIN-MADISON
432 N Murray St.
Madison, WI 53706-1496
Tel: (608)262-3060
Fax: (608)262-9068
E-mail: askbucky@uwmad.wisc.edu
Web Site: http://www.wisc.edu
To support UW-Madison students in their education.
Title of Award: University of Wisconsin-Madison Music Scholarships **Area, Field, or Subject:** Music. **Level of Education for which Award is Granted:** Undergraduate **Number Awarded:** Varies. **Funds Available:** $1,000-$5,000.
Eligibility Requirements: Applicants must be Wisconsin outstanding musicians as demonstrated by a musical background and an audition with the School of Music. **Application Requirements:** Applicants must fill out the School of Music application and attend the audition. **Deadline for Receipt:** February. **Additional Information:** School of Music, at 608-263-5986, or baabrams@wisc.edu.

2961 ■ UNIVERSITY OF WISCONSIN-MADISON
432 N Murray St.
Madison, WI 53706-1496
Tel: (608)262-3060
Fax: (608)262-9068
E-mail: askbucky@uwmad.wisc.edu
Web Site: http://www.wisc.edu
To support UW-Madison students in their education.
Title of Award: Wisconsin-Madison Music Clinic Scholarships **Area, Field, or Subject:** Music. **Level of Education for which Award is Granted:** Undergraduate **Number Awarded:** 10. **Funds Available:** Wisconsin resident tuition for four years of study.
Eligibility Requirements: Applicants must be Wisconsin high school graduates with outstanding musical talent who attended the UW-Madison Summer Music Clinic both summers before enrolling at UW-Madison. **Application Requirements:** Applicants must contact the Music Clinic Coordinator for information. **Deadline for Receipt:** May 15 of junior year in high school. **Additional Information:** School of Music, Music Clinic Coordinator, at 608-263-2242, or maaley@facstaff.wisc.edu.

2962 ■ VIOLIN SOCIETY OF AMERICA
48 Academy St.
Poughkeepsie, NY 12601
Tel: (845)452-7557
Web Site: http://www.vsa.to

To provide financial assistance for needy and deserving students of the art of violin and bow making and restoration.
Title of Award: Violin Society of America Scholarships **Area, Field, or Subject:** Music. **Level of Education for which Award is Granted:** Undergraduate **Funds Available:** No amount mentioned.
Eligibility Requirements: Applicant must be a student U.S. citizen, have satisfactorily completed at least one full year of study in the program, have shown serious effort, talent and future promise and have financial need. **Application Requirements:** Teachers and faculty of leading American violin making schools annually submit the names of those students most worthy of scholarship aid.

2963 ■ THE WASHINGTON GROUP
720 Park Blvd.
PO Box 73
Boise, ID 83729
Tel: (208)386-5000
E-mail: membership@washingtongroup.org
Web Site: http://www.wgint.com
To encourage active participation in Ukrainian community.
Title of Award: Marusia Yaworska Entrance Scholarships **Area, Field, or Subject:** Music. **Level of Education for which Award is Granted:** Undergraduate **Number Awarded:** 2. **Funds Available:** $5,000.
Eligibility Requirements: Applicants must be high school seniors already attending an accredited college or university; must be members of the Ukrainian Fraternal Association for two years. **Application Requirements:** Applicants must fill out the application and supporting materials. **Deadline for Receipt:** March 31. **Additional Information:** Department of Music, faculty of Arts, University of Ottawa, 50 University Private, Ottawa, Ontario, K1N 5N5, Canada.

2964 ■ WINSTON-SALEM FOUNDATION
860 W Fifth St.
Winston-Salem, NC 27101-2506
Tel: (336)725-2382
Fax: (336)727-0581
E-mail: info@wsfoundation.org
Web Site: http://www.wsfoundation.org
To award freshman who will pursue a degree in music from one of the following institutions: North Carolina School of the Arts, Salem College, Wake Forest University, or Winston-Salem State University.
Title of Award: Douglas Gray Kinel Scholarships **Area, Field, or Subject:** Music. **Level of Education for which Award is Granted:** Undergraduate **Funds Available:** $500.
Eligibility Requirements: This scholarship seeks to identify those students who: will pursue a degree in music; demonstrate a minimum, cumulative, unweighted GPA of 3.5; have financial need (scholarship is not restricted to lowest family incomes); are residents of Forsyth County; are Moravian, preferably; are studying to enter a church-related vocation, preferably. **Application Requirements:** Scholarship applications will be available online. Students must: complete the scholarship application; provide grade transcript through the 1st semester of 12th grade; submit one recommendation as outlined on the application; attend an interview if so advised. **Deadline for Receipt:** March 31. **Additional Information:** WSF Student Aid Department, 336-714-3445.

2965 ■ WOLF TRAP FOUNDATION FOR THE PERFORMING ARTS
1645 Trap Rd.
Vienna, VA 22182
Tel: (703)255-1900
E-mail: wolftrap@wolftrap.org
Web Site: http://www.wolf-trap.org
To provide training program for the performing arts.
Title of Award: The Wolf Trap Internship Program **Area, Field, or Subject:** Performing arts. **Level of Education for which Award is Granted:** Graduate, Professional, Undergraduate **Funds Available:** No specific amount. **Duration:** Summer: 12 weeks, full-time (40-plus hours per week); Fall and Spring: 12 weeks, part-time (maximum of 24 hours per week).
Eligibility Requirements: Applicants must be undergraduate students (completed one year of study or equivalent), graduate students, or recent graduates (up to two years out of school); career-changers enrolled in a degree program; and international students (J-1 or F-1 Visa required). **Ap-

plication Requirements: Applicants must submit a cover letter with a brief personal statement and an outline of career goals; a resume; two academic or professional recommendations; two contrasting writing samples, (maximum of 3 pages each). Applicants must send the requirements to Internship Program Wolf Trap Foundation for the Performing Arts, 1645 Trap Road, Vienna, VA 22182, 703255-1924 (fax), internships@wolftrap.org (e-mail). **Deadline for Receipt:** March 1, July 1, and November 1. **Additional Information:** (703)255-1933, (800)404-8461, or e-mail internships@wolftrap.org.

2966 ■ XAVIER UNIVERSITY

3800 Victory Pky.
Cincinnati, OH 45207
Tel: (513)745-3000
Free: 800-344-GOXU
Web Site: http://www.xavier.edu
To financially support students with their education.
Title of Award: Edgecliff McAuley Music Scholarships **Area, Field, or Subject:** Music. **Level of Education for which Award is Granted:** Undergraduate **Number Awarded:** 1. **Funds Available:** Full-tuition.
Eligibility Requirements: Applicant must be an incoming student. **Application Requirements:** Students admitted at the Xavier University are automatically considered. Applicants must pass the audition held on January 26, February 2, and February 23.

Philosophy

2967 ■ ARAB AMERICAN INSTITUTE

1600 K St. NW, Ste. 601
Washington, DC 20006
Tel: (202)429-9210
Fax: (202)429-9214
E-mail: aai@aaiusa.org
Web Site: http://www.aaiusa.org
To promote academic excellence and to provide an opportunity for outstanding student to reach their fullest potential.
Title of Award: Ameen Rihani Scholarship Program **Area, Field, or Subject:** Literature; Philosophy; Political science. **Level of Education for which Award is Granted:** Undergraduate **Funds Available:** $1,500.
Eligibility Requirements: Individual must: be a Lebanese or other Arab Descent; be a citizen or legal permanent residents of the United States; have attained a cumulative GPA of 3.25 on a 4.0 scale; enter a college or university as a full-time, degree-seeking freshman in the fall of the year; have demonstrated leadership abilities through participation in community service, extracurricular or other activities. **Application Requirements:**

Teachers, counselors, and principals are invited to nominate students with outstanding academic qualifications, particularly those who would promote success in the fields of literature, philosophy, or political science. **Deadline for Receipt:** May 31. **Additional Information:** Ameen Rihani Scholarship Program, The Ameen Rihani Organization, 1010 Wayne Ave. Ste 420 Silver Spring, MD 20910.

Theology

2968 ■ ARMENIAN STUDENTS' ASSOCIATION OF AMERICA

333 Atlantic Ave.
Warwick, RI 02888
Tel: (401)461-6114
E-mail: asa@asainc.org
Web Site: http://www.asainc.org
To provide financial assistance to those students who are in need.
Title of Award: Rev. and Mrs. A.K. Jizmejian Educational Fund **Area, Field, or Subject:** Theology. **Level of Education for which Award is Granted:** Undergraduate **Funds Available:** $500-$1,500.
Eligibility Requirements: Applicants must be full-time theological seminary students and fourth-year undergraduate students who intend to continue their education in a theological seminary. **Application Requirements:** Applicants must check the available website for more information. **Deadline for Receipt:** June 30. **Additional Information:** Armenian Evangelical Church; Mr. Mihran Jizmejian, Chairman 816-60 Pavane Linkway Don Mills, Ontario, M3C 1A2 Canada.

2969 ■ CATHOLIC BIBLICAL ASSOCIATION OF AMERICA

Catholic University of America
433 Caldwell Hall
Washington, DC 20064
Tel: (202)319-5519
Fax: (202)319-4799
E-mail: cua-cathbib@cua.edu
Web Site: http://cba.cua.edu
To provide support to students who want to pursue their biblical studies.
Title of Award: Catholic Biblical Association of America Scholarships **Area, Field, or Subject:** Bible studies. **Level of Education for which Award is Granted:** Undergraduate **Funds Available:** Full tuition fee and a stipend of $12,500. **Duration:** One year.
Eligibility Requirements: Applicant must be a full-time student in doctoral programs on biblical studies at four institutions: (a) Catholic University of America; (b) Graduate Theological Union at Barkeley; (c) University of Notre Dame. **Application Requirements:** For further information, applicants are advised to contact the Association at Catholic University of America, 433 Caldwell Hall, Washington, DC 20064.

General

2970 ■ AMERICAN ASSOCIATION OF CANDY TECHNOLOGISTS
175 Rock Rd.
Glen Rock, NJ 07452
Tel: (201)652-2655; (201)652-3419
E-mail: aactinfo@gomc.com
Web Site: http://www.aactcandy.org
To provide support for individuals pursuing their career.
Title of Award: National Candy Technologist Scholarship Program **Area, Field, or Subject:** Food science and technology, Biological and clinical sciences. **Level of Education for which Award is Granted:** Undergraduate **Funds Available:** $5,000.
Eligibility Requirements: Applicants must be Sophomore, Junior, or Senior Status; have demonstrated interest in confectionery technology; attend an accredited four-year college or university within North America; be majoring in a food science, chemical science, biological science, or related area; minimum 3.0 GPA required (or equivalent on another scale). **Application Requirements:** Applicants must submit a complete application with short statement of personal and professional goals; must attach the academic activities including those relating to confectionery technology; must have the current copy of college transcript and a recommendation letter. Application must be mailed to: Warrell Corp., 1250 Slate Hill Rd., Camp Hill, PA 17011. **Deadline for Receipt:** April 18. **Additional Information:** Mr. Karen Silva at the above address.

2971 ■ AMERICAN ASSOCIATION OF PROFESSIONAL APICULTURISTS
c/o Dept. of Entomology University of Minnesota
219 Hodson Hall
1980 Folwell Ave.
St. Paul, MN 55108-6125
Tel: (612)624-4798
Fax: (612)625-5299
Web Site: http://entomology.ucdavis.edu/home.cfm
To recognize and promote outstanding research by students in the field of apiculture.
Title of Award: AAPA Research Scholarships **Area, Field, or Subject:** Entomology. **Level of Education for which Award is Granted:** Undergraduate **Funds Available:** $1,000.
Eligibility Requirements: Applicants must be undergraduate or graduate students working in North America with completed research on Apis; must be active AAPA members. **Application Requirements:** Research proposal package must include a curriculum vitae of the nominee, one letter of recommendation, and a summary of the research problem not exceeding three pages including: objectives, significance, and methods. Nominees may also include: up to three publication reprints, submitted manuscripts or abstracts of theses or dissertations. Four copies of the proposal package should be sent to the Chair of the AAPA Student Award Committee at least one month prior to the annual meeting.

2972 ■ AMERICAN ASSOCIATION OF STRATIGRAPHIC PALYNOLOGISTS
University of North Carolina at Pembroke
Geology, Old Main 213
Pembroke, NC 28372
Tel: (910)521-6478
E-mail: mbfarley@sigmaxi.net
Web Site: http://www.palynology.org
To support research in the field or any aspect related to paleontology.
Title of Award: Paleontological Society Student Research Grants **Area, Field, or Subject:** Earth Sciences; Geology. **Level of Education for which Award is Granted:** Graduate, Undergraduate **Funds Available:** $750. **Duration:** One year.
Eligibility Requirements: Applicant must be undergraduate or graduate student member of the Paleontological Society conducting a research on any aspect of paleontology. **Application Requirements:** Applicants must submit a completed application form (available at the website) and a letter of support from research advisor (must be sent to michalk@vt.edu). **Deadline for Receipt:** February 25.

2973 ■ ARKANSAS ENVIRONMENTAL FEDERATION
1400 W Markham St., Ste. 302
Little Rock, AR 72201
Tel: (501)374-0263
Fax: (501)374-8752
Web Site: http://www.environmentark.org
To provide financial assistance for selected students from Arkansas universities.
Title of Award: Randall Matthis for Environmental Studies Scholarships **Area, Field, or Subject:** Environmental science; Health education; Natural resources. **Level of Education for which Award is Granted:** Graduate, Undergraduate **Funds Available:** $2,500. **Duration:** One year.
Eligibility Requirements: Applicants must be U.S. citizens residing in Arkansas and must be undergraduate or graduate students with at least 2.8 cumulative GPA based on 4.0 system. **Application Requirements:** Applicants must submit a completed application form along with current official transcript(s) and letters. **Deadline for Receipt:** April 11.

2974 ■ BIOCOMMUNICATIONS ASSOCIATION
220 Southwind Ln.
Hillsborough, NC 27278
Tel: (919)245-0906
E-mail: office@bca.org
Web Site: http://www.bca.org
To promote and assist study and research in the field of biological communication.
Title of Award: Endowment Fund for Education Grants **Area, Field, or Subject:** Biological and clinical sciences. **Level of Education for which Award is Granted:** Undergraduate **Funds Available:** $500 or less. **Duration:** One year.
Eligibility Requirements: High school students and students currently enrolled in their freshman year at a university or college are not eligible for grant funds. Applicants who are currently enrolled in sophomore, junior and senior years must present documentary evidence to demonstrate that they are in good academic standing for all courses directly related to their major. **Application Requirements:** Applicants must submit the following documentation: (1) Current curriculum vitae; (2) A full and complete statement of what the applicant/ applicants intend(s) to accomplish within the field of biological photography; (3) Time frame for the project; (4) Details of how the project will benefit biomedical communications and biocommu-

nicators as a whole, and of how this will be measured; (5) An agreement to provide the EFFE Committee with a final report describing the results of the project and its impact on biocommunication; (6) Description of plan to share the resulting educational benefits with the BCA membership; (7) An agreement that the BioCommunications Association, Inc., shall have the right of first publication on any results from project funded wholly or partially from the Endowment Fund for Education. **Deadline for Receipt:** April 25.

2975 ■ BIOCOMMUNICATIONS ASSOCIATION

220 Southwind Ln.
Hillsborough, NC 27278
Tel: (919)245-0906
E-mail: office@bca.org
Web Site: http://www.bca.org
To promote and assist study and research in the field of biological communication.

Title of Award: Endowment Fund for Education (Loan) **Area, Field, or Subject:** Biological and clinical sciences. **Level of Education for which Award is Granted:** Undergraduate **Funds Available:** $500 or less. **Duration:** One year.

Eligibility Requirements: Applicants must be high school students or students currently enrolled in their freshman year at a university or college; must present documentary evidence to demonstrate that they are in good academic standing for all courses directly related to their major (for sophomore, junior and senior years of high school). **Application Requirements:** Applicants must submit the following documentation: (1) Current curriculum vitae; (2) A financial statement; (3) High school graduates applying for a loan to be used as tuition for the freshman year must present documentation to assure the EFFE Committee that they are in good academic standing for their full senior year. Application forms are available online. **Deadline for Receipt:** April 25.

2976 ■ BIOCOMMUNICATIONS ASSOCIATION

220 Southwind Ln.
Hillsborough, NC 27278
Tel: (919)245-0906
E-mail: office@bca.org
Web Site: http://www.bca.org
To promote and assist study and research in the field of biological communication.

Title of Award: Endowment Fund for Education (Loan/Grants for Equipment) **Area, Field, or Subject:** Biological and clinical sciences. **Level of Education for which Award is Granted:** Undergraduate **Funds Available:** $500 or less. **Duration:** One year.

Eligibility Requirements: High school students and students currently enrolled in their freshman year at a university or college are not eligible for grant funds. Applicants who are currently enrolled in sophomore, junior and senior years must present documentary evidence to demonstrate that they are in good academic standing for all courses directly related to their major. **Application Requirements:** Applicants must submit the following documentation: (1) A complete description of each piece of equipment; (2) The life expectancy of each piece of equipment; (3) The role each piece of equipment will play in the education of biocommunicators; (4) The number of students who can be expected to benefit from the equipment; (5) The total cost of the equipment; (6) The intended supplier of the equipment; (7) An agreement to provide the EFFE Committee with reports at six and twelve months after installation stating how the equipment has been used to benefit the education of biophotography students. **Deadline for Receipt:** April 25.

2977 ■ BIOCOMMUNICATIONS ASSOCIATION

220 Southwind Ln.
Hillsborough, NC 27278
Tel: (919)245-0906
E-mail: office@bca.org
Web Site: http://www.bca.org
To promote and assist study and research in the field of biological communication.

Title of Award: Endowment Fund for Education (Loans/Grants for Educational Materials) **Area, Field, or Subject:** Biological and clinical sciences. **Level of Education for which Award is Granted:** Undergraduate **Funds Available:** $500 or less. **Duration:** One year.

Eligibility Requirements: High school students and students currently enrolled in their freshman year at a university or college are not eligible for grant funds. Applicants who are currently enrolled in sophomore, junior and senior years must present documentary evidence to demonstrate that they are in good academic standing for all courses directly related to their major. **Application Requirements:** Applicants must submit the following materials: (1) A complete description of the materials to be purchased; (2) Information about where the materials will be housed and who is to be responsible for their security; (3) Details on how the materials will be made available to the students; (4) The life expectancy of the materials; (5) The relevance of the material to biophotography; (6) The number of students who will use the materials; (7) The total cost and supplier of the materials. **Deadline for Receipt:** April 25.

2978 ■ CANADIAN SOCIETY OF PETROLEUM GEOLOGISTS

600-640 8th Ave. SW
Calgary, AB, Canada T2P 1G7
Tel: (403)264-5610
Fax: (403)264-5898
E-mail: tim.howard@cspg.org
Web Site: http://www.cspg.org
To encourage educational pursuits in the field of geology.

Title of Award: Canadian Society of Petroleum Geologists Regional Undergraduate Scholarships **Area, Field, or Subject:** Earth Sciences. **Level of Education for which Award is Granted:** Undergraduate **Funds Available:** $1,250.

Eligibility Requirements: Program is open to all undergraduates enrolled in an accredited Earth Science program of a Canadian University who are in their second or third year. Candidates must hold Canadian citizenship or landed immigrants status. **Application Requirements:** Applicants must submit the following: high school transcript; university transcript (second semester midterm results accepted if received under separate cover and signed by department head); recommendation by department head and another teaching faculty member of the department. **Additional Information:** Shawna Christensen; 403-218-1625; Schristensen@petrelrob.com.

2979 ■ ENERGY AND MINERAL LAW FOUNDATION

340 S Broadway, Ste. 101
Lexington, KY 40508
Tel: (859)231-0271
Fax: (859)226-0485
E-mail: eml@aol.com
Web Site: http://www.blairchiropractic.com
To provide educational assistance to encourage the study of energy, environmental, natural resources, and mineral law.

Title of Award: EMLF Law Student Scholarships **Area, Field, or Subject:** Environmental science, Natural resources, Mineralogy, Energy-related areas. **Level of Education for which Award is Granted:** Undergraduate **Funds Available:** $1,000-$3,000.

Eligibility Requirements: Applicants must be law school students for the current academic year and must demonstrate an interest in the study of natural resources, energy or mineral law. **Deadline for Receipt:** April 11.

2980 ■ GRAND HAVEN AREA COMMUNITY FOUNDATION

1 S. Harbor Dr.
Grand Haven, MI 49417
Tel: (616)842-6378
Fax: (616)842-9518
E-mail: bpost@ghacf.org
Web Site: http://www.ghacf.org
To improve and enhance the quality of life in the Tri-Cities area by serving as a leader, catalyst and resource for philanthropy; to strive for community improvement through strategic grantmaking in such fields as arts, education, health, environment, youth, social services and other human needs.

Title of Award: Grand Haven Offshore Challenge Scholarships Fund **Area, Field, or Subject:** Natural resources. **Level of Education for which Award is Granted:** Undergraduate **Funds Available:** No specific amount.

Eligibility Requirements: Applicants must be graduating high school seniors from the Tri-Cities area who plan to pursue a career in natural resources such as fisheries, wildlife and environmental water quality at any public or private college or university. **Application Requirements:**

Applicants must submit: completed application form; current high school or college transcript; Student Aid Report (SAR) from the Free Application for Federal Student Aid (FAFSA), unless applying for scholarships that do not consider financial need; and letter of recommendation. **Deadline for Receipt:** March 7. **Additional Information:** 616-842-6378.

2981 ■ LEWIS-CLARK STATE COLLEGE
500 8th Ave.
Lewiston, ID 83501
Tel: (208)792-5272
Web Site: http://www.lcsc.edu
To assist Lewis-Clark State College students who are majoring in mathematics.
Title of Award: Laura Ann Peck Memorial Endowed Scholarships **Area, Field, or Subject:** Natural Science. **Level of Education for which Award is Granted:** Undergraduate **Funds Available:** No specific amount.
Eligibility Requirements: Applicants must have successfully completed three semesters of calculus; must have at least a 2.5 cumulative GPA; and must be registered as degree-seeking, full-time (12 credits) students. **Application Requirements:** Applicants must submit a general application.

2982 ■ LEWIS-CLARK STATE COLLEGE
500 8th Ave.
Lewiston, ID 83501
Tel: (208)792-5272
Web Site: http://www.lcsc.edu
To inspire educational pursuits among less capable individuals by providing financial assistance.
Title of Award: Susan P. Schroeder Memorial Scholarships **Area, Field, or Subject:** Natural Sciences; English Language and Literature. **Level of Education for which Award is Granted:** Undergraduate **Funds Available:** No specific amount.
Eligibility Requirements: Applicants must be graduates of Idaho high school; must be majoring in Natural Sciences or English; and must have a cumulative 3.0 GPA. **Application Requirements:** Applicants must accomplish a general application available at the website. **Deadline for Receipt:** March 1.

2983 ■ MATANUSKA-SUSITNA COLLEGE
PO Box 2889
Palmer, AK 99645
Tel: (907)745-9774
Fax: (907)745-9711
E-mail: info@matsu.alaska.edu
Web Site: http://www.matsu.alaska.edu
To provide support to deserving students in Alaska who want to pursue an education in any campus of the University of Alaska.
Title of Award: Guy A. Woodings Scholarships **Area, Field, or Subject:** Natural resources. **Level of Education for which Award is Granted:** Undergraduate **Funds Available:** $500.
Eligibility Requirements: Applicants must be majoring in Natural Resource Management; must have been enrolled at least 2 years pursuing a 4-year degree. **Application Requirements:** Applicant must complete the application forms available at the website; must attach a personal essay, two letters of recommendation, and current transcripts. **Deadline for Receipt:** February 15.

2984 ■ NATIONAL FEDERATION OF THE BLIND
1800 Johnson St.
Baltimore, MD 21230
Tel: (410)659-9314
Fax: (410)685-5653
Web Site: http://www.nfb.org
To recognize achievement of blind scholars and to create opportunity for all blind people.
Title of Award: Howard B. Rickard Scholarships **Area, Field, or Subject:** Law; Medicine; Engineering; Architecture; Natural Science. **Level of Education for which Award is Granted:** Undergraduate **Funds Available:** $3,000.
Eligibility Requirements: All applicants must be legally blind; he/she must be pursuing or planning to study in the field of law, medicine,

engineering, architecture or the natural science; he/she must be participant in NFB national convention and in all scheduled scholarship program activities. **Application Requirements:** Applicant must fill out the application form; he/she must submit two letters of recommendation from individuals that can describe the academic ability, leadership skills, and/or community involvement; copies of transcript of record and a photocopy of score reports for all standardized tests taken for college admission (ACT, SAT or other); an applicant must provide a letter of proof of legal blindness from a qualified professional; and an affiliate President's letter. **Deadline for Receipt:** March 31.

2985 ■ NATIONAL TAXIDERMISTS ASSOCIATION
108 Branch Dr.
Slidell, LA 70461
Tel: (866)662-9054
Fax: (985)641-9463
E-mail: ntahq@aol.com
Web Site: http://www.nationaltaxidermists.com
To provide cash scholarships for qualified NTA members, or their dependents, to further their education in Taxidermy, or to attain higher education.
Title of Award: Charlie Fleming Education Fund Scholarships **Area, Field, or Subject:** Taxonomy. **Level of Education for which Award is Granted:** Undergraduate **Funds Available:** $500 **Duration:** One year.
Eligibility Requirements: Applicants must be NTA members and/or their children; member must be in the third year of continuous NTA membership. **Application Requirements:** Applicants must complete application form and file a statement outlining the reasons for furthering their education, as well as an explanation of how this education will benefit their future in the field of taxidermy. **Deadline for Receipt:** April 30.

2986 ■ REDLANDS COMMUNITY SCHOLARSHIP FOUNDATION
c/o Kathleen Venegas-Boge, Admin. Asst.
PO Box 1683
Redlands, CA 92373
Tel: (909)307-9892
Fax: (909)307-9892
Web Site: http://www.redlandsscholarships.org
To encourage educational pursuits among Redlands Unified School District graduates by providing educational assistance.
Title of Award: Aquatics Booster Club Scholarships **Area, Field, or Subject:** Aquaculture. **Level of Education for which Award is Granted:** Undergraduate **Funds Available:** No specific amount.
Eligibility Requirements: Applicant must be a graduating senior who ha participated for at least three consecutive years in the water polo and swimming program. Student must have maintained at least a 3.0 GPA a be planning to continue in an aquatic program in college. **Applica Requirements:** Applicants must submit a completed application together with the scantron sheet; cover sheet; student activity and munity activity sheets; personal essay; and a copy of unofficial tran (signed by the counselor). **Additional Information:** No electronic su sions of application will be accepted. Submit two printed copies application and use a No. 2 pencil on the scantron sheet. **Dead Receipt:** February 20.

2987 ■ SINO-AMERICAN PHARMACEUTICAL PROFESSIONA SOCIATION
PO Box 282
Nanuet, NY 10954
E-mail: information@sapaweb.org
Web Site: http://www.sapaweb.org
To recognize and support excellence on the part of outst school students, and to encourage the finest high school develop career in life science.
Title of Award: SAPA Scholarships **Area, Field, or Sub ences. **Level of Education for which Award is Granted: Funds Available:** $1,000. **Duration:** One year.
Eligibility Requirements: Applicant must be a full-ti graduate who plans full-time undergraduate study at ar year college in the upcoming academic year; must have minimum SAT 1400 and be in the top tenth of the class States citizen, or a legal resident alien; must demonstr and commitment to a career in life sciences. **Applicati**

Applicant must submit an essay of approximately 600 words, two letters of recommendation from teachers who can discuss the nominee's potential for a career in life sciences including a teacher in the applicant's field of study and another who can attest the nominee's potential; must have a list of awards received; must have a list of Advanced Placement of Honors courses with grades. **Deadline for Receipt:** April 30.

2988 ■ STARK COMMUNITY FOUNDATION
400 Market Ave. N, Ste. 200
Canton, OH 44702-2107
Tel: (330)454-3426
Fax: (330)454-5855
Web Site: http://www.starkcommunityfoundation.org
To provide scholarship assistance to qualified individuals who want to pursue their studies.
Title of Award: Margaret S. Gilbert Scholarship Fund **Area, Field, or Subject:** Natural sciences; Mathematics and mathematical sciences; History. **Level of Education for which Award is Granted:** Undergraduate **Number Awarded:** 2. **Funds Available:** $37,000. **Duration:** One year. **Eligibility Requirements:** Applicants must be Stark County public high school female graduates who attend or will attend Oberlin College; must have a major in one of the natural sciences, mathematics, or history; must have extracurricular activities, especially those demonstrating interest in science; must demonstrate diligent effort, responsibility and financial need. **Application Requirements:** Applicants must have academic record; must submit the application form and requirements at 400 Market Ave. N, Ste. 200, Canton, OH 44702. **Deadline for Receipt:** May 1.

2989 ■ UNIVERSITY OF TORONTO
315 Bloor St. W
Toronto, ON, Canada M5S 1A3
Tel: (416)978-2011
E-mail: information.commonsats@utoronto.ca
Web Site: http://www.utoronto.ca
To support students with their educational pursuits.
Title of Award: J.P. Bickell Mining Scholarships **Area, Field, or Subject:** Geophysics; Earth sciences; Mining; Environmental science. **Level of Education for which Award is Granted:** Undergraduate **Funds** Approximately $2000.
Requirements: Applicant must be a student of U of T; an undergraduate student in second or higher years studying mining (includ-ing geological and geophysical fields as well as environmental sci-ences, natural sciences, earth science programs and mining engineer-ing; minimum GPA of B or better and have demonstrated interest in the mining industry or field. **Application Requirements:** Applicants must submit of application together with a letter outlining the inter-est in mining industry. **Deadline for Receipt:** October 31.

AGRICULTURE FUTURE OF AMERICA

PROFESSIONALS AS-

for a career in the agriculture and food

Title of Award: Agriculture Future of America Community Scholarships **Area, Field, or Subject:** Agricultural economics. **Level of Education for which Award is Granted:** Undergraduate **Funds Available:** No specific

Eligibility Requirements: Applicants must be graduating high school seniors who plan to pursue a degree in an agriculture-related field. **Application Requirements:** Applicants must contact AFA to

request an application for a four-year accredited institution with a GPA above 3.3, a **Title of Award:** Life sci-**Level of Education:** Undergraduate high school students must be a United States citizen; and must have demonstrated a potential for a career. **Application Requirements:**

Fax: (816)472-4239
Web Site: http://www.agfuture.org
To support academic development through partnerships with rural com-munities, agriculture organizations, colleges and universities.
Title of Award: Agriculture Future of America Scholarship Program **Area, Field, or Subject:** Agricultural economics. **Level of Education for which Award is Granted:** Undergraduate **Funds Available:** No specific amount.
Eligibility Requirements: Applicants must be students who plan to pursue a four year degree in an agriculture-related field. **Application Requirements:** Applicants must contact AFA to request an application form.

2992 ■ ALABAMA HORSE COUNCIL
PO Box 260
Morris, AL 35116
800-945-8033
E-mail: info@alabamahorsecouncil.org
Web Site: http://www.alabamahorsecouncil.org
To provide financial assistance and recognition to students with strong ties to the beef cattle industry.
Title of Award: Cecil Lane Family Scholarships **Area, Field, or Subject:** Agricultural sciences. **Level of Education for which Award is Granted:** Undergraduate **Funds Available:** $1750. **Duration:** One year.
Eligibility Requirements: Applicants must be resident of Alabama; must be incoming freshman at the Auburn University College of Agriculture; and must be children or grandchildren of ACA members for two consecutive years. **Application Requirements:** Applicants must submit a completed application form. **Deadline for Receipt:** December. **Additional Informa-tion:** Martha Davis.

2993 ■ ALABAMA HORSE COUNCIL
PO Box 260
Morris, AL 35116
800-945-8033
E-mail: info@alabamahorsecouncil.org
Web Site: http://www.alabamahorsecouncil.org
To provide financial assistance for female students.
Title of Award: Ina E. Powell Memorial Scholarships **Area, Field, or Subject:** Agricultural sciences; Forestry; Education--Curricula. **Level of Education for which Award is Granted:** Undergraduate **Funds Avail-able:** $1500.
Eligibility Requirements: Applicants must be female students from Alabama; must be high school seniors accepted at the Auburn University; must be planning to pursue agricultural-related courses at the College of Agriculture, School of Forestry and Wildlife sciences, College of Human Sciences or College of Education; must demonstrate leadership abilities; must have GPA of 3.0 or above; and must be children or grandchildren of ACA members for two consecutive years. **Application Requirements:** Applicants must submit a completed application form. **Deadline for Receipt:** December. **Additional Information:** Martha Davis.

2994 ■ ALABAMA HORSE COUNCIL
PO Box 260
Morris, AL 35116
800-945-8033
E-mail: info@alabamahorsecouncil.org
Web Site: http://www.alabamahorsecouncil.org
To support the education of AHC members and their children.
Title of Award: Samuel Upchurch Memorial Scholarships **Area, Field, or Subject:** Agricultural economics; Animal science and behavior. **Level of Education for which Award is Granted:** Undergraduate **Funds Avail-able:** $4000.
Eligibility Requirements: Applicants must be children or grandchildren of ACA members for two consecutive years; and must be accepted in Animal Science or Agriculture Economics at Auburn University. **Applica-tion Requirements:** Applicants must submit a completed application form. **Deadline for Receipt:** December. **Additional Information:** Martha Davis.

2995 ■ ALABAMA HORSE COUNCIL
PO Box 260
Morris, AL 35116

453

800-945-8033
E-mail: info@alabamahorsecouncil.org
Web Site: http://www.alabamahorsecouncil.org
To financially support students studying agriculture at the Auburn University.
Title of Award: The Wax Company Scholarships **Area, Field, or Subject:** Agricultural sciences. **Level of Education for which Award is Granted:** Undergraduate **Funds Available:** $1000.
Eligibility Requirements: Applicants must be high senior or college students studying agriculture at the Auburn University; and must be children of ACA members. **Application Requirements:** Applicants must submit a completed application form. **Additional Information:** Funded through the sale of Marshall and Jackson ryegrass seed. **Deadline for Receipt:** December. **Additional Information:** Martha Davis.

2996 ■ ALBERTA BARLEY COMMISSION
3601A21 St. NE, No. 200
Calgary, AB, Canada T2E 6T5
Tel: (403)291-9111
Free: 800-265-9111
E-mail: barleyinfo@albertabarley.com
Web Site: http://www.albertabarley.com
To provide scholarship opportunity to the students of Alberta, Canada.
Title of Award: Eugene Boyko Scholarships **Area, Field, or Subject:** Agricultural sciences. **Level of Education for which Award is Granted:** Undergraduate **Funds Available:** $500.
Eligibility Requirements: Applicants must be: Canadian citizens or permanent Canadian residents living in Alberta; attending a post-secondary institution in Alberta; enrolled full-time in the second or subsequent year of post-secondary study. **Application Requirements:** Application forms are available from Alberta Scholarship Programs and from Alberta post-secondary institutions. Mail completed application and an official transcript to: Alberta Scholarship Programs 4th Floor - 9940 106 St. Box 28000 Station Main, Edmonton, AB TGJ 4R4. **Deadline for Receipt:** August 1. **Additional Information:** Alberta Scholarship Program, 780-427-8640, scholarships@gov.ab.ca.

2997 ■ ALBERTA LEARNING INFORMATION SERVICE - ALBERTA SCHOLARSHIP PROGRAM
Box 28000 Sta. Main
Edmonton, AB, Canada T5J 4R4
Tel: (780)427-8640
Fax: (780)427-1288
E-mail: scholarship@gov.ab.ca
Web Site: http://www.alis.alberta.ca
To recognize and reward the academic and leadership accomplishments of three students graduating from Sexsmith Secondary School who are entering post-secondary studies.
Title of Award: Dr. Robert and Anna Shaw Scholarships **Area, Field, or Subject:** Agriculture; Engineering; Art industries and trade; Fine arts. **Level of Education for which Award is Granted:** Undergraduate **Funds Available:** $500.
Eligibility Requirements: Applicants must be Alberta residents and plan to enroll full-time in a post-secondary program related to agriculture, engineering/trades or fine arts. **Application Requirements:** Applicants may obtain application form from Alberta Scholarship Programs and from the Counseling Office at Sexsmith Secondary School. **Deadline for Receipt:** June 1. **Additional Information:** Alberta Scholarship Programs at the above address.

2998 ■ CALIFORNIA ASSOCIATION OF PEST CONTROL ADVISERS
1143 Market Blvd., Ste. 7
Sacramento, CA 95834
Tel: (916)928-1625
Fax: (916)928-0705
Web Site: http://www.capca.com
To support and promote agricultural pest control advisers or professional production consultants who serve California agricultural and horticultural producers.
Title of Award: Stanley W. Strew Educational Fund Scholarship **Area, Field, or Subject:** Agricultural economics. **Level of Education for which Award is Granted:** Undergraduate **Number Awarded:** 2. **Funds Available:** $3,000; $2,000.

Eligibility Requirements: Applicants must be currently attending, entering or returning to college in agricultural or horticultural fields; must plan to pursue a career in pest management; must have a 2.5 GPA or better. **Application Requirements:** Applicants must submit a completed application form; must include a current official transcript of records; must submit at least two letters of recommendation. **Deadline for Receipt:** May 15. **Additional Information:** 916-928-1625.

2999 ■ EDON FARMERS COOPERATIVE ASSOCIATION
PO Box 308
Edon, OH 43518
Tel: (419)272-2121
Free: 800-878-4093
Fax: (419)272-2304
E-mail: efcrdunbar@williams-net.com
Web Site: http://edonfarmerscoop.com
To provide financial assistance for high school seniors to further their education as full-time students in any post high school institution.
Title of Award: Edon Farmers Cooperative Scholarships **Area, Field, or Subject:** Agricultural sciences. **Level of Education for which Award is Granted:** Undergraduate **Funds Available:** $1,000.
Eligibility Requirements: Applicants must be dependents of a stockholder going into any field of study or any students going into an agricultural field. **Application Requirements:** Applicants must submit all the required application information. **Deadline for Receipt:** April 1.

3000 ■ FLORIDA FERTILIZER AND AGRICHEMICAL ASSOCIATION
58 4th St. NW, Ste 200
Winter Haven, FL 33881
Tel: (863)293-4827
Fax: (863)294-8626
E-mail: mhartney@ffaa.org
Web Site: http://www.ffaa.org
To promote the study of agriculture in higher education and to encourage students pursuing agriculture studies.
Title of Award: Florida Fertilizer and Agrichemical Association Scholarships **Area, Field, or Subject:** Agricultural sciences. **Level of Education for which Award is Granted:** Undergraduate **Funds Available:** No specific amount.
Eligibility Requirements: Applicants must be agriculture junior, senior, or graduate students at the University of Florida, Florida A&M or Florida Southern; must plan to enroll for the semester immediately following the fall semester; must have a minimum GPA of 3.0 on a 4.0 scale. **Application Requirements:** Applicants must submit a completed application form. **Additional Information:** 863-293-4827.

3001 ■ FUR TAKERS OF AMERICA
853 E 1000 N Rd.
Onarga, IL 60955
Tel: (217)394-2577
E-mail: krumui@illicom.net
Web Site: http://www.furtakersofamerica.com
To promote interest in the accumulation and dissemination of knowledge concerning the trapping of fur bearing animals among persons interested therein.
Title of Award: Charles Dobbins FTA Scholarships **Area, Field, or Subject:** Agricultural Science; Biology; Wildlife Conservation and management. **Level of Education for which Award is Granted:** Undergraduate **Funds Available:** $250.
Eligibility Requirements: Applicants must be members of FTA or their immediate relatives; must be majoring in agriculture, biology, wildlife management or related courses in an accredited two-year or four-year college, university, or vocational/technical school. **Application Requirements:** Applicants must provide proof of high school graduation or pending graduation; official documents indicating that they have been accepted in an institution as first year students, or registration of classes if applicants are already in school. Applicants must also submit an essay that discusses career goals and how the scholarship would help to achieve these goals. **Deadline for Receipt:** June 1. **Additional Information:** Carol Krumwiede at the above address.

3002 ■ KEITH GILMORE FOUNDATION
5160 Skyline Way NE
Calgary, AB, Canada T2E 6V1

Tel: (403)274-1734
E-mail: kgf@keithgilmorefoundation.com
Web Site: http://www.keithgilmorefoundation.com
To provide scholarships for deserving individuals.
Title of Award: Keith Gilmore Foundation - Undergraduate Scholarships **Area, Field, or Subject:** Agriculture, Economic aspects; Medicine, Veterinary; Journalism; Communications. **Level of Education for which Award is Granted:** Undergraduate **Number Awarded:** 4. **Funds Available:** $1,500. **Duration:** One year.
Eligibility Requirements: Applicant must be an individual enrolled in an undergraduate degree program in agriculture, veterinary medicine, journalism and/or communications at a recognized university, leading to a career in the field of agriculture. **Application Requirements:** Application forms are available online at www.keithgilmorefoundation.com. Completed application must be sent to Keith Gilmore Foundation, 5160 Skyline Way NE, Calgary, AB T2E 6V1. **Deadline for Receipt:** July 1.

3003 ■ HARTFORD FOUNDATION FOR PUBLIC GIVING
10 Columbus Blvd., 8th Flr.
Hartford, CT 06106
Tel: (860)548-1888
Fax: (860)524-8346
E-mail: hfpg@hfpg.org
Web Site: http://www.hfpg.org
To provide scholarship for freshman students of College of Agriculture and Natural Resources at University of Connecticut or Raddcliffe Hicks School.
Title of Award: College of Agriculture and Natural Resources Scholarships **Area, Field, or Subject:** Allied health; Agricultural sciences. **Level of Education for which Award is Granted:** Undergraduate **Funds Available:** $500-$2,000. **Duration:** 1 semester.
Eligibility Requirements: Applicants must be freshman students interested in Allied Health Sciences, Animal Science, Cytotechnology, Diagnostic Genetic Sciences, Dietetics, Environmental Sciences, Health Promotion Sciences, Horticulture, Landscape Architecture, Medical Technology, Natural Resources, Nutritional Sciences, Pathobiology, Pre-veterinary Science, Resource Economics, Turfgrass and Soil Science, Allied Science; must attend College of Agriculture and Natural Resources at University of Connecticut or Radcliffe Hicks School; and must demonstrate academic excellence. **Application Requirements:** Applicants may obtain application materials from University of Connecticut College of Agricultural and Natural Resources, Associate Dean, 1376 Storrs Rd. Unit 4090 Storrs, CT 06269-4090. Phone: 860486-2919. acadprog@canr.uconn.edu.

3004 ■ INDEPENDENT PROFESSIONAL SEED ASSOCIATION
PO Box 241312
Omaha, NE 68124-5312
Tel: (402)991-3550
Fax: (402)489-2394
E-mail: IPSAGreg@aol.com
Web Site: http://www.ipsaweb.com
To promote education in the field of agriculture.
Title of Award: Myron Asplin Foundation Scholarships **Area, Field, or Subject:** Agricultural sciences. **Level of Education for which Award is Granted:** Undergraduate **Number Awarded:** 1. **Funds Available:** $750.
Eligibility Requirements: Applicants must be active students continuing their education in an agriculture-related field of study. **Application Requirements:** Applicants must submit application form (available at the website) with high school transcript; list of courses taken and grades received during senior year (if not included in transcript); recent photo (name printed at the back). **Deadline for Receipt:** May 15. **Additional Information:** Greg Ruehle at the above address. IPSAGreg@aol.com. 402-483-2571.

3005 ■ INDEPENDENT PROFESSIONAL SEED ASSOCIATION
PO Box 241312
Omaha, NE 68124-5312
Tel: (402)991-3550
Fax: (402)489-2394
E-mail: IPSAGreg@aol.com
Web Site: http://www.ipsaweb.com
To promote education in the field of agriculture.

Title of Award: IPSA Student Recognition Awards **Area, Field, or Subject:** Agriculture. **Level of Education for which Award is Granted:** Undergraduate **Funds Available:** $700.
Eligibility Requirements: Applicants must be an active student entering junior/senior year or graduate students studying agriculture or related field. **Application Requirements:** Application form is available at the website. Applicants must attach student transcript; two recommendation letters from professors; a statement about personal and professional goals and objectives; work experience for the last two years; and recommendation from the nominator along with any relationship to IPSA member or Associate member company. **Additional Information:** The Award was created in 1997 with donations from Independent Corn Breeders Association. **Deadline for Receipt:** May 15. **Additional Information:** 402-486-2571.

3006 ■ INTERNATIONAL CODE COUNCIL FOUNDATION
500 New Jersey Ave. NW, 6th Fl.
Washington, DC 20001-2070
Tel: 888-422-7233
E-mail: leslie@flash.org
Web Site: http://www.icc-foundation.org
To provide financial assistance for children of ICC governmental members.
Title of Award: International Code Council Foundation General Scholarship Fund **Area, Field, or Subject:** Architectural Engineering. **Level of Education for which Award is Granted:** Undergraduate **Number Awarded:** 2. **Funds Available:** $2,500.
Eligibility Requirements: Applicants must be children of code enforcement agency personnel. The jurisdiction authority must be an active Governmental Member of the International Code Council; Children must be dependents as defined by the Internal Revenue Service. Typically, this includes birth children, stepchildren, legally adopted children, or a legal ward financially supported by the employee. **Application Requirements:** Applications and instructions are available in the ICC and ICCF websites. **Deadline for Receipt:** June 30. **Additional Information:** International Code Council Foundation, Attn: Scholarships c/o: COO 900 Montclair Road Birmingham, AL 35213-1206; scholarships@iccsafe.org.

3007 ■ INTERNATIONAL CODE COUNCIL FOUNDATION
500 New Jersey Ave. NW, 6th Fl.
Washington, DC 20001-2070
Tel: 888-422-7233
E-mail: leslie@flash.org
Web Site: http://www.icc-foundation.org
To provide financial assistance for children of ICC governmental members.
Title of Award: J.W. "Bill" Neese Scholarships **Area, Field, or Subject:** Architectural Engineering. **Level of Education for which Award is Granted:** Undergraduate **Number Awarded:** 1. **Funds Available:** $1,000.
Eligibility Requirements: Applicants must be children of code enforcement agency personnel. The jurisdiction authority must be an active governmental member of the International Code Council. Children must be dependents as defined by the Internal Revenue Service. Typically, this includes birth children, stepchildren, legally adopted children, or a legal ward financially supported by the employee. **Application Requirements:** Applications and instructions are available at the ICC and ICCF websites. **Deadline for Receipt:** June 30. **Additional Information:** International Code Council Foundation, Attn: Scholarships c/o: COO 900 Montclair Road Birmingham, AL 35213-1206; scholarships@iccsafe.org.

3008 ■ INTERNATIONAL CODE COUNCIL FOUNDATION
500 New Jersey Ave. NW, 6th Fl.
Washington, DC 20001-2070
Tel: 888-422-7233
E-mail: leslie@flash.org
Web Site: http://www.icc-foundation.org
To provide financial assistance for children of ICC members intending to pursue higher education.
Title of Award: William J. Tangye Scholarships **Area, Field, or Subject:** Architectural Engineering. **Level of Education for which Award is Granted:** Undergraduate **Number Awarded:** 1. **Funds Available:** $2,500.

Eligibility Requirements: Applicants must be children of code enforcement agency personnel. The jurisdiction authority must be an active Governmental Member of the International Code Council; Children must be dependents as defined by the Internal Revenue Service. Typically, this includes birth children, stepchildren, legally adopted children, or a legal ward financially supported by the employee. Applicants must be enrolled in engineering, architecture or construction technology programs in a recognized and/or accredited school such as a university, trade school, business college or other institutions as approved by the ICC prior to distribution of the award. **Application Requirements:** Applications and instructions are available at the ICC and ICCF websites. **Deadline for Receipt:** June 30. **Additional Information:** International Code Council Foundation, Attn: Scholarships c/o: COO 900 Montclair Road Birmingham, AL 35213-1206; scholarships@iccsafe.org.

3009 ■ JAPANESE AMERICAN CITIZENS LEAGUE
1765 Sutter St.
San Francisco, CA 94115
Tel: (415)921-5225
Fax: (415)921-4671
E-mail: jacl@jacl.org
Web Site: http://www.jacl.org
To provide financial assistance for qualified individuals.
Title of Award: Kyutaro & Yasuo Abiko Memorial Scholarships **Area, Field, or Subject:** Journalism; Agricultural economics. **Level of Education for which Award is Granted:** Undergraduate **Funds Available:** $60,000. **Duration:** One year.
Eligibility Requirements: Applicant must be an active National JACL member at either an individual or student/youth level; must be planning to attend full-time at a college, university, trade school, business school, or any other institution of higher learning within the United States at the undergraduate or graduate school level. Entering freshman applicant must be a high school senior. **Application Requirements:** Application forms are available online at www.jacl.org/join.html. **Deadline for Receipt:** March 1 (entering freshman) and April 1 (all applications excluding entering freshman).

3010 ■ JAPANESE AMERICAN CITIZENS LEAGUE
1765 Sutter St.
San Francisco, CA 94115
Tel: (415)921-5225
Fax: (415)921-9946
E-mail: jacl@jacl.org
Web Site: http://www.jacl.org
To provide financial support for qualified students intending to pursue their education.
Title of Award: Sam S. Kuwahara Memorial Scholarships **Area, Field, or Subject:** Agricultural economics. **Level of Education for which Award is Granted:** Undergraduate **Funds Available:** $60,000. **Duration:** One year.
Eligibility Requirements: Applicant must be an active National JACL member at either an individual or Student/Youth level; must be planning to attend full-time at a college, university, trade school, business school, or any other institution of higher learning within the United States at the undergraduate or graduate school level. Entering freshman applicants must be a high school senior. **Application Requirements:** Application forms are available online at www.jacl.org/join.html. **Deadline for Receipt:** March 1 (entering freshman) and April 1 (all applications excluding entering freshman).

3011 ■ MIDWEST FOOD PROCESSORS ASSOCIATION
4600 American Pkwy., Ste. 110
Madison, WI 53718-8334
Tel: (608)255-9946
Free: 800-369-6220
Fax: (608)255-9838
E-mail: info@mwfpa.org
Web Site: http://www.mwfpa.org
To enhance and promote the business interests of the Midwest food processing industry.
Title of Award: Carleton A. Friday Memorial Scholarships **Area, Field, or Subject:** Agricultural sciences. **Level of Education for which Award is Granted:** Undergraduate **Number Awarded:** 3. **Funds Available:** Up to $1,500.

Eligibility Requirements: Applicants must be undergraduate students who are majoring in agriculture or food science within the University of Wisconsin system. **Application Requirements:** Applicants must submit completed application form indicating GPA; a letter of recommendation from advisor or other faculty member; a letter of interest; letter of recommendation from past employer; document/s indicating financial need; and contact information. **Deadline for Receipt:** June 13.

3012 ■ MIDWEST FOOD PROCESSORS ASSOCIATION
4600 American Pkwy., Ste. 110
Madison, WI 53718-8334
Tel: (608)255-9946
Free: 800-369-6220
Fax: (608)255-9838
E-mail: info@mwfpa.org
Web Site: http://www.mwfpa.org
To enhance and promote the business interests of the Midwest food processing industry.
Title of Award: Kenneth G. Weckel Scholarships **Area, Field, or Subject:** Agricultural sciences. **Level of Education for which Award is Granted:** Undergraduate **Number Awarded:** 3. **Funds Available:** $1,500.
Eligibility Requirements: Applicants must be undergraduate students who are majoring in agriculture or food science within the University of Wisconsin system. **Application Requirements:** Applicants must submit completed application form indicating GPA; a letter of recommendation from advisor or other faculty member; a letter of interest from students; letter of recommendation from past employer; documents indicating financial need; and contact information. **Deadline for Receipt:** June 13.

3013 ■ MONSANTO COMPANY
800 N Lindbergh Blvd.
St. Louis, MO 63167
Tel: (314)694-1000
Web Site: http://www.monsanto.com
To support the education of students who have long-term career interest in agriculture.
Title of Award: Monsanto Company Agriculture Scholarships **Area, Field, or Subject:** Agricultural sciences. **Level of Education for which Award is Granted:** Undergraduate **Number Awarded:** 100. **Funds Available:** $1,500.
Eligibility Requirements: Applicant must be a high school senior from a farm family; must have an above-average academic record; and must plan to enroll as a full-time student in an agriculture-related academic major at an accredited school. **Application Requirements:** Applicants may contact the Program Administrator for the application. **Additional Information:** In association with the National Association of Farm Broadcasters (NAFB). **Additional Information:** Program Administrator, Commitment to Agriculture Scholarship Program, c/o National FFA Organization, Scholarship Office, PO Box 68960 Indianapolis, IN 46268-0960; Phone: 317-802-6060, or E-mail: scholarships@ffa.org.

3014 ■ NATIONAL ASSOCIATION OF AGRICULTURAL EDUCATORS
300 Garrigus Bldg.
University of Kentucky
Lexington, KY 40546-0215
Tel: (859)257-2224
Free: 800-509-0204
Web Site: http://www.naae.org
To provide educational opportunities to students majoring in agricultural education.
Title of Award: Delmar Cengage Learning-NAAE Upper Division Scholarships **Area, Field, or Subject:** Education; Agricultural sciences. **Level of Education for which Award is Granted:** Undergraduate **Number Awarded:** 15. **Funds Available:** $750.
Eligibility Requirements: Applicants must be agricultural education majors who want to be agricultural teachers; must be members of NAAE. **Application Requirements:** Applicants must submit original copy and eight copies of application form; description of applicant's leadership and service activities; an essay entitled "Why I Want to Teach Agriculture"; a letter of recommendation from an agricultural education teacher in the applicant's college or university or from an agricultural education teacher at the local, state or national level; official transcript; and a photograph in a CD. **Deadline for Receipt:** May 15.

3015 ■ NATIONAL ASSOCIATION OF CONSERVATION DISTRICT EMPLOYEES
1607 W Jackson St.
Macomb, IL 61455
Tel: (309)833-1711
Fax: (309)837-1512
E-mail: cindy.moon@il.nacdnet.net
Web Site: http://www.ncdea.org
To provide financial support to a district employee or member of their immediate family who is participating in a resource conservation curriculum while enrolled in an accredited college or university.
Title of Award: National Association of Conservation District Employees Scholarships **Area, Field, or Subject:** Agriculture. **Level of Education for which Award is Granted:** Undergraduate **Funds Available:** $1,000. **Duration:** Not stated.
Eligibility Requirements: Applicant must be currently employed for a period of one year by a conservation district of the United States. Applicant must demonstrate integrity, ability, and competence in their work and possess skills gained through training or experience; or applicant must be an immediate family member of a conservation district employee. He/she must demonstrate an interest in soil and water conservation and have the intent to pursue a course in natural resource conservation. **Application Requirements:** Applicant must fill out the application form and provide proof that he/she is currently enrolled. **Deadline for Receipt:** May 1. **Additional Information:** Rich Duesterhaus at 509 Capitol Court, NE Washington, DC 20002; 202-547-6223.

3016 ■ NATIONAL CATTLEMEN'S FOUNDATION
9110 E Nichols Ave., Ste. 300
Centennial, CO 80112
Tel: (303)694-0305
E-mail: ncf@beef.org
Web Site: http://www.nationalcattlemensfoundation.org
To identify and encourage talented and thoughtful students who will emerge as industry leaders.
Title of Award: Beef Industry Scholarships **Area, Field, or Subject:** Agricultural sciences. **Level of Education for which Award is Granted:** Undergraduate **Number Awarded:** 10. **Funds Available:** $1,500.
Eligibility Requirements: Applicant must be a graduating high school senior or full-time undergraduate student enrolled at a two or four-year institution and have demonstrated commitment to a career in the beef industry through classes, internships or life experiences. **Application Requirements:** Applicants must submit proof of enrollment (as a full-time student); a one page letter of career goals; the essay (maximum of 750 words); and two letters of reference. **Deadline for Receipt:** October 1.

3017 ■ NATIONAL JUNIOR SWINE ASSOCIATION
PO Box 2517
West Lafayette, IN 47996
Tel: (765)463-3594
Fax: (765)497-2959
E-mail: nsr@nationalsine.com
Web Site: http://www.nationalswine.com
To provide a network uniting purebred swine enthusiast through a youth organization.
Title of Award: Gregory D. Johnson Memorial Scholarships **Area, Field, or Subject:** Agricultural economics. **Level of Education for which Award is Granted:** Graduate, Undergraduate **Funds Available:** $1,000.
Eligibility Requirements: Applicant must be a spring college graduate with a bachelor's degree in an agricultural field or a current graduate student pursuing a master's or doctorate degree in swine genetics, swine reproduction or swine nutrition. **Application Requirements:** Applicant must enclose one letter of recommendation from a college advisor who can verify participant's graduate school acceptance or enrollment, in addition to their college activities and involvement; Applicants must submit graduate school acceptance letter or proof of graduate school enrollment. **Deadline for Receipt:** May 15. **Additional Information:** NSR at the above address.

3018 ■ NATIONAL JUNIOR SWINE ASSOCIATION
PO Box 2517
West Lafayette, IN 47996
Tel: (765)463-3594

Fax: (765)497-2959
E-mail: nsr@nationalsine.com
Web Site: http://www.nationalswine.com
To provide a network uniting purebred swine enthusiast through a youth organization.
Title of Award: The Maschhoffs Inc. Pork Production Scholarships **Area, Field, or Subject:** Agricultural economics. **Level of Education for which Award is Granted:** Undergraduate **Funds Available:** $1,500 for the first-place and $1,000 For the second-place.
Eligibility Requirements: Applicants must be a member of the National Junior Swine Association (NJSA). Applicants must be 18-21 years old and enrolled in an agricultural program at a recognized college/ university. **Application Requirements:** Applicants may download an application form online. **Deadline for Receipt:** May 23. **Additional Information:** NSR at the above address.

3019 ■ NATIONAL JUNIOR SWINE ASSOCIATION
PO Box 2517
West Lafayette, IN 47996
Tel: (765)463-3594
Fax: (765)497-2959
E-mail: nsr@nationalsine.com
Web Site: http://www.nationalswine.com
To provide a network uniting purebred swine enthusiast through a youth organization.
Title of Award: Claude Robinson Scholarships **Area, Field, or Subject:** Agricultural economics. **Level of Education for which Award is Granted:** Undergraduate **Funds Available:** $1,000.
Eligibility Requirements: Scholarship applicants must be a sophomore, junior or senior enrolled in a collegiate. **Application Requirements:** Applicant must send in two letters of reference. One letter should be written by their college coach, and the second letter should be written by a non-family member who has knowledge of the applicant's involvement in the livestock industry. **Deadline for Receipt:** March 1. **Additional Information:** National Swine Registry at the above address.

3020 ■ NATIONAL JUNIOR SWINE ASSOCIATION
PO Box 2517
West Lafayette, IN 47996
Tel: (765)463-3594
Fax: (765)497-2959
E-mail: nsr@nationalsine.com
Web Site: http://www.nationalswine.com
To provide a network uniting purebred swine enthusiast through a youth organization.
Title of Award: Jason Shipley Memorial Scholarships **Area, Field, or Subject:** Agricultural economics. **Level of Education for which Award is Granted:** Undergraduate **Funds Available:** No specific amount.
Eligibility Requirements: Applicants must be incoming freshman, sophomore or junior enrolled in an agriculturally related field. **Application Requirements:** Applicant must send in two letters of reference. One letter should be written by an athletic coach, and the second letter should be written by a non-family member who has knowledge of the applicant's involvement in the swine industry. **Deadline for Receipt:** May 15.

3021 ■ NATIONAL POULTRY AND FOOD DISTRIBUTORS ASSOCIATION
958 McEver Rd. Ext., Unit B-8
Gainesville, GA 30504
Tel: (770)535-9901; 877-845-1545
Fax: (770)535-7385
E-mail: info@npfda.org
Web Site: http://www.npfda.org
To help build "people resources" for the poultry and food industries.
Title of Award: National Poultry and Food Distributors Association Scholarships **Area, Field, or Subject:** Poultry Science; Food science and technology; Dietetics; Agribusiness; Agricultural economics; Agriculture, Economic aspects; Agricultural sciences. **Level of Education for which Award is Granted:** Undergraduate **Number Awarded:** 5. Cash prizes will go to the top four; the fifth student chosen will be the alternate student should one of the award recipients not use all of his/her funds (early graduation). **Funds Available:** $2,000. **Duration:** Entire length of study.
Eligibility Requirements: Applicant must be a full time junior or senior at a U.S. institution for the upcoming award year, and must be pursuing a

poultry or related agricultural degree. **Application Requirements:** Applicant must submit an application form; official transcript; letter of recommendation from his/her Dean; and a one-page letter describing his/her goals and aspirations. **Additional Information:** This scholarship foundation was established in 1979. **Deadline for Receipt:** May 31.

3022 ■ NEBRASKA GRAIN SORGHUM PRODUCERS ASSOCIATION
PO Box 94982
Lincoln, NE 68509
Tel: (402)471-3552
Fax: (402)470-3040
E-mail: sorghum@nrcdec.nrc.state.ne.us
Web Site: http://nesorghum.nol.org
To aid and promote higher education in agriculture; to promote the study of sorghum and its impact on agriculture.
Title of Award: Nebraska Grain Sorghum Producers Association Scholarships **Area, Field, or Subject:** Agricultural economics. **Level of Education for which Award is Granted:** Undergraduate **Funds Available:** $400.
Eligibility Requirements: Applicants must be graduating high school seniors or students who are currently enrolled in post-secondary education; must plan to pursue a course of study which will prepare him or her a career in agriculture or an ag-related field. **Application Requirements:** Applicants must submit a completed application form; must submit a copy of transcript of records; letter of recommendation from a counselor or advisor with necessary signatures. Applicant must have membership status. **Deadline for Receipt:** February 1. **Additional Information:** 402-471-3552.

3023 ■ NEW YORK STATE ASSOCIATION OF AGRICULTURAL FAIRS
714 Nellis St.
Watertown, NY 13601
Tel: (315)771-3003
E-mail: carousels4@aol.com
Web Site: http://www.nyfairs.org
To provide financial assistance to those high school and college students who have been active in their local fairs and who intend to pursue higher education in an agricultural or fair management related field.
Title of Award: New York State Association of Agricultural Fairs Scholarships **Area, Field, or Subject:** Agricultural economics. **Level of Education for which Award is Granted:** Undergraduate **Funds Available:** $1,000.
Eligibility Requirements: Applicants must be in their senior year of high school in New York State or New York residents planning to pursue or already attending college in an agricultural or fair management-related field at an accredited institution of higher education. **Application Requirements:** Applicants must complete the application form.

3024 ■ NORTH CAROLINA SIMMENTAL ASSOCIATION
1341 Hwy. 21
Hamptonville, NC 27020
Tel: (336)468-1679
Fax: (336)468-1686
E-mail: ncsa@yadtel.net
Web Site: http://www.ncsimmental.com
To develop and promote the Simmental breed of cattle in the state of North Carolina; to help members of the North Carolina Simmental Association promote, improve and market their cattle.
Title of Award: Jim Graham Scholarships **Area, Field, or Subject:** Agricultural sciences. **Level of Education for which Award is Granted:** Undergraduate **Funds Available:** $1,000.
Eligibility Requirements: Applicants must be high school or college students planning to pursue or pursuing a career in an agricultural-related field of study; must maintain a 2.0 GPA. **Application Requirements:** Applicants must complete the application form; attach a photo; submit a transcript of high school grades or college grades with SAT scores. **Deadline for Receipt:** July 15. **Additional Information:** ncsa@yadtel.net

3025 ■ NORTH DAKOTA FARMERS UNION
PO Box 2136
Jamestown, ND 58401
Tel: (701)252-2341

Free: 800-366-8331
Fax: (701)252-6584
Web Site: http://www.ndfu.org
To provide financial assistance for students who deserve to pursue college but financially constrained.
Title of Award: North Dakota Farmers Union Agricultural Studies Scholarships **Area, Field, or Subject:** Agricultural sciences. **Level of Education for which Award is Granted:** Undergraduate **Funds Available:** $750.
Eligibility Requirements: Applicants must be first or second year students in an agricultural two-year program; must be enrolled in a school located at the Cenex Harvest States market area where curriculum is approved by the U.S. office of Education. **Application Requirements:** Applicants must submit all the required application information. **Deadline for Receipt:** March 1.

3026 ■ OHIO FARM BUREAU FEDERATION
280 Plaza
PO Box 182383
Columbus, OH 43218-2383
Tel: (614)249-2400
Web Site: http://ofbf.org
To provide financial support to deserving women.
Title of Award: Women's Leadership in Agriculture Scholarship Program **Area, Field, or Subject:** Agricultural Sciences. **Level of Education for which Award is Granted:** Undergraduate **Funds Available:** No specific amount.
Eligibility Requirements: Applicants must be enrolled in an accredited college or university. **Application Requirements:** Applicants must submit a completed application form. **Additional Information:** Ohio Farm Bureau Federation at the above address.

3027 ■ OREGON FARM BUREAU
3415 Commercial St. SE
Salem, OR 97302
Tel: (503)399-1701
Free: 800-334-6323
Fax: (503)399-8082
E-mail: annemarie@oregonfb.org
Web Site: http://www.oregonfb.org
To promote involvement in agriculture; to help those interested in an agricultural future; to further the education of those involved in the field, thus promoting a stronger future for the industry.
Title of Award: Clackamas County Farm Bureau Scholarships **Area, Field, or Subject:** Agricultural economics. **Level of Education for which Award is Granted:** Undergraduate **Number Awarded:** 3. **Funds Available:** $1,000.
Eligibility Requirements: Applicants must be residents of Clackamas County at the time of the application; must be interested in pursuing a career in agriculture or a related field; must have a GPA of at least 2.8. **Application Requirements:** Applicants must submit: two letters of recommendation, from which one must come from an Ag Advisor or teacher and the other from another non-relative; transcript of records from most recent school attended; written statement detailing reasons for interest in an agricultural profession, leadership, community service experience and experience in agriculture. **Deadline for Receipt:** April 1. **Additional Information:** 33814 S Meridian Rd., Woodburn, OR 97071.

3028 ■ OREGON FARM BUREAU
3415 Commercial St. SE
Salem, OR 97302
Tel: (503)399-1701
Free: 800-334-6323
Fax: (503)399-8082
E-mail: annemarie@oregonfb.org
Web Site: http://www.oregonfb.org
To promote educational improvement, economic opportunity and social achievement for its members and the farming, ranching and natural resources industry as a whole.
Title of Award: Oregon Farm Bureau Memorial Scholarships **Area, Field, or Subject:** Agricultural economics. **Level of Education for which Award is Granted:** Undergraduate **Funds Available:** $1,000.
Eligibility Requirements: Applicants must be full-time students pursuing an agriculture-related major. **Application Requirements:** Applicants

must complete an application form; must submit a transcript of records and three letters of recommendation. **Deadline for Receipt:** April 1. **Additional Information:** Dana Eckfield at the above address.

3029 ■ OREGON FARM BUREAU
3415 Commercial St. SE
Salem, OR 97302
Tel: (503)399-1701
Free: 800-334-6323
Fax: (503)399-8082
E-mail: annemarie@oregonfb.org
Web Site: http://www.oregonfb.org
To promote educational improvement, economic opportunity and social achievement for its members and the farming, ranching and natural resources industry as a whole.
Title of Award: Washington County Farm Bureau Scholarships **Area, Field, or Subject:** Agricultural economics. **Level of Education for which Award is Granted:** Undergraduate **Number Awarded:** 5. **Funds Available:** $1,000.
Eligibility Requirements: Applicants must be graduating high school seniors or college students enrolled in an agriculture degree program. **Application Requirements:** Applicants must submit a completed application form. **Deadline for Receipt:** May 5. **Additional Information:** 503-648-9442.

3030 ■ OREGON FARM BUREAU
3415 Commercial St. SE
Salem, OR 97302
Tel: (503)399-1701
Free: 800-334-6323
Fax: (503)399-8082
E-mail: annemarie@oregonfb.org
Web Site: http://www.oregonfb.org
To support Oregon High School graduates that plan to attend an Oregon university to study an area that would have a positive impact on production agriculture or other agricultural related fields.
Title of Award: Willamette Valley AG Association Scholarships **Area, Field, or Subject:** Agricultural economics. **Level of Education for which Award is Granted:** Undergraduate **Funds Available:** $1,000.
Eligibility Requirements: Applicants must be full-time students who are college level juniors or seniors pursuing an agriculture-related major at an Oregon college or university, and students seeking a graduate level teaching degree. **Application Requirements:** Applicants must submit a completed application form; a transcript of records and three letters of recommendation. **Deadline for Receipt:** April 1. **Additional Information:** Dana Eckfield at the above address.

3031 ■ OREGON FARM BUREAU
3415 Commercial St. SE
Salem, OR 97302
Tel: (503)399-1701
Free: 800-334-6323
Fax: (503)399-8082
E-mail: annemarie@oregonfb.org
Web Site: http://www.oregonfb.org
To assist Yamhill County high school graduates in furthering their education.
Title of Award: Yamhill County Farm Bureau Scholarships **Area, Field, or Subject:** Agricultural economics. **Level of Education for which Award is Granted:** Undergraduate **Number Awarded:** 2. **Funds Available:** $1,500. **Duration:** 1 year.
Eligibility Requirements: Applicants must be full-time students who have successfully completed at least one year of higher education at an accredited college or university; must have plans to continue their education at an accredited college; must have a major in agriculture or related field; must have a minimum of 2.5 GPA for the last college term; must have a minimum of 12 credits per term; must be graduates of Yamhill County. **Application Requirements:** Applicants must submit a completed and signed application form, two letters of recommendation from non-related persons and official transcripts from all colleges attended. **Deadline for Receipt:** August 1. **Additional Information:** 1215 N Adams St., Ste. C, McMinnville, OR 97128.

3032 ■ PARKERSBURG AREA COMMUNITY FOUNDATION
501 Avery St.
Parkersburg, WV 26101
Tel: (304)428-4438; (866)428-4438
Fax: (304)428-1200
E-mail: info@pacfwv.com
Web Site: http://www.pacfwv.com
To encourage graduating students to pursue their education.
Title of Award: Everett Oscar Shimp Memorial Scholarships **Area, Field, or Subject:** Agriculture, Economic aspects; History. **Level of Education for which Award is Granted:** Undergraduate **Funds Available:** $500-$1,000.
Eligibility Requirements: Applicant must be a graduate of Jackson or Roane County high schools who is currently enrolled full-time and has completed college credits equivalent to junior or senior status; must have a minimum of 3.0 college GPA; and must be majoring in agriculture or history or pursuing an education degree majoring in agriculture or history. **Application Requirements:** Applicants must submit a cover sheet (3 pages) and application form (4 pages); a personal essay; a high school and/or post-secondary transcript; a letter of recommendation; a signed copy of the page of their or their parent's most recent tax return that indicates adjusted gross income; and a Student Aid Report showing estimated family contribution from FAFSA. Application form and other supporting documents must be sent to Our Community's Foundation, P.O Box 1762, Parkersburg, WV 26102. **Deadline for Receipt:** March 20.

3033 ■ PARKERSBURG AREA COMMUNITY FOUNDATION
501 Avery St.
Parkersburg, WV 26101
Tel: (304)428-4438; (866)428-4438
Fax: (304)428-1200
E-mail: info@pacfwv.com
Web Site: http://www.pacfwv.com
To encourage graduating students to pursue their degree in the business or agriculture field.
Title of Award: Pat Shimp Memorial Scholarships **Area, Field, or Subject:** Business; Agriculture, Economic aspects. **Level of Education for which Award is Granted:** Undergraduate **Funds Available:** $500.
Eligibility Requirements: Applicant must be a Roane County High School graduating senior pursuing a degree in the business or agriculture field with a minimum of 2.0 GPA. **Application Requirements:** Applicants must submit a cover sheet (3 pages) and application form (4 pages); a personal essay; a high school and/or post-secondary transcript; a letter of recommendation; a signed copy of the page of their or their parent's most recent tax return that indicates adjusted gross income; and a Student Aid Report showing estimated family contribution from FAFSA. Application form and other supporting documents must be sent to Our Community's Foundation, P.O Box 1762, Parkersburg, WV 26102. **Deadline for Receipt:** March 20.

3034 ■ SOUTHWEST FLORIDA COMMUNITY FOUNDATION
8260 College Pkwy., Ste. 101
Fort Myers, FL 33919
Tel: (239)274-5900
Fax: (239)274-5930
Web Site: http://www.floridacommunity.com
To fund students pursuing degrees or advanced degrees in medicine, law, dentistry, teaching (math and science), ministry, engineering, accounting, architecture and computer science.
Title of Award: John M. and Mary A. Shanley Memorial Scholarships **Area, Field, or Subject:** Medicine; Law; Dentistry; Teaching; Ministry; Engineering; Accounting; Agriculture; Economic aspects; Architecture; Computer and information sciences **Level of Education for which Award is Granted:** Undergraduate **Funds Available:** $5,000. **Duration:** One year.
Eligibility Requirements: Applicant must be a resident of Charlotte, Hendry or Lee County. **Application Requirements:** Application forms are available online. Applicants must submit a letter of interest, letter of recommendation and transcript. **Deadline for Receipt:** February 15.

3035 ■ STEUBEN COUNTY COMMUNITY FOUNDATION
1701 N Wayne St.
Angola, IN 46703

Tel: (260)665-6656
Fax: (260)665-8420
Web Site: http://www.steubenfoundation.org
To provide financial assistance to those students who are in need.
Title of Award: Dr. M.G. "Doc" Headley Scholarships **Area, Field, or Subject:** Agriculture; Veterinary Science. **Level of Education for which Award is Granted:** Undergraduate **Number Awarded:** Minimum of 3 persons. **Funds Available:** No specific amount.
Eligibility Requirements: Applicants must be pursuing a certified or degreed agricultural or veterinarian program at an institution of higher education. Applicants must be graduating students from Angola, Fremont, Hamilton or Prairie Heights High School. **Application Requirements:** Applicants must check the website for the application process and required materials. **Deadline for Receipt:** March 15. **Additional Information:** Steuben County Community Foundation at the above address.

3036 ■ UNIVERSITY OF WISCONSIN-MADISON
432 N Murray St.
Madison, WI 53706-1496
Tel: (608)262-3060
Fax: (608)262-9068
E-mail: askbucky@uwmad.wisc.edu
Web Site: http://www.wisc.edu
To support UW-Madison students in their education.
Title of Award: University of Wisconsin-Madison/CALS Continuing Student Scholarships **Area, Field, or Subject:** Agricultural sciences; Life sciences. **Level of Education for which Award is Granted:** Undergraduate **Number Awarded:** Up to 200. **Funds Available:** $500-$3,000.
Eligibility Requirements: Applicant must be a UW-Madison sophomore, junior, or senior student enrolled in the College of Agricultural and Life Sciences (CALS). **Application Requirements:** Applicants must submit a completed application form together with a letter of recommendation. **Deadline for Receipt:** February 1.

3037 ■ UNIVERSITY OF WISCONSIN-MADISON
432 N Murray St.
Madison, WI 53706-1496
Tel: (608)262-3060
Fax: (608)262-9068
E-mail: askbucky@uwmad.wisc.edu
Web Site: http://www.wisc.edu
To support UW-Madison students in their education.
Title of Award: University of Wisconsin-Madison/CALS Minority Scholarships **Area, Field, or Subject:** Agricultural sciences; Life sciences. **Level of Education for which Award is Granted:** Undergraduate **Number Awarded:** Varies. **Funds Available:** $500-$2,000.
Eligibility Requirements: Applicants must be UW-Madison students of color enrolled in the College of Agricultural and Life Sciences (CALS). **Application Requirements:** Students must submit a completed CALS Scholarship Application along with the letter of recommendation. **Deadline for Receipt:** January 15.

3038 ■ WORKING FOR FARMERS' SUCCESS
PO Box 68
Truman, MN 56088
Tel: (507)524-4130
Free: 800-776-2871
Fax: (507)776-2871
E-mail: wfsinfo@wfsag.com
Web Site: http://www.wfsag.com
To encourage young people to pursue an agricultural career.
Title of Award: Working for Farmers' Success Scholarships **Area, Field, or Subject:** Agricultural economics. **Level of Education for which Award is Granted:** Undergraduate **Number Awarded:** 20. **Funds Available:** $500.
Eligibility Requirements: Applicants must be senior students who are graduating from the WFS trade territory. **Application Requirements:** Applicants must submit a completed application form. **Deadline for Receipt:** March 30. **Additional Information:** Jo Ann Gumto at the above address.

Animal Sciences

3039 ■ ALABAMA HORSE COUNCIL
PO Box 260
Morris, AL 35116

800-945-8033
E-mail: info@alabamahorsecouncil.org
Web Site: http://www.alabamahorsecouncil.org
To support the education of an AHC members and their children.
Title of Award: Alabama Horse Council Scholarships **Area, Field, or Subject:** Equine studies. **Level of Education for which Award is Granted:** Undergraduate **Funds Available:** $1000.
Eligibility Requirements: Applicants or their parents/grandparents must be current members of AHC; must be majoring in a field of study for a career in the equine industry; must have demonstrated record of activity in the equine industry prior to college application. **Application Requirements:** Applicants must submit 4 copies of: one page-cover form; two letters of references attesting to the applicant's commitment to the equine industry, activity in the industry and character; short (500 word maximum) essay about how horses have shaped the lives and the goals that applicant want to pursue in the horse industry; and a list of activities and honors received. **Deadline for Receipt:** June 1. **Additional Information:** Charlotte Collins at the above address.

3040 ■ ALABAMA HORSE COUNCIL
PO Box 260
Morris, AL 35116
800-945-8033
E-mail: info@alabamahorsecouncil.org
Web Site: http://www.alabamahorsecouncil.org
To support the education of AHC members and their children.
Title of Award: Samuel Upchurch Memorial Scholarships **Area, Field, or Subject:** Agricultural economics; Animal science and behavior. **Level of Education for which Award is Granted:** Undergraduate **Funds Available:** $4000.
Eligibility Requirements: Applicants must be children or grandchildren of ACA members for two consecutive years; and must be accepted in Animal Science or Agriculture Economics at Auburn University. **Application Requirements:** Applicants must submit a completed application form. **Deadline for Receipt:** December. **Additional Information:** Martha Davis.

3041 ■ ALABAMA HORSE COUNCIL
PO Box 260
Morris, AL 35116
800-945-8033
E-mail: info@alabamahorsecouncil.org
Web Site: http://www.alabamahorsecouncil.org
To support the education of AHC members and their children.
Title of Award: Ed Wadsworth Memorial Scholarships **Area, Field, or Subject:** Animal science and behavior. **Level of Education for which Award is Granted:** Undergraduate **Funds Available:** $1500.
Eligibility Requirements: Applicants must be resident of Alabama; must be junior or senior in the Animal Sciences Department at Auburn University; involved in beef cattle production; have demonstrated leadership abilities; have a GPA of 3.0 and above; and must be children or grandchildren of ACA members for two consecutive years. **Application Requirements:** Applicants must submit a completed application form. **Deadline for Receipt:** December. **Additional Information:** Martha Davis.

3042 ■ AMERICAN BIRDING ASSOCIATION
4945 N 30th St., Ste. 200
Colorado Springs, CO 80919
Tel: (719)578-9703
Free: 800-850-2473
Fax: (719)578-1480
E-mail: member@aba.org
Web Site: http://www.americanbirding.org
To recognize and stimulate interest in birds. To promote the pursuit of educational and other bird-related activities.
Title of Award: ABA Scholarships **Area, Field, or Subject:** Animal science and behavior; Animal rights. **Level of Education for which Award is Granted:** Undergraduate **Funds Available:** No specific amount.
Eligibility Requirements: Scholarship is open to American Birding Association active members only. **Application Requirements:** Applicants must submit a complete application form available from the ABA office and can be downloaded from the website; an essay about the importance of a

bird; a letter of recommendation from a teacher, bird club member or mentor. Send complete documents to: Lori L. Fujimoto, Youth Scholarships, American Birding Association, 4945 N 30th St., Ste. 200, Colorado Springs, CO 80919. **Deadline for Receipt:** April 30.

3043 ■ AMERICAN BIRDING ASSOCIATION
4945 N 30th St., Ste. 200
Colorado Springs, CO 80919
Tel: (719)578-9703
Free: 800-850-2473
Fax: (719)578-1480
E-mail: member@aba.org
Web Site: http://www.americanbirding.org
To provide financial assistance to young birders.
Title of Award: Richard E. Andrews Memorial Scholarships **Area, Field, or Subject:** Animal science and behavior; Animal rights. **Level of Education for which Award is Granted:** Undergraduate **Funds Available:** No specific amount.
Eligibility Requirements: Scholarship is open to American Birding Association active members. **Application Requirements:** Applicants must submit a complete application form available from the ABA office and can be downloaded from the website; an essay explaining why he/she deserves the Andrews Scholarships; a letter of recommendation from a teacher, bird club member or mentor. Send complete documents to: Youth Scholarships, American Birding Association, 4945 N 30th St., Ste. 200, Colorado Springs, CO 80919. **Deadline for Receipt:** April 30.

3044 ■ AMERICAN BIRDING ASSOCIATION
4945 N 30th St., Ste. 200
Colorado Springs, CO 80919
Tel: (719)578-9703
Free: 800-850-2473
Fax: (719)578-1480
E-mail: member@aba.org
Web Site: http://www.americanbirding.org
To recognize and stimulate interest in birds by promoting the pursuit of educational and other bird-related activities.
Title of Award: WildBird/Clements Memorial Scholarships **Area, Field, or Subject:** Animal science and behavior; Animal rights. **Level of Education for which Award is Granted:** Undergraduate **Funds Available:** $500. **Duration:** One academic year.
Eligibility Requirements: Scholarship is open to American Birding Association active members only. **Application Requirements:** Applicants must submit a complete application form available from the ABA office and can be downloaded from the website; an essay explaining why he/she believes that he/she qualifies for the Clements Scholarships; a letter of recommendation from a teacher, bird club member or mentor. Send complete documents to: Youth Scholarships, American Birding Association, 4945 N. 30th St., Ste. 200, Colorado Springs, CO 80919. **Deadline for Receipt:** April 30.

3045 ■ HARTFORD FOUNDATION FOR PUBLIC GIVING
10 Columbus Blvd., 8th Flr.
Hartford, CT 06106
Tel: (860)548-1888
Fax: (860)524-8346
E-mail: hfpg@hfpg.org
Web Site: http://www.hfpg.org
To provide scholarship to students attending the University of Connecticut.
Title of Award: Ratcliffe Hicks School of Agriculture Heritage Scholarships **Area, Field, or Subject:** Animal science and behavior; Horticulture; Turfgrass management. **Level of Education for which Award is Granted:** Undergraduate **Number Awarded:** 20. **Funds Available:** $1,200. **Duration:** One semester.
Eligibility Requirements: Applicants must be graduating seniors planning to attend the University of Connecticut, Ratcliffe Hicks School of Agriculture majoring in Animal Science, Ornamental Horticulture and Turfgrass management. **Application Requirements:** Applicants may obtain application materials from the University of Connecticut Ratcliffe Hicks School of Agriculture (RHSA). 1376 Storrs Rd., Unit 4090, Storrs, CT 06269-4090. Phone: 860486-2919
Fax: 860486-4643, acadprog@canr.uconn.edu.

3046 ■ NATIONAL CATTLEMEN'S FOUNDATION
9110 E Nichols Ave., Ste. 300
Centennial, CO 80112
Tel: (303)694-0305
E-mail: ncf@beef.org
Web Site: http://www.nationalcattlemensfoundation.org
To promote study in animal science with an emphasis in bovine practice.
Title of Award: NCF Fort Dodge Animal Health Legacy Scholarships for Undergraduate Students **Area, Field, or Subject:** Animal science and behavior. **Level of Education for which Award is Granted:** Undergraduate **Number Awarded:** 2. **Funds Available:** $5,000 each.
Eligibility Requirements: Applicant must be a U.S. citizen; an undergraduate junior or senior enrolled at a two-or four-year institution of higher learning; have demonstrated commitment to a career in the beef industry through classes, internships or life experience. **Application Requirements:** Applicants must submit a completed scholarship application form together with the essay and two letters of recommendation. **Additional Information:** In partnership with Fort Dodge Animal Health. **Deadline for Receipt:** April 30.

3047 ■ STARK COMMUNITY FOUNDATION
400 Market Ave. N, Ste. 200
Canton, OH 44702-2107
Tel: (330)454-3426
Fax: (330)454-5855
Web Site: http://www.starkcommunityfoundation.org
To provide scholarship assistance to qualified individuals who want to pursue their studies.
Title of Award: Stark County Dairy Promoters Scholarships **Area, Field, or Subject:** Dairy science; Animal science and behavior; Medicine, Veterinary; Nutrition; Food science and technology. **Level of Education for which Award is Granted:** Undergraduate **Funds Available:** No specific amount. **Duration:** One year.
Eligibility Requirements: Applicants must be residents of Stark County, OH; must be pursuing college-level study in the field of dairy science, animal science, veterinary medicine, human nutrition, or food science; must have 2.5 high school GPA; must have demonstrated financial need. **Application Requirements:** Applicants must complete and submit the application form and requirements to Stark County Diary Promoters Scholarship Committee, Stark Community Foundation, 400 Market Ave. N, Ste. 200, Canton, OH 44702. **Deadline for Receipt:** April 15.

Biology

3048 ■ AMERICAN ASSOCIATION FOR THE ADVANCEMENT OF SCIENCE
1200 New York Ave. NW
Washington, DC 20005
Tel: (202)326-6400
E-mail: webmaster@aaas.org
Web Site: http://www.aaas.org
To enhance undergraduate education through research experience that emphasize the interrelationship between chemistry and biology; to encourage students to pursue graduate education in chemistry and life sciences; to foster undergraduate programs and activities that bridge chemistry and biology;
Title of Award: Merck Undergraduate Science Research Scholarships **Area, Field, or Subject:** Chemistry; Biology; Life Sciences. **Level of Education for which Award is Granted:** Undergraduate **Number Awarded:** 15. **Funds Available:** $60,000. **Duration:** 3 years.
Eligibility Requirements: Applicants must be located in 50 United States; offered American Chemical Society-approved program in Chemistry; confer ten or fewer graduate degrees annually in Biology and Chemistry combined; defined by the U.S. Internal Revenue Service Tax Code as a not-for-profit entity under section 501; must not be current Merck/AAAS USRP Award Recipient. **Application Requirements:** Applicants must submit an application cover page; eligibility form including a copy of the school's 501(c)(3) certification letter from the U.S. Internal Revenue Service. **Deadline for Receipt:** November 2.

3049 ■ AMERICAN SOCIETY FOR MICROBIOLOGY
1752 N St. NW
Washington, DC 20036-2904

Tel: (202)942-9207
Fax: (202)942-9333
E-mail: chouston@utmb.edu
Web Site: http://www.asm.org
To increase the number of underrepresented undergraduate students who have demonstrated the ability to pursue graduate careers in microbiology.
Title of Award: Microbiology Undergraduate Research Fellowships **Area, Field, or Subject:** Microbiology. **Level of Education for which Award is Granted:** Undergraduate **Funds Available:** $3,500-student; $850-lodging; $500-roundtrip travel; $1,000 travel support.
Eligibility Requirements: Applicants must be enrolled as full-time matriculating undergraduate in an accredited U.S. institution; must be either freshmen with college level research experience or sophomores, juniors, or seniors who will not graduate before the completion date of the summer program; must be members of underrepresented group of microbiology; must have taken introductory courses in biology, chemistry and preferably microbiology prior to submission of the application; must have strong interests in obtaining a Ph.D. or M.D/Ph.D. in the microbiological sciences; must have laboratory research experience. **Application Requirements:** Applicants must submit a complete application form. **Deadline for Receipt:** February 1.

3050 ■ ASSOCIATION FOR WOMEN IN SCIENCE
1200 New York Ave. NW, Ste. 650
Washington, DC 20005
Tel: (202)326-8940
Fax: (202)326-8960
E-mail: awis@awis.org
Web Site: http://www.awis.org
To promote education in science.
Title of Award: AWIS College Scholarships **Area, Field, or Subject:** Astronomy and astronomical sciences; Geosciences; Biology; Mathematics and mathematical sciences; Chemistry; Physics; Computer and information sciences; Engineering; Psychology. **Level of Education for which Award is Granted:** Undergraduate **Number Awarded:** 2-5. **Funds Available:** No specific amount.
Eligibility Requirements: Applicant must be a female high school senior; U.S. citizen or permanent resident; have at least 3.75 GPA; at least 1200 score in SAT or a composite score of 25 in ACT; planning to study in any field of Astronomy, Geoscience, Biology, Mathematics, Chemistry, Physics, Computer and Information Science, Engineering, Psychology; planning to become a researcher or teacher. **Application Requirements:** Applicants must send five copies of: summary form; essay describing research experience; resume; two recommendation letters from science or research teachers; high school transcript and score of standardized test if available. **Deadline for Receipt:** January 17.

3051 ■ BENTON COUNTY FOUNDATION
PO Box 911
Corvallis, OR 97339
Tel: (541)753-1603
Web Site: http://www.bentoncountyfoundation.org
To encourage and support ethnic minority undergraduate women enrolled in the College of Science.
Title of Award: Margaret Dowell-Gravatt, M.D. Scholarship **Area, Field, or Subject:** Zoology; Microbiology; Medical technology; Medicine; Nursing; Physical therapy; Occupational therapy. **Level of Education for which Award is Granted:** Undergraduate **Funds Available:** No specific amount.
Eligibility Requirements: Applicant must: be pursuing a degree in Zoology or Microbiology or one of the following pre-health programs: Medical Technology, Medicine, Nursing, Physical and/or Occupational therapy. Applicant must: be enrolled full-time at the sophomore, junior, or senior level; have a GPA of 2.5 overall and 3.0 in science courses required in their major field or pre-health curriculum; qualify for financial assistance as defined by the Financial Aid Office of OSU. **Application Requirements:** Applicant may contact the Foundation for application form and other requirements. **Additional Information:** Benton County Foundation at the above address.

3052 ■ ENTOMOLOGICAL SOCIETY OF AMERICA
10001 Derekwood Ln., Ste. 100
Lanham, MD 20706-4876

Tel: (301)731-4535
Fax: (301)731-4538
E-mail: esa@entsoc.org
Web Site: http://www.entsoc.org
To provide educational assistance for needy students at the graduate or undergraduate level of their education in entomology and related disciplines at a college or university in the United States, Mexico, or Canada.
Title of Award: Stan Beck Fellowships **Area, Field, or Subject:** Biology. **Level of Education for which Award is Granted:** Undergraduate **Funds Available:** No specific amount.
Eligibility Requirements: Applicants must be graduate or undergraduate students in entomology or related disciplines at colleges or universities in the United States, Mexico, or Canada. **Application Requirements:** Applicants must submit a letter of nomination; description of applicant's academic studies including academic plan; a statement of the applicant's need or challenge (not more than 2 pages); letter of recommendation from the applicant's academic advisor; and two letters of support demonstrating the applicant's need or challenge. **Deadline for Receipt:** July 1. **Additional Information:** Entomological Foundation, 9331 Annapolis Rd. Ste. 210, Lanham, MD 20706.

3053 ■ ENTOMOLOGICAL SOCIETY OF AMERICA
10001 Derekwood Ln., Ste. 100
Lanham, MD 20706-4876
Tel: (301)731-4535
Fax: (301)731-4538
E-mail: esa@entsoc.org
Web Site: http://www.entsoc.org
To help students achieve their goal of obtaining a degree in entomology or pursuing a career as an entomologist.
Title of Award: BioQuip Scholarships **Area, Field, or Subject:** Biology. **Level of Education for which Award is Granted:** Undergraduate **Funds Available:** No stated amount.
Eligibility Requirements: Applicants must be enrolled as undergraduate students in entomology in any college or university in the United States, Mexico, and Canada. **Application Requirements:** Applicants must fill out an application form. Applicants must submit letter of nomination; statement not exceeding two-pages in length stating interest in entomology, career goals, financial need, and other pertinent factors which illustrate qualifications for the scholarship; three statements from school officials or other knowledgeable individuals attesting to entomological interests, character, aptitude and financial need; and current official transcript of college grades. **Deadline for Receipt:** July 1. **Additional Information:** Entomological Foundation, 9332 Annapolis Rd. Ste. 210, Lanham MD 20706.

3054 ■ FOUNDATION FOR THE CAROLINAS
217 S Tryon St.
Charlotte, NC 28202
Tel: (704)973-4500
Free: 800-973-7244
Web Site: http://www.fftc.org
To provide financial assistance for students at Clemson University and the University of North Carolina at Charlotte who are preparing for a career in a technological field appropriate to meet the requirements of the U.S. Patent Office as a patent agent or attorney.
Title of Award: Julian E. Carnes Scholarship Fund **Area, Field, or Subject:** Engineering; Chemistry; Physics; Biology; Computer and information sciences. **Level of Education for which Award is Granted:** Undergraduate **Funds Available:** No specific amount.
Eligibility Requirements: Applicants must be legal residents of North or South Carolina; must be rising juniors or seniors at Clemson University or UNC Charlotte whose academic major is appropriate to meet the requirements of the U.S. Patent Office for admission as a patent agent or attorney (including but not limited to engineering, chemistry, physics, biology and computer science); and must have at least a 3.0 cumulative grade point average (on a 4.0 scale). **Application Requirements:** Applicants must submit all the required application information. **Additional Information:** Clemson University Office of Student Financial Aid, 864-656-2280 or the UNC Charlotte Student Financial Aid Office, 704-687-2461.

3055 ■ FUR TAKERS OF AMERICA

853 E 1000 N Rd.
Onarga, IL 60955
Tel: (217)394-2577
E-mail: krumui@illicom.net
Web Site: http://www.furtakersofamerica.com
To promote interest in the accumulation and dissemination of knowledge concerning the trapping of fur bearing animals among persons interested therein.

Title of Award: Charles Dobbins FTA Scholarships **Area, Field, or Subject:** Agricultural Science; Biology; Wildlife Conservation and management. **Level of Education for which Award is Granted:** Undergraduate **Funds Available:** $250.

Eligibility Requirements: Applicants must be members of FTA or their immediate relatives; must be majoring in agriculture, biology, wildlife management or related courses in an accredited two-year or four-year college, university, or vocational/technical school. **Application Requirements:** Applicants must provide proof of high school graduation or pending graduation; official documents indicating that they have been accepted in an institution as first year students, or registration of classes if applicants are already in school. Applicants must also submit an essay that discusses career goals and how the scholarship would help to achieve these goals. **Deadline for Receipt:** June 1. **Additional Information:** Carol Krumwiede at the above address.

3056 ■ GULF AND CARIBBEAN FISHERIES INSTITUTE

Marine Research Institute
2796 Overseas Hwy., Ste. 119
Marathon, FL 33050
Tel: (305)289-2330
Fax: (305)289-2334
Web Site: http://www.gcfi.org
To encourage students with interest in marine recreational fisheries.

Title of Award: Ronald L. Schmied Scholarships **Area, Field, or Subject:** Fisheries sciences/management; Marine biology. **Level of Education for which Award is Granted:** Professional, Undergraduate **Funds Available:** $1,500 (covers airfare, lodging, and research-related expenses).

Eligibility Requirements: Applicant must be enrolled at a college/university degree program in the wider Caribbean or in one of Gulf of Mexico states (Mexico and the United States); or a student engaged in a research project in the Gulf of Mexico and wider Caribbean region. **Application Requirements:** Applicants must submit electronically an application letter (includes name, address, contact numbers, educational institution department, degree level, description of current marine research, career goals, and reasons for the needing financial assistance); an endorsement letter from a faculty; and a vita. **Deadline for Receipt:** August 1. **Additional Information:** Scholarship Committee, Robert B. Ditton, r-ditton@tamu.edu.

3057 ■ LAKSELAGET

c/o Ingeborg Sorensen
1235 Yale Place, No. 1305
Minneapolis, MN 55403
E-mail: president@lakselaget.org
Web Site: http://www.lakselaget.org
To promote the international connections between Norway and Minnesota, and learn, teach and share knowledge that will benefit women in their complex roles in today's society.

Title of Award: Lakselaget Foundation Scholarships **Area, Field, or Subject:** Biology; Mathematics and mathematical sciences; Science. **Level of Education for which Award is Granted:** Graduate, Undergraduate **Number Awarded:** Varies. **Funds Available:** $1,000.

Eligibility Requirements: Applicant must be female; an American citizen residing in Minnesota, enrolled in undergraduate or graduate studies at an accredited Minnesota college or university or at the University of North Dakota, Grand Forks and wish to study in Norway; or must be a Norwegian citizen attending undergraduate or graduate studies at an accredited Norwegian college or university, who wishes to study at a Minnesota college or university or at the University of North Dakota, Grand Forks. Study areas may include, but are not limited to, non-traditional women's studies such as biotechnology, mathematics, and the sciences. Applicants must be full-time undergraduates who have completed at least one year or full-time graduate students. American students should have a

GPA of 3.0 or better, Norwegians the equivalent. **Application Requirements:** Applicant must submit a completed application form with official transcripts, two letters or recommendation, a letter from an individual who can assess the applicant's Norwegian language skills (if an American), and a 1000-word essay. **Deadline for Receipt:** March 15. **Additional Information:** scholarships@lakselaget.org.

3058 ■ LEWIS-CLARK STATE COLLEGE

500 8th Ave.
Lewiston, ID 83501
Tel: (208)792-5272
Web Site: http://www.lcsc.edu
To provide financial assistance to students who are majoring in these fields: Accounting, Biology, Business, Communications, Computer Science, Economics, Environmental Science, Engineering, Mathematics, Natural Resources, Political Science, Statistics.

Title of Award: Avista Corporation Minds in Motion Scholarships **Area, Field, or Subject:** Accounting; Biology; Business; Communications; Computer and Information Sciences; Economics; Environmental Science; Engineering; Mathematics; Natural Resources; Political Science; Statistics. **Level of Education for which Award is Granted:** Undergraduate **Number Awarded:** 2. **Funds Available:** No specific Amount.

Eligibility Requirements: Applicants must be full-time students attending LCSC and must have a cumulative GPA of 2.5. **Application Requirements:** Applicants must submit general application. **Deadline for Receipt:** March 1.

3059 ■ LEWIS-CLARK STATE COLLEGE

500 8th Ave.
Lewiston, ID 83501
Tel: (208)792-5272
Web Site: http://www.lcsc.edu
To inspire educational pursuits among less capable individuals by providing financial assistance.

Title of Award: Lewis-Clark State College Presidential Technical Out-of-State Scholarships **Area, Field, or Subject:** Chemistry; Computer Science; Engineering; Information Systems Analysis; Industrial Electronics; Biology; Earth Information Systems; Radiology; Heating/Air Conditioning; Automated Manufacturing Technology; Mathematics; Printing Technology; Graphic Arts or Web Development. **Level of Education for which Award is Granted:** Undergraduate **Funds Available:** No specific amount.

Eligibility Requirements: Applicants must be new non-resident high school or transfer students who have at least 14 transferable semester credits. **Application Requirements:** Applicants must accomplish a general application available in the website. **Deadline for Receipt:** March 1 for Fall enrollment or November 1 for Spring enrollment.

3060 ■ MARINE BIOLOGICAL LABORATORY

7 MBL St.
Woods Hole, MA 02543
Tel: (508)548-3705
E-mail: mdonovan@mbl.edu
Web Site: http://www.mbl.edu
To provide support for a graduate or post-doctoral student taking a summer course in fundamental biological science.

Title of Award: John and Elisabeth Buck Endowed Scholarships **Area, Field, or Subject:** Biology. **Level of Education for which Award is Granted:** Undergraduate **Funds Available:** No specific amount.

Eligibility Requirements: Applicants must be attending a summer course at Marine Biological Laboratory. **Application Requirements:** Applicants must complete the application form.

3061 ■ MARINE BIOLOGICAL LABORATORY

7 MBL St.
Woods Hole, MA 02543
Tel: (508)548-3705
E-mail: mdonovan@mbl.edu
Web Site: http://www.mbl.edu
To provide support for students attending the Embryology and Frontiers in Reproduction courses.

Title of Award: C. Lalor Burdick Scholarships **Area, Field, or Subject:** Biology. **Level of Education for which Award is Granted:** Undergraduate **Funds Available:** No specific amount.

Eligibility Requirements: Applicants must be attending a summer course at Marine Biological Laboratory. **Application Requirements:** Applicants must complete the application form.

3062 ■ MARINE BIOLOGICAL LABORATORY
7 MBL St.
Woods Hole, MA 02543
Tel: (508)548-3705
E-mail: mdonovan@mbl.edu
Web Site: http://www.mbl.edu
To provide support for students attending the Embryology course.
Title of Award: Max M. Burger Endowed Scholarships in Embryology **Area, Field, or Subject:** Biology. **Level of Education for which Award is Granted:** Undergraduate **Funds Available:** No specific amount.
Eligibility Requirements: Applicants must be attending a summer course at Marine Biological Laboratory. **Application Requirements:** Applicants must complete the application form.

3063 ■ MARINE BIOLOGICAL LABORATORY
7 MBL St.
Woods Hole, MA 02543
Tel: (508)548-3705
E-mail: mdonovan@mbl.edu
Web Site: http://www.mbl.edu
To provide support for students studying at the Marine Biological Laboratory.
Title of Award: Robertson Lola Ellis Scholarships **Area, Field, or Subject:** Biology. **Level of Education for which Award is Granted:** Undergraduate **Funds Available:** No specific amount.
Eligibility Requirements: Applicants must be attending a summer course at Marine Biological Laboratory. **Application Requirements:** Applicants must complete the application form.

3064 ■ MARINE BIOLOGICAL LABORATORY
7 MBL St.
Woods Hole, MA 02543
Tel: (508)548-3705
E-mail: mdonovan@mbl.edu
Web Site: http://www.mbl.edu
To provide support for students studying in any Marine Biological Laboratory summer courses.
Title of Award: Thomas B. Grave and Elizabeth F. Grave Scholarships **Area, Field, or Subject:** Biology. **Level of Education for which Award is Granted:** Undergraduate **Funds Available:** No specific amount.
Eligibility Requirements: Applicants must be attending a summer course at Marine Biological Laboratory. **Application Requirements:** Applicants must complete the application form.

3065 ■ MARINE BIOLOGICAL LABORATORY
7 MBL St.
Woods Hole, MA 02543
Tel: (508)548-3705
E-mail: mdonovan@mbl.edu
Web Site: http://www.mbl.edu
To provide support for students studying in any Marine Biological Laboratory summer courses.
Title of Award: Caswell Grave Scholarships **Area, Field, or Subject:** Biology. **Level of Education for which Award is Granted:** Undergraduate **Funds Available:** No specific amount.
Eligibility Requirements: Applicants must be attending a summer course at Marine Biological Laboratory. **Application Requirements:** Applicants must complete the application form.

3066 ■ MARINE BIOLOGICAL LABORATORY
7 MBL St.
Woods Hole, MA 02543
Tel: (508)548-3705
E-mail: mdonovan@mbl.edu
Web Site: http://www.mbl.edu
To provide support for students studying in any Marine Biological Laboratory summer courses.
Title of Award: William Randolph Hearst Educational Endowments **Area, Field, or Subject:** Biology. **Level of Education for which Award is Granted:** Undergraduate **Funds Available:** No specific amount.

Eligibility Requirements: Applicants must be attending a summer course at Marine Biological Laboratory. **Application Requirements:** Applicants must complete the application form.

3067 ■ MARINE BIOLOGICAL LABORATORY
7 MBL St.
Woods Hole, MA 02543
Tel: (508)548-3705
E-mail: mdonovan@mbl.edu
Web Site: http://www.mbl.edu
To provide support for students studying in any Marine Biological Laboratory summer courses in Physiology.
Title of Award: Benjamin Kaminer Endowed Scholarships in Physiology **Area, Field, or Subject:** Physiology. **Level of Education for which Award is Granted:** Undergraduate **Funds Available:** No specific amount.
Eligibility Requirements: Applicants must be attending a summer course at Marine Biological Laboratory. **Application Requirements:** Applicants must complete the application form.

3068 ■ MARINE BIOLOGICAL LABORATORY
7 MBL St.
Woods Hole, MA 02543
Tel: (508)548-3705
E-mail: mdonovan@mbl.edu
Web Site: http://www.mbl.edu
To provide support for students in their courses and for research fellows working independently in laboratories.
Title of Award: Arthur Klorfein Scholarships and Fellowship Funds **Area, Field, or Subject:** Biology. **Level of Education for which Award is Granted:** Undergraduate **Funds Available:** No specific amount.
Eligibility Requirements: Applicants must be attending a summer course at Marine Biological Laboratory. **Application Requirements:** Applicants must complete the application form.

3069 ■ MARINE BIOLOGICAL LABORATORY
7 MBL St.
Woods Hole, MA 02543
Tel: (508)548-3705
E-mail: mdonovan@mbl.edu
Web Site: http://www.mbl.edu
To provide support for students in their courses and for research fellows working independently in laboratories.
Title of Award: Frank R. Lillie Fellowships and Scholarships **Area, Field, or Subject:** Biology. **Level of Education for which Award is Granted:** Undergraduate **Funds Available:** No specific amount.
Eligibility Requirements: Applicants must be attending a Marine Biological Laboratory summer course. **Application Requirements:** Applicants must complete the application form.

3070 ■ MARINE BIOLOGICAL LABORATORY
7 MBL St.
Woods Hole, MA 02543
Tel: (508)548-3705
E-mail: mdonovan@mbl.edu
Web Site: http://www.mbl.edu
To provide support for students attending a Marine Biological Laboratory.
Title of Award: Marine Biological Laboratory Pioneers Fund **Area, Field, or Subject:** Biology. **Level of Education for which Award is Granted:** Undergraduate **Funds Available:** No specific amount.
Eligibility Requirements: Applicants must be attending a Marine Biological Laboratory summer course. **Application Requirements:** Applicants must complete the application form.

3071 ■ MARINE BIOLOGICAL LABORATORY
7 MBL St.
Woods Hole, MA 02543
Tel: (508)548-3705
E-mail: mdonovan@mbl.edu
Web Site: http://www.mbl.edu
To provide support for students attending a Marine Biological Laboratory.
Title of Award: S.O. Mast Founder's Scholarships **Area, Field, or Subject:** Biology. **Level of Education for which Award is Granted:** Undergraduate **Funds Available:** No specific amount.

Eligibility Requirements: Applicants must be attending a Marine Biological Laboratory summer course. **Application Requirements:** Applicants must complete the application form.

3072 ■ MARINE BIOLOGICAL LABORATORY
7 MBL St.
Woods Hole, MA 02543
Tel: (508)548-3705
E-mail: mdonovan@mbl.edu
Web Site: http://www.mbl.edu
To provide support for students attending a neurobiology course.
Title of Award: Frank Morrell Endowed Memorial Scholarships **Area, Field, or Subject:** Biology. **Level of Education for which Award is Granted:** Undergraduate **Funds Available:** No specific amount.
Eligibility Requirements: Applicants must be attending a Marine Biological Laboratory summer course. **Application Requirements:** Applicants must complete the application form.

3073 ■ MARINE BIOLOGICAL LABORATORY
7 MBL St.
Woods Hole, MA 02543
Tel: (508)548-3705
E-mail: mdonovan@mbl.edu
Web Site: http://www.mbl.edu
To provide support for students who studying at the Marine Biological Laboratory.
Title of Award: Pfizer Inc. Endowed Scholarships **Area, Field, or Subject:** Biology. **Level of Education for which Award is Granted:** Undergraduate **Funds Available:** No specific amount.
Eligibility Requirements: Applicants must be attending a summer course at Marine Biological Laboratory. **Application Requirements:** Applicants must complete the application form.

3074 ■ MARINE BIOLOGICAL LABORATORY
7 MBL St.
Woods Hole, MA 02543
Tel: (508)548-3705
E-mail: mdonovan@mbl.edu
Web Site: http://www.mbl.edu
To provide support for students in their courses and for research fellows working independently in laboratories.
Title of Award: Herbert W. Rand Fellowships and Scholarships **Area, Field, or Subject:** Biology. **Level of Education for which Award is Granted:** Undergraduate **Funds Available:** No specific amount.
Eligibility Requirements: Applicants must be attending a summer course at Marine Biological Laboratory. **Application Requirements:** Applicants must complete the application form.

3075 ■ MARINE BIOLOGICAL LABORATORY
7 MBL St.
Woods Hole, MA 02543
Tel: (508)548-3705
E-mail: mdonovan@mbl.edu
Web Site: http://www.mbl.edu
To provide support for students from Dartmouth studying at the Marine Biological Laboratory.
Title of Award: Florence C. Rose and S. Meryl Rose Scholarships **Area, Field, or Subject:** Biology. **Level of Education for which Award is Granted:** Undergraduate **Funds Available:** No specific amount.
Eligibility Requirements: Applicants must be attending a summer course at Marine Biological Laboratory. **Application Requirements:** Applicants must complete the application form.

3076 ■ MARINE BIOLOGICAL LABORATORY
7 MBL St.
Woods Hole, MA 02543
Tel: (508)548-3705
E-mail: mdonovan@mbl.edu
Web Site: http://www.mbl.edu
To provide support for women students studying at the Marine Biological Laboratory.
Title of Award: Ruth Sager Scholarships **Area, Field, or Subject:** Biology. **Level of Education for which Award is Granted:** Undergraduate **Funds Available:** No specific amount.

Eligibility Requirements: Applicants must be attending a summer course at Marine Biological Laboratory. **Application Requirements:** Applicants must complete the application form.

3077 ■ MARINE BIOLOGICAL LABORATORY
7 MBL St.
Woods Hole, MA 02543
Tel: (508)548-3705
E-mail: mdonovan@mbl.edu
Web Site: http://www.mbl.edu
To provide support for students from Dartmouth College studying at the Marine Biological Laboratory.
Title of Award: Milton L. Shifman Endowed Scholarships **Area, Field, or Subject:** Biology. **Level of Education for which Award is Granted:** Undergraduate **Funds Available:** No specific amount.
Eligibility Requirements: Applicants must be attending a summer course at Marine Biological Laboratory. **Application Requirements:** Applicants must complete the application form.

3078 ■ MARINE BIOLOGICAL LABORATORY
7 MBL St.
Woods Hole, MA 02543
Tel: (508)548-3705
E-mail: mdonovan@mbl.edu
Web Site: http://www.mbl.edu
To provide support for students studying at the Marine Biological Laboratory.
Title of Award: Horace W. Stunkard Scholarships **Area, Field, or Subject:** Biology. **Level of Education for which Award is Granted:** Undergraduate **Funds Available:** No specific amount.
Eligibility Requirements: Applicants must be attending a summer course at Marine Biological Laboratory. **Application Requirements:** Applicants must complete the application form.

3079 ■ MARINE BIOLOGICAL LABORATORY
7 MBL St.
Woods Hole, MA 02543
Tel: (508)548-3705
E-mail: mdonovan@mbl.edu
Web Site: http://www.mbl.edu
To provide support for students studying at the Marine Biological Laboratory in the embryology course.
Title of Award: J.P. Madeline Trinkaus Endowed Scholarships in Embryology **Area, Field, or Subject:** Biology. **Level of Education for which Award is Granted:** Undergraduate **Funds Available:** No specific amount.
Eligibility Requirements: Applicants must be attending a summer course at Marine Biological Laboratory. **Application Requirements:** Applicants must complete the application form.

3080 ■ MARINE BIOLOGICAL LABORATORY
7 MBL St.
Woods Hole, MA 02543
Tel: (508)548-3705
E-mail: mdonovan@mbl.edu
Web Site: http://www.mbl.edu
To provide support for students participating in the microbial diversity course.
Title of Award: Selma A. Waksman Endowed Scholarships in Microbial Diversity **Area, Field, or Subject:** Microbiology. **Level of Education for which Award is Granted:** Undergraduate **Funds Available:** No specific amount.
Eligibility Requirements: Applicants must be attending a summer course at Marine Biological Laboratory. **Application Requirements:** Applicants must complete the application form.

3081 ■ MARINE TECHNOLOGY SOCIETY
5565 Sterrett Pl., Ste. 108
Columbia, MD 21044
Tel: (410)884-5330
Fax: (410)884-9060
E-mail: membership@mtsociety.org
Web Site: http://www.mtsociety.org

To help students achieve success.
Title of Award: Marine Technology Society ROV Scholarships **Area, Field, or Subject:** Marine. **Level of Education for which Award is Granted:** Undergraduate **Funds Available:** $2,000.
Eligibility Requirements: Applicants must be students interested in remotely operated vehicles (ROVs) or underwater work that furthers the use of ROVs. Applicants must be graduate, undergraduate or high school students. **Application Requirements:** Applicants must submit a written recommendation from a current teacher or counselor in a marine-related field; a written letter of reference from someone who is not a teacher or counselor; an official sealed transcript. For high school seniors, proof of acceptance to a two-year or four-year academic program must be submitted. Applicants must submit a biographical sketch including academic, personal and professional goals.

3082 ■ MARINE TECHNOLOGY SOCIETY
5565 Sterrett Pl., Ste. 108
Columbia, MD 21044
Tel: (410)884-5330
Fax: (410)884-9060
E-mail: membership@mtsociety.org
Web Site: http://www.mtsociety.org
To help students achieve success.
Title of Award: Marine Technology Society Scholarships for Graduate and Undergraduate Students **Area, Field, or Subject:** Marine. **Level of Education for which Award is Granted:** Undergraduate **Funds Available:** $2,000.
Eligibility Requirements: Applicants must be a graduate or undergraduate student, enrolled full-time in a marine-related field. **Application Requirements:** Applicants must submit a written recommendation from a current teacher or counselor in a marine-related field; a written letter of reference from someone who is not a teacher or counselor; an official sealed transcript. For high school seniors, proof of acceptance to a two-year or four-year academic program must be submitted. **Additional Information:** scholarships@mtsociety.org.

3083 ■ MARINE TECHNOLOGY SOCIETY
5565 Sterrett Pl., Ste. 108
Columbia, MD 21044
Tel: (410)884-5330
Fax: (410)884-9060
E-mail: membership@mtsociety.org
Web Site: http://www.mtsociety.org
To help students achieve success.
Title of Award: Marine Technology Society Student Scholarships for Graduating High School Seniors **Area, Field, or Subject:** Marine. **Level of Education for which Award is Granted:** Undergraduate **Funds Available:** $2,000.
Eligibility Requirements: Applicants must be high school seniors who have been accepted into a full-time undergraduate program. **Application Requirements:** Applicants must submit a written recommendation from a current teacher or counselor in a marine-related field; a written letter of reference from someone who is not a teacher or counselor; an official sealed transcript; proof of acceptance to a two-year or four-year academic program. **Additional Information:** scholarships@mtsociety.org.

3084 ■ MARINE TECHNOLOGY SOCIETY
5565 Sterrett Pl., Ste. 108
Columbia, MD 21044
Tel: (410)884-5330
Fax: (410)884-9060
E-mail: membership@mtsociety.org
Web Site: http://www.mtsociety.org
To help students achieve success.
Title of Award: Marine Technology Society Student Scholarships for Two-year Technical, Engineering and Community College Students **Area, Field, or Subject:** Marine; Marine Engineering. **Level of Education for which Award is Granted:** Undergraduate **Funds Available:** $2,000.
Eligibility Requirements: Applicants must be enrolled in a two-year technical, engineering or community college in a marine-related field. **Application Requirements:** Applicants must submit a written recommendation from a current teacher or counselor in a marine-related field; a written letter of reference from someone who is not a teacher or counselor; an

official sealed transcript. For high school seniors, proof of acceptance to a two-year or four-year academic program must be submitted. **Additional Information:** scholarships@mtsociety.org.

3085 ■ MARINE TECHNOLOGY SOCIETY
5565 Sterrett Pl., Ste. 108
Columbia, MD 21044
Tel: (410)884-5330
Fax: (410)884-9060
E-mail: membership@mtsociety.org
Web Site: http://www.mtsociety.org
To help students achieve success.
Title of Award: The Paros-Digiquartz Scholarships **Area, Field, or Subject:** Marine. **Level of Education for which Award is Granted:** Undergraduate **Funds Available:** $2,000.
Eligibility Requirements: Applicants must be high school seniors who have been accepted into a full-time undergraduate program, or undergraduate or graduate students. Applicants must have an interest in marine instrumentation. **Application Requirements:** Applicants must submit a written recommendation from a current teacher or counselor in a marine-related field; a written letter of reference from someone who is not a teacher or counselor; an official sealed transcript. For high school seniors, proof of acceptance to a two-year or four-year academic program must be submitted. **Additional Information:** scholarships@mtsociety.org.

3086 ■ MATANUSKA-SUSITNA COLLEGE
PO Box 2889
Palmer, AK 99645
Tel: (907)745-9774
Fax: (907)745-9711
E-mail: info@matsu.alaska.edu
Web Site: http://www.matsu.alaska.edu
To provide financial support for deserving students in Alaska intending to pursue an education in any campus of the University of Alaska.
Title of Award: Alaska Support Industry Alliance Scholarships **Area, Field, or Subject:** Resource management, Biology, Wildlife conservation, management, and science, Petroleum engineering. **Level of Education for which Award is Granted:** Undergraduate **Funds Available:** $500.
Eligibility Requirements: Applicants must be full-time students and Alaska residents who have at least 3.0 GPA majoring in a field that will support the industry growth in Alaska and at the same time showing concern for the environment and how industry is developed. **Application Requirements:** Applicants must complete the application forms available in the website; must attach a personal essay, two letters of recommendation, and their current transcripts. **Deadline for Receipt:** February 15.

3087 ■ PMCA: AN INTERNATIONAL ASSOCIATION OF CONFECTIONERS
2980 Linden St., Ste. E3
Bethlehem, PA 18017
Tel: (610)625-4655
Fax: (610)625-4567
E-mail: info@pmca.com
Web Site: http://www.pmca.com
To foster education students involved in confectionery technology.
Title of Award: AACT Undergraduate Scholarships **Area, Field, or Subject:** Food science and technology; Chemistry; Biology. **Level of Education for which Award is Granted:** Undergraduate **Funds Available:** $5,000 (two $2,500 installments). **Duration:** One year.
Eligibility Requirements: Applicants must be sophomores, juniors or seniors majoring in food science, chemical science, biological science, or related field at an accredited four-year college or university in North America; must have a GPA of 3.0; and must be interested in confectionery technology. **Application Requirements:** Applicants must submit a completed application form together with a letter of recommendation; copy of college transcript; and a list of academic activities, experience, other activities, honors and awards, and a short statement of personal and professional goals. Send materials to Kevin Silva, Warrell Corp. 2150 Slate Hill Road Camp Hill, PA 17011. **Deadline for Receipt:** April 18. **Additional Information:** Kevin Silva, kevins@warrellcorp.com

3088 ■ REDLANDS COMMUNITY SCHOLARSHIP FOUNDATION
c/o Kathleen Venegas-Boge, Admin. Asst.
PO Box 1683
Redlands, CA 92373

Tel: (909)307-9892
Fax: (909)307-9892
Web Site: http://www.redlandsscholarships.org
To encourage educational pursuits among Redlands Unified School District graduates by providing educational assistance.
Title of Award: Friends and Family of Jennifer Balber Scholarships **Area, Field, or Subject:** Marine biology; Oceanography. **Level of Education for which Award is Granted:** Undergraduate **Number Awarded:** 1. **Funds Available:** $500.
Eligibility Requirements: Applicant must be a graduating senior who has a cumulative GPA of 2.5 or higher; must demonstrate financial need; must be involved in school and community activities; must demonstrate strong character and citizenship; and must be pursuing a career in marine biology, oceanography, or a closely-related field. **Application Requirements:** Applicants must submit a completed application form together with the scantron sheet; cover sheet; student activity and community activity sheets; personal essay; and a copy of unofficial transcript (signed by the counselor). **Additional Information:** No electronic submissions of application will be accepted. Submit two printed copies of the application and use a No. 2 pencil on the scantron sheet. **Deadline for Receipt:** February 20.

3089 ■ THE SAN DIEGO FOUNDATION
2508 Historic Decatur Rd., Ste. 200
San Diego, CA 92106
Tel: (619)235-2300
Fax: (619)239-1710
E-mail: info@sdfoundation.org
Web Site: http://www.sdfoundation.org
To support the education of students from California.
Title of Award: Biocom Scholarships **Area, Field, or Subject:** Biology; Chemistry; Biomedical engineering. **Level of Education for which Award is Granted:** Undergraduate **Number Awarded:** 5. **Funds Available:** $1,500. **Duration:** One year.
Eligibility Requirements: Applicant must be a graduating high school senior with a minimum 3.50 GPA on a 4.0 scale; planning to attend an accredited two-year college or four-year university in the U.S.; must demonstrate a likelihood of achieving academic success with primary emphasis in biology, chemistry, physical and computational biosciences or biomedical engineering; committed in serving San Diego life sciences community; maintain a minimum 3.20 cumulative GPA on a 4.0 scale while in college; and exhibit the traits modeled by BIOCOM co-founder, James McGraw (leadership, passion for life sciences, integrity, and community service). **Application Requirements:** Applicants must submit a completed Common Scholarship Application together with personal statement; two letters of recommendation on official letterhead (written within the last six months); official transcript in an official and sealed envelope; and copy of most recent tax form (Form 1040-pages 1 & 2; Form 1040A-pages 1 & 2; Form 1040EZ-page 1). **Additional Information:** In memory of James McGraw. **Deadline for Receipt:** January 28. **Additional Information:** Arzo Mansury, Dir. Scholarships at 619-814-1343, or scholarships@sdfoundation.org.

3090 ■ THE SAN DIEGO FOUNDATION
2508 Historic Decatur Rd., Ste. 200
San Diego, CA 92106
Tel: (619)235-2300
Fax: (619)239-1710
E-mail: info@sdfoundation.org
Web Site: http://www.sdfoundation.org
To support the education of students from California.
Title of Award: Helm Family Scholarships **Area, Field, or Subject:** Biology; Computer and information sciences; Chemistry; Technology; Engineering; Physics. **Level of Education for which Award is Granted:** Undergraduate **Number Awarded:** 2. **Funds Available:** $5,00.
Eligibility Requirements: Applicant must be an entering junior or senior student at San Diego State University or the University of California, San Diego; have declared a major in mathematics or a scientific field such as, but not limited to, biology, computer science, chemistry, technology, engineering, physics, etc.; have a minimum 3.0 GPA on a 4.0 scale; and have demonstrated financial need. **Application Requirements:** Applicants must submit a completed Common Scholarship Application together with personal statement; two letters of recommendation on of-

ficial letterhead (written within the last six months); official transcript in an official and sealed envelope; and a copy of most recent tax form (Form 1040-pages 1 & 2; Form 1040Apages 1 & 2; Form 1040EZ-page 1). **Deadline for Receipt:** January 28. **Additional Information:** Arzo Mansury, Dir. Scholarships at 619-814-1343, or scholarships@sdfoundation.org.

3091 ■ UNIVERSITY OF ALASKA ANCHORAGE
3211 Providence Dr.
Anchorage, AK 99508
Tel: (907)786-1800
Web Site: http://www.uaa.alaska.edu
To provide financial assistance for tuition and other educational expenses to full-time students who are formally admitted to a degreeseeking program in the area of biochemistry, immunology, or microbiology at the University of Alaska Anchorage.
Title of Award: UAA Kris Knudson Memorial Scholarships **Area, Field, or Subject:** Biochemistry; Immunology; Microbiology. **Level of Education for which Award is Granted:** Graduate, Undergraduate **Funds Available:** $500-$885.
Eligibility Requirements: Applicant must demonstrate motivation, academic and leadership potential; must be in good academic standing with a minimum cumulative GPA of 3.0; must be formally admitted to an undergraduate or graduate degree-seeking program in the area of biochemistry, immunology, or microbiology at the University of Alaska Anchorage; must plan on enrolling full-time (12 credits) for undergraduate and (9 credits) for graduate at the University of Alaska Anchorage; must have completed at least fifteen credits in chemistry, biological sciences, and/or natural sciences; must be involved in a research project within the area of biochemistry, immunology, or microbiology; may be a U.S citizen, non-U.S. citizen, Alaska resident, or out-of-state resident; must be enrolled in the semester for which the award is made. **Application Requirements:** Applicants must submit a brief essay (250 words max) describing their involvement in a research project related to biochemistry, immunology, or microbiology. Application forms are available at www.uaa.alaska.edu/scholarships/kris.cfm. **Deadline for Receipt:** February 15.

3092 ■ VIRGINIA FOUNDATION FOR INDEPENDENT COLLEGES
8010 Ridge Rd., Ste. B
Richmond, VA 23229-7288
Tel: (804)288-6609
Free: 800-230-6757
Fax: (804)282-4635
E-mail: info@vfic.org
Web Site: http://www.vfic.org
To provide financial assistance for the students in their junior year at a VFIC college or university.
Title of Award: Phillip Morris USA Scholarships **Area, Field, or Subject:** Accounting; Biology; Business; Chemistry; Computer and information sciences; Economics; Engineering; Finance; Physics. **Level of Education for which Award is Granted:** Undergraduate **Funds Available:** $5,000.
Eligibility Requirements: Applicants must be U.S. citizens and current full-time sophomores attending a VFIC college or university (students from underrepresented populations are encouraged to apply); have minimum of 3.5 cumulative GPA; committed to applying for an internship with Phillip Morris USA for the summer after junior year; have declared, or intend to declare, a major in one of the following disciplines: accounting, biology, business, chemistry, computer science, economics, engineering, finance, or physics. **Application Requirements:** Applicants must submit completed application form along with two letters of recommendation and other required application information. **Deadline for Receipt:** November 1.

Forestry

3093 ■ ALABAMA HORSE COUNCIL
PO Box 260
Morris, AL 35116
800-945-8033
E-mail: info@alabamahorsecouncil.org
Web Site: http://www.alabamahorsecouncil.org

To provide financial assistance for female students.

Title of Award: Ina E. Powell Memorial Scholarships **Area, Field, or Subject:** Agricultural sciences; Forestry; Education--Curricula. **Level of Education for which Award is Granted:** Undergraduate **Funds Available:** $1500.

Eligibility Requirements: Applicants must be female students from Alabama; must be high school seniors accepted at the Auburn University; must be planning to pursue agricultural-related courses at the College of Agriculture, School of Forestry and Wildlife sciences, College of Human Sciences or College of Education; must demonstrate leadership abilities; must have GPA of 3.0 or above; and must be children or grandchildren of ACA members for two consecutive years. **Application Requirements:** Applicants must submit a completed application form. **Deadline for Receipt:** December. **Additional Information:** Martha Davis.

3094 ■ BEN MEADOWS

PO Box 5277
Janesville, WI 53547-5277
800-241-6401
Fax: (608)743-8007
E-mail: mail@benmeadows.com
Web Site: http://www.benmeadows.com
To provide fund for students enrolled in a natural resource program.

Title of Award: Ben Meadows Natural Resource Scholarships - Academic Achievement Scholarships **Area, Field, or Subject:** Forestry; Environmental science; Natural resources; Wildlife conservation, management, and science; Fisheries sciences/management. **Level of Education for which Award is Granted:** Undergraduate **Number Awarded:** 1. **Funds Available:** $2,500.

Eligibility Requirements: Applicant must be a junior or senior student enrolled in a natural resource program working toward a bachelor of arts or science degree, which includes, but not limited to, agro forestry, urban forestry, environmental studies, natural resource management, natural resource recreation, wildlife management, wood science and fisheries management. Student must have a GPA of 3.2 or higher on a 4.0 scale. **Application Requirements:** Applicants must complete the online scholarship application and must provide a letter of recommendation from educational superior (professor, teacher, advisor), and attach official copies of transcripts reflecting the GPA. **Deadline for Receipt:** June 30.

3095 ■ BEN MEADOWS

PO Box 5277
Janesville, WI 53547-5277
800-241-6401
Fax: (608)743-8007
E-mail: mail@benmeadows.com
Web Site: http://www.benmeadows.com
To provide fund for students enrolled in a natural resource program.

Title of Award: Ben Meadows Natural Resource Scholarships - Leadership Scholarships **Area, Field, or Subject:** Forestry; Environmental science; Natural resources; Wildlife conservation, management, and science; Fisheries sciences/management. **Level of Education for which Award is Granted:** Undergraduate **Number Awarded:** 1. **Funds Available:** $2,500.

Eligibility Requirements: Applicant must be a junior or senior student enrolled in a natural resource program working toward a bachelor of arts or science degree, which includes, but not limited to, agro forestry, urban forestry, environmental studies, natural resource management, natural resource recreation, wildlife management, wood science and fisheries management. Student must have a GPA of 2.5 or higher on a 4.0 scale. **Application Requirements:** Applicants must complete the online scholarship application and must provide a letter of recommendation from educational superior (professor, teacher, advisor), and attach official copies of transcripts reflecting the GPA. **Deadline for Receipt:** June 30.

3096 ■ COMPOSITE PANEL ASSOCIATION

19465 Deerfield Ave., Ste. 306
Leesburg, VA 20176
Tel: (703)724-1128
Fax: (703)724-1588
Web Site: http://www.pbmdf.com
To provide financial assistance to students pursuing a career in the composite panel and affiliated industries.

Title of Award: Robert E. Dougherty Scholarships **Area, Field, or Subject:** Forestry; Chemistry; Engineering. **Level of Education for which Award is Granted:** Undergraduate **Number Awarded:** 8. **Funds Available:** 5,000.

Eligibility Requirements: Applicant must be North American citizen; and nominated by a member of the Robert E. Dougherty Education Foundation. **Application Requirements:** Scholarship Application forms can be downloaded at the website and must be filled out and returned to the Foundation. **Deadline for Receipt:** March 21.

3097 ■ FOUNDATION FOR ENHANCING COMMUNITIES

200 N Third St., PO Box 678
Harrisburg, PA 17108-0678
Tel: (717)236-5040
Fax: (717)231-4463
E-mail: dawn@tfec.org
Web Site: http://www.ghf.org
To assist Susquenita High School students with their college expenses in the field of Forestry and/or Agriculture with an emphasis in forestry.

Title of Award: Dr. Harry V. Pfautz Memorial Scholarship Fund **Area, Field, or Subject:** Forestry. **Level of Education for which Award is Granted:** Undergraduate **Funds Available:** No specific amount.

Eligibility Requirements: Applicants must be graduating senior students of Susquenita High School who have a GPA of 2.5 on a 4.0 point scale. **Application Requirements:** Applicants must complete the attached form and requested supporting documents and send to the foundation. The supporting documents include: official transcript of the complete high school record, including GPA, through the first half of final year, on which the raised school seal is imprinted; list of extracurricular or non-academic activities; and reference letter. **Deadline for Receipt:** April 10. **Additional Information:** Dawn Morris, Program Officer at the above address.

3098 ■ HARTFORD FOUNDATION FOR PUBLIC GIVING

10 Columbus Blvd., 8th Flr.
Hartford, CT 06106
Tel: (860)548-1888
Fax: (860)524-8346
E-mail: hfpg@hfpg.org
Web Site: http://www.hfpg.org
To award scholarship to the students of Connecticut.

Title of Award: James L. and Genevieve H. Goodwin Scholarships **Area, Field, or Subject:** Forestry. **Level of Education for which Award is Granted:** Undergraduate **Number Awarded:** 5-10. **Funds Available:** $1,000-$5,000.

Eligibility Requirements: Applicants must be enrolled in an undergraduate or graduate curriculum in silviculture or forest resource management. **Application Requirements:** Applicants may complete the General Scholarship Application and include a personal statement indicating why you are interested in Forest Management and submit to Connecticut forest and Park Association, Inc. **Deadline for Receipt:** March 20. **Additional Information:** Adam Moore, Executive Dir., 16 Meriden Rd. Rockfall, CT 06481. Phone: 860-346-2372 Fax: 860-347-7463; info@ctwoodlands.org.

3099 ■ THE WASHINGTON GROUP

720 Park Blvd.
PO Box 73
Boise, ID 83729
Tel: (208)386-5000
E-mail: membership@washingtongroup.org
Web Site: http://www.wgint.com
To encourage active participation in Ukrainian community.

Title of Award: Chopivsky Fellowships **Area, Field, or Subject:** Forestry; Environmental Studies; Economics. **Level of Education for which Award is Granted:** Undergraduate **Number Awarded:** 2. **Funds Available:** No specific amount.

Eligibility Requirements: Applicants must be Ukrainian citizens and must be first admitted to the appropriate faculties at Yale; must be in graduate degree program leading to master's degree at the Yale School of Management at the Yale School of Forestry and Environmental Studies, and in the Departments of International Relations, International Economics, and Developmental Studies. **Application Requirements:** Applicants must fill out the application form and supporting materials. **Deadline for**

Receipt: January 1. **Additional Information:** PO Box 208206, New Haven, CT 06520-8606; 1203-432-3423; 12034325963.

Horticulture

3100 ■ AMERICAN CONIFER SOCIETY
175 Charisma Ln.
Lewisville, NC 27023-9611
Tel: (336)945-0483
Fax: (336)945-0484
E-mail: nationaloffice@conifersociety.org
Web Site: http://conifersociety.org
To provide financial assistance to ACS members to pursue their education.
Title of Award: American Conifer Society Scholarships **Area, Field, or Subject:** Horticulture. **Level of Education for which Award is Granted:** Undergraduate **Funds Available:** $1,000.
Eligibility Requirements: Applicant must be a current ACS member. **Application Requirements:** Application form may be downloaded from The American Conifer Society Web Page; www.conifersociety.org or you may request a form from; The American Conifer Society Scholarship Committee, 900 Winston Rd. N., Rochester, NY 14609. Forms are also available from the National Office. **Deadline for Receipt:** April 30.

3101 ■ AMERICAN FLORAL ENDOWMENT
1601 Duke St.
Alexandria, VA 22314
Tel: (703)838-5211
Fax: (703)838-5212
E-mail: afe@endowment.org
Web Site: http://endowment.org
To further the advancement of education and science in the floriculture and environmental horticulture field by funding research and studies and financing scholarships and other educational activities for individuals interested in the field.
Title of Award: American Floral Endowment Scholarships **Area, Field, or Subject:** Horticulture. **Level of Education for which Award is Granted:** Undergraduate **Funds Available:** Maximum of $2,000.
Eligibility Requirements: Applicants must be pursuing a career in a horticulture-related field; must have a minimum of 3.0 GPA; must be residents of the United States or Canada. **Application Requirements:** Applicants must send a completed online application form; must submit two letters of recommendations and a transcript of records. **Deadline for Receipt:** May 1. **Additional Information:** afe@endowment.org.

3102 ■ AMERICAN FLORAL ENDOWMENT
1601 Duke St.
Alexandria, VA 22314
Tel: (703)838-5211
Fax: (703)838-5212
E-mail: afe@endowment.org
Web Site: http://endowment.org
To further the advancement of education and science in the floriculture and environmental horticulture field by funding research and studies and financing scholarships and other educational activities for individuals interested in the field.
Title of Award: Ball Horticultural Company Scholarships **Area, Field, or Subject:** Horticulture. **Level of Education for which Award is Granted:** Undergraduate **Funds Available:** No specific amount.
Eligibility Requirements: Applicants must be students currently enrolled in their third to fifth year of college; must be pursuing a career in commercial floriculture. **Application Requirements:** Applicants must send a completed online application form; must submit two letters of recommendation and transcript of records.

3103 ■ AMERICAN FLORAL ENDOWMENT
1601 Duke St.
Alexandria, VA 22314
Tel: (703)838-5211
Fax: (703)838-5212
E-mail: afe@endowment.org
Web Site: http://endowment.org
To further the advancement of education and science in the floriculture and environmental horticulture field by funding research and studies and financing scholarships and other educational activities for individuals interested in the field; to assure continuance of practical experience opportunities.
Title of Award: Vic and Margaret Ball Student Intern Scholarships **Area, Field, or Subject:** Horticulture. **Level of Education for which Award is Granted:** Undergraduate **Funds Available:** varies. **Duration:** Maximum of six months.
Eligibility Requirements: Applicants must be full-time undergraduate students who are currently enrolled in a floriculture/environmental horticulture program at a two or four year college/university within the United States; must be U.S. citizens; must maintain "C" or better GPA with satisfactory progress in a degree or certificate program. **Application Requirements:** Applicants must submit a completed and signed application form, official transcript from all institutions attended, a statement explaining the reasons for applying and future career goals, a letter of recommendation and endorsement by a faculty member. Applicants must submit a 500 word report evaluating the experience within 30 days of completing the program; pictures of the student working at the intern location must be included. Applicants must have permission to interrupt studies for the length of the training period. **Deadline for Receipt:** March 1 and October 1.

3104 ■ AMERICAN FLORAL ENDOWMENT
1601 Duke St.
Alexandria, VA 22314
Tel: (703)838-5211
Fax: (703)838-5212
E-mail: afe@endowment.org
Web Site: http://endowment.org
To further the advancement of education and science in the floriculture and environmental horticulture field by funding research and studies and financing scholarships and other educational activities for individuals interested in the field.
Title of Award: Harold Bettinger Scholarships **Area, Field, or Subject:** Horticulture. **Level of Education for which Award is Granted:** Undergraduate **Funds Available:** No specific amount.
Eligibility Requirements: Applicants must be sophomore or graduate students pursuing a career in business and/or marketing with the intent to apply it to a horticulture-related business. **Application Requirements:** Applicants must send a completed online application form; must submit two letters of recommendation and transcript of records.

3105 ■ AMERICAN FLORAL ENDOWMENT
1601 Duke St.
Alexandria, VA 22314
Tel: (703)838-5211
Fax: (703)838-5212
E-mail: afe@endowment.org
Web Site: http://endowment.org
To further the advancement of education and science in the floriculture and environmental horticulture field by funding research and studies and financing scholarships and other educational activities for individuals interested in the field.
Title of Award: Leonard Bettinger Scholarships **Area, Field, or Subject:** Horticulture. **Level of Education for which Award is Granted:** Undergraduate **Funds Available:** No specific amount.
Eligibility Requirements: Applicants must be vocational students in a one or two-year program who intend to become growers or greenhouse managers. **Application Requirements:** Applicants must send a completed online application form; must submit two letters of recommendation and transcript of records.

3106 ■ AMERICAN FLORAL ENDOWMENT
1601 Duke St.
Alexandria, VA 22314
Tel: (703)838-5211
Fax: (703)838-5212
E-mail: afe@endowment.org
Web Site: http://endowment.org
To further the advancement of education and science in the floriculture and environmental horticulture field by funding research and studies and

financing scholarships and other educational activities for individuals interested in the field.
Title of Award: James Bridenbaugh Memorial Scholarship **Area, Field, or Subject:** Horticulture. **Level of Education for which Award is Granted:** Undergraduate **Funds Available:** No specific amount.
Eligibility Requirements: Applicants must be sophomore to fifth-year students pursuing a career in floral design and marketing fresh flowers and plants. **Application Requirements:** Applicants must send a completed online application form; must submit two letters of recommendation and transcript of records.

3107 ■ AMERICAN FLORAL ENDOWMENT
1601 Duke St.
Alexandria, VA 22314
Tel: (703)838-5211
Fax: (703)838-5212
E-mail: afe@endowment.org
Web Site: http://endowment.org
To further the advancement of education and science in the floriculture and environmental horticulture field by funding research and studies and financing scholarships and other educational activities for individuals interested in the field.
Title of Award: John Carew Memorial Scholarships **Area, Field, or Subject:** Horticulture. **Level of Education for which Award is Granted:** Undergraduate **Funds Available:** No specific amount.
Eligibility Requirements: Applicants must be graduate students with an interest in greenhouse crops. **Application Requirements:** Applicants must send a completed online application form; must submit two letters of recommendation and transcript of records.

3108 ■ AMERICAN FLORAL ENDOWMENT
1601 Duke St.
Alexandria, VA 22314
Tel: (703)838-5211
Fax: (703)838-5212
E-mail: afe@endowment.org
Web Site: http://endowment.org
To further the advancement of education and science in the floriculture and environmental horticulture field by funding research and studies and financing scholarships and other educational activities for individuals interested in the field.
Title of Award: Earl Deadman Memorial Scholarships **Area, Field, or Subject:** Horticulture. **Level of Education for which Award is Granted:** Undergraduate **Funds Available:** No specific amount.
Eligibility Requirements: Applicants must be sophomore to fifth-year students who plan to become greenhouse growers; must be from the Northwestern area of the U.S. **Application Requirements:** Applicants must send a completed online application form; must submit two letters of recommendation and transcript of records.

3109 ■ AMERICAN FLORAL ENDOWMENT
1601 Duke St.
Alexandria, VA 22314
Tel: (703)838-5211
Fax: (703)838-5212
E-mail: afe@endowment.org
Web Site: http://endowment.org
To further the advancement of education and science in the floriculture and environmental horticulture field by funding research and studies and financing scholarships and other educational activities for individuals interested in the field.
Title of Award: Dosatron International Inc. Scholarships **Area, Field, or Subject:** Horticulture. **Level of Education for which Award is Granted:** Undergraduate **Funds Available:** No specific amount.
Eligibility Requirements: Applicants must be third to fifth year students who are interested in floriculture production and plan to work in the greenhouse environment. **Application Requirements:** Applicants must send a completed online application form; must submit two letters of recommendation and transcript of records.

3110 ■ AMERICAN FLORAL ENDOWMENT
1601 Duke St.
Alexandria, VA 22314

Tel: (703)838-5211
Fax: (703)838-5212
E-mail: afe@endowment.org
Web Site: http://endowment.org
To further the advancement of education and science in the floriculture and environmental horticulture field by funding research and studies and financing scholarships and other educational activities for individuals interested in the field.
Title of Award: Paris Fracasso Production Floriculture Scholarships **Area, Field, or Subject:** Horticulture. **Level of Education for which Award is Granted:** Undergraduate **Funds Available:** No specific amount.
Eligibility Requirements: Applicants must be third to fifth year students who plan to work in floriculture production. **Application Requirements:** Applicants must send a completed online application form; must submit two letters of recommendation and transcript of records.

3111 ■ AMERICAN FLORAL ENDOWMENT
1601 Duke St.
Alexandria, VA 22314
Tel: (703)838-5211
Fax: (703)838-5212
E-mail: afe@endowment.org
Web Site: http://endowment.org
To further the advancement of education and science in the floriculture and environmental horticulture field by funding research and studies and financing scholarships and other educational activities for individuals interested in the field.
Title of Award: John Holden Vocational Scholarships **Area, Field, or Subject:** Horticulture. **Level of Education for which Award is Granted:** Undergraduate **Funds Available:** No specific amount.
Eligibility Requirements: Applicants must be vocational students in a one or two-year program who intend to become growers or greenhouse managers. **Application Requirements:** Applicants must send a completed online application form; must submit two letters of recommendation and transcript of records.

3112 ■ AMERICAN FLORAL ENDOWMENT
1601 Duke St.
Alexandria, VA 22314
Tel: (703)838-5211
Fax: (703)838-5212
E-mail: afe@endowment.org
Web Site: http://endowment.org
To further the advancement of education and science in the floriculture and environmental horticulture field by funding research and studies and financing scholarships and other educational activities for individuals interested in the field.
Title of Award: Ed Markham International Scholarships **Area, Field, or Subject:** Horticulture. **Level of Education for which Award is Granted:** Undergraduate **Funds Available:** No specific amount.
Eligibility Requirements: Applicants must be sophomore to graduate students pursuing a career in horticulture marketing through international travel. **Application Requirements:** Applicants must send a completed online application form; must submit two letters of recommendation and transcript of records.

3113 ■ AMERICAN FLORAL ENDOWMENT
1601 Duke St.
Alexandria, VA 22314
Tel: (703)838-5211
Fax: (703)838-5212
E-mail: afe@endowment.org
Web Site: http://endowment.org
To provide quality professional training for selected, motivated floriculture and environmental horticulture students.
Title of Award: Mossmiller Student Intern Scholarships Program **Area, Field, or Subject:** Horticulture. **Level of Education for which Award is Granted:** Undergraduate **Funds Available:** $2,000.
Eligibility Requirements: Applicants must be full-time undergraduate students who are currently enrolled in a recognized floriculture/ environmental horticulture or business program at a two or four year college or university in the U.S.; must maintain a "C" average with satisfac-

tory progress in a degree or certificate program. **Application Requirements:** Applicants must submit: completed and signed application form; official transcript from all institutions attended; a statement explaining the reasons for applying and future career goals; a letter of recommendation and endorsement by a faculty member. Applicants must submit a 500 word report evaluating the experience within 30 days of completing the program; pictures of the student working at the intern location must be included. Applicants must have permission to interrupt studies for the length of the training period. **Deadline for Receipt:** March 1 and October 1.

3114 ■ AMERICAN FLORAL ENDOWMENT
1601 Duke St.
Alexandria, VA 22314
Tel: (703)838-5211
Fax: (703)838-5212
E-mail: afe@endowment.org
Web Site: http://endowment.org
To further the advancement of education and science in the floriculture and environmental horticulture field by funding research and studies and financing scholarships and other educational activities for individuals interested in the field.
Title of Award: National Greenhouse Manufacturers Association Scholarships **Area, Field, or Subject:** Horticulture. **Level of Education for which Award is Granted:** Undergraduate **Funds Available:** No specific amount.
Eligibility Requirements: Applicants must be junior, senior or graduate students pursuing a career in horticulture and bio-engineering or the equivalent at a four-year college. **Application Requirements:** Applicants must send a completed online application form; must submit two letters of recommendation and transcript of records.

3115 ■ AMERICAN FLORAL ENDOWMENT
1601 Duke St.
Alexandria, VA 22314
Tel: (703)838-5211
Fax: (703)838-5212
E-mail: afe@endowment.org
Web Site: http://endowment.org
To further the advancement of education and science in the floriculture and environmental horticulture field by funding research and studies and financing scholarships and other educational activities for individuals interested in the field.
Title of Award: Mike and Flo Novovesky Scholarships **Area, Field, or Subject:** Horticulture. **Level of Education for which Award is Granted:** Undergraduate **Funds Available:** No specific amount.
Eligibility Requirements: Applicants must be second year to graduating married students with a GPA of 2.5 or higher. **Application Requirements:** Applicants must send a completed online application form; must submit two letters of recommendation and transcript of records.

3116 ■ AMERICAN FLORAL ENDOWMENT
1601 Duke St.
Alexandria, VA 22314
Tel: (703)838-5211
Fax: (703)838-5212
E-mail: afe@endowment.org
Web Site: http://endowment.org
To further the advancement of education and science in the floriculture and environmental horticulture field by funding research and studies and financing scholarships and other educational activities for individuals interested in the field.
Title of Award: Lawrence "Bud" Ohlman Memorial Scholarships **Area, Field, or Subject:** Horticulture. **Level of Education for which Award is Granted:** Undergraduate **Funds Available:** No specific amount.
Eligibility Requirements: Applicant must be in his or her third to final year in college, with a career goal to become a bedding plant grower for an established business. **Application Requirements:** Applicants must send a completed online application form; must submit two letters of recommendation and transcript of records.

3117 ■ AMERICAN FLORAL ENDOWMENT
1601 Duke St.
Alexandria, VA 22314

Tel: (703)838-5211
Fax: (703)838-5212
E-mail: afe@endowment.org
Web Site: http://endowment.org
To further the advancement of education and science in the floriculture and environmental horticulture field by funding research and studies and financing scholarships and other educational activities for individuals interested in the field.
Title of Award: Jim Perry Vocational Scholarships **Area, Field, or Subject:** Horticulture. **Level of Education for which Award is Granted:** Undergraduate **Funds Available:** No specific amount.
Eligibility Requirements: Applicant must be a vocational student in a one or two-year program with the intent of becoming a grower or greenhouse manager. **Application Requirements:** Applicants must send a completed online application form; must submit two letters of recommendation and transcript of records.

3118 ■ AMERICAN FLORAL ENDOWMENT
1601 Duke St.
Alexandria, VA 22314
Tel: (703)838-5211
Fax: (703)838-5212
E-mail: afe@endowment.org
Web Site: http://endowment.org
To further the advancement of education and science in the floriculture and environmental horticulture field by funding research and studies and financing scholarships and other educational activities for individuals interested in the field.
Title of Award: James K. Rathmell Jr. Scholarships **Area, Field, or Subject:** Horticulture. **Level of Education for which Award is Granted:** Undergraduate **Funds Available:** No specific amount.
Eligibility Requirements: Applicants must be in their third to final year of undergraduate studies or be graduate students; must plan to work or study outside of the United States. **Application Requirements:** Applicants must send a completed online application form; must submit two letters of recommendation, transcript of records, and specific plan for horticulture work/study outside of the USA.

3119 ■ AMERICAN FLORAL ENDOWMENT
1601 Duke St.
Alexandria, VA 22314
Tel: (703)838-5211
Fax: (703)838-5212
E-mail: afe@endowment.org
Web Site: http://endowment.org
To further the advancement of education and science in the floriculture and environmental horticulture field by funding research and studies and financing scholarships and other educational activities for individuals interested in the field.
Title of Award: Seed Companies Scholarships **Area, Field, or Subject:** Horticulture. **Level of Education for which Award is Granted:** Undergraduate **Funds Available:** No specific amount.
Eligibility Requirements: Applicants must be third to final year or graduate students who are pursuing a career in the seed industry in sales, breeding, research or marketing. **Application Requirements:** Applicants must send a completed online application form; must submit two letters of recommendation and transcript of records.

3120 ■ AMERICAN FLORAL ENDOWMENT
1601 Duke St.
Alexandria, VA 22314
Tel: (703)838-5211
Fax: (703)838-5212
E-mail: afe@endowment.org
Web Site: http://endowment.org
To further the advancement of education and science in the floriculture and environmental horticulture field by funding research and studies and financing scholarships and other educational activities for individuals interested in the field.
Title of Award: John Tomasovic, Sr. Scholarships **Area, Field, or Subject:** Horticulture. **Level of Education for which Award is Granted:** Undergraduate **Funds Available:** No specific amount.
Eligibility Requirements: Applicants must be in their second to final year in college and pursuing a career in a horticulture-related field; must have

3.0-3.5 GPA. **Application Requirements:** Applicants must send a completed online application form; must submit two letters of recommendation and transcript of records.

3121 ■ AMERICAN FLORAL ENDOWMENT
1601 Duke St.
Alexandria, VA 22314
Tel: (703)838-5211
Fax: (703)838-5212
E-mail: afe@endowment.org
Web Site: http://endowment.org
To further the advancement of education and science in the floriculture and environmental horticulture field by funding research and studies and financing scholarships and other educational activities for individuals interested in the field.
Title of Award: Edward Tuinier Memorial Scholarships **Area, Field, or Subject:** Horticulture. **Level of Education for which Award is Granted:** Undergraduate **Funds Available:** No specific amount.
Eligibility Requirements: Applicants must be in their second to final year in a floriculture program at Michigan State University. **Application Requirements:** Applicants must send a completed online application form; must submit two letters of recommendation and transcript of records.

3122 ■ AMERICAN FLORAL ENDOWMENT
1601 Duke St.
Alexandria, VA 22314
Tel: (703)838-5211
Fax: (703)838-5212
E-mail: afe@endowment.org
Web Site: http://endowment.org
To further the advancement of education and science in the floriculture and environmental horticulture field by funding research and studies and financing scholarships and other educational activities for individuals interested in the field.
Title of Award: Jacob VanNamen-Vans Marketing Scholarships **Area, Field, or Subject:** Horticulture. **Level of Education for which Award is Granted:** Undergraduate **Funds Available:** No specific amount.
Eligibility Requirements: Applicants must be in their second to final year in college; must be interested in agribusiness marketing and distribution of floral products. **Application Requirements:** Applicants must send a completed online application form; must submit two letters of recommendation and transcript of records.

3123 ■ AMERICAN FLORAL ENDOWMENT
1601 Duke St.
Alexandria, VA 22314
Tel: (703)838-5211
Fax: (703)838-5212
E-mail: afe@endowment.org
Web Site: http://endowment.org
To further the advancement of education and science in the floriculture and environmental horticulture field by funding research and studies and financing scholarships and other educational activities for individuals interested in the field.
Title of Award: Western Michigan Greenhouse Association Scholarships **Area, Field, or Subject:** Horticulture. **Level of Education for which Award is Granted:** Undergraduate **Funds Available:** No specific amount.
Eligibility Requirements: Applicants must be in their second to final year in a Michigan college; must be studying commercial horticulture. **Application Requirements:** Applicants must send a completed online application form; must submit two letters of recommendation and transcript of records.

3124 ■ AMERICAN SOCIETY FOR HORTICULTURAL SCIENCE
113 SW St., Ste. 200
Alexandria, VA 22314-2851
Tel: (703)836-4606
Fax: (703)836-2024
E-mail: webmaster@ashs.org
Web Site: http://www.ashs.org
To provide financial assistance to students in the area of horticulture.

Title of Award: American Society for Horticultural Science Student Travel Grants **Area, Field, or Subject:** General studies. **Level of Education for which Award is Granted:** Graduate, Undergraduate **Number Awarded:** Varies. **Funds Available:** $500 (domestic graduate and undergraduate students); $750 (international students). **Duration:** One year.
Eligibility Requirements: Applicants must be enrolled in horticultural science as a major course of study and must have submitted an abstract title or complete abstract for presentation at the ASHS Annual Conference. **Application Requirements:** Applicants must accomplish application and abstract. Application forms and instructions are available at the website. **Deadline for Receipt:** March 4. **Additional Information:** ASHS Headquarters, 113 S West St., Ste. 200, Alexandria, VA 22314-2851, phone: 703-836-4606; fax: 703-836-2024.

3125 ■ AMERICAN SOCIETY FOR HORTICULTURAL SCIENCE
113 SW St., Ste. 200
Alexandria, VA 22314-2851
Tel: (703)836-4606
Fax: (703)836-2024
E-mail: webmaster@ashs.org
Web Site: http://www.ashs.org
To provide financial assistance to students in the area of horticulture who are attending the ASHS Annual Conference.
Title of Award: ASHS Industry Division Student Travel Grants **Area, Field, or Subject:** Horticulture. **Level of Education for which Award is Granted:** Graduate, Undergraduate **Funds Available:** $750. **Duration:** One year.
Eligibility Requirements: Award is open to all undergraduate and graduate Horticulture students. **Application Requirements:** Applicants must submit transcripts, completed application, letter of recommendation from undergraduate advisor or faculty member, and a 500-word essay outlining interest in horticulture and career goals.

3126 ■ AMERICAN SOCIETY FOR HORTICULTURAL SCIENCE
113 SW St., Ste. 200
Alexandria, VA 22314-2851
Tel: (703)836-4606
Fax: (703)836-2024
E-mail: webmaster@ashs.org
Web Site: http://www.ashs.org
To recognize and support scholastic achievement and to encourage career development in horticultural science at the undergraduate level.
Title of Award: ASHS Scholars Awards **Area, Field, or Subject:** Horticulture. **Level of Education for which Award is Granted:** Undergraduate **Number Awarded:** 2. **Funds Available:** $1,500.
Eligibility Requirements: Applicant must be an undergraduate student of any class standing at the time of the application; must be registered as a full-time student (minimum 10 credit hours) and actively pursuing a degree in horticulture. **Application Requirements:** Applicants must be nominated by the chair/head of the department in which they are majoring; must submit completed application supported by a 250-500 essay, complete resume, three letters of reference, and official university/college transcripts. Forms and information are available at the website. **Deadline for Receipt:** February 4. **Additional Information:** Mary McGuire, email: mmcguire@ashs.org.

3127 ■ AMERICAN SOCIETY OF LANDSCAPE ARCHITECTS
636 Eye St. NW
Washington, DC 20001-3736
Tel: (202)898-2444; 888-999-2752
Fax: (202)898-1185
E-mail: dsaunders@asla.org
Web Site: http://www.asla.org
To assist undergraduate or graduate students enrolled in programs in landscape architecture and ornamental horticulture in California.
Title of Award: Class Fund Ornamental Horticulture Scholarship Program **Area, Field, or Subject:** Landscape architecture; Horticulture. **Level of Education for which Award is Granted:** Undergraduate **Number Awarded:** 1. **Funds Available:** $3,000.
Eligibility Requirements: Applicants must be undergraduate or graduate students in financial need who show promise and commitment to the profession; must be continuing their studies in landscape architecture or ornamental horticulture. **Application Requirements:** Applicants must

submit a 300-word statement on the profession; 100-word statement indicating intended use of funds; two letters of recommendation from the faculty; and one confidential letter of recommendation from the department head. **Deadline for Receipt:** February 15.

3128 ■ ARIZONA NURSERY ASSOCIATION
1430 W. Broadway, Ste. 110
Tempe, AZ 85282
Tel: (480)966-1610
Fax: (480)966-0923
E-mail: info@azna.org
Web Site: http://www.azna.org
To promote and advance the nursery industry for its members and the public they serve.
Title of Award: Arizona Nursery Association Scholarships **Area, Field, or Subject:** Horticulture. **Level of Education for which Award is Granted:** Undergraduate **Funds Available:** $500-$3,000.
Eligibility Requirements: Applicants must be residents of Arizona currently or planning to be enrolled in a horticultural-related curriculum at a university, community college or continuing education program; must be currently employed in or have an interest in the nursery industry as a career; must have above-average scholastic achievement or at least two years work experience in the industry; must display involvement in extracurricular activities related to industry. **Application Requirements:** Applicants must complete the online application form. **Deadline for Receipt:** April 15. **Additional Information:** 480-966-1610.

3129 ■ CALIFORNIA WATERFOWL ASSOCIATION
4630 Northgate Blvd., Ste. 150
Sacramento, CA 95834
Tel: (916)648-1406
Fax: (916)648-1665
E-mail: cwa@calwaterfowl.org
Web Site: http://www.calwaterfowl.org
To provide field experience a training in the tools, methods, concepts of waterfowl, wetlands research and management.
Title of Award: Dennis Raveling Scholarships **Area, Field, or Subject:** Wildlife conservation, management and sciences; Zoology; Botany; Ecology. **Level of Education for which Award is Granted:** Undergraduate **Number Awarded:** 2. **Funds Available:** $2,000 for first place; $1,000 for 2nd place.
Eligibility Requirements: Applicants must be students with a desire to pursue a career in waterfowl or wetlands ecology. **Application Requirements:** Applicants must submit a "one-page" proposal summary description on an original research or management project; must submit a detailed proposal if required or "one-page" statement explaining the course of study for which they need to support. **Deadline for Receipt:** October 31. **Additional Information:** Nocole Berset at the above address.

3130 ■ THE COMMUNITY FOUNDATION OF MIDDLE TENNESSEE
3833 Cleghorn Ave., Ste. 400
Nashville, TN 37215-2519
Tel: (615)321-4939; 888-540-5200
E-mail: mail@cfmt.org
Web Site: http://www.cfmt.org
To help students in planning their postsecondary education.
Title of Award: Howard A. Clark Horticulture Scholarships **Area, Field, or Subject:** Horticulture. **Level of Education for which Award is Granted:** Undergraduate **Funds Available:** No specific amount.
Eligibility Requirements: Applicants must be graduating seniors from Avery County High School, North Carolina, attending a two or four-year college to study horticulture or agriculture. Applicants must have at least a 2.5 GPA in high school. **Application Requirements:** Applicants must complete the application form. Applicants must submit two applicant appraisals; transcript of grades; student essay describing educational plans and how these will help in career goals. Applicants must submit one recent photograph. **Deadline for Receipt:** March 15. **Additional Information:** pcole@cfmt.org

3131 ■ FLORIDA NURSERY, GROWERS, AND LANDSCAPE ASSOCIATION
1533 Park Center Dr.
Orlando, FL 32835-5705

Tel: (407)295-7994
Free: 800-375-3642
Fax: (407)295-1619
E-mail: info@fngla.org
Web Site: http://www.fngla.org
To encourage students to pursue careers in Florida's horticulture industry and related pursuits by providing financial assistance for undergraduate, post-graduate, or other advanced education programs in Florida.
Title of Award: James H. Davis Scholarships **Area, Field, or Subject:** Horticulture. **Level of Education for which Award is Granted:** Undergraduate **Funds Available:** No specific amount.
Eligibility Requirements: Applicants must be incoming college freshmen, sophomores, juniors, seniors and/or graduate students planning to attend a community college, college or university in the state of Florida; must be full-time students in horticulture program or related field with the intent to graduate in the field; must have a 2.0 or above GPA. **Application Requirements:** Applicants must complete the application form; must submit a high school or college transcript; an essay and two letters of recommendation.

3132 ■ FOUNDATION FOR ENHANCING COMMUNITIES
200 N Third St., PO Box 678
Harrisburg, PA 17108-0678
Tel: (717)236-5040
Fax: (717)231-4463
E-mail: dawn@tfec.org
Web Site: http://www.ghf.org
To encourage and recognize two senior students from the Mechanicsburg Area School District who demonstrate good citizenship.
Title of Award: Bertha and Byron L. Reppert Scholarship Fund **Area, Field, or Subject:** Political science; Horticulture. **Level of Education for which Award is Granted:** Undergraduate **Funds Available:** No specific amount.
Eligibility Requirements: Applicants must have an interest in political science or horticulture; must be in the top one-third of the graduating class; must be accepted to an accredited college or university; must demonstrate good citizenship within the school and local community; and must complete an essay explaining how they meet the criteria. **Application Requirements:** Application form can be obtained online. Applicants must attach the following documents: official transcript of the complete high school/college record, including GPA, through the first half of the present year, with the raised school seal imprinted; list of extracurricular or non-academic activities; FAFSA Student Aid Report; and an essay describing how they meet the eligibility criteria of this scholarship. **Deadline for Receipt:** March 1. **Additional Information:** Dawn Morris, Program Officer at the above address.

3133 ■ GARDEN CLUB OF AMERICA
14 East 60th St., 3rd Fl.
New York, NY 10022
Tel: (212)753-8287
Fax: (212)753-0134
Web Site: http://www.gcamerica.org
To provide financial assistance to students who wish to pursue study of horticulture and related field.
Title of Award: Katherine M. Grosscup Scholarships **Area, Field, or Subject:** Horticulture. **Level of Education for which Award is Granted:** Graduate, Undergraduate **Number Awarded:** varies. **Funds Available:** $3,000.
Eligibility Requirements: Applicants must be current college sophomores, juniors, seniors or master's degree candidates majoring in horticulture. **Application Requirements:** Applicants must submit a completed application form; one letter of recommendation; transcript of college record. **Deadline for Receipt:** January.

3134 ■ GRAND HAVEN AREA COMMUNITY FOUNDATION
1 S. Harbor Dr.
Grand Haven, MI 49417
Tel: (616)842-6378
Fax: (616)842-9518
E-mail: bpost@ghacf.org
Web Site: http://www.ghacf.org

To assist graduating high school seniors and currently enrolled college students to pursue a horticulture or green industry career.

Title of Award: West Michigan Nursery and Landscape Association Scholarships Fund **Area, Field, or Subject:** Horticulture. **Level of Education for which Award is Granted:** Undergraduate **Funds Available:** No specific amount.

Eligibility Requirements: Applicants must be graduating high school seniors or currently enrolled college students planning to pursue a horticulture or green industry career at a two-or-four-year college or university; must be residents of Ottawa, Oceana, Newaygo, Muskegon or Allegan Counties. **Application Requirements:** Applicants must submit: completed application form; current high school or college transcript; Student Aid Report (SAR) from the Free Application for Federal Student Aid (FAFSA), unless applying for scholarships that do not consider financial need; and letter of recommendation. **Deadline for Receipt:** March 7. **Additional Information:** 616-842-6378.

3135 ■ THE GREATER TACOMA COMMUNITY FOUNDATION

PO Box 1995
Tacoma, WA 98401
Tel: (253)383-5622
Web Site: http://www.tacomafoundation.org
To foster generosity by connecting people who care with causes that matter; to benefit Washington State University Puyallup Research and Extension Center graduates, undergraduate students or a Pierce County high school student.

Title of Award: The Master Gardeners of Pierce County Scholarships **Area, Field, or Subject:** Horticulture. **Level of Education for which Award is Granted:** Undergraduate **Funds Available:** No specific amount.

Eligibility Requirements: Applicants must plan to study horticulture or the environment. **Application Requirements:** Applicants must contact W.S.U. Puyallup Research and Extension Center Scholarship Committee for application form. **Additional Information:** 7612 Pioneer Way E Puyallup, WA 98371-4998 or 253-445-4500.

3136 ■ HARTFORD FOUNDATION FOR PUBLIC GIVING

10 Columbus Blvd., 8th Flr.
Hartford, CT 06106
Tel: (860)548-1888
Fax: (860)524-8346
E-mail: hfpg@hfpg.org
Web Site: http://www.hfpg.org
To provide scholarship to students attending the University of Connecticut.

Title of Award: Ratcliffe Hicks School of Agriculture Heritage Scholarships **Area, Field, or Subject:** Animal science and behavior; Horticulture; Turfgrass management. **Level of Education for which Award is Granted:** Undergraduate **Number Awarded:** 20. **Funds Available:** $1,200. **Duration:** One semester.

Eligibility Requirements: Applicants must be graduating seniors planning to attend the University of Connecticut, Ratcliffe Hicks School of Agriculture majoring in Animal Science, Ornamental Horticulture and Turfgrass management. **Application Requirements:** Applicants may obtain application materials from the University of Connecticut Ratcliffe Hicks School of Agriculture (RHSA). 1376 Storrs Rd., Unit 4090, Storrs, CT 06269-4090. Phone: 860486-2919
Fax: 860486-4643, acadprog@canr.uconn.edu.

3137 ■ THE HERB SOCIETY OF AMERICA

9019 Kirtland Chardon Rd.
Kirtland, OH 44094
Tel: (440)256-0514
Fax: (440)256-0541
E-mail: herbs@herbsociety.org
Web Site: http://herbsociety.org
To educate its members and the public on the cultivation of herbs and the study of their history and uses.

Title of Award: Nashville Unit Scholarships **Area, Field, or Subject:** Horticulture. **Level of Education for which Award is Granted:** Undergraduate **Funds Available:** $2,500.

Eligibility Requirements: Applicants must be permanent residents of Tennessee; must be current college freshman, sophomore or junior students who are American citizens. **Application Requirements:** Applicants must submit a completed application form and two letters of reference. **Deadline for Receipt:** April 1.

3138 ■ THE HERB SOCIETY OF AMERICA

9019 Kirtland Chardon Rd.
Kirtland, OH 44094
Tel: (440)256-0514
Fax: (440)256-0541
E-mail: herbs@herbsociety.org
Web Site: http://herbsociety.org
To educate its members and the public on the cultivation of herbs and the study of their history and uses.

Title of Award: Pennsylvania Heartland Unit Scholarships **Area, Field, or Subject:** Horticulture. **Level of Education for which Award is Granted:** Undergraduate **Funds Available:** $1,500.

Eligibility Requirements: Applicants must be third or fourth year students of an associate degree program within the study of horticulture; must be residents of Berks, Montgomery, York, Lancaster or Schuylkill county. **Application Requirements:** Applicants must submit: a completed application form; two letters of reference from which one must come from an advisor or professor and one from a reference of the student's choice; must submit an official school transcript; and an essay stating their reasons for choosing the field of horticulture and future plans. **Deadline for Receipt:** April 1. **Additional Information:** jetlan1@aol.com.

3139 ■ THE HERB SOCIETY OF AMERICA

9019 Kirtland Chardon Rd.
Kirtland, OH 44094
Tel: (440)256-0514
Fax: (440)256-0541
E-mail: herbs@herbsociety.org
Web Site: http://herbsociety.org
To educate its members and the public on the cultivation of herbs and the study of their history and uses.

Title of Award: South Texas Unit Scholarships **Area, Field, or Subject:** Horticulture. **Level of Education for which Award is Granted:** Undergraduate **Funds Available:** $1,000.

Eligibility Requirements: Applicants must be students who are studying agronomy, horticulture, botany or a closely-related discipline at an accredited four-year college or university; must be either permanent residents of Texas or attending an accredited college or university in Texas; must have completed two full years of college and be entering their junior or senior year of studies. **Application Requirements:** Applicants must submit a completed application form and recommendation from professor or guidance counselor. **Deadline for Receipt:** May 1. **Additional Information:** 713-513-7808.

3140 ■ THE HERB SOCIETY OF AMERICA

9019 Kirtland Chardon Rd.
Kirtland, OH 44094
Tel: (440)256-0514
Fax: (440)256-0541
E-mail: herbs@herbsociety.org
Web Site: http://herbsociety.org
To educate its members and the public on the cultivation of herbs and the study of their history and uses.

Title of Award: Western Reserve Herb Society Scholarships **Area, Field, or Subject:** Horticulture. **Level of Education for which Award is Granted:** Undergraduate **Funds Available:** $4,000.

Eligibility Requirements: Applicants must be: undergraduate students; Ohio residents; studying horticulture or a related field such as landscape architecture or horticultural therapy; planning a career involving teaching/research or work in the public sector; entering their second to fifth year of an undergraduate program at an accredited college or university. **Application Requirements:** Applicants must submit a completed application form.

3141 ■ THE HERB SOCIETY OF AMERICA

9019 Kirtland Chardon Rd.
Kirtland, OH 44094
Tel: (440)256-0514
Fax: (440)256-0541
E-mail: herbs@herbsociety.org

Web Site: http://herbsociety.org
To educate its members and the public on the cultivation of herbs and the study of their history and uses.
Title of Award: Francis Sylvia Zverina Scholarship **Area, Field, or Subject:** Horticulture. **Level of Education for which Award is Granted:** Undergraduate **Funds Available:** $5,000.
Eligibility Requirements: Applicants must be students in good scholastic standing who are studying horticulture or related fields such as landscape architecture or horticultural therapy; must have horticultural career goals involving teaching/research or work in the public sector; must be U.S. citizens; must have completed their second or third year of undergraduate school at an accredited college or university anywhere in United States. **Application Requirements:** Applicants must submit a completed application form.

3142 ■ IDAHO NURSERY AND LANDSCAPE ASSOCIATION

PO Box 2065
Idaho Falls, ID 83403
Tel: (208)522-7307
Free: 800-462-4769
Fax: (208)529-0832
E-mail: abates@inlagrow.org
Web Site: http://www.inlagrow.org
To encourage the study of Horticulture, Floriculture, Plant Pathology, Landscape Design, Turfgrass Management, Botany and allied subjects that pertain to the Green Industry.
Title of Award: Idaho Nursery and Landscape Association Scholarships **Area, Field, or Subject:** Horticulture. **Level of Education for which Award is Granted:** Undergraduate **Funds Available:** $750.
Eligibility Requirements: Applicants must be students in an accredited two or four-year program in the State of Idaho pursuing studies in the Green Industry. **Application Requirements:** Applicants must submit "one-page, typed" essay stating their reasons for interest in this particular field of endeavor, future plans and goals; must submit a letter of recommendation from someone in the community who will evaluate citizenship; must submit school transcript and letter of recommendation from a professor in the applicant's major field of study. **Additional Information:** Ann Bates at the above address.

3143 ■ ILLINOIS LANDSCAPE CONTRACTORS ASSOCIATION

2625 Buterfield Rd., Ste. 204 W
Oak Brook, IL 60523
Tel: (630)472-2851
Fax: (630)472-3150
E-mail: sgrams@ilca.net
Web Site: http://www.ilca.net
To enhance the professionalism and capabilities of members by providing leadership, education and valued services while promoting environmental awareness within the landscape industry.
Title of Award: Illinois Landscape Contractors Association Scholarships **Area, Field, or Subject:** Horticulture. **Level of Education for which Award is Granted:** Undergraduate **Funds Available:** Varies.
Eligibility Requirements: Applicants must be residents of Illinois and enrolled full-time in an accredited two or four-year college horticultural program in Illinois or a bordering state. **Application Requirements:** Applicants must submit a completed application form; a letter describing their goals and aspirations in the field of horticulture, a transcript of record; must attach evaluation/letters from employers, internships, work study or any horticulture/landscape experience. **Deadline for Receipt:** February 28. **Additional Information:** 630-472-2851.

3144 ■ LANDSCAPE ARCHITECTURE FOUNDATION

818 18th St. NW, Ste. 810
Washington, DC 20006
Tel: (202)331-7070
Fax: (202)331-7079
E-mail: scholarships@lafoundation.org
Web Site: http://www.lafoundation.org
To recognize an outstanding landscape architecture, horticulture or irrigation science student.
Title of Award: Rain Bird Intelligent Use of Water Scholarships **Area, Field, or Subject:** Landscape architecture and design; Horticulture. **Level of Education for which Award is Granted:** Undergraduate **Number Awarded:** 1. **Funds Available:** $2,500.

Eligibility Requirements: Applicants must be students in the final two years of undergraduate study (third-, fourth-, or fifth-year students) who have demonstrated commitment to these professions through participation in extracurricular activities and exemplary scholastic achievements. **Application Requirements:** Applicants must submit an entry form, a photo (head shot with a plain background; 300 ppi, size 4 x 6 inches in extracurricular activities and financial information); a cover letter; a typed, double-spaced 300-word essay stating career goals and explaining how the applicant will contribute to the advancement of the profession of landscape architecture, horticulture or irrigation science. All application materials (with the exception of reference letters) must be sent through email as a single document. Each document must be formatted as follows: create one-inch minimum margins; include page number and surname/document name/award name on all pages of all documents prepared by applicant. **Deadline for Receipt:** February 15.

3145 ■ MICHIGAN STATE HORTICULTURAL SOCIETY

63806 90th Ave.
Hartford, MI 49057
Tel: (269)424-3990
Fax: (269)424-3096
E-mail: mihortsociety@aol.com
Web Site: http://www.mihortsociety.org
To encourage among the people a greater love for choice fruit products; to awaken a larger interest in Michigan's horticultural possibilities; to offer practical suggestions along modern cultural and marketing methods; and to encourage the improved methods in the production, harvest, handling, storage, marketing and utilization of fruit and vegetable crops as well as a full farm marketers program.
Title of Award: Fruits and Vegetable Industries Scholarships **Area, Field, or Subject:** Horticulture. **Level of Education for which Award is Granted:** Undergraduate **Funds Available:** $1,000.
Eligibility Requirements: Applicants must be students who intend to pursue a career in the Midwest fruit industry or vegetable industry. **Application Requirements:** Applicants must complete the application form. **Deadline for Receipt:** September 30. **Additional Information:** mihortsociety@aol.com.

3146 ■ MICHIGAN STATE HORTICULTURAL SOCIETY

63806 90th Ave.
Hartford, MI 49057
Tel: (269)424-3990
Fax: (269)424-3096
E-mail: mihortsociety@aol.com
Web Site: http://www.mihortsociety.org
To encourage among the people a greater love for choice fruit products; to awaken a larger interest in Michigan's horticultural possibilities; to offer practical suggestions along modern cultural and marketing methods; and to encourage the improved methods in the production, harvest, handling, storage, marketing and utilization of fruit and vegetable crops as well as a full farm marketers program.
Title of Award: Jordan B. Tatter Scholarships **Area, Field, or Subject:** Horticulture. **Level of Education for which Award is Granted:** Undergraduate **Funds Available:** No specific amount.
Eligibility Requirements: Applicants must be graduates or junior undergraduate students who show interest in working in the fruit and/or vegetable industry. **Application Requirements:** Applicants must complete the application form. **Deadline for Receipt:** October 1. **Additional Information:** 517-355-5191.

3147 ■ NATIONAL JUNIOR HORTICULTURAL ASSOCIATION

15 Railroad Ave.
Homer City, PA 15748-1378
Tel: (724)479-3254
E-mail: carole@njha.org
Web Site: http://www.njha.org
To help young people develop their skills and obtain an understanding of horticulture.
Title of Award: National Junior Horticultural Association Alumni Scholarships **Area, Field, or Subject:** Horticulture. **Level of Education for which Award is Granted:** Undergraduate **Funds Available:** No specific amount.
Eligibility Requirements: Program is open to any youth intending to return to the NJHA convention to expand their knowledge within NJHA.

Application Requirements: Applicants must submit a resume which must include a one paragraph statement about self, one paragraph about NJHA involvement, one paragraph about non-NJHA involvement, one paragraph about financial need, and a letter of recommendation from an NJHA leader. Applicants are advised to contact Mike Ensor who may be reached at 2336 Mt. Carmel Rd., Parkton, MD 21120-9608; phone: 410-357-0315, email: mensor@umd.ecu. **Deadline for Receipt:** September 1. **Additional Information:** mensor@umd.ecu.

3148 ■ NORTH CAROLINA COMMERCIAL FLOWER GROWERS ASSOCIATION

PO Box 58220
Raleigh, NC 27658
Tel: (919)334-0093
Fax: (919)877-0940
E-mail: smgbryan@aol.com
Web Site: http://www.nccfga.org
To support research on biological control of sweet potato and other integrated pest management approaches for greenhouse insect control.
Title of Award: North Carolina Commercial Flower Growers Association Floriculture Scholarships **Area, Field, or Subject:** Horticulture. **Level of Education for which Award is Granted:** Undergraduate **Funds Available:** $500.
Eligibility Requirements: Applicants must be full-time horticulture, entomology, or plant pathology students with an emphasis in greenhouse floriculture production; must be in their final year at a two-year, four-year or graduate institution. **Application Requirements:** Applicants must submit a completed application form.

3149 ■ NORTH CAROLINA NURSERY AND LANDSCAPE ASSOCIATION

968 Trinity Rd.
Raleigh, NC 27607
Tel: (919)816-9119
Fax: (919)816-9118
E-mail: rgelvin@ncan.com
Web Site: http://www.ncnla.com
To identify and reward horticulture students who exemplify scholastic aptitude, positive attitude and industry potential.
Title of Award: North Carolina Nursery and Landscape Association Horticulture Scholarships **Area, Field, or Subject:** Horticulture. **Level of Education for which Award is Granted:** Undergraduate **Funds Available:** No specific amount.
Eligibility Requirements: Applicants must be full-time students who are enrolled in a two-to-four year horticulture program in North Carolina. **Application Requirements:** Applicants must complete the application form; must submit a resume, transcripts and a wallet size black and white photograph. **Deadline for Receipt:** May 14.

3150 ■ OREGON ASSOCIATION OF NURSERIES

29751 SW Town Center Loop W
Wilsonville, OR 97070
Tel: (503)682-5089
Free: 800-342-6401
Fax: (503)682-5099
E-mail: info@oan.org
Web Site: http://www.oan.org
To provide opportunities for education, research and business development to members, including landscapers and allied businesses, that supply goods and services to those who grow, handle and retail ornamental horticultural products in Oregon.
Title of Award: Christmas Tree Chapter Scholarship Awards **Area, Field, or Subject:** Horticulture. **Level of Education for which Award is Granted:** Undergraduate **Funds Available:** $500.
Eligibility Requirements: Applicants must be students pursuing a degree in the field of horticulture. **Application Requirements:** Applicants must submit one copy of official transcript of records and three current letters of reference supporting the applicant's horticulture abilities. **Deadline for Receipt:** April 1. **Additional Information:** 29751 SW Town Center Loop W, Wilsonville, OR 97070.

3151 ■ OREGON ASSOCIATION OF NURSERIES

29751 SW Town Center Loop W
Wilsonville, OR 97070

Tel: (503)682-5089
Free: 800-342-6401
Fax: (503)682-5099
E-mail: info@oan.org
Web Site: http://www.oan.org
To provide opportunities for education, research and business development to members, including landscapers and allied businesses, that supply goods and services to those who grow, handle and retail ornamental horticultural products in Oregon.
Title of Award: Clackamas Chapter Scholarship Awards **Area, Field, or Subject:** Horticulture. **Level of Education for which Award is Granted:** Undergraduate **Funds Available:** $1,000.
Eligibility Requirements: Applicants must be freshmen students in an ornamental horticulture field. **Application Requirements:** Applicants must submit one copy of official transcript of records and three current letters of reference supporting the applicant's horticulture abilities. **Deadline for Receipt:** April 1. **Additional Information:** 29751 SW Town Center Loop W, Wilsonville, OR 97070.

3152 ■ OREGON ASSOCIATION OF NURSERIES

29751 SW Town Center Loop W
Wilsonville, OR 97070
Tel: (503)682-5089
Free: 800-342-6401
Fax: (503)682-5099
E-mail: info@oan.org
Web Site: http://www.oan.org
To provide opportunities for education, research and business development to members, including landscapers and allied businesses, that supply goods and services to those who grow, handle and retail ornamental horticultural products in Oregon.
Title of Award: Bill Egan Scholarship Program **Area, Field, or Subject:** Horticulture. **Level of Education for which Award is Granted:** Undergraduate **Funds Available:** $500.
Eligibility Requirements: Applicants must be college students majoring in horticulture with an emphasis on the greenhouse/floriculture areas. **Application Requirements:** Applicants must submit one copy of official transcript of records and three current letters of reference supporting the applicant's horticulture abilities. **Deadline for Receipt:** April 1. **Additional Information:** 29751 SW Town Center Loop W, Wilsonville, OR 97070.

3153 ■ OREGON ASSOCIATION OF NURSERIES

29751 SW Town Center Loop W
Wilsonville, OR 97070
Tel: (503)682-5089
Free: 800-342-6401
Fax: (503)682-5099
E-mail: info@oan.org
Web Site: http://www.oan.org
To provide opportunities for education, research and business development to members, including landscapers and allied businesses, that supply goods and services to those who grow, handle and retail ornamental horticultural products in Oregon.
Title of Award: Emerald Empire Chapter Scholarship Awards **Area, Field, or Subject:** Horticulture. **Level of Education for which Award is Granted:** Undergraduate **Funds Available:** $500.
Eligibility Requirements: Applicants must be junior or senior college students majoring in horticulture, landscape architecture or landscape construction who have graduated from an Oregon high school. **Application Requirements:** Applicants must submit one copy of official transcript of records and three current letters of reference supporting the applicant's horticulture abilities. **Deadline for Receipt:** April 1. **Additional Information:** 29751 SW Town Center Loop W, Wilsonville, OR 97070.

3154 ■ OREGON ASSOCIATION OF NURSERIES

29751 SW Town Center Loop W
Wilsonville, OR 97070
Tel: (503)682-5089
Free: 800-342-6401
Fax: (503)682-5099
E-mail: info@oan.org
Web Site: http://www.oan.org

To provide opportunities for education, research and business development to members, including landscapers and allied businesses, that supply goods and services to those who grow, handle and retail ornamental horticultural products in Oregon.
Title of Award: Martin Holmason Memorial Scholarship Awards **Area, Field, or Subject:** Horticulture. **Level of Education for which Award is Granted:** Undergraduate **Funds Available:** $500.
Eligibility Requirements: Applicants must be college junior or senior students majoring in ornamental horticulture. **Application Requirements:** Applicants must submit one copy of official transcript of records and three current letters of reference supporting the applicant's horticulture abilities. **Deadline for Receipt:** April 1. **Additional Information:** 29751 SW Town Center Loop W, Wilsonville, OR 97070.

3155 ■ OREGON ASSOCIATION OF NURSERIES
29751 SW Town Center Loop W
Wilsonville, OR 97070
Tel: (503)682-5089
Free: 800-342-6401
Fax: (503)682-5099
E-mail: info@oan.org
Web Site: http://www.oan.org
To provide opportunities for education, research and business development to members, including landscapers and allied businesses that supply goods and services to those who grow, handle and retail ornamental horticultural products in Oregon.
Title of Award: Joseph H. Klupenger Scholarship Awards **Area, Field, or Subject:** Horticulture. **Level of Education for which Award is Granted:** Undergraduate **Funds Available:** $550.
Eligibility Requirements: Applicants must be students majoring in ornamental horticulture; must intend to work in the ornamental industry. **Application Requirements:** Applicants must submit one copy of official transcript of records and three current letters of reference supporting the applicant's horticulture abilities. **Deadline for Receipt:** April 1. **Additional Information:** 29751 SW Town Center Loop W, Wilsonville, OR 97070.

3156 ■ OREGON ASSOCIATION OF NURSERIES
29751 SW Town Center Loop W
Wilsonville, OR 97070
Tel: (503)682-5089
Free: 800-342-6401
Fax: (503)682-5099
E-mail: info@oan.org
Web Site: http://www.oan.org
To provide opportunities for education, research and business development to members, including landscapers and allied businesses, that supply goods and services to those who grow, handle and retail ornamental horticultural products in Oregon.
Title of Award: Mt. Hood Chapter Scholarship Awards **Area, Field, or Subject:** Horticulture. **Level of Education for which Award is Granted:** Undergraduate **Funds Available:** $1,000.
Eligibility Requirements: Applicants must be college students majoring in ornamental horticulture. **Application Requirements:** Applicants must submit one copy of official transcript of records and three current letters of reference supporting the applicant's horticulture abilities. **Deadline for Receipt:** April 1. **Additional Information:** 29751 SW Town Center Loop W, Wilsonville, OR 97070.

3157 ■ OREGON ASSOCIATION OF NURSERIES
29751 SW Town Center Loop W
Wilsonville, OR 97070
Tel: (503)682-5089
Free: 800-342-6401
Fax: (503)682-5099
E-mail: info@oan.org
Web Site: http://www.oan.org
To provide opportunities for education, research and business development to members, including landscapers and allied businesses, that supply goods and services to those who grow, handle and retail ornamental horticultural products in Oregon.
Title of Award: Nurseries Foundation Scholarship Awards **Area, Field, or Subject:** Horticulture. **Level of Education for which Award is Granted:** Undergraduate **Funds Available:** $1,000.

Eligibility Requirements: Applicants must be college students majoring in the field of horticulture. **Application Requirements:** Applicants must submit one copy of official transcript of records and three current letters of reference supporting the applicant's horticulture abilities. **Deadline for Receipt:** April 1. **Additional Information:** 29751 SW Town Center Loop W, Wilsonville, OR 97070.

3158 ■ OREGON ASSOCIATION OF NURSERIES
29751 SW Town Center Loop W
Wilsonville, OR 97070
Tel: (503)682-5089
Free: 800-342-6401
Fax: (503)682-5099
E-mail: info@oan.org
Web Site: http://www.oan.org
To provide opportunities for education, research and business development to members, including landscapers and allied businesses, that supply goods and services to those who grow, handle and retail ornamental horticultural products in Oregon.
Title of Award: Oregon Association of Nurseries Scholarship Program **Area, Field, or Subject:** Horticulture. **Level of Education for which Award is Granted:** Undergraduate **Funds Available:** No specific amount.
Eligibility Requirements: Applicants must be students preparing for a career in ornamental horticulture and related fields. **Application Requirements:** Applicants must submit one copy of official transcript of records and three current letters of reference supporting the applicants' horticulture abilities. **Deadline for Receipt:** April 1. **Additional Information:** 29751 SW Town Center Loop W, Wilsonville, OR 97070.

3159 ■ OREGON ASSOCIATION OF NURSERIES
29751 SW Town Center Loop W
Wilsonville, OR 97070
Tel: (503)682-5089
Free: 800-342-6401
Fax: (503)682-5099
E-mail: info@oan.org
Web Site: http://www.oan.org
To provide opportunities for education, research and business development to members, including landscapers and allied businesses, that supply goods and services to those who grow, handle and retail ornamental horticultural products in Oregon.
Title of Award: Retail Chapter Scholarship Awards **Area, Field, or Subject:** Horticulture. **Level of Education for which Award is Granted:** Undergraduate **Funds Available:** $1,000.
Eligibility Requirements: Applicants must be students majoring in ornamental horticulture and related fields. **Application Requirements:** Applicants must submit one copy of official transcript of records and three current letters of reference supporting applicant's horticulture abilities. **Deadline for Receipt:** April 1. **Additional Information:** 29751 SW Town Center Loop W, Wilsonville, OR 97070.

3160 ■ OREGON ASSOCIATION OF NURSERIES
29751 SW Town Center Loop W
Wilsonville, OR 97070
Tel: (503)682-5089
Free: 800-342-6401
Fax: (503)682-5099
E-mail: info@oan.org
Web Site: http://www.oan.org
To provide opportunities for education, research and business development to members, including landscapers and allied businesses, that supply goods and services to those who grow, handle and retail ornamental horticultural products in Oregon.
Title of Award: Willamette Chapter Scholarship Awards **Area, Field, or Subject:** Horticulture. **Level of Education for which Award is Granted:** Undergraduate **Funds Available:** $1,000.
Eligibility Requirements: Applicants must be students majoring in ornamental horticulture and related fields. **Application Requirements:** Applicants must submit one copy of official transcript of records and three current letters of reference supporting the applicant's horticulture abilities. **Deadline for Receipt:** April 1. **Additional Information:** 29751 SW Town Center Loop W, Wilsonville, OR 97070.

3161 ■ OREGON ASSOCIATION OF NURSERIES

29751 SW Town Center Loop W
Wilsonville, OR 97070
Tel: (503)682-5089
Free: 800-342-6401
Fax: (503)682-5099
E-mail: info@oan.org
Web Site: http://www.oan.org
To provide opportunities for education, research and business development to members, including landscapers and allied businesses, that supply goods and services to those who grow, handle and retail ornamental horticultural products in Oregon.
Title of Award: Ed Wood Memorial Scholarship Awards **Area, Field, or Subject:** Horticulture. **Level of Education for which Award is Granted:** Undergraduate **Funds Available:** $1,500.
Eligibility Requirements: Applicants must be currently enrolled in a college horticulture program in Oregon. **Application Requirements:** Applicants must submit one copy of official transcript of records and three current letters of reference supporting the applicant's horticulture abilities. **Deadline for Receipt:** April 1. **Additional Information:** 29751 SW Town Center Loop W, Wilsonville, OR 97070.

3162 ■ WINSTON-SALEM FOUNDATION

860 W Fifth St.
Winston-Salem, NC 27101-2506
Tel: (336)725-2382
Fax: (336)727-0581
E-mail: info@wsfoundation.org
Web Site: http://www.wsfoundation.org
To provide financial support for educational opportunities to legal residents of North Carolina who will attend a two and/or four year college and have been accepted into the Horticulture Technology or Landscape Architecture curriculums at Forsyth Technical Community College or other accredited post-secondary schools in North Carolina.
Title of Award: Garden Club Council of Winston-Salem and Forsyth County Council **Area, Field, or Subject:** Horticulture; Landscape architecture and design. **Level of Education for which Award is Granted:** Undergraduate **Funds Available:** No specific amount.
Eligibility Requirements: Applicants must demonstrate academic potential; financial need; full-time attendance (minimum of 12 credit hours/ semester); pursuit of undergraduate associate or baccalaureate degree (first-time degrees preferred); must be US citizens. The scholarship is renewable for a second consecutive year if student maintains a cumulative college GPA of 2.0, continues full-time enrollment and continues in horticulture or landscape architecture; otherwise, scholarship is forfeited. Available to traditional and non-traditional age students. **Application Requirements:** Application must be completed and submitted with all required materials to the Student Aid Department at The Winston-Salem Foundation. Supplemental materials listed on the last page of the application include previous year's federal tax return for student and parent, if student is a dependent; academic year-end grade transcript; Federal Student Aid Report; federal award notice and interview with student aid staff. **Deadline for Receipt:** March 31. **Additional Information:** Edna Barker, 336-714-3445; Kay Dillon, 336-714-3446.

Mortuary Sciences

3163 ■ AMERICAN BOARD OF FUNERAL SERVICE EDUCATION

3432 Ashland Ave., Ste. U
St. Joseph, MO 64506
Tel: (816)233-3747
Fax: (816)233-3793
Web Site: http://www.abfse.org
To provide financial awards to students enrolled in funeral service or mortuary science programs to assist them in obtaining their professional education.
Title of Award: ABFSE National Scholarship Program **Area, Field, or Subject:** Funeral services, Mortuary science. **Level of Education for which Award is Granted:** Undergraduate **Funds Available:** $500 - $2,500. **Duration:** One year.
Eligibility Requirements: Applicant must have at least completed one semester (or quarter) of study in a funeral service or mortuary science education accredited by the American Board of Funeral Service Education; must have one term or semester remaining in his/her program which will commence after the award date in order to be considered for a full award; must be a citizen of the United States. **Application Requirements:** Application forms are available online. Applicant must have the tax forms, letter of recommendation and transcript of records. Application materials must be sent to: Scholarship Committee, ABFSE, 3432 Ashland Ave., Ste. U, St. Joseph, MO 64506. **Deadline for Receipt:** March 1 and September 1.

3164 ■ FUNERAL SERVICE FOUNDATION

13625 Bishop's Dr.
Brookfield, WI 53005
Tel: 877-402-5900
Fax: (262)789-6977
E-mail: info@funeralservicefoundation.org
Web Site: http://www.funeralservicefoundation.org
To provide financial assistance for tuition and travel stipend for selected individuals who attended the National Funeral Directors Association Professional Women's Conference.
Title of Award: NFDA Professional Women's Conference Scholarships **Area, Field, or Subject:** Funeral service; Mortuary science. **Level of Education for which Award is Granted:** Undergraduate **Funds Available:** $400.
Eligibility Requirements: Applicants must be verifiably employed in funeral service or a related occupation or mortuary science school students enrolled in school accredited by the American Board of Funeral Service Education. **Application Requirements:** Applicants must submit all the required application information.

3165 ■ NATIONAL FUNERAL DIRECTORS AND MORTICIANS ASSOCIATION

13625 Bishop's Dr.
Brookfield, WI 53005
Tel: (262)789-1880
Free: 800-228-6332
Fax: (262)789-6977
E-mail: nfda@nfda.org
Web Site: http://www.nfda.org
To provide financial support to the students in mortuary science or funeral service education.
Title of Award: Bishop State Community College Scholarships **Area, Field, or Subject:** Funeral services, Mortuary science. **Level of Education for which Award is Granted:** Undergraduate **Funds Available:** $1,800. **Duration:** One year.
Eligibility Requirements: Applicant must be a student enrolled in mortuary science or funeral service education. **Application Requirements:** For more information regarding the scholarship, applicants are advised to contact Bishop State Community College 351 Broad St., Mobile, AL, 36603.

3166 ■ NATIONAL FUNERAL DIRECTORS AND MORTICIANS ASSOCIATION

13625 Bishop's Dr.
Brookfield, WI 53005
Tel: (262)789-1880
Free: 800-228-6332
Fax: (262)789-6977
E-mail: nfda@nfda.org
Web Site: http://www.nfda.org
To provide financial support to the students in funeral service education.
Title of Award: Vincennes University Scholarships **Area, Field, or Subject:** Funeral services. **Level of Education for which Award is Granted:** Undergraduate **Number Awarded:** 5. **Funds Available:** $500.
Eligibility Requirements: Applicant must have completed one semester in funeral service education program at Vincennes University. **Application Requirements:** For further information about the scholarship, applicants are advised to contact the school at: Vincennes University, 1002 N 1st St., Vincennes, IN 47591. **Additional Information:** John Alsobrooks.

Zoology

3167 ■ BENTON COUNTY FOUNDATION
PO Box 911
Corvallis, OR 97339
Tel: (541)753-1603
Web Site: http://www.bentoncountyfoundation.org
To encourage and support ethnic minority undergraduate women enrolled in the College of Science.
Title of Award: Margaret Dowell-Gravatt, M.D. Scholarship **Area, Field, or Subject:** Zoology; Microbiology; Medical technology; Medicine; Nursing; Physical therapy; Occupational therapy. **Level of Education for which Award is Granted:** Undergraduate **Funds Available:** No specific amount.
Eligibility Requirements: Applicant must: be pursuing a degree in Zoology or Microbiology or one of the following pre-health programs: Medical Technology, Medicine, Nursing, Physical and/or Occupational therapy. Applicant must: be enrolled full-time at the sophomore, junior, or senior level; have a GPA of 2.5 overall and 3.0 in science courses required in their major field or pre-health curriculum; qualify for financial assistance as defined by the Financial Aid Office of OSU. **Application Requirements:** Applicant may contact the Foundation for application form and other requirements. **Additional Information:** Benton County Foundation at the above address.

3168 ■ CALIFORNIA WATERFOWL ASSOCIATION
4630 Northgate Blvd., Ste. 150
Sacramento, CA 95834
Tel: (916)648-1406
Fax: (916)648-1665
E-mail: cwa@calwaterfowl.org
Web Site: http://www.calwaterfowl.org
To provide field experience a training in the tools, methods, concepts of waterfowl, wetlands research and management.
Title of Award: Dennis Raveling Scholarships **Area, Field, or Subject:** Wildlife conservation, management and sciences; Zoology; Botany; Ecology. **Level of Education for which Award is Granted:** Undergraduate **Number Awarded:** 2. **Funds Available:** $2,000 for first place; $1,000 for 2nd place.
Eligibility Requirements: Applicants must be students with a desire to pursue a career in waterfowl or wetlands ecology. **Application Requirements:** Applicants must submit a "one-page" proposal summary description on an original research or management project; must submit a detailed proposal if required or "one-page" statement explaining the course of study for which they need to support. **Deadline for Receipt:** October 31. **Additional Information:** Nocole Berset at the above address.

General

3169 ■ ACMPE SCHOLARSHIP FUND
104 Inverness Terr. E
Englewood, CO 80112-5306
Tel: (303)799-1111; 877-275-6462
Fax: (303)643-4439
E-mail: acmpe@mgma.com
Web Site: http://www.mgma.com
To support and promote health care leaders' personal and professional growth toward advancement of the profession.
Title of Award: ACMPE Scholarship Fund Program **Area, Field, or Subject:** Health care services. **Level of Education for which Award is Granted:** Graduate, Undergraduate **Funds Available:** $1,000 to $5,000. **Eligibility Requirements:** Applicants must be students enrolled in an undergraduate or graduate degree program relevant to medical practice management, including public health, business administration, health care administration and other related areas. **Application Requirements:** Applicants must complete the online application and submit a recent unofficial academic transcript; a current resume; two reference letters; and for students recently accepted, documentation indicating acceptance into a graduate or undergraduate college or university. **Deadline for Receipt:** May 1.

3170 ■ ALABAMA HORSE COUNCIL
PO Box 260
Morris, AL 35116
800-945-8033
E-mail: info@alabamahorsecouncil.org
Web Site: http://www.alabamahorsecouncil.org
To promote Veterinary Medicine education in Alabama.
Title of Award: Auburn University College of Veterinary Medicine Scholarships **Area, Field, or Subject:** Veterinary science and medicine. **Level of Education for which Award is Granted:** Undergraduate **Funds Available:** $1500. **Eligibility Requirements:** Applicants must be currently enrolled at Auburn's College of Veterinary Medicine; must have strong background in Alabama's livestock industry; and intending to pursue a career involving large animal medicine. **Application Requirements:** Applicants must submit a completed application form. **Deadline for Receipt:** December. **Additional Information:** Martha Davis.

3171 ■ ALBERTA LEARNING INFORMATION SERVICE - ALBERTA SCHOLARSHIP PROGRAM
Box 28000 Sta. Main
Edmonton, AB, Canada T5J 4R4
Tel: (780)427-8640
Fax: (780)427-1288
E-mail: scholarship@gov.ab.ca
Web Site: http://www.alis.alberta.ca
To recognize and reward the exceptional achievement of a student graduating from Sexsmith Secondary School who is entering post-secondary studies in a health-related field.
Title of Award: Dr. Robert Norman Shaw Scholarship **Area, Field, or Subject:** Health sciences. **Level of Education for which Award is Granted:** Undergraduate **Funds Available:** $1,500. **Eligibility Requirements:** Applicants must have completed Grade 12 at Sexsmith Secondary School; be Alberta residents and plan to enroll full-time in a health-related post-secondary program of at least one semester in length. **Application Requirements:** Applicants may obtain an application form from the Counseling Office at Sexsmith Secondary School and also from Alberta Scholarship Programs. **Deadline for Receipt:** June 1. **Additional Information:** Alberta Scholarship Programs at the above address.

3172 ■ AMERICAN ACADEMY OF NEUROLOGY
1080 Montreal Ave.
St. Paul, MN 55116
Tel: (651)695-2717
Free: 800-879-1960
Fax: (651)695-2791
E-mail: memberservices@aan.com
Web Site: http://www.aan.com
To provide financial support for projects in either institutional, clinical, or laboratory setting where there are ongoing programs of research, service or training, or a private practice.
Title of Award: Medical Student Summer Research Scholarships **Area, Field, or Subject:** Neurology. **Level of Education for which Award is Granted:** Undergraduate **Funds Available:** $3,000. **Eligibility Requirements:** Applicants must be second-year medical students who have a supporting preceptor and a project with clearly defined goals, third-year medical students who are on an official summer break will also be considered with accompanying documentation, whose project is conducted through US or Canadian institution of the students' choice and jointly designed by the students and sponsoring institutions. **Application Requirements:** Applicant must submit completed application form, 1-2 page project proposal, 1-2 page curriculum vitae, 2 letters of recommendation: one from the project preceptor and one from the SIGN faculty advisor, completed tax form with institution information. **Deadline for Receipt:** February 15.

3173 ■ AMERICAN ASSOCIATION OF BOVINE PRACTITIONERS
PO Box 3610
Auburn, AL 36831-3610
Tel: (334)821-0442
Fax: (334)821-9532
E-mail: aabphq@aabp.org
Web Site: http://www.aabp.org
To enhance the professional lives of its members through relevant continuing education that will improve the well-being of cattle and the economic success of the owners; increase awareness; to promote leadership for issues critical to cattle industries; to improve opportunities for careers in bovine medicine.
Title of Award: AABP Amstutz Scholarships **Area, Field, or Subject:** Veterinary science and medicine. **Level of Education for which Award is Granted:** Undergraduate **Funds Available:** $2,000. **Eligibility Requirements:** Applicant must be student enrolled in college of veterinary medicine in Canada and United States; applicant must be in second year of the veterinarian curriculum at the time of the application. **Application Requirements:** Applicants must submit a current cumulative school GPA through December, 2007 and a current class rank; he/she

must submit a biographical account that outlines the background of the cattle industry; an applicant must prepare a one-page or less list factors that stimulate the interest and involvement in bovine medicine and extracurricular activities; ten lines or less description of plans following graduation from veterinary school; 30 lines or less answer about the experiences that stimulate in pursuing a career in food/animal/bovine medicine; 30 lines or less answering the question "What is our role today and in the future as a veterinarian in shaping public perception of food animal welfare in U.S. or Canada?"; an essay about the plans in using the money acquired from the award if considered; applicant must submit two letters of recommendation from either veterinarian or faculty members regarding the applicant's worthiness for the award. **Deadline for Receipt:** March 31.

3174 ■ AMERICAN ASSOCIATION OF BOVINE PRACTITIONERS
PO Box 3610
Auburn, AL 36831-3610
Tel: (334)821-0442
Fax: (334)821-9532
E-mail: aabphq@aabp.org
Web Site: http://www.aabp.org
To provide awards to 3rd and/or 4th year veterinary students who are interested in dairy and/or beef veterinary medicine.
Title of Award: AABP Bovine Veterinary Student Recognition Award **Area, Field, or Subject:** Veterinary science and medicine. **Level of Education for which Award is Granted:** Undergraduate **Funds Available:** $1,500.
Eligibility Requirements: Applicant must be a student member of AABP enrolled at Veterinary Colleges and Schools during the 2nd year and/or 3rd year. **Application Requirements:** An applicant must fill out the on-line application form which outlines the background, work, and academic experience, primary interests in veterinary medicine, career goals and providing the name of a faculty sponsor. **Deadline for Receipt:** March 15.

3175 ■ AMERICAN ASSOCIATION OF BOVINE PRACTITIONERS
PO Box 3610
Auburn, AL 36831-3610
Tel: (334)821-0442
Fax: (334)821-9532
E-mail: aabphq@aabp.org
Web Site: http://www.aabp.org
To help expand the skills and knowledge base of the cattle production medicine practitioner.
Title of Award: AABP Education Grants **Area, Field, or Subject:** Veterinary science and medicine. **Level of Education for which Award is Granted:** Undergraduate **Funds Available:** $500.
Eligibility Requirements: An applicant must be a member or student member of the AABP. **Application Requirements:** Applicant must fill out the online application form including the career goal, current job description, prior experience with food animal production medicine, and goals of advanced education program; an applicant must submit a brief course outline, a letter of recommendation, a signed hold harmless agreement release form; and applicant must obtain a completion of the advanced training, and the successful applicants will be required to submit an evaluation from detailing the experience. **Deadline for Receipt:** April 15.

3176 ■ AMERICAN ASSOCIATION OF BOVINE PRACTITIONERS
PO Box 3610
Auburn, AL 36831-3610
Tel: (334)821-0442
Fax: (334)821-9532
E-mail: aabphq@aabp.org
Web Site: http://www.aabp.org
To support veterinary students.
Title of Award: AABP Student Externship Program **Area, Field, or Subject:** Veterinary science and medicine. **Level of Education for which Award is Granted:** Undergraduate **Funds Available:** $500.
Eligibility Requirements: Applicant must be admitted to veterinary school and complete an externship of at least two weeks in bovine practice; applicant must be a student and AABP member; applicants must be full-time veterinary students at an American, Canadian, or Caribbean veterinary college or be a newly admitted freshmen at such college. **Application Requirements:** An applicant must submit the filled out online

application form including dates of expected externship, practice where it is to take place, projected cost support to be provided by the practice and amount of aid requested, and student's career interests, prior experience with food producing animals, and goals for the externship; an applicant must provide a letter from the practice describing what the students will be doing; a letter from a faculty member at the student's veterinary college; he/she must submit a completed release agreement. **Deadline for Receipt:** May 1-October 31.

3177 ■ AMERICAN ASSOCIATION OF EQUINE PRACTITIONERS
4075 Iron Works Pkwy.
Lexington, KY 40511
Tel: (859)233-0147
Fax: (859)233-1968
E-mail: aaepoffice@aaep.org
Web Site: http://www.aaep.org
To advance the health and welfare of horses by promoting the discovery and sharing of new knowledge; to enhance awareness of the need to the targeted research; to educate the public; to expand fundraising opportunities; to facilitate cooperation among funding agencies.
Title of Award: AAEP/ALSIC Scholarships **Area, Field, or Subject:** Veterinary science and medicine. **Level of Education for which Award is Granted:** Undergraduate **Number Awarded:** 8. **Funds Available:** $2,500.
Eligibility Requirements: Applicants must be senior veterinary students who have indicated a strong desire to pursue a career in equine medicine at schools nationwide. **Application Requirements:** An applicant must fill out the online application form. **Deadline for Receipt:** October 1.

3178 ■ AMERICAN ASSOCIATION OF NEUROLOGICAL SURGEONS
5550 Meadowbrook Dr.
Rolling Meadows, IL 60008
Tel: (847)378-0500; 888-566-2267
Fax: (847)378-0600
E-mail: info@aans.org
Web Site: http://www.aans.org
To provide first or second year medical students the opportunity to participate in neurosurgical research through a summer fellowship within an academic department of neurosurgery in the United States or Canada.
Title of Award: AANS Medical Student Summer Research Fellowships (MSSRF) **Area, Field, or Subject:** Neurology. **Level of Education for which Award is Granted:** Undergraduate **Number Awarded:** 15. **Funds Available:** $2,500.
Eligibility Requirements: Applicants must be American or Canadian medical students. **Application Requirements:** Applicants must submit applications through mail (hard-copy format) or electronically to nref@aans.org which must include the curriculum vitae and bio-sketch, a description of future plans, and a statement of why this fellowship is of interest to the applicant and why it would be beneficial to him/her. **Deadline for Receipt:** February 1.

3179 ■ AMERICAN ASSOCIATION OF NEUROLOGICAL SURGEONS
5550 Meadowbrook Dr.
Rolling Meadows, IL 60008
Tel: (847)378-0500; 888-566-2267
Fax: (847)378-0600
E-mail: info@aans.org
Web Site: http://www.aans.org
To provide financial support to a post neurosurgical resident for foreign travel for scientific enrichment, prior to beginning an academic career in neurological surgery.
Title of Award: William P. Van Wagenen Fellowships **Area, Field, or Subject:** Neurology. **Level of Education for which Award is Granted:** Undergraduate **Funds Available:** $60,000.
Eligibility Requirements: Applicants must be senior neurosurgical residents whose country of study is different from the country of residence in approved neurosurgery residency programs and whose intent is to pursue an academic career in neurological surgery. **Application Requirements:** Applicants must submit completed application together with the letter of reference. **Deadline for Receipt:** October 1.

3180 ■ AMERICAN COLLEGE OF HEALTHCARE EXECUTIVES
1 N Franklin, Ste. 1700
Chicago, IL 60606-3529

Tel: (312)424-2800
Fax: (312)424-0023
E-mail: geninfo@ache.org
Web Site: http://www.ache.org
To help ACHE Student Associates finance their education.
Title of Award: Albert W. Dent Graduate Student Scholarships **Area, Field, or Subject:** Health care services. **Level of Education for which Award is Granted:** Undergraduate **Number Awarded:** 15-25. **Funds Available:** $4,000. **Duration:** One year.
Eligibility Requirements: Applicant must be a Student Associate in good standing in the American College of Healthcare Executives; must be enrolled in full-time study for the upcoming term; must demonstrate financial need; must be a U.S or Canadian citizen; must have not been a previous recipient of the scholarship. **Application Requirements:** Applicants must submit and complete the application form available online; must submit a current curriculum vitae or resume; an official undergraduate and graduate transcript; must provide three current letters of recommendation and essay. **Additional Information:** American College of Healthcare Executives established the scholarship in honor of Foster G. McGaw, the founder of the American Hospital Supply Corporation. **Deadline for Receipt:** March 31.

3181 ■ AMERICAN COLLEGE OF HEALTHCARE EXECUTIVES
1 N Franklin, Ste. 1700
Chicago, IL 60606-3529
Tel: (312)424-2800
Fax: (312)424-0023
E-mail: geninfo@ache.org
Web Site: http://www.ache.org
To help ACHE Student Associates finance their education.
Title of Award: Foster G. McGaw Graduate Student Scholarships **Area, Field, or Subject:** Health care services. **Level of Education for which Award is Granted:** Undergraduate **Number Awarded:** 15-25. **Funds Available:** $4,000. **Duration:** One year.
Eligibility Requirements: Applicant must be a Student Associate in good standing in the American College of Healthcare Executives; must be enrolled in full-time study for the upcoming term; must demonstrate financial need; must be a U.S or Canadian citizen; must have not been a previous recipient of the scholarship. **Application Requirements:** Applicants must submit and complete the application form available online; must submit a current curriculum vitae or resume; an official undergraduate and graduate transcript; must provide three current letters of recommendation and essay. **Additional Information:** Foundation of the American College of Healthcare Executives established the scholarship in honor of Foster G. McGaw, the founder of the American Hospital Supply Corporation. **Deadline for Receipt:** March 31.

3182 ■ AMERICAN COUNCIL ON EXERCISE
4851 Paramount Dr.
San Diego, CA 92123
Tel: (858)279-8227; 888-825-3636
Fax: (858)279-8064
Web Site: http://www.acefitness.org
To provide support to the Penn State students.
Title of Award: Joe Q. Bryant American Council on Exercise Educational Scholarships **Area, Field, or Subject:** Health care services. **Level of Education for which Award is Granted:** Undergraduate **Funds Available:** $1,000.
Eligibility Requirements: Candidates must a student of Penn State; must maintain at least a 3.0 GPA on a 4.0 scale (verified by academic transcript); must meet the eligibility requirements for the ACE Certification Exam; must have perform two (2) hours of community service monthly during any term in which the student is enrolled. **Application Requirements:** Applicant must submit the following: (1) Applicant information form; (2) An official copy of academic transcript; (3) Two recommendation forms and statements of support: One academic reference and one non-academic reference; (4) Academic/ Leadership/Awards Form; (5) Essay form and 500-word essay.

3183 ■ AMERICAN COUNCIL ON EXERCISE
4851 Paramount Dr.
San Diego, CA 92123
Tel: (858)279-8227; 888-825-3636

Fax: (858)279-8064
Web Site: http://www.acefitness.org
To provide support to the Manhattan College students.
Title of Award: William J. Merriman American Council on Exercise Educational Scholarships **Area, Field, or Subject:** Health care services. **Level of Education for which Award is Granted:** Undergraduate **Funds Available:** $1.000.
Eligibility Requirements: Applicant must be a student of Manhattan College; must have at least a 3.0 GPA on a 4.0 scale (verified by academic transcript); must meet the eligibility requirements for the ACE Certification Exam; must perform two hours of community service monthly during any term in which the student is enrolled. **Application Requirements:** Applicant must have the following: (1) Applicant information form; (2) An official copy of academic transcript; (3) Two recommendation forms and statement of support: One academic reference and One non-academic reference; (4) Activities/Leadership/Awards form; (5) Essay form and 500-word essay.

3184 ■ AMERICAN COUNCIL ON EXERCISE
4851 Paramount Dr.
San Diego, CA 92123
Tel: (858)279-8227; 888-825-3636
Fax: (858)279-8064
Web Site: http://www.acefitness.org
To provide support to the student and employee of Duke University.
Title of Award: William Shannon American Council on Exercise Certification Scholarships **Area, Field, or Subject:** Health care services. **Level of Education for which Award is Granted:** Professional, Undergraduate **Funds Available:** $1.000.
Eligibility Requirements: Applicant must be a student or employee of Duke University; must meet the requirements for the ACE Certification Exam; must perform two hours of community service monthly during any term in which the student is enrolled. **Application Requirements:** Application form must consists of the following: (1) Applicant information form; (2) An official copy academic transcript; (3) Two recommendation forms and statements of support: One academic reference and one non-academic reference; (4) Activities/Leadership/Awards form; (5) Essay form and 500 word essay.

3185 ■ AMERICAN INDIAN EDUCATION FOUNDATION
2401 Eglin St.
Rapid City, SD 57703
Tel: (866)866-8642; (866)866-8642
Fax: (605)342-4113
E-mail: info@programs.org
Web Site: http://www.nrcprograms.org
To give American Indian students the tools, resources and opportunities to learn and succeed.
Title of Award: Indian Health Service Scholarship Program **Area, Field, or Subject:** Health sciences. **Level of Education for which Award is Granted:** Undergraduate **Funds Available:** No specific amount.
Eligibility Requirements: Applicants must be enrolled members of state or federally recognized tribes; must be undergraduate or graduate students who are majoring in any health-related pre-professional program. **Application Requirements:** Applicants may submit their application to the Foundation or to the Indian Health Service Scholarship Program 801 Thompson Ave. Ste. 120 Rockville, MD 20852; 301-443-6197. **Deadline for Receipt:** February.

3186 ■ AMERICAN MEDICAL ASSOCIATION
515 N State St.
Chicago, IL 60610
Tel: (312)464-4200
Free: 800-621-8335
Fax: (312)464-4142
E-mail: steven.churchill@ama-assn.org
Web Site: http://www.ama-assn.org
To advance health care through support of programs in medical education, research, and service.
Title of Award: AMA Foundation Minority Scholars Award **Area, Field, or Subject:** Medical Education. **Level of Education for which Award is Granted:** Undergraduate **Number Awarded:** 10. **Funds Available:** $10,000.

Eligibility Requirements: Applicant must be a current first or second year student and a permanent resident or citizen of the U.S.; must be African American, American Indian, Native American, Alaska Native, or Hispanic/Latino. **Application Requirements:** Applicants must complete the application form. Detailed requirement will be sent by the AMA Foundation to each medical school's Office of the Dean, Office of the Student Affairs, and Office of Financial Aid. **Deadline for Receipt:** April 15.

3187 ■ AMERICAN MEDICAL ASSOCIATION
515 N State St.
Chicago, IL 60610
Tel: (312)464-4200
Free: 800-621-8335
Fax: (312)464-4142
E-mail: steven.churchill@ama-assn.org
Web Site: http://www.ama-assn.org
To advance health care through support of programs in medical education, research, and service.
Title of Award: AMA Foundation Physicians of Tomorrow Scholarships **Area, Field, or Subject:** Medical Education. **Level of Education for which Award is Granted:** Undergraduate **Number Awarded:** 8. **Funds Available:** $10,000.
Eligibility Requirements: Applicants must be current third year medical students who are entering their fourth year of study. **Application Requirements:** Applicants must complete the application form. Detailed requirements will be sent by the AMA Foundation to each medical school's Office of the Dean, Office of the Student Affairs, and Office of Financial Aid. **Deadline for Receipt:** May 30.

3188 ■ AMERICAN MEDICAL ASSOCIATION
515 N State St.
Chicago, IL 60610
Tel: (312)464-4200
Free: 800-621-8335
Fax: (312)464-4142
E-mail: steven.churchill@ama-assn.org
Web Site: http://www.ama-assn.org
To advance health care through support of programs in medical education, research, and service.
Title of Award: The Arthur N. Wilson, MD, Scholarships **Area, Field, or Subject:** Medical Education. **Level of Education for which Award is Granted:** Undergraduate **Funds Available:** $5,000.
Eligibility Requirements: Applicants must be medical students who attended high school in Alaska. **Application Requirements:** Applicants must submit completed application form; a one-page personal statement outlining the career goals in the field of medicine; a curriculum vitae; official transcript from the applicant's high school in Southeast Alaska; official Medical school transcript; and letter of recommendation from a faculty member at the medical school or office of the dean. **Deadline for Receipt:** June 16. **Additional Information:** dina.lindenberg@ama-assn.org; 312-464-4193.

3189 ■ AMERICAN SOCIETY FOR CLINICAL LABORATORY SCIENCE
6701 Democracy Blvd., Ste. 300
Bethesda, MD 20817
Tel: (301)657-2768
Fax: (301)657-2909
E-mail: ascls@ascls.org
Web Site: http://www.ascls.org
To provide financial assistance for professionals who are involved in advancement of clinical laboratory sciences.
Title of Award: Alpha Mu Tau Undergraduate Scholarships **Area, Field, or Subject:** Clinical Laboratory sciences. **Level of Education for which Award is Granted:** Undergraduate **Funds Available:** $15,000.
Eligibility Requirements: Applicants must be United States citizens or permanent residents of the United States; accepted into an NAACLS accredited program in Clinical Laboratory Science, to include Clinical Laboratory Science, Medical Technology, Clinical Laboratory Technician/Medical Laboratory Technician, Cytotechnology or Histotechnology; in or entering their last year of study on September 1st. **Application Requirements:** Applicants must submit the completed application form. **Deadline for Receipt:** April 1.

3190 ■ AMERICAN SOCIETY FOR CLINICAL LABORATORY SCIENCE
6701 Democracy Blvd., Ste. 300
Bethesda, MD 20817
Tel: (301)657-2768
Fax: (301)657-2909
E-mail: ascls@ascls.org
Web Site: http://www.ascls.org
To provide financial assistance for professionals who are involved in advancement of clinical laboratory sciences.
Title of Award: Dorothy Morrison Undergraduate Scholarships **Area, Field, or Subject:** Clinical Laboratory sciences. **Level of Education for which Award is Granted:** Undergraduate **Funds Available:** $2,000.
Eligibility Requirements: Applicants must be United States citizens or permanent residents of the United States; accepted into an NAACLS accredited program in Clinical Laboratory Science, to include Clinical Laboratory Science/Medical Technology, Clinical Laboratory Technician/Medical Laboratory Technician, Cytotechnology or Histotechnology; in or entering their last year of study on September 1st. **Application Requirements:** Applicants must submit the completed application form. **Deadline for Receipt:** April 1.

3191 ■ AMERICAN SOCIETY OF ECHOCARDIOGRAPHY
1500 Sunday Dr., Ste. 102
Raleigh, NC 27607
Tel: (919)861-5574
Fax: (919)787-4916
E-mail: ase@asecho.org
Web Site: http://www.asecho.org
To financially support the graduating students in the cardiac sonography program.
Title of Award: Cardiac Sonographer Education Development Grants **Area, Field, or Subject:** Cardiology. **Level of Education for which Award is Granted:** Professional, Undergraduate **Funds Available:** $50,000. **Duration:** One year.
Eligibility Requirements: Applicant must be involved in the cardiac sonography programs. **Application Requirements:** Applicant must send application form and other supporting documents including lists of participants in the submission process (academic titles and affiliations, participants contribution to the proposal), summary of the proposal not exceeding 400 words (specific aims, how the program will use the money to increase qualified sonographer graduates, how the program will sustain the effort after the grant ended); budget, proposed method, additional supporting material, if any. **Deadline for Receipt:** April 18.

3192 ■ AMERICAN SOCIETY OF PODIATRIC MEDICAL ASSISTANTS
2124 S Austin Blvd.
Cicero, IL 60804
Tel: (708)863-6303; 888-882-7762
E-mail: aspmaex@aol.com
Web Site: http://www.aspma.org
To improve the profession of Podiatric Medical Assisting by providing educational opportunities for ASPMA members.
Title of Award: Zelda Walling Vicha Memorial Scholarships **Area, Field, or Subject:** Podiatry. **Level of Education for which Award is Granted:** Undergraduate **Funds Available:** $2,000.
Eligibility Requirements: Applicant must be a student entering his/her fourth year of school; must have a high scholastic achievement and a definite financial need. **Application Requirements:** Application forms are available in the website address. Applicant must submit the proof of financial need provided by the Financial Aid Office; must prepare an essay which describes the applicant's personal background, career, vocational or academic goals. **Deadline for Receipt:** May 1.

3193 ■ AMERICAN SOCIETY OF RADIOLOGIC TECHNOLOGISTS
15000 Central Ave. SE
Albuquerque, NM 87123-3909
Tel: (505)298-4500
Free: 800-444-2778
Fax: (505)298-5063
E-mail: customerinfo@asrt.org
Web Site: http://www.asrt.org

To provide resources for radiologic technologists intending to improve patient care and to support education and research in the radiologic sciences.

Title of Award: Jerman-Cahoon Student Scholarship Program **Area, Field, or Subject:** Radiology. **Level of Education for which Award is Granted:** Undergraduate **Funds Available:** $2,500.
Eligibility Requirements: Applicants must be students attending an entry-level radiologic sciences program. **Application Requirements:** Applicants must complete the application form and submit along with an essay, summary of financial need and scholastic information documents. **Additional Information:** foundation@asrt.org.

3194 ■ AMERICAN SOCIETY OF RADIOLOGIC TECHNOLOGISTS
15000 Central Ave. SE
Albuquerque, NM 87123-3909
Tel: (505)298-4500
Free: 800-444-2778
Fax: (505)298-5063
E-mail: customerinfo@asrt.org
Web Site: http://www.asrt.org
To provide resources for radiologic technologists intending to improve patient care and to support education and research in the radiologic sciences.

Title of Award: Royce-Osborn Minority Scholarship Program **Area, Field, or Subject:** Radiology. **Level of Education for which Award is Granted:** Undergraduate **Number Awarded:** 5. **Funds Available:** $4,000.
Eligibility Requirements: Applicants must be minority students attending an entry-level radiologic sciences program. **Application Requirements:** Applicants must complete the application form and submit along with an essay, summary of financial need and scholastic information documents. **Additional Information:** foundation@asrt.org.

3195 ■ ASSOCIATION OF AMERICAN MEDICAL COLLEGES
2450 N St. NW
Washington, DC 20037-1126
Tel: (202)828-0400
Fax: (202)828-1125
E-mail: amcas@aamc.org
Web Site: http://www.aamc.org
To eliminate inequities in medical education and health care and demonstrated leadership efforts in addressing educational, societal, and health care needs of minorities in United States.

Title of Award: Herbert W. Nickens Medical Student Scholarships **Area, Field, or Subject:** Medicinal Education. **Level of Education for which Award is Granted:** Undergraduate **Funds Available:** $5,000.
Eligibility Requirements: Applicants must be US citizens or permanent residents; must be entering third year of study in an accredited US medical school. **Application Requirements:** Applicants must submit one original and nine photocopies of nomination letter from the medical school's dean or the dean's designate discussing the leadership, academic achievement, awards and honors; letters of recommendation from the medical school and faculty member; personal statement (does not exceed 250 words) discussing motivation for pursuing medical career; curriculum vitae; and official medical school academic transcript. **Deadline for Receipt:** May 2. **Additional Information:** nickensawards@aamc.org

3196 ■ ASSOCIATION OF ZOO VETERINARY TECHNICIANS (AZVT)
903 10th St. SW
Albuquerque, NM 87102
Tel: (505)764-6264
Fax: (505)764-6275
E-mail: gdragoo@cabq.gov
Web Site: http://www.azvt.org
To provide educational assistance for veterinary or medical technology students.

Title of Award: Laurie Page-Peck Scholarships Fund **Area, Field, or Subject:** Veterinary science and medicine. **Level of Education for which Award is Granted:** Undergraduate **Funds Available:** $1,000.
Eligibility Requirements: Applicant must be a veterinary or medical technology student interested in zoo veterinary technology. **Application Requirements:** The applicant must submit a paper about zoo veterinary

technology. **Deadline for Receipt:** Deadline for receipt of abstracts-March 10; Deadline for first- draft paper submission- April 28; Deadline for final draft of paper July 7. **Additional Information:** Gwen A. Dragoo, B.S., R.V.T. Head Veterinary Technician Albuquerque Biological Park 903 10th Street SW Albuquerque, NM 87102.

3197 ■ AUTISM SOCIETY OF AMERICA
7910 Woodmont Ave., Ste. 300
Bethesda, MD 20814-3067
Tel: (301)657-0881
Free: 800-328-8476
Web Site: http://www.autism-society.org
To assist individuals with autism intending to pursue education.

Title of Award: CVS/All Kids Can Scholars Program **Area, Field, or Subject:** Mental health. **Level of Education for which Award is Granted:** Undergraduate **Number Awarded:** 5. **Funds Available:** $1,000.
Eligibility Requirements: Candidate must be an individual with autism completing post-secondary educational or vocational program. **Application Requirements:** Applicant must submit the documentation of status as an individual with autism; secondary school transcripts; documentation of acceptance into an accredited, post-secondary educational or vocational program of study; two recommendation letters; and a personal statement (maximum of 500 words) outlining the applicant's qualifications and proposed plan of study.

3198 ■ BECA FOUNDATION
830 E Grand Ave., Ste. B
Escondido, CA 92025
Tel: (760)741-8246
E-mail: sdbeca@sbcglobal.net
Web Site: http://www.becafoundation.org
To seek promising students and provide them with the necessary financial assistance, moral support and guidance to complete their education, thereby promoting higher educational and leadership standards within the Hispanic community.

Title of Award: Alice Newell Joslyn Medical Fund **Area, Field, or Subject:** Medical Education. **Level of Education for which Award is Granted:** Undergraduate **Funds Available:** $1,000.
Eligibility Requirements: Applicants must be entering medical/health care professions. **Application Requirements:** Applicants must complete the application form. **Deadline for Receipt:** March 3. **Additional Information:** sdbeca@sbcglobal.net; 760-741-8246.

3199 ■ ALEXANDER GRAHAM BELL ASSOCIATION FOR THE DEAF AND HARD OF HEARING
3417 Volta Pl. NW
Washington, DC 20007
Tel: (202)337-5220
Fax: (202)337-8314
E-mail: info@agbell.org
Web Site: http://www.agbell.org
To promote communication for people with hearing loss.

Title of Award: College Scholarship Awards **Area, Field, or Subject:** Hearing and Deafness. **Level of Education for which Award is Granted:** Undergraduate **Number Awarded:** Varies. **Funds Available:** $5,000. **Duration:** Entire length of undergraduate study.
Eligibility Requirements: Must be enrolled in or applied to a mainstream and accredited college/university as a full-time student. **Application Requirements:** Applicants must submit an application, with pages in numbered order; For children who use hearing aids, an unaided Audiogram performed within the last twelve (12) months or for those with cochlear implants, the most recent mapping report (first page only); Verification of the student's application, acceptance or enrollment to a mainstream and accredited university/college; Official transcripts for the most recent two years completed of high school or college; Student essay; Recommendation from a hearing health professional (maximum of two single-sided pages); Recommendation from a current AG Bell member (Maximum of two singe-sided pages). If you do not know an AG Bell member, please provide a recommendation from an educational or therapeutic professional; Recommendation from a non-relative who is familiar with the family's financial need (maximum of two single-sided pages). **Deadline for Receipt:** February 15.

3200 ■ ALEXANDER GRAHAM BELL ASSOCIATION FOR THE DEAF AND HARD OF HEARING
3417 Volta Pl. NW
Washington, DC 20007
Tel: (202)337-5220
Fax: (202)337-8314
E-mail: info@agbell.org
Web Site: http://www.agbell.org
To promote communication for people with hearing loss.
Title of Award: School Age Financial Aid Program **Area, Field, or Subject:** Hearing and Deafness. **Level of Education for which Award is Granted:** Undergraduate **Number Awarded:** Varies. **Funds Available:** No specific amount. **Duration:** Entire length of undergraduate study.
Eligibility Requirements: Applicants must be a resident of the United States (including territories) or Canada, and must be enrolled or registered for enrollment on a full-time basis in a parochial, independent or private school in which the child participates in a mainstream setting. **Application Requirements:** Applicants must submit an application, with pages in numbered order; For children who use hearing aids, an unaided Audiogram performed within the last twelve months or for those with cochlear implants, the most recent mapping report (first page only); Verification of the child's enrollment, and a narrative from a teacher or principal on the child's progress on school letterhead; Recommendation from a hearing health professional (maximum of two single-sided pages); Recommendation from a current AG Bell member (Maximum of two singe-sided pages). If you do not know an AG Bell member, please provide a recommendation from an educational or therapeutic professional; Recommendation from a non-relative who is familiar with the family's financial need (maximum of two single-sided pages). **Deadline for Receipt:** April 1.

3201 ■ BETHESDA LUTHERAN HOMES AND SERVICES
600 Hoffmann Dr.
Watertown, WI 53094
800-369-4636
E-mail: dwinter@blhs.org
Web Site: http://www.blhs.org
To financially support Lutheran students pursuing degrees in any area of service to people with developmental disabilities.
Title of Award: Scholarships for Lutheran College Students **Area, Field, or Subject:** Mental health. **Level of Education for which Award is Granted:** Undergraduate **Number Awarded:** 3. **Funds Available:** $1500. **Duration:** Annually.
Eligibility Requirements: Applicant must be active communicant member of a Lutheran church; have achieved sophomore status or higher at a college or university; have a 3.0 overall GPA; and have an interest in a career in the field of developmental disabilities. **Application Requirements:** Applicants must submit a completed application form together with an essay (1-2 pages, double-spaced) on planned career in the field of developmental disabilities; four letters of recommendations; an official college transcript; an autobiography (1 page, double-spaced); a documentation of service to people who are developmentally disabled (minimum of 100 hrs); and other materials helpful from the application. **Deadline for Receipt:** April 15. **Additional Information:** ncrc@blhs.org.

3202 ■ CALIFORNIA SOCIETY OF RADIOLOGIC TECHNOLOGISTS
PO Box 14502
Torrance, CA 90503
Tel: (310)782-0927
Fax: (310)787-0478
Web Site: http://www.csrt.org
To provide financial assistance to radiologic science students enrolled in JRCERT-approved California schools.
Title of Award: Anna Ames Clinical Excellence Student Grants **Area, Field, or Subject:** Radiology. **Level of Education for which Award is Granted:** Undergraduate **Funds Available:** $500.
Eligibility Requirements: Applicants must be CSRT members or apply for membership at the time of application; must be enrolled full-time in California Department of Health Services approved and Joint Review Committee for Education in Radiologic Technology (JRCERT) accredited education program of Radiologic Sciences; must be enrolled in the program for at least 6 months at the time of receipt of the award; and, must possess exceptional skills in the clinical environment. **Application**

Requirements: Applicants must submit the completed application form and all other required materials for the Grant. **Deadline for Receipt:** September 30.

3203 ■ CALIFORNIA SOCIETY OF RADIOLOGIC TECHNOLOGISTS
PO Box 14502
Torrance, CA 90503
Tel: (310)782-0927
Fax: (310)787-0478
Web Site: http://www.csrt.org
To provide financial assistance to radiologic science students enrolled in approved California schools.
Title of Award: Ruth McMillan Student Grants **Area, Field, or Subject:** Radiology. **Level of Education for which Award is Granted:** Undergraduate **Funds Available:** $500. **Duration:** One year.
Eligibility Requirements: Applicants must be CSRT members enrolled full-time in a California Department of Health Services approved and CSRT-recognized education program of Radiologic Sciences (at least 6 months enrolled in the program at the time of receipt of the award); must possess a minimum grade point average of 2.5 in all college courses. **Application Requirements:** Applicants must submit completed application form obtained from the CSRT office and other required materials for the Grant. **Deadline for Receipt:** September 30.

3204 ■ CALIFORNIA SOCIETY OF RADIOLOGIC TECHNOLOGISTS
PO Box 14502
Torrance, CA 90503
Tel: (310)782-0927
Fax: (310)787-0478
Web Site: http://www.csrt.org
To provide an opportunity to radiologic science students enrolled in approved California schools, through financial assistance, in order for them to participate in the legislative process.
Title of Award: Superior District Legislative Mentoring Student Grants **Area, Field, or Subject:** Radiology. **Level of Education for which Award is Granted:** Undergraduate **Number Awarded:** 4. **Funds Available:** $250.
Eligibility Requirements: Applicants must be CSRT members enrolled full-time in a California Department of Health Services-approved and CSRT-recognized education program of Radiologic Sciences for at least 6 months at the time of receipt of the award; and, must possess exceptional interest in leadership and the legislative process. **Application Requirements:** Applicants must submit the completed application form obtained from the CSRT office and the all other required application information materials. **Deadline for Receipt:** May 15.

3205 ■ CALIFORNIA SOCIETY OF RADIOLOGIC TECHNOLOGISTS
PO Box 14502
Torrance, CA 90503
Tel: (310)782-0927
Fax: (310)787-0478
Web Site: http://www.csrt.org
To provide an opportunity to radiologic science students enrolled in approved California schools, through financial assistance, in order for them to participate in the legislative process.
Title of Award: Superior District Legislative Mentoring Student Grants RT to DC **Area, Field, or Subject:** Radiology. **Level of Education for which Award is Granted:** Undergraduate **Number Awarded:** 2. **Funds Available:** $1,300.
Eligibility Requirements: Applicants must be CSRT members enrolled full-time in a California Department of Health Services approved and CSRT-recognized education program of Radiologic Sciences for at least 6 months at the time of receipt of the award; must possess exceptional interest in leadership and the legislative process. **Application Requirements:** Applicants must submit the completed application form obtained from the CSRT office and the other required materials for the award. **Deadline for Receipt:** February 1.

3206 ■ CAMDEN COUNTY COLLEGE
200 N Broadway
Camden, NJ 08102-1185
Tel: (856)338-1817
Web Site: http://www.camdencc.edu

To provide opportunity to qualified students to pursue an education at CCC.

Title of Award: Diane Basilone-Engle Memorial Scholarships **Area, Field, or Subject:** Theater arts; Secretarial sciences; Veterinary science and medicine; Education. **Level of Education for which Award is Granted:** Undergraduate **Funds Available:** No specific amount. **Duration:** One academic year.
Eligibility Requirements: Applicants must be students who want to continue their degree or certificate in theater, secretariat science, veterinary science or education. **Application Requirements:** Applicants must submit one recommendation from a faculty member or administrator at Camden County College. Application forms are available online and must be sent to Camden County College Foundation, PO Box 200, College Dr., Blackwood, NJ 08012. **Deadline for Receipt:** February 18.

3207 ■ CENTRAL OHIO DIABETES ASSOCIATION
1100 Dennison Ave.
Columbus, OH 43201
Tel: (614)884-4400
Fax: (614)884-4484
Web Site: http://www.diabetesohio.org
To provide scholarships to those students with diabetes.
Title of Award: The Youth Scholarship Program **Area, Field, or Subject:** Diabetes. **Level of Education for which Award is Granted:** Undergraduate **Funds Available:** No specific amount.
Eligibility Requirements: Applicants must be full-time undergraduate students with diabetes in the Central Ohio area; must demonstrate exemplary adjustment to living with diabetes; show financial need; and demonstrate involvement in extracurricular activities which help others and foster personal growth. **Application Requirements:** Applicants must submit a completed application form. **Deadline for Receipt:** February. **Additional Information:** Central Ohio Diabetes Association at the above address.

3208 ■ CENTRASTATE HEALTHCARE FOUNDATION
916 Rte. 33, Ste. 6
Freehold, NJ 07728
Tel: (732)294-7030
Web Site: http://www.centrastatefoundation.org
To provide scholarship assistance to a deserving student who wants to pursue the health care field.
Title of Award: CentraState Associated Auxiliaries Scholarships **Area, Field, or Subject:** Health care services. **Level of Education for which Award is Granted:** Undergraduate **Number Awarded:** 3. **Funds Available:** $500. **Duration:** One year.
Eligibility Requirements: Applicant must be a student or adult who lives and volunteers in the CentraState service area; must be pursuing a career in the health care field. **Application Requirements:** Applicant must submit the application form along with transcript, two letters of recommendation, and complete essay requirements to Mrs. Valerie MacPhee, PO Box 32, Perrineville, NJ 08535. **Deadline for Receipt:** April 25.

3209 ■ CENTRASTATE HEALTHCARE FOUNDATION
916 Rte. 33, Ste. 6
Freehold, NJ 07728
Tel: (732)294-7030
Web Site: http://www.centrastatefoundation.org
To provide scholarship assistance to a graduating high school senior who attends the Freehold Regional High School District's Medical Science Program.
Title of Award: CentraState Band Aid Open Committee Scholarships **Area, Field, or Subject:** Health sciences. **Level of Education for which Award is Granted:** Undergraduate **Funds Available:** $2,000. **Duration:** One year.
Eligibility Requirements: Applicant must be planning to pursue a career in the health profession; must be a student enrolled in the Medical Sciences Program in the Freehold Regional High School District. **Application Requirements:** Applicant must submit a current transcript, letters of recommendation from two teachers and/or counselors and the completed essay requirements. Scholarship application form may be obtained from Dr. Nicholas Mennuti at the school or from CentraState Healthcare Foundation Office by calling 732-294-7030. Application form and requirements must be sent to CentraState Healthcare Foundation, 916 Rte. 33, Ste. 6, Freehold, NJ 07728. **Deadline for Receipt:** March 30.

3210 ■ CENTRASTATE HEALTHCARE FOUNDATION
916 Rte. 33, Ste. 6
Freehold, NJ 07728
Tel: (732)294-7030
Web Site: http://www.centrastatefoundation.org
To provide scholarship assistance to a deserving student who wants to pursue the healthcare field.
Title of Award: CentraState Healthcare Foundation Health Professional Scholarships **Area, Field, or Subject:** Health care services. **Level of Education for which Award is Granted:** Undergraduate **Number Awarded:** 3. **Funds Available:** $1,000. **Duration:** One year.
Eligibility Requirements: Applicant must be a graduating student who has chosen to pursue a career in the health profession. **Application Requirements:** Applicant must submit the appropriate form along with transcript, two letters of recommendation, and the complete essay requirements. **Deadline for Receipt:** April 30. **Additional Information:** Alicia Zicha at the above address.

3211 ■ CENTRASTATE HEALTHCARE FOUNDATION
916 Rte. 33, Ste. 6
Freehold, NJ 07728
Tel: (732)294-7030
Web Site: http://www.centrastatefoundation.org
To provide scholarship assistance to a graduating high school senior who attends the Freehold Regional High School District's Medical Science Program.
Title of Award: DCH Freehold Toyota Scholarships **Area, Field, or Subject:** Health sciences. **Level of Education for which Award is Granted:** Undergraduate **Funds Available:** $1,000. **Duration:** One year.
Eligibility Requirements: Applicant must be planning to pursue a career in the health profession; must be a student enrolled in the Medical Sciences Program in the Freehold Regional High School District. **Application Requirements:** Applicant must submit a current transcript, letters of recommendation from two teachers and/or counselors and the completed essay requirements. Scholarship application form may be obtained from Dr. Nicholas Mennuti at the school or from CentraState Healthcare Foundation Office by calling 732-294-7030. Application form and requirements must be sent to CentraState Healthcare Foundation, 916 Rte. 33, Ste. 6, Freehold, NJ 07728. **Deadline for Receipt:** March 30.

3212 ■ CENTRASTATE HEALTHCARE FOUNDATION
916 Rte. 33, Ste. 6
Freehold, NJ 07728
Tel: (732)294-7030
Web Site: http://www.centrastatefoundation.org
To provide scholarship assistance to a graduating high school senior who attends the Freehold Regional High School District's Medical Science Program.
Title of Award: Norkus Charitable Foundation Scholarships **Area, Field, or Subject:** Health sciences. **Level of Education for which Award is Granted:** Undergraduate **Funds Available:** $1,000. **Duration:** One year.
Eligibility Requirements: Applicant must be planning to pursue a career in the health profession; must be a student enrolled in the Medical Sciences Program in the Freehold Regional High School District. **Application Requirements:** Applicant must submit a current transcript, letters of recommendation from two teachers and/or counselors and the completed essay requirements. Scholarship application form may be obtained from Dr. Nicholas Mennuti at the school or from CentraState Healthcare Foundation Office by calling 732-294-7030. Application form and requirements must be sent to CentraState Healthcare Foundation, 916 Rte. 33, Ste. 6, Freehold, NJ 07728. **Deadline for Receipt:** March 30.

3213 ■ CENTRASTATE HEALTHCARE FOUNDATION
916 Rte. 33, Ste. 6
Freehold, NJ 07728
Tel: (732)294-7030
Web Site: http://www.centrastatefoundation.org
To provide scholarship assistance to a graduating high school senior who attends the Freehold Regional High School District's Medical Science Program.
Title of Award: Star and Barry Tobias Scholarships **Area, Field, or Subject:** Health sciences. **Level of Education for which Award is Granted:** Undergraduate **Funds Available:** $2,500. **Duration:** One year.

Eligibility Requirements: Applicant must be planning to pursue a career in the health profession; must be a student enrolled in the Medical Sciences Program in the Freehold Regional High School District. **Application Requirements:** Applicant must submit a current transcript, letters of recommendation from two teachers and/or counselors and the completed essay requirements. Scholarship application form may be obtained from Dr. Nicholas Mennuti at the school or from CentraState Healthcare Foundation Office by calling 732-294-7030. Application form and requirements must be sent to CentraState Healthcare Foundation, 916 Rte. 33, Ste. 6, Freehold, NJ 07728. **Deadline for Receipt:** March 30.

3214 ■ CHILDHOOD CANCER FOUNDATION

1300 Yonge St., Ste. No. 405
Toronto, ON, Canada M4T 1X3
Tel: (416)489-6440
Free: 800-363-1062
Fax: (416)489-9812
E-mail: info@childhoodcancer.ca
Web Site: http://www.candlelighters.ca
To provide scholarships to young Canadians who are in treatment or who have survived childhood care.
Title of Award: Childhood Cancer Foundation Scholarships **Area, Field, or Subject:** Cancer. **Level of Education for which Award is Granted:** Undergraduate **Number Awarded:** 51 in 2007. **Funds Available:** $300-$1,000, depending on the availability of funds. **Duration:** One year.
Eligibility Requirements: Applicant must be a Canadian citizen or landed immigrant; must be between the ages of 17-25 years and be either treated for some form of childhood cancer or still be on treatment. **Application Requirements:** Applicant must write a 300-500 word letter describing their future academic goals and reasons for applying for the scholarship; must provide a letter of acceptance; a statement from their doctor, pediatrician or oncologist stating that they have had some form of childhood cancer; must print and complete the application form available online. Application form and requirements must be sent to Scholarship Program, Childhood Cancer Foundation, 1300 Yonge St., Ste. 405, Toronto, ON M4T 1X3. **Deadline for Receipt:** June 30.

3215 ■ CHILDREN'S HOSPITAL OF PHILADELPHIA

34th St. and Civic Center Blvd.
Philadelphia, PA 19104-4399
Tel: (215)590-1000
Free: 800-879-2467
E-mail: fordg@email.edu
Web Site: http://www.chop.edu
To abolish childhood cancers and enhance the lives of children and families in their communities.
Title of Award: Eagles Fly for Leukemia Scholarships **Area, Field, or Subject:** Health care services. **Level of Education for which Award is Granted:** Undergraduate **Number Awarded:** 3. **Funds Available:** $1,500.
Eligibility Requirements: Applicants must be survivors of childhood cancer. **Application Requirements:** Applicants must submit a complete application form. **Additional Information:** efleukemia@aol.com.

3216 ■ CHILDREN'S HOSPITAL OF PHILADELPHIA

34th St. and Civic Center Blvd.
Philadelphia, PA 19104-4399
Tel: (215)590-1000
Free: 800-879-2467
E-mail: fordg@email.edu
Web Site: http://www.chop.edu
To advance healthcare for children by integrating patient care, innovative research and quality professional education into all programs.
Title of Award: Tim and Tom Gullikson Foundation Scholarships **Area, Field, or Subject:** General studies. **Level of Education for which Award is Granted:** Undergraduate **Funds Available:** $20,000.
Eligibility Requirements: Program is open to individuals with brain tumor; patients/survivors and/or children of brain tumor patients/survivors who intend to pursue programs at an accredited four-year college, university,vocational-technical school or other institution of higher learning. **Application Requirements:** Applicants must submit a complete application form. **Deadline for Receipt:** May 1.

3217 ■ CHILDREN'S HOSPITAL OF PHILADELPHIA

34th St. and Civic Center Blvd.
Philadelphia, PA 19104-4399
Tel: (215)590-1000
Free: 800-879-2467
E-mail: fordg@email.edu
Web Site: http://www.chop.edu
To help improve the quality of life for those affected by leukemia.
Title of Award: Michael A. Hunter Memorial Scholarships **Area, Field, or Subject:** General Studies. **Level of Education for which Award is Granted:** Undergraduate **Number Awarded:** 2. **Funds Available:** $5,000.
Eligibility Requirements: Applicants must be graduating high school seniors, community college and four-year university students who are leukemia patients and/or children of non-surviving leukemia patients; must be enrolled full-time; and must have a minimum GPA of 3.0 or "B" average. **Application Requirements:** Applicants must submit a complete application form. **Deadline for Receipt:** May 1.

3218 ■ CHILDREN'S HOSPITAL OF PHILADELPHIA

34th St. and Civic Center Blvd.
Philadelphia, PA 19104-4399
Tel: (215)590-1000
Free: 800-879-2467
E-mail: fordg@email.edu
Web Site: http://www.chop.edu
To support the financial needs of young adults who have been affected by cancer and intend to pursue higher education.
Title of Award: Matt Stauffer Memorial Scholarships **Area, Field, or Subject:** Health care services. **Level of Education for which Award is Granted:** Undergraduate **Funds Available:** varies.
Eligibility Requirements: Applicants must be 35 years or younger at the time of application; must be young adult cancer survivor/patients diagnosed between the ages of 15 and 35; must be currently attending or accepted at a two- to four-year college, university or vocational program including graduate and professional schools; and must be degree-seeking. **Application Requirements:** Applicants must submit a complete application form.

3219 ■ CHILDREN'S HOSPITAL OF PHILADELPHIA

34th St. and Civic Center Blvd.
Philadelphia, PA 19104-4399
Tel: (215)590-1000
Free: 800-879-2467
E-mail: fordg@email.edu
Web Site: http://www.chop.edu
To support the financial needs of young adults who have lost a parent/guardian to cancer or have a parent/guardian with cancer and are seeking higher education.
Title of Award: Marilyn Yetso Memorial Scholarships **Area, Field, or Subject:** Health care services. **Level of Education for which Award is Granted:** Undergraduate **Funds Available:** Varies.
Eligibility Requirements: Applicants must be 35 years at younger time of application; must be young adults who have lost a parent/guardian to cancer or have a parent/guardian with cancer or the parent/guardian experienced a cancer diagnosis between the ages of 15 and 35; must be currently attending or accepted to a two- to four-year college, university or vocational program including graduate and professional schools; and must be degree-seeking. **Application Requirements:** Applicants must submit a completed application form.

3220 ■ COLLEGE OF HEALTHCARE INFORMATION MANAGEMENT EXECUTIVES

3300 Washtenaw Ave., Ste. 225
Ann Arbor, MI 48104-4250
Tel: (734)665-0000
Fax: (734)665-4922
E-mail: staff@cio-chime.org
Web Site: http://www.cio-chime.org
To acknowledge IT staff members who show potential for advancement to a CIO and who are dedicated to professional development.
Title of Award: John Glaser Scholarships **Area, Field, or Subject:** Health care services. **Level of Education for which Award is Granted:** Undergraduate **Number Awarded:** 2. **Funds Available:** $3,000. **Duration:** One year.

Eligibility Requirements: Candidates must be employed and nominated by a current CHIME member. **Application Requirements:** Candidates may visit the website to apply online, or download the application form and mail to: John Glaser, Scholarship Committee c/o CHIME 3300 Washtenaw Ave., Ste. 225 Ann Arbor, MI 48104. **Deadline for Receipt:** August 15.

3221 ■ THE COMMUNITY FOUNDATION OF MIDDLE TENNESSEE
3833 Cleghorn Ave., Ste. 400
Nashville, TN 37215-2519
Tel: (615)321-4939; 888-540-5200
E-mail: mail@cfmt.org
Web Site: http://www.cfmt.org
To help students in planning their postsecondary education.
Title of Award: Leigh Carter Scholarships **Area, Field, or Subject:** Health care services. **Level of Education for which Award is Granted:** Undergraduate **Funds Available:** No specific amount.
Eligibility Requirements: Applicants must be full-time students attending one of the nation's accredited chiropractic colleges or universities. **Application Requirements:** Applicants must complete the application form. Applicants must submit two applicant appraisals; transcript of grades; student essay describing educational plans and how these will help in career goals. Applicants must submit one recent photograph. **Deadline for Receipt:** March 15. **Additional Information:** pcole@cfmt.org

3222 ■ COMMUNITY FOUNDATION OF SARASOTA COUNTY
PO Box 49587
Sarasota, FL 34237
Tel: (941)955-3000
Fax: (941)952-1951
E-mail: stewart@cfsarasota.org
Web Site: http://www.cfsarasota.org
To encourage and enable caring individuals to easily and effectively support the charitable causes that they care about; to help students obtain a college degree or vocational training to pursue a career in nursing or the medical field.
Title of Award: Davis Educational Scholarship Fund **Area, Field, or Subject:** Medical education. **Level of Education for which Award is Granted:** Undergraduate **Funds Available:** No specific amount.
Eligibility Requirements: Applicants must be accepted into a health related program. **Application Requirements:** Applicants must complete the application form; must submit a parent or guardian's most recent 1040 federal tax form; must provide two letters of reference from people who know the applicant well; official acceptance letter from college or vocational school; and a copy of SAT and ACT scores.

3223 ■ DELTA ZETA SORORITY
202 E Church St.
Oxford, OH 45056
Tel: (513)523-7597
Web Site: http://www.deltazeta.org
To provide financial assistance to all qualified undergraduate students.
Title of Award: Houston/Nancy Holliman Scholarships **Area, Field, or Subject:** Speech and language pathology/audiology; Hearing and deafness; Allied health. **Level of Education for which Award is Granted:** Undergraduate **Funds Available:** $1,000-$2,500. **Duration:** One academic year.
Eligibility Requirements: Applicant must be a junior or senior active, continuing member majoring in hearing and speech, audiology or an allied field; must have an academic achievements (maintaining a 3.0 average), campus honors and activities, and service to Delta Zeta. **Application Requirements:** Scholarship applications are available on the website and must be completed properly. Applicant must have the FAFSA reply form. **Deadline for Receipt:** February 15.

3224 ■ EAST TENNESSEE FOUNDATION
625 Market St., Ste. 1400
Knoxville, TN 37902
Tel: (865)524-1223; 877-524-1223
Fax: (865)637-6039
Web Site: http://www.easttennesseefoundation.org
To benefit graduates of high schools in Blount, Loudon, and Knox counties in Tennessee who wish to pursue or who are pursuing college education in a health care or medical-related field.

Title of Award: Gordon W. and Agnes P. Cobb Scholarships **Area, Field, or Subject:** Health Sciences. **Level of Education for which Award is Granted:** Undergraduate **Funds Available:** $10,000 per year. **Duration:** Maximum of 4 years.
Eligibility Requirements: Applicants must show proof of maintaining full-time enrollment and a 3.0 or better academic standing in a health care or medical related curriculum each year through the submission of academic transcripts to the foundation at the end of each semester. **Application Requirements:** Applicants must check the application process online. **Additional Information:** Applicants from single-parent families will be given special consideration. **Deadline for Receipt:** April 4. **Additional Information:** East Tennessee Foundation at the above address

3225 ■ EQUITY FOUNDATION
P.O Box 5696
Portland, OR 97228
Tel: (503)231-5759
E-mail: info@equityfoundation.org
Web Site: http://www.equityfoundation.org
To provide financial assistance and to encourage members of the gay, lesbian, bisexual and transgender communities and their children, in Northwest Oregon and Southwest Washington to pursue careers in healthcare.
Title of Award: Kaiser Permanente Northwest Pride Scholarships **Area, Field, or Subject:** Healthcare. **Level of Education for which Award is Granted:** Undergraduate **Funds Available:** No specific amount.
Eligibility Requirements: Applicants must be members of the LGBT communities. **Application Requirements:** Applicants must check the available website for the required materials. **Deadline for Receipt:** June 30. **Additional Information:** Equity Foundation at the above address

3226 ■ KEITH GILMORE FOUNDATION
5160 Skyline Way NE
Calgary, AB, Canada T2E 6V1
Tel: (403)274-1734
E-mail: kgf@keithgilmorefoundation.com
Web Site: http://www.keithgilmorefoundation.com
To provide scholarships for deserving individuals.
Title of Award: Keith Gilmore Foundation - Undergraduate Scholarships **Area, Field, or Subject:** Agriculture, Economic aspects; Medicine, Veterinary; Journalism; Communications. **Level of Education for which Award is Granted:** Undergraduate **Number Awarded:** 4. **Funds Available:** $1,500. **Duration:** One year.
Eligibility Requirements: Applicant must be an individual enrolled in an undergraduate degree program in agriculture, veterinary medicine, journalism and/or communications at a recognized university, leading to a career in the field of agriculture. **Application Requirements:** Application forms are available online at www.keithgilmorefoundation.com. Completed application must be sent to Keith Gilmore Foundation, 5160 Skyline Way NE, Calgary, AB T2E 6V1. **Deadline for Receipt:** July 1.

3227 ■ HARTFORD FOUNDATION FOR PUBLIC GIVING
10 Columbus Blvd., 8th Flr.
Hartford, CT 06106
Tel: (860)548-1888
Fax: (860)524-8346
E-mail: hfpg@hfpg.org
Web Site: http://www.hfpg.org
To provide scholarships for graduating Hispanic students from a public high school in the City of Hartford.
Title of Award: Maria Borrero Scholarships **Area, Field, or Subject:** Health care services. **Level of Education for which Award is Granted:** Undergraduate **Number Awarded:** 1. **Funds Available:** $3,000.
Eligibility Requirements: Applicants must be entering a four-year college or university (full-time enrollment) pursuing a health-related field; must demonstrate financial need; must be top third with good academic record; and must be active volunteers in school, community, or other extracurricular activities. **Application Requirements:** Application form can be downloaded online. Applicants must complete the scholarship application. Applicants must also attach the following requirements: letter of recommendation from your guidance counselor or a teacher; official high school transcript (including SAT or ACT scores); copy of the essay you submitted with your college application (If you did not have to submit one,

write a brief (no more than two pages) essay regarding your future goals); and copy of pages 1 and 2 of your parents' 2006 or most recent completed federal tax form 1040. Mail everything to Hartford Foundation College Scholarship Program. **Deadline for Receipt:** February 6. **Additional Information:** Hartford Foundation College Scholarship Program, Scholarship Management Services, Scholarship America, One Scholarship Way, PO Box 297, St. Peter, MN 56082. 800-537-4180.

3228 ■ HARTFORD FOUNDATION FOR PUBLIC GIVING
10 Columbus Blvd., 8th Flr.
Hartford, CT 06106
Tel: (860)548-1888
Fax: (860)524-8346
E-mail: hfpg@hfpg.org
Web Site: http://www.hfpg.org
To provide scholarship for freshman students of College of Agriculture and Natural Resources at University of Connecticut or Raddcliffe Hicks School.
Title of Award: College of Agriculture and Natural Resources Scholarships **Area, Field, or Subject:** Allied health; Agricultural sciences. **Level of Education for which Award is Granted:** Undergraduate **Funds Available:** $500-$2,000. **Duration:** 1 semester.
Eligibility Requirements: Applicants must be freshman students interested in Allied Health Sciences, Animal Science, Cytotechnology, Diagnostic Genetic Sciences, Dietetics, Environmental Sciences, Health Promotion Sciences, Horticulture, Landscape Architecture, Medical Technology, Natural Resources, Nutritional Sciences, Pathobiology, Preveterinary Science, Resource Economics, Turfgrass and Soil Science, Allied Science; must attend College of Agriculture and Natural Resources at University of Connecticut or Radcliffe Hicks School; and must demonstrate academic excellence. **Application Requirements:** Applicants may obtain application materials from University of Connecticut College of Agricultural and Natural Resources, Associate Dean, 1376 Storrs Rd. Unit 4090 Storrs, CT 06269-4090. Phone: 860486-2919. acadprog@canr.uconn.edu.

3229 ■ HEALTH RESOURCES AND SERVICES ADMINISTRATION - BUREAU OF HEALTH PROFESSIONS
5600 Fishers Ln.
Rockville, MD 20857
Tel: (301)443-2194
Free: 800-221-9393
E-mail: callcenter@hrsa.gov
Web Site: http://bhpr.hrsa.gov
To provide scholarships for full-time, financially needy students from disadvantaged backgrounds who are enrolled in health professions and nursing programs.
Title of Award: Scholarships for Disadvantaged Students **Area, Field, or Subject:** Health sciences. **Level of Education for which Award is Granted:** Undergraduate **Funds Available:** No specific amount.
Eligibility Requirements: Applicant must be an individual from a disadvantaged background as defined by the US Department of Health and Human Services and must come from an environment that has inhibited the individual from obtaining the knowledge, skill, and abilities required to enroll in and graduate from a health professions school, or from a program providing education or training in an allied health profession; or must come from a family with an annual income below low income thresholds according to family size published by the US Bureau of Census, adjusted annually for changes in the Consumer Price Index, and adjusted by the Secretary, HHS, for use in health professions and nursing programs; must be a citizen, national, or a lawful permanent resident of the United States. **Application Requirements:** All applicants must submit an electronic application. Required supporting documentation is available within the online application and includes: A verification of Acceptance/Good Standing Report and Data Collection for Tuition and Fees; an Authorization to Re lease Information; Form W-4; Standard form 1199A (EG) Direct Deposit Sign Up Form; and a Signed Contract. **Additional Information:** HRSA at the above address.

3230 ■ HEMOPHILIA FEDERATION OF AMERICA
1405 W Pinhook Rd., Ste. 101
Lafayette, LA 70503
Tel: (337)261-9787

Free: 800-230-9797
Fax: (337)261-1787
E-mail: info@hemophiliafed.org
Web Site: http://www.hemophiliafed.org
To assists and advocates for the bleeding disorders community.
Title of Award: Hemophilia Federation of America Educational Scholarships **Area, Field, or Subject:** Hemophilia. **Level of Education for which Award is Granted:** Undergraduate **Funds Available:** $1,500.
Eligibility Requirements: Applicants must have hemophilia or von Willlebrand (VWD) and must be seeking a post-secondary education from a college, university, or trade school. The applicant must also be able to demonstrate a commitment to improving quality of life by pursuing his/her goals with determination. **Application Requirements:** Applicants must submit a complete application; essay; proof of academic standing; statement of financial need and parents previous year's tax return (if applicant is a dependent, otherwise the applicant's tax return); proof of enrollment; two letters of reference (one professional reference the other from the HTC or physician) **Deadline for Receipt:** April 30.

3231 ■ HILLEL MONTREAL
3460 Stanley St.
Montreal, QC, Canada H3A 1R8
Tel: (514)845-9171
Fax: (514)345-6418
E-mail: romy@hillel.ca
Web Site: http://montreal.hillel.ca
To improve the quality and diversity of Hillel Montreal.
Title of Award: Karen E. Latt Memorial Scholarship **Area, Field, or Subject:** Medical education. **Level of Education for which Award is Granted:** Undergraduate **Funds Available:** No specific amount.
Eligibility Requirements: Applicants must be female graduates entering medical school. **Application Requirements:** Applicants must submit a letter stating the objectives and reasons for request; letter of acceptance to medical school for the coming academic year; transcript of grades; two letters of recommendation from professors and Social Insurance Number. **Deadline for Receipt:** May 30.

3232 ■ HUNTINGTON'S DISEASE SOCIETY OF AMERICA
505 8th Ave., Ste. 902
New York, NY 10018
Tel: (212)242-1968
Free: 800-345-4372
Fax: (212)239-3430
E-mail: hdsainfo@hdsa.org
Web Site: http://www.hdsa.org
To sponsor HD investigations that can be conducted over a 10-week period.
Title of Award: Don King Student Fellowships **Area, Field, or Subject:** Huntington's disease. **Level of Education for which Award is Granted:** Undergraduate **Funds Available:** $3,000.
Eligibility Requirements: Applicants must be matriculated undergraduate life sciences students, pre-medical students, and first-year medical students who are currently attending accredited institutions in the United States where HDSA sponsors ongoing HD research. **Deadline for Receipt:** May 1.

3233 ■ ILLINOIS STUDENT ASSISTANCE COMMISSION
1755 Lake Cook Rd.
Deerfield, IL 60015-5209
Tel: 800-899-4722
E-mail: collegezone@isac.org
Web Site: http://www.collegezone.com
To increase the number of nurse practitioners, physician assistants and certified nurse midwives practicing in areas of Illinois. To provide financial support to a qualified allied health care professional students.
Title of Award: Allied Health Care Professional Scholarships **Area, Field, or Subject:** Allied health. **Level of Education for which Award is Granted:** Undergraduate **Funds Available:** $7,500. **Duration:** One academic year.
Eligibility Requirements: Applicant must be nurse practitioner, physician assistant or certified nurse midwife student must be accepted or enrolled in a school located in Illinois and accredited in its field; must be fulltime or part-time students, although part-time students must be enrolled for at

least one-third of the number of hours required per term by the school for its full-time students; must demonstrate financial need and must apply to their school's financial aid department on or before the school's designated application deadline date. **Application Requirements:** Applicant must complete the application forms available online; must have the financial aid award information; must have the proof of enrollment or letter of acceptance into the program. Application form must be sent to: Allied Health Care Professional Scholarship Program, Illinois Department of Public Health, Center for Rural Health, 535 W Jefferson St., Springfield, IL 62761. **Deadline for Receipt:** June 30.

3234 ■ ILLINOIS STUDENT ASSISTANCE COMMISSION
1755 Lake Cook Rd.
Deerfield, IL 60015-5209
Tel: 800-899-4722
E-mail: collegezone@isac.org
Web Site: http://www.collegezone.com
To increase the number of podiatric physicians practicing in underserved areas of Illinois.
Title of Award: Illinois Student Assistance Commission Podiatric Scholarship Program **Area, Field, or Subject:** Podiatry. **Level of Education for which Award is Granted:** Undergraduate **Funds Available:** Awards provides full tuition, matriculation fees and a living stipend. **Duration:** One academic year.
Eligibility Requirements: Applicant must be a podiatric medicine student; must be an Illinois resident at the time of application and must be accepted or enrolled in a school located in Illinois and accredited in its field; must demonstrate financial need and must apply to their school's financial aid department on or before the school's designated application deadline date. **Application Requirements:** Applicant must complete the application form available online; must have the financial aid award information; must provide the proof of enrollment or letter of acceptance into the program. Application materials must be sent to: Illinois Podiatric Scholarship Program, Illinois Department of Public Health, Center for Rural Health, 535 W Jefferson St., Springfield, IL 62761. **Deadline for Receipt:** June 30.

3235 ■ IMMUNE DEFICIENCY FOUNDATION
40 W Chesapeake Ave., Ste. 308
Towson, MD 21204
Tel: (410)321-6647
Free: 800-296-4433
Fax: (410)321-9165
E-mail: idf@primaryimmune.org
Web Site: http://www.primaryimmune.org
To improve the diagnosis and treatment of patients with primary immune deficiency diseases through research, education, and advocacy.
Title of Award: The Eric Marder Scholarships **Area, Field, or Subject:** Disabilities. **Level of Education for which Award is Granted:** Undergraduate **Funds Available:** No specific amount.
Eligibility Requirements: Applicants must be undergraduate students living with primary immune deficiency diseases planning to complete their secondary education. **Application Requirements:** Applicants must complete the application form.

3236 ■ JACKSON COUNTY COMMUNITY FOUNDATION
One Jackson Square, 100 E Michigan Ave., Ste. 308
Jackson, MI 49201-1406
Tel: (517)787-1321
Fax: (517)787-4333
E-mail: jcf@jacksoncf.org
Web Site: http://www.jacksoncf.org
To assist all citizens of greater Jackson in improving the quality of their lives; to support its work as a community grantmaker and community leader.
Title of Award: The Eileen J. Smith, R.N. Memorial Scholarship **Area, Field, or Subject:** Health care services. **Level of Education for which Award is Granted:** Undergraduate **Funds Available:** $1,000.
Eligibility Requirements: Applicants must be enrolled in an accredited college or university with a major in a medical profession; must be part or full-time students with cumulative 3.0 GPA or higher. **Application Requirements:** Applicants must submit a completed application form.

3237 ■ JACKSON COUNTY COMMUNITY FOUNDATION
One Jackson Square, 100 E Michigan Ave., Ste. 308
Jackson, MI 49201-1406
Tel: (517)787-1321
Fax: (517)787-4333
E-mail: jcf@jacksoncf.org
Web Site: http://www.jacksoncf.org
To assist all citizens of greater Jackson in improving the quality of their lives; to support its work as a community grantmaker and community leader.
Title of Award: Paul Tejada Memorial Scholarship **Area, Field, or Subject:** Health care services. **Level of Education for which Award is Granted:** Undergraduate **Funds Available:** $1,500.
Eligibility Requirements: Applicants must have plans to pursue a course of study leading to a degree in health services administration, nursing or human medicine; must be full or part-time students who maintain a minimum of 12 credit hours with a minimum of 3.0 GPA. **Application Requirements:** Applicants must submit a completed application form.

3238 ■ JAMAICAN CANADIAN ASSOCIATION
995 Arrow Rd.
Toronto, ON, Canada M9M 2Z5
Tel: (416)746-5772
Fax: (416)746-7035
E-mail: info@jcassoc.org
Web Site: http://www.jcassoc.org
To provide financial assistance to students from the Caribbean or African community, who are pursuing postsecondary studies in Ontario universities/colleges.
Title of Award: Dr. Ezra Nesbeth Scholarships **Area, Field, or Subject:** Business; Technology; Computer and information sciences; Health sciences. **Level of Education for which Award is Granted:** Undergraduate **Funds Available:** $2,000. **Duration:** One year.
Eligibility Requirements: Applicants must be college or university students studying business, technology, computer science or health science; must have a high academic standing; must demonstrate leadership; must have completed at least one year of college or university in Canada; must demonstrate strong oral and written communication skills; must have an involvement in extracurricular activities within the university, AfroCanadian community, or wider Canadian community; must have landed immigrant or Canadian citizenship; must not be receiving more than one other award of equal or greater value in the receiving year; must have a good understanding of the importance of economic self-sufficiency and entrepreneurship to the success of African Canadians in the Greater Toronto Area and elsewhere in Canada. **Application Requirements:** Application forms are available online and must be sent to The Jamaican Canadian Association Center, 995 Arrow Rd., Toronto M9M 2Z5. **Additional Information:** Sponsored by Dr. Ezra Nesbeth, a graduate of the University of Waterloo and the University of Toronto with varied and extensive experience in community and health programs. **Deadline for Receipt:** July 25.

3239 ■ LAPPER COUNTY COMMUNITY FOUNDATION
220 W Nepressing St., Ste. 202
Lapeer, MI 48446
Tel: (810)664-0691
E-mail: lccf@charterinternet.com
Web Site: http://www.lapeercountycommunityfoundation.org
To promote various medical related purposes.
Title of Award: Lapeer County Medical Scholarships Fund **Area, Field, or Subject:** Medical education. **Level of Education for which Award is Granted:** Undergraduate **Funds Available:** No specific amount.
Eligibility Requirements: Applicants must be residents of Lapeer County; must be accepted into and enrolled in an accredited medical program and maintain a GPA of 3.2. **Application Requirements:** Applicants must be prepared to participate in a brief interview; must submit a transcript of records, test scores, photos and federal tax return for self or family. **Deadline for Receipt:** April 15.

3240 ■ LEWIS-CLARK STATE COLLEGE
500 8th Ave.
Lewiston, ID 83501
Tel: (208)792-5272

Web Site: http://www.lcsc.edu
To inspire educational pursuits among less capable individuals by providing financial assistance.
Title of Award: Lewis-Clark State College Presidential Technical Out-of-State Scholarships **Area, Field, or Subject:** Chemistry; Computer Science; Engineering; Information Systems Analysis; Industrial Electronics; Biology; Earth Information Systems; Radiology; Heating/Air Conditioning; Automated Manufacturing Technology; Mathematics; Printing Technology; Graphic Arts or Web Development. **Level of Education for which Award is Granted:** Undergraduate **Funds Available:** No specific amount.
Eligibility Requirements: Applicants must be new non-resident high school or transfer students who have at least 14 transferable semester credits. **Application Requirements:** Applicants must accomplish a general application available in the website. **Deadline for Receipt:** March 1 for Fall enrollment or November 1 for Spring enrollment.

3241 ■ LLOYDMINSTER REGION HEALTH FOUNDATION
218 5704-44 St.
Lloydminster, AB, Canada T9V 2A1
Tel: (306)820-6161
Fax: (780)875-9172
Web Site: http://www.lrhf.ca
To provide financial assistant to qualified individuals who want to pursue their education.
Title of Award: George Phillips Scholarships **Area, Field, or Subject:** Health care services. **Level of Education for which Award is Granted:** Undergraduate **Number Awarded:** 1. **Funds Available:** $1,000. **Duration:** One year.
Eligibility Requirements: Applicant must be an individual studying full-time in a healthcare field at an accredited college or university; must demonstrate commitment and dedication to his/her work/education; must be a permanent resident in the Llyodminster area; must have good academic ability **Application Requirements:** Applicant must submit a letter of reference from an accredited instructor together with the application form to Lloydminster Region Health Foundation, 3820-43 Ave., Lloydminster, SK S9V 1Y5. **Additional Information:** Scholarship was created to honor George's remarkable leadership, loyalty, and forward-thinking contributions while serving on the Board of Directors. **Deadline for Receipt:** July 31.

3242 ■ LLOYDMINSTER REGION HEALTH FOUNDATION
218 5704-44 St.
Lloydminster, AB, Canada T9V 2A1
Tel: (306)820-6161
Fax: (780)875-9172
Web Site: http://www.lrhf.ca
To provide financial assistant to qualified individual who wants to pursue their education.
Title of Award: Ken Stanley Memorial Scholarships **Area, Field, or Subject:** Health care services. **Level of Education for which Award is Granted:** Undergraduate **Number Awarded:** 1. **Funds Available:** $1,000. **Duration:** One year.
Eligibility Requirements: Applicant must be an individual studying full-time in a healthcare field at an accredited college or university; must demonstrate commitment and dedication to his/her work/education; must be a permanent resident in the Llyodminster area; must have good academic ability **Application Requirements:** Applicant must submit a letter of reference from an accredited instructor together with the application form to Lloydminster Region Health Foundation, 3820-43 Ave., Lloydminster, SK S9V 1Y5. **Additional Information:** Scholarship was established in honor of Ken Stanley a long-time board member of the Lloydminster Hospital and the Hospital Region Health Foundation. **Deadline for Receipt:** July 31.

3243 ■ MATANUSKA-SUSITNA COLLEGE
PO Box 2889
Palmer, AK 99645
Tel: (907)745-9774
Fax: (907)745-9711
E-mail: info@matsu.alaska.edu
Web Site: http://www.matsu.alaska.edu
To provide financial support to qualified individuals.
Title of Award: Mat-Su Health Foundation Scholarships **Area, Field, or Subject:** Health care services. **Level of Education for which Award is

Granted: Undergraduate **Funds Available:** $2,500-$5000.
Eligibility Requirements: Applicant must be a Matanuske-Susitna Borough resident enrolling or currently enrolled in higher education in any health care field. **Application Requirements:** Scholarship application forms are available at: Mat-Su Regional Outpatient Center in Wasilla, 950 E Bogard, Ste. 218, online at www.matsuhealthfoundation.org. **Deadline for Receipt:** April 4.

3244 ■ MICHIGAN ASSOCIATION FOR DEAF AND HARD HEARING
2929 Covington Court, Ste. 200
Lansing, MI 48912-4939
Tel: (517)487-0066
Free: 800-968-7327
Fax: (517)487-2586
E-mail: info@madhh.org
Web Site: http://www.madhh.org
To improve the quality of life for deaf and hard of hearing individuals in Michigan through advocacy, education, leadership, and service.
Title of Award: Brian McCartney Scholarships **Area, Field, or Subject:** Hearing and deafness. **Level of Education for which Award is Granted:** Undergraduate **Funds Available:** $500.
Eligibility Requirements: Applicants must be deaf or hard of hearing high school seniors who intend to further their education at a college, university, state-certified trade school or a state-certified technical school, or a high school senior who is presently speech and/or language impaired. Applicants must be citizens of the United States; must be of good character and self-motivated. **Application Requirements:** Applicant must submit a copy of the applicant's IEPC or a letter from an appropriate school representative stating that the applicant meets the requirements; transcript of grades from senior year; three letters of recommendation from school representative, member of clergy, representative of community service organization, employer, or parent/guardian; must write an essay describing the volunteer activities and/or experiences that demonstrate their leadership skills, their career goals and plans to use the scholarship. Applicant must submit a letter of acceptance after the selection process. **Deadline for Receipt:** March 31.

3245 ■ MINNESOTA MINORITY JUNIOR GOLF ASSOCIATION
230 TriTech Ctr.
331 2nd Ave. S
Minneapolis, MN 55401-2240
Tel: (612)333-7309
E-mail: info@mmjga.org
Web Site: http://www.mmjga.org
To support minority junior golf.
Title of Award: Evans Scholarships **Area, Field, or Subject:** Sports. **Level of Education for which Award is Granted:** Undergraduate **Number Awarded:** 3. **Funds Available:** No specific amount.
Eligibility Requirements: Applicants must have completed two full years in the MMJGA Caddie Program; must document at least 40 loops of caddying in the two-year period (with at least 25 loops at a private country club in the two-year period); must be assisting in training new caddies; must achieve "A" level or above caddie status at a country club; must be accepted at a post-secondary educational program or enrolled at a post-secondary educational program; and must maintain 2.0 or better grade point average. **Application Requirements:** Applicants must complete an application form and provide an essay.

3246 ■ MINNESOTA STATE ARCHERY ASSOCIATION
4021 W Tischer Rd.
Duluth, MN 55803
Tel: (218)393-4181
E-mail: president.msaa@mnachery.org
Web Site: http://www.mnarchery.org
To encourage outstanding students to prepare for worthwhile careers at the college of their choice and to promote the sport of archery.
Title of Award: Minnesota State Archery Association Scholarship Program **Area, Field, or Subject:** General studies. **Level of Education for which Award is Granted:** Undergraduate **Funds Available:** $250.
Eligibility Requirements: Applicants must be graduating high school students who are academically successful and who can also demonstrate a sincere interest in the sport of archery. **Application Requirements:** Applicants must submit a completed application form and a resume. **Deadline for Receipt:** June 15.

3247 ■ RYAN MULLALY SECOND CHANCE FUND
26 Meadow Ln.
Pennington, NJ 08534
E-mail: the2dchancefund@aol.com
Web Site: http://ryan2dchancefund.org
To provide financial assistance to young people who are fighting cancer to attend college.
Title of Award: Ryan Mullaly Second Chance Fund Scholarships **Area, Field, or Subject:** Cancer. **Level of Education for which Award is Granted:** Undergraduate **Funds Available:** $1,000.
Eligibility Requirements: Applicants must be citizens or permanent residents of the United States; must be diagnosed with cancer or encounter a recurrence of cancer between age 13 and graduation from high school; must be under active treatment for cancer while in high school, resulting in a substantial impact on their ability to attend class; must have a treatment history which includes chemotherapy and/or radiation; must be age 22 or younger; must have not previously been awarded a scholarship from the fund; must be currently pursuing an associate's or bachelor's degree at an accredited 2-year or 4-year college or currently enrolled in an accredited post-secondary vocational or trade program which will culminate in certification. **Application Requirements:** Applicants who are students still undergoing treatment, those with permanent effects from treatment and those at the beginning of their post-high school education are given priority.

3248 ■ MYASTHENIA GRAVIS FOUNDATION OF AMERICA
1821 University Ave. W, Ste. S256
St. Paul, MN 55104
Tel: (651)917-6256
Free: 800-541-5454
Fax: (651)917-1835
E-mail: mgfa@myasthenia.org
Web Site: http://www.myasthenia.org
To provide financial support to current medical students or graduate students interested in the scientific basis of myasthenia gravis or related neuromuscular conditions, serving both to further scientific inquiries into the nature of these disorders and to encourage more research.
Title of Award: MGFA Student Fellowships **Area, Field, or Subject:** Myasthenia Gravis. **Level of Education for which Award is Granted:** Undergraduate **Funds Available:** $5,000.
Eligibility Requirements: Applicants must be medical or graduate students. **Application Requirements:** Applicants must submit one hardcopy or one PDF file of the letter of interest, summary of the research and its significance to myasthenia gravis or related neuromuscular conditions, proposed budget, curriculum vitae of applicant and sponsoring preceptor and letter of recommendation from preceptor that indicates acceptance of the candidate and outlines the proposed work plan for the research study. **Deadline for Receipt:** March 15.

3249 ■ MYASTHENIA GRAVIS FOUNDATION OF AMERICA
1821 University Ave. W, Ste. S256
St. Paul, MN 55104
Tel: (651)917-6256
Free: 800-541-5454
Fax: (651)917-1835
E-mail: mgfa@myasthenia.org
Web Site: http://www.myasthenia.org
To provide financial assistance to nurses or nursing students interested in studying problems encountered by patients with myasthenia gravis or related neuromuscular conditions.
Title of Award: Myasthenia Gravis Foundation of America Nursing Fellowships **Area, Field, or Subject:** Myasthenia gravis. **Level of Education for which Award is Granted:** Undergraduate **Funds Available:** $5,000.
Eligibility Requirements: Applicants must be professional nurses or nursing students. **Application Requirements:** Applicant must submit four copies of a cover letter and the completed application form to the Chief Executive of the MGFA national office. **Deadline for Receipt:** October 15.

3250 ■ NATIONAL ASSOCIATION OF HEALTH SERVICES EXECUTIVES
1140 Connecticut Ave., NW
Suite 505
Washington, DC 20036
Tel: (202)429-6060
Fax: (202)429-6767
E-mail: nahsehq@nahse.org
Web Site: http://www.nahse.org
To financially assist minority students in health care management or related field.
Title of Award: Ellis J. Bonner Scholarships **Area, Field, or Subject:** Health care services; Health services administration. **Level of Education for which Award is Granted:** Doctorate, Graduate, Undergraduate **Number Awarded:** 1. **Funds Available:** No specific amount.
Eligibility Requirements: Applicant must be a NAHSE member; enrolled in college/university in Bachelor of Science, Master of Science or Doctorate Degree major in health care administration or related field; have minimum of 2.5 GPA for undergraduates and 3.0 for graduates; must have demonstrated financial need. **Application Requirements:** Applicant must submit a scholarship application; resume; transcripts (if applicable); three letters of reference; composition; tax returns; two pictures 3x5; membership application and dues. **Deadline for Receipt:** July 1.

3251 ■ NATIONAL ASSOCIATION OF HEALTH SERVICES EXECUTIVES
1140 Connecticut Ave., NW
Suite 505
Washington, DC 20036
Tel: (202)429-6060
Fax: (202)429-6767
E-mail: nahsehq@nahse.org
Web Site: http://www.nahse.org
To financially assist minority students in health care management or related field.
Title of Award: Florence S. Gaynor Scholarships **Area, Field, or Subject:** Health care services; Health services administration. **Level of Education for which Award is Granted:** Doctorate, Graduate, Undergraduate **Number Awarded:** 1. **Funds Available:** No specific amount.
Eligibility Requirements: Applicant must be a NAHSE member; enrolled in college/university in Bachelor of Science, Master of Science or Doctorate Degree major in health care administration or related field; have minimum of 2.5 GPA for undergraduates and 3.0 for graduates; must have demonstrated financial need. **Application Requirements:** Applicant must submit a scholarship application; resume; transcripts (if applicable); three letters of reference; composition; tax returns; two pictures 3x5; membership application and dues. **Additional Information:** The scholarship is established in memory of Mrs. Florence Small Gaynor. **Deadline for Receipt:** July 1.

3252 ■ NATIONAL ASSOCIATION OF HEALTH SERVICES EXECUTIVES
1140 Connecticut Ave., NW
Suite 505
Washington, DC 20036
Tel: (202)429-6060
Fax: (202)429-6767
E-mail: nahsehq@nahse.org
Web Site: http://www.nahse.org
To financially assist minority students in health care management or related field.
Title of Award: Haynes Rice Scholarships **Area, Field, or Subject:** Health care services; Health services administration. **Level of Education for which Award is Granted:** Doctorate, Graduate, Undergraduate **Number Awarded:** 1. **Funds Available:** No specific amount.
Eligibility Requirements: Applicant must be a NAHSE member; enrolled in college/university in a Bachelor of Science, Master of Science or Doctorate Degree major in health care administration or related field; have minimum of 2.5 GPA for undergraduates and 3.0 for graduates; must have demonstrated financial need. **Application Requirements:** Applicant must submit a scholarship application; resume; transcripts (if applicable); three letters of reference; composition; tax returns; two pictures 3x5; membership application and dues. **Additional Information:** The scholarship is established in memory of Mr. Haynes Rice. **Deadline for Receipt:** July 1.

3253 ■ NATIONAL CATTLEMEN'S FOUNDATION
9110 E Nichols Ave., Ste. 300
Centennial, CO 80112

Tel: (303)694-0305
E-mail: ncf@beef.org
Web Site: http://www.nationalcattlemensfoundation.org
To promote veterinary study and encourage bovine practice.
Title of Award: NCF Fort Dodge Animal Health Legacy Scholarships for Veterinary Students **Area, Field, or Subject:** Veterinary science and medicine. **Level of Education for which Award is Granted:** Undergraduate **Number Awarded:** 3. **Funds Available:** $5,000 each.
Eligibility Requirements: Applicant must be a U.S. citizen, and a veterinary student with an emphasis in bovine practice. **Application Requirements:** Applicants must submit a completed scholarship application form together with the essay and two letters of recommendation. **Additional Information:** In partnership with Fort Dodge Animal Health. **Deadline for Receipt:** April 30.

3254 ■ NATIONAL INSTITUTE OF HEALTH
2 Center Dr. Rm. 2E24, MSC 0230
Bethesda, MD 20892-0230
Tel: 888-352-3001; 888-352-3001
Fax: (301)480-3123
E-mail: ugsp@nih.gov
Web Site: http://www.ugsp.nih.gov
To provide competitive scholarships for students from disadvantaged backgrounds.
Title of Award: National Institute of Health Undergraduate Scholarship Program **Area, Field, or Subject:** Biomedical research; Behavioral sciences; Social sciences. **Level of Education for which Award is Granted:** Undergraduate **Funds Available:** No specific amount.
Eligibility Requirements: Applicants must be US citizens, nationals, or qualified noncitizens; must be enrolled or accepted for enrollment as full-time students for the current academic year at an accredited, 4-year undergraduate institution; must be from a disadvantaged background (disadvantage background means that the financial aid office has certified student as having "exceptional financial need"); and must have a 3.5 GPA or higher (on a 4.0 scale) or be within the top 5 percent of their class. **Application Requirements:** Applicants are encouraged to apply online at www.ugsp.nih.gov or may visit the website for the application forms. **Deadline for Receipt:** March 31. **Additional Information:** NIH Undergraduate Scholarship Program at the above address.

3255 ■ NATIONAL TECHNICAL HONOR SOCIETY
PO Box 1336
Flat Rock, NC 28731
Tel: (828)698-8011
Fax: (828)698-8564
Web Site: http://www.nths.org
To promote career opportunities in health care; to enhance the delivery of quality health care to all people.
Title of Award: HOSA Scholarships **Area, Field, or Subject:** Health care services. **Level of Education for which Award is Granted:** Undergraduate **Funds Available:** $2,000.
Eligibility Requirements: Applicant must be either a senior secondary or postsecondary student who plans to continue his/her education in the health care field; **Application Requirements:** Applicants must submit and mail in one envelope the typed, word-processed or legible handwriting application; he/she must submit letters of reference, and official transcript of record; all applications must be submitted directly to the National HOSA Headquarters; there is no limit to the number of applications per school or per state association. **Deadline for Receipt:** April 20.

3256 ■ NEBRASKA HIGH SCHOOL RODEO ASSOCIATION
PO Box 10
Arnold, NE 69120
Tel: (308)848-2664
Fax: (308)848-2544
E-mail: becky.dailey@hotmail.com
Web Site: http://www.hsrodeo-nebraska.com
To assist a graduating student who participates in Steer Wrestling at Nebraska High School.
Title of Award: Swede Swanson Memorial Scholarships **Area, Field, or Subject:** Sports. **Level of Education for which Award is Granted:** Undergraduate **Funds Available:** $500.
Eligibility Requirements: Applicants must be graduating senior boys who participate in the Steer Wrestling event in the Nebraska High School

Rodeo Association. **Application Requirements:** Applicants must submit a cover sheet including name, address and GPA; must submit at least one page essay stating their career goals, one letter of recommendation and a copy of their grade transcripts. **Deadline for Receipt:** June 1. **Additional Information:** 8696 S. Hershey Dickens Road Hershey, NE 69143.

3257 ■ NEBRASKA HOSPITAL ASSOCIATION
3255 Salt Creek Circle, Ste. 100
Lincoln, NE 68504-4761
Tel: (402)742-8140
Fax: (402)742-8191
E-mail: info@nhanet.org
Web Site: http://www.nhanet.org
To advance the improvement of the health of the people of Nebraska through the provision of better health care; to foster and sponsor educational programs for training of health career personnel; to provide financial aid for Nebraska hospital employees needing assistance in the pursuit of an education in the health care field; to promote and sponsor research in health care issues.
Title of Award: Nebraska Hospital Association Tuition Aid and Scholarships **Area, Field, or Subject:** Medical education. **Level of Education for which Award is Granted:** Undergraduate **Funds Available:** No specific amount.
Eligibility Requirements: Applicants must be enrolled in an accredited program leading to registration, licensure or a clinical laboratory science degree; must be employed by a member hospital of the Nebraska Hospital Association. **Application Requirements:** Applicants must complete the application form.

3258 ■ NORTH CAROLINA ASSOCIATION OF HEALTH CARE RECRUITERS
High Point Regional Hospital PO Box HP-5
High Point, NC 27261
Tel: (336)878-6029
Fax: (336)878-6709
E-mail: cglover@hprhs.com
Web Site: http://www.ncahcr.org
To assist, encourage and enable deserving students currently enrolled in an accredited program for health professions.
Title of Award: North Carolina Association of Health Care Recruiters Scholarships **Area, Field, or Subject:** Health care services. **Level of Education for which Award is Granted:** Undergraduate **Funds Available:** $500.
Eligibility Requirements: Applicants must be full-time students in North Carolina who have been accepted into an accredited ADN, BSN or allied health program. **Application Requirements:** Applicants must complete the application form.

3259 ■ NORTH DAKOTA VETERINARY MEDICAL ASSOCIATION
921 S 9th St., Ste.120
Bismarck, ND 58504
Tel: (701)221-7740
Fax: (701)221-9005
E-mail: nkopp@btinet.net
Web Site: http://www.ndvma.com
To promote veterinary medicine and quality animal care through communication, fellowship and professional growth.
Title of Award: Dr. Roger E. Meisner Veterinary Medicine Educational Scholarship Fund **Area, Field, or Subject:** Veterinary science and medicine. **Level of Education for which Award is Granted:** Undergraduate **Funds Available:** No specific amount.
Eligibility Requirements: Applicants must be students who have graduated from North Dakota High School and have been accepted in a college of veterinary medicine in North America. **Application Requirements:** Applicants must submit a completed application form and a statement of less than one page of their reasons for choosing veterinary medicine as a career, plans and extracurricular activities.

3260 ■ NORTH DAKOTA VETERINARY MEDICAL ASSOCIATION
921 S 9th St., Ste.120
Bismarck, ND 58504
Tel: (701)221-7740
Fax: (701)221-9005

E-mail: nkopp@btinet.net
Web Site: http://www.ndvma.com
To promote veterinary medicine and quality animal care through communication, fellowship and professional growth.
Title of Award: North Dakota Veterinary Medical Association Scholarships **Area, Field, or Subject:** Veterinary science and medicine. **Level of Education for which Award is Granted:** Undergraduate **Funds Available:** No specific amount.
Eligibility Requirements: Applicants must be students pursuing a career in veterinary medicine who graduated from North Dakota High School; must be residents of North Dakota for two years prior to application; must be enrolled in the professional school of any accredited college of veterinary medicine in North America. **Application Requirements:** Applicants must submit a completed application form; must send references, and residency verification for those applicants who have not applied before for the NDVMA scholarship. **Deadline for Receipt:** May 15. **Additional Information:** nkopp@btinet.net.

3261 ■ NORTH DAKOTA VETERINARY MEDICAL ASSOCIATION
921 S 9th St., Ste.120
Bismarck, ND 58504
Tel: (701)221-7740
Fax: (701)221-9005
E-mail: nkopp@btinet.net
Web Site: http://www.ndvma.com
To promote veterinary medicine and quality animal care through communication, fellowship and professional growth.
Title of Award: Dr. William "Tim" Whalen Memorial Scholarship **Area, Field, or Subject:** Veterinary science and medicine. **Level of Education for which Award is Granted:** Undergraduate **Funds Available:** $5,000.
Eligibility Requirements: Applicants must be residents of North Dakota or Clay County for at least one year prior to scholarship application; must be accepted in the professional school of any AVMA accredited college of veterinary medicine in North America. **Application Requirements:** Applicants must submit: completed application form; a typed and short autobiography including educational objectives, veterinary-related work experiences, career plans and other activities, awards, honors and special interests; college transcript; three references; verification of one year residency; and verification of acceptance to veterinary school. **Deadline for Receipt:** May 15. **Additional Information:** 701-293-8888.

3262 ■ ORPHAN FOUNDATION OF AMERICA
21351 Gentry Dr., Ste. 130
Sterling, VA 20166
Tel: (571)203-0270
Fax: (571)203-0273
E-mail: help@orphan.org
Web Site: http://www.orphan.org
To provide opportunities and resources for America's foster youth to pursue their education and succeed in life.
Title of Award: Casey Family Scholars Scholarships **Area, Field, or Subject:** Health care services. **Level of Education for which Award is Granted:** Undergraduate **Funds Available:** $10,000.
Eligibility Requirements: Applicants must be accepted or enrolled in an accredited post-secondary program at the undergraduate level in a college, university, vocational or technical institute. Applicants must be children under the age of 25, who have spent at least 12 months in foster care and who were not subsequently adopted. **Application Requirements:** Applicants must complete the application form. **Additional Information:** scholarships@orphan.org

3263 ■ PARKERSBURG AREA COMMUNITY FOUNDATION
501 Avery St.
Parkersburg, WV 26101
Tel: (304)428-4438; (866)428-4438
Fax: (304)428-1200
E-mail: info@pacfwv.com
Web Site: http://www.pacfwv.com
To encourage individuals to pursue their career in medical school.
Title of Award: S. William & Martha R. Golf Educational Scholarships **Area, Field, or Subject:** Medical education. **Level of Education for which Award is Granted:** Undergraduate **Funds Available:** $2,000.
Eligibility Requirements: Applicants must have attended high school in Wood County and must be entering or currently in medical school. **Application Requirements:** Applicants must submit a cover sheet (3 pages) and application form (4 pages); must have a personal essay; must have a high school and/or postsecondary transcript; must provide a letter of recommendation and a signed copy of the page of their or their parent's most recent tax return that indicates adjusted gross income; and must have a Student Aid Report showing estimated family contribution from FAFSA. Application form and other supporting documents must be sent to Our Community's Foundation, P.O Box 1762, Parkersburg, WV 26102. **Deadline for Receipt:** March 20.

3264 ■ PARKERSBURG AREA COMMUNITY FOUNDATION
501 Avery St.
Parkersburg, WV 26101
Tel: (304)428-4438; (866)428-4438
Fax: (304)428-1200
E-mail: info@pacfwv.com
Web Site: http://www.pacfwv.com
To provide financial assistance for qualified Wood County residents intending to pursue their studies.
Title of Award: Gail Hartshorn Scholarships **Area, Field, or Subject:** Emergency and disaster services; Paramedics. **Level of Education for which Award is Granted:** Undergraduate **Funds Available:** $240.
Eligibility Requirements: Applicants must be Wood County residents who are pursuing emergency medical technician or paramedic training. **Application Requirements:** Applicants must submit a cover sheet (3 pages) and application form (4 pages); must have a personal essay; must have a high school and/or post-secondary transcript; must provide a letter of recommendation; copy of the page of their or their parent's most recent tax return that indicates adjusted gross income; and a Student Aid Report, showing estimated family contribution, from FAFSA. Application form and other supporting documents must be sent to Our Community's Foundation, P.O Box 1762, Parkersburg, WV 26102. **Deadline for Receipt:** March 20.

3265 ■ PARKERSBURG AREA COMMUNITY FOUNDATION
501 Avery St.
Parkersburg, WV 26101
Tel: (304)428-4438; (866)428-4438
Fax: (304)428-1200
E-mail: info@pacfwv.com
Web Site: http://www.pacfwv.com
To provide financial assistance for qualified graduating seniors intending to pursue their degree in health care field.
Title of Award: Rhonda Knopp Memorial Scholarships **Area, Field, or Subject:** Health care services. **Level of Education for which Award is Granted:** Undergraduate **Funds Available:** $250-$500.
Eligibility Requirements: Applicant must be a Roane County High School graduating senior pursuing a degree in the health care field with a minimum of 2.0 GPA. **Application Requirements:** Applicants must submit a cover sheet (3 pages) and application form (4 pages); must have a personal essay; must have a high school and/or post-secondary transcript; must provide a letter of recommendation; copy of the page of their or their parent's most recent tax return that indicates adjusted gross income; and a Student Aid Report showing estimated family contribution from FAFSA. Application form and other supporting documents must be sent to Our Community's Foundation, P.O Box 1762, Parkersburg, WV 26102. **Deadline for Receipt:** March 20.

3266 ■ PARKERSBURG AREA COMMUNITY FOUNDATION
501 Avery St.
Parkersburg, WV 26101
Tel: (304)428-4438; (866)428-4438
Fax: (304)428-1200
E-mail: info@pacfwv.com
Web Site: http://www.pacfwv.com
To encourage graduating seniors to pursue their degrees in any field specializing in services for individuals with disabilities.
Title of Award: Whitaker-Minard Memorial Scholarships **Area, Field, or Subject:** Disabilities. **Level of Education for which Award is Granted:** Undergraduate **Funds Available:** $1,000.
Eligibility Requirements: Applicant must be a graduating high school senior admitted to attend college, or a currently enrolled college student; must be pursuing associate or bachelor level degrees in any field special-

izing in services for individuals with disabilities; must have a minimum of 2.5 GPA; must be a resident of Wood, Pleasants, Ritchie, Wirt, Gilmer, Calhoun, Jackson, Roane or Tyler Counties, West Virginia or Washington County, Ohio. **Application Requirements:** Applicants must submit a cover sheet (3 pages) and application form (4 pages); must have a personal essay; must have a high school and/or post-secondary transcript; must provide a letter of recommendation and a signed copy of the page of their or their parent's most recent tax return that indicates adjusted gross income; and must have a Student Aid Report showing estimated family contribution from FAFSA. Application form and other supporting documents must be sent to Our Community's Foundation, P.O Box 1762, Parkersburg, WV 26102. **Deadline for Receipt:** March 20.

3267 ■ PATIENT ADVOCATE FOUNDATION
700 Thimble Shoals Blvd., Ste. 200
Newport News, VA 23606
800-532-5274
Fax: (757)873-8999
E-mail: help@patientadvocate.org
Web Site: http://www.patientadvocate.org
To provide financial support to individuals under the age of 25 who have been diagnosed with cancer or another life-threatening disease.
Title of Award: Patient Advocate Foundations Scholarships **Area, Field, or Subject:** General studies. **Level of Education for which Award is Granted:** Undergraduate **Funds Available:** $3,000.
Eligibility Requirements: Applicants must be survivors or current patients diagnosed with cancer or another life-threatening disease; must write an essay on how their diagnosis has impacted their lives and their future goals, (1000 word maximum); must submit a copy of an acceptance letter from their chosen college, university, or vocational-technical school; must submit written documentation from physician of medical history; must provide two letters of recommendation from non-related persons (examples: teachers, coaches, community leaders). Please ask that each reference include their name, address and phone number within the letter; must provide an official high school and/or current college transcript (with school seal); financial form that demonstrates financial need with a copy of the first two pages of tax returns. **Application Requirements:** Applicants must maintain an overall 3.0 G.P.A.; must be full-time students; must sign an agreement to complete 20 hours of community service for the year the scholarship will be dispensed and provide PAF with a written confirmation from a supervisor when that service has been completed. **Additional Information:** Patient Advocate Foundation at the above address

3268 ■ PEDORTHIC FOOTWEAR ASSOCIATION
2025 M St. NW, Ste. 800
Washington, DC 20036
Tel: (202)367-1145
Free: 800-673-8447
Fax: (202)367-2145
E-mail: info@pedorthics.org
Web Site: http://www.pedorthics.org
For students committed to attending the New York College of Podiatric Medicine/EPI course.
Title of Award: The Eneslow Pedorthic Institute Scholarships **Area, Field, or Subject:** Orthotics prosthetics technology; Pathology. **Level of Education for which Award is Granted:** Undergraduate **Funds Available:** $500-$2,500.
Eligibility Requirements: Applicants must be at least 18 years old and have at least a high school diploma or equivalent; have an experience related to footwear for foot care; must describe their educational plans, including the school(s), the approximate timetable, the approximate date on which they plan to take the pedorthic certification exam (Applicants need not be enrolled in a course at the time of application); must sit for the certification exam within two years of completing course work supported by the Foundation scholarship; must agree in advance that, if selected to receive a scholarship, they will serve as advisors to the Foundation Scholarship Committee for two years immediately after receipt of a scholarship (such service shall not exceed 16 hours of consultation, generally by telephone or e-mail, over the course of those years); must describe their preferred area of concentration in pedorthics. **Application Requirements:** Applicants must submit a completed application form to the Scholarship Review Committee. Applicants must also submit three

recommendations from individuals not related to them. **Deadline for Receipt:** January 15.

3269 ■ PEDORTHIC FOOTWEAR ASSOCIATION
2025 M St. NW, Ste. 800
Washington, DC 20036
Tel: (202)367-1145
Free: 800-673-8447
Fax: (202)367-2145
E-mail: info@pedorthics.org
Web Site: http://www.pedorthics.org
To provide financial assistance to students who are interested in a career in pedorthics.
Title of Award: The Dawn Janisse Scholarships **Area, Field, or Subject:** Orthotics prosthetics technology; Pathology. **Level of Education for which Award is Granted:** Undergraduate **Funds Available:** $500-$2,500.
Eligibility Requirements: Applicants must be at least 18 years old and have at least a high school diploma or equivalent; have an experience related to footwear for foot care; must describe their educational plans, including the school(s), the approximate timetable, the approximate date on which they plan to take the pedorthic certification exam (Applicants need not be enrolled in a course at the time of application); must sit for the certification exam within two years of completing course work supported by the Foundation scholarship; must agree in advance that, if selected to receive a scholarship, they will serve as advisors to the Foundation Scholarship Committee for two years immediately after receipt of a scholarship (such service shall not exceed 16 hours of consultation, generally by telephone or e-mail, over the course of those years); must describe their preferred area of concentration in pedorthics. **Application Requirements:** Applicants must submit a completed application form to the Scholarship Review Committee. Applicants must also submit three recommendations from individuals not related to them. **Deadline for Receipt:** January 15.

3270 ■ PEDORTHIC FOOTWEAR ASSOCIATION
2025 M St. NW, Ste. 800
Washington, DC 20036
Tel: (202)367-1145
Free: 800-673-8447
Fax: (202)367-2145
E-mail: info@pedorthics.org
Web Site: http://www.pedorthics.org
To financially assist students interested in a career in pedorthics.
Title of Award: The Aristotle Mirones Scholarships **Area, Field, or Subject:** Orthotics prosthetics technology; Pathology. **Level of Education for which Award is Granted:** Undergraduate **Funds Available:** $500-$2,500.
Eligibility Requirements: Applicants must be at least 18 years old and have at least a high school diploma or equivalent; have an experience related to footwear for foot care; must describe their educational plans, including the school(s), the approximate timetable, the approximate date on which they plan to take the pedorthic certification exam (Applicants need not be enrolled in a course at the time of application); must sit for the certification exam within two years of completing course work supported by the Foundation scholarship; must agree in advance that, if selected to receive a scholarship, they will serve as advisors to the Foundation Scholarship Committee for two years immediately after receipt of a scholarship (such service shall not exceed 16 hours of consultation, generally by telephone or e-mail, over the course of those years); must describe their preferred area of concentration in pedorthics. **Application Requirements:** Applicants must submit a completed application form to the Scholarship Review Committee. Applicants must also submit three recommendations from individuals not related to them. **Additional Information:** In memory of Aristotle Mirones, founder of ARIMED Orthotics, Prosthetics and Pedorthics.

3271 ■ PEDORTHIC FOOTWEAR ASSOCIATION
2025 M St. NW, Ste. 800
Washington, DC 20036
Tel: (202)367-1145
Free: 800-673-8447
Fax: (202)367-2145

E-mail: info@pedorthics.org

Web Site: http://www.pedorthics.org

To students pursuing Fundamentals Course at Oklahoma State University. **Title of Award:** The Oklahoma State University at Okmulgee Scholarships **Area, Field, or Subject:** Orthotics prosthetics technology; Pathology. **Level of Education for which Award is Granted:** Undergraduate **Funds Available:** $500-$2,500.

Eligibility Requirements: Applicants must be at least 18 years old and have at least a high school diploma or equivalent; have an experience related to footwear for foot care; must describe their educational plans, including the school(s), the approximate timetable, the approximate date on which they plan to take the pedorthic certification exam (Applicants need not be enrolled in a course at the time of application); must sit for the certification exam within two years of completing course work supported by the Foundation scholarship; must agree in advance that, if selected to receive a scholarship, they will serve as advisors to the Foundation Scholarship Committee for two years immediately after receipt of a scholarship (such service shall not exceed 16 hours of consultation, generally by telephone or e-mail, over the course of those years); must describe their preferred area of concentration in pedorthics. **Application Requirements:** Applicants must submit a completed application form to the Scholarship Review Committee. Applicants must also submit three recommendations from individuals not related to them. **Deadline for Receipt:** January 15.

3272 ■ PEDORTHIC FOOTWEAR ASSOCIATION

2025 M St. NW, Ste. 800

Washington, DC 20036

Tel: (202)367-1145

Free: 800-673-8447

Fax: (202)367-2145

E-mail: info@pedorthics.org

Web Site: http://www.pedorthics.org

To provide financial assistance to students who are interested in a career in pedorthics.

Title of Award: The Sidney M. Pols Scholarships **Area, Field, or Subject:** Orthotics prosthetics technology; Pathology. **Level of Education for which Award is Granted:** Undergraduate **Funds Available:** $500-$2,500.

Eligibility Requirements: Applicants must be at least 18 years old and have at least a high school diploma or equivalent; have an experience related to footwear for foot care; must describe their educational plans, including the school(s), the approximate timetable, the approximate date on which they plan to take the pedorthic certification exam (Applicants need not be enrolled in a course at the time of application); must sit for the certification exam within two years of completing course work supported by the Foundation scholarship; must agree in advance that, if selected to receive a scholarship, they will serve as advisors to the Foundation Scholarship Committee for two years immediately after receipt of a scholarship (such service shall not exceed 16 hours of consultation, generally by telephone or e-mail, over the course of those years); must describe their preferred area of concentration in pedorthics. **Application Requirements:** Applicants must submit a completed application form to the Scholarship Review Committee. Applicants must also submit three recommendations from individuals not related to them. **Additional Information:** Scholarship is created by P.W. Minor and Son, Inc. **Deadline for Receipt:** January 15.

3273 ■ PEDORTHIC FOOTWEAR ASSOCIATION

2025 M St. NW, Ste. 800

Washington, DC 20036

Tel: (202)367-1145

Free: 800-673-8447

Fax: (202)367-2145

E-mail: info@pedorthics.org

Web Site: http://www.pedorthics.org

To students pursuing Basic Course at Finch University.

Title of Award: The Dr. William M. Scholl College of Podiatric Medicine Scholarships **Area, Field, or Subject:** Orthotics prosthetics technology; Pathology. **Level of Education for which Award is Granted:** Undergraduate **Funds Available:** $500-$2,500.

Eligibility Requirements: Applicants must be at least 18 years old and have at least a high school diploma or equivalent; have an experience

related to footwear for foot care; must describe their educational plans, including the school(s), the approximate timetable, the approximate date on which they plan to take the pedorthic certification exam (Applicants need not be enrolled in a course at the time of application); must sit for the certification exam within two years of completing course work supported by the Foundation scholarship; must agree in advance that, if selected to receive a scholarship, they will serve as advisors to the Foundation Scholarship Committee for two years immediately after receipt of a scholarship (such service shall not exceed 16 hours of consultation, generally by telephone or e-mail, over the course of those years); must describe their preferred area of concentration in pedorthics. **Application Requirements:** Applicants must submit a completed application form to the Scholarship Review Committee. Applicants must also submit three recommendations from individuals not related to them. **Deadline for Receipt:** January 15.

3274 ■ PEDORTHIC FOOTWEAR ASSOCIATION

2025 M St. NW, Ste. 800

Washington, DC 20036

Tel: (202)367-1145

Free: 800-673-8447

Fax: (202)367-2145

E-mail: info@pedorthics.org

Web Site: http://www.pedorthics.org

To provide financial assistance to students who are interested in a career in pedorthics.

Title of Award: The Xtra Depth University Scholarships **Area, Field, or Subject:** Orthotics prosthetics technology; Pathology. **Level of Education for which Award is Granted:** Undergraduate **Funds Available:** $500-$2,500.

Eligibility Requirements: Applicants must be at least 18 years old and have at least a high school diploma or equivalent; have an experience related to footwear for foot care; must describe their educational plans, including the school(s), the approximate timetable, the approximate date on which they plan to take the pedorthic certification exam (Applicants need not be enrolled in a course at the time of application); must sit for the certification exam within two years of completing course work supported by the Foundation scholarship; must agree in advance that, if selected to receive a scholarship, they will serve as advisors to the Foundation Scholarship Committee for two years immediately after receipt of a scholarship (such service shall not exceed 16 hours of consultation, generally by telephone or e-mail, over the course of those years); must describe their preferred area of concentration in pedorthics. **Application Requirements:** Applicants must submit a completed application form to the Scholarship Review Committee. Applicants must also submit three recommendations from individuals not related to them. **Additional Information:** Scholarship is created by P.W. Minor and Son, Inc. **Deadline for Receipt:** January 15.

3275 ■ PINNACLE WEST CAPITAL CORPORATION

PO Box 53999

Phoenix, AZ 85072-3999

Tel: (602)250-1000

Free: 800-457-2983

Web Site: http://www.pinnaclewest.com

To provide financial assistance to qualified individuals who want to pursue their career.

Title of Award: APS/Maricopa County Community Colleges Scholarships **Area, Field, or Subject:** Mechanical engineering; Electrical engineering; Civil engineering; Chemical engineering; Trades training; Information science and technology; Marketing and distribution; Accounting; Finance; Economics; Management; Education; Health care services. **Level of Education for which Award is Granted:** Undergraduate **Number Awarded:** 25. **Funds Available:** $1,000. **Duration:** One year.

Eligibility Requirements: Applicant must be an Arizona resident; must have a cumulative GPA of at least 3.0; must demonstrate financial need; must be a high school senior or current Maricopa Community College student; must be enrolled in a minimum of nine credit hours per semester. **Application Requirements:** Applicant must complete the application form available online and must be sent to ASU Scholarship Office, Arizona State University, PO Box 470412, Tempe, AZ 85287-0412. **Additional Information:** Louise Moskowitz at louise.moskowitz@aps.com.

3276 ■ PORTUGUESE AMERICAN POLICE ASSOCIATION

PO Box 51523
New Bedford, MA 02745-0045
Tel: (508)994-5390
E-mail: info@papamass.org
Web Site: http://www.papamass.org
To provide support for deserving students intending to pursue a career in either Health Care, Social Service, Law Enforcement, or other related fields.
Title of Award: Portuguese American Police Association Scholarships **Area, Field, or Subject:** Health care services, Social work, Law enforcement. **Level of Education for which Award is Granted:** Undergraduate **Number Awarded:** 6. **Funds Available:** $500. **Duration:** One year.
Eligibility Requirements: Applicant must be a Portuguese descent; must be a resident of Massachusetts; must be enrolled full-time in an accredited college or university or a graduating senior applying to full-time status in an accredited or another college or university; must be majoring in either health care, social services, law enforcement or another related field; must maintain a GPA of 2.0 or higher. **Application Requirements:** Application forms are available online. Applicant must submit an essay of no more than three paragraphs stating the reason stating their career goals; must have a high school transcript that includes the class rank; must have the current college/university transcript; must have a letter of reference from each of the following: (1) Guidance counselor or advisor and (2) Personal reference, preferably from someone with whom the applicants have work. Application materials must be sent to: Scholarship Committee, Portuguese American Police Association, Inc., PO Box 51523, New Bedford, MA 02745-0045. **Deadline for Receipt:** June 1.

3277 ■ PRIDE FOUNDATION

PO Box 2194, 1122 E Pike St. PMB 1001
Seattle, WA 98112
Tel: (206)323-3318
Free: 800-735-7287
Fax: (206)323-1017
E-mail: prideweb@pridefoundation.org
Web Site: http://www.pridefoundation.org
To provide scholarship to the students who have been stigmatized, isolated or closeted because of sexual identity issues.
Title of Award: Bill Bendiner and Doug Morgenson Scholarships **Area, Field, or Subject:** Human relations; Health sciences; Visual arts. **Level of Education for which Award is Granted:** Undergraduate **Funds Available:** No specific amount.
Eligibility Requirements: Applicant must be pursing a career in human services, health sciences or visual arts. **Application Requirements:** Qualified students are asked to submit an application to determine eligibility for scholarships. Applicants may download an application form from the Foundation's website. **Additional Information:** Pride Foundation at the above address.

3278 ■ PRIDE FOUNDATION

PO Box 2194, 1122 E Pike St. PMB 1001
Seattle, WA 98112
Tel: (206)323-3318
Free: 800-735-7287
Fax: (206)323-1017
E-mail: prideweb@pridefoundation.org
Web Site: http://www.pridefoundation.org
To provide scholarship to the students who have been stigmatized, isolated or closeted because of sexual identity issues.
Title of Award: Robert Browning Scholarships **Area, Field, or Subject:** Health sciences. **Level of Education for which Award is Granted:** Undergraduate **Funds Available:** No specific amount.
Eligibility Requirements: Applicant must be majoring in health sciences program. **Application Requirements:** Qualified students are asked to submit an application to determine eligibility for scholarships. Applicants may download an application form from the Foundation's website. **Additional Information:** Pride Foundation at the above address.

3279 ■ PRIDE FOUNDATION

PO Box 2194, 1122 E Pike St. PMB 1001
Seattle, WA 98112
Tel: (206)323-3318

Free: 800-735-7287
Fax: (206)323-1017
E-mail: prideweb@pridefoundation.org
Web Site: http://www.pridefoundation.org
To provide scholarship to the students who have been stigmatized, isolated or closeted because of sexual identity issues.
Title of Award: Derivative Duo Scholarships **Area, Field, or Subject:** Mental health; Human relations. **Level of Education for which Award is Granted:** Undergraduate **Funds Available:** No specific amount.
Eligibility Requirements: Applicant must be a resident of Washington studying mental health or human services. **Application Requirements:** Qualified students are asked to submit an application to determine eligibility for scholarships. Applicants may download an application form from the Foundation's website. **Additional Information:** Pride Foundation at the above address.

3280 ■ PUBLIC EDUCATION FOUNDATION

3360 W Sahara Ave., Ste. 160
Las Vegas, NV 89102
Tel: (702)799-1042
Fax: (702)799-5247
E-mail: steelej@ccpef.org
Web Site: http://ccpef.org
To support individuals pursuing a career in the field of health services.
Title of Award: Adelson Scholarships **Area, Field, or Subject:** Health care services. **Level of Education for which Award is Granted:** Undergraduate **Number Awarded:** 3. **Funds Available:** $2,000. **Duration:** One year.
Eligibility Requirements: Applicants must be CCSD seniors interested in pursuing a career in the field of health services at an accredited college/ university; must have a minimum 3.5 cumulative GPA; and must demonstrate financial need. **Application Requirements:** Applicants must submit a completed application form together with an essay, two letters of recommendation, transcript and a resume of awards. **Deadline for Receipt:** March 4. **Additional Information:** Shana Venenga at 702-799-1042.

3281 ■ PUBLIC EDUCATION FOUNDATION

3360 W Sahara Ave., Ste. 160
Las Vegas, NV 89102
Tel: (702)799-1042
Fax: (702)799-5247
E-mail: steelej@ccpef.org
Web Site: http://ccpef.org
To provide educational opportunities for individuals intending to pursue higher studies.
Title of Award: MSPT Sports Medicine Scholarships **Area, Field, or Subject:** Health care services; Sports medicine. **Level of Education for which Award is Granted:** Undergraduate **Number Awarded:** 2. **Funds Available:** $2,500.
Eligibility Requirements: Applicants must be CCSD seniors intending to pursue a career in healthcare/sports medicine; must be planning to attend at an accredited post-secondary institution; and must have a minimum 3.2 unweighted cumulative GPA. **Application Requirements:** Applicants must submit a completed application form along with an essay, transcript, and resume of awards. **Deadline for Receipt:** March 7. **Additional Information:** Shana Venenga at 702-799-1042.

3282 ■ REACH OUT FOR YOUTH WITH ILEITIS AND COLITIS

84 Northgate Circle
Melville, NY 11747
Tel: (631)293-3102
E-mail: info@reachourforyouth.org
Web Site: http://www.reachoutforyouth.org
To encourage students to set high educational standards.
Title of Award: ROFY Scholarships **Area, Field, or Subject:** Ileitis and Colitis. **Level of Education for which Award is Granted:** Undergraduate **Funds Available:** No specific amount.
Eligibility Requirements: Applicant must be graduating from high school; must be from a family with a paid membership. **Application Requirements:** Students applying for the scholarship must submit an essay of approximately 1000 words to the organization about living with IBD or how Reach Out for Youth helped them deal with their illness. **Deadline**

for Receipt: June 1. **Additional Information:** ROfY at the above address.

3283 ■ REDLANDS COMMUNITY SCHOLARSHIP FOUNDATION
c/o Kathleen Venegas-Boge, Admin. Asst.
PO Box 1683
Redlands, CA 92373
Tel: (909)307-9892
Fax: (909)307-9892
Web Site: http://www.redlandsscholarships.org
To encourage educational pursuits among Redlands Unified School District graduates by providing educational assistance.
Title of Award: Soroptimist International of Redlands Scholarships **Area, Field, or Subject:** Health care services; Law; Engineering; Computer and information sciences; Education; Business. **Level of Education for which Award is Granted:** Undergraduate **Number Awarded:** 1. **Funds Available:** $750.
Eligibility Requirements: Applicant must be a graduating senior who has participated in community service and who will be attending an accredited college on a full-time basis and is planning to major in one of the following fields: health care, law, engineering, computer science, education and/or business administration. **Application Requirements:** Applicants must submit a completed application form together with the scantron sheet; cover sheet; student activity and community activity sheets; personal essay; and a copy of unofficial transcript (signed by the counselor). **Additional Information:** No electronic submissions of application will be accepted. Submit two printed copies of the application and use a No. 2 pencil on the scantron sheet. **Deadline for Receipt:** February 20.

3284 ■ REGISTRY OF INTERPRETERS FOR THE DEAF
333 Commerce St.
Alexandria, VA 22314
Tel: (703)838-0030
Fax: (703)838-0454
Web Site: http://www.rid.org
To provide financial assistance to members enrolled to ITP or IPP.
Title of Award: Elizabeth Benson Scholarship Awards **Area, Field, or Subject:** Hearing and deafness. **Level of Education for which Award is Granted:** Undergraduate **Funds Available:** $500.
Eligibility Requirements: Applicants must have dual membership; enrolled full-time or 9-hours in an interpreter or transliterator program; must have completed at least one semester of ITP or IPP; have 3.0 GPA in ITP or IPP. **Application Requirements:** Applicants must submit eight copies of a letter of interest specifying financial need; an application form (can be downloaded from the website); transcripts; three letters of recommendation (must be from an ITP or IPP chair, instructor and personal reference); copies of current RID and affiliate chapter membership card. **Deadline for Receipt:** April.

3285 ■ REGISTRY OF INTERPRETERS FOR THE DEAF
333 Commerce St.
Alexandria, VA 22314
Tel: (703)838-0030
Fax: (703)838-0454
Web Site: http://www.rid.org
To provide financial support to members applying for a certification.
Title of Award: Daniel H. Pokorny Memorial Scholarship Awards **Area, Field, or Subject:** Hearing and deafness. **Level of Education for which Award is Granted:** Undergraduate **Funds Available:** No specific amount.
Eligibility Requirements: Applicant must be a member for least one year. **Application Requirements:** Applicant must send eight copies of the application form (can be downloaded from the website). **Additional Information:** If not chosen as a recipient, the applicant may re-apply for the next cycle. **Deadline for Receipt:** April 1.

3286 ■ SAFE SCHOOLS COALITION
1002 E Seneca St.
Seattle, WA 98122-4203
Tel: (206)957-1621
Fax: (206)325-2689
Web Site: http://www.safeschoolscoalition.org
To provide financial assistance for transgender-identified students.

Title of Award: Transgender Scholarships and Education Legacy Fund **Area, Field, or Subject:** Social Services; Health Care Services; Religious Education; Teaching; Law. **Level of Education for which Award is Granted:** Undergraduate **Funds Available:** No specific amount.
Eligibility Requirements: Applicants must be students of one of these fields of studies. **Application Requirements:** Applicants must check the contact information for more inquiries. **Additional Information:** The awards are sponsored by the International Foundation for Gender Education. **Deadline for Receipt:** February 1. **Additional Information:** International Foundation for Gender Education (IFGE) TSELF Awards Committee PO Box 540229 Waltham, MA 02454-0229 Phone: 781-899-2212
Fax: 781-899-2212 URL: www.tself.org.

3287 ■ THE SAN DIEGO FOUNDATION
2508 Historic Decatur Rd., Ste. 200
San Diego, CA 92106
Tel: (619)235-2300
Fax: (619)239-1710
E-mail: info@sdfoundation.org
Web Site: http://www.sdfoundation.org
To support the education of students from California.
Title of Award: Vincent Trotter Health Care Scholarships **Area, Field, or Subject:** Health care services. **Level of Education for which Award is Granted:** Undergraduate **Number Awarded:** 1-2. **Funds Available:** $1,000-$2,000.
Eligibility Requirements: Applicant must be a graduating high school senior or adult re-entry student pursuing a career in the health care field (nurse, doctor, health care aid, or medical researcher) who will attend an accredited four-year university, two-year college or licensed trade/vocational school in the U.S. Student must have a minimum 2.50 GPA or better on a 4.0 scale. **Application Requirements:** Applicants must submit a completed Common Scholarship Application together with personal statement; two letters of recommendation on official letterhead (written within the last six months); official transcript in an official and sealed envelope; a copy of most recent tax form (Form 1040-pages 1 & 2; Form 1040A-pages 1 & 2; Form 1040EZ-page 1); and an essay (maximum one page, typed, double-spaced) describing how the applicant has made a real difference in somebody's life or getting something significant accomplished. **Deadline for Receipt:** January 28. **Additional Information:** Arzo Mansury, Dir. Scholarships at 619-814-1343, or scholarships@sdfoundation.org.

3288 ■ THE SAN DIEGO FOUNDATION
2508 Historic Decatur Rd., Ste. 200
San Diego, CA 92106
Tel: (619)235-2300
Fax: (619)239-1710
E-mail: info@sdfoundation.org
Web Site: http://www.sdfoundation.org
To support the education of students from California.
Title of Award: Leon Williams Scholarships **Area, Field, or Subject:** Health care services. **Level of Education for which Award is Granted:** Undergraduate **Number Awarded:** 1. **Funds Available:** $1,000.
Eligibility Requirements: Applicant must be a graduating African-American high school senior from San Diego County; have a minimum 2.50 GPA on a 4.0 scale; attending an accredited four-year university in the U.S.; involved in communities as demonstrated by extra-curricular, work, church, or volunteer activities; have demonstrated financial need; and pursuing a career in health or the healthcare field. **Application Requirements:** Applicants must submit a completed Common Scholarship Application together with personal statement; two letters of recommendation on official letterhead (written within the last six months); official transcript in an official and sealed envelope; and a copy of most recent tax form (Form 1040-pages 1 & 2; Form 1040A-pages 1 & 2; Form 1040EZ-page 1); and an essay (maximum of two pagess, typed, double-spaced) on "Improving the Health of our Underserved Community." **Deadline for Receipt:** January 28. **Additional Information:** Arzo Mansury, Dir. Scholarships at 619-814-1343, or scholarships@sdfoundation.org.

3289 ■ SHORELINE COMMUNITY COLLEGE FOUNDATION
16101 Greenwood Ave. N, Ste. 1005
Shoreline, WA 98133-5696

Tel: (206)546-4755
Fax: (206)546-5826
E-mail: rmanchester@shoreline.edu
Web Site: http://www.shoreline.edu
To increase access and success of Shoreline Community College students.
Title of Award: Ivan Braga Scholarships **Area, Field, or Subject:** Surgery. **Level of Education for which Award is Granted:** Undergraduate **Funds Available:** No specific amount.
Eligibility Requirements: Applicants must be part-time or full-time students who are currently enrolled at Shoreline Community College. **Application Requirements:** Applicants must complete the application form.

3290 ■ SIGMA KAPPA FOUNDATION
8733 Founder Rd.
Indianapolis, IN 46268
Tel: (317)872-3275
E-mail: alewis@sigmakappa.org
Web Site: http://www.sigmakappafoundation.org
To encourage and support the scholastic development of the collegiate and alumnae sisters of the foundation.
Title of Award: Sigma Kappa Foundation Alzheimer's/Gerontology Scholarships **Area, Field, or Subject:** Alzheimer's disease, Gerontology. **Level of Education for which Award is Granted:** Undergraduate **Number Awarded:** 3. **Funds Available:** $1,000.
Eligibility Requirements: Applicant must be a graduate students or alumnae studying Alzheimer, Gerontology (the study of aging), or a related field. **Application Requirements:** Application forms are available online. Applicant must submit the transcript and recommendation letter through online. **Deadline for Receipt:** March 1.

3291 ■ SIGMA KAPPA FOUNDATION
8733 Founder Rd.
Indianapolis, IN 46268
Tel: (317)872-3275
E-mail: alewis@sigmakappa.org
Web Site: http://www.sigmakappafoundation.org
To encourage and support the scholastic development of the collegiate and alumnae sisters of the foundation.
Title of Award: Sigma Kappa Foundation Gerontology Scholarships **Area, Field, or Subject:** Gerontology. **Level of Education for which Award is Granted:** Undergraduate **Number Awarded:** 1. **Funds Available:** $1,000.
Eligibility Requirements: Applicant must be a junior, senior, or graduate student with at least one year study remaining; must be a member in good standing, majoring in Gerontology (the study of aging) or a related field; must have a minimum cumulative GPA: 3.0. **Application Requirements:** Application forms are available online. Applicant must submit the transcript and recommendation letter through online. **Deadline for Receipt:** March 1.

3292 ■ SJOGRENS SYNDROME FOUNDATION
6707 Democracy Blvd. Ste. 325
Bethesda, MD 20817
Tel: (301)530-4420
Free: 800-475-6473
Fax: (301)530-4415
E-mail: tms@sjogrens.org
Web Site: http://www.sjogrens.org
To provide financial support for students working on a semester or summer research project in Sjogren's Syndrome.
Title of Award: SSF Student Fellowships **Area, Field, or Subject:** Medical research. **Level of Education for which Award is Granted:** Graduate, Undergraduate **Funds Available:** $2,000.
Eligibility Requirements: Applicants must be medical, dental, or PhD graduate and undergraduate students; must be conducting research at an institution in the United States. **Application Requirements:** Applicants must submit a complete application package which includes: an Application Face page; abstract for the research proposal; publications; budget; letters of recommendation; statement of guarantee of adequate facilities and budget for the research proposal; and a principal investigators signed statement of responsibility. Applicants must send the documents electronically to research@sjogrens.org with a subject line: Applicant NameRe-

search Grant Application, or send on a CD to: Sjogren's Syndrome Foundation Attn: Research Grant 6707 Democracy Blvd., Ste. 325 Bethesda, MD 20817. **Deadline for Receipt:** February 1.

3293 ■ SOCIETY OF NUCLEAR MEDICINE
1850 Samuel Morse Dr.
Reston, VA 20190
Tel: (703)708-9000
Fax: (703)708-9015
Web Site: http://www.snm.org
To provide financial support to students for educational careers in line with nuclear medicine technology.
Title of Award: Paul Cole Scholarships **Area, Field, or Subject:** Nuclear medicine. **Level of Education for which Award is Granted:** Undergraduate **Funds Available:** $1,000.
Eligibility Requirements: Applicants must demonstrate financial need; be enrolled or accepted in an institution accredited through the Joint Review Committee on Educational Programs in Nuclear Medicine Technology (JRCNMT); have a minimum cumulative GPA of 2.5 or better (on a 4.0 scale) or B average in a nuclear medicine technology core curriculum. **Application Requirements:** Applicants must submit complete application, which includes statement and program director's signature; official transcripts of all format education; letter of recommendation from the program director verifying the applicant's acceptance into or enrollment in the nuclear medicine technology program. **Deadline for Receipt:** October 17.

3294 ■ STEUBEN COUNTY COMMUNITY FOUNDATION
1701 N Wayne St.
Angola, IN 46703
Tel: (260)665-6656
Fax: (260)665-8420
Web Site: http://www.steubenfoundation.org
To provide financial assistance to those students who are in need.
Title of Award: Dr. M.G. "Doc" Headley Scholarships **Area, Field, or Subject:** Agriculture; Veterinary Science. **Level of Education for which Award is Granted:** Undergraduate **Number Awarded:** Minimum of 3 persons. **Funds Available:** No specific amount.
Eligibility Requirements: Applicants must be pursuing a certified or degreed agricultural or veterinarian program at an institution of higher education. Applicants must be graduating students from Angola, Fremont, Hamilton or Prairie Heights High School. **Application Requirements:** Applicants must check the website for the application process and required materials. **Deadline for Receipt:** March 15. **Additional Information:** Steuben County Community Foundation at the above address.

3295 ■ STRAIGHTFORWARD MEDIA
508 7th St., Ste 202
Rapid City, SD 57701
Tel: (605)348-3042
Fax: (605)348-3043
E-mail: info@straightforwardmedia.com
Web Site: http://www.straightforwardmedia.com
To financially assist students in their educational pursuits.
Title of Award: StraightForward Media's Medical Professions Scholarships **Area, Field, or Subject:** Health care services. **Level of Education for which Award is Granted:** Undergraduate **Number Awarded:** 4. **Funds Available:** $500.
Eligibility Requirements: Applicant must be a student majoring in the medical field. **Application Requirements:** Applicants must complete scholarship application online. **Additional Information:** Awards are given four times a year. **Deadline for Receipt:** March, June, September, December.

3296 ■ TANANA VALLEY CAMPUS
604 Barnette St.
Fairbanks, AK 99701
Tel: (907)455-2800; 877-882-8827
Web Site: http://www.tvc.uaf.edu
To provide support for deserving students intending to pursue their careers in radiologic technology.
Title of Award: Stacy Kaiser Memorial Funds **Area, Field, or Subject:** Radiology. **Level of Education for which Award is Granted:** Undergraduate **Funds Available:** $1,000. **Duration:** One year.

Eligibility Requirements: Applicants must be residents of Alaska; must be in the second year of program in radiologic technology. **Application Requirements:** Scholarship applications are available online and must be completed and sent to: uaonline.alaska.edu (to access the scholarship application, applicant must choose to "Login to secured area "if they have a UA ID or apply for admission for the new students).

3297 ■ TANANA VALLEY CAMPUS
604 Barnette St.
Fairbanks, AK 99701
Tel: (907)455-2800; 877-882-8827
Web Site: http://www.tvc.uaf.edu
To assist students in the health care services field at Tahana Valley Campus and/or Kuskokwim Campus within the college of Rural and Community Development at UAF.
Title of Award: Schaible Health Care Services Scholarships **Area, Field, or Subject:** Health care services. **Level of Education for which Award is Granted:** Undergraduate **Funds Available:** $500. **Duration:** One year. **Eligibility Requirements:** Applicants must be attending at Kuskokwom Campus or Tahana Valley Campus; must be enrolled in health care service. **Application Requirements:** Scholarship applications are available online at uaonline.alaska.edu (to access the scholarship application, applicant must choose "Login to secured area" if they have a UA ID or apply for admission for the new students).

3298 ■ UNIVERSITY OF ALASKA ANCHORAGE
3211 Providence Dr.
Anchorage, AK 99508
Tel: (907)786-1800
Web Site: http://www.uaa.alaska.edu
To provide financial assistance for tuition and other educational expenses to full-time students who are formally admitted to a degreeseeking program in the area of biochemistry, immunology, or microbiology at the University of Alaska Anchorage.
Title of Award: UAA Kris Knudson Memorial Scholarships **Area, Field, or Subject:** Biochemistry; Immunology; Microbiology. **Level of Education for which Award is Granted:** Graduate, Undergraduate **Funds Available:** $500-$885.
Eligibility Requirements: Applicant must demonstrate motivation, academic and leadership potential; must be in good academic standing with a minimum cumulative GPA of 3.0; must be formally admitted to an undergraduate or graduate degree-seeking program in the area of biochemistry, immunology, or microbiology at the University of Alaska Anchorage; must plan on enrolling full-time (12 credits) for undergraduate and (9 credits) for graduate at the University of Alaska Anchorage; must have completed at least fifteen credits in chemistry, biological sciences, and/or natural sciences; must be involved in a research project within the area of biochemistry, immunology, or microbiology; may be a U.S citizen, non-U.S. citizen, Alaska resident, or out-of-state resident; must be enrolled in the semester for which the award is made. **Application Requirements:** Applicants must submit a brief essay (250 words max) describing their involvement in a research project related to biochemistry, immunology, or microbiology. Application forms are available at www.uaa. alaska.edu/scholarships/kris.cfm. **Deadline for Receipt:** February 15.

3299 ■ UNIVERSITY OF CALIFORNIA, BERKELEY
301B Campbell Hall No. 2922
Berkeley, CA 94720-2922
Tel: (510)643-6929
E-mail: scholarships@learning.berkeley.edu
Web Site: http://www.berkeley.edu
To provide financial support for outstanding sophomore and junior students.
Title of Award: Udall Scholarships **Area, Field, or Subject:** Environmental science, Health care services. **Level of Education for which Award is Granted:** Undergraduate **Funds Available:** $5,000 for educational expenses. UC Berkeley selection committee will select the university's nominee based on the application materials and criteria.
Eligibility Requirements: Applicant must be a student who studies the environmental and related fields; must be a Native American or Alaska Native in fields related to health care or tribal public policy; Applicant must be a full-time sophomore or junior students; must be a U.S. citizen or resident alien; must have a minimum of 3.0 GPA. **Application Require-**

ments: Applicant must complete the application form; must have a 800-word essay discussing a significant public speech, legislative act, or public policy statement by Congressman Udall and its relationship to the applicant's interest or coursework; must have a three letters of recommendation from: (1) a faculty member who can discuss the applicant's potential; (2) a faculty member in the applicant's of study; (3) another individual who can attest to the applicant's capabilities; must have the official college transcripts. **Deadline for Receipt:** February 20.

3300 ■ UNIVERSITY OF NORTH CAROLINA SCHOOL OF JOURNALISM AND MASS COMMUNICATION
University of North Carolina, Carol Hall CB 3365
Chapel Hill, NC 27599-3365
Tel: (919)962-1204
Fax: (919)962-0620
E-mail: jomc@unc.edu
Web Site: http://www.jomc.unc.edu
To educate journalists so that they can communicate about science and medicine effectively.
Title of Award: Victoria M. Gardner Scholarships **Area, Field, or Subject:** Medical. **Level of Education for which Award is Granted:** Undergraduate **Funds Available:** $5,500.
Eligibility Requirements: Applicants must be students interested in families, children, and medical issues. **Application Requirements:** Applicants must complete the application form. **Deadline for Receipt:** October 1.

3301 ■ UNIVERSITY OF TORONTO
315 Bloor St. W
Toronto, ON, Canada M5S 1A3
Tel: (416)978-2011
E-mail: information.commonsats@utoronto.ca
Web Site: http://www.utoronto.ca
To support students with their educational pursuit.
Title of Award: City of Toronto Scholarships for Aboriginal Students **Area, Field, or Subject:** Health services administration. **Level of Education for which Award is Granted:** Graduate, Undergraduate **Funds Available:** Approximately $4500.
Eligibility Requirements: Applicants must be an undergraduate or graduate aboriginal student studying in any of the health professional programs. **Application Requirements:** Applicants must submit a completed application form along with the required materials and informations. **Deadline for Receipt:** October 31.

3302 ■ USDA ANIMAL AND PLANT HEALTH INSPECTION SERVICE
USDA, APHIS, Human Resources/Employment
4700 River Rd., Unit 106
Riverdale, MD 20737
Tel: (301)734-5596
Web Site: http://www.aphis.usda.gov
To provide financial assistance to graduates and undergraduates of veterinary medicine and biomedical sciences.
Title of Award: Saul T. Wilson, Jr. Scholarships **Area, Field, or Subject:** Veterinary; Medicine, Veterinary; Biomedical sciences. **Level of Education for which Award is Granted:** Graduate, Undergraduate **Funds Available:** $5,000 up to $10,000. **Duration:** One year.
Eligibility Requirements: Applicants must be U.S. citizens enrolled in an accredited college or university within the United States as full-time students in good academic standing; must be undergraduate students who have completed at least 2 years (60 semester or 90 quarter hours) of a 4-year preveterinary medicine or other biomedical science curriculum or graduate students who have completed not more than 1 year (18 semester or 27 quarter hours) of study in veterinary medicine; must be willing to work for the agency during school breaks (both summer and holiday periods). **Application Requirements:** Applicants must submit resume, including current and summer addresses and telephone numbers; transcripts of all college courses completed; letter of acceptance, if entering graduate school; three letters of recommendation from college officials; original essay, not exceeding 500 words on the topic: "Why I should receive a Saul T. Wilson, Jr., Scholarship and what contributions I would make to APHIS, Veterinary Services"; documentation of service, if they have served in the U.S. Armed Forces. **Deadline for Receipt:** March 1.

3303 ■ VENTURA COUNTY MEDICAL ASSOCIATION ALLIANCE
601 ELLA.MDaily Dr.
Camarillo, CA 93010
Tel: (805)484-6822
E-mail: info@vcma-alliance.com
Web Site: http://www.vcma-alliance.com
To educate and protect the health and well-being of the people of Ventura County.
Title of Award: Ventura County Medical Association Alliance Scholarships **Area, Field, or Subject:** Medicine. **Level of Education for which Award is Granted:** Undergraduate **Funds Available:** No specific amount.
Eligibility Requirements: Applicants must be accepted or currently enrolled in a health career program; must be students of Ventura County.
Application Requirements: Applicants must submit a copy of health career acceptance notification, most recent transcript or progress report (for students attending technical/vocational school), brief biography, recent photo, completed application form and letter of recommendation from a person who can speak to the character and motivation of applicant. **Deadline for Receipt:** June 20.

3304 ■ WASHINGTON HOSPITAL HEALTH CARE SYSTEM
2000 Mowry Ave.
Fremont, CA 94538
Tel: (510)797-1111
E-mail: foundation@whhs.com
Web Site: http://www.whhs.com
To meet the healthcare needs of the district residents through medical services, education and research.
Title of Award: Medical Staff Scholarships **Area, Field, or Subject:** Health sciences. **Level of Education for which Award is Granted:** Undergraduate **Number Awarded:** 2. **Funds Available:** $1,500.
Eligibility Requirements: Applicants must be students residing within the Washington Township Health Care District who are pursuing careers in the health sciences field. **Application Requirements:** Applicants must submit a completed application form. **Additional Information:** 510-791-3446.

3305 ■ WASHINGTON HOSPITAL HEALTH CARE SYSTEM
2000 Mowry Ave.
Fremont, CA 94538
Tel: (510)797-1111
E-mail: foundation@whhs.com
Web Site: http://www.whhs.com
To meet the healthcare needs of district residents through medical services, education and research.
Title of Award: Service League Volunteer Scholarships **Area, Field, or Subject:** Health care services. **Level of Education for which Award is Granted:** Undergraduate **Number Awarded:** 2. **Funds Available:** $1,000. **Duration:** 3 years.
Eligibility Requirements: Applicants must be graduating high school seniors or college students who are pursuing studies in a health-related field; must have 2.50 GPA or higher; must be U.S. citizens and residents of Washington Hospital District; must have been accepted by an accredited school, college or university offering a bachelor or higher degree program in a health-related field; must be full-time students and must have comleted 100 hours of volunteer service or employment in a health-related field. **Application Requirements:** Applicants must submit: completed application form; current letters of recommendation from a Director of Volunteer Services, employer, counselor, advisor or teacher; high school or college transcript and proof of citizenship. **Deadline for Receipt:** April 1. **Additional Information:** 510-791-3465.

3306 ■ WEST VIRGINIA RURAL HEALTH EDUCATION PARTNERSHIPS
PO Box 9003
Morgantown, WV 26506-9003
Tel: (304)293-6753
E-mail: klrobinson@hsc.wvu.edu
Web Site: http://www.wvrhep.org
To increase the number of primary care providers in rural West Virginia.
Title of Award: Health Sciences Scholarship Program **Area, Field, or Subject:** Health sciences. **Level of Education for which Award is Granted:** Undergraduate **Funds Available:** $20,000.

Eligibility Requirements: Applicants must be fourth year medical students at a West Virginia school of medicine or osteopathy who are entering primary care internship or residency programs in West Virginia; applicants must either be students who are in the final year of a primary care educational program in West Virginia for nurse practitioners or physician assistants, or a master's degree nursing education; or students who are in the final year of a graduate program in physical therapy. **Application Requirements:** Applicants must submit a complete application form. **Additional Information:** tyler@hepc.wvnet.edu.

3307 ■ WEST VIRGINIA RURAL HEALTH EDUCATION PARTNERSHIPS
PO Box 9003
Morgantown, WV 26506-9003
Tel: (304)293-6753
E-mail: klrobinson@hsc.wvu.edu
Web Site: http://www.wvrhep.org
To provide loans to students at schools of medicine or osteopathy in West Virginia.
Title of Award: Medical Students Loan Program **Area, Field, or Subject:** Health sciences. **Level of Education for which Award is Granted:** Undergraduate **Funds Available:** $10,000.
Eligibility Requirements: Applicants must be accepted for enrollment or be enrolled full-time in a West Virginia school of medicine or osteopathy. **Application Requirements:** Applicants must submit completed application form.

3308 ■ WINSTON-SALEM FOUNDATION
860 W Fifth St.
Winston-Salem, NC 27101-2506
Tel: (336)725-2382
Fax: (336)727-0581
E-mail: info@wsfoundation.org
Web Site: http://www.wsfoundation.org
To provide grants to the North Carolina residents pursuing education in the allied health fields.
Title of Award: Oliver Joel and Ellen Pell Denny Healthcare Scholarship Fund **Area, Field, or Subject:** Health care services. **Level of Education for which Award is Granted:** Undergraduate **Funds Available:** $1,200. **Duration:** One year.
Eligibility Requirements: Applicants must be seeking a two or four year degree or be enrolled in a program leading to a certificate or diploma; be attending an accredited North Carolina school pursuing healthcare education such as, but not limited, registered nursing, licensed practical nursing, nuclear medicine, radiography, and respiratory therapy; provide an acceptance letter for all programs; have a family adjusted gross income that does not exceed $80,000; have a high school/college cumulative GPA of at least 2.5 for all healthcare programs, including nursing. Students must be North Carolina residents and US citizens. Preference will be given to those living in Forsyth, Davidson, Davie, Stokes, Surry, and Yadkin counties. **Application Requirements:** The Winston-Salem Foundation's General Financial Aid Application will be used to apply for this scholarship. The General Financial Aid Applications are available in high school guidance office and on the website. **Deadline for Receipt:** March 31. **Additional Information:** WSF Student Aid Department, 336-714-3445.

Allied Health

3309 ■ AMBUCS RESOURCE CENTER
PO Box 5127
High Point, NC 27262
800-838-1845
Fax: (336)852-6830
E-mail: janiceb@ambucs.org
Web Site: http://www.ambucs.org
To ensure that a new generation of therapists will continue to enhance the lives of people with disabilities.
Title of Award: AMBUCS Scholarships for Therapists Program **Area, Field, or Subject:** Physical therapy; Occupational therapy; Speech and language pathology/audiology. **Level of Education for which Award is Granted:** Graduate, Undergraduate **Funds Available:** $500-$1,500.
Eligibility Requirements: Applicant must be a citizen of the United States; with documented financial need; with good scholastic standing; be

accepted at the junior or senior undergraduate, or graduate level in a program which qualifies the applicant for clinical practice in occupational therapy, physical therapy, speech and language pathology and hearing audiology; express an intent to enter clinical practice in chosen field of therapy in the United States upon completion of course of study for which aid is requested. **Application Requirements:** Applicants should complete online application and must submit most current IRS form 1040, narrative statement and enrollment certification. **Deadline for Receipt:** Mid-January until April 15 annually.

3310 ■ BENTON COUNTY FOUNDATION
PO Box 911
Corvallis, OR 97339
Tel: (541)753-1603
Web Site: http://www.bentoncountyfoundation.org
To encourage and support ethnic minority undergraduate women enrolled in the College of Science.
Title of Award: Margaret Dowell-Gravatt, M.D. Scholarship **Area, Field, or Subject:** Zoology; Microbiology; Medical technology; Medicine; Nursing; Physical therapy; Occupational therapy. **Level of Education for which Award is Granted:** Undergraduate **Funds Available:** No specific amount.
Eligibility Requirements: Applicant must: be pursuing a degree in Zoology or Microbiology or one of the following pre-health programs: Medical Technology, Medicine, Nursing, Physical and/or Occupational therapy. Applicant must: be enrolled full-time at the sophomore, junior, or senior level; have a GPA of 2.5 overall and 3.0 in science courses required in their major field or pre-health curriculum; qualify for financial assistance as defined by the Financial Aid Office of OSU. **Application Requirements:** Applicant may contact the Foundation for application form and other requirements. **Additional Information:** Benton County Foundation at the above address.

3311 ■ FIRST COMMUNITY FOUNDATION OF PENNSYLVANIA, WILLIAMSPORT-LYCOMING
330 Pine St., Suite 401
Williamsport, PA 17701
Tel: (570)321-1500; (866)901-2372
Fax: (570)321-6434
E-mail: fcfpa@fcfpa.org
Web Site: http://www.wlfoundation.org
To provide academic support for Danville Area High School seniors who have been accepted into a full-time undergraduate program at an accredited institution of higher education and who are entering a health-related field.
Title of Award: Eleanor McWilliams Burke Fund **Area, Field, or Subject:** Medicine; Nursing; Nutrition; Pharmacy; or Physical therapy. **Level of Education for which Award is Granted:** Undergraduate **Funds Available:** No specific amount.
Eligibility Requirements: Applicants must be entering a health related field. **Application Requirements:** Applicants may request an application from the Guidance Counselor of Danville Area School District. **Additional Information:** Gary Grozier, Guidance Counselor of Danville Area School District, 600 Walnut St., Danvilled, PA 17821; 570-271-3268 ext. 2006; ggrozier@danville.k12.pa.us.

3312 ■ FIRST COMMUNITY FOUNDATION OF PENNSYLVANIA, WILLIAMSPORT-LYCOMING
330 Pine St., Suite 401
Williamsport, PA 17701
Tel: (570)321-1500; (866)901-2372
Fax: (570)321-6434
E-mail: fcfpa@fcfpa.org
Web Site: http://www.wlfoundation.org
To provide scholarship for Montoursville Area High School seniors of high scholastic standing who are enrolled at a college or other educational institution pursuing a major in physical therapy.
Title of Award: Monica M. Weaver Memorial Fund **Area, Field, or Subject:** Physical therapy. **Level of Education for which Award is Granted:** Undergraduate **Funds Available:** No specific amount.
Eligibility Requirements: Students must have resided in the Montoursville Area School District for a minimum of three years prior to graduation. **Application Requirements:** Applicants may contact and request an ap-

plication from the Montoursville Area High School. **Additional Information:** Ronda Albert, Montoursville Area High School, 100 N Arch St, Montoursville, PA 17754; 570-368-3509; ralbert@montoursville.k12.pa.us.

3313 ■ FOUNDATION FOR THE CAROLINAS
217 S Tryon St.
Charlotte, NC 28202
Tel: (704)973-4500
Free: 800-973-7244
Web Site: http://www.fftc.org
To assist North Iredell High School graduates in obtaining a degree in physical therapy, medicine or nursing from a post-secondary accredited institution.
Title of Award: The Sibyl Jennings Vorheis Memorial Scholarship Program **Area, Field, or Subject:** Physical therapy; Medicine; Nursing. **Level of Education for which Award is Granted:** Undergraduate **Funds Available:** $3,000. **Duration:** One year.
Eligibility Requirements: Applicants must have graduated from North Iredell High School with a minimum cumulative grade point average of 3.0 (on 4.0 scale). **Application Requirements:** Applicants must submit completed application form; verification of acceptance into the accredited graduate program; official copy of college transcript; two recommendation forms and letters of recommendation; and a typewritten application statement of eligibility expressing applicant's educational and career goals, reasons for applying for the scholarship, and why the applicant feels they are a good candidate for the scholarship. **Deadline for Receipt:** April 1.

3314 ■ HARTFORD FOUNDATION FOR PUBLIC GIVING
10 Columbus Blvd., 8th Flr.
Hartford, CT 06106
Tel: (860)548-1888
Fax: (860)524-8346
E-mail: hfpg@hfpg.org
Web Site: http://www.hfpg.org
To provide scholarship to the students enrolled in an accredited school of Occupational or Physical Therapy.
Title of Award: Hartford Foundation for Public Giving Occupational Therapy Scholarships **Area, Field, or Subject:** Art therapy; Music therapy; Physical therapy. **Level of Education for which Award is Granted:** Undergraduate **Funds Available:** $500.
Eligibility Requirements: Applicants must: be a US citizen; be enrolled in an Occupational (including art and music) or Physical Therapy; have a letter of sponsorship form local DAR chapter. **Application Requirements:** For Connecticut residents, to obtain application materials, send a self-addressed stamped envelope to: National Society Daughters of American Revolution, 215 Loomis St., North Granby, CT 06060. **Deadline for Receipt:** February 15 or August 15. **Additional Information:** Mrs. Michael L. Stewart, CT State Chairperson, NSDAR Scholarship Committee. L2stew@yahoo.com; 860-653-4203.

3315 ■ JEWISH FOUNDATION FOR EDUCATION OF WOMEN
135 E 64th St.
New York, NY 10065
Tel: (212)288-3931
Fax: (212)288-5798
E-mail: info@jfew.org
Web Site: http://www.jfew.org
To provide financial support for emigres from the former Soviet Union to train in medicine, dentistry, dental hygiene, nursing, pharmacy, occupational and physical therapy, physician assistant, CVT, and sonography programs.
Title of Award: Scholarships for Emigres in the Health Sciences **Area, Field, or Subject:** Medicine; Dentistry; Nursing; Pharmacy; Physical therapy; Physiology. **Level of Education for which Award is Granted:** Undergraduate **Funds Available:** $5,000. **Duration:** One year.
Eligibility Requirements: Applicants must be students from the former Soviet Union; must be residents of New York City or the counties of Nassau, Suffolk or Westchester; must already be enrolled in or about to enroll in a health science program within that geographic area; and must be enrolled full-time, in good standing, and demonstrate financial need. **Application Requirements:** Applicants must submit all the required application information.

3316 ■ PARKERSBURG AREA COMMUNITY FOUNDATION
501 Avery St.
Parkersburg, WV 26101
Tel: (304)428-4438; (866)428-4438
Fax: (304)428-1200
E-mail: info@pacfwv.com
Web Site: http://www.pacfwv.com
To provide financial assistance for qualified individuals intending to pursue studies involving massage therapy or physical or occupational therapy.
Title of Award: Dave Couch Memorial Scholarships **Area, Field, or Subject:** Physical therapy; Occupational therapy. **Level of Education for which Award is Granted:** Undergraduate **Funds Available:** $500.
Eligibility Requirements: Applicant must be a resident of Wood, Wirt, Jackson, Pleasants, Ritchie, Roane, Mason, Calhoun, Gilmer, or Doddridge in WV or Washington County, OH; must be actively pursuing a course of study involving massage therapy or physical or occupational therapy. **Application Requirements:** Applicants must submit a cover sheet (3 pages) and application form (4 pages); must have a personal essay; must have high school and/or post-secondary transcripts; must provide a letter of recommendation in a signed and sealed envelope; a copy of the page of their or their parent's most recent tax return that indicates adjusted gross income; must have a Student Aid Report, showing estimated family contribution, from FAFSA. Application form and other supporting documents must be sent to Our Community's Foundation, P.O Box 1762, Parkersburg, WV 26102. **Deadline for Receipt:** March 20.

Chiropractic

3317 ■ BLAIR CHIROPRACTIC SOCIETY
8603 34th St. N
Lake Elmo, MN 55042
Tel: (651)748-5731
Web Site: http://www.blairchiropractic.com
To enhance the educational opportunities of chiropractic students with an interest in specific upper cervical Blair technique by providing financial assistance to eligible students attending chiropractic schools.
Title of Award: Beatrice K. Blair Scholarships **Area, Field, or Subject:** Chiropractic. **Level of Education for which Award is Granted:** Undergraduate **Funds Available:** 1,000.
Eligibility Requirements: The applicant must be a student in good standing at an accredited chiropractic college and a member of a student Blair club if available at their school. **Deadline for Receipt:** June 30. **Additional Information:** Dr. Alfred Tomp, Blair Scholarship Committee, 22421 Gilberto No. F, Rancho Santa Margarita, CA 92688.

Dentistry .

3318 ■ ALBERTA LEARNING INFORMATION SERVICE - ALBERTA SCHOLARSHIP PROGRAM
Box 28000 Sta. Main
Edmonton, AB, Canada T5J 4R4
Tel: (780)427-8640
Fax: (780)427-1288
E-mail: scholarship@gov.ab.ca
Web Site: http://www.alis.alberta.ca
To reward the outstanding academic achievement of Alberta post-secondary students who are continuing full-time in an undergraduate program in Alberta.
Title of Award: Jason Lang Scholarship **Area, Field, or Subject:** Law; Medicine; Pharmacy; Dentistry. **Level of Education for which Award is Granted:** Undergraduate **Funds Available:** $1,000.
Eligibility Requirements: Nominees must be enrolled full-time in an undergraduate or professional program, such as Law, Medicine, Pharmacy or Dentistry at an eligible Alberta post-secondary institution. These include publicly-funded colleges, technical institutes, universities, private colleges accredited to grant degrees, and the Banff Centre. **Application Requirements:** Recipients are nominated by the Awards Office at participating Alberta institutions where they have obtained qualifying grades. For information on the nomination process and eligibility, contact the Awards Office. **Deadline for Receipt:** October 15 and February 15. **Additional Information:** Alberta Scholarship Programs at the above address.

3319 ■ AMERICAN DENTAL ASSOCIATION
211 E Chicago Ave.
Chicago, IL 60611-2678
Tel: (312)440-2500
E-mail: membership@ada.org
Web Site: http://www.ada.org
To provide financial assistance for furthering education of students in pursuing the field of dentistry.
Title of Award: American Dental Association Dental Assisting Scholarship Program **Area, Field, or Subject:** Dentistry. **Level of Education for which Award is Granted:** Undergraduate **Number Awarded:** 10. **Funds Available:** $1,000.
Eligibility Requirements: Applicants must be a U.S. citizen (permanent resident status does not qualify); entering as student at the time of application and enrolled in a dental assisting program accredited by the Commission on Dental Accreditation of the American Dental Association; enrolled as a full-time student, a minimum of 12 credit hours; demonstrate a minimum financial need of $1,000; have a minimum accumulative grade point average of 3.0 based on a 4.0 scale; and, two reference forms, one from a dentist or dental assisting representative and/or one from a school representative in support of the application must be submitted as part of the application form. **Application Requirements:** Applicant must submit an application form that is typed or printed in black ink, completed and signed by school officials; completed application form, including the Academic Achievement Record Form and Financial Needs Assessment Form, which are a part of the application form, and signed by school official; a copy of the school's letter of acceptance, if entering first-year student; two completed reference forms, sealed and signed on the back flap of the envelopes by the referrers (required forms must be used which are a part of the scholarship application form); typed, biographical sketch questionnaire (required form must be used which is a part of the scholarship application form); a self-addressed, stamped postcard, which can be mailed upon receipt of the application (if the applicant wishes to have verification that the application was received). **Deadline for Receipt:** September 5.

3320 ■ AMERICAN DENTAL ASSOCIATION
211 E Chicago Ave.
Chicago, IL 60611-2678
Tel: (312)440-2500
E-mail: membership@ada.org
Web Site: http://www.ada.org
To provide financial assistance for furthering education of students in pursuing the field of dentistry.
Title of Award: American Dental Association Dental Hygiene Scholarship Program **Area, Field, or Subject:** Dentistry. **Level of Education for which Award is Granted:** Undergraduate **Number Awarded:** 15. **Funds Available:** $1,000.
Eligibility Requirements: Applicants must be U.S. citizen (permanent resident status does not qualify); entering final year student at the time of application and currently attending a dental hygiene program accredited by the Commission on Dental Accreditation of the American Dental Association; enrolled as a full-time student, a minimum of 12 credit hours; demonstrate a minimum financial need of $1,000; have a minimum accumulative grade point average of 3.0 based on a 4.0 scale; and two reference forms from two dental hygiene program representatives in support of the application must be submitted as part of the application form. **Application Requirements:** Applicant must submit an application form that is typed or printed in black ink, completed and signed by school officials; completed application form, including the Academic Achievement Record Form and Financial Needs Assessment Form, which are a part of the application form, and signed by school official; a copy of the school's letter of acceptance, if entering first-year student; two completed reference forms, sealed and signed on the back flap of the envelopes by the referrers (required forms must be used which are a part of the scholarship application form); typed, biographical sketch questionnaire (required form must be used which is a part of the scholarship application form); a self-addressed, stamped postcard, which can be mailed upon receipt of the application (if the applicant wishes to have verification that the application was received). **Deadline for Receipt:** June 2.

3321 ■ AMERICAN DENTAL ASSOCIATION
211 E Chicago Ave.
Chicago, IL 60611-2678

Tel: (312)440-2500
E-mail: membership@ada.org
Web Site: http://www.ada.org
To provide financial assistance for students to further their education in the field of dentistry.

Title of Award: American Dental Association Dental Laboratory Technology Scholarship Program **Area, Field, or Subject:** Dentistry. **Level of Education for which Award is Granted:** Undergraduate **Number Awarded:** 5. **Funds Available:** $1,000.

Eligibility Requirements: Applicants must be a U.S. citizen (permanent resident status does not qualify); entering final year student at the time of application and currently attending a dental laboratory technology program accredited by the Commission on Dental Accreditation of the American Dental Association; enrolled as a full-time student, a minimum of 12 credit hours; demonstrate a minimum financial need of $1,000; have a minimum accumulative grade point average of 3.0 based on a 4.0 scale; and, must have two reference forms from two dental laboratory technology program representatives in support of the application must be submitted as part of the application form. **Application Requirements:** Applicant must submit an application form that is typed or printed in black ink, completed and signed by school officials; completed application form, including the Academic Achievement Record Form and Financial Needs Assessment Form, which are a part of the application form, and signed by school official; a copy of the school's letter of acceptance, if entering first-year student; two completed reference forms, sealed and signed on the back flap of the envelopes by the referrers (required forms must be used which are a part of the scholarship application form); typed, biographical sketch questionnaire (required form must be used which is a part of the scholarship application form); a self-addressed, stamped postcard, which can be mailed upon receipt of the application (if the applicant wishes to have verification that the application was received). **Deadline for Receipt:** September 5.

3322 ■ AMERICAN DENTAL ASSOCIATION
211 E Chicago Ave.
Chicago, IL 60611-2678
Tel: (312)440-2500
E-mail: membership@ada.org
Web Site: http://www.ada.org
To provide financial assistance for furthering education of dental students.

Title of Award: American Dental Association Dental Student Scholarship **Area, Field, or Subject:** Dentistry. **Level of Education for which Award is Granted:** Undergraduate **Number Awarded:** 25. **Funds Available:** $2,500.

Eligibility Requirements: Applicant must be a U.S. Citizen (permanent resident status does not qualify); entering second year student at the time of application and currently attending or enrolled at a dental school accredited by the Commission on Dental Accreditation of the American Dental Association; enrolled as a full-time student, a minimum of 12 credit hours; must demonstrate a minimum financial need of $2,500; have a minimum accumulative grade point average of 3.0 based on a 4.0 scale; and two reference forms from two dental school representatives. **Application Requirements:** Applicant must submit an application form that is typed or printed in black ink, completed and signed by school officials; completed application form, including the Academic Achievement Record Form and Financial Needs Assessment Form, which are a part of the application form, and signed by school official; a copy of the school's letter of acceptance, if entering first-year student; two completed reference forms, sealed and signed on the back flap of the envelopes by the referrers (required forms must be used which are a part of the scholarship application form); typed, biographical sketch questionnaire (required form must be used which is a part of the scholarship application form); a self-addressed, stamped postcard, which can be mailed upon receipt of the application (if the applicant wishes to have verification that the application was received). **Deadline for Receipt:** June 2.

3323 ■ AMERICAN DENTAL ASSOCIATION
211 E Chicago Ave.
Chicago, IL 60611-2678
Tel: (312)440-2500
E-mail: membership@ada.org
Web Site: http://www.ada.org

To provide financial assistance for furthering education of the minority dental students.

Title of Award: American Dental Association Minority Dental Student Scholarships **Area, Field, or Subject:** Dentistry. **Level of Education for which Award is Granted:** Undergraduate **Number Awarded:** 25. **Funds Available:** $2,500.

Eligibility Requirements: Applicants must be U.S. Citizen (permanent resident status does not qualify); entering second year student at the time of application and currently attending or enrolled at a dental school accredited by the Commission on Dental Accreditation of the American Dental Association; enrolled as a full-time student, a minimum of 12 credit hours; demonstrate a minimum financial need of $2,500; have a minimum accumulative grade point average of 3.0 based on a 4.0 scale; and two reference forms from two dental school representatives (i.e., professor or academic advisor) in support of the application must be submitted as part of the application form. **Application Requirements:** Applicant must submit an application form that is typed or printed in black ink, completed and signed by school officials; completed application form, including the Academic Achievement Record Form and Financial Needs Assessment Form, which are a part of the application form, and signed by school official; a copy of the school's letter of acceptance, if entering first-year student; two completed reference forms, sealed and signed on the back flap of the envelopes by the referrers (required forms must be used which are a part of the scholarship application form); typed, biographical sketch questionnaire (required form must be used which is a part of the scholarship application form); a self-addressed, stamped postcard, which can be mailed upon receipt of the application (if the applicant wishes to have verification that the application was received). **Deadline for Receipt:** June 2.

3324 ■ AMERICAN SCHOOL HEALTH ASSOCIATION
7263 State Rte. 43
Kent, OH 44240
Tel: (330)678-1601
Fax: (330)678-4526
E-mail: asha@ashaweb.org
Web Site: http://www.ashaweb.org
To provide financial assistance to students concentrating on school health education, school nursing, and pediatric or adolescent medicine or dentistry.

Title of Award: ASHA Scholarships **Area, Field, or Subject:** Health education; Nursing; Pediatric medicine; Medicine; Dentistry; Nutrition; Counseling/Guidance. **Level of Education for which Award is Granted:** Graduate, Undergraduate **Number Awarded:** 3. **Funds Available:** $500 and a complimentary registration to ASHA's annual school health conference and a one-year ASHA membership. **Duration:** One year.

Eligibility Requirements: Applicants must be a junior, senior or graduate student; enrolled full-time at institution of higher education; have 3.0 GPA on a 4.0 scale; have a major related to School Health Education or School Nursing or Pediatric or Adolescent Medicine or Dentistry or other school health specializations (nutrition, counseling, etc.); not a previous recipient of this award. **Application Requirements:** Applicants must send one original and nine copies of the completed application form (application form available online); current resume; transcript; one page personal statement; three letters of recommendation. **Deadline for Receipt:** April 4. **Additional Information:** Pamela Dorazio Dean, pdean@ashaweb.org.

3325 ■ AMERICAN SCHOOL HEALTH ASSOCIATION
7263 State Rte. 43
Kent, OH 44240
Tel: (330)678-1601
Fax: (330)678-4526
E-mail: asha@ashaweb.org
Web Site: http://www.ashaweb.org
To provide financial assistance for research in areas related to the mission of ASHA.

Title of Award: ASHA Student Research Grants **Area, Field, or Subject:** Health education; Nursing; Pediatric medicine; Medicine; Dentistry; Nutrition; Counseling/Guidance. **Level of Education for which Award is Granted:** Graduate, Undergraduate **Funds Available:** No specific amount.

Eligibility Requirements: Applicants must be student members of ASHA. **Application Requirements:** Applicants must send one original and five

3326 ■ MEDICAL SCIENCES ■ DENTISTRY

copies of a proposal which includes a cover sheet; a narrative (title-problem, review of related literature, methodology, data analyst, institution IRB protocol documented); and a budget. Proposal should have one inch margins, doubled spaced and a font size not smaller than 12. Forward the original and 5 copies to: ASHA Student Research Grants, PO Box 708, Kent, OH 44240. **Deadline for Receipt:** April 4. **Additional Information:** Pamela Dorazio, pdean@ashaweb.org, 330-678-1601.

3326 ■ CHINESE AMERICAN MEDICAL SOCIETY
281 Edgewood Ave.
New York, NY 10013
Tel: (212)965-0723
Web Site: http://www.camsociety.org
To support clinical and basic science research among Chinese American, medical and dental students.
Title of Award: Chinese American Medical Society Summer Research Outreach Programs **Area, Field, or Subject:** Medical technology; Dental laboratory technology. **Level of Education for which Award is Granted:** Undergraduate **Funds Available:** $400 per week. **Duration:** Up to 8 weeks.
Eligibility Requirements: Applicant must be a current student in an accredited medical or dental school in the United States; working on a project in the basic science or clinical research. **Application Requirements:** The Applicants must submit completed CAMS Summer Research Fellowship Application; Project description; personal statement; curriculum vitae; a two letter from a supervising investigator supporting the research project and from the Dean verifying good standing. Send all materials to: Jerry Huo, MD, Chairman of CAMS Scholarship Committee 32 Aspen Road Scardale, NY 10583, jerryhuomd@gmail.com. **Deadline for Receipt:** March 31. **Additional Information:** Jerry Huo, MD, Chairman of CAMS Scholarship Committee, (718)670-0066, or jerryhuomd@gmail.com.

3327 ■ CHINESE AMERICAN MEDICAL SOCIETY
281 Edgewood Ave.
New York, NY 10013
Tel: (212)965-0723
Web Site: http://www.camsociety.org
To provide educational assistance to medical, dental students, and scientists.
Title of Award: Esther Lim Memorial Scholarships **Area, Field, or Subject:** Medical technology; Dental laboratory technology. **Level of Education for which Award is Granted:** Undergraduate **Number Awarded:** 3-5. **Funds Available:** No specific amount.
Eligibility Requirements: Applicant must be a medical or dental student or scientist matriculated in a medical or dental school. **Application Requirements:** Application form is available at the website. Applicants must submit completed application form along with a letter from the Dean of Students verifying good standing; two letters of recommendation; a personal statement; and a current vitae. Send all materials to: Jerry Huo MD, Chairman, CAMS Scholarship Committee 32 Aspen Road, Scarsdale NY 10583, jerryhuomd@gmail.com. **Additional Information:** Established as a result of a bequest by Dr. Lim, a late member of the society, and her family. **Deadline for Receipt:** March 31. **Additional Information:** Jerry Huo MD, Chairman of the CAMS Scholarship Committee, (718)670-0066, or jerryhuomd@gmail.com.

3328 ■ CHINESE AMERICAN MEDICAL SOCIETY
281 Edgewood Ave.
New York, NY 10013
Tel: (212)965-0723
Web Site: http://www.camsociety.org
To provide educational assistance to medical, dental students, and scientists.
Title of Award: Ruth Liu Memorial Scholarships **Area, Field, or Subject:** Medical technology; Dental laboratory technology. **Level of Education for which Award is Granted:** Undergraduate **Number Awarded:** 3-5. **Funds Available:** No specific amount.
Eligibility Requirements: Applicant must be a medical or dental student or scientist matriculated in a medical or dental school. **Application Requirements:** Application form is available at the website. Applicants must submit completed application form along with a letter from the Dean of Students verifying good standing; two letters of recommendation; a

personal statement; and a current vitae. Send all materials to: Jerry Huo MD, Chairman, CAMS Scholarship Committee 32 Aspen Road, Scarsdale NY 10583, jerryhuomd@gmail.com. **Additional Information:** Established in 1996 by her husband Dr. George Liu and friends. **Deadline for Receipt:** March 31. **Additional Information:** Jerry Huo MD, Chairman of the CAMS Scholarship Committee, (718)670-0066, or jerryhuomd@gmail.com.

3329 ■ THE COMMUNITY FOUNDATION OF MIDDLE TENNESSEE
3833 Cleghorn Ave., Ste. 400
Nashville, TN 37215-2519
Tel: (615)321-4939; 888-540-5200
E-mail: mail@cfmt.org
Web Site: http://www.cfmt.org
To help students in planning their postsecondary education.
Title of Award: Dr. Mac Scholarships **Area, Field, or Subject:** Dentistry. **Level of Education for which Award is Granted:** Undergraduate **Funds Available:** No specific amount.
Eligibility Requirements: Applicants must be enrolled at the University of Tennessee at Memphis School of Dentistry and entering their third year of school with a minimum of 2.7 GPA. **Application Requirements:** Applicants must complete the application form. Applicants must submit two applicant appraisals; transcript of grades; student essay describing educational plans and how these will help in career goals. Applicants must submit one recent photograph. **Deadline for Receipt:** March 15. **Additional Information:** pcole@cfmt.org

3330 ■ COMMUNITY FOUNDATION FOR SOUTHEAST MICHIGAN
333 West Fort St., Ste. 2010
Detroit, MI 48226-3134
Tel: (313)961-6675
Fax: (313)961-2886
E-mail: cfsem@cfsem.org
Web Site: http://www.cfsem.org
To provide financial assistance to students of Southeast Michigan region for their education.
Title of Award: Jeptha Wade Schureman Scholarship Program **Area, Field, or Subject:** Law; Nursing; Medicine; Dentistry. **Level of Education for which Award is Granted:** Undergraduate **Funds Available:** $7,500.
Eligibility Requirements: Applicants must be residents of Wayne, Oakland, Macomb, Lenawee, Monroe, Livingston, Washtenaw, or St. Clair counties at the time of high school graduation; must be fatherless either through death or through termination of parental rights; must be pursuing, or planning to pursue, a degree in the fields of law, nursing, medicine or dentistry. **Application Requirements:** Applicants must submit the completed application form and other required documents. **Deadline for Receipt:** June 2.

3331 ■ FOUNDATION FOR THE CAROLINAS
217 S Tryon St.
Charlotte, NC 28202
Tel: (704)973-4500
Free: 800-973-7244
Web Site: http://www.fftc.org
To provide financial assistance for students attending the College of Dental Medicine at the Medical University of South Carolina.
Title of Award: Howard B. Higgins South Carolina Dental Scholarships **Area, Field, or Subject:** Dentistry. **Level of Education for which Award is Granted:** Undergraduate **Funds Available:** No specific amount.
Eligibility Requirements: Applicants must be students at the College of Dental Medicine at the Medical University of South Carolina; must have at least a 3.0 cumulative grade point average (on a 4.0 scale); and must be legal residents of South Carolina. **Application Requirements:** Applicants must submit all the required application information. **Additional Information:** College of Dental Medicine Office of Academic and Student Affairs; 843-792-2344.

3332 ■ HARTFORD FOUNDATION FOR PUBLIC GIVING
10 Columbus Blvd., 8th Flr.
Hartford, CT 06106
Tel: (860)548-1888
Fax: (860)524-8346
E-mail: hfpg@hfpg.org

Web Site: http://www.hfpg.org
To award scholarship to a first-year student attending the University of Connecticut School of Dental Medicine.
Title of Award: Nicholas J. Piergrossi Scholarships **Area, Field, or Subject:** Dentistry. **Level of Education for which Award is Granted:** Undergraduate **Number Awarded:** 1. **Funds Available:** $1,000.
Eligibility Requirements: Applicants must be a resident of Connecticut who demonstrates financial need and academic excellence. **Application Requirements:** Applicants may obtain application materials from University of Connecticut School of Dental Medicine. 263 Farmington Ave., MC 1827 Farmington, CT 06030. **Deadline for Receipt:** March 20. **Additional Information:** Andrea Deveraux, Director of Financial Aid, Phone: 860-679-3574
Fax: 860-679-1902; devereux@uchc.edu.

3333 ■ HARTFORD FOUNDATION FOR PUBLIC GIVING
10 Columbus Blvd., 8th Flr.
Hartford, CT 06106
Tel: (860)548-1888
Fax: (860)524-8346
E-mail: hfpg@hfpg.org
Web Site: http://www.hfpg.org
To award scholarship to students attending the University of Connecticut School of Dental Medicine.
Title of Award: Dr. Sidney Rafal Memorial Scholarships **Area, Field, or Subject:** Dentistry; Dental hygiene. **Level of Education for which Award is Granted:** Undergraduate **Number Awarded:** 1. **Funds Available:** $1,200.
Eligibility Requirements: Applicants must demonstrate financial need and academic excellence. **Application Requirements:** Applicants may obtain application materials from University of Connecticut School of Dental Medicine. 263 Farmington Ave., MC 1827 Farmington, CT 06030. **Deadline for Receipt:** March 20. **Additional Information:** Andrea Deveraux, Director of Financial Aid, Phone: 860-679-3574
Fax: 860-679-1902; devereux@uchc.edu.

3334 ■ INTERNATIONAL ASSOCIATION FOR DENTAL RESEARCH
1619 Duke St.
Alexandria, VA 22314-3406
Tel: (703)548-1883
Fax: (703)548-0066
E-mail: cfox@iadr.org
Web Site: http://www.iadr.com
To improve knowledge on oral health by advancing and supporting research projects; to support and represent the oral health research community; and to facilitate the communication and application of research findings.
Title of Award: IADR David B. Scott Fellowships **Area, Field, or Subject:** Dental Hygiene. **Level of Education for which Award is Granted:** Undergraduate **Funds Available:** $2,500.
Eligibility Requirements: Program is open to students who are training to become dentists; must be registered in an accredited or acceptable dental school; and must be sponsored by a dental researcher with the approval of their school's dean. Candidates may not have received their dental degree nor should they be due to receive their degree in the year of the award; may have a college or advanced degree in a discipline other than the industry; and must be IADR members. **Application Requirements:** Applicants and their sponsors must submit a research project proposal to the division not exceeding 8 pages (including references), typed and double-spaced. Proposal should include aims, objectives, and significance of the proposal; rationale and background to the study; materials and methods; statistical treatment of data; facilities and equipment; and budget. **Deadline for Receipt:** October 15. **Additional Information:** Central Office of IADR at the above address.

3335 ■ JEWISH FOUNDATION FOR EDUCATION OF WOMEN
135 E 64th St.
New York, NY 10065
Tel: (212)288-3931
Fax: (212)288-5798
E-mail: info@jfew.org
Web Site: http://www.jfew.org

To provide financial support for emigres from the former Soviet Union to train in medicine, dentistry, dental hygiene, nursing, pharmacy, occupational and physical therapy, physician assistant, CVT, and sonography programs.
Title of Award: Scholarships for Emigres in the Health Sciences **Area, Field, or Subject:** Medicine; Dentistry; Nursing; Pharmacy; Physical therapy; Physiology. **Level of Education for which Award is Granted:** Undergraduate **Funds Available:** $5,000. **Duration:** One year.
Eligibility Requirements: Applicants must be students from the former Soviet Union; must be residents of New York City or the counties of Nassau, Suffolk or Westchester; must already be enrolled in or about to enroll in a health science program within that geographic area; and must be enrolled full-time, in good standing, and demonstrate financial need. **Application Requirements:** Applicants must submit all the required application information.

3336 ■ NATIONAL ARAB AMERICAN MEDICAL ASSOCIATION
801 S Adams Rd., Ste. 208
Birmingham, MI 48009
Tel: (248)646-3661
Fax: (248)646-0617
E-mail: naama@naama.com
Web Site: http://www.naama.com
To provide financial assistance to Arabic students who are studying in a medical, osteopathic, or dental school.
Title of Award: NAAMA Scholarships **Area, Field, or Subject:** Medicine, Osteopathic; Dentistry. **Level of Education for which Award is Granted:** Undergraduate **Number Awarded:** 2. **Funds Available:** $1,000.
Eligibility Requirements: Applicants must be Arabic students enrolled in a U.S. or Canadian medical, osteopathic, or dental school. **Application Requirements:** Applicants must send completed application form together with a brief description on the applicant's education; transcripts; description of financial need; description of involvement in the Arab American community after completing studies; and recent 1040 tax return (with spouse and parents). **Deadline for Receipt:** July.

3337 ■ NATIONAL DENTAL HYGIENISTS' ASSOCIATION
PO Box 22463
Tampa, FL 33622
800-234-1096
E-mail: forndha@aol.com
Web Site: http://ndhaonline.org
To increase interest in dental hygiene particularly among African American students by providing financial assistance.
Title of Award: National Dental Hygienists' Association Scholarships **Area, Field, or Subject:** Dental hygiene. **Level of Education for which Award is Granted:** Undergraduate **Funds Available:** No specific amount.
Eligibility Requirements: Applicant must be a current member of the NDHA; must be a U.S. citizen particularly African American; must have minimum of 2.5 GPA or greater. **Application Requirements:** Applicant must send completed application form (downloadable from the website); NDHA student membership of $35; a copy of official sealed transcript; a print verification of enrollment form signed by Registrar/Office of Dean of Students; a passport type photo; two recommendation letters (one from a dental hygiene director and the other one from dental hygiene teacher or employer); proof of financial need; statement of leadership skills; and stated ideas on how to promote the profession of dental hygiene and the NDHA Organization. **Deadline for Receipt:** March 15.

3338 ■ ROYAL BANK OF CANADA
260 Adelaide St. E
Toronto, ON, Canada M5A 1N1
(866)363-1722
E-mail: 4edu@sympatico.ca
Web Site: http://www.rbcroyalbank.com
To provide scholarship assistance to qualified individuals who want to pursue their studies.
Title of Award: RBC Royal Bank Scholarships for First Year Medical & Dental Students **Area, Field, or Subject:** Medical education; Dentistry. **Level of Education for which Award is Granted:** Undergraduate **Number Awarded:** 27. **Funds Available:** $5,000. **Duration:** One year.
Eligibility Requirements: Applicants must be Canadian citizens or permanent residents of Canada; must be accepted into the first year of a

recognized medical or dental program at a university in Canada for the academic year; must be full-time students studying to become an accredited medical doctors or dentists. **Application Requirements:** Applicants must complete the application form available online; must provide basic contact details, including their email, address, phone number, mailing address, and must provide information on their current undergraduate or graduate school, as well as details on the medical or dental school they will be attending. **Deadline for Receipt:** September 30.

3339 ■ SHORELINE COMMUNITY COLLEGE FOUNDATION
16101 Greenwood Ave. N, Ste. 1005
Shoreline, WA 98133-5696
Tel: (206)546-4755
Fax: (206)546-5826
E-mail: rmanchester@shoreline.edu
Web Site: http://www.shoreline.edu
To increase access and success of Shoreline Community College students.
Title of Award: Co Dental Hygiene Scholarships **Area, Field, or Subject:** Dental hygiene. **Level of Education for which Award is Granted:** Undergraduate **Funds Available:** $500.
Eligibility Requirements: Applicants must be full-time or part-time students at the Shoreline/Lake Forest Park area who are enrolling at SCC. **Application Requirements:** Applicants must complete the application form.

3340 ■ SHORELINE COMMUNITY COLLEGE FOUNDATION
16101 Greenwood Ave. N, Ste. 1005
Shoreline, WA 98133-5696
Tel: (206)546-4755
Fax: (206)546-5826
E-mail: rmanchester@shoreline.edu
Web Site: http://www.shoreline.edu
To increase access and success of Shoreline Community College students; to provide emergency assistance for Shoreline Community College dental hygiene students who are in need of financial assistance.
Title of Award: Dr. Princeton L. Co Emergency Fund for Dental Hygiene Scholarships **Area, Field, or Subject:** Dental hygiene. **Level of Education for which Award is Granted:** Undergraduate **Funds Available:** $300. **Duration:** One year.
Eligibility Requirements: Applicants must be currently enrolled as full-time dental hygiene students at Shoreline Community College; must be survivors of domestic abuse; must be Washington State residents for a minimum of one year; must not have previous two or four year college degree; must earn and maintain minimum cumulative GPA of 2.50 (minimum GPA of 3.0 in dental hygiene coursework); and must not be currently included on the Scholarship Selection Committee or related (first degree) to a person on the Selection Committee. **Application Requirements:** Applicants must complete the application form; must submit statement or documentation of income and need; unofficial SCC transcript; and current class schedule. **Additional Information:** mbaker@shoreline.edu

3341 ■ SHORELINE COMMUNITY COLLEGE FOUNDATION
16101 Greenwood Ave. N, Ste. 1005
Shoreline, WA 98133-5696
Tel: (206)546-4755
Fax: (206)546-5826
E-mail: rmanchester@shoreline.edu
Web Site: http://www.shoreline.edu
To increase access and success of Shoreline Community College students; to provide First Nation students (indigenous to the Americas and associated territories) with financial assistance in times of need.
Title of Award: Ken LaFountaine First Nations Scholarships **Area, Field, or Subject:** General studies. **Level of Education for which Award is Granted:** Undergraduate **Funds Available:** $300. **Duration:** One year.
Eligibility Requirements: Applicants must be returning or part-time students at Shoreline Community College; must have demonstrated active involvement in the First Nation community in the Puget Sound area, either on campus or in the broader community; and must not be currently included on the Scholarship Selection Committee or related (first degree) to a person on the Selection Committee. **Application Requirements:** Applicants must submit evidence of likelihood of academic success with a minimum of 2.0 GPA or 2.0 during most recent quarter attended; evidence

of the other venues of financial support; letter of recommendation from a teacher, professor, or employer. **Additional Information:** bpeace-g@shoreline.edu

3342 ■ SOUTHWEST FLORIDA COMMUNITY FOUNDATION
8260 College Pkwy., Ste. 101
Fort Myers, FL 33919
Tel: (239)274-5900
Fax: (239)274-5930
Web Site: http://www.floridacommunity.com
To fund students pursuing degrees or advanced degrees in medicine, law, dentistry, teaching (math and science), ministry, engineering, accounting, architecture and computer science.
Title of Award: John M. and Mary A. Shanley Memorial Scholarships **Area, Field, or Subject:** Medicine; Law; Dentistry; Teaching; Ministry; Engineering; Accounting; Agriculture; Economic aspects; Architecture; Computer and information sciences. **Level of Education for which Award is Granted:** Undergraduate **Funds Available:** $5,000. **Duration:** One year.
Eligibility Requirements: Applicant must be a resident of Charlotte, Hendry or Lee County. **Application Requirements:** Application forms are available online. Applicants must submit a letter of interest, letter of recommendation and transcript. **Deadline for Receipt:** February 15.

3343 ■ WASHINGTON HIGHER EDUCATION COORDINATING BOARD
PO Box 43430
Olympia, WA 98504-3430
Tel: (360)753-7800
E-mail: info@hecb.wa.gov
Web Site: http://www.hecb.wa.gov
To attract and retain health professionals to serve in critical shortage areas in Washington state.
Title of Award: Washington Higher Education Coordinating Board Health Professional Scholarships **Area, Field, or Subject:** Physics; Nursing; Midwifery; Pharmacy; Dentistry. **Level of Education for which Award is Granted:** Undergraduate **Funds Available:** Varies by educational program.
Eligibility Requirements: Applicant must be a student training to become a primary care health professional in an eligible profession; a U.S. citizen; have completed all prerequisite course work; not be in default on any educational loans; and must sign a Promissory Note agreeing to serve for a minimum of three years in a designated shortage area in Washington state or pay back funds with double penalty plus interest. **Application Requirements:** Applicants must submit a completed application form along with the required materials and information. **Additional Information:** Participants must agree, in return for the assistance, to provide primary care health care in rural or underserved urban areas with designated shortages for a minimum of three years. **Deadline for Receipt:** April 30.

Medicine

3344 ■ ACADEMY OF MEDICAL-SURGICAL NURSES
E Holly Ave., Box 56
Pitman, NJ 08071-0056
(866)877-2676
E-mail: amsn@ajj.com
Web Site: http://www.medsurgnurse.org/
To provide financial assistance for AMSN members who with to further their education.
Title of Award: Career Mobility Scholarship Awards **Area, Field, or Subject:** Nursing; Surgery; Medicine. **Level of Education for which Award is Granted:** Doctorate, Undergraduate **Number Awarded:** 1. **Funds Available:** $500. **Duration:** One year.
Eligibility Requirements: Applicants must be members of AMSN for at least one year. **Application Requirements:** Applicants must submit a completed application form; a brief description (one page, double-spaced with size 12 font) discussing how additional education will enhance the care of Adult Medical-Surgical patient; and a self-addressed stamped postcard. Electronic submission is preferred; otherwise applicant must submit additional 9 blinded photocopies of application and of required

documentation. **Additional Information:** Fax copies will not be considered. **Deadline for Receipt:** August 1.

3345 ■ ALBERTA LEARNING INFORMATION SERVICE - ALBERTA SCHOLARSHIP PROGRAM
Box 28000 Sta. Main
Edmonton, AB, Canada T5J 4R4
Tel: (780)427-8640
Fax: (780)427-1288
E-mail: scholarship@gov.ab.ca
Web Site: http://www.alis.alberta.ca
To reward the outstanding academic achievement of Alberta post-secondary students who are continuing full-time in an undergraduate program in Alberta.
Title of Award: Jason Lang Scholarship **Area, Field, or Subject:** Law; Medicine; Pharmacy; Dentistry. **Level of Education for which Award is Granted:** Undergraduate **Funds Available:** $1,000.
Eligibility Requirements: Nominees must be enrolled full-time in an undergraduate or professional program, such as Law, Medicine, Pharmacy or Dentistry at an eligible Alberta post-secondary institution. These include publicly-funded colleges, technical institutes, universities, private colleges accredited to grant degrees, and the Banff Centre. **Application Requirements:** Recipients are nominated by the Awards Office at participating Alberta institutions where they have obtained qualifying grades. For information on the nomination process and eligibility, contact the Awards Office. **Deadline for Receipt:** October 15 and February 15. **Additional Information:** Alberta Scholarship Programs at the above address.

3346 ■ ALBERTA LEARNING INFORMATION SERVICE - ALBERTA SCHOLARSHIP PROGRAM
Box 28000 Sta. Main
Edmonton, AB, Canada T5J 4R4
Tel: (780)427-8640
Fax: (780)427-1288
E-mail: scholarship@gov.ab.ca
Web Site: http://www.alis.alberta.ca
To increase the number of trained professionals in Northern Alberta and to encourage students from Northern Alberta to obtain a post-secondary education.
Title of Award: Northern Alberta Development Council Bursary for Medical Students **Area, Field, or Subject:** Medicine. **Level of Education for which Award is Granted:** Undergraduate **Funds Available:** $5,000.
Eligibility Requirements: Applicants must be residents of Alberta and enrolled in a medical program. Applicants must not be in default of a provincial student loan. **Application Requirements:** Applicants may obtain an application form from www.benorth.ca. Application forms for these bursaries are also available from Alberta Scholarship Programs, Student Awards Offices and from the Northern Alberta Development Council. **Deadline for Receipt:** June 1. **Additional Information:** Northern Alberta Development Council, 2nd Fl., Provincial Bldg. 9621 - 96 Ave. Postal Bag 900-14 Peace River, AB T8S 1T4; 780-624-6545; nadc.council@gov.ab.ca.

3347 ■ AMERICAN ASSOCIATION FOR THORACIC SURGERY
900 Cummings Center, Ste. 221-U
Beverly, MA 01915
Tel: (978)927-8330
Fax: (978)524-8890
Web Site: http://www.aats.org
To promote unique opportunity for clinical research involving thoracoesophageal surgery and/or interventions endoscopy.
Title of Award: Massachusetts General Hospital Summer Scholars Program **Area, Field, or Subject:** Medicine. **Level of Education for which Award is Granted:** Undergraduate **Funds Available:** No specific amount.
Eligibility Requirements: Applicants must be first or second year medical students. **Application Requirements:** Applicants must send a letter of interest and curriculum vitae. **Deadline for Receipt:** March 1. **Additional Information:** Douglas J. Mathisen.

3348 ■ AMERICAN ASSOCIATION FOR THORACIC SURGERY
900 Cummings Center, Ste. 221-U
Beverly, MA 01915

Tel: (978)927-8330
Fax: (978)524-8890
Web Site: http://www.aats.org
To introduce the field of cardiothoracic surgery.
Title of Award: Summer Intern Scholarships in Cardiothoracic Surgery **Area, Field, or Subject:** Medicine. **Level of Education for which Award is Granted:** Undergraduate **Funds Available:** $5,000.
Eligibility Requirements: Applicants must have the approval of the prospective sponsoring institutions; must be a member of the AATS; must be first or second year medical students. **Application Requirements:** Applicants must complete an online application and include a one-page outline of what they hope to accomplish during their eight weeks internship. Applicants must also submit a letter of support from the host sponsor. **Deadline for Receipt:** January 15. **Additional Information:** AATS at the above address.

3349 ■ AMERICAN INDIAN GRADUATE CENTER SCHOLARS (AIGCS)
4520 Montgomery Blvd., NE, Ste. 1B
Albuquerque, NM 87109
Tel: (505)881-4584
Free: 800-628-1920
Web Site: http://www.aigc.com
To provide financial assistance to undergraduate and graduate American Indians in furthering their education.
Title of Award: Accenture American Indian Scholarship Program **Area, Field, or Subject:** Technology; Engineering; Medicine; Law; Business. **Level of Education for which Award is Granted:** Graduate, Undergraduate **Funds Available:** No specific amount.
Eligibility Requirements: Applicants must be American Indians who are incoming freshmen with a cumulative GPA of 3.25 or greater on a 4.0 scale at the end of the seventh semester of high school or graduates/professionals who have attained a cumulative GPA of 3.25 or greater on a 4.0 scale, as measured by undergraduate transcripts; must be enrolled members of a U.S. federally-recognized American Indian tribe or Alaska Native group; must be seeking a degree and career in fields of study including technology, engineering, medicine, law, and business. **Application Requirements:** Applicants must submit completed application form; copy of certificate of Indian Blood (CIB); unofficial undergraduate and/or graduate academic transcripts; biographical data and/or resume; essay describing their character, personal merit and commitment to community and heritage; two personal letters of recommendation (one must come from an education professional who is familiar with their academic work and the other one must come from an individual having knowledge of their leadership and community service activities); and financial aid award letter from the institution they will attend. **Deadline for Receipt:** June 2.

3350 ■ AMERICAN RADIO RELAY LEAGUE (ARRL) FOUNDATION
225 Main St.
Newington, CT 06111
Tel: (860)594-0200
Fax: (860)594-0259
E-mail: foundation@arrl.org
Web Site: http://www.arrlf.org
To support the education of students holding a valid FCC-granted Amateur Radio license for post-secondary education.
Title of Award: William R. Goldfarb Memorial Scholarships **Area, Field, or Subject:** Radio and television; Business; Computer and information sciences; Medicine; Nursing; Engineering; Science. **Level of Education for which Award is Granted:** Undergraduate **Number Awarded:** 1. **Funds Available:** No specific amount.
Eligibility Requirements: Applicant must hold an FCC amateur radio license; must be studying baccalaureate courses in business-related, computers, medical, nursing, engineering or sciences; be a high school senior; and must demonstrate financial need. **Application Requirements:** Applicants must submit a completed scholarship application form along with a recent high school (or equivalent) or college transcript, and the Free Application for Federal Student Aid (FAFSA) or Student Aid Report (SAR). **Deadline for Receipt:** February 1.

3351 ■ AMERICAN SCHOOL HEALTH ASSOCIATION
7263 State Rte. 43
Kent, OH 44240

Tel: (330)678-1601
Fax: (330)678-4526
E-mail: asha@ashaweb.org
Web Site: http://www.ashaweb.org
To provide financial assistance to students concentrating on school health education, school nursing, and pediatric or adolescent medicine or dentistry.

Title of Award: ASHA Scholarships **Area, Field, or Subject:** Health education; Nursing; Pediatric medicine; Medicine; Dentistry; Nutrition; Counseling/Guidance. **Level of Education for which Award is Granted:** Graduate, Undergraduate **Number Awarded:** 3. **Funds Available:** $500 and a complimentary registration to ASHA's annual school health conference and a one-year ASHA membership. **Duration:** One year.

Eligibility Requirements: Applicants must be a junior, senior or graduate student; enrolled full-time at institution of higher education; have 3.0 GPA on a 4.0 scale; have a major related to School Health Education or School Nursing or Pediatric or Adolescent Medicine or Dentistry or other school health specializations (nutrition, counseling, etc.); not a previous recipient of this award. **Application Requirements:** Applicants must send one original and nine copies of the completed application form (application form available online); current resume; transcript; one page personal statement; three letters of recommendation. **Deadline for Receipt:** April 4. **Additional Information:** Pamela Dorazio Dean, pdean@ashaweb.org.

3352 ■ AMERICAN SCHOOL HEALTH ASSOCIATION

7263 State Rte. 43
Kent, OH 44240
Tel: (330)678-1601
Fax: (330)678-4526
E-mail: asha@ashaweb.org
Web Site: http://www.ashaweb.org
To provide financial assistance for research in areas related to the mission of ASHA.

Title of Award: ASHA Student Research Grants **Area, Field, or Subject:** Health education; Nursing; Pediatric medicine; Medicine; Dentistry; Nutrition; Counseling/Guidance. **Level of Education for which Award is Granted:** Graduate, Undergraduate **Funds Available:** No specific amount.

Eligibility Requirements: Applicants must be student members of ASHA. **Application Requirements:** Applicants must send one original and five copies of a proposal which includes a cover sheet; a narrative (title-problem, review of related literature, methodology, data analyst, institution IRB protocol documented); and a budget. Proposal should have one inch margins, doubled spaced and a font size not smaller than 12. Forward the original and 5 copies to: ASHA Student Research Grants, PO Box 708, Kent, OH 44240. **Deadline for Receipt:** April 4. **Additional Information:** Pamela Dorazio, pdean@ashaweb.org, 330-678-1601.

3353 ■ ARMENIAN RELIEF SOCIETY - EASTERN UNITED STATES

80 Bigelow Avenue, Ste. 200
Watertown, MA 02472
Tel: (617)926-3801
Fax: (617)924-7238
E-mail: arseastus@aol.com
Web Site: http://www.arseastus.com
To encourage educational pursuits among undergraduate students of Armenian descent.

Title of Award: ARS Undergraduate Scholarships **Area, Field, or Subject:** Law; History; Political science; Journalism; Government; Economics; Business administration; Medicine; Public service. **Level of Education for which Award is Granted:** Four Year College, Two Year College, Undergraduate **Funds Available:** No specific amount. **Duration:** One year.

Eligibility Requirements: Applicants must be of Armenian descent; must be undergraduate students who have completed at least one semester at an accredited four-year college or university in the United States or must be enrolled in a two-year college and are transferring to a four-year college or university as a full-time student in the Fall. **Application Requirements:** Application must include financial aid forms, recent official transcript, two letters of recommendation and tuition costs. Forward materials to: Scholarship Committee, Armenian Relief Society of Eastern USA, Inc., 80 Bigelow Ave., Ste. 200, Watertown, MA 02472. **Deadline for Receipt:** April 1.

3354 ■ ARMENIAN STUDENTS' ASSOCIATION OF AMERICA

333 Atlantic Ave.
Warwick, RI 02888
Tel: (401)461-6114
E-mail: asa@asainc.org
Web Site: http://www.asainc.org
To provide financial assistance to those students who are in need.

Title of Award: Armenian American Medical Association Scholarships **Area, Field, or Subject:** Medicine. **Level of Education for which Award is Granted:** Undergraduate **Number Awarded:** 3. **Funds Available:** $1,000-2,000.

Eligibility Requirements: Applicants must be students enrolled in a U.S. medical school. Award is primarily intended for students residing and studying in a private New England medical school. **Application Requirements:** Applicants must check the available website for the required materials. **Deadline for Receipt:** September 15; October 30. **Additional Information:** For more information, please contact Dr. Edward Karian, Chairperson; 324 Common St. Watertown, MA 02472-4940

3355 ■ ASSOCIATION OF BLACK WOMEN PHYSICIANS

4712 Admiralty Way, Ste. No. 175
Marina Del Rey, CA 90292
Tel: (310)364-1438
Web Site: http://www.blackwomenphysicians.org
To provide educational assistance for female medical students who are permanent residents of Southern California or enrolled in Southern California medical schools.

Title of Award: Rebecca Lee, M.D. Scholarships **Area, Field, or Subject:** Medicine. **Level of Education for which Award is Granted:** Undergraduate **Funds Available:** $1,000-$5,000.

Eligibility Requirements: Applicants must be permanent residents of Southern California at any medical school, or students at a Southern California medical school, who are in good academic standing. **Application Requirements:** Applicants must submit academic and financial aid transcripts, medical school acceptance letter or medical school dean's letter of good standing, three letters of recommendation, curriculum vitae and typed personal statement. **Deadline for Receipt:** September 5.

3356 ■ ASSOCIATION OF FAMILY PRACTICE PHYSICIAN ASSISTANTS

1905 Woodstock Rd., Ste. 2150
Roswell, GA 30075
Tel: (770)640-7605; 877-890-0181
Fax: (770)640-1095
Web Site: http://www.afppa.org
To financially assist first and second year physician students.

Title of Award: AFPPA Student Scholarships **Area, Field, or Subject:** Medicine. **Level of Education for which Award is Granted:** Undergraduate **Number Awarded:** 2. **Funds Available:** $500 for first year students and $1,000 for second year students.

Eligibility Requirements: Applicants must be PA students attending an accredited PA program for more than 12 months or students with 12 months or less of PA education. **Application Requirements:** Applicants must submit an essay (maximum of 750 words or less) describing the commitment to family practice medicine and how the current and past community involvement demonstrates this commitment. **Deadline for Receipt:** September 1.

3357 ■ BENTON COUNTY FOUNDATION

PO Box 911
Corvallis, OR 97339
Tel: (541)753-1603
Web Site: http://www.bentoncountyfoundation.org
To encourage and support ethnic minority undergraduate women enrolled in the College of Science.

Title of Award: Margaret Dowell-Gravatt, M.D. Scholarship **Area, Field, or Subject:** Zoology; Microbiology; Medical technology; Medicine; Nursing; Physical therapy; Occupational therapy. **Level of Education for which Award is Granted:** Undergraduate **Funds Available:** No specific amount.

Eligibility Requirements: Applicant must: be pursuing a degree in Zoology or Microbiology or one of the following pre-health programs: Medical Technology, Medicine, Nursing, Physical and/or Occupational therapy. Applicant must: be enrolled full-time at the sophomore, junior, or senior level; have a GPA of 2.5 overall and 3.0 in science courses required in their major field or pre-health curriculum; qualify for financial assistance as defined by the Financial Aid Office of OSU. **Application Requirements:** Applicant may contact the Foundation for application form and other requirements. **Additional Information:** Benton County Foundation at the above address.

3358 ■ CANADIAN SANITATION SUPPLY ASSOCIATION
910 Dundas St., W
PO Box 10009
Whitby, ON, Canada L1P 1P7
Tel: (905)430-7267
Fax: (905)430-6418
Web Site: http://cssa.com
To provide scholarship assistance to qualified Canadian students who will be attending college or university in Canada.
Title of Award: Sam Tughan Scholarships **Area, Field, or Subject:** Medicine. **Level of Education for which Award is Granted:** Undergraduate **Funds Available:** $2,000. **Duration:** One year.
Eligibility Requirements: Applicant must be a student who will be graduating high school; must be an individual who is already enrolled in a college or university in Canada; must be a young Canadian who has achieved a high level of academic and leadership standards. **Application Requirements:** Applicant must complete the application form available online; must have a photograph, and official high school or college transcript; must provide an essay on: "What does your school custodian or facilities manager think about the Green cleaning Movement?"; must have a typed resume with name, planned occupation or profession, high school information, college or university information, employment history, activity and leadership record, and applicant evaluation form completed by a counselor or teacher. **Deadline for Receipt:** June 1.

3359 ■ CDC FOUNDATION
55 Park Place, Ste. 400
Atlanta, GA 30303
Tel: (404)653-0790; 888-880-4CDC
Fax: (404)653-0330
Web Site: http://www.cdcfoundation.org
To provide an opportunity for third and fourth-year medical and veterinary students to gain public health experience in an international setting.
Title of Award: CDC Foundation Scholarships **Area, Field, or Subject:** Medicine; Veterinary science and medicine. **Level of Education for which Award is Granted:** Undergraduate **Funds Available:** $3,000. **Duration:** One year.
Eligibility Requirements: Applicants must be attending an LCME-accredited medical school or an AVMA-accredited veterinary school; must be current or incoming third or fourth-year students; must be either U.S. citizens or valid greencard holders. **Application Requirements:** Applicants must submit all application materials on 8 1/2" x 11" white paper, in triplicate, which includes three copies of the application form; two (2) letters of recommendation; current curriculum vitae; one personal statement; and signed insurance coverage statement.

3360 ■ CLINICAL LABORATORY MANAGEMENT ASSOCIATION
989 Old Eagle School Rd., Ste. 815
Wayne, PA 19087-1704
Tel: (610)995-9580
Fax: (610)995-9568
Web Site: http://www.meclma.com
To financially assist talented people pursuing education in the field of laboratory medicine.
Title of Award: Clinical Laboratory Management Association High School Senior Scholarships **Area, Field, or Subject:** Medicine. **Level of Education for which Award is Granted:** High School **Funds Available:** $500. **Duration:** One year.
Eligibility Requirements: Applicants must be undergraduate students who are Maine residents and who wish to become Medical Technologists (Clinical Laboratory Scientists), Medical Laboratory Technicians, Histotechnologists, or Cytologists. **Application Requirements:** Applicants must submit completed application form; printed essay; transcript of high school grades; two letters of recommendation (at least one must come from an academic source, e.g. teacher, guidance counselor, or

principal). **Deadline for Receipt:** May 17. **Additional Information:** Sonia E. Russell MT (ASCP); DCPA; 417 State Street, Webber W. Suite 541, Bangor, Maine 04401; 207-561-2413.

3361 ■ CLINICAL LABORATORY MANAGEMENT ASSOCIATION
989 Old Eagle School Rd., Ste. 815
Wayne, PA 19087-1704
Tel: (610)995-9580
Fax: (610)995-9568
Web Site: http://www.meclma.com
To financially assist talented people pursuing education in the field of laboratory medicine.
Title of Award: Clinical Laboratory Management Association Undergraduate Scholarships **Area, Field, or Subject:** Medicine. **Level of Education for which Award is Granted:** Undergraduate **Number Awarded:** 3. **Funds Available:** $1,000. **Duration:** One year.
Eligibility Requirements: Applicant must be a clinical laboratory scientist working towards an advanced degree or a student who is a Maine resident and wishes to become a Medical Technologist, a Medical Laboratory Technician, a Histotechnologist or a Cytologist. **Application Requirements:** Applicants must submit completed application form; printed essay, completed as described on the application; transcript of college grades; and two letters of recommendation from teachers or employers. **Deadline for Receipt:** May 3.

3362 ■ COMMUNITY FOUNDATION FOR SOUTHEAST MICHIGAN
333 West Fort St., Ste. 2010
Detroit, MI 48226-3134
Tel: (313)961-6675
Fax: (313)961-2886
E-mail: cfsem@cfsem.org
Web Site: http://www.cfsem.org
To provide financial assistance to students of Southeast Michigan region for their education.
Title of Award: Jeptha Wade Schureman Scholarship Program **Area, Field, or Subject:** Law; Nursing; Medicine; Dentistry. **Level of Education for which Award is Granted:** Undergraduate **Funds Available:** $7,500.
Eligibility Requirements: Applicants must be residents of Wayne, Oakland, Macomb, Lenawee, Monroe, Livingston, Washtenaw, or St. Clair counties at the time of high school graduation; must be fatherless either through death or through termination of parental rights; must be pursuing, or planning to pursue, a degree in the fields of law, nursing, medicine or dentistry. **Application Requirements:** Applicants must submit the completed application form and other required documents. **Deadline for Receipt:** June 2.

3363 ■ CROHN'S AND COLITIS FOUNDATION OF AMERICA
386 Park Ave. S, 17th Fl.
New York, NY 10016
800-932-2423
E-mail: info@ccfa.org
Web Site: http://www.ccfa.org
To fund a research on topics relevant to inflammatory bowel disease.
Title of Award: CCFA Student Research Fellowship Awards **Area, Field, or Subject:** Medicine. **Level of Education for which Award is Granted:** Graduate, Undergraduate **Number Awarded:** 16. **Funds Available:** $2,500. **Duration:** Ten weeks.
Eligibility Requirements: Applicants must be undergraduates, medical, or graduate students in an accredited institution in the United States. **Application Requirements:** Applicants must download, complete and submit the application form and SRFA forms available at the website. **Deadline for Receipt:** March 15.

3364 ■ FIRST COMMUNITY FOUNDATION OF PENNSYLVANIA, WILLIAMSPORT-LYCOMING
330 Pine St., Suite 401
Williamsport, PA 17701
Tel: (570)321-1500; (866)901-2372
Fax: (570)321-6434
E-mail: fcfpa@fcfpa.org
Web Site: http://www.wlfoundation.org
To provide academic support for Danville Area High School seniors who have been accepted into a full-time undergraduate program at an accredited institution of higher education and who are entering a health-related field.

Title of Award: Eleanor McWilliams Burke Fund **Area, Field, or Subject:** Medicine; Nursing; Nutrition; Pharmacy; or Physical therapy. **Level of Education for which Award is Granted:** Undergraduate **Funds Available:** No specific amount.

Eligibility Requirements: Applicants must be entering a health related field. **Application Requirements:** Applicants may request an application from the Guidance Counselor of Danville Area School District. **Additional Information:** Gary Grozier, Guidance Counselor of Danville Area School District, 600 Walnut St., Danvilled, PA 17821; 570-271-3268 ext. 2006; ggrozier@danville.k12.pa.us.

3365 ■ FIRST COMMUNITY FOUNDATION OF PENNSYLVANIA, WILLIAMSPORT-LYCOMING
330 Pine St., Suite 401
Williamsport, PA 17701
Tel: (570)321-1500; (866)901-2372
Fax: (570)321-6434
E-mail: fcfpa@fcfpa.org
Web Site: http://www.wlfoundation.org
To support the education of current and/or aspiring Lycoming County medical professionals who plan to dedicate their lives to helping others.
Title of Award: Joseph R. Calder, Jr., MD Scholarship Fund **Area, Field, or Subject:** Medicine; Nursing; Pharmacy; Allied health. **Level of Education for which Award is Granted:** Undergraduate **Funds Available:** No specific amount.

Eligibility Requirements: Applicants must be accepted into a full-time or part-time medical or any other related specialty at an accredited institution of higher education. Applicants should be residents of Lycoming County. **Application Requirements:** Applicant must submit an essay not to exceed one page outlining why he/she is pursuing a career in the medical field and summarizing his/her ultimate career objectives. Applicants may download an application form the Foundation's web site. **Additional Information:** Candy Bower, 570-321-1500; candyb@fcfpa.org

3366 ■ FOUNDATION FOR THE CAROLINAS
217 S Tryon St.
Charlotte, NC 28202
Tel: (704)973-4500
Free: 800-973-7244
Web Site: http://www.fftc.org
To assist North Iredell High School graduates in obtaining a degree in physical therapy, medicine or nursing from a post-secondary accredited institution.
Title of Award: The Sibyl Jennings Vorheis Memorial Scholarship Program **Area, Field, or Subject:** Physical therapy; Medicine; Nursing. **Level of Education for which Award is Granted:** Undergraduate **Funds Available:** $3,000. **Duration:** One year.

Eligibility Requirements: Applicants must have graduated from North Iredell High School with a minimum cumulative grade point average of 3.0 (on 4.0 scale). **Application Requirements:** Applicants must submit completed application form; verification of acceptance into the accredited graduate program; official copy of college transcript; two recommendation forms and letters of recommendation; and a typewritten application statement of eligibility expressing applicant's educational and career goals, reasons for applying for the scholarship, and why the applicant feels they are a good candidate for the scholarship. **Deadline for Receipt:** April 1.

3367 ■ FOUNDATION FOR ENHANCING COMMUNITIES
200 N Third St., PO Box 678
Harrisburg, PA 17108-0678
Tel: (717)236-5040
Fax: (717)231-4463
E-mail: dawn@tfec.org
Web Site: http://www.ghf.org
To provide financial assistance for Lebanon County residents pursuing higher education degrees.
Title of Award: Family and Children's Services of Lebanon County Fund **Area, Field, or Subject:** Medicine; Nursing, Social work, Mental health. **Level of Education for which Award is Granted:** Undergraduate **Funds Available:** No specific amount.

Eligibility Requirements: Applicants must be enrolled full-time in schools of advanced education in the fields of medicine, nursing, social work, mental health and other specialized therapies in the treatment of physical

and mental disabilities; must demonstrate financial need, academic aptitude and achievement, and commitment to a career in human services; and must be residents of Lebanon County. **Application Requirements:** Applicants may obtain the application online. Applicants must provide the most recent, either a certified high school transcript or a certified college transcript. **Additional Information:** Dawn Morris, Program Officer; 717-236-5040; dawn@tfec.org.

3368 ■ FOUNDATION OF THE PENNSYLVANIA MEDICAL SOCIETY
777 E Park Dr.
PO Box 8820
Harrisburg, PA 17105-8820
Tel: (717)558-7750
Free: 800-228-7823
Fax: (717)558-7818
E-mail: foundation@pamedsoc.org
Web Site: http://www.foundationpamedsoc.org
To assist local students with the cost of attending a Pennsylvania medical school.
Title of Award: Allegheny County Medical Society (ACMS) Medical Student Scholarship **Area, Field, or Subject:** Medicine. **Level of Education for which Award is Granted:** Undergraduate **Number Awarded:** 2. **Funds Available:** $2,000.

Eligibility Requirements: Applicants must be Pennsylvania residents from one of the following counties: Allegheny, Armstrong, Beaver, Butler, Washington, or Westmoreland. **Application Requirements:** Applicant must submit: completed scholarship application form; two reference letters, from persons other than family members, documenting integrity, interpersonal skills, and potential as a future physician (one must come from either a medical school professor or a physician); letter, on school letterhead, from the applicant's medical school verifying that he/she enrolled full time as a third or fourth-year medical student at that institution; and a typed, one-page essay addressing the following: Where do you see yourself in 10 years? How do you plan to give back to the community? **Deadline for Receipt:** September 30.

3369 ■ FOUNDATION OF THE PENNSYLVANIA MEDICAL SOCIETY
777 E Park Dr.
PO Box 8820
Harrisburg, PA 17105-8820
Tel: (717)558-7750
Free: 800-228-7823
Fax: (717)558-7818
E-mail: foundation@pamedsoc.org
Web Site: http://www.foundationpamedsoc.org
To financially assist a deserving medical student enrolled in a Pennsylvania medical school.
Title of Award: Alliance Medical Education Scholarship Fund (AMES) **Area, Field, or Subject:** Medicine. **Level of Education for which Award is Granted:** Undergraduate **Funds Available:** $2,500.

Eligibility Requirements: Applicants must be residents of Pennsylvania who are enrolled in a Pennsylvania medical school as full-time second- or third-year medical students. **Application Requirements:** Applicants must submit: the completed application form; two reference letters from persons who know them well (other than their families); letter from their medical school verifying that they are enrolled full-time and currently second or third-year medical students; and a typed statement of one page describing their vision for the future of Pennsylvania Medicine. **Deadline for Receipt:** January 15.

3370 ■ FOUNDATION OF THE PENNSYLVANIA MEDICAL SOCIETY
777 E Park Dr.
PO Box 8820
Harrisburg, PA 17105-8820
Tel: (717)558-7750
Free: 800-228-7823
Fax: (717)558-7818
E-mail: foundation@pamedsoc.org
Web Site: http://www.foundationpamedsoc.org
To financially assist deserving second-year medical students at Penn State College of Medicine.
Title of Award: Scott A. Gunder, MD, DCMS Presidential Scholarships **Area, Field, or Subject:** Medicine. **Level of Education for which Award is Granted:** Undergraduate **Funds Available:** $1,500.

Eligibility Requirements: Applicants must have been residents of Pennsylvania for at least 12 months before registering as medical students; must be second-year medical students; must be enrolled full-time at Penn State College of Medicine; and must be members of Pennsylvania Medical Society and their county medical society. **Application Requirements:** Applicants must submit: completed application form; two reference letters, from persons other than family members, documenting the applicants' integrity, interpersonal skills, and potential as future physicians; letter, on school letterhead, from Penn State College of Medicine verifying that they are enrolled full-time and second-year medical students; one-page typed essay describing the person or event that most influenced them to become physicians and how they see themselves leading others into medicine; and completed Pennsylvania Medical Society membership applications if students are not current members. **Deadline for Receipt:** April 15.

3371 ■ FOUNDATION OF THE PENNSYLVANIA MEDICAL SOCIETY
777 E Park Dr.
PO Box 8820
Harrisburg, PA 17105-8820
Tel: (717)558-7750
Free: 800-228-7823
Fax: (717)558-7818
E-mail: foundation@pamedsoc.org
Web Site: http://www.foundationpamedsoc.org
To provide financial assistance for medical students who are residents of Lycoming County.
Title of Award: Lycoming County Medical Society (LCMS) Scholarships **Area, Field, or Subject:** Medicine. **Level of Education for which Award is Granted:** Undergraduate **Funds Available:** $2,000.
Eligibility Requirements: Applicants must be residents of Lycoming County in the state of Pennsylvania; must be enrolled full-time in an accredited allopathic or osteopathic medical school within the United States. **Application Requirements:** Applicants must submit: completed application form; two reference letters, from persons other than family members, documenting the applicants' integrity, interpersonal skills, and potential as future physicians; letter, on school letterhead, from applicants' medical school verifying that they are enrolled full-time as medical students at their respective institutions; and, one-page, typed essay specifically describing why they chose to become physicians and what contributions they expect to make to the health profession. **Deadline for Receipt:** September 30.

3372 ■ FOUNDATION OF THE PENNSYLVANIA MEDICAL SOCIETY
777 E Park Dr.
PO Box 8820
Harrisburg, PA 17105-8820
Tel: (717)558-7750
Free: 800-228-7823
Fax: (717)558-7818
E-mail: foundation@pamedsoc.org
Web Site: http://www.foundationpamedsoc.org
To provide financial assistance for medical students who are residents of Montgomery County.
Title of Award: Montgomery County Medical Society (MCMS) Scholarships **Area, Field, or Subject:** Medicine. **Level of Education for which Award is Granted:** Undergraduate **Funds Available:** $1,000.
Eligibility Requirements: Applicants must be residents of Montgomery County in the state of Pennsylvania; must have been Pennsylvania residents for at least 12 months prior to registering as medical students; must be enrolled full-time in an accredited United States medical school; must be enrolled or entering their first year of medical school. **Application Requirements:** Applicants must submit completed application form; two reference letters, from persons other than family members, documenting the applicants' integrity, interpersonal skills, and potential as physicians; letter, on school letterhead, from their medical schools verifying that they are enrolled full time as first-year medical students at that institution; one-page, typed essay addressing the reasons for pursuing medical career, personal goals, and plans for future within the profession. **Deadline for Receipt:** September 30.

3373 ■ FOUNDATION OF THE PENNSYLVANIA MEDICAL SOCIETY
777 E Park Dr.
PO Box 8820
Harrisburg, PA 17105-8820

Tel: (717)558-7750
Free: 800-228-7823
Fax: (717)558-7818
E-mail: foundation@pamedsoc.org
Web Site: http://www.foundationpamedsoc.org
To provide financial assistance to qualified first-year medical students residing in Berks, Lehigh, or Northampton County.
Title of Award: Myrtle Siegfried, MD and Michael Vigilante, MD Scholarships **Area, Field, or Subject:** Medicine. **Level of Education for which Award is Granted:** Undergraduate **Funds Available:** No specific amount.
Eligibility Requirements: Applicants must be residents of Berks, Lehigh, or Northampton County; must be entering first year of medical school; must be enrolled full-time in an accredited United States medical school. **Application Requirements:** Applicants must submit completed application form; two reference letters documenting the applicants' integrity, interpersonal skills, and potential as future physicians (letters must come from persons who know the applicants well but are not family members); letter, on school letterhead, from their medical school verifying that they are enrolled full-time at that institution and first-year medical students; one-page, typed essay specifically describing why they chose to become physicians and what contributions they expect to make to the health profession. **Deadline for Receipt:** June 1.

3374 ■ GRAND RAPIDS COMMUNITY FOUNDATION
161 Ottawa Ave. NW
Ste. 209-C Waters Bldg.
Grand Rapids, MI 49503
Tel: (616)454-1751
Fax: (616)454-6455
E-mail: grfound@grfoundation.org
Web Site: http://www.grfoundation.org
To provide financial assistance to those students who are in need.
Title of Award: Dr. Noyes L. Avery, Jr. & Ann E. Avery Scholarships **Area, Field, or Subject:** Medicine. **Level of Education for which Award is Granted:** Undergraduate **Funds Available:** No specific amount.
Eligibility Requirements: Applicants must be full-time students from Kent County who are attending the University of Michigan for a medical doctor degree. Applicants must have a minimum of 3.0 GPA. Applicants must have financial need. **Application Requirements:** Applicants must check the available website for the required materials. **Additional Information:** Grand Rapids Community Foundation at the above address

3375 ■ GRAND RAPIDS COMMUNITY FOUNDATION
161 Ottawa Ave. NW
Ste. 209-C Waters Bldg.
Grand Rapids, MI 49503
Tel: (616)454-1751
Fax: (616)454-6455
E-mail: grfound@grfoundation.org
Web Site: http://www.grfoundation.org
To provide financial assistance to those students who are in need.
Title of Award: Dr. William E. & Norma Sprague Scholarships **Area, Field, or Subject:** Medicine. **Level of Education for which Award is Granted:** Undergraduate **Funds Available:** No specific amount.
Eligibility Requirements: Applicants must be full-time students and permanent residents in the Michigan counties of Kent, Allegan, Barry, Ionia, Montcalm, Muskegon, Newaygo or Athens County, Ohio, who are pursuing a full-time undergraduate or graduate degree in medicine at Ohio University. Applicants must have financial need. Applicants must have a minimum of 3.0 GPA. **Application Requirements:** Applicants must check the available website for the required materials. **Additional Information:** Grand Rapids Community Foundation at the above address

3376 ■ HARTFORD FOUNDATION FOR PUBLIC GIVING
10 Columbus Blvd., 8th Flr.
Hartford, CT 06106
Tel: (860)548-1888
Fax: (860)524-8346
E-mail: hfpg@hfpg.org
Web Site: http://www.hfpg.org
To provide scholarship to the students entering or enrolled in Medical school.
Title of Award: Dr. Frank and Florence Marino Scholarships **Area, Field, or Subject:** Medicine. **Level of Education for which Award is Granted:**

Undergraduate **Funds Available:** $1,000.

Eligibility Requirements: Applicants must: have attended Connecticut school for at least 8 years (K-12) and graduated from Connecticut public or parochial high school; demonstrate financial need; have academic excellence. **Application Requirements:** Applicants may contact Mrs. Rita Fry to obtain application materials. **Deadline for Receipt:** March 20. **Additional Information:** Scholarship Fund c/o Mrs. Rita Fry, PO Box 75 Brookfield, CT 06804. 203-775-3114; rfry@charter.net.

3377 ■ HARTFORD FOUNDATION FOR PUBLIC GIVING
10 Columbus Blvd., 8th Flr.
Hartford, CT 06106
Tel: (860)548-1888
Fax: (860)524-8346
E-mail: hfpg@hfpg.org
Web Site: http://www.hfpg.org
To provide scholarship to the students attending the University of Connecticut School of Medicine.
Title of Award: Sylvia Parkinson Scholarships **Area, Field, or Subject:** Medicine. **Level of Education for which Award is Granted:** Undergraduate **Funds Available:** $1,500-$3,000.
Eligibility Requirements: Applicants must: be a Capitol Region resident; demonstrate financial need; have an academic excellence; intend to practice in the Greater Hartford area. **Application Requirements:** Applicants may obtain application materials from University of Connecticut School of Medicine. 263 Farmington Ave. MC 1827 Farmington, CT 06030. **Deadline for Receipt:** March 20. **Additional Information:** Andrea Deveraux, Director of Financial Aid, Phone: 860-679-3574 Fax: 860-679-1902; devereux@uchc.edu.

3378 ■ HARTFORD FOUNDATION FOR PUBLIC GIVING
10 Columbus Blvd., 8th Flr.
Hartford, CT 06106
Tel: (860)548-1888
Fax: (860)524-8346
E-mail: hfpg@hfpg.org
Web Site: http://www.hfpg.org
To provide financial assistance to students accepted by an accredited medical school.
Title of Award: Alice W. Rooke Scholarships **Area, Field, or Subject:** Medicine. **Level of Education for which Award is Granted:** Undergraduate **Funds Available:** $5,000. **Duration:** Renewable.
Eligibility Requirements: Applicants must be pursuing a course of study in medicine, not pre-med; must be a US citizen; have a letter of sponsorship from local DAR chapter. **Application Requirements:** For Connecticut residents, to obtain application materials, send a self-addressed stamped envelope to: National Society Daughters of American Revolution, 215 Loomis St., North Granby, CT 06060. **Deadline for Receipt:** April 15. **Additional Information:** Mrs. Michael L. Stewart, CT State Chairperson, NSDAR Scholarship Committee. L2stew@yahoo.com; 860-653-4203.

3379 ■ HILLEL MONTREAL
3460 Stanley St.
Montreal, QC, Canada H3A 1R8
Tel: (514)845-9171
Fax: (514)345-6418
E-mail: romy@hillel.ca
Web Site: http://montreal.hillel.ca
To provide scholarship through Hillel Montreal as recognition of the financial assistance received by Dr. Cohen as a medical student through the Levitt Family Foundation and Hillel Montreal.
Title of Award: Dr. Mark Cohen Scholarship **Area, Field, or Subject:** Medicine. **Level of Education for which Award is Granted:** Undergraduate **Funds Available:** $5,000.
Eligibility Requirements: Applicants must be students enrolled in the Faculty of Medicine or the Faculty of Dentistry at McGill University or University de Montreal. **Application Requirements:** Applicants must submit a letter stating goals and reasons for request, transcript of grades, curriculum vitae, one academic recommendation, proof of Quebec residency, and Social Insurance Number. **Deadline for Receipt:** May 30. **Additional Information:** 514-842-6405.

3380 ■ JEWISH FOUNDATION FOR EDUCATION OF WOMEN
135 E 64th St.
New York, NY 10065

Tel: (212)288-3931
Fax: (212)288-5798
E-mail: info@jfew.org
Web Site: http://www.jfew.org
To provide financial support for emigres from the former Soviet Union to train in medicine, dentistry, dental hygiene, nursing, pharmacy, occupational and physical therapy, physician assistant, CVT, and sonography programs.
Title of Award: Scholarships for Emigres in the Health Sciences **Area, Field, or Subject:** Medicine; Dentistry; Nursing; Pharmacy; Physical therapy; Physiology. **Level of Education for which Award is Granted:** Undergraduate **Funds Available:** $5,000. **Duration:** One year.
Eligibility Requirements: Applicants must be students from the former Soviet Union; must be residents of New York City or the counties of Nassau, Suffolk or Westchester; must already be enrolled in or about to enroll in a health science program within that geographic area; and must be enrolled full-time, in good standing, and demonstrate financial need. **Application Requirements:** Applicants must submit all the required application information.

3381 ■ JEWISH VOCATIONAL SERVICE
216 W Jackson Blvd., Ste. 700
Chicago, IL 60606
Tel: (312)673-3400
Fax: (312)553-5544
E-mail: jvs@jvschicago.org
Web Site: http://www.jvschicago.org
To support the education of a Jewish college or graduate student.
Title of Award: Jewish Federation Academic Scholarships **Area, Field, or Subject:** Medicine; Education; Social work; Arts; Public health; Urban affairs/design/planning; Law. **Level of Education for which Award is Granted:** Graduate, Undergraduate **Funds Available:** More than $500,000 each year.
Eligibility Requirements: Applicant must be Jewish; be born or raised in either: Cook County, Chicago metropolitan area, or Northwest Indiana; or have one continuous year of full-time employment in Cook County or Chicago metropolitan area prior to starting professional education; must intend to remain in the Chicago metropolitan area after completing school; must be entering as a full-time student in an accredited professional graduate program or entering as junior or senior undergraduate student at an accredited professional education program; and must be demonstrating career promise in a helping profession. **Application Requirements:** Applicants must submit a completed Application Data Form; Career Statement Form; Budget Worksheet; and Academic Budget form as an attachment to jvsscholarship@jvschicago.org. In addition, applicants must send by mail a Legal Domicility Form; two letter of reference form; IRS Forms; parents' or spouse's IRS; documentation of tuition cost; Release of Information form; and official transcripts. **Deadline for Receipt:** February 15. **Additional Information:** 312-673-3457.

3382 ■ NATIONAL FEDERATION OF THE BLIND
1800 Johnson St.
Baltimore, MD 21230
Tel: (410)659-9314
Fax: (410)685-5653
Web Site: http://www.nfb.org
To recognize achievement of blind scholars and to create opportunity for all blind people.
Title of Award: Howard B. Rickard Scholarships **Area, Field, or Subject:** Law; Medicine; Engineering; Architecture; Natural Science. **Level of Education for which Award is Granted:** Undergraduate **Funds Available:** $3,000.
Eligibility Requirements: All applicants must be legally blind; he/she must be pursuing or planning to study in the field of law, medicine, engineering, architecture or the natural science; he/she must be participant in NFB national convention and in all scheduled scholarship program activities. **Application Requirements:** Applicant must fill out the application form; he/she must submit two letters of recommendation from individuals that can describe the academic ability, leadership skills, and/or community involvement; copies of transcript of record and a photocopy of score reports for all standardized tests taken for college admission (ACT, SAT or other); an applicant must provide a letter of proof of legal blindness from a qualified professional; and an affiliate President's letter. **Deadline for Receipt:** March 31.

3383 ■ NATIONAL MEDICAL FELLOWSHIPS
5 Hanover Sq., 15th Fl.
New York, NY 10004
Tel: (212)483-8880
Fax: (212)483-8897
E-mail: info@nmfonline.org
Web Site: http://www.nmfonline.org
To encourage future physicians to establish community-based primary care practices in California.
Title of Award: California Community Service Scholarships **Area, Field, or Subject:** Medicine. **Level of Education for which Award is Granted:** Undergraduate **Funds Available:** $7500.
Eligibility Requirements: Applicant must be a third or fourth year student; enrolled at MD degree granting schools in California; an African-American, mainland Puerto Rican, Mexican-American, Native Hawaiian, Alaska Native, or American Indian; a U.S. citizen; and must demonstrate commitment to practice in California. **Application Requirements:** Applicants must submit a completed application form together with the required materials. **Deadline for Receipt:** January. **Additional Information:** CSSP Interim Program Coordinator, Mary Wade at 415-397-2526 or marywade@nmfonline.org.

3384 ■ NATIONAL MEDICAL FELLOWSHIPS
5 Hanover Sq., 15th Fl.
New York, NY 10004
Tel: (212)483-8880
Fax: (212)483-8897
E-mail: info@nmfonline.org
Web Site: http://www.nmfonline.org
To encourage future physicians to establish community-based primary care practices in California.
Title of Award: California Community Service Scholarships - Bay Area **Area, Field, or Subject:** Medicine. **Level of Education for which Award is Granted:** Undergraduate **Funds Available:** $7500-$15,000.
Eligibility Requirements: Applicant must be a third or fourth year student; enrolled at MD degree granting schools in California; an African-American, mainland Puerto Rican, Mexican-American, Native Hawaiian, Alaska Native, or American Indian; a U.S. citizen; and must demonstrate commitment to practice in the San Francisco Bay Area. **Application Requirements:** Applicants must submit a completed application form together with the required materials. **Deadline for Receipt:** January. **Additional Information:** CSSP Interim Program Coordinator, Mary Wade at 415-397-2526 or marywade@nmfonline.org.

3385 ■ NATIONAL MEDICAL FELLOWSHIPS
5 Hanover Sq., 15th Fl.
New York, NY 10004
Tel: (212)483-8880
Fax: (212)483-8897
E-mail: info@nmfonline.org
Web Site: http://www.nmfonline.org
To support medical students in educational pursuits.
Title of Award: National Medical Fellowships Need-Based Scholarships **Area, Field, or Subject:** Medicine. **Level of Education for which Award is Granted:** Undergraduate **Funds Available:** $500-$10,000.
Eligibility Requirements: Applicants must be first or second year medical student; an African-American, Mexican-American, Native American, Alaska Native, Native Hawaiian, or mainland Puerto Ricans who permanently reside within the 50 U.S. states; and accepted to AAMC or AOA-accredited U.S. medical schools for study leading to M.D. or D.O. degrees. Applicants born outside of the U.S. must submit a proof of citizenship. **Application Requirements:** Applicants must submit a completed application together with the required documents. **Deadline for Receipt:** June 30.

3386 ■ OREGON MEDICAL ASSOCIATION
11740 SW, 68th Pkwy., Ste.100
Portland, OR 97223
Tel: (503)619-8000
Fax: (503)619-0609
E-mail: oma@theoma.org
Web Site: http://www.theoma.org
To advance medical science through education.
Title of Award: Linn Benton Scholarships **Area, Field, or Subject:** Medicine. **Level of Education for which Award is Granted:** Undergradu-

ate **Number Awarded:** 3. **Funds Available:** $1,000.
Eligibility Requirements: Applicants must be high school seniors or graduates seeking a career in medicine or nursing. **Application Requirements:** Applicants must complete the application form. **Deadline for Receipt:** April 1.

3387 ■ THE SAN DIEGO FOUNDATION
2508 Historic Decatur Rd., Ste. 200
San Diego, CA 92106
Tel: (619)235-2300
Fax: (619)239-1710
E-mail: info@sdfoundation.org
Web Site: http://www.sdfoundation.org
To support the education of students from California.
Title of Award: Mission Bay Hospital Auxiliary Scholarships **Area, Field, or Subject:** Medicine. **Level of Education for which Award is Granted:** Undergraduate **Number Awarded:** 1. **Funds Available:** $5,000.
Eligibility Requirements: Applicant must be a graduating college senior pursuing a career in medicine; a resident of San Diego County; planning to attend an accredited medical school in the U.S.; have a minimum 3.50 GPA on a 4.0 scale; and demonstrated financial need. **Application Requirements:** Applicants must submit a completed Common Scholarship Application together with personal statement; two letters of recommendation on official letterhead (written within the last six months); official transcript in an official and sealed envelope; and a copy of most recent tax form (Form 1040-pages 1 & 2; Form 1040A-pages 1 & 2; Form 1040EZ-page 1). **Deadline for Receipt:** January 28. **Additional Information:** Arzo Mansury, Dir. Scholarships at 619-814-1343, or scholarships@sdfoundation.org.

3388 ■ SILICON VALLEY COMMUNITY FOUNDATION
2240 W El Camino Real Ste. 300
Mountain View, CA 94040-1498
Tel: (650)450-5400
Fax: (650)450-5401
Web Site: http://www.siliconvalleycf.org
To recognize students who demonstrate excellence in both character and academic achievement by giving them scholarships.
Title of Award: Dr. James L. Hutchinson and Evelyn Ribbs Hutchinson Medical School Scholarship Fund **Area, Field, or Subject:** Medicine. **Level of Education for which Award is Granted:** Undergraduate **Number Awarded:** 1. **Funds Available:** $2,000. **Duration:** 1 year.
Eligibility Requirements: Applicants must be United States citizens; must be college seniors and accepted to medical school, or currently enrolled full-time in an accredited medical school program; must demonstrate personal motivation for excellence in both character and academic achievement. Personal integrity, as exemplified by leadership, community involvement, and concern for others, will be considered. **Application Requirements:** Applicants must check the available website for the required materials. **Deadline for Receipt:** May 16. **Additional Information:** Silicon Valley Community Foundation at the above address

3389 ■ SOUTHWEST FLORIDA COMMUNITY FOUNDATION
8260 College Pkwy., Ste. 101
Fort Myers, FL 33919
Tel: (239)274-5900
Fax: (239)274-5930
Web Site: http://www.floridacommunity.com
To fund a student who will attend: FGCU, university of Florida/Gainesville, Florida State University/Tallahassee, Flagler College, Stetson University/Deland, University of Miami, University of Tampa, or Embry Riddle Aeronautical University/Daytona Beach.
Title of Award: D&A Florida Scholarships **Area, Field, or Subject:** Architecture; Business; Engineering; International affairs and relations; Journalism; Computer and information sciences; Law; Literature; Medicine; Physics; Chemistry; Political science. **Level of Education for which Award is Granted:** Undergraduate **Funds Available:** $10,000. **Duration:** One year.
Eligibility Requirements: Applicants must have graduated from a public or private high school in Charlotte, Glades, Hendry or Lee County; must pursue a degree in Architecture, Business, Engineering, International affairs and relations, Journalism, Computer and information sciences, Law, Literature, Medicine, Physics, Chemistry, or Political science. **Application**

Requirements: Application forms are available online. Applicants must submit a letter of interest and letter of recommendation, a transcript and financial need documentation. **Deadline for Receipt:** February 15.

3390 ■ SOUTHWEST FLORIDA COMMUNITY FOUNDATION
8260 College Pkwy., Ste. 101
Fort Myers, FL 33919
Tel: (239)274-5900
Fax: (239)274-5930
Web Site: http://www.floridacommunity.com
To fund students studying Christian ministry/youth ministry, Christian counseling, nursing and medicine.
Title of Award: Dorris W. Frey Memorial Scholarships **Area, Field, or Subject:** Ministry; Christian education; Nursing; Medicine. **Level of Education for which Award is Granted:** Undergraduate **Funds Available:** Scholarship amount is determined by selection committee. **Duration:** One year.
Eligibility Requirements: Applicants must have graduated from a public or private high school in Charlotte, Collier, Glades, Hendry or Lee County; must pursue one of the above named degrees of study; must maintain satisfactory grades; must be committed to Jesus Christ and show commitment through action in ministering to others; and must have recognized ability and academic performance with standard measures of grades and appropriate test scores. **Application Requirements:** Applicants must submit an essay of future commitment, transcript, and references. **Deadline for Receipt:** February 15.

3391 ■ SOUTHWEST FLORIDA COMMUNITY FOUNDATION
8260 College Pkwy., Ste. 101
Fort Myers, FL 33919
Tel: (239)274-5900
Fax: (239)274-5930
Web Site: http://www.floridacommunity.com
To fund students pursuing degrees or advanced degrees in medicine, law, dentistry, teaching (math and science), ministry, engineering, accounting, architecture and computer science.
Title of Award: John M. and Mary A. Shanley Memorial Scholarships **Area, Field, or Subject:** Medicine; Law; Dentistry; Teaching; Ministry; Engineering; Accounting; Agriculture; Economic aspects; Architecture; Computer and information sciences. **Level of Education for which Award is Granted:** Undergraduate **Funds Available:** $5,000. **Duration:** One year.
Eligibility Requirements: Applicant must be a resident of Charlotte, Hendry or Lee County. **Application Requirements:** Application forms are available online. Applicants must submit a letter of interest, letter of recommendation and transcript. **Deadline for Receipt:** February 15.

3392 ■ UNIVERSITY OF ALASKA ANCHORAGE
3211 Providence Dr.
Anchorage, AK 99508
Tel: (907)786-1800
Web Site: http://www.uaa.alaska.edu
To provide financial support to students who want to pursue their degree in the field of medicine.
Title of Award: Providence Alaska Medical Center Auxiliary Scholarships **Area, Field, or Subject:** Medicine. **Level of Education for which Award is Granted:** Undergraduate **Funds Available:** $1,000.
Eligibility Requirements: Applicant must be admitted to a degree-seeking clinical major; must be currently enrolled as a first year student or beyond at one of the institutions of higher education in Alaska; must have a minimum GPA of 2.7. **Application Requirements:** Applicants must complete the scholarship application form; must have the current official transcript of grades; must have two letters of recommendation from university or college faculty members; must have a two- or three-page statement that includes: (1) Name, permanent address, phone number, social security number and student ID number; (2) A short history of the applicant and family; (3) A statement of goals; (4) A summary of interest and community involvement; (5) A summary of work experience and financial need. Application must be sent to: Providence Alaska Medical Center Auxiliary, Scholarship Committee, 3200 Providence Dr., PO Box 196604, Anchorage, AK 99519-6604. **Deadline for Receipt:** June 30.

3393 ■ UNIVERSITY OF TORONTO
315 Bloor St. W
Toronto, ON, Canada M5S 1A3

Tel: (416)978-2011
E-mail: information.commonsats@utoronto.ca
Web Site: http://www.utoronto.ca
To support students with their educational pursuit.
Title of Award: Dr. Anderson Abbott Awards **Area, Field, or Subject:** Medicine; Health sciences. **Level of Education for which Award is Granted:** Undergraduate **Number Awarded:** 1. **Funds Available:** $4000.
Eligibility Requirements: Applicant must be a black student of UofT. **Application Requirements:** Applicants must submit a completed Abbot application form along with the required materials and information. **Deadline for Receipt:** March 28.

3394 ■ WORCESTER DISTRICT MEDICAL SOCIETY
Mechanics Hall, 321 Main St.
Worcester, MA 01608
Tel: (508)753-1579
Fax: (508)754-6246
E-mail: info@wdms.org
Web Site: http://www.wdms.org
To provide educational assistance to medical students.
Title of Award: Worcester District Medical Society Scholarship Fund **Area, Field, or Subject:** Medicine. **Level of Education for which Award is Granted:** Undergraduate **Funds Available:** No specific amount.
Eligibility Requirements: Applicants must be second, third, or fourth year students enrolled, (with tuition obligation), in an accredited medical or osteophathic school and legal residents of Central Massachusetts at the time of applying to medical school. **Application Requirements:** Applicants must submit completed application form; current transcript; two letters of recommendation; and an essay stating the reasons for selecting a career in medicine and why they feel deserving of the award. **Deadline for Receipt:** August 31.

3395 ■ ZETA PHI BETA SORORITY
1734 New Hampshire Ave. NW
Washington, DC 20009
Tel: (202)387-3103
Fax: (202)232-4593
E-mail: ihq@zphib1920.org
Web Site: http://www.zphib1920.org
To support students in pursuit of higher education.
Title of Award: S. Evelyn Lewis Memorial Scholarships in Medical Health Sciences **Area, Field, or Subject:** Medicine; Health sciences. **Level of Education for which Award is Granted:** Graduate, Undergraduate **Number Awarded:** 1. **Funds Available:** $500-$1000. **Duration:** One academic year.
Eligibility Requirements: Applicant must be a full-time graduate or undergraduate woman enrolled in a program leading to a degree in medicine or health sciences. **Application Requirements:** Applicants must submit completed application forms along with the required materials. **Deadline for Receipt:** February 1.

Neurosciences

3396 ■ AMERICAN ASSOCIATION OF NEUROSCIENCE NURSES
4700 W Lake Ave.
Glenview, IL 60025
Tel: (847)375-4733; 888-557-2266
Fax: (847)375-3430
E-mail: info@aann.org
Web Site: http://www.aann.org
To promote excellence in neuroscience nursing.
Title of Award: NNF Scholarships Program **Area, Field, or Subject:** Neuroscience; Nursing. **Level of Education for which Award is Granted:** Graduate, Undergraduate **Funds Available:** $1,500.
Eligibility Requirements: Applicants must be registered nurses pursuing a career in neuroscience nursing at the undergraduate or graduate level. **Application Requirements:** Applications must be typed or word-processed. The application is available at the NNF web site, www.aann.org. Complete all information as requested. Incomplete applications will not be considered and will be returned to the applicants. School which the applicant attends, or plans to attend must be accredited. Submit one copy of Form A, four copies of Form B (including personal statement). **Deadline for Receipt:** January 15. **Additional Information:** AANN at the above address.

3397 ■ EPILEPSY FOUNDATION
8301 Professional Place
Landover, MD 20785
800-332-1000
Web Site: http://www.epilepsyfoundation.org
To encourage individuals to pursue careers in epilepsy in either the research or practice setting.
Title of Award: Behavioral Sciences Student Fellowships **Area, Field, or Subject:** Behavioral sciences; Epilepsy. **Level of Education for which Award is Granted:** Graduate, Undergraduate **Funds Available:** $3,000.
Eligibility Requirements: Applicants must be in an appropriate undergraduate or graduate program in the behavioral sciences and must have a defined epilepsy-related study or research plan. **Application Requirements:** Applicants may visit the website or contact Epilepsy Foundation for more details. **Deadline for Receipt:** March 2.

Nursing

3398 ■ ACADEMY OF MEDICAL-SURGICAL NURSES
E Holly Ave., Box 56
Pitman, NJ 08071-0056
(866)877-2676
E-mail: amsn@ajj.com
Web Site: http://www.medsurgnurse.org/
To provide financial assistance for AMSN members who with to further their education.
Title of Award: Career Mobility Scholarship Awards **Area, Field, or Subject:** Nursing; Surgery; Medicine. **Level of Education for which Award is Granted:** Doctorate, Undergraduate **Number Awarded:** 1. **Funds Available:** $500. **Duration:** One year.
Eligibility Requirements: Applicants must be members of AMSN for at least one year. **Application Requirements:** Applicants must submit a completed application form; a brief description (one page, double-spaced with size 12 font) discussing how additional education will enhance the care of Adult Medical-Surgical patient; and a self-addressed stamped postcard. Electronic submission is preferred; otherwise applicant must submit additional 9 blinded photocopies of application and of required documentation. **Additional Information:** Fax copies will not be considered. **Deadline for Receipt:** August 1.

3399 ■ AMERICAN ASSOCIATION OF AMBULATORY CARE NURSING
PO Box 56
Pitman, NJ 08071-0056
800-262-6877
E-mail: aaacn@ajj.com
Web Site: http://www.aaacn.org
To provide financial support for researches.
Title of Award: AAACN Scholarships **Area, Field, or Subject:** Nursing. **Level of Education for which Award is Granted:** Undergraduate **Funds Available:** $100 to $1,000.
Eligibility Requirements: Applicants must be members of American Academy of Ambulatory Care Nursing (AAACN) for a minimum of two years; currently enrolled in accredited school of nursing or a program deemed by the committee to advance the profession of nursing; request for payment of tuition, books, academic supplies; proof of acceptance in course; must submit a research abstract and proof of acceptance of research study by academic institution or by Investigational Review Board of employing or sponsoring institution; willing to present research findings at AAACN Annual Conference following receipt of award; willing to publish article in Viewpoint describing research study and outcome. **Application Requirements:** Applicants must complete application fully and submit two copies to the AAACN National Office. **Deadline for Receipt:** January 15.

3400 ■ AMERICAN ASSOCIATION OF COLLEGES OF NURSING
One Dupont Circle NW, Ste. 530
Washington, DC 20036
Tel: (202)463-6930
Fax: (202)785-8320
E-mail: scasey@aacn.nche.edu
Web Site: http://www.aacn.nche.edu
To promote education in nursing.

Title of Award: AACN Excellence in Academics Nursing Scholarships **Area, Field, or Subject:** Nursing. **Level of Education for which Award is Granted:** Undergraduate **Number Awarded:** 2. **Funds Available:** $2500.
Eligibility Requirements: Applicant must have a GPA of 3.5 or better; enrolled full-time in a baccalaureate program; a junior student pursuing a Bachelor of Science in Nursing (BSN) program. **Application Requirements:** Applicants must submit a completed application form together with the required materials. Send application and materials to Laura Guetter at AACN via email scholarship@aacn.nche.edu, or fax to 202785-8320. **Additional Information:** In partnership with Lydia's Professional Uniforms, a leading supplier of apparel for health professionals. **Deadline for Receipt:** August 1 and November 1.

3401 ■ AMERICAN ASSOCIATION OF COLLEGES OF NURSING
One Dupont Circle NW, Ste. 530
Washington, DC 20036
Tel: (202)463-6930
Fax: (202)785-8320
E-mail: scasey@aacn.nche.edu
Web Site: http://www.aacn.nche.edu
To promote education in nursing.
Title of Award: AfterCollege/AACN Nursing Scholarships **Area, Field, or Subject:** Nursing. **Level of Education for which Award is Granted:** Graduate, Undergraduate **Funds Available:** $2500.
Eligibility Requirements: Applicant must be enrolled at an AACN member institution; seeking baccalaureate, master's or doctoral degree in nursing; and have a GPA of 3.25 or higher. **Application Requirements:** Applicants are advised to visit the website for the application forms. **Additional Information:** In partnership with AfterCollege, the leading employment website for nursing/allied health care student. **Deadline for Receipt:** January 31, April 30, July 31 and October 31. **Additional Information:** scholarship@aacn.nche.edu.

3402 ■ AMERICAN ASSOCIATION OF CRITICAL-CARE NURSES
101 Columbia
Aliso Viejo, CA 92656-4109
Tel: (949)362-2000
Free: 800-899-2226
Fax: (949)362-2020
E-mail: info@aacn.org
Web Site: http://www.aacn.org
To provide financial assistance to AACN members who are registered nurses completing a baccalaureate or graduate degree program in nursing.
Title of Award: American Association of Critical-Care Nurses BSN Scholarships **Area, Field, or Subject:** Nursing. **Level of Education for which Award is Granted:** Undergraduate **Funds Available:** $1,500.
Eligibility Requirements: Applicant must be a bonafide AACN member; have an active RN license; cumulative GPA of 3.0 or better; currently working in critical care or have worked in critical care for at least one year in the past three years; junior or upper division status for the following fall semester; and currently enrolled in or accepted to a nursing program accredited by the state Board of Nursing for the following fall semester. **Application Requirements:** Applicants must submit application online, completed along with a cover checklist page and supporting documents. **Deadline for Receipt:** April 1.

3403 ■ AMERICAN ASSOCIATION OF NEUROSCIENCE NURSES
4700 W Lake Ave.
Glenview, IL 60025
Tel: (847)375-4733; 888-557-2266
Fax: (847)375-3430
E-mail: info@aann.org
Web Site: http://www.aann.org
To promote excellence in neuroscience nursing.
Title of Award: NNF Scholarships Program **Area, Field, or Subject:** Neuroscience; Nursing. **Level of Education for which Award is Granted:** Graduate, Undergraduate **Funds Available:** $1,500.
Eligibility Requirements: Applicants must be registered nurses pursuing a career in neuroscience nursing at the undergraduate or graduate level. **Application Requirements:** Applications must be typed or word-processed. The application is available at the NNF web site, www.aann.

org. Complete all information as requested. Incomplete applications will not be considered and will be returned to the applicants. School which the applicant attends, or plans to attend must be accredited. Submit one copy of Form A, four copies of Form B (including personal statement). **Deadline for Receipt:** January 15. **Additional Information:** AANN at the above address.

3404 ■ AMERICAN COLLEGE OF NURSE-MIDWIVES FOUNDATION

8403 Colesville Rd., Ste. 1550
Silver Spring, MD 20910
Tel: (240)485-1800
Fax: (240)485-1818
Web Site: http://www.midwife.org
To provide assistance to students of nurse-midwifery.
Title of Award: Basic Midwifery Student Scholarship Program **Area, Field, or Subject:** Nursing; Midwifery. **Level of Education for which Award is Granted:** Undergraduate **Funds Available:** No specific amount. **Duration:** One year.
Eligibility Requirements: Applicants must be students in good standing in an ACNM DOA accredited basic midwifery education program; must have successfully completed one academic or clinical semester/quarter or clinical module; and must be current members of the American College of Nurse-Midwives (ACNM). **Application Requirements:** Applicants must submit application information form; statement of career goals and plans; financial assessment form; statement of financial need; program director form; and the faculty recommendation form. **Deadline for Receipt:** March 17.

3405 ■ AMERICAN COLLEGE OF NURSING PRACTITIONERS

1501 Wilson Blvd., Ste. 509
Arlington, VA 22209
Tel: (703)740-2529
Fax: (703)740-2533
E-mail: acnp@acnpweb.org
Web Site: http://www.acnpweb.org
To recognize an outstanding student in the field of nursing.
Title of Award: ACNP Nurse Practitioner Student Scholarship Awards **Area, Field, or Subject:** Nursing. **Level of Education for which Award is Granted:** Undergraduate **Funds Available:** $1,000.
Eligibility Requirements: Applicants must be a member of ACNP; enrolled in an accredited NP program; have a GPA of 3.4. **Application Requirements:** Applicants must complete the application form and submit with the following supporting documents: proof of Student Membership in ACNP; official transcript of an accredited NP program that indicates a 3.4 GPA; curriculum vitae (not more than 2 pages); two letters from professional colleagues indicating leadership roles and involvement in any organizational policy development; statement of the applicant's goals related to the ACNP Mission (not more than 200 words). **Deadline for Receipt:** June 30.

3406 ■ AMERICAN QUARTER HORSE YOUTH ASSOCIATION

PO Box 200
Amarillo, TX 79168
Tel: (806)376-4811
Web Site: http://www.aqha.com/youth.html
To develop and educate the future professionals.
Title of Award: American Quarter Horse Foundation Scholarships **Area, Field, or Subject:** Education; Nursing; Journalism; Veterinary science and medicine. **Level of Education for which Award is Granted:** Undergraduate **Funds Available:** No specific amount.
Eligibility Requirements: An applicant must be enrolled in college specializing degree programs such as education, nursing, journalism, veterinary and racing. **Application Requirements:** Applicant must fill out the application form and submit proof that he/she is currently enrolled in a college or university. **Deadline for Receipt:** not stated. **Additional Information:** 806-378-5000.

3407 ■ AMERICAN RADIO RELAY LEAGUE (ARRL) FOUNDATION

225 Main St.
Newington, CT 06111
Tel: (860)594-0200
Fax: (860)594-0259
E-mail: foundation@arrl.org

Web Site: http://www.arrlf.org
To support the education of students holding a valid FCC-granted Amateur Radio license for post-secondary education.
Title of Award: William R. Goldfarb Memorial Scholarships **Area, Field, or Subject:** Radio and television; Business; Computer and information sciences; Medicine; Nursing; Engineering; Science. **Level of Education for which Award is Granted:** Undergraduate **Number Awarded:** 1. **Funds Available:** No specific amount.
Eligibility Requirements: Applicant must hold an FCC amateur radio license; must be studying baccalaureate courses in business-related, computers, medical, nursing, engineering or sciences; be a high school senior; and must demonstrate financial need. **Application Requirements:** Applicants must submit a completed scholarship application form along with a recent high school (or equivalent) or college transcript, and the Free Application for Federal Student Aid (FAFSA) or Student Aid Report (SAR). **Deadline for Receipt:** February 1.

3408 ■ AMERICAN RED CROSS

2025 E St. NW
Washington, DC 20006
Tel: (703)206-6000
Free: 800-733-2767
E-mail: williamscaro@usa.redcross.org
Web Site: http://www.redcross.org
To advance nursing as a career option and to promote the involvement of young nurses in the Red Cross.
Title of Award: Jane Delano Society Scholarships **Area, Field, or Subject:** Nursing. **Level of Education for which Award is Granted:** Undergraduate **Number Awarded:** 2. **Funds Available:** $1,000.
Eligibility Requirements: Applicants must have contributed volunteer service to a Red Cross unit during the past five years; must have current enrollment in an associate degree, diploma, or baccalaureate program preparing students for Registered Nurse licensure, or an RN to BSN completion program; and must have at least one semester, or quarter, left before graduation. **Application Requirements:** Candidates must submit the required documentation including: application which includes a one-page personal statement from student; letter of endorsement from Red Cross Unit (chapter, Blood Services region, or SAF station) leadership; and letter of endorsement from College/School of Nursing saying that the applicant is in good academic standing and verifying that student is enrolled (attach form to application). **Additional Information:** Established in 2001. **Deadline for Receipt:** April 7. **Additional Information:** Carolyn Williams at the above address.

3409 ■ AMERICAN SCHOOL HEALTH ASSOCIATION

7263 State Rte. 43
Kent, OH 44240
Tel: (330)678-1601
Fax: (330)678-4526
E-mail: asha@ashaweb.org
Web Site: http://www.ashaweb.org
To provide financial assistance to students concentrating on school health education, school nursing, and pediatric or adolescent medicine or dentistry.
Title of Award: ASHA Scholarships **Area, Field, or Subject:** Health education; Nursing; Pediatric medicine; Medicine; Dentistry; Nutrition; Counseling/Guidance. **Level of Education for which Award is Granted:** Graduate, Undergraduate **Number Awarded:** 3. **Funds Available:** $500 and a complimentary registration to ASHA's annual school health conference and a one-year ASHA membership. **Duration:** One year.
Eligibility Requirements: Applicants must be a junior, senior or graduate student; enrolled full-time at institution of higher education; have 3.0 GPA on a 4.0 scale; have a major related to School Health Education or School Nursing or Pediatric or Adolescent Medicine or Dentistry or other school health specializations (nutrition, counseling, etc.); not a previous recipient of this award. **Application Requirements:** Applicants must send one original and nine copies of the completed application form (application form available online); current resume; transcript; one page personal statement; three letters of recommendation. **Deadline for Receipt:** April 4. **Additional Information:** Pamela Dorazio Dean, pdean@ashaweb.org.

3410 ■ AMERICAN SCHOOL HEALTH ASSOCIATION

7263 State Rte. 43
Kent, OH 44240

Tel: (330)678-1601
Fax: (330)678-4526
E-mail: asha@ashaweb.org
Web Site: http://www.ashaweb.org
To provide financial assistance for research in areas related to the mission of ASHA.
Title of Award: ASHA Student Research Grants **Area, Field, or Subject:** Health education; Nursing; Pediatric medicine; Medicine; Dentistry; Nutrition; Counseling/Guidance. **Level of Education for which Award is Granted:** Graduate, Undergraduate **Funds Available:** No specific amount.
Eligibility Requirements: Applicants must be student members of ASHA. **Application Requirements:** Applicants must send one original and five copies of a proposal which includes a cover sheet; a narrative (title-problem, review of related literature, methodology, data analyst, institution IRB protocol documented); and a budget. Proposal should have one inch margins, doubled spaced and a font size not smaller than 12. Forward the original and 5 copies to: ASHA Student Research Grants, PO Box 708, Kent, OH 44240. **Deadline for Receipt:** April 4. **Additional Information:** Pamela Dorazio, pdean@ashaweb.org, 330-678-1601.

3411 ■ ARIZONA NURSES ASSOCIATION

1850 E Southern Ave., Ste. 1
Tempe, AZ 85282
Tel: (480)831-0404
Web Site: http://www.aznurse.org
To enhance the development of Arizona nurses and further the nursing profession in Arizona.
Title of Award: Arizona Nurses Foundation Scholarships **Area, Field, or Subject:** Nursing. **Level of Education for which Award is Granted:** Graduate, Undergraduate **Funds Available:** No specific amount.
Eligibility Requirements: Applicants must be undergraduate and graduate students enrolled in or accepted in an academic education program; must be enrolled part-time or full-time. **Application Requirements:** Applicants must submit: completed application form; evidence of admission such as official or unofficial transcript of records, current courses schedule, copy of letter or certificate of admission or a written statement from an appropriate academic official; a brief statement describing the professional's activities, community service and other activities in the last three years that demonstrate the potential for leadership; a statement describing the need for financial assistance; one confidential reference form from an immediate supervisor, the student's academic advisor or another faculty member. **Deadline for Receipt:** March 1; October 15. **Additional Information:** carol@aznurse.org

3412 ■ ARMY NURSE CORPS ASSOCIATION

PO Box 39235
San Antonio, TX 78218-1235
Tel: (210)650-3534
Fax: (210)650-3494
E-mail: education@e-anca.org
Web Site: http://e-anca.org
To provide financial assistance to nursing students.
Title of Award: ANCA Scholarships **Area, Field, or Subject:** Nursing. **Level of Education for which Award is Granted:** Graduate, Undergraduate **Funds Available:** Scholarship amount not specified.
Eligibility Requirements: Applicants must be a student in a nursing program approved by an agency acceptable to the United States Secretary of Education; have Internal Revenue Service tax-exempt status; have scholarship fund under the school control; been a supportive of Army Nurse Corps recruitment. **Application Requirements:** Applicants must submit application template consist of school and location; agency accreditation; internal revenue status; scholarship program; support of army nurse corps recruitment activities; award criteria; application for specific student; and agreement to Education Committee. **Deadline for Receipt:** May 15.

3413 ■ ASSOCIATION OF INDEPENDENT COLLEGES AND UNIVERSITIES OF PENNSYLVANIA

101 N Front St.
Harrisburg, PA 17101-1405
Tel: (717)232-8649
Fax: (717)233-8574

E-mail: duck@aicup.org
Web Site: http://www.aicup.org
To help full-time undergraduate students who are enrolled in a Nursing or Physician's Assistant program.
Title of Award: McLean Scholarships **Area, Field, or Subject:** Nursing. **Level of Education for which Award is Granted:** Undergraduate **Number Awarded:** 7. **Funds Available:** $2,500.
Eligibility Requirements: Applicant must be a full-time undergraduate student enrolled in a Nursing or Physician Assistant program at one of the Association of Independent Colleges and Universities of Pennsylvania's member institutions, and have at least a 3.0 GPA. Ideal candidates are campus leaders and community volunteers. **Application Requirements:** Application forms are available at the Financial Aid office. Along with the completed applications, students may submit a copy of their transcript, a letter of recommendation, and any other materials that they feel will be helpful to the committee in making their decision. Students must also submit a brief essay describing their college experience, including the following information: why they chose their major; What steps they are taking to ensure that they succeed in their major; what they plan to do upon graduating and their academic/career goals. Applicants should also describe the primary volunteer/extracurricular activities in which they participate; how these activities relate to their major and what leadership roles they have taken. Completed applications should be returned to the applicants' Financial Aid office, which will then select one application to submit to AICUP. **Deadline for Receipt:** April 29. **Additional Information:** Mary Maronic, 717-232-8649 ext. 232; maronic@aicup.org.

3414 ■ ASSOCIATION OF PERIOPERATIVE REGISTERED NURSES

2170 S Parker Rd., Ste. 300
Denver, CO 80231
Tel: (303)755-6304
Free: 800-755-2676
Web Site: http://www.aorn.org
To provide financial assistance to students enrolled in nursing schools and to perioperative nurses pursuing bachelors, masters, or doctoral degrees.
Title of Award: AORN Foundation Scholarship Program **Area, Field, or Subject:** Nursing. **Level of Education for which Award is Granted:** Undergraduate **Funds Available:** $1,000 up to $5,000.
Eligibility Requirements: Nursing students must be enrolled in an accredited program as a nursing major for the 2008-2009 academic year; must be a program leading to licensure as an RN. Current nurses must have a commitment to perioperative nursing; must be enrolled in an accredited master's degree program in nursing or in an accredited master's degree program in another discipline for the 2008-2009 academic year. **Application Requirements:** Applicant must submit all the required application information. **Deadline for Receipt:** June 15.

3415 ■ ASSOCIATION OF REHABILITATION NURSES

4700 W Lake Ave.
Glenview, IL 60025-1485
Tel: (847)375-4710
Free: 800-229-7530
Fax: (847)375-6481
E-mail: info@rehabnurse.org
Web Site: http://www.rehabnurse.org
To provide financial assistance to rehabilitation nurses working toward a Bachelor of Science in Nursing (BSN) degree.
Title of Award: Association of Rehabilitation Nurses Scholarship Program **Area, Field, or Subject:** Nursing. **Level of Education for which Award is Granted:** Undergraduate **Funds Available:** $1,000.
Eligibility Requirements: Applicants must be a member of ARN currently enrolled in a BSN degree program, in good standing, completed at least one course and practices rehabilitation nursing at present, a minimum of two years. **Application Requirements:** Applicants must submit completed form; transcript documenting enrollment in a BSN program; typed 1-3 page summary of professional and educational goals and achievements, which includes, involvement in ARN at the national and local levels, continuing education participation in the past three to five years, professional publications or presentations, community involvement, particularly related to advocating for individuals with disabilities, efforts made to improve rehabilitation nursing practice and the delivery of care in your work setting. **Deadline for Receipt:** June 2. **Additional Information:** ARN Scholarship Program

Fax: 888/458-0456; email: nwallace@connect2amc.com.

3416 ■ ASSOCIATION OF REHABILITATION NURSES
4700 W Lake Ave.
Glenview, IL 60025-1485
Tel: (847)375-4710
Free: 800-229-7530
Fax: (847)375-6481
E-mail: info@rehabnurse.org
Web Site: http://www.rehabnurse.org
To provide financial assistance covering full tuition of the Professional Rehabilitation Nursing course.
Title of Award: Mary Ann Mikulic Scholarships **Area, Field, or Subject:** Nursing. **Level of Education for which Award is Granted:** Undergraduate **Funds Available:** No amount specified.
Eligibility Requirements: Applicants must be registered nurses with current license currently practicing in the specialty of rehabilitation nursing and able to meet all other financial responsibilities incurred by participating in the course. **Application Requirements:** Applicants must submit the completed application and supporting materials to ARN. **Deadline for Receipt:** June 2. **Additional Information:** Nicole Wallace; ARN; Email: nwallace@connect2amc.com
Fax: 888/458-0456.

3417 ■ HOWARD BAKER FOUNDATION
12313 County Rd. 10
Ranburne, AL 36273
Tel: (313)268-0636
Fax: (256)568-5714
Web Site: http://www.howardbakerfoundation.org
To provide assistance to City of Detroit residents in financing their education at Wayne State University, to encourage continued progress towards a degree and to recognize scholastic achievement.
Title of Award: Howard Baker Foundation Scholarships **Area, Field, or Subject:** Nursing. **Level of Education for which Award is Granted:** Undergraduate **Funds Available:** No specific amount.
Eligibility Requirements: Applicants must be undergraduate minority students of Wayne State University or from minority students accepted for full-time study at Wayne State University; must be majoring nursing or in a natural science curriculum; must be Detroit (public, private or parochial) high school graduates, residents of the City of Detroit and United States citizens; must have a minimum of 2.5 cumulative Grade Point Average (GPA) at the time of the selection. **Application Requirements:** Applicants must submit all required application information.

3418 ■ BENTON COUNTY FOUNDATION
PO Box 911
Corvallis, OR 97339
Tel: (541)753-1603
Web Site: http://www.bentoncountyfoundation.org
To encourage and support ethnic minority undergraduate women enrolled in the College of Science.
Title of Award: Margaret Dowell-Gravatt, M.D. Scholarship **Area, Field, or Subject:** Zoology; Microbiology; Medical technology; Medicine; Nursing; Physical therapy; Occupational therapy. **Level of Education for which Award is Granted:** Undergraduate **Funds Available:** No specific amount.
Eligibility Requirements: Applicant must: be pursuing a degree in Zoology or Microbiology or one of the following pre-health programs: Medical Technology, Medicine, Nursing, Physical and/or Occupational therapy. Applicant must: be enrolled full-time at the sophomore, junior, or senior level; have a GPA of 2.5 overall and 3.0 in science courses required in their major field or pre-health curriculum; qualify for financial assistance as defined by the Financial Aid Office of OSU. **Application Requirements:** Applicant may contact the Foundation for application form and other requirements. **Additional Information:** Benton County Foundation at the above address.

3419 ■ BETHESDA LUTHERAN HOMES AND SERVICES
600 Hoffmann Dr.
Watertown, WI 53094
800-369-4636
E-mail: dwinter@blhs.org

Web Site: http://www.blhs.org
To financially support Lutheran students pursuing degrees in nursing and planning to serve people with developmental disabilities.
Title of Award: Scholarships for Lutheran Nursing Students **Area, Field, or Subject:** Mental health; Nursing. **Level of Education for which Award is Granted:** Undergraduate **Number Awarded:** 2. **Funds Available:** $1500. **Duration:** Annually.
Eligibility Requirements: Applicant must be an active communicant member of a Lutheran church; achieved sophomore status or higher at a college or university, or completed one year of a two-year ADN program; have a 3.0 overall GPA; and have an interest in working as a nurse in the field of developmental disabilities. **Application Requirements:** Applicants must submit a completed application form together with an essay (1-2 pages, double-spaced) on planned career in the field of developmental disabilities; four letters of recommendations; an official college transcript; an autobiography (1 page, double-spaced); a documentation of service to people who are developmentally disabled (minimum of 100 hrs); and other materials helpful from the application. **Deadline for Receipt:** April 15.

3420 ■ NOORALI BHARWANI PROFESSIONAL CORPORATION
821A 5th St. SW
Medicine Hat, AB, Canada T1A 4H7
Tel: (403)527-0099
E-mail: nb786@shaw.ca
Web Site: http://nbharwani.com
To provide financial assistance to qualified individuals who want to pursue their studies.
Title of Award: Dr. Noorali & Sabiya Bharwani Endowment **Area, Field, or Subject:** Nursing. **Level of Education for which Award is Granted:** Undergraduate **Funds Available:** No specific amount.
Eligibility Requirements: Applicants must be first year nursing students with a minimum GPA of B, equivalent of 3.0. **Application Requirements:** For further information about the scholarship and application form, applicants are advice to contact Noorali Bharwani Professional Corporation, 821A 5th St. SW, Medicine Hat, AB T1A 4H7.

3421 ■ NOORALI BHARWANI PROFESSIONAL CORPORATION
821A 5th St. SW
Medicine Hat, AB, Canada T1A 4H7
Tel: (403)527-0099
E-mail: nb786@shaw.ca
Web Site: http://nbharwani.com
To provide financial assistance to qualified individuals who wants to pursue their studies.
Title of Award: Hussein Jina Bharwani Memorial Endowment **Area, Field, or Subject:** Nursing. **Level of Education for which Award is Granted:** Undergraduate **Number Awarded:** 2. **Funds Available:** No specific amount. **Duration:** One year.
Eligibility Requirements: Applicants must be nursing students having completed the second year of the nursing program; must have maintained a GPA of 3.0 or better; must have demonstrated a keen interest in the nursing patient; must demonstrate strong clinical skills including good organization and assessment skills and have the ability to establish a positive and constructive rapport with patients, their families and co-workers. **Application Requirements:** For further information about the scholarship and application form, applicants are advice to contact Noorali Bharwani Professional Corporation, 821A 5th St. SW, Medicine Hat, AB T1A 4H7.

3422 ■ BLACK NURSES ASSOCIATION OF GREATER WASHINGTON
PO Box 55285
Washington, DC 20040
Tel: (202)291-8866
E-mail: contactus@bnaofgwdca.org
Web Site: http://www.bnaofgwdca.org
To empower the community through education, service and caring.
Title of Award: Dr. Johnella Banks Memorial Scholarships **Area, Field, or Subject:** Nursing. **Level of Education for which Award is Granted:** Undergraduate **Funds Available:** No specific amount.
Eligibility Requirements: Applicants must be sophomore, junior or first-semester senior nursing students in a registered nursing or practical nurs-

ing program; must be currently enrolled in a National League for Nursing accredited program and be in good academic standing with a cumulative grade point average of at least 2.8. **Application Requirements:** Applicants must submit a current official transcript from their nursing program, two letters of recommendation from which one must come from current faculty member and one must come from the Nursing Faculty Advisor or Designee; must submit a written essay that describes the applicant's objectives and need-based reasons for scholarship application; documented evidence to add support for the applicant's desirability that includes participation in student and nursing activities, community service in the Greater Washington area, awards, letters and certificates; must provide a proof of United States citizenship and evidence of financial need. **Deadline for Receipt:** December 31. **Additional Information:** 202-291-8866.

3423 ■ BLACK NURSES ASSOCIATION OF GREATER WASHINGTON

PO Box 55285
Washington, DC 20040
Tel: (202)291-8866
E-mail: contactus@bnaofgwdca.org
Web Site: http://www.bnaofgwdca.org
To empower the community through education, service and caring.
Title of Award: Margaret Pemberton Scholarships **Area, Field, or Subject:** Nursing. **Level of Education for which Award is Granted:** Undergraduate **Funds Available:** $2,000.
Eligibility Requirements: Applicants must be graduating high school senior students who have been accepted into an accredited National League for Nursing baccalaureate program at a college or university in the United States; must be currently enrolled in a District of Columbia High School in good academic standing with a cumulative GPA of at least 2.8. **Application Requirements:** Applicants must submit an at least one-page long written essay describing personal and educational goals, contributions to the community and reasons they should be selected; must submit documented evidence for support, including participation in activities and organizations, awards, certificates, and/or letters of commendation; must submit an official high school transcript, copy of letter of acceptance to a Baccalaureate Nursing Program in a college or university in the United States of America; must submit two letters of recommendation, from which one must come from a high school counselor or designee and the other one must come from non-related adult who has knowledge of the applicant's potential for success. **Deadline for Receipt:** April 15. **Additional Information:** 202-291-8866.

3424 ■ CANADIAN NURSES FOUNDATION

50 Driveway St.
Ottawa, ON, Canada K2P 1E2
Tel: (613)237-2159
Free: 800-361-8404
Fax: (613)237-3520
E-mail: info@cnf-fiic.ca
Web Site: http://www.canadiannursesfoundation.com/overview.htm
To support students who want to pursue their education.
Title of Award: Birks Family Foundation Scholarships **Area, Field, or Subject:** Nursing. **Level of Education for which Award is Granted:** Undergraduate **Funds Available:** No specific amount. **Duration:** One year.
Eligibility Requirements: Applicant must be a Canadian citizen or permanent resident status; must be studying in Canada; must be entering at least year 2 as a full-time student of a baccalaureate-nursing program. **Application Requirements:** Applicants must complete and print the application form available online. For further information, applicants are advice to contact, Jacqueline Solis, Foundation Coordinator at 613237-2159. **Additional Information:** Scholarship was established by the Birks Family Foundation out of an interest in contributing to a higher standard of living and quality of life by supporting higher education, the hospital sector, and health organizations. **Deadline for Receipt:** March 31.

3425 ■ CANADIAN NURSES FOUNDATION

50 Driveway St.
Ottawa, ON, Canada K2P 1E2
Tel: (613)237-2159
Free: 800-361-8404

Fax: (613)237-3520
E-mail: info@cnf-fiic.ca
Web Site: http://www.canadiannursesfoundation.com/overview.htm
To support students who want to pursue their education.
Title of Award: Canadian Nurses Foundation Northern Scholarships **Area, Field, or Subject:** Nursing. **Level of Education for which Award is Granted:** Undergraduate **Funds Available:** No specific amount. **Duration:** One year.
Eligibility Requirements: Applicant must be a student intending to work in Canada's North. **Application Requirements:** Applicants must complete and print the application form available online. For further information, applicants are advised to contact, Jacqueline Solis, Foundation Coordinator at 613237-2159. **Deadline for Receipt:** March 31.

3426 ■ CANADIAN NURSES FOUNDATION

50 Driveway St.
Ottawa, ON, Canada K2P 1E2
Tel: (613)237-2159
Free: 800-361-8404
Fax: (613)237-3520
E-mail: info@cnf-fiic.ca
Web Site: http://www.canadiannursesfoundation.com/overview.htm
To support students who want to pursue their education.
Title of Award: Canadian Nurses Foundation Scholarships **Area, Field, or Subject:** Nursing. **Level of Education for which Award is Granted:** Undergraduate **Funds Available:** No specific amount. **Duration:** One year.
Eligibility Requirements: Applicants must be Canadian citizens or permanent residents status; must be studying in Canada; must be entering at least year 2 as a full-time student of a baccalaureate-nursing program. **Application Requirements:** Applicants must complete and print the application form available online. For further information, applicants are advice to contact, Jacqueline Solis, Foundation Coordinator at 613237-2159. **Deadline for Receipt:** MArch 31.

3427 ■ CANADIAN NURSES FOUNDATION

50 Driveway St.
Ottawa, ON, Canada K2P 1E2
Tel: (613)237-2159
Free: 800-361-8404
Fax: (613)237-3520
E-mail: info@cnf-fiic.ca
Web Site: http://www.canadiannursesfoundation.com/overview.htm
To support students who want to pursue their education.
Title of Award: Judy Hill Scholarships **Area, Field, or Subject:** Nursing. **Level of Education for which Award is Granted:** Undergraduate **Funds Available:** No specific amount. **Duration:** One year.
Eligibility Requirements: Applicant must be a student who has worked in the north and must sign a statement that they will practice nursing in the north for a period of 12 months; must be Canadian citizen or permanent resident status; must be studying in Canada; must be entering at least year 2 as a full-time student of a baccalaureate-nursing program. **Application Requirements:** Applicants must complete and print the application form available online; for further information, applicants are advised to contact, Jacqueline Solis, Foundation Coordinator at 6132372159. **Deadline for Receipt:** March 31.

3428 ■ CANADIAN NURSES FOUNDATION

50 Driveway St.
Ottawa, ON, Canada K2P 1E2
Tel: (613)237-2159
Free: 800-361-8404
Fax: (613)237-3520
E-mail: info@cnf-fiic.ca
Web Site: http://www.canadiannursesfoundation.com/overview.htm
To support students who want to pursue their education.
Title of Award: Johnson & Johnson Scholarships **Area, Field, or Subject:** Nursing. **Level of Education for which Award is Granted:** Undergraduate **Funds Available:** No specific amount. **Duration:** One year.
Eligibility Requirements: Applicant must be a student who plans to practice nursing in an operating room or a critical care area; must be a Canadian citizen or permanent resident status; must be studying in

Canada; must be entering at least year 2 as a full-time student of a baccalaureate-nursing program. **Application Requirements:** Applicants must complete and print the application form available online. For further information, applicants are advised to contact, Jacqueline Solis, Foundation Coordinator at 613237-2159. **Deadline for Receipt:** March 31.

3429 ■ CANADIAN NURSES FOUNDATION
50 Driveway St.
Ottawa, ON, Canada K2P 1E2
Tel: (613)237-2159
Free: 800-361-8404
Fax: (613)237-3520
E-mail: info@cnf-fiic.ca
Web Site: http://www.canadiannursesfoundation.com/overview.htm
To support students who want to pursue their education.
Title of Award: Tecla Lin & Nelia Laroza Memorial Scholarships **Area, Field, or Subject:** Nursing. **Level of Education for which Award is Granted:** Undergraduate **Funds Available:** No specific amount. **Duration:** One year.
Eligibility Requirements: Applicant must be a foreign educated nurse working towards baccalaureate degree; must be a Canadian citizen or permanent resident status; must be studying in Canada; must be entering at least year 2 as a full-time student of a baccalaureate-nursing program. **Application Requirements:** Applicants must complete and print the application form available online. For further information, applicants are advised to contact, Jacqueline Solis, Foundation Coordinator at 613237-2159. **Deadline for Receipt:** March 31.

3430 ■ CANADIAN NURSES FOUNDATION
50 Driveway St.
Ottawa, ON, Canada K2P 1E2
Tel: (613)237-2159
Free: 800-361-8404
Fax: (613)237-3520
E-mail: info@cnf-fiic.ca
Web Site: http://www.canadiannursesfoundation.com/overview.htm
To support students who want to pursue their education.
Title of Award: Margaret Munro Scholarships **Area, Field, or Subject:** Nursing. **Level of Education for which Award is Granted:** Undergraduate **Funds Available:** No specific amount. **Duration:** One year.
Eligibility Requirements: Applicant must be a student form Prince Edward Island; must be a Canadian citizen or permanent resident status; must be studying in Canada; must be entering at least year 2 as a full-time student of a baccalaureate-nursing program. **Application Requirements:** Applicants must complete and print the application form available online. For further information, applicants are advised to contact, Jacqueline Solis, Foundation Coordinator at 613237-2159. **Deadline for Receipt:** March 31.

3431 ■ CANADIAN NURSES FOUNDATION
50 Driveway St.
Ottawa, ON, Canada K2P 1E2
Tel: (613)237-2159
Free: 800-361-8404
Fax: (613)237-3520
E-mail: info@cnf-fiic.ca
Web Site: http://www.canadiannursesfoundation.com/overview.htm
To support students who want to pursue their education.
Title of Award: Sharon Nield Memorial Scholarships **Area, Field, or Subject:** Nursing. **Level of Education for which Award is Granted:** Undergraduate **Funds Available:** No specific amount. **Duration:** One year.
Eligibility Requirements: Applicants must be registered nurses returning to school; must be Canadian citizens or permanent residents status; must be studying in Canada; must be entering at least year 2 as a full-time students of a baccalaureate-nursing program. **Application Requirements:** Applicants must complete and print the application form available online; for further information, applicants are advised to contact, Jacqueline Solis, Foundation Coordinator at 613237-2159. **Deadline for Receipt:** March 31.

3432 ■ CANADIAN NURSES FOUNDATION
50 Driveway St.
Ottawa, ON, Canada K2P 1E2

Tel: (613)237-2159
Free: 800-361-8404
Fax: (613)237-3520
E-mail: info@cnf-fiic.ca
Web Site: http://www.canadiannursesfoundation.com/overview.htm
To support students who want to pursue their education.
Title of Award: John Vanderlee Scholarships **Area, Field, or Subject:** Nursing. **Level of Education for which Award is Granted:** Undergraduate **Funds Available:** No specific amount. **Duration:** One year.
Eligibility Requirements: Applicant must be a male student entering at least year 2 as a full-time student of a baccalaureate-nursing program; must be a Canadian citizen or permanent resident status; must be studying in Canada. **Application Requirements:** Applicants must complete and print the application form available online; for further information, applicants are advised to contact, Jacqueline Solis, Foundation Coordinator at 613237-2159. **Deadline for Receipt:** March 31.

3433 ■ CHI ETA PHI SORORITY
3029 13th St. NW
Washington, DC 20009
Tel: (202)232-3858
Fax: (202)232-3460
Web Site: http://www.chietaphi.com
To recognize the life long commitment made by Soror Staupers to America's struggle for complete equality for all people.
Title of Award: The Mabel Keaton Staupers National Scholarship Award **Area, Field, or Subject:** Nursing. **Level of Education for which Award is Granted:** Doctorate, Graduate, Undergraduate **Funds Available:** $50,000.
Eligibility Requirements: Applicants must be current members of Chi Eta Phi Sorority, Inc. and the American Nurses Association and must be enrolled in a program of study leading to the Baccalaureate, masters or doctoral degree in a nationally accredited school of nursing. **Application Requirements:** Applicants must submit completed applications to the Chi Eta Phi, Inc.

3434 ■ CHILDREN'S HOSPITAL OF PHILADELPHIA
34th St. and Civic Center Blvd.
Philadelphia, PA 19104-4399
Tel: (215)590-1000
Free: 800-879-2467
E-mail: fordg@email.edu
Web Site: http://www.chop.edu
To support the financial needs of young adults who have lost a parent/guardian to cancer or have a parent/guardian with cancer and are seeking higher education in the field of nursing.
Title of Award: Barbara Palo Foster Memorial Scholarships **Area, Field, or Subject:** Nursing. **Level of Education for which Award is Granted:** Undergraduate **Funds Available:** Varies.
Eligibility Requirements: Applicant must be 35 years or younger at the time of the application; must be a young adult who has lost a parent/guardian to cancer or has a parent/guardian with cancer; must be currently attending, or planning to attend a two- to four-year college or university or training program, and seeking a degree in the field of nursing (including graduate and professional schools); and must demonstrate an interest in furthering patient education, focusing on persons from medically underserved communities and/or women's health issues. **Application Requirements:** Applicants must complete application.

3435 ■ COLORADO NURSES FOUNDATION
7831 Lewis Court
Arvada, CO 80005
Tel: (303)758-4291
E-mail: conursesfoundation@comcast.net
Web Site: http://www.coloradonursesfoundation.org
To provide scholarships for qualified nursing students from both rural and urban settings.
Title of Award: Roy Anderson Memorial Scholarships **Area, Field, or Subject:** Nursing. **Level of Education for which Award is Granted:** Graduate, Undergraduate **Funds Available:** $2,000. **Duration:** One year.
Eligibility Requirements: Applicant must be a Colorado resident committed to practicing nursing in Colorado; must be a student in an approved Colorado Nursing Program; must have a minimum of 3.25 GPA (for

undergraduate applicants) or 3.5 GPA (for graduate applicants); and must have one of the following student statuses: (1) Junior or senior level BSN undergraduate student; (2) RN enrolled in a baccalaureate or higher degree nursing program in a school of nursing; (3) Student in second year of nursing studies in an associate degree in nursing program; (4) RN with master's degree in nursing, currently practicing in Colorado and enrolled in a doctoral program; (5) Student in second or third year of a Doctorate Nursing Practice (DNP) program. **Application Requirements:** Applicants are advised to contact the foundation at Colorado Nurses Foundation, 7831 Lewis Court, Arvada, CO 80005 for further information.

3436 ■ COLORADO NURSES FOUNDATION

7831 Lewis Court
Arvada, CO 80005
Tel: (303)758-4291
E-mail: conursesfoundation@comcast.net
Web Site: http://www.coloradonursesfoundation.org
To provide scholarships for qualified nursing students from both rural and urban settings.
Title of Award: Banner Health System - McKee Medical Center, Loveland: Nightingale Scholarships **Area, Field, or Subject:** Nursing. **Level of Education for which Award is Granted:** Graduate, Undergraduate **Funds Available:** $1,000. **Duration:** One year. Applicants are advised to contact the foundation at Colorado Nurses Foundation, 7831 Lewis Court, Arvada, CO 80005 for further information.
Eligibility Requirements: Applicants must be Colorado residents committed to practicing nursing in Colorado; must be students in an approved Colorado Nursing Program; must have a minimum of 3.25 GPA (undergraduate) and 3.5 GPA (graduate); and must have one of the following student statuses: (1) Junior or senior level BSN undergraduate student; (2) RN enrolled in a baccalaureate or higher degree nursing program in a school of nursing; (3) Student in second year of nursing studies in an associate degree in nursing program; (4) RN with master's degree in nursing, currently practicing in Colorado and enrolled in a doctoral program; (5) Student in second or third year of a Doctorate Nursing Practice (DNP) program.

3437 ■ COLORADO NURSES FOUNDATION

7831 Lewis Court
Arvada, CO 80005
Tel: (303)758-4291
E-mail: conursesfoundation@comcast.net
Web Site: http://www.coloradonursesfoundation.org
To provide scholarships for qualified nursing students from both rural and urban settings.
Title of Award: Banner Health System - North Colorado Medical Center, Greeley: Nightingale Scholarships **Area, Field, or Subject:** Nursing. **Level of Education for which Award is Granted:** Graduate, Undergraduate **Funds Available:** $1,000. **Duration:** One year.
Eligibility Requirements: Applicant must be a Colorado resident committed to practicing nursing in Colorado; must be a student in an approved Colorado Nursing Program; must have a minimum of 3.25 GPA undergraduate and 3.5 GPA graduate; and must have one of the following student statuses: (1) Junior or senior level BSN undergraduate student; (2) RN enrolled in a baccalaureate or higher degree nursing program in a school of nursing; (3) Student in second year of nursing studies in an associate degree in nursing program; (4) RN with master's degree in nursing, currently practicing in Colorado and enrolled in a doctoral program; (5) Student in second or third year of a Doctorate Nursing Practice (DNP) program. **Application Requirements:** Applicants are advised to contact the foundation at Colorado Nurses Foundation, 7831 Lewis Court, Arvada, CO 80005 for further information.

3438 ■ COLORADO NURSES FOUNDATION

7831 Lewis Court
Arvada, CO 80005
Tel: (303)758-4291
E-mail: conursesfoundation@comcast.net
Web Site: http://www.coloradonursesfoundation.org
To provide scholarships for qualified nursing students from both rural and urban settings.
Title of Award: Marcy and Bruce Benson: Nightingale Scholarships **Area, Field, or Subject:** Nursing. **Level of Education for which Award is**

Granted: Graduate, Undergraduate **Funds Available:** $1,000. **Duration:** One year.
Eligibility Requirements: Applicant must be a Colorado resident committed to practicing nursing in Colorado; must be a student in an approved Colorado Nursing Program; must have a minimum of 3.25 GPA undergraduate and 3.5 GPA graduate; and must have one of the following student statuses: (1) Junior or senior level BSN undergraduate student; (2) RN enrolled in a baccalaureate or higher degree nursing program in a school of nursing; (3) Student in second year of nursing studies in an associate degree in nursing program; (4) RN with master's degree in nursing, currently practicing in Colorado and enrolled in a doctoral program; (5) Student in second or third year of a Doctorate Nursing Practice (DNP) program. **Application Requirements:** Applicants are advised to contact the foundation at Colorado Nurses Foundation, 7831 Lewis Court, Arvada, CO 80005 for further information.

3439 ■ COLORADO NURSES FOUNDATION

7831 Lewis Court
Arvada, CO 80005
Tel: (303)758-4291
E-mail: conursesfoundation@comcast.net
Web Site: http://www.coloradonursesfoundation.org
To provide scholarships for qualified nursing students from both rural and urban settings.
Title of Award: Colorado Nurses Association: Nightingale Scholarships **Area, Field, or Subject:** Nursing. **Level of Education for which Award is Granted:** Graduate, Undergraduate **Funds Available:** $1,000. **Duration:** One year.
Eligibility Requirements: Applicant must be a Colorado resident committed to practicing nursing in Colorado; must be a student in an approved Colorado Nursing Program; must have a minimum of 3.25 GPA undergraduate and 3.5 GPA graduate; and must have one of the following student statuses: (1) Junior or senior level BSN undergraduate student; (2) RN enrolled in a baccalaureate or higher degree nursing program in a school of nursing; (3) Student in second year of nursing studies in an associate degree in nursing program; (4) RN with master's degree in nursing, currently practicing in Colorado and enrolled in a doctoral program; (5) Student in second or third year of a Doctorate Nursing Practice (DNP) program. **Application Requirements:** Applicants are advised to contact the foundation at Colorado Nurses Foundation, 7831 Lewis Court, Arvada, CO 80005 for further information.

3440 ■ COLORADO NURSES FOUNDATION

7831 Lewis Court
Arvada, CO 80005
Tel: (303)758-4291
E-mail: conursesfoundation@comcast.net
Web Site: http://www.coloradonursesfoundation.org
To provide scholarships for qualified nursing students from both rural and urban settings.
Title of Award: Colorado Nurses Association: Virginia Paulson Memorial Scholarships **Area, Field, or Subject:** Nursing. **Level of Education for which Award is Granted:** Graduate, Undergraduate **Funds Available:** $2,000. **Duration:** One year.
Eligibility Requirements: Applicant must be a Colorado resident committed to practicing nursing in Colorado; must be a student in an approved Colorado Nursing Program; must have a minimum of 3.25 GPA (for undergraduate applicants) or 3.5 GPA (for graduate applicants); and must have one of the following student statuses: (1) Junior or senior level BSN undergraduate student; (2) RN enrolled in a baccalaureate or higher degree nursing program in a school of nursing; (3) Student in second year of nursing studies in an associate degree in nursing program; (4) RN with master's degree in nursing, currently practicing in Colorado and enrolled in a doctoral program; (5) Student in second or third year of a Doctorate Nursing Practice (DNP) program. **Application Requirements:** Applicants are advised to contact the foundation at Colorado Nurses Foundation, 7831 Lewis Court, Arvada, CO 80005 for further information.

3441 ■ COLORADO NURSES FOUNDATION

7831 Lewis Court
Arvada, CO 80005
Tel: (303)758-4291
E-mail: conursesfoundation@comcast.net

Web Site: http://www.coloradonursesfoundation.org
To provide scholarships for qualified nursing students from both rural and urban settings.

Title of Award: Colorado Nurses Foundation Nightingale Scholarships **Area, Field, or Subject:** Nursing. **Level of Education for which Award is Granted:** Graduate, Undergraduate **Number Awarded:** 10. **Funds Available:** $1,000. **Duration:** One year.

Eligibility Requirements: Applicant must be a Colorado resident committed to practicing nursing in Colorado; must be a student in an approved Colorado Nursing Program; must have a minimum of 3.25 GPA (for undergraduate applicants) or 3.5 GPA (for graduate applicants); and must have one of the following student statuses: (1) Junior or senior level BSN undergraduate student; (2) RN enrolled in a baccalaureate or higher degree nursing program in a school of nursing; (3) Student in second year of nursing studies in an associate degree in nursing program; (4) RN with master's degree in nursing, currently practicing in Colorado and enrolled in a doctoral program; (5) Student in second or third year of a Doctorate Nursing Practice (DNP) program. **Application Requirements:** Applicants are advised to contact the foundation at Colorado Nurses Foundation, 7831 Lewis Court, Arvada, CO 80005 for further information.

3442 ■ COLORADO NURSES FOUNDATION
7831 Lewis Court
Arvada, CO 80005
Tel: (303)758-4291
E-mail: conursesfoundation@comcast.net
Web Site: http://www.coloradonursesfoundation.org
To provide scholarships for qualified nursing students from both rural and urban settings.

Title of Award: Colorado Organization of Nursing Leaders Scholarships **Area, Field, or Subject:** Nursing. **Level of Education for which Award is Granted:** Graduate, Undergraduate **Funds Available:** $1,000. **Duration:** One year.

Eligibility Requirements: Applicant must be a Colorado resident committed to practicing nursing in Colorado; must be a student in an approved Colorado Nursing Program; must have a minimum of 3.25 GPA (for undergraduate applicants) or 3.5 GPA (for graduate applicants); and must have one of the following student statuses: (1) Junior or senior level BSN undergraduate student; (2) RN enrolled in a baccalaureate or higher degree nursing program in a school of nursing; (3) Student in second year of nursing studies in an associate degree in nursing program; (4) RN with master's degree in nursing, currently practicing in Colorado and enrolled in a doctoral program; (5) Student in second or third year of a Doctorate Nursing Practice (DNP) program. **Application Requirements:** Applicants are advised to contact the foundation at Colorado Nurses Foundation, 7831 Lewis Court, Arvada, CO 80005 for further information.

3443 ■ COLORADO NURSES FOUNDATION
7831 Lewis Court
Arvada, CO 80005
Tel: (303)758-4291
E-mail: conursesfoundation@comcast.net
Web Site: http://www.coloradonursesfoundation.org
To provide scholarships for qualified nursing students from both rural and urban settings.

Title of Award: Arthur L. Davis Publishing Agency Scholarships **Area, Field, or Subject:** Nursing. **Level of Education for which Award is Granted:** Graduate, Undergraduate **Funds Available:** $1,000. **Duration:** One year.

Eligibility Requirements: Applicant must be a Colorado resident committed to practicing nursing in Colorado; must be a student in an approved Colorado Nursing Program; must have a minimum of 3.25 GPA (for undergraduate applicants) or 3.5 GPA (for graduate applicants); and must have one of the following student statuses: (1) Junior or senior level BSN undergraduate student; (2) RN enrolled in a baccalaureate or higher degree nursing program in a school of nursing; (3) Student in second year of nursing studies in an associate degree in nursing program; (4) RN with master's degree in nursing, currently practicing in Colorado and enrolled in a doctoral program; (5) Student in second or third year of a Doctorate Nursing Practice (DNP) program. **Application Requirements:** Applicants are advised to contact the foundation at Colorado Nurses Foundation, 7831 Lewis Court, Arvada, CO 80005 for further information.

3444 ■ COLORADO NURSES FOUNDATION
7831 Lewis Court
Arvada, CO 80005
Tel: (303)758-4291
E-mail: conursesfoundation@comcast.net
Web Site: http://www.coloradonursesfoundation.org
To provide scholarships for qualified nursing students from both rural and urban settings.

Title of Award: Red and Lola Fehr: Nightingale Scholarships **Area, Field, or Subject:** Nursing. **Level of Education for which Award is Granted:** Graduate, Undergraduate **Funds Available:** $1,000. **Duration:** One year.

Eligibility Requirements: Applicant must be a Colorado resident committed to practicing nursing in Colorado; must be a student in an approved Colorado Nursing Program; must have a minimum of 3.25 GPA (for undergraduate applicants) or 3.5 GPA (for graduate applicants); and must have one of the following student statuses: (1) Junior or senior level BSN undergraduate student; (2) RN enrolled in a baccalaureate or higher degree nursing program in a school of nursing; (3) Student in second year of nursing studies in an associate degree in nursing program; (4) RN with master's degree in nursing, currently practicing in Colorado and enrolled in a doctoral program; (5) Student in second or third year of a Doctorate Nursing Practice (DNP) program. **Application Requirements:** Applicants are advised to contact the foundation at Colorado Nurses Foundation, 7831 Lewis Court, Arvada, CO 80005 for further information.

3445 ■ COLORADO NURSES FOUNDATION
7831 Lewis Court
Arvada, CO 80005
Tel: (303)758-4291
E-mail: conursesfoundation@comcast.net
Web Site: http://www.coloradonursesfoundation.org
To provide scholarships for qualified nursing students from both rural and urban settings.

Title of Award: Amy and Horace Hagedorn Trust: Nightingale Scholarships **Area, Field, or Subject:** Nursing. **Level of Education for which Award is Granted:** Graduate, Undergraduate **Funds Available:** $1,000. **Duration:** One year.

Eligibility Requirements: Applicants must be Colorado residents committed to practicing nursing in Colorado; must be students in an approved Colorado Nursing Program; must have a minimum of 3.25 undergraduate GPA and 3.5 graduate GPA; and must have one of the following student statuses: (1) Junior or senior level BSN undergraduate student; (2) RN enrolled in a baccalaureate or higher degree nursing program in a school of nursing; (3) Student in second year of nursing studies in an associate degree in nursing program; (4) RN with master's degree in nursing, currently practicing in Colorado and enrolled in a doctoral program; (5) Student in second or third year of a Doctorate Nursing Practice (DNP) program. **Application Requirements:** Applicants are advised to contact the foundation at Colorado Nurses Foundation, 7831 Lewis Court, Arvada, CO 80005 for application.

3446 ■ COLORADO NURSES FOUNDATION
7831 Lewis Court
Arvada, CO 80005
Tel: (303)758-4291
E-mail: conursesfoundation@comcast.net
Web Site: http://www.coloradonursesfoundation.org
To provide scholarships for qualified nursing students from both rural and urban settings.

Title of Award: Johnson and Johnson: Nightingale Scholarships **Area, Field, or Subject:** Nursing. **Level of Education for which Award is Granted:** Graduate, Undergraduate **Funds Available:** $1,000. **Duration:** One year.

Eligibility Requirements: Applicant must be a Colorado resident committed to practicing nursing in Colorado; must be a student in an approved Colorado Nursing Program; must have a minimum of 3.25 GPA (for undergraduate applicants) or 3.5 GPA (for graduate applicants); and must have one of the following student statuses: (1) Junior or senior level BSN undergraduate student; (2) RN enrolled in a baccalaureate or higher degree nursing program in a school of nursing; (3) Student in second year of nursing studies in an associate degree in nursing program; (4) RN with master's degree in nursing, currently practicing in Colorado and enrolled in a doctoral program; (5) Student in second or third year of a Doctorate

Nursing Practice (DNP) program. **Application Requirements:** Applicants are advised to contact the foundation at Colorado Nurses Foundation, 7831 Lewis Court, Arvada, CO 80005 for further information.

3447 ■ COLORADO NURSES FOUNDATION
7831 Lewis Court
Arvada, CO 80005
Tel: (303)758-4291
E-mail: conursesfoundation@comcast.net
Web Site: http://www.coloradonursesfoundation.org
To provide scholarships for qualified nursing students from both rural and urban settings.
Title of Award: Kaiser Permanente: Nightingale Scholarships **Area, Field, or Subject:** Nursing. **Level of Education for which Award is Granted:** Graduate, Undergraduate **Funds Available:** $1,000. **Duration:** One year.
Eligibility Requirements: Applicant must be a Colorado resident committed to practicing nursing in Colorado; must be a student in an approved Colorado Nursing Program; must have a minimum of 3.25 GPA (for undergraduate applicants) or 3.5 GPA (for graduate applicants); and must have one of the following student statuses: (1) Junior or senior level BSN undergraduate student; (2) RN enrolled in a baccalaureate or higher degree nursing program in a school of nursing; (3) Student in second year of nursing studies in an associate degree in nursing program; (4) RN with master's degree in nursing, currently practicing in Colorado and enrolled in a doctoral program; (5) Student in second or third year of a Doctorate Nursing Practice (DNP) program. **Application Requirements:** Applicants are advised to contact the foundation at Colorado Nurses Foundation, 7831 Lewis Court, Arvada, CO 80005 for further information.

3448 ■ COLORADO NURSES FOUNDATION
7831 Lewis Court
Arvada, CO 80005
Tel: (303)758-4291
E-mail: conursesfoundation@comcast.net
Web Site: http://www.coloradonursesfoundation.org
To provide scholarships for qualified nursing students from both rural and urban settings.
Title of Award: Metropolitan State College of Denver, President's Office: Nightingale Scholarships **Area, Field, or Subject:** Nursing. **Level of Education for which Award is Granted:** Graduate, Undergraduate **Funds Available:** $1,000. **Duration:** One year.
Eligibility Requirements: Applicant must be a Colorado resident committed to practicing nursing in Colorado; must be a student in an approved Colorado Nursing Program; must have a minimum of 3.25 GPA (for undergraduate applicants) or 3.5 GPA (for graduate applicants); and must have one of the following student statuses: (1) Junior or senior level BSN undergraduate student; (2) RN enrolled in a baccalaureate or higher degree nursing program in a school of nursing; (3) Student in second year of nursing studies in an associate degree in nursing program; (4) RN with master's degree in nursing, currently practicing in Colorado and enrolled in a doctoral program; (5) Student in second or third year of a Doctorate Nursing Practice (DNP) program. **Application Requirements:** Applicants are advised to contact the foundation at Colorado Nurses Foundation, 7831 Lewis Court, Arvada, CO 80005 for further information.

3449 ■ COLORADO NURSES FOUNDATION
7831 Lewis Court
Arvada, CO 80005
Tel: (303)758-4291
E-mail: conursesfoundation@comcast.net
Web Site: http://www.coloradonursesfoundation.org
To provide scholarships for qualified nursing students from both rural and urban settings.
Title of Award: H.M. Muffly Memorial Scholarships **Area, Field, or Subject:** Nursing. **Level of Education for which Award is Granted:** Graduate, Undergraduate **Funds Available:** $1,000. **Duration:** One year.
Eligibility Requirements: Applicant must be a Colorado resident committed to practicing nursing in Colorado; must be a student in an approved Colorado Nursing Program; must have a minimum of 3.25 GPA (for undergraduate applicants) or 3.5 GPA (for graduate applicants); and must have one of the following student statuses: (1) Junior or senior level BSN undergraduate student; (2) RN enrolled in a baccalaureate or higher

degree nursing program in a school of nursing; (3) Student in second year of nursing studies in an associate degree in nursing program; (4) RN with master's degree in nursing, currently practicing in Colorado and enrolled in a doctoral program; (5) Student in second or third year of a Doctorate Nursing Practice (DNP) program. **Application Requirements:** Applicants are advised to contact the foundation at Colorado Nurses Foundation, 7831 Lewis Court, Arvada, CO 80005 for further information.

3450 ■ COLORADO NURSES FOUNDATION
7831 Lewis Court
Arvada, CO 80005
Tel: (303)758-4291
E-mail: conursesfoundation@comcast.net
Web Site: http://www.coloradonursesfoundation.org
To provide scholarships for qualified nursing students from both rural and urban settings.
Title of Award: Poudre Valley Health System, Fort Collins: Nightingale Scholarships **Area, Field, or Subject:** Nursing. **Level of Education for which Award is Granted:** Graduate, Undergraduate **Funds Available:** $1,000. **Duration:** One year.
Eligibility Requirements: Applicant must be a Colorado resident committed to practicing nursing in Colorado; must be a student in an approved Colorado Nursing Program; must have a minimum of 3.25 GPA (for undergraduate applicants) or 3.5 GPA (for graduate applicants); and must have one of the following student statuses: (1) Junior or senior level BSN undergraduate student; (2) RN enrolled in a baccalaureate or higher degree nursing program in a school of nursing; (3) Student in second year of nursing studies in an associate degree in nursing program; (4) RN with master's degree in nursing, currently practicing in Colorado and enrolled in a doctoral program; (5) Student in second or third year of a Doctorate Nursing Practice (DNP) program. **Application Requirements:** Applicants are advised to contact the foundation at Colorado Nurses Foundation, 7831 Lewis Court, Arvada, CO 80005 for further information.

3451 ■ COLORADO NURSES FOUNDATION
7831 Lewis Court
Arvada, CO 80005
Tel: (303)758-4291
E-mail: conursesfoundation@comcast.net
Web Site: http://www.coloradonursesfoundation.org
To provide scholarships for qualified nursing students from both rural and urban settings.
Title of Award: Rocky Mountain Region of Wound Ostomy Continence Nurses Society Scholarships **Area, Field, or Subject:** Nursing. **Level of Education for which Award is Granted:** Graduate, Undergraduate **Funds Available:** $1,500. **Duration:** One year.
Eligibility Requirements: Applicant must be a Colorado resident committed to practicing nursing in Colorado; must be a student in an approved Colorado Nursing Program; must have a minimum of 3.25 GPA (for undergraduate applicants) or 3.5 GPA (for graduate applicants); and must have one of the following student statuses: (1) Junior or senior level BSN undergraduate student; (2) RN enrolled in a baccalaureate or higher degree nursing program in a school of nursing; (3) Student in second year of nursing studies in an associate degree in nursing program; (4) RN with master's degree in nursing, currently practicing in Colorado and enrolled in a doctoral program; (5) Student in second or third year of a Doctorate Nursing Practice (DNP) program. **Application Requirements:** Applicants are advised to contact the foundation at Colorado Nurses Foundation, 7831 Lewis Court, Arvada, CO 80005 for further information.

3452 ■ COLORADO NURSES FOUNDATION
7831 Lewis Court
Arvada, CO 80005
Tel: (303)758-4291
E-mail: conursesfoundation@comcast.net
Web Site: http://www.coloradonursesfoundation.org
To provide scholarships for qualified nursing students from both rural and urban settings.
Title of Award: Rose Medical Center, Denver: Nightingale Scholarships **Area, Field, or Subject:** Nursing. **Level of Education for which Award is Granted:** Graduate, Undergraduate **Funds Available:** $1,000. **Duration:** One year.
Eligibility Requirements: Applicant must be a Colorado resident committed to practicing nursing in Colorado; must be a student in an approved

Colorado Nursing Program; must have a minimum of 3.25 GPA (for undergraduate applicants) or 3.5 GPA (for graduate applicants); and must have one of the following student statuses: (1) Junior or senior level BSN undergraduate student; (2) RN enrolled in a baccalaureate or higher degree nursing program in a school of nursing; (3) Student in second year of nursing studies in an associate degree in nursing program; (4) RN with master's degree in nursing, currently practicing in Colorado and enrolled in a doctoral program; (5) Student in second or third year of a Doctorate Nursing Practice (DNP) program. **Application Requirements:** Applicants are advised to contact the foundation at Colorado Nurses Foundation, 7831 Lewis Court, Arvada, CO 80005 for further information.

3453 ■ COLORADO NURSES FOUNDATION
7831 Lewis Court
Arvada, CO 80005
Tel: (303)758-4291
E-mail: conursesfoundation@comcast.net
Web Site: http://www.coloradonursesfoundation.org
To provide scholarships for qualified nursing students from both rural and urban settings.
Title of Award: St. Anthony's Hospitals, Denver: Nightingale Scholarships **Area, Field, or Subject:** Nursing. **Level of Education for which Award is Granted:** Graduate, Undergraduate **Number Awarded:** 2. **Funds Available:** $1,000. **Duration:** One year.
Eligibility Requirements: Applicant must be a Colorado resident committed to practicing nursing in Colorado; must be a student in an approved Colorado Nursing Program; must have a minimum of 3.25 GPA (for undergraduate applicants) or 3.5 GPA (for graduate applicants); and must have one of the following student statuses: (1) Junior or senior level BSN undergraduate student; (2) RN enrolled in a baccalaureate or higher degree nursing program in a school of nursing; (3) Student in second year of nursing studies in an associate degree in nursing program; (4) RN with master's degree in nursing, currently practicing in Colorado and enrolled in a doctoral program; (5) Student in second or third year of a Doctorate Nursing Practice (DNP) program. **Application Requirements:** Applicants are advised to contact the foundation at Colorado Nurses Foundation, 7831 Lewis Court, Arvada, CO 80005 for further information.

3454 ■ COLORADO NURSES FOUNDATION
7831 Lewis Court
Arvada, CO 80005
Tel: (303)758-4291
E-mail: conursesfoundation@comcast.net
Web Site: http://www.coloradonursesfoundation.org
To provide scholarships for qualified nursing students from both rural and urban settings.
Title of Award: St. Mary's Hospital and Medical Center, Grand Junction: Nightingale Scholarships **Area, Field, or Subject:** Nursing. **Level of Education for which Award is Granted:** Graduate, Undergraduate **Number Awarded:** 2. **Funds Available:** $1,000. **Duration:** One year.
Eligibility Requirements: Applicant must be a Colorado resident committed to practicing nursing in Colorado; must be a student in an approved Colorado Nursing Program; must have a minimum of 3.25 GPA (for undergraduate applicants) or 3.5 GPA (for graduate applicants); and must have one of the following student statuses: (1) Junior or senior level BSN undergraduate student; (2) RN enrolled in a baccalaureate or higher degree nursing program in a school of nursing; (3) Student in second year of nursing studies in an associate degree in nursing program; (4) RN with master's degree in nursing, currently practicing in Colorado and enrolled in a doctoral program; (5) Student in second or third year of a Doctorate Nursing Practice (DNP) program. **Application Requirements:** Applicants are advised to contact the foundation at Colorado Nurses Foundation, 7831 Lewis Court, Arvada, CO 80005 for further information.

3455 ■ COLORADO NURSES FOUNDATION
7831 Lewis Court
Arvada, CO 80005
Tel: (303)758-4291
E-mail: conursesfoundation@comcast.net
Web Site: http://www.coloradonursesfoundation.org
To provide scholarships for qualified nursing students from both rural and urban settings.
Title of Award: Seedworks Fund: Nightingale Scholarships **Area, Field, or Subject:** Nursing. **Level of Education for which Award is Granted:**

Graduate, Undergraduate **Funds Available:** $1,000. **Duration:** One year.
Eligibility Requirements: Applicant must be a Colorado resident committed to practicing nursing in Colorado; must be a student in an approved Colorado Nursing Program; must have a minimum of 3.25 GPA (for undergraduate applicants) or 3.5 GPA (for graduate applicants); and must have one of the following student statuses: (1) Junior or senior level BSN undergraduate student; (2) RN enrolled in a baccalaureate or higher degree nursing program in a school of nursing; (3) Student in second year of nursing studies in an associate degree in nursing program; (4) RN with master's degree in nursing, currently practicing in Colorado and enrolled in a doctoral program; (5) Student in second or third year of a Doctorate Nursing Practice (DNP) program. **Application Requirements:** Applicants are advised to contact the foundation at Colorado Nurses Foundation, 7831 Lewis Court, Arvada, CO 80005 for further information.

3456 ■ COLORADO NURSES FOUNDATION
7831 Lewis Court
Arvada, CO 80005
Tel: (303)758-4291
E-mail: conursesfoundation@comcast.net
Web Site: http://www.coloradonursesfoundation.org
To provide scholarships for qualified nursing students from both rural and urban settings.
Title of Award: Patty Walter Memorial Scholarships **Area, Field, or Subject:** Nursing. **Level of Education for which Award is Granted:** Graduate, Undergraduate **Funds Available:** $1,000. **Duration:** One year.
Eligibility Requirements: Applicant must be a Colorado resident committed to practicing nursing in Colorado; must be a student in an approved Colorado Nursing Program; must have a minimum of 3.25 GPA (for undergraduate applicants) or 3.5 GPA (for graduate applicants); and must have one of the following student statuses: (1) Junior or senior level BSN undergraduate student; (2) RN enrolled in a baccalaureate or higher degree nursing program in a school of nursing; (3) Student in second year of nursing studies in an associate degree in nursing program; (4) RN with master's degree in nursing, currently practicing in Colorado and enrolled in a doctoral program; (5) Student in second or third year of a Doctorate Nursing Practice (DNP) program. **Application Requirements:** Applicants are advised to contact the foundation at Colorado Nurses Foundation, 7831 Lewis Court, Arvada, CO 80005 for further information.

3457 ■ COMMUNITY FOUNDATION OF CALHOUN COUNTY
PO Box 1826
Anniston, AL 36202-1826
Tel: (256)231-5160
Fax: (256)231-5161
E-mail: info@yourcommunityfirst.org
Web Site: http://www.yourcommunityfirst.org
To promote and celebrate the nursing profession.
Title of Award: Gadsden State/McClellan Campus Nursing Scholarships Award **Area, Field, or Subject:** Nursing. **Level of Education for which Award is Granted:** Undergraduate **Funds Available:** $2,500.
Eligibility Requirements: Applicants must be graduates of an accredited public or private high school within Calhoun County currently attending Gadsden State/McClellan Campus; must be enrolled in LPN Nursing Program. **Application Requirements:** Applicants must submit a completed application form and an essay describing their personal aspirations and contributions to nursing profession. **Deadline for Receipt:** February 1. **Additional Information:** info@yourcommunityfirst.org.

3458 ■ COMMUNITY FOUNDATION OF CALHOUN COUNTY
PO Box 1826
Anniston, AL 36202-1826
Tel: (256)231-5160
Fax: (256)231-5161
E-mail: info@yourcommunityfirst.org
Web Site: http://www.yourcommunityfirst.org
To promote and celebrate the nursing profession.
Title of Award: Edyie G. Kirby Nursing Scholarships Award **Area, Field, or Subject:** Nursing. **Level of Education for which Award is Granted:** Undergraduate **Funds Available:** $2,500.
Eligibility Requirements: Applicants must be graduates of an accredited public or private high school within Calhoun County. **Application Requirements:** Applicants must submit a completed application form and

an essay describing their personal aspirations and contributions to nursing profession. **Deadline for Receipt:** February 1. **Additional Information:** info@yourcommunityfirst.org.

3459 ■ COMMUNITY FOUNDATION OF CALHOUN COUNTY
PO Box 1826
Anniston, AL 36202-1826
Tel: (256)231-5160
Fax: (256)231-5161
E-mail: info@yourcommunityfirst.org
Web Site: http://www.yourcommunityfirst.org
To promote and celebrate the nursing profession.
Title of Award: Gertie S. Lowe Nursing Scholarships Award **Area, Field, or Subject:** Nursing. **Level of Education for which Award is Granted:** Undergraduate **Funds Available:** $2,500.
Eligibility Requirements: Applicants must be full- or part-time students in the LPN or RN program at Gadsten State Community College; must be graduates of any accredited public or private high school within Calhoun County currently attending Gadsden State Community College. **Application Requirements:** Applicants must submit a completed application form and an essay describing their personal aspirations and contributions to nursing profession. **Additional Information:** info@yourcommunityfirst.org.

3460 ■ COMMUNITY FOUNDATION OF CALHOUN COUNTY
PO Box 1826
Anniston, AL 36202-1826
Tel: (256)231-5160
Fax: (256)231-5161
E-mail: info@yourcommunityfirst.org
Web Site: http://www.yourcommunityfirst.org
To promote and celebrate the nursing profession.
Title of Award: Jerry Medforth Nursing Scholarships Award **Area, Field, or Subject:** Nursing. **Level of Education for which Award is Granted:** Undergraduate **Funds Available:** $2,500.
Eligibility Requirements: Applicants must be graduates of any accredited public or private high school within Calhoun County possessing an unencumbered Registered Nurse License; must be full-time students enrolled at the Jacksonville State University Lurleen B. Wallace College of Nursing and Health Sciences RN to BSN Strategic Teaching for Enhanced Professional Preparation program. **Application Requirements:** Applicants must submit a completed application form and an essay describing their personal aspirations and contributions to nursing profession. **Additional Information:** info@yourcommunityfirst.org.

3461 ■ COMMUNITY FOUNDATION OF CALHOUN COUNTY
PO Box 1826
Anniston, AL 36202-1826
Tel: (256)231-5160
Fax: (256)231-5161
E-mail: info@yourcommunityfirst.org
Web Site: http://www.yourcommunityfirst.org
To promote and celebrate the nursing profession.
Title of Award: The Nightingale Scholarships Award **Area, Field, or Subject:** Nursing. **Level of Education for which Award is Granted:** Undergraduate **Funds Available:** $20,000. **Duration:** 4 years.
Eligibility Requirements: Applicants must be full-time students attending an accredited four-year college or university within the United States in pursuit of a bachelor's degree in nursing; must be graduates of an accredited public or private high school within Calhoun County; must have a 3.0 overall high school GPA on a 4.0 scale. **Application Requirements:** Applicants must submit a completed application form and an essay describing the person or experience that has been the greatest influence in their life. **Deadline for Receipt:** February 1. **Additional Information:** info@yourcommunityfirst.org.

3462 ■ COMMUNITY FOUNDATION OF SARASOTA COUNTY
PO Box 49587
Sarasota, FL 34237
Tel: (941)955-3000
Fax: (941)952-1951
E-mail: stewart@cfsarasota.org
Web Site: http://www.cfsarasota.org

To encourage and enable caring individuals to easily and effectively support the charitable causes that they care about.
Title of Award: byourself Scholarship Fund **Area, Field, or Subject:** Nursing. **Level of Education for which Award is Granted:** Undergraduate **Funds Available:** No specific amount.
Eligibility Requirements: Applicants must be non-traditional students, males or females in Sarasota County pursuing RN, LPN, or CNA; must be accepted into the nursing programs at Manatee Community College or Sarasota County Technical Institute; and must maintain a 2.8 GPA to retain scholarship. **Application Requirements:** Applicants must complete the application form; must submit a parent or guardian's most recent 1040 federal tax form; and must provide two letters of reference from people who know the applicant well; official acceptance letter from college or vocational school; and a copy of SAT and ACT scores.

3463 ■ COMMUNITY FOUNDATION FOR SOUTHEAST MICHIGAN
333 West Fort St., Ste. 2010
Detroit, MI 48226-3134
Tel: (313)961-6675
Fax: (313)961-2886
E-mail: cfsem@cfsem.org
Web Site: http://www.cfsem.org
To provide financial assistance to students of Southeast Michigan region for their education.
Title of Award: Jeptha Wade Schureman Scholarship Program **Area, Field, or Subject:** Law; Nursing; Medicine; Dentistry. **Level of Education for which Award is Granted:** Undergraduate **Funds Available:** $7,500.
Eligibility Requirements: Applicants must be residents of Wayne, Oakland, Macomb, Lenawee, Monroe, Livingston, Washtenaw, or St. Clair counties at the time of high school graduation; must be fatherless either through death or through termination of parental rights; must be pursuing, or planning to pursue, a degree in the fields of law, nursing, medicine or dentistry. **Application Requirements:** Applicants must submit the completed application form and other required documents. **Deadline for Receipt:** June 2.

3464 ■ DADE COMMUNITY FOUNDATION, INC.
200 S Biscayne Blvd., Ste. 505
Miami, FL 33131-2343
Tel: (305)371-2711
Fax: (305)371-5342
Web Site: http://www.dadecommunityfoundation.org
To provide financial assistance to students in their junior or senior year of undergraduate nursing degree, who are Florida residents and enrolled full-time in a Florida public or private university.
Title of Award: Jennet Colliflower Nursing Scholarships **Area, Field, or Subject:** Nursing. **Level of Education for which Award is Granted:** Undergraduate **Number Awarded:** 2. **Funds Available:** $1,000. **Duration:** One year.
Eligibility Requirements: Applicants must be entering junior or senior year undergraduate studies; must be full-time students (minimum of 12 credits hours per semester) in a public or private four-year Florida university or college; and, must be seeking an undergraduate degree in Nursing. **Application Requirements:** Applicants must submit the completed application form along with the required materials. **Deadline for Receipt:** May 7.

3465 ■ EAST TENNESSEE FOUNDATION
625 Market St., Ste. 1400
Knoxville, TN 37902
Tel: (865)524-1223; 877-524-1223
Fax: (865)637-6039
Web Site: http://www.easttennesseefoundation.org
To benefit health nurses seeking to continue their nursing education.
Title of Award: Ruby A. Brown Memorial Scholarships **Area, Field, or Subject:** Nursing. **Level of Education for which Award is Granted:** Undergraduate **Funds Available:** $3,250.
Eligibility Requirements: Applicant must be currently employed as a public health nurse. Applicant must be a resident in one of 15 counties (Anderson, Blount, Campbell, Claiborne, Cocke, Grainger, Hamblen, Jefferson, Loudon, Monroe, Morgan, Roane, Scott, Sevier or Union). **Application Requirements:** Applicant must check the application process online as well as the required materials. **Deadline for Receipt:** April 25.

Additional Information: East Tennessee Foundation at the above address

3466 ■ EMERGENCY NURSES ASSOCIATION
915 Lee St.
Des Plaines, IL 60016-6569
Tel: (847)460-4123
Fax: (847)460-4001
E-mail: education@ena.org
Web Site: http://www.ena.org
To promote education or research on emergency care.
Title of Award: BCEN Undergraduate Scholarships **Area, Field, or Subject:** Nursing. **Level of Education for which Award is Granted:** Undergraduate **Number Awarded:** 1. **Funds Available:** $2,000.
Eligibility Requirements: Applicants must be attending a NLN or AACN accredited school; must be an ENA member for at least one year. **Application Requirements:** Applicants must provide a letter verifying the school's current accreditation with the application (visit the website for the application). If not a member, applicant must provide a letter of reference from an ENA member. **Additional Information:** Do not staple materials, use paper clips or binder clips. Faxed materials will be disqualified. **Deadline for Receipt:** June 1. **Additional Information:** ENA Foundation Office, 800-900-9658 x-4100, foundation@ena.org.

3467 ■ EMERGENCY NURSES ASSOCIATION
915 Lee St.
Des Plaines, IL 60016-6569
Tel: (847)460-4123
Fax: (847)460-4001
E-mail: education@ena.org
Web Site: http://www.ena.org
To promote education or research on emergency care.
Title of Award: Emergency Nurses Association Undergraduate Scholarships **Area, Field, or Subject:** Nursing. **Level of Education for which Award is Granted:** Undergraduate **Number Awarded:** 3. **Funds Available:** $3,000 for the highest scoring applicant and $2,500 for the two next highest scoring.
Eligibility Requirements: Applicants must be attending a NLN or AACN accredited school; must be an ENA member for at least one year. **Application Requirements:** Applicants must provide a letter verifying the school's current accreditation together with the application form. If not a member, applicant must provide a letter of reference from an ENA member. **Additional Information:** Do not staple materials, use paper clips or binder clips. Faxed materials will be disqualified. **Deadline for Receipt:** June 1.

3468 ■ EMERGENCY NURSES ASSOCIATION
915 Lee St.
Des Plaines, IL 60016-6569
Tel: (847)460-4123
Fax: (847)460-4001
E-mail: education@ena.org
Web Site: http://www.ena.org
To promote education or research on emergency care.
Title of Award: ENA Foundation Advanced Practice Scholarships **Area, Field, or Subject:** Nursing. **Level of Education for which Award is Granted:** Undergraduate **Number Awarded:** 4. **Funds Available:** $4,000.
Eligibility Requirements: Applicants must be attending a NLN or AACN accredited school; must be an ENA member for at least one year applicants; working on a dissertation related to emergency nursing. **Application Requirements:** Applicants must provide a letter verifying the school's current accreditation with the application (visit the website for the application). If not a member, applicant must provide a letter of reference from an ENA member. **Additional Information:** Do not staple materials, use paper clips or binder clips. Faxed materials will be disqualified. **Deadline for Receipt:** June 1. **Additional Information:** ENA Foundation Office, 800-900-9658 x-4100, foundation@ena.org.

3469 ■ FIRST COMMUNITY FOUNDATION OF PENNSYLVANIA, WILLIAMSPORT-LYCOMING
330 Pine St., Suite 401
Williamsport, PA 17701

Tel: (570)321-1500; (866)901-2372
Fax: (570)321-6434
E-mail: fcfpa@fcfpa.org
Web Site: http://www.wlfoundation.org
To provide academic support for Danville Area High School seniors who have been accepted into a full-time undergraduate program at an accredited institution of higher education and who are entering a health-related field.
Title of Award: Eleanor McWilliams Burke Fund **Area, Field, or Subject:** Medicine; Nursing; Nutrition; Pharmacy; or Physical therapy. **Level of Education for which Award is Granted:** Undergraduate **Funds Available:** No specific amount.
Eligibility Requirements: Applicants must be entering a health related field. **Application Requirements:** Applicants may request an application from the Guidance Counselor of Danville Area School District. **Additional Information:** Gary Grozier, Guidance Counselor of Danville Area School District, 600 Walnut St., Danvilled, PA 17821; 570-271-3268 ext. 2006; ggrozier@danville.k12.pa.us.

3470 ■ FIRST COMMUNITY FOUNDATION OF PENNSYLVANIA, WILLIAMSPORT-LYCOMING
330 Pine St., Suite 401
Williamsport, PA 17701
Tel: (570)321-1500; (866)901-2372
Fax: (570)321-6434
E-mail: fcfpa@fcfpa.org
Web Site: http://www.wlfoundation.org
To support the education of current and/or aspiring Lycoming County medical professionals who plan to dedicate their lives to helping others.
Title of Award: Joseph R. Calder, Jr., MD Scholarship Fund **Area, Field, or Subject:** Medicine; Nursing; Pharmacy; Allied health. **Level of Education for which Award is Granted:** Undergraduate **Funds Available:** No specific amount.
Eligibility Requirements: Applicants must be accepted into a full-time or part-time medical or any other related specialty at an accredited institution of higher education. Applicants should be residents of Lycoming County. **Application Requirements:** Applicant must submit an essay not to exceed one page outlining why he/she is pursuing a career in the medical field and summarizing his/her ultimate career objectives. Applicants may download an application form the Foundation's web site. **Additional Information:** Candy Bower, 570-321-1500; candyb@fcfpa.org

3471 ■ FIRST COMMUNITY FOUNDATION OF PENNSYLVANIA, WILLIAMSPORT-LYCOMING
330 Pine St., Suite 401
Williamsport, PA 17701
Tel: (570)321-1500; (866)901-2372
Fax: (570)321-6434
E-mail: fcfpa@fcfpa.org
Web Site: http://www.wlfoundation.org
To provide financial assistance for Bloomsburg University students who are pursuing a career in nursing.
Title of Award: Joseph and Catherine Missigman Memorial Nursing Scholarships **Area, Field, or Subject:** Nursing. **Level of Education for which Award is Granted:** Undergraduate **Funds Available:** No specific amount.
Eligibility Requirements: Candidates must be Bloomsburg University students who have identified nursing as their major; must be completing their second or third year's curricula in the University's nursing education program; have a GPA of 2.5 or greater for all nursing coursework; and have a demonstrated financial need as determined by Bloomsburg University's methods and practices for assessing its student's financial capacities. **Application Requirements:** Candidates must have completed and filed an application for the scholarship and must include a one-page cover letter describing his/her rational for applying for the scholarship as well as his/her interest in the nursing field. **Additional Information:** Margie Eckroth-Bucher, Associate Professor Department of Nursing, Bloomsburg University, 570-389-4607, mekroth@bloomu.edu.

3472 ■ FLORIDA ASSOCIATION DIRECTORS OF NURSING ADMINISTRATION
200 Butler St., Ste. 305
West Palm Beach, FL 33407

Tel: (561)659-2167
Fax: (561)659-1291
E-mail: fadona@fadona.org
Web Site: http://www.fadona.org
To provide financial assistance to individuals in nursing looking to continue their education in the LTC setting.
Title of Award: Florida Association District of Nursing Administration Scholarships **Area, Field, or Subject:** Nursing. **Level of Education for which Award is Granted:** Undergraduate **Funds Available:** $500.
Eligibility Requirements: Applicants must be currently licensed registered nurses, LPN or certified nursing assistants; must be currently enrolled or accepted in a RN, LPN or undergraduate health care program; or be currently accepted or enrolled in a baccalaureate or master's program in nursing or gerontology program; must have at least two years employment history in long-term care. **Application Requirements:** Applicants must submit a completed application form; must submit a list of employers and dates of employment.

3473 ■ FLORIDA ASSOCIATION DIRECTORS OF NURSING ADMINISTRATION
200 Butler St., Ste. 305
West Palm Beach, FL 33407
Tel: (561)659-2167
Fax: (561)659-1291
E-mail: fadona@fadona.org
Web Site: http://www.fadona.org
To provide financial assistance to individuals in nursing looking to continue their education in the LTC setting.
Title of Award: Imogene Ward Nursing Scholarships **Area, Field, or Subject:** Nursing. **Level of Education for which Award is Granted:** Undergraduate **Funds Available:** No specific amount.
Eligibility Requirements: Applicants must be pursuing education to become registered nurses; must be enrolled in an accredited Florida Nursing program; must be willing to pledge a minimum of two years, working full-time in long-term care in the state of Florida. **Application Requirements:** Applicants must submit a completed application form including name and full contact information; must submit a 300-word or less narrative essay which outlines what it takes to be an exceptional nurse and also expresses reasons they should be considered for the Imogene Ward Nursing Scholarship Award.

3474 ■ FOUNDATION FOR THE CAROLINAS
217 S Tryon St.
Charlotte, NC 28202
Tel: (704)973-4500
Free: 800-973-7244
Web Site: http://www.fftc.org
To provide undergraduate scholarships for students attending Limestone College in Gaffney, South Carolina.
Title of Award: Albert and Eloise Midyette Memorial Scholarship Fund **Area, Field, or Subject:** Nursing; Education, Medical. **Level of Education for which Award is Granted:** Undergraduate **Funds Available:** No specific amount.
Eligibility Requirements: Applicants must be full-time U.S. citizen students at Limestone College; must be majoring in the fields of religious and ministry studies, nursing or other medical academic fields; and must have a cumulative unweighted grade point average of at least 2.5 (on a 4.0 scale). **Application Requirements:** Applicants must submit all the required application information and materials.

3475 ■ FOUNDATION FOR THE CAROLINAS
217 S Tryon St.
Charlotte, NC 28202
Tel: (704)973-4500
Free: 800-973-7244
Web Site: http://www.fftc.org
To assist North Iredell High School graduates in obtaining a degree in physical therapy, medicine or nursing from a post-secondary accredited institution.
Title of Award: The Sibyl Jennings Vorheis Memorial Scholarship Program **Area, Field, or Subject:** Physical therapy; Medicine; Nursing. **Level of Education for which Award is Granted:** Undergraduate **Funds Available:** $3,000. **Duration:** One year.

Eligibility Requirements: Applicants must have graduated from North Iredell High School with a minimum cumulative grade point average of 3.0 (on 4.0 scale). **Application Requirements:** Applicants must submit completed application form; verification of acceptance into the accredited graduate program; official copy of college transcript; two recommendation forms and letters of recommendation; and a typewritten application statement of eligibility expressing applicant's educational and career goals, reasons for applying for the scholarship, and why the applicant feels they are a good candidate for the scholarship. **Deadline for Receipt:** April 1.

3476 ■ FOUNDATION FOR ENHANCING COMMUNITIES
200 N Third St., PO Box 678
Harrisburg, PA 17108-0678
Tel: (717)236-5040
Fax: (717)231-4463
E-mail: dawn@tfec.org
Web Site: http://www.ghf.org
To provide financial assistance for Lebanon County residents pursuing higher education degrees.
Title of Award: Family and Children's Services of Lebanon County Fund **Area, Field, or Subject:** Medicine; Nursing, Social work, Mental health. **Level of Education for which Award is Granted:** Undergraduate **Funds Available:** No specific amount.
Eligibility Requirements: Applicants must be enrolled full-time in schools of advanced education in the fields of medicine, nursing, social work, mental health and other specialized therapies in the treatment of physical and mental disabilities; must demonstrate financial need, academic aptitude and achievement, and commitment to a career in human services; and must be residents of Lebanon County. **Application Requirements:** Applicants may obtain the application online. Applicants must provide the most recent, either a certified high school transcript or a certified college transcript. **Additional Information:** Dawn Morris, Program Officer; 717-236-5040; dawn@tfec.org.

3477 ■ FOUNDATION FOR ENHANCING COMMUNITIES
200 N Third St., PO Box 678
Harrisburg, PA 17108-0678
Tel: (717)236-5040
Fax: (717)231-4463
E-mail: dawn@tfec.org
Web Site: http://www.ghf.org
To assist students from Franklin County with their nursing studies at a college or university of their choice.
Title of Award: Gordon B. and Josephine Hewlet Memorial Fund **Area, Field, or Subject:** Nursing. **Level of Education for which Award is Granted:** Undergraduate **Funds Available:** No specific amount.
Eligibility Requirements: Applicants must be nursing undergraduate students, however if there are no qualified undergraduate student applicants, scholarships may be given to graduate students. **Application Requirements:** The application and the required attachments must be completed and postmarked on or before the deadline. Required attachments include: completed student background sheet (attached); official high school transcript with raised school seal; 1st and 2nd page of parents and students IRS 1040 and/or 1040 A form(s); completed student essay (question attached); and two personal reference letters (one letter should be from a teacher and the other letter should be from an employer or a supervisor of community service volunteer agency). Letters of reference may not be from a family member. Application form can be obtained online. **Deadline for Receipt:** March 28. **Additional Information:** Dawn Morris, Program Officer at the above address.

3478 ■ FOUNDATION FOR ENHANCING COMMUNITIES
200 N Third St., PO Box 678
Harrisburg, PA 17108-0678
Tel: (717)236-5040
Fax: (717)231-4463
E-mail: dawn@tfec.org
Web Site: http://www.ghf.org
To assist students from Cumberland, Dauphin and Perry Counties studying nursing at a college or university of their choice.
Title of Award: Roberta L. Houpt Scholarship Fund **Area, Field, or Subject:** Nursing. **Level of Education for which Award is Granted:** Undergraduate **Funds Available:** $2,000. **Duration:** Annual.

Eligibility Requirements: Applicants must be nursing undergraduate students and residents of Dauphin, Cumberland or Perry Counties. **Application Requirements:** Application and the required attachments must be completed and postmarked on or before the deadline. Required attachments include: completed student background sheet; high school transcript or college transcript; letter of acceptance in nursing program or college transcript showing enrollment in program; FAFSA student aid report form (financial aid form); completed essay (question attached); and two personal reference letters (one letter should be from a science teacher and the other letter should be from an individual who can speak to applicant's ability to successfully complete studies), such as a teacher, employer, or mentor. Application form can be obtained online. **Additional Information:** Established in 1998. **Deadline for Receipt:** March 31. **Additional Information:** Dawn Morris, Program Officer at the above address.

3479 ■ FOUNDATION OF THE NATIONAL STUDENT NURSES ASSOCIATION
45 Main St., Ste. 606
Brooklyn, NY 11201
Tel: (718)210-0705
Fax: (718)210-0710
E-mail: nsna@nsna.org
Web Site: http://www.nsna.org
To provide financial support to qualified nursing students.
Title of Award: Breakthrough to Nursing Scholarships **Area, Field, or Subject:** Nursing. **Level of Education for which Award is Granted:** Undergraduate **Funds Available:** $1,000-$5,000. **Duration:** One year.
Eligibility Requirements: Applicant must be a student committed to providing quality health care services to underserved population; must possess the necessary leadership skills to influence the delivery of quality care; must be a U.S citizen or Alien with U.S permanent resident status/Alien Registration Number; must establish academic achievement; must have an involvement in student nursing organizations and community health activities; must be attending classes and taking no less than six credits per semester. **Application Requirements:** Applicants must submit and complete the application form available online; must submit an official transcript of records. Application form and other supporting documents must be sent to Foundation of the National Nurses' Association, 45 Main St., Ste. 606, Brooklyn, NY 11201. **Deadline for Receipt:** June 16.

3480 ■ FOUNDATION OF THE NATIONAL STUDENT NURSES ASSOCIATION
45 Main St., Ste. 606
Brooklyn, NY 11201
Tel: (718)210-0705
Fax: (718)210-0710
E-mail: nsna@nsna.org
Web Site: http://www.nsna.org
To provide financial support to qualified nursing students.
Title of Award: Career Mobility Scholarships **Area, Field, or Subject:** Nursing. **Level of Education for which Award is Granted:** Graduate, Undergraduate **Funds Available:** $1,000-$5,000. **Duration:** One year.
Eligibility Requirements: Applicants must be nursing or pre-nursing students who are registered nurses (RNs) enrolled in RN and BSN and RN to MSN completion programs or a licensed practical/vocational nurses enrolled in programs leading to RN licensure; must be U.S. citizens or Alien with U.S. permanent residents status/Alien Registration Number; must have established academic achievement; must have an involvement in student nursing organizations and community health activities; must be attending classes and taking no less than six credits per semester. **Application Requirements:** Applicants must submit and complete the application form available online; must submit an official transcript of records; application form and other supporting documents must be sent to Foundation of the National Nurses' Association, 45 Main St., Ste. 606, Brooklyn, NY 11201. **Deadline for Receipt:** June 16.

3481 ■ FOUNDATION OF THE NATIONAL STUDENT NURSES ASSOCIATION
45 Main St., Ste. 606
Brooklyn, NY 11201
Tel: (718)210-0705
Fax: (718)210-0710

E-mail: nsna@nsna.org
Web Site: http://www.nsna.org
To provide financial support to qualified nursing students.
Title of Award: McKesson Scholarships **Area, Field, or Subject:** Nursing. **Level of Education for which Award is Granted:** Undergraduate **Funds Available:** $1,000-$5,000. **Duration:** One year.
Eligibility Requirements: Applicants must be pre-nursing students taking courses to prepare for matriculation into a nursing program; must be U.S citizens or Alien with U.S permanent residents status/Alien Registration Number; must establish academic achievement; must have an involvement in student nursing organizations and community health activities; must be attending classes and taking no less than six credits per semester. **Application Requirements:** Applicants must submit and complete the application form available online; must submit an official transcript of records. Application form and other supporting documents must be sent to Foundation of the National Nurses' Association, 45 Main St., Ste. 606, Brooklyn, NY 11201. **Deadline for Receipt:** June 16.

3482 ■ FOUNDATION OF THE NATIONAL STUDENT NURSES ASSOCIATION
45 Main St., Ste. 606
Brooklyn, NY 11201
Tel: (718)210-0705
Fax: (718)210-0710
E-mail: nsna@nsna.org
Web Site: http://www.nsna.org
To provide financial support to qualified nursing students.
Title of Award: Specialty Nursing Scholarships **Area, Field, or Subject:** Nursing. **Level of Education for which Award is Granted:** Undergraduate **Funds Available:** $1,000-$5,000. **Duration:** One year.
Eligibility Requirements: Applicant must be a student interested in pursuing specialized areas of nursing practice; must be a U.S citizen or Alien with U.S permanent resident status/Alien Registration Number; must establish academic achievement; must have an involvement in student nursing organizations and community health activities; must be attending classes and taking no less than six credits per semester. **Application Requirements:** Applicants must submit and complete the application form available online; must submit an official transcript of records. Application form and other supporting documents must be sent to Foundation of the National Nurses' Association, 45 Main St., Ste. 606, Brooklyn, NY 11201. **Deadline for Receipt:** June 16.

3483 ■ GRAND HAVEN AREA COMMUNITY FOUNDATION
1 S. Harbor Dr.
Grand Haven, MI 49417
Tel: (616)842-6378
Fax: (616)842-9518
E-mail: bpost@ghacf.org
Web Site: http://www.ghacf.org
To improve and enhance the quality of life in the Tri-Cities area by serving as a leader, catalyst and resource for philanthropy; to strive for community improvement through strategic grantmaking in such fields as arts, education, health, environment, youth, social services and other human needs.
Title of Award: North Ottawa Hospital Auxiliary Scholarships Fund **Area, Field, or Subject:** Nursing. **Level of Education for which Award is Granted:** Undergraduate **Funds Available:** No specific amount.
Eligibility Requirements: Applicants must be from the Tri-Cities area; currently enrolled as college students who have taken their core requirements and been accepted into their health-care related program of study. **Application Requirements:** Applicants must submit: completed application form; current high school or college transcript; Student Aid Report (SAR) from the Free Application for Federal Student Aid (FAFSA), unless applying for scholarships that do not consider financial need; and letter of recommendation. **Deadline for Receipt:** March 7. **Additional Information:** 616-842-6378.

3484 ■ THE GREATER TACOMA COMMUNITY FOUNDATION
PO Box 1995
Tacoma, WA 98401
Tel: (253)383-5622
Web Site: http://www.tacomafoundation.org
To foster generosity by connecting people who care with causes that matter.

Title of Award: Ruth Murphy Evans Scholarship **Area, Field, or Subject:** Nursing. **Level of Education for which Award is Granted:** Undergraduate **Funds Available:** No specific amount.
Eligibility Requirements: Applicants must be students in a nursing program at Highline Community College, Olympic College, South Puget Sound Community College or Tacoma Community College. **Application Requirements:** Applicants must request an application form at their guidance office.

3485 ■ HARTFORD FOUNDATION FOR PUBLIC GIVING
10 Columbus Blvd., 8th Flr.
Hartford, CT 06106
Tel: (860)548-1888
Fax: (860)524-8346
E-mail: hfpg@hfpg.org
Web Site: http://www.hfpg.org
To provide scholarship to the Jewish high school senior or college students.
Title of Award: Rhea Sourifman Caplin Memorial Scholarships **Area, Field, or Subject:** Nursing; Health care services. **Level of Education for which Award is Granted:** Undergraduate **Number Awarded:** 1-2. **Funds Available:** $1,000-$2,000.
Eligibility Requirements: Applicants must: be a Greater Hartford resident; be pursuing nursing or health care profession; have a minimum B average in sciences; have a good citizenship and active involvement in the community. **Application Requirements:** Applicants may obtain application materials from Jewish Community Foundation of Greater Hartford, 333 Bloomfield Ave. Ste. D West Hartford, CT 06117. **Deadline for Receipt:** April 15. **Additional Information:** Michael Elfenbaum, Phone: 860-523-7460
Fax: 860-231-0576; melfenbaum@jcfhartford.org.

3486 ■ HARTFORD FOUNDATION FOR PUBLIC GIVING
10 Columbus Blvd., 8th Flr.
Hartford, CT 06106
Tel: (860)548-1888
Fax: (860)524-8346
E-mail: hfpg@hfpg.org
Web Site: http://www.hfpg.org
To provide educational assistance for senior nursing students or graduate students attending a Connecticut nursing school.
Title of Award: Connecticut League of Nursing Scholarships **Area, Field, or Subject:** Nursing. **Level of Education for which Award is Granted:** Undergraduate **Number Awarded:** 2. **Funds Available:** $1,000.
Eligibility Requirements: Applicants must have completed a minimum of 18 credits in a Nursing Program and must demonstrate financial need and academic excellence. **Application Requirements:** Applicants may obtain application materials from Connecticut League for Nursing, PO Box 365 Wallingford, CT 06492. **Deadline for Receipt:** October 15. **Additional Information:** Marcia Proto, Executive Dir. education@ctleaguefornursing.org
Fax: 203-265-5311.

3487 ■ HARTFORD FOUNDATION FOR PUBLIC GIVING
10 Columbus Blvd., 8th Flr.
Hartford, CT 06106
Tel: (860)548-1888
Fax: (860)524-8346
E-mail: hfpg@hfpg.org
Web Site: http://www.hfpg.org
To award scholarship to a graduating high school senior from Newington or Hartford Public High School.
Title of Award: William G. and Mayme J. Green Scholarships **Area, Field, or Subject:** Nursing. **Level of Education for which Award is Granted:** Undergraduate **Number Awarded:** 1. **Funds Available:** $2,500.
Eligibility Requirements: Applicants must: be entering a four-year college or university (full-time enrollment) pursuing a degree in Nursing; must demonstrate financial need; be on the class rank - top third with a good academic record; be an active volunteer in school, community, or other extracurricular activities. **Application Requirements:** Application form can be downloaded online. Applicants must complete the scholarship application. Applicants must also attach the following requirements: letter of

recommendation from your guidance counselor or a teacher; official high school transcript. Including SAT or ACT scores; copy of the essay you submitted with your college application. If you did not have to submit one, write a brief (no more than two pages) essay regarding your future goals; copy of pages 1 and 2 of your parents' most recent completed federal tax form 1040. Mail everything to Hartford Foundation College Scholarship Program. **Deadline for Receipt:** February 13. **Additional Information:** Hartford Foundation College Scholarship Program, Scholarship Management Services, Scholarship America, One Scholarship Way, PO Box 297, St. Peter, MN 56082. 800-537-4180.

3488 ■ HARTFORD FOUNDATION FOR PUBLIC GIVING
10 Columbus Blvd., 8th Flr.
Hartford, CT 06106
Tel: (860)548-1888
Fax: (860)524-8346
E-mail: hfpg@hfpg.org
Web Site: http://www.hfpg.org
To award scholarship to the undergraduate student enrolled in a Nursing Program.
Title of Award: Caroline Holt Nursing Scholarships **Area, Field, or Subject:** Nursing. **Level of Education for which Award is Granted:** Undergraduate **Funds Available:** $500.
Eligibility Requirements: Applicants must: be a US citizen; be attending an accredited School of Nursing; demonstrate financial need; have a letter of sponsorship from local DAR chapter. **Application Requirements:** For Connecticut residents to obtain materials, send a self-addressed stamped envelope to National Society Daughters of the American Revolution, 215 Loomis Rd. North Granby, CT 06060. **Deadline for Receipt:** February 15 or August 15. **Additional Information:** Mrs. Michael L. Stewart, CT State Chairperson. 860-653-4203. L2stew@yahoo.com.

3489 ■ HARTFORD FOUNDATION FOR PUBLIC GIVING
10 Columbus Blvd., 8th Flr.
Hartford, CT 06106
Tel: (860)548-1888
Fax: (860)524-8346
E-mail: hfpg@hfpg.org
Web Site: http://www.hfpg.org
To provide financial support to the graduating high school senior.
Title of Award: Katherine Portnoy Mattleson Scholarships **Area, Field, or Subject:** Nursing. **Level of Education for which Award is Granted:** Undergraduate **Number Awarded:** 1. **Funds Available:** $500.
Eligibility Requirements: Applicants must: be enrolled in a School of Nursing; be a Jewish faith; have an academic excellence; be involved in community service. **Application Requirements:** Applicants may obtain an application from Nona Dorman, Scholarship Chairperson, 31 Woodland St., 6L Hartford, CT 06105. 860724-2323. **Deadline for Receipt:** April 10.

3490 ■ HEALTH RESOURCES AND SERVICES ADMINISTRATION - BUREAU OF HEALTH PROFESSIONS
5600 Fishers Ln.
Rockville, MD 20857
Tel: (301)443-2194
Free: 800-221-9393
E-mail: callcenter@hrsa.gov
Web Site: http://bhpr.hrsa.gov
To award scholarships to individuals for attendance at schools of nursing.
Title of Award: Nursing Scholarship Program **Area, Field, or Subject:** Nursing. **Level of Education for which Award is Granted:** Undergraduate **Funds Available:** $1,233.
Eligibility Requirements: Applicants must be US citizens or nationals (permanent residents are not eligible); must be enrolled or accepted for enrollment as full-time or part-time students in an accredited school of nursing in a professional registered nurse program; must begin classes for the fall term on or after July 1 and no later than September 30; must be free from any Federal judgment liens; must be free from existing service commitments; and must not be delinquent on a federal debt. **Application Requirements:** All applicants (regardless of funding preference) must submit an electronic application. Required supporting documentation is available within the online application and includes: a verification of Acceptance/Good Standing Report and Data Collection for Tuition and

Fees; an Authorization to Release Information; Form W-4; Standard form 1199A (EG) Direct Deposit Sign Up Form; and a Signed Contract. **Deadline for Receipt:** June 6. **Additional Information:** HRSA at the above address.

3491 ■ IDAHO COMMUNITY FOUNDATION
210 W State St.
Boise, ID 83702
Tel: (208)342-3535
Free: 800-657-5357
Fax: (208)342-3577
E-mail: info@idcomfdn.org
Web Site: http://www.idcomfdn.org
To assist recipients with educational expenses at any Idaho accredited nursing program.
Title of Award: Idaho Nursing Scholarships **Area, Field, or Subject:** Nursing. **Level of Education for which Award is Granted:** Undergraduate **Funds Available:** No specific amount.
Eligibility Requirements: Applicants must be students that have been accepted by an accredited Idaho nursing program or be in the top third of the academic ranking of the class. **Application Requirements:** Applicants must send three copies of signed and completed application form. **Deadline for Receipt:** April 30.

3492 ■ ILLINOIS STUDENT ASSISTANCE COMMISSION
1755 Lake Cook Rd.
Deerfield, IL 60015-5209
Tel: 800-899-4722
E-mail: collegezone@isac.org
Web Site: http://www.collegezone.com
To provide financial support to a qualified individual intending to pursue a career in professional or practical nursing education in Illinois.
Title of Award: Illinois Student Assistance Commission Nurse Educator Scholarships **Area, Field, or Subject:** Practical nursing. **Level of Education for which Award is Granted:** Undergraduate **Funds Available:** $10,000 to cover the cost of attendance, including living expenses. **Duration:** One academic year.
Eligibility Requirements: Applicant must be a U.S citizen or an eligible non-citizen; must be an Illinois resident; must be a recipient of at least a bachelor's degree; must be enrolled, or accepted for enrollment, on at least a half-time basis in an approved program of practical nursing education at the graduate level at an eligible Illinois college; must have a satisfactory academic progress as determined by the college; must comply with federal Selective Service registration requirements. **Application Requirements:** Application forms are available to download and print from College Zone. **Deadline for Receipt:** March 1.

3493 ■ ILLINOIS STUDENT ASSISTANCE COMMISSION
1755 Lake Cook Rd.
Deerfield, IL 60015-5209
Tel: 800-899-4722
E-mail: collegezone@isac.org
Web Site: http://www.collegezone.com
To provide financial assistance to qualified individuals pursuing an associate degree in nursing, an associate degree in applied sciences in nursing, a hospital based diploma in nursing, a baccalaureate degree in nursing, a graduate degree in nursing or a certificate in practical nursing.
Title of Award: Illinois Student Assistance Commission Nursing Education Scholarships **Area, Field, or Subject:** Nursing. **Level of Education for which Award is Granted:** Undergraduate **Funds Available:** $1,603-$5,943.
Eligibility Requirements: Applicant must be a resident of Illinois for at least one year prior to application, and be a citizen or lawful permanent resident alien of the United States; must be enrolled in or accepted for admission to a nursing program in Illinois that is approved by the Illinois Department of Financial and Professional Regulation, Division of Professional Regulation; must be in need of financial assistance based on applicant's Student Aid Report. **Application Requirements:** Applicant must submit a completed, signed and dated application form prior to the deadline; must have a copy of his/her Illinois registered professional nurse license or Illinois practical nurse license; must include a current copy of an official transcript or other current official school form that indicates a cumulative grade point average; must include a copy of a current Student Aid Report (SAR) that indicates an estimated financial contribution. A current SAR is required, even if you are not eligible for or have not applied for other financial assistance. **Deadline for Receipt:** May 31.

3494 ■ JACKSON COUNTY COMMUNITY FOUNDATION
One Jackson Square, 100 E Michigan Ave., Ste. 308
Jackson, MI 49201-1406
Tel: (517)787-1321
Fax: (517)787-4333
E-mail: jcf@jacksoncf.org
Web Site: http://www.jacksoncf.org
To assist all citizens of greater Jackson in improving the quality of their lives; to support its work as a community grantmaker and community leader.
Title of Award: Sue Walicki Nursing Scholarship **Area, Field, or Subject:** Nursing. **Level of Education for which Award is Granted:** Undergraduate **Funds Available:** $5,000.
Eligibility Requirements: Applicants must be Jackson County residents or current employees of a Jackson county health care facility; must be full or part-time students at an accredited Michigan college or university; must have plans to start, continue or advance education in the field of nursing-related field. **Application Requirements:** Applicants must submit a proof of acceptance in an accredited Nursing Program and proof of financial need.

3495 ■ JAMAICAN CANADIAN ASSOCIATION
995 Arrow Rd.
Toronto, ON, Canada M9M 2Z5
Tel: (416)746-5772
Fax: (416)746-7035
E-mail: info@jcassoc.org
Web Site: http://www.jcassoc.org
To provide financial assistance to students from the Caribbean/ African community, who are pursuing postsecondary studies in Ontario universities/colleges.
Title of Award: Jamaica National Building Society Scholarships **Area, Field, or Subject:** Business; Law; Science; Technology; Nursing. **Level of Education for which Award is Granted:** Undergraduate **Number Awarded:** 2. **Funds Available:** $1,000. **Duration:** One year.
Eligibility Requirements: Applicant must be a Canadian citizen or landed immigrant of Caribbean or African background; must be enrolled as a full-time first-year student at an Ontario university/college or other postsecondary institution; must demonstrate remarkable academic performance or progress in high school; must demonstrate involvement and leadership in campus and/or community activities; must demonstrate financial need. **Application Requirements:** Application forms are available online and must be sent to The Jamaican Canadian Association Center, 995 Arrow Rd., Toronto M9M 2Z5. **Additional Information:** Scholarship is donated by the Jamaica National Building Society, a financial institution that facilitates money transfers from Canada. **Deadline for Receipt:** July 25.

3496 ■ JEWISH FOUNDATION FOR EDUCATION OF WOMEN
135 E 64th St.
New York, NY 10065
Tel: (212)288-3931
Fax: (212)288-5798
E-mail: info@jfew.org
Web Site: http://www.jfew.org
To provide financial support for emigres from the former Soviet Union to train in medicine, dentistry, dental hygiene, nursing, pharmacy, occupational and physical therapy, physician assistant, CVT, and sonography programs.
Title of Award: Scholarships for Emigres in the Health Sciences **Area, Field, or Subject:** Medicine; Dentistry; Nursing; Pharmacy; Physical therapy; Physiology. **Level of Education for which Award is Granted:** Undergraduate **Funds Available:** $5,000. **Duration:** One year.
Eligibility Requirements: Applicants must be students from the former Soviet Union; must be residents of New York City or the counties of Nassau, Suffolk or Westchester; must already be enrolled in or about to enroll in a health science program within that geographic area; and must be enrolled full-time, in good standing, and demonstrate financial need. **Application Requirements:** Applicants must submit all the required application information.

3497 ■ LEWIS-CLARK STATE COLLEGE

500 8th Ave.
Lewiston, ID 83501
Tel: (208)792-5272
Web Site: http://www.lcsc.edu
To inspire educational pursuits among less capable individuals by providing financial assistance.
Title of Award: Gretchen Dimico Memorial Scholarships **Area, Field, or Subject:** Nursing. **Level of Education for which Award is Granted:** Undergraduate **Funds Available:** No specific amount.
Eligibility Requirements: Applicants must be full or part-time students at the LCSC Coeur d'Alene Center; must have a cumulative GPA of 2.75; and must be current or former members of Professional Nursing Organization. **Application Requirements:** Applicants must accomplish a general application available at the website. **Deadline for Receipt:** March 1.

3498 ■ LEWIS-CLARK STATE COLLEGE

500 8th Ave.
Lewiston, ID 83501
Tel: (208)792-5272
Web Site: http://www.lcsc.edu
To encourage promising students from Timberline High School, Clearwater County to continue their education.
Title of Award: Bus and Mary Ellen Durant Timberline High School Endowed Scholarships **Area, Field, or Subject:** Nursing; Technical; Industrial. **Level of Education for which Award is Granted:** Undergraduate **Funds Available:** No specific amount.
Eligibility Requirements: Applicants must be alumni of Timberline High School or their successor in Clearwater County, Idaho; must be enrolled full-time who majoring in any other discipline offered at LCSC. **Application Requirements:** Applicants must accomplish a general application available in the website. **Deadline for Receipt:** March 1.

3499 ■ LLOYDMINSTER REGION HEALTH FOUNDATION

218 5704-44 St.
Lloydminster, AB, Canada T9V 2A1
Tel: (306)820-6161
Fax: (780)875-9172
Web Site: http://www.lrhf.ca
To support nursing students to complete their studies and to assist the future staffing needs of nursing professionals in Lloydminster.
Title of Award: Goodfellow Nursing Scholarships **Area, Field, or Subject:** Nursing. **Level of Education for which Award is Granted:** Undergraduate **Number Awarded:** 5. **Funds Available:** $2,000. **Duration:** One year.
Eligibility Requirements: Applicant must be an individual studying Nursing at a Canadian recognized university or post-secondary institution; must be willing to work in Lloydminster at a facility or program run by the Prairie North Health Region; must be a permanent resident in the Lloydminster region; must have good academic ability; must demonstrate community leadership and volunteering. **Application Requirements:** Applicant must submit a letter of reference from an accredited instructor together with the application form to Lloydminster Region Health Foundation, 3820-43 Ave., Lloydminster, SK S9V 1Y5. **Additional Information:** Scholarship was established in memory of Miss Kitty Goodfellow, a longtime resident of Lloydminster. **Deadline for Receipt:** July 31.

3500 ■ LLOYDMINSTER REGION HEALTH FOUNDATION

218 5704-44 St.
Lloydminster, AB, Canada T9V 2A1
Tel: (306)820-6161
Fax: (780)875-9172
Web Site: http://www.lrhf.ca
To support nursing students to complete their studies and to assist in meeting future staffing needs of Lloydminster.
Title of Award: Pat Redden Memorial Scholarships **Area, Field, or Subject:** Nursing. **Level of Education for which Award is Granted:** Undergraduate **Funds Available:** $5,000. **Duration:** One year.
Eligibility Requirements: Applicant must be a Nursing student at a Canadian recognized university or post-secondary institution; must be enrolled and have successfully completed 50% of a minimum two-year fully-accredited program in nursing leading to a RN designation. Applicant

must be a permanent resident in the Lloydminster region; must have good academic ability; must demonstrate community leadership and volunteering. **Application Requirements:** Applicant must submit a letter of reference from an accredited instructor together with the application to Lloydminster Region Health Foundation, 3820-43 Ave., Lloydminster, SK S9V 1Y5. **Additional Information:** Pat Redden was a pillar for both Hillmond and Lloydminster communities and served for many years as a registered nurse at the Lloydminster Hospital. **Deadline for Receipt:** July 31.

3501 ■ MATANUSKA-SUSITNA COLLEGE

PO Box 2889
Palmer, AK 99645
Tel: (907)745-9774
Fax: (907)745-9711
E-mail: info@matsu.alaska.edu
Web Site: http://www.matsu.alaska.edu
To provide support to deserving students in Alaska who want to pursue an education in any campus of the University of Alaska.
Title of Award: Joan C. Yoder Memorial Nursing Scholarships **Area, Field, or Subject:** Nursing. **Level of Education for which Award is Granted:** Undergraduate **Funds Available:** $500.
Eligibility Requirements: Applicants must be full-time students majoring in nursing who have completed one clinical nursing course and is in good academic standing. **Application Requirements:** Applicant must complete the application forms available at the website; must attach a personal essay, two letters of recommendation, and current transcripts. **Deadline for Receipt:** February 15.

3502 ■ MATANUSKA-SUSITNA COLLEGE

PO Box 2889
Palmer, AK 99645
Tel: (907)745-9774
Fax: (907)745-9711
E-mail: info@matsu.alaska.edu
Web Site: http://www.matsu.alaska.edu
To provide support to deserving students in Alaska who want to pursue an education in any campus of the University of Alaska.
Title of Award: Yukon Delta Fisheries Development Association Scholarships **Area, Field, or Subject:** General studies. **Level of Education for which Award is Granted:** Undergraduate **Funds Available:** $500.
Eligibility Requirements: Applicants must be undergraduate or graduate students from Alakanuk, Emmonak, Grayling, Kotlik, Mountain Village, Nunam Iqua, Pitka's Point, St. Mary's, Pilot Station, Marshall, Russian Mission, Holy Cross, Anvik and Shageluk; must demonstrate a subsistence and/or commercial fishing relationship to the lower Yukon Delta region and maintain a minimum cumulative GPA of 2.5 or higher. **Application Requirements:** Applicant must complete the application forms available at the website; must attach a personal essay, two letters of recommendation, and current transcripts. **Deadline for Receipt:** February 15.

3503 ■ MICHIGAN LEAGUE FOR NURSING

2410 Woodlake Dr.
Okemos, MI 48864
Tel: (517)347-8091
Fax: (517)347-4096
E-mail: cstacy@mhc.org
Web Site: http://www.michleaguenursing.org
To promote professional growth and continuous quality improvement of educators for the nursing workforce; to enhance collaboration between nursing education and healthcare delivery systems; and to support recruitment for the nursing workforce.
Title of Award: Michigan League for Nursing Scholarships **Area, Field, or Subject:** Nursing. **Level of Education for which Award is Granted:** Undergraduate **Number Awarded:** 4. **Funds Available:** $500.
Eligibility Requirements: Applicants must be enrolled in a program leading to a Licensed Practical Nurse certification, an Associate Degree in Nursing, or a Bachelor of Science in Nursing. Applicants must have successfully completed at least one nursing course with a clinical component and must have received a "C" grade or better. **Application Requirements:** Applicants must submit an unfolded, completed application form in an 8 1/2 x 11 envelope. Must also submit an unfolded letter of endorsement and essay. **Deadline for Receipt:** March 15.

3504 ■ MICHIGAN NURSES FOUNDATION

2310 Jolly Oak Rd.
Okemos, MI 48864
Tel: (517)349-5640
Web Site: http://www.michigannursesfoundation.org
To assist deserving nursing students who want to pursue their studies.
Title of Award: Michigan Nurses Foundation Scholarships **Area, Field, or Subject:** Nursing. **Level of Education for which Award is Granted:** Undergraduate **Funds Available:** $500. **Duration:** One year.
Eligibility Requirements: Applicant must be a student currently enrolled in a Michigan college/school of nursing that grants a certificate or degree for practicing nursing; must be in good academic standing with demonstrated progress toward degree completion. **Application Requirements:** Applicant must complete the application form and application requirements before the deadline; send to: Scholarship Committee, Michigan Nurses Foundation, 2310 Jolly Oak Rd., Okemos, MI 48864. **Deadline for Receipt:** July 15.

3505 ■ NATIONAL AMERICAN ARAB NURSES ASSOCIATION

PO Box 43
Dearborn Heights, MI 48127
Tel: (313)680-5049
E-mail: info@n-aana.org
Web Site: http://www.n-aana.org
To provide financial assistance to applicants who are engaged in studying nursing at the associate degree, bachelor's degree, and master's degree or RN-BSN levels.
Title of Award: National American Arab Nurses Association Scholarships **Area, Field, or Subject:** Nursing. **Level of Education for which Award is Granted:** Undergraduate **Funds Available:** No specific amount.
Eligibility Requirements: Applicants must be U.S. residents enrolled in an accredited nursing program at the time of the application, should be pursuing a nursing program during the year for which the award is made. **Application Requirements:** Applicants must submit a copy of the most recent college or university transcript; two letters of recommendation from nursing faculty members that addresses the overall academic performance of the student and leadership activities; a one-page essay by the applicant describing eligibility why he/she is deserving for the award; a typewritten scholarship information sheet. **Deadline for Receipt:** June 20.

3506 ■ NATIONAL ASSOCIATION OF FINANCIAL AID AND ADMINISTRATORS

1101 Connecticut Ave. NW, Ste. 1100
Washington, DC 20036-4303
Tel: (202)785-0453
Fax: (202)785-1487
E-mail: web@nasfaa.org
Web Site: http://www.nasfaa.org
To provide certain costs of education in exchange for service at a health care facility with a critical shortage of nurses.
Title of Award: National Association of Financial Aid and Administrators Nursing Scholarships **Area, Field, or Subject:** Nursing. **Level of Education for which Award is Granted:** Undergraduate **Funds Available:** $1,233.
Eligibility Requirements: Applicants must be U.S. citizens or nationals. Applicants must be enrolled or accepted for enrollment as full- or part-time students in an accredited school of nursing in a professional registered nurse program. **Application Requirements:** Applicants must submit an application form; a verification of acceptance; an authorization to release information; a student aid report. **Deadline for Receipt:** June 6.

3507 ■ NATIONAL ASSOCIATION OF FINANCIAL AID AND ADMINISTRATORS

1101 Connecticut Ave. NW, Ste. 1100
Washington, DC 20036-4303
Tel: (202)785-0453
Fax: (202)785-1487
E-mail: web@nasfaa.org
Web Site: http://www.nasfaa.org
To provide financial aid to disadvantaged students.
Title of Award: National Association of Financial Aid and Administrators Scholarships for Disadvantaged Students **Area, Field, or Subject:** Nursing. **Level of Education for which Award is Granted:** Undergraduate **Funds Available:** No specific amount.

Eligibility Requirements: Applicants must be full-time students from disadvantaged backgrounds, enrolled in health professions and nursing programs. Applicants must be citizens or permanent residents of the United States. **Application Requirements:** Applicants must complete the application form.

3508 ■ NATIONAL ASSOCIATION OF PEDIATRIC NURSE PRACTITIONERS

20 Brace Rd., Ste. 200
Cherry Hill, NJ 08034-2634
Tel: (856)857-9700
Fax: (856)857-1600
E-mail: info@napnap.org
Web Site: http://www.napnap.org
To support the education of a nurse practitioner student who demonstrating the ability to articulate and follow through an innovative solution through clinical competence, academic achievement and involvement in political activism relating to a pediatric health care issue.
Title of Award: Elaine Gelman Scholarship Award **Area, Field, or Subject:** Nursing. **Level of Education for which Award is Granted:** Undergraduate **Funds Available:** $1,000.
Eligibility Requirements: Applicant must be a full or part time NP student enrolled in an accredited NP program with an expected graduation date of two years or less. **Application Requirements:** Applicants must submit completed Elaine Gelman Scholaship Award Application Form; personal statement (200 words or less) describing why the individual is competing for this award and specifically what goals would be accomplished if he/she receives the award; two letters of reference from a faculty member and professional colleague. **Deadline for Receipt:** June 30.

3509 ■ NATIONAL ASSOCIATION OF PEDIATRIC NURSE PRACTITIONERS

20 Brace Rd., Ste. 200
Cherry Hill, NJ 08034-2634
Tel: (856)857-9700
Fax: (856)857-1600
E-mail: info@napnap.org
Web Site: http://www.napnap.org
To provide financial assistance to students enrolled in pediatric nurse practitioner programs.
Title of Award: NAPNAP McNeil Annual Scholarships **Area, Field, or Subject:** Nursing. **Level of Education for which Award is Granted:** Undergraduate **Funds Available:** $2,000.
Eligibility Requirements: Applicant must be a registered nursing student who has completed at least 2 semesters or quarters as defined by the university; enrolled at a recognized PNP program; and have no previous formal pediatric nurse practitioner education. **Application Requirements:** Applicants must submit five copies of the application and accompanying needed materials to the NAPNAP Foundation. **Deadline for Receipt:** April 30.

3510 ■ NATIONAL BLACK NURSES ASSOCIATION

8630 Fenton St., Ste. 330
Silver Spring, MD 20910-3803
Tel: (301)589-3200
Free: 800-575-6298
Fax: (301)589-3223
E-mail: NBNA@erols.com
Web Site: http://www.nbna.org
To provide funding for continuing education.
Title of Award: National Black Nurses Association Scholarships **Area, Field, or Subject:** Nursing. **Level of Education for which Award is Granted:** Undergraduate **Funds Available:** $500 to $2,000.
Eligibility Requirements: Applicants must be member of NBNA and a local chapter currently enrolled in a nursing program (B.S.N., A.D., Diploma or L.P.N./L.V.N.) and in good scholastic standing at the time of application and must have at least one full year of school remaining. **Application Requirements:** Applicants must submit official transcript from an accredited school of nursing; two (2) page written essay; two letters of recommendation (one from applicant's school of nursing and one from the local chapter, or a nurse in the area if a local chapter does not exist); letters of recommendation and essay must be attached to the application;

additional items to accompany the application in support of the candidates eligibility and desirability may include documented evidence of: a. participation in student nurse activities and b. involvement in the African American Community, i.e., letters, news clippings, awards, certificates, etc.

3511 ■ NATIONAL SLOVAK SOCIETY OF THE USA
351 Valley Brook Rd.
McMurray, PA 15317-3337
Tel: (724)731-0094
Free: 800-488-1890
Fax: (724)731-0145
E-mail: dblazek@nsslife.org
Web Site: http://www.nsslife.org
To financially assist members in attending college or trade school.
Title of Award: National Slovak Society of the USA Scholarships **Area, Field, or Subject:** Nursing; Education, Vocational-technical **Level of Education for which Award is Granted:** Undergraduate **Number Awarded:** Varies. **Funds Available:** $400 per year. **Duration:** Four years.
Eligibility Requirements: Applicant must be a member of the National Slovak Society for a minimum of two years; completed high school; have a minimum of $10,000 of permanent life insurance in force, or $5000 annuity; accepted by a college or university; a junior college, nursing, trade, technical or business school (2 years); or other institutions approved by the NSS Board of Directors. **Application Requirements:** Applicants must submit completed applications along with latest transcript; proof of acceptance as a full-time student; a resume/biographical sketch with recent photograph; and proof of fraternal activities. **Deadline for Receipt:** May 1.

3512 ■ NATIONAL STUDENT NURSES' ASSOCIATION
45 Main St., Ste. 606
Brooklyn, NY 11201
Tel: (718)210-0705
Fax: (718)210-0710
E-mail: nsna@nsna.org
Web Site: http://www.nsna.org
To promote education in nursing.
Title of Award: The Foundation of the National Student Nurses' Association Scholarships **Area, Field, or Subject:** Nursing. **Level of Education for which Award is Granted:** Graduate, Undergraduate **Funds Available:** $1000-$2500.
Eligibility Requirements: Applicant must be U.S. citizen enrolled in a State-approved school of nursing or pre-nursing in associate degree, baccalaureate, diploma, generic doctorate, and generic master's programs. **Application Requirements:** Applicants must submit a copy of recent nursing school and college transcripts; proof of membership (for NSNA members); and a copy of RN license (if applicable). **Additional Information:** In Memory of Frances Tompkins. **Deadline for Receipt:** January 9. **Additional Information:** FNSNA at (718) 210-0705.

3513 ■ NORTHAMPTON COUNTY MEDICAL SOCIETY ALLIANCE
PO Box 21271
Lehigh Valley, PA 18002-1271
E-mail: jakat2255@aol.com
Web Site: http://www.ncmsa.org
To provide financial assistance to medical, nursing and physician assistant students.
Title of Award: Northampton County Medical Society Alliance Scholarships **Area, Field, or Subject:** Medical assisting; Nursing; Physics. **Level of Education for which Award is Granted:** Undergraduate **Funds Available:** $1000.
Eligibility Requirements: Applicant must be a U.S. citizen residing in Northampton County, Pennsylvania, or have a Bethlehem mailing address; and must be accepted or enrolled in a fully accredited institute of medicine. **Application Requirements:** Applicants must complete the application form and submit along with the required materials to the Chairperson, Scholarship/Loan Fund, Northampton County Medical Society Alliance, PO Box 21271, Lehigh Valley, PA 18002-1217. **Deadline for Receipt:** April 15. **Additional Information:** Angela S. Carlin at angie@thecarlins.net.

3514 ■ PARKERSBURG AREA COMMUNITY FOUNDATION
501 Avery St.
Parkersburg, WV 26101

Tel: (304)428-4438; (866)428-4438
Fax: (304)428-1200
E-mail: info@pacfwv.com
Web Site: http://www.pacfwv.com
To encourage graduating students to pursue their education.
Title of Award: St. Joseph's Hospital School of Nursing Alumnae Scholarships **Area, Field, or Subject:** Nursing. **Level of Education for which Award is Granted:** Undergraduate **Funds Available:** $500.
Eligibility Requirements: Applicant must be a resident of Wood, Ritchie, Wirt, Calhoun, Jackson, Gilmer, Roane, Pleasants, or Doddridge in WV or Washington County, OH; must be planning to attend an accredited college/nursing school to become a RN; must have a financial need and a minimum of 2.0 GPA; must be willing to make a written pledge attesting to their intention to return to the area covered by the service region of the Foundation to practice for at least two years. **Application Requirements:** Applicants must submit a cover sheet (3 pages) and application form (4 pages); a personal essay; a high school and/or post-secondary transcript; a letter of recommendation; a signed copy of the page of their or their parent's most recent tax return that indicates adjusted gross income; and a Student Aid Report showing estimated family contribution from FAFSA. Application form and other supporting documents must be sent to Our Community's Foundation, P.O Box 1762, Parkersburg, WV 26102. **Deadline for Receipt:** March 20.

3515 ■ PARKERSBURG AREA COMMUNITY FOUNDATION
501 Avery St.
Parkersburg, WV 26101
Tel: (304)428-4438; (866)428-4438
Fax: (304)428-1200
E-mail: info@pacfwv.com
Web Site: http://www.pacfwv.com
To provide support for qualified individuals intending to pursue their nursing degree.
Title of Award: West Virginia Nurses Association District No. 3 Scholarships **Area, Field, or Subject:** Nursing. **Level of Education for which Award is Granted:** Undergraduate **Funds Available:** $800.
Eligibility Requirements: Applicants must reside in Wood, Wirt, Calhoun, Jackson, or Roane Counties and must be pursuing an associate nursing degree as full-time students. **Application Requirements:** Applicants must submit a cover sheet (3 pages) and application form (4 pages); a personal essay; a high school and/or post-secondary transcript; a letter of recommendation; a signed copy of the page of their or their parent's most recent tax return that indicates adjusted gross income; and a Student Aid Report showing estimated family contribution from FAFSA. Application form and other supporting documents must be sent to Our Community's Foundation, P.O Box 1762, Parkersburg, WV 26102. **Deadline for Receipt:** March 20.

3516 ■ PEDIATRIC ENDOCRINOLOGY NURSING SOCIETY
7794 Grow Dr.
Pensacola, FL 32514
Tel: (850)484-5223; 877-936-7367
Fax: (850)484-8762
E-mail: pens@puetzamc.com
Web Site: http://www.pens.org
To promote the study and development of pediatric endocrine nursing.
Title of Award: Pediatric Endocrinology Nursing Society Academic Education Scholarships **Area, Field, or Subject:** Nursing, Pediatric. **Level of Education for which Award is Granted:** Undergraduate **Funds Available:** $1,000. **Duration:** One year.
Eligibility Requirements: Applicant must be an active PENS member for at least three years; currently employed in pediatric endocrine nursing; and pursuing a nursing degree. **Application Requirements:** Applicants must submit a completed application form; copy of RN License; curriculum vitae or resume; receipt of registration from college or university; transcript of records or acceptance letter. **Deadline for Receipt:** April and September.

3517 ■ PEDIATRIC ENDOCRINOLOGY NURSING SOCIETY
7794 Grow Dr.
Pensacola, FL 32514
Tel: (850)484-5223; 877-936-7367
Fax: (850)484-8762

E-mail: pens@puetzamc.com
Web Site: http://www.pens.org
To promote the study and development of pediatric endocrine nursing.
Title of Award: Pediatric Endocrinology Nursing Society Continuing Education Scholarships **Area, Field, or Subject:** Nursing, Pediatric. **Level of Education for which Award is Granted:** Undergraduate **Funds Available:** $1,000.
Eligibility Requirements: Applicant must be an active PENS member for at least three years. **Application Requirements:** Applicants must send a completed application form and a 2-4 page clinical exemplar. Send documents via email. **Deadline for Receipt:** January 15. **Additional Information:** Patricia Barlow, pmbarlow@puetzamc.com.

3518 ■ PINNACLE WEST CAPITAL CORPORATION
PO Box 53999
Phoenix, AZ 85072-3999
Tel: (602)250-1000
Free: 800-457-2983
Web Site: http://www.pinnaclewest.com
To provide financial assistance to qualified individuals who want to pursue their career.
Title of Award: APS/ASU Scholarships **Area, Field, or Subject:** Chemical engineering; Electrical engineering; Mechanical engineering; Civil engineering; Construction; Telecommunications systems; Accounting; Finance; Economics; Information science and technology; Education, Elementary; Education, Secondary; Special education; Nursing. **Level of Education for which Award is Granted:** Undergraduate **Number Awarded:** 10. **Funds Available:** $2,000. **Duration:** One year.
Eligibility Requirements: Applicant must be an Arizona resident; must have a cumulative GPA of at least 3.0; must demonstrate financial need. **Application Requirements:** Applicant must complete the application form available online and send it to ASU Scholarship Office, Arizona State University, PO Box 470412, Tempe, AZ 85287-0412. **Deadline for Receipt:** March 1. **Additional Information:** Louise Moskowitz at louise. moskowitz@aps.com.

3519 ■ REDLANDS COMMUNITY SCHOLARSHIP FOUNDATION
c/o Kathleen Venegas-Boge, Admin. Asst.
PO Box 1683
Redlands, CA 92373
Tel: (909)307-9892
Fax: (909)307-9892
Web Site: http://www.redlandsscholarships.org
To encourage educational pursuits among Redlands Unified School District graduates by providing educational assistance.
Title of Award: Liz Roberts Memorial Scholarships **Area, Field, or Subject:** Nursing. **Level of Education for which Award is Granted:** Undergraduate **Number Awarded:** 1. **Funds Available:** $500.
Eligibility Requirements: Applicant must be a graduating senior who will attend a training school, college, or university; must be pursuing a degree in nursing; must demonstrate financial need; must have maintained a 3.0 GPA; must have good citizenship; must have demonstrated community service; and must have a desire to help others. **Application Requirements:** Applicants must submit a completed application form together with the scantron sheet; cover sheet; student activity and community activity sheets; personal essay; and a copy of unofficial transcript (signed by the counselor). **Additional Information:** No electronic submissions of application will be accepted. Submit two printed copies of the application and use a No. 2 pencil on the scantron sheet. **Deadline for Receipt:** February 20.

3520 ■ THE SAN DIEGO FOUNDATION
2508 Historic Decatur Rd., Ste. 200
San Diego, CA 92106
Tel: (619)235-2300
Fax: (619)239-1710
E-mail: info@sdfoundation.org
Web Site: http://www.sdfoundation.org
To support the education of students from California.
Title of Award: Jean Wright-Elson Scholarships **Area, Field, or Subject:** Nursing. **Level of Education for which Award is Granted:** Graduate, Undergraduate **Number Awarded:** 2. **Funds Available:** $1,000.
Eligibility Requirements: Applicant must be a college student who completed two full academic years (60 semester units or 72 quarter units);

pursuing a career in nursing; have a minimum 3.0 GPA on a 4.0 scale; demonstrated financial need; a resident of San Diego County; attending an accredited two-year college or four-year university in the U.S. Scholarship is also open to a student pursuing Masters degree or Ph.D. in nursing. **Application Requirements:** Applicants must submit a completed Common Scholarship Application together with personal statement; two letters of recommendation on official letterhead (written within the last six months); official transcript in an official and sealed envelope; copy of most recent tax form (Form 1040-pages 1 & 2; Form 1040A-pages 1 & 2; Form 1040EZ-page 1); a letter of recommendation on official letterhead from a health-related employer or volunteer supervisor; and an essay (maximum one page, typed, double-spaced) emphasizing applicant's career goals in nursing. **Deadline for Receipt:** January 28. **Additional Information:** Arzo Mansury, Dir. Scholarships at 619-814-1343, or scholarships@sdfoundation.org.

3521 ■ SHORELINE COMMUNITY COLLEGE FOUNDATION
16101 Greenwood Ave. N, Ste. 1005
Shoreline, WA 98133-5696
Tel: (206)546-4755
Fax: (206)546-5826
E-mail: rmanchester@shoreline.edu
Web Site: http://www.shoreline.edu
To increase access and success of Shoreline Community College students; to assist promising students to continue their studies at an accredited four year college or university.
Title of Award: Mallet Nursing Scholarships **Area, Field, or Subject:** Nursing. **Level of Education for which Award is Granted:** Undergraduate **Funds Available:** No specific amount.
Eligibility Requirements: Applicants must be part-time or full-time students who are currently enrolled at Shoreline Community College. **Application Requirements:** Applicants must complete the application form.

3522 ■ SOUTHWEST FLORIDA COMMUNITY FOUNDATION
8260 College Pkwy., Ste. 101
Fort Myers, FL 33919
Tel: (239)274-5900
Fax: (239)274-5930
Web Site: http://www.floridacommunity.com
To fund a student studying nursing at Edison College or Florida Gulf Coast University.
Title of Award: Doctors IRA & UDAYA Nursing Scholarships **Area, Field, or Subject:** Nursing. **Level of Education for which Award is Granted:** Undergraduate **Funds Available:** No specific amount. **Duration:** One year.
Eligibility Requirements: Applicants must plan to attend or be attending Edison College or Florida Gulf Coast University; must be enrolled in a nursing program; and must demonstrate financial need. **Application Requirements:** Applicants must submit a student letter of interest, documentation of financial need, transcript, and letter of recommendation. **Deadline for Receipt:** February 15.

3523 ■ SOUTHWEST FLORIDA COMMUNITY FOUNDATION
8260 College Pkwy., Ste. 101
Fort Myers, FL 33919
Tel: (239)274-5900
Fax: (239)274-5930
Web Site: http://www.floridacommunity.com
To fund students studying Christian ministry/youth ministry, Christian counseling, nursing and medicine.
Title of Award: Dorris W. Frey Memorial Scholarships **Area, Field, or Subject:** Ministry; Christian education; Nursing; Medicine. **Level of Education for which Award is Granted:** Undergraduate **Funds Available:** Scholarship amount is determined by selection committee. **Duration:** One year.
Eligibility Requirements: Applicants must have graduated from a public or private high school in Charlotte, Collier, Glades, Hendry or Lee County; must pursue one of the above named degrees of study; must maintain satisfactory grades; must be committed to Jesus Christ and show commitment through action in ministering to others; and must have recognized ability and academic performance with standard measures of grades and appropriate test scores. **Application Requirements:** Applicants must submit an essay of future commitment, transcript, and references. **Deadline for Receipt:** February 15.

3524 ■ SOUTHWEST FLORIDA COMMUNITY FOUNDATION

8260 College Pkwy., Ste. 101
Fort Myers, FL 33919
Tel: (239)274-5900
Fax: (239)274-5930
Web Site: http://www.floridacommunity.com
To fund scholarships for female students pursuing a career in technical studies, court reporting, computer training or nursing.
Title of Award: Faye Lynn Roberts Educational Scholarships **Area, Field, or Subject:** Technical training; Computer and information sciences; Nursing. **Level of Education for which Award is Granted:** Undergraduate **Funds Available:** $5,000. **Duration:** One year.
Eligibility Requirements: Applicants must be 21 years of age or older; must be residents of Lee County; and must demonstrate financial need. **Application Requirements:** Application forms are available online. Applicants must submit a personal essay, financial need documentation, high school/college transcript and letter of recommendation. **Deadline for Receipt:** March 20.

3525 ■ SOUTHWEST FLORIDA COMMUNITY FOUNDATION

8260 College Pkwy., Ste. 101
Fort Myers, FL 33919
Tel: (239)274-5900
Fax: (239)274-5930
Web Site: http://www.floridacommunity.com
To endow nursing scholarships for members or children of members of St. Andrew Catholic Church in Cape Coral.
Title of Award: Anne Sturrock Nursing Scholarships **Area, Field, or Subject:** Nursing. **Level of Education for which Award is Granted:** Undergraduate **Funds Available:** Scholarship award amount is determined by committee. **Duration:** One year.
Eligibility Requirements: Applicant must be a member or a child of a member of St. Andrew Catholic Church; must pursue a career in nursing; and must demonstrate financial need. **Application Requirements:** Application forms are available online. Applicants must submit a letter of interest, letter of recommendation from pastor of St. Andrew, transcript and financial need documentation. **Deadline for Receipt:** February 15.

3526 ■ SOUTHWEST FLORIDA COMMUNITY FOUNDATION

8260 College Pkwy., Ste. 101
Fort Myers, FL 33919
Tel: (239)274-5900
Fax: (239)274-5930
Web Site: http://www.floridacommunity.com
To fund students pursuing degrees in teaching, nursing, paramedic training or emergency medical technician training.
Title of Award: John I. and Madeleine R. Taeni Scholarships **Area, Field, or Subject:** Teaching; Nursing; Paramedics; Emergency and disaster services. **Level of Education for which Award is Granted:** Undergraduate **Funds Available:** $1,000.
Eligibility Requirements: Applicant must be a resident of Charlotte, Collier, Glades, Hendry or Lee County; must be highly motivated; must pursue teaching, nursing paramedic training, or emergency medical technician training; and must have graduated high school at least two years ago. **Application Requirements:** Application forms are available online. Applicants must submit a letter of interest, letter of recommendation, and transcript. **Deadline for Receipt:** March 20.

3527 ■ STARK COMMUNITY FOUNDATION

400 Market Ave. N, Ste. 200
Canton, OH 44702-2107
Tel: (330)454-3426
Fax: (330)454-5855
Web Site: http://www.starkcommunityfoundation.org
To provide scholarship assistance to qualified individuals who want to pursue their studies.
Title of Award: Joan Blend Scholarship Fund **Area, Field, or Subject:** Nursing. **Level of Education for which Award is Granted:** Undergraduate **Funds Available:** No specific amount. **Duration:** One year.
Eligibility Requirements: Applicants must be attending or planning to attend university or nursing school offering a Registered Nursing Degree; must have GPA of 2.5 or higher; must demonstrate financial need. **Application Requirements:** Applicants must complete and submit the ap-

plication form and other supporting documents to Mr. Dan Blend, 1684 Markley St. NW N. Canton, OH 44720. **Deadline for Receipt:** April 15.

3528 ■ STARK COMMUNITY FOUNDATION

400 Market Ave. N, Ste. 200
Canton, OH 44702-2107
Tel: (330)454-3426
Fax: (330)454-5855
Web Site: http://www.starkcommunityfoundation.org
To provide scholarship assistance to qualified individuals who want to pursue their studies.
Title of Award: Virginia C. Jack and Ralph L. Jack Scholarships **Area, Field, or Subject:** Vocational-technical education; Nursing. **Level of Education for which Award is Granted:** Undergraduate **Funds Available:** $2,000. **Duration:** One year.
Eligibility Requirements: Applicants must be Stark County residents; must be admitted to technical school, college or university, or school of nursing; must be full or part time students; must be traditional or non-traditional students; must have 2.50 or higher GPA on a 4.0 scale. **Application Requirements:** Applicants must submit two letters of recommendation and essay. Application form and other supporting documents must be sent to Stark Community Foundation, 400 Market Ave. N, Ste. 200, Canton, OH 44702. **Deadline for Receipt:** April 1.

3529 ■ STARK COMMUNITY FOUNDATION

400 Market Ave. N, Ste. 200
Canton, OH 44702-2107
Tel: (330)454-3426
Fax: (330)454-5855
Web Site: http://www.starkcommunityfoundation.org
To provide scholarship assistance to qualified individuals who want to pursue their studies.
Title of Award: Lake Dollars for Scholars Endowment Fund **Area, Field, or Subject:** Education, Vocational-technical; Nursing. **Level of Education for which Award is Granted:** Undergraduate **Funds Available:** No specific amount. **Duration:** One year.
Eligibility Requirements: Applicants must be graduating seniors residing within the boundaries of the Lake Local District, Lake Township, and Stark County, OH; must have been accepted into a two-year or four-year college or university, nursing school, or other post high school vocational education program; must meet the requirements of the application form provided by Lake Dollars For Scholars. **Application Requirements:** Applicants must submit completed application form and are advised to contact the Lake High School Guidance Office at 330877-4285. **Deadline for Receipt:** March 20.

3530 ■ STARK COMMUNITY FOUNDATION

400 Market Ave. N, Ste. 200
Canton, OH 44702-2107
Tel: (330)454-3426
Fax: (330)454-5855
Web Site: http://www.starkcommunityfoundation.org
To provide scholarship assistance to qualified individuals who want to pursue their studies.
Title of Award: Fizz and Dutch Miller Scholarship Fund **Area, Field, or Subject:** Vocational-technical education; Nursing. **Level of Education for which Award is Granted:** Undergraduate **Funds Available:** No specific amount. **Duration:** One year.
Eligibility Requirements: Applicants must be graduates of Strasburg High School or current residents of Strasburg; must have been admitted to and enrolled in a college, university, technical school, vocational school or nursing school; must demonstrate participation in school and community activities; must demonstrate good citizenship; must demonstrate financial assistance to pursue the best level of education. **Application Requirements:** Applicants must submit two letters of reference. Application form and other supporting documents must be sent to The Strasburg High School Guidance Office. **Deadline for Receipt:** May 10.

3531 ■ STEUBEN COUNTY COMMUNITY FOUNDATION

1701 N Wayne St.
Angola, IN 46703
Tel: (260)665-6656
Fax: (260)665-8420

Web Site: http://www.steubenfoundation.org
To provide financial support to those students in health-related fields.
Title of Award: Mandel & Lauretta Abrahamer Scholarships **Area, Field, or Subject:** Nursing. **Level of Education for which Award is Granted:** Undergraduate **Funds Available:** No specific amount.
Eligibility Requirements: Applicants must be residents of Steuben County; must be entering in a Nursing School; must have a cumulative 3.0 GPA; must demonstrate financial need. **Application Requirements:** Applicants must submit the following: copy of school transcripts; any supporting statement from former teachers or supervisors of any paid or volunteer work in your chosen field will be considered; an essay answering the question, "What characteristics are necessary to be a successful nurse?". **Deadline for Receipt:** March 15. **Additional Information:** Steuben County Community Foundation at the above address.

3532 ■ STEUBEN COUNTY COMMUNITY FOUNDATION
1701 N Wayne St.
Angola, IN 46703
Tel: (260)665-6656
Fax: (260)665-8420
Web Site: http://www.steubenfoundation.org
To provide financial assistance to those students who will be continuing their education through an accredited nursing program at any Indiana institution of higher education.
Title of Award: Don and Eileen Fulton Nursing Scholarships **Area, Field, or Subject:** Nursing. **Level of Education for which Award is Granted:** Undergraduate **Funds Available:** No specific amount.
Eligibility Requirements: Applicants must be graduating seniors or have graduated from a Steuben County High School; must provide two references, preferably demonstrating nursing experience. **Application Requirements:** Applicants must check the website for the application process and required materials. **Deadline for Receipt:** March 15. **Additional Information:** Steuben County Community Foundation at the above address.

3533 ■ STEUBEN COUNTY COMMUNITY FOUNDATION
1701 N Wayne St.
Angola, IN 46703
Tel: (260)665-6656
Fax: (260)665-8420
Web Site: http://www.steubenfoundation.org
To provide financial support to those students who are pursuing a career in Nursing.
Title of Award: Helen R. Greenamyer Memorial Scholarships **Area, Field, or Subject:** Nursing. **Level of Education for which Award is Granted:** Undergraduate **Funds Available:** No specific amount.
Eligibility Requirements: Applicants must be graduates of any Steuben County High School, including Prairie Heights, Fremont, Hamilton or MSD of Steuben County; must be pursuing a career in Nursing. **Application Requirements:** Applicants must check the website for the application process and required materials. **Deadline for Receipt:** March 15. **Additional Information:** Steuben County Community Foundation at the above address.

3534 ■ STRAIGHTFORWARD MEDIA
508 7th St., Ste 202
Rapid City, SD 57701
Tel: (605)348-3042
Fax: (605)348-3043
E-mail: info@straightforwardmedia.com
Web Site: http://www.straightforwardmedia.com
To financially assist students in their educational pursuits.
Title of Award: StraightForward Media's Nursing School Scholarships **Area, Field, or Subject:** Nursing. **Level of Education for which Award is Granted:** Undergraduate **Funds Available:** $500.
Eligibility Requirements: Applicant must be a nursing student. **Application Requirements:** Applicants must complete the scholarship application online. **Additional Information:** Awards are given four times a year. **Deadline for Receipt:** January, April, July, October.

3535 ■ TANANA VALLEY CAMPUS
604 Barnette St.
Fairbanks, AK 99701

Tel: (907)455-2800; 877-882-8827
Web Site: http://www.tvc.uaf.edu
To provide financial support for qualified students intending to pursue their nursing education.
Title of Award: Mary Ghezzi Nursing Scholarships **Area, Field, or Subject:** Nursing. **Level of Education for which Award is Granted:** Undergraduate **Funds Available:** $2,000. **Duration:** One year.
Eligibility Requirements: Applicants must be enrolled in Tahana Valley Campus; must be students who want to pursue their career in Nursing. **Application Requirements:** Applicants are advised to contact Allied Health at 455-2822 for further information about the scholarship application.

3536 ■ TANANA VALLEY CAMPUS
604 Barnette St.
Fairbanks, AK 99701
Tel: (907)455-2800; 877-882-8827
Web Site: http://www.tvc.uaf.edu
To provide support for deserving students intending to pursue their degree in pre-medicine or nursing.
Title of Award: Anna Doris Southall Nursing Scholarships **Area, Field, or Subject:** Nursing. **Level of Education for which Award is Granted:** Undergraduate **Funds Available:** $1,000. **Duration:** One year.
Eligibility Requirements: Applicants must be second year students enrolled in a pre-medicine or nursing program. **Application Requirements:** The applicants are advised to contact Allied Health at 455-2822 for further scholarship information and instructions.

3537 ■ UNIVERSITY OF ALASKA ANCHORAGE
3211 Providence Dr.
Anchorage, AK 99508
Tel: (907)786-1800
Web Site: http://www.uaa.alaska.edu
To provide scholarships in the name of the Alaska Kidney Foundation to prepare new nurses to provide safe and effective care to individuals experiencing chronic kidney disease in Alaska.
Title of Award: UAA Alaska Kidney Foundation Scholarships **Area, Field, or Subject:** Nursing. **Level of Education for which Award is Granted:** Graduate, Undergraduate **Number Awarded:** 19. **Funds Available:** $1,000-$2,400. **Duration:** One year.
Eligibility Requirements: Applicants must have been a resident of Alaska for three years prior to the start of the semester the award is given; must be formally admitted to a nursing degree program that leads to RN licensure; must plan on being enrolled at least part-time (six credits); must have completed one clinical nursing course by the start of the semester the award is given, unless a new student. Applicants who have successfully completed a clinical nursing course must have a minimum cumulative GPA of 2.5 and nursing course minimum cumulative GPA of 2.0. Applicants who are new students beginning clinical studies and have not completed a clinical nursing course must have a minimum cumulative GPA of 2.8. **Application Requirements:** Applicants must submit a brief essay (250 words max) describing the following: (1) A career plan that includes working with a clientele that could result in working with individuals with chronic or acute kidney disease or with clients at risk for the development of chronic renal disease; (2) A plan to remain in practice in Alaska. Applicants must complete the electronic scholarship application available online at www.uaa.alaska.edu/scholarships/kidney.cfm. **Deadline for Receipt:** February 15.

3538 ■ UNIVERSITY OF ALASKA ANCHORAGE
3211 Providence Dr.
Anchorage, AK 99508
Tel: (907)786-1800
Web Site: http://www.uaa.alaska.edu
To provide financial assistance for tuition and other educational expenses to students currently enrolled in a nursing degree program through the Recruitment and Retention of Alaska Natives into Nursing at the UAA.
Title of Award: UAA RRANN Program Scholarships **Area, Field, or Subject:** Nursing. **Level of Education for which Award is Granted:** Undergraduate **Number Awarded:** 18. **Funds Available:** $639-$1,500. **Duration:** One year.
Eligibility Requirements: Applicants must be in good academic standing with a minimum cumulative GPA of 2.0; must be formally admitted to a

degree program within the School of Nursing through the RRANN program; may be an incoming or continuing student at the UAA; must be an Alaskan resident; must be enrolled in the semester for which the award is to be in effect. **Application Requirements:** Applicants must complete the electronic scholarship application available online at www.uaa.alaska.edu/scholarships/rrann.cfm. **Deadline for Receipt:** February 15.

3539 ■ UNIVERSITY OF TORONTO
315 Bloor St. W
Toronto, ON, Canada M5S 1A3
Tel: (416)978-2011
E-mail: information.commonsats@utoronto.ca
Web Site: http://www.utoronto.ca
To support students with their educational pursuits.
Title of Award: City of Toronto Queen Elizabeth II Sesquicentennial Scholarships in Community Health Nursing (Undergraduate) **Area, Field, or Subject:** Nursing. **Level of Education for which Award is Granted:** Undergraduate **Number Awarded:** 1. **Funds Available:** $5000.
Eligibility Requirements: Applicant must be undergraduate student completing the first year of the second-entry two year BScN program. **Application Requirements:** Applicants must submit a completed application form along with the required materials and information. **Deadline for Receipt:** June 30. **Additional Information:** osap.staff@utoronto.ca.

3540 ■ WASHINGTON HIGHER EDUCATION COORDINATING BOARD
PO Box 43430
Olympia, WA 98504-3430
Tel: (360)753-7800
E-mail: info@hecb.wa.gov
Web Site: http://www.hecb.wa.gov
To attract and retain health professionals to serve in critical shortage areas in Washington state.
Title of Award: Washington Higher Education Coordinating Board Health Professional Scholarships **Area, Field, or Subject:** Physics; Nursing; Midwifery; Pharmacy; Dentistry. **Level of Education for which Award is Granted:** Undergraduate **Funds Available:** Varies by educational program.
Eligibility Requirements: Applicant must be a student training to become a primary care health professional in an eligible profession; a U.S. citizen; have completed all prerequisite course work; not be in default on any educational loans; and must sign a Promissory Note agreeing to serve for a minimum of three years in a designated shortage area in Washington state or pay back funds with double penalty plus interest. **Application Requirements:** Applicants must submit a completed application form along with the required materials and information. **Additional Information:** Participants must agree, in return for the assistance, to provide primary care health care in rural or underserved urban areas with designated shortages for a minimum of three years. **Deadline for Receipt:** April 30.

3541 ■ WINSTON-SALEM FOUNDATION
860 W Fifth St.
Winston-Salem, NC 27101-2506
Tel: (336)725-2382
Fax: (336)727-0581
E-mail: info@wsfoundation.org
Web Site: http://www.wsfoundation.org
Provides scholarships for N.C. residents pursuing two and four-year Nursing degrees at accredited N.C. colleges.
Title of Award: Virginia Elizabeth and Alma Vane Taylor Student Nurse Scholarships **Area, Field, or Subject:** Nursing. **Level of Education for which Award is Granted:** Undergraduate **Funds Available:** $1,200.
Eligibility Requirements: Applicants must: be accepted into an accredited North Carolina school of nursing program, as verified by an acceptance letter; have a family adjusted gross income that does not exceed $80,000; have a high school/college cumulative GPA of at least 2.5. Preference will be given to those seeking first time associate or baccalaureate degrees; those with masters degrees in any area will be ineligible to apply. **Application Requirements:** The Winston-Salem Foundation's General Financial Aid Application will be used to apply for this scholarship. The General Financial Aid Application is available online or you may request an application to the Foundation's Student Aid Com-

mittee. **Deadline for Receipt:** March 31. **Additional Information:** WSF Student Aid Department, 336-714-3445.

3542 ■ WINSTON-SALEM FOUNDATION
860 W Fifth St.
Winston-Salem, NC 27101-2506
Tel: (336)725-2382
Fax: (336)727-0581
E-mail: info@wsfoundation.org
Web Site: http://www.wsfoundation.org
To provide educational need-based scholarships for Forsyth County residents seeking nursing degrees at accredited two year and four year colleges and who will, upon completing a degree, practice nursing in Forsyth County, N.C. Preference will be given to those seeking first-time associate or baccalaureate nursing degree.
Title of Award: Forsyth County Nursing Scholarships **Area, Field, or Subject:** Nursing. **Level of Education for which Award is Granted:** Undergraduate **Funds Available:** No specific amount.
Eligibility Requirements: Applicants must have a family adjusted gross income within the table guidelines (table is based on up to 330% above the federal poverty level); have achieved a current cumulative grade point average of at least 2.0; be a US citizen; be a child of a living or deceased Vietnam veteran; be a Forsyth County N.C. resident; and provide a letter of acceptance into a nursing program. **Application Requirements:** The following items are required to complete the application process: Submittal of completed application and signed signature page; Signed copy of parents'/guardians'/family's previous year's 1040, 1040A, or 1040EZ income tax return (for dependent students); Signed copy of applicant's previous year's tax return; Official high school grade transcript through at least 1st semester of the 12th grade or college grade transcript, whichever is the most recent (request from the school's Registrar and forward to the Foundation); Copy of the Student Aid Report if applicant has applied for federal aid; Copy of the financial aid award letter. Please submit the application on-line and follow with additional items as soon as you receive them. **Deadline for Receipt:** March 31. **Additional Information:** WSF Student Aid Department, 336-714-3445.

3543 ■ WINSTON-SALEM FOUNDATION
860 W Fifth St.
Winston-Salem, NC 27101-2506
Tel: (336)725-2382
Fax: (336)727-0581
E-mail: info@wsfoundation.org
Web Site: http://www.wsfoundation.org
To provide educational need-based scholarships for Forsyth County residents seeking nursing degrees at Forsyth Technical Community College or Winston-Salem State University.
Title of Award: Orthopaedic Specialists Nursing Scholarships **Area, Field, or Subject:** Nursing. **Level of Education for which Award is Granted:** Undergraduate **Funds Available:** No specific amount.
Eligibility Requirements: Applicants must be pursuing a first-time associate degree or a bachelors degree in nursing. Must provide a copy of letter of admission to the nursing program at FTCC or WSSU (students ineligible until accepted into nursing program); demonstration of academic promise. Must have achieved 3.0 cumulative, unweighted GPA for graduating high school senior or 2.6 cumulative GPA as a college student; demonstrate financial need based on 300% of federal poverty guidelines. Scholarship recipients are expected to make themselves available for scholarship presentation events. **Application Requirements:** Scholarship application may be obtained online and submitted after January 1 each year for the next academic year. In addition to the application, the following items are required for first-time applicants: signed copy of parent/guardian federal income tax return (for dependent students); signed copy of applicant's federal income tax return; current official transcript of academic record (obtain from school Registrar); copy of Student Aid Report if student applied for federal aid; copy of financial aid notice from college if student applied for federal aid. **Deadline for Receipt:** March 31. **Additional Information:** Edna Barker, 336-714-3445.

3544 ■ WOUND, OSTOMY AND CONTINENCE NURSES SOCIETY
15000 Commerce Pkwy., Ste. C
Mount Laurel, NJ 08054
888-224-9626

Web Site: http://www.wocn.org
To support individuals seeking education in wound, ostomy and continence nursing specialties.
Title of Award: WOCN Accredited Nursing Education Scholarships **Area, Field, or Subject:** Nursing. **Level of Education for which Award is Granted:** Graduate, Undergraduate **Funds Available:** No specific amount.
Eligibility Requirements: Applicants must be pursuing an education in wound, ostomy and continence nursing care; accepted in a WOCN-accredited WOC Educational Program. **Application Requirements:** Application form is available at the website. **Deadline for Receipt:** November and May 1.

3545 ■ WOUND, OSTOMY AND CONTINENCE NURSES SOCIETY
15000 Commerce Pkwy., Ste. C
Mount Laurel, NJ 08054
888-224-9626
Web Site: http://www.wocn.org
To support individual seeking education in wound, ostomy and continence nursing specialties.
Title of Award: WOCN Advanced Education Scholarships **Area, Field, or Subject:** Nursing. **Level of Education for which Award is Granted:** Doctorate, Graduate, Undergraduate **Funds Available:** No specific amount.
Eligibility Requirements: Applicant must be seeking a baccalaureate, master's or doctoral degree or NP certificate; a member of WOCN; employed (for at least three years) as a wound, ostomy or continence nurse; accepted in an NLN-accredited nursing program or other accredited college/university program for non-nursing degree. **Application Requirements:** Application form is available at the website. **Deadline for Receipt:** November and May 1.

3546 ■ XAVIER UNIVERSITY
3800 Victory Pky.
Cincinnati, OH 45207
Tel: (513)745-3000
Free: 800-344-GOXU
Web Site: http://www.xavier.edu
To financially support students with their education.
Title of Award: Catholic Healthcare Partners Scholarships **Area, Field, or Subject:** Nursing. **Level of Education for which Award is Granted:** Undergraduate **Funds Available:** $10,000.
Eligibility Requirements: Applicant must be an incoming student majoring in nursing. **Application Requirements:** Applicants must apply for financial aid by completing the FAFSA and submit a completed application form. **Additional Information:** In partnership with The Catholic Healthcare Partners. **Deadline for Receipt:** FAFSA: February 15; Application: March 1.

Nutrition

3547 ■ AMERICAN SCHOOL HEALTH ASSOCIATION
7263 State Rte. 43
Kent, OH 44240
Tel: (330)678-1601
Fax: (330)678-4526
E-mail: asha@ashaweb.org
Web Site: http://www.ashaweb.org
To provide financial assistance to students concentrating on school health education, school nursing, and pediatric or adolescent medicine or dentistry.
Title of Award: ASHA Scholarships **Area, Field, or Subject:** Health education; Nursing; Pediatric medicine; Medicine; Dentistry; Nutrition; Counseling/Guidance. **Level of Education for which Award is Granted:** Graduate, Undergraduate **Number Awarded:** 3. **Funds Available:** $500 and a complimentary registration to ASHA's annual school health conference and a one-year ASHA membership. **Duration:** One year.
Eligibility Requirements: Applicants must be a junior, senior or graduate student; enrolled full-time at institution of higher education; have 3.0 GPA on a 4.0 scale; have a major related to School Health Education or School Nursing or Pediatric or Adolescent Medicine or Dentistry or other school health specializations (nutrition, counseling, etc.); not a previous recipient

of this award. **Application Requirements:** Applicants must send one original and nine copies of the completed application form (application form available online); current resume; transcript; one page personal statement; three letters of recommendation. **Deadline for Receipt:** April 4. **Additional Information:** Pamela Dorazio Dean, pdean@ashaweb.org.

3548 ■ AMERICAN SCHOOL HEALTH ASSOCIATION
7263 State Rte. 43
Kent, OH 44240
Tel: (330)678-1601
Fax: (330)678-4526
E-mail: asha@ashaweb.org
Web Site: http://www.ashaweb.org
To provide financial assistance for research in areas related to the mission of ASHA.
Title of Award: ASHA Student Research Grants **Area, Field, or Subject:** Health education; Nursing; Pediatric medicine; Medicine; Dentistry; Nutrition; Counseling/Guidance. **Level of Education for which Award is Granted:** Graduate, Undergraduate **Funds Available:** No specific amount.
Eligibility Requirements: Applicants must be student members of ASHA. **Application Requirements:** Applicants must send one original and five copies of a proposal which includes a cover sheet; a narrative (title-problem, review of related literature, methodology, data analyst, institution IRB protocol documented); and a budget. Proposal should have one inch margins, doubled spaced and a font size not smaller than 12. Forward the original and 5 copies to: ASHA Student Research Grants, PO Box 708, Kent, OH 44240. **Deadline for Receipt:** April 4. **Additional Information:** Pamela Dorazio, pdean@ashaweb.org, 330-678-1601.

3549 ■ FIRST COMMUNITY FOUNDATION OF PENNSYLVANIA, WILLIAMSPORT-LYCOMING
330 Pine St., Suite 401
Williamsport, PA 17701
Tel: (570)321-1500; (866)901-2372
Fax: (570)321-6434
E-mail: fcfpa@fcfpa.org
Web Site: http://www.wlfoundation.org
To provide academic support for Danville Area High School seniors who have been accepted into a full-time undergraduate program at an accredited institution of higher education and who are entering a health-related field.
Title of Award: Eleanor McWilliams Burke Fund **Area, Field, or Subject:** Medicine; Nursing; Nutrition; Pharmacy; or Physical therapy. **Level of Education for which Award is Granted:** Undergraduate **Funds Available:** No specific amount.
Eligibility Requirements: Applicants must be entering a health related field. **Application Requirements:** Applicants may request an application from the Guidance Counselor of Danville Area School District. **Additional Information:** Gary Grozier, Guidance Counselor of Danville Area School District, 600 Walnut St., Danvilled, PA 17821; 570-271-3268 ext. 2006; ggrozier@danville.k12.pa.us.

3550 ■ INTERNATIONAL FOODSERVICE EDITORIAL COUNCIL
PO Box 491
Hyde Park, NY 12538
Tel: (845)229-6973
Fax: (845)229-6993
E-mail: info@ifeconline.com
Web Site: http://www.ifec-is-us.com
To increase awareness and understanding of the career opportunities available in the field of food service communications and to encourage entry of qualified professionals in the field.
Title of Award: International Foodservice Editorial Council Scholarships **Area, Field, or Subject:** Culinary arts; Communications; Food service careers; Food science and technology; Photography; Hotel, institutional, and restaurant management; Nutrition; Dietetics; Journalism; Public relations; Graphic art and design. **Level of Education for which Award is Granted:** Graduate, Undergraduate **Number Awarded:** Varies. **Funds Available:** $3,750.
Eligibility Requirements: Applicants must be full-time students in a U.S. accredited post-secondary educational institution working towards an associate's, bachelor's or master's degree. **Application Requirements:** Ap-

plicants must submit a complete application together with academic transcript and two letters of recommendation. Application requirements must be typewritten and submitted using U.S. Postal Service's Return Receipt Service. **Deadline for Receipt:** March 15.

3551 ■ MIDWEST DAIRY ASSOCIATION
2015 Rice St.
St. Paul, MN 55113
800-642-3895
Web Site: http://www.midwestdairy.com
To provide financial assistance to those deserving students.
Title of Award: North Dakota Division Scholarships **Area, Field, or Subject:** Food Nutrition; Education. **Level of Education for which Award is Granted:** Undergraduate **Number Awarded:** 2. **Funds Available:** $1,000.
Eligibility Requirements: Applicants must be juniors or non-graduating seniors majoring in food nutrition, family and consumer science education or education. **Application Requirements:** Applicants must check the available website for the required materials. **Additional Information:** For more information, contact: Char Heer, Industry Relations Manager at 701-782-4154

3552 ■ NATIONAL POULTRY AND FOOD DISTRIBUTORS ASSOCIATION
958 McEver Rd. Ext., Unit B-8
Gainesville, GA 30504
Tel: (770)535-9901; 877-845-1545
Fax: (770)535-7385
E-mail: info@npfda.org
Web Site: http://www.npfda.org
To help build "people resources" for the poultry and food industries.
Title of Award: National Poultry and Food Distributors Association Scholarships **Area, Field, or Subject:** Poultry Science; Food science and technology; Dietetics; Agribusiness; Agricultural economics; Agriculture, Economic aspects; Agricultural sciences. **Level of Education for which Award is Granted:** Undergraduate **Number Awarded:** 5. Cash prizes will go to the top four; the fifth student chosen will be the alternate student should one of the award recipients not use all of his/her funds (early graduation). **Funds Available:** $2,000. **Duration:** Entire length of study.
Eligibility Requirements: Applicant must be a full time junior or senior at a U.S. institution for the upcoming award year, and must be pursuing a poultry or related agricultural degree. **Application Requirements:** Applicant must submit an application form; official transcript; letter of recommendation from his/her Dean; and a one-page letter describing his/her goals and aspirations. **Additional Information:** This scholarship foundation was established in 1979. **Deadline for Receipt:** May 31.

3553 ■ PHI UPSILON OMICRON
PO Box 329
Fairmont, WV 26555
Tel: (304)368-0612
E-mail: info@phiu.org
Web Site: http://www.phiu.org
To promote education in advance family and consumer sciences and related areas.
Title of Award: Nell Bryant Robinson Scholarships **Area, Field, or Subject:** Family planning; Consumer affairs; Nutrition. **Level of Education for which Award is Granted:** Undergraduate **Funds Available:** No specific amount.
Eligibility Requirements: Applicant must be a Phi U member; pursuing a baccalaureate degree in family and consumer sciences or one of its related areas. **Application Requirements:** Applicants must submit an application; transcripts; recommendations. Application documents must be assembled in order, clipped together with a paper clip and placed in a 10" x 13" envelope. Enclose a self-addressed stamped postcard. **Additional Information:** Applicants may apply for more than one fellowship. **Deadline for Receipt:** February 1.

3554 ■ PHI UPSILON OMICRON
PO Box 329
Fairmont, WV 26555
Tel: (304)368-0612
E-mail: info@phiu.org

Web Site: http://www.phiu.org
To promote education in advance family and consumer sciences and related areas.
Title of Award: Margaret Jerome Sampson Scholarships **Area, Field, or Subject:** Family planning; Consumer affairs; Nutrition. **Level of Education for which Award is Granted:** Undergraduate **Number Awarded:** 4. **Funds Available:** $3000.
Eligibility Requirements: Applicant must be a Phi U member; enrolled full-time in a baccalaureate degree program in family and consumer sciences or a related area. **Application Requirements:** Applicants must submit an application; transcripts; recommendations (one must be from the Phi U chapter advisor). Application documents must be assembled in order, clipped together with a paper clip and placed in a 10" x 13" envelope. Enclose a self-addressed stamped postcard, a financial statement and one double-spaced typewritten page about the reasons for needing an additional financial assistance. **Additional Information:** Applicants may apply for more than one fellowship. **Deadline for Receipt:** February 1.

3555 ■ THE SAN DIEGO FOUNDATION
2508 Historic Decatur Rd., Ste. 200
San Diego, CA 92106
Tel: (619)235-2300
Fax: (619)239-1710
E-mail: info@sdfoundation.org
Web Site: http://www.sdfoundation.org
To support the education of students from California.
Title of Award: California Association of Family and Consumer Sciences (CAFCS)-San Diego Chapter Scholarships **Area, Field, or Subject:** Food science and technology; Diabetes; Nutrition; Food service careers; Home Economics; Fashion design; Textile science; Housing; Management. **Level of Education for which Award is Granted:** Graduate, Undergraduate **Number Awarded:** To be determined. **Funds Available:** To be determined.
Eligibility Requirements: Applicant must be a graduating high school senior, current college student, or graduate student majoring in Food Sciences; Dietetics; Nutrition; Food Services; Hospitality; Human, Child and Family Development; Apparel, Fashion and Textile Services; Housing and Interiors; Consumer Economics; Management and Resources; or Family and Consumer Science Education. Student must have a minimum 2.50 GPA on a 4.0 scale; planning to attend an accredited two-year college, four-year university, or licensed trade-vocational school in the U.S. Undergraduate student must be enrolled in school full-time (12 units per semester or 9 per quarter). Graduate student may be enrolled full-time or part-time with awards allocated appropriately based upon enrollment units. **Application Requirements:** Applicants must submit a completed Common Scholarship Application together with personal statement; two letters of recommendation on official letterhead (written within the last six months); official transcript in an official and sealed envelope; copy of 2006 or most recent tax form (Form 1040-pages 1 & 2; Form 1040A-pages 1 & 2; Form 1040EZ -page 1); and a letter of recommendation on official letterhead from an instructor or professional indicating the applicant's interest in pursing one of the above listed fields. **Deadline for Receipt:** January 28. **Additional Information:** Arzo Mansury, Dir. Scholarships at 619-814-1343, or scholarships@sdfoundation.org.

3556 ■ STARK COMMUNITY FOUNDATION
400 Market Ave. N, Ste. 200
Canton, OH 44702-2107
Tel: (330)454-3426
Fax: (330)454-5855
Web Site: http://www.starkcommunityfoundation.org
To provide scholarship assistance to qualified individuals who want to pursue their studies.
Title of Award: Stark County Dairy Promoters Scholarships **Area, Field, or Subject:** Dairy science; Animal science and behavior; Medicine, Veterinary; Nutrition; Food science and technology. **Level of Education for which Award is Granted:** Undergraduate **Funds Available:** No specific amount. **Duration:** One year.
Eligibility Requirements: Applicants must be residents of Stark County, OH; must be pursuing college-level study in the field of dairy science, animal science, veterinary medicine, human nutrition, or food science; must have 2.5 high school GPA; must have demonstrated financial need.

Application Requirements: Applicants must complete and submit the application form and requirements to Stark County Diary Promoters Scholarship Committee, Stark Community Foundation, 400 Market Ave. N, Ste. 200, Canton, OH 44702. **Deadline for Receipt:** April 15.

3557 ■ UNIVERSITY OF TORONTO
315 Bloor St. W
Toronto, ON, Canada M5S 1A3
Tel: (416)978-2011
E-mail: information.commonsats@utoronto.ca
Web Site: http://www.utoronto.ca
To support students with their educational pursuit.
Title of Award: Gertrude and Edith Lowidt and Mary Catherine Preiss Memorial Bursaries in Nutritional Sciences **Area, Field, or Subject:** Nutrition. **Level of Education for which Award is Granted:** Undergraduate **Number Awarded:** 2. **Funds Available:** $500.
Eligibility Requirements: Applicant must be a UofT student registered in the Faculty of Arts and Science, St. George Campus entering or in a third or fourth year course offered by the Department of Nutritional Sciences. **Application Requirements:** Applicants must submit a completed application form along with the required materials and informations. **Deadline for Receipt:** November 30.

Optometry

3558 ■ SPIE (THE INTERNATIONAL SOCIETY FOR OPTICAL ENGINEERING)
PO Box 10
Bellingham, WA 98227-0010
Tel: (360)676-3290; 888-504-8171
Fax: (360)647-1445
E-mail: customerservice@spie.org
Web Site: http://www.spie.org
To provide education assistance to students in field of microlithography.
Title of Award: BACUS Scholarships **Area, Field, or Subject:** Optical engineering; Optics. **Level of Education for which Award is Granted:** Graduate, Undergraduate **Number Awarded:** 2. **Funds Available:** $4000.
Eligibility Requirements: Applicants must be student members of SPIE; must be enrolled full-time, undergraduate or graduate students in the field of microlithography emphasizing on optical tooling or semiconductor manufacturing technologies. **Application Requirements:** Applicants must submit a completed scholarship application form (available at the website); a 450-word essay; and two letters of recommendation sent separately by the recommender. Application materials must not exceed more than ten pages. **Additional Information:** Scholarships are sponsored by BACUS, the International Technical Group of SPIE dedicated to the advancement of photomask technology. **Deadline for Receipt:** January 11. **Additional Information:** scholarships@spie.org.

3559 ■ SPIE (THE INTERNATIONAL SOCIETY FOR OPTICAL ENGINEERING)
PO Box 10
Bellingham, WA 98227-0010
Tel: (360)676-3290; 888-504-8171
Fax: (360)647-1445
E-mail: customerservice@spie.org
Web Site: http://www.spie.org
To provide education assistance to a student in optical design.
Title of Award: D.J. Lovell Scholarships **Area, Field, or Subject:** Optics; Optical engineering. **Level of Education for which Award is Granted:** Graduate, Undergraduate **Funds Available:** $11,000. **Duration:** One year.
Eligibility Requirements: Applicants must be student members of SPIE; must be enrolled full-time in an optics photonics imaging or optoelectronics program or related discipline at an accredited school; must be in high school or secondary school, undergraduate or post-secondary school, or graduate school. **Application Requirements:** Applicants must submit a completed scholarship application form (available at the website); a 450-word essay; and two letters of recommendation sent separately by the recommender. Application materials must not exceed more than ten pages. **Additional Information:** The scholarship is sponsored in part by

SPIE with contributions from Labsphere Inc. **Deadline for Receipt:** January 11. **Additional Information:** scholarships@spie.org.

3560 ■ SPIE (THE INTERNATIONAL SOCIETY FOR OPTICAL ENGINEERING)
PO Box 10
Bellingham, WA 98227-0010
Tel: (360)676-3290; 888-504-8171
Fax: (360)647-1445
E-mail: customerservice@spie.org
Web Site: http://www.spie.org
To provide education assistance to a student in optical design.
Title of Award: William H. Price Scholarships **Area, Field, or Subject:** Optical engineering; Optics. **Level of Education for which Award is Granted:** Graduate, Undergraduate **Funds Available:** $3000.
Eligibility Requirements: Applicants must be student members of SPIE; must be enrolled full-time, undergraduate or graduate in an optical design and engineering. **Application Requirements:** Applicants must submit a completed scholarship application form (available at the website); a 450-word essay; and two letters of recommendation sent separately by the recommender. Application materials must not exceed more than ten pages. **Additional Information:** Established in 1985 in honor of Bill Price, a well-respected member of the SPIE technical community. **Deadline for Receipt:** January 11. **Additional Information:** scholarships@spie.org.

3561 ■ SPIE (THE INTERNATIONAL SOCIETY FOR OPTICAL ENGINEERING)
PO Box 10
Bellingham, WA 98227-0010
Tel: (360)676-3290; 888-504-8171
Fax: (360)647-1445
E-mail: customerservice@spie.org
Web Site: http://www.spie.org
To supplement travel support for students presenting a paper at any of SPIE's meetings.
Title of Award: Student Travel Grants **Area, Field, or Subject:** Optical engineering; Optics. **Level of Education for which Award is Granted:** Graduate, Undergraduate **Funds Available:** Covers travel expenses.
Eligibility Requirements: Applicants must be fulltime student members of SPIE; must be authors of an accepted paper presented at the conference; and must have not received any SPIE funding in the past 12 months. **Application Requirements:** Applicant must submit a student travel grant application form (available at the website); a letter of recommendation from faculty advisor or head department; and a written support from the chair of the conference which the paper will be presented.

Osteopathy

3562 ■ AMERICAN ASSOCIATION OF COLLEGES OF OSTEOPATHIC MEDICINE
5550 Friendship Blvd., Ste. 310
Chevy Chase, MD 20815-7231
Tel: (301)968-4100
Fax: (301)968-4101
Web Site: http://www.aacom.org
To promote leadership roles in the profession and positions of influence in health policy.
Title of Award: AACOM Scholar in Residence Program **Area, Field, or Subject:** Osteopathic medicine. **Level of Education for which Award is Granted:** Graduate, Undergraduate **Funds Available:** $2,225.
Eligibility Requirements: Individuals with a professional connection to the osteopathic profession. Applicants must be an undergraduate, graduate or continuing medical education. **Application Requirements:** Applicants must be nominated by their dean and together with the dean and department chair, develop a proposal for study that will enhance both their college's medical education and provide leadership to the greater osteopathic medical education community. **Deadline for Receipt:** December 31. **Additional Information:** Linda Heun 5550 Friendship Blvd., Suite 310 Chevy Chase MD 20815; Phone: 301-968-4143, Fax: 301-968-4101; meded@.aacom.org.

3563 ■ AMERICAN OSTEOPATHIC FOUNDATION
142 East Ontario St., Ste. 502
Chicago, IL 60611

Tel: (312)202-8234
Fax: (312)202-8216
E-mail: info@aof-foundation.org
Web Site: http://www.aof-foundation.org
To provide monetary scholarship to help defer the cost of students' osteopathic medical education.
Title of Award: William G. Anderson, DO, Minority Scholarship **Area, Field, or Subject:** Osteopathic medicine. **Level of Education for which Award is Granted:** Undergraduate **Funds Available:** $5,000.
Eligibility Requirements: Any osteopathic student who will be entering his or her second- to fourth-year studies at an AOA accredited college/school of osteopathic medicine. **Application Requirements:** Applicant shall meet the following criteria: Strong interest in osteopathic medicine, its philosophy and principles; Excellent academic achievement; Demonstrated leadership efforts in addressing the educational, societal, and health needs of minorities; Demonstrated leadership efforts to eliminate inequities in medical education and health care; Noteworthy accomplishments, awards and honors, clerkship or special projects, and extracurricular activities in which the student has shown leadership abilities; Financial need. **Deadline for Receipt:** March 28.

3564 ■ AMERICAN OSTEOPATHIC FOUNDATION
142 East Ontario St., Ste. 502
Chicago, IL 60611
Tel: (312)202-8234
Fax: (312)202-8216
E-mail: info@aof-foundation.org
Web Site: http://www.aof-foundation.org
To provide monetary scholarship to help defer the cost of students' osteopathic medical education.
Title of Award: Russell C. McCaughan, DO, Education Scholarships **Area, Field, or Subject:** Osteopathic medicine. **Level of Education for which Award is Granted:** Undergraduate **Funds Available:** $400.
Eligibility Requirements: Any osteopathic medical student who will be entering their second year of studies in an AOA approved college/school of osteopathic medicine is eligible to be nominated for this scholarship. **Application Requirements:** Applicant must submit the following in one packet: Completed, typewritten or computer generated Nomination form; Letter of recommendation from the nominator; Letter from Dean certifying that the applicant is in good academic standing and states the applicant's class ranking; Letter from the Director of Financial Aid verifying the students financial need for educational assistance; Personal statement of one page or less expressing why the nominee believes he or she should receive third scholarship and should emphasize how they meet the eligibility criteria; Official medical school academic transcript. **Deadline for Receipt:** April 25.

3565 ■ AMERICAN OSTEOPATHIC FOUNDATION
142 East Ontario St., Ste. 502
Chicago, IL 60611
Tel: (312)202-8234
Fax: (312)202-8216
E-mail: info@aof-foundation.org
Web Site: http://www.aof-foundation.org
To provide monetary aid to osteopathic medical students to help defray the costs involved of taking COMPLEX-USA Level 2-PE.
Title of Award: Procter and Gamble Complex PE Scholars Grant **Area, Field, or Subject:** Osteopathic medicine. **Level of Education for which Award is Granted:** Undergraduate **Funds Available:** $1,000.
Eligibility Requirements: Any osteopathic student who will be an OMS III or OMS IV during December of the year the grant is offered, and is currently enrolled at an AOA accredited college/school of osteopathic medicine, is eligible to be nominated for this grant. **Application Requirements:** The Dean at each COM/SOM is invited to nominate one student who best meets the eligibility criteria. The following should be sent in own complete packet: Completed, typewritten or computer generated nomination form; Letter of recommendation from the Dean (nominator); One letter of recommendation from someone involved with the nominee's osteopathic education that can speak to the nominee's qualifications for this grant based on the eligibility criteria. **Deadline for Receipt:** April 4.

3566 ■ AMERICAN OSTEOPATHIC FOUNDATION
142 East Ontario St., Ste. 502
Chicago, IL 60611

Tel: (312)202-8234
Fax: (312)202-8216
E-mail: info@aof-foundation.org
Web Site: http://www.aof-foundation.org
To provide funding for osteopathic medical students.
Title of Award: Savvy Student Traveler Grant Program **Area, Field, or Subject:** Osteopathic medicine. **Level of Education for which Award is Granted:** Undergraduate **Funds Available:** $750.
Eligibility Requirements: Any osteopathic student who will be entering his or her second- to fourth year of studies at an AOA accredited college/school of osteopathic medicine. **Application Requirements:** Applicant must submit the following in one packet: Completed, typewritten, or computer generated Nomination form; Letter of recommendation from the nominator; Letter from Dean certifying that the applicant is in good academic standing and states the applicant's class ranking; Personal statement; Official COM/SOM transcript; Current curriculum vitae or resume. **Deadline for Receipt:** April 4.

3567 ■ AMERICAN OSTEOPATHIC FOUNDATION
142 East Ontario St., Ste. 502
Chicago, IL 60611
Tel: (312)202-8234
Fax: (312)202-8216
E-mail: info@aof-foundation.org
Web Site: http://www.aof-foundation.org
To promote education within the osteopathic profession.
Title of Award: Welch Scholars Grants **Area, Field, or Subject:** Osteopathic medicine. **Level of Education for which Award is Granted:** Undergraduate **Funds Available:** $2,000.
Eligibility Requirements: Any osteopathic student who will be entering his or her second to fourth year of studies at an AOA accredited college/school of osteopathic medicine. **Application Requirements:** Applicant must submit the following in one packet: Completed, typewritten or computer generated Nomination form; Letter from Dean certifying that the applicant is in good academic standing and states the applicant's class ranking; Letter from the Director of Financial Aid verifying the student's financial need for educational assistance; Letters of recommendation from two references who can speak to the applicant's qualification for this grant based on the eligibility criteria; Personal statement of not more than two pages; Personal financial need statement of not more than one page. Official medical school academic transcript (may be mailed separately). **Deadline for Receipt:** April 25.

3568 ■ NATIONAL ARAB AMERICAN MEDICAL ASSOCIATION
801 S Adams Rd., Ste. 208
Birmingham, MI 48009
Tel: (248)646-3661
Fax: (248)646-0617
E-mail: naama@naama.com
Web Site: http://www.naama.com
To provide financial assistance to Arabic students who are studying in a medical, osteopathic, or dental school.
Title of Award: NAAMA Scholarships **Area, Field, or Subject:** Medicine, Osteopathic; Dentistry. **Level of Education for which Award is Granted:** Undergraduate **Number Awarded:** 2. **Funds Available:** $1,000.
Eligibility Requirements: Applicants must be Arabic students enrolled in a U.S. or Canadian medical, osteopathic, or dental school. **Application Requirements:** Applicants must send completed application form together with a brief description on the applicant's education; transcripts; description of financial need; description of involvement in the Arab American community after completing studies; and recent 1040 tax return (with spouse and parents). **Deadline for Receipt:** July.

3569 ■ NEW JERSEY ASSOCIATION OF OSTEOPATHIC PHYSICIANS AND SURGEONS
1 Distribution Way, Ste. 201
Monmouth Junction, NJ 08852
Tel: (732)940-9000
Fax: (732)940-8899
E-mail: njaops@njosteo.com
Web Site: http://www.njosteo.com
To promote public health, unite professionals for the maintenance of high standards of practice and osteopathic education; to promote scientific research.

Title of Award: New Jersey Association of Osteopathic Physicians and Surgeons Scholarships **Area, Field, or Subject:** Osteopathic medicine. **Level of Education for which Award is Granted:** Undergraduate **Funds Available:** No specific amount.
Eligibility Requirements: Applicants must be students entering their first year in an osteopathic college; must be residents of New Jersey and have completed four years of pre-medical education. **Application Requirements:** Applicants must submit a completed application form, four completed reference evaluation forms, MCAT scores, pre-med college transcript and an essay stating their reasons for becoming an osteopathic physician. **Deadline for Receipt:** April 30. **Additional Information:** njaops@njosteo.com.

3570 ■ STUDENT OSTEOPATHIC MEDICAL ASSOCIATION
142 E Ontario St.
Chicago, IL 60611
Tel: (312)202-8193
Free: 800-621-1773
Fax: (312)202-8200
E-mail: somanat@studentdo.com
Web Site: http://www.studentdo.com
To help medical students pursue their studies.
Title of Award: Humanism in Medicine Scholarships **Area, Field, or Subject:** Osteopathic Medicine. **Level of Education for which Award is Granted:** Undergraduate **Funds Available:** No specific amount.
Eligibility Requirements: Applicant must be a third- or fourth-year osteopathic medical student attending any accredited osteopathic medical colleges. **Application Requirements:** Applicants must complete the application form. Applicants must submit a 500-word essay. Applicants must submit a curriculum vitae. **Deadline for Receipt:** September 22. **Additional Information:** sabeena.rahman@nv.touro.edu

3571 ■ STUDENT OSTEOPATHIC MEDICAL ASSOCIATION
142 E Ontario St.
Chicago, IL 60611
Tel: (312)202-8193
Free: 800-621-1773
Fax: (312)202-8200
E-mail: somanat@studentdo.com
Web Site: http://www.studentdo.com
To provide funds for medical students who are currently or will be conducting a research project in the field of osteopathy.
Title of Award: Student Osteopathic Medical Student Fellowships and Research **Area, Field, or Subject:** Osteopathic medicine. **Level of Education for which Award is Granted:** Undergraduate **Funds Available:** $2,000.
Eligibility Requirements: Applicants must be osteopathic medical students. **Application Requirements:** Applicants must present an abstract. **Deadline for Receipt:** January 4. **Additional Information:** allisaco@pcom.edu

3572 ■ STUDENT OSTEOPATHIC MEDICAL ASSOCIATION
142 E Ontario St.
Chicago, IL 60611
Tel: (312)202-8193
Free: 800-621-1773
Fax: (312)202-8200
E-mail: somanat@studentdo.com
Web Site: http://www.studentdo.com
To benefit students pursuing a career in specialty medicine.
Title of Award: Marvin H. and Kathleen G. Teget Leadership Scholarships **Area, Field, or Subject:** Specialty Medicine. **Level of Education for which Award is Granted:** Undergraduate **Number Awarded:** 2. **Funds Available:** $500.
Eligibility Requirements: Applicants must be currently enrolled in a specialty medicine program at an institution, college, or university. **Application Requirements:** Applicants must submit a personal statement and complete the application form. **Deadline for Receipt:** March 15.

Pediatrics

3573 ■ AMERICAN SCHOOL HEALTH ASSOCIATION
7263 State Rte. 43
Kent, OH 44240
Tel: (330)678-1601
Fax: (330)678-4526
E-mail: asha@ashaweb.org
Web Site: http://www.ashaweb.org
To provide financial assistance to students concentrating on school health education, school nursing, and pediatric or adolescent medicine or dentistry.
Title of Award: ASHA Scholarships **Area, Field, or Subject:** Health education; Nursing; Pediatric medicine; Medicine; Dentistry; Nutrition; Counseling/Guidance. **Level of Education for which Award is Granted:** Graduate, Undergraduate **Number Awarded:** 3. **Funds Available:** $500 and a complimentary registration to ASHA's annual school health conference and a one-year ASHA membership. **Duration:** One year.
Eligibility Requirements: Applicants must be a junior, senior or graduate student; enrolled full-time at institution of higher education; have 3.0 GPA on a 4.0 scale; have a major related to School Health Education or School Nursing or Pediatric or Adolescent Medicine or Dentistry or other school health specializations (nutrition, counseling, etc.); not a previous recipient of this award. **Application Requirements:** Applicants must send one original and nine copies of the completed application form (application form available online); current resume; transcript; one page personal statement; three letters of recommendation. **Deadline for Receipt:** April 4. **Additional Information:** Pamela Dorazio Dean, pdean@ashaweb.org.

3574 ■ AMERICAN SCHOOL HEALTH ASSOCIATION
7263 State Rte. 43
Kent, OH 44240
Tel: (330)678-1601
Fax: (330)678-4526
E-mail: asha@ashaweb.org
Web Site: http://www.ashaweb.org
To provide financial assistance for research in areas related to the mission of ASHA.
Title of Award: ASHA Student Research Grants **Area, Field, or Subject:** Health education; Nursing; Pediatric medicine; Medicine; Dentistry; Nutrition; Counseling/Guidance. **Level of Education for which Award is Granted:** Graduate, Undergraduate **Funds Available:** No specific amount.
Eligibility Requirements: Applicants must be student members of ASHA. **Application Requirements:** Applicants must send one original and five copies of a proposal which includes a cover sheet; a narrative (title-problem, review of related literature, methodology, data analyst, institution IRB protocol documented); and a budget. Proposal should have one inch margins, doubled spaced and a font size not smaller than 12. Forward the original and 5 copies to: ASHA Student Research Grants, PO Box 708, Kent, OH 44240. **Deadline for Receipt:** April 4. **Additional Information:** Pamela Dorazio, pdean@ashaweb.org, 330-678-1601.

3575 ■ NATIONAL MEDICAL FELLOWSHIPS
5 Hanover Sq., 15th Fl.
New York, NY 10004
Tel: (212)483-8880
Fax: (212)483-8897
E-mail: info@nmfonline.org
Web Site: http://www.nmfonline.org
To provide support for a minority medical student or resident doing ongoing research in the area of pediatric nutrition.
Title of Award: Gerber Fellowships in Pediatric Nutrition **Area, Field, or Subject:** Medicine, Pediatric. **Level of Education for which Award is Granted:** Undergraduate **Number Awarded:** 1. **Funds Available:** $3000.
Eligibility Requirements: Applicant must be a second or third year student; an African-American, mainland Puerto Rican, Mexican-American, Native Hawaiian, Alaska Native, or American Indian; a U.S. citizen attending a M.D. degree-granting institutions accredited by the Liaison Committee on Medical Education of the Association of American Medical Colleges, or in D.O. degree-granting colleges of osteopathic medicine accredited by the Bureau of Professional Education of the American Osteopathic Association; and pursuing careers in pediatric nutrition research. **Application Requirements:** Applicants must submit a competed application form together with a letter of recommendation from medical school dean or director; a letter of commitment; an official academic transcript; a curriculum vitae; a personal statement on career goals; and a description of the research project. **Additional Information:**

Created in 1997 with support from the Gerber Companies Foundation. **Deadline for Receipt:** October.

3576 ■ SOCIETY OF PEDIATRIC PSYCHOLOGY
PO Box 170231
Atlanta, GA 30317
E-mail: pedpsychol@aol.com
Web Site: http://www.apa.org/divisions/div54
To provide assistance to research related to prevention of injuries to children and adolescents.
Title of Award: Lizette Peterson Homer Injury Prevention Grant Awards **Area, Field, or Subject:** Pediatric medicine. **Level of Education for which Award is Granted:** Professional, Undergraduate **Funds Available:** $1500.
Eligibility Requirements: Applicants must be students and faculty members. **Application Requirements:** Applicants must submit a seven pages summary of proposed research which includes abstract (maximum of 100 words), project descriptions with introduction, budget, reference; curriculum vitae; letter of recommendation by faculty supervisor; and proof of IRB approval send by email at palermot@ohsu.edu on one single Word format. **Deadline for Receipt:** October 1. **Additional Information:** Tonya Palermo, PhD, Phone: 503-494-0848, Fax: 503-494-5945, palermo@ohsu.edu.

3577 ■ SOCIETY OF PEDIATRIC PSYCHOLOGY
PO Box 170231
Atlanta, GA 30317
E-mail: pedpsychol@aol.com
Web Site: http://www.apa.org/divisions/div54
To provide assistance to research related to field of pediatric psychology.
Title of Award: Routh Student Research Grants **Area, Field, or Subject:** Pediatric medicine. **Level of Education for which Award is Granted:** Undergraduate **Funds Available:** $1000.
Eligibility Requirements: Applicants must be student members of APA. **Application Requirements:** Applicants must submit summary of proposed research (maximum of 100 words); project objectives (maximum of 7 pages); a detailed budget; a statement about the qualifications, training, membership of the applicant; and a letter of recommendation by faculty supervisor, send materials by email in MS Word format to: palermot@ohsu.edu. **Deadline for Receipt:** October 1. **Additional Information:** Tonya Palermo, PhD, Phone: 503-494-0848, Fax: 503-494-5945, palermo@ohsu.edu.

3578 ■ SOCIETY FOR PEDIATRIC UROLOGY
900 Cummings Center, Ste. 221-U
Beverly, MA 01915
Tel: (978)927-8330
Fax: (978)524-8890
Web Site: http://www.spuonline.org
to promote pediatric urology, appropriate practice, education as well as exchanges between practitioners involve din the treatment of genito urinary disorders of children.
Title of Award: John W. Duckett Jr., AFUD Pediatric Research Scholarships **Area, Field, or Subject:** Pediatric medicine. **Level of Education for which Award is Granted:** Undergraduate **Funds Available:** $10,000.
Eligibility Requirements: Applicant must be taking up pediatric medicine. **Application Requirements:** Applicant must fill out the application form and submit to the American Foundation of Urologic Disease.

3579 ■ SOCIETY FOR PEDIATRIC UROLOGY
900 Cummings Center, Ste. 221-U
Beverly, MA 01915
Tel: (978)927-8330
Fax: (978)524-8890
Web Site: http://www.spuonline.org
To promote pediatric urology, an appropriate practice, education as well as exchanges between practitioners involved in the treatment of genito urinary disorders of children.
Title of Award: Society for Pediatric Urology Research Grant Program **Area, Field, or Subject:** Pediatric medicine. **Level of Education for which Award is Granted:** Undergraduate **Funds Available:** $30,000. **Duration:** 1 year.
Eligibility Requirements: Applicant must have a knowledge in pediatric urology and must be officially enrolled in an accredited institution. **Ap-**

plication Requirements: Applicants must attach a copy of Principal Investigator's Curriculum Vitae; a letter of commitment from the chair of the Principal Investigator's Department; must attach an abstract of the research plan which summarizes the long-term objectives, scientific aims, and methodology; a grant budget; and must provide a justification which describes any large or unusual expenses in any category or any cost of the need which may not be obvious. **Deadline for Receipt:** February 20.

Pharmacy

3580 ■ ALBERTA LEARNING INFORMATION SERVICE - ALBERTA SCHOLARSHIP PROGRAM
Box 28000 Sta. Main
Edmonton, AB, Canada T5J 4R4
Tel: (780)427-8640
Fax: (780)427-1288
E-mail: scholarship@gov.ab.ca
Web Site: http://www.alis.alberta.ca
To reward the outstanding academic achievement of Alberta post-secondary students who are continuing full-time in an undergraduate program in Alberta.
Title of Award: Jason Lang Scholarship **Area, Field, or Subject:** Law; Medicine; Pharmacy; Dentistry. **Level of Education for which Award is Granted:** Undergraduate **Funds Available:** $1,000.
Eligibility Requirements: Nominees must be enrolled full-time in an undergraduate or professional program, such as Law, Medicine, Pharmacy or Dentistry at an eligible Alberta post-secondary institution. These include publicly-funded colleges, technical institutes, universities, private colleges accredited to grant degrees, and the Banff Centre. **Application Requirements:** Recipients are nominated by the Awards Office at participating Alberta institutions where they have obtained qualifying grades. For information on the nomination process and eligibility, contact the Awards Office. **Deadline for Receipt:** October 15 and February 15. **Additional Information:** Alberta Scholarship Programs at the above address.

3581 ■ ALBERTA LEARNING INFORMATION SERVICE - ALBERTA SCHOLARSHIP PROGRAM
Box 28000 Sta. Main
Edmonton, AB, Canada T5J 4R4
Tel: (780)427-8640
Fax: (780)427-1288
E-mail: scholarship@gov.ab.ca
Web Site: http://www.alis.alberta.ca
To increase the number of trained professionals in Northern Alberta and to encourage students from Northern Alberta to obtain a post-secondary education.
Title of Award: Northern Alberta Development Council Bursary for Pharmacy Students **Area, Field, or Subject:** Pharmacy. **Level of Education for which Award is Granted:** Undergraduate **Funds Available:** $3,500.
Eligibility Requirements: Applicants must be: a resident of Alberta based on Students Finance Regulations; enrolled in a four year pharmacy degree program; planning to live and work in northern Alberta upon completion of studies; in good standing with any provincial student loan. **Application Requirements:** Applicants may obtain an application form from www.benorth.ca. Application forms for these bursaries are also available from Alberta Scholarship Programs, Student Awards Offices and from the Northern Alberta Development Council. **Deadline for Receipt:** May 15. **Additional Information:** Northern Alberta Development Council, 2nd Fl., Provincial Bldg. 9621 - 96 Ave. Postal Bag 900-14 Peace River, AB T8S 1T4; 780-624-6545; nadc.council@gov.ab.ca.

3582 ■ FIRST COMMUNITY FOUNDATION OF PENNSYLVANIA, WILLIAMSPORT-LYCOMING
330 Pine St., Suite 401
Williamsport, PA 17701
Tel: (570)321-1500; (866)901-2372
Fax: (570)321-6434
E-mail: fcfpa@fcfpa.org
Web Site: http://www.wlfoundation.org

To provide academic support for Danville Area High School seniors who have been accepted into a full-time undergraduate program at an accredited institution of higher education and who are entering a health-related field.

Title of Award: Eleanor McWilliams Burke Fund **Area, Field, or Subject:** Medicine; Nursing; Nutrition; Pharmacy; or Physical therapy. **Level of Education for which Award is Granted:** Undergraduate **Funds Available:** No specific amount.

Eligibility Requirements: Applicants must be entering a health related field. **Application Requirements:** Applicants may request an application from the Guidance Counselor of Danville Area School District. **Additional Information:** Gary Grozier, Guidance Counselor of Danville Area School District, 600 Walnut St., Danvilled, PA 17821; 570-271-3268 ext. 2006; ggrozier@danville.k12.pa.us.

3583 ■ FIRST COMMUNITY FOUNDATION OF PENNSYLVANIA, WILLIAMSPORT-LYCOMING

330 Pine St., Suite 401
Williamsport, PA 17701
Tel: (570)321-1500; (866)901-2372
Fax: (570)321-6434
E-mail: fcfpa@fcfpa.org
Web Site: http://www.wlfoundation.org

To support the education of current and/or aspiring Lycoming County medical professionals who plan to dedicate their lives to helping others.

Title of Award: Joseph R. Calder, Jr., MD Scholarship Fund **Area, Field, or Subject:** Medicine; Nursing; Pharmacy; Allied health. **Level of Education for which Award is Granted:** Undergraduate **Funds Available:** No specific amount.

Eligibility Requirements: Applicants must be accepted into a full-time or part-time medical or any other related specialty at an accredited institution of higher education. Applicants should be residents of Lycoming County. **Application Requirements:** Applicant must submit an essay not to exceed one page outlining why he/she is pursuing a career in the medical field and summarizing his/her ultimate career objectives. Applicants may download an application form the Foundation's web site. **Additional Information:** Candy Bower, 570-321-1500; candyb@fcfpa.org

3584 ■ JEWISH FOUNDATION FOR EDUCATION OF WOMEN

135 E 64th St.
New York, NY 10065
Tel: (212)288-3931
Fax: (212)288-5798
E-mail: info@jfew.org
Web Site: http://www.jfew.org

To provide financial support for emigres from the former Soviet Union to train in medicine, dentistry, dental hygiene, nursing, pharmacy, occupational and physical therapy, physician assistant, CVT, and sonography programs.

Title of Award: Scholarships for Emigres in the Health Sciences **Area, Field, or Subject:** Medicine; Dentistry; Nursing; Pharmacy; Physical therapy; Physiology. **Level of Education for which Award is Granted:** Undergraduate **Funds Available:** $5,000. **Duration:** One year.

Eligibility Requirements: Applicants must be students from the former Soviet Union; must be residents of New York City or the counties of Nassau, Suffolk or Westchester; must already be enrolled in or about to enroll in a health science program within that geographic area; and must be enrolled full-time, in good standing, and demonstrate financial need. **Application Requirements:** Applicants must submit all the required application information.

3585 ■ NATIONAL COMMUNITY PHARMACISTS ASSOCIATION

100 Daingerfield Rd.
Alexandria, VA 22314
Tel: (703)683-8200
Free: 800-544-7477
Fax: (703)683-3619
E-mail: info@ncpanet.org
Web Site: http://www.ncpanet.org

To promote the continuing growth and prosperity of independent community pharmacy in the United States.

Title of Award: J.C. and Rheba Cobb Memorial Scholarships **Area, Field, or Subject:** Pharmacy. **Level of Education for which Award is

Granted: Undergraduate **Number Awarded:** 1. **Funds Available:** $2,500.

Eligibility Requirements: Applicants must be full-time pharmacy students in an accredited United States college of pharmacy. **Application Requirements:** Applicants must submit a copy of the most recent official transcript of record. Applicants must submit a letter from school official familiar with the students activities; a letter from a pharmacy owner or manager, preferably an NCPA member; a letter from the applicants to the NCPA Foundation Scholarships Award Committee outlining his or her school and civic accomplishments and objectives for the future; a resume or curriculum vitae describing the students work and professional experience. **Deadline for Receipt:** March 15.

3586 ■ NATIONAL COMMUNITY PHARMACISTS ASSOCIATION

100 Daingerfield Rd.
Alexandria, VA 22314
Tel: (703)683-8200
Free: 800-544-7477
Fax: (703)683-3619
E-mail: info@ncpanet.org
Web Site: http://www.ncpanet.org

To provide undergraduate pharmacy students with an opportunity to become more aware of the vast opportunities that exist in independent pharmacy practice. To provide an experience that demonstrates the importance of a national pharmacy association to the profession.

Title of Award: National Community Pharmacists Association Internship Programs **Area, Field, or Subject:** Pharmacy. **Level of Education for which Award is Granted:** Undergraduate **Funds Available:** No specific amount. **Duration:** 10 weeks.

Eligibility Requirements: Applicants must be enrolled in a full-time pharmacy program in pursuit of their first professional pharmacy degree; applicants must have a minimum of 2.50 cumulative GPA at an accredited U.S. college of pharmacy; a demonstrated interest in independent pharmacy practice through school activities and work experience; exhibit an interest in organizational involvement through participation in student organizations in college and/or community organizations. **Application Requirements:** Applicants must submit a letter of recommendation explaining their interest in the internship, career goals, and how the internship will help to meet the goals; a resume or curriculum vitae; a school transcript to verify a cumulative GPA of at least 2.5; two letters of recommendation, one from pharmacy school dean and one from the state pharmacy association executive, current recent employer, or NCPA Faculty Liaison. **Deadline for Receipt:** January 15.

3587 ■ NATIONAL COMMUNITY PHARMACISTS ASSOCIATION

100 Daingerfield Rd.
Alexandria, VA 22314
Tel: (703)683-8200
Free: 800-544-7477
Fax: (703)683-3619
E-mail: info@ncpanet.org
Web Site: http://www.ncpanet.org

To promote the continuing growth and prosperity of independent community pharmacy in the United States.

Title of Award: National Community Pharmacists Association Presidential Scholarships **Area, Field, or Subject:** Pharmacy. **Level of Education for which Award is Granted:** Undergraduate **Number Awarded:** 15. **Funds Available:** $2,000.

Eligibility Requirements: Applicants must be full-time pharmacy students at an accredited college of pharmacy. **Application Requirements:** Applicants must submit a copy of the most recent official transcript of record. Applicants must submit a letter from a school official familiar with the students activities; a letter from a pharmacy owner or manager, preferably an NCPA member; a letter from the applicant to the NCPA Foundation Scholarships Award Committee outlining his or her school and civic accomplishments and objectives for the future; a resume or curriculum vitae describing the students work and professional experience. **Deadline for Receipt:** March 15.

3588 ■ NATIONAL COMMUNITY PHARMACISTS ASSOCIATION

100 Daingerfield Rd.
Alexandria, VA 22314
Tel: (703)683-8200

Free: 800-544-7477
Fax: (703)683-3619
E-mail: info@ncpanet.org
Web Site: http://www.ncpanet.org
To promote the continuing growth and prosperity of independent community pharmacy in the United States.
Title of Award: Neil Pruitt, Sr. Memorial Scholarships **Area, Field, or Subject:** Pharmacy. **Level of Education for which Award is Granted:** Undergraduate **Number Awarded:** 1. **Funds Available:** $2,500.
Eligibility Requirements: Applicants must be full-time pharmacy students at an accredited United States college of pharmacy. **Application Requirements:** Applicants must submit a copy of the most recent official transcript of record; a letter from a school official familiar with the students activities; a letter from a pharmacy owner or manager, preferably an NCPA member; a letter from the applicant to the NCPA Foundation Scholarships Award Committee outlining his or her school and civic accomplishments and objectives for the future; a resume or curriculum vitae describing the students work and professional experience. **Deadline for Receipt:** March 15.

3589 ■ NATIONAL COMMUNITY PHARMACISTS ASSOCIATION
100 Daingerfield Rd.
Alexandria, VA 22314
Tel: (703)683-8200
Free: 800-544-7477
Fax: (703)683-3619
E-mail: info@ncpanet.org
Web Site: http://www.ncpanet.org
To promote the continuing growth and prosperity of independent community pharmacy in the United States.
Title of Award: Williard B. Simmons Sr. Memorial Scholarships **Area, Field, or Subject:** Pharmacy. **Level of Education for which Award is Granted:** Undergraduate **Number Awarded:** 1. **Funds Available:** $2,500.
Eligibility Requirements: Applicants must be full-time pharmacy students at an accredited United States college of pharmacy. **Application Requirements:** Applicants must submit a copy of the most recent official transcript of record. Applicants must submit a letter from school official familiar with the students activities; a letter from a pharmacy owner or manager, preferably an NCPA member; a letter from the applicants to the NCPA Foundation Scholarships Award Committee outlining his or her school and civic accomplishments and objectives for the future; a resume or curriculum vitae describing the students work and professional experience. **Deadline for Receipt:** March 15.

3590 ■ STARK COMMUNITY FOUNDATION
400 Market Ave. N, Ste. 200
Canton, OH 44702-2107
Tel: (330)454-3426
Fax: (330)454-5855
Web Site: http://www.starkcommunityfoundation.org
To provide scholarship assistance to qualified individuals who want to pursue their studies.
Title of Award: Thomas W. Gallagher Scholarship Fund **Area, Field, or Subject:** Pharmacy. **Level of Education for which Award is Granted:** Undergraduate **Funds Available:** No specific amount. **Duration:** One year.
Eligibility Requirements: Applicants must be seniors attending Minerva High School, Minerva, OH or will be graduated with his/her class; must be full-time students who have been accepted into a four-year college or university to pursue a degree in pharmacy; must be full-time students who have been accepted into a four-year college or university to study in the field of science (if no students pursuing a degree in pharmacy have applied). **Application Requirements:** Applicants must complete and submit the application form available online at Guidance High School, 501 Almeda Ave., Minerva, OH 44657. **Deadline for Receipt:** April 10.

3591 ■ UNIVERSITY OF WISCONSIN-MADISON
432 N Murray St.
Madison, WI 53706-1496
Tel: (608)262-3060
Fax: (608)262-9068
E-mail: askbucky@uwmad.wisc.edu

Web Site: http://www.wisc.edu
To support UW-Madison students in their education.
Title of Award: School of Pharmacy Continuing Student Scholarships **Area, Field, or Subject:** Pharmacology; Toxicology; Pharmacy. **Level of Education for which Award is Granted:** Undergraduate **Number Awarded:** More than 60. **Funds Available:** Varies.
Eligibility Requirements: Applicants must be students who are continuing their education in the School of Pharmacy. **Application Requirements:** Applicants must contact the Student Services Office for the details and application materials. **Deadline for Receipt:** Third week of April. **Additional Information:** School of Pharmacy at 608-262-6234, or pharminfo@pharmacy.wisc.edu.

3592 ■ UNIVERSITY OF WISCONSIN-MADISON
432 N Murray St.
Madison, WI 53706-1496
Tel: (608)262-3060
Fax: (608)262-9068
E-mail: askbucky@uwmad.wisc.edu
Web Site: http://www.wisc.edu
To support UW-Madison students in their education.
Title of Award: University of Wisconsin-Madison Pharmacy New Student Scholarships **Area, Field, or Subject:** Pharmacology; Toxicology; Pharmacy. **Level of Education for which Award is Granted:** Undergraduate **Funds Available:** Varies.
Eligibility Requirements: Applicants must be Wisconsin students entering as first year students in the School of Pharmacy. **Application Requirements:** Applicants must contact the Student Services Office for the details and application materials. **Deadline for Receipt:** First week of May. **Additional Information:** School of Pharmacy, at 608-262-6234, or pharminfo@pharmacy.wisc.edu.

3593 ■ WASHINGTON HIGHER EDUCATION COORDINATING BOARD
PO Box 43430
Olympia, WA 98504-3430
Tel: (360)753-7800
E-mail: info@hecb.wa.gov
Web Site: http://www.hecb.wa.gov
To attract and retain health professionals to serve in critical shortage areas in Washington state.
Title of Award: Washington Higher Education Coordinating Board Health Professional Scholarships **Area, Field, or Subject:** Physics; Nursing; Midwifery; Pharmacy; Dentistry. **Level of Education for which Award is Granted:** Undergraduate **Funds Available:** Varies by educational program.
Eligibility Requirements: Applicant must be a student training to become a primary care health professional in an eligible profession; a U.S. citizen; have completed all prerequisite course work; not be in default on any educational loans; and must sign a Promissory Note agreeing to serve for a minimum of three years in a designated shortage area in Washington state or pay back funds with double penalty plus interest. **Application Requirements:** Applicants must submit a completed application form along with the required materials and information. **Additional Information:** Participants must agree, in return for the assistance, to provide primary care health care in rural or underserved urban areas with designated shortages for a minimum of three years. **Deadline for Receipt:** April 30.

Pharmacology

3594 ■ UNIVERSITY OF WISCONSIN-MADISON
432 N Murray St.
Madison, WI 53706-1496
Tel: (608)262-3060
Fax: (608)262-9068
E-mail: askbucky@uwmad.wisc.edu
Web Site: http://www.wisc.edu
To support UW-Madison students in their education.
Title of Award: School of Pharmacy Continuing Student Scholarships **Area, Field, or Subject:** Pharmacology; Toxicology; Pharmacy. **Level of Education for which Award is Granted:** Undergraduate **Number Awarded:** More than 60. **Funds Available:** Varies.

Eligibility Requirements: Applicants must be students who are continuing their education in the School of Pharmacy. **Application Requirements:** Applicants must contact the Student Services Office for the details and application materials. **Deadline for Receipt:** Third week of April. **Additional Information:** School of Pharmacy at 608-262-6234, or pharminfo@pharmacy.wisc.edu.

3595 ■ UNIVERSITY OF WISCONSIN-MADISON
432 N Murray St.
Madison, WI 53706-1496
Tel: (608)262-3060
Fax: (608)262-9068
E-mail: askbucky@uwmad.wisc.edu
Web Site: http://www.wisc.edu
To support UW-Madison students in their education.
Title of Award: University of Wisconsin-Madison Pharmacy New Student Scholarships **Area, Field, or Subject:** Pharmacology; Toxicology; Pharmacy. **Level of Education for which Award is Granted:** Undergraduate **Funds Available:** Varies.
Eligibility Requirements: Applicants must be Wisconsin students entering as first year students in the School of Pharmacy. **Application Requirements:** Applicants must contact the Student Services Office for the details and application materials. **Deadline for Receipt:** First week of May. **Additional Information:** School of Pharmacy, at 608-262-6234, or pharminfo@pharmacy.wisc.edu.

Psychiatry

3596 ■ AMERICAN PSYCHIATRIC PUBLISHING INC.
1000 Wilson Blvd., Ste. 1825
Arlington, VA 22209-3901
800-368-5777
E-mail: appi@psych.org
Web Site: http://pn.psychiatryonline.org
To support minority medical students who have primary interest in services related to HIV/AIDS and substance abuse and its relationship to the mental health or psychological well-being of ethnic minorities.
Title of Award: Minority Medical Student Fellowships in HIV Psychiatry **Area, Field, or Subject:** Psychology. **Level of Education for which Award is Granted:** Undergraduate **Funds Available:** No specific amount.
Eligibility Requirements: Applicants must be minority medical students. **Application Requirements:** Applicants must submit a completed application form. **Deadline for Receipt:** March 31. **Additional Information:** More information is available from Carol Svoboda at 703-907-8642 or csvoboda@psych.org; or Diane Pennessi at 703-907-8668 or dpennessi@psych.org.

3597 ■ AMERICAN PSYCHOLOGICAL ASSOCIATION OF GRADUATE STUDENTS
750 1st St. NE
Washington, DC 20002-4242
Tel: (202)336-6014
E-mail: apags@apa.org
Web Site: http://www.apa.org/apags
To provide funds for research on the regulation of psychology.
Title of Award: ASPPB Larry J. Bass Jr., PhD. Memorial Scholarship Awards **Area, Field, or Subject:** Psychology. **Level of Education for which Award is Granted:** Graduate, Undergraduate **Funds Available:** $1,000. **Duration:** One year.
Eligibility Requirements: Applicants must be psychology graduate students or advanced undergraduate psychology majors. **Application Requirements:** Applicants must submit a curriculum vitae/resume; a recommendation from a professor or advisor who will mentor the research; a written proposal that includes: outline of the desired area of research, description of the proposed methodology and estimate of project timeline. **Additional Information:** The Scholarship was named after the former president of the Association of State and Provincial Psychology Boards (ASPPB) Larry J. Bass Jr. PhD (1999-2000). **Deadline for Receipt:** May. **Additional Information:** Larry J. Bass, Jr., PhD. Memorial Scholarship Award, c/o The ASPPB Foundation, 7177 Halcyon Summit Dr., Montgomery, AL 36117.

3598 ■ ARMENIAN STUDENTS' ASSOCIATION OF AMERICA
333 Atlantic Ave.
Warwick, RI 02888
Tel: (401)461-6114
E-mail: asa@asainc.org
Web Site: http://www.asainc.org
To provide financial assistance to those students who are in need.
Title of Award: Garikian Scholarship Fund **Area, Field, or Subject:** Armenian Studies; Sociology; Psychology; Political Science; Middle Eastern History; Journalism; Education; Music. **Level of Education for which Award is Granted:** Undergraduate **Funds Available:** $750-$1,000.
Eligibility Requirements: Applicants must have completed their first academic year in college or university in California; must be pursuing one of the above field of studies. **Application Requirements:** Applicants must apply to the Executive Board for application forms and return them, completed, before the deadline. **Deadline for Receipt:** August 31. **Additional Information:** Berj S. Baghdoyan c/o Western Prelacy at 4401 Russell Avenue, Los Angeles, CA 90027.

3599 ■ ASSOCIATION FOR PSYCHOLOGICAL SCIENCE
1133 15th St. NW, Ste. 1000
Washington, DC 20005
Tel: (202)293-9300
Fax: (202)293-9350
Web Site: http://www.psychologicalscience.org
To provide financial support for APS students for their research currently in early development.
Title of Award: APS Student Grants **Area, Field, or Subject:** Psychology. **Level of Education for which Award is Granted:** Graduate, Undergraduate **Number Awarded:** 3 for graduate student and 2 for undergraduate student. **Funds Available:** $500 per graduate student and $300 per undergraduate student.
Eligibility Requirements: Applicant must be an APS undergraduate or graduate student. **Application Requirements:** Applicant must submit a cover letter; project summary; and review board approval. Submit through E-mail at grad.advocate@gmail.com, with a subject, APSSC Student Grant Submission except the Review Board Approval, or mail to Ewa J. Szymanska Department of Psychology University of Pennsylvania 3720 Walnut Street, Solomon Lab Bldg. Philadelphia, PA 19104. **Deadline for Receipt:** November 1. **Additional Information:** Ewa J. Szymanska grad. advocate@gmail.com.

3600 ■ ASSOCIATION FOR WOMEN IN SCIENCE
1200 New York Ave. NW, Ste. 650
Washington, DC 20005
Tel: (202)326-8940
Fax: (202)326-8960
E-mail: awis@awis.org
Web Site: http://www.awis.org
To promote education in science.
Title of Award: AWIS College Scholarships **Area, Field, or Subject:** Astronomy and astronomical sciences; Geosciences; Biology; Mathematics and mathematical sciences; Chemistry; Physics; Computer and information sciences; Engineering; Psychology. **Level of Education for which Award is Granted:** Undergraduate **Number Awarded:** 2-5. **Funds Available:** No specific amount.
Eligibility Requirements: Applicant must be a female high school senior; U.S. citizen or permanent resident; have at least 3.75 GPA; at least 1200 score in SAT or a composite score of 25 in ACT; planning to study in any field of Astronomy, Geoscience, Biology, Mathematics, Chemistry, Physics, Computer and Information Science, Engineering, Psychology; planning to become a researcher or teacher. **Application Requirements:** Applicants must send five copies of: summary form; essay describing research experience; resume; two recommendation letters from science or research teachers; high school transcript and score of standardized test if available. **Deadline for Receipt:** January 17.

3601 ■ HUMAN RESOURCES RESEARCH MANAGEMENT
66 Canal Center Plz., Ste. 400
Alexandria, VA 22314
Tel: (703)549-3611
Fax: (703)549-9025

Web Site: http://www.humrro.org
To provide financial support while the student completes his/her dissertation in the field of Industrial-Organizational (I-O) Psychology, or in a field congruent with the objectives of the Society for Industrial Psychology, Inc. (SIOP).
Title of Award: Meredith P. Crawford Fellowship in I/O Psychology **Area, Field, or Subject:** Psychology. **Level of Education for which Award is Granted:** Undergraduate **Number Awarded:** 1. **Funds Available:** $12,000.
Eligibility Requirements: Applicants must be doctoral candidates whose dissertation topic has been proposed and approved by his/ her graduate faculty in Industrial-Organizational (I-O) Psychology, Inc. **Application Requirements:** Applicants must provide a completed application form, a personal statement, three completed recommendation forms, and an official transcript from each institution attended for graduate academic work. **Deadline for Receipt:** March 14.

3602 ■ MENTAL HEALTH ASSOCIATION OF TARRANT COUNTY
3136 W St.
Fort Worth, TX 76107
Tel: (817)335-5405
Fax: (817)334-0025
E-mail: mhatc@mhatc.org
Web Site: http://www.mhatc.org
To provide financial support to those students pursuing a degree in the mental health field.
Title of Award: Patricia Pownder Conolly Memorial Scholarships **Area, Field, or Subject:** Psychiatry; Psychology; Sociology; Social work; Counseling; Rehabilitation counseling. **Level of Education for which Award is Granted:** Undergraduate **Funds Available:** No specific amount.
Eligibility Requirements: Applicants must be college students pursuing a degree in the mental health field. **Application Requirements:** Applicants must check the available website to download the application form. **Additional Information:** Mental Health Association of Tarrant County at the above address.

3603 ■ MENTAL HEALTH ASSOCIATION OF TARRANT COUNTY
3136 W St.
Fort Worth, TX 76107
Tel: (817)335-5405
Fax: (817)334-0025
E-mail: mhatc@mhatc.org
Web Site: http://www.mhatc.org
To provide financial support to those students pursuing a degree in the mental health field.
Title of Award: Linda Lyons Memorial Scholarship Fund **Area, Field, or Subject:** Psychiatry; Psychology; Sociology; Social work; Counseling; Rehabilitation counseling. **Level of Education for which Award is Granted:** Undergraduate **Funds Available:** No specific amount.
Eligibility Requirements: Applicants must be college students pursuing a degree in the mental health field. **Application Requirements:** Applicants must check the available website to download the application form. **Additional Information:** Mental Health Association of Tarrant County at the above address.

3604 ■ PARAPSYCHOLOGY FOUNDATION
PO Box 1562
New York, NY 10021
Tel: (212)628-1550
Fax: (212)628-1559
E-mail: info@parapsychology.org
Web Site: http://www.parapsychology.org
To promote education in the field of psychology while stimulating interest in the field of Parapsychology.
Title of Award: Eileen J. Garrett Scholarships **Area, Field, or Subject:** Psychology. **Level of Education for which Award is Granted:** Undergraduate **Number Awarded:** 1. **Funds Available:** $3,000. **Duration:** One year.
Eligibility Requirements: Applicants must be currently enrolled full-time in an accredited school or university; must be pursuing academic study in parapsychology; and must be members of the foundation. **Application Requirements:** Applicants must submit an application form together with

letters of reference from individuals familiar with the applicant's work or studies in parapsychology. **Deadline for Receipt:** July 15.

3605 ■ PARAPSYCHOLOGY FOUNDATION
PO Box 1562
New York, NY 10021
Tel: (212)628-1550
Fax: (212)628-1559
E-mail: info@parapsychology.org
Web Site: http://www.parapsychology.org
To support a research that deals directly with some aspect of parapsychology.
Title of Award: Charles T. and Judith A. Tart Student Incentive Awards **Area, Field, or Subject:** Psychology. **Level of Education for which Award is Granted:** Graduate, Postdoctoral, Undergraduate **Number Awarded:** 1. **Funds Available:** $500. **Duration:** One year.
Eligibility Requirements: Applicants must be undergraduate, graduate or post-graduate students seeking either psychology course or any related field; must be enrolled full-time in an accredited school or university; and must have a great interest in parapsychology. **Application Requirements:** Applicants must submit an application form together with letters of recommendation from individuals familiar with the applicant's work and studies; a project description (maximum of 2 pages); and a one-page statement of budget needed for the research. **Deadline for Receipt:** October 15.

3606 ■ PEPPERDINE UNIVERSITY SCHOOL OF LAW
24255 Pacific Coast Highway
Malibu, CA 90263
Tel: (310)506-4611
E-mail: soladmis@pepperdine.edu
Web Site: http://law.pepperdine.edu
To assist students at Pepperdine University School.
Title of Award: Associated Women for Pepperdine (AWP) Scholarships **Area, Field, or Subject:** Education; Psychology; Law. **Level of Education for which Award is Granted:** Undergraduate **Funds Available:** No specific amount.
Eligibility Requirements: Applicants must be admitted at Pepperdine University; and be members of the Church of Christ. **Application Requirements:** Applicants must submit a completed scholarship application form together with a resume, letter of qualifications, and a letter confirming active membership in a local Church of Christ congregation. **Deadline for Receipt:** October 31.

3607 ■ STEUBEN COUNTY COMMUNITY FOUNDATION
1701 N Wayne St.
Angola, IN 46703
Tel: (260)665-6656
Fax: (260)665-8420
Web Site: http://www.steubenfoundation.org
To provide financial support to those students who will be entering a four-year college or university with intent of pursuing a Bachelor's Degree.
Title of Award: Tara Lynne Arnold Scholarships **Area, Field, or Subject:** Psychology; Women's Studies. **Level of Education for which Award is Granted:** Undergraduate **Funds Available:** No specific amount.
Eligibility Requirements: Applicants must attend or have attended Angola High School; must be in good academic standing. **Application Requirements:** Applicants must check the website for the application process online and required materials. **Deadline for Receipt:** March 15.

3608 ■ UNIVERSITY OF ALASKA ANCHORAGE
3211 Providence Dr.
Anchorage, AK 99508
Tel: (907)786-1800
Web Site: http://www.uaa.alaska.edu
To provide a monetary award to an outstanding student in the UAA Master of Science in Clinical Psychology program.
Title of Award: UAA Chris L. Kleinke Scholarships **Area, Field, or Subject:** Psychology. **Level of Education for which Award is Granted:** Graduate, Undergraduate **Funds Available:** $1,500. **Duration:** One year.
Eligibility Requirements: Applicants must demonstrate motivation, academic and leadership potential; must be in good academic standing with a minimum cumulative GPA of 3.0; must be formally admitted to the Master of Science in Clinical Psychology program at the UAA; must plan

on enrolling full-time (nine credits of graduate course work) at the University of Alaska Anchorage; applicant may be an incoming or continuing student at the UAA; may be a U.S citizen, non-U.S. citizen, Alaska resident, or out-of-state resident; must be enrolled in the semester for which the award is made. **Application Requirements:** Applicants must provide two letters of recommendation from professors and/or professionals in the clinical psychology field; must complete the electronic scholarship application available online at www.uaa.alaska.edu/scholarships/chris.cfm. **Deadline for Receipt:** February 15.

3609 ■ UNIVERSITY OF ALASKA ANCHORAGE

3211 Providence Dr.
Anchorage, AK 99508
Tel: (907)786-1800
Web Site: http://www.uaa.alaska.edu
To offer financial assistance for tuition and other educational expenses to full-time University of Alaska Anchorage students who are admitted to the Psychology program.
Title of Award: UAA Dr. Jon Baker Memorial Scholarships **Area, Field, or Subject:** Psychology. **Level of Education for which Award is Granted:** Graduate, Undergraduate **Number Awarded:** 2. **Funds Available:** $500. **Duration:** One year.
Eligibility Requirements: Applicants must demonstrate motivation, academic and leadership potential; must be in good academic standing with a minimum cumulative GPA of 2.0 for undergraduate and 3.0 for graduate; must be formally admitted to an undergraduate, graduate, certificate, and/or vocational degree-seeking program at the University of Alaska Anchorage; may be a U.S. citizen, nonU.S. citizen, Alaska resident, or out-of-state resident. **Application Requirements:** Applicants must complete the electronic scholarship application available online at www.uaa.alaska.edu/scholarships/jon.cfm. **Deadline for Receipt:** February 15.

Rehabilitation

3610 ■ MENTAL HEALTH ASSOCIATION OF TARRANT COUNTY

3136 W St.
Fort Worth, TX 76107
Tel: (817)335-5405
Fax: (817)334-0025
E-mail: mhatc@mhatc.org
Web Site: http://www.mhatc.org
To provide financial support to those students pursuing a degree in the mental health field.
Title of Award: Patricia Pownder Conolly Memorial Scholarships **Area, Field, or Subject:** Psychiatry; Psychology; Sociology; Social work; Counseling; Rehabilitation counseling. **Level of Education for which Award is Granted:** Undergraduate **Funds Available:** No specific amount.
Eligibility Requirements: Applicants must be college students pursuing a degree in the mental health field. **Application Requirements:** Applicants must check the available website to download the application form. **Additional Information:** Mental Health Association of Tarrant County at the above address.

3611 ■ MENTAL HEALTH ASSOCIATION OF TARRANT COUNTY

3136 W St.
Fort Worth, TX 76107
Tel: (817)335-5405
Fax: (817)334-0025
E-mail: mhatc@mhatc.org
Web Site: http://www.mhatc.org
To provide financial support to those students pursuing a degree in the mental health field.
Title of Award: Linda Lyons Memorial Scholarship Fund **Area, Field, or Subject:** Psychiatry; Psychology; Sociology; Social work; Counseling; Rehabilitation counseling. **Level of Education for which Award is Granted:** Undergraduate **Funds Available:** No specific amount.
Eligibility Requirements: Applicants must be college students pursuing a degree in the mental health field. **Application Requirements:** Applicants must check the available website to download the application form. **Additional Information:** Mental Health Association of Tarrant County at the above address.

Physical Sciences

General

3612 ■ AMERICAN COUNCIL OF INDEPENDENT LABORATORIES
1629 K St. NW, Ste. 400
Washington, DC 20006-1633
Tel: (202)887-5872
Fax: (202)887-0021
E-mail: info@acil.org
Web Site: http://www.acil.org
To provide financial assistance for helping to ensure future generations of skilled employees for the laboratory testing community.
Title of Award: American Council of Independent Laboratories Scholarships **Area, Field, or Subject:** Physical sciences. **Level of Education for which Award is Granted:** Undergraduate **Funds Available:** $1,000 to 4,000.
Eligibility Requirements: Applicants must be students attending their junior year or higher in a four-year, bachelor degree major in any of the physical sciences practiced by ACIL members: physics, chemistry, engineering, geology, biology, or environmental science in granting institution or graduate program within the United States. **Application Requirements:** Applicant must submit a brief resume or personal statement outlining the activities in college, including field of study and future plans; two letters of recommendation from faculty members of the university currently attending; transcript of grades; and information on any other scholarship or grant aid now receiving. **Deadline for Receipt:** April 4.

3613 ■ AMERICAN SOCIETY FOR PHOTOGRAMMETRY AND REMOTE SENSING
5410 Grosvenor Ln., Ste. 210
Bethesda, MD 20814-2160
Tel: (301)493-0290
Fax: (301)493-0208
E-mail: asprs@asprs.org
Web Site: http://www.asprs.org
To promote study in surveying and photogrammetry leading to a career in the geospatial mapping profession.
Title of Award: Francis H. Moffitt Memorial Scholarships **Area, Field, or Subject:** Remote sensing; Photogrammetry. **Level of Education for which Award is Granted:** Graduate, Undergraduate **Funds Available:** $2,500.
Eligibility Requirements: Applicants must be students currently enrolled or planning to enroll in a college/university in the United States or Canada; pursuing a program of study in surveying or photogrammetry. **Application Requirements:** Applicants must submit an application form; a listing of courses taken and/or those to be taken in surveying and photogrammetry and other related geospatial information technologies; a transcript of all college/university level courses completed; a listing of internships, special projects or work experience; two letters of recommendation or reference form; a statement (maximum of 2 pages) detailing the applicant's educational and research goals. **Additional Information:** Established in memory of Frank Moffitt for his lifetime contributions to the photogrammetric surveying profession. **Deadline for Receipt:** December 3.

3614 ■ AMERICAN SOKOL
122 W 22nd St.
Oak Brook, IL 60523-1557

Tel: (630)368-0771
Fax: (630)368-0758
E-mail: aso@american-sokol.org
Web Site: http://american-sokol.com
To help incoming students pursue their studies in college.
Title of Award: American Sokol Merit Awards **Area, Field, or Subject:** Physical education; Physical sciences. **Level of Education for which Award is Granted:** Undergraduate **Number Awarded:** 2 students per district. **Funds Available:** $500. **Duration:** One year.
Eligibility Requirements: Applicants must be Sokol Youth or Sokol Adult members who are planning a full-time course or program in an accredited college. Applications must be made in advance of the year of study. **Application Requirements:** Successful candidates must submit a recommendation proof of the Unit or District Physical Director; a parent or guardian will be required to sign to the condition that if the candidate cannot submit the needed requirements completely, he or she should repaid the whole amount of the award. **Additional Information:** The award was instituted by the XIIth American Sokol Convention to be paid from the American Sokol Future Leaders Fund. **Deadline for Receipt:** June 1.

3615 ■ ASSOCIATION FOR IRON AND STEEL TECHNOLOGY
186 Thorn Hill Rd.
Warrendale, PA 15086-7528
Tel: (724)776-6040
Fax: (724)776-1880
E-mail: info@aist.org
Web Site: http://www.aist.org
To enhance education and careers in engineering, metallurgy, physical science, computer technology or an engineering technology field.
Title of Award: Ohio Valley Chapter Scholarships **Area, Field, or Subject:** Engineering; Metallurgy; Physical sciences. **Level of Education for which Award is Granted:** Undergraduate **Number Awarded:** 2. **Funds Available:** $1,000. **Duration:** One year.
Eligibility Requirements: Applicant must be a dependent or member of Ohio Valley Chapter of the AIST; planning to attend or currently enrolled full-time curriculum at an accredited university or college; pursuing a degree in Mechanical Engineering, Electrical Engineering, Engineering/Engineering Technology, Environmental Engineering/Sciences, Metallurgy, Physical Sciences, Computer Technology, Computer Programming, Information Systems Technology, Chemistry, Biology/Microbiology, Physics, other engineering-related fields, or other related fields approved by the committee. **Application Requirements:** Applicants must submit an application form available at the website; a resume; a recommendation/evaluation from a counselor and teacher or professor; copy of SAT/ACT scores; copy of transcripts; an essay (maximum of 2 pages) with either one of the topics: purpose in going to college; beneficial experience during the last two summers; most significant experiences and effect on future plans; accomplishments providing the greatest satisfaction; reasons why he/she should be chosen as the recipient of the award. All requirements must be sent to: Jeff McKain, 11451 Reading Road Cincinnati, OH 45241. Or thru email, Attn: AIST Scholarship, E-mail subject: AIST Scholarship to jeff.mckain@xtek.com. **Deadline for Receipt:** March 31. **Additional Information:** Jeff Mckain 513-200-3000.

3616 ■ ASSOCIATION FOR WOMEN GEOSCIENTISTS
PO Box 30645
Lincoln, NE 68503-0645
Tel: (402)470-3110
Fax: (402)470-3110
E-mail: office@awg.org
Web Site: http://www.awg.org
To support students with their educational pursuits.
Title of Award: AWG Maria Luisa Crawford Field Camp Scholarships **Area, Field, or Subject:** Geosciences. **Level of Education for which Award is Granted:** Undergraduate **Number Awarded:** 2. **Funds Available:** $500.
Eligibility Requirements: Applicant must be a full-time undergraduate student pursuing a degree in geosciences and must have a GPA of 3.0.
Application Requirements: Applicants must submit a completed application form together with an essay; two letters of recommendations; and college transcripts. **Deadline for Receipt:** February 16. **Additional Information:** Alice L. Hoersch, PhD, hoersch@lasalle.edu.

3617 ■ ASSOCIATION FOR WOMEN GEOSCIENTISTS
PO Box 30645
Lincoln, NE 68503-0645
Tel: (402)470-3110
Fax: (402)470-3110
E-mail: office@awg.org
Web Site: http://www.awg.org
To support students with their educational pursuits.
Title of Award: AWG Minority Scholarships **Area, Field, or Subject:** Geosciences. **Level of Education for which Award is Granted:** Undergraduate **Number Awarded:** 1. **Funds Available:** $5000. **Duration:** June 30.
Eligibility Requirements: Applicant must be a woman who is African-American, Hispanic, or Native American; full-time student pursuing an undergraduate degree in the geosciences at an accredited college or university (high school students who will enter one of these fields during their freshman year may also apply). **Application Requirements:** Applicants must submit a completed application form together with a statement of academic career goals; two letters of recommendation; transcript; and SAT/ACT scores. **Deadline for Receipt:** June 30. **Additional Information:** Christina Tapia, awgscholarship@yahoo.com.

3618 ■ ASSOCIATION FOR WOMEN GEOSCIENTISTS
PO Box 30645
Lincoln, NE 68503-0645
Tel: (402)470-3110
Fax: (402)470-3110
E-mail: office@awg.org
Web Site: http://www.awg.org
To support students with their educational pursuit.
Title of Award: Penelope Hanshaw Scholarships **Area, Field, or Subject:** Geosciences. **Level of Education for which Award is Granted:** Graduate, Undergraduate **Funds Available:** $500.
Eligibility Requirements: Applicant must be enrolled full-time graduate or undergraduate geosciences major; and have a GPA of 3.0. **Application Requirements:** Applicant must submit a nomination letter from a geoscience professor; a recommendation letter from a geoscience faculty; a letter of application; and academic transcripts. Send materials to Laurel M. Bybell, US Geological Survey 926 National Center Reston, VA 20192. **Additional Information:** Sponsored by AWG Potomac Area Chapter. **Deadline for Receipt:** April 30. **Additional Information:** Laurel M. Bybell.

3619 ■ ASSOCIATION FOR WOMEN GEOSCIENTISTS
PO Box 30645
Lincoln, NE 68503-0645
Tel: (402)470-3110
Fax: (402)470-3110
E-mail: office@awg.org
Web Site: http://www.awg.org
To encourage women to study geoscience.
Title of Award: Puget Sound Chapter Scholarships **Area, Field, or Subject:** Geosciences. **Level of Education for which Award is Granted:** Undergraduate **Funds Available:** $1000.

Eligibility Requirements: Applicant must be an undergraduate woman committed to completing a Bachelor's Degree; pursuing a career or graduate work in the geosciences; a sophomore, junior, or senior woman enrolled in a university or two year college in Washington state west of the Columbia and Okanogan Rivers; have a minimum of 3.2 GPA (or equivalent academic achievement). **Application Requirements:** Applicants must submit their name, address, phone number, and email (if available); One paragraph each describing your (1) financial needs, (2) current resources, and (3) academic achievements; One-page essay summarizing your commitment to a career in the geosciences; Copies of all college transcripts (photocopies accepted); Three letters of reference; provide names, affiliations, phone numbers. **Additional Information:** Sponsored by AWG Puget Sound Chapter. **Deadline for Receipt:** November 3.

3620 ■ ASSOCIATION FOR WOMEN GEOSCIENTISTS
PO Box 30645
Lincoln, NE 68503-0645
Tel: (402)470-3110
Fax: (402)470-3110
E-mail: office@awg.org
Web Site: http://www.awg.org
To support students with educational pursuits.
Title of Award: William Rucker Greenwood Scholarships **Area, Field, or Subject:** Geosciences. **Level of Education for which Award is Granted:** Graduate, Undergraduate **Funds Available:** $1000.
Eligibility Requirements: Applicant must be a minority woman; enrolled full-time graduate or undergraduate geosciences major. **Application Requirements:** Applicants must submit a letter of recommendation from a geoscience professor or chairperson, and another from a geoscience faculty or employer; and a letter of application. Send materials to Laurel M. Bybell, US Geological Survey 926 National Center Reston, VA 20192. **Additional Information:** Sponsored by AWG Potomac Area Chapter. **Deadline for Receipt:** April 30. **Additional Information:** Laurel M. Bybell.

3621 ■ CANADIAN SOCIETY OF PETROLEUM GEOLOGISTS
600-640 8th Ave. SW
Calgary, AB, Canada T2P 1G7
Tel: (403)264-5610
Fax: (403)264-5898
E-mail: tim.howard@cspg.org
Web Site: http://www.cspg.org
To encourage educational pursuits among aboriginal students involved in the earth sciences.
Title of Award: Canadian Aboriginal Science and Technology Society Scholarships **Area, Field, or Subject:** Geosciences. **Level of Education for which Award is Granted:** Undergraduate **Funds Available:** $1,250.
Eligibility Requirements: Applicants must be aboriginal students pursuing academic programs in the earth sciences. The program of study must be at least two years in length and the student must have completed the first year of his/her studies. **Application Requirements:** Applicants must submit the following: high school transcript; university transcript (second semester midterm results accepted if received under separate cover and signed by department head); recommendation by department head and another teaching faculty member of the department. **Additional Information:** Shawna Christensen; 403-218-1625; Schristensen@petrelrob.com.

3622 ■ CANADIAN SOCIETY OF PETROLEUM GEOLOGISTS
600-640 8th Ave. SW
Calgary, AB, Canada T2P 1G7
Tel: (403)264-5610
Fax: (403)264-5898
E-mail: tim.howard@cspg.org
Web Site: http://www.cspg.org
To promote excellence in petroleum geology and geophysics by assisting in the development of future geoscientists.
Title of Award: Glen Ruby Memorial Scholarships **Area, Field, or Subject:** Geoscience. **Level of Education for which Award is Granted:** Undergraduate **Funds Available:** $2,000-$4,000.
Eligibility Requirements: Applicants must be students in their second, third or fourth year of studies in areas related to petroleum geology and geophysics. **Application Requirements:** Applicants must submit the

completed application form together with copy of transcripts. Application forms are available online. **Additional Information:** Scholarships will be administered through the CSPG Trust Fund. **Deadline for Receipt:** October 31. **Additional Information:** June Hamm, Conoco Philips Canada; PO Box 130, 401-9th Avenue S.W., Calgary, AB, T2P 2H7.

3623 ■ ENERGY AND MINERAL LAW FOUNDATION
340 S Broadway, Ste. 101
Lexington, KY 40508
Tel: (859)231-0271
Fax: (859)226-0485
E-mail: eml@aol.com
Web Site: http://www.blairchiropractic.com
To provide educational assistance to encourage the study of energy, environmental, natural resources, and mineral law.

Title of Award: EMLF Law Student Scholarships **Area, Field, or Subject:** Environmental science, Natural resources, Mineralogy, Energy-related areas. **Level of Education for which Award is Granted:** Undergraduate **Funds Available:** $1,000-$3,000.

Eligibility Requirements: Applicants must be law school students for the current academic year and must demonstrate an interest in the study of natural resources, energy or mineral law. **Deadline for Receipt:** April 11.

3624 ■ FEI COMPANY
5350 NE Dawson Creek Dr.
Hillsboro, OR 97124
Tel: (503)726-7500; (866)693-3426
Fax: (503)726-2615
Web Site: http://www.fei.com
To assist high school seniors who plan careers in the fields of Physical Sciences or Materials Sciences.

Title of Award: Casey Bennett Scholarships **Area, Field, or Subject:** Physical sciences. **Level of Education for which Award is Granted:** Undergraduate **Number Awarded:** 2. **Funds Available:** $1,000.

Eligibility Requirements: Applicant must be a high school senior (from either the Beaverton or Hillsboro School Districts); planning to pursue a career in Physical Sciences or Materials Sciences; and must have a 3.5 GPA or above. **Application Requirements:** Applicants must complete the online scholarship application; submit a brief essay (approximately 1/2-1 page) explaining why they should receive the award and an explanation of education/career "roadmap"; a letter of recommendation from a science-related faculty member; and high school transcript (copy or scan). Applications are to be submitted online to scholarships@fei.com (include your name in the subject line of the email). **Deadline for Receipt:** April 30.

3625 ■ GEMOLOGICAL INSTITUTE OF AMERICA
The Robert Mouawad Campus
5345 Amada Dr.
Carlsbad, CA 92008
Tel: (760)603-4031
Free: 800-421-7250
E-mail: financialaid@gia.edu
Web Site: http://www.gia.edu
To promote education in Gemology.

Title of Award: William Argo Scholarships **Area, Field, or Subject:** Gemology. **Level of Education for which Award is Granted:** Undergraduate **Number Awarded:** 1. **Funds Available:** $500.

Eligibility Requirements: Applicant must be U.S. citizen and permanent resident; at least 17 years old; have a high school diploma or GED equivalency; currently employed or planning to enter in the jewelry industry; applying for On Campus or Distance Education School of Gemology course or program; past recipient of GIA scholarship within last five years are not eligible. **Application Requirements:** Applicant must complete the GIA Scholarship application (available at the website), with a letter of recommendation from a person in the jewelry industry. Send application and supporting documents to: Gemological Institute of America, Office of Student Financial Assistance, MS 7 The Robert Mouawad Campus 5345 Armada Drive Carlsbad, CA 92008. **Deadline for Receipt:** June 15 October 15. **Additional Information:** Financial aid representative, 800-421-7250 x-4175, financialaid@gia.edu.

3626 ■ GEMOLOGICAL INSTITUTE OF AMERICA
The Robert Mouawad Campus
5345 Amada Dr.
Carlsbad, CA 92008
Tel: (760)603-4031
Free: 800-421-7250
E-mail: financialaid@gia.edu
Web Site: http://www.gia.edu
To promote education in Gemology.

Title of Award: ColorMasters Scholarships **Area, Field, or Subject:** Gemology. **Level of Education for which Award is Granted:** Undergraduate **Number Awarded:** 8. **Funds Available:** $390.

Eligibility Requirements: Applicant must be U.S. citizen and permanent resident; at least 17 years old; have a high school diploma or GED equivalency; currently employed or planning to enter in the jewelry industry (ColorMasters products); applying for Distance Education School of Gemology Accredited Jewelry Professionals (AJP) diploma program; past recipient of GIA scholarship within last five years are not eligible. **Application Requirements:** Applicant must complete the GIA Scholarship application (available at the website), with a letter of recommendation from a person in the jewelry industry. Send application and supporting documents to: Gemological Institute of America, Office of Student Financial Assistance, MS 7 The Robert Mouawad Campus 5345 Armada Drive Carlsbad, CA 92008. **Deadline for Receipt:** June 15 - October 15. **Additional Information:** Financial aid representative, 800-421-7250 x-4175, financialaid@gia.edu.

3627 ■ GEMOLOGICAL INSTITUTE OF AMERICA
The Robert Mouawad Campus
5345 Amada Dr.
Carlsbad, CA 92008
Tel: (760)603-4031
Free: 800-421-7250
E-mail: financialaid@gia.edu
Web Site: http://www.gia.edu
To promote education in Gemology.

Title of Award: Eye On Jewels Scholarships **Area, Field, or Subject:** Gemology. **Level of Education for which Award is Granted:** Undergraduate **Number Awarded:** 2. **Funds Available:** $395

Eligibility Requirements: Applicant must be U.S. citizen and permanent resident; at least 17 years old; have a high school diploma or GED equivalency; currently employed or planning to enter in the jewelry industry; applying for Distance Education School of Gemology Accredited Jewelry Professionals (AJP) diploma program; past recipient of GIA scholarship within last five years are not eligible. **Application Requirements:** Applicant must complete the GIA Scholarship application (available at the website), with a letter of recommendation from a person in the jewelry industry. Send application and supporting documents to: Gemological Institute of America, Office of Student Financial Assistance, MS 7 The Robert Mouawad Campus 5345 Armada Drive Carlsbad, CA 92008. **Deadline for Receipt:** June 15 October 15. **Additional Information:** Financial aid representative, 800-421-7250 x-4175, financialaid@gia.edu.

3628 ■ GEMOLOGICAL INSTITUTE OF AMERICA
The Robert Mouawad Campus
5345 Amada Dr.
Carlsbad, CA 92008
Tel: (760)603-4031
Free: 800-421-7250
E-mail: financialaid@gia.edu
Web Site: http://www.gia.edu
To promote education in Gemology.

Title of Award: GIA Endowment Scholarships - School of Business **Area, Field, or Subject:** Gemology; Business. **Level of Education for which Award is Granted:** Undergraduate **Funds Available:** Varies.

Eligibility Requirements: Applicant must be U.S. citizen and permanent resident; at least 17 years old; have a high school diploma or GED equivalency; currently employed or planning to enter in the jewelry industry; applying for On Campus and Distance Education courses at the School of Business; past recipient of GIA scholarship within last five years are not eligible. **Application Requirements:** Applicant must complete the GIA Scholarship application (available at the website), with a letter of recommendation from a person in the jewelry industry. Send application and supporting documents to: Gemological Institute of America, Office of Student Financial Assistance, MS 7 The Robert Mouawad Campus 5345 Armada Drive Carlsbad, CA 92008. **Deadline for Receipt:** June 15 October 15. **Additional Information:** Financial aid representative, 800-421-7250 x-4175, financialaid@gia.edu.

3629 ■ GEMOLOGICAL INSTITUTE OF AMERICA
The Robert Mouawad Campus
5345 Amada Dr.
Carlsbad, CA 92008
Tel: (760)603-4031
Free: 800-421-7250
E-mail: financialaid@gia.edu
Web Site: http://www.gia.edu
To promote education in Gemology.
Title of Award: Ray Glynn Scholarships **Area, Field, or Subject:** Gemology. **Level of Education for which Award is Granted:** Undergraduate **Number Awarded:** 1. **Funds Available:** $500.
Eligibility Requirements: Applicant must be U.S. citizen and legal resident of the state of Alaska, Idaho, Oregon, Montana, or Washington; at least 17 years old; have a high school diploma or GED equivalency; currently employed or planning to enter in the jewelry industry; applying for Distance Education School of Gemology course for Diamonds, Colored Stones, or Gem Identification; past recipient of GIA scholarship within last five years are not eligible. **Application Requirements:** Applicant must complete the GIA Scholarship application (available at the website), with a letter of recommendation from a person in the jewelry industry. Send application and supporting documents to: Gemological Institute of America, Office of Student Financial Assistance, MS 7 The Robert Mouawad Campus 5345 Armada Drive Carlsbad, CA 92008. **Deadline for Receipt:** June 15 October 15. **Additional Information:** Financial aid representative, 800-421-7250 x-4175, financialaid@gia.edu.

3630 ■ GEMOLOGICAL INSTITUTE OF AMERICA
The Robert Mouawad Campus
5345 Amada Dr.
Carlsbad, CA 92008
Tel: (760)603-4031
Free: 800-421-7250
E-mail: financialaid@gia.edu
Web Site: http://www.gia.edu
To promote education in Gemology.
Title of Award: Morris Hanauer Scholarships **Area, Field, or Subject:** Gemology. **Level of Education for which Award is Granted:** Undergraduate **Number Awarded:** 1. **Funds Available:** $600.
Eligibility Requirements: Applicant must be U.S. citizen and permanent resident; at least 17 years old; have a high school diploma or GED equivalency; currently employed or planning to enter in the jewelry industry; applying for Distance Education School of Gemology course or program; past recipient of GIA scholarship within last five years are not eligible. **Application Requirements:** Applicant must complete the GIA Scholarship application (available at the website), with a letter of recommendation from a person in the jewelry industry. Send application and supporting documents to: Gemological Institute of America, Office of Student Financial Assistance, MS 7 The Robert Mouawad Campus 5345 Armada Drive Carlsbad, CA 92008. **Deadline for Receipt:** June 15 - October 15. **Additional Information:** Financial aid representative, 800-421-7250 x-4175, financialaid@gia.edu.

3631 ■ GEMOLOGICAL INSTITUTE OF AMERICA
The Robert Mouawad Campus
5345 Amada Dr.
Carlsbad, CA 92008
Tel: (760)603-4031
Free: 800-421-7250
E-mail: financialaid@gia.edu
Web Site: http://www.gia.edu
To promote education in Gemology.
Title of Award: Kazanjian Scholarships **Area, Field, or Subject:** Gemology. **Level of Education for which Award is Granted:** Undergraduate **Number Awarded:** 2. **Funds Available:** $10,000.
Eligibility Requirements: Applicant must be U.S. citizen and permanent resident; at least 17 years old; have a high school diploma or GED

equivalency; currently employed or planning to enter in the jewelry industry; applying for any School of Gemology course or program; past recipient of GIA scholarship within last five years are not eligible. **Application Requirements:** Applicant must complete the GIA Scholarship application (available at the website), with a letter of recommendation from a person in the jewelry industry. Send application and supporting documents to: Gemological Institute of America, Office of Student Financial Assistance, MS 7 The Robert Mouawad Campus 5345 Armada Drive Carlsbad, CA 92008. **Deadline for Receipt:** June 15 - October 15. **Additional Information:** Financial aid representative, 800-421-7250 x-4175, financialaid@gia.edu.

3632 ■ GEMOLOGICAL INSTITUTE OF AMERICA
The Robert Mouawad Campus
5345 Amada Dr.
Carlsbad, CA 92008
Tel: (760)603-4031
Free: 800-421-7250
E-mail: financialaid@gia.edu
Web Site: http://www.gia.edu
To promote education in Gemology.
Title of Award: Richard Kern Scholarships **Area, Field, or Subject:** Gemology. **Level of Education for which Award is Granted:** Undergraduate **Number Awarded:** 1. **Funds Available:** $500.
Eligibility Requirements: Applicant must be U.S. citizen and permanent resident; at least 17 years old; have a high school diploma or GED equivalency; currently employed or planning to enter in the jewelry industry; applying for On Campus or Distance Education School of Gemology course or program; past recipient of GIA scholarship within last five years are not eligible. **Application Requirements:** Applicant must complete the GIA Scholarship application (available at the website), with a letter of recommendation from a person in the jewelry industry. Send application and supporting documents to: Gemological Institute of America, Office of Student Financial Assistance, MS 7 The Robert Mouawad Campus 5345 Armada Drive Carlsbad, CA 92008. **Deadline for Receipt:** June 15 October 15. **Additional Information:** Financial aid representative, 800-421-7250 x-4175, financialaid@gia.edu.

3633 ■ GEMOLOGICAL INSTITUTE OF AMERICA
The Robert Mouawad Campus
5345 Amada Dr.
Carlsbad, CA 92008
Tel: (760)603-4031
Free: 800-421-7250
E-mail: financialaid@gia.edu
Web Site: http://www.gia.edu
To promote education in Gemology.
Title of Award: Irene Mack Scholarships **Area, Field, or Subject:** Gemology. **Level of Education for which Award is Granted:** Undergraduate **Number Awarded:** 2. **Funds Available:** $500.
Eligibility Requirements: Applicant must be U.S. citizen and permanent resident; at least 17 years old; have a high school diploma or GED equivalency; currently employed or planning to enter in the jewelry industry; applying for Distance Education School of Gemology course or program; past recipient of GIA scholarship within last five years are not eligible. **Application Requirements:** Applicant must complete the GIA Scholarship application (available at the website), with a letter of recommendation from a person in the jewelry industry. Send application and supporting documents to: Gemological Institute of America, Office of Student Financial Assistance, MS 7 The Robert Mouawad Campus 5345 Armada Drive Carlsbad, CA 92008. **Deadline for Receipt:** June 15 - October 15. **Additional Information:** Financial aid representative, 800-421-7250 x-4175, financialaid@gia.edu.

3634 ■ GEMOLOGICAL INSTITUTE OF AMERICA
The Robert Mouawad Campus
5345 Amada Dr.
Carlsbad, CA 92008
Tel: (760)603-4031
Free: 800-421-7250
E-mail: financialaid@gia.edu
Web Site: http://www.gia.edu
To promote education in Gemology.

Title of Award: Matthew A. Runci, MJSA Scholarships **Area, Field, or Subject:** Gemology; Art industries and trade. **Level of Education for which Award is Granted:** Undergraduate **Number Awarded:** 1. **Funds Available:** $500.

Eligibility Requirements: Applicant must be U.S. citizen and permanent resident; at least 17 years old; have a high school diploma or GED equivalency; currently employed or planning to enter in the jewelry industry; applying for On Campus School of Jewelry Manufacturing Arts courses; past recipient of GIA scholarship within last five years are not eligible. **Application Requirements:** Applicant must complete the GIA Scholarship application (available at the website), with a letter of recommendation from a person in the jewelry industry. Send application and supporting documents to: Gemological Institute of America, Office of Student Financial Assistance, MS 7 The Robert Mouawad Campus 5345 Armada Drive Carlsbad, CA 92008. **Deadline for Receipt:** June 15 - October 15. **Additional Information:** Financial aid representative, 800-421-7250 x-4175, financialaid@gia.edu.

3635 ■ GEMOLOGICAL INSTITUTE OF AMERICA

The Robert Mouawad Campus
5345 Amada Dr.
Carlsbad, CA 92008
Tel: (760)603-4031
Free: 800-421-7250
E-mail: financialaid@gia.edu
Web Site: http://www.gia.edu
To promote education in Gemology.

Title of Award: Trillion Diamond Company Scholarships **Area, Field, or Subject:** Gemology. **Level of Education for which Award is Granted:** Undergraduate **Number Awarded:** 2. **Funds Available:** $500.

Eligibility Requirements: Applicant must be U.S. citizen and residing in the state of New York, New Jersey, or Connecticut; at least 17 years old; have a high school diploma or GED equivalency; currently employed or planning to enter in the jewelry industry; applying for Distance Education School of Gemology courses; past recipient of GIA scholarship within last five years are not eligible. **Application Requirements:** Applicant must complete the GIA Scholarship application (available at the website), with a letter of recommendation from a person in the jewelry industry. Send application and supporting documents to: Gemological Institute of America, Office of Student Financial Assistance, MS 7 The Robert Mouawad Campus 5345 Armada Drive Carlsbad, CA 92008. **Deadline for Receipt:** June 15 - October 15. **Additional Information:** Financial aid representative, 800-421-7250 x-4175, financialaid@gia.edu.

3636 ■ GEMOLOGICAL INSTITUTE OF AMERICA

The Robert Mouawad Campus
5345 Amada Dr.
Carlsbad, CA 92008
Tel: (760)603-4031
Free: 800-421-7250
E-mail: financialaid@gia.edu
Web Site: http://www.gia.edu
To promote education in Gemology.

Title of Award: William Goldberg Diamond Corp. Scholarships **Area, Field, or Subject:** Gemology. **Level of Education for which Award is Granted:** Undergraduate **Number Awarded:** 1. **Funds Available:** $10,000.

Eligibility Requirements: Applicant must be U.S. citizen and permanent resident; at least 17 years old; have a high school diploma or GED equivalency; currently employed or planning to enter in the jewelry industry; applying for any School of Gemology course or program; past recipient of GIA scholarship within last five years are not eligible. **Application Requirements:** Applicant must complete the GIA Scholarship application (available at the website), with a letter of recommendation from a person in the jewelry industry. Send application and supporting documents to: Gemological Institute of America, Office of Student Financial Assistance, MS 7 The Robert Mouawad Campus 5345 Armada Drive Carlsbad, CA 92008. **Deadline for Receipt:** June 15 - October 15. **Additional Information:** Financial aid representative, 800-421-7250 x-4175, financialaid@gia.edu.

3637 ■ REDLANDS COMMUNITY SCHOLARSHIP FOUNDATION

c/o Kathleen Venegas-Boge, Admin. Asst.
PO Box 1683
Redlands, CA 92373
Tel: (909)307-9892
Fax: (909)307-9892
Web Site: http://www.redlandsscholarships.org
To encourage educational pursuits among Redlands Unified School District graduates by providing educational assistance.

Title of Award: Harold Leeming Memorial Scholarships **Area, Field, or Subject:** Engineering; Physical sciences. **Level of Education for which Award is Granted:** Undergraduate **Number Awarded:** 2. **Funds Available:** $1,000.

Eligibility Requirements: Applicant must be a graduating senior who has an interest in engineering or physical science; must have played an active part in school and community activities; and must be enrolled in engineering or physical science courses. **Application Requirements:** Applicants must submit a completed application form together with the scantron sheet; cover sheet; student activity and community activity sheets; personal essay; and a copy of unofficial transcript (signed by the counselor). **Additional Information:** No electronic submissions of application will be accepted. Submit two printed copies of the application and use a No. 2 pencil on the scantron sheet. **Deadline for Receipt:** February 20.

3638 ■ SHELL OIL COMPANY

PO Box 2463
Houston, TX 77252
Tel: (713)241-6161; 888-467-4355
E-mail: shellcustomercare@shell.com
Web Site: http://www.shell.com
To offer scholarships to selected students pursuing two and four-year college degrees in certain engineering or geosciences disciplines at certain colleges.

Title of Award: Shell Incentive Scholarships Fund **Area, Field, or Subject:** Engineering; Geosciences. **Level of Education for which Award is Granted:** Undergraduate **Funds Available:** $5,000.

Eligibility Requirements: Applicants must be underrepresented students pursuing a four-year degree in a specific technical field of study at certain colleges. **Application Requirements:** Applicants must submit a completed application form.

3639 ■ SHELL OIL COMPANY

PO Box 2463
Houston, TX 77252
Tel: (713)241-6161; 888-467-4355
E-mail: shellcustomercare@shell.com
Web Site: http://www.shell.com
To help students who seek an education to obtain employment in the industries that use and control mechanical, physical or chemical processes to produce a final product.

Title of Award: Shell Process Technology Scholarships **Area, Field, or Subject:** Engineering; Geosciences. **Level of Education for which Award is Granted:** Undergraduate **Funds Available:** $2,000.

Eligibility Requirements: Applicants must be currently enrolled or planning to enroll in the Process Technology two-year degree program. **Application Requirements:** Applicants must submit a completed application form.

3640 ■ SHELL OIL COMPANY

PO Box 2463
Houston, TX 77252
Tel: (713)241-6161; 888-467-4355
E-mail: shellcustomercare@shell.com
Web Site: http://www.shell.com
To offer scholarships to selected students pursuing two and four-year college degrees in certain engineering or geosciences disciplines at certain colleges.

Title of Award: Shell Technical Scholarships **Area, Field, or Subject:** Engineering; Geosciences. **Level of Education for which Award is Granted:** Undergraduate **Funds Available:** $5,000. **Duration:** 4 years.

Eligibility Requirements: Applicants must be students pursuing a four-year college degree in certain engineering or geosciences disciplines at certain colleges. **Application Requirements:** Applicants must submit a completed application form.

3641 ■ SOCIETY OF EXPLORATION GEOPHYSICISTS
PO Box 702740
Tulsa, OK 74170-2740
Tel: (918)497-5500
Fax: (918)497-5557
E-mail: membership@seg.org
Web Site: http://www.seg.org
To reduce the financial burden of tuition of geoscience students and promote study in geoscience.

Title of Award: Society of Exploration Geophysicists Foundation Scholarships **Area, Field, or Subject:** Geosciences. **Level of Education for which Award is Granted:** Graduate, Undergraduate **Funds Available:** $500-$14,000.

Eligibility Requirements: Applicant must be a student pursuing a college curriculum directed toward a career in applied geophysics, or a closely related field such as geosciences, physics, geology, or earth and environmental sciences; must be attending high school and planning to enter college next fall or be an undergraduate or graduate college student whose grades are above average. **Application Requirements:** Applicants must submit a completed scholarship application form and materials. **Deadline for Receipt:** February 1. **Additional Information:** scholarships@seg.org

3642 ■ SOCIETY FOR MINING, METALLURGY AND EXPLORATION
8307 Shaffer Pkwy.
Littleton, CO 80127-4102
Tel: (303)973-9550
Free: 800-763-3132
Fax: (303)973-3845
E-mail: estrada@smenet.org
Web Site: http://www.smenet.org
To provide support to students seeking advanced education in the minerals industry profession and field.

Title of Award: SME Coal and Energy Division Scholarships **Area, Field, or Subject:** Metallurgy; Mineralogy; Mining; Engineering, Mining and Mineral. **Level of Education for which Award is Granted:** Undergraduate **Number Awarded:** 15. **Funds Available:** $1,500. **Duration:** One year.

Eligibility Requirements: Applicants must be junior or senior students majoring in mining or mineral engineering programs that are accredited by the Accreditation Board for Engineering and Technology (ABET). Applicants must be a student member of SME and must have a minimum cumulative 2.50 GPA. Applicants who have received a previous Coal and Energy Division Scholarship may, upon submitting a new application, be granted a scholarship, subject to the recommendations of the college or university the recipient is attending and review by the Scholarship Committee. **Application Requirements:** Applicants must submit a completed application form, transcript and two letters of recommendation, one of which must be from the Program Chair or Department Head. Application form should include a brief outline of the applicant's participation in mining industry-related activities (such as the student chapter or local section of SME), coal industry employment or employment commitment, scholastic achievements and an explanation why the applicant is interested in a career in coal and is deserving of Coal and Energy Division support. **Deadline for Receipt:** October 30. **Additional Information:** Ann Marie Estrada at the above address.

3643 ■ SOCIETY FOR MINING, METALLURGY AND EXPLORATION
8307 Shaffer Pkwy.
Littleton, CO 80127-4102
Tel: (303)973-9550
Free: 800-763-3132
Fax: (303)973-3845
E-mail: estrada@smenet.org
Web Site: http://www.smenet.org
To provide support to students seeking advanced education in the minerals industry profession and field.

Title of Award: SME Environmental Division Scholarships **Area, Field, or Subject:** Metallurgy; Mineralogy; Mining; Engineering, Mining and Mineral. **Level of Education for which Award is Granted:** Undergraduate **Funds Available:** $2,000. **Duration:** One academic year.

Eligibility Requirements: Candidates must be promising college students who desire to develop their skills related to mining and the environment. Candidates must be of good character and must have demonstrated scholastic aptitude; must be a member of SME, attending a college or university of his or her choice that provides a curriculum leading to an undergraduate degree related to mining and the environment and a faculty advisor with special interests in an environmentally oriented program. **Application Requirements:** Applicants must submit a completed application form, transcript and two references from faculty members, people from industry, or others who can write about his/her academic potential and professional interests. **Deadline for Receipt:** October 30. **Additional Information:** Ann Marie Estrada at the above address.

3644 ■ U.S. AIR FORCE ROTC
551 E Maxwell Blvd.
Maxwell AFB, AL 36112-5917
Tel: (334)953-6167
Fax: (866)423-7682
Web Site: http://www.afrotc.com
To provide financial assistance for college students enrolled in specific fields.

Title of Award: U.S. Air Force ROTC Express Scholarships **Area, Field, or Subject:** Engineering; Aerospace sciences; Aeronautics; Atmospheric sciences. **Level of Education for which Award is Granted:** Undergraduate **Funds Available:** $15,000.

Eligibility Requirements: Applicants must be United States citizens by the end of the projected term of activation; must pass the Air Force Officer Qualifying Test; must pass the Air Force ROTC Physical Fitness Test; must have at least a 2.5 cumulative college grade point average; must a physical examination and be certified; must not be a contracted scholarship recipient; and must meet the age, moral and other scholarship eligibility requirements for Air force ROTC. **Application Requirements:** Applications for the Express Scholarship are processed and approved at the detachment level. Applicant must contact the detachment serving the school that he/she wishes to attend and the school will work to nominate the student for the appropriate scholarship program.

3645 ■ UNITED STATES GEOSPATIAL INTELLIGENCE FOUNDATION
2325 Dulles Corner Blvd., Ste. 450
Herndon, VA 20171
Tel: (703)793-0109
Free: 800-698-7443
Fax: (703)793-9069
E-mail: stu.shea@usgif.org
Web Site: http://www.usgif.org
To help further the geospatial tradecraft. To assist promising students interested in the geospatial sciences.

Title of Award: United States Geospatial Intelligence Foundation High School Scholarships **Area, Field, or Subject:** Geosciences. **Level of Education for which Award is Granted:** Undergraduate **Funds Available:** No specific amount.

Eligibility Requirements: Applicants must be senior high school students interested in geospatial sciences. **Application Requirements:** Applicants must complete the application form. Applicants must submit an essay describing their understanding of the geospatial intelligence tradecraft, future goals and how they relate to geospatial tradecraft, their understanding of the variety of careers and opportunities available within the geospatial intelligence tradecraft, and their motivation for pursuing this field. Applicants must submit two letters of recommendation. **Deadline for Receipt:** May 30.

3646 ■ UNITED STATES GEOSPATIAL INTELLIGENCE FOUNDATION
2325 Dulles Corner Blvd., Ste. 450
Herndon, VA 20171
Tel: (703)793-0109
Free: 800-698-7443
Fax: (703)793-9069
E-mail: stu.shea@usgif.org
Web Site: http://www.usgif.org
To help further the geospatial tradecraft. To assist promising students interested in the geospatial sciences.

Title of Award: United States Geospatial Intelligence Foundation Undergraduate Scholarships **Area, Field, or Subject:** Geosciences.

Level of Education for which Award is Granted: Undergraduate **Funds Available:** No specific amount.

Eligibility Requirements: Applicants must be undergraduate students interested in geospatial sciences. **Application Requirements:** Applicants must complete the application form. Applicants must submit an essay describing their understanding of the geospatial intelligence tradecraft, future goals and how they relate to geospatial tradecraft, their understanding of the variety of careers and opportunities available within the geospatial intelligence tradecraft, and their motivation for pursuing this field. Applicants must submit two letters of recommendation. **Deadline for Receipt:** May 30. **Additional Information:** scholarships@usgif.org

3647 ■ UNIVERSITY OF ALASKA ANCHORAGE

3211 Providence Dr.
Anchorage, AK 99508
Tel: (907)786-1800
Web Site: http://www.uaa.alaska.edu
To provide financial assistance for tuition and other educational expenses to full-time students who are formally admitted to a degreeseeking program in the area of biochemistry, immunology, or microbiology at the University of Alaska Anchorage.

Title of Award: UAA Kris Knudson Memorial Scholarships **Area, Field, or Subject:** Biochemistry; Immunology; Microbiology. **Level of Education for which Award is Granted:** Graduate, Undergraduate **Funds Available:** $500-$885.

Eligibility Requirements: Applicant must demonstrate motivation, academic and leadership potential; must be in good academic standing with a minimum cumulative GPA of 3.0; must be formally admitted to an undergraduate or graduate degree-seeking program in the area of biochemistry, immunology, or microbiology at the University of Alaska Anchorage; must plan on enrolling full-time (12 credits) for undergraduate and (9 credits) for graduate at the University of Alaska Anchorage; must have completed at least fifteen credits in chemistry, biological sciences, and/or natural sciences; must be involved in a research project within the area of biochemistry, immunology, or microbiology; may be a U.S citizen, non-U.S. citizen, Alaska resident, or out-of-state resident; must be enrolled in the semester for which the award is made. **Application Requirements:** Applicants must submit a brief essay (250 words max) describing their involvement in a research project related to biochemistry, immunology, or microbiology. Application forms are available at www.uaa.alaska.edu/scholarships/kris.cfm. **Deadline for Receipt:** February 15.

3648 ■ UNIVERSITY OF NEW HAMPSHIRE

Office of Admission
4 Garrison Ave.
Durham, NH 03824
Tel: (603)862-1360
Fax: (603)862-0077
E-mail: admission@unh.edu
Web Site: http://www.unh.edu
To provide financial assistance to students who want to continue their education at UNH.

Title of Award: CEPS-Tyco Scholarships **Area, Field, or Subject:** Engineering; Physical sciences. **Level of Education for which Award is Granted:** Undergraduate **Number Awarded:** 2. **Funds Available:** $10,000. **Duration:** One year.

Eligibility Requirements: Applicants must be high school seniors admitted to the University's College of Engineering and Physical Sciences. **Application Requirements:** Applicants must have an application for admission to a major within the College of Engineering and Physical Sciences at the University of New Hampshire; must have official high school transcripts, including the first marking period of senior year; must have the official test scores for either the SAT Reasoning Test or ACT with writing test; must submit an additional scholarship essay through the online form; must submit a Free Application for Federal Student Aid (FAFSA) form. Application form and other supporting documents must be sent to University of New Hampshire, Office of Admission/CEPS-Tyco Scholarship, Grant House, 4 Garrison Ave., Durham, NH 03824. **Deadline for Receipt:** November 15.

Chemistry

3649 ■ AMERICAN ASSOCIATION FOR THE ADVANCEMENT OF SCIENCE

1200 New York Ave. NW
Washington, DC 20005
Tel: (202)326-6400
E-mail: webmaster@aaas.org
Web Site: http://www.aaas.org
To enhance undergraduate education through research experience that emphasize the interrelationship between chemistry and biology; to encourage students to pursue graduate education in chemistry and life sciences; to foster undergraduate programs and activities that bridge chemistry and biology;

Title of Award: Merck Undergraduate Science Research Scholarships **Area, Field, or Subject:** Chemistry; Biology; Life Sciences. **Level of Education for which Award is Granted:** Undergraduate **Number Awarded:** 15. **Funds Available:** $60,000. **Duration:** 3 years.

Eligibility Requirements: Applicants must be located in 50 United States; offered American Chemical Society-approved program in Chemistry; confer ten or fewer graduate degrees annually in Biology and Chemistry combined; defined by the U.S. Internal Revenue Service Tax Code as a not-for-profit entity under section 501; must not be current Merck/AAAS USRP Award Recipient. **Application Requirements:** Applicants must submit an application cover page; eligibility form including a copy of the school's 501(c)(3) certification letter from the U.S. Internal Revenue Service. **Deadline for Receipt:** November 2.

3650 ■ ASSOCIATION FOR WOMEN IN SCIENCE

1200 New York Ave. NW, Ste. 650
Washington, DC 20005
Tel: (202)326-8940
Fax: (202)326-8960
E-mail: awis@awis.org
Web Site: http://www.awis.org
To promote education in science.

Title of Award: AWIS College Scholarships **Area, Field, or Subject:** Astronomy and astronomical sciences; Geosciences; Biology; Mathematics and mathematical sciences; Chemistry; Physics; Computer and information sciences; Engineering; Psychology. **Level of Education for which Award is Granted:** Undergraduate **Number Awarded:** 2-5. **Funds Available:** No specific amount.

Eligibility Requirements: Applicant must be a female high school senior; U.S. citizen or permanent resident; have at least 3.75 GPA; at least 1200 score in SAT or a composite score of 25 in ACT; planning to study in any field of Astronomy, Geoscience, Biology, Mathematics, Chemistry, Physics, Computer and Information Science, Engineering, Psychology; planning to become a researcher or teacher. **Application Requirements:** Applicants must send five copies of: summary form; essay describing research experience; resume; two recommendation letters from science or research teachers; high school transcript and score of standardized test if available. **Deadline for Receipt:** January 17.

3651 ■ COMPOSITE PANEL ASSOCIATION

19465 Deerfield Ave., Ste. 306
Leesburg, VA 20176
Tel: (703)724-1128
Fax: (703)724-1588
Web Site: http://www.pbmdf.com
To provide financial assistance to students pursuing a career in the composite panel and affiliated industries.

Title of Award: Robert E. Dougherty Scholarships **Area, Field, or Subject:** Forestry; Chemistry; Engineering. **Level of Education for which Award is Granted:** Undergraduate **Number Awarded:** 8. **Funds Available:** 5,000.

Eligibility Requirements: Applicant must be North American citizen; and nominated by a member of the Robert E. Dougherty Education Foundation. **Application Requirements:** Scholarship Application forms can be downloaded at the website and must be filled out and returned to the Foundation. **Deadline for Receipt:** March 21.

3652 ■ FOUNDATION FOR THE CAROLINAS

217 S Tryon St.
Charlotte, NC 28202

Tel: (704)973-4500
Free: 800-973-7244
Web Site: http://www.fftc.org
To provide financial assistance for students at Clemson University and the University of North Carolina at Charlotte who are preparing for a career in a technological field appropriate to meet the requirements of the U.S. Patent Office as a patent agent or attorney.
Title of Award: Julian E. Carnes Scholarship Fund **Area, Field, or Subject:** Engineering; Chemistry; Physics; Biology; Computer and information sciences. **Level of Education for which Award is Granted:** Undergraduate **Funds Available:** No specific amount.
Eligibility Requirements: Applicants must be legal residents of North or South Carolina; must be rising juniors or seniors at Clemson University or UNC Charlotte whose academic major is appropriate to meet the requirements of the U.S. Patent Office for admission as a patent agent or attorney (including but not limited to engineering, chemistry, physics, biology and computer science); and must have at least a 3.0 cumulative grade point average (on a 4.0 scale). **Application Requirements:** Applicants must submit all the required application information. **Additional Information:** Clemson University Office of Student Financial Aid, 864-656-2280 or the UNC Charlotte Student Financial Aid Office, 704-687-2461.

3653 ■ LEWIS-CLARK STATE COLLEGE
500 8th Ave.
Lewiston, ID 83501
Tel: (208)792-5272
Web Site: http://www.lcsc.edu
To encourage African-American, Hispanic, and American Indian students to pursue undergraduate college degrees in the chemical sciences and chemical technology.
Title of Award: Lewis-Clark State College/American Chemical Society Scholars Program **Area, Field, or Subject:** Chemistry; Science Technologies; Chemical Engineering. **Level of Education for which Award is Granted:** Undergraduate **Funds Available:** $3,000. **Duration:** One year.
Eligibility Requirements: Applicants must be students who want to enter the fields of chemistry, biochemistry, or chemical engineering, and students seeking a two-year degree in chemical technology; high school seniors planning a science preparatory program of study and college students who are currently from freshmen to juniors who are committed to the study of chemistry, biochemistry, chemical engineering or other chemically related fields such as environmental science, materials science or toxicology and are interested in pursuing careers in one of these fields; students who have strong academic records and show an interest in and potential for careers in the chemical sciences. **Application Requirements:** Applicants must accomplish general application available at the website.

3654 ■ LEWIS-CLARK STATE COLLEGE
500 8th Ave.
Lewiston, ID 83501
Tel: (208)792-5272
Web Site: http://www.lcsc.edu
To inspire educational pursuits among less capable individuals by providing financial assistance.
Title of Award: Lewis-Clark State College Presidential Technical Out-of-State Scholarships **Area, Field, or Subject:** Chemistry; Computer Science; Engineering; Information Systems Analysis; Industrial Electronics; Biology; Earth Information Systems; Radiology; Heating/Air Conditioning; Automated Manufacturing Technology; Mathematics; Printing Technology; Graphic Arts or Web Development. **Level of Education for which Award is Granted:** Undergraduate **Funds Available:** No specific amount.
Eligibility Requirements: Applicants must be new non-resident high school or transfer students who have at least 14 transferable semester credits. **Application Requirements:** Applicants must accomplish a general application available in the website. **Deadline for Receipt:** March 1 for Fall enrollment or November 1 for Spring enrollment.

3655 ■ PMCA: AN INTERNATIONAL ASSOCIATION OF CONFECTIONERS
2980 Linden St., Ste. E3
Bethlehem, PA 18017
Tel: (610)625-4655

Fax: (610)625-4567
E-mail: info@pmca.com
Web Site: http://www.pmca.com
To foster education students involved in confectionery technology.
Title of Award: AACT Undergraduate Scholarships **Area, Field, or Subject:** Food science and technology; Chemistry; Biology. **Level of Education for which Award is Granted:** Undergraduate **Funds Available:** $5,000 (two $2,500 installments). **Duration:** One year.
Eligibility Requirements: Applicants must be sophomores, juniors or seniors majoring in food science, chemical science, biological science, or related field at an accredited four-year college or university in North America; must have a GPA of 3.0; and must be interested in confectionery technology. **Application Requirements:** Applicants must submit a completed application form together with a letter of recommendation; copy of college transcript; and a list of academic activities, experience, other activities, honors and awards, and a short statement of personal and professional goals. Send materials to Kevin Silva, Warrell Corp. 2150 Slate Hill Road Camp Hill, PA 17011. **Deadline for Receipt:** April 18. **Additional Information:** Kevin Silva, kevins@warrellcorp.com

3656 ■ RUBBER DIVISION AMERICAN CHEMICAL SOCIETY
PO Box 499
Akron, OH 44309-0499
Tel: (330)972-7814
Fax: (330)972-5269
Web Site: http://www.rubber.org
To provide financial assistance to students pursuing a college degree related to rubber technology, polymer science or the chemical profession.
Title of Award: Rubber Division American Chemical Society Scholarships **Area, Field, or Subject:** Chemistry; Physics; Chemical engineering; Mechanical engineering. **Level of Education for which Award is Granted:** Undergraduate **Funds Available:** $5,000. **Duration:** One academic year.
Eligibility Requirements: Applicants must be enrolled in an accredited university or college where rubber division has a partner organization; must be students majoring in chemistry, physics, chemical engineering, mechanical engineering, polymer science or any other field related to the rubber industry. **Application Requirements:** Applicants must send application form; two nomination letters; and transcript mailed by school registrar via regular mail. **Deadline for Receipt:** March. **Additional Information:** Christie Robinson, Education & Publications Manager, 330-972-7815.

3657 ■ THE SAN DIEGO FOUNDATION
2508 Historic Decatur Rd., Ste. 200
San Diego, CA 92106
Tel: (619)235-2300
Fax: (619)239-1710
E-mail: info@sdfoundation.org
Web Site: http://www.sdfoundation.org
To support the education of students from California.
Title of Award: Biocom Scholarships **Area, Field, or Subject:** Biology; Chemistry; Biomedical engineering. **Level of Education for which Award is Granted:** Undergraduate **Number Awarded:** 5. **Funds Available:** $1,500. **Duration:** One year.
Eligibility Requirements: Applicant must be a graduating high school senior with a minimum 3.50 GPA on a 4.0 scale; planning to attend an accredited two-year college or four-year university in the U.S.; must demonstrate a likelihood of achieving academic success with primary emphasis in biology, chemistry, physical and computational biosciences or biomedical engineering; committed in serving San Diego life sciences community; maintain a minimum 3.20 cumulative GPA on a 4.0 scale while in college; and exhibit the traits modeled by BIOCOM co-founder, James McGraw (leadership, passion for life sciences, integrity, and community service). **Application Requirements:** Applicants must submit a completed Common Scholarship Application together with personal statement; two letters of recommendation on official letterhead (written within the last six months); official transcript in an official and sealed envelope; and copy of most recent tax form (Form 1040-pages 1 & 2; Form 1040A-pages 1 & 2; Form 1040EZ-page 1). **Additional Information:** In memory of James McGraw. **Deadline for Receipt:** January 28. **Additional Information:** Arzo Mansury, Dir. Scholarships at 619-814-1343, or scholarships@sdfoundation.org.

3658 ■ THE SAN DIEGO FOUNDATION
2508 Historic Decatur Rd., Ste. 200
San Diego, CA 92106
Tel: (619)235-2300
Fax: (619)239-1710
E-mail: info@sdfoundation.org
Web Site: http://www.sdfoundation.org
To support the education of students from California.
Title of Award: Helm Family Scholarships **Area, Field, or Subject:** Biology; Computer and information sciences; Chemistry; Technology; Engineering; Physics. **Level of Education for which Award is Granted:** Undergraduate **Number Awarded:** 2. **Funds Available:** $5,00.
Eligibility Requirements: Applicant must be an entering junior or senior student at San Diego State University or the University of California, San Diego; have declared a major in mathematics or a scientific field such as, but not limited to, biology, computer science, chemistry, technology, engineering, physics, etc.; have a minimum 3.0 GPA on a 4.0 scale; and have demonstrated financial need. **Application Requirements:** Applicants must submit a completed Common Scholarship Application together with personal statement; two letters of recommendation on official letterhead (written within the last six months); official transcript in an official and sealed envelope; and a copy of most recent tax form (Form 1040-pages 1 & 2; Form 1040Apages 1 & 2; Form 1040EZ-page 1). **Deadline for Receipt:** January 28. **Additional Information:** Arzo Mansury, Dir. Scholarships at 619-814-1343, or scholarships@sdfoundation.org.

3659 ■ SOUTHWEST FLORIDA COMMUNITY FOUNDATION
8260 College Pkwy., Ste. 101
Fort Myers, FL 33919
Tel: (239)274-5900
Fax: (239)274-5930
Web Site: http://www.floridacommunity.com
To fund a student who will attend: FGCU, university of Florida/Gainesville, Florida State University/Tallahassee, Flagler College, Stetson University/Deland, University of Miami, University of Tampa, or Embry Riddle Aeronautical University/Daytona Beach.
Title of Award: D&A Florida Scholarships **Area, Field, or Subject:** Architecture; Business; Engineering; International affairs and relations; Journalism; Computer and information sciences; Law; Literature; Medicine; Physics; Chemistry; Political science. **Level of Education for which Award is Granted:** Undergraduate **Funds Available:** $10,000. **Duration:** One year.
Eligibility Requirements: Applicants must have graduated from a public or private high school in Charlotte, Glades, Hendry or Lee County; must pursue a degree in Architecture, Business, Engineering, International affairs and relations, Journalism, Computer and information sciences, Law, Literature, Medicine, Physics, Chemistry, or Political science. **Application Requirements:** Application forms are available online. Applicants must submit a letter of interest and letter of recommendation, a transcript and financial need documentation. **Deadline for Receipt:** February 15.

3660 ■ UNIVERSITY OF ALASKA ANCHORAGE
3211 Providence Dr.
Anchorage, AK 99508
Tel: (907)786-1800
Web Site: http://www.uaa.alaska.edu
To provide financial assistance for tuition and other educational expenses to full-time students who are formally admitted to a chemistry degree-seeking program at the University of Alaska Anchorage.
Title of Award: UAA Ardell French Memorial Scholarships **Area, Field, or Subject:** Chemistry. **Level of Education for which Award is Granted:** Undergraduate **Funds Available:** $1,000-$2,000.
Eligibility Requirements: Applicants must demonstrate motivation, academic and leadership potential; must be in good academic standing with a minimum cumulative GPA of 2.0; must be formally admitted to a undergraduate chemistry degree-seeking program at the University of Alaska Anchorage; must plan on enrolling full-time (12 credits) at the University of Alaska Anchorage; may be a U.S citizen, non-U.S citizen, Alaska resident, or out-of-state resident; must be enrolled in the semester for which the award is made. **Application Requirements:** Applicants must complete the electronic scholarship application available online at www.uaa.alaska.edu/scholarships/ardell.cfm. **Deadline for Receipt:** February 15.

3661 ■ VIRGINIA FOUNDATION FOR INDEPENDENT COLLEGES
8010 Ridge Rd., Ste. B
Richmond, VA 23229-7288
Tel: (804)288-6609
Free: 800-230-6757
Fax: (804)282-4635
E-mail: info@vfic.org
Web Site: http://www.vfic.org
To provide financial assistance for the students in their junior year at a VFIC college or university.
Title of Award: Phillip Morris USA Scholarships **Area, Field, or Subject:** Accounting; Biology; Business; Chemistry; Computer and information sciences; Economics; Engineering; Finance; Physics. **Level of Education for which Award is Granted:** Undergraduate **Funds Available:** $5,000.
Eligibility Requirements: Applicants must be U.S. citizens and current full-time sophomores attending a VFIC college or university (students from underrepresented populations are encouraged to apply); have minimum of 3.5 cumulative GPA; committed to applying for an internship with Phillip Morris USA for the summer after junior year; have declared, or intend to declare, a major in one of the following disciplines: accounting, biology, business, chemistry, computer science, economics, engineering, finance, or physics. **Application Requirements:** Applicants must submit completed application form along with two letters of recommendation and other required application information. **Deadline for Receipt:** November 1.

3662 ■ XAVIER UNIVERSITY
3800 Victory Pky.
Cincinnati, OH 45207
Tel: (513)745-3000
Free: 800-344-GOXU
Web Site: http://www.xavier.edu
To financially support students with their education.
Title of Award: Xavier University Departmental Scholarships **Area, Field, or Subject:** Chemistry; Classical studies; History; Mathematics and mathematical sciences; Modern languages; Physics. **Level of Education for which Award is Granted:** Undergraduate **Funds Available:** $2500.
Eligibility Requirements: Applicant must top the score in either of the six departmental exams (chemistry, classics (Latin), history, mathematics, modern languages (French, German or Spanish) and physics). Student must major in the area for which the scholarship is awarded. **Application Requirements:** Participants will take an exam in the appropriate subject area and have an opportunity to speak with faculty and learn more about the department.

Geology

3663 ■ AMERICAN ASSOCIATION OF STRATIGRAPHIC PALYNOLOGISTS
University of North Carolina at Pembroke
Geology, Old Main 213
Pembroke, NC 28372
Tel: (910)521-6478
E-mail: mbfarley@sigmaxi.net
Web Site: http://www.palynology.org
To support research in the field or any aspect related to paleontology.
Title of Award: Paleontological Society Student Research Grants **Area, Field, or Subject:** Earth Sciences; Geology. **Level of Education for which Award is Granted:** Graduate, Undergraduate **Funds Available:** $750. **Duration:** One year.
Eligibility Requirements: Applicant must be undergraduate or graduate student member of the Paleontological Society conducting a research on any aspect of paleontology. **Application Requirements:** Applicants must submit a completed application form (available at the website) and a letter of support from research advisor (must be sent to michalk@vt.edu). **Deadline for Receipt:** February 25.

3664 ■ ASSOCIATION OF DESK AND DERRICK CLUBS
5153 E 51st St., Ste. 107
Tulsa, OK 74135
Tel: (918)622-1749
Fax: (918)622-1675

E-mail: adotulsa@swbell.net
Web Site: http://www.addc.org
To provide financial assistance to college students planning a career in the petroleum energy or allied industries.
Title of Award: Association of Desk and Derrick Clubs Education Trust Scholarships **Area, Field, or Subject:** Geology; Geophysics; Engineering, Petroleum; Engineering, Nuclear; Engineering, Mechanical; Energy-related areas. **Level of Education for which Award is Granted:** Undergraduate **Funds Available:** $1,500.
Eligibility Requirements: Applicant must have completed at least two years or be currently enrolled in the second year of undergraduate study at an accredited college or university; be a U.S. or Canadian citizen; maintain a GPA of 3.2 or above on a 4.0 scale; be pursuing a career in the field of petroleum, energy or allied industry. **Application Requirements:** Applicants must submit a completed application form to Desk and Derrick Educational Trust, 5153 E 51st St., Ste. 107, Tulsa, OK 74135. **Deadline for Receipt:** April 1.

3665 ■ CAMECO CORPORATION
2121-11th St. W
Saskatoon, SK, Canada S7M 1J3
Tel: (306)956-6290
Fax: (306)956-6201
Web Site: http://www.cameco.com
To support the students who want to pursue their career in geological sciences.
Title of Award: Cameco Corporation Scholarships in the Geological Sciences - Continuing Students **Area, Field, or Subject:** Geology. **Level of Education for which Award is Granted:** Undergraduate **Number Awarded:** 2. **Funds Available:** No specific amount. **Duration:** One year.
Eligibility Requirements: Applicants must be full-time students who are Canadian citizens entering their second year of university study and pursuing Bachelor of Science degrees; must have declared majors in the geological sciences; must be registered in 200 level courses related to their majors; must have a sessional weighted average of at least 70% for all credit units attempted in the last regular session. **Application Requirements:** Application form can be obtained from: Continuing Students, Student Central, University of Saskatchewan, 105 Administration Place, Saskatoon, SK S7N 5A2. **Deadline for Receipt:** June 1.

3666 ■ CAMECO CORPORATION
2121-11th St. W
Saskatoon, SK, Canada S7M 1J3
Tel: (306)956-6290
Fax: (306)956-6201
Web Site: http://www.cameco.com
To support the students who want to pursue their career in geological sciences.
Title of Award: Cameco Corporation Scholarships in the Geological Sciences - Entering Students **Area, Field, or Subject:** Geology. **Level of Education for which Award is Granted:** Undergraduate **Number Awarded:** 2. **Funds Available:** No specific amount. **Duration:** One year.
Eligibility Requirements: Applicants must be full-time students who are Canadian citizens pursuing Bachelor of Science degrees and are entering their first year of university study and are registered in specified courses as outlined in guidelines. **Application Requirements:** Application form can be obtained from: Entering Students, Recruitment and Admissions, University of Saskatchewan, 105 Administration Place, Saskatoon, SK S7N 5A2. **Deadline for Receipt:** February 15.

3667 ■ GEOLOGICAL SOCIETY OF AMERICA
PO Box 9140
Boulder, CO 80301-9140
Tel: (303)357-1000; 888-443-4472
Fax: (303)257-1070
E-mail: gsaservice@geosociety.org
Web Site: http://www.geosociety.org
To encourage and support desert studies by students in their senior year of undergraduate studies, or at the master's or Ph.D. level.
Title of Award: Farouk El-Baz Student Research Grants **Area, Field, or Subject:** Geology. **Level of Education for which Award is Granted:** Doctorate, Graduate, Undergraduate **Funds Available:** No specified amount.

Eligibility Requirements: Applicants must be a GSA member; applicants must be in their senior year of their undergraduate studies, or at the master's or Ph.D. level. **Application Requirements:** Applicants must submit a one-page description of proposed research under title; letter of recommendation by university research advisor. **Deadline for Receipt:** June 1. **Additional Information:** awards@geosociety.org;

3668 ■ HISPANIC SCHOLARSHIP FUND
55 Second St., Ste. 1500
San Francisco, CA 94105
877-473-4636
Fax: (415)808-2302
E-mail: info@hsf.net
Web Site: http://www.hsf.net
To provide financial assistance to students of Hispanic heritage.
Title of Award: HSF/Wal-Mart Stores Inc. Scholarship Program **Area, Field, or Subject:** Marketing and distribution; Accounting; Business; Finance; Management; Computer and information sciences; Information science and technology; Civil engineering; Construction; Electrical engineering; Geology; Engineering, Industrial; Fashion design; Law; **Level of Education for which Award is Granted:** Graduate, Undergraduate **Funds Available:** $2,500.
Eligibility Requirements: Applicant must be of Hispanic heritage; U.S. citizen or legal permanent resident with a valid permanent resident card or passport stamped I-551; enrolled as sophomore, junior, senior undergraduate or First or Second year Master student in a full-time degree-seeking program at an accredited U.S. institution in the U.S., Puerto Rico, U.S. Virgin Islands or Guam; have a minimum 3.0 GPA on a 4.0 scale or 4.00 on a 5.00 scale; must apply for Federal Financing Aid; pursuing his/her first undergraduate or graduate degree. Undergraduate students must be majoring in: Marketing, Accounting, Business, Finance, Management, Computer Science, Computer Programming, Information Technology (IT), Civil Engineering, Construction, Electrical Engineering, Environmental/Geological Engineering, Industrial Engineering, and Fashion. Master's students must be majoring in: Business, Finance, Marketing, Civil Engineering, Construction, Electrical Engineering, Environmental/Geological Engineering and Law. **Application Requirements:** Applications must be submitted using the HSF online application system. **Additional Information:** In partnership with Wal-Mart Stores, Inc. **Deadline for Receipt:** March 15. **Additional Information:** scholar1@hsf.net.

3669 ■ HISPANIC SCHOLARSHIP FUND
55 Second St., Ste. 1500
San Francisco, CA 94105
877-473-4636
Fax: (415)808-2302
E-mail: info@hsf.net
Web Site: http://www.hsf.net
To provide financial assistance to those who are studying engineering.
Title of Award: Marathon Oil Corporation College Scholarship Program **Area, Field, or Subject:** Chemical engineering; Civil engineering; Electrical engineering; Mechanical engineering; Petroleum engineering; Geology; Geophysics; Accounting; Marketing and distribution; Land management; Transportation; Logistics; Engineering, Petroleum **Level of Education for which Award is Granted:** Graduate, Undergraduate **Funds Available:** $20,000. **Duration:** Two academic years.
Eligibility Requirements: Applicant must be of Hispanic American, African American, Asian Pacific Islander American or American Indian/Alaskan Native heritage; U.S. citizen or legal permanent resident with a valid Social Security Number and a permanent resident card or passport stamped I-551; have a minimum 3.0 GPA on a 4.0 scale; a sophomore majoring in chemical engineering, civil engineering, electrical engineering, mechanical engineering, petroleum engineering, geology, geophysics, accounting, marketing, global procurement or supply chain management, environmental health & safety, energy management or petroleum land management, transportation & logistics or geotechnical engineering; or a senior pursuing a Masters degree in geology or geophysics; must participate in a possible paid summer internship opportunity in Marathon Oil Corporation; must apply for federal financing aid using the Free Application for Federal Student Aid (FAFSA) at www.fafsa.ed.gov. **Application Requirements:** Applications must be submitted using the HSF online application system. **Additional Information:** Scholars will be paired with a Marathon Oil Corporation employee as a professional mentor. **Deadline for Receipt:** November 1. **Additional Information:** scholar1@hsf.net.

3670 ■ NATIONAL SPELEOLOGICAL SOCIETY

2813 Cave Ave.
Huntsville, AL 35810-4431
Tel: (256)852-1300
Fax: (256)851-9241
E-mail: nss@caves.org
Web Site: http://www.caves.org
To support research done by younger members of the society.
Title of Award: Young Investigator Grants **Area, Field, or Subject:** Cave studies. **Level of Education for which Award is Granted:** Undergraduate **Funds Available:** $500.
Eligibility Requirements: Applicant must be a NSS member under 22 years old. **Application Requirements:** Applicants must send an application including a narrative (four pages, double-spaced) about the motivation of the study, objectives and methodology, and a brief discussion of related literature. The application must also include a detailed budget; transcript; a brief statement of experience and interest (maximum of 250 words); and two letters of recommendation. Submit applications electronically (Word or .pdf files) to the Chair of the NSS Research Advisory Committee, dmcfarla@jsd.claremont.edu. **Deadline for Receipt:** February 1.

3671 ■ NATIONAL STONE SAND AND GRAVEL ASSOCIATION

1605 King St.
Alexandria, VA 22314
Tel: (703)525-8788
Web Site: http://www.nssga.org
To provide scholarships to students pursuing a career in the crushed stone industry.
Title of Award: Samuel C. Kraus, Jr. Memorial Scholarships **Area, Field, or Subject:** Engineering, Mining and Mineral; Geology. **Level of Education for which Award is Granted:** Undergraduate **Funds Available:** No specific amount. **Duration:** One year.
Eligibility Requirements: Applicant must be a mining engineering or geology student at the University of Missouri Rolla. **Application Requirements:** Contact the School of Mines and Metallurgy, University of Missouri Rolla for the application procedures. **Additional Information:** 64501-0249.

3672 ■ UNIVERSITY OF ALASKA ANCHORAGE

3211 Providence Dr.
Anchorage, AK 99508
Tel: (907)786-1800
Web Site: http://www.uaa.alaska.edu
To provide financial assistance for tuition and other related educational expenses to University of Alaska Anchorage or University of Alaska Fairbanks students who are admitted in a Geology degree-seeking program.
Title of Award: Chugach Gem & Mineral Society Scholarships **Area, Field, or Subject:** Geology. **Level of Education for which Award is Granted:** Undergraduate **Number Awarded:** 2. **Funds Available:** $2,000. **Duration:** One academic year.
Eligibility Requirements: Applicant must be in good academic standing with a minimum cumulative GPA of 2.0; must demonstrate motivation, academic and leadership potential; must be formally admitted to an undergraduate Geology major or minor degree-seeking program at the University of Alaska Anchorage or Fairbanks by the start of the fall semester; must plan on enrolling at least half-time (six credits) at the University of Alaska Anchorage or the University of Alaska Fairbanks; must be junior or senior standing; must be an Alaska resident; must be enrolled in the semester for which the award is made. **Application Requirements:** Applicant must complete the UAA Scholarship Application Form available online; must attach a list of activities/community service in which the applicant have participated; must submit a resume and personal essay; must have two letters of recommendation and transcript; must provide a proof of Alaska residency. Application must be received by the UAA Office of Student Financial Aid, Attn: CGMS Rasmusson Memorial Earth Science Scholarship, PO Box 141608, Anchorage, AK 99514. **Deadline for Receipt:** October 6.

3673 ■ UNIVERSITY OF TORONTO

315 Bloor St. W
Toronto, ON, Canada M5S 1A3
Tel: (416)978-2011
E-mail: information.commonsats@utoronto.ca
Web Site: http://www.utoronto.ca
To support students with their educational pursuits.
Title of Award: J.P. Bickell Mining Scholarships **Area, Field, or Subject:** Geology; Geophysics; Earth sciences; Mining; Environmental science. **Level of Education for which Award is Granted:** Undergraduate **Funds Available:** Approximately $2000.
Eligibility Requirements: Applicant must be a student of U of T; an undergraduate student in second or higher years studying mining (including the geological and geophysical fields as well as environmental sciences, geological sciences, earth science programs and mining engineering); have a minimum GPA of B or better and have demonstrated interest in the mining industry or field. **Application Requirements:** Applicants must submit a letter of application together with a letter outlining the interest in the mining industry. **Deadline for Receipt:** October 31.

Geophysics

3674 ■ ASSOCIATION OF DESK AND DERRICK CLUBS

5153 E 51st St., Ste. 107
Tulsa, OK 74135
Tel: (918)622-1749
Fax: (918)622-1675
E-mail: adotulsa@swbell.net
Web Site: http://www.addc.org
To provide financial assistance to college students planning a career in the petroleum energy or allied industries.
Title of Award: Association of Desk and Derrick Clubs Education Trust Scholarships **Area, Field, or Subject:** Geology; Geophysics; Engineering, Petroleum; Engineering, Nuclear; Engineering, Mechanical; Energy-related areas. **Level of Education for which Award is Granted:** Undergraduate **Funds Available:** $1,500.
Eligibility Requirements: Applicant must have completed at least two years or be currently enrolled in the second year of undergraduate study at an accredited college or university; be a U.S. or Canadian citizen; maintain a GPA of 3.2 or above on a 4.0 scale; be pursuing a career in the field of petroleum, energy or allied industry. **Application Requirements:** Applicants must submit a completed application form to Desk and Derrick Educational Trust, 5153 E 51st St., Ste. 107, Tulsa, OK 74135. **Deadline for Receipt:** April 1.

3675 ■ HISPANIC SCHOLARSHIP FUND

55 Second St., Ste. 1500
San Francisco, CA 94105
877-473-4636
Fax: (415)808-2302
E-mail: info@hsf.net
Web Site: http://www.hsf.net
To provide financial assistance to those who are studying engineering.
Title of Award: Marathon Oil Corporation College Scholarship Program **Area, Field, or Subject:** Chemical engineering; Civil engineering; Electrical engineering; Mechanical engineering; Petroleum engineering; Geology; Geophysics; Accounting; Marketing and distribution; Land management; Transportation; Logistics; Engineering, Petroleum **Level of Education for which Award is Granted:** Graduate, Undergraduate **Funds Available:** $20,000. **Duration:** Two academic years.
Eligibility Requirements: Applicant must be of Hispanic American, African American, Asian Pacific Islander American or American Indian/Alaskan Native heritage; U.S. citizen or legal permanent resident with a valid Social Security Number and a permanent resident card or passport stamped I-551; have a minimum 3.0 GPA on a 4.0 scale; a sophomore majoring in chemical engineering, civil engineering, electrical engineering, mechanical engineering, petroleum engineering, geology, geophysics, accounting, marketing, global procurement or supply chain management, environmental health & safety, energy management or petroleum land management, transportation & logistics or geotechnical engineering; or a senior pursuing a Masters degree in geology or geophysics; must participate in a possible paid summer internship opportunity in Marathon Oil Corporation; must apply for federal financing aid using the Free Application for Federal Student Aid (FAFSA) at www.fafsa.ed.gov. **Application Requirements:** Applications must be submitted using the HSF online application system. **Additional Information:** Scholars will be paired with

a Marathon Oil Corporation employee as a professional mentor. **Deadline for Receipt:** November 1. **Additional Information:** scholar1@hsf.net.

3676 ■ UNIVERSITY OF TORONTO
315 Bloor St. W
Toronto, ON, Canada M5S 1A3
Tel: (416)978-2011
E-mail: information.commonsats@utoronto.ca
Web Site: http://www.utoronto.ca
To support students with their educational pursuits.
Title of Award: J.P. Bickell Mining Scholarships **Area, Field, or Subject:** Geology; Geophysics; Earth sciences; Mining; Environmental science. **Level of Education for which Award is Granted:** Undergraduate **Funds Available:** Approximately $2000.
Eligibility Requirements: Applicant must be a student of U of T; an undergraduate student in second or higher years studying mining (including the geological and geophysical fields as well as environmental sciences, geological sciences, earth science programs and mining engineering); have a minimum GPA of B or better and have demonstrated interest in the mining industry or field. **Application Requirements:** Applicants must submit a letter of application together with a letter outlining the interest in the mining industry. **Deadline for Receipt:** October 31.

Physics

3677 ■ AMERICAN ASSOCIATION OF PHYSICS TEACHERS
One Physics Ellipse
College Park, MD 20740-3845
Tel: (301)209-3300
Fax: (301)209-0845
E-mail: webmaster@aapt.org
Web Site: http://www.aapt.org
To provide scholarships for future high school physics teachers.
Title of Award: Barbara Lotze Scholarships for Future Teachers **Area, Field, or Subject:** Physics. **Level of Education for which Award is Granted:** Undergraduate **Number Awarded:** 2. **Funds Available:** $2,000.
Eligibility Requirements: Applicants must be U.S. citizens attending U.S. schools. Undergraduate students who are enrolled or planning to enroll in physics teacher preparation curricula or high school seniors entering such programs are eligible to apply. **Application Requirements:** Application materials are available as a PDF or may be requested from Programs Department, American Association of Physics Teachers at the above address. **Deadline for Receipt:** December 1.

3678 ■ AMERICAN PHYSICAL SOCIETY
One Physics Ellipse
College Park, MD 20740-3844
Tel: (301)209-3200
Fax: (301)209-0865
E-mail: alinger@aps.org
Web Site: http://www.aps.org
To advance and diffuse the knowledge of physics.
Title of Award: American Physical Society Undergraduate Scholarships **Area, Field, or Subject:** Physics. **Level of Education for which Award is Granted:** Undergraduate **Funds Available:** Maximum amount of $2,000.
Eligibility Requirements: Applicants must be African American, Hispanic American, or Native American US citizens or permanent residents who are majoring or planning to major in physics; must be high school seniors, college freshmen, or sophomores. **Application Requirements:** Applicants must complete an application form and other materials that will be sent by the office after November 30. **Deadline for Receipt:** February 6.

3679 ■ ARMED FORCES COMMUNICATIONS AND ELECTRONICS ASSOCIATION
4400 Fair Lakes Court
Fairfax, VA 22033
Tel: (703)631-6141
Free: 800-336-4583
Fax: (703)631-4693
Web Site: http://www.afcea.org

To provide scholarship for the general public.
Title of Award: AFCEA Distance Learning/Online Scholarships **Area, Field, or Subject:** Engineering; Mathematics; Physics; Communications; Electronics. **Level of Education for which Award is Granted:** Undergraduate **Funds Available:** $1,500.
Eligibility Requirements: Applicants must be U.S. citizens currently enrolled full time pursuing either a Bachelor of Science or Master's of Science degree through distance learning or online program (only a few second-year students only will be accepted). **Application Requirements:** Applicants may apply online at AFFECT website. Applicants must also submit two letters of recommendation printed in school stationery and with signature from field-of-study professors. **Deadline for Receipt:** June 1. **Additional Information:** Norma Corrales; 703-631-6149.

3680 ■ ARMED FORCES COMMUNICATIONS AND ELECTRONICS ASSOCIATION
4400 Fair Lakes Court
Fairfax, VA 22033
Tel: (703)631-6141
Free: 800-336-4583
Fax: (703)631-4693
Web Site: http://www.afcea.org
To provide scholarship to the general public.
Title of Award: AFCEA General John A. Wickham Scholarships **Area, Field, or Subject:** Engineering; Mathematics; Physics; Communications; Electronics. **Level of Education for which Award is Granted:** Undergraduate **Funds Available:** $2,000.
Eligibility Requirements: Applicants must be US citizens; must have GPA of 3.5 on 4.0 scale. **Application Requirements:** Applicants may apply at AFCEA web site. Applicants must also submit two letters of recommendation printed in school stationery and with signature from field-of-study professors. **Deadline for Receipt:** May 1. **Additional Information:** Norma Corrales; 703-631-6149.

3681 ■ ARMED FORCES COMMUNICATIONS AND ELECTRONICS ASSOCIATION
4400 Fair Lakes Court
Fairfax, VA 22033
Tel: (703)631-6141
Free: 800-336-4583
Fax: (703)631-4693
Web Site: http://www.afcea.org
To provide scholarship for the general public.
Title of Award: William E. "Buck" Bragunier Scholarships **Area, Field, or Subject:** Engineering; Mathematics; Physics; Communications; Electronics. **Level of Education for which Award is Granted:** Undergraduate **Funds Available:** $2,000.
Eligibility Requirements: Applicants must be at least second year college students; must be enrolled full time as sophomores or juniors at the time of application; must have an outstanding record of demonstrated leadership within university or local community. **Application Requirements:** Applicants may apply online at AFFECT website. Applicants must also submit two letters of recommendation printed in school stationery and with signature from field-of-study professors. **Deadline for Receipt:** May 1. **Additional Information:** Norma Corrales; 703-631-6149.

3682 ■ ARMED FORCES COMMUNICATIONS AND ELECTRONICS ASSOCIATION
4400 Fair Lakes Court
Fairfax, VA 22033
Tel: (703)631-6141
Free: 800-336-4583
Fax: (703)631-4693
Web Site: http://www.afcea.org
To provide scholarships to students connected to the US Military.
Title of Award: LT.G. Douglas D. Buchholz Memorial Scholarships **Area, Field, or Subject:** Engineering; Mathematics; Physics; Communications. **Level of Education for which Award is Granted:** Undergraduate **Funds Available:** $2,000.
Eligibility Requirements: Applicants must be currently active enlisted soldiers assigned to Fort Gordon, Georgia; must have completed a minimum of 15 semester hours/25 quarter hours; must be currently enrolled either full or part time in an accredited US college; and must have

a minimum GPA of 2.5 on a 4.0 scale. **Application Requirements:** Students may apply online at the AFCEA web site. **Deadline for Receipt:** November 15. **Additional Information:** Mr. Joseph S. Yavorsky, President; president@afcea-augusta.org.

3683 ■ ARMED FORCES COMMUNICATIONS AND ELECTRONICS ASSOCIATION
4400 Fair Lakes Court
Fairfax, VA 22033
Tel: (703)631-6141
Free: 800-336-4583
Fax: (703)631-4693
Web Site: http://www.afcea.org
To provide educational incentives, opportunities and assistance for people engaged in information management, communications and intelligence efforts and fostering excellence in education particularly in the "hard science" disciplines related to C4ISR.

Title of Award: Disabled War Veterans Scholarships **Area, Field, or Subject:** Engineering; Mathematics; Physics; Communications. **Level of Education for which Award is Granted:** Undergraduate **Funds Available:** $2,500.
Eligibility Requirements: Applicants must be currently enrolled and attending either a two year or four year in an accredited college or university in the United States; must be enrolled in an accredited distance learning or online degree granting program affiliated with major, accredited two year or four year college or university in the United States. **Application Requirements:** Applicants may apply online at AFFECT website. Applicants must also submit two letters of recommendation printed on school stationery and with signature from field-of-study professors. **Deadline for Receipt:** November 1. **Additional Information:** Norma Corrales; 703-631-6149.

3684 ■ ARMED FORCES COMMUNICATIONS AND ELECTRONICS ASSOCIATION
4400 Fair Lakes Court
Fairfax, VA 22033
Tel: (703)631-6141
Free: 800-336-4583
Fax: (703)631-4693
Web Site: http://www.afcea.org
To provide scholarship to the general public.

Title of Award: Lockheed Martin IT Scholarships **Area, Field, or Subject:** Engineering; Mathematics; Physics; Communications. **Level of Education for which Award is Granted:** Undergraduate **Funds Available:** $3,000.
Eligibility Requirements: Applicants must be at least second year college students, must be enrolled full time as sophomores or juniors at the time of application. **Application Requirements:** Applicants may apply online. Applicants must also submit two letters of recommendation printed in school stationery and with signature from field-of-study professors; and official transcript of all college level study. **Deadline for Receipt:** May 1. **Additional Information:** Norma Corrales; 703-631-6149.

3685 ■ ARMED FORCES COMMUNICATIONS AND ELECTRONICS ASSOCIATION
4400 Fair Lakes Court
Fairfax, VA 22033
Tel: (703)631-6141
Free: 800-336-4583
Fax: (703)631-4693
Web Site: http://www.afcea.org
To provide scholarships to students connected to the US Military.

Title of Award: AFCEA General Emmett Paige Scholarships **Area, Field, or Subject:** Engineering; Mathematics; Physics; Communications. **Level of Education for which Award is Granted:** Undergraduate **Funds Available:** $2,000.
Eligibility Requirements: Applicants must be US citizens; must have a minimum GPA of 3.0 on 4.0 scale. **Application Requirements:** Applicants may apply online at the AFCEA web site. Applicants must also submit a copy of Certificate of Service, Discharge From DD214, or facsimile of current Department of Defense or Coast Guard Identification Card; and two letters of recommendation printed in school stationery and with signature from field-of-study professors. **Deadline for Receipt:** March 1. **Additional Information:** Norma Corrales; 703-631-6149.

3686 ■ ARMED FORCES COMMUNICATIONS AND ELECTRONICS ASSOCIATION
4400 Fair Lakes Court
Fairfax, VA 22033
Tel: (703)631-6141
Free: 800-336-4583
Fax: (703)631-4693
Web Site: http://www.afcea.org
To provide scholarships to students connected to the US military.

Title of Award: Veterans of Enduring Freedom (Afghanistan) and Iraqi Freedom Scholarships **Area, Field, or Subject:** Engineering; Mathematics; Physics; Communications. **Level of Education for which Award is Granted:** Undergraduate **Funds Available:** $2,500. **Duration:** One year.
Eligibility Requirements: Applicants must be currently enrolled and attending either a two year accredited college or university in the United States. **Application Requirements:** Applicants may apply online at AFCEA web site. **Additional Information:** The AFCEA Educational Foundation is pleased to co-sponsor this scholarship opportunity for U.S. War Veterans. **Deadline for Receipt:** April 1 and November 1. **Additional Information:** Norma Corrales 703-631-6149.

3687 ■ ARMED FORCES COMMUNICATIONS AND ELECTRONICS ASSOCIATION
4400 Fair Lakes Court
Fairfax, VA 22033
Tel: (703)631-6141
Free: 800-336-4583
Fax: (703)631-4693
Web Site: http://www.afcea.org
To provide scholarships to students connected with the US Military.

Title of Award: Marine Corps Sgt. Jeannette L. Winters Memorial Scholarships **Area, Field, or Subject:** Engineering; Mathematics; Physics; Communications. **Level of Education for which Award is Granted:** Undergraduate **Funds Available:** $2,000.
Eligibility Requirements: Applicants must be enrolled full time in a Bachelor of Science degree program in accredited colleges or universities in the United States; and must have a minimum GPA of 3.0 on 4.0 scale. Majors directly related to the support of US Intelligence enterprises or national security with relevance to the mission of AFCEA are also eligible. **Application Requirements:** Applicants may apply online at the AFCEA web site. Applicants must also submit two letters of recommendation printed in school stationery and with signature from field-of-study professors. **Deadline for Receipt:** September 1. **Additional Information:** Norma Corrales; 703-631-6149.

3688 ■ ASSOCIATION FOR WOMEN IN SCIENCE
1200 New York Ave. NW, Ste. 650
Washington, DC 20005
Tel: (202)326-8940
Fax: (202)326-8960
E-mail: awis@awis.org
Web Site: http://www.awis.org
To promote education in science.

Title of Award: AWIS College Scholarships **Area, Field, or Subject:** Astronomy and astronomical sciences; Geosciences; Biology; Mathematics and mathematical sciences; Chemistry; Physics; Computer and information sciences; Engineering; Psychology. **Level of Education for which Award is Granted:** Undergraduate **Number Awarded:** 2-5. **Funds Available:** No specific amount.
Eligibility Requirements: Applicant must be a female high school senior; U.S. citizen or permanent resident; have at least 3.75 GPA; at least 1200 score in SAT or a composite score of 25 in ACT; planning to study in any field of Astronomy, Geoscience, Biology, Mathematics, Chemistry, Physics, Computer and Information Science, Engineering, Psychology; planning to become a researcher or teacher. **Application Requirements:** Applicants must send five copies of: summary form; essay describing research experience; resume; two recommendation letters from science or research teachers; high school transcript and score of standardized test if available. **Deadline for Receipt:** January 17.

3689 ■ FOUNDATION FOR THE CAROLINAS
217 S Tryon St.
Charlotte, NC 28202

Tel: (704)973-4500
Free: 800-973-7244
Web Site: http://www.fftc.org
To provide financial assistance for students at Clemson University and the University of North Carolina at Charlotte who are preparing for a career in a technological field appropriate to meet the requirements of the U.S. Patent Office as a patent agent or attorney.
Title of Award: Julian E. Carnes Scholarship Fund **Area, Field, or Subject:** Engineering; Chemistry; Physics; Biology; Computer and information sciences. **Level of Education for which Award is Granted:** Undergraduate **Funds Available:** No specific amount.
Eligibility Requirements: Applicants must be legal residents of North or South Carolina; must be rising juniors or seniors at Clemson University or UNC Charlotte whose academic major is appropriate to meet the requirements of the U.S. Patent Office for admission as a patent agent or attorney (including but not limited to engineering, chemistry, physics, biology and computer science); and must have at least a 3.0 cumulative grade point average (on a 4.0 scale). **Application Requirements:** Applicants must submit all the required application information. **Additional Information:** Clemson University Office of Student Financial Aid, 864-656-2280 or the UNC Charlotte Student Financial Aid Office, 704-687-2461.

3690 ■ MATANUSKA-SUSITNA COLLEGE
PO Box 2889
Palmer, AK 99645
Tel: (907)745-9774
Fax: (907)745-9711
E-mail: info@matsu.alaska.edu
Web Site: http://www.matsu.alaska.edu
To provide support to deserving students in Alaska who want to pursue an education in any campus of the University of Alaska.
Title of Award: Alaska Aerospace Development Corporation Scholarships **Area, Field, or Subject:** Applied mathematics; Physics; Engineering; Business; Technical communications. **Level of Education for which Award is Granted:** Undergraduate **Funds Available:** $5,000.
Eligibility Requirements: Applicant must be a freshman student majoring in mathematics, physics, engineering, business, or a technical science field such as computer science who has graduated from the Kodiak Island Borough School District; must be a full-time student enrolled in 14 credits and in good academic standing. **Application Requirements:** Applicants must submit a written statement verifying that he/she has not been convicted of a crime other than a minor traffic violation; must complete the application forms available at the website; must attach a personal essay, two letters of recommendation, and current transcripts. **Deadline for Receipt:** February 15.

3691 ■ NATIONAL SOCIETY OF BLACK PHYSICISTS
1100 N. Glebe Rd., Ste. 1010
Arlington, VA 22201
Tel: (703)536-4207
Fax: (703)536-4203
E-mail: headquarters@nsbp.org
Web Site: http://www.nsbp.org
To support interest in physics by providing educational assistance to skilled physics majors.
Title of Award: Michael P. Anderson Scholarships in Space Science **Area, Field, or Subject:** Physics. **Level of Education for which Award is Granted:** Undergraduate **Number Awarded:** 1. **Funds Available:** $1,000.
Eligibility Requirements: Applicants must be physics majors in their junior or senior year. **Application Requirements:** Applicant must send the complete application package along with official transcripts and a stamped envelope to: Scholarship Committee Chair, National Society of Black Physicists, 6704G Lee Highway, Arlington, VA 22205. **Additional Information:** Established to commemorate Dr. Michael P. Anderson, an accomplished physicist and a NASA astronaut who perished in a space shuttle accident. **Deadline for Receipt:** January 12.

3692 ■ NATIONAL SOCIETY OF BLACK PHYSICISTS
1100 N. Glebe Rd., Ste. 1010
Arlington, VA 22201
Tel: (703)536-4207

Fax: (703)536-4203
E-mail: headquarters@nsbp.org
Web Site: http://www.nsbp.org
To inspire pursuits in physics education specifically among minority undergraduates.
Title of Award: APS Scholarships for Minority Undergraduate Physics Majors **Area, Field, or Subject:** Physics. **Level of Education for which Award is Granted:** Undergraduate **Funds Available:** $2,000 (for new minority scholars); $3,000 (for renewal students) to be used for tuition, room & board and educational materials. **Duration:** One year.
Eligibility Requirements: Any African-American, Hispanic American, or Native American U.S. citizen or permanent resident who is majoring or planning to major in physics; a high school senior, college freshman, or sophomore is eligible to apply for the scholarship. **Application Requirements:** Applicants may download application materials in the website. **Additional Information:** Established in 1980. **Deadline for Receipt:** February 6.

3693 ■ NATIONAL SOCIETY OF BLACK PHYSICISTS
1100 N. Glebe Rd., Ste. 1010
Arlington, VA 22201
Tel: (703)536-4207
Fax: (703)536-4203
E-mail: headquarters@nsbp.org
Web Site: http://www.nsbp.org
To support interest in physics by providing educational assistance to skilled physics majors.
Title of Award: Harvey Washington Banks Scholarships in Astronomy **Area, Field, or Subject:** Physics. **Level of Education for which Award is Granted:** Undergraduate **Number Awarded:** 1. **Funds Available:** $1,000.
Eligibility Requirements: Applicants must be physics majors in their junior or senior year. **Application Requirements:** Applicant must send the complete application package along with official transcripts and a stamped envelope to: Scholarship Committee Chair, National Society of Black Physicists, 6704G Lee Highway, Arlington, VA 22205. **Additional Information:** Established to commemorate Dr. Harvey Washington Banks, the first African-American to receive a Ph.D. degree in astronomy. **Deadline for Receipt:** January 12.

3694 ■ NATIONAL SOCIETY OF BLACK PHYSICISTS
1100 N. Glebe Rd., Ste. 1010
Arlington, VA 22201
Tel: (703)536-4207
Fax: (703)536-4203
E-mail: headquarters@nsbp.org
Web Site: http://www.nsbp.org
To inspire the next generation of physicians by providing financial assistance to individuals pursuing further studies in the field of physics.
Title of Award: Charles S. Brown Scholarships in Physics **Area, Field, or Subject:** Physics. **Level of Education for which Award is Granted:** Graduate, Undergraduate **Number Awarded:** 1. **Funds Available:** $1,000.
Eligibility Requirements: Graduate students and undergraduate students with a declared major in physics are eligible for this scholarship. **Application Requirements:** Applicant must send complete application package available in the website with official transcript and supply a stamped envelope addressed to: Scholarship Committee Chair, National Society of Black Physicists, 6704G Lee Highway, Arlington, VA 22205. **Additional Information:** Established to commemorate Dr. Charles S. Brown, who had extensive contributions in the development of science and technology in Africa. **Deadline for Receipt:** January 12.

3695 ■ NATIONAL SOCIETY OF BLACK PHYSICISTS
1100 N. Glebe Rd., Ste. 1010
Arlington, VA 22201
Tel: (703)536-4207
Fax: (703)536-4203
E-mail: headquarters@nsbp.org
Web Site: http://www.nsbp.org
To support interest in physics by providing educational assistance to skilled physics majors.
Title of Award: Robert A. Ellis Scholarships in Physics **Area, Field, or Subject:** Physics. **Level of Education for which Award is Granted:**

Undergraduate **Number Awarded:** 1. **Funds Available:** $1,000.
Eligibility Requirements: Applicants must be physics majors in their junior or senior year. **Application Requirements:** Applicant must send the complete application package along with official transcripts and a stamped envelope to: Scholarship Committee Chair, National Society of Black Physicists, 6704G Lee Highway, Arlington, VA 22205. **Additional Information:** Established to commemorate Dr. Robert A. Ellis, an internationally-recognized pioneer in modern experimental plasma physics. **Deadline for Receipt:** January 12.

3696 ■ NATIONAL SOCIETY OF BLACK PHYSICISTS
1100 N. Glebe Rd., Ste. 1010
Arlington, VA 22201
Tel: (703)536-4207
Fax: (703)536-4203
E-mail: headquarters@nsbp.org
Web Site: http://www.nsbp.org
To support interest in physics by providing educational assistance to skilled physics majors.
Title of Award: Elmer S. Imes Scholarships in Physics **Area, Field, or Subject:** Physics. **Level of Education for which Award is Granted:** Undergraduate **Number Awarded:** 1. **Funds Available:** $1,000.
Eligibility Requirements: Applicants must be physics majors in their junior or senior year. **Application Requirements:** Applicant must send the complete application package along with official transcripts and a stamped envelope to: Scholarship Committee Chair, National Society of Black Physicists, 6704G Lee Highway, Arlington, VA 22205. **Additional Information:** Established to honor Elmer S. Imes, one of the first African-Americans to receive a Ph.D. degree in physics. **Deadline for Receipt:** January 12.

3697 ■ NATIONAL SOCIETY OF BLACK PHYSICISTS
1100 N. Glebe Rd., Ste. 1010
Arlington, VA 22201
Tel: (703)536-4207
Fax: (703)536-4203
E-mail: headquarters@nsbp.org
Web Site: http://www.nsbp.org
To support interest in physics by providing educational assistance to skilled physics majors.
Title of Award: Walter Samuel McAfee Scholarships in Space Physics **Area, Field, or Subject:** Physics. **Level of Education for which Award is Granted:** Undergraduate **Number Awarded:** 1. **Funds Available:** $1,000.
Eligibility Requirements: Applicants must be physics majors in their junior or senior year. **Application Requirements:** Applicant must send the complete application package along with official transcripts and a stamped envelope to: Scholarship Committee Chair, National Society of Black Physicists, 6704G Lee Highway, Arlington, VA 22205. **Additional Information:** Established to commemorate Dr. Walter Samuel McAfee and his significant contributions in space communications, radar, and general understanding of electromagnetic propagation. **Deadline for Receipt:** January 12.

3698 ■ NATIONAL SOCIETY OF BLACK PHYSICISTS
1100 N. Glebe Rd., Ste. 1010
Arlington, VA 22201
Tel: (703)536-4207
Fax: (703)536-4203
E-mail: headquarters@nsbp.org
Web Site: http://www.nsbp.org
To support interest in physics by providing educational assistance to skilled physics majors.
Title of Award: Ronald E. McNair Scholarships in Space and Optical Physics **Area, Field, or Subject:** Physics. **Level of Education for which Award is Granted:** Undergraduate **Number Awarded:** 1. **Funds Available:** $1,000.
Eligibility Requirements: Applicants must be physics majors in their junior or senior year. **Application Requirements:** Applicant must send the complete application package along with official transcripts and a stamped envelope to: Scholarship Committee Chair, National Society of Black Physicists, 6704G Lee Highway, Arlington, VA 22205. **Additional Information:** Established to commemorate Dr. Ronald E. McNair, an ac-

complished physicist and a NASA astronaut who perished in a space shuttle accident. **Deadline for Receipt:** January 12.

3699 ■ NATIONAL SOCIETY OF BLACK PHYSICISTS
1100 N. Glebe Rd., Ste. 1010
Arlington, VA 22201
Tel: (703)536-4207
Fax: (703)536-4203
E-mail: headquarters@nsbp.org
Web Site: http://www.nsbp.org
To support interest in physics by providing educational assistance to skilled physics majors.
Title of Award: Willie Hobbs Moore Scholarships **Area, Field, or Subject:** Physics. **Level of Education for which Award is Granted:** Undergraduate **Number Awarded:** 1. **Funds Available:** $1,000.
Eligibility Requirements: Applicants must be physics majors in their junior or senior year. **Application Requirements:** Applicant must send the complete application package along with official transcripts and a stamped envelope to: Scholarship Committee Chair, National Society of Black Physicists, 6704G Lee Highway, Arlington, VA 22205. **Additional Information:** Established to commemorate Dr. Willie Hobbs Moore, the first African-American female to earn a Ph.D. degree in physics. **Deadline for Receipt:** January 12.

3700 ■ NATIONAL SOCIETY OF BLACK PHYSICISTS
1100 N. Glebe Rd., Ste. 1010
Arlington, VA 22201
Tel: (703)536-4207
Fax: (703)536-4203
E-mail: headquarters@nsbp.org
Web Site: http://www.nsbp.org
To support interest in physics by providing educational assistance to skilled physics majors.
Title of Award: Harry L. Morrison Scholarships **Area, Field, or Subject:** Physics. **Level of Education for which Award is Granted:** Undergraduate **Number Awarded:** 1. **Funds Available:** $1,000.
Eligibility Requirements: Applicants must be physics majors in their junior or senior year. **Application Requirements:** Applicant must send the complete application package along with official transcripts and a stamped envelope to: Scholarship Committee Chair, National Society of Black Physicists, 6704G Lee Highway, Arlington, VA 22205. **Additional Information:** Established to commemorate Dr. Harry L. Morrison, a legendary figure in mathematical statistical physics. **Deadline for Receipt:** January 12.

3701 ■ NATIONAL SOCIETY OF BLACK PHYSICISTS
1100 N. Glebe Rd., Ste. 1010
Arlington, VA 22201
Tel: (703)536-4207
Fax: (703)536-4203
E-mail: headquarters@nsbp.org
Web Site: http://www.nsbp.org
To support interest in physics by providing educational assistance to skilled physics majors.
Title of Award: Arthur BC Walker Scholarships **Area, Field, or Subject:** Physics. **Level of Education for which Award is Granted:** Undergraduate **Number Awarded:** 1. **Funds Available:** $1,000.
Eligibility Requirements: Applicants must be physics majors in their junior or senior year. **Application Requirements:** Applicant must send the complete application package along with official transcripts and a stamped envelope to: Scholarship Committee Chair, National Society of Black Physicists, 6704G Lee Highway, Arlington, VA 22205. **Additional Information:** Established to commemorate Dr. Arthur BC Walker, one of the most brilliant x-ray spectroscopists who ever lived. **Deadline for Receipt:** January 12.

3702 ■ NORTHAMPTON COUNTY MEDICAL SOCIETY ALLIANCE
PO Box 21271
Lehigh Valley, PA 18002-1271
E-mail: jakat2255@aol.com
Web Site: http://www.ncmsa.org
To provide financial assistance to medical, nursing and physician assistant students.

Title of Award: Northampton County Medical Society Alliance Scholarships **Area, Field, or Subject:** Medical assisting; Nursing; Physics. **Level of Education for which Award is Granted:** Undergraduate **Funds Available:** $1000.

Eligibility Requirements: Applicant must be a U.S. citizen residing in Northampton County, Pennsylvania, or have a Bethlehem mailing address; and must be accepted or enrolled in a fully accredited institute of medicine. **Application Requirements:** Applicants must complete the application form and submit along with the required materials to the Chairperson, Scholarship/Loan Fund, Northampton County Medical Society Alliance, PO Box 21271, Lehigh Valley, PA 18002-1217. **Deadline for Receipt:** April 15. **Additional Information:** Angela S. Carlin at angie@thecarlins.net.

3703 ■ RUBBER DIVISION AMERICAN CHEMICAL SOCIETY

PO Box 499
Akron, OH 44309-0499
Tel: (330)972-7814
Fax: (330)972-5269
Web Site: http://www.rubber.org
To provide financial assistance to students pursuing a college degree related to rubber technology, polymer science or the chemical profession.

Title of Award: Rubber Division American Chemical Society Scholarships **Area, Field, or Subject:** Chemistry; Physics; Chemical engineering; Mechanical engineering. **Level of Education for which Award is Granted:** Undergraduate **Funds Available:** $5,000. **Duration:** One academic year.

Eligibility Requirements: Applicants must be enrolled in an accredited university or college where rubber division has a partner organization; must be students majoring in chemistry, physics, chemical engineering, mechanical engineering, polymer science or any other field related to the rubber industry. **Application Requirements:** Applicants must send application form; two nomination letters; and transcript mailed by school registrar via regular mail. **Deadline for Receipt:** March. **Additional Information:** Christie Robinson, Education & Publications Manager, 330-972-7815.

3704 ■ THE SAN DIEGO FOUNDATION

2508 Historic Decatur Rd., Ste. 200
San Diego, CA 92106
Tel: (619)235-2300
Fax: (619)239-1710
E-mail: info@sdfoundation.org
Web Site: http://www.sdfoundation.org
To support the education of students from California.

Title of Award: Helm Family Scholarships **Area, Field, or Subject:** Biology; Computer and information sciences; Chemistry; Technology; Engineering; Physics. **Level of Education for which Award is Granted:** Undergraduate **Number Awarded:** 2. **Funds Available:** $5,00.

Eligibility Requirements: Applicant must be an entering junior or senior student at San Diego State University or the University of California, San Diego; have declared a major in mathematics or a scientific field such as, but not limited to, biology, computer science, chemistry, technology, engineering, physics, etc.; have a minimum 3.0 GPA on a 4.0 scale; and have demonstrated financial need. **Application Requirements:** Applicants must submit a completed Common Scholarship Application together with personal statement; two letters of recommendation on official letterhead (written within the last six months); official transcript in an official and sealed envelope; and a copy of most recent tax form (Form 1040-pages 1 & 2; Form 1040Apages 1 & 2; Form 1040EZ-page 1). **Deadline for Receipt:** January 28. **Additional Information:** Arzo Mansury, Dir. Scholarships at 619-814-1343, or scholarships@sdfoundation.org.

3705 ■ SOCIETY OF ALLIED WEIGHT ENGINEERS

PO Box 60024, Terminal Annex
Los Angeles, CA 90060
Tel: (562)596-2873
Fax: (562)596-2874
Web Site: http://www.sawe.org
To provide financial assistance for the education of the dependents of SAWE members.

Title of Award: Frank Fong Scholarships **Area, Field, or Subject:** Engineering; Physics; Mathematics and mathematical sciences; Computer and information sciences. **Level of Education for which Award is Granted:** Undergraduate **Number Awarded:** 5. **Funds Available:** $1000. **Duration:** One year.

Eligibility Requirements: Applicants must be children or grandchildren of SAWE members; must be aged 25 or below; full-time undergraduate students; pursuing a technical course of study (engineering, physics, mathematics, computer sciences, etc.). **Application Requirements:** Application forms are available at the website. Applicants must submit completed application form and send together with a complete transcript of grades. **Deadline for Receipt:** April. **Additional Information:** Ginny Miller, Scholarship Management Services, Telephone: (507)931-1682, Toll-free: (800)537-4180.

3706 ■ SOCIETY OF PHYSICS STUDENTS

One Physics Ellipse
College Park, MD 20740
Tel: (301)209-3007
Fax: (301)209-0839
E-mail: sps@aip.org
Web Site: http://www.spsnational.org
To support students from a two-year college transitioning into a physics bachelor's degree program.

Title of Award: Peggy Dixon Two-Year Scholarships **Area, Field, or Subject:** Physics. **Level of Education for which Award is Granted:** Undergraduate **Funds Available:** $2000.

Eligibility Requirements: Applicants must have completed at least one semester or quarter of the introductory physics sequence; and currently registered in the appropriate subsequent physics courses. **Application Requirements:** Application forms are available online. Applicants must submit completed application form; certified and official transcript (submitted directly by the applicant's college/university); letters from at least two full-time members of the faculty. **Additional Information:** The scholarship is established in memory of Dr. Peggy A. Dixon, SPS and Sigma Pi Sigma Historian from 19922003. **Deadline for Receipt:** February 15.

3707 ■ SOCIETY OF PHYSICS STUDENTS

One Physics Ellipse
College Park, MD 20740
Tel: (301)209-3007
Fax: (301)209-0839
E-mail: sps@aip.org
Web Site: http://www.spsnational.org
To provide financial assistance to promising physics students.

Title of Award: Herbert Levy Memorial Endowment Fund Scholarships **Area, Field, or Subject:** Physics. **Level of Education for which Award is Granted:** Undergraduate **Funds Available:** $2,000.

Eligibility Requirements: Applicants must be full-time undergraduate students applying in their junior year (except for two-year college applicants who should apply after completing one semester of physics); and must be SPS members. **Application Requirements:** Application forms are available online. Applicants must submit completed application form; certified and official transcript (submitted directly by the applicant's college/university); letters from at least two full-time members of the faculty. **Additional Information:** Scholarships establish by Margaret Sussman Levy in memory of her husband Dr. Herbert Levy. **Deadline for Receipt:** February 15.

3708 ■ SOCIETY OF PHYSICS STUDENTS

One Physics Ellipse
College Park, MD 20740
Tel: (301)209-3007
Fax: (301)209-0839
E-mail: sps@aip.org
Web Site: http://www.spsnational.org
To support local chapter activities that would contribute to the strengthening of the SPS program.

Title of Award: Sigma Pi Sigma Undergraduate Research Awards **Area, Field, or Subject:** Physics. **Level of Education for which Award is Granted:** Undergraduate **Funds Available:** $2000.

Eligibility Requirements: Applicants must be active chapter members of SPS. **Application Requirements:** Applicants must submit a proposal containing a budget and must be signed by the advisor and officers of the chapter. **Deadline for Receipt:** November 15.

3709 ■ SOCIETY OF PHYSICS STUDENTS
One Physics Ellipse
College Park, MD 20740
Tel: (301)209-3007
Fax: (301)209-0839
E-mail: sps@aip.org
Web Site: http://www.spsnational.org
To award SPS members participating in a teacher education program and pursuing a career in physics education.
Title of Award: SPS Future Teacher Scholarships **Area, Field, or Subject:** Physics. **Level of Education for which Award is Granted:** Undergraduate **Funds Available:** $2000.
Eligibility Requirements: Applicants must be undergraduate students applying in their junior year majoring in physics; and must be SPS members. **Application Requirements:** Application forms are available online. Applicants must submit completed application form; certified and official transcript (submitted directly by the applicant's college/university); letters from at least two full-time members of the faculty; and a statement from an SPS advisor that certifies the applicant's participation in a teacher education program. **Deadline for Receipt:** February 15.

3710 ■ SOCIETY OF PHYSICS STUDENTS
One Physics Ellipse
College Park, MD 20740
Tel: (301)209-3007
Fax: (301)209-0839
E-mail: sps@aip.org
Web Site: http://www.spsnational.org
To encourage the students to pursue their career in study of physics.
Title of Award: SPS Leadership Scholarships **Area, Field, or Subject:** Physics. **Level of Education for which Award is Granted:** Undergraduate **Funds Available:** $5000 and $2000.
Eligibility Requirements: Applicants must be full-time undergraduate students applying in their junior year (except for two-year college applicants who should apply after completing one semester of physics); and must be SPS members. **Application Requirements:** Application forms are available online. Applicants must submit completed application form; certified and official transcript (submitted directly by the applicant's college/university); letters from at least two full-time members of the faculty. **Deadline for Receipt:** February 15.

3711 ■ SOUTHWEST FLORIDA COMMUNITY FOUNDATION
8260 College Pkwy., Ste. 101
Fort Myers, FL 33919
Tel: (239)274-5900
Fax: (239)274-5930
Web Site: http://www.floridacommunity.com
To fund a student who will attend: FGCU, university of Florida/Gainesville, Florida State University/Tallahassee, Flagler College, Stetson University/Deland, University of Miami, University of Tampa, or Embry Riddle Aeronautical University/Daytona Beach.
Title of Award: D&A Florida Scholarships **Area, Field, or Subject:** Architecture; Business; Engineering; International affairs and relations; Journalism; Computer and information sciences; Law; Literature; Medicine; Physics; Chemistry; Political science. **Level of Education for which Award is Granted:** Undergraduate **Funds Available:** $10,000. **Duration:** One year.
Eligibility Requirements: Applicants must have graduated from a public or private high school in Charlotte, Glades, Hendry or Lee County; must pursue a degree in Architecture, Business, Engineering, International affairs and relations, Journalism, Computer and information sciences, Law, Literature, Medicine, Physics, Chemistry, or Political science. **Application Requirements:** Application forms are available online. Applicants must submit a letter of interest and letter of recommendation, a transcript and financial need documentation. **Deadline for Receipt:** February 15.

3712 ■ VIRGINIA FOUNDATION FOR INDEPENDENT COLLEGES
8010 Ridge Rd., Ste. B
Richmond, VA 23229-7288
Tel: (804)288-6609
Free: 800-230-6757
Fax: (804)282-4635
E-mail: info@vfic.org
Web Site: http://www.vfic.org
To provide financial assistance for the students in their junior year at a VFIC college or university.
Title of Award: Phillip Morris USA Scholarships **Area, Field, or Subject:** Accounting; Biology; Business; Chemistry; Computer and information sciences; Economics; Engineering; Finance; Physics. **Level of Education for which Award is Granted:** Undergraduate **Funds Available:** $5,000.
Eligibility Requirements: Applicants must be U.S. citizens and current full-time sophomores attending a VFIC college or university (students from underrepresented populations are encouraged to apply); have minimum of 3.5 cumulative GPA; committed to applying for an internship with Phillip Morris USA for the summer after junior year; have declared, or intend to declare, a major in one of the following disciplines: accounting, biology, business, chemistry, computer science, economics, engineering, finance, or physics. **Application Requirements:** Applicants must submit completed application form along with two letters of recommendation and other required application information. **Deadline for Receipt:** November 1.

3713 ■ WASHINGTON HIGHER EDUCATION COORDINATING BOARD
PO Box 43430
Olympia, WA 98504-3430
Tel: (360)753-7800
E-mail: info@hecb.wa.gov
Web Site: http://www.hecb.wa.gov
To attract and retain health professionals to serve in critical shortage areas in Washington state.
Title of Award: Washington Higher Education Coordinating Board Health Professional Scholarships **Area, Field, or Subject:** Physics; Nursing; Midwifery; Pharmacy; Dentistry. **Level of Education for which Award is Granted:** Undergraduate **Funds Available:** Varies by educational program.
Eligibility Requirements: Applicant must be a student training to become a primary care health professional in an eligible profession; a U.S. citizen; have completed all prerequisite course work; not be in default on any educational loans; and must sign a Promissory Note agreeing to serve for a minimum of three years in a designated shortage area in Washington state or pay back funds with double penalty plus interest. **Application Requirements:** Applicants must submit a completed application form along with the required materials and information. **Additional Information:** Participants must agree, in return for the assistance, to provide primary care health care in rural or underserved urban areas with designated shortages for a minimum of three years. **Deadline for Receipt:** April 30.

3714 ■ WOMEN IN DEFENSE
2111 Wilson Blvd., Ste. 400
Arlington, VA 22201-3061
Tel: (703)247-2552
Fax: (703)522-1885
E-mail: wid@ndia.org
Web Site: http://wid.ndia.org
To provide financial assistance to further educational objectives of women either employed or planning careers in defense or national security areas.
Title of Award: Women In Defense HORIZONS Scholarships **Area, Field, or Subject:** National security; Military history; Government; Engineering; Computer and information sciences; Physics; Mathematics and mathematical sciences; Business; Law; International affairs and relations; Political science; Economics. **Level of Education for which Award is Granted:** Graduate, Undergraduate **Funds Available:** No specific amount.
Eligibility Requirements: Applicant must be currently enrolled at an accredited university/college, either full-time or part-time; must have junior, senior or graduate status; demonstrate interest in pursuing a career related to national security or defense; demonstrate financial need; have a minimum GPA of 3.25. Applicant must be a female citizen of the United States. **Application Requirements:** Applicants must submit a completed scholarship application form with the essays, recommendations, and transcripts. **Additional Information:** Established in 1988. **Deadline for Receipt:** July 1.

3715 ■ XAVIER UNIVERSITY

3800 Victory Pky.
Cincinnati, OH 45207
Tel: (513)745-3000
Free: 800-344-GOXU
Web Site: http://www.xavier.edu
To financially support students with their education.
Title of Award: Xavier University Departmental Scholarships **Area, Field, or Subject:** Chemistry; Classical studies; History; Mathematics and mathematical sciences; Modern languages; Physics. **Level of Education for which Award is Granted:** Undergraduate **Funds Available:** $2500. **Eligibility Requirements:** Applicant must top the score in either of the six departmental exams (chemistry, classics (Latin), history, mathematics, modern languages (French, German or Spanish) and physics). Student must major in the area for which the scholarship is awarded. **Application Requirements:** Participants will take an exam in the appropriate subject area and have an opportunity to speak with faculty and learn more about the department.

General

3716 ■ ALBERTA LEARNING INFORMATION SERVICE - ALBERTA SCHOLARSHIP PROGRAM
Box 28000 Sta. Main
Edmonton, AB, Canada T5J 4R4
Tel: (780)427-8640
Fax: (780)427-1288
E-mail: scholarship@gov.ab.ca
Web Site: http://www.alis.alberta.ca
To recognize student's leadership and community service.
Title of Award: Lois Hole Humanities and Social Sciences Scholarship **Area, Field, or Subject:** Humanities; Social sciences. **Level of Education for which Award is Granted:** Undergraduate **Funds Available:** $5,000.
Eligibility Requirements: Applicants must be students enrolled full-time in the second or subsequent year of post-secondary study in the Faculty of Humanities or the Faculty of Social Sciences, at the University of Alberta, the University of Calgary, the University of Lethbridge, or Athabasca University. **Application Requirements:** Applicants may contact the Student Awards Office at participating educational institutions for other application requirements. **Deadline for Receipt:** October 15 for University of Alberta and Athabasca University; November 15 for University Lethbridge and the University of Calgary. **Additional Information:** Alberta Scholarship Programs at the above address.

3717 ■ AMERICAN UNIVERSITY - SCHOOL OF PUBLIC AFFAIRS
Ward Circle Bldg.
4400 Massachusetts Ave. NW
Washington, DC 20016
Tel: (202)885-2940
Fax: (202)885-2353
E-mail: spagrad@american.edu
Web Site: http://spa.american.edu
To provide financial assistance to School of Public Administration students.
Title of Award: Jane R. Glaser Scholarships **Area, Field, or Subject:** Public affairs. **Level of Education for which Award is Granted:** Undergraduate **Funds Available:** $2,500. **Duration:** One year.
Eligibility Requirements: Applicants should be undergraduate students of School of Public Administration. **Application Requirements:** Applicants must submit one page formal recommendation from advisor; outline of grade point average; activities; reason for studying at Hebrew University; and statement stating interest in receiving the scholarship and studying abroad. **Deadline for Receipt:** May 15 and September **Additional Information:** Jenine Rabine; 202-885-3968; rabin@american.edu

3718 ■ BLACK COACHES AND ADMINISTRATORS
Pan American Plaza, 201 S Capitol Ave., Ste. 495
Indianapolis, IN 46225
Tel: (317)829-5600
Fax: (317)829-5601
Web Site: http://www.bcasports.cstv.com

To support and encourage minorities who wish to pursue a career in athletics.
Title of Award: BCA Ethnic Minority Postgraduate Scholarships for Careers in Athletics **Area, Field, or Subject:** Sports studies. **Level of Education for which Award is Granted:** Undergraduate **Funds Available:** $2,500.
Eligibility Requirements: Applicants must be seeking admission or have been accepted into a sports-administration or related program that will assist the applicant in obtaining a career in athletics. **Application Requirements:** Program application is available at the website. **Deadline for Receipt:** May 1. **Additional Information:** Lauren Peterson, Director of Operations and Administration at 317-829-5619.

3719 ■ CENTER FOR LESBIAN AND GAY STUDIES
City University of New York; 365 Fifth Ave
New York, NY 10016
Tel: (212)817-1955
E-mail: clags@gc.cuny.edu
Web Site: http://web.gc.cuny.edu/clags
To supports research into the impact of lesbians and/or gay men on U.S. society and culture.
Title of Award: Joan Heller-Diane Bernard Fellowships **Area, Field, or Subject:** Homosexuality. **Level of Education for which Award is Granted:** Graduate, Undergraduate **Number Awarded:** 2. **Funds Available:** $5,000.
Eligibility Requirements: Applicants must be junior scholars, graduate students, untenured professors, independent researchers, or senior scholars. **Application Requirements:** Applicants must submit a cover letter with contact information; a proposal of 5-10 pages; evidence of contribution to the field of LGTBQ studies; curriculum vitae; and two letters of recommendation. **Deadline for Receipt:** November.

3720 ■ EISENHOWER INSTITUTE
915 15th St. NW, 8th Fl.
Washington, DC 20005
Tel: (202)628-4444
Fax: (202)628-4445
E-mail: ei@eisenhowerinstitute.org
Web Site: http://www.eisenhowerinstitute.org
To help American students study abroad.
Title of Award: Conrad N. Hilton Scholarships **Area, Field, or Subject:** Social sciences. **Level of Education for which Award is Granted:** Undergraduate **Number Awarded:** 1. **Funds Available:** $10,000. **Duration:** Annually.
Eligibility Requirements: Applicant must be a Gettysburg College senior or junior undergraduate student planning to study abroad; have at least a 3.0 cumulative GPA(can be waived for applicants with strong needs or qualifications); and must be social science or interdisciplinary majors. **Application Requirements:** Applicant must submit academic transcript; a resume; a statement of career aspirations (maximum of 1,000 words); a letter of recommendation from the candidate's faculty advisor or department chair; and a copy of a 10-15 page paper (within the last four months) from a course in the applicant's major field of study. Submit it at Gettysburg College. **Deadline for Receipt:** First day of Spring semester.

3721 ■ GAY ASIAN PACIFIC ALLIANCE

PO Box 421884
San Francisco, CA 94142-1884
E-mail: info@gapa.org
Web Site: http://www.gapa.org

To provide financial assistance to lesbian, gay, bisexual and transgender Asian and Pacific Islanders in educational pursuits.

Title of Award: GAPA Scholarships **Area, Field, or Subject:** Homosexuality. **Level of Education for which Award is Granted:** Undergraduate **Funds Available:** $1000.

Eligibility Requirements: Applicant must be an Asian/Pacific Islander; applying or attending school in one of the nine-Bay Area counties; and have a minimum GPA of 2.75. **Application Requirements:** Applicants must submit a completed horizons Foundation's scholarship application form together with a transcript; letter of recommendation; and an essay of 500 words. Send materials to Horizons Foundation, 870 Market St., Suite 728, San Francisco, CA 94102. **Additional Information:** In memory of George Choy. The scholarship is administered by the Horizons Foundation. **Deadline for Receipt:** July 31. **Additional Information:** Hao Thai, hao@gapa.org.

3722 ■ THE GREATER TACOMA COMMUNITY FOUNDATION

PO Box 1995
Tacoma, WA 98401
Tel: (253)383-5622
Web Site: http://www.tacomafoundation.org

To foster generosity by connecting people who care with causes that matter.

Title of Award: Fuchs-Harden Educational Scholarships Fund **Area, Field, or Subject:** Engineering; Business Administration; Social sciences. **Level of Education for which Award is Granted:** Undergraduate **Funds Available:** No specific amount.

Eligibility Requirements: Applicant must be an African American residing in the legal limits of the city of Tacoma, Washington; must be enrolled in and maintain a satisfactory GPA at a college or university in the courses for Business Administration, Engineering, Applied Physics, Dentistry, Medicine, Law, Sociology, Journalism or Home Economics. **Application Requirements:** Applicants must submit a completed application form available through R. Merle Palmer Minority Scholarship Fund. **Additional Information:** PO Box 7119, Tacoma, WA 98406-0119.

3723 ■ JACKSON COUNTY COMMUNITY FOUNDATION

One Jackson Square, 100 E Michigan Ave., Ste. 308
Jackson, MI 49201-1406
Tel: (517)787-1321
Fax: (517)787-4333
E-mail: jcf@jacksoncf.org
Web Site: http://www.jacksoncf.org

To participate in the sport while maintaining high academic standards in preparation for future educational enrichment.

Title of Award: Bernice Barabash Sports Scholarship **Area, Field, or Subject:** Athletics. **Level of Education for which Award is Granted:** Undergraduate **Number Awarded:** 2. **Funds Available:** $1,000.

Eligibility Requirements: Applicants must be students in grades seven to twelve who hold a minimum of 3.0 GPA; must play hockey during the school year; must be residing in Jackson County or surrounding communities that do not have ice arenas in the area; must plan to attend an accredited college or university program or vocational/technical institute. **Application Requirements:** Applicants must submit a completed application form and a copy of report card or transcript from the 2nd semester. **Additional Information:** 517-787-1321.

3724 ■ MATANUSKA-SUSITNA COLLEGE

PO Box 2889
Palmer, AK 99645
Tel: (907)745-9774
Fax: (907)745-9711
E-mail: info@matsu.alaska.edu
Web Site: http://www.matsu.alaska.edu

To provide support to deserving students in Alaska who want to pursue an education in any campus of the University of Alaska.

Title of Award: Lydia Fohn-Hansen/Lola Hill Memorial Scholarships **Area, Field, or Subject:** Family planning; Consumer affairs. **Level of Education for which Award is Granted:** Undergraduate **Funds Available:** $1,000.

Eligibility Requirements: Applicant must be full-time undergraduate or degree-seeking graduate students majoring in Family and Consumer Sciences or a related field; must have a minimum GPA of 3.0 and must be a resident of Alaska. **Application Requirements:** Applicant must complete the application forms available at the website; must attach a personal essay, two letters of recommendation, and current transcripts. **Deadline for Receipt:** February 15.

3725 ■ NATIONAL ORGANIZATION FOR HUMAN SERVICES

90 Madison St., Ste. 206
Denver, CO 80206
Tel: (303)320-5430
Fax: (303)322-1455
Web Site: http://www.nationalhumanservices.org

To support the education of a student in a human service program.

Title of Award: David C. Maloney Scholarship Program **Area, Field, or Subject:** Humanities; Human relation. **Level of Education for which Award is Granted:** Undergraduate **Funds Available:** No specific amount.

Eligibility Requirements: Applicant must be an Associate, Baccalaureate, or Master's student member of NOHS; have a GPA of 3.0 and above on a 4.0 scale; enrolled in a Human Services studies program. **Application Requirements:** Applicants must submit an official transcript (sent by the university in a sealed envelope); a resume; an essay (500-words) about the applicant's commitment to the field of helping and quality of Human Service Education; copy of current NOHS membership card; and two reference letters. Send applications as email attachments to Linda Wark, PhD, LMFT, Chair, Professional Development Committee at warkl@ipfw. edu. **Deadline for Receipt:** May 1.

3726 ■ NATIONAL STONE SAND AND GRAVEL ASSOCIATION

1605 King St.
Alexandria, VA 22314
Tel: (703)525-8788
Web Site: http://www.nssga.org

To provide scholarships to students who plan to pursue a career in the aggregates industry.

Title of Award: The Jennifer Curtis Byler Scholarships **Area, Field, or Subject:** Public affairs. **Level of Education for which Award is Granted:** Undergraduate **Funds Available:** No specific amount.

Eligibility Requirements: Applicants must be graduating high school seniors or students enrolled in a public affairs major. Applicants must also be dependents of an aggregates company employee. **Application Requirements:** Applicants must submit a completed form; a letter of recommendation from a faculty advisor; a 300 to 500-word statement about the plans for a career in public affairs; a letter or recommendation from employer (if the applicant worked in public affairs as a summer employee). **Deadline for Receipt:** May 31.

3727 ■ PHI UPSILON OMICRON

PO Box 329
Fairmont, WV 26555
Tel: (304)368-0612
E-mail: info@phiu.org
Web Site: http://www.phiu.org

To promote education in advance family and consumer sciences and related areas.

Title of Award: Geraldine Clewell Scholarships - Undergraduate **Area, Field, or Subject:** Family planning; Consumer affairs. **Level of Education for which Award is Granted:** Undergraduate **Funds Available:** No specific amount.

Eligibility Requirements: Applicant must be a Phi U member; enrolled full-time in a baccalaureate degree program in family and consumer sciences or a related area. **Application Requirements:** Applicants must submit an application; transcripts; recommendations. Application documents must be assembled in order, clipped together with a paper clip and placed in a 10" x 13" envelope. Enclose a self-addressed stamped postcard. **Additional Information:** Applicants may apply for more than one fellowship. **Deadline for Receipt:** February 1.

3728 ■ PHI UPSILON OMICRON

PO Box 329
Fairmont, WV 26555

Tel: (304)368-0612
E-mail: info@phiu.org
Web Site: http://www.phiu.org
To promote education in advance family and consumer sciences and related areas.
Title of Award: Closs/Parnitzke/Clarke Scholarships **Area, Field, or Subject:** Family planning; Consumer affairs. **Level of Education for which Award is Granted:** Undergraduate **Funds Available:** No specific amount.
Eligibility Requirements: Applicant must be a Phi U member; enrolled full-time in a baccalaureate degree program in family and consumer sciences or a related area. **Application Requirements:** Applicants must submit an application; transcripts; recommendations. Application documents must be assembled in order, clipped together with a paper clip and placed in a 10" x 13" envelope. Enclose a self-addressed stamped postcard. **Additional Information:** Applicants may apply for more than one fellowship. **Deadline for Receipt:** February 1.

3729 ■ PHI UPSILON OMICRON
PO Box 329
Fairmont, WV 26555
Tel: (304)368-0612
E-mail: info@phiu.org
Web Site: http://www.phiu.org
To promote education in advance family and consumer sciences and related areas.
Title of Award: Genevieve Forthun Scholarships **Area, Field, or Subject:** Family planning; Consumer affairs. **Level of Education for which Award is Granted:** Undergraduate **Funds Available:** No specific amount.
Eligibility Requirements: Applicant must be a Phi U member; enrolled full-time in a baccalaureate degree program in family and consumer sciences or a related area. **Application Requirements:** Applicants must submit an application; transcripts; recommendations. Application documents must be assembled in order, clipped together with a paper clip and placed in a 10" x 13" envelope. Enclose a self-addressed stamped postcard. **Additional Information:** Applicants may apply for more than one fellowship. **Deadline for Receipt:** February 1.

3730 ■ PHI UPSILON OMICRON
PO Box 329
Fairmont, WV 26555
Tel: (304)368-0612
E-mail: info@phiu.org
Web Site: http://www.phiu.org
To promote education in advance family and consumer sciences and related areas.
Title of Award: Mary Weiking Franken Scholarships **Area, Field, or Subject:** Family planning; Consumer affairs. **Level of Education for which Award is Granted:** Undergraduate **Funds Available:** No specific amount.
Eligibility Requirements: Applicant must be a Phi U member; enrolled full-time in a baccalaureate degree program in family and consumer sciences or a related area. **Application Requirements:** Applicants must submit an application; transcripts; recommendations. Application documents must be assembled in order, clipped together with a paper clip and placed in a 10" x 13" envelope. Enclose a self-addressed stamped postcard. **Additional Information:** Applicants may apply for more than one fellowship. **Deadline for Receipt:** February 1.

3731 ■ PHI UPSILON OMICRON
PO Box 329
Fairmont, WV 26555
Tel: (304)368-0612
E-mail: info@phiu.org
Web Site: http://www.phiu.org
To promote education in advance family and consumer sciences and related areas.
Title of Award: Tommie J. Hamner Scholarships **Area, Field, or Subject:** Family planning; Consumer affairs. **Level of Education for which Award is Granted:** Undergraduate **Funds Available:** No specific amount.
Eligibility Requirements: Applicant must be a Phi U member; enrolled full-time in a baccalaureate degree program in family and consumer sci-

ences or a related area; and have shown exemplary commitment to Phi Upsilon Omicron. **Application Requirements:** Applicants must submit an application; transcripts; recommendations. Application documents must be assembled in order, clipped together with a paper clip and placed in a 10" x 13" envelope. Enclose a self-addressed stamped postcard. **Additional Information:** Applicants may apply for more than one fellowship. **Deadline for Receipt:** February 1.

3732 ■ PHI UPSILON OMICRON
PO Box 329
Fairmont, WV 26555
Tel: (304)368-0612
E-mail: info@phiu.org
Web Site: http://www.phiu.org
To promote education in advance family and consumer sciences and related areas.
Title of Award: Jackman Scholarships **Area, Field, or Subject:** Family planning; Consumer affairs. **Level of Education for which Award is Granted:** Undergraduate **Funds Available:** No specific amount.
Eligibility Requirements: Applicant must be a Phi U member; enrolled full-time in a baccalaureate degree program in family and consumer sciences or a related area; and have shown exemplary commitment to Phi Upsilon Omicron. **Application Requirements:** Applicants must submit an application; transcripts; recommendations. Application documents must be assembled in order, clipped together with a paper clip and placed in a 10" x 13" envelope. Enclose a self-addressed stamped postcard. **Additional Information:** Applicants may apply for more than one fellowship. **Deadline for Receipt:** February 1.

3733 ■ PHI UPSILON OMICRON
PO Box 329
Fairmont, WV 26555
Tel: (304)368-0612
E-mail: info@phiu.org
Web Site: http://www.phiu.org
To promote education in advance family and consumer sciences and related areas.
Title of Award: Martha Combs Jenkins Scholarships **Area, Field, or Subject:** Family planning; Consumer affairs. **Level of Education for which Award is Granted:** Undergraduate **Funds Available:** No specific amount.
Eligibility Requirements: Applicant must be a Phi U member; pursuing a baccalaureate degree in family and consumer sciences or one of its related areas; and has shown exemplary commitment to Phi Upsilon Omicron. **Application Requirements:** Applicants must submit an application; transcripts; recommendations. Application documents must be assembled in order, clipped together with a paper clip and placed in a 10" x 13" envelope. Enclose a self-addressed stamped postcard. **Additional Information:** Applicants may apply for more than one fellowship. **Deadline for Receipt:** February 1.

3734 ■ PHI UPSILON OMICRON
PO Box 329
Fairmont, WV 26555
Tel: (304)368-0612
E-mail: info@phiu.org
Web Site: http://www.phiu.org
To promote education in advance family and consumer sciences and related areas.
Title of Award: Treva C. Kintner Scholarships **Area, Field, or Subject:** Family planning; Consumer affairs. **Level of Education for which Award is Granted:** Undergraduate **Funds Available:** No specific amount.
Eligibility Requirements: Applicant must be a Phi U member; a non-traditional student; completed at least half of the academic work toward a baccalaureate degree in family and consumer sciences or a related area. **Application Requirements:** Applicants must submit an application; transcripts; recommendations. Application documents must be assembled in order, clipped together with a paper clip and placed in a 10" x 13" envelope. Enclose a self-addressed stamped postcard. **Additional Information:** Applicants may apply for more than one fellowship. **Deadline for Receipt:** February 1.

3735 ■ PHI UPSILON OMICRON
PO Box 329
Fairmont, WV 26555

Tel: (304)368-0612
E-mail: info@phiu.org
Web Site: http://www.phiu.org
To promote education in advance family and consumer sciences and related areas.
Title of Award: Phi Upsilon Omicron Challenge Scholarships **Area, Field, or Subject:** Family planning; Consumer affairs. **Level of Education for which Award is Granted:** Undergraduate **Funds Available:** No specific amount.
Eligibility Requirements: Applicant must be a Phi U member; enrolled full-time in a baccalaureate degree program in family and consumer sciences or a related area. **Application Requirements:** Applicants must submit an application; transcripts; recommendations. Application documents must be assembled in order, clipped together with a paper clip and placed in a 10" x 13" envelope. Enclose a self-addressed stamped postcard. **Additional Information:** Applicants may apply for more than one fellowship. **Deadline for Receipt:** February 1.

3736 ■ PHI UPSILON OMICRON
PO Box 329
Fairmont, WV 26555
Tel: (304)368-0612
E-mail: info@phiu.org
Web Site: http://www.phiu.org
To promote education in advance family and consumer sciences and related areas.
Title of Award: Phi Upsilon Omicron Golden Anniversary Scholarships **Area, Field, or Subject:** Family planning; Consumer affairs. **Level of Education for which Award is Granted:** Undergraduate **Funds Available:** No specific amount.
Eligibility Requirements: Applicant must be a Phi U member; enrolled full-time in a baccalaureate degree program in family and consumer sciences or a related area. **Application Requirements:** Applicants must submit an application; transcripts; recommendations. Application documents must be assembled in order, clipped together with a paper clip and placed in a 10" x 13" envelope. Enclose a self-addressed stamped postcard. **Additional Information:** Applicants may apply for more than one fellowship. **Deadline for Receipt:** February 1.

3737 ■ PHI UPSILON OMICRON
PO Box 329
Fairmont, WV 26555
Tel: (304)368-0612
E-mail: info@phiu.org
Web Site: http://www.phiu.org
To promote education in advance family and consumer sciences and related areas.
Title of Award: Phi Upsilon Omicron Past Presidents Scholarships **Area, Field, or Subject:** Family planning; Consumer affairs. **Level of Education for which Award is Granted:** Undergraduate **Funds Available:** No specific amount.
Eligibility Requirements: Applicant must be a Phi U member; enrolled full-time in a baccalaureate degree program in family and consumer sciences or a related area. **Application Requirements:** Applicants must submit an application; transcripts; recommendations. Application documents must be assembled in order, clipped together with a paper clip and placed in a 10" x 13" envelope. Enclose a self-addressed stamped postcard. **Additional Information:** Applicants may apply for more than one fellowship. **Deadline for Receipt:** February 1.

3738 ■ PHI UPSILON OMICRON
PO Box 329
Fairmont, WV 26555
Tel: (304)368-0612
E-mail: info@phiu.org
Web Site: http://www.phiu.org
To promote education in advance family and consumer sciences and related areas.
Title of Award: Nell Bryant Robinson Scholarships **Area, Field, or Subject:** Family planning; Consumer affairs; Nutrition. **Level of Education for which Award is Granted:** Undergraduate **Funds Available:** No specific amount.
Eligibility Requirements: Applicant must be a Phi U member; pursuing a baccalaureate degree in family and consumer sciences or one of its

related areas. **Application Requirements:** Applicants must submit an application; transcripts; recommendations. Application documents must be assembled in order, clipped together with a paper clip and placed in a 10" x 13" envelope. Enclose a self-addressed stamped postcard. **Additional Information:** Applicants may apply for more than one fellowship. **Deadline for Receipt:** February 1.

3739 ■ PHI UPSILON OMICRON
PO Box 329
Fairmont, WV 26555
Tel: (304)368-0612
E-mail: info@phiu.org
Web Site: http://www.phiu.org
To promote education in advance family and consumer sciences and related areas.
Title of Award: Lucile Rust Scholarships **Area, Field, or Subject:** Family planning; Consumer affairs. **Level of Education for which Award is Granted:** Undergraduate **Funds Available:** No specific amount.
Eligibility Requirements: Applicant must be a Phi U member; enrolled full-time in a baccalaureate degree program in family and consumer sciences or a related area. **Application Requirements:** Applicants must submit an application; transcripts; recommendations. Application documents must be assembled in order, clipped together with a paper clip and placed in a 10" x 13" envelope. Enclose a self-addressed stamped postcard. **Additional Information:** Applicants may apply for more than one fellowship. **Deadline for Receipt:** February 1.

3740 ■ PHI UPSILON OMICRON
PO Box 329
Fairmont, WV 26555
Tel: (304)368-0612
E-mail: info@phiu.org
Web Site: http://www.phiu.org
To promote education in advance family and consumer sciences and related areas.
Title of Award: Margaret Jerome Sampson Scholarships **Area, Field, or Subject:** Family planning; Consumer affairs; Nutrition. **Level of Education for which Award is Granted:** Undergraduate **Number Awarded:** 4. **Funds Available:** $3000.
Eligibility Requirements: Applicant must be a Phi U member; enrolled full-time in a baccalaureate degree program in family and consumer sciences or a related area. **Application Requirements:** Applicants must submit an application; transcripts; recommendations (one must be from the Phi U chapter advisor). Application documents must be assembled in order, clipped together with a paper clip and placed in a 10" x 13" envelope. Enclose a self-addressed stamped postcard, a financial statement and one double-spaced typewritten page about the reasons for needing an additional financial assistance. **Additional Information:** Applicants may apply for more than one fellowship. **Deadline for Receipt:** February 1.

3741 ■ PHI UPSILON OMICRON
PO Box 329
Fairmont, WV 26555
Tel: (304)368-0612
E-mail: info@phiu.org
Web Site: http://www.phiu.org
To promote education in advance family and consumer sciences and related areas.
Title of Award: Lillian P. Schoephoerster Scholarships **Area, Field, or Subject:** Family planning; Consumer affairs. **Level of Education for which Award is Granted:** Undergraduate **Number Awarded:** 2. **Funds Available:** $1000.
Eligibility Requirements: Applicant must be a Phi U member; a non-traditional student enrolled full-time in a baccalaureate degree program in family and consumer sciences or a related area. **Application Requirements:** Applicants must submit an application; transcripts; recommendations. Application documents must be assembled in order, clipped together with a paper clip and placed in a 10" x 13" envelope. Enclose a self-addressed stamped postcard. **Additional Information:** Applicants may apply for more than one fellowship. **Deadline for Receipt:** February 1.

3742 ■ PRIDE FOUNDATION
PO Box 2194, 1122 E Pike St. PMB 1001
Seattle, WA 98112
Tel: (206)323-3318
Free: 800-735-7287
Fax: (206)323-1017
E-mail: prideweb@pridefoundation.org
Web Site: http://www.pridefoundation.org
To provide scholarship to the students who have been stigmatized, isolated or closeted because of sexual identity issues.
Title of Award: Athletic Excellence Scholarships **Area, Field, or Subject:** Sports studies. **Level of Education for which Award is Granted:** Undergraduate **Funds Available:** No specific amount.
Eligibility Requirements: Applicant must be an LGBT individual who plans to pursue or study athletics through college, or for athletes pursuing national/international excellence in sports through an accredited institution or program. **Application Requirements:** Qualified students are asked to submit an application to determine eligibility for scholarships. Applicants may download an application form from the Foundation's website. **Additional Information:** Pride Foundation at the above address.

3743 ■ PRIDE FOUNDATION
PO Box 2194, 1122 E Pike St. PMB 1001
Seattle, WA 98112
Tel: (206)323-3318
Free: 800-735-7287
Fax: (206)323-1017
E-mail: prideweb@pridefoundation.org
Web Site: http://www.pridefoundation.org
To provide scholarship to the students who have been stigmatized, isolated or closeted because of sexual identity issues.
Title of Award: Bill Bendiner and Doug Morgenson Scholarships **Area, Field, or Subject:** Human relations; Health sciences; Visual arts. **Level of Education for which Award is Granted:** Undergraduate **Funds Available:** No specific amount.
Eligibility Requirements: Applicant must be pursing a career in human services, health sciences or visual arts. **Application Requirements:** Qualified students are asked to submit an application to determine eligibility for scholarships. Applicants may download an application form from the Foundation's website. **Additional Information:** Pride Foundation at the above address.

3744 ■ PRIDE FOUNDATION
PO Box 2194, 1122 E Pike St. PMB 1001
Seattle, WA 98112
Tel: (206)323-3318
Free: 800-735-7287
Fax: (206)323-1017
E-mail: prideweb@pridefoundation.org
Web Site: http://www.pridefoundation.org
To provide scholarship to the students who have been stigmatized, isolated or closeted because of sexual identity issues.
Title of Award: Derivative Duo Scholarships **Area, Field, or Subject:** Mental health; Human relations. **Level of Education for which Award is Granted:** Undergraduate **Funds Available:** No specific amount.
Eligibility Requirements: Applicant must be a resident of Washington studying mental health or human services. **Application Requirements:** Qualified students are asked to submit an application to determine eligibility for scholarships. Applicants may download an application form from the Foundation's website. **Additional Information:** Pride Foundation at the above address.

3745 ■ PUBLIC EDUCATION FOUNDATION
3360 W Sahara Ave., Ste. 160
Las Vegas, NV 89102
Tel: (702)799-1042
Fax: (702)799-5247
E-mail: steelej@ccpef.org
Web Site: http://ccpef.org
To provide educational opportunities for individuals intending to pursue higher studies.
Title of Award: Corporal Joseph Martinez U.S. Army Memorial Scholarships **Area, Field, or Subject:** Maritime studies. **Level of Education for which Award is Granted:** Undergraduate **Number Awarded:** 1 or 2. **Funds Available:** $500-$1,000. **Duration:** One year.

Eligibility Requirements: Applicants must be Durango High School AFJROTC program seniors planning to attend an accredited post-secondary institution either during or immediately following enlistment in any branch of the U.S. military may apply. **Application Requirements:** Applicants must submit a completed application form along with the letter from military recruiter, one letter of recommendation, transcript, and resume. **Deadline for Receipt:** March 7. **Additional Information:** Shana Venenga at 702-799-1042.

3746 ■ ROYAL CANADIAN GOLF ASSOCIATION
1333 Dorval Dr., Ste. 1
Oakville, ON, Canada L6M 4X7
Tel: (905)849-9700
Fax: (905)845-7040
E-mail: ssimmons@rcga.org
Web Site: http://www.rcga.org
To assist a promising university student.
Title of Award: Georgia Hilton Academic Scholarships **Area, Field, or Subject:** Sports studies; Business administration. **Level of Education for which Award is Granted:** Undergraduate **Funds Available:** $5,000. **Duration:** One year.
Eligibility Requirements: Applicants must be university students studying towards a degree in sport/business administration; must show a minimum average of 80% in the last two years of high school, or CEGEP, and have attained a graduation diploma (minimum Grade 12). Must also have completed at least one full year of education in a post-secondary degree program at a recognized institution; must intend to continue in an undergraduate or graduate program in sport/business administration; must have experience in competitive golf at a regional, provincial, or national level; must have participated in community and/or extracurricular activities; must be a Canadian citizen or landed immigrant. **Application Requirements:** Application forms are available online and must be sent to RCGA, 1333 Dorval Dr., Ste. 1, Oakville, ON L6M 4X7. **Deadline for Receipt:** June 30.

3747 ■ UNIVERSITY OF ALASKA ANCHORAGE
3211 Providence Dr.
Anchorage, AK 99508
Tel: (907)786-1800
Web Site: http://www.uaa.alaska.edu
To provide financial assistance for tuition and other educational expenses to students who are formally admitted to a degree-seeking program at the University of Alaska Anchorage who have an intent to explore human-nature relationships through writing or other creative expression.
Title of Award: UAA April Relyea Scholarships **Area, Field, or Subject:** Human relations. **Level of Education for which Award is Granted:** Graduate, Undergraduate **Funds Available:** $500. **Duration:** One academic year.
Eligibility Requirements: Applicants must demonstrate environmental interest with intent to explore the topic of human-nature relationships through writing or other creative expressions; must be in good academic standing with a minimum cumulative GPA of 2.0 for undergraduates and 3.0 for graduates; must be formally admitted to an undergraduate, graduate, certificate, and/or vocational degree-seeking program at the University of Alaska Anchorage; may be a U.S citizen, non-U.S citizen, Alaska resident, or out-of-state resident; must complete a project to receive a second semester scholarship. **Application Requirements:** Applicants must submit an essay about their interest in human-nature relationships and how they intend to pursue that interest at UAA; must submit two letters of reference from source having knowledge of their environmental interest. Application forms and other supporting documents must be sent to the UAA Office of Student Financial Assistance, April Relyea Scholarship, PO Box 141608, Anchorage, AK 99503. **Deadline for Receipt:** February 15.

3748 ■ UNIVERSITY OF ALASKA ANCHORAGE
3211 Providence Dr.
Anchorage, AK 99508
Tel: (907)786-1800
Web Site: http://www.uaa.alaska.edu
To provide financial assistance to University of Alaska Anchorage students who are formally admitted to the journalism & public communication degree-seeking program.

Title of Award: UAA Elaine Atwood Scholarships **Area, Field, or Subject:** Journalism; Public affairs. **Level of Education for which Award is Granted:** Undergraduate **Funds Available:** $2,500-5,000. **Duration:** One year.
Eligibility Requirements: Applicants must demonstrate motivation, academic and leadership potential; must be in good academic standing with a minimum cumulative GPA of 3.0; must be formally admitted to the Journalism and Public Communication degree program at UAA; must plan on enrolling full-time (12 credits) at the University of Alaska Anchorage; may be an incoming or continuing student at the University of Alaska Anchorage; must be an Alaska resident who will pursue a career in Alaska. **Application Requirements:** Applicants must complete the electronics scholarship application available online at www.uaa.alaska.edu/scholarships/elaine.cfm. **Deadline for Receipt:** February 15.

3749 ■ UNIVERSITY OF ALASKA ANCHORAGE
3211 Providence Dr.
Anchorage, AK 99508
Tel: (907)786-1800
Web Site: http://www.uaa.alaska.edu
To provide financial assistance to cover a student-designated sociology project to be conducted while the student is enrolled at UAA and to encourage the students to pursue sociology as a career.
Title of Award: UAA Eveline Schuster Memorial Award/Scholarships **Area, Field, or Subject:** Sociology. **Level of Education for which Award is Granted:** Graduate, Undergraduate **Funds Available:** No specific amount. **Duration:** One year.
Eligibility Requirements: Applicants must demonstrate motivation, academic, and leadership potential; must be in good academic standing with a 3.0 GPA and a sociology GPA of 3.3 or better; must be formally admitted to a sociology degree-seeking program or interdisciplinary master's degree-seeking program with sociology as one of the disciplines, at the UAA; must plan on enrolling full-time (12 credits for undergraduates, 9 credits for graduates) at the UAA; must have at least a junior class standing; must have been enrolled in at least six (6) credits prior to the semester the award is granted; may be a U.S citizen, non-U.S. citizen, Alaska resident, or out-of-state resident. **Application Requirements:** Applicants must submit a cover letter indicating if they are applying for the scholarship or for project funding; must submit two (2) letters of recommendation; must submit a project budget and statement indicating the project intent; must complete the electronic scholarship application available online at www.uaa.alaska.edu/scholarships/eveline.cfm. **Deadline for Receipt:** February 15.

3750 ■ UNIVERSITY OF ALASKA ANCHORAGE
3211 Providence Dr.
Anchorage, AK 99508
Tel: (907)786-1800
Web Site: http://www.uaa.alaska.edu
To provide financial assistance for tuition and other educational expenses to full-time students who are formally admitted to a journalism & public communications degree-seeking program at the University of Alaska Anchorage and who are in financial need.
Title of Award: UAA GCI, Inc. Scholarships **Area, Field, or Subject:** Journalism; Public affairs. **Level of Education for which Award is Granted:** Undergraduate **Funds Available:** No specific amount.
Eligibility Requirements: Applicants must demonstrate motivation, academic and leadership potential; must be in good academic standing with a minimum cumulative GPA of 3.0; must be formally admitted to a journalism & public communications degree-seeking program at the University of Alaska Anchorage; must plan on enrolling full-time (12 credits) at the University of Alaska Anchorage; must be able to demonstrate financial need; must be enrolled in the semester for which the award is made; may be an incoming or continuing student at the University of Alaska Anchorage; may be a U.S citizen, non-U.S citizen, Alaska resident, or out-of-state resident. **Application Requirements:** Applicants must complete the electronic scholarship application available online at www.uaa.alaska.edu/scholarships/sturgulewski_family.cfm. **Deadline for Receipt:** February 15.

3751 ■ UNIVERSITY OF ALASKA ANCHORAGE
3211 Providence Dr.
Anchorage, AK 99508
Tel: (907)786-1800
Web Site: http://www.uaa.alaska.edu
To provide financial assistance for tuition and other educational expenses to full-time students who are formally admitted to an undergraduate social sciences program or enrolled in an interdisciplinary masters program which includes sociology as one of the disciplines.
Title of Award: UAA Michael Baring-Gould Memorial Scholarships **Area, Field, or Subject:** Social sciences; Sociology. **Level of Education for which Award is Granted:** Graduate, Undergraduate **Funds Available:** No specific amount.
Eligibility Requirements: Applicants must be in good academic standing with a minimum cumulative GPA of 2.5 for undergraduates and 3.0 for graduates; must be formally admitted to an undergraduate social sciences major or an Interdisciplinary Master's degree program that includes sociology as one of the disciplines at the University of Alaska Anchorage; must have completed at least thirty credits (undergraduate applicants); must have completed at least six credits prior to the semester of the award at the University of Alaska Anchorage; must plan on enrolling full-time (12 credits for undergraduates and nine credits for graduates) at the University of Alaska Anchorage the semester the award is granted; must demonstrate involvement in a project or area of study which reflects a commitment to social justice, peace, equality, and/or empowerment of minorities; may be a U.S. citizen, non-U.S. citizen, Alaska resident, or out-of-state resident. **Application Requirements:** Applicants must submit two letters of recommendation and an essay (250 words) describing the student's involvement in a project or area of study which reflects a commitment to social justice, peace, equality, and/or empowerment of minorities. Application material must be mailed to the UAA Office of Student Financial Assistance, PO Box 141608, Anchorage, AK 99514-1608. **Deadline for Receipt:** February 15.

3752 ■ UNIVERSITY OF CALIFORNIA, BERKELEY
301B Campbell Hall No. 2922
Berkeley, CA 94720-2922
Tel: (510)643-6929
E-mail: scholarships@learning.berkeley.edu
Web Site: http://www.berkeley.edu
To encourage a junior student to continue studies in the arts, humanities, or social sciences.
Title of Award: Beinecke Brothers Memorial Scholarships **Area, Field, or Subject:** Arts, Humanities, Social sciences. **Level of Education for which Award is Granted:** Undergraduate **Funds Available:** $34,000.
Eligibility Requirements: Applciant must be a junior student; must be a U.S citizen or U.S national from American Samoa or the Commonwealth of Northern Mariana Islands; must have a superior intellectual ability (typically a minimum 3.5 GPA); must have a financial need. **Application Requirements:** Applicant must complete a application form (available online); must have a current resume; must provide a 1000-word personal statement describing background, interests, career goals, and plan for graduate study; must have a official copies of all college transcripts; must have three letters of recommendation from faculty members. **Deadline for Receipt:** February 15.

3753 ■ WOMEN MARINES ASSOCIATION
PO Box 8405
Falls Church, VA 22041-8405
888-525-1943
E-mail: wma@womenmarines.org
Web Site: http://www.womenmarines.org
To financially assist students with their educational pursuits.
Title of Award: LaRue A. Ditmore Music Scholarships **Area, Field, or Subject:** Maritime studies. **Level of Education for which Award is Granted:** Undergraduate **Funds Available:** $1500.
Eligibility Requirements: Applicant must have served, or be serving in the U.S. Marine Corps or Reserve; or a direct descendant by blood, or legal adoption or stepchild of a Marine on active duty, or who has served in the U.S. Marine Corps, Regular or Reserve; or a sibling or a descendant of a sibling by blood, or legal adoption or stepchild of a Marine on active duty, or who has served in the U.S. Marine Corps, Regular or Reserve; or have completed two years in a Marine Corps JROTC program. High school applicant must have maintained a B+ average for the sophomore or junior years; have a SAT score of 1100 (combined Math/Verbal); have an ACT score of 25 (combined Math/

Verbal). College students must have a GPA of 3.5. Applicant must have a WMA member sponsor. **Application Requirements:** Applicants must submit a completed application form together with a copy of Sponsor's National Membership Card; a wallet size photo (name written on lower back); three letters of reference from a school personnel (on official letterhead signed and sealed envelope); proof of relationship to a U.S. Marine; and a permanent and alternate Email addresses. High school students must also send official transcripts (mailed directly from the school) and a letter of acceptance for the following year. College freshmen students must send an additional official final high school transcript (including SAT/ACT scores) and current college transcript. Send all materials to Luann Weeks, 251 SW 1300th Road, Chilhowee, MO 64733-8133, ldweeks@pocketmail.com. **Additional Information:** Male applicants must submit a proof of draft registration when applying on or after their eighteenth birthday. **Deadline for Receipt:** March 31.

3754 ■ WOMEN MARINES ASSOCIATION
PO Box 8405
Falls Church, VA 22041-8405
888-525-1943
E-mail: wma@womenmarines.org
Web Site: http://www.womenmarines.org
To financially assist students with their educational pursuits.
Title of Award: Lily H. Gridley Memorial Scholarships **Area, Field, or Subject:** Maritime studies. **Level of Education for which Award is Granted:** Undergraduate **Funds Available:** $1500.
Eligibility Requirements: Applicant must have served, or be serving in the U.S. Marine Corps or Reserve; or a direct descendant by blood, or legal adoption or stepchild of a Marine on active duty, or has served in the U.S. Marine Corps, Regular or Reserve; or a sibling or a descendant of a sibling by blood, or legal adoption or stepchild of a Marine on active duty, or who has served in the U.S. Marine Corps, Regular or Reserve; or have completed two years in a Marine Corps JROTC program. High school applicant must have maintained a B+ average for the sophomore or junior years; have a SAT score of 1100 (combined Math/Verbal); have an ACT score of 25 (combined Math/Verbal). College students must have a GPA of 3.5. Applicant must have a WMA member sponsor. **Application Requirements:** Applicants must submit a completed application form together with a copy of Sponsor's National Membership Card; a wallet size photo (name written on lower back); three letters of reference from a school personnel (on official letterhead signed and sealed envelope); proof of relationship to a U.S. Marine; and a permanent and alternate Email addresses. High schools students must also send official transcripts (mailed directly from the school) and a letter of acceptance for the following year. College freshmen students must send an additional official final high school transcript (including SAT/ACT scores) and current college transcript. Send all materials to Luann Weeks, 251 SW 1300th Road, Chilhowee, MO 64733-8133, ldweeks@pocketmail.com. **Additional Information:** Male applicants must submit a proof of draft registration when applying on or after their eighteenth birthday. **Deadline for Receipt:** March 31.

3755 ■ WOMEN MARINES ASSOCIATION
PO Box 8405
Falls Church, VA 22041-8405
888-525-1943
E-mail: wma@womenmarines.org
Web Site: http://www.womenmarines.org
To financially assist students with their educational pursuits.
Title of Award: Ethyl and Armin Wiebke Memorial Scholarships **Area, Field, or Subject:** Maritime studies. **Level of Education for which Award is Granted:** Undergraduate **Number Awarded:** 1. **Funds Available:** $1500.
Eligibility Requirements: Applicant must have served, or be serving in the U.S. Marine Corps or Reserve; or a direct descendant by blood, or legal adoption or stepchild of a Marine on active duty, or who has served in the U.S. Marine Corps, Regular or Reserve; or a sibling or a descendant of a sibling by blood, or legal adoption or stepchild of a Marine on active duty, or who has served in the U.S. Marine Corps, Regular or Reserve; or have completed two years in a Marine Corps JROTC program. High school applicant must have maintained a B+ average for the sophomore or junior years; have a SAT score of 1100 (combined Math/Verbal); have an ACT score of 25 (combined Math/

Verbal). College students must have a GPA of 3.5. Applicant must have a WMA member sponsor. **Application Requirements:** Applicants must submit a completed application form together with a copy of Sponsor's National Membership Card; a wallet size photo (name written on lower back); three letters of reference from a school personnel (on official letterhead signed and sealed envelope); proof of relationship to a U.S. Marine; and a permanent and alternate Email addresses. High schools students must also send official transcripts (mailed directly from the school) and a letter of acceptance for the following year. College freshmen students must send an additional official final high school transcript (including SAT/ACT scores) and current college transcript. Send all materials to Luann Weeks, 251 SW 1300th Road, Chilhowee, MO 64733-8133, ldweeks@pocketmail.com. **Additional Information:** Male applicants must submit a proof of draft registration when applying on or after their eighteenth birthday. **Deadline for Receipt:** March 31.

3756 ■ WOMEN MARINES ASSOCIATION
PO Box 8405
Falls Church, VA 22041-8405
888-525-1943
E-mail: wma@womenmarines.org
Web Site: http://www.womenmarines.org
To financially assist students with their educational pursuits.
Title of Award: WMA Memorial Scholarships **Area, Field, or Subject:** Maritime studies. **Level of Education for which Award is Granted:** Undergraduate **Funds Available:** $1500.
Eligibility Requirements: Applicant must have served, or be serving in the U.S. Marine Corps or Reserve; or a direct descendant by blood, or legal adoption or stepchild of a Marine on active duty, or who has served in the U.S. Marine Corps, Regular or Reserve; or a sibling or a descendant of a sibling by blood, or legal adoption or stepchild of a Marine on active duty, or who has served in the U.S. Marine Corps, Regular or Reserve; or have completed two years in a Marine Corps JROTC program. High school applicant must have maintained a B+ average for the sophomore or junior years; have a SAT score of 1100 (combined Math/Verbal); have an ACT score of 25 (combined Math/Verbal). College students must have a GPA of 3.5. Applicant must have a WMA member sponsor. **Application Requirements:** Applicants must submit a completed application form together with a copy of Sponsor's National Membership Card; a wallet size photo (name written on lower back); three letters of reference from a school personnel (on official letterhead signed and sealed envelope); proof of relationship to a U.S. Marine; and a permanent and alternate Email addresses. High schools students must also send official transcripts (mailed directly from the school) and a letter of acceptance for the following year. College freshmen students must send an additional official final high school transcript (including SAT/ACT scores) and current college transcript. Send all materials to Luann Weeks, 251 SW 1300th Road, Chilhowee, MO 64733-8133, ldweeks@pocketmail.com. **Additional Information:** Male applicants must submit a proof of draft registration when applying on or after their eighteenth birthday. **Deadline for Receipt:** March 31.

3757 ■ YOUTH MARITIME TRAINING ASSOCIATION
PO Box 70425
Seattle, WA 98127-0425
Tel: (206)782-1080
E-mail: info@ymta.net
Web Site: http://www.ymta.net
To support students pursuing maritime training and education.
Title of Award: Norm Manly - YMTA Maritime Educational Scholarships **Area, Field, or Subject:** Maritime studies. **Level of Education for which Award is Granted:** Undergraduate **Number Awarded:** 4. **Funds Available:** $1,000, $3,000, and $5,000. **Duration:** One year.
Eligibility Requirements: Applicants must have attended at least one semester or quarter in an YMTA-supported program or be a current active member of a Sea Scout ship for the past 6 months; must be under 21 at time of application; must be enrolled as a senior in a high school in the State of Washington; and have GPA of at least 2.5. Relatives of YMTA Executive, Honorary and Advisory Board members are not eligible for YMTA Scholarships. **Application Requirements:** Applicants are required to complete the application form and submit along with the required documents to Youth Maritime Training Association PO Box 70425 Seattle, WA 98127. **Deadline for Receipt:** February and April. **Additional Information:** Carleen See, arleeninballard@yahoo.com.

Anthropology

3758 ■ MASSACHUSETTS OFFICE OF STUDENT FINANCIAL ASSISTANCE
454 Broadway, Ste. 200
Revere, MA 02151
Tel: (617)727-9420
Fax: (617)727-0667
E-mail: osfa@osfa.mass.edu
Web Site: http://www.osfa.mass.edu
To provide financial assistance for currently employed early childhood educators and providers who enroll in an associate or bachelor degree program in early childhood education or related program.
Title of Award: Early Childhood Educators Scholarship Program **Area, Field, or Subject:** Child care. **Level of Education for which Award is Granted:** Undergraduate **Funds Available:** No specific amount.
Eligibility Requirements: Applicants must be permanent legal residents of Massachusetts; United States citizens or eligible non-citizens; eligible under Title IV Regulations and not in default of a state or federal education loan or grant; enrolled, as matriculated students without a bachelor's degree, in an undergraduate degree program (full- or part-time) in early childhood education or a related field (i.e., elementary education, sociology, psychology); employed as early childhood educators or licensed family child care providers in Massachusetts for at least one year; and must continue employment while enrolled in the required degree program. **Application Requirements:** Applicants must submit all the required application information.

Behavioral Sciences

3759 ■ AMERICAN SCHOOL HEALTH ASSOCIATION
7263 State Rte. 43
Kent, OH 44240
Tel: (330)678-1601
Fax: (330)678-4526
E-mail: asha@ashaweb.org
Web Site: http://www.ashaweb.org
To provide financial assistance to students concentrating on school health education, school nursing, and pediatric or adolescent medicine or dentistry.
Title of Award: ASHA Scholarships **Area, Field, or Subject:** Health education; Nursing; Pediatric medicine; Medicine; Dentistry; Nutrition; Counseling/Guidance. **Level of Education for which Award is Granted:** Graduate, Undergraduate **Number Awarded:** 3. **Funds Available:** $500 and a complimentary registration to ASHA's annual school health conference and a one-year ASHA membership. **Duration:** One year.
Eligibility Requirements: Applicants must be a junior, senior or graduate student; enrolled full-time at institution of higher education; have 3.0 GPA on a 4.0 scale; have a major related to School Health Education or School Nursing or Pediatric or Adolescent Medicine or Dentistry or other school health specializations (nutrition, counseling, etc.); not a previous recipient of this award. **Application Requirements:** Applicants must send one original and nine copies of the completed application form (application form available online); current resume; transcript; one page personal statement; three letters of recommendation. **Deadline for Receipt:** April 4. **Additional Information:** Pamela Dorazio Dean, pdean@ashaweb.org.

3760 ■ AMERICAN SCHOOL HEALTH ASSOCIATION
7263 State Rte. 43
Kent, OH 44240
Tel: (330)678-1601
Fax: (330)678-4526
E-mail: asha@ashaweb.org
Web Site: http://www.ashaweb.org
To provide financial assistance for research in areas related to the mission of ASHA.
Title of Award: ASHA Student Research Grants **Area, Field, or Subject:** Health education; Nursing; Pediatric medicine; Medicine; Dentistry; Nutrition; Counseling/Guidance. **Level of Education for which Award is Granted:** Graduate, Undergraduate **Funds Available:** No specific amount.
Eligibility Requirements: Applicants must be student members of ASHA.
Application Requirements: Applicants must send one original and five copies of a proposal which includes a cover sheet; a narrative (title-problem, review of related literature, methodology, data analyst, institution IRB protocol documented); and a budget. Proposal should have one inch margins, doubled spaced and a font size not smaller than 12. Forward the original and 5 copies to: ASHA Student Research Grants, PO Box 708, Kent, OH 44240. **Deadline for Receipt:** April 4. **Additional Information:** Pamela Dorazio, pdean@ashaweb.org, 330-678-1601.

3761 ■ BULLETIN OF THE ATOMIC SCIENTISTS
77 W Washington St., Ste. 2120
Chicago, IL 60602
Tel: (312)364-9715
Fax: (312)364-9715
E-mail: kbenedict@thebulletin.org
Web Site: http://www.thebulletin.org/index.htm
To provide financial support to undergraduate students pursuing a project relating to interaction of science, global security, and public policy.
Title of Award: Rieser Fellowships **Area, Field, or Subject:** Peace studies; National security. **Level of Education for which Award is Granted:** Undergraduate **Number Awarded:** 3-5. **Funds Available:** $2500 $5000.
Duration: One year.
Eligibility Requirements: Applicant must be undergraduate student at a U.S. college/university. **Application Requirements:** Applicant must send an application form (available at the website); resume; proposal (800-1000 words); official letters confirming internships, acceptance to conference; an essay (one-page, single-spaced) explaining how the fellowship would be benefit to the applicant; project budget; and two letters of recommendation. **Deadline for Receipt:** December. **Additional Information:** Rieser Fellowship rieser@thebulletin.org.

3762 ■ CATCHING THE DREAM
8200 Mountain Rd. NE., Ste. 203
Albuquerque, NM 87110
Tel: (505)262-2351
E-mail: nscholarships@aol.com
Web Site: http://www.catchingthedream.org
To support paraprofessionals native students in Native American Schools planning to complete their degree in education, counseling, or school administration.
Title of Award: Native American Leadership Education (NALE) Scholarships **Area, Field, or Subject:** Education; Counseling/Guidance; Educational administration. **Level of Education for which Award is Granted:** Postdoctoral, Undergraduate **Funds Available:** $500-$5000.
Duration: One academic year.
Eligibility Requirements: Applicants must be 1/4 or more degree Native American; an enrolled member of a "U.S. tribe"; attending or planning to attend a college/university within the U.S. on a full-time basis that is fully accredited (college level and can range from bachelor's degrees to postdoctoral study); have excellent grades; high ACT or SAT scores; and have a strong commitment to their Native American community. **Application Requirements:** Applicants must submit a completed application form (available at the website); financial need analysis; a copy of the IRS 1040 Federal Tax Return for the previous year; Certificate of Native American Blood; an essay explaining career goals; three letters of recommendation; official transcripts; a copy of standardized test scores; copy of letter of admission from an accredited college/university or graduate school and degree program in the US; and a photograph (2X3) of head and shoulders. **Deadline for Receipt:** March 15, April 15, and September 15.

3763 ■ DELTA ZETA SORORITY
202 E Church St.
Oxford, OH 45056
Tel: (513)523-7597
Web Site: http://www.deltazeta.org
To provide financial assistance to all qualified undergraduate students.
Title of Award: Huenefeld/Denton Scholarships **Area, Field, or Subject:** Child development, Education, Library and archival sciences. **Level of Education for which Award is Granted:** Undergraduate **Funds Available:** $1,000-$2,500. **Duration:** One academic year.
Eligibility Requirements: Applicant must be a junior or senior initiated, active continuing members in need of financial help, seeking an undergraduate degree in child development/primary education or library science. **Application Requirements:** Scholarship applications are avail-

able on the website and must be completed properly. Applicant must have the FAFSA reply form. **Deadline for Receipt:** February 15.

3764 ■ EPILEPSY FOUNDATION
8301 Professional Place
Landover, MD 20785
800-332-1000
Web Site: http://www.epilepsyfoundation.org
To encourage individuals to pursue careers in epilepsy in either the research or practice setting.
Title of Award: Behavioral Sciences Student Fellowships **Area, Field, or Subject:** Behavioral sciences; Epilepsy. **Level of Education for which Award is Granted:** Graduate, Undergraduate **Funds Available:** $3,000. **Eligibility Requirements:** Applicants must be in an appropriate undergraduate or graduate program in the behavioral sciences and must have a defined epilepsy-related study or research plan. **Application Requirements:** Applicants may visit the website or contact Epilepsy Foundation for more details. **Deadline for Receipt:** March 2.

3765 ■ HARTFORD FOUNDATION FOR PUBLIC GIVING
10 Columbus Blvd., 8th Flr.
Hartford, CT 06106
Tel: (860)548-1888
Fax: (860)524-8346
E-mail: hfpg@hfpg.org
Web Site: http://www.hfpg.org
To provide scholarship to the resident of Connecticut or student attending a Connecticut high school or college/university.
Title of Award: Gail Burns-Smith "Dare to Dream" Fund **Area, Field, or Subject:** Aggression and violence. **Level of Education for which Award is Granted:** Undergraduate **Number Awarded:** 1. **Funds Available:** $1,000.
Eligibility Requirements: Applicants be paid or volunteer work experience in the field women's issues or sexual violence prevention/advocacy and planned commitment to continuing work in the field of sexual violence prevention/advocacy. **Application Requirements:** Applicants must complete the application form provided by CONNSACS together with the following requirements: two written essays in response to questions listed on application; two character references, submitted as letters of recommendation on behalf of applicant. Applicants may obtain application from address below and submit to CONNSACS, Inc. **Deadline for Receipt:** March 1. **Additional Information:** Tara Martin, Dir. of Resource Development, 96 Pitkin St. E Hartford, CT 06108. Fax: 860-291-9335; Phone: 860-282-9881. tara@connsacs.org.

3766 ■ HISPANIC SCHOLARSHIP FUND
55 Second St., Ste. 1500
San Francisco, CA 94105
877-473-4636
Fax: (415)808-2302
E-mail: info@hsf.net
Web Site: http://www.hsf.net
To provide financial resources to assist outstanding Latino high school graduates.
Title of Award: Toyota High School Scholarship Program **Area, Field, or Subject:** Accounting; Actuarial science; Advertising; Architecture; Automotive technology; Bioengineering; Business; Chemical engineering; Civil engineering; Engineering, Computer; Electronics; Computer and information sciences; Construction; Drafting; Economics; Education; Education, Bilingual and cross-cultural; Education, Early childhood; Education, Special; Counseling/Guidance; Electrical engineering; Engineering; Environmental design; Environmental science; Geology; Educational administration; Education-Curricula; Personnel administration/human resources; Industrial design; Engineering, Industrial; Information science and technology; Management; Marketing and distribution; International trade; Manufacturing; Mechanical engineering; Engineering, Nuclear; Public administration; Public relations; Transportation. **Level of Education for which Award is Granted:** Undergraduate **Funds Available:** $5,000.
Eligibility Requirements: Applicant must be of Hispanic heritage; U.S. citizen or legal permanent resident with a valid permanent resident card or passport stamped I-551; have a minimum GPA of 3.0 on a 4.0 scale or equivalent; must apply for federal financing aid using the Free Application

for Federal Student Aid (FAFSA) at www.fafsa.ed.gov; enrolling as full-time freshman at: Arizona State University; Central Missouri University; Colorado State University, Pueblo; Cornell University; Ferris State; Florida International University; Harvard University; Indiana University; Massachusetts Institute of Technology; New York University; Northwestern University; Pennsylvania Tech College; Pittsburg State University; Southern Illinois University; Stanford University; Texas A&M University; University of Arizona; University of California, Berkeley; University of California, Davis; University of California, Los Angeles; University of California, San Diego; University of Florida; University of Houston; University of Illinois at Chicago; University of Illinois at Urbana-Champaign; University of Michigan; University of New Mexico; University of Pennsylvania; University of Southern California; University of Texas at Austin; University of Texas at El Paso; University of Texas at San Antonio; University of Texas, Pan American; or Weber State University. Applicants must pursue a degree in: Accounting; Actuarial Science; Advertising; Architecture; Automotive Technology; Bio-Engineering; Business; Chemical Engineering; Civil Engineering; Computer Electronics; Computer Engineering; Computer Information Systems (CIS); Computer Programming; Computer Science; Construction; Drafting/CAD; Economics; Education Admin./Leadership; Education/Teaching; Education: Bilingual; Education: Early Childhood/ Elementary; Education: Special; Educational Counseling; Electrical Engineering; Engineering; Environmental Design/Landscaping; Environmental Management/Science; Environmental/Geological Engineering; Human Resource Management; Industrial Design; Industrial Engineering; Information Technology (IT); International Business; Management; Management Information Systems (MIS); Manufacturing Engineering; Marketing; Materials/ Manufacturing; Mechanical Engineering; Network Administration; Non-Profit Management; Nuclear Engineering; Office Administration; Public Administration; Public Relations; Supply Chain Management; or Transportation. **Application Requirements:** Applications must be submitted using the HSF online application system. **Additional Information:** In partnership with Toyota Motor Sales, USA. **Deadline for Receipt:** July 16. **Additional Information:** highschool@hsf.net.

3767 ■ MENTAL HEALTH ASSOCIATION OF TARRANT COUNTY
3136 W St.
Fort Worth, TX 76107
Tel: (817)335-5405
Fax: (817)334-0025
E-mail: mhatc@mhatc.org
Web Site: http://www.mhatc.org
To provide financial support to those students pursuing a degree in the mental health field.
Title of Award: Patricia Pownder Conolly Memorial Scholarships **Area, Field, or Subject:** Psychiatry; Psychology; Sociology; Social work; Counseling; Rehabilitation counseling. **Level of Education for which Award is Granted:** Undergraduate **Funds Available:** No specific amount.
Eligibility Requirements: Applicants must be college students pursuing a degree in the mental health field. **Application Requirements:** Applicants must check the available website to download the application form. **Additional Information:** Mental Health Association of Tarrant County at the above address.

3768 ■ MENTAL HEALTH ASSOCIATION OF TARRANT COUNTY
3136 W St.
Fort Worth, TX 76107
Tel: (817)335-5405
Fax: (817)334-0025
E-mail: mhatc@mhatc.org
Web Site: http://www.mhatc.org
To provide financial support to those students pursuing a degree in the mental health field.
Title of Award: Linda Lyons Memorial Scholarship Fund **Area, Field, or Subject:** Psychiatry; Psychology; Sociology; Social work; Counseling; Rehabilitation counseling. **Level of Education for which Award is Granted:** Undergraduate **Funds Available:** No specific amount.
Eligibility Requirements: Applicants must be college students pursuing a degree in the mental health field. **Application Requirements:** Applicants must check the available website to download the application form. **Additional Information:** Mental Health Association of Tarrant County at the above address.

3769 ■ NATIONAL INSTITUTE OF HEALTH
2 Center Dr. Rm. 2E24, MSC 0230
Bethesda, MD 20892-0230
Tel: 888-352-3001; 888-352-3001
Fax: (301)480-3123
E-mail: ugsp@nih.gov
Web Site: http://www.ugsp.nih.gov
To provide competitive scholarships for students from disadvantaged backgrounds.
Title of Award: National Institute of Health Undergraduate Scholarship Program **Area, Field, or Subject:** Biomedical research; Behavioral sciences; Social sciences. **Level of Education for which Award is Granted:** Undergraduate **Funds Available:** No specific amount.
Eligibility Requirements: Applicants must be US citizens, nationals, or qualified noncitizens; must be enrolled or accepted for enrollment as full-time students for the current academic year at an accredited, 4-year undergraduate institution; must be from a disadvantaged background (disadvantaged background means that the financial aid office has certified student as having "exceptional financial need"); and must have a 3.5 GPA or higher (on a 4.0 scale) or be within the top 5 percent of their class. **Application Requirements:** Applicants are encouraged to apply online at www.ugsp.nih.gov or may visit the website for the application forms. **Deadline for Receipt:** March 31. **Additional Information:** NIH Undergraduate Scholarship Program at the above address.

3770 ■ ZETA PHI BETA SORORITY
1734 New Hampshire Ave. NW
Washington, DC 20009
Tel: (202)387-3103
Fax: (202)232-4593
E-mail: ihq@zphib1920.org
Web Site: http://www.zphib1920.org
To support students in pursuit of higher education.
Title of Award: Lullelia W. Harrison Scholarships in Counseling **Area, Field, or Subject:** Counseling/Guidance. **Level of Education for which Award is Granted:** Graduate, Undergraduate **Number Awarded:** 1. **Funds Available:** $500-$1000. **Duration:** One academic year.
Eligibility Requirements: Applicant must be a full-time graduate or undergraduate level student enrolled in a degree program in counseling. **Application Requirements:** Applicants must submit completed application forms along with the required materials. **Deadline for Receipt:** February 1.

Business and Economics

3771 ■ ALBERTA AGRICULTURAL ECONOMICS ASSOCIATION
University of Alberta
515 General Services Bldg.
Edmonton, AB, Canada T6G 2H1
Tel: (780)492-4562
E-mail: info@aaea.ab.ca
Web Site: http://www.aaea.ab.ca
To recognize the deserving students in Alberta.
Title of Award: Alberta Agricultural Economics Association Undergraduate Scholarships **Area, Field, or Subject:** Economics; Agribusiness. **Level of Education for which Award is Granted:** Undergraduate **Funds Available:** $500. **Duration:** One year.
Eligibility Requirements: Applicants must be full-time students enrolled in the third or fourth year of a B.Sc. Applied Economics or Agri-Food Business Management program in the faculty of Agriculture, Forestry and Home Economics; must have a GPA of 7.5 in their most recent academic year. **Application Requirements:** For further information about the scholarship and requirements, applicants are advised to contact the Association at AAEA, 515 General Services Bldg., University of Alberta, Edmonton, AB T6G 2H1.

3772 ■ ALBERTA LEARNING INFORMATION SERVICE - ALBERTA SCHOLARSHIP PROGRAM
Box 28000 Sta. Main
Edmonton, AB, Canada T5J 4R4
Tel: (780)427-8640
Fax: (780)427-1288
E-mail: scholarship@gov.ab.ca
Web Site: http://www.alis.alberta.ca
To recognize and reward the academic and leadership accomplishments of three students graduating from Sexsmith Secondary School who are entering post-secondary studies.
Title of Award: Dr. Robert and Anna Shaw Scholarships **Area, Field, or Subject:** Agriculture; Engineering; Art industries and trade; Fine arts. **Level of Education for which Award is Granted:** Undergraduate **Funds Available:** $500.
Eligibility Requirements: Applicants must be Alberta residents and plan to enroll full-time in a post-secondary program related to agriculture, engineering/trades or fine arts. **Application Requirements:** Applicants may obtain application form from Alberta Scholarship Programs and from the Counseling Office at Sexsmith Secondary School. **Deadline for Receipt:** June 1. **Additional Information:** Alberta Scholarship Programs at the above address.

3773 ■ AMERICAN ADVERTISING FEDERATION-CLEVELAND
20325 Center Ridge Rd., Ste. 670
Cleveland, OH 44116
Tel: (440)673-0020
Fax: (440)673-0025
E-mail: adassoc@aafcleveland.com
Web Site: http://clevead.com
To bring advertising, public relations, sales and marketing professionals together to build networks and create business solutions.
Title of Award: American Advertising Federation-Cleveland College Scholarships **Area, Field, or Subject:** Advertising. **Level of Education for which Award is Granted:** Undergraduate **Funds Available:** No specific amount.
Eligibility Requirements: Applicants must be Ohio college students majoring in advertising, marketing and communications; must be Ohio residents and enrolled on a full-time basis; must have a current minimum cumulative 3.0 GPA; must be seniors, juniors or in the last semester of the sophomore year. **Application Requirements:** Applicants must submit a completed application form, transcript of records, two letters of recommendation from faculty and/or professionals and a one page, double-spaced essay stating their career goals. **Deadline for Receipt:** October 29.

3774 ■ AMERICAN ADVERTISING FEDERATION-CLEVELAND
20325 Center Ridge Rd., Ste. 670
Cleveland, OH 44116
Tel: (440)673-0020
Fax: (440)673-0025
E-mail: adassoc@aafcleveland.com
Web Site: http://clevead.com
To provide opportunity for students who plan to pursue careers in advertising, marketing, communication, photography and graphic design.
Title of Award: American Advertising Federation-Cleveland High School Scholarships **Area, Field, or Subject:** Advertising. **Level of Education for which Award is Granted:** Undergraduate **Funds Available:** No specific amount.
Eligibility Requirements: Applicants must be enrolled in a Cleveland Municipal School District high school; must be planning to enroll in a communication/marketing-related major at an accredited college or university with the goal of pursuing a degree; must carry a full course-load and hold a current minimum cumulative GPA of 2.5 or higher on a 4.0 scale; must be in their senior year. **Application Requirements:** Applicants must submit a completed application form, two letters of recommendation from teachers or other professionals and a typed one page, double-spaced essay describing their career goals. **Deadline for Receipt:** January 22.

3775 ■ AMERICAN INDIAN COLLEGE FUND
8333 Greenwood Blvd.
Denver, CO 80221
Tel: (303)426-8900
Free: 800-776-3863
Fax: (303)426-1200
E-mail: info@collegefund.org
Web Site: http://www.collegefund.org

To award scholarships to outstanding American Indian students who are currently enrolled at a tribal college and who have an interest in business or the financial services industry.
Title of Award: Morgan Stanley Tribal Scholars Program **Area, Field, or Subject:** Business or related field. **Level of Education for which Award is Granted:** Undergraduate **Funds Available:** $2,500. **Duration:** Annually.
Eligibility Requirements: Applicants must have at least a 3.0 grade point average; must have declared a major in business or a related field; must be enrolled full-time at an eligible tribal college; must be American Indian or Alaskan Native with proof of enrollment or descendancy; and must have demonstrated exceptional academic achievement. **Application Requirements:** Applicants must check the available website to download the application form. **Additional Information:** American Indian College Fund at the above address.

3776 ■ AMERICAN INDIAN EDUCATION FOUNDATION
2401 Eglin St.
Rapid City, SD 57703
Tel: (866)866-8642; (866)866-8642
Fax: (605)342-4113
E-mail: info@programs.org
Web Site: http://www.nrcprograms.org
To give American Indian students the tools, resources and opportunities to learn and succeed.
Title of Award: Catching the Dream Scholarship **Area, Field, or Subject:** Education; Business; Science; Engineering. **Level of Education for which Award is Granted:** Graduate, Undergraduate **Funds Available:** $500-$5,000.
Eligibility Requirements: Applicants must be enrolled members of a federally recognized tribe; both undergraduate and graduate students may apply. **Application Requirements:** Applicants may submit an application to the Scholarship Affairs Office of Catching the Dream. **Deadline for Receipt:** March 15-Summer; April 15-Fall; September 15-spring. **Additional Information:** Catching the Dream 8200 Mountain Rd. NE Ste. 203 Albuquerque, NM 87110; 505-262-2351 x 116; nscholarsh@aol.com.

3777 ■ AMERICAN INDIAN GRADUATE CENTER SCHOLARS (AIGCS)
4520 Montgomery Blvd., NE, Ste. 1B
Albuquerque, NM 87109
Tel: (505)881-4584
Free: 800-628-1920
Web Site: http://www.aigc.com
To provide financial assistance to undergraduate and graduate American Indians in furthering their education.
Title of Award: Accenture American Indian Scholarship Program **Area, Field, or Subject:** Technology; Engineering; Medicine; Law; Business. **Level of Education for which Award is Granted:** Graduate, Undergraduate **Funds Available:** No specific amount.
Eligibility Requirements: Applicants must be American Indians who are incoming freshmen with a cumulative GPA of 3.25 or greater on a 4.0 scale at the end of the seventh semester of high school or graduates/professionals who have attained a cumulative GPA of 3.25 or greater on a 4.0 scale, as measured by undergraduate transcripts; must be enrolled members of a U.S. federally-recognized American Indian tribe or Alaska Native group; must be seeking a degree and career in fields of study including technology, engineering, medicine, law, and business. **Application Requirements:** Applicants must submit completed application form; copy of certificate of Indian Blood (CIB); unofficial undergraduate and/or graduate academic transcripts; biographical data and/or resume; essay describing their character, personal merit and commitment to community and heritage; two personal letters of recommendation (one must come from an education professional who is familiar with their academic work and the other one must come from an individual having knowledge of their leadership and community service activities); and financial aid award letter from the institution they will attend. **Deadline for Receipt:** June 2.

3778 ■ AMERICAN INDIAN GRADUATE CENTER SCHOLARS (AIGCS)
4520 Montgomery Blvd., NE, Ste. 1B
Albuquerque, NM 87109

Tel: (505)881-4584
Free: 800-628-1920
Web Site: http://www.aigc.com
To provide financial assistance to American Indian tribe or Alaska Native group in furthering their education.
Title of Award: Wall-Mart Stores, Inc. Fellowships - Graduate **Area, Field, or Subject:** Banking; Gaming industry; Management; Accounting; Finance; Information science and technology; Human resource.s **Level of Education for which Award is Granted:** Undergraduate **Funds Available:** No specific amount.
Eligibility Requirements: Applicants must be enrolled members of a United States federally-recognized American Indian tribe or Alaska Native group; pursuing a career and degree in fields relating to banking, resort management, gaming operations, management and administration, including accounting, finance, information technology, and human resources. Full-time graduate students at U.S. accredited colleges or universities with a cumulative GPA of 3.0 on 4.0 scale at the time of application are eligible. **Application Requirements:** Applicants must submit all the required application information.

3779 ■ AMERICAN MARKETING ASSOCIATION FOUNDATION
311 S Wacker Dr., Ste. 5800
Chicago, IL 60606
Tel: (312)542-9000
Fax: (312)542-9001
E-mail: lchernick@ama.org
Web Site: http://www.themarketingfoundation.org
To provide an annual scholarship award for students who are enrolled in the Marketing Program.
Title of Award: Richard A. Hammill Scholarships Fund **Area, Field, or Subject:** Marketing and distribution. **Level of Education for which Award is Granted:** Undergraduate **Funds Available:** No specific amount.
Eligibility Requirements: Applicants must be students enrolled at Georgia State University. **Application Requirements:** Interested applicants may apply online via the AMAF website. **Additional Information:** AMA Foundation at the above address.

3780 ■ AMERICAN RADIO RELAY LEAGUE (ARRL) FOUNDATION
225 Main St.
Newington, CT 06111
Tel: (860)594-0200
Fax: (860)594-0259
E-mail: foundation@arrl.org
Web Site: http://www.arrlf.org
To support the education of students holding a valid FCC-granted Amateur Radio license for post-secondary education.
Title of Award: William R. Goldfarb Memorial Scholarships **Area, Field, or Subject:** Radio and television; Business; Computer and information sciences; Medicine; Nursing; Engineering; Science. **Level of Education for which Award is Granted:** Undergraduate **Number Awarded:** 1. **Funds Available:** No specific amount.
Eligibility Requirements: Applicant must hold an FCC amateur radio license; must be studying baccalaureate courses in business-related, computers, medical, nursing, engineering or sciences; be a high school senior; and must demonstrate financial need. **Application Requirements:** Applicants must submit a completed scholarship application form along with a recent high school (or equivalent) or college transcript, and the Free Application for Federal Student Aid (FAFSA) or Student Aid Report (SAR). **Deadline for Receipt:** February 1.

3781 ■ AMERICAN RESEARCH INSTITUTE IN TURKEY
3260 S St.
Philadelphia, PA 19104-6324
Tel: (215)898-3474
Fax: (215)898-0657
E-mail: leinwand@sas.upenn.edu
Web Site: http://www.ccat.sas.upenn.edu
To expand the number of Americans studying and mastering critical need foreign languages.
Title of Award: Critical Language Scholarships for Intensive Summer Institutes **Area, Field, or Subject:** Business; Engineering; Science; Social Sciences; Humanities. **Level of Education for which Award is Granted:** Graduate, Undergraduate **Funds Available:** no stated amount.

Eligibility Requirements: Applicants must be U.S. citizens; must be currently enrolled in a degree-granting program at the undergraduate or graduate level; must have graduated from an undergraduate or graduate program no more than two-years ago; undergraduate students must have completed at least one year of general college course-work by program start date (one year is defined as two semesters or three quarters); or students in all disciplines including business, engineering, science, the social sciences and humanities are encourage to apply. **Application Requirements:** Applicants must submit completed application form; transcript of records; and letters of recommendation. **Deadline for Receipt:** January 25.

3782 ■ AMERICAN SOCIETY OF MILITARY COMPTROLLERS
415 N Alfred
Alexandria, VA 22314
Tel: (703)549-0360
Free: 800-462-5637
Fax: (703)549-3181
E-mail: asmchq@asmconline.org
Web Site: http://www.asmconline.org
To provide financial assistance to seniors to accomplish their future financial management baccalaureate educational goals.
Title of Award: American Society of Military Comptrollers National Scholarship Program **Area, Field, or Subject:** Business Administration, Economics, Public Administration, Accounting, Finance. **Level of Education for which Award is Granted:** Undergraduate **Number Awarded:** One. **Funds Available:** $3,000.
Eligibility Requirements: Applicants must be entering a field of study directly related to financial/resource management. **Application Requirements:** Applicants must have endorsement letters from ASMC chapters. Applicants must submit completed application form and three letters of recommendation from local ASMC chapter president, high school principal, academic dean, or guidance counselor, and a high school teacher. **Deadline for Receipt:** March 31. **Additional Information:** Linda Ryan; 301-227-6341; linda.c.ryan@nga.mil.

3783 ■ ARMENIAN RELIEF SOCIETY - EASTERN UNITED STATES
80 Bigelow Avenue, Ste. 200
Watertown, MA 02472
Tel: (617)926-3801
Fax: (617)924-7238
E-mail: arseastus@aol.com
Web Site: http://www.arseastus.com
To encourage educational pursuits among undergraduate students of Armenian descent.
Title of Award: ARS Undergraduate Scholarships **Area, Field, or Subject:** Law; History; Political science; Journalism; Government; Economics; Business administration; Medicine; Public service. **Level of Education for which Award is Granted:** Four Year College, Two Year College, Undergraduate **Funds Available:** No specific amount. **Duration:** One year.
Eligibility Requirements: Applicants must be of Armenian descent; must be undergraduate students who have completed at least one semester at an accredited four-year college or university in the United States or must be enrolled in a two-year college and are transferring to a four-year college or university as a full-time student in the Fall. **Application Requirements:** Application must include financial aid forms, recent official transcript, two letters of recommendation and tuition costs. Forward materials to: Scholarship Committee, Armenian Relief Society of Eastern USA, Inc., 80 Bigelow Ave., Ste. 200, Watertown, MA 02472. **Deadline for Receipt:** April 1.

3784 ■ ASSOCIATION FOR INTERNATIONAL TRAINING
10400 Little Patuxent Parkway, Ste. 250
Columbia, MD 21044-3519
Tel: (410)992-3924
Fax: (410)992-3924
E-mail: aipt@aipt.org
Web Site: http://www.aipt.org
to help defray some of the costs associating with relocating overseas.
Title of Award: Jessica King Scholarships **Area, Field, or Subject:** Hospitals-Administration. **Level of Education for which Award is Granted:** Undergraduate **Funds Available:** No specific amount. **Duration:** Entire length of undergraduate study.

Eligibility Requirements: All applicants must be 18 years old and not older than 35; he/she must have been participating in an AIPT-sponsored program; must have been approved for the work permit to take up that position; must have been offered an overseas position; must have a degree in the hospitality industry; he/she must be currently employed for at least one year in hospitality industry; must be a U.S. citizen only. **Application Requirements:** An applicant must complete and submit a filled out application form. **Additional Information:** aipt@aipt.org

3785 ■ ASSOCIATION OF SEVENTH-DAY ADVENTIST LIBRARIANS
James White Library, Andrews University
Berrien Springs, MI 49104-1400
E-mail: helmsc@andrews.edu
Web Site: http://www.asdal.org
To financially support Hispanic students pursuing studies in accounting, finance, IT or related field.
Title of Award: ALPFA Scholarship Programs **Area, Field, or Subject:** Business; Finance; Accounting. **Level of Education for which Award is Granted:** Postgraduate, Undergraduate **Funds Available:** $1,250-$1,500. **Duration:** One academic year.
Eligibility Requirements: Applicants must be full-time Hispanic students or of Hispanic descent; U.S. citizens or permanent residents of the United States or Puerto Rico; attending an accredited university; have a cumulative grade point average of 3.0 and above on a 4.0 scale; must demonstrate financial need; and pursuing an undergraduate or master's degree in business, finance and accounting. **Application Requirements:** Applicants must register first in order to apply online (please visit the website). Applicants must submit an official transcript; proof of family income and citizen status; an essay; letter of recommendation; resume; and The Financial Aid Verification (for semi-finalist only). **Deadline for Receipt:** March 15. **Additional Information:** Hispanic College Fund, HCF-info@hispanicfund.org.

3786 ■ AUTOMOTIVE HALL OF FAME
21400 Oakwood Blvd.
Dearborn, MI 48124
Tel: (313)240-4000
Fax: (313)240-8641
Web Site: http://www.automotivehalloffame.org
To financially support students pursuing education in an automotive related career.
Title of Award: Society of Automotive Analyst Scholarships **Area, Field, or Subject:** Automotive technology; Engineering, Automotive; Economics; Finance; Business administration; Marketing and distribution. **Level of Education for which Award is Granted:** Undergraduate **Funds Available:** No specific amount.
Eligibility Requirements: Applicant must be an undergraduate student; interested in careers in automotive analysis; have a 3.0 GPA; and enrolled full-time at an accredited college or university majoring in economics, finance, business administration, or marketing management. **Application Requirements:** Application form is available at the website or send a letter of request with a self-addressed stamped envelope. Applicants must submit a completed application form; an official transcript; two recommendation letters; and a letter of acceptance for an associate, bachelor or masters program. Send all materials to: Automotive Hall of Fame, Scholarship Programs 21400 Oakwood Blvd. Dearborn, MI 48124. **Deadline for Receipt:** May 30.

3787 ■ AUTOMOTIVE RECYCLERS ASSOCIATION
3975 Fair Ridge Dr., Ste. 20-N
Fairfax, VA 22033
Tel: (703)385-1001; 888-385-1005
Fax: (703)385-1494
E-mail: kelly@a-r-a.org
Web Site: http://www.a-r-a.org
To assist outstanding students to pursue their educational goal.
Title of Award: ARA Scholarship Awards **Area, Field, or Subject:** Business; Trades training; Technical training. **Level of Education for which Award is Granted:** Undergraduate **Funds Available:** Scholarship amount not specified. **Duration:** One year.
Eligibility Requirements: Applicants must be children of an employee of a direct ARA member company; must be a high school senior or pursuing a full-time post high school program in an institution providing trade, busi-

ness, or technical programs; have at least 3.0 GPA or equivalent. **Application Requirements:** Applicants must submit a completed application form and profile sheet. Transcript of academic record must be sent by the applicant's school/college directly to the ARA Scholarship Advisor. Applicants must obtain a certification and letter of verification from the parents' employer who is a direct member of ARA (should include current employment and the hiring date). Send all requirements to the ARA Scholarship Foundation Advisor. **Deadline for Receipt:** March 15. **Additional Information:** ARA Scholarship Advisor, arascholar@sbcglobal.net.

3788 ■ BLACK BUSINESS AND PROFESSIONAL ASSOCIATION
675 King St. W, Ste. 210
Toronto, ON, Canada M5V 1M9
Tel: (416)504-4097
Fax: (416)504-7343
E-mail: bbpa@bellnet.ca
Web Site: http://www.bbpa.org
To provide support for Black Canadian students.
Title of Award: Urban Financial Services Coalition Scholarships **Area, Field, or Subject:** Business, Economics, Finance, Information science and technology. **Level of Education for which Award is Granted:** Undergraduate **Number Awarded:** 2. **Funds Available:** $2,000. **Duration:** One year.
Eligibility Requirements: Applicant must be a student pursuing studies in business, economics, finance or information technology; must be a Canadian citizen or a permanent resident; must be 17 to 30 years of age; and must be enrolled in a full-time degree (graduate or undergraduate), diploma or certificate program at a Canadian college or university for the academic year. **Application Requirements:** Applicants must complete the application form and submit along with a letter describing the reasons why they would be worthy recipients of a BBPA National Scholarship; a completed financial information schedule stating their budget for the coming year including information on their expected sources of funding, family income and related information; and a letter of reference from the two individuals named in their application (must be a teacher from their high school, college or university, and an individual who is familiar with their community service). Application form and requirements must be sent to The Board of Trustees, BBPA National Scholarship Fund, 675 King St., W, Ste. 210, Toronto, ON M5V 1M9. **Deadline for Receipt:** May 30.

3789 ■ BUSINESS PROFESSIONALS OF AMERICA
5454 Cleveland Ave.
Columbus, OH 43231-4021
Tel: (614)895-7277
Free: 800-334-2007
Fax: (614)895-1165
Web Site: http://www.bpanet.org
To assist outstanding seniors of Business Professionals of America in the Secondary Division.
Title of Award: National Honor Roll Scholarships **Area, Field, or Subject:** Business. **Level of Education for which Award is Granted:** Undergraduate **Funds Available:** $2,000.
Eligibility Requirements: Applicants must be members of Business Professionals of America who are graduating high school seniors with minimum grade point average of 3.0. **Application Requirements:** Applicants must submit completed application form along with the school grade transcript or letter form school principal verifying GPA; one page, typed resume of activities involving both Business Professionals of America and other school and community activities; three signed recommendation letters on official letterhead from local advisor and two individuals of their choice; one page, double spaced, typed essay on topic "Where I see myself professionally in ten years." **Deadline for Receipt:** April 15.

3790 ■ CATCHING THE DREAM
8200 Mountain Rd. NE., Ste. 203
Albuquerque, NM 87110
Tel: (505)262-2351
E-mail: nscholarships@aol.com
Web Site: http://www.catchingthedream.org
To support the education of Native Schools.
Title of Award: MESBEC Scholarships **Area, Field, or Subject:** Mathematics and mathematical sciences; Engineering; Science; Busi-

ness; Education; Computer and information sciences. **Level of Education for which Award is Granted:** Undergraduate **Funds Available:** $500-$5000. **Duration:** One academic year.
Eligibility Requirements: Applicants must be 1/4 or more degree Native American; an enrolled member of a "U.S. tribe"; attending or planning to attend a college/university within the U.S. on a full-time basis that is fully accredited; studying in the field of business, finance, management, economics, banking, hotel management, and related field; have excellent grades; high ACT or SAT scores; and have a strong commitment to their Native American community. **Application Requirements:** Applicants must submit a completed application form (available at the website); financial need analysis; a copy of the IRS 1040 Federal Tax Return for the previous year; Certificate of Native American Blood; an essay explaining career goals; three letters of recommendation; official transcripts; a copy of standardized test scores; copy of letter of admission from an accredited college or university or graduate school and degree program in the US; and a photograph (2X3) of head and shoulders. **Deadline for Receipt:** March 15, April 15, and September 15.

3791 ■ CATCHING THE DREAM
8200 Mountain Rd. NE., Ste. 203
Albuquerque, NM 87110
Tel: (505)262-2351
E-mail: nscholarships@aol.com
Web Site: http://www.catchingthedream.org
To support students planning to work in economic development for tribes.
Title of Award: Tribal Business Management Program (TBM) Scholarships **Area, Field, or Subject:** Business; Finance; Management; Economics; Banking; Hotel, institutional, and restaurant management. **Level of Education for which Award is Granted:** Undergraduate **Funds Available:** $500-$5000. **Duration:** One academic year.
Eligibility Requirements: Applicants must be 1/4 or more degree Native American; an enrolled member of a "U.S. tribe"; attending or planning to attend a college/university within the U.S. on a full-time basis that is fully accredited; studying in the field of business, finance, management, economics, banking, hotel management, and related field; have excellent grades; high ACT or SAT scores; and have a strong commitment to their Native American community. **Application Requirements:** Applicants must submit a completed application form (available at the website); financial need analysis; a copy of the IRS 1040 Federal Tax Return for the previous year; Certificate of Native American Blood; an essay explaining career goals; three letters of recommendation; official transcripts; a copy of standardized test scores; copy of letter of admission from an accredited college or university or graduate school and degree program in the US; and a photograph (2X3) of head and shoulders. **Deadline for Receipt:** March 15, April 15, and September 15.

3792 ■ COASTAL BEND COMMUNITY FOUNDATION
600 Leopard St., Ste. 1716
Corpus Christi, TX 78473
Tel: (361)882-9745
Fax: (361)882-2865
Web Site: http://www.cbcfoundation.org
To assist students majoring in business with an interest in human resources.
Title of Award: C.C.H.R.M.A. Scholarships **Area, Field, or Subject:** Business; Personnel administration/human resources. **Level of Education for which Award is Granted:** High School, Undergraduate **Number Awarded:** 1. **Funds Available:** $500.
Eligibility Requirements: Applicants must: be high school seniors or undergraduate college students majoring in business; be enrolled as full-time students in the Coastal Bend seven-county service area; maintain a 3.0 GPA on a 4.0 scale (85% on 100% scale if high school students). **Application Requirements:** Applicants must download application form from the website of the Foundation or obtain it by calling the Foundation at 361-882-9745. **Deadline for Receipt:** March 15.

3793 ■ COASTAL BEND COMMUNITY FOUNDATION
600 Leopard St., Ste. 1716
Corpus Christi, TX 78473
Tel: (361)882-9745
Fax: (361)882-2865
Web Site: http://www.cbcfoundation.org

To provide financial assistance to further the education of deserving students in Coastal Bend.
Title of Award: Jim Springer Memorial Scholarships **Area, Field, or Subject:** Public relations; Marketing and distribution; Advertising; Communications. **Level of Education for which Award is Granted:** Undergraduate **Number Awarded:** 1. **Funds Available:** $500.
Eligibility Requirements: Applicants must be Coastal Bend residents; full-time college sophomore, junior or senior students with grade point average of 2.5; majoring in public relations, marketing, advertising or communications. **Application Requirements:** Applicants must submit all the required application information. **Deadline for Receipt:** March 14.

3794 ■ COMMUNITY FOUNDATION OF NORTHERN ILLINOIS
946 N 2nd St.
Rockford, IL 61107
Tel: (815)962-2110
Fax: (815)962-2116
Web Site: http://www.cfnil.org
To serve the four county area (Boone, Ogle, Stephenson and Winnebago) through philanthropy; to provide leadership in meeting charitable needs and to be a responsible steward to the Foundation's donors and of the Foundation's endowment; to provide educational resources to Winnebago County high school graduating seniors to pursue a degree in business.
Title of Award: International Management Council (IMC) Scholarships **Area, Field, or Subject:** Business. **Level of Education for which Award is Granted:** Undergraduate **Funds Available:** No specific amount.
Eligibility Requirements: Applicants must be graduating seniors residing in Winnebago County who are pursuing a degree in business; must have a GPA of at least 3.0 on a 4.0 scale and have been active in community service. **Application Requirements:** Applicants must submit a completed application form, verification form, an official transcript in a sealed envelope and two letters of recommendation. **Deadline for Receipt:** March 1. **Additional Information:** jpatterson@cfnil.org.

3795 ■ COMMUNITY FOUNDATION OF NORTHERN ILLINOIS
946 N 2nd St.
Rockford, IL 61107
Tel: (815)962-2110
Fax: (815)962-2116
Web Site: http://www.cfnil.org
To serve the four county area (Boone, Ogle, Stephenson and Winnebago) through philanthropy; to provide leadership in meeting charitable needs and to be a responsible steward to the Foundation's donors and of the Foundation's endowment.
Title of Award: Paul and Ruth Neidhold Business Scholarship **Area, Field, or Subject:** Business. **Level of Education for which Award is Granted:** Undergraduate **Funds Available:** No specific amount.
Eligibility Requirements: Applicants must be Harvard High School seniors with a minimum GPA of 2.0 ; must have plans to pursue an education or training in a business field. **Application Requirements:** Applicants must submit a completed application form, verification form, an official transcript in a sealed envelope, two letters of recommendation and a copy of their FAFSA. **Deadline for Receipt:** March 1. **Additional Information:** jpatterson@cfnil.org.

3796 ■ COMMUNITY FOUNDATION OF SARASOTA COUNTY
PO Box 49587
Sarasota, FL 34237
Tel: (941)955-3000
Fax: (941)952-1951
E-mail: stewart@cfsarasota.org
Web Site: http://www.cfsarasota.org
To encourage and enable caring individuals to easily and effectively support the charitable causes that they care about.
Title of Award: American Business Women's Association Sarasota Chapter Scholarships **Area, Field, or Subject:** Business. **Level of Education for which Award is Granted:** Undergraduate **Funds Available:** No specific amount.
Eligibility Requirements: Applicants must be female students with 3.0 unweighted high school GPA and must be of good character and have a career goal related to their college or university studies. **Application Requirements:** Applicants must complete the application form; must submit a parent or guardian's most recent 1040 federal tax form; must

provide two letters of reference from people who know the applicant well; official acceptance letter from college or vocational school; and a copy of SAT and ACT scores.

3797 ■ CONSTRUCTION FINANCIAL MANAGEMENT ASSOCIATION
29 Emmons Dr., Ste. F-50
Princeton, NJ 08540
Tel: (609)452-8000
Fax: (609)452-0474
Web Site: http://www.cfma.org
To provide resources to meet challenges of construction financial professionals. To support the qualified individual who want to pursue a degree in business or construction management.
Title of Award: Cindy P. Dennis Scholarship Fund **Area, Field, or Subject:** Business, Construction. **Level of Education for which Award is Granted:** Undergraduate **Funds Available:** $500.
Eligibility Requirements: Applicant must be a resident of Atascosa, Bandera, Bexar, Comal, Guadalupe, Kendall, Medina, or Wilson County; must be a candidate for a degree in business or construction management at any accredited college or university, taking a minimum of 12 hours; must have a high school scholastic B average at the end of fall semester of senior year or have a minimum 3.0 cumulative GPA, if already in college. **Application Requirements:** Applicant must submit the following: name, address, and telephone numbers; must have the high school transcript through fall semester of senior year or cumulative college transcripts for classes taken to date; must prepare an essay (not to exceed 500 words); must have a letter of recommendation from a nonfamily member; must have a summary of extracurricular and outside activities. Application and other supporting documents must be sent to: CFMA - San Antonio Chapter Scholarship Committee, 100 NE Loop 410, Ste. 1100, San Antonio, TX 78216. **Deadline for Receipt:** April 15.

3798 ■ DADE COMMUNITY FOUNDATION, INC.
200 S Biscayne Blvd., Ste. 505
Miami, FL 33131-2343
Tel: (305)371-2711
Fax: (305)371-5342
Web Site: http://www.dadecommunityfoundation.org
To provide financial assistance to students at Miami Springs Senior High School who are enrolled in a college program related to public education, political science, history or social work.
Title of Award: Randy Green Memorial Scholarship Fund **Area, Field, or Subject:** Political science; economics; Social work. **Level of Education for which Award is Granted:** High School **Number Awarded:** 2. **Funds Available:** $1,000. **Duration:** One year.
Eligibility Requirements: Applicants must be permanent residents or citizens of the U.S. and domiciled in South Florida; must have minimum high school grade point average of 3.0; must be Miami Springs high-school seniors demonstrating merit and financial need; must be accepted into accredited university and plan to be enrolled in two year or four year university programs concentrating in public education, political science, history, social work, or other major related to community service. **Application Requirements:** Applicants must submit the completed application form and all other required application information. **Deadline for Receipt:** June 3.

3799 ■ DADE COMMUNITY FOUNDATION, INC.
200 S Biscayne Blvd., Ste. 505
Miami, FL 33131-2343
Tel: (305)371-2711
Fax: (305)371-5342
Web Site: http://www.dadecommunityfoundation.org
To provide financial assistance to business students entering their junior/senior year of undergraduate studies.
Title of Award: Dr. Felix H. Reyler Memorial Scholarships **Area, Field, or Subject:** Business; Finance. **Level of Education for which Award is Granted:** Undergraduate **Number Awarded:** 2. **Funds Available:** $2,500. **Duration:** One year.
Eligibility Requirements: Applicants must be permanent residents or citizens of the U.S. and domiciled in Florida; must be business students entering their junior/senior year of undergraduate studies; must be students graduating from the Academy for International Business and Finance at Miami Jackson Senior High and the children of FIBA members;

must be currently or enrolling as full-time students in four-year Florida college/university and seeking for a degree in Business. **Application Requirements:** Applicants must submit completed application form; personal statement; official transcript; original recommendation letter on school letterhead; and, one photocopy of the entire completed application. **Deadline for Receipt:** April 25.

3800 ■ DADE COMMUNITY FOUNDATION, INC.
200 S Biscayne Blvd., Ste. 505
Miami, FL 33131-2343
Tel: (305)371-2711
Fax: (305)371-5342
Web Site: http://www.dadecommunityfoundation.org
To assist students pursuing career in the insurance industry and business. **Title of Award:** The Rodney Thaxton Justice Fund **Area, Field, or Subject:** Business; Insurance and insurance-related fields. **Level of Education for which Award is Granted:** Undergraduate **Number Awarded:** 2. **Funds Available:** $1,500. **Duration:** One year. **Eligibility Requirements:** Applicants must be high school seniors with minimum high school grade point average of 3.0 who have interest in pursuing career in business or the insurance industry. **Application Requirements:** Applicants must submit completed application form and all required application materials and information. **Deadline for Receipt:** March 9.

3801 ■ DADE COMMUNITY FOUNDATION, INC.
200 S Biscayne Blvd., Ste. 505
Miami, FL 33131-2343
Tel: (305)371-2711
Fax: (305)371-5342
Web Site: http://www.dadecommunityfoundation.org
To provide financial assistance to African-American students to pursue their professional careers. **Title of Award:** Jacki Tuckfield Memorial Graduate Business Scholarship Fund **Area, Field, or Subject:** Business. **Level of Education for which Award is Granted:** Undergraduate **Funds Available:** $1,000. **Eligibility Requirements:** Applicants must be African American United States citizen, resident of South Florida, enrolled in a graduate business degree program (master's or doctoral), at Florida University during the Fall, Winter, Spring or Summer term of the 2008-2009 academic year; must be planning to pursue professional career in South Florida. **Application Requirements:** Applicants must submit the completed application form; essay; transcripts; color passport photo; letter of recommendation; and resume. **Deadline for Receipt:** May 25.

3802 ■ DADE COMMUNITY FOUNDATION, INC.
200 S Biscayne Blvd., Ste. 505
Miami, FL 33131-2343
Tel: (305)371-2711
Fax: (305)371-5342
Web Site: http://www.dadecommunityfoundation.org
To assist students pursuing careers in the insurance industry and business. **Title of Award:** Seitlin Franklin E. Wheeler Scholarship Fund **Area, Field, or Subject:** Insurance and insurance-related fields; Business. **Level of Education for which Award is Granted:** Undergraduate **Number Awarded:** 2. **Funds Available:** $1,500. **Duration:** One year. **Eligibility Requirements:** Applicants must be high school seniors with minimum high school grade point average of 3.0 and demonstrate interest in pursuing career in business or the insurance industry. **Application Requirements:** Applicants must submit all the required application information. **Deadline for Receipt:** May 9.

3803 ■ DIRECT MARKETING FUNDRAISERS ASSOCIATION
PO Box 1038
New York, NY 10028
Tel: (646)675-7314
Fax: (646)417-6493
Web Site: http://www.dmfa.org
To enhance the skills a new member in direct marketing fundraising. **Title of Award:** Sanky Perlowin Memorial Scholarships **Area, Field, or Subject:** Marketing and distribution. **Level of Education for which Award is Granted:** Undergraduate **Funds Available:** $500.

Eligibility Requirements: Nominees must be involved or interested in fundraising by direct mail and related techniques. **Application Requirements:** Applicants must fill up the and complete the nomination form. **Additional Information:** Mrs. Sanky Perlowin was the head of Sanky Perlowin Associates, a direct mail fundraising consulting firm.

3804 ■ DULUTH SUPERIOR AREA COMMUNITY FOUNDATION
324 W Superior St., Ste. 212
Duluth, MN 55802
Tel: (218)726-0232
Fax: (218)726-0257
E-mail: info@communityfoundation.com
Web Site: http://www.dsacommunityfoundation.com
To provide financial assistance for students studying business and accounting. **Title of Award:** Hubert A. Nelson Scholarships **Area, Field, or Subject:** Business; Accounting. **Level of Education for which Award is Granted:** Undergraduate **Funds Available:** $1,400. **Duration:** One year. **Eligibility Requirements:** Applicants must be graduating seniors of public or private high schools in Duluth and Superior; must be planning to major in business/accounting at the University of Minnesota-Duluth or the University of Wisconsin-Superior; must be in the top 25% of their high school. **Application Requirements:** Applicants must submit all the required application information. **Additional Information:** The award is co-payable to the institution and the recipient. **Deadline for Receipt:** January 15.

3805 ■ EDIS COMPANY
PO Box 2697
Wilmington, DE 19805
Tel: (302)421-5700
Fax: (302)421-5715
Web Site: http://www.ediscompany.com
To recognize members of the community who played a part in the growth of EDiS. **Title of Award:** Gen III Scholarships **Area, Field, or Subject:** Architecture; Engineering; Business. **Level of Education for which Award is Granted:** Undergraduate **Number Awarded:** 2. **Funds Available:** $1,000 renewable. **Duration:** One year. **Eligibility Requirements:** Applicant must be a resident within the community in which EDiS is currently working; must not be any employee of an EDiS Company or a relative of an employee of an EDiS Company; must be pursuing either an Associate's degree or Bachelor's degree; field of study is limited to business or construction-related degrees; and must have a cumulative GPA of 2.5 or greater for renewal. **Application Requirements:** Applicants must submit a completed scholarship application together with official transcript (from current institution), and a copy of best SAT score. **Deadline for Receipt:** May 2. **Additional Information:** Ms. Cyndi Slothour.

3806 ■ FIRST COMMUNITY FOUNDATION OF PENNSYLVANIA, WILLIAMSPORT-LYCOMING
330 Pine St., Suite 401
Williamsport, PA 17701
Tel: (570)321-1500; (866)901-2372
Fax: (570)321-6434
E-mail: fcfpa@fcfpa.org
Web Site: http://www.wlfoundation.org
To provide financial assistance for Montgomery Area High School students intending to pursue higher education in finance, engineering, business or science. **Title of Award:** Robert E. and Judy More Scholarship Fund **Area, Field, or Subject:** Finance; Engineering; Business; Science. **Level of Education for which Award is Granted:** Undergraduate **Funds Available:** No specific amount. **Eligibility Requirements:** Candidates must exhibit leadership qualities, academic excellence and a cooperative spirit. **Application Requirements:** Candidates must complete and submit the application. Scholarship application can be requested from Montgomery Area High School or may be downloaded from the Foundation's web site. **Deadline for Receipt:** April 15. **Additional Information:** Tara Bozella, Guidance Counselor, Montgomery Area High School, 120 Penn Street, Montgomery, PA 17752, 570-547-1608 ext. 116, tbozella@montasd.org.

3807 ■ FOUNDATION FOR THE CAROLINAS
217 S Tryon St.
Charlotte, NC 28202
Tel: (704)973-4500
Free: 800-973-7244
Web Site: http://www.fftc.org
To provide financial support for undergraduate students who have expressed an interest in business through their service to Junior Achievement in Atlanta, GA.
Title of Award: Bank of America Junior Achievement Scholarship Fund **Area, Field, or Subject:** Business; Technology. **Level of Education for which Award is Granted:** Undergraduate **Funds Available:** No specific amount.
Eligibility Requirements: Applicants must be graduating high school seniors with a minimum cumulative GPA of 3.0 on a 4.0 scale and who have actively participated in Junior Achievement of Georgia and are planning to major in business or computer technology. **Application Requirements:** Applicants must submit all the required application information.

3808 ■ THE FUND FOR AMERICAN STUDIES
1706 New Hampshire Ave.
Washington, DC 20009
Tel: (202)986-0384
Free: 800-741-6964
Fax: (202)986-0390
E-mail: info@tfas.org
Web Site: http://www.tfas.org
To provide financial support for students who wish to attend the Institute on Business and Government Affairs (IBGA) at Georgetown University.
Title of Award: Congressional Scholarships Award **Area, Field, or Subject:** Business; Local government. **Level of Education for which Award is Granted:** Undergraduate **Funds Available:** No specific amount. **Duration:** One year.
Eligibility Requirements: Applicant must be an undergraduate student. **Application Requirements:** Applicants can contact Kristy Khachigian for the scholarship information and application. **Additional Information:** Established in 1990. **Additional Information:** Kristy Khachigian Tel. No. 202-986-0384.

3809 ■ GEMOLOGICAL INSTITUTE OF AMERICA
The Robert Mouawad Campus
5345 Amada Dr.
Carlsbad, CA 92008
Tel: (760)603-4031
Free: 800-421-7250
E-mail: financialaid@gia.edu
Web Site: http://www.gia.edu
To promote education in Gemology.
Title of Award: GIA Endowment Scholarships - School of Business **Area, Field, or Subject:** Gemology; Business. **Level of Education for which Award is Granted:** Undergraduate **Funds Available:** Varies.
Eligibility Requirements: Applicant must be U.S. citizen and permanent resident; at least 17 years old; have a high school diploma or GED equivalency; currently employed or planning to enter in the jewelry industry; applying for On Campus and Distance Education courses at the School of Business; past recipient of GIA scholarship within last five years are not eligible. **Application Requirements:** Applicant must complete the GIA Scholarship application (available at the website), with a letter of recommendation from a person in the jewelry industry. Send application and supporting documents to: Gemological Institute of America, Office of Student Financial Assistance, MS 7 The Robert Mouawad Campus 5345 Armada Drive Carlsbad, CA 92008. **Deadline for Receipt:** June 15 - October 15. **Additional Information:** Financial aid representative, 800-421-7250 x-4175, financialaid@gia.edu.

3810 ■ GEMOLOGICAL INSTITUTE OF AMERICA
The Robert Mouawad Campus
5345 Amada Dr.
Carlsbad, CA 92008
Tel: (760)603-4031
Free: 800-421-7250
E-mail: financialaid@gia.edu
Web Site: http://www.gia.edu
To promote education in Gemology.
Title of Award: Matthew A. Runci, MJSA Scholarships **Area, Field, or Subject:** Gemology; Art industries and trade. **Level of Education for which Award is Granted:** Undergraduate **Number Awarded:** 1. **Funds Available:** $500.
Eligibility Requirements: Applicant must be U.S. citizen and permanent resident; at least 17 years old; have a high school diploma or GED equivalency; currently employed or planning to enter in the jewelry industry; applying for On Campus School of Jewelry Manufacturing Arts courses; past recipient of GIA scholarship within last five years are not eligible. **Application Requirements:** Applicant must complete the GIA Scholarship application (available at the website), with a letter of recommendation from a person in the jewelry industry. Send application and supporting documents to: Gemological Institute of America, Office of Student Financial Assistance, MS 7 The Robert Mouawad Campus 5345 Armada Drive Carlsbad, CA 92008. **Deadline for Receipt:** June 15 - October 15. **Additional Information:** Financial aid representative, 800-421-7250 x-4175, financialaid@gia.edu.

3811 ■ GOLDEN KEY INTERNATIONAL HONOUR SOCIETY
621 Noeth Ave. NE., Ste. C-100
Atlanta, GA 30308
Tel: (404)377-2400
Free: 800-377-2401
Fax: (678)420-6757
E-mail: memberservices@goldenkey.org
Web Site: http://www.goldenkey.org
To financially assist students studying business.
Title of Award: Boeing Business Scholarships **Area, Field, or Subject:** Business. **Level of Education for which Award is Granted:** Undergraduate **Number Awarded:** 1. **Funds Available:** $1000.
Eligibility Requirements: Applicant must be a U.S. undergraduate member currently enrolled in classes in a degree-granting program. **Application Requirements:** Applicants must submit a letter of recommendation from a professor in the discipline; and a current, comprehensive official academic transcript. Submit materials to awards@goldenkey. org. **Additional Information:** Applicants can apply more than one scholarships. **Deadline for Receipt:** May 15. **Additional Information:** awards@goldenkey.org.

3812 ■ GRAND HAVEN AREA COMMUNITY FOUNDATION
1 S. Harbor Dr.
Grand Haven, MI 49417
Tel: (616)842-6378
Fax: (616)842-9518
E-mail: bpost@ghacf.org
Web Site: http://www.ghacf.org
To improve and enhance the quality of life in the Tri-Cities area by serving as a leader, catalyst and resource for philanthropy; to strive for community improvement through strategic grantmaking in such fields as arts, education, health, environment, youth, social services and other human needs.
Title of Award: Floto-Peel Family Scholarships Fund **Area, Field, or Subject:** Nursing; Business. **Level of Education for which Award is Granted:** Undergraduate **Funds Available:** No specific amount.
Eligibility Requirements: Applicants must be Tri-Cities area residents planning to attend a two-to-four year college, university or vocational school; must plan to study in the field of nursing or business; must have 2.5 GPA. **Application Requirements:** Applicants must submit: completed application form; current high school or college transcript; Student Aid Report (SAR) from the Free Application for Federal Student Aid (FAFSA), unless applying for scholarships that do not consider financial need; and letter of recommendation. **Deadline for Receipt:** March 7. **Additional Information:** 616-842-6378.

3813 ■ GRAND HAVEN AREA COMMUNITY FOUNDATION
1 S. Harbor Dr.
Grand Haven, MI 49417
Tel: (616)842-6378
Fax: (616)842-9518
E-mail: bpost@ghacf.org
Web Site: http://www.ghacf.org
To improve and enhance the quality of life in the Tri-Cities area by serving as a leader, catalyst and resource for philanthropy; to strive for community

improvement through strategic grantmaking in such fields as arts, education, health, environment, youth, social services and other human needs. **Title of Award:** Paul J. Laninga Memorial Scholarship Fund **Area, Field, or Subject:** Business; Accounting. **Level of Education for which Award is Granted:** Undergraduate **Funds Available:** No specific amount. **Eligibility Requirements:** Applicants must be graduating seniors of Northwest Ottawa County who plan to attend a public university; must be pursuing education and long-term careers in the areas of business and/or accounting. **Application Requirements:** Applicants must submit: completed application form; current high school or college transcript; Student Aid Report (SAR) from the Free Application for Federal Student Aid (FAFSA), unless applying for scholarships that do not consider financial need; and letter of recommendation. **Deadline for Receipt:** March 7. **Additional Information:** 616-842-6378.

3814 ■ GRAND HAVEN AREA COMMUNITY FOUNDATION

1 S. Harbor Dr.
Grand Haven, MI 49417
Tel: (616)842-6378
Fax: (616)842-9518
E-mail: bpost@ghacf.org
Web Site: http://www.ghacf.org
To provide financial assistance to graduates of Spring Lake or Grand Haven High school who demonstrate financial need.
Title of Award: Rick and Beverly Lattin Education Scholarships Fund **Area, Field, or Subject:** Business. **Level of Education for which Award is Granted:** Undergraduate **Funds Available:** No specific amount. **Eligibility Requirements:** Applicants must be graduates of Spring Lake or Grand Haven High School; must have 2.0 to 3.0 GPA and wish to continue their education; must be pursuing skills in the area of business or technical training. **Application Requirements:** Applicants must submit completed application form; current high school or college transcript; Student Aid Report (SAR) from the Free Application for Federal Student Aid (FAFSA), unless applying for scholarships that do not consider financial need; and letter of recommendation. **Deadline for Receipt:** March 7. **Additional Information:** 616-842-6378.

3815 ■ GRAND HAVEN AREA COMMUNITY FOUNDATION

1 S. Harbor Dr.
Grand Haven, MI 49417
Tel: (616)842-6378
Fax: (616)842-9518
E-mail: bpost@ghacf.org
Web Site: http://www.ghacf.org
To improve and enhance the quality of life in the Tri-Cities area by serving as a leader, catalyst and resource for philanthropy; to strive for community improvement through strategic grantmaking in such fields as arts, education, health, environment, youth, social services and other human needs. **Title of Award:** David and Sharon Seaver Family Scholarship Fund **Area, Field, or Subject:** Business. **Level of Education for which Award is Granted:** Undergraduate **Funds Available:** No specific amount. **Eligibility Requirements:** Applicants must be graduating seniors who plan to pursue a career in Business. **Application Requirements:** Applicants must submit: completed application form; current high school or college transcript; Student Aid Report (SAR) from the Free Application for Federal Student Aid (FAFSA), unless applying for scholarships that do not consider financial need; and letter of recommendation. **Deadline for Receipt:** March 7. **Additional Information:** 616-842-6378.

3816 ■ GRAND HAVEN AREA COMMUNITY FOUNDATION

1 S. Harbor Dr.
Grand Haven, MI 49417
Tel: (616)842-6378
Fax: (616)842-9518
E-mail: bpost@ghacf.org
Web Site: http://www.ghacf.org
To improve and enhance the quality of life in the Tri-Cities area by serving as a leader, catalyst and resource for philanthropy; to strive for community improvement through strategic grantmaking in such fields as arts, education, health, environment, youth, social services and other human needs. **Title of Award:** Edward P. Suchecki Family Scholarship Fund **Area, Field, or Subject:** Business. **Level of Education for which Award is Granted:** Undergraduate **Funds Available:** No specific amount.

Eligibility Requirements: Applicants must be high school senior athletes from Grand Haven High School, preferably planning to pursue a career in business. **Application Requirements:** Applicants must submit: completed application form; current high school or college transcript; Student Aid Report (SAR) from the Free Application for Federal Student Aid (FAFSA), unless applying for scholarships that do not consider financial need; and letter of recommendation. **Deadline for Receipt:** March. **Additional Information:** 616-842-6378.

3817 ■ GRAND RAPIDS COMMUNITY FOUNDATION

161 Ottawa Ave. NW
Ste. 209-C Waters Bldg.
Grand Rapids, MI 49503
Tel: (616)454-1751
Fax: (616)454-6455
E-mail: grfound@grfoundation.org
Web Site: http://www.grfoundation.org
To provide financial assistance to deserving students.
Title of Award: Paul Collins Scholarships **Area, Field, or Subject:** Applied Arts; Fine Arts. **Level of Education for which Award is Granted:** Undergraduate **Funds Available:** No specific amount. **Eligibility Requirements:** Applicants must be undergraduate level students studying Fine or Applied Arts at Aquinas, Calvin, GVSU, GRCC or Kendall. Applicants must be residents of Kent County. Applicants must have a minimum of 2.5 GPA, financial need and demonstrate artistic talent. **Application Requirements:** Applicants must check the available website for more information. **Additional Information:** Grand Rapids Community Foundation at the above address

3818 ■ HARTFORD FOUNDATION FOR PUBLIC GIVING

10 Columbus Blvd., 8th Flr.
Hartford, CT 06106
Tel: (860)548-1888
Fax: (860)524-8346
E-mail: hfpg@hfpg.org
Web Site: http://www.hfpg.org
To provide educational assistance for undergraduate students enrolled in a college or university in Connecticut.
Title of Award: Malcolm Baldrige Scholarships **Area, Field, or Subject:** Manufacturing; International trade. **Level of Education for which Award is Granted:** Undergraduate **Number Awarded:** 1-3. **Funds Available:** 4,000. **Eligibility Requirements:** Applicant must be an International trade and manufacturing related major; must demonstrate academic excellence; must be studying foreign language, if majoring in International Business; and must be a resident of Connecticut. **Application Requirements:** Applicants may obtain the application materials from the website at www.conncf.org. **Deadline for Receipt:** March 1. **Additional Information:** Connecticut Community Foundation. Tallitha Richardson-Selby, Program/Scholarship Associate, 43 Field St. Waterbury, CT 06702. info@conncf.org. fax: 203-756-3054.

3819 ■ HARTFORD FOUNDATION FOR PUBLIC GIVING

10 Columbus Blvd., 8th Flr.
Hartford, CT 06106
Tel: (860)548-1888
Fax: (860)524-8346
E-mail: hfpg@hfpg.org
Web Site: http://www.hfpg.org
To provide scholarship for graduating high school seniors who live in or are attending school in Greater Hartford.
Title of Award: Connecticut Mortgage Bankers Scholarships-Social Affairs Committee **Area, Field, or Subject:** Business; Real estate. **Level of Education for which Award is Granted:** Undergraduate **Number Awarded:** 1. **Funds Available:** $3,000. **Eligibility Requirements:** Applicants must be entering a four-year college or university (full-time enrollment) pursuing a career in business, mortgage or real estate; must have a financial need; must be on a class rank - top third with good academic record; and must be active volunteers in school, community, or other extracurricular activities. **Application Requirements:** Application form can be downloaded on-line. Applicants must complete the scholarship application. Applicants must also attach the following requirements: letter of recommendation from your guidance

counselor or a teacher; official high school transcript. Including SAT or ACT scores; copy of the essay you submitted with your college application. If you did not have to submit one, write a brief (no more than two pages) essay regarding your future goals; copy of pages 1 and 2 of your parents' most recent completed federal tax form 1040. Mail everything to Hartford Foundation College Scholarship Program. **Deadline for Receipt:** February 6. **Additional Information:** Hartford Foundation College Scholarship Program, Scholarship Management Services, Scholarship America, One Scholarship Way, PO Box 297, St. Peter, MN 56082. 800-537-4180.

3820 ■ HARTFORD FOUNDATION FOR PUBLIC GIVING
10 Columbus Blvd., 8th Flr.
Hartford, CT 06106
Tel: (860)548-1888
Fax: (860)524-8346
E-mail: hfpg@hfpg.org
Web Site: http://www.hfpg.org
To provide scholarship to students entering or enrolled in a four-year program at the University of Connecticut.
Title of Award: Michael Jewelers Foundation Scholarships for Athletes **Area, Field, or Subject:** Business. **Level of Education for which Award is Granted:** Undergraduate **Number Awarded:** 8. **Funds Available:** $2,000.
Eligibility Requirements: Applicants must: be a graduating high school senior residing in Connecticut; be a Business major; participate in intercollegiate athletics. **Application Requirements:** Applicants may obtain application materials from University of Connecticut Athletic Department. www.michaelsjewelers.com. **Deadline for Receipt:** March 1. **Additional Information:** Michael Jewelers Foundation, 203-597-4905. gems@michaelsjewelers.com.

3821 ■ HISPANIC ASSOCIATION OF COLLEGES AND UNIVERSITIES
8415 Datapoint Dr., Ste. 400
San Antonio, TX 78229
Tel: (210)698-3805
Fax: (210)692-0823
E-mail: hacu@hacu.net
Web Site: http://www.hacu.net
To promote the development of member colleges and universities; to improve access to and the quality of post-secondary educational opportunities for Hispanic students; and to meet the needs of business, industry and government through the development and sharing of resources, information and expertise.
Title of Award: Office Depot Scholarships **Area, Field, or Subject:** Business; Marketing and Distribution; Information Science and Technology. **Level of Education for which Award is Granted:** Undergraduate **Funds Available:** $1,000.
Eligibility Requirements: Applicants must be undergraduate students attending four year institutions and must possess a minimum cumulative GPA of 3.0. **Application Requirements:** Applicants must fill out the application form and must provide any documents showing that they are currently enrolled or accepted by a college, university, or institution. **Deadline for Receipt:** May 23.

3822 ■ HISPANIC ASSOCIATION OF COLLEGES AND UNIVERSITIES
8415 Datapoint Dr., Ste. 400
San Antonio, TX 78229
Tel: (210)698-3805
Fax: (210)692-0823
E-mail: hacu@hacu.net
Web Site: http://www.hacu.net
To promote the development of member colleges and universities; to improve access to and the quality of post-secondary educational opportunities for Hispanic students; and to meet the needs of business, industry and government through the development and sharing of resources, information and expertise.
Title of Award: Wendell Scott Awards **Area, Field, or Subject:** Business; Engineering; Public Relation; Technology; Management. **Level of Education for which Award is Granted:** Graduate, Undergraduate **Funds Available:** $1,500-undergraduate; $2,000-graduate.

Eligibility Requirements: Applicants must be full-time or part-time, undergraduate and graduate students attending four year institutions; must possess a minimum cumulative GPA of 3.0. Applying graduate students must be attending school at least on a part-time basis and must possess a minimum cumulative GPA of 3.0. **Application Requirements:** Applicants must fill out the application form and must provide any documents showing that they are currently enrolled or accepted by a college, university, or institution. **Deadline for Receipt:** May 23.

3823 ■ HISPANIC NATIONAL BAR ASSOCIATION
1111 Pennysylvania Ave. NW
Washington, DC 20004
Tel: (202)223-4777
Web Site: http://www.hnba.com
To support and help the nation's top college students to pursue their careers.
Title of Award: Hispanic College Fund Scholarship Programs **Area, Field, or Subject:** Business, Finance, Engineering, Science. **Level of Education for which Award is Granted:** Undergraduate **Funds Available:** $500-$5,000.
Eligibility Requirements: Applicant must be of Hispanic descent and a U.S. citizen or a permanent resident; must be studying at an accredited university in the U.S. or Puerto Rico; must be enrolled full-time as an undergraduate student for the upcoming academic year; must have earned and maintain a grade point of no less than 3.0 on a 4.0 scale; must demonstrate financial need. **Application Requirements:** Applicants must submit an official transcript, proof of family income, proof of citizenship status, essay, resume, and financial verification (if chosen as semi finalist only). **Deadline for Receipt:** March 22.

3824 ■ HISPANIC SCHOLARSHIP FUND
55 Second St., Ste. 1500
San Francisco, CA 94105
877-473-4636
Fax: (415)808-2302
E-mail: info@hsf.net
Web Site: http://www.hsf.net
For sophomore students who will be transferring to a four-year college.
Title of Award: HSBC-North America Scholarship Program **Area, Field, or Subject:** Accounting; Actuarial science; Advertising; Public relations; Business; Engineering; Computer; Computer and information sciences; Economics; Finance; International trade; Marketing and distribution; Management. **Level of Education for which Award is Granted:** Undergraduate **Funds Available:** $2,500.
Eligibility Requirements: Applicant must be of Hispanic heritage; U.S. citizen or legal permanent resident with a valid permanent resident card or passport stamped I-551; be a current sophomore or community college student transferring to a four-year college/university and will be a junior status for the upcoming academic year; be enrolled full-time in a degree-seeking program at an accredited institution in the U.S., Puerto Rico, U.S. Virgin Islands or Guam; have a minimum 3.0 GPA on a 4.0 scale or 4.00 on a 5.00 scale; must be majoring in one of the following: Accounting, Actuarial Science, Advertising, Public Relations, Business, Computer Engineering, Computer Information Systems (CIS), Computer Science, Economics, Finance, International Business, Marketing or Management; must submit a resume; have applied for Federal Financial Aid; must be a resident of: Los Angeles, CA (LA, Orange, Riverside, San Bernardino, Ventura); Monterey/Salinas, CA (Salinas); San Diego, CA (San Diego); Tampa, FL (Hernando, Hillsborough, Pasco, Pinella); Jacksonville, FL (Nassau, Duval, Clay, St. Johns); Chicago, IL (Cook, DuPage, Grundy, Kane, Kankakee, Kendall, Lake, LaSalle, Will, McHenry); New York, NY (Bronx, Kings, New York, Queens, Richmond); Las Vegas, NV (Clark); Phoenix, AZ (Phoenix-Mesa); Wilmington, DC (New Castle); Bridgewater, NJ (Sussex); or Chesapeake, VA. Applicants must also submit a resume; must have applied for federal financial aid and must be pursuing his/her first undergraduate degree. **Application Requirements:** Applicants must use the HSF online application system. **Additional Information:** In partnership with HSBC. **Deadline for Receipt:** November 1. **Additional Information:** scholar1@hsf.net.

3825 ■ HISPANIC SCHOLARSHIP FUND
55 Second St., Ste. 1500
San Francisco, CA 94105

877-473-4636
Fax: (415)808-2302
E-mail: info@hsf.net
Web Site: http://www.hsf.net
To provide financial assistance for Hispanic junior and senior students.
Title of Award: HSF/Citi Fellows Program **Area, Field, or Subject:** Business administration; Economics; Finance. **Level of Education for which Award is Granted:** Undergraduate **Funds Available:** $10,000. **Duration:** Two years.
Eligibility Requirements: Applicant must be of Hispanic heritage; U.S. citizen or legal permanent resident with a valid permanent resident card or passport stamped I-551; a sophomore enrolled full-time at a four-year accredited college/university in the U.S. (must be enrolled as junior in the following academic year); be pursuing a Business Administration, Economics or Finance degree; have a minimum 3.0 GPA on a 4.0 scale or the equivalent; must be a resident or attending college in: New York City metropolitan area; Miami/Fort Lauderdale area; Tampa, Florida; Dallas, Texas; Austin, Texas; Los Angeles, California; San Francisco Bay Area, California. Or must attend college at: Columbia University, Cornell University, Dartmouth College, Duke University, Georgetown University, Harvard University, New York University, Northwestern University, Princeton University, Rutgers University, Stanford University, University of California - Los Angeles, University of Chicago, University of Pennsylvania, University of Virginia, University of Texas at Austin, or Yale University. **Application Requirements:** Applicants must use the HSF online application system. **Additional Information:** Fellows will be paired with a Citi employee as a professional mentor and offer career guidance. **Deadline for Receipt:** March 15. **Additional Information:** scholar1@hsf.net.

3826 ■ HISPANIC SCHOLARSHIP FUND
55 Second St., Ste. 1500
San Francisco, CA 94105
877-473-4636
Fax: (415)808-2302
E-mail: info@hsf.net
Web Site: http://www.hsf.net
To provide financial resources to outstanding Latinos pursuing degrees in engineering and business.
Title of Award: HSF/General Motors Scholarship Program **Area, Field, or Subject:** Electrical engineering; Engineering, Industrial; Manufacturing; Mechanical engineering; Accounting; Business administration; Economics; Finance; Personnel administration/human resources. **Level of Education for which Award is Granted:** Undergraduate **Funds Available:** $2,500.
Eligibility Requirements: Applicants must be of Hispanic heritage; U.S. citizens or legal permanent residents with a valid permanent resident card or passport stamped I-551; enrolled full-time in a degree-seeking program at any four-year U.S. accredited institution in the U.S., Puerto Rico, U.S. Virgin Islands or Guam; have a minimum 3.0 GPA on a 4.0 scale or the equivalent; pursue degrees in Engineering, Business or Human Resources; must apply for federal financing aid using the Free Application for Federal Student Aid (FAFSA) at www.fafsa.ed.gov. For semi-finalists, applicants must complete the GM Online Assessment. **Application Requirements:** Applicants must use the HSF online application system. **Additional Information:** Given in partnership with General Motors (GM). **Deadline for Receipt:** June 30. **Additional Information:** scholar1@hsf.net.

3827 ■ HISPANIC SCHOLARSHIP FUND
55 Second St., Ste. 1500
San Francisco, CA 94105
877-473-4636
Fax: (415)808-2302
E-mail: info@hsf.net
Web Site: http://www.hsf.net
To support outstanding Community College Transfer Students.
Title of Award: HSF/Nissan Community College Transfer Scholarship Program **Area, Field, or Subject:** Business; Engineering; Communications; Media arts. **Level of Education for which Award is Granted:** Undergraduate **Funds Available:** $2,500.
Eligibility Requirements: Applicant must be of Hispanic heritage; U.S. citizen or legal permanent resident with a valid permanent resident card or passport stamped I-551; currently enrolled part-time or full-time at a com-

munity college; planning to transfer and enroll full-time in a degree-seeking program at a four-year U.S. accredited institution; must reside or transfer to a four-year institution in Atlanta, Georgia; Chicago Illinois; Greater Dallas/Forth Worth, Texas; Jackson/Canton, Mississippi; Los Angeles, California; Nashville, Tennessee; Northern California; New York City/New Jersey; be pursuing a degree in Business, Engineering, Communications or Media Arts; have a minimum GPA of 3.0 on a 4.0 scale; must apply for federal financing aid using the Free Application for Federal Student Aid (FAFSA) at www.fafsa.ed.gov. **Application Requirements:** Applications must be submitted using the HSF online application system. **Additional Information:** In partnership with Nissan North America, Inc. **Deadline for Receipt:** March 15. **Additional Information:** cctransfer@hsf.net.

3828 ■ HISPANIC SCHOLARSHIP FUND
55 Second St., Ste. 1500
San Francisco, CA 94105
877-473-4636
Fax: (415)808-2302
E-mail: info@hsf.net
Web Site: http://www.hsf.net
To provide financial assistance to students of Hispanic heritage.
Title of Award: HSF/Wal-Mart Stores Inc. Scholarship Program **Area, Field, or Subject:** Marketing and distribution; Accounting; Business; Finance; Management; Computer and information sciences; Information science and technology; Civil engineering; Construction; Electrical engineering; Geology; Engineering, Industrial; Fashion design; Law; **Level of Education for which Award is Granted:** Graduate, Undergraduate **Funds Available:** $2,500.
Eligibility Requirements: Applicant must be of Hispanic heritage; U.S. citizen or legal permanent resident with a valid permanent resident card or passport stamped I-551; enrolled as sophomore, junior, senior undergraduate or First or Second year Master student in a full-time degree-seeking program at an accredited U.S. institution in the U.S., Puerto Rico, U.S. Virgin Islands or Guam; have a minimum 3.0 GPA on a 4.0 scale or 4.00 on a 5.00 scale; must apply for Federal Financing Aid; pursuing his/her first undergraduate or graduate degree. Undergraduate students must be majoring in: Marketing, Accounting, Business, Finance, Management, Computer Science, Computer Programming, Information Technology (IT), Civil Engineering, Construction, Electrical Engineering, Environmental/Geological Engineering, Industrial Engineering, and Fashion. Master's students must be majoring in: Business, Finance, Marketing, Civil Engineering, Construction, Electrical Engineering, Environmental/Geological Engineering and Law. **Application Requirements:** Applications must be submitted using the HSF online application system. **Additional Information:** In partnership with Wal-Mart Stores, Inc. **Deadline for Receipt:** March 15. **Additional Information:** scholar1@hsf.net.

3829 ■ HISPANIC SCHOLARSHIP FUND
55 Second St., Ste. 1500
San Francisco, CA 94105
877-473-4636
Fax: (415)808-2302
E-mail: info@hsf.net
Web Site: http://www.hsf.net
To provide financial assistance to those who are studying engineering.
Title of Award: Marathon Oil Corporation College Scholarship Program **Area, Field, or Subject:** Chemical engineering; Civil engineering; Electrical engineering; Mechanical engineering; Petroleum engineering; Geology; Geophysics; Accounting; Marketing and distribution; Land management; Transportation; Logistics; Engineering, Petroleum **Level of Education for which Award is Granted:** Graduate, Undergraduate **Funds Available:** $20,000. **Duration:** Two academic years.
Eligibility Requirements: Applicant must be of Hispanic American, African American, Asian Pacific Islander American or American Indian/Alaskan Native heritage; U.S. citizen or legal permanent resident with a valid Social Security Number and a permanent resident card or passport stamped I-551; have a minimum 3.0 GPA on a 4.0 scale; a sophomore majoring in chemical engineering, civil engineering, electrical engineering, mechanical engineering, petroleum engineering, geology, geophysics, accounting, marketing, global procurement or supply chain management, environmental health & safety, energy management or petroleum land management, transportation & logistics or geotechnical engineering; or a

senior pursuing a Masters degree in geology or geophysics; must participate in a possible paid summer internship opportunity in Marathon Oil Corporation; must apply for federal financing aid using the Free Application for Federal Student Aid (FAFSA) at www.fafsa.ed.gov. **Application Requirements:** Applications must be submitted using the HSF online application system. **Additional Information:** Scholars will be paired with a Marathon Oil Corporation employee as a professional mentor. **Deadline for Receipt:** November 1. **Additional Information:** scholar1@hsf.net.

3830 ■ HISPANIC SCHOLARSHIP FUND

55 Second St., Ste. 1500
San Francisco, CA 94105
877-473-4636
Fax: (415)808-2302
E-mail: info@hsf.net
Web Site: http://www.hsf.net
To provide financial resources to assist outstanding Latino high school graduates.

Title of Award: Toyota High School Scholarship Program **Area, Field, or Subject:** Accounting; Actuarial science; Advertising; Architecture; Automotive technology; Bioengineering; Business; Chemical engineering; Civil engineering; Engineering, Computer; Electronics; Computer and information sciences; Construction; Drafting; Economics; Education; Education, Bilingual and cross-cultural; Education, Early childhood; Education, Special; Counseling/Guidance; Electrical engineering; Engineering; Environmental design; Environmental science; Geology; Educational administration; Education-Curricula; Personnel administration/human resources; Industrial design; Engineering, Industrial; Information science and technology; Management; Marketing and distribution; International trade; Manufacturing; Mechanical engineering; Engineering, Nuclear; Public administration; Public relations; Transportation. **Level of Education for which Award is Granted:** Undergraduate **Funds Available:** $5,000.

Eligibility Requirements: Applicant must be of Hispanic heritage; U.S. citizen or legal permanent resident with a valid permanent resident card or passport stamped I-551; have a minimum GPA of 3.0 on a 4.0 scale or equivalent; must apply for federal financing aid using the Free Application for Federal Student Aid (FAFSA) at www.fafsa.ed.gov; enrolling as full-time freshman at: Arizona State University; Central Missouri University; Colorado State University, Pueblo; Cornell University; Ferris State; Florida International University; Harvard University; Indiana University; Massachusetts Institute of Technology; New York University; Northwestern University; Pennsylvania Tech College; Pittsburg State University; Southern Illinois University; Stanford University; Texas A&M University; University of Arizona; University of California, Berkeley; University of California, Davis; University of California, Los Angeles; University of California, San Diego; University of Florida; University of Houston; University of Illinois at Chicago; University of Illinois at Urbana-Champaign; University of Michigan; University of New Mexico; University of Pennsylvania; University of Southern California; University of Texas at Austin; University of Texas at El Paso; University of Texas at San Antonio; University of Texas, Pan American; or Weber State University. Applicants must pursue a degree in: Accounting; Actuarial Science; Advertising; Architecture; Automotive Technology; Bio-Engineering; Business; Chemical Engineering; Civil Engineering; Computer Electronics; Computer Engineering; Computer Information Systems (CIS); Computer Programming; Computer Science; Construction; Drafting/CAD; Economics; Education Admin./Leadership; Education/Teaching; Education: Bilingual; Education: Early Childhood/ Elementary; Education: Special; Educational Counseling; Electrical Engineering; Engineering; Environmental Design/ Landscaping; Environmental Management/Science; Environmental/ Geological Engineering; Human Resource Management; Industrial Design; Industrial Engineering; Information Technology (IT); International Business; Management; Management Information Systems (MIS); Manufacturing Engineering; Marketing; Materials/ Manufacturing; Mechanical Engineering; Network Administration; Non-Profit Management; Nuclear Engineering; Office Administration; Public Administration; Public Relations; Supply Chain Management; or Transportation. **Application Requirements:** Applications must be submitted using the HSF online application system. **Additional Information:** In partnership with Toyota Motor Sales, USA. **Deadline for Receipt:** July 16. **Additional Information:** highschool@hsf.net.

3831 ■ HISPANIC SCHOLARSHIP FUND

55 Second St., Ste. 1500
San Francisco, CA 94105
877-473-4636
Fax: (415)808-2302
E-mail: info@hsf.net
Web Site: http://www.hsf.net
To provide financial assistance to college students of Hispanic heritage.

Title of Award: Verizon Scholarship Program **Area, Field, or Subject:** Accounting; Business; Economics; Finance; Personnel administration/human resources; Marketing and distribution; Engineering, Computer; Information science and technology; Computer and information sciences; Civil engineering; Electrical engineering; Engineering, Industrial; Engineering, Mechanical. **Level of Education for which Award is Granted:** Undergraduate **Funds Available:** $5,000.

Eligibility Requirements: Applicant must be of Hispanic heritage; U.S. citizen or legal permanent resident with a valid permanent resident card or passport stamped I-551; enrolled as sophomore, junior or senior in a full-time degree-seeking program at an accredited U.S. institution in the U.S., Puerto Rico, U.S. Virgin Islands or Guam; have a minimum 3.0 GPA on a 4.0 scale or 4.00 on a 5.00 scale; must apply for federal financing aid using the Free Application for Federal Student Aid (FAFSA) at www.fafsa. ed.gov; must submit a resume with application; must be pursuing his/her first undergraduate degree; must be majoring in: Accounting, Business, Economics, Finance, Human Resource Management, Marketing, Computer Science, Computer Engineering, Computer Programming, Computer Electronics, Information Technology (IT), Management Information Systems (MIS), Network Administration, Computer Information Systems (CIS), Civil, Electrical, Industrial, or Mechanical Engineering; must be a resident of: (NY counties) Bronx, Kings, New York, Queens, and Richmond; (NJ) Town of Basking Ridge in Somerset County; (PA Counties) Bucks, Montgomery, Chester, Delaware, Philadelphia; (FL counties) Hernando, Hillsborough, Pasco, and Pinella; (MA counties) Essex, Middlesex, Plymouth, Suffolk; (TX counties) Collin, Dallas, Denton, Dexar, Dorris, Ellis, Henderson, Hood, Hunt, Johnson, Kaufman, Parker, Rockwall, and Tarrant; (VA county) Arlington, Loudoun; (DC) Washington; (Southern CA counties) Los Angeles, Orange, Riverside, San Bernardino, Ventura; Maine, New Hampshire, Washington State. **Application Requirements:** Applications must be submitted using the HSF online application system. **Additional Information:** In partnership with Verizon. **Deadline for Receipt:** March 15. **Additional Information:** scholar1@hsf. net.

3832 ■ HISPANIC SCHOLARSHIP FUND

55 Second St., Ste. 1500
San Francisco, CA 94105
877-473-4636
Fax: (415)808-2302
E-mail: info@hsf.net
Web Site: http://www.hsf.net
To assist college students who are interested in financial and banking based careers.

Title of Award: Wells Fargo Scholarship Program **Area, Field, or Subject:** Banking; Finance. **Level of Education for which Award is Granted:** Graduate, Undergraduate **Funds Available:** $2,000.

Eligibility Requirements: Applicants must be of Hispanic heritage; U.S. citizen or legal permanent resident with a valid permanent resident card or passport stamped I-551; a sophomore enrolled full-time at a four-year accredited college/university in the U.S. (must be enrolled as a junior in the following academic year); pursuing a degree in Business, Economics, Finance, Accounting or IT, including CIS, MIS and Computer Engineering; have a minimum 3.0 GPA on a 4.0 scale or the equivalent; must apply for Federal Financing Aid. **Application Requirements:** Applicants must use the HSF online application system, and visit website www.hsf.net. **Additional Information:** In partnership with Wells Fargo. **Deadline for Receipt:** March 15. **Additional Information:** scholar1@hsf.net.

3833 ■ INTERNATIONAL ASSOCIATION OF ADMINISTRATIVE PROFESSIONALS

PO Box 20404
Kansas City, MO 64195-0404
Tel: (816)891-6600
Fax: (816)891-9118

Web Site: http://www.iaap-wings.org

To provide financial assistance for qualified individuals from the Greater Miami Valley area who are pursuing careers as office professionals.

Title of Award: IAAP Wings Chapter Scholarships **Area, Field, or Subject:** Business. **Level of Education for which Award is Granted:** Undergraduate **Funds Available:** No specific amount. **Duration:** One year.

Eligibility Requirements: Applicants must have applied and have been accepted or be currently attending an accredited university, college, junior college, community college, or technical or vocational school. **Application Requirements:** Applicants must submit all the required application information. **Deadline for Receipt:** February 29.

3834 ■ INTERNATIONAL DAIRY-DELI-BAKERY ASSOCIATION

PO Box 5528
Madison, WI 53705-0528
Tel: (608)310-5000
Fax: (608)238-6330
Web Site: http://www.iddba.org

To support employees of IDDBA-member companies.

Title of Award: International Dairy-Deli-Bakery Association Undergraduate Scholarships **Area, Field, or Subject:** Culinary arts; Food service careers; Business. **Level of Education for which Award is Granted:** Graduate, Undergraduate **Funds Available:** $1,000. May be prorated among applicants. **Duration:** One semester.

Eligibility Requirements: Applicants must have an academic field of study in a food-related field such as culinary arts, baking/pastry arts or food science, business or marketing program. Applicants must also have a 2.5 grade-point average on a 4.0 scale, or equivalent which may be waived for first-time returning adult students. **Application Requirements:** Applicants must submit a completed application form together with at least one letter of reference on letterhead from a department/store manager and/or professional academic contact. Incomplete or illegible applications will not be considered. **Deadline for Receipt:** January 1, April 1, July 1, October 1. **Additional Information:** Karen Peckham at the above address.

3835 ■ JAMAICAN CANADIAN ASSOCIATION

995 Arrow Rd.
Toronto, ON, Canada M9M 2Z5
Tel: (416)746-5772
Fax: (416)746-7035
E-mail: info@jcassoc.org
Web Site: http://www.jcassoc.org

To provide financial assistance to students from the Caribbean/ African community, who are pursuing postsecondary studies in Ontario universities/colleges.

Title of Award: Jamaica National Building Society Scholarships **Area, Field, or Subject:** Business; Law; Science; Technology; Nursing. **Level of Education for which Award is Granted:** Undergraduate **Number Awarded:** 2. **Funds Available:** $1,000. **Duration:** One year.

Eligibility Requirements: Applicant must be a Canadian citizen or landed immigrant of Caribbean or African background; must be enrolled as a full-time first-year student at an Ontario university/college or other postsecondary institution; must demonstrate remarkable academic performance or progress in high school; must demonstrate involvement and leadership in campus and/or community activities; must demonstrate financial need. **Application Requirements:** Application forms are available online and must be sent to The Jamaican Canadian Association Center, 995 Arrow Rd., Toronto M9M 2Z5. **Additional Information:** Scholarship is donated by the Jamaica National Building Society, a financial institution that facilitates money transfers from Canada. **Deadline for Receipt:** July 25.

3836 ■ JAMAICAN CANADIAN ASSOCIATION

995 Arrow Rd.
Toronto, ON, Canada M9M 2Z5
Tel: (416)746-5772
Fax: (416)746-7035
E-mail: info@jcassoc.org
Web Site: http://www.jcassoc.org

To provide financial assistance to students from the Caribbean or African community, who are pursuing postsecondary studies in Ontario universities/colleges.

Title of Award: Dr. Ezra Nesbeth Scholarships **Area, Field, or Subject:** Business; Technology; Computer and information sciences; Health sciences. **Level of Education for which Award is Granted:** Undergraduate **Funds Available:** $2,000. **Duration:** One year.

Eligibility Requirements: Applicants must be college or university students studying business, technology, computer science or health science; must have a high academic standing; must demonstrate leadership; must have completed at least one year of college or university in Canada; must demonstrate strong oral and written communication skills; must have an involvement in extracurricular activities within the university, AfroCanadian community, or wider Canadian community; must have landed immigrant or Canadian citizenship; must not be receiving more than one other award of equal or greater value in the receiving year; must have a good understanding of the importance of economic self-sufficiency and entrepreneurship to the success of African Canadians in the Greater Toronto Area and elsewhere in Canada. **Application Requirements:** Application forms are available online and must be sent to The Jamaican Canadian Association Center, 995 Arrow Rd., Toronto M9M 2Z5. **Additional Information:** Sponsored by Dr. Ezra Nesbeth, a graduate of the University of Waterloo and the University of Toronto with varied and extensive experience in community and health programs. **Deadline for Receipt:** July 25.

3837 ■ JUNIOR ACHIEVEMENT

One Education Way
Colorado Springs, CO 80906
Tel: (719)540-8000; 888-4JA-ALUM
Fax: (719)540-6299
E-mail: newmedia@ja.org
Web Site: http://www.ja.org

To allow educational advancements by providing financial assistance.

Title of Award: Johnson and Wales University Scholarships **Area, Field, or Subject:** Business; Culinary arts; Technology; Teaching. **Level of Education for which Award is Granted:** Undergraduate **Number Awarded:** Varies. **Funds Available:** $500 to cover full tuition. **Duration:** One year.

Eligibility Requirements: Program is open to individuals who are majoring in the field of business, culinary arts, hospitality, technology or teacher education. **Application Requirements:** Applicants must submit a completed application form together with other supporting materials. Mail all materials to Johnson and Wales University, 8 Abbott Park Place, Providence, RI 02903. **Deadline for Receipt:** February 1. **Additional Information:** National Student Organizations Office at Johnson and Wales University, 8 Abbott Park Place, Providence, RI 02903, at 800DIAL-JWU x-2345, or nso@jwu.edu.

3838 ■ THE LAGRANT FOUNDATION

626 Wilshire Blvd., Ste. 700
Los Angeles, CA 90017-2920
Tel: (323)469-8680
Fax: (323)469-8683
Web Site: http://www.lagrantfoundation.org

To provide financial support for the education of undergraduate students who belong to ethnic groups: African American, Asian Pacific American, Hispanic or Native American or Alaska Native.

Title of Award: The Lagrant Foundation - Undergraduate Students Scholarship **Area, Field, or Subject:** Public relations; Marketing and distribution; Advertising. **Level of Education for which Award is Granted:** Undergraduate **Funds Available:** No amount specified.

Eligibility Requirements: Applicants must be U.S. citizens and full-time students at a four-year, accredited institution, carrying a total of 12 units or more per semester/quarter; must have a minimum of 2.75 GPA; and must major in a field of study that has an emphasis on public relations, marketing or advertising or must minor in communications with desire to pursue a career in public relations, marketing or advertising. **Application Requirements:** Applicants must submit a one- to two-page typewritten essay outlining their career goals and what steps they will take to increase the lack of ethnic representation in the fields of advertising, marketing and public relations (must define the role of advertising, marketing or public relations practitioner depending on emphasis); accomplishments relevant to increasing awareness about diversity in their community; brief paragraph describing any honors and awards that they have received (must put the particular dates); a letter of reference from a college professor or internship advisor. **Additional Information:** If chosen, the applicant must attend the Lagrant Foundation's career development workshop and awards reception to receive the scholarship. **Deadline for Receipt:** February 29.

3839 ■ LEWIS-CLARK STATE COLLEGE
500 8th Ave.
Lewiston, ID 83501
Tel: (208)792-5272
Web Site: http://www.lcsc.edu
To provide financial assistance to students who are majoring in these fields: Accounting, Biology, Business, Communications, Computer Science, Economics, Environmental Science, Engineering, Mathematics, Natural Resources, Political Science, Statistics.
Title of Award: Avista Corporation Minds in Motion Scholarships **Area, Field, or Subject:** Accounting; Biology; Business; Communications; Computer and Information Sciences; Economics; Environmental Science; Engineering; Mathematics; Natural Resources; Political Science; Statistics. **Level of Education for which Award is Granted:** Undergraduate **Number Awarded:** 2. **Funds Available:** No specific Amount.
Eligibility Requirements: Applicants must be full-time students attending LCSC and must have a cumulative GPA of 2.5. **Application Requirements:** Applicants must submit general application. **Deadline for Receipt:** March 1.

3840 ■ LEWIS-CLARK STATE COLLEGE
500 8th Ave.
Lewiston, ID 83501
Tel: (208)792-5272
Web Site: http://www.lcsc.edu
To provide financial assistance for outstanding junior or senior students in the Business Division.
Title of Award: Banner Bank Business Scholarships **Area, Field, or Subject:** Business. **Level of Education for which Award is Granted:** Undergraduate **Funds Available:** $1,000.
Eligibility Requirements: Program is open to students pursuing a degree in business and entering their junior or senior year. Applicants must demonstrate financial need as determined by the FAFSA form. **Application Requirements:** Applicants must accomplish the required general application available in the website. **Deadline for Receipt:** March 1.

3841 ■ LEWIS-CLARK STATE COLLEGE
500 8th Ave.
Lewiston, ID 83501
Tel: (208)792-5272
Web Site: http://www.lcsc.edu
To assist students pursuing a degree in business at Lewis-Clark State College.
Title of Award: First Security Foundation Business Scholarships **Area, Field, or Subject:** Business. **Level of Education for which Award is Granted:** Undergraduate **Number Awarded:** 2. **Funds Available:** $1,500.
Eligibility Requirements: Applicants must be students at Lewis-Clark State College and must have a cumulative GPA of 3.0. **Application Requirements:** Applicants must submit a general application. **Deadline for Receipt:** March 1.

3842 ■ LEWIS-CLARK STATE COLLEGE
500 8th Ave.
Lewiston, ID 83501
Tel: (208)792-5272
Web Site: http://www.lcsc.edu
To provide financial assistance to students who are currently enrolled in a vocational program.
Title of Award: Margaret G. Johnson and Marge J. Stout Scholarships **Area, Field, or Subject:** Vocational; Business. **Level of Education for which Award is Granted:** Undergraduate **Funds Available:** No specific amount.
Eligibility Requirements: Applicants must have completed at least 12 credits; must be residents of Idaho; must be enrolled in a two year vocational-technical program at LCSC; and must demonstrate a minimum GPA of 3.0. **Application Requirements:** Applicants must accomplish a general application available at the website. **Deadline for Receipt:** March 1.

3843 ■ LEWIS-CLARK STATE COLLEGE
500 8th Ave.
Lewiston, ID 83501
Tel: (208)792-5272
Web Site: http://www.lcsc.edu
To encourage educational pursuits among individuals who have experienced congenital heart defects.
Title of Award: Kaia Lynn Markwalter Endowed Scholarships **Area, Field, or Subject:** Business. **Level of Education for which Award is Granted:** Undergraduate **Funds Available:** No specific amount.
Eligibility Requirements: Applicants must be students at Lewis-Clark State College who have been directly impacted by congenital heart defects. The applicant must also have a 3.0 cumulative G.P.A. and be enrolled in 12 credits each semester. **Application Requirements:** Applicants must submit a general application. **Deadline for Receipt:** March 1.

3844 ■ LUSO-AMERICAN EDUCATION FOUNDATION
PO Box 2967
Dublin, CA 94568
Tel: (925)828-3883
Fax: (925)828-3883
E-mail: odom@luso-american.org
To provide financial assistance to qualified students to further their education.
Title of Award: Luso-American Education Foundation C-1 General Scholarships **Area, Field, or Subject:** Business. **Level of Education for which Award is Granted:** Undergraduate **Funds Available:** $1,500. **Duration:** One year.
Eligibility Requirements: Applicant must be a California resident; enrolled in trade business school, junior or four-year college/university; have minimum of 3.5 GPA; a Portuguese descent; or currently taking Portuguese language classes with 3.0 GPA. **Application Requirements:** Applicants must submit a completed application form; an official transcript; SAT or ACT scores; and two letters of recommendation. **Deadline for Receipt:** March 1.

3845 ■ MATANUSKA-SUSITNA COLLEGE
PO Box 2889
Palmer, AK 99645
Tel: (907)745-9774
Fax: (907)745-9711
E-mail: info@matsu.alaska.edu
Web Site: http://www.matsu.alaska.edu
To provide support to deserving students in Alaska who want to pursue an education in any campus of the University of Alaska.
Title of Award: Alaska Aerospace Development Corporation Scholarships **Area, Field, or Subject:** Applied mathematics; Physics; Engineering; Business; Technical communications. **Level of Education for which Award is Granted:** Undergraduate **Funds Available:** $5,000.
Eligibility Requirements: Applicant must be a freshman student majoring in mathematics, physics, engineering, business, or a technical science field such as computer science who has graduated from the Kodiak Island Borough School District; must be a full-time student enrolled in 14 credits and in good academic standing. **Application Requirements:** Applicants must submit a written statement verifying that he/she has not been convicted of a crime other than a minor traffic violation; must complete the application forms available at the website; must attach a personal essay, two letters of recommendation, and current transcripts. **Deadline for Receipt:** February 15.

3846 ■ MATANUSKA-SUSITNA COLLEGE
PO Box 2889
Palmer, AK 99645
Tel: (907)745-9774
Fax: (907)745-9711
E-mail: info@matsu.alaska.edu
Web Site: http://www.matsu.alaska.edu
To provide support to deserving students in Alaska who want to pursue an education in any campus of the University of Alaska.
Title of Award: Mable B. Crawford Memorial Scholarships **Area, Field, or Subject:** Accounting; Economics; Law; Business. **Level of Education for which Award is Granted:** Undergraduate **Funds Available:** $500.

Eligibility Requirements: Applicants must be students who have been residents of Alaska for at least two years. **Application Requirements:** Applicant must complete the application forms available at the website; must attach a personal essay, two letters of recommendation, and current transcripts. **Deadline for Receipt:** February 15.

3847 ■ MATANUSKA-SUSITNA COLLEGE
PO Box 2889
Palmer, AK 99645
Tel: (907)745-9774
Fax: (907)745-9711
E-mail: info@matsu.alaska.edu
Web Site: http://www.matsu.alaska.edu
To provide financial assistance for tuition and other educational expenses to students who are formally admitted to a business degreeseeking program and attending the Matanuska-Susitna College.
Title of Award: NAPMW Mat-Su Valley Alaska Scholarships **Area, Field, or Subject:** Business. **Level of Education for which Award is Granted:** Undergraduate **Funds Available:** $2,000. **Duration:** One academic year. **Eligibility Requirements:** Applicant must be in good academic standing with a minimum cumulative GPA of 2.5; must be formally admitted to an undergraduate business degreeseeking program at the University of Alaska Anchorage; must plan to attend at least half-time (6 credits) at the Matanuska-Susitna College; must be an incoming or continuing student. **Application Requirements:** Applicant must complete the MSC scholarship application form; must attach a list of activities/community service in which they have participated; must attach a resume of their work experience over the past four years; must attach a personal essay (not more than 500 words); must have two letters of recommendation and transcript. **Deadline for Receipt:** May 31.

3848 ■ MILL CREEK BUSINESS ASSOCIATION
13300 Bothell-Everett Hwy.
Mill Creek, WA 98012
Tel: (425)673-6200
E-mail: info@millcreekbiz.com
Web Site: http://www.millcreekbiz.com
To encourage and assist local high school students in their pursuit of higher learning in Business or Fine Arts.
Title of Award: Mill Creek Business Association Scholarships **Area, Field, or Subject:** Business; Fine Arts. **Level of Education for which Award is Granted:** Undergraduate **Funds Available:** No specific amount.
Eligibility Requirements: Applicants must live in Mill Creek and/or attend school at Jacksonville High school or Archbishop Murphy High School; must be senior students in good standing at the time of application; must be accepted to attend a full-time accredited college, university or Fine Arts school; must be planning an academic course of study in the field of business/fine arts and/or plan to pursue a career in business or fine arts. **Application Requirements:** Applicants must complete the application form; must submit two letters of reference and recommendation from teachers, advisors, and/or local business people; a copy of the letter of acceptance from their institution; must provide a 200 word, typed essay stating their academic and career plans. **Deadline for Receipt:** May 1. **Additional Information:** 13300 Bothell-Everett Hwy., Mill Creek, WA 98012.

3849 ■ NATIONAL ASSOCIATION OF BLACK ACCOUNTANTS
7249-A Hanover Pkwy.
Greenbelt, MD 20770
Tel: (301)474-6222; 888-571-2939
Fax: (301)474-3114
E-mail: customerservice@nabainc.org
Web Site: http://www.nabainc.org
To support deserving students planning to enter a business related field.
Title of Award: Donald J. Bristow Memorial Scholarship Program **Area, Field, or Subject:** Business; Accounting; Finance. **Level of Education for which Award is Granted:** Graduate, Undergraduate **Funds Available:** $3,500. **Duration:** One academic year.
Eligibility Requirements: Applicant must be a member of an ethic minority; an active NABA student member; enrolled full-time at a four-year United States college or university; must be a freshman, sophomore, junior or first-year senior undergraduate pursuing a major in accounting,

finance, or business; or a graduate student in a master's-level business program; must meet the minimum requirement of 3.5 major GPA and 3.3 overall GPA or equivalent. **Application Requirements:** Applicant must submit a completed National Scholarship Application (NSA) available at the website; a current official transcript; a copy of Student/Permanent Resident Visa (for non-U.S. citizen applicants); a resume; two letters of recommendation; a personal biography (maximum of 500 words) discussing career objectives, leadership skills, community activities, and involvement in NABA. **Deadline for Receipt:** January 31.

3850 ■ NATIONAL ASSOCIATION OF BLACK ACCOUNTANTS
7249-A Hanover Pkwy.
Greenbelt, MD 20770
Tel: (301)474-6222; 888-571-2939
Fax: (301)474-3114
E-mail: customerservice@nabainc.org
Web Site: http://www.nabainc.org
To support deserving students planning to enter a business related field.
Title of Award: Mark Miller Award **Area, Field, or Subject:** Business; Accounting; Finance. **Level of Education for which Award is Granted:** Graduate, Undergraduate **Funds Available:** $2,500. **Duration:** One academic year.
Eligibility Requirements: Applicant must be a member of an ethic minority; an active NABA student member; enrolled full-time at a four-year United States college or university; a freshman, sophomore, junior or first-year senior undergraduate pursuing a major in accounting, finance, or business; or a graduate student in a master's-level business program; must meet the minimum requirement of 2.0 major GPA and 2.5 overall GPA or equivalent. **Application Requirements:** Applicant must submit a completed National Scholarship Application (NSA) available at the website; a current official transcript; a copy of Student/Permanent Resident Visa (for non-U.S. citizen applicants); a resume; two letters of recommendation; a personal biography (maximum of 500 words) discussing career objectives, leadership skills, community activities, and involvement in NABA. **Deadline for Receipt:** January 31.

3851 ■ NATIONAL ASSOCIATION OF BLACK ACCOUNTANTS
7249-A Hanover Pkwy.
Greenbelt, MD 20770
Tel: (301)474-6222; 888-571-2939
Fax: (301)474-3114
E-mail: customerservice@nabainc.org
Web Site: http://www.nabainc.org
To support deserving students planning to enter a business related field.
Title of Award: NABA Corporate Scholarship Program **Area, Field, or Subject:** Business; Accounting; Finance. **Level of Education for which Award is Granted:** Graduate, Undergraduate **Funds Available:** $2,000-$10,000. **Duration:** One academic year.
Eligibility Requirements: Applicant must be a member of an ethic minority, an active NABA student member, enrolled full-time at a four-year United States college or university; must be a freshman, sophomore, junior or first-year senior undergraduate pursuing a major in accounting, finance, or business; or a graduate student in a master's-level business program; must meet the minimum requirement of 3.5 major GPA and 3.3 overall GPA or equivalent. **Application Requirements:** Applicant must submit a completed National Scholarship Application (NSA) available at the website; a current official transcript; a copy of Student/Permanent Resident Visa (for non-U.S. citizen applicants); a resume; two letters of recommendation; a personal biography (maximum of 500 words) discussing career objectives, leadership skills, community activities, and involvement in NABA. **Deadline for Receipt:** January 31.

3852 ■ NATIONAL ASSOCIATION OF BLACK ACCOUNTANTS
7249-A Hanover Pkwy.
Greenbelt, MD 20770
Tel: (301)474-6222; 888-571-2939
Fax: (301)474-3114
E-mail: customerservice@nabainc.org
Web Site: http://www.nabainc.org
To support deserving students planning to enter a business related field.
Title of Award: NABA National Scholarship Program **Area, Field, or Subject:** Business; Accounting; Finance. **Level of Education for which Award is Granted:** Graduate, Undergraduate **Funds Available:** $3,000-$6,000. **Duration:** One academic year.

Eligibility Requirements: Applicant must be a member of an ethic minority; an active NABA student member; enrolled full-time at a four-year United States college or university; must be a freshman, sophomore, junior or first-year senior undergraduate pursuing a major in accounting, finance, or business; or a graduate student in a master's-level business program; must meet the minimum requirement of 3.5 major GPA and 3.3 overall GPA or equivalent. **Application Requirements:** Applicants must submit a completed National Scholarship Application (NSA) available at the website; a current official transcript; a copy of the Student/Permanent Resident Visa (for non-U.S. citizen applicants); a resume; two letters of recommendation; a personal biography (maximum of 500 words) discussing career objectives, leadership skills, community activities, and involvement in NABA. **Deadline for Receipt:** January 31.

3853 ■ NATIONAL ASSOCIATION OF BLACK ACCOUNTANTS
7249-A Hanover Pkwy.
Greenbelt, MD 20770
Tel: (301)474-6222; 888-571-2939
Fax: (301)474-3114
E-mail: customerservice@nabainc.org
Web Site: http://www.nabainc.org
To support deserving students planning to enter a business related field.
Title of Award: TDC Scholarship Program **Area, Field, or Subject:** Business; Accounting; Finance. **Level of Education for which Award is Granted:** Graduate, Undergraduate **Funds Available:** $1,000. **Duration:** One academic year.
Eligibility Requirements: Applicant must be a member of an ethic minority; an active NABA student member; enrolled full-time at a four-year United States college or university; must be a freshman, sophomore, junior or first-year senior undergraduate pursuing a major in accounting, finance, or business; or a graduate student in a master's-level business program; must meet the minimum requirement of 3.5 major GPA and 3.3 overall GPA or equivalent. **Application Requirements:** Applicant must submit a completed National Scholarship Application (NSA) available at the website; a current official transcript; a copy of Student/Permanent Resident Visa (for non-U.S. citizen applicants); a resume; two letters of recommendation; a personal biography (maximum of 500 words) discussing career objectives, leadership skills, community activities, and involvement in NABA. **Deadline for Receipt:** January 31.

3854 ■ NATIONAL ASSOCIATION OF BLACK ACCOUNTANTS
7249-A Hanover Pkwy.
Greenbelt, MD 20770
Tel: (301)474-6222; 888-571-2939
Fax: (301)474-3114
E-mail: customerservice@nabainc.org
Web Site: http://www.nabainc.org
To support deserving students planning to enter a business related field.
Title of Award: Ralph and Valerie Thomas Scholarship Program **Area, Field, or Subject:** Business; Accounting; Finance. **Level of Education for which Award is Granted:** Graduate, Undergraduate **Funds Available:** $1,000. **Duration:** One academic year.
Eligibility Requirements: Applicant must be a member of an ethic minority; an active NABA student member; enrolled full-time at a four-year United States college or university; must be a freshman, sophomore, junior or first-year senior undergraduate pursuing a major in accounting, finance, or business; or a graduate student in a master's-level business program; must meet the minimum requirement of 3.5 major GPA and 3.3 overall GPA or equivalent. **Application Requirements:** Applicant must submit a completed National Scholarship Application (NSA) available at the website; a current official transcript; a copy of Student/Permanent Resident Visa (for non-U.S. citizen applicants); a resume; two letters of recommendation; a personal biography (maximum of 500 words) discussing career objectives, leadership skills, community activities, and involvement in NABA. **Deadline for Receipt:** January 31.

3855 ■ NATIONAL ASSOCIATION OF BLACK ACCOUNTANTS
7249-A Hanover Pkwy.
Greenbelt, MD 20770
Tel: (301)474-6222; 888-571-2939
Fax: (301)474-3114
E-mail: customerservice@nabainc.org
Web Site: http://www.nabainc.org

To support deserving students planning to enter a business related field.
Title of Award: Travis C. Tomlin Memorial Scholarship Program **Area, Field, or Subject:** Business; Accounting; Finance. **Level of Education for which Award is Granted:** Graduate, Undergraduate **Funds Available:** $2,000. **Duration:** One academic year.
Eligibility Requirements: Applicant must be a member of an ethic minority; an active NABA student member; enrolled full-time at a four-year United States college or university; must be a freshman, sophomore, junior or first-year senior undergraduate pursuing a major in accounting, finance, or business; or a graduate student in a master's-level business program; must meet the minimum requirement of 3.5 major GPA and 3.3 overall GPA or equivalent. **Application Requirements:** Applicant must submit a completed National Scholarship Application (NSA) available at the website; a current official transcript; a copy of Student/Permanent Resident Visa (for non-U.S. citizen applicants); a resume; two letters of recommendation; a personal biography (maximum of 500 words) discussing career objectives, leadership skills, community activities, and involvement in NABA. **Deadline for Receipt:** January 31.

3856 ■ NATIONAL ASSOCIATION OF BLACK ACCOUNTANTS
7249-A Hanover Pkwy.
Greenbelt, MD 20770
Tel: (301)474-6222; 888-571-2939
Fax: (301)474-3114
E-mail: customerservice@nabainc.org
Web Site: http://www.nabainc.org
To support deserving students planning to enter a business related field.
Title of Award: Thomas S. Watson, Jr. Memorial Scholarships **Area, Field, or Subject:** Business; Accounting; Finance. **Level of Education for which Award is Granted:** Graduate, Undergraduate **Funds Available:** $1,000. **Duration:** One academic year.
Eligibility Requirements: Applicant must be a member of an ethic minority; an active NABA student member; enrolled full-time at a four-year United States college or university; must be a freshman, sophomore, junior or first-year senior undergraduate pursuing a major in accounting, finance, or business; or a graduate student in a master's-level business program; must meet the minimum requirement of 3.5 major GPA and 3.3 overall GPA or equivalent. **Application Requirements:** Applicant must submit a completed National Scholarship Application (NSA) available at the website; a current official transcript; a copy of Student/Permanent Resident Visa (for non-U.S. citizen applicants); a resume; two letters of recommendation; a personal biography (maximum of 500 words) discussing career objectives, leadership skills, community activities, and involvement in NABA. **Deadline for Receipt:** January 31.

3857 ■ NATIONAL ASSOCIATION FOR THE SELF-EMPLOYED
PO Box 612067
DFW Airport, TX 75261-2067
800-232-6273
Fax: 800-551-4446
E-mail: koberlander@nase.org
Web Site: http://www.nase.org
To promote entrepreneurial philosophy.
Title of Award: NASE Future Entrepreneur Scholarships **Area, Field, or Subject:** Business. **Level of Education for which Award is Granted:** Undergraduate **Number Awarded:** 1. **Funds Available:** $12,000 scholarship for the first year and $4,000 for the next three years. **Duration:** Four years.
Eligibility Requirements: Applicants must be dependents of NASE members. **Application Requirements:** Applicants must submit a completed application form and original copies of transcripts and test scores. **Deadline for Receipt:** April 25.

3858 ■ NATIONAL FEDERATION OF REPUBLICAN WOMEN
124 N Alfred St.
Alexandria, VA 22314
Tel: (703)548-9688
Fax: (703)548-9836
E-mail: mail@nfrw.org
Web Site: http://www.nfrw.org
To support students with their education.
Title of Award: Betty Rendel Scholarships **Area, Field, or Subject:** Political science; Government; Economics. **Level of Education for which**

Award is Granted: Undergraduate **Number Awarded:** 3. **Funds Available:** $1000. **Duration:** Annual.
Eligibility Requirements: Applicant must be an undergraduate student majoring in political science, government or economics; and have completed at least two years of college coursework. **Application Requirements:** Applicants must submit a completed application form together with three letters of recommendation (include contact numbers of the authors); an official copy of recent college transcript; a 1-page typed essay stating why deserve the scholarship; another 1-page typed essay on career goals; a photograph (optional); and State Federation President Certification. **Additional Information:** Established in 1995 in honor of NFRW Past President Betty Rendel's extraordinary leadership skills and dedication to the Republican Party in her home state of Indiana. **Deadline for Receipt:** June 1.

3859 ■ NATIONAL IRANIAN AMERICAN COUNCIL
1411 K St. NW, Ste. 600
Washington, DC 20005
Tel: (202)386-6325
Fax: (202)386-6409
Web Site: http://www.niacouncil.org
To provide outstanding Iranian-American college students with internships in political and media organizations.
Title of Award: National Iranian American Council Fellowships **Area, Field, or Subject:** Political science; Economics; International affairs and relations; Journalism. **Level of Education for which Award is Granted:** Graduate, Undergraduate **Funds Available:** Travel expenses covered to and from DC; $500 monthly stipend; $700 monthly towards rent.
Eligibility Requirements: Applicant must be a college junior, senior, and graduate student who is a U.S. citizen or a legal permanent resident of Iranian descent. **Application Requirements:** Applicant must submit the following requirements: a completed application form; three letters of recommendation (two academic and one from an employment supervisor); resume; current college transcript; a 500-word essay answering the question: "How has being Iranian-American influenced your decision to pursue a career in public service or journalism?" **Deadline for Receipt:** February 15. **Additional Information:** NIAC at the above address.

3860 ■ NATIONAL SOCIETY, DAUGHTERS OF THE AMERICAN REVOLUTION
1776 D St. NW
Washington, DC 20006-5303
Tel: (202)628-1776
Web Site: http://www.dar.org
To encourage students to pursue an undergraduate degree.
Title of Award: Enid Hall Griswold Memorial Scholarships **Area, Field, or Subject:** Political science; History; Government; Economics. **Level of Education for which Award is Granted:** Undergraduate **Funds Available:** $1,000. **Duration:** One year.
Eligibility Requirements: Applicants must be juniors or seniors enrolled in an accredited college or university in the United States; pursuing a major in political science, history, government, or economics. **Application Requirements:** Applicants must obtain a letter of sponsorship from their local DAR chapter. Application forms and other supporting documents must be completed correctly and submitted in one package. **Deadline for Receipt:** February 15.

3861 ■ NEW YORK FINANCIAL WRITERS ASSOCIATION
PO Box 338
Ridgewood, NJ 07451-0338
Tel: (201)612-0100
Fax: (201)612-9915
E-mail: info@nyfwa.org
Web Site: http://www.nyfwa.org
To provide financial assistance to those studying business, finance, and journalism.
Title of Award: New York Financial Writers' Associations Scholarships **Area, Field, or Subject:** Business; Finance; Journalism. **Level of Education for which Award is Granted:** Graduate, Undergraduate **Funds Available:** No specific amount.
Eligibility Requirements: Undergraduate or graduate journalism students in the Metropolitan New York area who are seriously interested in pursuing a career in business and financial journalism. **Application**

Requirements: Applicants must send an application form together with an essay explaining why the applicant is pursuing a career in business and financial journalism, current resume, list of other scholarships received and samples of financial writings and clippings created. If an application form is unavailable, applicants may submit a cover letter with the requirements listed. **Deadline for Receipt:** April 15. **Additional Information:** NYFWS Scholarship Committee at the above address.

3862 ■ NEW YORK WOMEN IN COMMUNICATIONS FOUNDATION
355 Lexington Ave., 15th Fl.
New York, NY 10017-6603
Tel: (212)297-2133
Fax: (212)370-9047
Web Site: http://www.nywici.org
To provide financial assistance for the education of the residents of NY, NJ, CT, or PA.
Title of Award: New York Women in Communications, Inc. Foundation Scholarships **Area, Field, or Subject:** Advertising; Broadcasting; Communications; Media arts; Journalism; Marketing and distribution; Media arts; Public relations. **Level of Education for which Award is Granted:** Graduate, Undergraduate **Funds Available:** No specific amount. **Duration:** One year.
Eligibility Requirements: Applicants must be high school seniors, or college undergraduate or graduate students who are permanent residents of NY, NJ, CT or PA majoring or declaring a major in a communications-related field, including but not limited to advertising, broadcasting, communications, English, film, journalism, marketing, new media, or public relations. Applicants must have an overall GPA of 3.2 or better (or the high school equivalent). **Application Requirements:** Applicants must submit completed application form and all other required application information and materials. **Deadline for Receipt:** January 30.

3863 ■ NORTH CAROLINA VENDING ASSOCIATION
2501 Aerial Center Pkwy., Ste. 103
Morrisville, NC 27560
Tel: (919)459-2070
Fax: (919)459-2075
E-mail: info@ncvend.com
Web Site: http://www.ncvend.com
To contribute to the educational advancement of North Carolina's young citizens.
Title of Award: North Carolina Vending Association Academic Scholarships **Area, Field, or Subject:** Business. **Level of Education for which Award is Granted:** Undergraduate **Funds Available:** $1,000.
Eligibility Requirements: Applicants must be entering or already enrolled in an advanced degree program. **Application Requirements:** Applicants must submit a completed application form. **Deadline for Receipt:** April 10.

3864 ■ ONTARIO TRUCKING ASSOCIATION
555 Dixon Rd.
Toronto, ON, Canada M9W 1H8
Tel: (416)249-7401
Fax: (416)245-6152
E-mail: info@ontruck.org
Web Site: http://www.ontruck.org
To assist the deserving students who demonstrate exemplary commitment to their academic studies and community.
Title of Award: Bison Transport Scholarships **Area, Field, or Subject:** Transportation; Logistics; Human resources; Business. **Level of Education for which Award is Granted:** Undergraduate **Funds Available:** $1,000. **Duration:** One year.
Eligibility Requirements: Applicant must be a postsecondary student who demonstrates an exemplary commitment to his/her academic studies and community; must be enrolled in full-time studies in Transportation, Logistics, Human resources, or a Business program at a recognized university or college in Canada. **Application Requirements:** Applicants must complete the Bison Transport Commitment to People Scholarship Statement of Volunteer Work/Community Services form; must attach a letter that explains how they help people in ways other than through volunteer/charitable work or community service; must submit an official transcript of their most recent marks; must include an essay of 500 words or less that explains what motivated them to embark on studies in their

chosen field and their career aspirations. **Deadline for Receipt:** August 15.

3865 ■ PARKERSBURG AREA COMMUNITY FOUNDATION

501 Avery St.
Parkersburg, WV 26101
Tel: (304)428-4438; (866)428-4438
Fax: (304)428-1200
E-mail: info@pacfwv.com
Web Site: http://www.pacfwv.com
To encourage graduating seniors of Wirt County High School to pursue their education.
Title of Award: Kenneth D. and Katherine D. Davis Scholarships **Area, Field, or Subject:** Business. **Level of Education for which Award is Granted:** Undergraduate **Funds Available:** $225.
Eligibility Requirements: Applicant must be a Wirt County High School graduating senior pursuing a career or major in business. **Application Requirements:** Applicants must submit a cover sheet (3 pages) and application form (4 pages); must have a personal essay; must have a high school and/or post- secondary transcript; must provide a letter of recommendation and a signed, copy of the page of their or their parent's most recent tax return that indicates adjusted gross income; and must have a Student Aid Report showing estimated family contribution from FAFSA. Application form and other supporting documents must be sent to Our Community's Foundation, P.O Box 1762, Parkersburg, WV 26102. **Deadline for Receipt:** March 20.

3866 ■ PARKERSBURG AREA COMMUNITY FOUNDATION

501 Avery St.
Parkersburg, WV 26101
Tel: (304)428-4438; (866)428-4438
Fax: (304)428-1200
E-mail: info@pacfwv.com
Web Site: http://www.pacfwv.com
To encourage graduating students to pursue their degree in the business or agriculture field.
Title of Award: Pat Shimp Memorial Scholarships **Area, Field, or Subject:** Business; Agriculture, Economic aspects. **Level of Education for which Award is Granted:** Undergraduate **Funds Available:** $500.
Eligibility Requirements: Applicant must be a Roane County High School graduating senior pursuing a degree in the business or agriculture field with a minimum of 2.0 GPA. **Application Requirements:** Applicants must submit a cover sheet (3 pages) and application form (4 pages); a personal essay; a high school and/or post-secondary transcript; a letter of recommendation; a signed copy of the page of their or their parent's most recent tax return that indicates adjusted gross income; and a Student Aid Report showing estimated family contribution from FAFSA. Application form and other supporting documents must be sent to Our Community's Foundation, P.O Box 1762, Parkersburg, WV 26102. **Deadline for Receipt:** March 20.

3867 ■ PARKERSBURG AREA COMMUNITY FOUNDATION

501 Avery St.
Parkersburg, WV 26101
Tel: (304)428-4438; (866)428-4438
Fax: (304)428-1200
E-mail: info@pacfwv.com
Web Site: http://www.pacfwv.com
To provide financial support for qualified individuals intending to pursue their education.
Title of Award: Glenn Wilson Broadcast Journalism Scholarships **Area, Field, or Subject:** Journalism; Communications; Marketing and distribution. **Level of Education for which Award is Granted:** Undergraduate **Funds Available:** $560.
Eligibility Requirements: Applicants must be current or previous Wood or Pleasant County, WV, or Washington County, OH, high school students; must be studying broadcast journalism, journalism, communications or marketing; and must have a minimum 2.5 GPA. **Application Requirements:** Applicants must submit a cover sheet (3 pages) and application form (4 pages); a personal essay; a high school and/or post-secondary transcript; a letter of recommendation; a signed copy of the page of their or their parent's most recent tax return that indicates adjusted gross income; and a Student Aid Report showing estimated fam-

ily contribution from FAFSA. Application form and other supporting documents must be sent to Our Community's Foundation, P.O Box 1762, Parkersburg, WV 26102. **Deadline for Receipt:** March 20.

3868 ■ PENNSYLVANIA STATE SYSTEM OF HIGHER EDUCATION FOUNDATION

2986 N 2nd St.
Harrisburg, PA 17110
Tel: (717)720-4086
Fax: (717)720-7082
Web Site: http://www.thepafoundation.org
To provide educational assistance to high school seniors graduating from a West Shore School District high school and planning to major in business or a related field at one of the State System universities.
Title of Award: Wayne G. Failor Scholarships **Area, Field, or Subject:** Business. **Level of Education for which Award is Granted:** High School **Funds Available:** No specific amount. **Duration:** One year.
Eligibility Requirements: Applicants must be students who are graduating seniors of a West Shore School District high school; full-time undergraduate students who plan to enroll at a State System university; must plan to major in business or a related field; must have a "B" average or better by the end of their junior year in high school. **Application Requirements:** Applicants must submit all the required application information. **Deadline for Receipt:** May 1.

3869 ■ PEPPERDINE UNIVERSITY SCHOOL OF LAW

24255 Pacific Coast Highway
Malibu, CA 90263
Tel: (310)506-4611
E-mail: soladmis@pepperdine.edu
Web Site: http://law.pepperdine.edu
To assist students at Pepperdine University School of Law.
Title of Award: JD/MBA Scholarships **Area, Field, or Subject:** Law; Business. **Level of Education for which Award is Granted:** Undergraduate **Funds Available:** No specific amount.
Eligibility Requirements: Applicant must be a student enrolled in the joint JD and MBA program at the School of Law and Graziadio School of Business and Management. Applicant must be in good standing in all areas of the University. **Application Requirements:** Applicants must submit a completed scholarship application form together with a resume and a letter of qualifications. **Deadline for Receipt:** October 31.

3870 ■ PHI CHI THETA

1508 E Beltline Rd., Ste. 104
Carrollton, TX 75006
Tel: (972)245-7202
E-mail: executivedirector@phichitheta.org
Web Site: http://www.phichitheta.org
To support students who have made a substantial contribution and impact to the organization or local community intending to pursue a degree in the fields of business and/or economics.
Title of Award: Anna E. Hall Memorial Scholarships **Area, Field, or Subject:** Business; Economics. **Level of Education for which Award is Granted:** Undergraduate **Funds Available:** $500.
Eligibility Requirements: Applicants must be national members of Phi Chi Theta in good standing; must be students who have completed at least one semester or two quarters of college in the United States and will be enrolled in and attending classes during the forthcoming academic year at an approved college or university in the United States (in pursuit of a degree in the fields of Business and/or Economics). **Application Requirements:** Applicants may visit the Phi Chi Theta Educational Foundation's website for application information and instructions. **Deadline for Receipt:** May 1.

3871 ■ PHI CHI THETA

1508 E Beltline Rd., Ste. 104
Carrollton, TX 75006
Tel: (972)245-7202
E-mail: executivedirector@phichitheta.org
Web Site: http://www.phichitheta.org
To support students who have made a substantial contribution and impact to the organization or local community pursuing a degree in the fields of business and/or economics.

Title of Award: Helen D. Snow Memorial Scholarships **Area, Field, or Subject:** Business; Economics. **Level of Education for which Award is Granted:** Undergraduate **Funds Available:** $500.
Eligibility Requirements: Applicants must be national members of Phi Chi Theta in good standing; must be students who have completed at least one semester or two quarters of college in the United States and will be enrolled in and attending classes during the forthcoming academic year at an approved college or university in the United States in pursuit of a degree in the fields of business and/or economics. **Application Requirements:** Applicants may visit the Phi Chi Theta Educational Foundation's website for application information and instructions. **Deadline for Receipt:** May 1.

3872 ■ PHI SIGMA EPSILON
3747 S Howell Ave.
Milwaukee, WI 53207
Tel: (414)328-1952
Free: 800-761-9350
Fax: (414)328-1953
E-mail: pse@pse.org
Web Site: http://www.pse.org
To advance education of Pi Sigma Epsilon student member in sales and marketing.
Title of Award: Anchor Plastics Scholarships **Area, Field, or Subject:** Marketing and distribution. **Level of Education for which Award is Granted:** Graduate, Undergraduate **Number Awarded:** 1. **Funds Available:** $1000.
Eligibility Requirements: Applicant must be enrolled in an undergraduate program and working toward an undergraduate degree with at least one semester, two quarters or summer session left before graduation; or enrolled or planning to enroll in a Graduate Program and working toward a post graduate degree (such as an MBA) with at least one semester, two quarters or summer session left before graduation; or a graduating senior with outstanding loans to his/her university. **Application Requirements:** Applicants must submit a completed application form together with a one page description of qualifications (Pi Sigma Epsilon activities; Mu Kappa Tau activities; Career objectives; Educational goals; Campus/Community activities; Special achievements/awards; Employment history; Percent of education financed by self, parents, scholarships, other); and two letters of recommendation. send materials electronically to scholarships@pse. org. **Additional Information:** Sponsored by Anchor Plastics. **Deadline for Receipt:** January 18.

3873 ■ PHI SIGMA EPSILON
3747 S Howell Ave.
Milwaukee, WI 53207
Tel: (414)328-1952
Free: 800-761-9350
Fax: (414)328-1953
E-mail: pse@pse.org
Web Site: http://www.pse.org
To advance education of Pi Sigma Epsilon student member in sales and marketing.
Title of Award: Anheuser-Busch International Scholarships **Area, Field, or Subject:** Marketing and distribution. **Level of Education for which Award is Granted:** Graduate, Undergraduate **Number Awarded:** 1. **Funds Available:** $1500.
Eligibility Requirements: Applicant must be enrolled in an undergraduate program and working toward an undergraduate degree with at least one semester, two quarters or summer session left before graduation; or enrolled or planning to enroll in a Graduate Program and working toward a post graduate degree (such as an MBA) with at least one semester, two quarters or summer session left before graduation; or a graduating senior with outstanding loans to his/her university. **Application Requirements:** Applicants must submit a completed application form together with a one page description of qualifications (Pi Sigma Epsilon activities; Mu Kappa Tau activities; Career objectives; Educational goals; Campus/Community activities; Special achievements/awards; Employment history; Percent of education financed by self, parents, scholarships, other); and two letters of recommendation. send materials electronically to scholarships@pse. org. **Additional Information:** Sponsored by Anheuser-Busch. **Deadline for Receipt:** January 18.

3874 ■ PHI SIGMA EPSILON
3747 S Howell Ave.
Milwaukee, WI 53207
Tel: (414)328-1952
Free: 800-761-9350
Fax: (414)328-1953
E-mail: pse@pse.org
Web Site: http://www.pse.org
To advance education of Pi Sigma Epsilon student member in sales and marketing.
Title of Award: Enterprise Rent-A-Car Scholarships **Area, Field, or Subject:** Marketing and distribution. **Level of Education for which Award is Granted:** Graduate, Undergraduate **Number Awarded:** 1. **Funds Available:** $1500.
Eligibility Requirements: Applicant must be enrolled in an undergraduate program and working toward an undergraduate degree with at least one semester, two quarters or summer session left before graduation; or enrolled or planning to enroll in a Graduate Program and working toward a post graduate degree (such as an MBA) with at least one semester, two quarters or summer session left before graduation; or a graduating senior with outstanding loans to his/her university. **Application Requirements:** Applicants must submit a completed application form together with a one page description of qualifications (Pi Sigma Epsilon activities; Mu Kappa Tau activities; Career objectives; Educational goals; Campus/Community activities; Special achievements/awards; Employment history; Percent of education financed by self, parents, scholarships, other); and two letters of recommendation. send materials electronically to scholarships@pse. org. **Additional Information:** Sponsored by Enterprise Rent-A-Car. **Deadline for Receipt:** January 18.

3875 ■ PHI SIGMA EPSILON
3747 S Howell Ave.
Milwaukee, WI 53207
Tel: (414)328-1952
Free: 800-761-9350
Fax: (414)328-1953
E-mail: pse@pse.org
Web Site: http://www.pse.org
To advance education of Pi Sigma Epsilon student member in sales and marketing.
Title of Award: Federated Insurance Scholarships **Area, Field, or Subject:** Marketing and distribution. **Level of Education for which Award is Granted:** Graduate, Undergraduate **Number Awarded:** 1. **Funds Available:** $1000.
Eligibility Requirements: Applicant must be enrolled in an undergraduate program and working toward an undergraduate degree with at least one semester, two quarters or summer session left before graduation; or enrolled or planning to enroll in a Graduate Program and working toward a post graduate degree (such as an MBA) with at least one semester, two quarters or summer session left before graduation; or a graduating senior with outstanding loans to his/her university. **Application Requirements:** Applicants must submit a completed application form together with a one page description of qualifications (Pi Sigma Epsilon activities; Mu Kappa Tau activities; Career objectives; Educational goals; Campus/Community activities; Special achievements/awards; Employment history; Percent of education financed by self, parents, scholarships, other); and two letters of recommendation. send materials electronically to scholarships@pse. org. **Additional Information:** Sponsored by Federated Insurance. **Deadline for Receipt:** January 18.

3876 ■ PHI SIGMA EPSILON
3747 S Howell Ave.
Milwaukee, WI 53207
Tel: (414)328-1952
Free: 800-761-9350
Fax: (414)328-1953
E-mail: pse@pse.org
Web Site: http://www.pse.org
To advance education of Pi Sigma Epsilon student member in sales and marketing.
Title of Award: William H. Harris Memorial Scholarships **Area, Field, or Subject:** Marketing and distribution. **Level of Education for which Award is Granted:** Graduate, Undergraduate **Number Awarded:** 1. **Funds Available:** $1500.

Eligibility Requirements: Applicant must be enrolled in an undergraduate program and working toward an undergraduate degree with at least one semester, two quarters or summer session left before graduation; or enrolled or planning to enroll in a Graduate Program and working toward a post graduate degree (such as an MBA) with at least one semester, two quarters or summer session left before graduation; or a graduating senior with outstanding loans to his/her university. **Application Requirements:** Applicants must submit a completed application form together with a one page description of qualifications (Pi Sigma Epsilon activities; Mu Kappa Tau activities; Career objectives; Educational goals; Campus/Community activities; Special achievements/awards; Employment history; Percent of education financed by self, parents, scholarships, other); and two letters of recommendation. send materials electronically to scholarships@pse. org. **Additional Information:** In memory of PSE co-founder, William H. Harris. **Deadline for Receipt:** January 18.

3877 ■ PHI SIGMA EPSILON
3747 S Howell Ave.
Milwaukee, WI 53207
Tel: (414)328-1952
Free: 800-761-9350
Fax: (414)328-1953
E-mail: pse@pse.org
Web Site: http://www.pse.org
To advance education of Pi Sigma Epsilon student member in sales and marketing.
Title of Award: Debbie Khalil Memorial Scholarships **Area, Field, or Subject:** Marketing and distribution. **Level of Education for which Award is Granted:** Graduate, Undergraduate **Number Awarded:** 1. **Funds Available:** $1500.
Eligibility Requirements: Applicant must be enrolled in an undergraduate program and working toward an undergraduate degree with at least one semester, two quarters or summer session left before graduation; or enrolled or planning to enroll in a Graduate Program and working toward a post graduate degree (such as an MBA) with at least one semester, two quarters or summer session left before graduation; or a graduating senior with outstanding loans to his/her university. **Application Requirements:** Applicants must submit a completed application form together with a one page description of qualifications (Pi Sigma Epsilon activities; Mu Kappa Tau activities; Career objectives; Educational goals; Campus/Community activities; Special achievements/awards; Employment history; Percent of education financed by self, parents, scholarships, other); and two letters of recommendation. send materials electronically to scholarships@pse. org. **Additional Information:** In memory of Debbie Khalil. **Deadline for Receipt:** January 18.

3878 ■ PHI SIGMA EPSILON
3747 S Howell Ave.
Milwaukee, WI 53207
Tel: (414)328-1952
Free: 800-761-9350
Fax: (414)328-1953
E-mail: pse@pse.org
Web Site: http://www.pse.org
To advance education of Pi Sigma Epsilon student member in sales and marketing.
Title of Award: Mach 1 Air Services Scholarships **Area, Field, or Subject:** Marketing and distribution. **Level of Education for which Award is Granted:** Graduate, Undergraduate **Number Awarded:** 1. **Funds Available:** $2000.
Eligibility Requirements: Applicant must be enrolled in an undergraduate program and working toward an undergraduate degree with at least one semester, two quarters or summer session left before graduation; or enrolled or planning to enroll in a Graduate Program and working toward a post graduate degree (such as an MBA) with at least one semester, two quarters or summer session left before graduation; or a graduating senior with outstanding loans to his/her university. **Application Requirements:** Applicants must submit a completed application form together with a one page description of qualifications (Pi Sigma Epsilon activities; Mu Kappa Tau activities; Career objectives; Educational goals; Campus/Community activities; Special achievements/awards; Employment history; Percent of education financed by self, parents, scholarships, other); and two letters of recommendation. send materials electronically to scholarships@pse.

org. **Additional Information:** Sponsored by Mach 1 Air Services. **Deadline for Receipt:** January 18.

3879 ■ PHI SIGMA EPSILON
3747 S Howell Ave.
Milwaukee, WI 53207
Tel: (414)328-1952
Free: 800-761-9350
Fax: (414)328-1953
E-mail: pse@pse.org
Web Site: http://www.pse.org
To advance education of Pi Sigma Epsilon student member in sales and marketing.
Title of Award: MPower Scholarships **Area, Field, or Subject:** Marketing and distribution. **Level of Education for which Award is Granted:** Graduate, Undergraduate **Number Awarded:** 1. **Funds Available:** $1000.
Eligibility Requirements: Applicant must be enrolled in an undergraduate program and working toward an undergraduate degree with at least one semester, two quarters or summer session left before graduation; or enrolled or planning to enroll in a Graduate Program and working toward a post graduate degree (such as an MBA) with at least one semester, two quarters or summer session left before graduation; or a graduating senior with outstanding loans to his/her university. **Application Requirements:** Applicants must submit a completed application form together with a one page description of qualifications (Pi Sigma Epsilon activities; Mu Kappa Tau activities; Career objectives; Educational goals; Campus/Community activities; Special achievements/awards; Employment history; Percent of education financed by self, parents, scholarships, other); and two letters of recommendation. send materials electronically to scholarships@pse. org. **Additional Information:** Sponsored by MPower. **Deadline for Receipt:** January 18.

3880 ■ PHI SIGMA EPSILON
3747 S Howell Ave.
Milwaukee, WI 53207
Tel: (414)328-1952
Free: 800-761-9350
Fax: (414)328-1953
E-mail: pse@pse.org
Web Site: http://www.pse.org
To advance education of Pi Sigma Epsilon student member in sales and marketing.
Title of Award: Northwestern Mutual Financial Network Scholarships **Area, Field, or Subject:** Marketing and distribution. **Level of Education for which Award is Granted:** Graduate, Undergraduate **Number Awarded:** 1. **Funds Available:** $1500.
Eligibility Requirements: Applicant must be enrolled in an undergraduate program and working toward an undergraduate degree with at least one semester, two quarters or summer session left before graduation; or enrolled or planning to enroll in a Graduate Program and working toward a post graduate degree (such as an MBA) with at least one semester, two quarters or summer session left before graduation; or a graduating senior with outstanding loans to his/her university. **Application Requirements:** Applicants must submit a completed application form together with a one page description of qualifications (Pi Sigma Epsilon activities; Mu Kappa Tau activities; Career objectives; Educational goals; Campus/Community activities; Special achievements/awards; Employment history; Percent of education financed by self, parents, scholarships, other); and two letters of recommendation. send materials electronically to scholarships@pse. org. **Additional Information:** Sponsored by Northwestern Mutual Life Insurance Company. **Deadline for Receipt:** January 18.

3881 ■ PHI SIGMA EPSILON
3747 S Howell Ave.
Milwaukee, WI 53207
Tel: (414)328-1952
Free: 800-761-9350
Fax: (414)328-1953
E-mail: pse@pse.org
Web Site: http://www.pse.org
To advance education of Pi Sigma Epsilon student member in sales and marketing.

Title of Award: Phi Sigma Epsilon Innovation Scholarships **Area, Field, or Subject:** Marketing and distribution. **Level of Education for which Award is Granted:** Graduate, Undergraduate **Number Awarded:** 1. **Funds Available:** $1500.
Eligibility Requirements: Applicant must be enrolled in an undergraduate program and working toward an undergraduate degree with at least one semester, two quarters or summer session left before graduation; or enrolled or planning to enroll in a Graduate Program and working toward a post graduate degree (such as an MBA) with at least one semester, two quarters or summer session left before graduation; or a graduating senior with outstanding loans to his/her university. **Application Requirements:** Applicants must submit a completed application form together with a one page description of qualifications (Pi Sigma Epsilon activities; Mu Kappa Tau activities; Career objectives; Educational goals; Campus/Community activities; Special achievements/awards; Employment history; Percent of education financed by self, parents, scholarships, other); and two letters of recommendation. send materials electronically to scholarships@pse. org. **Additional Information:** Presented by 3M Corporation. **Deadline for Receipt:** January 18.

3882 ■ PHI SIGMA EPSILON
3747 S Howell Ave.
Milwaukee, WI 53207
Tel: (414)328-1952
Free: 800-761-9350
Fax: (414)328-1953
E-mail: pse@pse.org
Web Site: http://www.pse.org
To advance education of Pi Sigma Epsilon student member in sales and marketing.
Title of Award: Phi Sigma Epsilon Past National President Scholarships **Area, Field, or Subject:** Marketing and distribution. **Level of Education for which Award is Granted:** Graduate, Undergraduate **Number Awarded:** 1. **Funds Available:** $1500.
Eligibility Requirements: Applicant must be enrolled in an undergraduate program and working toward an undergraduate degree with at least one semester, two quarters or summer session left before graduation; or enrolled or planning to enroll in a Graduate Program and working toward a post graduate degree (such as an MBA) with at least one semester, two quarters or summer session left before graduation; or a graduating senior with outstanding loans to his/her university. **Application Requirements:** Applicants must submit a completed application form together with a one page description of qualifications (Pi Sigma Epsilon activities; Mu Kappa Tau activities; Career objectives; Educational goals; Campus/Community activities; Special achievements/awards; Employment history; Percent of education financed by self, parents, scholarships, other); and two letters of recommendation. send materials electronically to scholarships@pse. org. **Additional Information:** Contributions came from past PSE National Presidents. **Deadline for Receipt:** January 18.

3883 ■ PHI SIGMA EPSILON
3747 S Howell Ave.
Milwaukee, WI 53207
Tel: (414)328-1952
Free: 800-761-9350
Fax: (414)328-1953
E-mail: pse@pse.org
Web Site: http://www.pse.org
To assist in the development of future sales and marketing professionals.
Title of Award: Sales and Marketing Executives International Scholarships **Area, Field, or Subject:** Marketing and distribution. **Level of Education for which Award is Granted:** Graduate, Undergraduate **Number Awarded:** 1. **Funds Available:** $1500.
Eligibility Requirements: Applicant must be enrolled in an undergraduate program and working toward an undergraduate degree with at least one semester, two quarters or summer session left before graduation; or enrolled or planning to enroll in a Graduate Program and working toward a post graduate degree (such as an MBA) with at least one semester, two quarters or summer session left before graduation; or a graduating senior with outstanding loans to his/her university. **Application Requirements:** Applicants must submit a completed application form together with a one page description of qualifications (Pi Sigma Epsilon activities; Mu Kappa Tau activities; Career objectives; Educational goals; Campus/Community

activities; Special achievements/awards; Employment history; Percent of education financed by self, parents, scholarships, other); and two letters of recommendation. send materials electronically to scholarships@pse. org. **Additional Information:** Sponsored by Sales and Marketing Executives International. **Deadline for Receipt:** January 18.

3884 ■ PHI SIGMA EPSILON
3747 S Howell Ave.
Milwaukee, WI 53207
Tel: (414)328-1952
Free: 800-761-9350
Fax: (414)328-1953
E-mail: pse@pse.org
Web Site: http://www.pse.org
To advance education of Pi Sigma Epsilon student member in sales and marketing.
Title of Award: The Standard Scholarships **Area, Field, or Subject:** Marketing and distribution. **Level of Education for which Award is Granted:** Graduate, Undergraduate **Number Awarded:** 1. **Funds Available:** $1000.
Eligibility Requirements: Applicant must be enrolled in an undergraduate program and working toward an undergraduate degree with at least one semester, two quarters or summer session left before graduation; or enrolled or planning to enroll in a Graduate Program and working toward a post graduate degree (such as an MBA) with at least one semester, two quarters or summer session left before graduation; or a graduating senior with outstanding loans to his/her university. **Application Requirements:** Applicants must submit a completed application form together with a one page description of qualifications (Pi Sigma Epsilon activities; Mu Kappa Tau activities; Career objectives; Educational goals; Campus/Community activities; Special achievements/awards; Employment history; Percent of education financed by self, parents, scholarships, other); and two letters of recommendation. send materials electronically to scholarships@pse. org. **Additional Information:** Sponsored by The Standard. **Deadline for Receipt:** January 18.

3885 ■ PHI SIGMA EPSILON
3747 S Howell Ave.
Milwaukee, WI 53207
Tel: (414)328-1952
Free: 800-761-9350
Fax: (414)328-1953
E-mail: pse@pse.org
Web Site: http://www.pse.org
To advance education of Pi Sigma Epsilon student member in sales and marketing.
Title of Award: Student Media Group Scholarships **Area, Field, or Subject:** Marketing and distribution. **Level of Education for which Award is Granted:** Graduate, Undergraduate **Number Awarded:** 1. **Funds Available:** $1000.
Eligibility Requirements: Applicant must be enrolled in an undergraduate program and working toward an undergraduate degree with at least one semester, two quarters or summer session left before graduation; or enrolled or planning to enroll in a Graduate Program and working toward a post graduate degree (such as an MBA) with at least one semester, two quarters or summer session left before graduation; or a graduating senior with outstanding loans to his/her university. **Application Requirements:** Applicants must submit a completed application form together with a one page description of qualifications (Pi Sigma Epsilon activities; Mu Kappa Tau activities; Career objectives; Educational goals; Campus/Community activities; Special achievements/awards; Employment history; Percent of education financed by self, parents, scholarships, other); and two letters of recommendation. send materials electronically to scholarships@pse. org. **Additional Information:** Sponsored by Student Media Group. **Deadline for Receipt:** January 18.

3886 ■ PHI SIGMA EPSILON
3747 S Howell Ave.
Milwaukee, WI 53207
Tel: (414)328-1952
Free: 800-761-9350
Fax: (414)328-1953
E-mail: pse@pse.org

Web Site: http://www.pse.org
To advance education of Pi Sigma Epsilon student member in sales and marketing.
Title of Award: Swivel Media Scholarships **Area, Field, or Subject:** Marketing and distribution. **Level of Education for which Award is Granted:** Graduate, Undergraduate **Number Awarded:** 1. **Funds Available:** $2000.
Eligibility Requirements: Applicant must be enrolled in an undergraduate program and working toward an undergraduate degree with at least one semester, two quarters or summer session left before graduation; or enrolled or planning to enroll in a Graduate Program and working toward a post graduate degree (such as an MBA) with at least one semester, two quarters or summer session left before graduation; or a graduating senior with outstanding loans to his/her university. **Application Requirements:** Applicants must submit a completed application form together with a one page description qualifications (Pi Sigma Epsilon activities; Mu Kappa Tau activities; Career objectives; Educational goals; Campus/Community activities; Special achievements/awards; Employment history; Percent of education financed by self, parents, scholarships, other); and two letters of recommendation. send materials electronically to scholarships@pse.org. **Additional Information:** Sponsored by Swivel Media. **Deadline for Receipt:** January 18.

3887 ■ PHI SIGMA EPSILON
3747 S Howell Ave.
Milwaukee, WI 53207
Tel: (414)328-1952
Free: 800-761-9350
Fax: (414)328-1953
E-mail: pse@pse.org
Web Site: http://www.pse.org
To advance education of Pi Sigma Epsilon student member in sales and marketing.
Title of Award: Thrivent Financial Scholarships **Area, Field, or Subject:** Marketing and distribution. **Level of Education for which Award is Granted:** Graduate, Undergraduate **Number Awarded:** 1. **Funds Available:** $1000.
Eligibility Requirements: Applicant must be enrolled in an undergraduate program and working toward an undergraduate degree with at least one semester, two quarters or summer session left before graduation; or enrolled or planning to enroll in a Graduate Program and working toward a post graduate degree (such as an MBA) with at least one semester, two quarters or summer session left before graduation; or a graduating senior with outstanding loans to his/her university. **Application Requirements:** Applicants must submit a completed application form together with a one page description of qualifications (Pi Sigma Epsilon activities; Mu Kappa Tau activities; Career objectives; Educational goals; Campus/Community activities; Special achievements/awards; Employment history; Percent of education financed by self, parents, scholarships, other); and two letters of recommendation. send materials electronically to scholarships@pse.org. **Additional Information:** Sponsored by Thrivent Financial. **Deadline for Receipt:** January 18.

3888 ■ PHI SIGMA EPSILON
3747 S Howell Ave.
Milwaukee, WI 53207
Tel: (414)328-1952
Free: 800-761-9350
Fax: (414)328-1953
E-mail: pse@pse.org
Web Site: http://www.pse.org
To advance education of Pi Sigma Epsilon student member in sales and marketing.
Title of Award: Valpak Scholarships **Area, Field, or Subject:** Marketing and distribution. **Level of Education for which Award is Granted:** Graduate, Undergraduate **Number Awarded:** 1. **Funds Available:** $1500.
Eligibility Requirements: Applicant must be enrolled in an undergraduate program and working toward an undergraduate degree with at least one semester, two quarters or summer session left before graduation; or enrolled or planning to enroll in a Graduate Program and working toward a post graduate degree (such as an MBA) with at least one semester, two quarters or summer session left before graduation; or a graduating senior

with outstanding loans to his/her university. **Application Requirements:** Applicants must submit a completed application form together with a one page description of qualifications (Pi Sigma Epsilon activities; Mu Kappa Tau activities; Career objectives; Educational goals; Campus/Community activities; Special achievements/awards; Employment history; Percent of education financed by self, parents, scholarships, other); and two letters of recommendation. send materials electronically to scholarships@pse.org. **Additional Information:** Sponsored by Valpak. **Deadline for Receipt:** January 18.

3889 ■ PHI SIGMA EPSILON
3747 S Howell Ave.
Milwaukee, WI 53207
Tel: (414)328-1952
Free: 800-761-9350
Fax: (414)328-1953
E-mail: pse@pse.org
Web Site: http://www.pse.org
To advance education of Pi Sigma Epsilon student member in sales and marketing.
Title of Award: Vector Marketing Scholarships **Area, Field, or Subject:** Marketing and distribution. **Level of Education for which Award is Granted:** Graduate, Undergraduate **Number Awarded:** 1. **Funds Available:** $1000.
Eligibility Requirements: Applicant must be enrolled in an undergraduate program and working toward an undergraduate degree with at least one semester, two quarters or summer session left before graduation; or enrolled or planning to enroll in a Graduate Program and working toward a post graduate degree (such as an MBA) with at least one semester, two quarters or summer session left before graduation; or a graduating senior with outstanding loans to his/her university. **Application Requirements:** Applicants must submit a completed application form together with a one page description of qualifications (Pi Sigma Epsilon activities; Mu Kappa Tau activities; Career objectives; Educational goals; Campus/Community activities; Special achievements/awards; Employment history; Percent of education financed by self, parents, scholarships, other); and two letters of recommendation. send materials electronically to scholarships@pse.org. **Additional Information:** Sponsored by Vector Marketing. **Deadline for Receipt:** January 18.

3890 ■ PHI SIGMA EPSILON
3747 S Howell Ave.
Milwaukee, WI 53207
Tel: (414)328-1952
Free: 800-761-9350
Fax: (414)328-1953
E-mail: pse@pse.org
Web Site: http://www.pse.org
To advance education of Pi Sigma Epsilon student member in sales and marketing.
Title of Award: Whan Memorial Scholarships **Area, Field, or Subject:** Marketing and distribution. **Level of Education for which Award is Granted:** Graduate, Undergraduate **Number Awarded:** 2. **Funds Available:** $1500.
Eligibility Requirements: Applicant must be enrolled in an undergraduate program and working toward an undergraduate degree with at least one semester, two quarters or summer session left before graduation; or enrolled or planning to enroll in a Graduate Program and working toward a post graduate degree (such as a MBA) with at least one semester, two quarters or summer session left before graduation; or a graduating senior with outstanding loans to his/her university. **Application Requirements:** Applicants must submit a completed application form together with a one page description of qualifications (Pi Sigma Epsilon activities; Mu Kappa Tau activities; Career objectives; Educational goals; Campus/Community activities; Special achievements/awards; Employment history; Percent of education financed by self, parents, scholarships, other); and two letters of recommendation. send materials electronically to scholarships@pse.org. **Additional Information:** In memory of Tony Whan, Past President of Sales & Marketing Executives International. **Deadline for Receipt:** January 18.

3891 ■ PHI SIGMA EPSILON
3747 S Howell Ave.
Milwaukee, WI 53207

Tel: (414)328-1952
Free: 800-761-9350
Fax: (414)328-1953
E-mail: pse@pse.org
Web Site: http://www.pse.org
To advance education of Pi Sigma Epsilon student member in sales and marketing.
Title of Award: Xilinx Scholarships **Area, Field, or Subject:** Marketing and distribution. **Level of Education for which Award is Granted:** Graduate, Undergraduate **Number Awarded:** 1. **Funds Available:** $1000.
Eligibility Requirements: Applicant must be enrolled in an undergraduate program and working toward an undergraduate degree with at least one semester, two quarters or summer session left before graduation; or enrolled or planning to enroll in a Graduate Program and working toward a post graduate degree (such as an MBA) with at least one semester, two quarters or summer session left before graduation; or a graduating senior with outstanding loans to his/her university. **Application Requirements:** Applicants must submit a completed application form together with a one page description of qualifications (Pi Sigma Epsilon activities; Mu Kappa Tau activities; Career objectives; Educational goals; Campus/Community activities; Special achievements/awards; Employment history; Percent of education financed by self, parents, scholarships, other); and two letters of recommendation. send materials electronically to scholarships@pse.org. **Additional Information:** Sponsored by Xilinx. **Deadline for Receipt:** January 18.

3892 ■ PINNACLE WEST CAPITAL CORPORATION
PO Box 53999
Phoenix, AZ 85072-3999
Tel: (602)250-1000
Free: 800-457-2983
Web Site: http://www.pinnaclewest.com
To provide financial assistance to qualified individuals who want to pursue their career.
Title of Award: APS/ASU Scholarships **Area, Field, or Subject:** Chemical engineering; Electrical engineering; Mechanical engineering; Civil engineering; Construction; Telecommunications systems; Accounting; Finance; Economics; Information science and technology; Education, Elementary; Education, Secondary; Special education; Nursing. **Level of Education for which Award is Granted:** Undergraduate **Number Awarded:** 10. **Funds Available:** $2,000. **Duration:** One year.
Eligibility Requirements: Applicant must be an Arizona resident; must have a cumulative GPA of at least 3.0; must demonstrate financial need. **Application Requirements:** Applicant must complete the application form available online and send it to ASU Scholarship Office, Arizona State University, PO Box 470412, Tempe, AZ 85287-0412. **Deadline for Receipt:** March 1. **Additional Information:** Louise Moskowitz at louise.moskowitz@aps.com.

3893 ■ PINNACLE WEST CAPITAL CORPORATION
PO Box 53999
Phoenix, AZ 85072-3999
Tel: (602)250-1000
Free: 800-457-2983
Web Site: http://www.pinnaclewest.com
To provide financial assistance to qualified individuals who want to pursue their career.
Title of Award: APS/Maricopa County Community Colleges Scholarships **Area, Field, or Subject:** Mechanical engineering; Electrical engineering; Civil engineering; Chemical engineering; Trades training; Information science and technology; Marketing and distribution; Accounting; Finance; Economics; Management; Education; Health care services. **Level of Education for which Award is Granted:** Undergraduate **Number Awarded:** 25. **Funds Available:** $1,000. **Duration:** One year.
Eligibility Requirements: Applicant must be an Arizona resident; must have a cumulative GPA of at least 3.0; must demonstrate financial need; must be a high school senior or current Maricopa Community College student; must be enrolled in a minimum of nine credit hours per semester. **Application Requirements:** Applicant must complete the application form available online and must be sent to ASU Scholarship Office, Arizona State University, PO Box 470412, Tempe, AZ 85287-0412. **Additional Information:** Louise Moskowitz at louise.moskowitz@aps.com.

3894 ■ PLUMBING-HEATING-COOLING CONTRACTORS ASSOCIATION
PO Box 6808
Falls Church, VA 22046
Tel: (703)237-8100
Free: 800-533-7694
Fax: (703)237-7442
E-mail: naphcc@naphcc.org
Web Site: http://www.phccweb.org
To establish a framework for the industry's first apprenticeship system and to spearhead education programs to keep pace with technological change.
Title of Award: American Standard Scholarships **Area, Field, or Subject:** Business. **Level of Education for which Award is Granted:** Undergraduate **Number Awarded:** 4. **Funds Available:** $2,500.
Eligibility Requirements: Applicants must be citizens of the United States or Canada and must be in a full-time undergraduate degree program at an accredited four-year college or university with a major directly relating to plumbing-heating-cooling profession. **Application Requirements:** Applicants must complete the application form and submit an official transcript of the high school grades; letter of recommendation from high school principal or counselor, college/university dean, academic advisor, or apprentice program instructor; SAT and ACT scores and cumulative GPA; and a letter of recommendation from an active member of the plumbing-heating-cooling contractors. **Deadline for Receipt:** May 1.

3895 ■ PLUMBING-HEATING-COOLING CONTRACTORS ASSOCIATION
PO Box 6808
Falls Church, VA 22046
Tel: (703)237-8100
Free: 800-533-7694
Fax: (703)237-7442
E-mail: naphcc@naphcc.org
Web Site: http://www.phccweb.org
To establish a framework for the industry's first apprenticeship system and to spearhead education programs to keep pace with technological change.
Title of Award: Delta Faucet Scholarships **Area, Field, or Subject:** Business. **Level of Education for which Award is Granted:** Undergraduate **Number Awarded:** 6. **Funds Available:** $2,500.
Eligibility Requirements: Applicants must be citizens of the United States or Canada and currently enrolled in or planning to enroll in plumbing, heating, cooling contractors; or must be enrolled full-time in an undergraduate degree program at an accredited four-year college or university with a major directly relating to the plumbing-heating-cooling profession. **Application Requirements:** Applicants must complete the application form; must submit an official transcript of the high school grades; letter of recommendation from high school principal or counselor, college/university dean, academic advisor, or apprentice program instructor; SAT and ACT scores and cumulative GPA. **Deadline for Receipt:** May 1.

3896 ■ PLUMBING-HEATING-COOLING CONTRACTORS ASSOCIATION
PO Box 6808
Falls Church, VA 22046
Tel: (703)237-8100
Free: 800-533-7694
Fax: (703)237-7442
E-mail: naphcc@naphcc.org
Web Site: http://www.phccweb.org
To establish a framework for the industry's first apprenticeship system and to spearhead educational programs to keep pace with technological change.
Title of Award: Plumbing-Heating-Cooling Contractors Association Educational Foundation Massachusetts Auxiliary Scholarships **Area, Field, or Subject:** Business. **Level of Education for which Award is Granted:** Undergraduate **Number Awarded:** 1. **Funds Available:** $1,500.
Eligibility Requirements: Applicants must be high school seniors who are citizens of the United States and residents of the Commonwealth of

Massachusetts, planning to enroll in a full-time undergraduate degree program at an accredited four-year college or university. **Application Requirements:** Applicants must complete the application form and submit an official transcript of high school grades; letter of recommendation from high school principal or counselor; SAT and ACT scores and cumulative GPA; and a letter of recommendation from an active member of the Plumbing-Heating-Cooling Contractors Association National Auxiliary. **Deadline for Receipt:** May 1.

3897 ■ PLUMBING-HEATING-COOLING CONTRACTORS ASSOCIATION
PO Box 6808
Falls Church, VA 22046
Tel: (703)237-8100
Free: 800-533-7694
Fax: (703)237-7442
E-mail: naphcc@naphcc.org
Web Site: http://www.phccweb.org
To establish a framework for the industry's first apprenticeship system and to spearhead educational programs to keep pace with technological change.
Title of Award: Plumbing-Heating-Cooling Contractors Association Educational Foundation Need-Based Scholarships **Area, Field, or Subject:** Business. **Level of Education for which Award is Granted:** Undergraduate **Number Awarded:** 1. **Funds Available:** $2,500.
Eligibility Requirements: Applicants must be citizens of the United States or Canada planning to enroll in a full-time undergraduate degree program at an accredited four-year college or university. **Application Requirements:** Applicants must complete the application form and submit an official transcript of high school grades; letter of recommendation from high school principal or counselor; SAT and ACT scores and cumulative GPA; and a letter of recommendation from an active member of the Plumbing-Heating-Cooling Contractors Association National Association. **Deadline for Receipt:** May 1.

3898 ■ PLUMBING-HEATING-COOLING CONTRACTORS ASSOCIATION
PO Box 6808
Falls Church, VA 22046
Tel: (703)237-8100
Free: 800-533-7694
Fax: (703)237-7442
E-mail: naphcc@naphcc.org
Web Site: http://www.phccweb.org
To establish a framework for the industry's first apprenticeship system and to spearhead educational programs to keep pace with technological change.
Title of Award: Plumbing-Heating-Cooling Contractors Association Educational Foundation Scholarships **Area, Field, or Subject:** Business. **Level of Education for which Award is Granted:** Undergraduate **Number Awarded:** 5. **Funds Available:** $3,000; $12,000.
Eligibility Requirements: Applicants must be citizens of the United States or Canada and are planning to enroll in a full-time undergraduate degree program at an accredited four-year college or university. **Application Requirements:** Applicants must complete the application form and submit an official transcript of the high school grades; letter of recommendation from high school principal or counselor; SAT and ACT scores and cumulative GPA; and a letter of recommendation from an active member of the Plumbing-Heating-Cooling Contractors Association National Association. **Deadline for Receipt:** May 1.

3899 ■ PLUMBING-HEATING-COOLING CONTRACTORS ASSOCIATION
PO Box 6808
Falls Church, VA 22046
Tel: (703)237-8100
Free: 800-533-7694
Fax: (703)237-7442
E-mail: naphcc@naphcc.org
Web Site: http://www.phccweb.org
To establish a framework for the industry's first apprenticeship system and to spearhead education programs to keep pace with technological change.

Title of Award: A.O. Smith Scholarships **Area, Field, or Subject:** Business. **Level of Education for which Award is Granted:** Undergraduate **Number Awarded:** 2. **Funds Available:** $2,500.
Eligibility Requirements: Applicants must be citizens of the United States or Canada and must be enrolled full-time in an undergraduate degree program at an accredited four-year college or university with a major directly to plumbing-heating-cooling profession. **Application Requirements:** Applicants must complete the application form and must submit an official transcript of the high school grades; letter of recommendation from high school principal or counselor, college/university dean, academic advisor, or apprentice program instructor; SAT and ACT scores as well as cumulative GPA; and a letter of recommendation from an active member of the plumbing-heating-cooling contractors. **Deadline for Receipt:** May 1.

3900 ■ PLUMBING-HEATING-COOLING CONTRACTORS ASSOCIATION
PO Box 6808
Falls Church, VA 22046
Tel: (703)237-8100
Free: 800-533-7694
Fax: (703)237-7442
E-mail: naphcc@naphcc.org
Web Site: http://www.phccweb.org
To establish a framework for the industry's first apprenticeship system and to spearhead education programs to keep pace with technological change.
Title of Award: Bradford White Scholarships **Area, Field, or Subject:** Business. **Level of Education for which Award is Granted:** Undergraduate **Number Awarded:** 3. **Funds Available:** $2,500.
Eligibility Requirements: Applicants must be citizens of the United States or Canada and must be enrolled full-time in an undergraduate degree program at an accredited two-year community college, technical college or trade school with a major directly related to the plumbing-heating-cooling profession. **Application Requirements:** Applicants must complete the application form and submit an official transcript of the high school grades; letter of recommendation from high school principal or counselor, college/university dean, academic advisor, or apprentice program instructor; SAT and ACT scores and cumulative GPA; and a letter of recommendation from an active member of the plumbing-heating-cooling contractors. **Deadline for Receipt:** May 1.

3901 ■ PUBLIC EDUCATION FOUNDATION
3360 W Sahara Ave., Ste. 160
Las Vegas, NV 89102
Tel: (702)799-1042
Fax: (702)799-5247
E-mail: steelej@ccpef.org
Web Site: http://ccpef.org
To support individuals aiming to acquire a degree in education or business.
Title of Award: Evelyn Abrams Memorial Scholarships **Area, Field, or Subject:** Education; Business. **Level of Education for which Award is Granted:** Undergraduate **Number Awarded:** 1. **Funds Available:** $750.
Eligibility Requirements: Applicants must be CCSD female seniors interested in pursuing a degree in education or business at an accredited college/university; must have a minimum 3.0 unweighted cumulative GPA; and must demonstrate financial need. **Application Requirements:** Applicants must submit a completed application form together with the required materials. **Deadline for Receipt:** March 7. **Additional Information:** Shana Venenga at 702-799-1042.

3902 ■ PUBLIC EDUCATION FOUNDATION
3360 W Sahara Ave., Ste. 160
Las Vegas, NV 89102
Tel: (702)799-1042
Fax: (702)799-5247
E-mail: steelej@ccpef.org
Web Site: http://ccpef.org
To promote education in business, economics or finance.
Title of Award: Clark High School Academy of Finance Scholarships **Area, Field, or Subject:** Business; Economics; Finance. **Level of Education for which Award is Granted:** Undergraduate **Number Awarded:** 1. **Funds Available:** $2,000.

Eligibility Requirements: Applicants must be Clark High School Academy of Finance (AOF) seniors interested in pursuing a degree in business, economics or finance at an accredited college/university and who have a minimum 3.0 GPA. **Application Requirements:** Applicants must submit a completed application form together with an essay, three letters of recommendation, transcript, resume of awards, and a copy of AOF Internship Evaluation. **Deadline for Receipt:** March 7. **Additional Information:** Shana Venenga at 702-799-1042.

3903 ■ PUBLIC EDUCATION FOUNDATION

3360 W Sahara Ave., Ste. 160
Las Vegas, NV 89102
Tel: (702)799-1042
Fax: (702)799-5247
E-mail: steelej@ccpef.org
Web Site: http://ccpef.org
To promote education in business, economics or finance.
Title of Award: Clark High School Alumni Leadership Circle Scholarships **Area, Field, or Subject:** Business; Economics; Finance. **Level of Education for which Award is Granted:** Undergraduate **Number Awarded:** 1. **Funds Available:** $500.
Eligibility Requirements: Applicants must be Clark High School Academy of Finance (AOF) seniors interested in pursuing a degree in business, economics or finance at an accredited college/university and who have a minimum 3.0 GPA. **Application Requirements:** Applicants must submit a completed application form together with an essay, two letters of recommendation, transcript, resume of awards, and a copy of AOF Internship Evaluation. **Deadline for Receipt:** March 7. **Additional Information:** Shana Venenga at 702-799-1042.

3904 ■ PUBLIC EDUCATION FOUNDATION

3360 W Sahara Ave., Ste. 160
Las Vegas, NV 89102
Tel: (702)799-1042
Fax: (702)799-5247
E-mail: steelej@ccpef.org
Web Site: http://ccpef.org
To provide educational opportunities for individuals intending to pursue higher studies.
Title of Award: Las Vegas Chinatown Scholarships **Area, Field, or Subject:** Business. **Level of Education for which Award is Granted:** Undergraduate **Number Awarded:** 2. **Funds Available:** $1,000.
Eligibility Requirements: Applicants must be CCSD seniors of Asian descent planning to attend an accredited college/university in Nevada and must have a minimum 3.0 cumulative GPA. **Application Requirements:** Applicants must submit a completed application form with an essay, two letters of recommendation, transcript, and resume of awards. **Deadline for Receipt:** March 7. **Additional Information:** Shana Venenga at 702-799-1042.

3905 ■ PUBLIC EDUCATION FOUNDATION

3360 W Sahara Ave., Ste. 160
Las Vegas, NV 89102
Tel: (702)799-1042
Fax: (702)799-5247
E-mail: steelej@ccpef.org
Web Site: http://ccpef.org
To provide educational opportunities for individuals intending to pursue higher studies.
Title of Award: Pardee Community Building Scholarships **Area, Field, or Subject:** Business; Civil engineering; Architecture; Construction. **Level of Education for which Award is Granted:** Undergraduate **Number Awarded:** 10. **Funds Available:** $1,500. **Duration:** One year.
Eligibility Requirements: Applicants must be CCSD seniors who have demonstrated an interest in home building and community development; must be planning to attend a Nevada accredited college or university; must be pursuing studies in areas of business, civil engineering, architecture or landscape architecture and construction management; and must have a minimum 2.8 cumulative GPA. **Application Requirements:** Applicants must submit a completed application form along with an essay, two letters of recommendation, transcript, and resume of awards. **Deadline for Receipt:** March 7. **Additional Information:** Shana Venenga at 702-799-1042.

3906 ■ PUBLIC EDUCATION FOUNDATION

3360 W Sahara Ave., Ste. 160
Las Vegas, NV 89102
Tel: (702)799-1042
Fax: (702)799-5247
E-mail: steelej@ccpef.org
Web Site: http://ccpef.org
To promote education in arts and business.
Title of Award: Silver Nugget Gaming Ambassadors Scholarships **Area, Field, or Subject:** Arts; Business. **Level of Education for which Award is Granted:** Undergraduate **Number Awarded:** 1. **Funds Available:** $3,000.
Eligibility Requirements: Applicants must be CCSD seniors who attended Rancho High School, Desert Pines High School, Community College East or Area Technical Trade Center; must have demonstrated an interest in the arts and business; and must have shown leadership skills. **Application Requirements:** Applicants must submit a completed application form together with an essay (400-500 words). **Deadline for Receipt:** March 31. **Additional Information:** Shana Venenga at 702-799-1042.

3907 ■ REDLANDS COMMUNITY SCHOLARSHIP FOUNDATION

c/o Kathleen Venegas-Boge, Admin. Asst.
PO Box 1683
Redlands, CA 92373
Tel: (909)307-9892
Fax: (909)307-9892
Web Site: http://www.redlandsscholarships.org
To encourage educational pursuits among Redlands Unified School District graduates by providing educational assistance.
Title of Award: Community Bank - Lee Guggisberg Foundation Memorial Scholarships **Area, Field, or Subject:** Business; Accounting. **Level of Education for which Award is Granted:** Undergraduate **Number Awarded:** 3. **Funds Available:** $300.
Eligibility Requirements: Applicant must complete the graduation requirements of the Redlands Unified School District; must be enrolled as a full-time student at an accredited college/university prior to Community Bank releasing the scholarship money; and must plan to further education in the field of business management or accounting. **Application Requirements:** Applicants must submit a completed application form together with the scantron sheet; cover sheet; student activity and community activity sheets; personal essay; and a copy of unofficial transcript (signed by the counselor). **Additional Information:** No electronic submissions of application will be accepted. Submit two printed copies of the application and use a No. 2 pencil on the scantron sheet. **Deadline for Receipt:** February 20.

3908 ■ REDLANDS COMMUNITY SCHOLARSHIP FOUNDATION

c/o Kathleen Venegas-Boge, Admin. Asst.
PO Box 1683
Redlands, CA 92373
Tel: (909)307-9892
Fax: (909)307-9892
Web Site: http://www.redlandsscholarships.org
To encourage educational pursuits among Redlands Unified School District graduates by providing educational assistance.
Title of Award: Doreen Legg Memorial Scholarships **Area, Field, or Subject:** Business; Teaching. **Level of Education for which Award is Granted:** Undergraduate **Number Awarded:** 9. **Funds Available:** $600 and $1000.
Eligibility Requirements: Applicant must be a graduating senior enrolling full-time at a four-year college or university; must be pursuing a business or teaching career; must have a minimum 3.0 GPA; and must have attended Redlands High School for at least three consecutive years. **Application Requirements:** Applicants must submit a completed application form together with the scantron sheet; cover sheet; student activity and community activity sheets; personal essay; and a copy of unofficial transcript (signed by the counselor). **Additional Information:** No electronic submissions of application will be accepted. Submit two printed copies of the application and use a No. 2 pencil on the scantron sheet. **Deadline for Receipt:** February 20.

3909 ■ REDLANDS COMMUNITY SCHOLARSHIP FOUNDATION

c/o Kathleen Venegas-Boge, Admin. Asst.
PO Box 1683
Redlands, CA 92373
Tel: (909)307-9892
Fax: (909)307-9892
Web Site: http://www.redlandsscholarships.org
To encourage educational pursuits among Redlands Unified School District graduates by providing educational assistance.
Title of Award: Soroptimist International of Redlands Scholarships **Area, Field, or Subject:** Health care services; Law; Engineering; Computer and information sciences; Education; Business. **Level of Education for which Award is Granted:** Undergraduate **Number Awarded:** 1. **Funds Available:** $750.
Eligibility Requirements: Applicant must be a graduating senior who has participated in community service and who will be attending an accredited college on a full-time basis and is planning to major in one of the following fields: health care, law, engineering, computer science, education and/or business administration. **Application Requirements:** Applicants must submit a completed application form together with the scantron sheet; cover sheet; student activity and community activity sheets; personal essay; and a copy of unofficial transcript (signed by the counselor). **Additional Information:** No electronic submissions of application will be accepted. Submit two printed copies of the application and use a No. 2 pencil on the scantron sheet. **Deadline for Receipt:** February 20.

3910 ■ ROYAL BANK OF CANADA

260 Adelaide St. E
Toronto, ON, Canada M5A 1N1
(866)363-1722
E-mail: 4edu@sympatico.ca
Web Site: http://www.rbcroyalbank.com
To provide scholarship assistance to qualified individuals who want to pursue their studies.
Title of Award: RBC Royal Bank Scholarships for Undergraduates **Area, Field, or Subject:** Business; Science; Visual arts. **Level of Education for which Award is Granted:** Undergraduate **Number Awarded:** 9. **Funds Available:** Gold: $5,000; Silver: $3,000; Bronze: $2,000. **Duration:** One year.
Eligibility Requirements: Applicants must be Canadian citizens or permanent residents; must be enrolled as full-time students in an accredited Canadian college or university; must be entering their second through final program year; must have minimum cumulative GPA equivalent to 70% average. **Application Requirements:** Applicants must provide basic contact details, including their email address, phone numbers, mailing address, and must provide information about their college or university, program of study, and cumulative GPA. **Deadline for Receipt:** June 9.

3911 ■ THE SAN DIEGO FOUNDATION

2508 Historic Decatur Rd., Ste. 200
San Diego, CA 92106
Tel: (619)235-2300
Fax: (619)239-1710
E-mail: info@sdfoundation.org
Web Site: http://www.sdfoundation.org
To support the education of students from California.
Title of Award: Julie Allen World Classroom Scholarships **Area, Field, or Subject:** International affairs and relations; Business; Economics; Civil rights; Foreign languages. **Level of Education for which Award is Granted:** Undergraduate **Number Awarded:** 1. **Funds Available:** $1,000.
Eligibility Requirements: Applicant must be an undergraduate student enrolled at the University of San Diego, UC San Diego, or San Diego State University; have a minimum 2.50 GPA on a 4.0 scale; demonstrated financial need; planning to study abroad for a minimum of one semester in a Second or Third World Country whose culture, language and customs are different than their own. **Application Requirements:** Applicants must submit a completed Common Scholarship Application together with personal statement; two letters of recommendation on official letterhead (written within the last six months); official transcript in an official and sealed envelope; copy of most recent tax form (Form 1040-pages 1 & 2; Form 1040A-pages 1 & 2; Form 1040EZ-page 1); and an essay (maximum one page, typed, double-spaced) addressing applicant's reason(s) for studying abroad, or coming to San Diego to pursue an education from the student's native country. **Deadline for Receipt:** January 28. **Additional Information:** Arzo Mansury, Dir. Scholarships at 619-814-1343, or scholarships@sdfoundation.org.

3912 ■ SOUTHWEST FLORIDA COMMUNITY FOUNDATION

8260 College Pkwy., Ste. 101
Fort Myers, FL 33919
Tel: (239)274-5900
Fax: (239)274-5930
Web Site: http://www.floridacommunity.com
To fund a student who will attend: FGCU, university of Florida/Gainesville, Florida State University/Tallahassee, Flagler College, Stetson University/Deland, University of Miami, University of Tampa, or Embry Riddle Aeronautical University/Daytona Beach.
Title of Award: D&A Florida Scholarships **Area, Field, or Subject:** Architecture; Business; Engineering; International affairs and relations; Journalism; Computer and information sciences; Law; Literature; Medicine; Physics; Chemistry; Political science. **Level of Education for which Award is Granted:** Undergraduate **Funds Available:** $10,000. **Duration:** One year.
Eligibility Requirements: Applicants must have graduated from a public or private high school in Charlotte, Glades, Hendry or Lee County; must pursue a degree in Architecture, Business, Engineering, International affairs and relations, Journalism, Computer and information sciences, Law, Literature, Medicine, Physics, Chemistry, or Political science. **Application Requirements:** Application forms are available online. Applicants must submit a letter of interest and letter of recommendation, a transcript and financial need documentation. **Deadline for Receipt:** February 15.

3913 ■ SOUTHWEST FLORIDA COMMUNITY FOUNDATION

8260 College Pkwy., Ste. 101
Fort Myers, FL 33919
Tel: (239)274-5900
Fax: (239)274-5930
Web Site: http://www.floridacommunity.com
To fund tuition for females pursuing a business career in college.
Title of Award: Ruth Messmer Memorial Scholarships **Area, Field, or Subject:** Business. **Level of Education for which Award is Granted:** Undergraduate **Funds Available:** $1,000. **Duration:** One year.
Eligibility Requirements: Applicants must have graduated from a public or private high school in Lee County with a documented "B" average; must be females pursuing a business career in college. **Application Requirements:** Applicants must submit a letter of interest, transcript, and letter of recommendation. Application forms are available online. **Deadline for Receipt:** February 15.

3914 ■ STARK COMMUNITY FOUNDATION

400 Market Ave. N, Ste. 200
Canton, OH 44702-2107
Tel: (330)454-3426
Fax: (330)454-5855
Web Site: http://www.starkcommunityfoundation.org
To provide scholarship assistance to qualified individuals who want to pursue their studies.
Title of Award: Raymond T. Hoge Scholarship Fund **Area, Field, or Subject:** Business; Education. **Level of Education for which Award is Granted:** Undergraduate **Funds Available:** No specific amount. **Duration:** One year.
Eligibility Requirements: Applicants must be graduating senior members of Perry High School or alumni who plan to attend an institution of higher learning; must be in good academic standing; must be planning to pursue a degree in the field of business or education; must demonstrate financial need. **Application Requirements:** Applicants must complete and submit the application form at Perry High School Guidance Office, 3737 13th St. SW, Massillon, OH 44646. **Deadline for Receipt:** April 15.

3915 ■ STRAIGHTFORWARD MEDIA

508 7th St., Ste 202
Rapid City, SD 57701
Tel: (605)348-3042
Fax: (605)348-3043

E-mail: info@straightforwardmedia.com
Web Site: http://www.straightforwardmedia.com
To financially assist students in their educational pursuits.
Title of Award: StraightForward Media's Business School Scholarships **Area, Field, or Subject:** Business. **Level of Education for which Award is Granted:** Undergraduate **Funds Available:** $500.
Eligibility Requirements: Applicants must be students attending business schools, including students getting MBAs. **Application Requirements:** Applicants must complete the online scholarship application. **Additional Information:** Awards are given four times a year. **Deadline for Receipt:** March, June, September, December.

3916 ■ SURETY AND FIDELITY ASSOCIATION OF AMERICA
1101 Connecticut Ave. NW, Ste. 800
Washington, DC 20036
Tel: (202)463-0600
Fax: (202)463-0606
Web Site: http://www.surety.org
To provide financial assistance to outstanding minority students to support their studies in the areas of insurance/risk management, accounting, or business/finance and to encourage their consideration of the surety industry and surety underwriting as a career choice.
Title of Award: Surety Industry Scholarship Program for Minority Students **Area, Field, or Subject:** Insurance and insurance-related fields; Management; Accounting; Business; Finance. **Level of Education for which Award is Granted:** Undergraduate **Funds Available:** $2,500.
Eligibility Requirements: Applicants must be majoring in insurance/risk management, accounting, or business/finance; must have an overall and major grade point average (GPA) of at least 3.0 on 4.0 scale; must be minority students who have satisfactorily completed at least 30 semester hours and at least 6 semester hours in their declared major; must be enrolled as full-time undergraduate students (minimum of 12 semester hours or equivalent) at an accredited four-year institution. **Application Requirements:** Applicants must submit all the required application information. **Deadline for Receipt:** April 30.

3917 ■ TAG AND LABEL MANUFACTURERS INSTITUTE
40 Shuman Blvd., Ste. 295
Naperville, IL 60563
Tel: (630)357-9222
Free: 800-533-8564
Fax: (630)357-0192
E-mail: office@tlmi.com
Web Site: http://www.tlmi.com
To promote education in the flexographic industry.
Title of Award: TLMI Scholarships - Four-Year Colleges **Area, Field, or Subject:** Management; Marketing and distribution; Graphic art and design. **Level of Education for which Award is Granted:** Undergraduate **Number Awarded:** 6. **Funds Available:** $5,000.
Eligibility Requirements: Applicant must be a second or third year full-time college student pursuing a career in the tag and table manufacturing industry; majoring in management, sales/ marketing, graphic arts, graphic design, or production; and must maintain a 3.00 or higher GPA. **Application Requirements:** Applicants must fill out the application online; must prepare a personal statement (one page) on personal information, work experiences, family financial report, career and educational goals and reasons why they deserve the award; a school transcript; three references; and samples of work (not mandatory). **Deadline for Receipt:** January 1-March 31. **Additional Information:** Karen Planzat.

3918 ■ U.S.-IRELAND ALLIANCE
2800 Clarendon Blvd., No. 502 West
Arlington, VA 22201
E-mail: vargo@us-irelandalliance.org
Web Site: http://us-irelandalliance.org
To introduce and connect generations of future American leaders to the island of Ireland, while recognizing and fostering intellectual achievement, leadership, and a commitment to public service and community.
Title of Award: George J. Mitchell Scholarships **Area, Field, or Subject:** Business. **Level of Education for which Award is Granted:** Undergraduate **Funds Available:** No specific amount.
Eligibility Requirements: Applicant must be a U.S. citizen between 18-30 years old. **Application Requirements:** Applicants must apply online. **Deadline for Receipt:** October 6.

3919 ■ UNIVERSITY OF ALASKA ANCHORAGE
3211 Providence Dr.
Anchorage, AK 99508
Tel: (907)786-1800
Web Site: http://www.uaa.alaska.edu
To provide financial assistance for tuition and other educational expenses to full-time students who are formally admitted to a degreeseeking program within the College of Business & Public Policy at the UAA.
Title of Award: UAA College of Business & Public Policy Scholarships **Area, Field, or Subject:** Business; Public service. **Level of Education for which Award is Granted:** Graduate, Undergraduate **Number Awarded:** 3. **Funds Available:** $500. **Duration:** One year.
Eligibility Requirements: Applicants must demonstrate motivation, academic and leadership potential; must be in good academic standing with a minimum cumulative GPA of 2.0 for undergraduates and 3.0 for graduates; must be formally admitted to an undergraduate, graduate, certificate, and/or vocational degree-seeking program within the College of Business & Public Policy at the UAA; must plan on enrolling full-time (12 credits for undergraduate and nine credits for graduate) at the UAA; may be an incoming or continuing student at the UAA; may be a U.S. citizen, non-U.S. citizen, Alaska resident, or out-of-state resident. **Application Requirements:** Applicants must complete the electronic scholarship application. **Deadline for Receipt:** February 15.

3920 ■ UNIVERSITY OF ALASKA ANCHORAGE
3211 Providence Dr.
Anchorage, AK 99508
Tel: (907)786-1800
Web Site: http://www.uaa.alaska.edu
To provide financial assistance to junior and senior students at UAA to help them pay for tuition and other related expenses.
Title of Award: UAA Diane Olsen Memorial Scholarships **Area, Field, or Subject:** Economics. **Level of Education for which Award is Granted:** Undergraduate **Funds Available:** $500. **Duration:** One year.
Eligibility Requirements: Applicants must demonstrate motivation, academic and leadership potential; must be in good academic standing with a minimum cumulative GPA of 2.75; must have a junior or senior standing; must be a declared economics major or have an interest in economics as demonstrated by the completion of at least 12 credits in economic courses; must plan on enrolling full-time (twelve credits for undergraduate) at the UAA; must be active in student clubs, student organizations or student governance; may be an incoming or continuing student at the UAA; may be a U.S. citizen, non-U.S. citizen, Alaska resident, or out-of-state resident. **Application Requirements:** Applicants must complete the electronic scholarship application available online at www.uaa.alaska.edu/scholarships/diane.cfm. **Deadline for Receipt:** February 15.

3921 ■ UNIVERSITY OF ALASKA ANCHORAGE
3211 Providence Dr.
Anchorage, AK 99508
Tel: (907)786-1800
Web Site: http://www.uaa.alaska.edu
To provide financial assistance for tuition and other educational expenses to full-time students who are formally admitted to a business degree-seeking program at the UAA.
Title of Award: UAA Jan & Glenn Fredericks Scholarships **Area, Field, or Subject:** Business. **Level of Education for which Award is Granted:** Graduate, Undergraduate **Funds Available:** No specific amount.
Eligibility Requirements: Applicants must demonstrate motivation, academic and leadership potential; must be in good academic standing with a minimum cumulative GPA of 2.0 for undergraduates and 3.0 for graduates; must be formally admitted to a business degreeseeking program at the UAA by the start of the semester; must plan on enrolling full-time (12 credits for undergraduate and nine credits for graduate) at the UAA by the start of the semester of the award; must have at least a junior, senior, or graduate class-standing by the start of the semester of the award; may be a U.S. citizen, non-U.S. citizen, Alaska resident, or out-of-state resident. **Application Requirements:** Applicants must complete the electronic scholarship application available online at www.uaa.alaska.edu/scholarships/jan.cfm. **Deadline for Receipt:** February 15.

3922 ■ UNIVERSITY OF ALASKA ANCHORAGE

3211 Providence Dr.
Anchorage, AK 99508
Tel: (907)786-1800
Web Site: http://www.uaa.alaska.edu
To provide financial assistance for tuition and other educational expenses to students who are in financial need.
Title of Award: UAA Mark A. Beltz Scholarships **Area, Field, or Subject:** Political science; Economics; Business administration; Science technologies. **Level of Education for which Award is Granted:** Graduate, Undergraduate **Funds Available:** $500$1,000.
Eligibility Requirements: Applicants must demonstrate motivation, academic and leadership potential; must be in good academic standing with a minimum cumulative GPA of 2.0 for undergraduates and 3.0 for graduates; must be formally admitted to a political science, economics, business administration, business and corporate law, or science and technology undergraduate, graduate, certificate, and/or vocational degree-seeking program at the University of Alaska Anchorage; must plan on enrolling at least half-time (6 credits) at the University of Alaska Anchorage; may be an incoming or continuing student at the University of Alaska Anchorage; may be a U.S. citizen, nonU.S. citizen, Alaska resident, or out-of-state resident. **Application Requirements:** Applicants must complete the electronics scholarship application available online. **Deadline for Receipt:** February 15.

3923 ■ UNIVERSITY OF ALASKA ANCHORAGE

3211 Providence Dr.
Anchorage, AK 99508
Tel: (907)786-1800
Web Site: http://www.uaa.alaska.edu
To encourage an Alaskan student to enter the field of business and to provide financial assistance for tuition and other educational expenses to full-time students who are formally admitted to a business degree-seeking program at the University of Alaska Anchorage.
Title of Award: UAA Michael D. Ford Memorial Scholarships **Area, Field, or Subject:** Business. **Level of Education for which Award is Granted:** Graduate, Undergraduate **Funds Available:** No specific amount.
Eligibility Requirements: Applicants must have been born in Alaska and be a current Alaska resident; must be in good academic standing with a minimum cumulative GPA of 3.0; must be formally admitted to a business degree-seeking program at the University of UAA; must plan on enrolling full-time (12 credits for undergraduate and nine credits for graduate) at the UAA. **Application Requirements:** Applicants must complete the electronic scholarship application available online at www.uaa.alaska.edu/scholarships/michael.cfm. **Deadline for Receipt:** February 15.

3924 ■ UNIVERSITY OF NORTH CAROLINA SCHOOL OF JOURNALISM AND MASS COMMUNICATION

University of North Carolina, Carol Hall CB 3365
Chapel Hill, NC 27599-3365
Tel: (919)962-1204
Fax: (919)962-0620
E-mail: jomc@unc.edu
Web Site: http://www.jomc.unc.edu
To educate journalists.
Title of Award: Donald Mauer Scholarships **Area, Field, or Subject:** Advertising. **Level of Education for which Award is Granted:** Undergraduate **Funds Available:** $500.
Eligibility Requirements: Applicants must be rising junior in the advertising sequence. **Application Requirements:** Applicants must complete the application form.

3925 ■ UNIVERSITY OF NORTH CAROLINA SCHOOL OF JOURNALISM AND MASS COMMUNICATION

University of North Carolina, Carol Hall CB 3365
Chapel Hill, NC 27599-3365
Tel: (919)962-1204
Fax: (919)962-0620
E-mail: jomc@unc.edu
Web Site: http://www.jomc.unc.edu
To educate journalists.
Title of Award: Hal Tanner Jr. Scholarships **Area, Field, or Subject:** Communication; Advertising. **Level of Education for which Award is Granted:** Undergraduate **Funds Available:** $1,500.

Eligibility Requirements: Applicants must be rising senior students majoring in advertising. **Application Requirements:** Applicants must complete the application form.

3926 ■ UNIVERSITY OF TORONTO

315 Bloor St. W
Toronto, ON, Canada M5S 1A3
Tel: (416)978-2011
E-mail: information.commonsats@utoronto.ca
Web Site: http://www.utoronto.ca
To support students with their educational pursuits.
Title of Award: Nortel Institute Undergraduate Scholarships **Area, Field, or Subject:** Applied art; Engineering. **Level of Education for which Award is Granted:** Undergraduate **Funds Available:** Approximately $5000.
Eligibility Requirements: Applicant must be a U of T student and a Canadian citizen or landed immigrant and a resident of Ontario; must be in the second or third year in the Faculty of Applied Science and Engineering, the Faculty of Arts and Science, University of Toronto Mississauga and University of Toronto Scarborough. **Application Requirements:** Applicants must submit a completed application form together with the required materials and information. **Deadline for Receipt:** November 1.

3927 ■ URBAN FINANCIAL SERVICES COALITION

1200 G St., Ste. 800
Washington, DC 20005
Tel: (202)289-8335
Free: 800-996-8335
Fax: (202)682-3058
E-mail: ufsc@ufscnet.org
Web Site: http://www.ufscnet.org
To provide assistance to minority students in their education.
Title of Award: Herbert W. Whiteman, Jr. Scholarships **Area, Field, or Subject:** Banking; Finance. **Level of Education for which Award is Granted:** Graduate, Undergraduate **Funds Available:** No specific amount. **Duration:** Annually.
Eligibility Requirements: Applicants must have a 3.0 GPA on a 4.0 scale; pursuing an undergraduate or advanced degree in finance or business at an accredited college/university. **Application Requirements:** Application form is available at the website. Applicants must submit a completed application form together with a reference letter; acceptance letter from the college/university; and a 400- to 500-word essay to: UFSC Foundation, Attn: Herbert W. Whiteman, Jr. Scholarship Fund, 2121 K. St. NW, Suite 800, Washington, DC 20037.

3928 ■ VECTOR MARKETING CORPORATION

5301 Limestone Rd., Ste. 105
Wilmington, DE 19808
Tel: (302)372-8020
E-mail: campus@cutco.com
Web Site: http://www.vectorscholarships.com
To recognize students who have excelled in their roles as sales representatives.
Title of Award: All-American Vector Marketing Scholarship Program **Area, Field, or Subject:** Marketing and distribution. **Level of Education for which Award is Granted:** Undergraduate **Funds Available:** $250-$1,000.
Eligibility Requirements: Applicants must be full-time students at an accredited college or university; active in the business at the conclusion of the Scholarship Race. **Application Requirements:** Applicants must provide current official transcript as well as a copy of current semester registration. Applicants may contact Vector Marketing Corporation for other requirements. **Additional Information:** Vector Marketing Corporation at the above address.

3929 ■ VECTOR MARKETING CORPORATION

5301 Limestone Rd., Ste. 105
Wilmington, DE 19808
Tel: (302)372-8020
E-mail: campus@cutco.com
Web Site: http://www.vectorscholarships.com
To provide financial assistance to student sales representatives and the institutions of higher education they attend.

Title of Award: Vector Marketing Canadian Scholarship Awards **Area, Field, or Subject:** Marketing and distribution. **Level of Education for which Award is Granted:** Undergraduate **Funds Available:** No specific amount.
Eligibility Requirements: Applicants must be full-time university or college students working with Vector. **Application Requirements:** Applicants must provide current official transcript as well as a copy of current semester registration. Applicants may contact Vector Marketing Corporation for other requirements. **Additional Information:** Vector Marketing Corporation at the above address.

3930 ■ VIRGINIA FOUNDATION FOR INDEPENDENT COLLEGES
8010 Ridge Rd., Ste. B
Richmond, VA 23229-7288
Tel: (804)288-6609
Free: 800-230-6757
Fax: (804)282-4635
E-mail: info@vfic.org
Web Site: http://www.vfic.org
To provide financial assistance to students who will be juniors at a VFIC member college.
Title of Award: Hilb, Rogal and Hobbs Scholarships **Area, Field, or Subject:** Marketing and distribution; Business; Economics; Finance; Mathematics and Mathematical sciences. **Level of Education for which Award is Granted:** Undergraduate **Funds Available:** $2,500.
Eligibility Requirements: Applicants must be full-time students at one of the fifteen private colleges/universities associated with the Virginia Foundation for Independent Colleges; must be first-semester juniors at the time of application with a cumulative grade point average of at least 3.0 on a 4.0 scale, who have declared, or intend to declare a major in one of the following disciplines: marketing, business, economics, finance, mathematics or related fields; must be U.S. citizens. **Application Requirements:** Applicants must submit all the required application information. **Deadline for Receipt:** November 1.

3931 ■ VIRGINIA FOUNDATION FOR INDEPENDENT COLLEGES
8010 Ridge Rd., Ste. B
Richmond, VA 23229-7288
Tel: (804)288-6609
Free: 800-230-6757
Fax: (804)282-4635
E-mail: info@vfic.org
Web Site: http://www.vfic.org
To provide financial assistance to students who will be juniors at a VFIC member college to defray educational expenses.
Title of Award: Norfolk Southern Scholarships **Area, Field, or Subject:** Economics; Business; Finance; Accounting. **Level of Education for which Award is Granted:** Undergraduate **Funds Available:** $5,000. **Duration:** One year.
Eligibility Requirements: Applicants must be full-time students at one of the fifteen private colleges/universities associated with the VFIC; first semester juniors at the time of application with a cumulative GPA of at least 3.0 on a 4.0 scale and declared major in economics, business, finance, accounting or related fields, and interested in a career in a Fortune 500 corporate setting; must be United States citizens. **Application Requirements:** Applicants must submit resume, college transcript, two letters of recommendation and the completed application form. **Deadline for Receipt:** November 1.

3932 ■ VIRGINIA FOUNDATION FOR INDEPENDENT COLLEGES
8010 Ridge Rd., Ste. B
Richmond, VA 23229-7288
Tel: (804)288-6609
Free: 800-230-6757
Fax: (804)282-4635
E-mail: info@vfic.org
Web Site: http://www.vfic.org
To provide financial assistance for the students in their junior year at a VFIC college or university.
Title of Award: Phillip Morris USA Scholarships **Area, Field, or Subject:** Accounting; Biology; Business; Chemistry; Computer and information sciences; Economics; Engineering; Finance; Physics. **Level of Education for which Award is Granted:** Undergraduate **Funds Available:** $5,000.

Eligibility Requirements: Applicants must be U.S. citizens and current full-time sophomores attending a VFIC college or university (students from underrepresented populations are encouraged to apply); have minimum of 3.5 cumulative GPA; committed to applying for an internship with Phillip Morris USA for the summer after junior year; have declared, or intend to declare, a major in one of the following disciplines: accounting, biology, business, chemistry, computer science, economics, engineering, finance, or physics. **Application Requirements:** Applicants must submit completed application form along with two letters of recommendation and other required application information. **Deadline for Receipt:** November 1.

3933 ■ THE WASHINGTON GROUP
720 Park Blvd.
PO Box 73
Boise, ID 83729
Tel: (208)386-5000
E-mail: membership@washingtongroup.org
Web Site: http://www.wgint.com
To encourage active participation in Ukrainian community.
Title of Award: Chopivsky Fellowships **Area, Field, or Subject:** Forestry; Environmental Studies; Economics. **Level of Education for which Award is Granted:** Undergraduate **Number Awarded:** 2. **Funds Available:** No specific amount.
Eligibility Requirements: Applicants must be Ukrainian citizens and must be first admitted to the appropriate faculties at Yale; must be in graduate degree program leading to master's degree at the Yale School of Management at the Yale School of Forestry and Environmental Studies, and in the Departments of International Relations, International Economics, and Developmental Studies. **Application Requirements:** Applicants must fill out the application form and supporting materials. **Deadline for Receipt:** January 1. **Additional Information:** PO Box 208206, New Haven, CT 06520-8606; 1203-432-3423; 12034325963.

3934 ■ WASHINGTON STATE BUSINESS EDUCATION ASSOCIATION
c/o Lori Finn
800 Abbott Rd.
Walla Walla, WA 99362
Tel: (509)526-8606
Fax: (509)526-8690
E-mail: lfinn@wwps.org
Web Site: http://www.wsbea.org
To provide financial assistance to those students who are in need.
Title of Award: Doris Y. and John J. Gerber Scholarships **Area, Field, or Subject:** Business. **Level of Education for which Award is Granted:** Undergraduate **Funds Available:** No specific amount.
Eligibility Requirements: Applicants must be junior or senior students majoring in Business Education. Applicants must be nominated by their advisor who is a current dues-paying member of WSBEA. **Application Requirements:** Applicants must inquire online for the application process. **Deadline for Receipt:** December 1. **Additional Information:** Jackie Floetke, WSBEA Scholarship Committee at PO Box 138 Wilson Creek, WA 98860

3935 ■ WILKINSON & COMPANY LLP
PO Box 757
Belleville, ON, Canada K8N 5B5
Tel: (613)966-5105; 888-728-3890
Fax: (613)962-7072
Web Site: http://www.wilkinson.net
To provide financial support for students.
Title of Award: Wilkinson & Company LLP Secondary School Scholarships **Area, Field, or Subject:** Business-related course. **Level of Education for which Award is Granted:** Undergraduate **Funds Available:** $300.
Eligibility Requirements: Applicants must have highest mark in business-related course. **Application Requirements:** Applicants must submit a completed application form. **Additional Information:** Wilkinson & Company LLP at the above address.

3936 ■ WOMEN IN DEFENSE
2111 Wilson Blvd., Ste. 400
Arlington, VA 22201-3061

Tel: (703)247-2552
Fax: (703)522-1885
E-mail: wid@ndia.org
Web Site: http://wid.ndia.org
To provide financial assistance to further educational objectives of women either employed or planning careers in defense or national security areas. **Title of Award:** Women In Defense HORIZONS Scholarships **Area, Field, or Subject:** National security; Military history; Government; Engineering; Computer and information sciences; Physics; Mathematics and mathematical sciences; Business; Law; International affairs and relations; Political science; Economics. **Level of Education for which Award is Granted:** Graduate, Undergraduate **Funds Available:** No specific amount.
Eligibility Requirements: Applicant must be currently enrolled at an accredited university/college, either full-time or part-time; must have junior, senior or graduate status; demonstrate interest in pursuing a career related to national security or defense; demonstrate financial need; have a minimum GPA of 3.25. Applicant must be a female citizen of the United States. **Application Requirements:** Applicants must submit a completed scholarship application form with the essays, recommendations, and transcripts. **Additional Information:** Established in 1988. **Deadline for Receipt:** July 1.

3937 ■ XAVIER UNIVERSITY
3800 Victory Pky.
Cincinnati, OH 45207
Tel: (513)745-3000
Free: 800-344-GOXU
Web Site: http://www.xavier.edu
To financially support students with their education.
Title of Award: Xavier University Williams Scholarships **Area, Field, or Subject:** Business. **Level of Education for which Award is Granted:** Undergraduate **Number Awarded:** 4. **Funds Available:** $3000.
Eligibility Requirements: Applicant must be a first year student declared a major in the Williams College of Business. **Application Requirements:** Applicants admitted at the Xavier University are automatically considered. **Deadline for Receipt:** February 15.

3938 ■ YOUNG MENSWEAR ASSOCIATION
36 W 20th St., 3rd Fl.
New York, NY 10011
Tel: (212)594-6422
E-mail: hharrison@ymafashionscholarshipfund.org
Web Site: http://the-yma.com
To promote education in the fashion industry.
Title of Award: YMA Fashion Scholarships **Area, Field, or Subject:** Fashion design; Business. **Level of Education for which Award is Granted:** Undergraduate **Funds Available:** No specific amount.
Eligibility Requirements: Applicant must be a full-time junior or senior student with a GPA of 3.0 or above in a 4.0 GPA system. **Application Requirements:** Educators can nominate up to eight applicants per school. Nominated applicants must submit all the student records and transcript; and an essay. For Design students, submit a portfolio (at least 2 designs/projects) not to exceed 8 1/2"x 11" folder size. For Business students, submit a project about merchandising, marketing or finance not to exceed 8 1/2"x 11" folder size. Application form is to be sent electronically to hharrison@ymafashionscholarshipfund.org; a box per school containing all other materials of the applicants must be sent to: The YMA Fashion Scholarship Fund, 36 West 20th St., 3rd Fl., New York, NY 10011. **Deadline for Receipt:** January 15.

Communications

3939 ■ ADVERTISING PRODUCTION CLUB OF NEW YORK
428 E State St.
Long Beach, NY 11561
Tel: (212)671-2975
Fax: (718)228-8202
E-mail: admin@apc-ny.org
Web Site: http://www.apc-ny.org
To provide financial assistance to students pursuing a full-time graphic arts/communications degree.

Title of Award: Advertising Production Club Scholarship Awards **Area, Field, or Subject:** Graphic art and design; Communications. **Level of Education for which Award is Granted:** Graduate, Undergraduate **Number Awarded:** 4. **Funds Available:** $500. Funds are applied to tuition expenses. **Duration:** One year.
Eligibility Requirements: Applicant must be a resident of New York City metro area attending a graphic arts/communications degree program full-time in any college in the New York City metro area. **Application Requirements:** Guidelines and application forms are available from the Advertising Production Club office or can be downloaded from the APC website. Applicants must submit a completed hard copy application with the APC office together with registration receipt for the new semester, college transcript and acceptance letter. **Deadline for Receipt:** October 15.

3940 ■ ADVERTISING PRODUCTION CLUB OF NEW YORK
428 E State St.
Long Beach, NY 11561
Tel: (212)671-2975
Fax: (718)228-8202
E-mail: admin@apc-ny.org
Web Site: http://www.apc-ny.org
To provide financial assistance to those studying graphic arts and communications.
Title of Award: APC High School Scholarships **Area, Field, or Subject:** Graphic art and design; Communications. **Level of Education for which Award is Granted:** Undergraduate **Number Awarded:** 2. **Funds Available:** $250. Funds are applied to tuition expenses. **Duration:** One year.
Eligibility Requirements: Applicants must present a positive identification and confirmation by the high school principal; graduate high school with at least a B average; be duly accepted as a full-time, matriculated student in an accredited graphic arts or communications program at a college in the United States. **Application Requirements:** Guidelines and application forms are available from the Advertising Production Club office or can be downloaded from the APC website. Applicants must submit a completed hard copy application with the APC office together with registration receipt for the new semester, college transcript and acceptance letter. **Deadline for Receipt:** October 15.

3941 ■ ADVERTISING PRODUCTION CLUB OF NEW YORK
428 E State St.
Long Beach, NY 11561
Tel: (212)671-2975
Fax: (718)228-8202
E-mail: admin@apc-ny.org
Web Site: http://www.apc-ny.org
To provide financial assistance to students pursuing graphic communications careers.
Title of Award: PGSF-GATF Scholarships **Area, Field, or Subject:** Graphic art and design; Communications. **Level of Education for which Award is Granted:** Graduate, Undergraduate **Number Awarded:** 2. **Funds Available:** $500. Funds are applied to tuition expenses. **Duration:** One year.
Eligibility Requirements: Applicant must be a resident of New York City metro area attending a graphic arts/communications degree program full-time in an accredited college in the U.S. **Application Requirements:** Guidelines and application forms are available from the Advertising Production Club office or can be downloaded from the APC website. Applicants must submit a completed hard copy application with the APC office together with registration receipt for the new semester, college transcript and acceptance letter. **Deadline for Receipt:** October 15.

3942 ■ AMERICAN INSTITUTE OF POLISH CULTURE
1440 79th St. Causeway, Ste. 117
Miami, FL 33141
Tel: (305)864-2349
Fax: (305)865-5150
E-mail: info@ampolinstitute.org
Web Site: http://www.ampolinstitute.org
To provide financial support American students of Polish descent who wish to continue their education after high school.
Title of Award: Harriet Irsay Scholarships **Area, Field, or Subject:** Communications; Education; Media arts; History; International affairs and relations; Journalism; Liberal arts; Polish studies; Public relations. **Level of**

Education for which Award is Granted: Graduate, Undergraduate **Number Awarded:** 10-15. **Funds Available:** $1,000.
Eligibility Requirements: Applicants must be of Polish heritage; an American citizen or permanent resident; full-time graduate or undergraduate students in the field of communication, education, film, history, International Relation, journalism, liberal arts, polish studies, public relations; or graduate student in business programs with a thesis related to Poland, or graduate students with a thesis with Polish subject. **Application Requirements:** Applicants must submit a completed application form; school transcripts; resume; essay (200-400 words) about "Why should I receive the scholarship"; an article about Poland (maximum of 700 words); and 3 signed recommendation letters on a letterhead stationary from teachers or other person knowledgeable about the applicant's academic background. A non-refundable $10 processing fee (check or money order) must also be included. **Deadline for Receipt:** April 20.

3943 ■ AMERICAN RADIO RELAY LEAGUE (ARRL) FOUNDATION
225 Main St.
Newington, CT 06111
Tel: (860)594-0200
Fax: (860)594-0259
E-mail: foundation@arrl.org
Web Site: http://www.arrlf.org
To support the education of students holding a valid FCC-granted Amateur Radio license for post-secondary education.
Title of Award: American Radio Relay League Louisiana Memorial Scholarships **Area, Field, or Subject:** Radio and television. **Level of Education for which Award is Granted:** Undergraduate **Number Awarded:** 1. **Funds Available:** $500.
Eligibility Requirements: Applicant must hold an FCC amateur radio license, and be a Louisiana resident or attending a four-year college/university in Louisiana. **Application Requirements:** Applicants must submit a completed scholarship application form along with a recent high school (or equivalent) or college transcript. **Deadline for Receipt:** February 1.

3944 ■ AMERICAN RADIO RELAY LEAGUE (ARRL) FOUNDATION
225 Main St.
Newington, CT 06111
Tel: (860)594-0200
Fax: (860)594-0259
E-mail: foundation@arrl.org
Web Site: http://www.arrlf.org
To support the education of students holding a valid FCC-granted Amateur Radio license for post-secondary education.
Title of Award: American Radio Relay League Scholarships Honoring Barry Goldwater, K7UGA **Area, Field, or Subject:** Radio and television. **Level of Education for which Award is Granted:** Undergraduate **Number Awarded:** 1. **Funds Available:** $5,000.
Eligibility Requirements: Applicant must hold an FCC amateur radio license. **Application Requirements:** Applicants must submit a completed scholarship application form along with a recent high school (or equivalent) or college transcript. **Deadline for Receipt:** February 1.

3945 ■ AMERICAN RADIO RELAY LEAGUE (ARRL) FOUNDATION
225 Main St.
Newington, CT 06111
Tel: (860)594-0200
Fax: (860)594-0259
E-mail: foundation@arrl.org
Web Site: http://www.arrlf.org
To support the education of students holding a valid FCC-granted Amateur Radio license for post-secondary education.
Title of Award: Earl I. Anderson Scholarships **Area, Field, or Subject:** Radio and television. **Level of Education for which Award is Granted:** Undergraduate **Number Awarded:** 3. **Funds Available:** $1,250.
Eligibility Requirements: Applicant must hold an FCC amateur radio license, and be an Illinois, Indiana, Michigan, or Florida resident. **Application Requirements:** Applicants must submit a completed scholarship application form along with a recent high school (or equivalent) or college transcript. **Deadline for Receipt:** February 1.

3946 ■ AMERICAN RADIO RELAY LEAGUE (ARRL) FOUNDATION
225 Main St.
Newington, CT 06111

Tel: (860)594-0200
Fax: (860)594-0259
E-mail: foundation@arrl.org
Web Site: http://www.arrlf.org
To support the education of students holding a valid FCC-granted Amateur Radio license for post-secondary education.
Title of Award: ARRL Foundation General Fund Scholarships **Area, Field, or Subject:** Radio and television. **Level of Education for which Award is Granted:** Undergraduate **Number Awarded:** Multiple. **Funds Available:** $1,000.
Eligibility Requirements: Applicant must hold an FCC amateur radio license. **Application Requirements:** Applicants must submit a completed scholarship application form along with a recent high school (or equivalent) or college transcript. **Deadline for Receipt:** February 1.

3947 ■ AMERICAN RADIO RELAY LEAGUE (ARRL) FOUNDATION
225 Main St.
Newington, CT 06111
Tel: (860)594-0200
Fax: (860)594-0259
E-mail: foundation@arrl.org
Web Site: http://www.arrlf.org
To support the education of students holding a valid FCC-granted Amateur Radio license for post-secondary education.
Title of Award: ARRLF Mississippi Scholarships **Area, Field, or Subject:** Radio and television; Electronics; Communications. **Level of Education for which Award is Granted:** Undergraduate **Number Awarded:** 1. **Funds Available:** $500.
Eligibility Requirements: Applicant must hold an FCC amateur radio license; be a Mississippi resident; be studying in baccalaureate or higher courses of study in electronics, communications or related fields; and be under 30 years of age. **Application Requirements:** Applicants must submit a completed scholarship application form along with a recent high school (or equivalent) or college transcript. **Deadline for Receipt:** February 1.

3948 ■ AMERICAN RADIO RELAY LEAGUE (ARRL) FOUNDATION
225 Main St.
Newington, CT 06111
Tel: (860)594-0200
Fax: (860)594-0259
E-mail: foundation@arrl.org
Web Site: http://www.arrlf.org
To support the education of students holding a valid FCC-granted Amateur Radio license for post-secondary education.
Title of Award: Richard W. Bendicksen Memorial Scholarships **Area, Field, or Subject:** Radio and television. **Level of Education for which Award is Granted:** Undergraduate **Number Awarded:** 1. **Funds Available:** $1,000.
Eligibility Requirements: Applicant must hold an FCC amateur radio license, and attending a four-year college/university. **Application Requirements:** Applicants must submit a completed scholarship application form along with a recent high school (or equivalent) or college transcript. **Deadline for Receipt:** February 1.

3949 ■ AMERICAN RADIO RELAY LEAGUE (ARRL) FOUNDATION
225 Main St.
Newington, CT 06111
Tel: (860)594-0200
Fax: (860)594-0259
E-mail: foundation@arrl.org
Web Site: http://www.arrlf.org
To support the education of students holding a valid FCC-granted Amateur Radio license for post-secondary education.
Title of Award: William Bennett W7PHO Memorial Scholarships **Area, Field, or Subject:** Radio and television. **Level of Education for which Award is Granted:** Undergraduate **Number Awarded:** 1. **Funds Available:** $500.
Eligibility Requirements: Applicant must hold an FCC amateur radio license; be a Northwest, Pacific or Southwest Division resident; be enrolled in a four-year college/university; and have a GPA of 3.0 or better for an ongoing course of study. **Application Requirements:** Applicants must submit a completed scholarship application form along with a recent high school (or equivalent) or college transcript. **Deadline for Receipt:** February 1.

3950 ■ AMERICAN RADIO RELAY LEAGUE (ARRL) FOUNDATION
225 Main St.
Newington, CT 06111
Tel: (860)594-0200
Fax: (860)594-0259
E-mail: foundation@arrl.org
Web Site: http://www.arrlf.org
To support the education of students holding a valid FCC-granted Amateur Radio license for post-secondary education.
Title of Award: Henry Broughton, K2AE Memorial Scholarships **Area, Field, or Subject:** Radio and television; Engineering; Science. **Level of Education for which Award is Granted:** Undergraduate **Number Awarded:** 1. **Funds Available:** $1,000.
Eligibility Requirements: Applicant must hold an FCC amateur radio license; reside within 70 miles of Schenectady NY; studying in baccalaureate or higher courses of study in engineering, sciences or a similar field in an accredited four-year college/university. **Application Requirements:** Applicants must submit a completed scholarship application form along with a recent high school (or equivalent) or college transcript. **Deadline for Receipt:** February 1.

3951 ■ AMERICAN RADIO RELAY LEAGUE (ARRL) FOUNDATION
225 Main St.
Newington, CT 06111
Tel: (860)594-0200
Fax: (860)594-0259
E-mail: foundation@arrl.org
Web Site: http://www.arrlf.org
To support the education of students holding a valid FCC-granted Amateur Radio license for post-secondary education.
Title of Award: Mary Lou Brown Scholarships **Area, Field, or Subject:** Radio and television. **Level of Education for which Award is Granted:** Undergraduate **Funds Available:** $2,500.
Eligibility Requirements: Applicant must hold an FCC amateur radio license; be a resident of ARRL Northwest Division (AK, ID, MT, OR, WA); studying baccalaureate or higher courses; and have a GPA of 3.0 or higher. **Application Requirements:** Applicants must submit a completed scholarship application form along with a recent high school (or equivalent) or college transcript. **Deadline for Receipt:** February 1.

3952 ■ AMERICAN RADIO RELAY LEAGUE (ARRL) FOUNDATION
225 Main St.
Newington, CT 06111
Tel: (860)594-0200
Fax: (860)594-0259
E-mail: foundation@arrl.org
Web Site: http://www.arrlf.org
To support the education of students holding a valid FCC-granted Amateur Radio license for post-secondary education.
Title of Award: L.B. Cebik, W4RNL, and Jean Cebik, N4TZP, Memorial Scholarships **Area, Field, or Subject:** Radio and television. **Level of Education for which Award is Granted:** Undergraduate **Number Awarded:** 1. **Funds Available:** $1,000.
Eligibility Requirements: Applicant must hold an FCC amateur radio license, and be attending a four-year college/university. **Application Requirements:** Applicants must submit a completed scholarship application form along with a recent high school (or equivalent) or college transcript. **Deadline for Receipt:** February 1.

3953 ■ AMERICAN RADIO RELAY LEAGUE (ARRL) FOUNDATION
225 Main St.
Newington, CT 06111
Tel: (860)594-0200
Fax: (860)594-0259
E-mail: foundation@arrl.org
Web Site: http://www.arrlf.org
To support the education of students holding a valid FCC-granted Amateur Radio license for post-secondary education.
Title of Award: Central Arizona DX Association Scholarships **Area, Field, or Subject:** Radio and television. **Level of Education for which Award is Granted:** Undergraduate **Number Awarded:** 1. **Funds Available:** $500.
Eligibility Requirements: Applicant must hold an FCC amateur radio license; be a resident of Arizona; and have a GPA of 3.2 or above. **Ap-**

plication **Requirements:** Applicants must submit a completed scholarship application form along with a recent high school (or equivalent) or college transcript. **Deadline for Receipt:** February 1.

3954 ■ AMERICAN RADIO RELAY LEAGUE (ARRL) FOUNDATION
225 Main St.
Newington, CT 06111
Tel: (860)594-0200
Fax: (860)594-0259
E-mail: foundation@arrl.org
Web Site: http://www.arrlf.org
To support the education of students holding a valid FCC-granted Amateur Radio license for post-secondary education.
Title of Award: Challenge Met Scholarships **Area, Field, or Subject:** Radio and television. **Level of Education for which Award is Granted:** Undergraduate **Funds Available:** $500.
Eligibility Requirements: Applicant must hold an FCC amateur radio license, and be attending an accredited two- or four-year college technical school or university. **Application Requirements:** Applicants must submit a completed scholarship application form along with a recent high school (or equivalent) or college transcript. **Deadline for Receipt:** February 1.

3955 ■ AMERICAN RADIO RELAY LEAGUE (ARRL) FOUNDATION
225 Main St.
Newington, CT 06111
Tel: (860)594-0200
Fax: (860)594-0259
E-mail: foundation@arrl.org
Web Site: http://www.arrlf.org
To support the education of students holding a valid FCC-granted Amateur Radio license for post-secondary education.
Title of Award: Chicago FM Club Scholarships **Area, Field, or Subject:** Radio and television. **Level of Education for which Award is Granted:** Undergraduate **Funds Available:** $500.
Eligibility Requirements: Applicant must hold an FCC amateur radio license; residency in FCC Ninth Call district (IN, IL, WI); be attending a post-secondary course of study at an accredited two- or four-year college or trade school; and must be a U.S. citizen or within three months of citizenship. **Application Requirements:** Applicants must submit a completed scholarship application form along with a recent high school (or equivalent) or college transcript. **Deadline for Receipt:** February 1.

3956 ■ AMERICAN RADIO RELAY LEAGUE (ARRL) FOUNDATION
225 Main St.
Newington, CT 06111
Tel: (860)594-0200
Fax: (860)594-0259
E-mail: foundation@arrl.org
Web Site: http://www.arrlf.org
To support the education of students holding a valid FCC-granted Amateur Radio license for post-secondary education.
Title of Award: Tom and Judith Comstock Scholarships **Area, Field, or Subject:** Radio and television. **Level of Education for which Award is Granted:** Undergraduate **Number Awarded:** 1. **Funds Available:** $2,000.
Eligibility Requirements: Applicant must hold an FCC amateur radio license; be a resident of Texas or Oklahoma; and be a high school senior accepted at a twoor four-year college. **Application Requirements:** Applicants must submit a completed scholarship application form along with a recent high school (or equivalent) or college transcript. **Deadline for Receipt:** February 1.

3957 ■ AMERICAN RADIO RELAY LEAGUE (ARRL) FOUNDATION
225 Main St.
Newington, CT 06111
Tel: (860)594-0200
Fax: (860)594-0259
E-mail: foundation@arrl.org
Web Site: http://www.arrlf.org
To support the education of students holding a valid FCC-granted Amateur Radio license for post-secondary education.
Title of Award: Irvine W. Cook WA0CGS Scholarships **Area, Field, or Subject:** Radio and television; Electronics; Communications. **Level of**

Education for which Award is Granted: Undergraduate **Number Awarded:** 1. **Funds Available:** $1,000.

Eligibility Requirements: Applicant must hold an FCC amateur radio license; residency in Kansas; and be studying baccalaureate or higher courses in electronics, communications or a related field. **Application Requirements:** Applicants must submit a completed scholarship application form along with a recent high school (or equivalent) or college transcript. **Deadline for Receipt:** February 1.

3958 ■ AMERICAN RADIO RELAY LEAGUE (ARRL) FOUNDATION
225 Main St.
Newington, CT 06111
Tel: (860)594-0200
Fax: (860)594-0259
E-mail: foundation@arrl.org
Web Site: http://www.arrlf.org
To support the education of students holding a valid FCC-granted Amateur Radio license for post-secondary education.
Title of Award: Charles Clarke Cordle Memorial Scholarships **Area, Field, or Subject:** Radio and television; Electronics; Communications. **Level of Education for which Award is Granted:** Undergraduate **Number Awarded:** 1. **Funds Available:** $1,000.
Eligibility Requirements: Applicant must hold an FCC amateur radio license; be a resident of Georgia or Alabama; have a GPA of 2.5 or higher; and be attending an institution in Georgia or Alabama. **Application Requirements:** Applicants must submit a completed scholarship application form along with a recent high school (or equivalent) or college transcript. **Deadline for Receipt:** February 1.

3959 ■ AMERICAN RADIO RELAY LEAGUE (ARRL) FOUNDATION
225 Main St.
Newington, CT 06111
Tel: (860)594-0200
Fax: (860)594-0259
E-mail: foundation@arrl.org
Web Site: http://www.arrlf.org
To support the education of students holding a valid FCC-granted Amateur Radio license for post-secondary education.
Title of Award: Albuquerque ARC/Toby Cross Scholarships **Area, Field, or Subject:** Radio and television. **Level of Education for which Award is Granted:** Undergraduate **Number Awarded:** 1. **Funds Available:** $500.
Eligibility Requirements: Applicant must hold an FCC amateur radio license, and be a New Mexico resident. **Application Requirements:** Applicants must submit a completed scholarship application form along with a recent high school (or equivalent) or college transcript. **Deadline for Receipt:** February 1.

3960 ■ AMERICAN RADIO RELAY LEAGUE (ARRL) FOUNDATION
225 Main St.
Newington, CT 06111
Tel: (860)594-0200
Fax: (860)594-0259
E-mail: foundation@arrl.org
Web Site: http://www.arrlf.org
To support the education of students holding a valid FCC-granted Amateur Radio license for post-secondary education.
Title of Award: Dayton Amateur Radio Association Scholarships **Area, Field, or Subject:** Radio and television. **Level of Education for which Award is Granted:** Undergraduate **Number Awarded:** 4. **Funds Available:** $1,000.
Eligibility Requirements: Applicant must hold an FCC amateur radio license and be attending an accredited four-year college/university. **Application Requirements:** Applicants must submit a completed scholarship application form along with a recent high school (or equivalent) or college transcript. **Deadline for Receipt:** February 1.

3961 ■ AMERICAN RADIO RELAY LEAGUE (ARRL) FOUNDATION
225 Main St.
Newington, CT 06111
Tel: (860)594-0200
Fax: (860)594-0259
E-mail: foundation@arrl.org

Web Site: http://www.arrlf.org
To support the education of students holding a valid FCC-granted Amateur Radio license for post-secondary education.
Title of Award: Charles N. Fisher Memorial Scholarships **Area, Field, or Subject:** Radio and television; Electronics; Communications. **Level of Education for which Award is Granted:** Undergraduate **Number Awarded:** 1. **Funds Available:** $1,000.
Eligibility Requirements: Applicant must hold an FCC amateur radio license; must be a resident of ARRL Southwestern Division (AZ, Los Angeles, Orange, San Diego, Santa Barbara); studying in electronics, communications or related fields. **Application Requirements:** Applicants must submit a completed scholarship application form along with a recent high school (or equivalent) or college transcript. **Deadline for Receipt:** February 1.

3962 ■ AMERICAN RADIO RELAY LEAGUE (ARRL) FOUNDATION
225 Main St.
Newington, CT 06111
Tel: (860)594-0200
Fax: (860)594-0259
E-mail: foundation@arrl.org
Web Site: http://www.arrlf.org
To support the education of students holding a valid FCC-granted Amateur Radio license for post-secondary education.
Title of Award: William R. Goldfarb Memorial Scholarships **Area, Field, or Subject:** Radio and television; Business; Computer and information sciences; Medicine; Nursing; Engineering; Science. **Level of Education for which Award is Granted:** Undergraduate **Number Awarded:** 1. **Funds Available:** No specific amount.
Eligibility Requirements: Applicant must hold an FCC amateur radio license; must be studying baccalaureate courses in business-related, computers, medical, nursing, engineering or sciences; be a high school senior; and must demonstrate financial need. **Application Requirements:** Applicants must submit a completed scholarship application form along with a recent high school (or equivalent) or college transcript, and the Free Application for Federal Student Aid (FAFSA) or Student Aid Report (SAR). **Deadline for Receipt:** February 1.

3963 ■ AMERICAN RADIO RELAY LEAGUE (ARRL) FOUNDATION
225 Main St.
Newington, CT 06111
Tel: (860)594-0200
Fax: (860)594-0259
E-mail: foundation@arrl.org
Web Site: http://www.arrlf.org
To support the education of students holding a valid FCC-granted Amateur Radio license for post secondary-education.
Title of Award: Paul and Helen L. Grauer Scholarships **Area, Field, or Subject:** Radio and television; Electronics; Communications. **Level of Education for which Award is Granted:** Undergraduate **Number Awarded:** 1. **Funds Available:** $1,000.
Eligibility Requirements: Applicant must hold an FCC amateur radio license; be a resident of ARRL Midwest Division (IA, KS, MO, NE); be studying in baccalaureate or higher courses in electronics, communications or related field; and be attending school in the Midwest Division. **Application Requirements:** Applicants must submit a completed scholarship application form along with a recent high school (or equivalent) or college transcript. **Deadline for Receipt:** February 1.

3964 ■ AMERICAN RADIO RELAY LEAGUE (ARRL) FOUNDATION
225 Main St.
Newington, CT 06111
Tel: (860)594-0200
Fax: (860)594-0259
E-mail: foundation@arrl.org
Web Site: http://www.arrlf.org
To support the education of students holding a valid FCC-granted Amateur Radio license for post-secondary education.
Title of Award: K2TEO Martin J. Green, Sr. Memorial Scholarships **Area, Field, or Subject:** Radio and television. **Level of Education for which Award is Granted:** Undergraduate **Number Awarded:** 1. **Funds Available:** $1,000.
Eligibility Requirements: Applicant must hold an FCC amateur radio license. **Application Requirements:** Applicants must submit a completed

scholarship application form along with a recent high school (or equivalent) or college transcript. **Deadline for Receipt:** February 1.

3965 ■ AMERICAN RADIO RELAY LEAGUE (ARRL) FOUNDATION
225 Main St.
Newington, CT 06111
Tel: (860)594-0200
Fax: (860)594-0259
E-mail: foundation@arrl.org
Web Site: http://www.arrlf.org
To support the education of students holding a valid FCC-granted Amateur Radio license for post-secondary education.
Title of Award: Perry F. Hadlock Memorial Scholarships **Area, Field, or Subject:** Radio and television; Technology; Engineering, Electrical. **Level of Education for which Award is Granted:** Undergraduate **Number Awarded:** 1. **Funds Available:** $2,000.
Eligibility Requirements: Applicant must hold an FCC amateur radio license; must be studying in baccalaureate or higher courses in a technology-related field; preference to electrical and electronics engineering. **Application Requirements:** Applicants must submit a completed scholarship application form along with a recent high school (or equivalent) or college transcript. **Deadline for Receipt:** February 1.

3966 ■ AMERICAN RADIO RELAY LEAGUE (ARRL) FOUNDATION
225 Main St.
Newington, CT 06111
Tel: (860)594-0200
Fax: (860)594-0259
E-mail: foundation@arrl.org
Web Site: http://www.arrlf.org
To support the education of students holding a valid FCC-granted Amateur Radio license for post-secondary education.
Title of Award: Albert H. Hix, W8AH Memorial Scholarships **Area, Field, or Subject:** Radio and television. **Level of Education for which Award is Granted:** Undergraduate **Number Awarded:** 1. **Funds Available:** $500.
Eligibility Requirements: Applicant must hold an FCC amateur radio license; be a resident and attending school in the WV Section; and have a GPA of 3.0 or higher. **Application Requirements:** Applicants must submit a completed scholarship application form along with a recent high school (or equivalent) or college transcript. **Deadline for Receipt:** February 1.

3967 ■ AMERICAN RADIO RELAY LEAGUE (ARRL) FOUNDATION
225 Main St.
Newington, CT 06111
Tel: (860)594-0200
Fax: (860)594-0259
E-mail: foundation@arrl.org
Web Site: http://www.arrlf.org
To support the education of students holding a valid FCC-granted Amateur Radio license for post-secondary education.
Title of Award: Seth Horen, K1LOM Memorial Scholarships **Area, Field, or Subject:** Radio and television. **Level of Education for which Award is Granted:** Undergraduate **Number Awarded:** 1. **Funds Available:** $500.
Eligibility Requirements: Applicant must hold an FCC amateur radio license, and be attending a four-year college/university. **Application Requirements:** Applicants must submit a completed scholarship application form along with a recent high school (or equivalent) or college transcript. **Deadline for Receipt:** February 1.

3968 ■ AMERICAN RADIO RELAY LEAGUE (ARRL) FOUNDATION
225 Main St.
Newington, CT 06111
Tel: (860)594-0200
Fax: (860)594-0259
E-mail: foundation@arrl.org
Web Site: http://www.arrlf.org
To support the education of students holding a valid FCC-granted Amateur Radio license for post-secondary education.
Title of Award: IRARC Memorial Joseph P. Rubino WA4MMD Scholarships **Area, Field, or Subject:** Radio and television; Electronics. **Level of Education for which Award is Granted:** Undergraduate **Funds Available:** $750.

Eligibility Requirements: Applicant must hold an FCC amateur radio license; have a minimum 2.5 GPA on a 4.0 scale; and be enrolled in an undergraduate degree or electronic technician certification program at an accredited institution. **Application Requirements:** Applicants must submit a completed scholarship application form along with a recent high school (or equivalent) or college transcript. **Deadline for Receipt:** February 1.

3969 ■ AMERICAN RADIO RELAY LEAGUE (ARRL) FOUNDATION
225 Main St.
Newington, CT 06111
Tel: (860)594-0200
Fax: (860)594-0259
E-mail: foundation@arrl.org
Web Site: http://www.arrlf.org
To support the education of students holding a valid FCC-granted Amateur Radio license for post-secondary education.
Title of Award: Dr. James L. Lawson Memorial Scholarships **Area, Field, or Subject:** Radio and television Electronics; Communications. **Level of Education for which Award is Granted:** Undergraduate **Number Awarded:** 1. **Funds Available:** $500.
Eligibility Requirements: Applicant must hold an FCC amateur radio license; be a resident of one of the New England states (ME, NH, VT, CT, RI) or New York State; and be studying in baccalaureate or higher courses in electronics, communications or related fields. **Application Requirements:** Applicants must submit a completed scholarship application form along with a recent high school (or equivalent) or college transcript. **Deadline for Receipt:** February 1.

3970 ■ AMERICAN RADIO RELAY LEAGUE (ARRL) FOUNDATION
225 Main St.
Newington, CT 06111
Tel: (860)594-0200
Fax: (860)594-0259
E-mail: foundation@arrl.org
Web Site: http://www.arrlf.org
To support the education of students holding a valid FCC-granted Amateur Radio license for post-secondary education.
Title of Award: Fred R. McDaniel Memorial Scholarships **Area, Field, or Subject:** Radio and television; Electronics; Communications. **Level of Education for which Award is Granted:** Undergraduate **Number Awarded:** 1. **Funds Available:** $500.
Eligibility Requirements: Applicant must hold an FCC amateur radio license; be a resident of the FCC 5th call district (TX, OK, AR, LA, MS, NM); be studying in baccalaureate or higher courses of study in electronics, communications or related fields. **Application Requirements:** Applicants must submit a completed scholarship application form along with a recent high school (or equivalent) or college transcript. **Deadline for Receipt:** February 1.

3971 ■ AMERICAN RADIO RELAY LEAGUE (ARRL) FOUNDATION
225 Main St.
Newington, CT 06111
Tel: (860)594-0200
Fax: (860)594-0259
E-mail: foundation@arrl.org
Web Site: http://www.arrlf.org
To support the education of students holding a valid FCC-granted Amateur Radio license for post-secondary education.
Title of Award: Edmond A. Metzger Scholarships **Area, Field, or Subject:** Radio and television; Electrical engineering. **Level of Education for which Award is Granted:** Undergraduate **Number Awarded:** 1. **Funds Available:** $500.
Eligibility Requirements: Applicant must hold an FCC amateur radio license; be a resident of ARRL Central Division (IL, IN, WI); be studying in baccalaureate or higher courses of study in electrical engineering; be an ARRL member; and attending school in the Central Division. **Application Requirements:** Applicants must submit a completed scholarship application form along with a recent high school (or equivalent) or college transcript. **Deadline for Receipt:** February 1.

3972 ■ AMERICAN RADIO RELAY LEAGUE (ARRL) FOUNDATION
225 Main St.
Newington, CT 06111

Tel: (860)594-0200
Fax: (860)594-0259
E-mail: foundation@arrl.org
Web Site: http://www.arrlf.org
To support the education of students holding a valid FCC-granted Amateur Radio license for post-secondary education.
Title of Award: David W. Misek, N8NPX Memorial Scholarships **Area, Field, or Subject:** Radio and television. **Level of Education for which Award is Granted:** Undergraduate **Number Awarded:** Up to 3. **Funds Available:** $1,500.
Eligibility Requirements: Applicant must hold an FCC amateur radio license; currently reside in one of nine Ohio counties: Greene, Montgomery, Champaign, Darke, Preble, Miami, Clark, Butler, Warren; and be attending four-year college/university. **Application Requirements:** Applicants must submit a completed scholarship application form along with a recent high school (or equivalent) or college transcript. **Deadline for Receipt:** February 1.

3973 ■ AMERICAN RADIO RELAY LEAGUE (ARRL) FOUNDATION
225 Main St.
Newington, CT 06111
Tel: (860)594-0200
Fax: (860)594-0259
E-mail: foundation@arrl.org
Web Site: http://www.arrlf.org
To support the education of students holding a valid FCC-granted Amateur Radio license for post-secondary education.
Title of Award: NCDXF Scholarships **Area, Field, or Subject:** Radio and television. **Level of Education for which Award is Granted:** Undergraduate **Number Awarded:** 2. **Funds Available:** $1,500.
Eligibility Requirements: Applicant must hold an FCC amateur radio license; be attending a junior college, four-year college/university or trade school in the U.S.; and must demonstrate activity and interest in DXing.
Application Requirements: Applicants must submit a completed scholarship application form along with a recent high school (or equivalent) or college transcript. **Deadline for Receipt:** February 1.

3974 ■ AMERICAN RADIO RELAY LEAGUE (ARRL) FOUNDATION
225 Main St.
Newington, CT 06111
Tel: (860)594-0200
Fax: (860)594-0259
E-mail: foundation@arrl.org
Web Site: http://www.arrlf.org
To support the education of students holding a valid FCC-granted Amateur Radio license for post-secondary education.
Title of Award: New England FEMARA Scholarships **Area, Field, or Subject:** Radio and television. **Level of Education for which Award is Granted:** Undergraduate **Funds Available:** $1,000.
Eligibility Requirements: Applicant must hold an FCC amateur radio license, and be a resident of one of the New England states (ME, NH, VT, CT, RI). **Application Requirements:** Applicants must submit a completed scholarship application form along with a recent high school (or equivalent) or college transcript. **Deadline for Receipt:** February 1.

3975 ■ AMERICAN RADIO RELAY LEAGUE (ARRL) FOUNDATION
225 Main St.
Newington, CT 06111
Tel: (860)594-0200
Fax: (860)594-0259
E-mail: foundation@arrl.org
Web Site: http://www.arrlf.org
To support the education of students holding a valid FCC-granted Amateur Radio license for post-secondary education.
Title of Award: Ray, NORP and Katie, WOKTE Pautz Scholarships **Area, Field, or Subject:** Radio and television; Electronics; Computer and information sciences. **Level of Education for which Award is Granted:** Undergraduate **Number Awarded:** 1. **Funds Available:** $500-$1,000.
Eligibility Requirements: Applicant must hold an FCC amateur radio license; be a resident of the ARRL Midwest Division (IA, KS, MO, NE); be enrolled in electronics, computer science or related field at an accredited 4-year college/university; and be an ARRL member. **Application Requirements:** Applicants must submit a completed scholarship applica-

tion form along with a recent high school (or equivalent) or college transcript. **Deadline for Receipt:** February 1.

3976 ■ AMERICAN RADIO RELAY LEAGUE (ARRL) FOUNDATION
225 Main St.
Newington, CT 06111
Tel: (860)594-0200
Fax: (860)594-0259
E-mail: foundation@arrl.org
Web Site: http://www.arrl.org
To support the education of students holding a valid FCC-granted Amateur Radio license for post-secondary education.
Title of Award: Peoria Area Amateur Radio Club Scholarships **Area, Field, or Subject:** Radio and television. **Level of Education for which Award is Granted:** Undergraduate **Number Awarded:** 1. **Funds Available:** $500.
Eligibility Requirements: Applicant must hold an FCC amateur radio license; be a resident of Central Illinois in one of these counties: Peoria, Tazewell, Woodford, Knox, McLean, Fulton, Logan, Marshall or Stark; and attending an accredited two- or four-year college/university. **Application Requirements:** Applicants must submit a completed scholarship application form along with a recent high school (or equivalent) or college transcript. **Deadline for Receipt:** February 1.

3977 ■ AMERICAN RADIO RELAY LEAGUE (ARRL) FOUNDATION
225 Main St.
Newington, CT 06111
Tel: (860)594-0200
Fax: (860)594-0259
E-mail: foundation@arrl.org
Web Site: http://www.arrlf.org
To support the education of students holding a valid FCC-granted Amateur Radio license for post-secondary education.
Title of Award: PHD ARA Scholarships **Area, Field, or Subject:** Radio and television; Journalism; Computer and information sciences; Electronics. **Level of Education for which Award is Granted:** Undergraduate **Number Awarded:** 1. **Funds Available:** $500.
Eligibility Requirements: Applicant must hold an FCC amateur radio license; be a resident of ARRL Midwest Division (IA, KS, MO, NE); with course sof study in journalism, computer science or electronic engineering; and be the child of a deceased radio amateur. **Application Requirements:** Applicants must submit a completed scholarship application form along with a recent high school (or equivalent) or college transcript. **Deadline for Receipt:** February 1.

3978 ■ AMERICAN RADIO RELAY LEAGUE (ARRL) FOUNDATION
225 Main St.
Newington, CT 06111
Tel: (860)594-0200
Fax: (860)594-0259
E-mail: foundation@arrl.org
Web Site: http://www.arrlf.org
To support the education of students holding a valid FCC-granted Amateur Radio license for post-secondary education.
Title of Award: Thomas W. Porter, W8KYZ Scholarships Honoring Michael Daugherty, W8LSE **Area, Field, or Subject:** Radio and television. **Level of Education for which Award is Granted:** Undergraduate **Number Awarded:** 1. **Funds Available:** $1,000.
Eligibility Requirements: Applicant must hold an FCC amateur radio license, and attending an accredited 2- or 4-year college/university or technical school. **Application Requirements:** Applicants must submit a completed scholarship application form along with a recent high school (or equivalent) or college transcript. **Deadline for Receipt:** February 1.

3979 ■ AMERICAN RADIO RELAY LEAGUE (ARRL) FOUNDATION
225 Main St.
Newington, CT 06111
Tel: (860)594-0200
Fax: (860)594-0259
E-mail: foundation@arrl.org
Web Site: http://www.arrlf.org
To support the education of students holding a valid FCC-granted Amateur Radio license for post-secondary education.

Title of Award: Donald Riebhoff Memorial Scholarships **Area, Field, or Subject:** Radio and television. **Level of Education for which Award is Granted:** Undergraduate **Number Awarded:** 1. **Funds Available:** $1,000.

Eligibility Requirements: Applicant must hold an FCC amateur radio license; be studying in baccalaureate or higher courses of study in international studies at an accredited post-secondary school; and be an ARRL member. **Application Requirements:** Applicants must submit a completed scholarship application form along with a recent high school (or equivalent) or college transcript. **Deadline for Receipt:** February 1.

3980 ■ AMERICAN RADIO RELAY LEAGUE (ARRL) FOUNDATION
225 Main St.
Newington, CT 06111
Tel: (860)594-0200
Fax: (860)594-0259
E-mail: foundation@arrl.org
Web Site: http://www.arrl.org
To support the education of students holding a valid FCC-granted Amateur Radio license for post-secondary education.
Title of Award: Bill Salerno, W2ONV, Memorial Scholarships **Area, Field, or Subject:** Radio and television. **Level of Education for which Award is Granted:** Undergraduate **Number Awarded:** 1. **Funds Available:** $1,000.

Eligibility Requirements: Applicant must hold an FCC amateur radio license; have a high school GPA of 3.7 or higher; have an annual family income not exceeding $100,000; and be enrolled at an accredited 4-year college/university. **Application Requirements:** Applicants must submit a completed scholarship application form along with a recent high school (or equivalent) or college transcript. **Deadline for Receipt:** February 1.

3981 ■ AMERICAN RADIO RELAY LEAGUE (ARRL) FOUNDATION
225 Main St.
Newington, CT 06111
Tel: (860)594-0200
Fax: (860)594-0259
E-mail: foundation@arrl.org
Web Site: http://www.arrl.org
To support the education of students holding a valid FCC-granted Amateur Radio license for post-secondary education.
Title of Award: Eugene Gene Sallee, W4YFR Memorial Scholarships **Area, Field, or Subject:** Radio and television. **Level of Education for which Award is Granted:** Undergraduate **Number Awarded:** 1. **Funds Available:** $500.

Eligibility Requirements: Applicant must hold an FCC amateur radio license; be a resident of the state of Georgia; and have a GPA of 3.0 or higher. **Application Requirements:** Applicants must submit a completed scholarship application form along with a recent high school (or equivalent) or college transcript. **Deadline for Receipt:** February 1.

3982 ■ AMERICAN RADIO RELAY LEAGUE (ARRL) FOUNDATION
225 Main St.
Newington, CT 06111
Tel: (860)594-0200
Fax: (860)594-0259
E-mail: foundation@arrl.org
Web Site: http://www.arrl.org
To support the education of students holding a valid FCC-granted Amateur Radio license for post-secondary education.
Title of Award: Scholarships of the Morris Radio Club of New Jersey **Area, Field, or Subject:** Radio and television. **Level of Education for which Award is Granted:** Undergraduate **Number Awarded:** 1. **Funds Available:** $1,000.
Eligibility Requirements: Applicant must hold an FCC amateur radio license, and be attending a four-year college/university. **Application Requirements:** Applicants must submit a completed scholarship application form along with a recent high school (or equivalent) or college transcript. **Deadline for Receipt:** February 1.

3983 ■ AMERICAN RADIO RELAY LEAGUE (ARRL) FOUNDATION
225 Main St.
Newington, CT 06111
Tel: (860)594-0200

Fax: (860)594-0259
E-mail: foundation@arrl.org
Web Site: http://www.arrlf.org
To support the education of students holding a valid FCC-granted Amateur Radio license for post-secondary education.
Title of Award: Six Meter Club of Chicago Scholarships **Area, Field, or Subject:** Radio and television. **Level of Education for which Award is Granted:** Undergraduate **Number Awarded:** 1. **Funds Available:** $500.
Eligibility Requirements: Applicant must hold an FCC amateur radio license; a resident of Illinois; and be enrolled in a post-secondary course of study leading to undergraduate degree. **Application Requirements:** Applicants must submit a completed scholarship application form along with a recent high school (or equivalent) or college transcript. **Deadline for Receipt:** February 1.

3984 ■ AMERICAN RADIO RELAY LEAGUE (ARRL) FOUNDATION
225 Main St.
Newington, CT 06111
Tel: (860)594-0200
Fax: (860)594-0259
E-mail: foundation@arrl.org
Web Site: http://www.arrlf.org
To support the education of students holding a valid FCC-granted Amateur Radio license for post-secondary education.
Title of Award: Zachary Taylor Stevens Memorial Scholarships **Area, Field, or Subject:** Radio and television. **Level of Education for which Award is Granted:** Undergraduate **Number Awarded:** 1. **Funds Available:** $750.

Eligibility Requirements: Applicant must hold an FCC amateur radio license, and be enrolled in an accredited two- or four-year college/university or technical school. **Application Requirements:** Applicants must submit a completed scholarship application form along with a recent high school (or equivalent) or college transcript. **Deadline for Receipt:** February 1.

3985 ■ AMERICAN RADIO RELAY LEAGUE (ARRL) FOUNDATION
225 Main St.
Newington, CT 06111
Tel: (860)594-0200
Fax: (860)594-0259
E-mail: foundation@arrl.org
Web Site: http://www.arrlf.org
To support the education of students holding a valid FCC-granted Amateur Radio license for post-secondary education.
Title of Award: Carole J. Streeter, KB9JBR Scholarships **Area, Field, or Subject:** Radio and television. **Level of Education for which Award is Granted:** Undergraduate **Number Awarded:** 1. **Funds Available:** $750.
Eligibility Requirements: Applicant must hold an FCC amateur radio license, and be enrolled in an accredited college/university studying healing arts. **Application Requirements:** Applicants must submit a completed scholarship application form along with a recent high school (or equivalent) or college transcript. **Deadline for Receipt:** February 1.

3986 ■ AMERICAN RADIO RELAY LEAGUE (ARRL) FOUNDATION
225 Main St.
Newington, CT 06111
Tel: (860)594-0200
Fax: (860)594-0259
E-mail: foundation@arrl.org
Web Site: http://www.arrlf.org
To support the education of students holding a valid FCC-granted Amateur Radio license for post-secondary education.
Title of Award: Norman E. Strohmeier, W2VRS Memorial Scholarships **Area, Field, or Subject:** Radio and television. **Level of Education for which Award is Granted:** Undergraduate **Number Awarded:** 1. **Funds Available:** $550.
Eligibility Requirements: Applicant must hold an FCC amateur radio license; be a resident of Western New York; and have a cumulative GPA of 3.2 or better. **Application Requirements:** Applicants must submit a completed scholarship application form along with a recent high school (or equivalent) or college transcript. **Deadline for Receipt:** February 1.

3987 ■ AMERICAN RADIO RELAY LEAGUE (ARRL) FOUNDATION
225 Main St.
Newington, CT 06111

Tel: (860)594-0200
Fax: (860)594-0259
E-mail: foundation@arrl.org
Web Site: http://www.arrlf.org
To support the education of students holding a valid FCC-granted Amateur Radio license for post-secondary education.
Title of Award: Gary Wagner, K3OMI Scholarships **Area, Field, or Subject:** Radio and television; Engineering. **Level of Education for which Award is Granted:** Undergraduate **Number Awarded:** 1. **Funds Available:** $1,000.
Eligibility Requirements: Applicant must hold an FCC amateur radio license; be a resident of NC, VA, WV, MD or TN; enrolled in an accredited four-year college/university (NC, VA, WV, MD, or TN) working towards a Bachelor's of Science in any field of engineering; and have financial need. **Application Requirements:** Applicants must submit a completed scholarship application form along with a recent high school (or equivalent) or college transcript. **Deadline for Receipt:** February 1.

3988 ■ AMERICAN RADIO RELAY LEAGUE (ARRL) FOUNDATION
225 Main St.
Newington, CT 06111
Tel: (860)594-0200
Fax: (860)594-0259
E-mail: foundation@arrl.org
Web Site: http://www.arrl.org
To support the education of students holding a valid FCC-granted Amateur Radio license for post-secondary education.
Title of Award: Francis Walton Memorial Scholarships **Area, Field, or Subject:** Radio and television. **Level of Education for which Award is Granted:** Undergraduate **Number Awarded:** 1 or more. **Funds Available:** $500.
Eligibility Requirements: Applicant must hold an FCC amateur radio license; be a resident of Illinois or Central Division (IL, IN, WI); and studying baccalaureate or higher degree. **Application Requirements:** Applicants must submit a completed scholarship application form along with a recent high school (or equivalent) or college transcript. **Deadline for Receipt:** February 1.

3989 ■ AMERICAN RADIO RELAY LEAGUE (ARRL) FOUNDATION
225 Main St.
Newington, CT 06111
Tel: (860)594-0200
Fax: (860)594-0259
E-mail: foundation@arrl.org
Web Site: http://www.arrlf.org
To support the education of students holding a valid FCC-granted Amateur Radio license for post-secondary education.
Title of Award: L. Phil Wicker Scholarships **Area, Field, or Subject:** Radio and television; Electronics; Communications. **Level of Education for which Award is Granted:** Undergraduate **Number Awarded:** 1. **Funds Available:** $1,000.
Eligibility Requirements: Applicant must hold an FCC amateur radio license; be a resident of ARRL Roanoke Division (NC, SC, VA, WV); enrolled in a baccalaureate or higher course in electronics, communications and related fields. **Application Requirements:** Applicants must submit a completed scholarship application form along with a recent high school (or equivalent) or college transcript. **Deadline for Receipt:** February 1.

3990 ■ AMERICAN RADIO RELAY LEAGUE (ARRL) FOUNDATION
225 Main St.
Newington, CT 06111
Tel: (860)594-0200
Fax: (860)594-0259
E-mail: foundation@arrl.org
Web Site: http://www.arrlf.org
To support the education of students holding a valid FCC-granted Amateur Radio license for post-secondary education.
Title of Award: Yankee Clipper Contest Club, Inc. Youth Scholarships **Area, Field, or Subject:** Radio and television. **Level of Education for which Award is Granted:** Undergraduate **Number Awarded:** 1. **Funds Available:** $1,000.
Eligibility Requirements: Applicant must hold an FCC amateur radio license; residency or college/university attendance within 175 miles of

YCCC Center in Erving MA, including MA, RI, CT, Long Island NY, some of VT, NH, ME, PA, and NJ; and be enrolled in a 2 or 4-year degree program at an accredited college/university. **Application Requirements:** Applicants must submit a completed scholarship application form along with a recent high school (or equivalent) or college transcript. **Deadline for Receipt:** February 1.

3991 ■ AMERICAN RADIO RELAY LEAGUE (ARRL) FOUNDATION
225 Main St.
Newington, CT 06111
Tel: (860)594-0200
Fax: (860)594-0259
E-mail: foundation@arrl.org
Web Site: http://www.arrlf.org
To support the education of students holding a valid FCC-granted Amateur Radio license for post-secondary education.
Title of Award: Yasme Foundation Scholarships **Area, Field, or Subject:** Radio and television; Science; Engineering. **Level of Education for which Award is Granted:** Undergraduate **Number Awarded:** 5 in 2006. **Funds Available:** $2,000.
Eligibility Requirements: Applicant must hold an FCC amateur radio license, and be enrolled in a science or engineering course at an accredited four-year college/university. **Application Requirements:** Applicants must submit a completed scholarship application form along with a recent high school (or equivalent) or college transcript. **Deadline for Receipt:** February 1.

3992 ■ ARMED FORCES COMMUNICATIONS AND ELECTRONICS ASSOCIATION
4400 Fair Lakes Court
Fairfax, VA 22033
Tel: (703)631-6141
Free: 800-336-4583
Fax: (703)631-4693
Web Site: http://www.afcea.org
To provide scholarship for the general public.
Title of Award: AFCEA Distance Learning/Online Scholarships **Area, Field, or Subject:** Engineering; Mathematics; Physics; Communications; Electronics. **Level of Education for which Award is Granted:** Undergraduate **Funds Available:** $1,500.
Eligibility Requirements: Applicants must be U.S. citizens currently enrolled full time pursuing either a Bachelor of Science or Master's of Science degree through distance learning or online program (only a few second-year students only will be accepted). **Application Requirements:** Applicants may apply online at AFFECT website. Applicants must also submit two letters of recommendation printed in school stationery and with signature from field-of-study professors. **Deadline for Receipt:** June 1. **Additional Information:** Norma Corrales; 703-631-6149.

3993 ■ ARMED FORCES COMMUNICATIONS AND ELECTRONICS ASSOCIATION
4400 Fair Lakes Court
Fairfax, VA 22033
Tel: (703)631-6141
Free: 800-336-4583
Fax: (703)631-4693
Web Site: http://www.afcea.org
To provide scholarship to the general public.
Title of Award: AFCEA General John A. Wickham Scholarships **Area, Field, or Subject:** Engineering; Mathematics; Physics; Communications; Electronics. **Level of Education for which Award is Granted:** Undergraduate **Funds Available:** $2,000.
Eligibility Requirements: Applicants must be US citizens; must have GPA of 3.5 on 4.0 scale. **Application Requirements:** Applicants may apply at AFCEA web site. Applicants must also submit two letters of recommendation printed in school stationery and with signature from field-of-study professors. **Deadline for Receipt:** May 1. **Additional Information:** Norma Corrales; 703-631-6149.

3994 ■ ARMED FORCES COMMUNICATIONS AND ELECTRONICS ASSOCIATION
4400 Fair Lakes Court
Fairfax, VA 22033

Tel: (703)631-6141
Free: 800-336-4583
Fax: (703)631-4693
Web Site: http://www.afcea.org
To provide scholarship for the general public.
Title of Award: William E. "Buck" Bragunier Scholarships **Area, Field, or Subject:** Engineering; Mathematics; Physics; Communications; Electronics. **Level of Education for which Award is Granted:** Undergraduate **Funds Available:** $2,000.
Eligibility Requirements: Applicants must be at least second year college students; must be enrolled full time as sophomores or juniors at the time of application; must have an outstanding record of demonstrated leadership within university or local community. **Application Requirements:** Applicants may apply online at AFFECT website. Applicants must also submit two letters of recommendation printed in school stationery and with signature from field-of-study professors. **Deadline for Receipt:** May 1. **Additional Information:** Norma Corrales; 703-631-6149.

3995 ■ ARMED FORCES COMMUNICATIONS AND ELECTRONICS ASSOCIATION
4400 Fair Lakes Court
Fairfax, VA 22033
Tel: (703)631-6141
Free: 800-336-4583
Fax: (703)631-4693
Web Site: http://www.afcea.org
To provide scholarships to students connected to the US Military.
Title of Award: LT.G. Douglas D. Buchholz Memorial Scholarships **Area, Field, or Subject:** Engineering; Mathematics; Physics; Communications. **Level of Education for which Award is Granted:** Undergraduate **Funds Available:** $2,000.
Eligibility Requirements: Applicants must be currently active enlisted soldiers assigned to Fort Gordon, Georgia; must have completed a minimum of 15 semester hours/25 quarter hours; must be currently enrolled either full or part time in an accredited US college; and must have a minimum GPA of 2.5 on a 4.0 scale. **Application Requirements:** Students may apply online at the AFCEA web site. **Deadline for Receipt:** November 15. **Additional Information:** Mr. Joseph S. Yavorsky, President; president@afcea-augusta.org.

3996 ■ ARMED FORCES COMMUNICATIONS AND ELECTRONICS ASSOCIATION
4400 Fair Lakes Court
Fairfax, VA 22033
Tel: (703)631-6141
Free: 800-336-4583
Fax: (703)631-4693
Web Site: http://www.afcea.org
To provide educational incentives, opportunities and assistance for people engaged in information management, communications and intelligence efforts and fostering excellence in education particularly in the "hard science" disciplines related to C4ISR.
Title of Award: Disabled War Veterans Scholarships **Area, Field, or Subject:** Engineering; Mathematics; Physics; Communications. **Level of Education for which Award is Granted:** Undergraduate **Funds Available:** $2,500.
Eligibility Requirements: Applicants must be currently enrolled and attending either a two year or four year in an accredited college or university in the United States; must be enrolled in an accredited distance learning or online degree granting program affiliated with major, accredited two year or four year college or university in the United States. **Application Requirements:** Applicants may apply online at AFFECT website. Applicants must also submit two letters of recommendation printed on school stationery and with signature from field-of-study professors. **Deadline for Receipt:** November 1. **Additional Information:** Norma Corrales; 703-631-6149.

3997 ■ ARMED FORCES COMMUNICATIONS AND ELECTRONICS ASSOCIATION
4400 Fair Lakes Court
Fairfax, VA 22033
Tel: (703)631-6141
Free: 800-336-4583

Fax: (703)631-4693
Web Site: http://www.afcea.org
To provide scholarship to the general public.
Title of Award: Lockheed Martin IT Scholarships **Area, Field, or Subject:** Engineering; Mathematics; Physics; Communications. **Level of Education for which Award is Granted:** Undergraduate **Funds Available:** $3,000.
Eligibility Requirements: Applicants must be at least second year college students, must be enrolled full time as sophomores or juniors at the time of application. **Application Requirements:** Applicants may apply online. Applicants must also submit two letters of recommendation printed in school stationery and with signature from field-of-study professors; and official transcript of all college level study. **Deadline for Receipt:** May 1. **Additional Information:** Norma Corrales; 703-631-6149.

3998 ■ ARMED FORCES COMMUNICATIONS AND ELECTRONICS ASSOCIATION
4400 Fair Lakes Court
Fairfax, VA 22033
Tel: (703)631-6141
Free: 800-336-4583
Fax: (703)631-4693
Web Site: http://www.afcea.org
To provide scholarships to students connected to the US Military.
Title of Award: AFCEA General Emmett Paige Scholarships **Area, Field, or Subject:** Engineering; Mathematics; Physics; Communications. **Level of Education for which Award is Granted:** Undergraduate **Funds Available:** $2,000.
Eligibility Requirements: Applicants must be US citizens; must have a minimum GPA of 3.0 on 4.0 scale. **Application Requirements:** Applicants may apply online at the AFCEA web site. Applicants must also submit a copy of Certificate of Service, Discharge From DD214, or facsimile of current Department of Defense or Coast Guard Identification Card; and two letters of recommendation printed in school stationery and with signature from field-of-study professors. **Deadline for Receipt:** March 1. **Additional Information:** Norma Corrales; 703-631-6149.

3999 ■ ARMED FORCES COMMUNICATIONS AND ELECTRONICS ASSOCIATION
4400 Fair Lakes Court
Fairfax, VA 22033
Tel: (703)631-6141
Free: 800-336-4583
Fax: (703)631-4693
Web Site: http://www.afcea.org
To provide scholarships to students connected to the US military.
Title of Award: Veterans of Enduring Freedom (Afghanistan) and Iraqi Freedom Scholarships **Area, Field, or Subject:** Engineering; Mathematics; Physics; Communications. **Level of Education for which Award is Granted:** Undergraduate **Funds Available:** $2,500. **Duration:** One year.
Eligibility Requirements: Applicants must be currently enrolled and attending either a two year accredited college or university in the United States. **Application Requirements:** Applicants may apply online at AFCEA web site. **Additional Information:** The AFCEA Educational Foundation is pleased to co-sponsor this scholarship opportunity for U.S. War Veterans. **Deadline for Receipt:** April 1 and November 1. **Additional Information:** Norma Corrales 703-631-6149.

4000 ■ ARMED FORCES COMMUNICATIONS AND ELECTRONICS ASSOCIATION
4400 Fair Lakes Court
Fairfax, VA 22033
Tel: (703)631-6141
Free: 800-336-4583
Fax: (703)631-4693
Web Site: http://www.afcea.org
To provide scholarships to students connected with the US Military.
Title of Award: Marine Corps Sgt. Jeannette L. Winters Memorial Scholarships **Area, Field, or Subject:** Engineering; Mathematics; Physics; Communications. **Level of Education for which Award is Granted:** Undergraduate **Funds Available:** $2,000.
Eligibility Requirements: Applicants must be enrolled full time in a Bachelor of Science degree program in accredited colleges or universities

in the United States; and must have a minimum GPA of 3.0 on 4.0 scale. Majors directly related to the support of US Intelligence enterprises or national security with relevance to the mission of AFCEA are also eligible. **Application Requirements:** Applicants may apply online at the AFCEA web site. Applicants must also submit two letters of recommendation printed in school stationery and with signature from field-of-study professors. **Deadline for Receipt:** September 1. **Additional Information:** Norma Corrales; 703-631-6149.

4001 ■ ASIAN AMERICAN JOURNALISTS ASSOCIATION
1182 Market St., Ste. 320
San Francisco, CA 94102
Tel: (415)346-2051
Fax: (415)346-6343
E-mail: national@aaja.org
Web Site: http://www.aaja.org
To provide financial assistance to students majoring in broadcast or online journalism.
Title of Award: AAJA/CNN Scholar Program **Area, Field, or Subject:** Journalism; Broadcasting. **Level of Education for which Award is Granted:** Graduate, Undergraduate **Number Awarded:** 4. **Funds Available:** $25,000. **Duration:** Four years.
Eligibility Requirements: Applicants must be graduating high school senior, undergraduate or graduate student enrolled full time with at least 12 credit units for each semester; must be currently taking or planning to take journalism courses. **Application Requirements:** Applicants must submit the completed application form; a resume; an official transcript; two letters of recommendation; a short essay, not exceeding 500 words, on the topic: "Describe any involvement or interest that you have in the Asian American community. If you were awarded an AAJA scholarship, propose how you would contribute to the field of journalism and/or media issues involving the Asian American and Pacific Islander community." **Deadline for Receipt:** March 28. **Additional Information:** Nao Vang; AAJA Student Programs Coordinator; 415-346-2051; programs@aaja.org.

4002 ■ ASIAN AMERICAN JOURNALISTS ASSOCIATION
1182 Market St., Ste. 320
San Francisco, CA 94102
Tel: (415)346-2051
Fax: (415)346-6343
E-mail: national@aaja.org
Web Site: http://www.aaja.org
To assist students who are interested in pursuing a career in print, broadcast, or photojournalism.
Title of Award: AAJA/COX Foundation Scholarships **Area, Field, or Subject:** Journalism; Broadcasting; Photography, Journalistic. **Level of Education for which Award is Granted:** Graduate, Undergraduate **Number Awarded:** 1. **Funds Available:** $1,250.
Eligibility Requirements: Applicants must be graduating high school senior, undergraduate or graduate student enrolled full time with at least 12 credit units for each semester; must be currently taking or planning to take journalism courses. **Application Requirements:** Applicants must submit the completed application form; a resume; an official transcript; two letters of recommendation; a short essay, not exceeding 500 words, on the topic: "Describe any involvement or interest that you have in the Asian American community. If you were awarded an AAJA scholarship, propose how you would contribute to the field of journalism and/or media issues involving the Asian American and Pacific Islander community." **Deadline for Receipt:** March 28. **Additional Information:** Nao Vang; AAJA Student Programs Coordinator; 415-346-2051; programs@aaja.org.

4003 ■ JOHN BAYLISS BROADCAST FOUNDATION
PO Box 51126
Pacific Grove, CA 93950
Tel: (831)655-5229
Fax: (831)655-5228
E-mail: cbutrum@baylissfoundation.org
Web Site: http://www.baylissfoundation.org
To enhance students' education at Bayliss Schools across the nation. To provide practical skills that will prepare them for a rewarding future.
Title of Award: John Bayliss Broadcast Foundation Internship Programs **Area, Field, or Subject:** Broadcasting. **Level of Education for which Award is Granted:** Undergraduate **Funds Available:** No specific amount.

Eligibility Requirements: Applicants must be studying for a career in the radio industry and have taken basic journalism courses as well as specialized courses in the radio communication fields. Applicants must have previous radio-related experience. Applicants must be enrolled in a degree program and entering their junior or senior year in college; must have a GPA of 3.0 or better; must be at least 18 years of age. **Application Requirements:** Applicants must submit a resume and complete the application form.

4004 ■ JOHN BAYLISS BROADCAST FOUNDATION
PO Box 51126
Pacific Grove, CA 93950
Tel: (831)655-5229
Fax: (831)655-5228
E-mail: cbutrum@baylissfoundation.org
Web Site: http://www.baylissfoundation.org
To support broadcasting students.
Title of Award: John Bayliss Broadcast Foundation Scholarships **Area, Field, or Subject:** Broadcasting. **Level of Education for which Award is Granted:** Undergraduate **Number Awarded:** 15. **Funds Available:** $5,000.
Eligibility Requirements: Applicants must be entering thier junior or senior year at an institution in the United States. Applicants must be preparing for a career in the radio industry, preferably commercial radio. Applicants must maintain a 3.0 GPA or better. **Application Requirements:** Applicants must provide a typewritten resume; an official transcript; three letters of recommendation written by people other than relatives. Applicant must submit a two-page typewritten essay describing his/her broadcasting goals as they relate to radio and the ways in which they hope to achieve their goals. **Deadline for Receipt:** March.

4005 ■ BLACK WOMEN IN SISTERHOOD FOR ACTION
PO Box 1592
Washington, DC 20013
Tel: (202)543-6013
Fax: (202)543-5719
E-mail: info@bisa-hq.org
Web Site: http://www.bisa-hq.org
To provide financial assistance to offset the cost of education for qualified students who have been accepted by an accredited college or university.
Title of Award: Richard Gregory Freeland, II Educational Scholarships **Area, Field, or Subject:** Computer and information sciences; Engineering; Telecommunications systems; Business administration. **Level of Education for which Award is Granted:** High School **Funds Available:** $500 to $2,500.
Eligibility Requirements: Applicants must be graduating high school students of African American ethnicity; reside in Maryland, Washington, DC or the Northern Virginia area; hold a grade point average of 2.5 or above; be pursuing a degree in the areas of computer science, information management, engineering, telecommunications, business management/administration or another technology-related field. **Application Requirements:** Applicants must submit all the required application information. **Deadline for Receipt:** May 5.

4006 ■ BLUES HEAVEN FOUNDATION
2120 S Michigan Ave.
Chicago, IL 60616
Tel: (312)808-1286
Fax: (312)808-0273
E-mail: info@bluesheaven.com
Web Site: http://www.bluesheaven.com
To provide financial assistance to students in Chicago.
Title of Award: Muddy Waters Scholarships **Area, Field, or Subject:** Music education, music, African-American studies, folklore, performing arts, journalism, radio and television. **Level of Education for which Award is Granted:** Undergraduate **Funds Available:** NO specific amount.
Eligibility Requirements: Applicant must have a full-time enrollment status in a Chicago area college or university; must be in at least their first year of undergraduate studies or graduate program. **Application Requirements:** Application form are available in the website address; must be sent to: Blues Heaven Foundation Inc., 2120 S Michigan Ave., Chicago, IL 60616. **Deadline for Receipt:** April 30.

4007 ■ BOWLING WRITERS ASSOCIATION OF AMERICA
8501 N Manor Ln.
Fox Point, WI 53217
Tel: (414)351-6085
E-mail: sjames2652@wi.rr.com
Web Site: http://www.bowlingwriters.com
To provide financial support for students pursuing a career in communications that involve the sport of bowling.
Title of Award: Chuck Pezzano Scholarships **Area, Field, or Subject:** Communication; Sports writing. **Level of Education for which Award is Granted:** Undergraduate **Funds Available:** $1000.
Eligibility Requirements: Applicants must have a minimum of 2.5 GPA; must be a high school or vocational school senior or college student. **Application Requirements:** Applicant must send application form (available at the website); transcript; at least one reference letter; and any other information to support your application. **Additional Information:** Established in honor of Chuck Pezzano a BWAA, American Bowling Congress and Professional Bowlers Association Hall of Fame journalist. **Deadline for Receipt:** May 15. **Additional Information:** Steve James, Executive Director

4008 ■ CANADIAN ASSOCIATION OF BROADCASTERS
PO Box 627, Sta. B
Ottawa, ON, Canada K1P 1A4
Tel: (613)233-4035
Fax: (613)233-6961
E-mail: cab@cab-acr.ca
Web Site: http://www.cab-acr.ca
To provide support to qualified individuals who want to pursue their career in broadcasting.
Title of Award: BBM Canada Scholarships **Area, Field, or Subject:** Broadcasting. **Level of Education for which Award is Granted:** Undergraduate **Funds Available:** $4,000. **Duration:** One year.
Eligibility Requirements: Applicant must be enrolled in a graduate studies program, or be in the final year of an honors degree with the intention of entering a graduate program, anywhere in Canada. **Application Requirements:** Applicant must submit a 250-word essay outlining their interest in and thoughts on audience research; must provide a recommendation from their course director. Application forms are available online and must be sent together with the application requirements to BBM Canada Scholarship, c/o The Canadian Association of Broadcasters, PO Box 627, Sta. B, Ottawa, ON K1P 5S2. **Deadline for Receipt:** June 30.

4009 ■ CANADIAN ASSOCIATION OF BROADCASTERS
PO Box 627, Sta. B
Ottawa, ON, Canada K1P 1A4
Tel: (613)233-4035
Fax: (613)233-6961
E-mail: cab@cab-acr.ca
Web Site: http://www.cab-acr.ca
To provide support to qualified individuals who want to pursue their career in broadcasting or broadcast sales/marketing.
Title of Award: Ruth Hancock Scholarships **Area, Field, or Subject:** Broadcasting. **Level of Education for which Award is Granted:** Undergraduate **Funds Available:** $1,500. **Duration:** One year.
Eligibility Requirements: Applicant must be a student enrolled in a recognized communication or marketing course in Canada; must have strong character and leadership qualities; must have a willingness to assist others; must have a genuine interest in pursuing a broadcasting career, as reflected in extracurricular activities related to broadcasting or broadcast sales/marketing, and/or self-initiated undertakings; must have community involvement and/ or volunteer work. **Application Requirements:** Applicant must provide 500-word outline and a signed recommendation from their course director. Application forms are available online and must be sent with the other supporting documents to Ruth Hancock Memorial Scholarships, c/o Canadian Association of Broadcasters, PO Box 627 Sta. B, Ottawa, K1P 5S2. **Deadline for Receipt:** June 30.

4010 ■ DADE COMMUNITY FOUNDATION, INC.
200 S Biscayne Blvd., Ste. 505
Miami, FL 33131-2343
Tel: (305)371-2711
Fax: (305)371-5342
Web Site: http://www.dadecommunityfoundation.org
To help talented South Florida students for aspiring a career in journalism, broadcast or mass communications.
Title of Award: Leo Suarez Journalism Scholarships **Area, Field, or Subject:** Journalism; Broadcasting; Communications. **Level of Education for which Award is Granted:** Undergraduate **Funds Available:** $1,000. **Duration:** One year.
Eligibility Requirements: Applicants must be high school seniors in Miami-Dade or Broward public school; must have minimum of 3.0 grade point average; must intend to major in journalism, broadcast or mass communications in undergraduate studies at four year university and/or two year college. **Application Requirements:** Applicants must submit the completed application form together with the three writing samples that have been published and letter of recommendation from the journalism sponsor or English professor at their high school. **Deadline for Receipt:** March 21.

4011 ■ DICKEY RURAL NETWORKS
9628 Hwy. 281
PO Box 69
Ellendale, ND 58436
877-559-4692
Web Site: http://www.drtel.net
To provide financial assistance for rural high school seniors to further their college education.
Title of Award: Dickey Rural Networks College Scholarship Program **Area, Field, or Subject:** Telecommunications systems. **Level of Education for which Award is Granted:** Undergraduate **Number Awarded:** 30. **Funds Available:** $2,500. **Duration:** One year.
Eligibility Requirements: Applicants must be graduating high school seniors; must receive local telecommunications service from a current NTCA member (except for students sponsored by an associate member company); must be accepted by an accredited two or four-year college, university or vocational-technical school; must have at least a C grade point average (GPA); must have academic credentials within an average to above-average range; must express an interest to return to a rural community following graduation; and must be sponsored by a contributor to, or supporter of, the Foundation for Rural Service. **Application Requirements:** Applicants must complete and print the DRN/FRS Scholarship Application online, which is also available from the school counselor, with the complete instructions and checklist of items to be considered. **Deadline for Receipt:** February 15.

4012 ■ FIRST COMMUNITY FOUNDATION OF PENNSYLVANIA, WILLIAMSPORT-LYCOMING
330 Pine St., Suite 401
Williamsport, PA 17701
Tel: (570)321-1500; (866)901-2372
Fax: (570)321-6434
E-mail: fcfpa@fcfpa.org
Web Site: http://www.wlfoundation.org
To provide financial assistance for Lycoming County high school seniors who have demonstrated an interest in furthering their education in international studies.
Title of Award: ISCALC International Scholarship Fund **Area, Field, or Subject:** International affairs and relations; Foreign languages. **Level of Education for which Award is Granted:** Undergraduate **Number Awarded:** 2-4. **Funds Available:** $250-$400.
Eligibility Requirements: Applicant must be a high school senior within Lycoming county who will be attending an accredited institution of higher education and who plans to pursue major coursework in the area of international studies, including but not limited to international affairs, foreign languages, overseas exchange programs, multicultural studies, and related areas. **Application Requirements:** Candidates must complete the application and submit it along with any requested additional information to the Williamsport-Lycoming Community Foundation. **Additional Information:** Candy Bower, Manager of Program and Scholarship Services, candyb@fcfpa.org.

4013 ■ ALLISON E. FISHER MEMORIAL FUND
PO Box 43402
Baltimore, MD 21236

Tel: (410)679-0595
E-mail: fishers@verizon.net
Web Site: http://www.allisonfisherfund.org
To provide financial assistance to students who are attending an accredited four-year university.
Title of Award: Allison E. Fisher Scholarships **Area, Field, or Subject:** Journalism; Photography; Radio and television. **Level of Education for which Award is Granted:** Undergraduate **Funds Available:** $2,500.
Eligibility Requirements: Applicants must be any foreign or U.S. students who are majoring in journalism-print, photography or radio and television or planning a career in one of those fields; must be currently attending accredited four-year university; must have cumulative grade point average of 3.0 and be enrolled in undergraduate or graduate school during the award year. **Application Requirements:** Applicants must submit all the required application information.

4014 ■ FLORIDA OUTDOOR WRITERS ASSOCIATION
24 NW, 33rd Court, Ste. A
Gainesville, FL 32607
Tel: (352)392-2801
E-mail: info@fowa.org
Web Site: http://www.fowa.org
To motivate and encourage young people to enter outdoor communications career fields.
Title of Award: Florida Outdoor Writers Association Scholarships **Area, Field, or Subject:** Communications; Journalism. **Level of Education for which Award is Granted:** Undergraduate **Funds Available:** $500-$1,000.
Eligibility Requirements: Applicants must be students at Florida Colleges and universities, or must be students whose applications are endorsed by a FOWA member or a faculty advisor. **Application Requirements:** Applicants must submit a completed application form; must submit an essay, 500-1,000-words, that expresses their appreciation for the outdoor experience; an up-to-date resume; a letter of endorsement from a FOWA member or faculty advisor. **Deadline for Receipt:** August 31.

4015 ■ FOUNDATION FOR THE CAROLINAS
217 S Tryon St.
Charlotte, NC 28202
Tel: (704)973-4500
Free: 800-973-7244
Web Site: http://www.fftc.org
To assist graduating seniors at East Mecklenburg High School in Charlotte, NC who demonstrate interest in foreign languages and/or journalism.
Title of Award: Pete and Ellen Bensley Memorial Scholarship Fund **Area, Field, or Subject:** Foreign languages; Journalism. **Level of Education for which Award is Granted:** Undergraduate **Funds Available:** Amount not specified.
Eligibility Requirements: Applicants must be legal residents of Mecklenburg County and graduating seniors at East Mecklenburg High School who are planning to major in foreign languages and/or journalism. **Application Requirements:** Applicants must submit all the required materials and complete application information. **Additional Information:** The Scholarship Coordinator at East Mecklenburg High School, 980-343-6430.

4016 ■ THE GERMAN SOCIETY OF PENNSYLVANIA
611 Spring Garden St.
Philadelphia, PA 19123
Tel: (215)627-2332
Fax: (215)627-5297
E-mail: info@germansociety.org
Web Site: http://www.germansociety.org
To provide financial assistance for undergraduate students majoring in German language and literature.
Title of Award: German Society Scholarships **Area, Field, or Subject:** Foreign languages; German studies. **Level of Education for which Award is Granted:** Undergraduate **Funds Available:** $2500.
Eligibility Requirements: Applicant must be a resident of the Greater Delaware Valley; and a high school senior intending to major in German, or a German major (Double majors are also eligible). **Application**

Requirements: Applicants must submit a completed application form; a German writing sample (up to one typewritten page); recent transcript; and two letters of reference. **Deadline for Receipt:** March 17.

4017 ■ KEITH GILMORE FOUNDATION
5160 Skyline Way NE
Calgary, AB, Canada T2E 6V1
Tel: (403)274-1734
E-mail: kgf@keithgilmorefoundation.com
Web Site: http://www.keithgilmorefoundation.com
To provide scholarships for deserving individuals.
Title of Award: Keith Gilmore Foundation - Undergraduate Scholarships **Area, Field, or Subject:** Agriculture, Economic aspects; Medicine, Veterinary; Journalism; Communications. **Level of Education for which Award is Granted:** Undergraduate **Number Awarded:** 4. **Funds Available:** $1,500. **Duration:** One year.
Eligibility Requirements: Applicant must be an individual enrolled in an undergraduate degree program in agriculture, veterinary medicine, journalism and/or communications at a recognized university, leading to a career in the field of agriculture. **Application Requirements:** Application forms are available online at www.keithgilmorefoundation.com. Completed application must be sent to Keith Gilmore Foundation, 5160 Skyline Way NE, Calgary, AB T2E 6V1. **Deadline for Receipt:** July 1.

4018 ■ GRAND RAPIDS COMMUNITY FOUNDATION
161 Ottawa Ave. NW
Ste. 209-C Waters Bldg.
Grand Rapids, MI 49503
Tel: (616)454-1751
Fax: (616)454-6455
E-mail: grfound@grfoundation.org
Web Site: http://www.grfoundation.org
To provide financial support to deserving students.
Title of Award: Audrey L. Wright Scholarships **Area, Field, or Subject:** Foreign Language; Education. **Level of Education for which Award is Granted:** Undergraduate **Funds Available:** No specific amount.
Eligibility Requirements: Applicants must be residents of Kent County; must be pursuing an undergraduate degree in Foreign Language or Education; must have financial need; must have a minimum of 3.0 GPA. **Application Requirements:** Applicants must check the available website for the application process and for the required materials. **Additional Information:** Grand Rapids Community Foundation at the above address

4019 ■ HARTFORD FOUNDATION FOR PUBLIC GIVING
10 Columbus Blvd., 8th Flr.
Hartford, CT 06106
Tel: (860)548-1888
Fax: (860)524-8346
E-mail: hfpg@hfpg.org
Web Site: http://www.hfpg.org
To provide financial assistance to students planning a career in Journalism.
Title of Award: Deedee Segel - Hartford Courant Internships **Area, Field, or Subject:** Journalism; Communication. **Level of Education for which Award is Granted:** Undergraduate **Funds Available:** No specific amount.
Eligibility Requirements: Applicants must be college students majoring in Journalism or Communication. **Application Requirements:** Applicants may obtain application materials from The Hartford Courant and include the following requirements: resume with cover letter; application; eight published writings samples; reporting experience; college grades; references. **Deadline for Receipt:** January 1. **Additional Information:** Lynne DeLucia, Asst. Managing Ed., State/Metro, 285 Broad St., Hartford, CT 06115.

4020 ■ HISPANIC SCHOLARSHIP FUND
55 Second St., Ste. 1500
San Francisco, CA 94105
877-473-4636
Fax: (415)808-2302
E-mail: info@hsf.net
Web Site: http://www.hsf.net
To support outstanding Community College Transfer Students.

Title of Award: HSF/Nissan Community College Transfer Scholarship Program **Area, Field, or Subject:** Business; Engineering; Communications; Media arts. **Level of Education for which Award is Granted:** Undergraduate **Funds Available:** $2,500.
Eligibility Requirements: Applicant must be of Hispanic heritage; U.S. citizen or legal permanent resident with a valid resident card or passport stamped I-551; currently enrolled part-time or full-time at a community college; planning to transfer and enroll full-time in a degree-seeking program at a four-year U.S. accredited institution; must reside or transfer to a four-year institution in Atlanta, Georgia; Chicago Illinois; Greater Dallas/Forth Worth, Texas; Jackson/Canton, Mississippi; Los Angeles, California; Nashville, Tennessee; Northern California; New York City/New Jersey; be pursuing a degree in Business, Engineering, Communications or Media Arts; have a minimum GPA of 3.0 on a 4.0 scale; must apply for federal financing aid using the Free Application for Federal Student Aid (FAFSA) at www.fafsa.ed.gov. **Application Requirements:** Applications must be submitted using the HSF online application system. **Additional Information:** In partnership with Nissan North America, Inc. **Deadline for Receipt:** March 15. **Additional Information:** cctransfer@hsf.net.

4021 ■ HISPANIC SCHOLARSHIP FUND
55 Second St., Ste. 1500
San Francisco, CA 94105
877-473-4636
Fax: (415)808-2302
E-mail: info@hsf.net
Web Site: http://www.hsf.net
To provide financial assistance to creative arts-related undergraduate and graduate students beginning or completing an art project.
Title of Award: McNamara Family Creative Arts Project Grants **Area, Field, or Subject:** Art; Media arts; Broadcasting; Filmmaking; Performing arts; Communications; Writing. **Level of Education for which Award is Granted:** Graduate, Undergraduate **Funds Available:** $5,000-$20,000.
Eligibility Requirements: Applicant must be of Hispanic heritage; U.S. citizen or legal permanent resident with a valid permanent resident card or passport stamped I-551; enrolled full-time undergraduate or graduate student in a degree-seeking program at a U.S. accredited institution in the U.S., Puerto Rico or U.S. Virgin Islands in the upcoming academic year; pursuing a major in Arts, including but not limited to media, film, performing arts, communications or writing; have a minimum 3.0 GPA on a 4.0 scale; must apply for federal financing aid using the Free Application for Federal Student Aid (FAFSA) at www.fafsa.ed.gov. **Application Requirements:** Applications must be submitted using the HSF online application system. **Additional Information:** In partnership with the McNamara Family Foundation. **Deadline for Receipt:** March 15. **Additional Information:** scholar1@hsf.net.

4022 ■ INDIANA BROADCASTERS ASSOCIATION
3003 ELLA., 98th St., Ste 161
Indianapolis, IN 46280
Tel: (317)573-0119
Free: 800-342-6276
Fax: (317)573-0895
E-mail: indba@aol.com
Web Site: http://www.indianabroadcasters.org
To promote cooperation and understanding among broadcasters, both radio and television as well as among businesses and other organizations associated with the broadcast industry; to foster and promote the development of the art of broadcasting; to encourage and promote customs and practices which will be in the best interests of the public and the broadcasting industry; to protect members in every lawful and proper manner from injuries and unjust actions; and to act as a contact with other broadcast associations.
Title of Award: Indiana Broadcasters Association for College Scholarship Program **Area, Field, or Subject:** Broadcasting. **Level of Education for which Award is Granted:** Undergraduate **Funds Available:** No specific amount.
Eligibility Requirements: Applicants must have an overall 3.0 GPA on a 4.0 scale; must be residents of Indiana; must be second semester seniors at an Indiana High school planning to attend an Indiana post-secondary school; must be actively participating in a high school broadcast facility while attending an Indiana high school; and must have received credit in a

High School Broadcasting, Telecommunications or Broadcast Journalism course. **Application Requirements:** Applicants must complete the Transcript Request Form and application form and send them to the College Records Office. **Deadline for Receipt:** March 3.

4023 ■ INDIANA BROADCASTERS ASSOCIATION
3003 ELLA., 98th St., Ste 161
Indianapolis, IN 46280
Tel: (317)573-0119
Free: 800-342-6276
Fax: (317)573-0895
E-mail: indba@aol.com
Web Site: http://www.indianabroadcasters.org
To promote cooperation and understanding among broadcasters, both radio and television as well as among businesses and other organizations associated with the broadcast industry; to foster and promote the development of the art of broadcasting; to encourage and promote customs and practices which will be in the best interests of the public and the broadcasting industry; to protect members in every lawful and proper manner from injuries and unjust actions; and to act as a contact with other broadcast associations.
Title of Award: Indiana Broadcasters Association High School Scholarship Program **Area, Field, or Subject:** Broadcasting. **Level of Education for which Award is Granted:** Undergraduate **Funds Available:** No specific amount.
Eligibility Requirements: Applicants must have an overall 3.0 GPA on a 4.0 scale; must be residents of Indiana; must be second-semester seniors at an Indiana High school planning to attend an Indiana post-secondary school; must be actively participating in a high school broadcast facility while attending an Indiana high school; and must have received credit in a High School Broadcasting, Telecommunications or Broadcast Journalism course. **Application Requirements:** Applicants must complete the application form and the High School Transcript Request Form and send them to the high school records office. **Deadline for Receipt:** March 3. **Additional Information:** 317-573-0119.

4024 ■ INTERNATIONAL FOODSERVICE EDITORIAL COUNCIL
PO Box 491
Hyde Park, NY 12538
Tel: (845)229-6973
Fax: (845)229-6993
E-mail: info@ifeconline.com
Web Site: http://www.ifec-is-us.com
To increase awareness and understanding of the career opportunities available in the field of food service communications and to encourage entry of qualified professionals in the field.
Title of Award: International Foodservice Editorial Council Scholarships **Area, Field, or Subject:** Culinary arts; Communications; Food service careers; Food science and technology; Photography; Hotel, institutional, and restaurant management; Nutrition; Dietetics; Journalism; Public relations; Graphic art and design. **Level of Education for which Award is Granted:** Graduate, Undergraduate **Number Awarded:** Varies. **Funds Available:** $3,750.
Eligibility Requirements: Applicants must be full-time students in a U.S. accredited post-secondary educational institution working towards an associate's, bachelor's or master's degree. **Application Requirements:** Applicants must submit a complete application together with academic transcript and two letters of recommendation. Application requirements must be typewritten and submitted using U.S. Postal Service's Return Receipt Service. **Deadline for Receipt:** March 15.

4025 ■ IOWA COURT REPORTERS ASSOCIATION
8345 University Blvd., Ste. F-1
Des Moines, IA 50325
Tel: (515)225-2323
E-mail: sylvia.kreamalmyer@jb.state.ia.us
Web Site: http://www.iacra.org
To promote and advance the interest of individuals engaged in the profession of shorthand reporting throughout the state of Iowa; to develop greater awareness and appreciation for the profession through public education and to promote the shorthand reporting industry.
Title of Award: Mary L. Brown Scholarships **Area, Field, or Subject:** Broadcasting. **Level of Education for which Award is Granted:** Undergraduate **Funds Available:** $750.

Eligibility Requirements: Applicant must be enrolled as a Realtime Reporting major in either Judicial or Captioning/CART service; must attend AIB College of Business; and must be a graduate of an Iowa high school. **Application Requirements:** Applicants must submit a completed application form along with two letters of recommendation and a 250-word essay. **Deadline for Receipt:** April 1. **Additional Information:** icra@assoc-serv.com

4026 ■ IOWA NEWSPAPER ASSOCIATION
319 E. 5th St.
Des Moines, IA 50309
Tel: (515)244-2145
Fax: (515)244-4855
E-mail: ina@inanews.com
Web Site: http://www.inanews.com
To champion the quality and future of Iowa's newspaper enterprises and the communities they serve.
Title of Award: Iowa Journalism Institute Scholarships **Area, Field, or Subject:** Journalism; Communication. **Level of Education for which Award is Granted:** Undergraduate **Funds Available:** No specific amount.
Eligibility Requirements: Applicants must be students studying journalism, communications, mass communications, photojournalism, graphic design, marketing or public relations at a college or university in Iowa, Illinois, or Wisconsin. **Application Requirements:** Applicants must attach two letters of reference including one from a teacher or guidance counselor; must attach a one-page statement about self, educational and career goals; two samples of writings or other examples of work which attest to the abilities of applicants in their intended career field. These samples should be printed on or affixed to 8.5" x 11" sheets of white copy paper. **Additional Information:** info@inanews.com.

4027 ■ LEWIS-CLARK STATE COLLEGE
500 8th Ave.
Lewiston, ID 83501
Tel: (208)792-5272
Web Site: http://www.lcsc.edu
To provide financial assistance to students who are majoring in these fields: Accounting, Biology, Business, Communications, Computer Science, Economics, Environmental Science, Engineering, Mathematics, Natural Resources, Political Science, Statistics.
Title of Award: Avista Corporation Minds in Motion Scholarships **Area, Field, or Subject:** Accounting; Biology; Business; Communications; Computer and Information Sciences; Economics; Environmental Science; Engineering; Mathematics; Natural Resources; Political Science; Statistics. **Level of Education for which Award is Granted:** Undergraduate **Number Awarded:** 2. **Funds Available:** No specific Amount.
Eligibility Requirements: Applicants must be full-time students attending LCSC and must have a cumulative GPA of 2.5. **Application Requirements:** Applicants must submit general application. **Deadline for Receipt:** March 1.

4028 ■ LIN TELEVISION CORPORATION
300 Wavy St.
Portsmouth, VA 23704
Tel: (757)673-5314
Fax: (757)673-5300
E-mail: rosetta.rolan@lintv.com
Web Site: http://www.lintv.com
To help educate and train outstanding minority candidates who seek to enter the television broadcast field.
Title of Award: LIN Television Corporation Minority Scholarships and Training Program **Area, Field, or Subject:** Broadcasting; Journalism. **Level of Education for which Award is Granted:** Undergraduate **Funds Available:** $20,000. **Duration:** One year.
Eligibility Requirements: Applicants must be citizens of the United States and of non-white origin; must be sophomores or have completed sufficient semester hours or similar educational units to be within two years of receiving an undergraduate bachelor's degree; must have a minimum of 3.0 cumulative GPA and with declared major in journalism, broadcast journalism, business or marketing at an accredited university or college. **Application Requirements:** Applicants must submit completed application form; list of organizations and activities in which they have

held leadership position where nature of involvement must be briefly described; three references, up to two faculty members (university or secondary) and one or two other references that will recommend their work; list of personal achievements and honors; description of career goals in 50 words or less; and, short essay about themselves (up to 500 words, double-spaced). **Deadline for Receipt:** March 15.

4029 ■ MATANUSKA-SUSITNA COLLEGE
PO Box 2889
Palmer, AK 99645
Tel: (907)745-9774
Fax: (907)745-9711
E-mail: info@matsu.alaska.edu
Web Site: http://www.matsu.alaska.edu
To provide an incentive for Alaska's middle and high school students to achieve academic excellence, and to encourage the top high school graduates from every community in Alaska to attend the University of Alaska.
Title of Award: Snodgrass Scholarships **Area, Field, or Subject:** Accounting; Engineering, Architectural; Computer and information sciences; Fires and fire prevention; Heating, air conditioning, and refrigeration; Business administration; Telecommunications systems. **Level of Education for which Award is Granted:** Undergraduate **Funds Available:** $500-$2,000. **Duration:** One academic year.
Eligibility Requirements: Applicant must be admitted to the given Matanuska-Susitna College degree programs; must be a continuing student at Matanuska-Susitna College who has earned at least 20 credit hours; must have a cumulative GPA of 3.0 or higher; must exhibit good moral character and conduct; must be registered for eight or more credit hours. **Application Requirements:** Applicants must complete the MSC scholarship application and attach a resume showing their work experience; must compose an essay of 500 words or less describing their educational and career goals and how they plan to attain them; must have two letters of recommendation, written within the last two years. Application form and other supporting documents must be sent to Snodgrass Scholarships, Matanuska-Susitna College, Student Service, FSM 102, Palmer, AK 99645. **Deadline for Receipt:** May 31.

4030 ■ MEDIA ACTION NETWORK FOR ASIAN AMERICANS
PO Box 11105
Burbank, CA 91510
Tel: (213)486-4433; 888-90-MANAA
E-mail: manaaletters@yahoo.com
Web Site: http://www.manaa.org
To promote education in filmmaking and in television production.
Title of Award: MANAA Media Scholarships **Area, Field, or Subject:** Filmmaking; Television. **Level of Education for which Award is Granted:** Graduate, Undergraduate **Number Awarded:** 1. **Funds Available:** $1000.
Eligibility Requirements: Applicants must be graduate or undergraduate students pursuing careers as filmmakers and in television production (not broadcast journalism). **Application Requirements:** Applicants must submit a copy of all official transcripts; copy of completed financial aid documents; two letters of recommendation; a double-spaced essay (maximum of 1,000 words); and a work sample consisting of a short film or screenplay (optional). Send applications to MANAA Scholarship, P.O. Box 11105, Burbank, CA 91510. Do not send applications via certified or registered mail. **Additional Information:** The scholarship was formed in 1992. **Deadline for Receipt:** May 9.

4031 ■ MONTANA BROADCASTERS ASSOCIATION
HC 70, Box 90
Bonner, MT 59823
Tel: (406)244-4622
Fax: (406)244-5518
E-mail: mba@mtbroadcasters.org
Web Site: http://www.mtbroadcasters.org
To promote the values of local, free over-the-air broadcasting to the business community, governmental bodies and the general public in Montana; and to support the Montana broadcasting industry by providing services, information, continuing education, recruitment and a strong unified voice.
Title of Award: Joe Durso Memorial Scholarships **Area, Field, or Subject:** Broadcasting. **Level of Education for which Award is Granted:** Undergraduate **Funds Available:** No specific amount.

Eligibility Requirements: Applicants must be students entering their senior year, majoring in Radio-TV or Broadcast Journalism. **Application Requirements:** Applicants must submit a completed application form.

4032 ■ MONTANA BROADCASTERS ASSOCIATION
HC 70, Box 90
Bonner, MT 59823
Tel: (406)244-4622
Fax: (406)244-5518
E-mail: mba@mtbroadcasters.org
Web Site: http://www.mtbroadcasters.org
To promote the values of local, free over-the-air broadcasting to the business community, governmental bodies and the general public in Montana; and to support the Montana broadcasting industry by providing services, information, continuing education, recruitment and a strong unified voice. **Title of Award:** Great Falls Broadcasters Association Scholarships **Area, Field, or Subject:** Broadcasting. **Level of Education for which Award is Granted:** Undergraduate **Funds Available:** No specific amount.
Eligibility Requirements: Applicants must be students who have graduated from North-Central Montana High School and are enrolled as at least second-year students in Radio-TV at any public or private Montana college or university. **Application Requirements:** Applicants must submit completed application form.

4033 ■ MONTANA BROADCASTERS ASSOCIATION
HC 70, Box 90
Bonner, MT 59823
Tel: (406)244-4622
Fax: (406)244-5518
E-mail: mba@mtbroadcasters.org
Web Site: http://www.mtbroadcasters.org
To promote the values of local, free over-the-air broadcasting to the business community, governmental bodies and the general public in Montana; and to support the Montana broadcasting industry by providing services, information, continuing education, recruitment and a strong unified voice. **Title of Award:** Montana Broadcasters Association Directors' Scholarships **Area, Field, or Subject:** Broadcasting; Theater Arts. **Level of Education for which Award is Granted:** Undergraduate **Funds Available:** No specific amount.
Eligibility Requirements: Applicants must be students majoring in media and theater arts. **Application Requirements:** Applicants must submit a completed application form.

4034 ■ MONTANA BROADCASTERS ASSOCIATION
HC 70, Box 90
Bonner, MT 59823
Tel: (406)244-4622
Fax: (406)244-5518
E-mail: mba@mtbroadcasters.org
Web Site: http://www.mtbroadcasters.org
To promote the values of local, free over-the-air broadcasting to the business community, governmental bodies and the general public in Montana; and to support the Montana broadcasting industry by providing services, information, continuing education, recruitment and a strong unified voice. **Title of Award:** Montana Broadcasters Association Engineers' Scholarships **Area, Field, or Subject:** Broadcasting; Engineering. **Level of Education for which Award is Granted:** Undergraduate **Funds Available:** No specific amount.
Eligibility Requirements: Applicants must be second year students, majoring in Engineering at the UM College of Technology, and interested in pursuing a career in Broadcast Engineering. **Application Requirements:** Applicants must submit completed application form.

4035 ■ NATIONAL ACADEMY OF TELEVISION ARTS AND SCIENCES
111 W 57th St., Ste. 600
New York, NY 10019
Tel: (212)586-8424
Fax: (212)246-8129
E-mail: axa24@psu.edu
Web Site: http://www.emmyonline.org
To provide educational assistance to an outstanding high school senior who intends to pursue a baccalaureate degree in communications with emphasis on any aspect of the television industry.

Title of Award: John Cannon Memorial Scholarships **Area, Field, or Subject:** Television. **Level of Education for which Award is Granted:** Undergraduate **Number Awarded:** 9. **Funds Available:** $40,000. **Duration:** 4 years.
Eligibility Requirements: Applicant must be a college-bound student within the United States who has demonstrated exceptional talent as a creator of video programming. **Application Requirements:** Application forms can be downloaded from the Foundation's scholarship web site or applicants may write to: Scholarship Committee, National Academy of Television Arts and Sciences, 111 W 57th St., Ste. 600, New York, NY 10019. **Deadline for Receipt:** November 5.

4036 ■ NATIONAL ASSOCIATION OF BLACK TELECOMMUNICATIONS PROFESSIONALS
2020 Pennsylvania Ave. NW
Washington, DC 20006
Tel: 877-349-8869
Fax: 877-349-8869
E-mail: office@nabtp.org
Web Site: http://www.nabtp.org
To provide financial assistance for students who wish to study telecommunications or a related field.
Title of Award: NABTP Collegian **Area, Field, or Subject:** Telecommunications. **Level of Education for which Award is Granted:** Undergraduate **Funds Available:** $2,000.
Eligibility Requirements: Applicants have notable achievements in academics, extra-curricular and/or community activities. Applicants must also illustrate an interest in telecommunications or a related field. **Application Requirements:** Applicant may download and fill out an application form online. Applicants are also required to submit the following documents: Evidence of household income; NABTP Collegian Applicants official college-university transcripts in a sealed envelope from your educational institution(s); Two signed Letters of Recommendation in a sealed envelope with author's signature signed across the back flap of the envelope; and a maximum 2-page essay which can downloaded online. **Deadline for Receipt:** July 23.

4037 ■ NEW YORK WOMEN IN COMMUNICATIONS FOUNDATION
355 Lexington Ave., 15th Fl.
New York, NY 10017-6603
Tel: (212)297-2133
Fax: (212)370-9047
Web Site: http://www.nywici.org
To provide financial assistance for the education of the residents of NY, NJ, CT, or PA.
Title of Award: New York Women in Communications, Inc. Foundation Scholarships **Area, Field, or Subject:** Advertising; Broadcasting; Communications; Media arts; Journalism; Marketing and distribution; Media arts; Public relations. **Level of Education for which Award is Granted:** Graduate, Undergraduate **Funds Available:** No specific amount. **Duration:** One year.
Eligibility Requirements: Applicants must be high school seniors, or college undergraduate or graduate students who are permanent residents of NY, NJ, CT or PA majoring or declaring a major in a communications-related field, including but not limited to advertising, broadcasting, communications, English, film, journalism, marketing, new media, or public relations. Applicants must have an overall GPA of 3.2 or better (or the high school equivalent). **Application Requirements:** Applicants must submit completed application form and all other required application information and materials. **Deadline for Receipt:** January 30.

4038 ■ OHIO ASSOCIATION OF BROADCASTERS
88 E Broad St., Ste.1180
Columbus, OH 43215
Tel: (614)228-4052; (866)228-5794
Fax: (614)228-8133
E-mail: oab@oab.org
Web Site: http://www.oab.org
To encourage high standards of professionalism in the industry; to foster a stronger relationship between higher education and the profession; to promote a greater understanding of the ethics and societal responsibility of broadcasters; to support potential and commitment in promising future broadcasters; to advance a continuing commitment to diversity in the industry.

Title of Award: Ohio Association of Broadcaster's Kids Scholarships **Area, Field, or Subject:** Broadcasting. **Level of Education for which Award is Granted:** Undergraduate **Funds Available:** $1,500.
Eligibility Requirements: Applicants must be high school seniors who are children of a full-time employee of an OAB member station; must plan to enroll in a postsecondary institution. **Application Requirements:** Applicants must submit a completed application form; a two page essay; a copy of high school transcript and one letter of recommendation. **Deadline for Receipt:** March 28. **Additional Information:** oab@oab.org.

4039 ■ OHIO ASSOCIATION OF BROADCASTERS
88 E Broad St., Ste.1180
Columbus, OH 43215
Tel: (614)228-4052; (866)228-5794
Fax: (614)228-8133
E-mail: oab@oab.org
Web Site: http://www.oab.org
To encourage high standards of professionalism in the industry; to foster a stronger relationship between higher education and the profession; to promote a greater understanding of the ethics and societal responsibility of broadcasters; to support potential and commitment in promising future broadcasters; to advance a continuing commitment to diversity in the industry.
Title of Award: Ohio Association of Broadcasters Scholarships **Area, Field, or Subject:** Broadcasting. **Level of Education for which Award is Granted:** Undergraduate **Number Awarded:** 3. **Funds Available:** No specific amount.
Eligibility Requirements: Applicants must be college students interested in pursuing a career in broadcasting; must be residents of Ohio; must be working toward a major or minor in their school's radio or television broadcasting or communications program; must have a minimum of 2.75 on a 4.0 scale, or the equivalent. **Application Requirements:** Applicants must complete the application form, transcripts and letters of recommendation. **Deadline for Receipt:** March 28. **Additional Information:** oab@oab.org.

4040 ■ OREGON ASSOCIATION OF BROADCASTERS
7150 SW Hampton St., Ste. 240
Portland, OR 97223-8366
Tel: (503)443-2299
Fax: (503)443-2488
E-mail: theoab@theoab.org
Web Site: http://www.theoab.org
To promote, enhance, strengthen and defend the broadcast industry. To encourage and promote sound broadcast customs and practices.
Title of Award: Oregon Association of Broadcasters Scholarships **Area, Field, or Subject:** Broadcasting. **Level of Education for which Award is Granted:** Undergraduate **Funds Available:** Varies.
Eligibility Requirements: Applicants must be graduating high school students, or students enrolled in two- or four-year college broadcast programs. Applicants must be Oregon residents, enrolled or intending to enroll at an Oregon college or university. **Application Requirements:** Applicants must complete the application form. Applicants must include an essay explaining the student's reasons for choosing a career in broadcasting or a related field. **Additional Information:** theoab@theoab.org

4041 ■ PARKERSBURG AREA COMMUNITY FOUNDATION
501 Avery St.
Parkersburg, WV 26101
Tel: (304)428-4438; (866)428-4438
Fax: (304)428-1200
E-mail: info@pacfwv.com
Web Site: http://www.pacfwv.com
To provide support for graduating or graduate students from a Wood County, WV high school.
Title of Award: George H. Clinton Scholarship Fund **Area, Field, or Subject:** Communications. **Level of Education for which Award is Granted:** Undergraduate **Funds Available:** $1,000.
Eligibility Requirements: Applicants must be graduating or have graduated from a Wood County, WV, high school; must be attending college full-time and majoring in the media communications field; must have a minimum of 3.0 GPA. **Application Requirements:** Applicants must

submit a cover sheet (3 pages) and application form (4 pages); must have a personal essay; must have a high school and/or post-secondary transcript; must provide a letter of recommendation and a signed copy of the page of their or their parent's most recent tax return that indicates adjusted gross income; and must have a Student Aid Report showing estimated family contribution from FAFSA. Application form and other supporting documents must be sent to Our Community's Foundation, P.O. Box 1762, Parkersburg, WV 26102. **Deadline for Receipt:** March 20.

4042 ■ PARKERSBURG AREA COMMUNITY FOUNDATION
501 Avery St.
Parkersburg, WV 26101
Tel: (304)428-4438; (866)428-4438
Fax: (304)428-1200
E-mail: info@pacfwv.com
Web Site: http://www.pacfwv.com
To provide financial support for qualified individuals intending to pursue their education.
Title of Award: Glenn Wilson Broadcast Journalism Scholarships **Area, Field, or Subject:** Journalism; Communications; Marketing and distribution. **Level of Education for which Award is Granted:** Undergraduate **Funds Available:** $560.
Eligibility Requirements: Applicants must be current or previous Wood or Pleasant County, WV, or Washington County, OH, high school students; must be studying broadcast journalism, journalism, communications or marketing; and must have a minimum 2.5 GPA. **Application Requirements:** Applicants must submit a cover sheet (3 pages) and application form (4 pages); a personal essay; a high school and/or post-secondary transcript; a letter of recommendation; a signed copy of the page of their or their parent's most recent tax return that indicates adjusted gross income; and a Student Aid Report showing estimated family contribution from FAFSA. Application form and other supporting documents must be sent to Our Community's Foundation, P.O Box 1762, Parkersburg, WV 26102. **Deadline for Receipt:** March 20.

4043 ■ PINNACLE WEST CAPITAL CORPORATION
PO Box 53999
Phoenix, AZ 85072-3999
Tel: (602)250-1000
Free: 800-457-2983
Web Site: http://www.pinnaclewest.com
To provide financial assistance to qualified individuals who want to pursue their career.
Title of Award: APS/ASU Scholarships **Area, Field, or Subject:** Chemical engineering; Electrical engineering; Mechanical engineering; Civil engineering; Construction; Telecommunications systems; Accounting; Finance; Economics; Information science and technology; Education, Elementary; Education, Secondary; Special education; Nursing. **Level of Education for which Award is Granted:** Undergraduate **Number Awarded:** 10. **Funds Available:** $2,000. **Duration:** One year.
Eligibility Requirements: Applicant must be an Arizona resident; must have a cumulative GPA of at least 3.0; must demonstrate financial need. **Application Requirements:** Applicant must complete the application form available online and send it to ASU Scholarship Office, Arizona State University, PO Box 470412, Tempe, AZ 85287-0412. **Deadline for Receipt:** March 1. **Additional Information:** Louise Moskowitz at louise.moskowitz@aps.com.

4044 ■ PUBLIC EDUCATION FOUNDATION
3360 W Sahara Ave., Ste. 160
Las Vegas, NV 89102
Tel: (702)799-1042
Fax: (702)799-5247
E-mail: steelej@ccpef.org
Web Site: http://ccpef.org
To promote education in communication.
Title of Award: Harvey N. Dondero Communication and Journalism Excellence Scholarships **Area, Field, or Subject:** Journalism; Communications. **Level of Education for which Award is Granted:** Undergraduate **Number Awarded:** 1. **Funds Available:** $1,200.
Eligibility Requirements: Applicants must be CCSD seniors planning to attend an accredited post-secondary institution pursuing a degree in journalism or communications. **Application Requirements:** Applicants

must submit a completed application form together with an essay, transcript, and a recommendation written by a journalism or English teacher. **Deadline for Receipt:** March 31. **Additional Information:** Shana Venenga at 702-799-1042.

4045 ■ PUBLIC EDUCATION FOUNDATION

3360 W Sahara Ave., Ste. 160
Las Vegas, NV 89102
Tel: (702)799-1042
Fax: (702)799-5247
E-mail: steelej@ccpef.org
Web Site: http://ccpef.org
To provide educational opportunities for individuals intending to pursue higher studies.
Title of Award: Palo Verde High School - Barbara Edwards Memorial Scholarships **Area, Field, or Subject:** Foreign languages. **Level of Education for which Award is Granted:** Undergraduate **Number Awarded:** 1. **Funds Available:** $1,000.
Eligibility Requirements: Applicants must be Palo Verde High School seniors who have completed seven semesters of the same foreign language and demonstrated academic excellence; must be planning to attend an accredited college or university; and must have a minimum 3.5 cumulative GPA. **Application Requirements:** Applicants must submit a completed application form along with an essay, transcript, resume of awards, and Foreign Language Teacher Evaluation Sheet. **Deadline for Receipt:** March 7. **Additional Information:** Shana Venenga at 702-799-1042.

4046 ■ PUBLIC RELATIONS SOCIETY OF AMERICA

33 Maiden Ln., 11th Fl.
New York, NY 10038-5150
Tel: (212)460-1474
Fax: (212)995-0757
E-mail: prssa@prsa.org
Web Site: http://www.prssa.org
To provide educational assistance for qualified students intending to pursue a career in the field of public relations.
Title of Award: Stephen D. Pisinski Memorial Scholarships **Area, Field, or Subject:** Public relations; Journalism; Communications. **Level of Education for which Award is Granted:** Undergraduate **Funds Available:** $1,500.
Eligibility Requirements: Applicants must be majoring in journalism, communications, or public relations; must be junior or senior level only; must have at least a 3.3 overall GPA on a 4.0 system; must be members of the Public Relations Student Society of America, and leadership positions are a plus. **Application Requirements:** Applicants must submit a resume including any academic honors, special projects, activities and/or work experience or training; an official transcript of all college studies, including grades of the preceding semester; an essay of 1,000 words or less stating your career goals; two strong writing samples; and two letters of academic and/or professional recommendations. Application form and other required items must be sent to PRSSA Headquarters by Stephen D. Pininski Memorial Scholarship, Public Relations Student Society of America, 33 Maiden Ln., 11th Fl., New York, NY 10038. **Deadline for Receipt:** June 2.

4047 ■ QUARTER CENTURY WIRELESS ASSOCIATION

PO Box 3247
Framingham, MA 01705
Tel: (508)405-1930
Fax: (508)405-1965
Web Site: http://www.qcwa.org
To provide financial support for students intending to pursue higher education.
Title of Award: QCWA Memorial Scholarships **Area, Field, or Subject:** Radio and television. **Level of Education for which Award is Granted:** Undergraduate **Funds Available:** $500-$3,000.
Eligibility Requirements: Applicants must be radio amateurs enrolled or planning to enroll in a full-time course which leads to a degree at an accredited college/university. **Application Requirements:** Applications are requested from the Foundation for Amateur Radio Scholarship Committee; applicant must be recommended by a QCWA member. **Additional Information:** Established in 1977. **Deadline for Receipt:** April 30. **Ad-**

ditional Information: Lalend Buddy Smith, QCWA Memorial Scholarship Fund, 504-721-4684, w4ye@aol.com.

4048 ■ SAFE SCHOOLS COALITION

1002 E Seneca St.
Seattle, WA 98122-4203
Tel: (206)957-1621
Fax: (206)325-2689
Web Site: http://www.safeschoolscoalition.org
To sponsor scholarships for gay, lesbian, bisexual and transgendered students pursuing a degree in journalism and communications at an accredited four-year college or university.
Title of Award: Messenger-Anderson Journalism Scholarships and Internships Program **Area, Field, or Subject:** Journalism; Communications. **Level of Education for which Award is Granted:** Undergraduate **Funds Available:** $5,000 for the first year and $2,500 for the second and third years.
Eligibility Requirements: Applicants must be high school seniors or current undergraduate students with a cumulative 2.8 GPA or better. **Application Requirements:** Applicants may check the available contact information for inquiries. **Additional Information:** The award is sponsored by the National Gay and Lesbian Task Force (NGLTF). Winners are required to participate in the Messenger-Anderson Scholarship Intern Program at NGLTF offices in Washington, DC, or New York City during the summer. **Deadline for Receipt:** February.

4049 ■ THE SAN DIEGO FOUNDATION

2508 Historic Decatur Rd., Ste. 200
San Diego, CA 92106
Tel: (619)235-2300
Fax: (619)239-1710
E-mail: info@sdfoundation.org
Web Site: http://www.sdfoundation.org
To support the education of students from California.
Title of Award: Julie Allen World Classroom Scholarships **Area, Field, or Subject:** International affairs and relations; Business; Economics; Civil rights; Foreign languages. **Level of Education for which Award is Granted:** Undergraduate **Number Awarded:** 1. **Funds Available:** $1,000.
Eligibility Requirements: Applicant must be an undergraduate student enrolled at the University of San Diego, UC San Diego, or San Diego State University; have a minimum 2.50 GPA on a 4.0 scale; demonstrated financial need; planning to study abroad for a minimum of one semester in a Second or Third World Country whose culture, language and customs are different than their own. **Application Requirements:** Applicants must submit a completed Common Scholarship Application together with personal statement; two letters of recommendation on official letterhead (written within the last six months); official transcript in an official and sealed envelope; copy of most recent tax form (Form 1040-pages 1 & 2; Form 1040A-pages 1 & 2; Form 1040EZ-page 1); and an essay (maximum one page, typed, double-spaced) addressing applicant's reason(s) for studying abroad, or coming to San Diego to pursue an education from the student's native country. **Deadline for Receipt:** January 28. **Additional Information:** Arzo Mansury, Dir. Scholarships at 619-814-1343, or scholarships@sdfoundation.org.

4050 ■ BERT SAPERSTEIN COMMUNICATIONS SCHOLARSHIP FUND

PO Box 42-Wykagyl Sta.
New Rochelle, NY 10804
Tel: (914)636-1281
E-mail: info@bsc-scholarshipfund.org
Web Site: http://www.bsc-scholarshipfund.org
To promote and increase interest in the field of Communication Arts which include film and television, creative writing, advertising, public relations, and communication design.
Title of Award: Bert Saperstein Communication Scholarships **Area, Field, or Subject:** Communication arts. **Level of Education for which Award is Granted:** Undergraduate **Funds Available:** $500-$2,000.
Eligibility Requirements: Applicants must be enrolled full-time in any college/university. **Application Requirements:** Applicants may submit their application letters and other requirements to the office. **Additional Information:** Bert Saperstein Communication at the above address.

4051 ■ SIGMA KAPPA FOUNDATION
8733 Founder Rd.
Indianapolis, IN 46268
Tel: (317)872-3275
E-mail: alewis@sigmakappa.org
Web Site: http://www.sigmakappafoundation.org
To encourage and support the scholastic development of the collegiate and alumnae sisters of the foundation.
Title of Award: Frances Warren Baker Memorial Scholarships **Area, Field, or Subject:** Journalism, Communications. **Level of Education for which Award is Granted:** Undergraduate **Number Awarded:** 1. **Funds Available:** $500.
Eligibility Requirements: Applicant must be a member in good standing enrolled in an undergraduate program in the fields of journalism or communication (print media); must have a minimum cumulative GPA: 3.0. **Application Requirements:** Application forms are available online. Applicant must submit the transcript and recommendation letter through online. **Deadline for Receipt:** March 1.

4052 ■ SOCIETY OF BROADCAST ENGINEERS
9102 North Meridian St., Ste. 150
Indianapolis, IN 46260
Tel: (317)846-9000
Fax: (317)846-9120
E-mail: mclappe@sbe.org
Web Site: http://www.sbe.org
To provide educational fund to deserving candidates who aspire to a career in the technical aspects of broadcasting.
Title of Award: Youth Scholarships **Area, Field, or Subject:** Broadcasting; Engineering. **Level of Education for which Award is Granted:** Undergraduate **Number Awarded:** 3. **Funds Available:** $1000 $3000.
Eligibility Requirements: Applicants must be high school seniors; planning to enroll at a technical school; pursuing studies leading to a career in broadcasting engineering or related field. **Application Requirements:** Application forms are available at the website. Complete only the B and C sections of the application form and send together with a brief autobiography; a summary of technical changes; and a copy of recent college transcripts (if applicable). **Deadline for Receipt:** July 1.

4053 ■ SOCIETY OF SATELLITE PROFESSIONALS INTERNATIONAL
55 Broad St., 14th Fl.
New York, NY 10004
Tel: (212)809-5199
Fax: (212)825-0075
E-mail: tbond@sspi.org
Web Site: http://www.hessberger.com/sspi/index.html
To recognize innovative work in the satellite field.
Title of Award: The Access Intelligence Scholarships **Area, Field, or Subject:** Telecommunications systems; Broadcasting. **Level of Education for which Award is Granted:** Graduate, Undergraduate **Funds Available:** No specific amount.
Eligibility Requirements: Applicant must be an SSPI member; pursue education in the satellite industry or a field making direct use of satellite technology; have academic and leadership achievement; show potential for significant contribution to the satellite communications industry; enrolled in an accredited college or university program at the time of the scholarship issuance. **Application Requirements:** Applicants may mail or fax their applications together with a current transcript. **Deadline for Receipt:** December 31. **Additional Information:** Membership Director Tamara Bond at the above address.

4054 ■ SOCIETY OF SATELLITE PROFESSIONALS INTERNATIONAL
55 Broad St., 14th Fl.
New York, NY 10004
Tel: (212)809-5199
Fax: (212)825-0075
E-mail: tbond@sspi.org
Web Site: http://www.hessberger.com/sspi/index.html
To assist students with financial need.
Title of Award: The A.W. Perigard Fund **Area, Field, or Subject:** Telecommunications systems. **Level of Education for which Award is Granted:** Graduate, Undergraduate **Funds Available:** No specific amount.

Eligibility Requirements: Applicant must be an SSPI member; must pursue education in the satellite industry or a field making direct use of satellite technology; have academic and leadership achievement; have potential for significant contribution to the satellite communications industry; enrolled in an accredited college or university program at the time of the scholarship issuance. **Application Requirements:** Applicants my mail or fax their applications together with a current transcript. **Deadline for Receipt:** December 31. **Additional Information:** Membership Director Tamara Bond at the above address.

4055 ■ SOCIETY OF SATELLITE PROFESSIONALS INTERNATIONAL
55 Broad St., 14th Fl.
New York, NY 10004
Tel: (212)809-5199
Fax: (212)825-0075
E-mail: tbond@sspi.org
Web Site: http://www.hessberger.com/sspi/index.html
To provide financial assistance to those who wish to study international satellite applications and distance education.
Title of Award: The PSSC Legacy Fund **Area, Field, or Subject:** Telecommunications systems. **Level of Education for which Award is Granted:** Graduate, Undergraduate **Funds Available:** No specific amount.
Eligibility Requirements: Applicant must be an SSPI member; pursue education in the satellite industry or a field making direct use of satellite technology; have academic and leadership achievement; show potential for significant contribution to the satellite communications industry; enrolled in an accredited college or university program at the time of the scholarship issuance. **Application Requirements:** Applicants may mail or fax their applications together with a current transcript. **Deadline for Receipt:** December 31. **Additional Information:** Membership Director Tamara Bond at the above address.

4056 ■ SOCIETY OF SATELLITE PROFESSIONALS INTERNATIONAL
55 Broad St., 14th Fl.
New York, NY 10004
Tel: (212)809-5199
Fax: (212)825-0075
E-mail: tbond@sspi.org
Web Site: http://www.hessberger.com/sspi/index.html
To provide financial assistance to those studying telecommunications systems.
Title of Award: The SSPI Mid-Atlantic Chapter Scholarships **Area, Field, or Subject:** Telecommunications systems. **Level of Education for which Award is Granted:** Graduate, Undergraduate **Funds Available:** No specific amount.
Eligibility Requirements: Applicant must be an SSPI member; pursue education in the satellite industry or a field making direct use of satellite technology; have academic and leadership achievement; show potential for significant contribution to the satellite communications industry; enrolled in an accredited college or university program at the time of the scholarship issuance. **Application Requirements:** Applicants may mail or fax their applications together with a current transcript. **Deadline for Receipt:** December 31. **Additional Information:** Membership Director Tamara Bond at the above address.

4057 ■ SOCIETY OF SATELLITE PROFESSIONALS INTERNATIONAL
55 Broad St., 14th Fl.
New York, NY 10004
Tel: (212)809-5199
Fax: (212)825-0075
E-mail: tbond@sspi.org
Web Site: http://www.hessberger.com/sspi/index.html
To provide financial assistance to those studying telecommunications systems.
Title of Award: The SSPI Northeast Chapter Scholarships **Area, Field, or Subject:** Telecommunications systems. **Level of Education for which Award is Granted:** Graduate, Undergraduate **Funds Available:** No specific amount.
Eligibility Requirements: Applicant must be an SSPI member; pursue education in the satellite industry or a field making direct use of satellite

technology; have academic and leadership achievement; potential for significant contribution to the satellite communications industry; enrolled in an accredited college or university program at the time of the scholarship issuance. **Application Requirements:** Applicants may mail or fax their applications together with a current transcript. **Deadline for Receipt:** December 31. **Additional Information:** Membership Director Tamara Bond at the above address.

4058 ■ SOCIETY OF SATELLITE PROFESSIONALS INTERNATIONAL
55 Broad St., 14th Fl.
New York, NY 10004
Tel: (212)809-5199
Fax: (212)825-0075
E-mail: tbond@sspi.org
Web Site: http://www.hessberger.com/sspi/index.html
To assist students with financial need.
Title of Award: The SSPI Southern California Scholarships **Area, Field, or Subject:** Telecommunications systems. **Level of Education for which Award is Granted:** Graduate, Undergraduate **Funds Available:** No specific amount.
Eligibility Requirements: Applicant must be a female SSPI member; current graduate or undergraduate of Southern California University System with a GPA of 3.2 or higher, pursue education in the satellite industry or a field making direct use of satellite technology; have academic and leadership achievement; show potential for significant contribution to the satellite communications industry; enrolled in an accredited college or university program at the time of the scholarship issuance. **Application Requirements:** Applicants may mail or fax their applications together with a current transcript to: Cynthia M. Dinkins, Vice President of Business and Program Development, T. Howard Foundation 601 13th St. NW, Ste. 710N Washington, DC 20005. **Deadline for Receipt:** December 31. **Additional Information:** Vice President of Business and Program Development Cynthia M. Dinkins e-mail at cdinkins@t-howard.org.

4059 ■ SOUTHWEST FLORIDA COMMUNITY FOUNDATION
8260 College Pkwy., Ste. 101
Fort Myers, FL 33919
Tel: (239)274-5900
Fax: (239)274-5930
Web Site: http://www.floridacommunity.com
To fund high school or undergraduate/graduate students planning to study at a 4-year accredited college in the area of Communications or Journalism.
Title of Award: Paul B. & Aline Flynn Scholarships **Area, Field, or Subject:** Communications; Journalism. **Level of Education for which Award is Granted:** Undergraduate **Funds Available:** No specific amount. **Duration:** One year.
Eligibility Requirements: Applicants must have graduated from a public or private high school in Charlotte, Collier, Glades, Hendry or Lee County; must pursue a degree in Communications, English or Journalism; and must maintain satisfactory grades. **Application Requirements:** Application forms are available online. Applicants must submit a student letter of interest, high school/college transcript, and letter of recommendation. **Deadline for Receipt:** February 15.

4060 ■ STARK COMMUNITY FOUNDATION
400 Market Ave. N, Ste. 200
Canton, OH 44702-2107
Tel: (330)454-3426
Fax: (330)454-5855
Web Site: http://www.starkcommunityfoundation.org
To provide scholarship assistance to qualified individuals who want to pursue their studies.
Title of Award: Louise Nader Khourey/Kappa Delta Pi Scholarships **Area, Field, or Subject:** Education; Foreign languages. **Level of Education for which Award is Granted:** Undergraduate **Funds Available:** No specific amount. **Duration:** One year.
Eligibility Requirements: Applicants must be graduating seniors from Stark County high schools who plan to attend an institution of higher learning; must be planning to pursue a degree in the field of education. **Application Requirements:** Applicants must submit completed applica-

tion forms and are advised to visit the High School Guidance Counselor. **Deadline for Receipt:** January.

4061 ■ STRAIGHTFORWARD MEDIA
508 7th St., Ste 202
Rapid City, SD 57701
Tel: (605)348-3042
Fax: (605)348-3043
E-mail: info@straightforwardmedia.com
Web Site: http://www.straightforwardmedia.com
To financially assist students in their educational pursuits.
Title of Award: StraightForward Media's Media and Communications Scholarships **Area, Field, or Subject:** Media arts; Communications. **Level of Education for which Award is Granted:** Undergraduate **Number Awarded:** 4. **Funds Available:** $500.
Eligibility Requirements: Applicant must be a student majoring in communications or media. **Application Requirements:** Applicants must complete scholarship application online. **Additional Information:** Awards are given four times a year. **Deadline for Receipt:** March, June, September, December.

4062 ■ TURF AND ORNAMENTAL COMMUNICATORS ASSOCIATION
120 W Main St.
New Prague, MN 56071
Tel: (952)758-6340
Fax: (952)758-5813
E-mail: tocaassociation@aol.com
Web Site: http://www.toca.org
To provide financial support for undergraduate college students pursuing a career in green industry communications.
Title of Award: Turf and Ornamental Communicators Association Scholarship Program **Area, Field, or Subject:** Communications. **Level of Education for which Award is Granted:** Undergraduate **Funds Available:** $2,500.
Eligibility Requirements: Applicants must major or minor in technical communications or a green industry related field such as horticulture, plant sciences, botany, agronomy, plant pathology, etc; must demonstrate an interest in using this course of study in the field of communications; must have overall GPA of 2.5 or above and a 3.0 in the major area of study (based on 4.0 scale). **Application Requirements:** Applicants must submit complete application form together with references, writing/editing sample, essay, resume, and transcript. **Deadline for Receipt:** March 1.

4063 ■ TURKISH COALITION OF AMERICA
1025 Connecticut Ave. NW, Ste. 1000
Washington, DC 20036
Tel: (202)370-1399
Fax: (202)370-1398
E-mail: info@turkishcoalitionofamerica.org
Web Site: http://www.turkishcoalition.org
To engage and cultivate a new generation of young Turkish American leaders.
Title of Award: TCA Turkish American Scholarships **Area, Field, or Subject:** Public Affairs; Political Science; International Affairs and Relations; Communications; Printing Trades; Public Relations. **Level of Education for which Award is Granted:** Undergraduate **Funds Available:** No specific amount.
Eligibility Requirements: Applicants must meet the following criteria: be a U.S. citizen or permanent resident (green card holder); have, and maintain through the course of the scholarship period, a cumulative minimum 3.3 GPA on a 4.0 scale; evidence of leadership commitment through participation in community service, particularly within the Turkish American community; and be a high school senior applying to an accredited college or university, or college student who plans to continue undergraduate study; or a college senior or graduate enrolled or about to enroll in graduate school. Graduate students who apply for the TCA must plan to pursue studies and a career in public affairs. **Application Requirements:** Applicants must submit three (3) collated, non-stapled, paperclipped copies of each of the following items: (1) Completed Application Form (2) Resume: Each copy should be submitted on one single-sided 8.5" x 11" sheet of paper. (3) Short essay: The essay should not exceed 500 words, must be typed and double-spaced. **Deadline for Receipt:** June 6. **Additional Information:** Turkish Coalition of America at the above address.

4064 ■ UNITED METHODIST COMMUNICATIONS

PO Box 320
Nashville, TN 37202-0320
Tel: (615)742-5400
E-mail: umcom@umcom.org
Web Site: http://www.umcom.org
To provide financial assistance to students who intend to pursue a career in religion journalism for communications.
Title of Award: Leonard M. Perryman Communications Scholarships for Ethnic Minority Students **Area, Field, or Subject:** Religion; Journalism; Communications. **Level of Education for which Award is Granted:** Undergraduate **Funds Available:** $2,500.
Eligibility Requirements: Applicants must be undergraduate United Methodist students, who intend to pursue a career in religion journalism for study at an accredited U.S. college or university. **Application Requirements:** Applicants must submit all the required application information. **Deadline for Receipt:** March 15.

4065 ■ UNIVERSITY OF HAWAII AT MANOA

2500 Campus Rd., Hawaii Hall 202
Honolulu, HI 96822
Tel: (808)956-8111
Web Site: http://www.uhm.hawaii.edu
To provide support for outstanding U.S. graduate students intending to pursue a career in language study.
Title of Award: National Security Education Program Fellowships **Area, Field, or Subject:** Foreign languages. **Level of Education for which Award is Granted:** Undergraduate **Funds Available:** $2,000. **Duration:** One Semester.
Eligibility Requirements: Applicant must be a U.S graduate student who wants to pursue their area of specialization in language study; must be a U.S. citizen. **Application Requirements:** For applications and information, applicants are advice to contact Dr. Chizuko Allen, Undergraduate and Fellowships Advisor, School of Pacific & Asian Studies, University of Hawaii, Honolulu, HI 96822, 808.956.2210. **Deadline for Receipt:** Early November.

4066 ■ UNIVERSITY OF NORTH CAROLINA SCHOOL OF JOURNALISM AND MASS COMMUNICATION

University of North Carolina, Carol Hall CB 3365
Chapel Hill, NC 27599-3365
Tel: (919)962-1204
Fax: (919)962-0620
E-mail: jomc@unc.edu
Web Site: http://www.jomc.unc.edu
To educate journalists.
Title of Award: Peggy Allen Community Newspaper Internships **Area, Field, or Subject:** Journalism; Communication. **Level of Education for which Award is Granted:** Undergraduate **Funds Available:** $5,000.
Eligibility Requirements: Applicants must be enrolled or plan to enroll in university and have an at least 2.9 GPA. **Application Requirements:** Applicants must complete the application form. **Deadline for Receipt:** February 1. **Additional Information:** PO Box 1080, Chapel Hill, NC 27514-1080.

4067 ■ UNIVERSITY OF NORTH CAROLINA SCHOOL OF JOURNALISM AND MASS COMMUNICATION

University of North Carolina, Carol Hall CB 3365
Chapel Hill, NC 27599-3365
Tel: (919)962-1204
Fax: (919)962-0620
E-mail: jomc@unc.edu
Web Site: http://www.jomc.unc.edu
To educate journalists.
Title of Award: Phillip Alston Scholarships **Area, Field, or Subject:** Journalism; Communications. **Level of Education for which Award is Granted:** Undergraduate **Funds Available:** $500.
Eligibility Requirements: Applicants must be undergraduate students in university. **Application Requirements:** Applicants must complete the application form.

4068 ■ UNIVERSITY OF NORTH CAROLINA SCHOOL OF JOURNALISM AND MASS COMMUNICATION

University of North Carolina, Carol Hall CB 3365
Chapel Hill, NC 27599-3365
Tel: (919)962-1204
Fax: (919)962-0620
E-mail: jomc@unc.edu
Web Site: http://www.jomc.unc.edu
To provide financial assistance to news-editorial journalism and community journalism students.
Title of Award: Jim Batten Community Newspaper Internships **Area, Field, or Subject:** Journalism; Communication. **Level of Education for which Award is Granted:** Undergraduate **Funds Available:** $5,000.
Eligibility Requirements: Applicants must be enrolled or plan to enroll in university and have at least 2.9 GPA. **Application Requirements:** Applicants must submit a completed application form. Applicants must contact the school's director of graduate studies for other application requirements. **Deadline for Receipt:** February 1. **Additional Information:** PO Box 1080, Chapel Hill, NC 27514-1080.

4069 ■ UNIVERSITY OF NORTH CAROLINA SCHOOL OF JOURNALISM AND MASS COMMUNICATION

University of North Carolina, Carol Hall CB 3365
Chapel Hill, NC 27599-3365
Tel: (919)962-1204
Fax: (919)962-0620
E-mail: jomc@unc.edu
Web Site: http://www.jomc.unc.edu
To educate journalists.
Title of Award: Tom Bost Scholarships **Area, Field, or Subject:** Journalism; Communications. **Level of Education for which Award is Granted:** Undergraduate **Funds Available:** $500.
Eligibility Requirements: Applicants must be undergraduate students in university. **Application Requirements:** Applicants must complete the application form.

4070 ■ UNIVERSITY OF NORTH CAROLINA SCHOOL OF JOURNALISM AND MASS COMMUNICATION

University of North Carolina, Carol Hall CB 3365
Chapel Hill, NC 27599-3365
Tel: (919)962-1204
Fax: (919)962-0620
E-mail: jomc@unc.edu
Web Site: http://www.jomc.unc.edu
To educate journalists.
Title of Award: Rick Brewer Scholarships **Area, Field, or Subject:** Broadcasting; Journalism; Public relations. **Level of Education for which Award is Granted:** Undergraduate **Funds Available:** $1,000.
Eligibility Requirements: Applicants must be undergraduate students with a keen interest in pursuing a career in sports journalism, broadcasting, or public relations. **Application Requirements:** Applicants must complete the application form.

4071 ■ UNIVERSITY OF NORTH CAROLINA SCHOOL OF JOURNALISM AND MASS COMMUNICATION

University of North Carolina, Carol Hall CB 3365
Chapel Hill, NC 27599-3365
Tel: (919)962-1204
Fax: (919)962-0620
E-mail: jomc@unc.edu
Web Site: http://www.jomc.unc.edu
To educate journalists.
Title of Award: Elton Casey Scholarships **Area, Field, or Subject:** Journalism. **Level of Education for which Award is Granted:** Undergraduate **Funds Available:** $750.
Eligibility Requirements: Applicants must be students who are interested in pursuing a career in sports journalism with a preference given to students from Orange or Durham counties. **Application Requirements:** Applicants must complete the application form.

4072 ■ UNIVERSITY OF NORTH CAROLINA SCHOOL OF JOURNALISM AND MASS COMMUNICATION

University of North Carolina, Carol Hall CB 3365
Chapel Hill, NC 27599-3365
Tel: (919)962-1204
Fax: (919)962-0620
E-mail: jomc@unc.edu

Web Site: http://www.jomc.unc.edu
To provide educational assistance for journalists intending to achieve better communication skills.
Title of Award: Ardis Cohoon Scholarships **Area, Field, or Subject:** Communications; Journalism. **Level of Education for which Award is Granted:** Undergraduate **Funds Available:** $500.
Eligibility Requirements: Applicants must be currently enrolled or plan to enroll in university with at least a 2.9 GPA. **Application Requirements:** Applicants must complete the application package.

4073 ■ UNIVERSITY OF NORTH CAROLINA SCHOOL OF JOURNALISM AND MASS COMMUNICATION
University of North Carolina, Carol Hall CB 3365
Chapel Hill, NC 27599-3365
Tel: (919)962-1204
Fax: (919)962-0620
E-mail: jomc@unc.edu
Web Site: http://www.jomc.unc.edu
To educate journalists.
Title of Award: Kathryn M. Cronin Scholarships **Area, Field, or Subject:** Journalism; Communications. **Level of Education for which Award is Granted:** Undergraduate **Funds Available:** $3,000.
Eligibility Requirements: Applicants must be enrolled or plan to enroll in university and have an at least 2.9 GPA. **Application Requirements:** Applicants must complete the application form; see Professor Tom Linden. **Deadline for Receipt:** March 1. **Additional Information:** PO Box 1080, Chapel Hill, NC 27514-1080.

4074 ■ UNIVERSITY OF NORTH CAROLINA SCHOOL OF JOURNALISM AND MASS COMMUNICATION
University of North Carolina, Carol Hall CB 3365
Chapel Hill, NC 27599-3365
Tel: (919)962-1204
Fax: (919)962-0620
E-mail: jomc@unc.edu
Web Site: http://www.jomc.unc.edu
To educate journalists; to support undergraduates who participate in meaningful out-of class activities that will help them in their mass communications careers.
Title of Award: Don and Barbara Curtis Excellence Fund for Extracurricular Student Activities **Area, Field, or Subject:** Journalism; Communication. **Level of Education for which Award is Granted:** Undergraduate **Funds Available:** $25,000.
Eligibility Requirements: Applicants must be students who are currently enrolled at the University of North Carolina and/or as a member of a student organization. **Application Requirements:** Applicants must complete the application form. **Deadline for Receipt:** October and February. **Additional Information:** PO Box 1080, Chapel Hill, NC 27514-1080.

4075 ■ UNIVERSITY OF NORTH CAROLINA SCHOOL OF JOURNALISM AND MASS COMMUNICATION
University of North Carolina, Carol Hall CB 3365
Chapel Hill, NC 27599-3365
Tel: (919)962-1204
Fax: (919)962-0620
E-mail: jomc@unc.edu
Web Site: http://www.jomc.unc.edu
To educate journalists.
Title of Award: James Davis Scholarships **Area, Field, or Subject:** Journalism; Communication. **Level of Education for which Award is Granted:** Undergraduate **Funds Available:** $4,000.
Eligibility Requirements: Applicants must be enrolled or plan to enroll in university and have an at least 2.9 GPA; Applicants must be studying North Carolina history, and North Carolina natives. **Application Requirements:** Applicants must complete the application form. **Deadline for Receipt:** February 1. **Additional Information:** PO Box 1080, Chapel Hill, NC 27514-1080.

4076 ■ UNIVERSITY OF NORTH CAROLINA SCHOOL OF JOURNALISM AND MASS COMMUNICATION
University of North Carolina, Carol Hall CB 3365
Chapel Hill, NC 27599-3365
Tel: (919)962-1204

Fax: (919)962-0620
E-mail: jomc@unc.edu
Web Site: http://www.jomc.unc.edu
To educate journalists.
Title of Award: Robert Winchester Dodson Scholarships **Area, Field, or Subject:** Communication. **Level of Education for which Award is Granted:** Undergraduate **Funds Available:** $1,500.
Eligibility Requirements: Applicants must be students who are currently enrolled or plan to enroll in university. **Application Requirements:** Applicants must complete the application form.

4077 ■ UNIVERSITY OF NORTH CAROLINA SCHOOL OF JOURNALISM AND MASS COMMUNICATION
University of North Carolina, Carol Hall CB 3365
Chapel Hill, NC 27599-3365
Tel: (919)962-1204
Fax: (919)962-0620
E-mail: jomc@unc.edu
Web Site: http://www.jomc.unc.edu
To provide financial assistance to journalism students.
Title of Award: Vivian Edmonds Scholarships **Area, Field, or Subject:** Journalism; Communication. **Level of Education for which Award is Granted:** Undergraduate **Funds Available:** $1,000.
Eligibility Requirements: Applicants must be sophomore students and must have a minimum of 2.9 GPA. **Application Requirements:** Applicants must submit a completed application form. **Deadline for Receipt:** February 1. **Additional Information:** PO Box 1080, Chapel Hill, NC 27514-1080.

4078 ■ UNIVERSITY OF NORTH CAROLINA SCHOOL OF JOURNALISM AND MASS COMMUNICATION
University of North Carolina, Carol Hall CB 3365
Chapel Hill, NC 27599-3365
Tel: (919)962-1204
Fax: (919)962-0620
E-mail: jomc@unc.edu
Web Site: http://www.jomc.unc.edu
To educate journalists.
Title of Award: Reese Felts Scholarships **Area, Field, or Subject:** Communication; Journalism. **Level of Education for which Award is Granted:** Undergraduate **Funds Available:** $2,500.
Eligibility Requirements: Applicants must be currently enrolled or plan to enroll in university. **Application Requirements:** Applicants must complete the application form.

4079 ■ UNIVERSITY OF NORTH CAROLINA SCHOOL OF JOURNALISM AND MASS COMMUNICATION
University of North Carolina, Carol Hall CB 3365
Chapel Hill, NC 27599-3365
Tel: (919)962-1204
Fax: (919)962-0620
E-mail: jomc@unc.edu
Web Site: http://www.jomc.unc.edu
To educate journalists.
Title of Award: Ameel J. Fisher Scholarships **Area, Field, or Subject:** Journalism; Communication. **Level of Education for which Award is Granted:** Undergraduate **Funds Available:** $4,000.
Eligibility Requirements: Applicants must be enrolled or plan to enroll in university and have an at least 2.9 GPA. **Application Requirements:** Applicants must complete the application form. **Deadline for Receipt:** February 1. **Additional Information:** PO Box 1080, Chapel Hill, NC 27514-1080.

4080 ■ UNIVERSITY OF NORTH CAROLINA SCHOOL OF JOURNALISM AND MASS COMMUNICATION
University of North Carolina, Carol Hall CB 3365
Chapel Hill, NC 27599-3365
Tel: (919)962-1204
Fax: (919)962-0620
E-mail: jomc@unc.edu
Web Site: http://www.jomc.unc.edu
To educate journalists.
Title of Award: Kays Gary Scholarships **Area, Field, or Subject:** Communications; Journalism. **Level of Education for which Award is Granted:** Undergraduate **Funds Available:** $500.

Eligibility Requirements: Applicants must be currently enrolled or plan to enroll in university and have an at least 2.9 GPA. **Application Requirements:** Applicants must complete the application form.

4081 ■ UNIVERSITY OF NORTH CAROLINA SCHOOL OF JOURNALISM AND MASS COMMUNICATION
University of North Carolina, Carol Hall CB 3365
Chapel Hill, NC 27599-3365
Tel: (919)962-1204
Fax: (919)962-0620
E-mail: jomc@unc.edu
Web Site: http://www.jomc.unc.edu
To educate journalists.
Title of Award: Stephen Gates Scholarships **Area, Field, or Subject:** Communication; Broadcasting. **Level of Education for which Award is Granted:** Undergraduate **Funds Available:** $2,000.
Eligibility Requirements: Applicants must be student currently enrolled or planing to enroll in university. **Application Requirements:** Applicants must complete the application form.

4082 ■ UNIVERSITY OF NORTH CAROLINA SCHOOL OF JOURNALISM AND MASS COMMUNICATION
University of North Carolina, Carol Hall CB 3365
Chapel Hill, NC 27599-3365
Tel: (919)962-1204
Fax: (919)962-0620
E-mail: jomc@unc.edu
Web Site: http://www.jomc.unc.edu
To educate journalists.
Title of Award: Joy Gibson Scholarships **Area, Field, or Subject:** Journalism; Communications. **Level of Education for which Award is Granted:** Undergraduate **Funds Available:** $500.
Eligibility Requirements: Applicants must be undergraduate students in university. **Application Requirements:** Applicants must complete the application form.

4083 ■ UNIVERSITY OF NORTH CAROLINA SCHOOL OF JOURNALISM AND MASS COMMUNICATION
University of North Carolina, Carol Hall CB 3365
Chapel Hill, NC 27599-3365
Tel: (919)962-1204
Fax: (919)962-0620
E-mail: jomc@unc.edu
Web Site: http://www.jomc.unc.edu
To educate journalists.
Title of Award: L.C. Gifford Distinguished Journalism Scholarships **Area, Field, or Subject:** Communication; Journalism. **Level of Education for which Award is Granted:** Undergraduate **Funds Available:** $2,000.
Eligibility Requirements: Applicants must be journalism students from the University of North Carolina Chapel Hill. **Application Requirements:** Applicants must complete the application form.

4084 ■ UNIVERSITY OF NORTH CAROLINA SCHOOL OF JOURNALISM AND MASS COMMUNICATION
University of North Carolina, Carol Hall CB 3365
Chapel Hill, NC 27599-3365
Tel: (919)962-1204
Fax: (919)962-0620
E-mail: jomc@unc.edu
Web Site: http://www.jomc.unc.edu
To educate journalists.
Title of Award: Charles Hauser Scholarships **Area, Field, or Subject:** Communications; Journalism. **Level of Education for which Award is Granted:** Undergraduate **Funds Available:** $500.
Eligibility Requirements: Applicants must be currently enrolled or plan to enroll in university and have an at least 2.9 GPA. **Application Requirements:** Applicants must complete the application form.

4085 ■ UNIVERSITY OF NORTH CAROLINA SCHOOL OF JOURNALISM AND MASS COMMUNICATION
University of North Carolina, Carol Hall CB 3365
Chapel Hill, NC 27599-3365
Tel: (919)962-1204

Fax: (919)962-0620
E-mail: jomc@unc.edu
Web Site: http://www.jomc.unc.edu
To educate journalists.
Title of Award: Paul Green Houston Scholarships **Area, Field, or Subject:** Communication; Journalism. **Level of Education for which Award is Granted:** Undergraduate **Funds Available:** $1,500.
Eligibility Requirements: Applicants must be students majoring in news editorial journalism. **Application Requirements:** Applicants must complete the application form.

4086 ■ UNIVERSITY OF NORTH CAROLINA SCHOOL OF JOURNALISM AND MASS COMMUNICATION
University of North Carolina, Carol Hall CB 3365
Chapel Hill, NC 27599-3365
Tel: (919)962-1204
Fax: (919)962-0620
E-mail: jomc@unc.edu
Web Site: http://www.jomc.unc.edu
To provide financial assistance to journalism students.
Title of Award: James F. Hurley III Bicentennial Merit Scholarships **Area, Field, or Subject:** Journalism; Communication. **Level of Education for which Award is Granted:** Undergraduate **Funds Available:** $7,250.
Eligibility Requirements: Applicants must be enrolled or plan to enroll in university and have an at least 2.9 GPA. **Application Requirements:** Applicants must submit a completed application form. Applicants must contact the school's director of graduate studies for other application requirements. **Deadline for Receipt:** February 1. **Additional Information:** PO Box 1080, Chapel Hill, NC 27514-1080.

4087 ■ UNIVERSITY OF NORTH CAROLINA SCHOOL OF JOURNALISM AND MASS COMMUNICATION
University of North Carolina, Carol Hall CB 3365
Chapel Hill, NC 27599-3365
Tel: (919)962-1204
Fax: (919)962-0620
E-mail: jomc@unc.edu
Web Site: http://www.jomc.unc.edu
To educate journalists; to help defray expenses associated with travel to foreign countries for courses.
Title of Award: Fred Hutchison Travel Scholarships **Area, Field, or Subject:** Journalism; Communication. **Level of Education for which Award is Granted:** Undergraduate **Funds Available:** No specific amount.
Eligibility Requirements: Applicants must be students who are currently enrolled or plan to enroll in university. **Application Requirements:** Applicants must complete the application form; see Professor Tom Linden. **Deadline for Receipt:** March 1. **Additional Information:** jyopp@email.unc.edu.

4088 ■ UNIVERSITY OF NORTH CAROLINA SCHOOL OF JOURNALISM AND MASS COMMUNICATION
University of North Carolina, Carol Hall CB 3365
Chapel Hill, NC 27599-3365
Tel: (919)962-1204
Fax: (919)962-0620
E-mail: jomc@unc.edu
Web Site: http://www.jomc.unc.edu
To educate journalists; to support undergraduate students in traveling to a European country to learn about it's politics, culture, and mass media by working there.
Title of Award: Edward Jackson International Scholarships **Area, Field, or Subject:** Communication; Journalism. **Level of Education for which Award is Granted:** Undergraduate **Funds Available:** $2,500.
Eligibility Requirements: Applicants must be news editorial undergraduate students, preferably from North Carolina. **Application Requirements:** Applicants must complete the application form. **Deadline for Receipt:** February 1.

4089 ■ UNIVERSITY OF NORTH CAROLINA SCHOOL OF JOURNALISM AND MASS COMMUNICATION
University of North Carolina, Carol Hall CB 3365
Chapel Hill, NC 27599-3365

Tel: (919)962-1204
Fax: (919)962-0620
E-mail: jomc@unc.edu
Web Site: http://www.jomc.unc.edu
To educate journalists.
Title of Award: Gene Jackson Scholarships **Area, Field, or Subject:** Communication; Journalism. **Level of Education for which Award is Granted:** Undergraduate **Funds Available:** $1,250.
Eligibility Requirements: Applicants must be graduate students of the school whve had a distinguished career in newspaper and worked in the University of North Carolina Chapel Hill Development Office. **Application Requirements:** Applicants must complete the application form.

4090 ■ UNIVERSITY OF NORTH CAROLINA SCHOOL OF JOURNALISM AND MASS COMMUNICATION
University of North Carolina, Carol Hall CB 3365
Chapel Hill, NC 27599-3365
Tel: (919)962-1204
Fax: (919)962-0620
E-mail: jomc@unc.edu
Web Site: http://www.jomc.unc.edu
To provide educational assistance for journalists to help them achieve effective communication in the fields of science and medicine.
Title of Award: Peter Lars Jacobson Scholarships **Area, Field, or Subject:** Journalism; Communications. **Level of Education for which Award is Granted:** Undergraduate **Funds Available:** $500.
Eligibility Requirements: Applicants must be journalism and mass communication students who are able to write the best medical story. **Application Requirements:** Applicants must submit completed application form; applicants must submit a story or stories with name, address, telephone number and class year to Professor Tom Linden. **Deadline for Receipt:** February 1.

4091 ■ UNIVERSITY OF NORTH CAROLINA SCHOOL OF JOURNALISM AND MASS COMMUNICATION
University of North Carolina, Carol Hall CB 3365
Chapel Hill, NC 27599-3365
Tel: (919)962-1204
Fax: (919)962-0620
E-mail: jomc@unc.edu
Web Site: http://www.jomc.unc.edu
To educate journalists.
Title of Award: Glenn Keever Scholarships **Area, Field, or Subject:** Communication; Journalism. **Level of Education for which Award is Granted:** Undergraduate **Funds Available:** $2,500.
Eligibility Requirements: Applicants must be undergraduate students, preferably in North Carolina. **Application Requirements:** Applicants must complete the application form.

4092 ■ UNIVERSITY OF NORTH CAROLINA SCHOOL OF JOURNALISM AND MASS COMMUNICATION
University of North Carolina, Carol Hall CB 3365
Chapel Hill, NC 27599-3365
Tel: (919)962-1204
Fax: (919)962-0620
E-mail: jomc@unc.edu
Web Site: http://www.jomc.unc.edu
To educate journalists.
Title of Award: Norval Neil Luxon Prize for Scholarship to a Junior Scholarships **Area, Field, or Subject:** Communications. **Level of Education for which Award is Granted:** Undergraduate **Funds Available:** $500.
Eligibility Requirements: Applicant must be junior with the highest grade point of average; applicants must have at least 36 credit hours of graded course work at the University of North Carolina and have completed approximately 90 credit hours by the end of the spring semester. **Application Requirements:** Applicants must complete the application form.

4093 ■ UNIVERSITY OF NORTH CAROLINA SCHOOL OF JOURNALISM AND MASS COMMUNICATION
University of North Carolina, Carol Hall CB 3365
Chapel Hill, NC 27599-3365
Tel: (919)962-1204

Fax: (919)962-0620
E-mail: jomc@unc.edu
Web Site: http://www.jomc.unc.edu
To educate journalists.
Title of Award: Mackey-Byars Scholarships for Communication Excellence **Area, Field, or Subject:** Communications. **Level of Education for which Award is Granted:** Undergraduate **Funds Available:** $500.
Eligibility Requirements: Applicants must be minority or disadvantaged students majoring in mass communications. **Application Requirements:** Applicants must complete the application form.

4094 ■ UNIVERSITY OF NORTH CAROLINA SCHOOL OF JOURNALISM AND MASS COMMUNICATION
University of North Carolina, Carol Hall CB 3365
Chapel Hill, NC 27599-3365
Tel: (919)962-1204
Fax: (919)962-0620
E-mail: jomc@unc.edu
Web Site: http://www.jomc.unc.edu
To educate journalists.
Title of Award: Raleigh Mann Scholarships **Area, Field, or Subject:** Journalism; Communications. **Level of Education for which Award is Granted:** Undergraduate **Funds Available:** $500.
Eligibility Requirements: Applicants must be undergraduate students in university. **Application Requirements:** Applicants must complete the application package.

4095 ■ UNIVERSITY OF NORTH CAROLINA SCHOOL OF JOURNALISM AND MASS COMMUNICATION
University of North Carolina, Carol Hall CB 3365
Chapel Hill, NC 27599-3365
Tel: (919)962-1204
Fax: (919)962-0620
E-mail: jomc@unc.edu
Web Site: http://www.jomc.unc.edu
To educate journalists.
Title of Award: Edward Heywood Megson Scholarships **Area, Field, or Subject:** Journalism; Communications. **Level of Education for which Award is Granted:** Undergraduate **Funds Available:** $750.
Eligibility Requirements: Applicants must be graduates of University of North Carolina- Chapel Hill. **Application Requirements:** Applicants must complete the application form.

4096 ■ UNIVERSITY OF NORTH CAROLINA SCHOOL OF JOURNALISM AND MASS COMMUNICATION
University of North Carolina, Carol Hall CB 3365
Chapel Hill, NC 27599-3365
Tel: (919)962-1204
Fax: (919)962-0620
E-mail: jomc@unc.edu
Web Site: http://www.jomc.unc.edu
To provide financial assistance to minority and disadvantaged students.
Title of Award: Quincy Sharpe Mills Scholarships **Area, Field, or Subject:** Journalism; Communication. **Level of Education for which Award is Granted:** Undergraduate **Funds Available:** $3,000.
Eligibility Requirements: Applicants must be currently enrolled in or planning to attend university and must have a minimum of 2.9 GPA. **Application Requirements:** Applicants must submit a completed application form. **Deadline for Receipt:** February 1. **Additional Information:** PO Box 1080, Chapel Hill, NC 27514-1080.

4097 ■ UNIVERSITY OF NORTH CAROLINA SCHOOL OF JOURNALISM AND MASS COMMUNICATION
University of North Carolina, Carol Hall CB 3365
Chapel Hill, NC 27599-3365
Tel: (919)962-1204
Fax: (919)962-0620
E-mail: jomc@unc.edu
Web Site: http://www.jomc.unc.edu
To provide financial assistance to journalism students.
Title of Award: Alexander Morisey Scholarships **Area, Field, or Subject:** Journalism; Communication. **Level of Education for which Award is Granted:** Undergraduate **Funds Available:** $1,000.
Eligibility Requirements: Applicants must be first year students and must have a minimum of 2.9 GPA. **Application Requirements:** Ap-

plicants must submit a completed application form. **Deadline for Receipt:** February 1. **Additional Information:** PO Box 1080, Chapel Hill, NC 27514-1080.

4098 ■ UNIVERSITY OF NORTH CAROLINA SCHOOL OF JOURNAL- ISM AND MASS COMMUNICATION
University of North Carolina, Carol Hall CB 3365
Chapel Hill, NC 27599-3365
Tel: (919)962-1204
Fax: (919)962-0620
E-mail: jomc@unc.edu
Web Site: http://www.jomc.unc.edu
To provide financial assistance to journalism students.
Title of Award: Robert Pittman Scholarships **Area, Field, or Subject:** Journalism; Communication. **Level of Education for which Award is Granted:** Undergraduate **Funds Available:** $7,000.
Eligibility Requirements: Applicants must be enrolled or plan to enroll in university and have at least 2.9 GPA; applicants must have an internship at St. Petersburg Times. **Application Requirements:** Applicants must submit a completed application form. Applicants must contact the School's Director of graduate studies for other application requirements. **Deadline for Receipt:** February 1. **Additional Information:** PO Box 1080, Chapel Hill, NC 27514-1080.

4099 ■ UNIVERSITY OF NORTH CAROLINA SCHOOL OF JOURNAL- ISM AND MASS COMMUNICATION
University of North Carolina, Carol Hall CB 3365
Chapel Hill, NC 27599-3365
Tel: (919)962-1204
Fax: (919)962-0620
E-mail: jomc@unc.edu
Web Site: http://www.jomc.unc.edu
To provide financial assistance to Latino students studying newspaper journalism.
Title of Award: Erwin Potts Scholarships **Area, Field, or Subject:** Journalism; Communication. **Level of Education for which Award is Granted:** Undergraduate **Funds Available:** $2,000.
Eligibility Requirements: Applicants must be currently enrolled or plan to attend in university and must have a minimum of 2.9 GPA. **Application Requirements:** Applicants must submit a completed application form. **Deadline for Receipt:** February 1. **Additional Information:** PO Box 1080, Chapel Hill, NC 27514-1080.

4100 ■ UNIVERSITY OF NORTH CAROLINA SCHOOL OF JOURNAL- ISM AND MASS COMMUNICATION
University of North Carolina, Carol Hall CB 3365
Chapel Hill, NC 27599-3365
Tel: (919)962-1204
Fax: (919)962-0620
E-mail: jomc@unc.edu
Web Site: http://www.jomc.unc.edu
To provide financial assistance to journalism students.
Title of Award: Peter DeWitt Pruden and Phyliss Harrill Pruden Scholarships **Area, Field, or Subject:** Journalism; Communication. **Level of Education for which Award is Granted:** Undergraduate **Funds Available:** $10,000.
Eligibility Requirements: Applicants must be enrolled or plan to enroll in a university in North Carolina, Tennessee, or Virginia and have an at least 2.9 GPA. **Application Requirements:** Applicants must submit a completed application form. Applicants must contact the school's director of graduate studies for other application requirements. **Deadline for Receipt:** February 1. **Additional Information:** PO Box 1080, Chapel Hill, NC 27514-1080.

4101 ■ UNIVERSITY OF NORTH CAROLINA SCHOOL OF JOURNAL- ISM AND MASS COMMUNICATION
University of North Carolina, Carol Hall CB 3365
Chapel Hill, NC 27599-3365
Tel: (919)962-1204
Fax: (919)962-0620
E-mail: jomc@unc.edu
Web Site: http://www.jomc.unc.edu
To educate journalists.
Title of Award: Bob Quincy Scholarships **Area, Field, or Subject:** Communication; Journalism. **Level of Education for which Award is**

Granted: Undergraduate **Funds Available:** $2,500.
Eligibility Requirements: Applicants must be currently enrolled or plan to enroll in university. **Application Requirements:** Applicants must complete the application form.

4102 ■ UNIVERSITY OF NORTH CAROLINA SCHOOL OF JOURNAL- ISM AND MASS COMMUNICATION
University of North Carolina, Carol Hall CB 3365
Chapel Hill, NC 27599-3365
Tel: (919)962-1204
Fax: (919)962-0620
E-mail: jomc@unc.edu
Web Site: http://www.jomc.unc.edu
To educate journalists.
Title of Award: Marjorie Usher Regan Scholarships **Area, Field, or Subject:** Communication; Journalism. **Level of Education for which Award is Granted:** Undergraduate **Funds Available:** $2,000.
Eligibility Requirements: Applicants must be women with a career interest in print journalism. **Application Requirements:** Applicants must complete the application form.

4103 ■ UNIVERSITY OF NORTH CAROLINA SCHOOL OF JOURNAL- ISM AND MASS COMMUNICATION
University of North Carolina, Carol Hall CB 3365
Chapel Hill, NC 27599-3365
Tel: (919)962-1204
Fax: (919)962-0620
E-mail: jomc@unc.edu
Web Site: http://www.jomc.unc.edu
To educate journalists.
Title of Award: Hal Tanner Jr. Scholarships **Area, Field, or Subject:** Communication; Advertising. **Level of Education for which Award is Granted:** Undergraduate **Funds Available:** $1,500.
Eligibility Requirements: Applicants must be rising senior students majoring in advertising. **Application Requirements:** Applicants must complete the application form.

4104 ■ UNIVERSITY OF NORTH CAROLINA SCHOOL OF JOURNAL- ISM AND MASS COMMUNICATION
University of North Carolina, Carol Hall CB 3365
Chapel Hill, NC 27599-3365
Tel: (919)962-1204
Fax: (919)962-0620
E-mail: jomc@unc.edu
Web Site: http://www.jomc.unc.edu
To educate journalists; to pay expenses for a student who has secured a summer internship in sports communication.
Title of Award: Jim and Pat Thacker Sports Communication Internships **Area, Field, or Subject:** Communication. **Level of Education for which Award is Granted:** Undergraduate **Funds Available:** $2,500.
Eligibility Requirements: Applicants must be currently enrolled or plan to enroll in university. **Application Requirements:** Applicants must complete the application form; applicants must contact Professor John Sweeney for details.

4105 ■ UNIVERSITY OF NORTH CAROLINA SCHOOL OF JOURNAL- ISM AND MASS COMMUNICATION
University of North Carolina, Carol Hall CB 3365
Chapel Hill, NC 27599-3365
Tel: (919)962-1204
Fax: (919)962-0620
E-mail: jomc@unc.edu
Web Site: http://www.jomc.unc.edu
To provide financial assistance to journalism students.
Title of Award: Tucker Family Scholarships **Area, Field, or Subject:** Journalism; Communication. **Level of Education for which Award is Granted:** Undergraduate **Funds Available:** $5,000.
Eligibility Requirements: Applicants must be enrolled or plan to enroll in university and have at least 2.9 GPA. **Application Requirements:** Applicants must submit a completed application form. **Deadline for Receipt:** February 1. **Additional Information:** PO Box 1080, Chapel Hill, NC 27514-1080.

4106 ■ UNIVERSITY OF NORTH CAROLINA SCHOOL OF JOURNAL-ISM AND MASS COMMUNICATION
University of North Carolina, Carol Hall CB 3365
Chapel Hill, NC 27599-3365
Tel: (919)962-1204
Fax: (919)962-0620
E-mail: jomc@unc.edu
Web Site: http://www.jomc.unc.edu
To educate journalists.
Title of Award: David Julian Wichard Scholarships **Area, Field, or Subject:** Communication; Journalism. **Level of Education for which Award is Granted:** Undergraduate **Funds Available:** $2,000.
Eligibility Requirements: Applicants must be currently enrolled or planning to enroll in university; applicants must be residents of North Carolina. **Application Requirements:** Applicants must complete the application form.

4107 ■ UNIVERSITY OF NORTH CAROLINA SCHOOL OF JOURNAL-ISM AND MASS COMMUNICATION
University of North Carolina, Carol Hall CB 3365
Chapel Hill, NC 27599-3365
Tel: (919)962-1204
Fax: (919)962-0620
E-mail: jomc@unc.edu
Web Site: http://www.jomc.unc.edu
To provide financial assistance to news-editorial graduate students.
Title of Award: Tom Wicker Scholarships **Area, Field, or Subject:** Journalism; Communication. **Level of Education for which Award is Granted:** Undergraduate **Funds Available:** $1,000.
Eligibility Requirements: Applicants must be enrolled or plan to enroll in university and have an at least 2.9 GPA. **Application Requirements:** Applicants must submit a completed application form. Applicants must contact the school's director of graduate studies for other application requirements. **Deadline for Receipt:** February 1. **Additional Information:** PO Box 1080, Chapel Hill, NC 27514-1080.

4108 ■ UNIVERSITY OF NORTH CAROLINA SCHOOL OF JOURNAL-ISM AND MASS COMMUNICATION
University of North Carolina, Carol Hall CB 3365
Chapel Hill, NC 27599-3365
Tel: (919)962-1204
Fax: (919)962-0620
E-mail: jomc@unc.edu
Web Site: http://www.jomc.unc.edu
To educate journalists.
Title of Award: WKIX Alumni Association Scholarships **Area, Field, or Subject:** Communications. **Level of Education for which Award is Granted:** Undergraduate **Funds Available:** $1,000.
Eligibility Requirements: Applicants must be student in the electronic communication sequence. **Application Requirements:** Applicants must complete the application form.

4109 ■ UNIVERSITY OF NORTH CAROLINA SCHOOL OF JOURNAL-ISM AND MASS COMMUNICATION
University of North Carolina, Carol Hall CB 3365
Chapel Hill, NC 27599-3365
Tel: (919)962-1204
Fax: (919)962-0620
E-mail: jomc@unc.edu
Web Site: http://www.jomc.unc.edu
To provide financial assistance to journalism students.
Title of Award: WTVD Endowment Scholarships **Area, Field, or Subject:** Journalism; Communication. **Level of Education for which Award is Granted:** Undergraduate **Funds Available:** $1,000.
Eligibility Requirements: Applicants must be enrolled or plan to enroll in university and have at least 2.9 GPA. **Application Requirements:** Applicants must submit a completed application form. **Deadline for Receipt:** February 1. **Additional Information:** PO Box 1080, Chapel Hill, NC 27514-1080.

4110 ■ WISCONSIN BROADCASTERS ASSOCIATION
44 E Mifflin St., Ste. 900
Madison, WI 53703
Tel: (608)255-2600
Free: 800-236-1922
Fax: (608)256-3986
E-mail: mendicott@wi-broadcasters.org
Web Site: http://www.wi-broadcasters.org
To assist students enrolled in broadcasting-related educational programs at four-year public or private colleges and universities.
Title of Award: Wisconsin Broadcasters Association Scholarships **Area, Field, or Subject:** Broadcasting. **Level of Education for which Award is Granted:** Undergraduate **Number Awarded:** 4. **Funds Available:** $2,000.
Eligibility Requirements: Applicants must have completed 60 credits and must be majoring in broadcasting, communications, or related field at a four-year public or private college or university; must have Wisconsin connection in that they must have either graduated from a Wisconsin high school or be attending a Wisconsin college or university; and must be planning a career in radio or television broadcasting. **Application Requirements:** Applicants must submit a completed application form; a current official transcript of college/university grades; two brief letters of recommendation supporting the application; maximum of three pages, original, typed, double-spaced essay written by the applicant forecasting what the broadcasting industry will be like in five years and how the applicant believes he or she will contribute to radio or television during that time. **Deadline for Receipt:** October 19. **Additional Information:** John Laabs at the above address.

Education

4111 ■ AMERICAN ASSOCIATION FOR HEALTH EDUCATION
1900 Association Dr.
Reston, VA 20191-1598
Tel: (703)476-3400
Free: 800-213-7193
Web Site: http://www.aahperd.org/aahe
To support members with their educational pursuit.
Title of Award: Ruth Abernathy Presidential Scholarships **Area, Field, or Subject:** Health education; Physical education. **Level of Education for which Award is Granted:** Graduate, Undergraduate **Number Awarded:** Three undergraduates; Two graduate students. **Funds Available:** $1000-$1500; and a three-year AAHPERD membership.
Eligibility Requirements: Applicant must be undergraduate or graduate student members majoring in a field related to one or more of the disciplines represented by AAHPERD and its associations; and have a cumulative GPA of 3.5. **Application Requirements:** Applicants must submit a completed application from together with the required materials. Application materials should be submitted by U.S. mail (fax copies will not be accepted). **Deadline for Receipt:** October 15. **Additional Information:** Deb Callis at dcallis@aahperd.org.

4112 ■ AMERICAN INDIAN EDUCATION FOUNDATION
2401 Eglin St.
Rapid City, SD 57703
Tel: (866)866-8642; (866)866-8642
Fax: (605)342-4113
E-mail: info@programs.org
Web Site: http://www.nrcprograms.org
To award scholarship to the students of Native American ancestry wishing to attend college.
Title of Award: Brown Foundation College Scholarship **Area, Field, or Subject:** Education. **Level of Education for which Award is Granted:** Undergraduate **Number Awarded:** 10. **Funds Available:** $1,000.
Eligibility Requirements: Applicants must be students wishing to attend college and major in education. **Application Requirements:** Applicants must: complete AIEF Scholarship Application; provide documentation of tribal enrollment for themselves or their parents; provide transcripts with ACT and GPA scores; attach an essay that outlines the following information: introduction, academics, career plans, service to the Native American community, leadership/community service, financial needs and unique circumstances. **Deadline for Receipt:** April 4. **Additional Information:** Brown Foundation Scholarship Program, 1515 SE Monroe, Topeka, KS 66612; Phone: 785-235-3939; brownfoundation@juno.com.

4113 ■ AMERICAN INDIAN EDUCATION FOUNDATION

2401 Eglin St.
Rapid City, SD 57703
Tel: (866)866-8642; (866)866-8642
Fax: (605)342-4113
E-mail: info@programs.org
Web Site: http://www.nrcprograms.org
To give American Indian students the tools, resources and opportunities to learn and succeed.
Title of Award: Catching the Dream Scholarship **Area, Field, or Subject:** Education; Business; Science; Engineering. **Level of Education for which Award is Granted:** Graduate, Undergraduate **Funds Available:** $500-$5,000.
Eligibility Requirements: Applicants must be enrolled members of a federally recognized tribe; both undergraduate and graduate students may apply. **Application Requirements:** Applicants may submit an application to the Scholarship Affairs Office of Catching the Dream. **Deadline for Receipt:** March 15-Summer; April 15-Fall; September 15-spring. **Additional Information:** Catching the Dream 8200 Mountain Rd. NE Ste. 203 Albuquerque, NM 87110; 505-262-2351 x 116; nscholarsh@aol.com.

4114 ■ AMERICAN INSTITUTE OF POLISH CULTURE

1440 79th St. Causeway, Ste. 117
Miami, FL 33141
Tel: (305)864-2349
Fax: (305)865-5150
E-mail: info@ampolinstitute.org
Web Site: http://www.ampolinstitute.org
To provide financial support American students of Polish descent who wish to continue their education after high school.
Title of Award: Harriet Irsay Scholarships **Area, Field, or Subject:** Communications; Education; Media arts; History; International affairs and relations; Journalism; Liberal arts; Polish studies; Public relations. **Level of Education for which Award is Granted:** Graduate, Undergraduate **Number Awarded:** 10-15. **Funds Available:** $1,000.
Eligibility Requirements: Applicants must be of Polish heritage; an American citizen or permanent resident; full-time graduate or undergraduate students in the field of communication, education, film, history, International Relation, journalism, liberal arts, polish studies, public relations; or graduate student in business programs with a thesis related to Poland, or graduate students with a thesis with Polish subject. **Application Requirements:** Applicants must submit a completed application form; school transcripts; resume; essay (200-400 words) about "Why should I receive the scholarship"; an article about Poland (maximum of 700 words); and 3 signed recommendation letters on a letterhead stationary from teachers or other person knowledgeable about the applicant's academic background. A non-refundable $10 processing fee (check or money order) must also be included. **Deadline for Receipt:** April 20.

4115 ■ AMERICAN MONTESSORI SOCIETY

281 Park Ave. S
New York, NY 10010-6102
Tel: (212)358-1250
Fax: (212)358-1256
E-mail: info@amshq.org
Web Site: http://www.amshq.org
To support the growth of Montessori teachers.
Title of Award: AMS Teacher Education Scholarships **Area, Field, or Subject:** Education, Teaching. **Level of Education for which Award is Granted:** Undergraduate **Funds Available:** $28,000.
Eligibility Requirements: Applicant must be accepted or in the process of acceptance by an affiliated AMS teacher education program. **Application Requirements:** Application forms are available on the website. Applicant must have a personal statement and three recommendation letters. Application materials must be sent to: The American Montessori Society, 281 Park Ave., S, New York, NY, 10010. **Deadline for Receipt:** May 1.

4116 ■ AMERICAN QUARTER HORSE YOUTH ASSOCIATION

PO Box 200
Amarillo, TX 79168
Tel: (806)376-4811

Web Site: http://www.aqha.com/youth.html
To develop and educate the future professionals.
Title of Award: American Quarter Horse Foundation Scholarships **Area, Field, or Subject:** Education; Nursing; Journalism; Veterinary science and medicine. **Level of Education for which Award is Granted:** Undergraduate **Funds Available:** No specific amount.
Eligibility Requirements: An applicant must be enrolled in college specializing degree programs such as education, nursing, journalism, veterinary and racing. **Application Requirements:** Applicant must fill out the application form and submit proof that he/she is currently enrolled in a college or university. **Deadline for Receipt:** not stated. **Additional Information:** 806-378-5000.

4117 ■ AMERICAN SCHOOL HEALTH ASSOCIATION

7263 State Rte. 43
Kent, OH 44240
Tel: (330)678-1601
Fax: (330)678-4526
E-mail: asha@ashaweb.org
Web Site: http://www.ashaweb.org
To provide financial assistance to students concentrating on school health education, school nursing, and pediatric or adolescent medicine or dentistry.
Title of Award: ASHA Scholarships **Area, Field, or Subject:** Health education; Nursing; Pediatric medicine; Medicine; Dentistry; Nutrition; Counseling/Guidance. **Level of Education for which Award is Granted:** Graduate, Undergraduate **Number Awarded:** 3. **Funds Available:** $500 and a complimentary registration to ASHA's annual school health conference and a one-year ASHA membership. **Duration:** One year.
Eligibility Requirements: Applicants must be a junior, senior or graduate student; enrolled full-time at institution of higher education; have 3.0 GPA on a 4.0 scale; have a major related to School Health Education or School Nursing or Pediatric or Adolescent Medicine or Dentistry or other school health specializations (nutrition, counseling, etc.); not a previous recipient of this award. **Application Requirements:** Applicants must send one original and nine copies of the completed application form (application form available online); current resume; transcript; one page personal statement; three letters of recommendation. **Deadline for Receipt:** April 4. **Additional Information:** Pamela Dorazio Dean, pdean@ashaweb.org.

4118 ■ AMERICAN SCHOOL HEALTH ASSOCIATION

7263 State Rte. 43
Kent, OH 44240
Tel: (330)678-1601
Fax: (330)678-4526
E-mail: asha@ashaweb.org
Web Site: http://www.ashaweb.org
To provide financial assistance for research in areas related to the mission of ASHA.
Title of Award: ASHA Student Research Grants **Area, Field, or Subject:** Health education; Nursing; Pediatric medicine; Medicine; Dentistry; Nutrition; Counseling/Guidance. **Level of Education for which Award is Granted:** Graduate, Undergraduate **Funds Available:** No specific amount.
Eligibility Requirements: Applicants must be student members of ASHA. **Application Requirements:** Applicants must send one original and five copies of a proposal which includes a cover sheet; a narrative (title-problem, review of related literature, methodology, data analyst, institution IRB protocol documented); and a budget. Proposal should have one inch margins, doubled spaced and a font size not smaller than 12. Forward the original and 5 copies to: ASHA Student Research Grants, PO Box 708, Kent, OH 44240. **Deadline for Receipt:** April 4. **Additional Information:** Pamela Dorazio, pdean@ashaweb.org, 330-678-1601.

4119 ■ AMERICAN SOCIETY FOR MICROBIOLOGY

1752 N St. NW
Washington, DC 20036-2904
Tel: (202)942-9207
Fax: (202)942-9333
E-mail: chouston@utmb.edu
Web Site: http://www.asm.org
To support students who are interested in a career as an elementary or secondary school science teacher.

Title of Award: Microbiology Undergraduate Teaching Fellowships **Area, Field, or Subject:** Education. **Level of Education for which Award is Granted:** Undergraduate **Funds Available:** $2,500-student; $500-supplies and instructional materials; $1,000-travel support. **Duration:** 2 years.
Eligibility Requirements: Applicants must be enrolled as full-time matriculating undergraduate in an accredited U.S. institution; must be involved in educational outreach project; must be a science major interested in education; must have strong faculty ASM members in their home institutions willing to serve as a co-mentor; must have not receive any financial support for the project during the fellowship. **Application Requirements:** Applicants must submit six copies of complete application form. **Deadline for Receipt:** April 1.

4120 ■ AMERICAN SOKOL
122 W 22nd St.
Oak Brook, IL 60523-1557
Tel: (630)368-0771
Fax: (630)368-0758
E-mail: aso@american-sokol.org
Web Site: http://american-sokol.com
To help incoming students pursue their studies in college.
Title of Award: American Sokol Merit Awards **Area, Field, or Subject:** Physical education; Physical sciences. **Level of Education for which Award is Granted:** Undergraduate **Number Awarded:** 2 students per district. **Funds Available:** $500. **Duration:** One year.
Eligibility Requirements: Applicants must be Sokol Youth or Sokol Adult members who are planning a full-time course or program in an accredited college. Applications must be made in advance of the year of study. **Application Requirements:** Successful candidates must submit a recommendation proof of the Unit or District Physical Director; a parent or guardian will be required to sign to the condition that if the candidate cannot submit the needed requirements completely, he or she should repaid the whole amount of the award. **Additional Information:** The award was instituted by the XIIth American Sokol Convention to be paid from the American Sokol Future Leaders Fund. **Deadline for Receipt:** June 1.

4121 ■ ARKANSAS ENVIRONMENTAL FEDERATION
1400 W Markham St., Ste. 302
Little Rock, AR 72201
Tel: (501)374-0263
Fax: (501)374-8752
Web Site: http://www.environmentark.org
To provide financial assistance for selected students from Arkansas universities.
Title of Award: Randall Matthis for Environmental Studies Scholarships **Area, Field, or Subject:** Environmental science; Health education; Natural resources. **Level of Education for which Award is Granted:** Graduate, Undergraduate **Funds Available:** $2,500. **Duration:** One year.
Eligibility Requirements: Applicants must be U.S. citizens residing in Arkansas and must be undergraduate or graduate students with at least 2.8 cumulative GPA based on 4.0 system. **Application Requirements:** Applicants must submit a completed application form along with current official transcript(s) and letters. **Deadline for Receipt:** April 11.

4122 ■ ARMENIAN STUDENTS' ASSOCIATION OF AMERICA
333 Atlantic Ave.
Warwick, RI 02888
Tel: (401)461-6114
E-mail: asa@asainc.org
Web Site: http://www.asainc.org
To provide financial support to those students who are in need.
Title of Award: Emmanuel Bible College Scholarships **Area, Field, or Subject:** Religious Education. **Level of Education for which Award is Granted:** Undergraduate **Funds Available:** No specific amount.
Eligibility Requirements: Applicants must be willing to pledge to work as a minister, evangelist, missionary, or youth director after graduation; must study in one of the institutions of Emmanuel Bible College. **Application Requirements:** Applicants must check the contact information for inquiries. **Deadline for Receipt:** June 30. **Additional Information:** Dr. Yeghia Babikian, Director; 1605 East Elizabeth Street, Pasadena, CA 91104 Fax: 818-398-2424 Tel: 818-791-2575.

4123 ■ ARMENIAN STUDENTS' ASSOCIATION OF AMERICA
333 Atlantic Ave.
Warwick, RI 02888
Tel: (401)461-6114
E-mail: asa@asainc.org
Web Site: http://www.asainc.org
To provide financial assistance to those students who are in need.
Title of Award: Garikian Scholarship Fund **Area, Field, or Subject:** Armenian Studies; Sociology; Psychology; Political Science; Middle Eastern History; Journalism; Education; Music. **Level of Education for which Award is Granted:** Undergraduate **Funds Available:** $750-$1,000.
Eligibility Requirements: Applicants must have completed their first academic year in college or university in California; must be pursuing one of the above field of studies. **Application Requirements:** Applicants must apply to the Executive Board for application forms and return them, completed, before the deadline. **Deadline for Receipt:** August 31. **Additional Information:** Berj S. Baghdoyan c/o Western Prelacy at 4401 Russell Avenue, Los Angeles, CA 90027.

4124 ■ ASSOCIATED LOCKSMITHS OF AMERICA
3500 Easy St.
Dallas, TX 75247
Tel: (214)819-9733
Free: 800-532-2562
Web Site: http://www.aloa.org
To provide financial assistance for educational services, programs and materials concerning locksmithing and security devices and procedures.
Title of Award: ALOA Scholarship Foundation **Area, Field, or Subject:** Technical training. **Level of Education for which Award is Granted:** Undergraduate **Funds Available:** No amount mentioned.
Eligibility Requirements: Applicants must be individuals desirous of entering the locksmithing field or individuals already in the field of locksmithing who wish to improve their professional skills through education. **Application Requirements:** Applicants must complete the application form provided in the website of the Foundation and submit it along with the letters of recommendation from locksmith industry references.

4125 ■ ASSOCIATION OF AMERICAN INDIAN PHYSICIANS
1225 Sovereign Row, Ste. 103
Oklahoma City, OK 73108
Tel: (405)946-7072
Fax: (405)946-7651
Web Site: http://www.aaip.org
To provide a framework for undergraduate and graduate students in the application process to a health professional school.
Title of Award: Association of American Indian Physicians Scholarships **Area, Field, or Subject:** Health Education. **Level of Education for which Award is Granted:** Graduate, Undergraduate **Funds Available:** No specific amount.
Eligibility Requirements: Applicants must be undergraduate and graduate medical students; must be American Indian and Alaska Native Students. **Application Requirements:** Applicants must submit the completed application form; AAIP Student Primary Data Sheet Scholarship Application; Recent College and/or University Transcripts; one letter of recommendation from a professor or academic advisor; copy of Certificate of Degree of Indian Blood or Tribal Identification Card; recent photograph for identification and publication purposes; one page personal statement answering: Why they are seeking a professional career in the health professions? What influenced them and the experience(s) they have had to support this decision? Their career goals and where they plan to work. The physician and medical students will use this in their mock interview. **Deadline for Receipt:** June 27.

4126 ■ AUTOMOTIVE RECYCLERS ASSOCIATION
3975 Fair Ridge Dr., Ste. 20-N
Fairfax, VA 22033
Tel: (703)385-1001; 888-385-1005
Fax: (703)385-1494
E-mail: kelly@a-r-a.org
Web Site: http://www.a-r-a.org
To assist outstanding students to pursue their educational goal.
Title of Award: ARA Scholarship Awards **Area, Field, or Subject:** Business; Trades training; Technical training. **Level of Education for which**

Award is Granted: Undergraduate **Funds Available:** Scholarship amount not specified. **Duration:** One year.

Eligibility Requirements: Applicants must be children of an employee of a direct ARA member company; must be a high school senior or pursuing a full-time post high school program in an institution providing trade, business, or technical programs; have at least 3.0 GPA or equivalent. **Application Requirements:** Applicants must submit a completed application form and profile sheet. Transcript of academic record must be sent by the applicant's school/college directly to the ARA Scholarship Advisor. Applicants must obtain a certification and letter of verification from the parents' employer who is a direct member of ARA (should include current employment and the hiring date). Send all requirements to the ARA Scholarship Foundation Advisor. **Deadline for Receipt:** March 15. **Additional Information:** ARA Scholarship Advisor, arascholar@sbcglobal. net.

4127 ■ THE BAILEY FAMILY FOUNDATION
912 W Platt St.
Tampa, FL 33606
Tel: (813)549-6140
Fax: (813)549-6141
E-mail: bailey@bailey-family.org
Web Site: http://www.bailey-family.org
To provide financial assistance for high school seniors intending to continue their post-secondary education.

Title of Award: The Bailey Family Foundation High School Scholarship Program **Area, Field, or Subject:** General studies. **Level of Education for which Award is Granted:** Undergraduate **Funds Available:** No specific amount.

Eligibility Requirements: Applicant must possess a minimum cumulative GPA of 2.5; must demonstrate financial need; must be a graduating senior from a participating high school; and must be pursuing an undergraduate degree. **Application Requirements:** Applicants must submit the completed scholarship application form and an essay of no more than 300 words.

4128 ■ BIG SANDY COMMUNITY AND TECHNICAL COLLEGE
1 Bert T. Combs Dr.
Prestonsburg, KY 41653
Tel: (606)886-3863; 888-641-4132
Web Site: http://www.bigsandy.kctcs.edu
To provide a seamless system to upgrade the professional development of child-care workers and trainers by providing financial assistance for qualified Kentucky students intending to pursue a childhood development degree.

Title of Award: Early Childhood Development Scholarships **Area, Field, or Subject:** Early childhood education. **Level of Education for which Award is Granted:** Undergraduate **Funds Available:** $1,800. **Duration:** One year.

Eligibility Requirements: Applicants must be residents of Kentucky; must be U.S. citizens, national, or permanent residents; must be enrolled in no more than 9 credit hours per academic term in the scholarship program curriculum at a participating Kentucky institution and must be pursuing at least one of the approved credentials and maintaining satisfactory academic progress; must be employed at least 20 hours weekly in a participating early childhood facility or must be providing training in early childhood development at least 12 times per year for an organization approved to offer training by the Office of Inspector General of the Cabinet for Health Services or must be employed as a preschool associate teacher in a state-funded preschool program; must have no unpaid financial obligation to the Kentucky Higher Education Assistance Authority or in default on any other Title IV program; and must be agreeable to a service commitment based on the credential pursued. **Application Requirements:** Applicants must submit completed application package which include the Free Application for Federal Student Aid which can be obtained up to three copies by calling the Federal Student Aid Information Center toll free at 800433-3243.

4129 ■ BIG SANDY COMMUNITY AND TECHNICAL COLLEGE
1 Bert T. Combs Dr.
Prestonsburg, KY 41653
Tel: (606)886-3863; 888-641-4132
Web Site: http://www.bigsandy.kctcs.edu

To provide financial aid for highly qualified Kentucky students intending to pursue initial teacher certification at participating Kentucky institutions.

Title of Award: KHEAA Teacher Scholarships **Area, Field, or Subject:** Teaching. **Level of Education for which Award is Granted:** Undergraduate **Funds Available:** $2,500 for each semester and $1,250 for summer awarded to juniors, seniors, post-baccalaureate or graduate students; $625 each semester and $325 for summer awarded to freshmen and sophomore recipients.

Eligibility Requirements: Applicants must be residents of Kentucky who are enrolled full-time in a teacher certification program; must demonstrate financial need; and must meet their institution's educational program GPA requirements. **Application Requirements:** Applicants must complete application package which include the Free Application for Federal Student Aid and a Teacher Scholarship application. Applicants are advised to contact the Federal Student Aid Information Center at 800433-3243 for further information and instructions. **Deadline for Receipt:** May 1.

4130 ■ MARY E. BIVINS FOUNDATION
301 S Polk Ste. 860
PO Box 1727
Amarillo, TX 79105-1727
Tel: (806)379-9400
Fax: (806)379-9404
E-mail: info@bivinsfoundation.org
Web Site: http://www.bivinsfoundations.org
To educate ministers to preach the Christian religion.

Title of Award: Mary E. Bivins Foundation Religious Scholarship Program **Area, Field, or Subject:** Religious Education. **Level of Education for which Award is Granted:** Graduate, Undergraduate **Funds Available:** $1,000 per semester for those students classified as freshmen or sophomores, $2,000 per semester for those students classified as a juniors or seniors and $3,000 per semester for graduate students to be used for tuition, books, fees, and other expenses as necessary for college/university attendance.

Eligibility Requirements: Applicants must be dedicated to seeking an undergraduate or graduate education leading to a Bachelors or Masters Degree in a field that prepares the students to preach the Christian religion; must have the intent to serve as pulpit pastors; must be committed to studies and maintain a cumulative undergraduate GPA of 2.75 or above or a cumulative graduate GPA of 3.0 or above; must be permanent residents of one of the 26 counties of the Texas Panhandle; must enroll and pass a minimum of 12 hours each semester at the undergraduate level or 9 hours each semester at the graduate level; must enroll in an accredited college or university. **Application Requirements:** Applicants must check the available website for the required materials. **Additional Information:** Scholarships are awarded on an annual basis, and the students are required to continue to meet all award criteria each semester and to complete an application annually. **Additional Information:** Mary E. Bivins Foundation at the above address.

4131 ■ BROWN FOUNDATION
1515 SE Monroe St.
Topeka, KS 66612
Tel: (785)235-3939
E-mail: brownfound@juno.com
Web Site: http://brownvboard.org
To assist qualified minority students to pursue a career in education by providing financial support.

Title of Award: Brown Foundation Academic Scholarships **Area, Field, or Subject:** Education. **Level of Education for which Award is Granted:** Undergraduate **Funds Available:** $1,000. **Duration:** Two academic years.

Eligibility Requirements: Applicants must be minority students entering their junior year of college; must be admitted to a teacher education program; must be enrolled at an institution of higher education with an accredited program in teacher education for at least half-time as defined by the higher education institution of attendance; must have minimum 3.0 grade point average on a 4.0 scale. **Application Requirements:** Applicants must submit all the required application information.

4132 ■ CAMDEN COUNTY COLLEGE
200 N Broadway
Camden, NJ 08102-1185

Tel: (856)338-1817
Web Site: http://www.camdencc.edu
To provide opportunity to qualified students to pursue an education at CCC.
Title of Award: Diane Basilone-Engle Memorial Scholarships **Area, Field, or Subject:** Theater arts; Secretarial sciences; Veterinary science and medicine; Education. **Level of Education for which Award is Granted:** Undergraduate **Funds Available:** No specific amount. **Duration:** One academic year.
Eligibility Requirements: Applicants must be students who want to continue their degree or certificate in theater, secretariat science, veterinary science or education. **Application Requirements:** Applicants must submit one recommendation from a faculty member or administrator at Camden County College. Application forms are available online and must be sent to Camden County College Foundation, PO Box 200, College Dr., Blackwood, NJ 08012. **Deadline for Receipt:** February 18.

4133 ■ CANADIAN SANITATION SUPPLY ASSOCIATION
910 Dundas St., W
PO Box 10009
Whitby, ON, Canada L1P 1P7
Tel: (905)430-7267
Fax: (905)430-6418
Web Site: http://cssa.com
To provide scholarship assistance to qualified Canadian students who will be attending college or university in Canada.
Title of Award: Geofrey H. Wood Scholarships **Area, Field, or Subject:** Education. **Level of Education for which Award is Granted:** Undergraduate **Funds Available:** $2,000. **Duration:** One year.
Eligibility Requirements: Applicant must be a student who will be graduating high school; must be an individual who is already enrolled in a college or university in Canada; must be a young Canadian who has achieved a high level of academic and leadership standards. **Application Requirements:** Applicant must complete the application form available online; must have a photograph and official high school or college transcript; must provide an essay on: "What does your school custodian or facilities manager think about the Green cleaning Movement?"; must have a typed resume with name, planned occupation or profession, high school information, college or university information, employment history, activity and leadership record, and applicant evaluation form completed by a counselor or teacher. **Deadline for Receipt:** June 1.

4134 ■ CATCHING THE DREAM
8200 Mountain Rd. NE., Ste. 203
Albuquerque, NM 87110
Tel: (505)262-2351
E-mail: nscholarships@aol.com
Web Site: http://www.catchingthedream.org
To support the education of Native Schools.
Title of Award: MESBEC Scholarships **Area, Field, or Subject:** Mathematics and mathematical sciences; Engineering; Science; Business; Education; Computer and information sciences. **Level of Education for which Award is Granted:** Undergraduate **Funds Available:** $500-$5000. **Duration:** One academic year.
Eligibility Requirements: Applicants must be 1/4 or more degree Native American; an enrolled member of a "U.S. tribe"; attending or planning to attend a college/university within the U.S. on a full-time basis that is fully accredited; studying in the field of business, finance, management, economics, banking, hotel management, and related field; have excellent grades; high ACT or SAT scores; and have a strong commitment to their Native American community. **Application Requirements:** Applicants must submit a completed application form (available at the website); financial need analysis; a copy of the IRS 1040 Federal Tax Return for the previous year; Certificate of Native American Blood; an essay explaining career goals; three letters of recommendation; official transcripts; a copy of standardized test scores; copy of letter of admission from an accredited college or university or graduate school and degree program in the US; and a photograph (2X3) of head and shoulders. **Deadline for Receipt:** March 15, April 15, and September 15.

4135 ■ CATCHING THE DREAM
8200 Mountain Rd. NE., Ste. 203
Albuquerque, NM 87110

Tel: (505)262-2351
E-mail: nscholarships@aol.com
Web Site: http://www.catchingthedream.org
To support paraprofessionals native students in Native American Schools planning to complete their degree in education, counseling, or school administration.
Title of Award: Native American Leadership Education (NALE) Scholarships **Area, Field, or Subject:** Education; Counseling/Guidance; Educational administration. **Level of Education for which Award is Granted:** Postdoctoral, Undergraduate **Funds Available:** $500-$5000. **Duration:** One academic year.
Eligibility Requirements: Applicants must be 1/4 or more degree Native American; an enrolled member of a "U.S. tribe"; attending or planning to attend a college/university within the U.S. on a full-time basis that is fully accredited (college level and can range from bachelor's degrees to postdoctoral study); have excellent grades; high ACT or SAT scores; and have a strong commitment to their Native American community. **Application Requirements:** Applicants must submit a completed application form (available at the website); financial need analysis; a copy of the IRS 1040 Federal Tax Return for the previous year; Certificate of Native American Blood; an essay explaining career goals; three letters of recommendation; official transcripts; a copy of standardized test scores; copy of letter of admission from an accredited college/university or graduate school and degree program in the US; and a photograph (2X3) of head and shoulders. **Deadline for Receipt:** March 15, April 15, and September 15.

4136 ■ COACH - CANADA'S HEALTH INFORMATICS ASSOCIATION
250 Consumers Rd., Ste. 301
Toronto, ON, Canada M2J 4V6
Tel: (416)494-9324; 888-253-8554
Fax: (416)495-8723
E-mail: info@coachorg.com
Web Site: http://www.coachorg.com
To encourage health education by providing financial assistance for post-secondary education.
Title of Award: Steven Huesing Scholarships **Area, Field, or Subject:** Health education. **Level of Education for which Award is Granted:** Undergraduate **Funds Available:** $500. **Duration:** One year.
Eligibility Requirements: Applicants must be enrolled in a health informatics or related program at an accredited post-secondary institution; and must demonstrate active involvement and achievement in health informatics. **Application Requirements:** Applicants must submit a transcript of records and an assessment by an academic advisor; must have proof of enrollment in a recognized Canadian post-secondary institution and current attendance in a health informatics and related program; must prepare a description (500 words) of their involvement and achievements in health informatics. Application forms and other supporting documents must be sent to: COACH, 301-250 Consumer Rd., Toronto, On M2J 4V6. **Additional Information:** Established in 1999 in recognition of Founding President Steven Huesing's contribution to COACH. **Deadline for Receipt:** September 17.

4137 ■ COASTAL BEND COMMUNITY FOUNDATION
600 Leopard St., Ste. 1716
Corpus Christi, TX 78473
Tel: (361)882-9745
Fax: (361)882-2865
Web Site: http://www.cbcfoundation.org
To provide financial assistance to high school seniors or graduates of a Coastal Bend high school in furthering their college education.
Title of Award: Cecil E. Burney Scholarships **Area, Field, or Subject:** Liberal arts; History; Political science; Music; Education. **Level of Education for which Award is Granted:** High School, Undergraduate **Funds Available:** $2,000.
Eligibility Requirements: Applicants must be high school seniors or graduates of a Coastal Bend high school pursuing a liberal arts degree majoring in history, political science, music or education; have a high school GPA of 90 percent or higher; maintain a college 3.0 GPA or higher and at least 12 hours per semester. **Application Requirements:** Applicants must submit all the required application information. **Deadline for Receipt:** March 14.

4138 ■ COASTAL BEND COMMUNITY FOUNDATION

600 Leopard St., Ste. 1716
Corpus Christi, TX 78473
Tel: (361)882-9745
Fax: (361)882-2865
Web Site: http://www.cbcfoundation.org
To help needy students in financing their college education.
Title of Award: Faye and Rendell Webb Scholarships **Area, Field, or Subject:** General studies. **Level of Education for which Award is Granted:** High School, Undergraduate **Number Awarded:** 2. **Funds Available:** $1,000.
Eligibility Requirements: Applicants must be students graduated from Miller or Moody high schools, with preference for students who attended Los Encinos, Lamar or Lozano elementary schools for at least one year; must be education majors who are attending college in the state of Texas; must be students who have an average of 85 percent or better or maintain 3.0 GPA on 4.0 scale and complete at least 12 credits per semester. **Application Requirements:** Applicants must download application form from the website of CBC Foundation or obtain it from Miller and Moody high school counselor's offices. **Deadline for Receipt:** March 14.

4139 ■ COASTAL BEND COMMUNITY FOUNDATION

600 Leopard St., Ste. 1716
Corpus Christi, TX 78473
Tel: (361)882-9745
Fax: (361)882-2865
Web Site: http://www.cbcfoundation.org
To provide educational assistance to students planning to become teachers or public school administrators.
Title of Award: Dr. Dana Williams Scholarships **Area, Field, or Subject:** Education. **Level of Education for which Award is Granted:** High School, Undergraduate **Number Awarded:** 1. **Funds Available:** $4,000. **Duration:** Four years.
Eligibility Requirements: Applicants must be: high school seniors graduating at the end of the spring semester; planning to become teachers or public school administrators; enrolled as full-time students in college (12 hours or more). Applicants must have a cumulative high school GPA of 90 percent or more; must be graduates from a high school in the Corpus Christi Independent School District and must be permanent residents of Corpus Christi. **Application Requirements:** Applicants must download application form from the website of the CBC Foundation or obtain it by calling 361-882-9745. **Deadline for Receipt:** March 14.

4140 ■ THE COMMUNITY FOUNDATION OF MIDDLE TENNESSEE

3833 Cleghorn Ave., Ste. 400
Nashville, TN 37215-2519
Tel: (615)321-4939; 888-540-5200
E-mail: mail@cfmt.org
Web Site: http://www.cfmt.org
To help students in planning their postsecondary education.
Title of Award: Maude Keisling/Cumberland County Extension Homemakers Scholarships **Area, Field, or Subject:** Ecology; Education; Social work. **Level of Education for which Award is Granted:** Undergraduate **Funds Available:** No specific amount.
Eligibility Requirements: Applicants must be residents of Cumberland County, Tennessee for a period of four years or more. Applicants must be graduating high school seniors, GED graduates, or current college undergraduates with a GPA of 2.5 or better. Applicants must pursue a field of study such as, but not limited to, human ecology, family and consumer science, education, and social services. **Application Requirements:** Applicants must complete the application form. Applicants must submit two applicant appraisals; transcript of grades; student essay describing educational plans and how these will help in career goals. Applicants must submit one recent photograph. **Deadline for Receipt:** March 15. **Additional Information:** pcole@cfmt.org

4141 ■ THE COMMUNITY FOUNDATION OF MIDDLE TENNESSEE

3833 Cleghorn Ave., Ste. 400
Nashville, TN 37215-2519
Tel: (615)321-4939; 888-540-5200
E-mail: mail@cfmt.org
Web Site: http://www.cfmt.org
To help students in planning their postsecondary education.

Title of Award: Edna Martin Scholarships **Area, Field, or Subject:** Education. **Level of Education for which Award is Granted:** Undergraduate **Funds Available:** No specific amount.
Eligibility Requirements: Applicants must be high school seniors, or individuals who previously graduated from the Davidson County-Metropolitan Nashville Public School System, who have a desire to pursue a career in teaching in elementary, middle, or high school. **Application Requirements:** Applicants must complete the application form. Applicants must submit two applicant appraisals; transcript of grades; student essay describing educational plans and how these will help in career goals. Applicants must submit one recent photograph. **Deadline for Receipt:** March 15. **Additional Information:** pcole@cfmt.org

4142 ■ COMMUNITY FOUNDATION OF NORTHERN ILLINOIS

946 N 2nd St.
Rockford, IL 61107
Tel: (815)962-2110
Fax: (815)962-2116
Web Site: http://www.cfnil.org
To serve the four county area (Boone, Ogle, Stephenson and Winnebago) through philanthropy; to provide leadership in meeting charitable needs.
Title of Award: Charles Lee Anderson Memorial Scholarship **Area, Field, or Subject:** Education. **Level of Education for which Award is Granted:** Undergraduate **Funds Available:** No specific amount.
Eligibility Requirements: Applicants must be Rock Valley or Sycamore High School graduating seniors who will enter a college or university to pursue a degree in education. **Application Requirements:** Applicants must submit a completed application form, verification form, an official college transcript in a sealed envelope and two completed recommendation forms. **Deadline for Receipt:** March 1. **Additional Information:** jpatterson@cfnil.org.

4143 ■ COMMUNITY FOUNDATION OF NORTHERN ILLINOIS

946 N 2nd St.
Rockford, IL 61107
Tel: (815)962-2110
Fax: (815)962-2116
Web Site: http://www.cfnil.org
To serve the four county area (Boone, Ogle, Stephenson and Winnebago) through philanthropy; to provide leadership in meeting charitable needs and to be a responsible steward to the Foundation's donors and of the Foundation's endowment.
Title of Award: Karen Harter Recruitment Scholarship Grant **Area, Field, or Subject:** Education. **Level of Education for which Award is Granted:** Undergraduate **Funds Available:** No specific amount.
Eligibility Requirements: Applicants must be female Rockford College or Northern Illinois University sophomore or junior students who are pursuing a career in secondary math or science education. **Application Requirements:** Applicants must submit a completed application form, verification form, an official transcript in a sealed envelope and two letters of recommendation. **Deadline for Receipt:** March 1. **Additional Information:** jpatterson@cfnil.org.

4144 ■ COMMUNITY FOUNDATION OF NORTHERN ILLINOIS

946 N 2nd St.
Rockford, IL 61107
Tel: (815)962-2110
Fax: (815)962-2116
Web Site: http://www.cfnil.org
To serve the four county area (Boone, Ogle, Stephenson and Winnebago) through philanthropy; to provide leadership in meeting charitable needs and to be a responsible steward to the Foundation's donors and of the Foundation's endowment; to provide educational resources to students pursuing a career in education.
Title of Award: Karen Harter Recruitment Scholarship Grant **Area, Field, or Subject:** Education. **Level of Education for which Award is Granted:** Undergraduate **Funds Available:** No specific amount.
Eligibility Requirements: Applicants must be female Rockford College or Northern Illinois University sophomore or junior students who are pursuing a career in secondary math or science education. **Application Requirements:** Applicants must submit a completed application form, verification form, an official transcript in a sealed envelope and two letters of recommendation. **Deadline for Receipt:** March 1. **Additional Information:** jpatterson@cfnil.org.

4145 ■ COMMUNITY FOUNDATION OF NORTHERN ILLINOIS

946 N 2nd St.
Rockford, IL 61107
Tel: (815)962-2110
Fax: (815)962-2116
Web Site: http://www.cfnil.org
To serve the four county area (Boone, Ogle, Stephenson and Winnebago) through philanthropy; to provide leadership in meeting charitable needs and to be a responsible steward to the Foundation's donors and of the Foundation's endowment.
Title of Award: La Voz Latina Scholarships **Area, Field, or Subject:** Education. **Level of Education for which Award is Granted:** Undergraduate **Funds Available:** No specific amount.
Eligibility Requirements: Applicants must be high school graduates of Hispanic origin who reside in Winnebago County; must be enrolled in a post-secondary education program. **Application Requirements:** Applicants must submit a completed application form. **Deadline for Receipt:** March 14. **Additional Information:** 815-965-5784.

4146 ■ COMMUNITY FOUNDATION OF NORTHERN ILLINOIS

946 N 2nd St.
Rockford, IL 61107
Tel: (815)962-2110
Fax: (815)962-2116
Web Site: http://www.cfnil.org
To serve the four county area (Boone, Ogle, Stephenson and Winnebago) through philanthropy; to provide leadership in meeting charitable needs and to be a responsible steward to the Foundation's donors and of the Foundation's endowment.
Title of Award: Bonnie Sorenson Scudder Scholarship **Area, Field, or Subject:** Physical education. **Level of Education for which Award is Granted:** Undergraduate **Funds Available:** No specific amount.
Eligibility Requirements: Applicants must be female senior students at Harvard High School who have exhibited an interest in women's physical education and who wish to pursue a degree in women's physical education. **Application Requirements:** Applicants must submit a completed application form and must contact Melissa Laffey for more information. **Additional Information:** 1103 N Jefferson, Harvard, IL 60033.

4147 ■ CSA FRATERNAL LIFE

122 W 22nd St.
Oak Brook, IL 60523
Tel: (630)472-0500
Free: 800-543-3272
Fax: (630)472-1100
Web Site: http://www.csafraternallife.org
To help students on their financial needs for studying in college.
Title of Award: CSA Fraternal Life Scholarships **Area, Field, or Subject:** Education. **Level of Education for which Award is Granted:** Undergraduate **Number Awarded:** Varies. **Funds Available:** $1,250. **Duration:** One year.
Eligibility Requirements: Applicants must be student-members with satisfactory class standing no less than a "B" or Better or 3.0 in average (minimum of two years); have at least $5,000 face value in permanent life insurance or $1,000 in a CSA annuity at the time of application. **Application Requirements:** Applicants must submit a completed application form to the Fraternal Department; a complete official transcript to be sent to CSA; submit a photo for publication in the Journal to be attached to the first page of the application over the cap and diploma and a 400-600 words essay about the applicant's interests. **Deadline for Receipt:** March 9.

4148 ■ DELTA DELTA DELTA

PO Box 5987
Arlington, TX 76005-5987
Tel: (817)633-8001
Fax: (817)652-0212
E-mail: info@trideltaeo.org
Web Site: http://www.tridelta.org
To provide financial assistance to qualified undergraduate students.
Title of Award: Margaret M. Alkek Scholarship **Area, Field, or Subject:** Education, Music, Theater arts. **Level of Education for which Award is Granted:** Undergraduate **Funds Available:** $500-$1,500. **Duration:** One academic year.

Eligibility Requirements: Applicant must be a Theta Xi chapter member at the University of Southern California; must have academic achievement at the collegiate level; must be an initiated sophomore or junior members. **Application Requirements:** Application forms are available on the website. Applicant must provide a personal statement about their educational and vocational goals; must have a recommendation letter from a faculty member; must have an official transcript from each undergraduate institution. Application materials must be sent to: Delta Delta Delta, PO Box 5987, Arlington, TX 76005. **Deadline for Receipt:** March 15.

4149 ■ DELTA DELTA DELTA

PO Box 5987
Arlington, TX 76005-5987
Tel: (817)633-8001
Fax: (817)652-0212
E-mail: info@trideltaeo.org
Web Site: http://www.tridelta.org
To provide financial assistance to qualified undergraduate students.
Title of Award: Avery Bayle Barth Scholarships **Area, Field, or Subject:** Education. **Level of Education for which Award is Granted:** Undergraduate **Funds Available:** $500-$1,500. **Duration:** One academic year.
Eligibility Requirements: Applicant must be a Theta Xi chapter member at the University of Southern California; must have an academic achievement at the collegiate level; must be an initiated sophomore and junior members. **Application Requirements:** Application forms are available on the website. Applicant must provide a personal statement about educational and vocational goals; must have a recommendation letter from a faculty member; must have an official transcript from each undergraduate institution. Application materials must be sent to: Delta Delta Delta, PO Box 5987, Arlington, TX 76005. **Deadline for Receipt:** March 15.

4150 ■ DELTA ZETA SORORITY

202 E Church St.
Oxford, OH 45056
Tel: (513)523-7597
Web Site: http://www.deltazeta.org
To provide financial assistance to all qualified undergraduate students.
Title of Award: Sarah Jane Houston Scholarships **Area, Field, or Subject:** Education, English as a second language. **Level of Education for which Award is Granted:** Undergraduate **Funds Available:** $1,000-$2,500. **Duration:** One academic year.
Eligibility Requirements: Applicant must be an undergraduate Delta Zeta member in good standing with 3.0 or higher grade point average; must have a major field in English or in related fields such as speech, debate, drama, theater, or education. **Application Requirements:** Scholarship applications are available in the website and must be completed properly. Applicant must have the FAFSA reply form. **Deadline for Receipt:** February 15.

4151 ■ DELTA ZETA SORORITY

202 E Church St.
Oxford, OH 45056
Tel: (513)523-7597
Web Site: http://www.deltazeta.org
To provide financial assistance to all qualified undergraduate students.
Title of Award: Huenefeld/Denton Scholarships **Area, Field, or Subject:** Child development, Education, Library and archival sciences. **Level of Education for which Award is Granted:** Undergraduate **Funds Available:** $1,000-$2,500. **Duration:** One academic year.
Eligibility Requirements: Applicant must be a junior or senior initiated, active continuing members in need of financial help, seeking an undergraduate degree in child development/primary education or library science. **Application Requirements:** Scholarship applications are available on the website and must be completed properly. Applicant must have the FAFSA reply form. **Deadline for Receipt:** February 15.

4152 ■ DULUTH SUPERIOR AREA COMMUNITY FOUNDATION

324 W Superior St., Ste. 212
Duluth, MN 55802
Tel: (218)726-0232
Fax: (218)726-0257

E-mail: info@communityfoundation.com

Web Site: http://www.dsacommunityfoundation.com

To provide financial assistance for students who plan to major in education or early childhood education.

Title of Award: John Hoffbauer Memorial Scholarships **Area, Field, or Subject:** Early childhood education. **Level of Education for which Award is Granted:** Undergraduate **Number Awarded:** 1. **Funds Available:** $1,000. **Duration:** One year.

Eligibility Requirements: Applicants must be graduating seniors from Proctor Senior High School and all Duluth public high schools who are planning to be teachers; must be in the top 25% of their high school class. **Application Requirements:** Applicants must submit a completed application form and a recently completed Student Aid Report (SAR) from the Free Application for Federal Student Aid (FAFSA). **Additional Information:** The Award is co-payable to the institution and the recipient. **Deadline for Receipt:** January 15.

4153 ■ DULUTH SUPERIOR AREA COMMUNITY FOUNDATION

324 W Superior St., Ste. 212

Duluth, MN 55802

Tel: (218)726-0232

Fax: (218)726-0257

E-mail: info@communityfoundation.com

Web Site: http://www.dsacommunityfoundation.com

To provide financial assistance for students majoring in education who are in financial need.

Title of Award: John A. Sullivan Scholarships **Area, Field, or Subject:** Education. **Level of Education for which Award is Granted:** Undergraduate **Number Awarded:** 1. **Funds Available:** $500. **Duration:** One year.

Eligibility Requirements: Applicants must be graduates of Senior High in Superior, Wisconsin, who will attend their junior and senior years at the University of Wisconsin-Superior with a major in education. **Application Requirements:** Applicants must complete the Scholarship application and must submit a recently completed Student Aid Report (SAR) from the Free Application for Federal Student Aid (FAFSA). **Deadline for Receipt:** January 15.

4154 ■ EASTER SEALS ONTARIO

1 Concorde Gate, Ste. 700

Toronto, ON, Canada M3C 3N6

Tel: (416)421-8377

Free: 800-668-6252

Fax: (416)696-1035

Web Site: http://www.easterseals.org

To assist young adults with physical disabilities with the cost of post-secondary education or vocational training.

Title of Award: The Leaders of Tomorrow Scholarships **Area, Field, or Subject:** Education, Vocational-technical. **Level of Education for which Award is Granted:** Undergraduate **Funds Available:** No specific amount.

Eligibility Requirements: Applicants must be seeking for post-secondary education; demonstrated consistent level of scholastic achievement throughout their secondary school curriculum; participated as a spokesperson for The Easter Seal Society; must served as models and inspirations to fellow students; and have applied for alternate financial assistance and still require assistance. **Application Requirements:** Applicants must submit the completed application form along with typed, one-page letter outlining the qualifications for the award, including scholastic achievement, motivation, initiative and extra-curricular activities; copy of secondary and, if applicable, post-secondary transcripts; any interim marks that are available before the deadline; and, proof of application to applicable alternate sources of financial assistance. **Deadline for Receipt:** May 15.

4155 ■ EASTER SEALS ONTARIO

1 Concorde Gate, Ste. 700

Toronto, ON, Canada M3C 3N6

Tel: (416)421-8377

Free: 800-668-6252

Fax: (416)696-1035

Web Site: http://www.easterseals.org

To assist young adults with physical disabilities with the cost of post-secondary education or vocational training.

Title of Award: Beatrice Drinnan Spence Scholarships **Area, Field, or Subject:** Education, Vocational-technical. **Level of Education for which Award is Granted:** Undergraduate **Funds Available:** $5,000. **Duration:** One year.

Eligibility Requirements: Applicants must be resident students of Ontario with disabilities who are currently applying to or enrolled in a post-secondary educational facility like university or community college. **Application Requirements:** Applicants must submit the completed application form along with a one-page letter outlining qualifications for the award including scholastic achievement, motivation, initiative and extra-curricular activities; copy of secondary and, if applicable, post-secondary transcripts; any interim marks that are available before the deadline; and, proof of application to applicable alternate sources of financial assistance. **Deadline for Receipt:** May 16.

4156 ■ FIRST COMMUNITY FOUNDATION OF PENNSYLVANIA, WILLIAMSPORT-LYCOMING

330 Pine St., Suite 401

Williamsport, PA 17701

Tel: (570)321-1500; (866)901-2372

Fax: (570)321-6434

E-mail: fcfpa@fcfpa.org

Web Site: http://www.wlfoundation.org

To provide financial assistance for Milton Area High school seniors planning to pursue a major in elementary education.

Title of Award: Gina L. Barnhart Memorial Scholarship Fund **Area, Field, or Subject:** Education, Elementary. **Level of Education for which Award is Granted:** Undergraduate **Funds Available:** No specific amount.

Eligibility Requirements: Candidates must be seniors in good standing and members of the cheerleading squad; must have been accepted by a qualified institution of higher education and plan to major in elementary education. Applicants who are planning to major in secondary education may be considered if there are no candidates that are planning to major in elementary education. Preference will be given to applicants with educational and/or career objectives focused on working with children or community service. **Application Requirements:** Candidates must submit of a 200-word short essay on the following topic: "How has my participating in cheerleading and sports helped to prepare me for a career in elementary education or other work on behalf of children?" **Additional Information:** Leslie Robinson, Milton Senior High School, 700 Mahoning St., Milton, PA 17847, 570-742-7611.

4157 ■ FIRST COMMUNITY FOUNDATION OF PENNSYLVANIA, WILLIAMSPORT-LYCOMING

330 Pine St., Suite 401

Williamsport, PA 17701

Tel: (570)321-1500; (866)901-2372

Fax: (570)321-6434

E-mail: fcfpa@fcfpa.org

Web Site: http://www.wlfoundation.org

To provide financial assistance for Canton Area High School seniors intending to pursue a course of study in elementary or secondary education.

Title of Award: Marian Jones Donaldson Scholarship Fund **Area, Field, or Subject:** Education, Elementary; Education, Secondary. **Level of Education for which Award is Granted:** Undergraduate **Number Awarded:** 1. **Funds Available:** No specific amount. **Duration:** Annual.

Eligibility Requirements: Applicants shall have a four-year overall minimum grade average of 85%. **Application Requirements:** Candidate must complete and submit an application, a 500-word or less essay describing why he or she wants to enter the field of education, and three letters of reference. **Deadline for Receipt:** April 1. **Additional Information:** Jamie May, Guidance Counselor, Canton Area High School, 570-673-5134, jmay@canton.k12.pa.us.

4158 ■ FIRST COMMUNITY FOUNDATION OF PENNSYLVANIA, WILLIAMSPORT-LYCOMING

330 Pine St., Suite 401

Williamsport, PA 17701

Tel: (570)321-1500; (866)901-2372

Fax: (570)321-6434
E-mail: fcfpa@fcfpa.org
Web Site: http://www.wlfoundation.org
To provide financial assistance for the Jersey Shore High School seniors intending to pursue a course of study in elementary education, preferably with an emphasis on education of special-needs children.
Title of Award: Lindsay M. Entz Memorial Scholarships **Area, Field, or Subject:** Education, elementary. **Level of Education for which Award is Granted:** Undergraduate **Number Awarded:** 1. **Funds Available:** $1,000. **Duration:** Annual.
Eligibility Requirements: Candidates must plan to pursue a course of study in elementary education, preferably with an emphasis on education of special-needs children; must have exhibited good citizenship and community involvement; must be a leader with a sense of humor; must be grounded; must show tolerance to others; must be honest; must have integrity; and must make a difference in the school community. **Application Requirements:** Candidate must complete an application; attach a cover letter (not to exceed two pages) outlining why he or she is applying for the scholarship and summarizing his/her ultimate career objectives; must provide proof that he or she has been accepted to an accredited two-/four-year college/university; and must provide at least one letter of reference. **Deadline for Receipt:** April 15. **Additional Information:** Jeannie Rombach, Guidance Counselor, Jersey Shore Area Senior High School, 570-398-7174 ext. 1009, jrombach@jsasd.k12.pa.us.

4159 ■ FIRST COMMUNITY FOUNDATION OF PENNSYLVANIA, WILLIAMSPORT-LYCOMING
330 Pine St., Suite 401
Williamsport, PA 17701
Tel: (570)321-1500; (866)901-2372
Fax: (570)321-6434
E-mail: fcfpa@fcfpa.org
Web Site: http://www.wlfoundation.org
To provide financial assistance for Danville Area High School seniors intending to pursue higher education goals, preferably in the field of secondary education.
Title of Award: Mollie Harter Memorial Fund **Area, Field, or Subject:** Education, Secondary. **Level of Education for which Award is Granted:** Undergraduate **Funds Available:** No specific amount.
Eligibility Requirements: Applicants must be planning to pursue a Bachelor of Arts or Sciences degree from a qualified institution of higher education. Applicants' experience with community service and volunteering, as well as their interest in working with children and the potential to succeed in pursuing their goals may be considered. Preference will be given to applicants interested in a career in education, ideally secondary education, and then to other careers working with children. **Application Requirements:** Applicants may request an application from the Guidance Counselor of Danville Area School District. **Additional Information:** Gary Grozier, Guidance Counselor of Danville Area School District, 600 Walnut St., Danvilled, PA 17821; 570-271-3268 ext. 2006; ggrozier@danville.k12.pa.us.

4160 ■ FIRST COMMUNITY FOUNDATION OF PENNSYLVANIA, WILLIAMSPORT-LYCOMING
330 Pine St., Suite 401
Williamsport, PA 17701
Tel: (570)321-1500; (866)901-2372
Fax: (570)321-6434
E-mail: fcfpa@fcfpa.org
Web Site: http://www.wlfoundation.org
To provide financial assistance for Danville Area High School graduating seniors who have been accepted into a full-time undergraduate program at an institution of higher education to study education or science.
Title of Award: Rechsteiner Family Scholarship Fund **Area, Field, or Subject:** Education; Science. **Level of Education for which Award is Granted:** Undergraduate **Funds Available:** No specific amount.
Eligibility Requirements: Applicants must be students studying education or science and who maintain a GPA of 2.7 on a 4.0 scale after the end of their freshman year and for the rest of their undergraduate education. **Application Requirements:** Applicants may request an application from the Guidance Counselor of Danville Area School District. **Additional Information:** Gary Grozier, Guidance Counselor of Danville Area School District, 600 Walnut St., Danville, PA 17821; 570-271-3268 ext. 2006; ggrozier@danville.k12.pa.us.

4161 ■ THOMAS B. FORDMAN FOUNDATION
1016 16th NW 8th Fl.
Washington, DC 20036
Tel: (202)223-5452
Fax: (202)223-9226
E-mail: letters@edexcellence.net
Web Site: http://www.edexcellence.net
To support more bright and ambitious people into the world of education policy.
Title of Award: Fordham Fellowships **Area, Field, or Subject:** Education. **Level of Education for which Award is Granted:** Undergraduate **Funds Available:** $25,000. **Duration:** 9 months.
Eligibility Requirements: Applicants must have undergraduate degree; have spent several years in the working; have keen interest in public policy. **Application Requirements:** Applicants must submit a resume; cover letter; contact information of three references. **Deadline for Receipt:** April. **Additional Information:** Liam Julian; Program Coordinator; ljulian@edexcellence.net.

4162 ■ FOUNDATION FOR THE CAROLINAS
217 S Tryon St.
Charlotte, NC 28202
Tel: (704)973-4500
Free: 800-973-7244
Web Site: http://www.fftc.org
To provide financial assistance for undergraduate students from Mecklenburg County, NC, primarily in the field of education.
Title of Award: William Tasse Alexander Scholarship Fund **Area, Field, or Subject:** Education. **Level of Education for which Award is Granted:** Undergraduate **Funds Available:** $1,000 to $3,500. **Duration:** One year.
Eligibility Requirements: Applicants must be legal residents of Mecklenburg County, NC who are matriculating full-time juniors or seniors in college; must have a minimum cumulative grade point average of 3.0 on a 4.0 scale; and must be majoring in the field of education or taking courses leading to a career in teaching. **Application Requirements:** Applicants must submit completed application form; official transcript(s) of academic coursework and grades for at least the last two years; copy of applicants' NTE/Praxis Series scores, if available; three recommendation forms (two from instructors or other campus administrators and one from an employer or other non-related individual); one to two pages typewritten statement expressing reasons for applying for scholarship, qualifications, and educational/career goals; and a copy of the estimated expense budget for tuition, room and board, books, etc. at the school they attended. **Deadline for Receipt:** March 1.

4163 ■ FOUNDATION FOR THE CAROLINAS
217 S Tryon St.
Charlotte, NC 28202
Tel: (704)973-4500
Free: 800-973-7244
Web Site: http://www.fftc.org
To provide financial assistance for students majoring in education at the University of North Carolina at Charlotte.
Title of Award: Lula Faye Clegg Memorial Scholarship Fund **Area, Field, or Subject:** Education. **Level of Education for which Award is Granted:** Undergraduate **Funds Available:** No specific amount.
Eligibility Requirements: Applicants must be graduates of a high school in the Charlotte-Mecklenburg public school system; must rank in the top 10% of graduating high school class; and must have strong interest and commitment to a career in teaching. **Application Requirements:** Applicants must submit all the required application information. **Additional Information:** UNC Charlotte Student Financial Aid Office, 704-687-2461.

4164 ■ FOUNDATION FOR THE CAROLINAS
217 S Tryon St.
Charlotte, NC 28202
Tel: (704)973-4500
Free: 800-973-7244
Web Site: http://www.fftc.org
To provide financial assistance for Winthrop University students with an interest in Education, Human Services and related majors.
Title of Award: Judy Crocker Memorial Scholarship Fund **Area, Field, or Subject:** Education. **Level of Education for which Award is Granted:** Undergraduate **Funds Available:** No specific amount.

Eligibility Requirements: Applicants must be legal residents of York County, SC who are rising juniors or seniors at Winthrop University, located in Rock Hill, SC, majoring in education, human services or a related field with 2.9 minimum cumulative grade point average (on a 4.0 scale) and who demonstrate financial need. **Application Requirements:** Applicants must submit all the required application information. **Additional Information:** Winthrop University Office of Financial Aid, 803-323-2189.

4165 ■ FOUNDATION FOR THE CAROLINAS
217 S Tryon St.
Charlotte, NC 28202
Tel: (704)973-4500
Free: 800-973-7244
Web Site: http://www.fftc.org
To provide financial assistance for children of Founders Federal Credit Union members intending to attend an accredited college, vocational or technical school of their choice.
Title of Award: Laura M. Fleming Scholarship Fund **Area, Field, or Subject:** General studies. **Level of Education for which Award is Granted:** Undergraduate **Funds Available:** $1,000 up to $2,500. **Duration:** One year.
Eligibility Requirements: Applicants must be children of Founders Federal Credit Union members defined as natural born or legally adopted children and stepchildren and wards of employees; must be high school seniors graduating in the spring of the current school year; must have a minimum 3.5 cumulative grade point average (on a 4.0 scale). Applicant's parents or legally appointed guardians must be Founders Credit Union members in good standing for a minimum of two years (24 months) prior to the application deadline. **Application Requirements:** Applicants must submit completed application form; official copy of most recent high school transcript; three recommendation forms (two from current teachers or other school personnel and one from an employer or other non-relative); two typed essays of 400 words or less on topics provided in the application form; documentation of school and community involvement; and a copy of Student Air Report (SAR) from FAFSA. **Deadline for Receipt:** March 1.

4166 ■ FOUNDATION FOR THE CAROLINAS
217 S Tryon St.
Charlotte, NC 28202
Tel: (704)973-4500
Free: 800-973-7244
Web Site: http://www.fftc.org
To provide financial assistance for graduating seniors from South Carolina's York School District One intending to attend an accredited college or technical school of their choice.
Title of Award: Wilbert L. and Zora F. Holmes Scholarship Endowment Fund **Area, Field, or Subject:** Vocational-technical education. **Level of Education for which Award is Granted:** Undergraduate **Funds Available:** No specific amount.
Eligibility Requirements: Applicants must be graduating seniors at York Comprehensive High School (currently the only high school in the York School District One) and must have been students at York Comprehensive High School for a minimum of two years as of the application deadline; must be legal residents of York County, South Carolina; and must have a minimum of 3.0 cumulative grade point average (on a 4.0 scale) at the end of the first semester of senior year. **Application Requirements:** Applicants must submit all the required application information. **Additional Information:** Guidance Office at York Comprehensive High School at 803-684-2336.

4167 ■ FOUNDATION FOR THE CAROLINAS
217 S Tryon St.
Charlotte, NC 28202
Tel: (704)973-4500
Free: 800-973-7244
Web Site: http://www.fftc.org
To provide financial assistance for North Mecklenburg High School students intending to pursue a degree in education.
Title of Award: North Mecklenburg Teachers' Memorial Scholarships **Area, Field, or Subject:** Education. **Level of Education for which Award is Granted:** Undergraduate **Funds Available:** $1,000. **Duration:** One year.

Eligibility Requirements: Applicants must be graduating seniors with a grade point average of 3.0 on a 4.0 scale at North Mecklenburg High School; must be planning to attend a four-year college or university; and must be majoring in education. **Application Requirements:** Applicants must submit a completed application form; copy of the Student Aid Report (SAR) from Free Application for Federal Student Aid; official transcript of academic coursework and grades; and a typewritten statement expressing the applicants' educational and career goals and reasons for applying for the scholarship. **Deadline for Receipt:** February 15.

4168 ■ FOUNDATION FOR THE CAROLINAS
217 S Tryon St.
Charlotte, NC 28202
Tel: (704)973-4500
Free: 800-973-7244
Web Site: http://www.fftc.org
To provide financial assistance for graduating high school seniors in Mecklenburg County intending to attend an accredited college or vocational school in Mecklenburg County.
Title of Award: Turner Family Scholarship Fund **Area, Field, or Subject:** Vocational-technical education. **Level of Education for which Award is Granted:** Undergraduate **Funds Available:** $1,000 to 4,000. **Duration:** One year.
Eligibility Requirements: Applicants must be graduating high school seniors who have a minimum cumulative grade point average of 2.5 (on a 4.0 scale) and whose parents or legally appointed guardians are full-time employees who worked for National Welders Supply Company, Inc. for at least two years. Children of employees shall be defined to include natural born or legally adopted dependent children and stepchildren and wards of employees (in the case of stepchildren and wards, the applicant must live in the home with the eligible employee). **Application Requirements:** Applicants must submit completed application form; copy of the Student Aid Report (SAR) from Free Application for Federal Student Aid (FAFSA); three recommendation forms (two from teachers or other school personnel and one from an employer or other non-related adult); one to two pages typed statement expressing reasons for applying for the scholarship, qualifications and educational/career goals; and a letter from an official of National Welders Supply Company, Inc. where the applicants' parents or legally appointed guardians are employed. **Deadline for Receipt:** February 15.

4169 ■ FOUNDATION FOR THE CAROLINAS
217 S Tryon St.
Charlotte, NC 28202
Tel: (704)973-4500
Free: 800-973-7244
Web Site: http://www.fftc.org
To provide financial assistance for residents of the Wilmore neighborhood in Charlotte, NC intending to attend college or vocational school.
Title of Award: The Wilmore Scholarship Fund **Area, Field, or Subject:** Vocational-technical education. **Level of Education for which Award is Granted:** Undergraduate **Funds Available:** $500 to $2,000. **Duration:** One year.
Eligibility Requirements: Applicants must be residents of the Wilmore Neighborhood which is defined by Summit Avenue on the north, Interstate 77 on the west, South Tryon Street on the east and Wilmore Drive on the south; must have lived in Wilmore Neighborhood for at least one year (12 months) prior to the application deadline; and must have a minimum cumulative grade point average of 2.0 (on a 4.0 scale) for the last completed years of education. **Application Requirements:** Applicants must submit completed application form; official transcript(s) of high school and/or college coursework and grades for at least the last two years attended, including SAT/ACT score reports if taken; one recommendation form from a teacher, other school personnel or employer; one to two page personal statement expressing the applicants' educational and career goals and financial need for scholarship assistance; and a copy of the Student Aid Report (SAR) from Free Application for Federal Student Aid (FAFSA). **Deadline for Receipt:** April 1.

4170 ■ FOUNDATION FOR ENHANCING COMMUNITIES
200 N Third St., PO Box 678
Harrisburg, PA 17108-0678
Tel: (717)236-5040

Fax: (717)231-4463
E-mail: dawn@tfec.org
Web Site: http://www.ghf.org
To assist students with their college tuition expenses.
Title of Award: Norma Gotwalt Scholarship Fund **Area, Field, or Subject:** Education, Elementary. **Level of Education for which Award is Granted:** Undergraduate **Funds Available:** $3,000.
Eligibility Requirements: Applicants must be female junior or senior students studying Elementary Education at the Penn State Capital College and who have maintained a minimum of 3.0 cumulative GPA while at Capital College. **Application Requirements:** Applicants must complete and submit the application and attachments on or before the deadline. **Deadline for Receipt:** February 28. **Additional Information:** Dawn Morris, Program Officer; 717-236-5040; dawn@tfec.org.

4171 ■ FOUNDATION FOR ENHANCING COMMUNITIES
200 N Third St., PO Box 678
Harrisburg, PA 17108-0678
Tel: (717)236-5040
Fax: (717)231-4463
E-mail: dawn@tfec.org
Web Site: http://www.ghf.org
To assist students from Mechanicsburg Area High School planning to pursue a career in elementary or early childhood education.
Title of Award: Carol Hoy Scholarship fund **Area, Field, or Subject:** Elementary Education; early childhood education. **Level of Education for which Award is Granted:** Undergraduate **Funds Available:** No specific amount. **Duration:** Annual.
Eligibility Requirements: Applicants must be graduating seniors from Mechanicsburg Area High School. **Application Requirements:** Application and the required attachments must be completed and postmarked on or before the deadline. The required attachments include: completed student background sheet; high school transcript; FAFSA student aid report form (financial aid form); completed student essay; resume including leadership and community service; and two personal reference letters. One letter should be from a teacher and the other letter should be from an individual who can speak to applicant's ability to successfully complete studies, such as a teacher, employer, or mentor. Application form can be obtained online. **Additional Information:** Established in 2006. **Deadline for Receipt:** April 10. **Additional Information:** Dawn Morris, Program Officer at the above address.

4172 ■ FOUNDATION FOR ENHANCING COMMUNITIES
200 N Third St., PO Box 678
Harrisburg, PA 17108-0678
Tel: (717)236-5040
Fax: (717)231-4463
E-mail: dawn@tfec.org
Web Site: http://www.ghf.org
To provide educational assistance for students attending Greenwood High School, Newport High School, Susquenita High School and West Perry High School.
Title of Award: Carie and George Lyter Scholarship Fund **Area, Field, or Subject:** Education, Elementary; Science; Mathematics and mathematical sciences. **Level of Education for which Award is Granted:** Undergraduate **Funds Available:** No specific amount.
Eligibility Requirements: Applicants must have a desire to pursue a career in elementary or middle school education with emphasis in science or mathematics; an academic achievement of a cumulative GPA of 2.5 to 3.0 on a 4.0 scale in their junior/senior year; demonstrated talent for leadership; a high moral character (must have attended and be involved in church activities); and must demonstrate financial need. **Application Requirements:** Applicants must submit the following required attachments: completed student background sheet; official high school transcript with raised school seal; FAFSA student aid report; completed student 300-word essay identifying their interest in Elementary or Middle School Education with an emphasis in science and mathematics (include professional goals); and two personal reference letters. One letter should be from a teacher and the other letter should be from an employer or a supervisor of a community service volunteer agency. Letters of reference may not be from a family member. **Deadline for Receipt:** April 24. **Additional Information:** Dawn Morris, Program Officer at the above address.

4173 ■ FOUNDATION FOR ENHANCING COMMUNITIES
200 N Third St., PO Box 678
Harrisburg, PA 17108-0678
Tel: (717)236-5040
Fax: (717)231-4463
E-mail: dawn@tfec.org
Web Site: http://www.ghf.org
To assist Susquenita High School students with their college expenses in the field of Elementary Education.
Title of Award: Ruth Cook Pfautz Memorial Scholarship Fund **Area, Field, or Subject:** Education, Elementary. **Level of Education for which Award is Granted:** Undergraduate **Funds Available:** No specific amount.
Eligibility Requirements: Applicants must be graduating senior students of Susquenita High School who have a GPA of 2.5 on a 4.0 point scale. **Application Requirements:** Application form can be obtained online. Applicants must complete the attached form and requested supporting documents and send to the Foundation. The supporting documents include: official transcript of the complete high school record, including GPA, through the first half of final year, on which the raised school seal is imprinted; list of extracurricular or non-academic activities; reference letter; and a 300-word student essay explaining why they have chosen Elementary Education as a career path and describing their educational plans to achieve their career goal. **Deadline for Receipt:** April 10. **Additional Information:** Dawn Morris, Program Officer at the above address.

4174 ■ GRAND HAVEN AREA COMMUNITY FOUNDATION
1 S. Harbor Dr.
Grand Haven, MI 49417
Tel: (616)842-6378
Fax: (616)842-9518
E-mail: bpost@ghacf.org
Web Site: http://www.ghacf.org
To improve and enhance the quality of life in the Tri-Cities area by serving as a leader, catalyst and resource for philanthropy; to strive for community improvement through strategic grantmaking in such fields as arts, education, health, environment, youth, social services and other human needs.
Title of Award: E.V. Erickson Field of Interest Education Scholarships Fund **Area, Field, or Subject:** Education. **Level of Education for which Award is Granted:** Undergraduate **Funds Available:** No specific amount.
Eligibility Requirements: Applicants must be graduating high school seniors who have excelled not only academically but also demonstrate leadership qualities; must have a 3.8 GPA or better on a 4.0 scale. **Application Requirements:** Applicants must submit: completed application form; current high school or college transcript; Student Aid Report (SAR) from the Free Application for Federal Student Aid (FAFSA), unless applying for scholarships that do not consider financial need; and letter of recommendation. **Deadline for Receipt:** March 7. **Additional Information:** 616-842-6378.

4175 ■ GRAND HAVEN AREA COMMUNITY FOUNDATION
1 S. Harbor Dr.
Grand Haven, MI 49417
Tel: (616)842-6378
Fax: (616)842-9518
E-mail: bpost@ghacf.org
Web Site: http://www.ghacf.org
To improve and enhance the quality of life in the Tri-Cities area by serving as a leader, catalyst and resource for philanthropy; to strive for community improvement through strategic grantmaking in such fields as arts, education, health, environment, youth, social services and other human needs.
Title of Award: Bertha M. Fase Memorial Scholarship Fund **Area, Field, or Subject:** Education. **Level of Education for which Award is Granted:** Undergraduate **Funds Available:** No specific amount.
Eligibility Requirements: Applicants must be Grand Haven High School graduating seniors with a 3.5 GPA or better; must plan to pursue studies in the field of Education. **Application Requirements:** Applicants must submit: completed application form; current high school or college transcript; Student Aid Report (SAR) from the Free Application for Federal Student Aid (FAFSA), unless applying for scholarships that do not consider financial need; and letter of recommendation. **Deadline for Receipt:** March 7. **Additional Information:** 616-842-6378.

4176 ■ GRAND HAVEN AREA COMMUNITY FOUNDATION
1 S. Harbor Dr.
Grand Haven, MI 49417
Tel: (616)842-6378
Fax: (616)842-9518
E-mail: bpost@ghacf.org
Web Site: http://www.ghacf.org
To improve and enhance the quality of life in the Tri-Cities area by serving as a leader, catalyst and resource for philanthropy; to strive for community improvement through strategic grantmaking in such fields as arts, education, health, environment, youth, social services and other human needs. **Title of Award:** Terry Linda Potter Scholarship Fund **Area, Field, or Subject:** Health education. **Level of Education for which Award is Granted:** Undergraduate **Funds Available:** No specific amount.
Eligibility Requirements: Applicants must be graduating high school seniors planning to pursue a health-related field at an accredited two-to-four year college. **Application Requirements:** Applicants must submit: completed application form; current high school or college transcript; Student Aid Report (SAR) from the Free Application for Federal Student Aid (FAFSA), unless applying for scholarships that do not consider financial need; and letter of recommendation. **Deadline for Receipt:** March 7. **Additional Information:** 616-842-6378.

4177 ■ GRAND HAVEN AREA COMMUNITY FOUNDATION
1 S. Harbor Dr.
Grand Haven, MI 49417
Tel: (616)842-6378
Fax: (616)842-9518
E-mail: bpost@ghacf.org
Web Site: http://www.ghacf.org
To improve and enhance the quality of life in the Tri-Cities area by serving as a leader, catalyst and resource for philanthropy; to strive for community improvement through strategic grantmaking in such fields as arts, education, health, environment, youth, social services and other human needs. **Title of Award:** Marion A. And Ruth Sherwood Family Fund Education Scholarships **Area, Field, or Subject:** Education. **Level of Education for which Award is Granted:** Undergraduate **Funds Available:** No specific amount.
Eligibility Requirements: Applicants must be planning to pursue a career in the field of Education. **Application Requirements:** Applicants must submit: completed application form; current high school or college transcript; Student Aid Report (SAR) from the Free Application for Federal Student Aid (FAFSA), unless applying for scholarships that do not consider financial need; and letter of recommendation. **Deadline for Receipt:** March 7. **Additional Information:** 616-842-6378.

4178 ■ GRAND HAVEN AREA COMMUNITY FOUNDATION
1 S. Harbor Dr.
Grand Haven, MI 49417
Tel: (616)842-6378
Fax: (616)842-9518
E-mail: bpost@ghacf.org
Web Site: http://www.ghacf.org
To assist local graduating high school seniors interested in obtaining a college degree in elementary education. **Title of Award:** Louise Wachter Wichman Scholarship Fund **Area, Field, or Subject:** Education. **Level of Education for which Award is Granted:** Undergraduate **Funds Available:** No specific amount.
Eligibility Requirements: Applicants must be graduating high school seniors interested in obtaining a college degree in elementary education; must have a good (but not necessarily perfect) academic record. **Application Requirements:** Applicants must submit: completed application form; current high school or college transcript; Student Aid Report (SAR) from the Free Application for Federal Student Aid (FAFSA), unless applying for scholarships that do not consider financial need; and letter of recommendation. **Deadline for Receipt:** March 7. **Additional Information:** 616-842-6378.

4179 ■ HARTFORD FOUNDATION FOR PUBLIC GIVING
10 Columbus Blvd., 8th Flr.
Hartford, CT 06106
Tel: (860)548-1888
Fax: (860)524-8346

E-mail: hfpg@hfpg.org
Web Site: http://www.hfpg.org
To provide scholarship for graduating seniors from any public or private high school in Connecticut.
Title of Award: ARTC Glenn Moon Scholarships **Area, Field, or Subject:** Education. **Level of Education for which Award is Granted:** Undergraduate **Number Awarded:** 4. **Funds Available:** $1,500 - one-time award; $2,000 renewable.
Eligibility Requirements: Applicants must be entering a four-year college or university and must demonstrate financial need and academic excellence. **Application Requirements:** Applicants may obtain application materials from their high school guidance counselor or online at the www.artcinc.org. **Deadline for Receipt:** March 31. **Additional Information:** ARTC Inc. 203-639-9628.

4180 ■ HARTFORD FOUNDATION FOR PUBLIC GIVING
10 Columbus Blvd., 8th Flr.
Hartford, CT 06106
Tel: (860)548-1888
Fax: (860)524-8346
E-mail: hfpg@hfpg.org
Web Site: http://www.hfpg.org
To provide scholarship to the graduating high school senior who lives in or attends school in Greater Hartford.
Title of Award: Ida L. Hartenberg Charitable Scholarships **Area, Field, or Subject:** Teaching. **Level of Education for which Award is Granted:** Undergraduate **Number Awarded:** 1. **Funds Available:** $3,000.
Eligibility Requirements: Applicants must: be entering a four-year college or university (full-time enrollment); be pursuing a career in teaching; demonstrate financial need; be on a class rank - top third with good academic record; be an active volunteer in school, community, or other extracurricular activities. **Application Requirements:** Application form can be downloaded online. Applicants must complete the scholarship application. Applicants must also attach the following requirements: letter of recommendation from your guidance counselor or a teacher; official high school transcript. Including SAT or ACT scores; copy of the essay you submitted with your college application. If you did not have to submit one, write a brief (no more than two pages) essay regarding your future goals; copy of pages 1 and 2 of your parents' 2006 or most recent completed federal tax form 1040. Mail everything to Hartford Foundation College Scholarship Program. **Deadline for Receipt:** February 13. **Additional Information:** Hartford Foundation College Scholarship Program, Scholarship Management Services, Scholarship America, One Scholarship Way, PO Box 297, St. Peter, MN 56082. 800-537-4180.

4181 ■ HARTFORD FOUNDATION FOR PUBLIC GIVING
10 Columbus Blvd., 8th Flr.
Hartford, CT 06106
Tel: (860)548-1888
Fax: (860)524-8346
E-mail: hfpg@hfpg.org
Web Site: http://www.hfpg.org
To provide scholarship to the graduating senior residing and attending high school in Hartford County.
Title of Award: Hartford County Retired Teachers Association Scholarships **Area, Field, or Subject:** Teaching. **Level of Education for which Award is Granted:** Undergraduate **Number Awarded:** 2. **Funds Available:** $1,500.
Eligibility Requirements: Applicants must: be entering a four-year college or university; be a teaching major; demonstrate financial need, community service, leadership abilities and good character; have work experience and school and community participation. **Application Requirements:** Applicants may obtain application materials from their high school guidance counselor and submit to Hartford County Retired Teachers Association Scholarship Committee. **Deadline for Receipt:** March 15. **Additional Information:** Mrs. Roberta Parlin, Chairperson. 35 Ledgecrest Drive, Newington, CT 06111; 860-666-5709.

4182 ■ HARTFORD FOUNDATION FOR PUBLIC GIVING
10 Columbus Blvd., 8th Flr.
Hartford, CT 06106
Tel: (860)548-1888
Fax: (860)524-8346

E-mail: hfpg@hfpg.org
Web Site: http://www.hfpg.org
To provide scholarship for students attending graduate education program at Saint Joseph College, or the University of Connecticut, Hartford campus, or the University of Hartford.
Title of Award: Peter T. Steinwedell Scholarships **Area, Field, or Subject:** Education. **Level of Education for which Award is Granted:** Undergraduate **Number Awarded:** 1. **Funds Available:** $1,250.
Eligibility Requirements: Applicant must be an Education major with strong preference given to applicants pursuing teaching career; must demonstrate financial need and academic excellence. **Application Requirements:** Applicants may obtain an application by contacting either: Dr. Kathleen Butler, Chair, Department of Education St. Joseph College, 860231-5322, kbutler@sjc.edu; Monica Gat, Dean's Office Teacher Certification Program for College Graduates UConn Greater Hartford Campus, 860570-9283; Dr. H. Frederick Sweitzer, Associate Dean College of Education, Nursing and Health Professions University of Hartford, 860768-4279, sweitzer@hartford.edu. **Deadline for Receipt:** March 24.

4183 ■ HILLEL MONTREAL
3460 Stanley St.
Montreal, QC, Canada H3A 1R8
Tel: (514)845-9171
Fax: (514)345-6418
E-mail: romy@hillel.ca
Web Site: http://montreal.hillel.ca
To improve the quality and diversity of Hillel Montreal.
Title of Award: Leila Klinger Kurtzman Mamorial Scholarship Fund **Area, Field, or Subject:** Education. **Level of Education for which Award is Granted:** Undergraduate **Funds Available:** $500.
Eligibility Requirements: Applicants must be students entering the first year of a certified university. **Application Requirements:** Applicants must submit a letter stating the goals and reasons for request; proof of Quebec residency; transcript of records; acceptance letter from Montreal University; two letters of recommendation and Social Insurance Number.

4184 ■ HISPANIC SCHOLARSHIP FUND
55 Second St., Ste. 1500
San Francisco, CA 94105
877-473-4636
Fax: (415)808-2302
E-mail: info@hsf.net
Web Site: http://www.hsf.net
To promote academic excellence and to provide an opportunity for outstanding students with significant financial need to reach their fullest potential.
Title of Award: The Gates Millennium Scholars **Area, Field, or Subject:** Mathematics and mathematical sciences; Science; Engineering; Education; Public health; Library and archival sciences. **Level of Education for which Award is Granted:** Undergraduate **Funds Available:** No specific amount.
Eligibility Requirements: Applicants must be African American, American Indian/Alaska Native, Asian pacific Islander American and Hispanic American heritage; a U.S. citizen or legal permanent resident; have a minimum 3.3 GPA on a 4.0 scale; must demonstrate leadership skills; must demonstrate financial need. **Application Requirements:** Applicants must complete all three required forms available at the award site www.gmsp.org. American Indian/Alaska Natives must submit proof of tribal enrollment or a certificate of descent if selected as finalists. **Additional Information:** Established in 1999 and funded by a grant from the Bill and Melinda Gates Foundation. **Deadline for Receipt:** December 31 (paper applications), January 11 (online applications). **Additional Information:** gmsinfo@hsf.nett.

4185 ■ HISPANIC SCHOLARSHIP FUND
55 Second St., Ste. 1500
San Francisco, CA 94105
877-473-4636
Fax: (415)808-2302
E-mail: info@hsf.net
Web Site: http://www.hsf.net
To provide financial resources to assist outstanding Latino high school graduates.

Title of Award: Toyota High School Scholarship Program **Area, Field, or Subject:** Accounting; Actuarial science; Advertising; Architecture; Automotive technology; Bioengineering; Business; Chemical engineering; Civil engineering; Engineering, Computer; Electronics; Computer and information sciences; Construction; Drafting; Economics; Education; Education, Bilingual and cross-cultural; Education, Early childhood; Education, Special; Counseling/Guidance; Electrical engineering; Engineering; Environmental design; Environmental science; Geology; Educational administration; Education-Curricula; Personnel administration/human resources; Industrial design; Engineering, Industrial; Information science and technology; Management; Marketing and distribution; International trade; Manufacturing; Mechanical engineering; Engineering, Nuclear; Public administration; Public relations; Transportation. **Level of Education for which Award is Granted:** Undergraduate **Funds Available:** $5,000.
Eligibility Requirements: Applicant must be of Hispanic heritage; U.S. citizen or legal permanent resident with a valid permanent resident card or passport stamped I-551; have a minimum GPA of 3.0 on a 4.0 scale or equivalent; must apply for federal financing aid using the Free Application for Federal Student Aid (FAFSA) at www.fafsa.ed.gov; enrolling as full-time freshman at: Arizona State University; Central Missouri University; Colorado State University, Pueblo; Cornell University; Ferris State; Florida International University; Harvard University; Indiana University; Massachusetts Institute of Technology; New York University; Northwestern University; Pennsylvania Tech College; Pittsburg State University; Southern Illinois University; Stanford University; Texas A&M University; University of Arizona; University of California, Berkeley; University of California, Davis; University of California, Los Angeles; University of California, San Diego; University of Florida; University of Houston; University of Illinois at Chicago; University of Illinois at Urbana-Champaign; University of Michigan; University of New Mexico; University of Pennsylvania; University of Southern California; University of Texas at Austin; University of Texas at El Paso; University of Texas at San Antonio; University of Texas, Pan American; or Weber State University. Applicants must pursue a degree in: Accounting; Actuarial Science; Advertising; Architecture; Automotive Technology; Bio-Engineering; Business; Chemical Engineering; Civil Engineering; Computer Electronics; Computer Engineering; Computer Information Systems (CIS); Computer Programming; Computer Science; Construction; Drafting/CAD; Economics; Education Admin./Leadership; Education/Teaching; Education: Bilingual; Education: Early Childhood/ Elementary; Education: Special; Educational Counseling; Electrical Engineering; Engineering; Environmental Design/ Landscaping; Environmental Management/Science; Environmental/ Geological Engineering; Human Resource Management; Industrial Design; Industrial Engineering; Information Technology (IT); International Business; Management; Management Information Systems (MIS); Manufacturing Engineering; Marketing; Materials/ Manufacturing; Mechanical Engineering; Network Administration; Non-Profit Management; Nuclear Engineering; Office Administration; Public Administration; Public Relations; Supply Chain Management; or Transportation. **Application Requirements:** Applications must be submitted using the HSF online application system. **Additional Information:** In partnership with Toyota Motor Sales, USA. **Deadline for Receipt:** July 16. **Additional Information:** highschool@hsf.net.

4186 ■ ILLINOIS STUDENT ASSISTANCE COMMISSION
1755 Lake Cook Rd.
Deerfield, IL 60015-5209
Tel: 800-899-4722
E-mail: collegezone@isac.org
Web Site: http://www.collegezone.com
To provide financial support to deserving individuals intending to pursue their careers as teachers.
Title of Award: Illinois Future Teacher Corps Scholarships **Area, Field, or Subject:** Teaching. **Level of Education for which Award is Granted:** Undergraduate **Funds Available:** $5,000 or $10,000 depending on the teaching commitment made. **Duration:** One academic year.
Eligibility Requirements: Applicant must be a U.S citizen or an eligible non-citizen; must be a resident of Illinois; must be a high school graduate or person who has received a General Education Development certificate; must be enrolled, or accepted for enrollment as a junior or above, on at least a half-time basis in a Teacher Education Program at an eligible Illinois public or private college, seeking initial teacher certification; must be

pursuing additional coursework needed to gain Illinois State Board of Education approval to teach, including alternative teacher certification; must maintain a cumulative grade point average of 2.5 on a 4.0 scale; must maintain satisfactory academic progress as determined by the college. **Application Requirements:** Applicant must complete the application for Teacher Education Scholarship Programs; must sign the application's Teaching Agreement/Promissory Note promising to fulfill the teaching commitment or repay funds received, plus interest. **Deadline for Receipt:** March 1.

4187 ■ ILLINOIS STUDENT ASSISTANCE COMMISSION

1755 Lake Cook Rd.
Deerfield, IL 60015-5209
Tel: 800-899-4722
E-mail: collegezone@isac.org
Web Site: http://www.collegezone.com
To provide support to deserving individuals intending to pursue their career in special education programs.
Title of Award: Illinois Special Education Teacher Tuition Waiver Scholarships **Area, Field, or Subject:** Special education. **Level of Education for which Award is Granted:** Undergraduate **Funds Available:** Full tuition and mandatory fees. **Duration:** One academic year.
Eligibility Requirements: Applicant must be a U.S. citizen or an eligible non-citizen; must be an Illinois resident; must have graduated from an approved high school in the academic year in the upper half of their graduating class according to performance-based academic data provided by the high school; or graduated from an approved high school prior to the academic year in which the award is made, and must hold a valid teaching certificate that is not in the discipline of special education; must be enrolled, or accepted for enrollment, at one of the eligible public four-year colleges in Illinois as an undergraduate or graduate student seeking initial certification in any area of special education; must be enrolled in a program of special education within ten days after the beginning of the term for which the waiver was initially awarded; must comply with federal Selective Service registration requirements. **Application Requirements:** Application forms are available online at the College Zone. **Deadline for Receipt:** March 1.

4188 ■ ILLINOIS STUDENT ASSISTANCE COMMISSION

1755 Lake Cook Rd.
Deerfield, IL 60015-5209
Tel: 800-899-4722
E-mail: collegezone@isac.org
Web Site: http://www.collegezone.com
To provide financial support to the qualified individuals intending to pursue their careers as a preschool, elementary or secondary school teacher.
Title of Award: Minority Teachers of Illinois Scholarships **Area, Field, or Subject:** Teaching. **Level of Education for which Award is Granted:** Undergraduate **Funds Available:** $5,000. **Duration:** One academic year.
Eligibility Requirements: Applicant must be a U.S citizen or an eligible noncitizen; must be a resident of Illinois; must be either a African American/ Black, Hispanic American, Asian American or Native American origin; must be a high school graduate, or hold a General Educational Development certificate; must be enrolled at least a hal-time basis as an undergraduate or graduate student; must be enrolled or accepted for enrollment at a qualified Illinois institutions of higher education in a course of study which, upon completion, qualifies to be certified as a preschool, elementary or secondary school teacher by the Illinois State Board of Education, including alternative teacher certification; must maintain a cumulative grade point average of 2.5 on a 4.0 scale; must maintain a satisfactory academic progress as determined by the college; must comply with federal Selective Service registration requirements. **Application Requirements:** Applicant must submit the complete application form for the Teacher Education Scholarship Programs (available online); must sign the application's Teaching Agreement or Promissory Note promising to fulfill the teaching commitment or repay funds received plus interest. **Deadline for Receipt:** March 1.

4189 ■ IMAGINE AMERICA FOUNDATION

1101 Connecticut Ave. NW, Ste. 901
Washington, DC 20036
Tel: (202)336-6800
Fax: (202)408-8102

E-mail: bobm@imagine-america.org
Web Site: http://www.imagine-america.org
To help high school seniors attend college.
Title of Award: Career Colleges Scholarships **Area, Field, or Subject:** Education. **Level of Education for which Award is Granted:** Undergraduate **Funds Available:** $1,000.
Eligibility Requirements: Applicants must be high school graduates who are pursuing postsecondary career education at participating career colleges across the United States. **Application Requirements:** Applicants must complete the online application form including name and contact information.

4190 ■ IMAGINE AMERICA FOUNDATION

1101 Connecticut Ave. NW, Ste. 901
Washington, DC 20036
Tel: (202)336-6800
Fax: (202)408-8102
E-mail: bobm@imagine-america.org
Web Site: http://www.imagine-america.org
To help high school seniors attend college.
Title of Award: High School Councilors Scholarships **Area, Field, or Subject:** Education. **Level of Education for which Award is Granted:** Undergraduate **Number Awarded:** 3. **Funds Available:** $1,000.
Eligibility Requirements: Applicants must be high school graduates who are pursuing postsecondary career education at participating career colleges across the United States; Applicants must have a high school grade point average of 2.5 or greater. **Application Requirements:** Applicants must complete the online application form including name and contact information.

4191 ■ IMAGINE AMERICA FOUNDATION

1101 Connecticut Ave. NW, Ste. 901
Washington, DC 20036
Tel: (202)336-6800
Fax: (202)408-8102
E-mail: bobm@imagine-america.org
Web Site: http://www.imagine-america.org
To support and promote the benefits of career colleges to the general public.
Title of Award: Imagine America Scholarships **Area, Field, or Subject:** General studies. **Level of Education for which Award is Granted:** Undergraduate **Number Awarded:** 3. **Funds Available:** $1,000.
Eligibility Requirements: Applicants must be graduating high school students planning to attend a career college; selected winners usually have a grade point average of 2.5 or greater. **Application Requirements:** Applicants must complete the application form.

4192 ■ IMAGINE AMERICA FOUNDATION

1101 Connecticut Ave. NW, Ste. 901
Washington, DC 20036
Tel: (202)336-6800
Fax: (202)408-8102
E-mail: bobm@imagine-america.org
Web Site: http://www.imagine-america.org
To help high school seniors attend college.
Title of Award: Parents Scholarships **Area, Field, or Subject:** Education. **Level of Education for which Award is Granted:** Undergraduate **Funds Available:** $1,000.
Eligibility Requirements: Applicants must be high school graduates who are pursuing postsecondary career education at participating career colleges across the United States. **Application Requirements:** Applicants must complete the online application form including name and contact information.

4193 ■ INDIANA STATE ALUMNI ASSOCIATION

200 N 7th St.
Terre Haute, IN 47809-9989
800-GO-TO-ISU
Web Site: http://www.indstate.edu/alum/alum_assoc.htm
To support educational pursuit of students.
Title of Award: Indiana State Alumni Association Creative and Performing Arts Award **Area, Field, or Subject:** Art; Music; English language and literature; Theater arts. **Level of Education for which Award is Granted:** Undergraduate **Funds Available:** $2000. **Duration:** One year.

Eligibility Requirements: Applicant must be entering college as freshmen at the Indiana State University; majoring or have a minor in Art, Music, English, Physical Education (Dance), Theater. **Application Requirements:** Applicant must submit an application form; portfolio review; must audition at the departments; and will be interview. Contact the department where the applicant is majoring. **Deadline for Receipt:** Must be admitted before February 1. **Additional Information:** Art: 812-237-3697; Music: 812-237-27771; English: 812-237-3163; Physical Education: 812-237-2520; Theater: 812-237-3331.

4194 ■ INDIANA STATE ALUMNI ASSOCIATION
200 N 7th St.
Terre Haute, IN 47809-9989
800-GO-TO-ISU
Web Site: http://www.indstate.edu/alum/alum_assoc.htm
To support educational pursuit of students.
Title of Award: Noyce Scholarships for Secondary Math and Science Education **Area, Field, or Subject:** Education, Secondary; Science; Mathematics and mathematical sciences. **Level of Education for which Award is Granted:** Undergraduate **Funds Available:** $10,000. **Duration:** One year.
Eligibility Requirements: Applicant must be a transfer student with a GPA of 2.75 in all science and mathematics work. **Application Requirements:** Applicants must submit a signed urban teaching commitment and a scholarship application checklist. **Additional Information:** Dr. Jay D. Gatrell, project director, 812-237-2785 or jgatrell@indstate.edu.

4195 ■ JACKSON COUNTY COMMUNITY FOUNDATION
One Jackson Square, 100 E Michigan Ave., Ste. 308
Jackson, MI 49201-1406
Tel: (517)787-1321
Fax: (517)787-4333
E-mail: jcf@jacksoncf.org
Web Site: http://www.jacksoncf.org
To assist all citizens of greater Jackson in improving the quality of their lives; to support its work as a community grantmaker and community leader.
Title of Award: June Danby and Pat Pearse Education Scholarship **Area, Field, or Subject:** Education. **Level of Education for which Award is Granted:** Undergraduate **Funds Available:** $1,000.
Eligibility Requirements: Applicants must be Jackson High School graduating senior students with cumulative GPA of 3.25 or higher; must be full or part-time students in an accredited college or university majoring in the field of education. **Application Requirements:** Applicants must submit a completed application form.

4196 ■ JACKSON COUNTY COMMUNITY FOUNDATION
One Jackson Square, 100 E Michigan Ave., Ste. 308
Jackson, MI 49201-1406
Tel: (517)787-1321
Fax: (517)787-4333
E-mail: jcf@jacksoncf.org
Web Site: http://www.jacksoncf.org
To assist all citizens of greater Jackson in improving the quality of their lives; to support its work as a community grantmaker and community leader.
Title of Award: Antonia Dellas Memorial Scholarship **Area, Field, or Subject:** Education. **Level of Education for which Award is Granted:** Undergraduate **Funds Available:** $2,000.
Eligibility Requirements: Applicants must be high school senior students with a minimum of 3.35 or above GPA; must be accepted or attending an accredited Michigan college or university; must intend to enroll or are already enrolled in a school of education. **Application Requirements:** Applicants must submit a completed application form and must provide a proof of financial need.

4197 ■ JACKSON COUNTY COMMUNITY FOUNDATION
One Jackson Square, 100 E Michigan Ave., Ste. 308
Jackson, MI 49201-1406
Tel: (517)787-1321
Fax: (517)787-4333
E-mail: jcf@jacksoncf.org
Web Site: http://www.jacksoncf.org

To recognize and encourage those who desire to enter the field of education within the intention of teaching in the classroom.
Title of Award: Martha and Oliver Hansen Memorial Scholarship **Area, Field, or Subject:** Education. **Level of Education for which Award is Granted:** Undergraduate **Funds Available:** $1,000.
Eligibility Requirements: Applicants must be incoming college junior or senior majoring in Education with the intention of teaching in the classroom; must attend an accredited Michigan college or university who holds 2.5 GPA or above. **Application Requirements:** Applicants must submit a completed application form.

4198 ■ JEWISH VOCATIONAL SERVICE
216 W Jackson Blvd., Ste. 700
Chicago, IL 60606
Tel: (312)673-3400
Fax: (312)553-5544
E-mail: jvs@jvschicago.org
Web Site: http://www.jvschicago.org
To support the education of a Jewish college or graduate student.
Title of Award: Jewish Federation Academic Scholarships **Area, Field, or Subject:** Medicine; Education; Social work; Arts; Public health; Urban affairs/design/planning; Law. **Level of Education for which Award is Granted:** Graduate, Undergraduate **Funds Available:** More than $500,000 each year.
Eligibility Requirements: Applicant must be Jewish; be born or raised in either: Cook County, Chicago metropolitan area, or Northwest Indiana; or have one continuous year of full-time employment in Cook County or Chicago metropolitan area prior to starting professional education; must intend to remain in the Chicago metropolitan area after completing school; must be entering as a full-time student in an accredited professional graduate program or entering as junior or senior undergraduate student at an accredited professional education program; and must be demonstrating career promise in a helping profession. **Application Requirements:** Applicants must submit a completed Application Data Form; Career Statement Form; Budget Worksheet; and Academic Budget form as an attachment to jvsscholarship@jvschicago.org. In addition, applicants must send by mail a Legal Domicility Form; two letter of reference form; IRS Forms; parents' or spouse's IRS; documentation of tuition cost; Release of Information form; and official transcripts. **Deadline for Receipt:** February 15. **Additional Information:** 312-673-3457.

4199 ■ JUNIOR ACHIEVEMENT
One Education Way
Colorado Springs, CO 80906
Tel: (719)540-8000; 888-4JA-ALUM
Fax: (719)540-6299
E-mail: newmedia@ja.org
Web Site: http://www.ja.org
To allow educational advancements by providing financial assistance.
Title of Award: Johnson and Wales University Scholarships **Area, Field, or Subject:** Business; Culinary arts; Technology; Teaching. **Level of Education for which Award is Granted:** Undergraduate **Number Awarded:** Varies. **Funds Available:** $500 to cover full tuition. **Duration:** One year.
Eligibility Requirements: Program is open to individuals who are majoring in the field of business, culinary arts, hospitality, technology or teacher education. **Application Requirements:** Applicants must submit a completed application form together with other supporting materials. Mail all materials to Johnson and Wales University, 8 Abbott Park Place, Providence, RI 02903. **Deadline for Receipt:** February 1. **Additional Information:** National Student Organizations Office at Johnson and Wales University, 8 Abbott Park Place, Providence, RI 02903, at 800DIAL-JWU x-2345, or nso@jwu.edu.

4200 ■ LEWIS-CLARK STATE COLLEGE
500 8th Ave.
Lewiston, ID 83501
Tel: (208)792-5272
Web Site: http://www.lcsc.edu
To encourage promising students from Timberline High School, Clearwater County to continue their education.
Title of Award: Bus and Mary Ellen Durant Timberline High School Endowed Scholarships **Area, Field, or Subject:** Nursing; Technical;

Industrial. **Level of Education for which Award is Granted:** Undergraduate **Funds Available:** No specific amount.
Eligibility Requirements: Applicants must be alumni of Timberline High School or their successor in Clearwater County, Idaho; must be enrolled full-time who majoring in any other discipline offered at LCSC. **Application Requirements:** Applicants must accomplish a general application available in the website. **Deadline for Receipt:** March 1.

4201 ■ LEWIS-CLARK STATE COLLEGE
500 8th Ave.
Lewiston, ID 83501
Tel: (208)792-5272
Web Site: http://www.lcsc.edu
To provide financial assistance to students who are currently enrolled in a vocational program.
Title of Award: Margaret G. Johnson and Marge J. Stout Scholarships **Area, Field, or Subject:** Vocational; Business. **Level of Education for which Award is Granted:** Undergraduate **Funds Available:** No specific amount.
Eligibility Requirements: Applicants must have completed at least 12 credits; must be residents of Idaho; must be enrolled in a two year vocational-technical program at LCSC; and must demonstrate a minimum GPA of 3.0. **Application Requirements:** Applicants must accomplish a general application available at the website. **Deadline for Receipt:** March 1.

4202 ■ LEWIS-CLARK STATE COLLEGE
500 8th Ave.
Lewiston, ID 83501
Tel: (208)792-5272
Web Site: http://www.lcsc.edu
To provide educational assistance for students intending to pursue a career in Special Education.
Title of Award: Military Order of the Perpetual Heart Foundation Scholarships **Area, Field, or Subject:** Special education. **Level of Education for which Award is Granted:** Undergraduate **Funds Available:** $1,500.
Duration: One year.
Eligibility Requirements: Program is open to students committed to pursue a teaching career in special education; must be accepted to the Teacher Education Program; must be enrolled for 12 credits; and must have a GPA of 3.25. **Application Requirements:** Applicants must accomplish a general application available at the website. **Deadline for Receipt:** March 1.

4203 ■ LEWIS-CLARK STATE COLLEGE
500 8th Ave.
Lewiston, ID 83501
Tel: (208)792-5272
Web Site: http://www.lcsc.edu
To offset the educationally-related expenses of Lewis-Clark State College students.
Title of Award: Bill Sawyer Memorial Scholarships **Area, Field, or Subject:** Technical. **Level of Education for which Award is Granted:** Undergraduate **Funds Available:** No specific amount.
Eligibility Requirements: Applicants must have a cumulative GPA consistent with the minimum required for admission and for progress toward their selected major. **Application Requirements:** Applicants must accomplish a general application available at the website. **Deadline for Receipt:** March 1.

4204 ■ LEWIS-CLARK STATE COLLEGE
500 8th Ave.
Lewiston, ID 83501
Tel: (208)792-5272
Web Site: http://www.lcsc.edu
To offset the educationally-related expenses of Lewis-Clark State College students.
Title of Award: Ethel Shinn Alumni-Vocational Scholarships **Area, Field, or Subject:** Technical. **Level of Education for which Award is Granted:** Undergraduate **Funds Available:** No specific amount.
Eligibility Requirements: Applicants must be professional/technical students; must have 12 or more credits per semester; and must have completed at least one full semester at LCSC with a cumulative GPA of at

least 2.5. **Application Requirements:** Applicants must accomplish a general application available at the website. **Deadline for Receipt:** March 1.

4205 ■ MATANUSKA-SUSITNA COLLEGE
PO Box 2889
Palmer, AK 99645
Tel: (907)745-9774
Fax: (907)745-9711
E-mail: info@matsu.alaska.edu
Web Site: http://www.matsu.alaska.edu
To provide support to deserving students in Alaska who want to pursue an education in any campus of the University of Alaska.
Title of Award: Mike Ardaw Scholarships **Area, Field, or Subject:** Science; Education; Engineering. **Level of Education for which Award is Granted:** Undergraduate **Funds Available:** $1,000.
Eligibility Requirements: Applicant must be a full-time student and have a minimum GPA of 2.5. **Application Requirements:** Applicant must complete the application forms available at the website; must attach a personal essay, two letters of recommendation, and current transcripts. **Deadline for Receipt:** February 15.

4206 ■ MATANUSKA-SUSITNA COLLEGE
PO Box 2889
Palmer, AK 99645
Tel: (907)745-9774
Fax: (907)745-9711
E-mail: info@matsu.alaska.edu
Web Site: http://www.matsu.alaska.edu
To provide support to deserving students in Alaska who want to pursue an education in any campus of the University of Alaska.
Title of Award: Patricia Ann Hughes Eastaugh Memorial Teaching Scholarships **Area, Field, or Subject:** Teaching. **Level of Education for which Award is Granted:** Undergraduate **Funds Available:** $8,000.
Eligibility Requirements: Applicants must be first-time incoming freshman students enrolled in a baccalaureate degree program; must intend to become an elementary or secondary school teacher in Alaska and be enrolled in academic programs leading toward that end; must be an Alaska resident and a graduate of a public or private school in Alaska. **Application Requirements:** Applicant must attach an additional statement of 1,000 words or less entitled "Why I Want to become a Teacher of Children in Alaska." Candidates should also briefly express their opinion of Alaska's educational system(s) and their thoughts on changes they would embrace therein. Applicant must complete the application forms available in the website; must attach a personal essay, two letters of recommendation, and current transcripts. **Deadline for Receipt:** February 15.

4207 ■ MATANUSKA-SUSITNA COLLEGE
PO Box 2889
Palmer, AK 99645
Tel: (907)745-9774
Fax: (907)745-9711
E-mail: info@matsu.alaska.edu
Web Site: http://www.matsu.alaska.edu
To provide support to deserving students in Alaska who want to pursue an education in any campus of the University of Alaska.
Title of Award: Patty Hamilton Early Childhood Development Scholarships **Area, Field, or Subject:** Early childhood education. **Level of Education for which Award is Granted:** Undergraduate **Funds Available:** $2,500.
Eligibility Requirements: Applicants must be Alaska residents entering their junior or senior year and majoring in early childhood development/education. **Application Requirements:** Applicant must complete the application forms available at the website; must attach a personal essay, two letters of recommendation, and current transcripts. **Deadline for Receipt:** February 15.

4208 ■ MATANUSKA-SUSITNA COLLEGE
PO Box 2889
Palmer, AK 99645
Tel: (907)745-9774
Fax: (907)745-9711

E-mail: info@matsu.alaska.edu
Web Site: http://www.matsu.alaska.edu
To provide financial assistance for tuition and other educational expenses to students who are enrolled in Early Childhood Development courses at Matanuska-Susitna College.
Title of Award: Molly Ann Mishler Memorial Scholarships **Area, Field, or Subject:** Early childhood education. **Level of Education for which Award is Granted:** Undergraduate **Funds Available:** $500. **Duration:** One academic year.
Eligibility Requirements: Applicant must demonstrate motivation, academic and leadership potential; must have a good academic standing with a minimum cumulative GPA of 2.0; must be formally admitted to a degree-seeking program at the University of Alaska at Anchorage or Matanuska-Susitna College; must plan on enrolling at least part-time (3 credits) at Matanuska-Susitna College; must be an incoming or continuing student at Matanuska-Susitna College; must be a U.S. citizen, non-U.S. citizen, Alaska resident, or out-of-state resident; must be enrolled in the semester(s) for which the award is offered; must be enrolled in at least three credits for Early Childhood Development courses. **Application Requirements:** Applicant must complete the MSC scholarship application form; must attach a list of activities/community service in which they have participated; must attach a resume of their work experience they have held over the past four years; must attach a personal essay (not more than 500 words); must have two letters of recommendation and transcripts. Application documents must be submitted to Molly Ann Mishler Memorial Scholarships, Matanuska-Susitna College, Student Services, FSM 102, PO Box 2889, Palmer, AK 99645. **Deadline for Receipt:** May 31.

4209 ■ MATANUSKA-SUSITNA COLLEGE
PO Box 2889
Palmer, AK 99645
Tel: (907)745-9774
Fax: (907)745-9711
E-mail: info@matsu.alaska.edu
Web Site: http://www.matsu.alaska.edu
To provide support to deserving students in Alaska who want to pursue an education in any campus of the University of Alaska.
Title of Award: Ralph Yetka Memorial Scholarships **Area, Field, or Subject:** Engineering; Education, Elementary; Education, Secondary; Computer and information sciences. **Level of Education for which Award is Granted:** Undergraduate **Funds Available:** $750.
Eligibility Requirements: Applicants must be full-time students and graduates of Ketchikan or Revilla High School with a minimum GPA of 2.5; must be majoring in engineering, elementary or secondary education, computer science or aviation. **Application Requirements:** Applicant must complete the application forms available at the website; must attach a personal essay, two letters of recommendation, and current transcripts. **Deadline for Receipt:** February 15.

4210 ■ MIDWEST DAIRY ASSOCIATION
2015 Rice St.
St. Paul, MN 55113
800-642-3895
Web Site: http://www.midwestdairy.com
To provide financial assistance to those deserving students.
Title of Award: North Dakota Division Scholarships **Area, Field, or Subject:** Food Nutrition; Education. **Level of Education for which Award is Granted:** Undergraduate **Number Awarded:** 2. **Funds Available:** $1,000.
Eligibility Requirements: Applicants must be juniors or non-graduating seniors majoring in food nutrition, family and consumer science education or education. **Application Requirements:** Applicants must check the available website for the required materials. **Additional Information:** For more information, contact: Char Heer, Industry Relations Manager at 701-782-4154

4211 ■ MINNESOTA HEALTH INFORMATION MANAGEMENT ASSOCIATION
PO Box 356
Stillwater, MN 55082
Tel: (651)342-0019
E-mail: mhima@comcast.net

Web Site: http://www.mnhima.org
To promote high quality health information and benefit the public, health care providers, and other clinical data users.
Title of Award: Minnesota Health Information Management Association Scholarships **Area, Field, or Subject:** Health education. **Level of Education for which Award is Granted:** Undergraduate **Funds Available:** No specific amount.
Eligibility Requirements: Applicants must be Minnesota residents enrolled in an in-state or out-of-state program or out-of-state students attending a Minnesota school; must have completed accredited Health Information Technology or Health Information Management program; must be in a graduate program related to HIM College or University and accredited by a nationally recognized accrediting agency that has a coding certificate program or AHIMA Coding Basics Interactive Campus program. Applicant must have a cumulative GPA of 3.0 out of 4.0. **Application Requirements:** Applicants must submit an application form; one letter of recommendation from faculty advisor, faculty member or mentor; a verification program; an essay with 500 words; and an official transcript of grades indicating cumulative grades.

4212 ■ MIRACOSTA COLLEGE
1 Barnard Dr.
Oceanside, CA 92056
Tel: (760)757-2121; 888-201-8480
Web Site: http://www.miracosta.cc.ca.us
To encourage educational pursuits among individuals inclined in the field of health.
Title of Award: TYLENOL Scholarships **Area, Field, or Subject:** Health education. **Level of Education for which Award is Granted:** Undergraduate **Number Awarded:** 170. **Funds Available:** $1,000-$5,000.
Eligibility Requirements: Applicants must be students intending to pursue their careers in health-related studies. **Application Requirements:** Application forms are available online. **Deadline for Receipt:** May 15.

4213 ■ MOLINE FOUNDATION
817 11th Ave.
Moline, IL 61265
Tel: (309)736-3800
Fax: (309)736-3721
E-mail: molinefoundation@gconline.com
Web Site: http://www.molinefoundation.org
To provide grants to health, human services, education, community development, the arts, and other charitable organizations which benefit the citizens of Moline Foundations. To provide funds to deserving students from Moline High School who plan to obtain a college degree in education.
Title of Award: Lee Womack Scholarships Fund **Area, Field, or Subject:** Education. **Level of Education for which Award is Granted:** Undergraduate **Funds Available:** No specific amount.
Eligibility Requirements: Applicants must be graduating high school seniors, or community college students preparing to transfer to four-year colleges. Applicants must intend to pursue a bachelor's degree on a full-time basis. Applicants must demonstrate financial need. Applicants must have achieved high school scholastic performance in the upper one-third of their class, or community college grade performance of 2.5 on a 4.0 scale, or equivalent. **Application Requirements:** Applicants must complete the application form. **Additional Information:** 309-736-3800.

4214 ■ NATIONAL ASSOCIATION OF AGRICULTURAL EDUCATORS
300 Garrigus Bldg.
University of Kentucky
Lexington, KY 40546-0215
Tel: (859)257-2224
Free: 800-509-0204
Web Site: http://www.naae.org
To provide educational opportunities to students majoring in agricultural education.
Title of Award: Delmar Cengage Learning-NAAE Upper Division Scholarships **Area, Field, or Subject:** Education; Agricultural sciences. **Level of Education for which Award is Granted:** Undergraduate **Number Awarded:** 15. **Funds Available:** $750.
Eligibility Requirements: Applicants must be agricultural education majors who want to be agricultural teachers; must be members of NAAE.

Application Requirements: Applicants must submit original copy and eight copies of application form; description of applicant's leadership and service activities; an essay entitled "Why I Want to Teach Agriculture"; a letter of recommendation from an agricultural education teacher in the applicant's college or university or from an agricultural education teacher at the local, state or national level; official transcript; and a photograph in a CD. **Deadline for Receipt:** May 15.

4215 ■ NATIONAL DAIRY HERD IMPROVEMENT ASSOCIATION

PO Box 930399
Verona, WI 53593-0399
Tel: (608)848-6455
Fax: (608)848-7675
E-mail: jmattison@requestltd.com
Web Site: http://www.dhia.org
To provide financial assistance for the education of incoming and continuing students at technical and two-year and four-year institutions.
Title of Award: National Dairy Herd Improvement Association Scholarship Program **Area, Field, or Subject:** General studies. **Level of Education for which Award is Granted:** Undergraduate **Funds Available:** $500.

Eligibility Requirements: Applicants must be family members or employees of a herd on DHIA testing, or family members of an employee, or employees of a DHIA affiliate. **Application Requirements:** Applicants must submit all the required application information. **Deadline for Receipt:** September 30.

4216 ■ NATIONAL FEDERATION OF THE BLIND

1800 Johnson St.
Baltimore, MD 21230
Tel: (410)659-9314
Fax: (410)685-5653
Web Site: http://www.nfb.org
To recognize achievement by blind scholars and create opportunity for all blind people; to keep alive the memory of a young woman who dealt with blindness and terminal illness with grace and strength, she frequently assured others she drew from the Federation and from her faith in God.
Title of Award: Jennica Ferguson Memorial Scholarships **Area, Field, or Subject:** Education, Elementary; Education, Secondary. **Level of Education for which Award is Granted:** Undergraduate **Number Awarded:** 14. **Funds Available:** $5,000.

Eligibility Requirements: Applicant must be legally blind; he/she must be pursuing or planning a career in elementary, secondary, or postsecondary teaching; he/she must be participant in NFB national convention and in all scheduled scholarship program activities. **Application Requirements:** Applicant must fill out the application form; he/she must submit two letters of recommendation from individuals that can describe the academic ability, leadership skills, and/or community involvement; copies of transcript of record and a photocopy of score reports for all standardized tests taken for college admission(ACT, SAT or other); applicant must provide a letter of proof of legal blindness from a qualified professional; and an affiliate President's letter. **Deadline for Receipt:** March 31.

4217 ■ NATIONAL FEDERATION OF THE BLIND

1800 Johnson St.
Baltimore, MD 21230
Tel: (410)659-9314
Fax: (410)685-5653
Web Site: http://www.nfb.org
To recognize achievement of blind scholars and to create opportunity for all blind people.
Title of Award: National Federation of the Blind Educator of Tomorrow Award **Area, Field, or Subject:** Education, Elementary; Education, Secondary. **Level of Education for which Award is Granted:** Undergraduate **Funds Available:** $3,000.

Eligibility Requirements: All applicants must be legally blind; he/she must be pursuing or planning a career in elementary, secondary, or postsecondary teaching; he/she must be participant in NFB national convention and in all scheduled scholarship program activities. **Application Requirements:** Applicant must fill out the application form; he/she must submit two letters of recommendation from individuals that can describe the academic ability, leadership skills, and/or community involvement; copies of transcript of record and a photocopy of score reports for

all standardized tests taken for college admission (ACT, SAT or other); applicant must provide a letter of proof of legal blindness from a qualified professional; and an affiliate President's letter. **Deadline for Receipt:** March 31.

4218 ■ NATIONAL SLOVAK SOCIETY OF THE USA

351 Valley Brook Rd.
McMurray, PA 15317-3337
Tel: (724)731-0094
Free: 800-488-1890
Fax: (724)731-0145
E-mail: dblazek@nsslife.org
Web Site: http://www.nsslife.org
To financially assist members in attending college or trade school.
Title of Award: National Slovak Society of the USA Scholarships **Area, Field, or Subject:** Nursing; Education, Vocational-technical **Level of Education for which Award is Granted:** Undergraduate **Number Awarded:** Varies. **Funds Available:** $400 per year. **Duration:** Four years.
Eligibility Requirements: Applicant must be a member of the National Slovak Society for a minimum of two years; completed high school; have a minimum of $10,000 of permanent life insurance in force, or $5000 annuity; accepted by a college or university; a junior college, nursing, trade, technical or business school (2 years); or other institutions approved by the NSS Board of Directors. **Application Requirements:** Applicants must submit completed applications along with latest transcript; proof of acceptance as a full-time student; a resume/biographical sketch with recent photograph; and proof of fraternal activities. **Deadline for Receipt:** May 1.

4219 ■ NATIONAL SLOVAK SOCIETY OF THE USA

351 Valley Brook Rd.
McMurray, PA 15317-3337
Tel: (724)731-0094
Free: 800-488-1890
Fax: (724)731-0145
E-mail: dblazek@nsslife.org
Web Site: http://www.nsslife.org
To encourage older members to continue their education and to make fuller use of their leisure time.
Title of Award: National Slovak Society of the USA Senior Scholarships **Area, Field, or Subject:** Education, Vocational-technical. **Level of Education for which Award is Granted:** Undergraduate **Funds Available:** One-half reimbursement of the tuition, limited up to $100.
Eligibility Requirements: Applicant must be a member of the National Slovak Society; 55 years and above; enrolled and successfully completed a continuing education or adult education course. Continuing education classes for the attainment or maintenance of a degree or certification are not qualified. **Application Requirements:** Applicants must enroll and pay for the course of their choice, after the applicant have finished the class, they must submit an application, along with the verification that the class was successfully completed.

4220 ■ NEW MEXICO ASSOCIATION FOR BILINGUAL EDUCATION

PO Box 5190
Clovis, NM 88102-5190
Tel: (505)309-3599
Fax: (505)769-0742
E-mail: nmabe@suddenlink.net
Web Site: http://www.nmabe.net
To provide financial support for deserving students intending to pursue studies in the area of bilingual education.
Title of Award: New Mexico Association for Bilingual Education Scholarships **Area, Field, or Subject:** Bilingual Education. **Level of Education for which Award is Granted:** Undergraduate **Funds Available:** No specific amount.
Eligibility Requirements: Applicants must be juniors or seniors in a New Mexico university bilingual education teacher preparation program. Applicants must have a GPA of 3.0 or better for initial consideration and for renewals. They must reapply by the appropriate deadline for consideration each semester. **Application Requirements:** Applicants must submit the completed application form; two letters of recommendation; a written essay in Spanish or a Native American language outlining their reasons for entering the field of Bilingual Education; and current university transcripts.

Additional Information: New Mexico Association for Bilingual Education at the above address.

4221 ■ NORTHWEST-SHOALS COMMUNITY COLLEGE
PO Box 2545
Muscle Shoals, AL 35662
Tel: (256)331-5200
Free: 800-645-8967
Fax: (256)331-5222
Web Site: http://www.nwscc.edu
To support students with their educational pursuit.
Title of Award: Northwest-Shoals Community College Applied Technology Scholarships **Area, Field, or Subject:** Education, Vocational-technical. **Level of Education for which Award is Granted:** Undergraduate **Funds Available:** $1500. **Eligibility Requirements:** Applicant must be entering freshmen and enrolled full-time in technical or occupational program; and have an overall GPA of 3.0. **Application Requirements:** To qualify, students must file a Northwest-Shoals Community College Application for Admission. Applicants must submit a completed scholarship application form together with the required materials and information. **Deadline for Receipt:** March 2. **Additional Information:** Office of Student Financial Services, at 235-331-5417/256-331-6232.

4222 ■ OPERATION HOMEFRONT
8930 Fourwinds Dr., Ste. 340
San Antonio, TX 78239
Tel: (210)659-7756
Free: 800-722-6098
Fax: (210)566-7544
E-mail: info@operationhomefront.net
Web Site: http://www.operationhomefront.net
To provide financial assistance to the spouses and children of active-duty personnel.
Title of Award: Operation Homefront Scholarships **Area, Field, or Subject:** Vocational-technical education. **Level of Education for which Award is Granted:** Undergraduate **Funds Available:** $1,000 up to $5,000. **Eligibility Requirements:** Applicants must be spouses and children of active-duty military personnel who plan to pursue post-secondary education, including college, vocational and technical training. **Application Requirements:** Applicants must submit all the required application information. **Deadline for Receipt:** May 30.

4223 ■ ORANGE COUNTY COMMUNITY FOUNDATION
30 Corporate Park, Ste. 410
Irvine, CA 92606
Tel: (949)553-4202
Fax: (949)553-4211
E-mail: cmontesano@oc-cf.org
Web Site: http://www.oc-cf.org
To support outstanding students in pursuing a career as a public school teacher.
Title of Award: Larry Acterman Public Education Awards **Area, Field, or Subject:** Education. **Level of Education for which Award is Granted:** Undergraduate **Funds Available:** $2,000. **Eligibility Requirements:** Applicants must: be a high school senior graduating from the Long Beach Unified School District; plan to enroll in a full-time course of study at an accredited four-year public college or university in the state of California to attain a degree and a teaching credential; demonstrate outstanding scholastic ability and a determination to graduate from college and become a public school teacher, Financial need will be considered as well. **Application Requirements:** Interested applicant may download an application from the Foundation's website. in a maximum one-page essay, write about any one of the following topics: Your interest in becoming a public school teacher; The importance of a strong public education system for society and democracy; How you would improve public schools and/or public education in California. **Deadline for Receipt:** March 28. **Additional Information:** Claudia Montesano, 949-553-4202 ext. 46; cmontesano@oc-cf.org.

4224 ■ PAINTING AND DECORATING CONTRACTORS OF AMERICA
1801 Park 270 Dr., Ste. 220
St. Louis, MO 63146

Tel: (314)514-7322
Free: 800-332-7322
Fax: (314)514-9417
E-mail: ihoren@pdca.org
Web Site: http://www.pdca.org
To assist students who wish to further their education.
Title of Award: A.E. Robert Friedman Scholarships **Area, Field, or Subject:** Adult education; Education, Vocational-technical. **Level of Education for which Award is Granted:** Postgraduate, Undergraduate **Number Awarded:** Varies. **Funds Available:** $1,500. **Eligibility Requirements:** Applicants must be at least seniors in high school, no more than 26 years old; nominated by an active PDCA member, unrelated to a PDCA member or employee and otherwise unconnected with the PDCA. **Application Requirements:** Applicants must submit a completed application form; essays; letters of recommendation and transcript. **Additional Information:** Scholarships are in honor of A.E. Robert Friedman, a legal counsel of PDCA and supporter of education. **Deadline for Receipt:** October 1.

4225 ■ PARKERSBURG AREA COMMUNITY FOUNDATION
501 Avery St.
Parkersburg, WV 26101
Tel: (304)428-4438; (866)428-4438
Fax: (304)428-1200
E-mail: info@pacfwv.com
Web Site: http://www.pacfwv.com
To encourage the graduating seniors of Parkersburg High School to pursue their career in teaching.
Title of Award: Jennifer Coulter Memorial Scholarships **Area, Field, or Subject:** Teaching. **Level of Education for which Award is Granted:** Undergraduate **Funds Available:** $1,000. **Eligibility Requirements:** Applicant must be a graduating senior from Parkersburg High School interested in pursuing a career in teaching and must be involved in extracurricular and/or community service activities. **Application Requirements:** Applicants must submit a cover sheet (3 pages) and application form (4 pages); must have a personal essay; must have a high school and/or post-secondary transcript; must provide a letter of recommendation and a signed copy of the page of their or their parent's most recent tax return that indicates adjusted gross income; and must have a Student Aid Report showing estimated family contribution from FAFSA. Application form and other supporting documents must be sent to Our Community's Foundation, P.O Box 1762, Parkersburg, WV 26102. **Deadline for Receipt:** March 20.

4226 ■ PARKERSBURG AREA COMMUNITY FOUNDATION
501 Avery St.
Parkersburg, WV 26101
Tel: (304)428-4438; (866)428-4438
Fax: (304)428-1200
E-mail: info@pacfwv.com
Web Site: http://www.pacfwv.com
To provide financial assistance for qualified graduating seniors intending to pursue their career in education.
Title of Award: Laverne L. Gibson Memorial Scholarships **Area, Field, or Subject:** Education; Special education. **Level of Education for which Award is Granted:** Undergraduate **Funds Available:** $390. **Eligibility Requirements:** Applicant must be a graduating senior from Wood County West Virginia or Washington County Ohio; must be majoring in education, and special education. **Application Requirements:** Applicants must submit a cover sheet (3 pages) and application form (4 pages); must have a personal essay; must have high school and/or post-secondary transcripts; must provide a letter of recommendation and a signed copy of the page of their or their parent's most recent tax return that indicates adjusted gross income; must have a Student Aid Report, showing estimated family contribution, from FAFSA. Application form and other supporting documents must be sent to Our Community's Foundation, P.O Box 1762, Parkersburg, WV 26102. **Deadline for Receipt:** March 20.

4227 ■ PARKERSBURG AREA COMMUNITY FOUNDATION
501 Avery St.
Parkersburg, WV 26101
Tel: (304)428-4438; (866)428-4438

Fax: (304)428-1200
E-mail: info@pacfwv.com
Web Site: http://www.pacfwv.com
To provide financial support for qualified individuals in Ritchie County intending to pursue their studies.
Title of Award: Harrisville Lions Club Scholarships **Area, Field, or Subject:** Education, Vocationaltechnical. **Level of Education for which Award is Granted:** Undergraduate **Funds Available:** $500.
Eligibility Requirements: Applicant must be a resident of Ritchie County; must be pursuing vocational, technical, or trade related education through an accredited institution or program; and must have a minimum 2.0 GPA (if a graduating senior or presently enrolled in school). **Application Requirements:** Applicants must submit a cover sheet (3 pages) and application form (4 pages); must have a personal essay; must have high school and/or post-secondary transcripts; must provide a letter of recommendation; copy of the page of their or their parent's most recent tax return that indicates adjusted gross income; and must have a Student Aid Report showing estimated family contribution; from FAFSA. Application form and other supporting documents must be sent to Our Community's Foundation, P.O Box 1762, Parkersburg, WV 26102. **Deadline for Receipt:** March 20.

4228 ■ PARKERSBURG AREA COMMUNITY FOUNDATION
501 Avery St.
Parkersburg, WV 26101
Tel: (304)428-4438; (866)428-4438
Fax: (304)428-1200
E-mail: info@pacfwv.com
Web Site: http://www.pacfwv.com
To assist graduating students in their educational pursuits.
Title of Award: William R. Pfalzgraf Scholarships **Area, Field, or Subject:** Law; Education, English as a second language; Music. **Level of Education for which Award is Granted:** Undergraduate **Funds Available:** $760.
Eligibility Requirements: Applicant must be a Parkersburg High School graduating senior with a minimum of 3.0 GPA. **Application Requirements:** Applicants must submit a cover sheet (3 pages) and application form (4 pages); a personal essay; a high school and/or post-secondary transcript; a letter of recommendation; a signed copy of the page of their or their parent's most recent tax return that indicates adjusted gross income; and a Student Aid Report showing estimated family contribution from FAFSA. Application form and other supporting documents must be sent to Our Community's Foundation, P.O Box 1762, Parkersburg, WV 26102. **Deadline for Receipt:** March 20.

4229 ■ PARKERSBURG AREA COMMUNITY FOUNDATION
501 Avery St.
Parkersburg, WV 26101
Tel: (304)428-4438; (866)428-4438
Fax: (304)428-1200
E-mail: info@pacfwv.com
Web Site: http://www.pacfwv.com
To encourage graduating students to pursue their college postsecondary education.
Title of Award: William Reaser Scholarships **Area, Field, or Subject:** Vocational-technical. **Level of Education for which Award is Granted:** Undergraduate **Funds Available:** $500.
Eligibility Requirements: Applicant must be a Ritchie County High School graduating senior planning to pursue post-secondary education in a technical or vocational field. **Application Requirements:** Applicants must submit a cover sheet (3 pages) and application form (4 pages); must have a personal essay; must have a high school and/or postsecondary transcript; must provide a letter of recommendation and a signed copy of the page of their or their parent's most recent tax return that indicates adjusted gross income; and must have a Student Aid Report showing estimated family contribution from FAFSA. Application form and other supporting documents must be sent to Our Community's Foundation, P.O. Box 1762, Parkersburg, WV 26102. **Deadline for Receipt:** March 20.

4230 ■ PARKERSBURG AREA COMMUNITY FOUNDATION
501 Avery St.
Parkersburg, WV 26101
Tel: (304)428-4438; (866)428-4438

Fax: (304)428-1200
E-mail: info@pacfwv.com
Web Site: http://www.pacfwv.com
To encourage graduating students to pursue their education.
Title of Award: Carl M. Rose Memorial Scholarship Fund **Area, Field, or Subject:** Education, Secondary. **Level of Education for which Award is Granted:** Undergraduate **Funds Available:** $390.
Eligibility Requirements: Applicant must be a Parkersburg South High School graduating senior; must have a 3.0 GPA; and must be planning to pursue a major in secondary education. **Application Requirements:** Applicants must submit a cover sheet (3 pages) and application form (4 pages); a personal essay; a high school and/or post-secondary transcript; a letter of recommendation; a signed copy of the page of their or their parent's most recent tax return that indicates adjusted gross income; and a Student Aid Report showing estimated family contribution from FAFSA. Application form and other supporting documents must be sent at Our Community's Foundation, P.O Box 1762, Parkersburg, WV 26102. **Deadline for Receipt:** March 20.

4231 ■ PARKERSBURG AREA COMMUNITY FOUNDATION
501 Avery St.
Parkersburg, WV 26101
Tel: (304)428-4438; (866)428-4438
Fax: (304)428-1200
E-mail: info@pacfwv.com
Web Site: http://www.pacfwv.com
To encourage graduating seniors to pursue their education.
Title of Award: Mary K. Smith Rector Scholarships **Area, Field, or Subject:** Vocational-technical education. **Level of Education for which Award is Granted:** Undergraduate **Funds Available:** $500-$1,500.
Eligibility Requirements: Applicants must be graduating seniors from Gilmer County High School; must be planning to attend an accredited college or university in West Virginia; must have a minimum of 2.5 GPA. **Application Requirements:** Applicants must submit a cover sheet (3 pages) and application form (4 pages); must have a personal essay; must have high school and/or post-secondary transcripts; must provide a letter of recommendation; copy of the page of their or their parent's most recent tax return that indicates adjusted gross income; and a Student Aid Report showing estimated family contribution from FAFSA. Application form and other supporting documents must be sent at Our Community's Foundation, P.O Box 1762, Parkersburg, WV 26102. **Deadline for Receipt:** March 20.

4232 ■ PARKERSBURG AREA COMMUNITY FOUNDATION
501 Avery St.
Parkersburg, WV 26101
Tel: (304)428-4438; (866)428-4438
Fax: (304)428-1200
E-mail: info@pacfwv.com
Web Site: http://www.pacfwv.com
To encourage graduating students to pursue their career as education professionals.
Title of Award: Charles A. Townsend Scholarships **Area, Field, or Subject:** Education. **Level of Education for which Award is Granted:** Undergraduate **Funds Available:** $985.
Eligibility Requirements: Applicant must be a graduating senior of Wood County schools planning to attend an accredited post-secondary school; must be interested in pursuing a career as an education professional; and must be pursuing a degree at St. John's College in Annapolis, MD, or Santa Fe, NM. **Application Requirements:** Applicants must submit a cover sheet (3 pages) and application form (4 pages); a personal essay; a high school and/or post-secondary transcript; a letter of recommendation; a signed copy of the page of their or their parent's most recent tax return that indicates adjusted gross income; and a Student Aid Report, showing estimated family contribution, from FAFSA. Application form and other supporting documents must be sent to Our Community's Foundation, P.O Box 1762, Parkersburg, WV 26102. **Deadline for Receipt:** March 20.

4233 ■ PEPPERDINE UNIVERSITY SCHOOL OF LAW
24255 Pacific Coast Highway
Malibu, CA 90263
Tel: (310)506-4611
E-mail: soladmis@pepperdine.edu

Web Site: http://law.pepperdine.edu
To assist students at Pepperdine University School.

Title of Award: Associated Women for Pepperdine (AWP) Scholarships **Area, Field, or Subject:** Education; Psychology; Law. **Level of Education for which Award is Granted:** Undergraduate **Funds Available:** No specific amount.

Eligibility Requirements: Applicants must be admitted at Pepperdine University; and be members of the Church of Christ. **Application Requirements:** Applicants must submit a completed scholarship application form together with a resume, letter of qualifications, and a letter confirming active membership in a local Church of Christ congregation. **Deadline for Receipt:** October 31.

4234 ■ PIERCE COLLEGE DISTRICT 11
9401 Farwest Dr. SW
Lakewood, WA 98498
Tel: (253)964-6500
Web Site: http://www.pierce.ctc.edu
To support Pierce College students with their education.

Title of Award: Pierce County Retired Teachers Scholarships **Area, Field, or Subject:** Teaching. **Level of Education for which Award is Granted:** Undergraduate **Number Awarded:** 1. **Funds Available:** $1,000. **Duration:** One academic year.

Eligibility Requirements: Applicants must be community college students in the second year of program and who will graduate with an AA degree; must be planning to transfer to a four-year university/college as full-time students; must be intending to pursue a career in teaching or education; and must have a minimum 2.5 GPA. **Application Requirements:** Applicants must complete the application form and submit together with the required materials to Ruth Ann Hatchett Pierce College District Rm. 108 Gaspard Building 1601 39th Ave. SE, Puyallup, WA 98374. **Additional Information:** Funded by the Retired Teacher Association - WSRTA Affiliate No. 27. **Deadline for Receipt:** May 2.

4235 ■ PINNACLE WEST CAPITAL CORPORATION
PO Box 53999
Phoenix, AZ 85072-3999
Tel: (602)250-1000
Free: 800-457-2983
Web Site: http://www.pinnaclewest.com
To provide financial assistance to qualified individuals who want to pursue their career.

Title of Award: APS/ASU Scholarships **Area, Field, or Subject:** Chemical engineering; Electrical engineering; Mechanical engineering; Civil engineering; Construction; Telecommunications systems; Accounting; Finance; Economics; Information science and technology; Education, Elementary; Education, Secondary; Special education; Nursing. **Level of Education for which Award is Granted:** Undergraduate **Number Awarded:** 10. **Funds Available:** $2,000. **Duration:** One year.

Eligibility Requirements: Applicant must be an Arizona resident; must have a cumulative GPA of at least 3.0; must demonstrate financial need. **Application Requirements:** Applicant must complete the application form available online and send it to ASU Scholarship Office, Arizona State University, PO Box 470412, Tempe, AZ 85287-0412. **Deadline for Receipt:** March 1. **Additional Information:** Louise Moskowitz at louise. moskowitz@aps.com.

4236 ■ PINNACLE WEST CAPITAL CORPORATION
PO Box 53999
Phoenix, AZ 85072-3999
Tel: (602)250-1000
Free: 800-457-2983
Web Site: http://www.pinnaclewest.com
To provide financial assistance to qualified individuals who want to pursue their career.

Title of Award: APS/Maricopa County Community Colleges Scholarships **Area, Field, or Subject:** Mechanical engineering; Electrical engineering; Civil engineering; Chemical engineering; Trades training; Information science and technology; Marketing and distribution; Accounting; Finance; Economics; Management; Education; Health care services. **Level of Education for which Award is Granted:** Undergraduate **Number Awarded:** 25. **Funds Available:** $1,000. **Duration:** One year.

Eligibility Requirements: Applicant must be an Arizona resident; must have a cumulative GPA of at least 3.0; must demonstrate financial need;

must be a high school senior or current Maricopa Community College student; must be enrolled in a minimum of nine credit hours per semester. **Application Requirements:** Applicant must complete the application form available online and must be sent to ASU Scholarship Office, Arizona State University, PO Box 470412, Tempe, AZ 85287-0412. **Additional Information:** Louise Moskowitz at louise.moskowitz@aps.com.

4237 ■ PRIDE FOUNDATION
PO Box 2194, 1122 E Pike St. PMB 1001
Seattle, WA 98112
Tel: (206)323-3318
Free: 800-735-7287
Fax: (206)323-1017
E-mail: prideweb@pridefoundation.org
Web Site: http://www.pridefoundation.org
To provide scholarship to the students who have been stigmatized, isolated or closeted because of sexual identity issues.

Title of Award: Deloris Carter Hampton Scholarships **Area, Field, or Subject:** Education; Dance. **Level of Education for which Award is Granted:** Undergraduate **Funds Available:** No specific amount.

Eligibility Requirements: Applicants must be women of color who have a demonstrated history of activism and/or leadership in the LGBT community and are pursuing a degree in education, women's health, or dance. **Application Requirements:** Qualified students are asked to submit an application to determine eligibility for scholarships. Applicants may download an application form from the Foundation's website. **Additional Information:** Pride Foundation at the above address.

4238 ■ PRIDE FOUNDATION
PO Box 2194, 1122 E Pike St. PMB 1001
Seattle, WA 98112
Tel: (206)323-3318
Free: 800-735-7287
Fax: (206)323-1017
E-mail: prideweb@pridefoundation.org
Web Site: http://www.pridefoundation.org
To provide scholarship to the students who have been stigmatized, isolated or closeted because of sexual identity issues.

Title of Award: Jacinta McKoy Memorial Scholarships **Area, Field, or Subject:** Education. **Level of Education for which Award is Granted:** Undergraduate **Funds Available:** No specific amount.

Eligibility Requirements: Applicant must be a student from the Black Hills community pursuing education in the healing arts. Preference is given to students who are self-identified lesbian, gay, bisexual or transgender (LGBT). **Application Requirements:** Qualified students are asked to submit an application to determine eligibility for scholarships. Applicants may download an application form from the Foundation's website. **Additional Information:** Pride Foundation at the above address.

4239 ■ PUBLIC EDUCATION FOUNDATION
3360 W Sahara Ave., Ste. 160
Las Vegas, NV 89102
Tel: (702)799-1042
Fax: (702)799-5247
E-mail: steelej@ccpef.org
Web Site: http://ccpef.org
To provide educational opportunities for individuals intending to pursue higher studies.

Title of Award: Jeannette Bautista Memorial Scholarships **Area, Field, or Subject:** Education. **Level of Education for which Award is Granted:** Undergraduate **Number Awarded:** 1. **Funds Available:** $250. **Duration:** One year.

Eligibility Requirements: Applicants must be CCSD seniors planning to attend an accredited post-secondary institution in the field of education; must have a minimum 3.5 cumulative GPA; and must demonstrate financial need. **Application Requirements:** Applicants must submit a completed application form together with an essay, two letters of recommendation, transcript and a resume of awards. **Deadline for Receipt:** March 7. **Additional Information:** Shana Venenga at 702-799-1042.

4240 ■ PUBLIC EDUCATION FOUNDATION
3360 W Sahara Ave., Ste. 160
Las Vegas, NV 89102

Tel: (702)799-1042
Fax: (702)799-5247
E-mail: steelej@ccpef.org
Web Site: http://ccpef.org
To provide educational opportunities for individuals intending to pursue higher studies.
Title of Award: Susan Brager Occupational Education Scholarships **Area, Field, or Subject:** Education. **Level of Education for which Award is Granted:** Undergraduate **Number Awarded:** 1. **Funds Available:** $1,000.
Eligibility Requirements: Applicants must be CCSD seniors; must have completed a minimum of two years of an established occupational education program; must have a minimum 2.5 cumulative GPA; and must be planning to attend a school in the Nevada Higher Education System within Clark County. **Application Requirements:** Applicants must submit a completed application form together with an essay, a letter of recommendation, transcript and a resume of awards. **Deadline for Receipt:** March 7. **Additional Information:** Shana Venenga at 702-799-1042.

4241 ■ PUBLIC EDUCATION FOUNDATION
3360 W Sahara Ave., Ste. 160
Las Vegas, NV 89102
Tel: (702)799-1042
Fax: (702)799-5247
E-mail: steelej@ccpef.org
Web Site: http://ccpef.org
To provide educational opportunities for individuals intending to pursue higher studies.
Title of Award: Clark High School Teacher Education Academy Scholarships **Area, Field, or Subject:** Education. **Level of Education for which Award is Granted:** Undergraduate **Number Awarded:** 1. **Funds Available:** $500.
Eligibility Requirements: Applicants must be Teacher Education Academy at Clark High School (TEACH) seniors interested in pursuing a degree in education at an accredited college/university; must have a minimum 2.8 cumulative GPA; and must be currently enrolled in the TEACH Educational Internship and Seminar course. **Application Requirements:** Applicants must submit a completed application form together with an essay, transcript, and resume of awards. **Additional Information:** In memory of Eleine Flemming-Smith. **Deadline for Receipt:** March 7. **Additional Information:** Shana Venenga at 702-799-1042.

4242 ■ PUBLIC EDUCATION FOUNDATION
3360 W Sahara Ave., Ste. 160
Las Vegas, NV 89102
Tel: (702)799-1042
Fax: (702)799-5247
E-mail: steelej@ccpef.org
Web Site: http://ccpef.org
To provide educational opportunities for individuals intending to pursue higher studies.
Title of Award: Flora English Creative Writing Scholarships **Area, Field, or Subject:** Education, English as a second language. **Level of Education for which Award is Granted:** Undergraduate **Number Awarded:** 1. **Funds Available:** $1,000. **Duration:** One year.
Eligibility Requirements: Applicants must be CCSD seniors interested in pursuing a degree in English at an accredited college or university; must have a minimum 3.0 cumulative GPA; and must demonstrate financial need. **Application Requirements:** Applicants must submit a completed application form together with an essay, two letters of recommendation, transcript, and resume of awards. **Deadline for Receipt:** March 7. **Additional Information:** Shana Venenga at 702-799-1042.

4243 ■ PUBLIC EDUCATION FOUNDATION
3360 W Sahara Ave., Ste. 160
Las Vegas, NV 89102
Tel: (702)799-1042
Fax: (702)799-5247
E-mail: steelej@ccpef.org
Web Site: http://ccpef.org
To provide educational opportunities for individuals intending to pursue higher studies.

Title of Award: Fraser Family Scholarships **Area, Field, or Subject:** Education. **Level of Education for which Award is Granted:** Undergraduate **Number Awarded:** 1. **Funds Available:** $1,000.
Eligibility Requirements: Applicants must be high school seniors from Durango with a 3.5 cumulative GPA planning to attend an accredited college/university and pursuing a degree in education or related field. **Application Requirements:** Applicants must submit a completed application form together with an essay, two letters of recommendation, transcript, and resume of awards. **Deadline for Receipt:** March 7. **Additional Information:** Shana Venenga at 702-799-1042.

4244 ■ PUBLIC EDUCATION FOUNDATION
3360 W Sahara Ave., Ste. 160
Las Vegas, NV 89102
Tel: (702)799-1042
Fax: (702)799-5247
E-mail: steelej@ccpef.org
Web Site: http://ccpef.org
To promote education in physical education.
Title of Award: Gretchen Hauff Memorial Scholarships **Area, Field, or Subject:** Physical education. **Level of Education for which Award is Granted:** Undergraduate **Number Awarded:** 1. **Funds Available:** $1,000.
Eligibility Requirements: Applicants must be CCSD female seniors interested in pursuing a degree in physical education at an accredited college/university; must have a minimum 2.5 unweighted cumulative GPA; and must have demonstrated financial need. **Application Requirements:** Applicants must submit a completed application form together with an essay, three letters of recommendation, transcript, and resume of awards. **Deadline for Receipt:** March 7. **Additional Information:** Shana Venenga at 702-799-1042.

4245 ■ PUBLIC EDUCATION FOUNDATION
3360 W Sahara Ave., Ste. 160
Las Vegas, NV 89102
Tel: (702)799-1042
Fax: (702)799-5247
E-mail: steelej@ccpef.org
Web Site: http://ccpef.org
To provide educational opportunities for individuals intending to pursue higher studies.
Title of Award: Nevada Parent Teacher Association Scholarships **Area, Field, or Subject:** Education. **Level of Education for which Award is Granted:** Undergraduate **Number Awarded:** 1. **Funds Available:** $500.
Eligibility Requirements: Applicants must be CCSD seniors who have attended a PTSA high school or Teacher Education Academy at Clark High School (TEACH); must be pursuing a degree in education; must be planning to attend a post-secondary college or university; and must have a minimum 2.8 cumulative GPA. **Application Requirements:** Applicants must submit a completed application form along with an essay, transcript, and resume of awards. **Deadline for Receipt:** March 7. **Additional Information:** Shana Venenga at 702-799-1042.

4246 ■ PUBLIC EDUCATION FOUNDATION
3360 W Sahara Ave., Ste. 160
Las Vegas, NV 89102
Tel: (702)799-1042
Fax: (702)799-5247
E-mail: steelej@ccpef.org
Web Site: http://ccpef.org
To provide educational opportunities for individuals intending to pursue higher studies.
Title of Award: Penn-Bird Family Memorial Scholarships **Area, Field, or Subject:** Education. **Level of Education for which Award is Granted:** Undergraduate **Number Awarded:** 2. **Funds Available:** $1,000.
Eligibility Requirements: Applicants must be CCSD seniors pursuing a degree in education and with a minimum 3.0 cumulative GPA. **Application Requirements:** Applicants must submit a completed application form along with the essay, transcript, and college letter of admission. **Deadline for Receipt:** March 7. **Additional Information:** Shana Venenga at 702-799-1042.

4247 ■ PUBLIC EDUCATION FOUNDATION
3360 W Sahara Ave., Ste. 160
Las Vegas, NV 89102

Tel: (702)799-1042
Fax: (702)799-5247
E-mail: steelej@ccpef.org
Web Site: http://ccpef.org
To provide educational opportunities for individuals intending to pursue higher studies.
Title of Award: R.M. Princ Scholarships **Area, Field, or Subject:** Education, Elementary; Education, Secondary. **Level of Education for which Award is Granted:** Undergraduate **Number Awarded:** 3. **Funds Available:** $2,000.
Eligibility Requirements: Applicants must be CCSD female seniors who have maintained a minimum 3.5 cumulative GPA; must demonstrate financial need; and must be planning to attend an accredited post-secondary college or university majoring in the field of education (elementary or secondary). **Application Requirements:** Applicants must submit a completed application form along with an essay, two letters of recommendation, transcript, and resume of awards. **Deadline for Receipt:** March 7. **Additional Information:** Shana Venenga at 702-799-1042.

4248 ■ PUBLIC EDUCATION FOUNDATION
3360 W Sahara Ave., Ste. 160
Las Vegas, NV 89102
Tel: (702)799-1042
Fax: (702)799-5247
E-mail: steelej@ccpef.org
Web Site: http://ccpef.org
To provide educational opportunities for individuals intending to pursue higher studies.
Title of Award: TEACH Scholarships **Area, Field, or Subject:** Education. **Level of Education for which Award is Granted:** Undergraduate **Number Awarded:** 3. **Funds Available:** $500.
Eligibility Requirements: Applicants must be Teacher Education Academy at Clark High School (TEACH) seniors interested in pursuing a degree in education at an accredited college/university; must have a minimum 2.8 cumulative GPA; and must be currently enrolled in the TEACH Educational Internship and Seminar course. **Application Requirements:** Applicants must submit a completed application form along with an essay, transcript, resume of awards, and a copy of recent TEACH Internship Evaluation. **Deadline for Receipt:** March 7. **Additional Information:** Shana Venenga at 702-799-1042.

4249 ■ QUALITY FUNCTION DEPLOYMENT (QFD) INSTITUTE
1140 Morehead Ct.
Ann Arbor, MI 48103
Tel: (734)995-0847
Fax: (206)203-0733
E-mail: registration@qfdi.org
Web Site: http://www.qfdi.org
To stimulate QFD research and education at higher education institutions worldwide by rewarding the university student who has written and submitted the best "Student QFD Paper" of the year.
Title of Award: Akao Scholarships for QFD **Area, Field, or Subject:** Education. **Level of Education for which Award is Granted:** Undergraduate **Funds Available:** No specific amount.
Eligibility Requirements: Applicants must be full-time working students; currently enrolled in an accredited university/college degree program. **Application Requirements:** Applicants must submit a paper reporting their own QFD application case study and/or research findings (must include QFD work objects and data, method(s) used, applicants' own analysis, conclusion and references, information about the applicant as well as any student co-authors). Working students must include their employers' name, employment location and short description of their job; recommendation letter from a professor of their school; proof of enrollment status issued by their school's registrar office. **Deadline for Receipt:** May 1.

4250 ■ REDLANDS COMMUNITY SCHOLARSHIP FOUNDATION
c/o Kathleen Venegas-Boge, Admin. Asst.
PO Box 1683
Redlands, CA 92373
Tel: (909)307-9892
Fax: (909)307-9892

Web Site: http://www.redlandsscholarships.org
To encourage educational pursuits among Redlands Unified School District graduates by providing educational assistance.
Title of Award: Quincy Brown Memorial Scholarships **Area, Field, or Subject:** Business; Teaching. **Level of Education for which Award is Granted:** Undergraduate **Number Awarded:** 7. **Funds Available:** $600; $1000.
Eligibility Requirements: Applicant must be a graduating senior enrolled as a full-time student in a four-year college or university; must be pursuing a business or teaching career; must have a 3.0 or higher GPA; and must have attended Redlands High School for at least three consecutive years. **Application Requirements:** Applicants must submit a completed application form together with the scantron sheet; cover sheet; student activity and community activity sheets; personal essay; and a copy of unofficial transcript (signed by the counselor). **Additional Information:** No electronic submissions of application will be accepted. Submit two printed copies of the application and use a No. 2 pencil on the scantron sheet. **Deadline for Receipt:** February 20.

4251 ■ REDLANDS COMMUNITY SCHOLARSHIP FOUNDATION
c/o Kathleen Venegas-Boge, Admin. Asst.
PO Box 1683
Redlands, CA 92373
Tel: (909)307-9892
Fax: (909)307-9892
Web Site: http://www.redlandsscholarships.org
To encourage educational pursuits among Redlands Unified School District graduates by providing educational assistance.
Title of Award: Doreen Legg Memorial Scholarships **Area, Field, or Subject:** Business; Teaching. **Level of Education for which Award is Granted:** Undergraduate **Number Awarded:** 9. **Funds Available:** $600 and $1000.
Eligibility Requirements: Applicant must be a graduating senior enrolling full-time at a four-year college or university; must be pursuing a business or teaching career; must have a minimum 3.0 GPA; and must have attended Redlands High School for at least three consecutive years. **Application Requirements:** Applicants must submit a completed application form together with the scantron sheet; cover sheet; student activity and community activity sheets; personal essay; and a copy of unofficial transcript (signed by the counselor). **Additional Information:** No electronic submissions of application will be accepted. Submit two printed copies of the application and use a No. 2 pencil on the scantron sheet. **Deadline for Receipt:** February 20.

4252 ■ REDLANDS COMMUNITY SCHOLARSHIP FOUNDATION
c/o Kathleen Venegas-Boge, Admin. Asst.
PO Box 1683
Redlands, CA 92373
Tel: (909)307-9892
Fax: (909)307-9892
Web Site: http://www.redlandsscholarships.org
To encourage educational pursuits among Redlands Unified School District graduates by providing educational assistance.
Title of Award: Charles and Ruth Ronin Memorial Scholarships **Area, Field, or Subject:** Political science; History; Education. **Level of Education for which Award is Granted:** Undergraduate **Number Awarded:** 1. **Funds Available:** $1,000.
Eligibility Requirements: Applicant must be a graduating senior with a 3.5 or higher GPA who will attend a four-year college/university on a full-time basis in pursuit of a bachelor's degree in political science, history, or education. **Application Requirements:** Applicants must submit a completed application form together with the scantron sheet; cover sheet; student activity and community activity sheets; personal essay; and a copy of unofficial transcript (signed by the counselor). **Additional Information:** No electronic submissions of application will be accepted. Submit two printed copies of the application and use a No. 2 pencil on the scantron sheet. **Deadline for Receipt:** February 20.

4253 ■ REDLANDS COMMUNITY SCHOLARSHIP FOUNDATION
c/o Kathleen Venegas-Boge, Admin. Asst.
PO Box 1683
Redlands, CA 92373
Tel: (909)307-9892

Fax: (909)307-9892
Web Site: http://www.redlandsscholarships.org
To encourage educational pursuits among Redlands Unified School District graduates by providing educational assistance.
Title of Award: Soroptimist International of Redlands Scholarships **Area, Field, or Subject:** Health care services; Law; Engineering; Computer and information sciences; Education; Business. **Level of Education for which Award is Granted:** Undergraduate **Number Awarded:** 1. **Funds Available:** $750.
Eligibility Requirements: Applicant must be a graduating senior who has participated in community service and who will be attending an accredited college on a full-time basis and is planning to major in one of the following fields: health care, law, engineering, computer science, education and/or business administration. **Application Requirements:** Applicants must submit a completed application form together with the scantron sheet; cover sheet; student activity and community activity sheets; personal essay; and a copy of unofficial transcript (signed by the counselor). **Additional Information:** No electronic submissions of application will be accepted. Submit two printed copies of the application and use a No. 2 pencil on the scantron sheet. **Deadline for Receipt:** February 20.

4254 ■ ROCKY MOUNTAIN COAL MINING INSTITUTE
8057 S Yukon Way
Littleton, CO 80128-5510
Tel: (303)948-3300
Fax: (303)948-1132
E-mail: mail@rmcmi.org
Web Site: http://www.rmcmi.org
To students in technical programs who would like to pursue their education in the coal industry.
Title of Award: Rocky Mountain Coal Mining Institute Technical Scholarships **Area, Field, or Subject:** Education, Vocational-technical; Trades training **Level of Education for which Award is Granted:** Undergraduate **Number Awarded:** 1 candidate from each state. **Funds Available:** $1,000. **Duration:** One year.
Eligibility Requirements: Applicant must be a first-year student at a two-year Technical/Trade School in a good standing at the time of selection; both a U.S. citizen and a legal resident of one of the Rocky Mountain Coal Mining Institute member states - Arizona, Colorado, Montana, New Mexico, North Dakota, Texas, Utah, or Wyoming; studying an applicable trade; interested in coal as a career path. **Application Requirements:** Applicants must submit a completed application form that can be downloaded from www.rmcmi.org. **Additional Information:** The fund is directly sent to the college, university, or technical school as tuition credit. **Deadline for Receipt:** February 1. **Additional Information:** Karen Inzano, RMCMI Executive Director, or Beth Coen.

4255 ■ SAFE SCHOOLS COALITION
1002 E Seneca St.
Seattle, WA 98122-4203
Tel: (206)957-1621
Fax: (206)325-2689
Web Site: http://www.safeschoolscoalition.org
To provide financial assistance for transgender-identified students.
Title of Award: Transgender Scholarships and Education Legacy Fund **Area, Field, or Subject:** Social Services; Health Care Services; Religious Education; Teaching; Law. **Level of Education for which Award is Granted:** Undergraduate **Funds Available:** No specific amount.
Eligibility Requirements: Applicants must be students of one of these fields of studies. **Application Requirements:** Applicants must check the contact information for more inquiries. **Additional Information:** The awards are sponsored by the International Foundation for Gender Education. **Deadline for Receipt:** February 1. **Additional Information:** International Foundation for Gender Education (IFGE) TSELF Awards Committee PO Box 540229 Waltham, MA 02454-0229 Phone: 781-899-2212 Fax: 781-899-2212 URL: www.tself.org.

4256 ■ THE SAN DIEGO FOUNDATION
2508 Historic Decatur Rd., Ste. 200
San Diego, CA 92106
Tel: (619)235-2300
Fax: (619)239-1710

E-mail: info@sdfoundation.org
Web Site: http://www.sdfoundation.org
To support the education of students from California.
Title of Award: Jonathan Hastings Foster Scholarships **Area, Field, or Subject:** Teaching. **Level of Education for which Award is Granted:** Undergraduate **Number Awarded:** 1. **Funds Available:** $1,500.
Eligibility Requirements: Applicant must be a graduating senior from Point Loma High School; or current San Diego State University student pursuing a career in teaching; must have a minimum 3.50 GPA on a 4.0 scale; and attending an accredited four-year university in the United States. **Application Requirements:** Applicants must submit a completed Common Scholarship Application together with personal statement; two letters of recommendation on official letterhead (written within the last six months); official transcript in an official and sealed envelope; and a copy of most recent tax form (Form 1040-pages 1 & 2; Form 1040A-pages 1 & 2; Form 1040EZ-page 1). **Deadline for Receipt:** January 28. **Additional Information:** Arzo Mansury, Dir. Scholarships at 619-814-1343, or scholarships@sdfoundation.org.

4257 ■ SIEMENS FOUNDATION
170 Wood Ave., S.
Iselin, NJ 08830
877-822-5233
Fax: (732)603-5890
E-mail: foundation.us@siemens.com
Web Site: http://www.siemens-foundation.org
To encourage minority students to consider careers teaching math and science; to provide financial assistance to those students who are in need.
Title of Award: Siemens Teacher Scholarships **Area, Field, or Subject:** Education. **Level of Education for which Award is Granted:** Graduate, Undergraduate **Funds Available:** No specific amount.
Eligibility Requirements: Applicants must be undergraduate or graduate students pursuing education; must be enrolled at one of the historically black colleges or universities. **Application Requirements:** Applicants must check the application process online.

4258 ■ SIGMA KAPPA FOUNDATION
8733 Founder Rd.
Indianapolis, IN 46268
Tel: (317)872-3275
E-mail: alewis@sigmakappa.org
Web Site: http://www.sigmakappafoundation.org
To encourage and support the scholastic development of the collegiate and alumnae sisters of the foundation.
Title of Award: Maridell Braham Condon Scholarships **Area, Field, or Subject:** Education. **Level of Education for which Award is Granted:** Undergraduate **Number Awarded:** 1. **Funds Available:** $500.
Eligibility Requirements: Applicants must be initiated, active members in good standing; must be majoring in education; must have a minimum cumulative GPA: 3.0. **Application Requirements:** Application forms are available online. Applicant must submit the transcript and recommendation letter through online. **Deadline for Receipt:** March 1.

4259 ■ SOUTHWEST FLORIDA COMMUNITY FOUNDATION
8260 College Pkwy., Ste. 101
Fort Myers, FL 33919
Tel: (239)274-5900
Fax: (239)274-5930
Web Site: http://www.floridacommunity.com
To provide educational assistance for Moore Haven High School students pursuing post-secondary education.
Title of Award: COUSE-Gram Scholarships **Area, Field, or Subject:** General studies. **Level of Education for which Award is Granted:** Undergraduate **Funds Available:** No specific amount. **Duration:** One year.
Eligibility Requirements: Applicant must be a Moore Haven High School senior; must pursue post-secondary education. **Application Requirements:** Applicants must submit a letter of interest, transcript, and letter of recommendation. Application forms are available online. **Deadline for Receipt:** February 15.

4260 ■ SOUTHWEST FLORIDA COMMUNITY FOUNDATION
8260 College Pkwy., Ste. 101
Fort Myers, FL 33919

Tel: (239)274-5900
Fax: (239)274-5930
Web Site: http://www.floridacommunity.com
To fund scholarships for female students pursuing a career in technical studies, court reporting, computer training or nursing.
Title of Award: Faye Lynn Roberts Educational Scholarships **Area, Field, or Subject:** Technical training; Computer and information sciences; Nursing. **Level of Education for which Award is Granted:** Undergraduate **Funds Available:** $5,000. **Duration:** One year.
Eligibility Requirements: Applicants must be 21 years of age or older; must be residents of Lee County; and must demonstrate financial need.
Application Requirements: Application forms are available online. Applicants must submit a personal essay, financial need documentation, high school/college transcript and letter of recommendation. **Deadline for Receipt:** March 20.

4261 ■ SOUTHWEST FLORIDA COMMUNITY FOUNDATION
8260 College Pkwy., Ste. 101
Fort Myers, FL 33919
Tel: (239)274-5900
Fax: (239)274-5930
Web Site: http://www.floridacommunity.com
To fund students pursuing degrees or advanced degrees in medicine, law, dentistry, teaching (math and science), ministry, engineering, accounting, architecture and computer science.
Title of Award: John M. and Mary A. Shanley Memorial Scholarships **Area, Field, or Subject:** Medicine; Law; Dentistry; Teaching; Ministry; Engineering; Accounting; Agriculture; Economic aspects; Architecture; Computer and information sciences. **Level of Education for which Award is Granted:** Undergraduate **Funds Available:** $5,000. **Duration:** One year.
Eligibility Requirements: Applicant must be a resident of Charlotte, Hendry or Lee County. **Application Requirements:** Application forms are available online. Applicants must submit a letter of interest, letter of recommendation and transcript. **Deadline for Receipt:** February 15.

4262 ■ SOUTHWEST FLORIDA COMMUNITY FOUNDATION
8260 College Pkwy., Ste. 101
Fort Myers, FL 33919
Tel: (239)274-5900
Fax: (239)274-5930
Web Site: http://www.floridacommunity.com
To fund students pursuing degrees in teaching, nursing, paramedic training or emergency medical technician training.
Title of Award: John I. and Madeleine R. Taeni Scholarships **Area, Field, or Subject:** Teaching; Nursing; Paramedics; Emergency and disaster services. **Level of Education for which Award is Granted:** Undergraduate **Funds Available:** $1,000.
Eligibility Requirements: Applicant must be a resident of Charlotte, Collier, Glades, Hendry or Lee County; must be highly motivated; must pursue teaching, nursing paramedic training, or emergency medical technician training; and must have graduated high school at least two years ago. **Application Requirements:** Application forms are available online. Applicants must submit a letter of interest, letter of recommendation, and transcript. **Deadline for Receipt:** March 20.

4263 ■ STARK COMMUNITY FOUNDATION
400 Market Ave. N, Ste. 200
Canton, OH 44702-2107
Tel: (330)454-3426
Fax: (330)454-5855
Web Site: http://www.starkcommunityfoundation.org
To provide scholarship assistance to qualified individuals who want to pursue their studies.
Title of Award: Emergency Medicine Physician Scholarships for Health Information Management Program **Area, Field, or Subject:** Health education. **Level of Education for which Award is Granted:** Undergraduate **Funds Available:** No specific amount. **Duration:** One year.
Eligibility Requirements: Applicants must be students beginning the second year of study at Stark State College and enrolled full time in the Health Information Management Technology program; must have minimum GPA of 3.0 on a 4.0 scale; must complete his/her education at the conclusion of spring semester; must have interview with the EMP

Manager of Coding and Senior Executives. **Application Requirements:** Applicants must submit an employment history, attitude and work ethic together with the application form to EMP Scholarship Program, Emergency Medicine Physicians, 4535 Dressler Rd. NW, Canton, OH 44718. **Deadline for Receipt:** July 27.

4264 ■ STARK COMMUNITY FOUNDATION
400 Market Ave. N, Ste. 200
Canton, OH 44702-2107
Tel: (330)454-3426
Fax: (330)454-5855
Web Site: http://www.starkcommunityfoundation.org
To provide scholarship assistance to qualified individuals who want to pursue their studies.
Title of Award: Raymond T. Hoge Scholarship Fund **Area, Field, or Subject:** Business; Education. **Level of Education for which Award is Granted:** Undergraduate **Funds Available:** No specific amount. **Duration:** One year.
Eligibility Requirements: Applicants must be graduating senior members of Perry High School or alumni who plan to attend an institution of higher learning; must be in good academic standing; must be planning to pursue a degree in the field of business or education; must demonstrate financial need. **Application Requirements:** Applicants must complete and submit the application form at Perry High School Guidance Office, 3737 13th St. SW, Massillon, OH 44646. **Deadline for Receipt:** April 15.

4265 ■ STARK COMMUNITY FOUNDATION
400 Market Ave. N, Ste. 200
Canton, OH 44702-2107
Tel: (330)454-3426
Fax: (330)454-5855
Web Site: http://www.starkcommunityfoundation.org
To provide scholarship assistance to qualified individuals who want to pursue their studies.
Title of Award: Virginia C. Jack and Ralph L. Jack Scholarships **Area, Field, or Subject:** Vocational-technical education; Nursing. **Level of Education for which Award is Granted:** Undergraduate **Funds Available:** $2,000. **Duration:** One year.
Eligibility Requirements: Applicants must be Stark County residents; must be admitted to technical school, college or university, or school of nursing; must be full or part time students; must be traditional or non-traditional students; must have 2.50 or higher GPA on a 4.0 scale. **Application Requirements:** Applicants must submit two letters of recommendation and essay. Application form and other supporting documents must be sent to Stark Community Foundation, 400 Market Ave. N, Ste. 200, Canton, OH 44702. **Deadline for Receipt:** April 1.

4266 ■ STARK COMMUNITY FOUNDATION
400 Market Ave. N, Ste. 200
Canton, OH 44702-2107
Tel: (330)454-3426
Fax: (330)454-5855
Web Site: http://www.starkcommunityfoundation.org
To provide scholarship assistance to qualified individuals who want to pursue their studies.
Title of Award: Louise Nader Khourey/Kappa Delta Pi Scholarships **Area, Field, or Subject:** Education; Foreign languages. **Level of Education for which Award is Granted:** Undergraduate **Funds Available:** No specific amount. **Duration:** One year.
Eligibility Requirements: Applicants must be graduating seniors from Stark County high schools who plan to attend an institution of higher learning; must be planning to pursue a degree in the field of education. **Application Requirements:** Applicants must submit completed application forms and are advised to visit the High School Guidance Counselor. **Deadline for Receipt:** January.

4267 ■ STARK COMMUNITY FOUNDATION
400 Market Ave. N, Ste. 200
Canton, OH 44702-2107
Tel: (330)454-3426
Fax: (330)454-5855
Web Site: http://www.starkcommunityfoundation.org

To provide scholarship assistance to qualified individuals who want to pursue their studies.
Title of Award: Lake Dollars for Scholars Endowment Fund **Area, Field, or Subject:** Education, Vocational-technical; Nursing. **Level of Education for which Award is Granted:** Undergraduate **Funds Available:** No specific amount. **Duration:** One year.
Eligibility Requirements: Applicants must be graduating seniors residing within the boundaries of the Lake Local District, Lake Township, and Stark County, OH; must have been accepted into a two-year or four-year college or university, nursing school, or other post high school vocational education program; must meet the requirements of the application form provided by Lake Dollars For Scholars. **Application Requirements:** Applicants must submit completed application form and are advised to contact the Lake High School Guidance Office at 330877-4285. **Deadline for Receipt:** March 20.

4268 ■ STARK COMMUNITY FOUNDATION
400 Market Ave. N, Ste. 200
Canton, OH 44702-2107
Tel: (330)454-3426
Fax: (330)454-5855
Web Site: http://www.starkcommunityfoundation.org
To provide scholarship assistance to qualified individuals who want to pursue their studies.
Title of Award: Fizz and Dutch Miller Scholarship Fund **Area, Field, or Subject:** Vocational-technical education; Nursing. **Level of Education for which Award is Granted:** Undergraduate **Funds Available:** No specific amount. **Duration:** One year.
Eligibility Requirements: Applicants must be graduates of Strasburg High School or current residents of Strasburg; must have been admitted to and enrolled in a college, university, technical school, vocational school or nursing school; must demonstrate participation in school and community activities; must demonstrate good citizenship; must demonstrate financial assistance to pursue the best level of education. **Application Requirements:** Applicants must submit two letters of reference. Application form and other supporting documents must be sent to The Strasburg High School Guidance Office. **Deadline for Receipt:** May 10.

4269 ■ STARK COMMUNITY FOUNDATION
400 Market Ave. N, Ste. 200
Canton, OH 44702-2107
Tel: (330)454-3426
Fax: (330)454-5855
Web Site: http://www.starkcommunityfoundation.org
To provide scholarship assistance to qualified individuals who want to pursue their studies.
Title of Award: Lt. Colonel Robert G. Moreland Vocational/Technical Fund **Area, Field, or Subject:** Education, Vocational-technical. **Level of Education for which Award is Granted:** Undergraduate **Funds Available:** No specific amount. **Duration:** One year.
Eligibility Requirements: Applicants must be residents of Stark County, OH; must be graduating high school seniors; must be older students desiring vocational/technical training or retraining GED certificate; must intend to pursue vocational or technical education or training in a school or college within the State of Ohio; must demonstrate financial assistance. **Application Requirements:** Applicants must complete and submit the application form and requirements to Lt. Colonel Robert G. Moreland Scholarship, Stark Community Foundation, 400 Market Ave. N, Ste. 200, Canton, OH 44702-2107. **Deadline for Receipt:** April 10.

4270 ■ STARK COMMUNITY FOUNDATION
400 Market Ave. N, Ste. 200
Canton, OH 44702-2107
Tel: (330)454-3426
Fax: (330)454-5855
Web Site: http://www.starkcommunityfoundation.org
To provide scholarship assistance to qualified individuals who want to pursue their studies.
Title of Award: Mary Kean White Memorial Scholarship Fund **Area, Field, or Subject:** Education, Elementary. **Level of Education for which Award is Granted:** Undergraduate **Funds Available:** No specific amount. **Duration:** One year.
Eligibility Requirements: Applicants must be graduates of Malvern High School or Carrollton High School; must be currently enrolled as full time

students at an accredited college or university; must have cumulative GPA of at least 3.0 on a 4.0 scale; must be pursuing a career in elementary education or related field; must demonstrate financial need.
Application Requirements: Applicants must complete and submit the application form and requirements to Carrollton High School Guidance Office, Malvern High School Guidance Office. **Deadline for Receipt:** April 1.

4271 ■ STARK COMMUNITY FOUNDATION
400 Market Ave. N, Ste. 200
Canton, OH 44702-2107
Tel: (330)454-3426
Fax: (330)454-5855
Web Site: http://www.starkcommunityfoundation.org
To provide scholarship assistance to qualified individuals who want to pursue their studies.
Title of Award: Workshop, Inc. and Stark MRDD Fostering Diversity Through Special Needs Scholarship Fund **Area, Field, or Subject:** Special education. **Level of Education for which Award is Granted:** Undergraduate **Funds Available:** No specific amount. **Duration:** One year.
Eligibility Requirements: Applicants must be residents of Stark County; must have at least a 3.0 cumulative GPA; must be majoring in Special Education or related field; must be juniors or seniors at a college or university. **Application Requirements:** Applicants must submit a 500-word essay, which describes, "Why you chose to major in special education or related field", and an essay review. Application form and other supporting documents must be sent to The Workshops, Inc. 2950 Whipple Ave. NW, Canton, OH 44708. **Deadline for Receipt:** June 15. **Additional Information:** Leslie Thomas at the above address.

4272 ■ STRAIGHTFORWARD MEDIA
508 7th St., Ste 202
Rapid City, SD 57701
Tel: (605)348-3042
Fax: (605)348-3043
E-mail: info@straightforwardmedia.com
Web Site: http://www.straightforwardmedia.com
To financially assist students in their educational pursuits.
Title of Award: StraightForward Media's Teacher Scholarships **Area, Field, or Subject:** Teaching. **Level of Education for which Award is Granted:** Undergraduate **Funds Available:** $500.
Eligibility Requirements: Applicant must be a student planning to be a teacher. **Application Requirements:** Applicants must complete the Online Scholarship Application. **Additional Information:** Awards are given four times a year. **Deadline for Receipt:** January, April, July, October.

4273 ■ STRAIGHTFORWARD MEDIA
508 7th St., Ste 202
Rapid City, SD 57701
Tel: (605)348-3042
Fax: (605)348-3043
E-mail: info@straightforwardmedia.com
Web Site: http://www.straightforwardmedia.com
To financially assist students in their educational pursuits.
Title of Award: StraightForward Media's Vocational-Technical School Scholarships **Area, Field, or Subject:** Education, Vocational-technical. **Level of Education for which Award is Granted:** Undergraduate **Funds Available:** $500.
Eligibility Requirements: Applicants must be a students pursuing degrees, licenses or certificates at vocational schools. **Application Requirements:** Applicants must complete the Online Scholarship Application. **Additional Information:** Awards are given four times a year. **Deadline for Receipt:** November, February, May, August.

4274 ■ TECHNICAL WOMEN'S ORGANIZATION
6905 S 1300 E No. 124
Midvale, UT 84047
Tel: (405)954-3247
E-mail: Emily.M.Godinet@faa.gov
Web Site: http://www.technicalwomen.org
To encourage students to take every opportunity to participate in training and education that will enhance or advance careers.

Title of Award: TWO Scholarship Program **Area, Field, or Subject:** Technical Training. **Level of Education for which Award is Granted:** Undergraduate **Funds Available:** $500.
Eligibility Requirements: Applicants must be in a training program that will advance or enhance the individual's career in a technical area. **Application Requirements:** Applicants must check the available website for more information. **Deadline for Receipt:** May 15. **Additional Information:** Application Mailing Address: Brenda Smith-Keene P.O. Box 20802 Kansas City, MO 64195

4275 ■ TEXAS MUTUAL INSURANCE COMPANY
6210 E Hwy. 290
Austin, TX 78723-1098
Tel: (512)224-3800
Free: 800-583-5995
E-mail: information@texasmutual.com
Web Site: http://www.texasmutual.com
To provide financial support for the surviving family members of employees who died from an on-the-job accident, and/or whose injuries qualify for lifetime income benefits, to have the chance to pursue education and training to help them build better futures.
Title of Award: Texas Mutual Scholarship Program **Area, Field, or Subject:** Vocational-technical education. **Level of Education for which Award is Granted:** Undergraduate **Funds Available:** $4,000. **Duration:** One year.
Eligibility Requirements: Applicants must be unmarried surviving children of an individual who died as a result of a work-related injury or whose severe injuries qualify them for a lifetime income benefits (LIBs) under the Texas Worker's Compensation Act. **Application Requirements:** Applicants must complete the application form available at the website of Texas Mutual Insurance Company and submit along with the other materials needed to qualify for the scholarship.

4276 ■ THUNDER BAY COMMUNITY FOUNDATION
PO Box 20120
Thunder Bay, ON, Canada P7E 6P2
Tel: (807)475-7279
E-mail: tbcf@tbaytel.net
Web Site: http://www.tbcf.org
To provide scholarship assistance to qualified graduating students from the Bachelor of Education program at Lakehead University.
Title of Award: John Alexander McLean Scholarships **Area, Field, or Subject:** Education. **Level of Education for which Award is Granted:** Undergraduate **Funds Available:** No specific amount. **Duration:** One year.
Eligibility Requirements: Applicant must be in their final year before graduation from the Bachelor of Education program at Lakehead University; must be pursuing a career in education; must have a minimum overall average of 80% in all university credits. **Application Requirements:** Applicant must submit: completed application form (available online); three reference letters (one from a school source, one from extracurricular source, and one from the nominating committee/individual sponsoring their application for the scholarship); must submit all required documents to the Thunder Bay Community Foundation. **Deadline for Receipt:** April 15.

4277 ■ UNIVERSITY OF ALASKA ANCHORAGE
3211 Providence Dr.
Anchorage, AK 99508
Tel: (907)786-1800
Web Site: http://www.uaa.alaska.edu
To provide financial assistance for tuition and other related educational expenses to a University of Alaska Anchorage student who has a declared major in English.
Title of Award: Arlene Kuhner Memorial Scholarships **Area, Field, or Subject:** Education, English as a second language. **Level of Education for which Award is Granted:** Undergraduate **Funds Available:** No specific amount.
Eligibility Requirements: Applicant must demonstrate academic excellence; must be in good academic standing with at least a cumulative GPA of 3.0; must be a student attending the University of Alaska Anchorage with a declared major in English; must take a minimum of six credits per semester. **Application Requirements:** For further information about the

scholarship, applicants are advised to visit the website at www.uaa.alaska.edu/scholarships/arlene.cfm. **Deadline for Receipt:** February 15.

4278 ■ UNIVERSITY OF ALASKA ANCHORAGE
3211 Providence Dr.
Anchorage, AK 99508
Tel: (907)786-1800
Web Site: http://www.uaa.alaska.edu
To provide financial assistance to students at UAA who are studying to become teachers.
Title of Award: Lillian Smith Scholarship for Teaching Students **Area, Field, or Subject:** Education. **Level of Education for which Award is Granted:** Graduate, Undergraduate **Number Awarded:** 2. **Funds Available:** $500. **Duration:** One year.
Eligibility Requirements: Applicants must demonstrate motivation, academic and leadership potential; must be in good academic standing with a minimum cumulative GPA of 2.0 for undergraduate and 3.0 for graduate; must be a full-time student attending the UAA (12 credits for undergraduates, 9 credits for graduates); must be fully admitted to the Education degree program at the UAA; may be an incoming or continuing student at the University of Alaska Anchorage; may be a U.S. citizen, non-U.S. citizen, Alaskan resident, or out-of-state resident. **Application Requirements:** Applicants must complete the electronic scholarship application available online. **Deadline for Receipt:** February 15.

4279 ■ UNIVERSITY OF ALASKA ANCHORAGE
3211 Providence Dr.
Anchorage, AK 99508
Tel: (907)786-1800
Web Site: http://www.uaa.alaska.edu
To provide financial assistance for tuition and other educational expenses to students admitted to pre-service teacher education programs at UAA.
Title of Award: Sheri Stears Education Scholarships **Area, Field, or Subject:** Education. **Level of Education for which Award is Granted:** Undergraduate **Funds Available:** $500-$2,500. **Duration:** One year.
Eligibility Requirements: Applicants must be in good academic standing with a minimum cumulative GPA of 3.0; must be involved in extracurricular activities; must be formally admitted to the College of Education pursuing an undergraduate education degree or the Master of Arts in Teaching at the UAA; must plan on enrolling at least half-time (6 credits) at the UAA; may be an incoming or continuing student at the UAA; may be a U.S. citizen, non-U.S. citizen, Alaska resident, or out-of-state resident. **Application Requirements:** Applicants must submit an essay responding to these questions: (1) How do you see yourself further advancing education in Alaska?; (2) How do your extracurricular activities enhance your educational experience?; Applicants must complete the electronic scholarship application available online at www.uaa.alaska.edu/scholarships/sheri.cfm. **Deadline for Receipt:** February 15.

4280 ■ UNIVERSITY OF ALASKA ANCHORAGE
3211 Providence Dr.
Anchorage, AK 99508
Tel: (907)786-1800
Web Site: http://www.uaa.alaska.edu
To provide financial assistance for tuition and other educational expenses to full-time students who are formally admitted to a journalism, engineering, or education degree-seeking program at the University of Alaska Anchorage.
Title of Award: Sturgulewski Family Scholarships **Area, Field, or Subject:** Journalism; Engineering; Education. **Level of Education for which Award is Granted:** Graduate, Undergraduate **Funds Available:** $500.
Eligibility Requirements: Applicants must demonstrate motivation, academic and leadership potential; must be in good academic standing with a minimum cumulative GPA of 2.0 for undergraduates and 3.0 for graduates; must be formally admitted to a journalism, engineering, or education undergraduate, graduate, certificate, and/or vocational degree-seeking program at the University of Alaska Anchorage; must have plan on enrolling full-time (12 credits for undergraduates and 9 for graduates) at the University of Alaska Anchorage; may be an incoming or continuing student at the University of Alaska Anchorage; may be a U.S citizen, non-US citizen, Alaska resident, or out-of-state resident; must be enrolled in the semester for which the award is made. **Application Require-**

ments: Applicants must complete the electronic scholarship application available online at www.uaa.alaska.edu/scholarships/sturgulewski_family. cfm. **Deadline for Receipt:** February 15.

4281 ■ UNIVERSITY OF OREGON
1217 University of Oregon
Eugene, OR 97403
Tel: (541)346-1000
Free: 800-232-3825
Fax: (541)346-5815
E-mail: stl@uoregon.edu
Web Site: http://www.uoregon.edu
To provide financial support to students who desire to further their education without financial burden.
Title of Award: Robert W. and Bernice Ingalls Staton Scholarships **Area, Field, or Subject:** Humanities; Fine arts; Education; Music. **Level of Education for which Award is Granted:** Undergraduate **Funds Available:** $5,000. **Duration:** One year.
Eligibility Requirements: Applicants must be Oregon residents and must have an extraordinary financial need. **Application Requirements:** Applicants must submit the Admission application available online to the Office of Admission. **Deadline for Receipt:** January 15.

4282 ■ UNIVERSITY OF WISCONSIN-MADISON
432 N Murray St.
Madison, WI 53706-1496
Tel: (608)262-3060
Fax: (608)262-9068
E-mail: askbucky@uwmad.wisc.edu
Web Site: http://www.wisc.edu
To support UW-Madison students in their education.
Title of Award: Mary Ann Brichta Scholarships **Area, Field, or Subject:** Education, Secondary. **Level of Education for which Award is Granted:** Undergraduate **Number Awarded:** Varies. **Funds Available:** No specific amount.
Eligibility Requirements: Applicants must be UW-Madison sophomore, junior, or senior underrepresented students of color majoring in elementary or secondary education. **Application Requirements:** Scholarship applications are available from the Office of the Dean. **Deadline for Receipt:** February.

4283 ■ UNIVERSITY OF WISCONSIN-MADISON
432 N Murray St.
Madison, WI 53706-1496
Tel: (608)262-3060
Fax: (608)262-9068
E-mail: askbucky@uwmad.wisc.edu
Web Site: http://www.wisc.edu
To support UW-Madison students in their education.
Title of Award: Patricia Buchanan Memorial Scholarships **Area, Field, or Subject:** Education, Secondary. **Level of Education for which Award is Granted:** Undergraduate **Number Awarded:** Varies. **Funds Available:** No specific amount.
Eligibility Requirements: Applicants must be UW-Madison sophomore, junior, or senior underrepresented students of color majoring in elementary or secondary education. **Application Requirements:** Scholarship applications are available from the Office of the Dean. **Deadline for Receipt:** February.

4284 ■ UNIVERSITY OF WISCONSIN-MADISON
432 N Murray St.
Madison, WI 53706-1496
Tel: (608)262-3060
Fax: (608)262-9068
E-mail: askbucky@uwmad.wisc.edu
Web Site: http://www.wisc.edu
To support UW-Madison students in their education.
Title of Award: George Koeppel and Roland W. Zinns Scholarships **Area, Field, or Subject:** Education, Secondary. **Level of Education for which Award is Granted:** Undergraduate **Number Awarded:** Varies. **Funds Available:** No specific amount.
Eligibility Requirements: Applicant must be UW-Madison freshmen students; must be Wisconsin residents with permanent home address in

Milwaukee County. **Application Requirements:** Scholarship applications are available from the Office of the Dean. **Deadline for Receipt:** February.

4285 ■ UNIVERSITY OF WISCONSIN-MADISON
432 N Murray St.
Madison, WI 53706-1496
Tel: (608)262-3060
Fax: (608)262-9068
E-mail: askbucky@uwmad.wisc.edu
Web Site: http://www.wisc.edu
To support UW-Madison students in their education.
Title of Award: John P. and Tashia F. Morgridge Scholarships **Area, Field, or Subject:** Education, Secondary. **Level of Education for which Award is Granted:** Undergraduate **Number Awarded:** 6. **Funds Available:** Varies.
Eligibility Requirements: Applicants must be UW-Madison sophomores, juniors, or seniors who are underrepresented students of color. Applicants must be preparing for a teaching career, preferably at the elementary level. **Application Requirements:** Scholarship applications are available from the Office of the Dean. **Deadline for Receipt:** February. **Additional Information:** School of Education, Office of the Dean, at 608-262-6137, or soeinfo@education.wisc.edu.

4286 ■ UNIVERSITY OF WISCONSIN-MADISON
432 N Murray St.
Madison, WI 53706-1496
Tel: (608)262-3060
Fax: (608)262-9068
E-mail: askbucky@uwmad.wisc.edu
Web Site: http://www.wisc.edu
To support UW-Madison students in their education.
Title of Award: Pi Lambda Theta Scholarships **Area, Field, or Subject:** Education. **Level of Education for which Award is Granted:** Undergraduate **Number Awarded:** 2. **Funds Available:** Varies.
Eligibility Requirements: Applicants must be UW-Madison junior students having the highest GPA in the School of Education; and must have completed at least one full semester (12 credits). **Application Requirements:** Scholarship applications are available from the Office of the Dean. **Deadline for Receipt:** February. **Additional Information:** School of Education, Office of the Dean, at 608-262-6137, soeinfo@education.wisc.edu.

4287 ■ UNIVERSITY OF WISCONSIN-MADISON
432 N Murray St.
Madison, WI 53706-1496
Tel: (608)262-3060
Fax: (608)262-9068
E-mail: askbucky@uwmad.wisc.edu
Web Site: http://www.wisc.edu
To support UW-Madison students in their education.
Title of Award: School of Education Scholarships for Students from Underrepresented Groups **Area, Field, or Subject:** Education. **Level of Education for which Award is Granted:** Undergraduate **Number Awarded:** Varies. **Funds Available:** Varies.
Eligibility Requirements: Applicants must be UW-Madison underrepresented students of color with demonstrated financial need majoring in Education. **Application Requirements:** Scholarship applications are available from the Office of the Dean. **Additional Information:** School of Education, Office of the Dean, at 608-262-6137, soeinfo@education.wisc.edu.

4288 ■ UNIVERSITY OF WISCONSIN-MADISON
432 N Murray St.
Madison, WI 53706-1496
Tel: (608)262-3060
Fax: (608)262-9068
E-mail: askbucky@uwmad.wisc.edu
Web Site: http://www.wisc.edu
To support UW-Madison students in their education.
Title of Award: University of Wisconsin-Madison Minority Teacher Loans **Area, Field, or Subject:** Education, Secondary. **Level of Education for which Award is Granted:** Professional, Undergraduate **Number Awarded:** Varies. **Funds Available:** $250-$3000.

Eligibility Requirements: Applicants must be UW-Madison juniors or seniors from underrepresented groups enrolled full-time in a teacher preparation program; must be Wisconsin residents planning to teach in selected school districts in Wisconsin; or degree-holders enrolled in a teacher certification program. **Application Requirements:** Scholarship applications are available from the Office of the Dean. **Additional Information:** 25 percent of the loan is forgiven for each year the recipient teaches in the selected school district. Teaching for 4 years eliminates 100 percent of the debt. Recipients who do not teach in selected districts must repay the loan at an interest rate of 5 percent. **Deadline for Receipt:** Varies.

4289 ■ WASHINGTON HIGHER EDUCATION COORDINATING BOARD
PO Box 43430
Olympia, WA 98504-3430
Tel: (360)753-7800
E-mail: info@hecb.wa.gov
Web Site: http://www.hecb.wa.gov
To encourage outstanding students and paraprofessionals to become teachers, and to encourage current teachers to obtain additional endorsements in teacher shortage subjects.
Title of Award: Future Teachers Conditional Scholarships and Loan Repayment **Area, Field, or Subject:** Teaching. **Level of Education for which Award is Granted:** Professional, Undergraduate **Funds Available:** Varies.
Eligibility Requirements: Applicant must be a resident student of Washington state; planning to complete an approved program leading to a residency teacher certificate or an additional shortage subject endorsement; planning to be employed as a certificated classroom teacher in Washington K-12 public schools; planning to attend an eligible college at least half-time; and not pursuing or planning to pursue a degree in theology. **Application Requirements:** Applicants must contact the Future Teachers Conditional Scholarship and Loan Repayment Program in order to apply. **Additional Information:** In return for conditional scholarships or loan repayments, participants agree to teach in Washington K-12 public schools.

4290 ■ WINSTON-SALEM FOUNDATION
860 W Fifth St.
Winston-Salem, NC 27101-2506
Tel: (336)725-2382
Fax: (336)727-0581
E-mail: info@wsfoundation.org
Web Site: http://www.wsfoundation.org
To provide a consecutive four-year renewable award to a graduating high school senior form a Forsyth County high school who will pursue post-secondary education.
Title of Award: Art and Dannie Weber Scholarships **Area, Field, or Subject:** General studies. **Level of Education for which Award is Granted:** Undergraduate **Funds Available:** $750. **Duration:** One year.
Eligibility Requirements: Applicants must: have demonstrated character and purpose as evidenced in school, community, church, and work activities; have financial need (however, the scholarship is not restricted to lower family incomes); demonstrate academic success by having achieved minimum, unweighted high school cumulative grade point average (GPA) between 2.5-3.5. **Application Requirements:** Students who are interested in applying for this scholarship should complete the application in its entirety and submit it by the deadline. In addition, the following supplemental items must be submitted: a grade transcript through the first semester of the 12th grade; family federal tax return for last year (deadline April 15); one recommendation from a teacher, guidance counselor, coach, principal, employer, clergy, or other community leader who has supervised, counseled or coached applicant in some capacity. **Deadline for Receipt:** March 31. **Additional Information:** WSF Student Aid Department, 336-714-3445.

4291 ■ WINSTON-SALEM FOUNDATION
860 W Fifth St.
Winston-Salem, NC 27101-2506
Tel: (336)725-2382
Fax: (336)727-0581
E-mail: info@wsfoundation.org

Web Site: http://www.wsfoundation.org
To provide scholarships to Forsyth County graduating seniors who will pursue post-secondary education at accredited institutions.
Title of Award: Winston-Salem Foundation Scholarships **Area, Field, or Subject:** General studies. **Level of Education for which Award is Granted:** Undergraduate **Funds Available:** No specific amount.
Eligibility Requirements: Applicants must have a minimum, cumulative, unweighted GPA of 2.5 to 3.0; a challenging course selection; must demonstrate leadership, school service, and community involvement; must demonstrate financial need (award is not restricted to lower family incomes). **Application Requirements:** Scholarship application will be available online. Students must: complete the scholarship application in its entirely; provide grade transcript through the 1st semester of the 12th grade. **Deadline for Receipt:** March 31. **Additional Information:** WSF Student Aid Department, 336-714-3445.

4292 ■ ZETA PHI BETA SORORITY
1734 New Hampshire Ave. NW
Washington, DC 20009
Tel: (202)387-3103
Fax: (202)232-4593
E-mail: ihq@zphib1920.org
Web Site: http://www.zphib1920.org
To support students in pursuit of higher education.
Title of Award: Isabel M. Herson Scholarships in Education **Area, Field, or Subject:** Education, Elementary; Education--Curricula. **Level of Education for which Award is Granted:** Graduate, Undergraduate **Number Awarded:** 1. **Funds Available:** $500-$1000. **Duration:** One academic year.
Eligibility Requirements: Applicant must be in graduate or undergraduate level student enrolled full-time in a degree program in either elementary or secondary education. **Application Requirements:** Applicants must submit completed application forms along with the required materials. **Deadline for Receipt:** February 1.

History

4293 ■ AMERICAN DIVISION VETERANS ASSOCIATION
3839 Ols Savannah Dr.
Kalamazoo, MI 49009
Tel: (269)372-2129
E-mail: c146thinf@aol.com
Web Site: http://www.americal.org
To provide college and vocational scholarships to the children and grandchildren, including those by adoption, of current and deceased ADVA members, provided the deceased member held good membership standing at the time of death, and to any child or adopted child of an American Division soldier who was killed or died while on active duty with the division.
Title of Award: American Division Veterans Association Scholarships **Area, Field, or Subject:** History, Military. **Level of Education for which Award is Granted:** Undergraduate **Funds Available:** No specific amount.
Eligibility Requirements: An applicant must be a high school graduate and planning to attend college. **Application Requirements:** Applicant must submit a letter from the sponsor attesting to the applicant's eligibility according to ADVA Scholarship Fund Purpose and By-Laws; a letter of admission from the applicant's college or vocational school of choice; a letter from the applicant's high school principal attesting to the applicant's character if applicant is attending or has graduated from high school; two letters of recommendation from current teachers concerning the applicant's progress in current classes or subjects; a photocopy of the applicant's high school or college transcript; a detailed statement of the applicant's academic accomplishments, extracurricular activities, and community service involvement; an applicant must submit a 200-300 word essay on subjects pertaining to American Division history, national pride, loyalty to the nation, and patriotism. **Additional Information:** Mr. Bob Short 3839 Old Savannah Drive Kalamazoo MI 49009; 269-372-2192; c146thinf@aol.com

4294 ■ AMERICAN INSTITUTE OF POLISH CULTURE
1440 79th St. Causeway, Ste. 117
Miami, FL 33141

Tel: (305)864-2349
Fax: (305)865-5150
E-mail: info@ampolinstitute.org
Web Site: http://www.ampolinstitute.org
To provide financial support American students of Polish descent who wish to continue their education after high school.

Title of Award: Harriet Irsay Scholarships **Area, Field, or Subject:** Communications; Education; Media arts; History; International affairs and relations; Journalism; Liberal arts; Polish studies; Public relations. **Level of Education for which Award is Granted:** Graduate, Undergraduate **Number Awarded:** 10-15. **Funds Available:** $1,000.

Eligibility Requirements: Applicants must be of Polish heritage; an American citizen or permanent resident; full-time graduate or undergraduate students in the field of communication, education, film, history, International Relation, journalism, liberal arts, polish studies, public relations; or graduate student in business programs with a thesis related to Poland, or graduate students with a thesis with Polish subject. **Application Requirements:** Applicants must submit a completed application form; school transcripts; resume; essay (200-400 words) about "Why should I receive the scholarship"; an article about Poland (maximum of 700 words); and 3 signed recommendation letters on a letterhead stationary from teachers or other person knowledgeable about the applicant's academic background. A non-refundable $10 processing fee (check or money order) must also be included. **Deadline for Receipt:** April 20.

4295 ■ ARMENIAN RELIEF SOCIETY - EASTERN UNITED STATES
80 Bigelow Avenue, Ste. 200
Watertown, MA 02472
Tel: (617)926-3801
Fax: (617)924-7238
E-mail: arseastus@aol.com
Web Site: http://www.arseastus.com
To encourage educational pursuits among undergraduate students of Armenian descent.

Title of Award: ARS Undergraduate Scholarships **Area, Field, or Subject:** Law; History; Political science; Journalism; Government; Economics; Business administration; Medicine; Public service. **Level of Education for which Award is Granted:** Four Year College, Two Year College, Undergraduate **Funds Available:** No specific amount. **Duration:** One year.

Eligibility Requirements: Applicants must be of Armenian descent; must be undergraduate students who have completed at least one semester at an accredited four-year college or university in the United States or must be enrolled in a two-year college and are transferring to a four-year college or university as a full-time student in the Fall. **Application Requirements:** Application must include financial aid forms, recent official transcript, two letters of recommendation and tuition costs. Forward materials to: Scholarship Committee, Armenian Relief Society of Eastern USA, Inc., 80 Bigelow Ave., Ste. 200, Watertown, MA 02472. **Deadline for Receipt:** April 1.

4296 ■ COASTAL BEND COMMUNITY FOUNDATION
600 Leopard St., Ste. 1716
Corpus Christi, TX 78473
Tel: (361)882-9745
Fax: (361)882-2865
Web Site: http://www.cbcfoundation.org
To provide financial assistance to high school seniors or graduates of a Coastal Bend high school in furthering their college education.

Title of Award: Cecil E. Burney Scholarships **Area, Field, or Subject:** Liberal arts; History; Political science; Music; Education. **Level of Education for which Award is Granted:** High School, Undergraduate **Funds Available:** $2,000.

Eligibility Requirements: Applicants must be high school seniors or graduates of a Coastal Bend high school pursuing a liberal arts degree majoring in history, political science, music or education; have a high school GPA of 90 percent or higher; maintain a college 3.0 GPA or higher and at least 12 hours per semester. **Application Requirements:** Applicants must submit all the required application information. **Deadline for Receipt:** March 14.

4297 ■ COMMUNITY FOUNDATION FOR SOUTHEAST MICHIGAN
333 West Fort St., Ste. 2010
Detroit, MI 48226-3134

Tel: (313)961-6675
Fax: (313)961-2886
E-mail: cfsem@cfsem.org
Web Site: http://www.cfsem.org
To provide financial assistance to graduating seniors from North Farmington High School who demonstrate leadership, good grades and male varsity athlete who will enter college majoring liberal studies, especially History and English.

Title of Award: Dick Depaolis Memorial Scholarships **Area, Field, or Subject:** History; English language and literature. **Level of Education for which Award is Granted:** Undergraduate **Funds Available:** $500.

Eligibility Requirements: Applicants must be members of the graduating class at North Farmington High School; must demonstrate exemplary desire, ability and have a GPA of 3.0 or higher; must be male athletes demonstrating leadership, academic discipline and good sportsmanship on and off the field; must be playing varsity sports (football preferred); have applied or been accepted as full-time students in an accredited educational institution in the United States with a major in liberal studies, especially History and English. **Application Requirements:** Applicants must use a computer, typewriter or print neatly in blue or black ink in completing the application form. **Deadline for Receipt:** April 2.

4298 ■ DEATH VALLEY '49ERS
10 Paseo de Pino
Rancho Palos Verdes, CA 90275-6383
Tel: (310)544-1207
Fax: (310)544-2178
E-mail: lcbaker@cox.net
Web Site: http://www.deathvalley49ers.org
To assist high school graduates living in the Death Valley Unified School District.

Title of Award: Death Valley '49ers Scholarships **Area, Field, or Subject:** Historic preservation. **Level of Education for which Award is Granted:** Undergraduate **Funds Available:** $4,000. **Duration:** Two semesters.

Eligibility Requirements: Applicants must be residents of the Death Valley Unified School District and/or Death Valley National Park for a minimum of two years and/or parent(s) are employed within the boundaries of Death Valley National Park and/or attended Death Valley Elementary School for a minimum of two years. Completes all the required subjects for high school graduation in their junior and senior academic years at Beatty, Pahrump, or Shoshone High Schools. **Application Requirements:** Applicants must submit a Death Valley '49ers Scholarship Application to the Scholarship Committee by the application deadline in the senior year of high school. **Deadline for Receipt:** March.

4299 ■ DELTA ZETA SORORITY
202 E Church St.
Oxford, OH 45056
Tel: (513)523-7597
Web Site: http://www.deltazeta.org
To provide financial assistance to all qualified undergraduate students.

Title of Award: Betsy B. and Garold A. Leach Scholarship for Museum Studies **Area, Field, or Subject:** Museum science. **Level of Education for which Award is Granted:** Undergraduate **Funds Available:** $1,000-$2,500. **Duration:** One academic year.

Eligibility Requirements: Applicant must be an initiated, continuing member of Delta Zeta pursuing a course of study that could lead to a career in museum work; must be entering his/her junior or senior year or graduate level; must have a financial need and have at least 3.0 average. **Application Requirements:** Scholarship applications are available on the website and must be completed properly. Applicant must have the FAFSA reply form. **Deadline for Receipt:** February 15.

4300 ■ NATIONAL ALLIANCE OF PRESERVATION COMMISSION
PO Box 1605
Athens, GA 30603
Tel: (706)542-4731
Fax: (706)583-0320
E-mail: napc@uga.edu
Web Site: http://www.sed.uga.edu
To provide financial assistance for graduating students in historic preservation.

Title of Award: National Alliance of Preservation Commission Student Scholarships **Area, Field, or Subject:** Historic Preservation. **Level of Education for which Award is Granted:** Undergraduate **Funds Available:** No specific amount.
Eligibility Requirements: Applicants must be a graduate student in historic preservation or related fields to participate in the National Commission Forum. **Application Requirements:** Applicants must submit a cover letter with name and contact information; a 500-word statement explaining interest and expectations in attending the Forum; an estimate of the Forum expenses and the anticipated financial contribution. Applicants must also submit a proof of current student status; current resume including two academic and/or professional references. **Deadline for Receipt:** May 5. **Additional Information:** NAPC Forum Scholarship, PO Box 1605, Athens, GA 30603; napc@uga.edu.

4301 ■ NATIONAL FEDERATION OF THE BLIND
1800 Johnson St.
Baltimore, MD 21230
Tel: (410)659-9314
Fax: (410)685-5653
Web Site: http://www.nfb.org
To recognize achievement of blind scholars and to create opportunity for all blind people.
Title of Award: Michael Marucci Memorial Scholarships **Area, Field, or Subject:** History; Geography; Political science. **Level of Education for which Award is Granted:** Undergraduate **Funds Available:** $5,000.
Eligibility Requirements: Applicants must be legally blind; he/she must be pursuing or planning a career in history, geography, or political science with a concentration in international studies or study requiring study abroad; he/she must be participant in NFB national convention and in all scheduled scholarship program activities. **Application Requirements:** Applicant must fill out the application form; he/she must submit two letters of recommendation from individuals that can describe the academic ability, leadership skills, and/or community involvement; copies of transcript of record and a photocopy of score reports for all standardized tests taken for college admission(ACT, SAT or other); applicant must provide a letter of proof of legal blindness from a qualified professional; and an affiliate President's letter. **Deadline for Receipt:** March 31.

4302 ■ NATIONAL SOCIETY, DAUGHTERS OF THE AMERICAN REVOLUTION
1776 D St. NW
Washington, DC 20006-5303
Tel: (202)628-1776
Web Site: http://www.dar.org
To provide financial assistance to individuals who wish to pursue their degrees.
Title of Award: J.E. Caldwell Centennial Scholarships **Area, Field, or Subject:** Historic preservation. **Level of Education for which Award is Granted:** Undergraduate **Funds Available:** $2,000. **Duration:** One year.
Eligibility Requirements: Applicants must be students who plan to pursue their course of graduate study in the field of historic preservation. **Application Requirements:** Applicants must obtain a letter of sponsorship from their local DAR chapter. Application forms and other supporting documents must be completed correctly and submitted in one package. **Deadline for Receipt:** February 15.

4303 ■ NATIONAL SOCIETY, DAUGHTERS OF THE AMERICAN REVOLUTION
1776 D St. NW
Washington, DC 20006-5303
Tel: (202)628-1776
Web Site: http://www.dar.org
To encourage students to pursue an undergraduate degree.
Title of Award: Enid Hall Griswold Memorial Scholarships **Area, Field, or Subject:** Political science; History; Government; Economics. **Level of Education for which Award is Granted:** Undergraduate **Funds Available:** $1,000. **Duration:** One year.
Eligibility Requirements: Applicants must be juniors or seniors enrolled in an accredited college or university in the United States; pursuing a major in political science, history, government, or economics. **Application Requirements:** Applicants must obtain a letter of sponsorship from their local DAR chapter. Application forms and other supporting documents

must be completed correctly and submitted in one package. **Deadline for Receipt:** February 15.

4304 ■ PARKERSBURG AREA COMMUNITY FOUNDATION
501 Avery St.
Parkersburg, WV 26101
Tel: (304)428-4438; (866)428-4438
Fax: (304)428-1200
E-mail: info@pacfwv.com
Web Site: http://www.pacfwv.com
To encourage graduating students to pursue their education.
Title of Award: Everett Oscar Shimp Memorial Scholarships **Area, Field, or Subject:** Agriculture, Economic aspects; History. **Level of Education for which Award is Granted:** Undergraduate **Funds Available:** $500-$1,000.
Eligibility Requirements: Applicant must be a graduate of Jackson or Roane County high schools who is currently enrolled full-time and has completed college credits equivalent to junior or senior status; must have a minimum of 3.0 college GPA; and must be majoring in agriculture or history or pursuing an education degree majoring in agriculture or history. **Application Requirements:** Applicants must submit a cover sheet (3 pages) and application form (4 pages); a personal essay; a high school and/or post-secondary transcript; a letter of recommendation; a signed copy of the page of their or their parent's most recent tax return that indicates adjusted gross income; and a Student Aid Report showing estimated family contribution from FAFSA. Application form and other supporting documents must be sent to Our Community's Foundation, P.O Box 1762, Parkersburg, WV 26102. **Deadline for Receipt:** March 20.

4305 ■ REDLANDS COMMUNITY SCHOLARSHIP FOUNDATION
c/o Kathleen Venegas-Boge, Admin. Asst.
PO Box 1683
Redlands, CA 92373
Tel: (909)307-9892
Fax: (909)307-9892
Web Site: http://www.redlandsscholarships.org
To encourage educational pursuits among Redlands Unified School District graduates by providing educational assistance.
Title of Award: Charles and Ruth Ronin Memorial Scholarships **Area, Field, or Subject:** Political science; History; Education. **Level of Education for which Award is Granted:** Undergraduate **Number Awarded:** 1. **Funds Available:** $1,000.
Eligibility Requirements: Applicant must be a graduating senior with a 3.5 or higher GPA who will attend a four-year college/university on a full-time basis in pursuit of a bachelor's degree in political science, history, or education. **Application Requirements:** Applicants must submit a completed application form together with the scantron sheet; cover sheet; student activity and community activity sheets; personal essay; and a copy of unofficial transcript (signed by the counselor). **Additional Information:** No electronic submissions of application will be accepted. Submit two printed copies of the application and use a No. 2 pencil on the scantron sheet. **Deadline for Receipt:** February 20.

4306 ■ STARK COMMUNITY FOUNDATION
400 Market Ave. N, Ste. 200
Canton, OH 44702-2107
Tel: (330)454-3426
Fax: (330)454-5855
Web Site: http://www.starkcommunityfoundation.org
To provide scholarship assistance to qualified individuals who want to pursue their studies.
Title of Award: Margaret S. Gilbert Scholarship Fund **Area, Field, or Subject:** Natural sciences; Mathematics and mathematical sciences; History. **Level of Education for which Award is Granted:** Undergraduate **Number Awarded:** 2. **Funds Available:** $37,000. **Duration:** One year.
Eligibility Requirements: Applicants must be Stark County public high school female graduates who attend or will attend Oberlin College; must have a major in one of the natural sciences, mathematics, or history; must have extracurricular activities, especially those demonstrating interest in science; must demonstrate diligent effort, responsibility and financial need. **Application Requirements:** Applicants must have academic record; must submit the application form and requirements at 400 Market Ave. N, Ste. 200, Canton, OH 44702. **Deadline for Receipt:** May 1.

4307 ■ STARK COMMUNITY FOUNDATION

400 Market Ave. N, Ste. 200
Canton, OH 44702-2107
Tel: (330)454-3426
Fax: (330)454-5855
Web Site: http://www.starkcommunityfoundation.org
To provide scholarship assistance to qualified individuals who want to pursue their studies.
Title of Award: Velma Shotwell Griffin Memorial Scholarship Fund **Area, Field, or Subject:** History; Writing; Music. **Level of Education for which Award is Granted:** Undergraduate **Number Awarded:** 1. **Funds Available:** $1,000. **Duration:** One year.
Eligibility Requirements: Applicants must be graduates of Conotton Valley High School or Carrollton High School; must be planning to enroll, or currently enrolled, at an accredited college or university to pursue further education in the following fields: (1) History; (2) Writing, not limited to, English Journalism, Language Arts, Communications and programs in Mass Media; (3) Music, not limited to vocal music, instrumental music, music history, music education, and music performance; (4) Any other program or field of study approved by the selection committee. **Application Requirements:** Applicants must submit completed application form and are advised to contact Carrollton High School Guidance Office, Connotton Valley High School Guidance Office. **Deadline for Receipt:** April 28.

4308 ■ TOURO SYNAGOGUE FOUNDATION

85 Touro St.
Newport, RI 02840
Tel: (401)847-4794
Fax: (401)845-8790
E-mail: info@tourosynagogue.org
Web Site: http://www.tourosynagogue.org
To educate future generations.
Title of Award: The Aaron and Rita Slom Scholarships **Area, Field, or Subject:** Historical preservation. **Level of Education for which Award is Granted:** Undergraduate **Funds Available:** $500.
Eligibility Requirements: Applicants must be a high school graduating students. **Application Requirements:** Students must submit an interpretative work (i.e. written submission, audio visual, documentary, film, Powerpoint...) focusing on the George Washington letter in context with the present time. Written submissions such as essays, stories, poems (no less than 500 words and no more than 1000 words), or audiovisual submissions such as documentaries, films or computer presentations (no more than 10 minutes) will be considered. **Deadline for Receipt:** April 4. **Additional Information:** Touro Synagogue Foundation at the above address.

4309 ■ UNIVERSITY OF ALASKA ANCHORAGE

3211 Providence Dr.
Anchorage, AK 99508
Tel: (907)786-1800
Web Site: http://www.uaa.alaska.edu
To provide financial assistance for tuition and other educational expenses to students who are formally admitted to a political science or history degree-seeking program or who are members of the Forty-Ninth State Fellows Program at the University of Alaska Anchorage.
Title of Award: UAA Governor William A. Egan Scholarships **Area, Field, or Subject:** Political science; History. **Level of Education for which Award is Granted:** Undergraduate **Funds Available:** $560. **Duration:** One year.
Eligibility Requirements: Applicant must demonstrate motivation, academic and leadership potential; must demonstrate a commitment to their community; must be in good academic standing with a minimum cumulative GPA of 2.0; must be formally admitted to a political science or history degreeseeking program at the University of Alaska Anchorage; must plan on enrolling full-time (12 credits) at the University of Alaska Anchorage; may be an incoming or continuing student at the University of Alaska Anchorage; may be a U.S citizen, non-U.S citizen, Alaska resident, out-of-state resident; must be enrolled in the semester for which the award is made. **Application Requirements:** Applicants must complete the electronic scholarship application available online at www.uaa.alaska.edu/scholarships/egan.cfm. **Deadline for Receipt:** February 15.

4310 ■ WOMEN IN DEFENSE

2111 Wilson Blvd., Ste. 400
Arlington, VA 22201-3061
Tel: (703)247-2552
Fax: (703)522-1885
E-mail: wid@ndia.org
Web Site: http://wid.ndia.org
To provide financial assistance to further educational objectives of women either employed or planning careers in defense or national security areas.
Title of Award: Women In Defense HORIZONS Scholarships **Area, Field, or Subject:** National security; Military history; Government; Engineering; Computer and information sciences; Physics; Mathematics and mathematical sciences; Business; Law; International affairs and relations; Political science; Economics. **Level of Education for which Award is Granted:** Graduate, Undergraduate **Funds Available:** No specific amount.
Eligibility Requirements: Applicant must be currently enrolled at an accredited university/college, either full-time or part-time; must have junior, senior or graduate status; demonstrate interest in pursuing a career related to national security or defense; demonstrate financial need; have a minimum GPA of 3.25. Applicant must be a female citizen of the United States. **Application Requirements:** Applicants must submit a completed scholarship application form with the essays, recommendations, and transcripts. **Additional Information:** Established in 1988. **Deadline for Receipt:** July 1.

4311 ■ XAVIER UNIVERSITY

3800 Victory Pky.
Cincinnati, OH 45207
Tel: (513)745-3000
Free: 800-344-GOXU
Web Site: http://www.xavier.edu
To financially support students with their education.
Title of Award: Xavier University Departmental Scholarships **Area, Field, or Subject:** Chemistry; Classical studies; History; Mathematics and mathematical sciences; Modern languages; Physics. **Level of Education for which Award is Granted:** Undergraduate **Funds Available:** $2500.
Eligibility Requirements: Applicant must top the score in either of the six departmental exams (chemistry, classics (Latin), history, mathematics, modern languages (French, German or Spanish) and physics). Student must major in the area for which the scholarship is awarded. **Application Requirements:** Participants will take an exam in the appropriate subject area and have an opportunity to speak with faculty and learn more about the department.

International Affairs

4312 ■ AMERICAN INSTITUTE OF POLISH CULTURE

1440 79th St. Causeway, Ste. 117
Miami, FL 33141
Tel: (305)864-2349
Fax: (305)865-5150
E-mail: info@ampolinstitute.org
Web Site: http://www.ampolinstitute.org
To provide financial support American students of Polish descent who wish to continue their education after high school.
Title of Award: Harriet Irsay Scholarships **Area, Field, or Subject:** Communications; Education; Media arts; History; International affairs and relations; Journalism; Liberal arts; Polish studies; Public relations. **Level of Education for which Award is Granted:** Graduate, Undergraduate **Number Awarded:** 10-15. **Funds Available:** $1,000.
Eligibility Requirements: Applicants must be of Polish heritage; an American citizen or permanent resident; full-time graduate or undergraduate students in the field of communication, education, film, history, International Relation, journalism, liberal arts, polish studies, public relations; or graduate student in business programs with a thesis related to Poland, or graduate students with a thesis with Polish subject. **Application Requirements:** Applicants must submit a completed application form; school transcripts; resume; essay (200-400 words) about "Why should I receive the scholarship"; an article about Poland (maximum of 700 words); and 3 signed recommendation letters on a letterhead stationary from teachers or other person knowledgeable about the applicant's

academic background. A non-refundable $10 processing fee (check or money order) must also be included. **Deadline for Receipt:** April 20.

4313 ■ ASHBURN INSTITUTE
444 North West Capitol St., NW
PO Box 77164
Washington, DC 20013-7164
Tel: (703)728-6482
Fax: (703)753-1910
E-mail: info@ashburninstutute.org
Web Site: http://www.ashburninstitute.org
To support the study of international integration and federalism at the graduate level.
Title of Award: Mayme and Herb Frank Scholarship Program **Area, Field, or Subject:** International affairs and relations. **Level of Education for which Award is Granted:** Graduate, Undergraduate **Funds Available:** $500-$2,000 depending on relevance of the goals of the fund.
Eligibility Requirements: Applicant must be a graduate student of strong academic standing; must have a thesis or dissertation relating to international integration and/or federalism and coursework that places major weight on international and/or federalism or must have an independent study project relating to international integration and federalism to be conducted as part of a graduate program. **Application Requirements:** Applicant must complete the FEF Application form and must have the description of any course planned to be completed by the applicant during the period of the proposed grant; must submit the copy of the graduate transcript if currently enrolled in a graduate program, or a copy of the applicant's undergraduate transcript if enrolled in a graduate program but ha not yet started it. Application form and other supporting materials must be submitted to: Association to Unite the Democracies c/o The Ashburn Institute, The Frank Educational Fund, PO Box 77164, Washington, DC, 200137164. **Deadline for Receipt:** April 1 for Fall term awards and October 1 for Spring term awards.

4314 ■ BETA THETA PI
PO Box 6277
Oxford, OH 45056
Tel: (513)523-7591
Free: 800-800-BETA
E-mail: beta@betathetapi.org
Web Site: http://www.betathetapi.org
To financially assist students in their pursuit of academic achievement.
Title of Award: Burton L. Gerber Scholarships **Area, Field, or Subject:** Military science and education; International affairs and relations. **Level of Education for which Award is Granted:** Graduate, Undergraduate **Number Awarded:** 1. **Funds Available:** $1025. **Duration:** One academic year.
Eligibility Requirements: Applicant must be undergraduate or graduate student; a member of Beta Theta Pi enrolled as full-time student; and a senior pursuing a career in military or international affairs. Previous recipients are not qualified. **Application Requirements:** Applicants must submit a completed standard application form along with transcript of grades and a passport type photo (head and shoulders, wallet size, in coat and tie). **Deadline for Receipt:** April 1.

4315 ■ FIRST COMMUNITY FOUNDATION OF PENNSYLVANIA, WILLIAMSPORT-LYCOMING
330 Pine St., Suite 401
Williamsport, PA 17701
Tel: (570)321-1500; (866)901-2372
Fax: (570)321-6434
E-mail: fcfpa@fcfpa.org
Web Site: http://www.wlfoundation.org
To provide financial assistance for Lycoming County high school seniors who have demonstrated an interest in furthering their education in international studies.
Title of Award: ISCALC International Scholarship Fund **Area, Field, or Subject:** International affairs and relations; Foreign languages. **Level of Education for which Award is Granted:** Undergraduate **Number Awarded:** 2-4. **Funds Available:** $250-$400.
Eligibility Requirements: Applicant must be a high school senior within Lycoming county who will be attending an accredited institution of higher education and who plans to pursue major coursework in the area of

international studies, including but not limited to international affairs, foreign languages, overseas exchange programs, multicultural studies, and related areas. **Application Requirements:** Candidates must complete the application and submit it along with any requested additional information to the Williamsport-Lycoming Community Foundation. **Additional Information:** Candy Bower, Manager of Program and Scholarship Services, candyb@fcfpa.org.

4316 ■ NATIONAL IRANIAN AMERICAN COUNCIL
1411 K St. NW, Ste. 600
Washington, DC 20005
Tel: (202)386-6325
Fax: (202)386-6409
Web Site: http://www.niacouncil.org
To provide outstanding Iranian-American college students with internships in political and media organizations.
Title of Award: National Iranian American Council Fellowships **Area, Field, or Subject:** Political science; Economics; International affairs and relations; Journalism. **Level of Education for which Award is Granted:** Graduate, Undergraduate **Funds Available:** Travel expenses covered to and from DC; $500 monthly stipend; $700 monthly towards rent.
Eligibility Requirements: Applicant must be a college junior, senior, and graduate student who is a U.S. citizen or a legal permanent resident of Iranian descent. **Application Requirements:** Applicant must submit the following requirements: a completed application form; three letters of recommendation (two academic and one from an employment supervisor); resume; current college transcript; a 500-word essay answering the question: "How has being Iranian-American influenced your decision to pursue a career in public service or journalism?" **Deadline for Receipt:** February 15. **Additional Information:** NIAC at the above address.

4317 ■ THE SAN DIEGO FOUNDATION
2508 Historic Decatur Rd., Ste. 200
San Diego, CA 92106
Tel: (619)235-2300
Fax: (619)239-1710
E-mail: info@sdfoundation.org
Web Site: http://www.sdfoundation.org
To support the education of students from California.
Title of Award: Julie Allen World Classroom Scholarships **Area, Field, or Subject:** International affairs and relations; Business; Economics; Civil rights; Foreign languages. **Level of Education for which Award is Granted:** Undergraduate **Number Awarded:** 1. **Funds Available:** $1,000.
Eligibility Requirements: Applicant must be an undergraduate student enrolled at the University of San Diego, UC San Diego, or San Diego State University; have a minimum 2.50 GPA on a 4.0 scale; demonstrated financial need; planning to study abroad for a minimum of one semester in a Second or Third World Country whose culture, language and customs are different than their own. **Application Requirements:** Applicants must submit a completed Common Scholarship Application together with personal statement; two letters of recommendation on official letterhead (written within the last six months); official transcript in an official and sealed envelope; copy of most recent tax form (Form 1040-pages 1 & 2; Form 1040A-pages 1 & 2; Form 1040EZ-page 1); and an essay (maximum one page, typed, double-spaced) addressing applicant's reason(s) for studying abroad, or coming to San Diego to pursue an education from the student's native country. **Deadline for Receipt:** January 28. **Additional Information:** Arzo Mansury, Dir. Scholarships at 619-814-1343, or scholarships@sdfoundation.org.

4318 ■ SOUTHWEST FLORIDA COMMUNITY FOUNDATION
8260 College Pkwy., Ste. 101
Fort Myers, FL 33919
Tel: (239)274-5900
Fax: (239)274-5930
Web Site: http://www.floridacommunity.com
To fund a student who will attend: FGCU, university of Florida/Gainesville, Florida State University/Tallahassee, Flagler College, Stetson University/Deland, University of Miami, University of Tampa, or Embry Riddle Aeronautical University/Daytona Beach.
Title of Award: D&A Florida Scholarships **Area, Field, or Subject:** Architecture; Business; Engineering; International affairs and relations;

Journalism; Computer and information sciences; Law; Literature; Medicine; Physics; Chemistry; Political science. **Level of Education for which Award is Granted:** Undergraduate **Funds Available:** $10,000. **Duration:** One year.
Eligibility Requirements: Applicants must have graduated from a public or private high school in Charlotte, Glades, Hendry or Lee County; must pursue a degree in Architecture, Business, Engineering, International affairs and relations, Journalism, Computer and information sciences, Law, Literature, Medicine, Physics, Chemistry, or Political science. **Application Requirements:** Application forms are available online. Applicants must submit a letter of interest and letter of recommendation, a transcript and financial need documentation. **Deadline for Receipt:** February 15.

4319 ■ TURKISH COALITION OF AMERICA
1025 Connecticut Ave. NW, Ste. 1000
Washington, DC 20036
Tel: (202)370-1399
Fax: (202)370-1398
E-mail: info@turkishcoalitionofamerica.org
Web Site: http://www.turkishcoalition.org
To engage and cultivate a new generation of young Turkish American leaders.
Title of Award: TCA Turkish American Scholarships **Area, Field, or Subject:** Public Affairs; Political Science; International Affairs and Relations; Communications; Printing Trades; Public Relations. **Level of Education for which Award is Granted:** Undergraduate **Funds Available:** No specific amount.
Eligibility Requirements: Applicants must meet the following criteria: be a U.S. citizen or permanent resident (green card holder); have, and maintain through the course of the scholarship period, a cumulative minimum 3.3 GPA on a 4.0 scale; evidence of leadership commitment through participation in community service, particularly within the Turkish American community; and be a high school senior applying to an accredited college or university, or college student who plans to continue undergraduate study; or a college senior or graduate enrolled or about to enroll in graduate school. Graduate students who apply for the TCA must plan to pursue studies and a career in public affairs. **Application Requirements:** Applicants must submit three (3) collated, non-stapled, paperclipped copies of each of the following items: (1) Completed Application Form (2) Resume: Each copy should be submitted on one single-sided 8.5" x 11" sheet of paper. (3) Short essay: The essay should not exceed 500 words, must be typed and double-spaced. **Deadline for Receipt:** June 6. **Additional Information:** Turkish Coalition of America at the above address.

4320 ■ UNIVERSITY OF HAWAII AT MANOA
2500 Campus Rd., Hawaii Hall 202
Honolulu, HI 96822
Tel: (808)956-8111
Web Site: http://www.uhm.hawaii.edu
To promote understanding between peoples and nations of the world through higher education.
Title of Award: University of Hawaii at Manoa Japan Travel Bureau Scholarships **Area, Field, or Subject:** International affairs and relations, Crosscultural studies. **Level of Education for which Award is Granted:** Graduate, Undergraduate **Funds Available:** $1,000.
Eligibility Requirements: Candidate must be a full-time classified UHM graduate student or upper class undergraduate interested in international relations or cross-cultural studies and have demonstrated high scholastic achievement. **Application Requirements:** Information and application materials may be obtained from the SPAS Office of Student Academic Services, 315 Moore Hall. **Deadline for Receipt:** March 1.

4321 ■ WOMEN IN DEFENSE
2111 Wilson Blvd., Ste. 400
Arlington, VA 22201-3061
Tel: (703)247-2552
Fax: (703)522-1885
E-mail: wid@ndia.org
Web Site: http://wid.ndia.org
To provide financial assistance to further educational objectives of women either employed or planning careers in defense or national security areas.
Title of Award: Women In Defense HORIZONS Scholarships **Area, Field, or Subject:** National security; Military history; Government;

Engineering; Computer and information sciences; Physics; Mathematics and mathematical sciences; Business; Law; International affairs and relations; Political science; Economics. **Level of Education for which Award is Granted:** Graduate, Undergraduate **Funds Available:** No specific amount.
Eligibility Requirements: Applicant must be currently enrolled at an accredited university/college, either full-time or part-time; must have junior, senior or graduate status; demonstrate interest in pursuing a career related to national security or defense; demonstrate financial need; have a minimum GPA of 3.25. Applicant must be a female citizen of the United States. **Application Requirements:** Applicants must submit a completed scholarship application form with the essays, recommendations, and transcripts. **Additional Information:** Established in 1988. **Deadline for Receipt:** July 1.

Law

4322 ■ AKRON BAR ASSOCIATION FOUNDATION
7 W Bowery St., Ste. 1100
Akron, OH 44308
Tel: (330)253-5007
E-mail: lindaf@akronbar.org
Web Site: http://www.akronbar.org
To provide scholarships to students enrolled in a law school.
Title of Award: Akron Bar Association Foundation Scholarships **Area, Field, or Subject:** Law. **Level of Education for which Award is Granted:** Undergraduate **Funds Available:** No specific amount.
Eligibility Requirements: Applicants must be citizens of the United States and in good academic standing with their respective schools. Applicants should demonstrate financial need, have an affiliation with Summit County, and demonstrate an established history of community involvement. Scholarship recipients are encouraged to become active members in the Akron Bar Association upon joining the legal profession. **Application Requirements:** An applicant must submit the following requirements: a formal letter indicating how and why they became a law student, their connections to Summit County, their volunteer and extracurricular involvement and the reasons they deserve the award; a completed application form; a certified or verified transcript from their school; a copy of their Federal Income Tax Return; an updated resume; and two letters of recommendation from people familiar with their character. Application may be downloaded online. **Deadline for Receipt:** April 14. **Additional Information:** ABAF at the above address.

4323 ■ ALABAMA LAW FOUNDATION
PO Box 671
Montgomery, AL 36101
Tel: (334)269-1515
E-mail: tdaniel@alfinc.org
Web Site: http://www.alfinc.org
To recognize and assist outstanding second-year law students in their academic pursuits.
Title of Award: Johnston Cabaniss Scholarships **Area, Field, or Subject:** Law. **Level of Education for which Award is Granted:** Undergraduate **Funds Available:** $5,000-first place; $1,000-second place.
Eligibility Requirements: Applicants must be resident of Alabama; and must be law students entering second year at any accredited law school in the United States. **Application Requirements:** Applicants may download an application form ALFINC website. Applicants must submit a completed application form with school transcript attached. **Additional Information:** ALFINC at the above address.

4324 ■ ALBERTA INDIAN INVESTMENT CORPORATION
PO Box 180
Enoch, AB, Canada T7X 3Y3
Tel: (780)470-3600; 888-308-6789
Fax: (780)470-3605
E-mail: info@aiicbusiness.org
Web Site: http://www.aiicbusiness.org
To provide scholarship assistance to qualified individuals who want to pursue their education.
Title of Award: Sam Bull Memorial Scholarships **Area, Field, or Subject:** Law; Political science. **Level of Education for which Award is Granted:** Undergraduate **Funds Available:** $1,000. **Duration:** One year.

Eligibility Requirements: Applicant must be a First Nation native who has resided in Alberta for at least one year; must demonstrate interest in law or political science education. **Application Requirements:** Applicant must prepare a 100 to 200 word statement of personal and academic objectives, which should emphasize how their proposed course of study will contribute to First Nation community development in Canada. Application forms are available online and must be sent together with other supporting documents to General Manager, PO Box 180, Enoch, AB T7X 3Y3. **Deadline for Receipt:** February 15.

4325 ■ ALBERTA INDIAN INVESTMENT CORPORATION
PO Box 180
Enoch, AB, Canada T7X 3Y3
Tel: (780)470-3600; 888-308-6789
Fax: (780)470-3605
E-mail: info@aiicbusiness.org
Web Site: http://www.aiicbusiness.org
To provide scholarship assistance to qualified individuals who want to pursue their education.
Title of Award: Senator James Gladstone Memorial Scholarships **Area, Field, or Subject:** Law; Political science. **Level of Education for which Award is Granted:** Undergraduate **Funds Available:** $750-$1,000. **Duration:** One year.
Eligibility Requirements: Applicant must be a First Nation native who has resided in Alberta for at least one year; must demonstrate interest in law or political science education. **Application Requirements:** Applicant must submit a transcript of record; must prepare a 100 to 200 word statement of personal and academic objectives which should emphasize how their proposed course of study will contribute to First Nation economic and business development in Canada. Application form and other supporting documents must be sent to General Manager, Alberta Indian Investment Corporation, PO Box 180, Enoch, AB T7X 3Y3. **Deadline for Receipt:** February 15.

4326 ■ ALBERTA LEARNING INFORMATION SERVICE - ALBERTA SCHOLARSHIP PROGRAM
Box 28000 Sta. Main
Edmonton, AB, Canada T5J 4R4
Tel: (780)427-8640
Fax: (780)427-1288
E-mail: scholarship@gov.ab.ca
Web Site: http://www.alis.alberta.ca
To provide financial assistance to aboriginal students who have successfully completed the first year of a program relating to criminal justice, criminology or law.
Title of Award: Robert C. Carson Memorial Bursary **Area, Field, or Subject:** Criminal justice; Criminology; Law. **Level of Education for which Award is Granted:** Undergraduate **Funds Available:** $500.
Eligibility Requirements: Applicants must be Alberta residents and full-time students enrolled in the second year of either Law Enforcement or Criminal Justice. The qualifying Alberta institutions are: Lethbridge Community College, Mount Royal College, Grant MacEwan College, the University of Calgary or the University of Alberta. **Application Requirements:** Application forms are available from the Institution's Student Award Office. **Deadline for Receipt:** October 1. **Additional Information:** Alberta Scholarship Program at the above address.

4327 ■ ALBERTA LEARNING INFORMATION SERVICE - ALBERTA SCHOLARSHIP PROGRAM
Box 28000 Sta. Main
Edmonton, AB, Canada T5J 4R4
Tel: (780)427-8640
Fax: (780)427-1288
E-mail: scholarship@gov.ab.ca
Web Site: http://www.alis.alberta.ca
To reward the outstanding academic achievement of Alberta post-secondary students who are continuing full-time in an undergraduate program in Alberta.
Title of Award: Jason Lang Scholarship **Area, Field, or Subject:** Law; Medicine; Pharmacy; Dentistry. **Level of Education for which Award is Granted:** Undergraduate **Funds Available:** $1,000.
Eligibility Requirements: Nominees must be enrolled full-time in an undergraduate or professional program, such as Law, Medicine,

Pharmacy or Dentistry at an eligible Alberta post-secondary institution. These include publicly-funded colleges, technical institutes, universities, private colleges accredited to grant degrees, and the Banff Centre. **Application Requirements:** Recipients are nominated by the Awards Office at participating Alberta institutions where they have obtained qualifying grades. For information on the nomination process and eligibility, contact the Awards Office. **Deadline for Receipt:** October 15 and February 15. **Additional Information:** Alberta Scholarship Programs at the above address.

4328 ■ AMERICAN ASSOCIATION OF ATTORNEY-CERTIFIED PUBLIC ACCOUNTANTS
3921 Old Lee Hwy., Ste. 71A
Fairfax, VA 22030
Tel: 888-288-9272
Fax: 888-272-2889
E-mail: info@attorney-cpa.com
Web Site: http://www.attorney-cpa.com
To promote the study and understanding of the fields of Law and Accounting and other related professions.
Title of Award: Attorney-CPA Foundation Scholarships **Area, Field, or Subject:** Law. **Level of Education for which Award is Granted:** Undergraduate **Funds Available:** $250-$1,000. **Duration:** One year.
Eligibility Requirements: Applicants must be graduating law students who have obtained CPA Certificate. **Application Requirements:** Applicants must submit the completed application form. **Deadline for Receipt:** March 15.

4329 ■ AMERICAN ASSOCIATION FOR JUSTICE
1050 31 St. NW
Washington, DC 20007
Tel: (202)965-3500
Free: 800-424-2725
E-mail: membership@justice.org
Web Site: http://www.justice.org
To assist law students to further their studies.
Title of Award: AAJ Trial Advocacy Scholarships **Area, Field, or Subject:** Law. **Level of Education for which Award is Granted:** Undergraduate **Funds Available:** $2,500.
Eligibility Requirements: Applicants must be second and third year AAJ law student members; must be enrolled in an ABA accredited law school. **Application Requirements:** Applicants must submit resume; 500-word essay on how the applicants will meet the criteria; up to three recommendations from a faculty adviser, trial advocacy professor, Dean, AAJ member, or trial lawyer; and a completed form verifying applicant's student status. **Deadline for Receipt:** April 30. **Additional Information:** Natalie Etori at the above address.

4330 ■ AMERICAN ASSOCIATION FOR JUSTICE
1050 31 St. NW
Washington, DC 20007
Tel: (202)965-3500
Free: 800-424-2725
E-mail: membership@justice.org
Web Site: http://www.justice.org
To assist law students to further their studies.
Title of Award: The Richard D. Hailey AAJ Law Student Scholarships **Area, Field, or Subject:** Law. **Level of Education for which Award is Granted:** Undergraduate **Number Awarded:** 6. **Funds Available:** $1,000. **Duration:** One year.
Eligibility Requirements: Applicants must be incoming first, second or third year African, American, Hispanic Asian American, Native American and bi-racial AAJ law student members; must be enrolled in an ABA accredited law school. **Application Requirements:** Applicants must submit resume; 500-word essay on how the applicants will meet the criteria; up to three recommendations from a faculty adviser, trial advocacy professor, Dean, AAJ member or trial lawyer; and a completed form verifying applicant's student status. **Deadline for Receipt:** April 30. **Additional Information:** Natalie Etori at the above address.

4331 ■ AMERICAN ASSOCIATION FOR JUSTICE
1050 31 St. NW
Washington, DC 20007

Tel: (202)965-3500
Free: 800-424-2725
E-mail: membership@justice.org
Web Site: http://www.justice.org
To assist law students to further their studies.
Title of Award: Alia Herrera Memorial Scholarships **Area, Field, or Subject:** Law. **Level of Education for which Award is Granted:** Undergraduate **Funds Available:** $3,000. **Duration:** One year.
Eligibility Requirements: Applicants must be students entering second or third year of law school, or having the equivalent of one year to complete; must be attending law schools in the Philadelphia, PA area; must be members of the law student section of AAJ; must be children of AAJ members. **Application Requirements:** Applicants must submit cover letter; resume; transcript; letter of recommendation from a law professor or Dean of law school; 500-word essay on the topic ("Damage Caps": Limiting Damage awards in Civil cases by State and/or federal statutes, compared to juries making damage awards, with judicial review; Who should bare the risk or loss, and why?). **Deadline for Receipt:** May 1. **Additional Information:** Cheryl Lange, 1643 Monaco Pkwy. Denver, CO 80220; cheryllange@yahoo.com.

4332 ■ AMERICAN ASSOCIATION FOR JUSTICE
1050 31 St. NW
Washington, DC 20007
Tel: (202)965-3500
Free: 800-424-2725
E-mail: membership@justice.org
Web Site: http://www.justice.org
To assist law students to further their studies.
Title of Award: The Leesfield/AAJ Law Student Scholarships **Area, Field, or Subject:** Law. **Level of Education for which Award is Granted:** Undergraduate **Funds Available:** $1,500.
Eligibility Requirements: Applicants must be first and second year AAJ law student members. **Application Requirements:** Applicants must submit resume; statement of financial need; 500-word written request substantiating the applicant's commitment to preserving the civil justice system; three recommendations from a faculty adviser, trial advocacy professor, dean AAJ member, or trial lawyer; and a completed form verifying applicant's student status. **Deadline for Receipt:** April 30. **Additional Information:** Natalie Etori at the above address.

4333 ■ AMERICAN BAR ASSOCIATION
321 North Clark St.
Chicago, IL 60610
Tel: (312)988-5927
Fax: (312)988-6392
E-mail: dfranklin3@staff.abanet.org
Web Site: http://www.abanet.org/fje
To provide law students with financial assistance.
Title of Award: The Allen E. Broussard Scholarships **Area, Field, or Subject:** Law. **Level of Education for which Award is Granted:** Undergraduate **Funds Available:** $5,000.
Eligibility Requirements: Applicants must be law students attending California Bay Area law schools. **Application Requirements:** Applicants need to complete single application available at ABA website. **Deadline for Receipt:** March 1. **Additional Information:** ABA at the above address.

4334 ■ AMERICAN BAR FOUNDATION
750 North Lake Shore Dr.
Chicago, IL 60611-4403
Tel: (312)988-6500
Web Site: http://www.abf-sociolegal.org
To promoted education in social sciences.
Title of Award: Summer Research Diversity Fellowships in Law and Social Science **Area, Field, or Subject:** Law; Social sciences. **Level of Education for which Award is Granted:** Undergraduate **Funds Available:** $3600. **Duration:** Annually.
Eligibility Requirements: Applicant must be an American citizen and permanent resident; an African American, Hispanic/Latino, Native American, or Puerto Rican, or individuals who will add diversity to the field of law and social science; a sophomore or junior student who have not yet received a degree; have a GPA of 3.0; and pursuing an academic major in the social sciences. **Application Requirements:** Applicants must send the completed application form together with the essay, official transcripts, and a letter of recommendation from a faculty. **Deadline for Receipt:** February 15. **Additional Information:** fellowships@abfn.org.

4335 ■ AMERICAN COUNSEL ASSOCIATION
150 Fayetteville St. PO Box 2611
Raleigh, NC 27602-2611
Tel: (919)821-1220
E-mail: jdorsett@smithlaw.com
Web Site: http://www.amcounsel.org
To provide scholarships to academically gifted and financially needy third-year law students.
Title of Award: American Counsel Association Scholarships **Area, Field, or Subject:** Law. **Level of Education for which Award is Granted:** Undergraduate **Funds Available:** No specific amount.
Eligibility Requirements: Applicants must be enrolled in a law school located within the Seventh Federal Judicial District. **Application Requirements:** The law school deans are invited to submit nominations which are reviewed by the Committee.

4336 ■ AMERICAN CRIMINAL JUSTICE ASSOCIATION
PO Box 601047
Sacramento, CA 95860-1047
Tel: (916)484-6553
E-mail: acjalae@aol.com
Web Site: http://www.acjalae.org
To provide financial support to members who are upper or lower division students or graduate students enrolled in a course of study in the criminal justice field.
Title of Award: American Criminal Justice Association Scholarships **Area, Field, or Subject:** Criminal Justice. **Level of Education for which Award is Granted:** Undergraduate **Funds Available:** $400; $200; $100.
Eligibility Requirements: Applicants must be US citizens or eligible non-citizens; must be ACJA/LAE chapter members; must be currently enrolled in a recognized course of study directly or indirectly associated with the criminal justice field; must have achieved a minimum overall GPA of 3.0 on a scale of 4.0; must be currently enrolled with a minimum course of at least two-thirds of full-time loads. **Application Requirements:** Applicants must fill out application form. Applicants must submit: five copies of school transcript; five copies of letters of recommendation from chapter officers and faculty advisors; career and educational goal statement. **Deadline for Receipt:** December 31. **Additional Information:** Dr. Archie Rainey at the above address.

4337 ■ AMERICAN INDIAN GRADUATE CENTER SCHOLARS (AIGCS)
4520 Montgomery Blvd., NE, Ste. 1B
Albuquerque, NM 87109
Tel: (505)881-4584
Free: 800-628-1920
Web Site: http://www.aigc.com
To provide financial assistance to undergraduate and graduate American Indians in furthering their education.
Title of Award: Accenture American Indian Scholarship Program **Area, Field, or Subject:** Technology; Engineering; Medicine; Law; Business. **Level of Education for which Award is Granted:** Graduate, Undergraduate **Funds Available:** No specific amount.
Eligibility Requirements: Applicants must be American Indians who are incoming freshmen with a cumulative GPA of 3.25 or greater on a 4.0 scale at the end of the seventh semester of high school or graduates/professionals who have attained a cumulative GPA of 3.25 or greater on a 4.0 scale, as measured by undergraduate transcripts; must be enrolled members of a U.S. federally-recognized American Indian tribe or Alaska Native group; must be seeking a degree and career in fields of study including technology, engineering, medicine, law, and business. **Application Requirements:** Applicants must submit completed application form; copy of certificate of Indian Blood (CIB); unofficial undergraduate and/or graduate academic transcripts; biographical data and/or resume; essay describing their character, personal merit and commitment to community and heritage; two personal letters of recommendation (one must come from an education professional who is familiar with their academic work and the other one must come from an individual having knowledge of their

leadership and community service activities); and financial aid award letter from the institution they will attend. **Deadline for Receipt:** June 2.

4338 ■ AMERICAN INSTITUTE FOR PARALEGAL STUDIES
2777 Finley Rd., Ste. 11
Downers Grove, IL 60515
800-553-2420
Fax: (630)916-6694
E-mail: info@americanparalegal.edu
Web Site: http://www.americanparalegal.edu
To advance the paralegal profession and to promote a global presence for the paralegal profession and leadership.
Title of Award: American Institute for Paralegal Studies Alumni Achievement Scholarships **Area, Field, or Subject:** Paralegal studies. **Level of Education for which Award is Granted:** Undergraduate **Funds Available:** $2,500.
Eligibility Requirements: Applicants must be students with a bachelor's degree; must have a minimum of 3.0 GPA at the undergraduate or graduate level; and must have three years or more legal work experience. **Application Requirements:** Applicants must submit completed application form; an official transcript of record; a personal statement; and letters of recommendation from AIPS Alumni.

4339 ■ AMERICAN INSTITUTE FOR PARALEGAL STUDIES
2777 Finley Rd., Ste. 11
Downers Grove, IL 60515
800-553-2420
Fax: (630)916-6694
E-mail: info@americanparalegal.edu
Web Site: http://www.americanparalegal.edu
To advance the paralegal profession and to promote a global presence for the paralegal profession and leadership.
Title of Award: American Institute for Paralegal Studies Alumni Competitive Scholarships **Area, Field, or Subject:** Paralegal studies. **Level of Education for which Award is Granted:** Undergraduate **Funds Available:** No specific amount.
Eligibility Requirements: Applicants must be students with a bachelor's degree, must have a minimum of 3.0 GPA at the undergraduate or graduate level, and must have a law-related work experience. **Application Requirements:** Applicants must submit completed application form; an official transcript of record; a personal statement; two letters of recommendation; and grade for the introductory course, American Jurisprudence.

4340 ■ AMERICAN INSTITUTE FOR PARALEGAL STUDIES
2777 Finley Rd., Ste. 11
Downers Grove, IL 60515
800-553-2420
Fax: (630)916-6694
E-mail: info@americanparalegal.edu
Web Site: http://www.americanparalegal.edu
To advance the paralegal profession and to promote a global presence for the paralegal profession and leadership.
Title of Award: American Institute for Paralegal Studies Merit Scholarships **Area, Field, or Subject:** Paralegal studies. **Level of Education for which Award is Granted:** Undergraduate **Funds Available:** No specific amount.
Eligibility Requirements: Applicants must be students with a bachelor's degree and must have a minimum of 3.0 GPA at the undergraduate or graduate level. **Application Requirements:** Applicants must complete the application form and submit along with an official transcript of record. Applicants are advised to contact admissions for details and availability.

4341 ■ AMERICAN INTELLECTUAL PROPERTY LAW EDUCATION FOUNDATION
485 Kinderkamack Rd.
Oradell, NJ 07649
Tel: (201)634-1870
Fax: (201)634-1871
E-mail: admin@aiplef.org
Web Site: http://www.aiplef.org
To increase the number of underrepresented minority groups serving as intellectual property law practitioners in law firms and departments of corporations.

Title of Award: Sidney B. Williams, Jr. Scholarships **Area, Field, or Subject:** Law. **Level of Education for which Award is Granted:** Undergraduate **Funds Available:** $10,000. **Duration:** 3 years.
Eligibility Requirements: Applicants must be entering or attending law school; **Application Requirements:** Applicants must submit completed scholarship application form; FAFSA form (or similar form) and other supporting documentation required. Applicants must also submit undergraduate transcript and graduate law transcript(if applicable); two letters of recommendation from, but not limited to former teachers, college administrators, community leaders, or other similar persons concerning the academic ability, character, reputation or professional aptitude of the applicant; evidence of being US citizen; personal or telephonic interview; and recent resume. **Deadline for Receipt:** February 25. **Additional Information:** Sophia Rogers Thurgood Marshall College Fund at 80 Maiden Lane, Ste. 2204, New York, NY 10038; srogers@tmcfund.org.

4342 ■ APPALACHIAN SCHOOL OF LAW
PO Box 2825
Grundy, VA 24614
Tel: (276)935-4349
Free: 800-895-7411
Fax: (276)935-8261
E-mail: aslinfo@asl.edu
Web Site: http://www.asl.edu
To support students financially in the form of credit against tuition charged.
Title of Award: Angela D. Dales Merit Scholarship Program **Area, Field, or Subject:** Law. **Level of Education for which Award is Granted:** Undergraduate **Funds Available:** No specific amount.
Eligibility Requirements: Applicants must be at least incoming first year law students. **Application Requirements:** Applicants must complete and submit an online application available at the website; online certification page; two letters of recommendation; and 500 words or less describing professional goals and qualifications. **Additional Information:** Scholarship is awarded on a first-come, first-served basis.

4343 ■ ARENT FOX LLP
1050 Connecticut Ave. NW
Washington, DC 20036-5339
Tel: (202)857-6000
Fax: (202)857-6395
E-mail: charyk.william@arentfox.com
Web Site: http://www.arentfox.com
To provide financial assistance for qualified individuals intending to pursue their law career.
Title of Award: Arent Fox Diversity Scholarships **Area, Field, or Subject:** Law. **Level of Education for which Award is Granted:** Undergraduate **Number Awarded:** 3. **Funds Available:** $15,000. **Duration:** One academic year.
Eligibility Requirements: Applicants must be U.S citizens or otherwise authorized to work in the United States; must have an excellent academic performance during college and law school; must have excellent oral and written communication skills; must have leadership qualities and community involvement; must be members of a diverse population that historically has been underrepresented in the legal profession; must agree to join the Arent Fox summer program after the first year of law school; and must be first-year law students. **Application Requirements:** Applicants must submit a resume with cover letter; must provide a undergraduate transcript and law school grades when available; must have three professional or academic references and Arent Fox essay. Application forms are available online and must be sent to Arent Fox LLP/Diversity Scholarship Program, Washington Office, Ms. Jessica L. Salvaterra, Recruitment and Career Development Manager, 1050 Connecticut Ave., N.W., Washington, D.C. 20036. **Deadline for Receipt:** January 15.

4344 ■ ARMENIAN RELIEF SOCIETY - EASTERN UNITED STATES
80 Bigelow Avenue, Ste. 200
Watertown, MA 02472
Tel: (617)926-3801
Fax: (617)924-7238
E-mail: arseastus@aol.com
Web Site: http://www.arseastus.com

To encourage educational pursuits among undergraduate students of Armenian descent.
Title of Award: ARS Undergraduate Scholarships **Area, Field, or Subject:** Law; History; Political science; Journalism; Government; Economics; Business administration; Medicine; Public service. **Level of Education for which Award is Granted:** Four Year College, Two Year College, Undergraduate **Funds Available:** No specific amount. **Duration:** One year.
Eligibility Requirements: Applicants must be of Armenian descent; must be undergraduate students who have completed at least one semester at an accredited four-year college or university in the United States or must be enrolled in a two-year college and are transferring to a four-year college or university as a full-time student in the Fall. **Application Requirements:** Application must include financial aid forms, recent official transcript, two letters of recommendation and tuition costs. Forward materials to: Scholarship Committee, Armenian Relief Society of Eastern USA, Inc., 80 Bigelow Ave., Ste. 200, Watertown, MA 02472. **Deadline for Receipt:** April 1.

4345 ■ ASIAN AMERICAN BAR ASSOCIATION

PO Box 190517
San Francisco, CA 94119-0571
Tel: (415)623-6433
E-mail: info@aaba-bay.com
Web Site: http://www.aaba-bay.com
To support newly admitted law students from groups historically underrepresented in the legal profession, who have committed to attend California Law School.
Title of Award: California Bar Foundation Diversity Scholarships **Area, Field, or Subject:** Law. **Level of Education for which Award is Granted:** Undergraduate **Funds Available:** $7,500.
Eligibility Requirements: Applicants must be students of California law school and come from racial or ethnic groups that are underrepresented in the legal profession; must have financial need; and must demonstrate leadership in making a positive impact to the community. **Application Requirements:** Applicants must submit two current letters of recommendation; certification and authorization form; evidence of acceptance to law school; resume; one-page between 250-400 words personal statement; undergraduate transcript; evidence of financial need; and optional statement of financial circumstance. **Deadline for Receipt:** June 18. **Additional Information:** California Bar Foundation, 180 Howard St., San Francisco, CA 94105.

4346 ■ ASIAN AMERICAN BAR ASSOCIATION

PO Box 190517
San Francisco, CA 94119-0571
Tel: (415)623-6433
E-mail: info@aaba-bay.com
Web Site: http://www.aaba-bay.com
To recognize the importance of fostering the growth of law students and to improve the future development of the Asian Pacific American Bar.
Title of Award: California Bar Law Foundation Scholarships **Area, Field, or Subject:** Law. **Level of Education for which Award is Granted:** Undergraduate **Funds Available:** No stated amount.
Eligibility Requirements: Applicants must be law students who are committed to advocating and improving their communities. **Application Requirements:** Applicants must submit completed application form; resume; personal statement of no more than three pages, double-spaced describing the perception in facing the Asian American community, including the role in advocating or engaging in such issues and experiences in overcoming the economic or other discriminatory barriers. **Deadline for Receipt:** February 1. **Additional Information:** amathai-jackson@hansonbridgett.com

4347 ■ ASIAN AMERICAN LAWYERS ASSOCIATION OF MASSACHUSETTS

PO Box 6254
Boston, MA 02114
Tel: (617)248-4865
E-mail: ckim@choate.com
Web Site: http://www.aalam.org
To promote and enhance the Asian American legal profession by furthering and encouraging professional interaction and the exchange of ideas among its members and with other individuals, groups, and organizations; to improve and facilitate the administration of law and justice through various means.
Title of Award: Asian American Lawyers Associations of Massachusetts Scholarships **Area, Field, or Subject:** Law. **Level of Education for which Award is Granted:** Undergraduate **Number Awarded:** 1. **Funds Available:** $2,500.
Eligibility Requirements: Applicants must be enrolled at a law school in the Commonwealth of Massachusetts and must be in good standing. **Application Requirements:** Applicants must complete the application form; must submit an official transcript of records; resume; one letter of recommendation written by a person who is not related to the candidate; and a signed certification contained at the end of the scholarship application form. **Deadline for Receipt:** April 3. **Additional Information:** 111 Huntington Ave., Boston MA 02199.

4348 ■ ASIAN/PACIFIC BAR ASSOCIATION OF SACRAMENTO

PO Box 2215
Sacramento, CA 95812
Tel: (916)492-3170
E-mail: brownd@insurance.ca.gov
Web Site: http://www.sacasianpacbar.com
To recognize law students and recent law school graduates who possess extraordinary skills, desire and potential to serve and lead the greater Sacramento Asian-Pacific Islander community.
Title of Award: Asian/Pacific Bar Association of Sacramento Law Foundation Scholarships **Area, Field, or Subject:** Law. **Level of Education for which Award is Granted:** Undergraduate **Funds Available:** $1,000-$4,000.
Eligibility Requirements: Applicants must be either currently enrolled and in good standing at a Sacramento area (including U.C. Davis) law school or currently residing in the Sacramento area; have graduated from law school in Spring/Summer 2007 or winter 2007-08. **Application Requirements:** Applicants must submit evidence of scholarship eligibility (a copy of current law school registration or law school diploma will suffice); a personal statement; a current resume; current law school transcripts; financial information; and two references. **Deadline for Receipt:** February 29.

4349 ■ THE BAILEY FAMILY FOUNDATION

912 W Platt St.
Tampa, FL 33606
Tel: (813)549-6140
Fax: (813)549-6141
E-mail: bailey@bailey-family.org
Web Site: http://www.bailey-family.org
To financially assist students in continuing their education.
Title of Award: The Bailey Family Foundation College Scholarship Program **Area, Field, or Subject:** General studies. **Level of Education for which Award is Granted:** Undergraduate **Funds Available:** No specific amount.
Eligibility Requirements: Applicants must possess a minimum cumulative GPA of 2.5; must demonstrate financial need; must be enrolled or accepted to one of the participating schools listed on the scholarship application; and must be pursuing an undergraduate degree. **Application Requirements:** Applicants must submit the completed scholarship application form and an essay of no more than 300 words.

4350 ■ BANNER & WITCOFF, LTD.

10 S Wacker Dr., Ste. 3000
Chicago, IL 60606-7407
Tel: (312)463-5000
Fax: (312)463-5001
E-mail: info@bannerwitcoff.com
Web Site: http://www.bannerwitcoff.com
To foster the development of intellectual property lawyers from diverse backgrounds.
Title of Award: Donald W. Banner Diversity Scholarship for Law Students **Area, Field, or Subject:** Law. **Level of Education for which Award is Granted:** Undergraduate **Funds Available:** $5,000. **Duration:** One year.
Eligibility Requirements: Applicants must be law students who have entered into a JD program at an ABA-accredited law school in the United States. **Application Requirements:** Applicants must complete the

Donald W. Banner Diversity Scholarship application form, available online; must submit a resume, academic transcripts (law, undergraduate/graduate school), a writing sample (5-10 pages), three references including contact information, and a one-page statement describing how diversity has impacted the candidate. **Deadline for Receipt:** October 1.

4351 ■ BAR ASSOCIATION OF SAN FRANCISCO

301 Battery St., 3rd Fl.
San Francisco, CA 94111
Tel: (415)982-1600
Fax: (415)477-2388
Web Site: http://www.sfbar.org
To reaffirm a commitment to diversity in legal education and the legal profession.
Title of Award: Bay Area Minority Law Student Scholarships **Area, Field, or Subject:** Law. **Level of Education for which Award is Granted:** Graduate, Undergraduate **Funds Available:** $10,000.
Eligibility Requirements: Applicants must be students from minority groups who are underrepresented in Bay Area law schools; and must have received a "letter of admission" from one of the eight Northern California law schools. **Application Requirements:** Applicants must submit a completed application with official undergraduate or graduate transcript; 500-word personal statement; copies of current IRS tax forms; statement of economic need (optional); copies of "letters of admissions" from any ABA accredited law school in Northern California. **Deadline for Receipt:** May 30. **Additional Information:** Jayne Salinger at 415-782-9000 x8710, or email at jsalinger@sfbar.org.

4352 ■ BERKS COUNTY BAR FOUNDATION

PO Box 1058
544 Court St.
Reading, PA 19603
Tel: (610)375-4591
Fax: (610)373-0256
E-mail: info@berksbarfoundation.org
Web Site: http://www.berksbarfoundation.org
To provide financial assistance for the education of Berks County residents planning to take up law courses.
Title of Award: Howard Fox Memorial Law Scholarship **Area, Field, or Subject:** Law. **Level of Education for which Award is Granted:** Undergraduate **Funds Available:** $3,000.
Eligibility Requirements: Applicants must be Berks County residents entering their second year at an accredited law school who demonstrate financial need, without discrimination to color, race, national origin or religion. **Application Requirements:** Applicant must submit the completed application form with two letters of reference from people who are not related to him or her; copy of law school transcript; and a written recommendation from a professor at the law school he or she is attending. **Deadline for Receipt:** April 1.

4353 ■ BLACK WOMEN LAWYERS' ASSOCIATION OF GREATER CHICAGO

321 S Plymouth Ct., Ste. 600
Chicago, IL 60604
Tel: (312)554-2088
Fax: (708)201-9342
E-mail: administrator@bwla.org
Web Site: http://www.bwla.org
To provide financial assistance to deserving law students from ABA accredited law schools.
Title of Award: DRI Law Student Diversity Scholarships **Area, Field, or Subject:** Law. **Level of Education for which Award is Granted:** Undergraduate **Number Awarded:** 2. **Funds Available:** $10,000.
Eligibility Requirements: Applicants must be second-year African American, Hispanic, Asian, Pan Asian or Native American students; or second-year female law students, regardless of race or ethnicity. **Application Requirements:** Applicants must submit three recommendations, one each from the following individuals: a) the dean of the student's law school, b) a current or past law professor, and c) an individual who is personally acquainted with the applicant, but who is not related by blood line or adoption; and a cover letter which identifies their academic, personal and/or professional accomplishments and how those accomplishments qualify him or her for DRI's Law Student Diversity Scholarship Award.

4354 ■ BLACK WOMEN LAWYERS ASSOCIATION OF LOS ANGELES

PO Box 8179
Los Angeles, CA 90008
Tel: (213)538-0137
Web Site: http://www.blackwomenlawyersla.org
To encourage careers and increase interest in the field of law.
Title of Award: Black Women Lawyers Association of Los Angeles Scholarships **Area, Field, or Subject:** Law. **Level of Education for which Award is Granted:** Undergraduate **Funds Available:** No specific amount.
Eligibility Requirements: Program is open to second or third year full-time law students as well as to fourth year law students enrolled in night programs intending to practice law in California. **Application Requirements:** Applicants must return completed application along with other required documents. Applications should be either typed or handwritten in black or dark blue ink. Applicants must submit the following attachments: current official school transcript, including school grading scale; letter from law school verifying the current academic status; and resume. Application forms are available at the website. **Deadline for Receipt:** March 31. **Additional Information:** Mika M. Hilaire, 15233 Ventura Blvd., Suite 420, Sherman Oaks, CA 91403; mika@ahblegal.com.

4355 ■ BOYS AND GIRLS CLUB OF OTTAWA

2825 Dumaurier Ave.
Ottawa, ON, Canada K2B 7W3
Tel: (613)232-0925
E-mail: sbradford@bgcottawa.org
Web Site: http://www.bgcottawa.org
To promote, encourage and sponsor promising individuals who would otherwise experience extreme hardships in pursuing a post-secondary education.
Title of Award: Ottawa Police 150th Anniversary Scholarships **Area, Field, or Subject:** Criminal justice. **Level of Education for which Award is Granted:** Undergraduate **Funds Available:** $5,000.
Eligibility Requirements: Applicants must be students pursuing a career in policing or a related criminal justice field. **Application Requirements:** Applicants must submit: a completed application form; completed expenses and income form; up-to-date resume; two letters of recommendation; copy of most recent school transcript; proof of citizenship status; copy of letter of acceptance to an accredited post-secondary school; professional quality color photo; and a 300-1,000 word essay discussing their community involvement, financial need, accomplishment and academics. **Deadline for Receipt:** March 30.

4356 ■ BRONX COUNTY BAR ASSOCIATION

New York State Supreme Court Bldg.
851 Grand Concourse
Bronx, NY 10451-2937
Tel: (718)293-2227
Fax: (718)681-0098
E-mail: info@bronxbar.com
Web Site: http://www.bronxbar.com
To provide financial assistance for the education of law school students who are domiciled in Bronx County.
Title of Award: Peggy Bernheim Memorial Scholarships **Area, Field, or Subject:** Law. **Level of Education for which Award is Granted:** Undergraduate **Funds Available:** $2,500.
Eligibility Requirements: Applicants must be first, second, or third year law students who are graduating in May or June; must be enrolled at an A.B.A. accredited school; may also be first year students who have completed one semester of study. **Application Requirements:** Applicants must submit general application. **Deadline for Receipt:** February 29.

4357 ■ BRONX COUNTY BAR ASSOCIATION

New York State Supreme Court Bldg.
851 Grand Concourse
Bronx, NY 10451-2937
Tel: (718)293-2227
Fax: (718)681-0098
E-mail: info@bronxbar.com
Web Site: http://www.bronxbar.com

To provide financial assistance for the education of law school students who are domiciled in Bronx County. **Title of Award:** Alexander A. DelleCese Memorial Scholarships **Area, Field, or Subject:** Law. **Level of Education for which Award is Granted:** Undergraduate **Funds Available:** $2,500.
Eligibility Requirements: Applicants must be first, second, or third year law students who are graduating in May or June; must be enrolled at an A.B.A. accredited school; may also be first year students who have completed one semester of study. **Application Requirements:** Applicants must submit general application. **Deadline for Receipt:** February 29.

4358 ■ BRONX COUNTY BAR ASSOCIATION
New York State Supreme Court Bldg.
851 Grand Concourse
Bronx, NY 10451-2937
Tel: (718)293-2227
Fax: (718)681-0098
E-mail: info@bronxbar.com
Web Site: http://www.bronxbar.com
To provide financial assistance for the education of law school students who are domiciled in Bronx County.
Title of Award: Craig Lensch Memorial Scholarships **Area, Field, or Subject:** Law. **Level of Education for which Award is Granted:** Undergraduate **Funds Available:** $2,500.
Eligibility Requirements: Applicants must be first, second, or third year law students who are graduating in May or June; must be enrolled at an A.B.A. accredited school; may also be first year students who have completed one semester of study. **Application Requirements:** Applicants must submit general application. **Deadline for Receipt:** February 29.

4359 ■ CALIFORNIA BAR ASSOCIATION
180 Howard St.
San Francisco, CA 94105-1939
Tel: (415)856-0780
Fax: (415)856-0788
Web Site: http://www.calbarfoundation.org
To help offset high cost of law school education.
Title of Award: Public Interest Scholarships **Area, Field, or Subject:** Law. **Level of Education for which Award is Granted:** Undergraduate **Funds Available:** No specific amount.
Eligibility Requirements: Candidates must be enrolled in a California law school or must have completed at least one year of study at a California law school (the candidates' law school must certify good ethical standing of the candidate while attending law school and must also attest to the candidate's financial need); must maintain at least a 2.5 or equivalent on a 4.0 scale (or provide an explanation of extenuating circumstances if GPA is lower than 2.5). **Application Requirements:** Applicants must accomplish complete application package which includes: application; certification and authorization form (which includes certification of non-relationship, authorization t use information, name and likeness and consent and authorization to obtain information); resume; personal statement describing the candidate's commitment and plans for a legal career in public service (not to exceed 400 words); three letters of recommendation; law school transcript; certification of financial need; certification of ethical standing and statement of nomination; and optional statement of financial circumstances. Candidate's name must appear in the upper right-hand corner of each page of every document submitted. **Deadline for Receipt:** March 19. **Additional Information:** California Bar Foundation at the above address.

4360 ■ CALIFORNIA BAR ASSOCIATION
180 Howard St.
San Francisco, CA 94105-1939
Tel: (415)856-0780
Fax: (415)856-0788
Web Site: http://www.calbarfoundation.org
To provide financial support for outstanding graduating California law students who are embarking on careers in public service law.
Title of Award: Rosenthal Bar Exam Scholarships **Area, Field, or Subject:** Law. **Level of Education for which Award is Granted:** Undergraduate **Funds Available:** $1,000.

Eligibility Requirements: Candidates must be graduating or have graduated from a California law school; must be taking the California Bar Exam for the first time; and must maintain at least a 2.5 GPA or equivalent on a 4.0 scale (or provide an explanation of extenuating circumstances if GPA is lower than 2.5). **Application Requirements:** Candidates must be nominated by their law school. **Deadline for Receipt:** February 14. **Additional Information:** CBF at the above address.

4361 ■ CANADIAN ASSOCIATION OF LAW LIBRARIES
PO Box 1570
Kingston, ON, Canada K7L 5C8
Tel: (613)531-9338
Fax: (613)531-0626
E-mail: office@callacbd.ca
Web Site: http://www.callacbd.ca
To encourage and support professional development in the area of law librarianship.
Title of Award: Diana M. Priestly Memorial Scholarships **Area, Field, or Subject:** Law. **Level of Education for which Award is Granted:** Undergraduate **Funds Available:** $2,500.
Eligibility Requirements: Program is open to Canadian citizens or landed immigrants; must have previous law library experience and will be enrolled in an accredited Canadian Library School during the next academic term or year; must have a degree from or are currently enrolled in an accredited Canadian Library School and will be enrolled in an approved Canadian Law School during the next academic term or year; or who have a degree from or are currently enrolled in an approved Canadian law School and will be enrolled in an accredited Canadian Library school during the next academic term/year; or who will be concurrently enrolled in an approved Canadian Law School and an accredited Canadian Library School during the next academic term/year. **Application Requirements:** Applicants must submit the completed application form available on the website along with resume; written statement from applicant; transcripts; and references. **Deadline for Receipt:** February 15. **Additional Information:** Janet Moss, Chair; CALL/ACBD Scholarships and Awards Committee, Head Law Librarian, Gerard V. La Forest Law Library, University of New Brunswick, Bag Service 44999 41 Dineen Dr. Fredericton, NB E3B 6C9; jmoss@unb.ca.

4362 ■ CHICAGO BAR FOUNDATION
21 S Plymouth Ct., Ste. 3B
Chicago, IL 60604
Tel: (312)554-1204
Fax: (312)554-1203
E-mail: khamilton@chicagobar.org
Web Site: http://www.chicagobarfoundation.org
To support a needy law student who is deeply committed to public interest work so that upon graduation financial need will not prevent the student from pursuing a public interest legal career.
Title of Award: Abraham Lincoln Marovitz Public Interest Law Scholarships **Area, Field, or Subject:** Law. **Level of Education for which Award is Granted:** Undergraduate **Funds Available:** $10,000 in the first year.
Eligibility Requirements: Applicants must be students attending one of the nine Illinois law schools (Chicago-Kent College of Law, University of Chicago Law School, DePaul University College of Law, University of Illinois College of Law, John Marshall Law School, Loyola University School of Law, Northern Illinois University Law School, Northwestern University School of Law and Southern Illinois University School of Law). **Application Requirements:** Applicants must submit cover letter with attached application form; resume; official transcript from undergraduate institution and graduate institution; two letters of reference about commitment to public interest work; brief essay (no more than three pages, explaining commitment to pursue a career in public interest law). **Deadline for Receipt:** April 15.

4363 ■ COLUMBIAN LAWYERS ASSOCIATION OF WESTCHESTER COUNTY
800 Westchester Ave., Ste. S608
Rye Brook, NY 10573
Tel: (914)253-6533
E-mail: awcornachio3@westcla.org
Web Site: http://www.westcla.org

To develop a program for Italian-American law students to give them an opportunity to serve as legal interns with judges who are associations members and to assist Italian-American educators and community members with their efforts to continue the teaching of the Italian language at several involving law, government, social, historical and contemporary issues.

Title of Award: Columbian Lawyers Association of Westchester County Scholarships **Area, Field, or Subject:** Law. **Level of Education for which Award is Granted:** Undergraduate **Funds Available:** No specific amount.

Eligibility Requirements: Applicants must be residents of Westchester County who are enrolled in any law school; must not be children of CLAW member; and should be ranked in the upper half of their class. **Application Requirements:** Applicants must submit a complete application form and a resume; a letter to scholarship committee demonstrating the Italian descent, academic achievement, financial need, aspirations and goals; and a firm adherence to the ideals championed by the association. **Deadline for Receipt:** October.

4364 ■ COLUMBIAN LAWYERS ASSOCIATION OF WESTCHESTER COUNTY

800 Westchester Ave., Ste. S608
Rye Brook, NY 10573
Tel: (914)253-6533
E-mail: awcornachio3@westcla.org
Web Site: http://www.westcla.org

To develop a program for Italian-American law students to give them an opportunity to serve as legal interns with judges who are associations members and to assist Italian-American educators and community members with their efforts to continue the teaching of the Italian language at several involving law, government, social, historical and contemporary issues.

Title of Award: PACE/Columbian Lawyers Association of Westchester County Endowed Scholarships **Area, Field, or Subject:** Law. **Level of Education for which Award is Granted:** Undergraduate **Funds Available:** $5,000.

Eligibility Requirements: Applicants must be Pace Law School students; should be of an Italian-American heritage; and must maintain an overall minimum academic 3.0 GPA. **Application Requirements:** Applicants must submit completed application form.

4365 ■ THE COMMUNITY FOUNDATION OF MIDDLE TENNESSEE

3833 Cleghorn Ave., Ste. 400
Nashville, TN 37215-2519
Tel: (615)321-4939; 888-540-5200
E-mail: mail@cfmt.org
Web Site: http://www.cfmt.org

To help students in planning their postsecondary education.

Title of Award: Colonel Richard M. Dawson Scholarships **Area, Field, or Subject:** Criminal justice. **Level of Education for which Award is Granted:** Undergraduate **Funds Available:** No specific amount.

Eligibility Requirements: Applicants must be children of employees of the Tennessee Highway Patrol who serve in uniform, undercover, or plainclothes. Applicants must be rising sophomores, juniors, or seniors in college who demonstrate a commitment to a career in criminal justice through their course of study. **Application Requirements:** Applicants must complete the application form. Applicants must submit two applicant appraisals; transcript of grades; student essay describing educational plans and how these will help in career goals. Applicants must submit one recent photograph. **Deadline for Receipt:** March 15. **Additional Information:** pcole@cfmt.org

4366 ■ THE COMMUNITY FOUNDATION OF MIDDLE TENNESSEE

3833 Cleghorn Ave., Ste. 400
Nashville, TN 37215-2519
Tel: (615)321-4939; 888-540-5200
E-mail: mail@cfmt.org
Web Site: http://www.cfmt.org

To help students in planning their postsecondary education.

Title of Award: Senator Carl O. Koella, Jr. Memorial Scholarships **Area, Field, or Subject:** Law. **Level of Education for which Award is Granted:** Undergraduate **Funds Available:** No specific amount.

Eligibility Requirements: Applicants must be legislative interns, either public or private, currently enrolled or planning to enroll in a four-year col-

lege the year of the application. **Application Requirements:** Applicants must complete the application form. Applicants must submit two applicant appraisals; transcript of grades; student essay describing educational plans and how these will help in career goals. Applicants must submit one recent photograph. **Deadline for Receipt:** March 15. **Additional Information:** pcole@cfmt.org

4367 ■ THE COMMUNITY FOUNDATION OF MIDDLE TENNESSEE

3833 Cleghorn Ave., Ste. 400
Nashville, TN 37215-2519
Tel: (615)321-4939; 888-540-5200
E-mail: mail@cfmt.org
Web Site: http://www.cfmt.org

To help students in planning their postsecondary education.

Title of Award: Emmett H. Turner Scholarships **Area, Field, or Subject:** Criminal justice. **Level of Education for which Award is Granted:** Undergraduate **Funds Available:** No specific amount.

Eligibility Requirements: Applicants must be students enrolling or currently enrolled at Tennessee University in the Criminal Justice program. **Application Requirements:** Applicants must complete the application form. Applicants must submit two applicant appraisals; transcript of grades; student essay describing educational plans and how these will help in career goals. Applicants must submit one recent photograph. **Deadline for Receipt:** March 15. **Additional Information:** pcole@cfmt.org

4368 ■ COMMUNITY FOUNDATION FOR SOUTHEAST MICHIGAN

333 West Fort St., Ste. 2010
Detroit, MI 48226-3134
Tel: (313)961-6675
Fax: (313)961-2886
E-mail: cfsem@cfsem.org
Web Site: http://www.cfsem.org

To provide financial assistance to students of Southeast Michigan region for their education.

Title of Award: Jeptha Wade Schureman Scholarship Program **Area, Field, or Subject:** Law; Nursing; Medicine; Dentistry. **Level of Education for which Award is Granted:** Undergraduate **Funds Available:** $7,500.

Eligibility Requirements: Applicants must be residents of Wayne, Oakland, Macomb, Lenawee, Monroe, Livingston, Washtenaw, or St. Clair counties at the time of high school graduation; must be fatherless either through death or through termination of parental rights; must be pursuing, or planning to pursue, a degree in the fields of law, nursing, medicine or dentistry. **Application Requirements:** Applicants must submit the completed application form and other required documents. **Deadline for Receipt:** June 2.

4369 ■ CORRECTIONAL EDUCATION ASSOCIATION

8182 Lark Brown Rd., Ste. 202
Elkridge, MD 21075
Tel: (443)459-3080
Free: 800-783-1232
Fax: (443)459-3088
Web Site: http://www.ceanational.org

To encourage students to continue a course of study in correctional education.

Title of Award: Correctional Education Association Scholarships **Area, Field, or Subject:** Criminal justice. **Level of Education for which Award is Granted:** Graduate, Undergraduate **Number Awarded:** Scholarship Committee will determine the number of scholarships to be awarded. **Funds Available:** $500. **Duration:** One year.

Eligibility Requirements: Applicant must be a graduate or undergraduate student in correctional education; must be a voting member of the Correctional Education Association and have been a member for a minimum of two years prior to application. **Application Requirements:** Application forms are available in the website (application format must be completed in full in order to be considered by the Committee). Application materials must be sent to: Correctional Educational Association, Scholarship Committee, 8182 Lark Brown Rd., Ste. 202, Elkridge, MD 21075.

4370 ■ DALLAS HISPANIC BAR ASSOCIATION

2101 Ross Ave.
Dallas, TX 75201

Tel: (214)924-3176
Fax: (214)634-9991
E-mail: mail@dallashispanicbar.com
Web Site: http://www.dallashispanicbar.com
To provide financial assistance for Texas law school students.
Title of Award: Dallas Hispanic Bar Association Scholarships **Area, Field, or Subject:** Law. **Level of Education for which Award is Granted:** Undergraduate **Number Awarded:** 5. **Funds Available:** $1,000-$2,000. **Duration:** One year.
Eligibility Requirements: Applicants must have high academic performance and demonstrated leadership and must be enrolled in a Texas law school. **Application Requirements:** Applicants must complete the application form available online and must send it to Martinez Ramirez Siewcynski LLC, 6318 Gaston Ave., Ste. 201, Dallas, TX 75214. **Deadline for Receipt:** August 22. **Additional Information:** Maricela Siewczynski, at the above address.

4371 ■ DAVIS WRIGHT TREMAINE LLP
701 W Eighth Ave.
Anchorage, AK 99501-3468
Tel: (907)257-5300; 877-398-8416
Fax: (907)257-5399
E-mail: info@dwt.com
Web Site: http://www.dwt.com
To provide financial assistance for qualified students intending to pursue their law degree.
Title of Award: Davis Wright Tremaine 1L Diversity Scholarships **Area, Field, or Subject:** Law. **Level of Education for which Award is Granted:** Undergraduate **Funds Available:** $7,500 for the student's second year tuition and expenses. **Duration:** One year.
Eligibility Requirements: Applicants must be first-year law students; must have a record of academic achievement in both undergraduate school and the first year of law school; must demonstrate promise for a successful career in law; must be committed to civic involvement that promotes diversity; be willing to continue that commitment upon entering the legal profession; and must commit to become a Summer Associate in DWT's Seattle Office between the student's first and second years of law school. **Application Requirements:** Applicants must submit a current resume; a complete undergraduate transcript; a grade from the first semester of law school; a short, personal essay indicating the applicant's eligibility for and interest in the scholarship, and a legal writing sample; and two or three references (one of whom should be a person qualified to comment on the applicant's law school work). Application materials must be sent to Davis Wright Tremaine LLP, IL Diversity Scholarship Program, 2600 Century Square, 1501 Fourth Ave., Seattle, WA 98101-1688. **Deadline for Receipt:** February 3.

4372 ■ DRAKE UNIVERSITY LAW SCHOOL
2621 Carpenter Ave.
Des Moines, IA 50311
Tel: (515)271-2824
Free: 800-44-DRAKE
E-mail: lawadmit@drake.edu
Web Site: http://www.law.drake.edu
To support the education of law students.
Title of Award: William Stone Ayres Scholarships **Area, Field, or Subject:** Law. **Level of Education for which Award is Granted:** Undergraduate **Funds Available:** No specific amount.
Eligibility Requirements: Applicants must be students of Drake University law school. **Application Requirements:** Applicants must file FAFSA and application form. **Additional Information:** Established by a bequest from Gladys L. Ayres in memory of her husband, a 1894 Law School graduate. **Additional Information:** Office of Admission and Financial Aid at 515-271-2782.

4373 ■ DRAKE UNIVERSITY LAW SCHOOL
2621 Carpenter Ave.
Des Moines, IA 50311
Tel: (515)271-2824
Free: 800-44-DRAKE
E-mail: lawadmit@drake.edu
Web Site: http://www.law.drake.edu
To support the education of law students.

Title of Award: Beverly Estate Scholarships **Area, Field, or Subject:** Law. **Level of Education for which Award is Granted:** Undergraduate **Funds Available:** No specific amount.
Eligibility Requirements: Applicants must be students of Drake University law school. **Application Requirements:** Applicants must file FAFSA and application form. **Additional Information:** Awards are made possible by bequests from Francis Cecile Beverly, LW'15, and Adda Brown Beverly, ED'14. **Additional Information:** Office of Admission and Financial Aid at 515-271-2782.

4374 ■ DRAKE UNIVERSITY LAW SCHOOL
2621 Carpenter Ave.
Des Moines, IA 50311
Tel: (515)271-2824
Free: 800-44-DRAKE
E-mail: lawadmit@drake.edu
Web Site: http://www.law.drake.edu
To support the education of law students.
Title of Award: George and Mary Brammer Scholarships **Area, Field, or Subject:** Law. **Level of Education for which Award is Granted:** Undergraduate **Funds Available:** No specific amount.
Eligibility Requirements: Applicants must be students of Drake University law school. **Application Requirements:** Applicants must file FAFSA and application form. **Additional Information:** Established by Mary and John Harper as a memorial to Mary's parents, 1908 and 1907 graduates of the Law School. **Additional Information:** Office of Admission and Financial Aid at 515-271-2782.

4375 ■ DRAKE UNIVERSITY LAW SCHOOL
2621 Carpenter Ave.
Des Moines, IA 50311
Tel: (515)271-2824
Free: 800-44-DRAKE
E-mail: lawadmit@drake.edu
Web Site: http://www.law.drake.edu
To support the education of law students.
Title of Award: Gregory Brunk Scholarships **Area, Field, or Subject:** Law. **Level of Education for which Award is Granted:** Undergraduate **Funds Available:** No specific amount.
Eligibility Requirements: Applicants must be students of Drake University law school. **Application Requirements:** Applicants must file the FAFSA and application form. **Additional Information:** The scholarship was made available by the late Gregory Brunk, LW'19. **Additional Information:** Office of Admission and Financial Aid at 515-271-2782.

4376 ■ DRAKE UNIVERSITY LAW SCHOOL
2621 Carpenter Ave.
Des Moines, IA 50311
Tel: (515)271-2824
Free: 800-44-DRAKE
E-mail: lawadmit@drake.edu
Web Site: http://www.law.drake.edu
To support the education of law students.
Title of Award: Donald C. and Doris K. Byers Scholarships **Area, Field, or Subject:** Law. **Level of Education for which Award is Granted:** Undergraduate **Funds Available:** No specific amount.
Eligibility Requirements: Applicants must be entering first year students. **Application Requirements:** Applicants must submit a completed application form. **Additional Information:** Sponsored by Donald C. and Doris K. Byers. **Additional Information:** Office of Admission and Financial Aid at 515-271-2782.

4377 ■ DRAKE UNIVERSITY LAW SCHOOL
2621 Carpenter Ave.
Des Moines, IA 50311
Tel: (515)271-2824
Free: 800-44-DRAKE
E-mail: lawadmit@drake.edu
Web Site: http://www.law.drake.edu
To support the education of law students.
Title of Award: Raymond DiPaglia Endowment Scholarships **Area, Field, or Subject:** Law. **Level of Education for which Award is Granted:** Undergraduate **Funds Available:** No specific amount.

Eligibility Requirements: Applicants must be returning law students in good standing at the Drake University law school. **Application Requirements:** Applicants must file FAFSA and application form. **Additional Information:** Office of Admission and Financial Aid at 515-271-2782.

4378 ■ DRAKE UNIVERSITY LAW SCHOOL
2621 Carpenter Ave.
Des Moines, IA 50311
Tel: (515)271-2824
Free: 800-44-DRAKE
E-mail: lawadmit@drake.edu
Web Site: http://www.law.drake.edu
To support the education of law students.
Title of Award: Grace O. Doane Scholarships **Area, Field, or Subject:** Law. **Level of Education for which Award is Granted:** Undergraduate **Funds Available:** No specific amount.
Eligibility Requirements: Applicants must be second year Iowa residents who rank in the top one-half of their class. **Application Requirements:** Applicants must file FAFSA and an application form. **Additional Information:** Office of Admission and Financial Aid at 515-271-2782.

4379 ■ DRAKE UNIVERSITY LAW SCHOOL
2621 Carpenter Ave.
Des Moines, IA 50311
Tel: (515)271-2824
Free: 800-44-DRAKE
E-mail: lawadmit@drake.edu
Web Site: http://www.law.drake.edu
To support the education of law students.
Title of Award: Joseph M. Dorgan Scholarships **Area, Field, or Subject:** Law. **Level of Education for which Award is Granted:** Undergraduate **Funds Available:** No specific amount.
Eligibility Requirements: Applicants must be African American law students. **Application Requirements:** Applicants must file FAFSA and application form. **Additional Information:** Office of Admission and Financial Aid at 515-271-2782.

4380 ■ DRAKE UNIVERSITY LAW SCHOOL
2621 Carpenter Ave.
Des Moines, IA 50311
Tel: (515)271-2824
Free: 800-44-DRAKE
E-mail: lawadmit@drake.edu
Web Site: http://www.law.drake.edu
To support the education of disadvantaged law students.
Title of Award: Drake University Law School Law Opportunity Scholarships - Disadvantage **Area, Field, or Subject:** Law. **Level of Education for which Award is Granted:** Undergraduate **Funds Available:** One-quarter tuition to full-tuition awards.
Eligibility Requirements: Applicants must have been admitted to the Law School and must demonstrate financial need as determined by the Free Application for Federal Student Aid. **Application Requirements:** Applicants must submit completed application form. **Additional Information:** Disadvantaged student is "one who, despite facing significant obstacles, has prepared himself or herself for a college education". **Additional Information:** Office of Admission and Financial Aid at 515-271-2782.

4381 ■ DRAKE UNIVERSITY LAW SCHOOL
2621 Carpenter Ave.
Des Moines, IA 50311
Tel: (515)271-2824
Free: 800-44-DRAKE
E-mail: lawadmit@drake.edu
Web Site: http://www.law.drake.edu
To promote the diversity of students in Drake University.
Title of Award: Drake University Law School Law Opportunity Scholarships - Diversity **Area, Field, or Subject:** Law. **Level of Education for which Award is Granted:** Undergraduate **Funds Available:** One-quarter tuition to full-tuition awards.
Eligibility Requirements: Applicants must have been admitted to the law school and must demonstrate financial need as determined by the Free

Application for Federal Student Aid. **Application Requirements:** Applicants must submit completed application form. **Additional Information:** Office of Admission and Financial Aid at 515-271-2782.

4382 ■ DRAKE UNIVERSITY LAW SCHOOL
2621 Carpenter Ave.
Des Moines, IA 50311
Tel: (515)271-2824
Free: 800-44-DRAKE
E-mail: lawadmit@drake.edu
Web Site: http://www.law.drake.edu
To support the education of law students.
Title of Award: Drake University Law School Public Service Scholarships **Area, Field, or Subject:** Law. **Level of Education for which Award is Granted:** Undergraduate **Funds Available:** Full-tuition.
Eligibility Requirements: Applicants must exhibit an extraordinary history of public service work and plan to continue that commitment during and after law school. **Application Requirements:** Applicants must submit completed application form along with essay, a short description of past work experiences/activities, letters of recommendation, relevant academic curriculum and statement of reasons for award. **Deadline for Receipt:** March 1. **Additional Information:** Office of Admission and Financial Aid at 515-271-2782.

4383 ■ DRAKE UNIVERSITY LAW SCHOOL
2621 Carpenter Ave.
Des Moines, IA 50311
Tel: (515)271-2824
Free: 800-44-DRAKE
E-mail: lawadmit@drake.edu
Web Site: http://www.law.drake.edu
To support the education of law students.
Title of Award: Robert E. Early Memorial Scholarships **Area, Field, or Subject:** Law. **Level of Education for which Award is Granted:** Undergraduate **Funds Available:** No specific amount.
Eligibility Requirements: Applicants must be second or third year full time students who are in need of financial assistance. **Application Requirements:** Applicants must file FAFSA and application form. **Additional Information:** Sponsored by Margaret M. Early in memory of her husband, LW'41. **Additional Information:** Office of Admission and Financial Aid at 515-271-2782.

4384 ■ DRAKE UNIVERSITY LAW SCHOOL
2621 Carpenter Ave.
Des Moines, IA 50311
Tel: (515)271-2824
Free: 800-44-DRAKE
E-mail: lawadmit@drake.edu
Web Site: http://www.law.drake.edu
To support the education of law students.
Title of Award: Electric Cooperative Pioneer Trust Fund Scholarships **Area, Field, or Subject:** Law. **Level of Education for which Award is Granted:** Undergraduate **Funds Available:** No specific amount.
Eligibility Requirements: Applicant must be second or third year law students interested in agricultural law. **Application Requirements:** Applicants may contact Office of Admission and Financial Aid for more information. **Additional Information:** Office of Admission and Financial Aid at 515-271-2782.

4385 ■ DRAKE UNIVERSITY LAW SCHOOL
2621 Carpenter Ave.
Des Moines, IA 50311
Tel: (515)271-2824
Free: 800-44-DRAKE
E-mail: lawadmit@drake.edu
Web Site: http://www.law.drake.edu
To support the education of law students.
Title of Award: Herman E. Elgar Memorial Scholarships **Area, Field, or Subject:** Law. **Level of Education for which Award is Granted:** Undergraduate **Funds Available:** No specific amount.
Eligibility Requirements: Applicants must be third year law students. **Application Requirements:** Applicants must file FAFSA and application form. **Additional Information:** Established in memory of Mr. Elgar, LW'11,

by his wife and children, John, LW'50, and Alanson, LW'51. **Additional Information:** Office of Admission and Financial Aid at 515-271-2782.

4386 ■ DRAKE UNIVERSITY LAW SCHOOL
2621 Carpenter Ave.
Des Moines, IA 50311
Tel: (515)271-2824
Free: 800-44-DRAKE
E-mail: lawadmit@drake.edu
Web Site: http://www.law.drake.edu
To support the education of law students.
Title of Award: D.J. Fairgrave Education Trust **Area, Field, or Subject:** Law. **Level of Education for which Award is Granted:** Undergraduate **Funds Available:** No specific amount. **Eligibility Requirements:** Applicants must be students of Drake University law school. **Application Requirements:** Applicants must file FAFSA and application form. **Additional Information:** Established by Denio John Fairgrave. **Additional Information:** Office of Admission and Financial Aid at 515-271-2782.

4387 ■ DRAKE UNIVERSITY LAW SCHOOL
2621 Carpenter Ave.
Des Moines, IA 50311
Tel: (515)271-2824
Free: 800-44-DRAKE
E-mail: lawadmit@drake.edu
Web Site: http://www.law.drake.edu
To support the education of law students.
Title of Award: Leland Stanford Forrest Scholarships **Area, Field, or Subject:** Law. **Level of Education for which Award is Granted:** Undergraduate **Funds Available:** No specific amount. **Eligibility Requirements:** Applicants must be accepted as first year students at Drake law school. **Application Requirements:** Applicants must fill up the General Information Form of Scholarship. **Additional Information:** Scholarship was established through the bequest of Leland Stanford Forrest, former dean of the law school.

4388 ■ DRAKE UNIVERSITY LAW SCHOOL
2621 Carpenter Ave.
Des Moines, IA 50311
Tel: (515)271-2824
Free: 800-44-DRAKE
E-mail: lawadmit@drake.edu
Web Site: http://www.law.drake.edu
To support the education of law students.
Title of Award: Lex and Scott Hawkins Endowed Scholarships **Area, Field, or Subject:** Law. **Level of Education for which Award is Granted:** Undergraduate **Funds Available:** No specific amount. **Eligibility Requirements:** Applicants must be the president of the Law School's Moot Court Board. **Application Requirements:** Applicants may contact Office of Admission and Financial Aid for more information. **Additional Information:** Established by Lex Hawkins, LW'51, and Scott Hawkins, LW'81. **Additional Information:** Office of Admission and Financial Aid at 515-271-2782.

4389 ■ DRAKE UNIVERSITY LAW SCHOOL
2621 Carpenter Ave.
Des Moines, IA 50311
Tel: (515)271-2824
Free: 800-44-DRAKE
E-mail: lawadmit@drake.edu
Web Site: http://www.law.drake.edu
To support the education of law students.
Title of Award: Edward and Cora Hayes Scholarships **Area, Field, or Subject:** Law. **Level of Education for which Award is Granted:** Undergraduate **Funds Available:** No specific amount. **Eligibility Requirements:** Applicants must be accepted as first year students at Drake University law school and not a graduate of Iowa high schools or colleges. **Application Requirements:** Applicants must fill up the General Information Form of Scholarship. **Additional Information:** Established by former associate dean Edward Hayes and his wife.

4390 ■ DRAKE UNIVERSITY LAW SCHOOL
2621 Carpenter Ave.
Des Moines, IA 50311

Tel: (515)271-2824
Free: 800-44-DRAKE
E-mail: lawadmit@drake.edu
Web Site: http://www.law.drake.edu
To support the education of law students.
Title of Award: Annamae Heaps Law Scholarships **Area, Field, or Subject:** Law. **Level of Education for which Award is Granted:** Undergraduate **Funds Available:** No specific amount. **Eligibility Requirements:** Applicants must be a second year students demonstrating financial need. **Application Requirements:** Applicants must file FAFSA and application form. **Additional Information:** Office of Admission and Financial Aid at 515-271-2782.

4391 ■ DRAKE UNIVERSITY LAW SCHOOL
2621 Carpenter Ave.
Des Moines, IA 50311
Tel: (515)271-2824
Free: 800-44-DRAKE
E-mail: lawadmit@drake.edu
Web Site: http://www.law.drake.edu
To support the education of law students.
Title of Award: John M. Helmick Law Scholarships **Area, Field, or Subject:** Law. **Level of Education for which Award is Granted:** Undergraduate **Funds Available:** No specific amount. **Eligibility Requirements:** Applicants must be students of Iowa backgrounds planning to enter the legal or educational professions in Iowa. **Application Requirements:** Applicants must file FAFSA and application form. **Additional Information:** Sponsored by Robert H. Helmick, LW'60, in memory of his grandfather, John Miller Helmick. **Additional Information:** Office of Admission and Financial Aid at 515-271-2782.

4392 ■ DRAKE UNIVERSITY LAW SCHOOL
2621 Carpenter Ave.
Des Moines, IA 50311
Tel: (515)271-2824
Free: 800-44-DRAKE
E-mail: lawadmit@drake.edu
Web Site: http://www.law.drake.edu
To support the education of law students.
Title of Award: James P. Irish Scholarships **Area, Field, or Subject:** Law. **Level of Education for which Award is Granted:** Undergraduate **Funds Available:** No specific amount. **Eligibility Requirements:** Applicants must be from Southeast Polk High School or members of the Law Review Board of Editor. **Application Requirements:** Applicants may contact Office of Admission and Financial Aid for more information. **Additional Information:** Established by Edwin Skinner and Donald Beattie in honor of their associate and law partner, James P. Irish, LW'31. **Additional Information:** Office of Admission and Financial Aid at 515-271-2782.

4393 ■ DRAKE UNIVERSITY LAW SCHOOL
2621 Carpenter Ave.
Des Moines, IA 50311
Tel: (515)271-2824
Free: 800-44-DRAKE
E-mail: lawadmit@drake.edu
Web Site: http://www.law.drake.edu
To support the education of law students.
Title of Award: Edward H. Jones Scholarships **Area, Field, or Subject:** Law. **Level of Education for which Award is Granted:** Undergraduate **Funds Available:** $2000. **Eligibility Requirements:** Applicants must be second year law students. **Application Requirements:** Applicants must submit a completed scholarship application form. **Additional Information:** Established in honor of the late Edward H. Jones, former executive director of the Iowa State Bar Association. **Additional Information:** Office of Admission and Financial Aid at 515-271-2782.

4394 ■ DRAKE UNIVERSITY LAW SCHOOL
2621 Carpenter Ave.
Des Moines, IA 50311
Tel: (515)271-2824
Free: 800-44-DRAKE

E-mail: lawadmit@drake.edu
Web Site: http://www.law.drake.edu
To support the education of law students.
Title of Award: Martin Luther King Law Scholarships **Area, Field, or Subject:** Law. **Level of Education for which Award is Granted:** Undergraduate **Funds Available:** No specific amount.
Eligibility Requirements: Applicants must be female African-American law students who embodies the spirit and values of Martin Luther King and who have demonstrated financial need. **Application Requirements:** Applicants must file FAFSA and application form. **Additional Information:** Established by Naomi Mercer, LW'68. **Additional Information:** Office of Admission and Financial Aid at 515-271-2782.

4395 ■ DRAKE UNIVERSITY LAW SCHOOL
2621 Carpenter Ave.
Des Moines, IA 50311
Tel: (515)271-2824
Free: 800-44-DRAKE
E-mail: lawadmit@drake.edu
Web Site: http://www.law.drake.edu
To support the education of law students.
Title of Award: Forest A. King Scholarships **Area, Field, or Subject:** Law. **Level of Education for which Award is Granted:** Undergraduate **Funds Available:** No specific amount.
Eligibility Requirements: Applicants must be students of Drake University law school. **Application Requirements:** Applicants must file FAFSA and application form. **Additional Information:** Established in memory of Mr. King, LW'25, by his wife, Nonnie. **Additional Information:** Office of Admission and Financial Aid at 515-271-2782.

4396 ■ DRAKE UNIVERSITY LAW SCHOOL
2621 Carpenter Ave.
Des Moines, IA 50311
Tel: (515)271-2824
Free: 800-44-DRAKE
E-mail: lawadmit@drake.edu
Web Site: http://www.law.drake.edu
To support the education of law students.
Title of Award: Verne Lawyer Scholarships **Area, Field, or Subject:** Law. **Level of Education for which Award is Granted:** Undergraduate **Funds Available:** No specific amount.
Eligibility Requirements: Applicants must be students of Drake University Law School. **Application Requirements:** Applicants must file FAFSA and application form. **Additional Information:** Established in 1992 in honor of D. Verne Lawyer, a 1949 graduate of the Law School. **Additional Information:** Office of Admission and Financial Aid at 515-271-2782.

4397 ■ DRAKE UNIVERSITY LAW SCHOOL
2621 Carpenter Ave.
Des Moines, IA 50311
Tel: (515)271-2824
Free: 800-44-DRAKE
E-mail: lawadmit@drake.edu
Web Site: http://www.law.drake.edu
To support the education of law students.
Title of Award: League of Attorneys' Wives Scholarships **Area, Field, or Subject:** Law. **Level of Education for which Award is Granted:** Undergraduate **Funds Available:** No specific amount.
Eligibility Requirements: Applicants must be second year or third year female law students planning a career in public interest law. **Application Requirements:** Applicants must file FAFSA and application form. **Additional Information:** Office of Admission and Financial Aid at 515-271-2782.

4398 ■ DRAKE UNIVERSITY LAW SCHOOL
2621 Carpenter Ave.
Des Moines, IA 50311
Tel: (515)271-2824
Free: 800-44-DRAKE
E-mail: lawadmit@drake.edu
Web Site: http://www.law.drake.edu
To support the education of law students.

Title of Award: Legal Research Service Scholarships **Area, Field, or Subject:** Law. **Level of Education for which Award is Granted:** Undergraduate **Funds Available:** No specific amount.
Eligibility Requirements: Applicants must be the presidents of the Student Legal Research Service. **Application Requirements:** Applicants may contact Office of Admission and Financial Aid for more information. **Additional Information:** Office of Admission and Financial Aid at 515-271-2782.

4399 ■ DRAKE UNIVERSITY LAW SCHOOL
2621 Carpenter Ave.
Des Moines, IA 50311
Tel: (515)271-2824
Free: 800-44-DRAKE
E-mail: lawadmit@drake.edu
Web Site: http://www.law.drake.edu
To support the education of law students.
Title of Award: Frederick D. Lewis Jr. Scholarships **Area, Field, or Subject:** Law. **Level of Education for which Award is Granted:** Undergraduate **Funds Available:** No specific amount.
Eligibility Requirements: Applicants must be students of Drake University law school. **Application Requirements:** Applicants must file FAFSA and application form. **Additional Information:** Established by Patrick D. Kelly, LW'53, in memory of Frederick D. Lewis Jr., a professor at Drake Law School from 1949 to 1959. **Additional Information:** Office of Admission and Financial Aid at 515-271-2782.

4400 ■ DRAKE UNIVERSITY LAW SCHOOL
2621 Carpenter Ave.
Des Moines, IA 50311
Tel: (515)271-2824
Free: 800-44-DRAKE
E-mail: lawadmit@drake.edu
Web Site: http://www.law.drake.edu
To support the education of law students.
Title of Award: Gordon and Delores Madson Scholarships **Area, Field, or Subject:** Law. **Level of Education for which Award is Granted:** Undergraduate **Funds Available:** No specific amount.
Eligibility Requirements: Applicants must be students of Drake University law school. **Application Requirements:** Applicants must file FAFSA and application form. **Additional Information:** Established by Gordon Madson, LW'57, and his wife, Delores. **Additional Information:** Office of Admission and Financial Aid at 515-271-2782.

4401 ■ DRAKE UNIVERSITY LAW SCHOOL
2621 Carpenter Ave.
Des Moines, IA 50311
Tel: (515)271-2824
Free: 800-44-DRAKE
E-mail: lawadmit@drake.edu
Web Site: http://www.law.drake.edu
To support the education of law students.
Title of Award: Jake S. More Scholarships **Area, Field, or Subject:** Law. **Level of Education for which Award is Granted:** Undergraduate **Funds Available:** No specific amount.
Eligibility Requirements: Applicants must be students of Drake University law school. **Application Requirements:** Applicants must file FAFSA and scholarship application form. **Additional Information:** Established by Jake S. More, LW'28. **Additional Information:** Office of Admission and Financial Aid at 515-271-2782.

4402 ■ DRAKE UNIVERSITY LAW SCHOOL
2621 Carpenter Ave.
Des Moines, IA 50311
Tel: (515)271-2824
Free: 800-44-DRAKE
E-mail: lawadmit@drake.edu
Web Site: http://www.law.drake.edu
To support the education of law students.
Title of Award: Dwight D. Opperman Scholarships **Area, Field, or Subject:** Law. **Level of Education for which Award is Granted:** Undergraduate **Number Awarded:** 5. **Funds Available:** Full-tuition plus $10,000. **Duration:** One year.

Eligibility Requirements: Applicants must be accepted as first year students at Drake Law School; must show evidence of superior academic record and potential; must have a high score in law entrance exam; and demonstrate significant community and extracurricular experiences. **Application Requirements:** Applicants must complete the application packet.

4403 ■ DRAKE UNIVERSITY LAW SCHOOL

2621 Carpenter Ave.
Des Moines, IA 50311
Tel: (515)271-2824
Free: 800-44-DRAKE
E-mail: lawadmit@drake.edu
Web Site: http://www.law.drake.edu
To support the education of law students.
Title of Award: Jerome S. Petz, S.J., Scholarships **Area, Field, or Subject:** Law. **Level of Education for which Award is Granted:** Undergraduate **Funds Available:** No specific amount.
Eligibility Requirements: Applicants must be students of Drake University law school. **Application Requirements:** Applicants must file FAFSA and application form. **Additional Information:** Established by the faculty as a memorial in honor of Father Jerome Petz, who taught at the Law School from 1971 to 1979. **Additional Information:** Office of Admission and Financial Aid at 515-271-2782.

4404 ■ DRAKE UNIVERSITY LAW SCHOOL

2621 Carpenter Ave.
Des Moines, IA 50311
Tel: (515)271-2824
Free: 800-44-DRAKE
E-mail: lawadmit@drake.edu
Web Site: http://www.law.drake.edu
To support the education of law students.
Title of Award: Janet Reynoldson Memorial Scholarships **Area, Field, or Subject:** Law. **Level of Education for which Award is Granted:** Undergraduate **Funds Available:** No specific amount.
Eligibility Requirements: Applicants must be students of Drake University law school. **Application Requirements:** Applicants must file FAFSA and application form. **Additional Information:** Established by the family of Janet Reynoldson, LW'65. **Additional Information:** Office of Admission and Financial Aid at 515-271-2782.

4405 ■ DRAKE UNIVERSITY LAW SCHOOL

2621 Carpenter Ave.
Des Moines, IA 50311
Tel: (515)271-2824
Free: 800-44-DRAKE
E-mail: lawadmit@drake.edu
Web Site: http://www.law.drake.edu
To support the education of law students.
Title of Award: Isador M. Robinson Endowment Scholarships **Area, Field, or Subject:** Law. **Level of Education for which Award is Granted:** Undergraduate **Funds Available:** No specific amount.
Eligibility Requirements: Applicants must be second or third year law students of Drake University law school. **Application Requirements:** Applicants must file FAFSA and application form. **Additional Information:** Office of Admission and Financial Aid at 515-271-2782.

4406 ■ DRAKE UNIVERSITY LAW SCHOOL

2621 Carpenter Ave.
Des Moines, IA 50311
Tel: (515)271-2824
Free: 800-44-DRAKE
E-mail: lawadmit@drake.edu
Web Site: http://www.law.drake.edu
To support the education of law students.
Title of Award: Walter and Rita Selvy Scholarships **Area, Field, or Subject:** Law. **Level of Education for which Award is Granted:** Undergraduate **Funds Available:** No specific amount.
Eligibility Requirements: Applicants must be students of Drake University law school. **Application Requirements:** Applicants must file FAFSA and application form. **Additional Information:** Established by Walter, LW'28, and his late wife, Rita Selvy. **Additional Information:** Office of Admission and Financial Aid at 515-271-2782.

4407 ■ DRAKE UNIVERSITY LAW SCHOOL

2621 Carpenter Ave.
Des Moines, IA 50311
Tel: (515)271-2824
Free: 800-44-DRAKE
E-mail: lawadmit@drake.edu
Web Site: http://www.law.drake.edu
To support the education of law students.
Title of Award: Charles "Buck" and Dora Taylor Endowed Law Scholarships **Area, Field, or Subject:** Law. **Level of Education for which Award is Granted:** Undergraduate **Funds Available:** No specific amount. **Duration:** One year.
Eligibility Requirements: Applicants must be students with financial need and have demonstrated a history of academic success while participating in sports at the undergraduate school level. **Application Requirements:** Applicants must submit the General Information Form for Scholarships along with the application for admission. **Additional Information:** Established in honor of 1933 Drake Law School graduate Charles Taylor. **Additional Information:** Office of Admission and Financial Aid at 515-271-2782.

4408 ■ DRAKE UNIVERSITY LAW SCHOOL

2621 Carpenter Ave.
Des Moines, IA 50311
Tel: (515)271-2824
Free: 800-44-DRAKE
E-mail: lawadmit@drake.edu
Web Site: http://www.law.drake.edu
To support the education of law students.
Title of Award: Haemer Wheatcraft Scholarships **Area, Field, or Subject:** Law. **Level of Education for which Award is Granted:** Undergraduate **Funds Available:** No specific amount.
Eligibility Requirements: Applicants must be students of Drake University law school. **Application Requirements:** Applicants must file the FAFSA and the scholarship application. **Additional Information:** Established by friends and associates in honor of Haemer Wheatcraft, LW'33. **Additional Information:** Office of Admission and Financial Aid at 515-271-2782.

4409 ■ DRAKE UNIVERSITY LAW SCHOOL

2621 Carpenter Ave.
Des Moines, IA 50311
Tel: (515)271-2824
Free: 800-44-DRAKE
E-mail: lawadmit@drake.edu
Web Site: http://www.law.drake.edu
To support the education of law students.
Title of Award: Zarley, McKee, Thomte, Voorhees, Sease Law Scholarships **Area, Field, or Subject:** Law. **Level of Education for which Award is Granted:** Undergraduate **Funds Available:** No specific amount.
Eligibility Requirements: Applicants must be students interested in intellectual property law. **Application Requirements:** Applicants must file FAFSA and application form. **Additional Information:** Established by Donald R. Zarley, LW'54; Bruce W. McKee; Dennis L. Thomte; Michael G. Voorhees, LW'68; Edmund J. Sease, LW'67; and John Beehner. **Additional Information:** Office of Admission and Financial Aid at 515-271-2782.

4410 ■ DUTCHESS COUNTY BAR ASSOCIATION

PO Box 4865
Poughkeepsie, NY 12602
Tel: (845)473-2488
Fax: (845)485-1484
E-mail: janna@dutchesscountybar.org
Web Site: http://www.dutchesscountybar.org
To provide financial assistance for the residents of Dutchess County intending to attend an accredited law school.
Title of Award: Joseph H. Gellert/Dutchess County Bar Association Scholarships **Area, Field, or Subject:** Law. **Level of Education for which Award is Granted:** Undergraduate **Funds Available:** $1,000.
Eligibility Requirements: Applicants must be Dutchess County residents who completed at least one year of law school. **Application Require-**

4411 ■ SOCIAL SCIENCES ■ LAW

ments: Applicants must submit application; copy of law school transcript; essay of approximately 500 words describing interest in the law and career aspirations; letter of recommendation; and resume. **Deadline for Receipt:** April 1.

4411 ■ EQUAL JUSTICE WORKS

2120 L St., NW, Ste. 450
Washington, DC 20037-1541
Tel: (202)466-3686
Fax: (202)429-9766
E-mail: info@equaljusticeworks.org
Web Site: http://www.equaljusticeworks.org
To address the shortage of attorneys working on behalf of traditionally under-served populations and causes in the United States and its territories while encouraging partnerships between law firms, corporations and public interest organizations to fund fellowships.
Title of Award: Equal Justice Works Fellowship Program **Area, Field, or Subject:** Law. **Level of Education for which Award is Granted:** Graduate, Undergraduate **Funds Available:** $37,500. **Duration:** Two years.
Eligibility Requirements: Applicants must be third year law students or graduates from an EJW law school who are committed to public interest.
Application Requirements: Applicants must provide a completed application, including a project proposal, a fellowship candidate to carry out the project, and a nonprofit public interest organization identified to host the project; Applicants must also submit a certification form and two hard copies of letters of recommendation; and must attend a scheduled interview if evaluated successfully. **Deadline for Receipt:** September.

4412 ■ EQUITY FOUNDATION

P.O Box 5696
Portland, OR 97228
Tel: (503)231-5759
E-mail: info@equityfoundation.org
Web Site: http://www.equityfoundation.org
To provide financial support to those who are in need.
Title of Award: Bill and Ann Sheperd Legal Scholarships Fund **Area, Field, or Subject:** Law. **Level of Education for which Award is Granted:** Undergraduate **Funds Available:** No specific amount.
Eligibility Requirements: Applicants must be third year law students dedicated to keeping Oregon a hate-free state. **Application Requirements:** Applicants must check the available website for the required materials. **Deadline for Receipt:** June 30. **Additional Information:** Equity Foundation at the above address

4413 ■ FAEGRE & BENSON LLP

2200 Wells Fargo Center
90 S 7th St.
Minneapolis, MN 55402-3901
Tel: (612)766-7000
Free: 800-328-4393
Fax: (612)766-1600
E-mail: info@faegre.com
Web Site: http://www.faegre.com
To encourage and support individuals intending to pursue their legal profession.
Title of Award: Faegre & Benson Diversity Scholarships **Area, Field, or Subject:** Law. **Level of Education for which Award is Granted:** Undergraduate **Number Awarded:** 2. **Funds Available:** $12,000.
Eligibility Requirements: Applicants must be enrolled full-time at an accredited law school in the United States. **Application Requirements:** Applicants must complete the application form, available online; must submit a resume and cover letter; must provide a personal statement explaining their interest in the scholarship program and how diversity has influenced their life and how it impacts the legal profession; must have an undergraduate transcript(s), legal writing sample and two professional recommendations, one of which must be from a law school professor. Application form and other supporting documents must be sent to Faegre & Benson LLP, 2200 Wells Fargo Center, 90 S 7th St., Minneapolis, MN 55402. **Deadline for Receipt:** January 3. **Additional Information:** Dana Gray, Manager of Legal Personnel Services.

4414 ■ FARELLA BRAUN MARTEL LLP

235 Montgomery St., 17th Fl.
Russ Bldg.
San Francisco, CA 94104

Tel: (415)954-4400
Fax: (415)954-4480
E-mail: cloof@fbm.com
Web Site: http://www.fbm.com
To support outstanding, diverse Bay Area law students.
Title of Award: Farella Braun Martel LLP Diversity Scholarships **Area, Field, or Subject:** Law. **Level of Education for which Award is Granted:** Undergraduate **Funds Available:** A total of $25,000 is available.
Eligibility Requirements: Applicants must be current first-year, full or part-time law students who are students of color or from underrepresented backgrounds, who currently attend one of the following local law schools: University of California, Berkeley (Boalt Hall); University of California, Davis (King Hall); University of California, Hastings College of the Law; Golden Gate University; Stanford University; Santa Clara University; or the University of San Francisco. **Application Requirements:** Applicants must submit the completed application form. **Deadline for Receipt:** March 14.

4415 ■ FEDERAL CIRCUIT BAR ASSOCIATION

1620 St. NW, Ste. 900
Washington, DC 20006
Tel: (202)466-3923
Fax: (202)833-1061
Web Site: http://www.fedcirbar.org
To provide financial support for qualified individuals intending to pursue their studies.
Title of Award: Howard T. Markey Memorial Scholarships **Area, Field, or Subject:** Law. **Level of Education for which Award is Granted:** Undergraduate **Funds Available:** $10,000. **Duration:** One year.
Eligibility Requirements: Applicants must be law students showing financial need, demonstrated academic promise, and service, either in undergraduate or in law school. **Application Requirements:** Applicants must submit a college and law school transcript and a one-page curriculum vitae. **Deadline for Receipt:** April 30.

4416 ■ FEDERAL CIRCUIT BAR ASSOCIATION

1620 St. NW, Ste. 900
Washington, DC 20006
Tel: (202)466-3923
Fax: (202)833-1061
Web Site: http://www.fedcirbar.org
To provide financial support for qualified individuals intending to pursue their studies.
Title of Award: Helen W. Nies Scholarships **Area, Field, or Subject:** Law. **Level of Education for which Award is Granted:** Undergraduate **Funds Available:** $10,000. **Duration:** One year.
Eligibility Requirements: Applicants must be women law students showing financial need, demonstrated academic promise, and service, either in undergraduate or in law school. **Application Requirements:** Applicants must submit a college and law school transcript and a one-page curriculum vitae. **Deadline for Receipt:** April 30.

4417 ■ FINNEGAN, HENDERSON, FARABOW, GARRETT & DUNNER LLP

901 New York Ave. NW
Washington, DC 20001
Tel: (202)408-4000
Fax: (202)408-4400
E-mail: info@finnegan.com
Web Site: http://www.finnegan.com
To develop diversity in the workplace and in the field of intellectual property law.
Title of Award: Finnegan, Henderson, Farabow, Garrett & Dunner, LLP Diversity Scholarships **Area, Field, or Subject:** Law. **Level of Education for which Award is Granted:** Undergraduate **Funds Available:** $15,000. **Duration:** One year, renewable.
Eligibility Requirements: Applicant must be enrolled in an American Bar Association accredited law school either as a first year full-time student or second-year part-time student. **Application Requirements:** Applicants must submit current resume; completed scholarship application; undergraduate and, if applicable, graduate transcripts; law school transcripts; a legal writing sample (10 pages); and one to three letters of recommendation. **Deadline for Receipt:** February 29.

4418 ■ FOUNDATION FOR ENHANCING COMMUNITIES
200 N Third St., PO Box 678
Harrisburg, PA 17108-0678
Tel: (717)236-5040
Fax: (717)231-4463
E-mail: dawn@tfec.org
Web Site: http://www.ghf.org
To provide high school students a meaningful, educational and highly-involved look at law and law-related career opportunities.
Title of Award: Pathways to Success Scholarships **Area, Field, or Subject:** Law; Paralegal studies. **Level of Education for which Award is Granted:** Undergraduate **Funds Available:** No specific amount.
Eligibility Requirements: Applicants must be minority students accepted by (in the case of high school students) or enrolled in an accredited institution of higher learning at its main campus or a branch campus located in Central Pennsylvania. **Application Requirements:** Application form can be obtained online. Applicants must provide a copy of high school or college transcript, certified as true and accurate by your guidance counselor, Registrar's Office or equivalent. Applicants must respond to the essay question (maximum of 500 words and typed). If you are in high school, attach a copy of your letter of acceptance to your application. Applicants pursuing post-secondary education should attach a copy of a certification of good standing from the educational institution which they are attending. Submit two letters of recommendation endorsing your candidacy for the Pathways to Success scholarship with your application. Letters of recommendation from teachers, administrators, or community members may be submitted and must reference at least one example of personal interaction with the applicant to underscore the applicant's academic/leadership and/or contribution to community. Applicants must attach a copy of your FAFSA Student Aid Report. With your FAFSA Student Aid Report, please make sure to include the cover letter of the report, which will indicate your EFC (Estimated Family Contribution). **Deadline for Receipt:** March 1. **Additional Information:** Central PA Chapter, Association of Corporate Counsel, c/o Frank Miles, Esq., 27 West Chocolate Ave., Hershey, PA 17033.

4419 ■ BILL AND MELINDA GATES FOUNDATION
PO Box 23350
Seattle, WA 98102
Tel: (206)709-3100
E-mail: info@gatesfoundation.org
Web Site: http://www.gatesfoundation.org
To recognize the critical role played by lawyers in establishing and preserving a civil society and their calling in the spirit of public service.
Title of Award: William H. Gates Public Service Law Scholarships **Area, Field, or Subject:** Law. **Level of Education for which Award is Granted:** Undergraduate **Funds Available:** No specific amount. **Duration:** One year renewable.
Eligibility Requirements: Applicants must be incoming first year students in the University of Washington Law School. **Application Requirements:** Applicants must submit a cover letter; an essay, not to exceed 750 words, discussing the factors that have shaped the applicants vision and influenced his/her public service commitment; two recommendations related to commitment to potential contributions to public service; Gates PSL Scholarship recommendation form; resume with details of public service experience; and signed application form. **Deadline for Receipt:** January 15. **Additional Information:** PO Box 353020 Seattle, WA 98195; gatespsl@u.washington.edu.

4420 ■ GONZAGA UNIVERSITY SCHOOL OF LAW
PO Box 3528
Spokane, WA 99220
Tel: (509)323-3700
E-mail: sharmon@lawschool.gonzaga.edu
Web Site: http://www.law.gonzaga.edu
To help individuals in the pursuit of their educational goals.
Title of Award: Thomas More Scholarships **Area, Field, or Subject:** Law. **Level of Education for which Award is Granted:** Undergraduate **Funds Available:** No specific amount. **Duration:** One year renewable.
Eligibility Requirements: Applicants must be US or Canadian citizens who are entering law school for the first time as first year students. **Application Requirements:** Applicants must submit their completed application and two letters of recommendation. **Deadline for Receipt:** March 1.

4421 ■ GRAND HAVEN AREA COMMUNITY FOUNDATION
1 S. Harbor Dr.
Grand Haven, MI 49417
Tel: (616)842-6378
Fax: (616)842-9518
E-mail: bpost@ghacf.org
Web Site: http://www.ghacf.org
To improve and enhance the quality of life in the Tri-Cities area by serving as a leader, catalyst and resource for philanthropy; to strive for community improvement through strategic grantmaking in such fields as arts, education, health, environment, youth, social services and other human needs.
Title of Award: Scott A. Flahive Memorial Scholarship Fund **Area, Field, or Subject:** Criminal justice. **Level of Education for which Award is Granted:** Undergraduate **Funds Available:** No specific amount.
Eligibility Requirements: Applicants must be students pursuing career in the field of law enforcement and/or criminal justice. **Application Requirements:** Applicants must submit: completed application form; current high school or college transcript; Student Aid Report (SAR) from the Free Application for Federal Student Aid (FAFSA), unless applying for scholarships that do not consider financial need; and letter of recommendation. **Deadline for Receipt:** March 7. **Additional Information:** 616-842-6378.

4422 ■ GRAND HAVEN AREA COMMUNITY FOUNDATION
1 S. Harbor Dr.
Grand Haven, MI 49417
Tel: (616)842-6378
Fax: (616)842-9518
E-mail: bpost@ghacf.org
Web Site: http://www.ghacf.org
To improve and enhance the quality of life in the Tri-Cities area by serving as a leader, catalyst and resource for philanthropy; to strive for community improvement through strategic grantmaking in such fields as the arts, education, health, environment, youth, social services and other human needs.
Title of Award: Hierholzer-Fojtik Scholarship Fund **Area, Field, or Subject:** Law. **Level of Education for which Award is Granted:** Undergraduate **Funds Available:** No specific amount.
Eligibility Requirements: Applicants must be Grand Haven High School graduates planning to pursue law as a career. **Application Requirements:** Applicants must submit: completed application form; current high school or college transcript; Student Aid Report (SAR) from the Free Application for Federal Student Aid (FAFSA), unless applying for scholarships that do not consider financial need; and letter of recommendation. **Deadline for Receipt:** March 7. **Additional Information:** 616-842-6378.

4423 ■ GREATER PHILADELPHIA LAW LIBRARY ASSOCIATION
PO Box 335
Philadelphia, PA 19105
Tel: (215)977-2779
E-mail: malmendarez@wolfblock.com
Web Site: http://www.gplla.org
To fulfill the educational mission of GPLLA; to support the recruitment of law librarians to the profession as a whole and to GPLLA in particular.
Title of Award: Greater Philadelphia Law Library Association Scholarships **Area, Field, or Subject:** Law. **Level of Education for which Award is Granted:** Undergraduate **Funds Available:** $1,000.
Eligibility Requirements: Applicants must be students interested in pursuing a career in law librarianship; must be students accepted and/or registered at an ALA-accredited library school (minimum of half-time status) who will continue as a student for another semester or quarter; must reside within the geographic area covered by GPLLA. **Application Requirements:** Applicants must submit a certified copy of the graduate library school transcript; must submit a completed application for the student scholarship; must submit a resume; two letters of recommendation from teachers and/or employers with application; must submit a personal statement that indicates a genuine interest in the profession of law librarianship with the application. **Deadline for Receipt:** May 16.

4424 ■ HARTFORD FOUNDATION FOR PUBLIC GIVING
10 Columbus Blvd., 8th Flr.
Hartford, CT 06106
Tel: (860)548-1888
Fax: (860)524-8346

E-mail: hfpg@hfpg.org
Web Site: http://www.hfpg.org
To provide educational assistance for students entering or enrolled as undergraduate students at Manchester Community College.
Title of Award: Officer Brian A. Aselton Memorial Scholarships **Area, Field, or Subject:** Criminal Justice. **Level of Education for which Award is Granted:** Undergraduate **Number Awarded:** 1. **Funds Available:** $500-$1,000.
Eligibility Requirements: Applicants must be Connecticut residents, majoring in Criminal Justice and planning a career in law enforcement. **Application Requirements:** Applicants may obtain the application materials from the Manchester Community College. **Deadline for Receipt:** March 1. **Additional Information:** Donna Nicholson, Coordinator, Criminal Justice Program, Manchester Community College, 60 Bidwell St., Manchester, CT 06040.

4425 ■ HARTFORD FOUNDATION FOR PUBLIC GIVING
10 Columbus Blvd., 8th Flr.
Hartford, CT 06106
Tel: (860)548-1888
Fax: (860)524-8346
E-mail: hfpg@hfpg.org
Web Site: http://www.hfpg.org
To provide scholarship for graduating high school seniors.
Title of Award: Connecticut Association of Women Police Scholarships **Area, Field, or Subject:** Criminal Justice. **Level of Education for which Award is Granted:** Undergraduate **Number Awarded:** 1-4. **Funds Available:** No specific amount.
Eligibility Requirements: Applicants must be residents of Connecticut; must be graduating high school senior entering a four-year college or university; must be majoring in criminal justice; and must demonstrate financial need. **Application Requirements:** Applicants may obtain application materials from their high school guidance counselor or download online at www.cawp.net. **Deadline for Receipt:** April 30. **Additional Information:** gmcdonnell@coventryct.org.

4426 ■ HISPANIC LAWYERS ASSOCIATION OF ILLINOIS
321 South Plymouth Court, Ste. 600
Chicago, IL 60604
Tel: (312)345-9200
E-mail: hlai-cs@att.net
Web Site: http://www.hlai.org
To help increase excellence among individuals pursuing careers in the legal field.
Title of Award: Barbri Scholarships for Bar Preparation **Area, Field, or Subject:** Law. **Level of Education for which Award is Granted:** Undergraduate **Funds Available:** $500-$1,000.
Eligibility Requirements: Program is open to post-graduation law students that secure legal or related employment with a government agency, a non-profit organization, or public interest agency intending to apply in a BARBRI preparation course. **Application Requirements:** Applicants may download application form at HLAI website. Complete and submit the application form (including the two short essays about the applicant's commitment to public interest law and to serving the legal and social needs of the Hispanic community). Applicants must also provide a copy of law school transcript. **Deadline for Receipt:** April 7. **Additional Information:** Christina Lopez-Nutzman; Wessels and Pautsch, P.C. 35 West Monroe, Suite 1120 Chicago, IL 60603; 312-629-9300 chlopez@chgo.w-p.com.

4427 ■ HISPANIC LAWYERS ASSOCIATION OF ILLINOIS
321 South Plymouth Court, Ste. 600
Chicago, IL 60604
Tel: (312)345-9200
E-mail: hlai-cs@att.net
Web Site: http://www.hlai.org
To help increase excellence among individuals pursuing careers in the legal field.
Title of Award: Hispanic Lawyers Association of Illinois Public Interest Fellowships **Area, Field, or Subject:** Law. **Level of Education for which Award is Granted:** Undergraduate **Funds Available:** $2,500.
Eligibility Requirements: Program is open to law students in need of a summer stipend and have secured legal or related employment with a

government agency, a non-profit organization, or public interest agency. **Application Requirements:** Applicants may download an application form at HLAI website. Complete and submit the application form (including the submission of two short essays about your commitment to public interest law and to serving the legal and social needs of the Hispanic community). Applicants must also provide a copy of law school transcript. **Deadline for Receipt:** April 7. **Additional Information:** Christina Lopez-Nutzman; Wessels and Pautsch, P.C. 35 West Monroe, Suite 1120 Chicago, IL 60603; 312-629-9300 chlopez@chgo.w-p.com.

4428 ■ HISPANIC LAWYERS ASSOCIATION OF ILLINOIS
321 South Plymouth Court, Ste. 600
Chicago, IL 60604
Tel: (312)345-9200
E-mail: hlai-cs@att.net
Web Site: http://www.hlai.org
To help increase excellence among individuals pursuing careers in the legal field.
Title of Award: Kaplan Scholarships **Area, Field, or Subject:** Law. **Level of Education for which Award is Granted:** Undergraduate **Funds Available:** No specific amount.
Eligibility Requirements: Program is open to law students that demonstrate a genuine interest in pursuing a legal career. **Application Requirements:** Applicants must submit completed application (available at the website) and submit along with two short essays about your commitment to public interest law and to serving the legal and social needs of the Hispanic community. Applicants must also provide a copy of law school transcript. **Deadline for Receipt:** April 7. **Additional Information:** Christina Lopez-Nutzman; Wessels and Pautsch, P.C. 35 West Monroe, Suite 1120 Chicago, IL 60603; 312-629-9300 chlopez@chgo.w-p.com.

4429 ■ HISPANIC NATIONAL BAR ASSOCIATION
1111 Pennysylvania Ave. NW
Washington, DC 20004
Tel: (202)223-4777
Web Site: http://www.hnba.com
To promote diversity in the legal profession by providing financial assistance to law students attending an ABA-accredited law school.
Title of Award: ABA Legal Opportunity Scholarship Funds **Area, Field, or Subject:** Law. **Level of Education for which Award is Granted:** Undergraduate **Funds Available:** $5,000 renewable up to $15,000. **Duration:** One year.
Eligibility Requirements: Applicants must be students entering their first year in law school; must have achieved a minimum cumulative grade point average of 2.5 on a 4.0 grading scale at their undergraduate degree at the time the application is submitted; must be citizens or permanent residents of the USA. **Application Requirements:** Applicants must complete the attached application form and must have the following documents: personal statement, recommendation, transcript, and personal, family and educational background. **Deadline for Receipt:** March 1.

4430 ■ HISPANIC NATIONAL BAR ASSOCIATION
1111 Pennysylvania Ave. NW
Washington, DC 20004
Tel: (202)223-4777
Web Site: http://www.hnba.com
To provide financial support to the nest generation of Hispanic leaders.
Title of Award: HNBF Princeton Review Duard Bradshaw Memorial Scholarships **Area, Field, or Subject:** Law. **Level of Education for which Award is Granted:** Undergraduate **Funds Available:** $1,000.
Eligibility Requirements: Applicants must be of Hispanic or Latino heritage; must be U.S. citizens or legal permanent residents; must be juniors enrolled at least part-time in an accredited U.S. college or university; must have a minimum cumulative grade point average of 2.75 on a 4.00 scale; must demonstrate active participation and leadership in an undergraduate student Hispanic/Latino organization. **Application Requirements:** Applicants must submit an information sheet, cover letter and resume, personal essay and a recommendation letter from a professor (sealed and mailed in with application packet). Application materials must be mailed in one envelope to: Hispanic National Bar Foundation, 1900 K St. NW, Ste. 100, Washington, DC 20006. **Deadline for Receipt:** June 1.

4431 ■ HISPANIC NATIONAL BAR ASSOCIATION

1111 Pennysylvania Ave. NW
Washington, DC 20004
Tel: (202)223-4777
Web Site: http://www.hnba.com
To assist graduating high school students who are interested in the law to attend college.
Title of Award: Justicia En Diversidad Scholarships **Area, Field, or Subject:** Law. **Level of Education for which Award is Granted:** Undergraduate **Funds Available:** 1,500.
Eligibility Requirements: Applicants must be high school students interested in law; must have à 2.5 grade point average on a 4.0 scale; must be attending a U.S. school and must be planning to attend law school; must attend an accredited two or four-year U.S. college on a full time basis during the academic year. **Application Requirements:** Candidates must attach the current transcript of record, two recommendation letters (should discuss any or all of the following: academic and extracurricular achievements, community involvement, motivation, and leadership), personal statement, honors, paid and volunteer work, and extracurricular activities, and financial information. Application form is available at the website; send completed application to: La Alianza, Justicia en Diversidad Foundation, c/o Alexander A. Boni-Saenz, Harvard Law School, Cambridge, MA 02138. **Deadline for Receipt:** February 1.

4432 ■ HISPANIC NATIONAL BAR ASSOCIATION

1111 Pennysylvania Ave. NW
Washington, DC 20004
Tel: (202)223-4777
Web Site: http://www.hnba.com
To provide financial assistance to qualified individuals in pursuit of higher education.
Title of Award: MALDEF Law School Scholarships **Area, Field, or Subject:** Law. **Level of Education for which Award is Granted:** Undergraduate **Funds Available:** $1,000-$4,000.
Eligibility Requirements: Applicants must be students entering their first, second or third year in law school; must have an outstanding academic records, including in their participation and leadership in extracurricular activities; must be enrolled as a full time student. **Application Requirements:** Applicants must complete and sign MALDEF scholarship application form; must submit a current resume; must provide a typed personal statement of 750 words or less; must have the official undergraduate transcript or photocopy of an official transcript; have a letter of recommendation describing their involvement in the Latino community from a person familiar with that involvement; have a letter of recommendation from a college, or law school professor; and a complete financial statement from the school they are or will be attending that indicates both the financial assistance. **Deadline for Receipt:** October 1.

4433 ■ HISPANIC SCHOLARSHIP FUND

55 Second St., Ste. 1500
San Francisco, CA 94105
877-473-4636
Fax: (415)808-2302
E-mail: info@hsf.net
Web Site: http://www.hsf.net
To provide financial assistance to students of Hispanic heritage.
Title of Award: HSF/Wal-Mart Stores Inc. Scholarship Program **Area, Field, or Subject:** Marketing and distribution; Accounting; Business; Finance; Management; Computer and information sciences; Information science and technology; Civil engineering; Construction; Electrical engineering; Geology; Engineering, Industrial; Fashion design; Law; **Level of Education for which Award is Granted:** Graduate, Undergraduate **Funds Available:** $2,500.
Eligibility Requirements: Applicant must be of Hispanic heritage; U.S. citizen or legal permanent resident with a valid permanent resident card or passport stamped I-551; enrolled as sophomore, junior, senior undergraduate or First or Second year Master student in a full-time degree-seeking program at an accredited U.S. institution in the U.S., Puerto Rico, U.S. Virgin Islands or Guam; have a minimum 3.0 GPA on a 4.0 scale or 4.00 on a 5.00 scale; must apply for Federal Financing Aid; pursuing his/her first undergraduate or graduate degree. Undergraduate students must be majoring in: Marketing, Accounting, Business, Finance, Management, Computer Science, Computer Programming, Information Technology (IT),

Civil Engineering, Construction, Electrical Engineering, Environmental/Geological Engineering, Industrial Engineering, and Fashion. Master's students must be majoring in: Business, Finance, Marketing, Civil Engineering, Construction, Electrical Engineering, Environmental/Geological Engineering and Law. **Application Requirements:** Applications must be submitted using the HSF online application system. **Additional Information:** In partnership with Wal-Mart Stores, Inc. **Deadline for Receipt:** March 15. **Additional Information:** scholar1@hsf.net.

4434 ■ INDIGENOUS BAR ASSOCIATION

9785-152B St., No. 9
Surrey, BC, Canada V3R 9W2
Tel: (604)951-8807
Fax: (604)951-8806
E-mail: glangan@indigenousbar.ca
Web Site: http://www.indigenousbar.ca
To provide assistance to qualified individuals who want to pursue their education.
Title of Award: IBA Law Student Scholarships Foundation **Area, Field, or Subject:** Law. **Level of Education for which Award is Granted:** Undergraduate **Funds Available:** $2,000. **Duration:** One year.
Eligibility Requirements: Applicant must be an Indigenous law student currently enrolled in law school who, at a minimum, has substantially completed their first year of legal studies; must have demonstrated interest in serving the Indigenous community and the creator with honor and integrity. **Application Requirements:** Applicant must complete the application form available online; must submit a short personal essay describing why they should receive the scholarship, including financial need, community involvement, as well as his/her goals and career aspirations; must enclose two letters of recommendations. Application form and other supporting documents must be sent to Germaine Langan, No. 9, 9785-152B St., Surrey, BC V3R 9W2. **Deadline for Receipt:** June 1.

4435 ■ INTELLECTUAL PROPERTY OWNERS ASSOCIATION

1255 23rd St. NW, Ste. 200
Washington, DC 20037
Tel: (202)466-2396
Fax: (202)466-2893
E-mail: info@ipo.org
Web Site: http://www.ipo.org
To improve knowledge and education in intellectual property rights and to recognize outstanding achievement in the fields of invention, creativity, and IP rights.
Title of Award: Donald W. Banner Corporate Intern Scholarships **Area, Field, or Subject:** Law. **Level of Education for which Award is Granted:** Undergraduate **Funds Available:** $10,000.
Eligibility Requirements: Applicants must be law students who have completed an internship in a corporate intellectual property law department and are intending to pursue a career in intellectual property law. **Application Requirements:** Applicants must complete the scholarship application form. **Additional Information:** 202-466-2396.

4436 ■ INTERNATIONAL ASSOCIATION OF LAW ENFORCEMENT INTELLIGENCE ANALYSTS

PO box 13857
Richmond, VA 23225
Tel: (804)565-2059
Fax: (804)565-2059
E-mail: admin@ialeia.org
Web Site: http://www.ialeia.org
To strive for professionalism in the intelligence field by promoting career development and continued education.
Title of Award: Jorge Espejal Contreras Memorial Scholarships **Area, Field, or Subject:** Intelligence Service; Statistics; Criminal Justice. **Level of Education for which Award is Granted:** Graduate, Undergraduate **Number Awarded:** 2. **Funds Available:** $1,000.
Eligibility Requirements: Program is open to active IALEIA members or immediate family members enrolled in an intelligence, analysis, criminal justice, or other related undergraduate or graduate program at an accredited academic institution; must be based on full-time or part-time enrollment in an accredited college/university and can be on campus or via distance-learning. **Application Requirements:** Applicants should download application from the IALEIA website and submit to the IALEIA

Training, Education, and Career Development Committee. Eligible submissions must be provided in English. Applicants must submit their work electronically to the attention of the TE&CD Director and a signed original copy to be mailed. Application must include a mandatory 1,000-1,500 word essay on: The Future of Law Enforcement Intelligence as a Profession. Mail application package to: IALEIA Scholarship Program, Attn: IALEIA TE&CD, 705 Somerset Drive, El Paso, Texas 79912, USA. **Deadline for Receipt:** May 16.

4437 ■ INTERNATIONAL CENTER FOR NOT-FOR-PROFIT LAW
1126 16th St. NW, Ste. 400
Washington, DC 20036
Tel: (202)452-8600
Fax: (202)452-8555
E-mail: andrea@ecnl.org.hu
Web Site: http://www.icnl.org
To provide financial assistance to develop projects that reflect student interests and skills and to assist with the student's career development.
Title of Award: Internships in International Civil Society Law **Area, Field, or Subject:** Law. **Level of Education for which Award is Granted:** Undergraduate **Number Awarded:** 1. **Funds Available:** No specific amount. **Duration:** Ten weeks.
Eligibility Requirements: Applicants should be enrolled in an accredited law school. Good research, writing and analytical skills and foreign language is a plus eligibility. **Application Requirements:** Applicants must submit resume, writing sample, and a cover letter. **Deadline for Receipt:** April 30. **Additional Information:** Human Resources at hr@icnl.org.

4438 ■ INTERNATIONAL CENTER FOR NOT-FOR-PROFIT LAW
1126 16th St. NW, Ste. 400
Washington, DC 20036
Tel: (202)452-8600
Fax: (202)452-8555
E-mail: andrea@ecnl.org.hu
Web Site: http://www.icnl.org
To provide financial assistance to students seeking a unique opportunity to be involved in the promotion of an enabling legal environment for civil society, freedom of association and public participation around the world.
Title of Award: Spring Internship in International NGO Law **Area, Field, or Subject:** Law. **Level of Education for which Award is Granted:** Undergraduate **Funds Available:** No specific amount.
Eligibility Requirements: Applicants must come from Washington, DC; must be enrolled in an accredited law school; must possess good research, writing and analytical skills; and must have demonstrable individual initiative and ability to work as part of a team. **Application Requirements:** Applicants must submit a cover letter, resume and writing samples (not longer than 5 pages). **Deadline for Receipt:** February 1.

4439 ■ INTERNATIONAL FRANCHISE ASSOCIATION
1501 K St. NW, Ste. 350
Washington, DC 20005
Tel: (202)628-8000
Fax: (202)628-0812
Web Site: http://www.franchise.org
To recognize and support academic achievement among diverse law students.
Title of Award: Franchise Law Diversity Scholarship Awards **Area, Field, or Subject:** Law. **Level of Education for which Award is Granted:** Undergraduate **Funds Available:** $4,000. **Duration:** One year.
Eligibility Requirements: Applicants must be enrolled in an ABA-accredited law schools. Applicants must have 2L or 3L status during the period of the scholarship, and they must be enrolled in at least one course oriented towards franchise law (e.g., Torts, Unfair Trade Practices, Trade Secrets, Antitrust, Trademarks, Contracts, Agency, Securities). Applicants must be considered members of diverse groups (African American, American Indian, Hispanic American, Asian American, or Gay/Lesbian). **Application Requirements:** Applicants must submit completed application form. **Deadline for Receipt:** February 15. **Additional Information:** Miriam L. Brewer, Director of Diversity, IFA Educational Foundation, 1501 K Street, N.W., Suite 350 Washington, D.C. 20005.

4440 ■ IRANIAN AMERICAN BAR ASSOCIATION
1025 Connecticut Ave. NW, Ste. 1012
Washington, DC 20036

E-mail: iaba@iaba.us
Web Site: http://www.iaba.us
To recognize the commitment of law students to the advancement of the Iranian American community.
Title of Award: Iranian American Bar Association Scholarships **Area, Field, or Subject:** Law. **Level of Education for which Award is Granted:** Undergraduate **Funds Available:** $2,000. **Duration:** One year.
Eligibility Requirements: Applicants must be of Iranian heritage or committed to the advancement of the Iranian American community and IABA's mission; must be enrolled in an accredited law school in US; must be in the position to accept the scholarship in the school year for which it is being awarded; and must be full-time students. **Application Requirements:** Applicants must submit a duly completed National Scholarship Application Form; a detailed resume; a statement or essay written by the applicant (no more than one single-sided 1.5 spaced typewritten page); and official law school and college transcripts. **Deadline for Receipt:** June.

4441 ■ ITALIAN AMERICAN LAWYERS ASSOCIATION
155 South El Molino Ave., Ste. 202
Pasadena, CA 91101
Tel: (626)793-7788
Fax: (626)793-1013
E-mail: jcapeloto@capelotolaw.com
Web Site: http://www.iala.lawzone.com
To inspire excellence in the practice of law by rendering financial aid and assistance for individuals intending to pursue legal education.
Title of Award: Italian American Lawyers Association Annual Scholarships **Area, Field, or Subject:** Law. **Level of Education for which Award is Granted:** Undergraduate **Funds Available:** $2,500. **Duration:** One year.
Eligibility Requirements: Program is open to individuals pursuing legal education. **Application Requirements:** Applicants must submit completed application available in the website and must provide a copy of their transcript. In some cases, applicants may also be asked to attend a personal interview. **Deadline for Receipt:** September 30. **Additional Information:** IALA.

4442 ■ JAMAICAN CANADIAN ASSOCIATION
995 Arrow Rd.
Toronto, ON, Canada M9M 2Z5
Tel: (416)746-5772
Fax: (416)746-7035
E-mail: info@jcassoc.org
Web Site: http://www.jcassoc.org
To provide financial assistance to students from the Caribbean/ African community, who are pursuing postsecondary studies in Ontario universities/colleges.
Title of Award: Jamaica National Building Society Scholarships **Area, Field, or Subject:** Business; Law; Science; Technology; Nursing. **Level of Education for which Award is Granted:** Undergraduate **Number Awarded:** 2. **Funds Available:** $1,000. **Duration:** One year.
Eligibility Requirements: Applicant must be a Canadian citizen or landed immigrant of Caribbean or African background; must be enrolled as a full-time first-year student at an Ontario university/college or other postsecondary institution; must demonstrate remarkable academic performance or progress in high school; must demonstrate involvement and leadership in campus and/or community activities; must demonstrate financial need. **Application Requirements:** Application forms are available online and must be sent to The Jamaican Canadian Association Center, 995 Arrow Rd., Toronto M9M 2Z5. **Additional Information:** Scholarship is donated by the Jamaica National Building Society, a financial institution that facilitates money transfers from Canada. **Deadline for Receipt:** July 25.

4443 ■ JAPANESE AMERICAN BAR ASSOCIATION
PO Box 86812
Los Angeles, CA 90086
Tel: (213)738-6746
E-mail: dyokoyama@swlaw.edu
Web Site: http://www.jabaonline.org
To encourage pursuits in legal education among law students with ethnic backgrounds.

Title of Award: Japanese American Bar Association Scholarships **Area, Field, or Subject:** Law. **Level of Education for which Award is Granted:** Undergraduate **Funds Available:** $1,500.
Eligibility Requirements: Applicants must be law students of various ethnic backgrounds. **Application Requirements:** Applicants must submit completed application along with their most recent law school transcript, current resume; and a personal statement of no more than 500 words. **Deadline for Receipt:** January 14. **Additional Information:** JABA Educational Foundation at the above address.

4444 ■ JAPANESE AMERICAN CITIZENS LEAGUE

1765 Sutter St.
San Francisco, CA 94115
Tel: (415)921-5225
Fax: (415)921-4671
E-mail: jacl@jacl.org
Web Site: http://www.jacl.org
To encourage individuals to pursue their legal profession.
Title of Award: Thomas T. Hayashi Memorial Scholarships **Area, Field, or Subject:** Law. **Level of Education for which Award is Granted:** Graduate, Undergraduate **Funds Available:** $60,000. **Duration:** One year.
Eligibility Requirements: Applicants must be active National JACL members at either an individual or student/youth level; must be planning to attend full-time at a college, university, trade school, business school, or any other institution of higher learning within the United States at the undergraduate or graduate school level. Entering freshman applicant must be a high school senior. **Application Requirements:** Application forms are available online at www.jacl.org/join.html. **Deadline for Receipt:** March 1 (entering freshman) and April 1 (all applications excluding entering freshman).

4445 ■ JEWISH VOCATIONAL SERVICE

216 W Jackson Blvd., Ste. 700
Chicago, IL 60606
Tel: (312)673-3400
Fax: (312)553-5544
E-mail: jvs@jvschicago.org
Web Site: http://www.jvschicago.org
To support the education of a Jewish college or graduate student.
Title of Award: Jewish Federation Academic Scholarships **Area, Field, or Subject:** Medicine; Education; Social work; Arts; Public health; Urban affairs/design/planning; Law. **Level of Education for which Award is Granted:** Graduate, Undergraduate **Funds Available:** More than $500,000 each year.
Eligibility Requirements: Applicant must be Jewish; be born or raised in either: Cook County, Chicago metropolitan area, or Northwest Indiana; or have one continuous year of full-time employment in Cook County or Chicago metropolitan area prior to starting professional education; must intend to remain in the Chicago metropolitan area after completing school; must be entering as a full-time student in an accredited professional graduate program or entering as junior or senior undergraduate student at an accredited professional education program; and must be demonstrating career promise in a helping profession. **Application Requirements:** Applicants must submit a completed Application Data Form; Career Statement Form; Budget Worksheet; and Academic Budget form as an attachment to jvsscholarship@jvschicago.org. In addition, applicants must send by mail a Legal Domicility Form; two letter of reference form; IRS Forms; parents' or spouse's IRS; documentation of tuition cost; Release of Information form; and official transcripts. **Deadline for Receipt:** February 15. **Additional Information:** 312-673-3457.

4446 ■ KEGLER, BROWN, HILL AND RITTER

Capitol Sq., Ste. 1800
65 E State St.
Columbus, OH 43215-4294
Tel: (614)462-5400
Fax: (614)464-2634
E-mail: info@keglerbrown.com
Web Site: http://www.keglerbrown.com
To assist minority students financially with their legal education.
Title of Award: Kegler Brown Minority Merit Scholarships **Area, Field, or Subject:** Law. **Level of Education for which Award is Granted:**

Undergraduate **Number Awarded:** 1. **Funds Available:** No specific amount.
Eligibility Requirements: Applicant must be a minority student studying law. **Application Requirements:** Students may contact the office for more information about the scholarship. **Additional Information:** Jeff Dennis at 614-462-5430, or jdennis@keglerbrown.com.

4447 ■ KENTUCKY PARALEGAL ASSOCIATION

PO Box 2675
Louisville, KY 40201-2675
E-mail: kentuckyparalegal@insightbb.com
Web Site: http://www.kypa.org
To provide financial assistance to those students who are in need.
Title of Award: Kentucky Paralegal Association Student Scholarships **Area, Field, or Subject:** Paralegal studies. **Level of Education for which Award is Granted:** Undergraduate **Funds Available:** $1,000.
Eligibility Requirements: Applicants must be enrolled in a paralegal program within the Commonwealth of Kentucky; must have at least 12 credit hours of paralegal course work completed with a GPA in those courses of 3.50 or higher and an overall GPA of 3.25 or higher. **Application Requirements:** Applicants must submit the following: application form (typed); 2 letters of recommendation and forms; one writing sample; an essay and Official transcript. **Deadline for Receipt:** June 30. **Additional Information:** Kentucky Paralegal Association at the above address.

4448 ■ LANE POWELL PC

1420 5th Ave., Ste. 4100
Seattle, WA 98101
Tel: (206)223-7000
Fax: (206)223-7107
E-mail: infoatslanepowell.com
Web Site: http://www.lanepowell.com
To support the education of a minority law student.
Title of Award: George V. Powell Diversity Scholarships **Area, Field, or Subject:** Law. **Level of Education for which Award is Granted:** Undergraduate **Funds Available:** $6,000.
Eligibility Requirements: Applicants must be second year students in good standing at an ABA accredited law school. Students in four-year joint degree programs will be considered after third year. **Application Requirements:** Applicants must submit a cover letter including a statement indicating eligibility to participate in the program; a resume; current copy of law school transcript; legal writing sample; and a list of two or three professional or academic references. **Additional Information:** Len Roden, Manager of Attorney Recruiting at 206-223-6123, or redenl@lanepowell.com.

4449 ■ LAW FOUNDATION OF BRITISH COLUMBIA

1340-605 Robson St.
Vancouver, BC, Canada V6B 5J3
Tel: (604)688-2337
Fax: (604)688-4586
E-mail: lfbc@tlfbc.org
Web Site: http://www.lawfoundationbc.org
To provide financial assistance to qualified individuals who want to pursue their law career.
Title of Award: Law Foundation of British Columbia Graduate Fellowships **Area, Field, or Subject:** Law. **Level of Education for which Award is Granted:** Undergraduate **Number Awarded:** 5. **Funds Available:** $13,750. **Duration:** One year.
Eligibility Requirements: Applicants must be either residents of British Columbia, graduates of British Columbia law school, or members of the British Columbia Bar; must devote themselves primarily to full-time graduate studies in law or a law related area. **Application Requirements:** Applicants must complete the application form available online; must have transcript of records, and three letters of reference. Application form and other supporting documents must be sent to Law Foundation of British Columbia, 1340-605 Robson St., Vancouver, BC V6B 5J3. **Deadline for Receipt:** January 4.

4450 ■ LAW SOCIETY OF PRINCE EDWARD ISLAND

PO Box 128
49 Water St.

Charlottetown, PE, Canada C1A 7K2
Tel: (902)566-1666
Fax: (902)368-7557
E-mail: lawsociety@lspei.pe.ca
Web Site: http://www.lspei.pe.ca
To provide scholarship assistance to deserving students who want to pursue their studies.
Title of Award: Prince Edward Island Law Student Scholarships **Area, Field, or Subject:** Law. **Level of Education for which Award is Granted:** Undergraduate **Funds Available:** $1,000. **Duration:** One year.
Eligibility Requirements: Applicant must be a student enrolled or accepted for enrollment as a full-time law student at an accredited university law school for the academic year; must be a resident of Prince Edward Island; must demonstrate scholastic achievement in his or her last year of academic study; and must demonstrate financial need. **Application Requirements:** Applicant must complete the application form available online; must submit an official transcript of record and curriculum vitae. Application form and other supporting documents must be sent to The Law Society of PEI Scholarship Committee, 49 Water St., PO Box 128, Charlottetown, PE C1A 7K2. **Deadline for Receipt:** July 31.

4451 ■ MACOMB COUNTY BAR FOUNDATION

40 N Main St., Ste. 435
Mount Clemens, MI 48043
Tel: (586)468-2940
Fax: (586)468-6926
E-mail: mcba@macombbar.org
Web Site: http://www.macombbar.org
To provide financial assistance for second or third year law students enrolled in evening classes at the University of Detroit Mercy Law School.
Title of Award: Philip F. Greco Memorial Scholarships **Area, Field, or Subject:** Law. **Level of Education for which Award is Granted:** Undergraduate **Funds Available:** $3,000.
Eligibility Requirements: Applicants must be enrolled as law degree candidates in evening classes at the University of Detroit Marcy Law School. They must demonstrate a need for financial assistance, good academic standing (2.5 GPA or above), and the ability to achieve success as a lawyer. **Application Requirements:** Applications can be downloaded online. The application packet must include: completed application; candidates most recent law school transcript; resume; three letters of recommendation; a personal statement in which the candidate discusses his/her inertness in law, reason for applying for scholarship, career goals and any other pertinent information he/she would like the Scholarship Committee to know. **Deadline for Receipt:** January 25. **Additional Information:** Macomb County Bar Foundation at the above address.

4452 ■ MACOMB COUNTY BAR FOUNDATION

40 N Main St., Ste. 435
Mount Clemens, MI 48043
Tel: (586)468-2940
Fax: (586)468-6926
E-mail: mcba@macombbar.org
Web Site: http://www.macombbar.org
To award scholarships for students enrolled in Macomb County Community College who have been affected by Michigan's economic circumstances.
Title of Award: Trustees College Scholarships **Area, Field, or Subject:** Law. **Level of Education for which Award is Granted:** Undergraduate **Funds Available:** $2,500 (Award is for tuition, fees and other educational expenses.)
Eligibility Requirements: Applicants for the Macomb County Bar Foundation Trustees Scholarship must be enrolled or accepted for enrollment at Macomb Community College at least part-time (six credit hours). **Application Requirements:** Applicants may download application online. The application packet must include: completed application; brief summary of applicant's educational and career goals; resume; three letters of recommendation; a personal statement in which the candidate discuss their interest in law, reason for applying for scholarship, career goals and any other pertinent information he/she would like the Scholarship Committee to know about. **Deadline for Receipt:** January 25. **Additional Information:** Macomb County Bar Foundation at the above address.

4453 ■ MACOMB COUNTY BAR FOUNDATION

40 N Main St., Ste. 435
Mount Clemens, MI 48043
Tel: (586)468-2940
Fax: (586)468-6926
E-mail: mcba@macombbar.org
Web Site: http://www.macombbar.org
To award scholarships for pursuits in the study of law.
Title of Award: Trustees Law School Scholarships **Area, Field, or Subject:** Law. **Level of Education for which Award is Granted:** Undergraduate **Funds Available:** $3,000.
Eligibility Requirements: Applicants must be second or third year law students who demonstrate a commitment to serve or contribute to the Macomb County legal community; must demonstrate a need for financial assistance; and must have high scholastic achievement. Applicants must be enrolled as a law degree candidate at one of the following Michigan Law Schools: Thomas M. Cooley, Michigan State University, University of Michigan, University of Detroit Mercy, Wayne State University. **Application Requirements:** Applicants may download application online. The application packet must include: complete application; candidate's undergraduate college transcript; candidate's most recent law school transcript; resume; three letters of recommendation; a personal statement in which the candidate discusses his/her interest in law, reason for applying for scholarship, career goals and any other pertinent information he/she would like the Scholarship Committee to know about. **Deadline for Receipt:** January 25. **Additional Information:** Macomb County Bar Foundation at the above address.

4454 ■ MASSACHUSETTS ASSOCIATION OF WOMEN LAWYERS

c/o Annette Hines, Esq.
20 Main St. Ste. No. 206A
Natick, MA 01760
E-mail: info@mawi.org
Web Site: http://www.mawi.org
To award scholarships to law students in Massachusetts.
Title of Award: Carol DiMaiti Scholarship Awards **Area, Field, or Subject:** Law. **Level of Education for which Award is Granted:** Undergraduate **Funds Available:** $1,000. **Duration:** One year.
Eligibility Requirements: Applicants must be entering their second or third year of law school; must be in good academic standing; must have demonstrated high financial need. **Application Requirements:** Applicants must submit a completed application form and must check the available website for details. **Additional Information:** This particular fund is maintained solely through voluntary contributions made throughout the year and fundraising events. **Additional Information:** Massachusetts Association of Women Lawyers at the above address.

4455 ■ MATANUSKA-SUSITNA COLLEGE

PO Box 2889
Palmer, AK 99645
Tel: (907)745-9774
Fax: (907)745-9711
E-mail: info@matsu.alaska.edu
Web Site: http://www.matsu.alaska.edu
To provide support to deserving students in Alaska who want to pursue an education in any campus of the University of Alaska.
Title of Award: Mable B. Crawford Memorial Scholarships **Area, Field, or Subject:** Accounting; Economics; Law; Business. **Level of Education for which Award is Granted:** Undergraduate **Funds Available:** $500.
Eligibility Requirements: Applicants must be students who have been residents of Alaska for at least two years. **Application Requirements:** Applicant must complete the application forms available at the website; must attach a personal essay, two letters of recommendation, and current transcripts. **Deadline for Receipt:** February 15.

4456 ■ MEXICAN AMERICAN LEGAL DEFENSE AND EDUCATIONAL FUND

634 S Spring St.
Los Angeles, CA 90014
Tel: (213)629-2512
Web Site: http://www.maldef.org
To increase the number of Latinos in the legal profession.
Title of Award: MALDEF Law School Scholarships **Area, Field, or Subject:** Law. **Level of Education for which Award is Granted:** Undergraduate **Funds Available:** $7,000.

Eligibility Requirements: Students must be enrolled full time in law school. Application Requirements: Applicants must complete and send the following materials: a completed and signed MALDEF Scholarship form; current resume; a typed personal statement of 750 words or less, double-spaced, detailing professional objectives, plans after school, and describing your past involvement in activities which applicant believes have served or benefited the Latino community and how these activities relate to your decision to pursue a career in the legal profession; an official undergraduate transcript or photocopy of an official transcript; For law schoolstudents who have already completed one year or more of law school, please, also provide: an official law school transcript or photocopy of an official transcript; a letter of recommendation describing your involvement in the Latino community from a person familiar with that involvement; a letter of recommendation from a college, or law school professor; and a completed financial need statement (enclose) from the school applicant is attending that indicates the financial assistance provided to you by the school's financial aid office. Deadline for Receipt: October 3. Additional Information: MALDEF Law School Scholarship Program at the above address.

4457 ■ MILBANK, TWEED, HADLEY & MCCLOY LLP
1 Chase Manhattan Plz.
New York, NY 10005
Tel: (212)530-5000
Fax: (212)530-5219
Web Site: http://www.milbank.com/en
To inspire career pursuits and excellence in the field of law by providing educational support for qualified law students.
Title of Award: Milbank Diversity Scholarships Area, Field, or Subject: Law. Level of Education for which Award is Granted: Undergraduate Number Awarded: 2. Funds Available: $50,000. Duration: One year.
Eligibility Requirements: Applicants must be members of groups traditionally underrepresented in large law firms; must be in good standing at an ABA accredited law school; must have successfully completed their first year of a full-time JD program; may not be the recipient of a similar scholarship award from another law firm; and must have completed two years of a JD program. Application Requirements: Applicants must complete the application form available online and submit along with an essay, official law school transcript and resume. Application form and other supporting documents must be sent to Elizabeth A. Crispino, Manager of Campus Recruiting. Deadline for Receipt: September 1.

4458 ■ MINNESOTA ASSOCIATION COUNTY PROBATION OFFICERS
Sherburne County Court Services
13880 Hwy. 10
Elk River, MN 55330
Tel: (763)241-2819
E-mail: christopher.maas@co.sherburne.mn.us
Web Site: http://www.macpo.org
To promote and attract quality students to consider Corrections as a career.
Title of Award: Minnesota Association County Probation Officers Scholarships Area, Field, or Subject: Criminal justice. Level of Education for which Award is Granted: Undergraduate Funds Available: $500.
Eligibility Requirements: Applicants must be junior or senior students majoring in Corrections, Sociology, Criminal justice, Psychology, Social Work, or other related fields who will be/are currently involved in an internship; must have a 2.5 GPA; and must be enrolled at an accredited two-year of four-year college or university. Application Requirements: Applicants must submit a completed application form; a school transcript; resume of related volunteer/community experience; one letter of reference; and a 500-word essay describing the impact as you prepare for a career in Corrections.

4459 ■ MINORITY CORPORATE COUNSEL ASSOCIATION
1111 Pennsylvania Ave. NW
Washington, DC 20004
Tel: (202)739-5901
Fax: (202)739-5999
Web Site: http://www.mcca.com
To provide scholarship opportunities for minority students seeking to study law.

Title of Award: MCCA Lloyd M. Johnson, Jr. Scholarships Area, Field, or Subject: Law. Level of Education for which Award is Granted: Undergraduate Number Awarded: 10. Funds Available: $10,000. Duration: Three years.
Eligibility Requirements: Program is open to college seniors and graduate students that are interested in obtaining a law degree; must have a grade point average of at least 2.5 on a 4.0 scale; must be in financial need; and must be considered a minority. Application Requirements: Applicants must accomplish online application. Deadline for Receipt: January 1.

4460 ■ NATIONAL ASIAN PACIFIC AMERICAN BAR ASSOCIATION
1612 K Street NW, Ste. 1400
Washington, DC 20006
Tel: (202)775-9555
Fax: (202)775-9333
E-mail: ed@napaba.org
Web Site: http://www.napaba.org
To award law students who demonstrate an outstanding leadership potential to serve the Asian Pacific American community.
Title of Award: Anheuser-Busch NAPABA Law Foundation Presidential Scholarships Area, Field, or Subject: Law. Level of Education for which Award is Granted: Undergraduate Funds Available: $7,500.
Eligibility Requirements: Applicants must be a student enrolled as a law degree candidate in an accredited law school in the United States at least half time as determined by the school is eligible. Application Requirements: Applicants must submit complete application form; official copy of most recent law school transcript; resume; two letters of recommendation; a copy of application to law school for financial assistance. Additional Information: Parkin Lee, Esq; New York Life Investment Management, LLC; 51 Madison Avenue Room 1104; New York, New York 10010.

4461 ■ NATIONAL ASIAN PACIFIC AMERICAN BAR ASSOCIATION
1612 K Street NW, Ste. 1400
Washington, DC 20006
Tel: (202)775-9555
Fax: (202)775-9333
E-mail: ed@napaba.org
Web Site: http://www.napaba.org
To award to law students who demonstrate a commitment to serve or contribute to the Asian Pacific American community as future leaders.
Title of Award: Lim, Ruger and Kim Scholarships Area, Field, or Subject: Law. Level of Education for which Award is Granted: Undergraduate Funds Available: $2,500.
Eligibility Requirements: Applicants must be a student enrolled as a law degree candidate in an accredited law school in the US at least half time as determined by the school. Application Requirements: Applicants must submit a completed and signed application form from foundation; official copy of the applicant's most recent law school transcript; resume; letter of recommendation from persons not related to the applicant. Additional Information: In 2004 the Foundation established its Lim, Ruger and Kim Scholarship through the generosity of the law firm of Lim, Ruger and Kim in Los Angeles.

4462 ■ NATIONAL ASIAN PACIFIC AMERICAN BAR ASSOCIATION
1612 K Street NW, Ste. 1400
Washington, DC 20006
Tel: (202)775-9555
Fax: (202)775-9333
E-mail: ed@napaba.org
Web Site: http://www.napaba.org
To award law students who demonstrate a commitment to serve or contribute to the Asian Pacific American community as future leaders.
Title of Award: NAPABA Law Foundation Scholarships Area, Field, or Subject: Law. Level of Education for which Award is Granted: Undergraduate Funds Available: $2,500.
Eligibility Requirements: Applicants must be a student enrolled as a law degree candidate in an accredited law school in the US at least half time as determined by the school. Application Requirements: Applicants must submit a completed and signed application form from foundation; official copy of the applicant's most recent law school transcript; resume; letter of recommendation from persons not related to the applicant. Additional Information: In 2003 the Foundation named one of these

scholarships in memory of Chris Nakamura; a leader of the Asian Pacific legal community of Arizona.

4463 ■ NATIONAL ASIAN PACIFIC AMERICAN BAR ASSOCIATION
1612 K Street NW, Ste. 1400
Washington, DC 20006
Tel: (202)775-9555
Fax: (202)775-9333
E-mail: ed@napaba.org
Web Site: http://www.napaba.org
To assist recent law graduates who are working in Asia Pacific American legal service organizations to repay a portion of their student loans.
Title of Award: Diane Yu Loan Repayment Assistance Program **Area, Field, or Subject:** Law. **Level of Education for which Award is Granted:** Undergraduate **Funds Available:** $5,500 for each of two years to be applied to their educational debt.
Eligibility Requirements: Applicants must be a student enrolled as a law degree candidate in an accredited law school in the US at least half time as determined by the school. **Application Requirements:** Applicants must submit a completed and signed application form from foundation; official copy of the applicant's most recent law school transcript; resume; letter of recommendation from persons not related to the applicant. **Additional Information:** Diane Yu is a long-time supporter of NAPABA and the NAPABA Law Foundation and generously funded a program in 2004.

4464 ■ NATIONAL ASSOCIATION OF WOMEN JUDGES
1341 Connecticut Ave. NW, Ste. 42
Washington, DC 20036-1834
Tel: (202)393-0222
Fax: (202)393-0125
E-mail: nawj@nawj.org
Web Site: http://www.nawj.org
To provide financial assistance for law students who have demonstrated a sustained commitment to diversity and equality in the system of justice.
Title of Award: Equal Access to Justice Scholarships **Area, Field, or Subject:** Law. **Level of Education for which Award is Granted:** Undergraduate **Funds Available:** No amount mentioned.
Eligibility Requirements: Applicants must be enrolled second- or third-year law student in good academic standing who demonstrate a sustained and passionate commitment to the achievement of equality of opportunity and access in the system of justice. **Application Requirements:** Applicant must submit the completed application form and a 500-word personal statement and a resume.

4465 ■ NATIONAL FEDERATION OF THE BLIND
1800 Johnson St.
Baltimore, MD 21230
Tel: (410)659-9314
Fax: (410)685-5653
Web Site: http://www.nfb.org
To recognize achievement of blind scholars and to create opportunity for all blind people.
Title of Award: Howard B. Rickard Scholarships **Area, Field, or Subject:** Law; Medicine; Engineering; Architecture; Natural Science. **Level of Education for which Award is Granted:** Undergraduate **Funds Available:** $3,000.
Eligibility Requirements: All applicants must be legally blind; he/she must be pursuing or planning to study in the field of law, medicine, engineering, architecture or the natural science; he/she must be participant in NFB national convention and in all scheduled scholarship program activities. **Application Requirements:** Applicant must fill out the application form; he/she must submit two letters of recommendation from individuals that can describe the academic ability, leadership skills, and/or community involvement; copies of transcript of record and a photocopy of score reports for all standardized tests taken for college admission (ACT, SAT or other); an applicant must provide a letter of proof of legal blindness from a qualified professional; and an affiliate President's letter. **Deadline for Receipt:** March 31.

4466 ■ NATIONAL FEDERATION OF PARALEGAL ASSOCIATIONS
PO Box 2016
Edmonds, WA 98020
Tel: (425)967-0045

Fax: (425)771-9588
E-mail: info@paralegals.org
Web Site: http://www.paralegals.org
To promote a global presence for the paralegal profession and leadership in the legal community.
Title of Award: NFPA and Thomson West Scholarships **Area, Field, or Subject:** Paralegal studies. **Level of Education for which Award is Granted:** Undergraduate **Funds Available:** $5,000. **Duration:** Not stated.
Eligibility Requirements: Applicant must be a part-time or full-time, currently-enrolled student or accepted student in an accredited paralegal education program or college level program with emphasis in paralegal studies. Applicants must demonstrate or maintain at least a "B" average. **Application Requirements:** Applicants must submit original and three copies of application form; letter of recommendation from the director of paralegal education program or an employer; a double-spaced essay of required topics (not more than four pages); recent official transcript showing at least a "B" average. High school transcripts are acceptable only if an applicant has not completed a college semester. **Deadline for Receipt:** In 2004, deadline was August 4. **Additional Information:** National Federation of Paralegal Associations at the above address.

4467 ■ NATIONAL HEMOPHILIA FOUNDATION
116 W 32nd St., 11th Fl.
New York, NY 10001
Tel: (212)328-3700
Free: 800-424-2631
Fax: (212)328-3777
E-mail: handi@hemophilia.org
Web Site: http://www.hemophilia.org
To encourage careers in the field of law among individuals with bleeding disorders.
Title of Award: Michael Bendix Sutton Foundation **Area, Field, or Subject:** Law. **Level of Education for which Award is Granted:** Undergraduate **Number Awarded:** 2. **Funds Available:** $2,000.
Eligibility Requirements: Students with hemophilia pursuing pre-law studies are eligible to apply. **Application Requirements:** Applicants must write for applications addressed to: Michael Bendix Sutton Foundation, c/o Marion B. Sutton, 300 Maritime Ave., White Plains, NY 10601. **Deadline for Receipt:** March 30.

4468 ■ NATIONAL SHERIFFS' ASSOCIATION
1450 Duke St.
Alexandria, VA 22314
Tel: (703)836-7827
Free: 800-424-7827
Fax: (703)683-6541
Web Site: http://www.sheriffs.org
To provide educational assistance to employees of a sheriff's office or their dependents.
Title of Award: NSA Scholarship Program **Area, Field, or Subject:** Criminal justice; Law. **Level of Education for which Award is Granted:** Undergraduate **Funds Available:** $1,000.
Eligibility Requirements: Applicant must be applying or enrolled in an undergraduate or graduate college program majoring in a criminal justice-related subject area; must be employed by a sheriff's office or a dependent of an individual employed by a sheriff's office; and must not be a previous recipient of the NSA scholarship. **Application Requirements:** Applicants must provide a completed Official NSA scholarship application form available at the website; a transcript from high school or college (if already attending college); two letters of recommendation (one must be from a principal, teacher, guidance counselor, or advisor); endorsement letter from the sheriff of applicant's county; statement of financial need; and an essay (minimum of 150 words) about the applicant's intents in pursuing a career in law enforcement. Required materials must be photocopied and forwarded to the NSA Awards and Scholarship Committee while the application form must be mailed to: Hilary Burgess, National Sheriff's Association 1450 Duke St. Alexandria, VA 22314, Attn: NSA Scholarship Program. **Deadline for Receipt:** April 1.

4469 ■ NATIVE WOMEN'S ASSOCIATION OF CANADA
PO Box 331
1721 Chiefswood Rd.
Ohsweken, ON, Canada N0A 1M0

Tel: (519)445-0990; (866)796-6053
Fax: (519)445-0924
Web Site: http://www.nwac-hq.org/en
To provide financial support for students intending to pursue their law careers.
Title of Award: Helen Bassett Commemorative Scholarships **Area, Field, or Subject:** Law. **Level of Education for which Award is Granted:** Undergraduate **Number Awarded:** 4. **Funds Available:** $1,000.
Eligibility Requirements: Applicants must be post-secondary students, specifically Aboriginal females, pursuing a law career; must be under 31 years old; must demonstrate financial need; and must demonstrate commitment to improving the situation of Aboriginal women and youth in Canada politically, culturally, economically or otherwise. **Application Requirements:** Applicants must submit application form, proof of age, and proof of Aboriginal descent; must have a proof of attending post-secondary studies: acceptance letter from a post-secondary institution; must have the most recent official transcript, proof of community involvement/interest and dedication in working on Aboriginal women's issues; one reference letter of support from a local community organization, or school, or any relevant organization/person; must provide a short essay of 1-2 pages, and statement of financial need in a letter, plus monthly or yearly budget and a list of other funding sources and scholarships. Application form and all other required documents must be sent to CDC-Youth Native Women's Association of Canada, 1292 Wellington St., W, Ottawa, ON K1Y 3A9. **Deadline for Receipt:** July 11.

4470 ■ NEBRASKA ASSOCIATION OF LEGAL ASSISTANTS
PO Box 24943
Omaha, NE 68124
E-mail: info@neala.org
Web Site: http://www.neala.org
To encourage and assist men and women in pursuit of training for careers as legal assistants.
Title of Award: Nebraska Association of Legal Assistants Student Scholarships **Area, Field, or Subject:** Law. **Level of Education for which Award is Granted:** Undergraduate **Funds Available:** No specific amount.
Eligibility Requirements: Applicants must be Nebraska residents admitted and committed to enroll as half-time or full-time students in a university, college, community college or business college located in Nebraska that offers an accredited legal assistant program; must be in good standing with at least 3.0 GPA at the time of application. **Application Requirements:** Applicants must submit a completed application form, resume, two letters of recommendation from instructors, employers or community leaders, a copy of a letter of acceptance to a Nebraska legal assistant program, a statement of good academic standing for the most recent college term; recipients must pass the interview. **Deadline for Receipt:** May 18.

4471 ■ NEBRASKA STATE BAR ASSOCIATION
PO Box 81809
Lincoln, NE 68501
Tel: (402)475-7091
Free: 800-927-0117
Fax: (402)475-7098
Web Site: http://www.nebar.com
To provide college tuition assistance and paid internships at the firm for students of African-American, Asian, Latino and Native American origins from low-income families in the Omaha metro area.
Title of Award: Fraser Stryker Diversity Scholarship Program **Area, Field, or Subject:** Law. **Level of Education for which Award is Granted:** Undergraduate **Funds Available:** $2,500 per academic year.
Eligibility Requirements: Applicants must be pursuing law studies; must be African-American, Asian, Latino or Native American students; must be from low-income families in the Omaha metro area. **Application Requirements:** Applicants must check the available website for the application process online. **Deadline for Receipt:** March 9. **Additional Information:** For more information or application for the Fraser Stryker Diversity Scholarship Program, please visit www.fraserstryker.com.

4472 ■ NORTHERN INDIANA COMMUNITY FOUNDATION
PO Box 807
Rochester, IN 46975

Tel: (574)223-2227; 877-432-6423
Fax: (574)224-3709
Web Site: http://www.nicf.org
To provide scholarships for qualified college graduates pursuing a degree in law.
Title of Award: Frederick Rakestraw Law Scholarships **Area, Field, or Subject:** Law. **Level of Education for which Award is Granted:** Undergraduate **Funds Available:** $1,000. **Duration:** One year.
Eligibility Requirements: Applicants must be residents of Fulton County Indiana for at least three years during their high school career. **Application Requirements:** Applicants must submit a completed scholarship form; an acceptance letter or other proof of enrollment in any school of law in the US; a current transcript; and three letters of recommendation. **Deadline for Receipt:** June 19.

4473 ■ OKLAHOMA CITY UNIVERSITY SCHOOL OF LAW
251 N Blackwelder Ave.
Oklahoma City, OK 73106
Tel: (405)208-5337
Web Site: http://www.okcu.edu/law/
To provide financial assistance for qualified law students intending to pursue their studies.
Title of Award: Kerr Foundation Scholarships **Area, Field, or Subject:** Law. **Level of Education for which Award is Granted:** Undergraduate **Number Awarded:** 20. **Funds Available:** No specific amount.
Eligibility Requirements: Applicants must be upper class students who have high GPA (generally 3.5 or above) and high LSAT (generally at the 80th percentile or above). **Application Requirements:** Applicants must complete the application form available online and submit along with their undergraduate transcript and letters of recommendation.

4474 ■ OKLAHOMA CITY UNIVERSITY SCHOOL OF LAW
251 N Blackwelder Ave.
Oklahoma City, OK 73106
Tel: (405)208-5337
Web Site: http://www.okcu.edu/law/
To provide financial assistance for qualified law students intending to pursue their studies.
Title of Award: Oklahoma City University Merit Scholarships **Area, Field, or Subject:** Law. **Level of Education for which Award is Granted:** Undergraduate **Funds Available:** Covers 2/3 of tuition. **Duration:** One year.
Eligibility Requirements: Applicants must have a high GPA (generally 3.5 or above) and high LSAT (generally at the 80th percentile or above). **Application Requirements:** Applicants must complete the application form available online and must also submit the undergraduate transcript and letters of recommendation. **Deadline for Receipt:** April 1.

4475 ■ OKLAHOMA CITY UNIVERSITY SCHOOL OF LAW
251 N Blackwelder Ave.
Oklahoma City, OK 73106
Tel: (405)208-5337
Web Site: http://www.okcu.edu/law/
To provide financial assistance for qualified law students intending to pursue their studies.
Title of Award: Hatton W. Sumners Scholarships **Area, Field, or Subject:** Law. **Level of Education for which Award is Granted:** Undergraduate **Funds Available:** Covers all tuition and other fees, $400 book allowance and $2,500 living stipend. **Duration:** One year.
Eligibility Requirements: Applicants must be U.S. citizens; must rank in the top quarter of their class; and must be residents of or students/graduates of colleges or universities in Oklahoma, Arkansas, Kansas, Missouri, Texas, Louisiana, Nebraska, or New Mexico. **Application Requirements:** Applicants must complete the application form available online must also submit their undergraduate transcript and letters of recommendation. **Deadline for Receipt:** February 15.

4476 ■ PACIFIC LEGAL FOUNDATION
3900 Lennane Dr., Ste. 200
Sacramento, CA 95834
Tel: (916)419-7111
Free: 800-847-7719
Fax: (916)419-7747

E-mail: plf@pacificlegal.org
Web Site: http://www.community.pacificlegal.org
To encourage legal scholarships related to Pacific Legal Foundation's Litigation.
Title of Award: Legal Scholarship for Law Students **Area, Field, or Subject:** Law. **Level of Education for which Award is Granted:** Undergraduate **Funds Available:** $5,000.
Eligibility Requirements: Applicants must be enrolled in law schools in the United States. **Application Requirements:** Applicants must submit original essays related to one or more of the legal objectives. **Deadline for Receipt:** July 1. **Additional Information:** Pacific Legal Foundation at the above address.

4477 ■ PARKERSBURG AREA COMMUNITY FOUNDATION
501 Avery St.
Parkersburg, WV 26101
Tel: (304)428-4438; (866)428-4438
Fax: (304)428-1200
E-mail: info@pacfwv.com
Web Site: http://www.pacfwv.com
To assist graduating students in their educational pursuits.
Title of Award: William R. Pfalzgraf Scholarships **Area, Field, or Subject:** Law; Education, English as a second language; Music. **Level of Education for which Award is Granted:** Undergraduate **Funds Available:** $760.
Eligibility Requirements: Applicant must be a Parkersburg High School graduating senior with a minimum of 3.0 GPA. **Application Requirements:** Applicants must submit a cover sheet (3 pages) and application form (4 pages); a personal essay; a high school and/or post-secondary transcript; a letter of recommendation; a signed copy of the page of their or their parent's most recent tax return that indicates adjusted gross income; and a Student Aid Report showing estimated family contribution from FAFSA. Application form and other supporting documents must be sent to Our Community's Foundation, P.O Box 1762, Parkersburg, WV 26102. **Deadline for Receipt:** March 20.

4478 ■ PARKERSBURG AREA COMMUNITY FOUNDATION
501 Avery St.
Parkersburg, WV 26101
Tel: (304)428-4438; (866)428-4438
Fax: (304)428-1200
E-mail: info@pacfwv.com
Web Site: http://www.pacfwv.com
To provide financial assistance for qualified individuals intending to pursue their law degree.
Title of Award: Wood County Bar Association Memorial Scholarships **Area, Field, or Subject:** Law. **Level of Education for which Award is Granted:** Undergraduate **Funds Available:** $250-$500.
Eligibility Requirements: Applicant must be a student attending an accredited law school in the United States and must have certain minimal contacts with Wood, Jackson, Ritchie, Wirt, or Pleasant Counties in West Virginia. **Application Requirements:** Applicants must submit a cover sheet (3 pages) and application form (4 pages); a personal essay; a high school and/or post-secondary transcript; a letter of recommendation; a signed copy of the page of their or their parent's most recent tax return that indicates adjusted gross income; and a Student Aid Report showing estimated family contribution from FAFSA. Application form and other supporting documents must be sent to Our Community's Foundation, P.O Box 1762, Parkersburg, WV 26102. **Deadline for Receipt:** March 20.

4479 ■ PEPPERDINE UNIVERSITY SCHOOL OF LAW
24255 Pacific Coast Highway
Malibu, CA 90263
Tel: (310)506-4611
E-mail: soladmis@pepperdine.edu
Web Site: http://law.pepperdine.edu
To assist students at Pepperdine University School.
Title of Award: Associated Women for Pepperdine (AWP) Scholarships **Area, Field, or Subject:** Education; Psychology; Law. **Level of Education for which Award is Granted:** Undergraduate **Funds Available:** No specific amount.
Eligibility Requirements: Applicants must be admitted at Pepperdine University; and be members of the Church of Christ. **Application**

Requirements: Applicants must submit a completed scholarship application form together with a resume, letter of qualifications, and a letter confirming active membership in a local Church of Christ congregation. **Deadline for Receipt:** October 31.

4480 ■ PEPPERDINE UNIVERSITY SCHOOL OF LAW
24255 Pacific Coast Highway
Malibu, CA 90263
Tel: (310)506-4611
E-mail: soladmis@pepperdine.edu
Web Site: http://law.pepperdine.edu
To assist students at Pepperdine University School of Law.
Title of Award: Beck-Pfann Memorial Scholarships **Area, Field, or Subject:** Law. **Level of Education for which Award is Granted:** Undergraduate **Funds Available:** No specific amount.
Eligibility Requirements: Applicants must be second-year students. **Application Requirements:** Applicants must submit a completed scholarship application form together with a resume and a letter of qualifications. **Additional Information:** Established in honor of R. Michael Beck and C. Lori Pfann. **Deadline for Receipt:** October 31.

4481 ■ PEPPERDINE UNIVERSITY SCHOOL OF LAW
24255 Pacific Coast Highway
Malibu, CA 90263
Tel: (310)506-4611
E-mail: soladmis@pepperdine.edu
Web Site: http://law.pepperdine.edu
To assist students at Pepperdine University School of Law.
Title of Award: David and Camille Boatwright Endowed Scholarships **Area, Field, or Subject:** Law. **Level of Education for which Award is Granted:** Undergraduate **Funds Available:** No specific amount.
Eligibility Requirements: Applicants must be a Pepperdine University School of Law students. **Application Requirements:** Applicants must submit a completed scholarship application form together with a resume, and letter of qualifications. **Deadline for Receipt:** October 31.

4482 ■ PEPPERDINE UNIVERSITY SCHOOL OF LAW
24255 Pacific Coast Highway
Malibu, CA 90263
Tel: (310)506-4611
E-mail: soladmis@pepperdine.edu
Web Site: http://law.pepperdine.edu
To assist students at Pepperdine University School of Law.
Title of Award: Ann Marie Bredefeld Scholarships **Area, Field, or Subject:** Law. **Level of Education for which Award is Granted:** Undergraduate **Funds Available:** No specific amount.
Eligibility Requirements: Applicants must be students who share the Christian values of Pepperdine. **Application Requirements:** Applicants must submit a completed scholarship application form together with a resume and a letter of qualifications. **Deadline for Receipt:** October 31.

4483 ■ PEPPERDINE UNIVERSITY SCHOOL OF LAW
24255 Pacific Coast Highway
Malibu, CA 90263
Tel: (310)506-4611
E-mail: soladmis@pepperdine.edu
Web Site: http://law.pepperdine.edu
To assist students at Pepperdine University School of Law.
Title of Award: Margaret Martin Brock Scholarships in Law **Area, Field, or Subject:** Law. **Level of Education for which Award is Granted:** Undergraduate **Funds Available:** No specific amount.
Eligibility Requirements: Applicants must be Pepperdine University School of Law students. **Application Requirements:** Applicants must submit a completed scholarship application form together with a resume and a letter of qualifications. **Additional Information:** Scholarship fund was established by the late Mrs. Margaret Martin Brock. **Deadline for Receipt:** October 31.

4484 ■ PEPPERDINE UNIVERSITY SCHOOL OF LAW
24255 Pacific Coast Highway
Malibu, CA 90263
Tel: (310)506-4611
E-mail: soladmis@pepperdine.edu

Web Site: http://law.pepperdine.edu
To assist students at Pepperdine University School of Law.
Title of Award: Kae and Kay Brockermeyer Endowed Scholarships **Area, Field, or Subject:** Law. **Level of Education for which Award is Granted:** Undergraduate **Funds Available:** No specific amount.
Eligibility Requirements: Applicants must be law students interested in trial advocacy. Applicant must also be a resident of the state of Texas.
Application Requirements: Applicants must submit a completed scholarship application form together with a resume and a letter of qualifications. **Deadline for Receipt:** October 31.

4485 ■ PEPPERDINE UNIVERSITY SCHOOL OF LAW
24255 Pacific Coast Highway
Malibu, CA 90263
Tel: (310)506-4611
E-mail: soladmis@pepperdine.edu
Web Site: http://law.pepperdine.edu
To assist students at Pepperdine University School of Law.
Title of Award: Shirley J. Brooke Endowed Scholarships **Area, Field, or Subject:** Law. **Level of Education for which Award is Granted:** Undergraduate **Funds Available:** No specific amount.
Eligibility Requirements: Applicants must be female law students who demonstrate above average academic achievement. **Application Requirements:** Applicants must submit a completed scholarship application form together with a resume and a letter of qualifications. **Deadline for Receipt:** October 31.

4486 ■ PEPPERDINE UNIVERSITY SCHOOL OF LAW
24255 Pacific Coast Highway
Malibu, CA 90263
Tel: (310)506-4611
E-mail: soladmis@pepperdine.edu
Web Site: http://law.pepperdine.edu
To assist students at Pepperdine University School of Law.
Title of Award: Athalie Clarke Endowed Scholarships **Area, Field, or Subject:** Law. **Level of Education for which Award is Granted:** Undergraduate **Funds Available:** No specific amount.
Eligibility Requirements: Applicants must be Pepperdine University School of Law students. **Application Requirements:** Applicants must submit a completed scholarship application form together with a resume and a letter of qualifications. **Additional Information:** Funded by the late Athalie Irvine Clarke. **Deadline for Receipt:** October 31.

4487 ■ PEPPERDINE UNIVERSITY SCHOOL OF LAW
24255 Pacific Coast Highway
Malibu, CA 90263
Tel: (310)506-4611
E-mail: soladmis@pepperdine.edu
Web Site: http://law.pepperdine.edu
To assist students at Pepperdine University School of Law.
Title of Award: Brian Dane Cleary Memorial Scholarships **Area, Field, or Subject:** Law. **Level of Education for which Award is Granted:** Undergraduate **Funds Available:** No specific amount.
Eligibility Requirements: Applicants must be Pepperdine University School of Law students. **Application Requirements:** Applicants must submit a completed scholarship application form together with a resume and a letter of qualifications. **Additional Information:** Established by the family members and friends of Brian Dane Cleary, member of the Class of 1991, died in a car accident 18 days before graduation. **Deadline for Receipt:** October 31.

4488 ■ PEPPERDINE UNIVERSITY SCHOOL OF LAW
24255 Pacific Coast Highway
Malibu, CA 90263
Tel: (310)506-4611
E-mail: soladmis@pepperdine.edu
Web Site: http://law.pepperdine.edu
To encourage students to remain enrolled at the School of Law.
Title of Award: Hugh and Hazel Darling Dean Scholarships **Area, Field, or Subject:** Law. **Level of Education for which Award is Granted:** Undergraduate **Funds Available:** No specific amount.
Eligibility Requirements: Applicants must be Pepperdine University School of Law students. **Application Requirements:** Applicants must

submit a completed scholarship application form together with a resume and a letter of qualifications. **Deadline for Receipt:** October 31.

4489 ■ PEPPERDINE UNIVERSITY SCHOOL OF LAW
24255 Pacific Coast Highway
Malibu, CA 90263
Tel: (310)506-4611
E-mail: soladmis@pepperdine.edu
Web Site: http://law.pepperdine.edu
To assist students at Pepperdine University School of Law.
Title of Award: Darling Foundation Endowed School of Law Scholarships **Area, Field, or Subject:** Law. **Level of Education for which Award is Granted:** Undergraduate **Funds Available:** No specific amount.
Eligibility Requirements: Applicants must be Pepperdine University School of Law students. **Application Requirements:** Applicants must submit a completed scholarship application form together with a resume and a letter of qualifications. **Deadline for Receipt:** October 31.

4490 ■ PEPPERDINE UNIVERSITY SCHOOL OF LAW
24255 Pacific Coast Highway
Malibu, CA 90263
Tel: (310)506-4611
E-mail: soladmis@pepperdine.edu
Web Site: http://law.pepperdine.edu
To assist students at Pepperdine University School of Law.
Title of Award: Martha Delman and Milton Arthur Krug Endowed Scholarships **Area, Field, or Subject:** Law. **Level of Education for which Award is Granted:** Undergraduate **Funds Available:** No specific amount.
Eligibility Requirements: Applicants must be Pepperdine University School of Law students. **Application Requirements:** Applicants must submit a completed scholarship application form together with a resume and a letter of qualifications. **Additional Information:** Funded by the late Martha Delman Krug. **Deadline for Receipt:** October 31.

4491 ■ PEPPERDINE UNIVERSITY SCHOOL OF LAW
24255 Pacific Coast Highway
Malibu, CA 90263
Tel: (310)506-4611
E-mail: soladmis@pepperdine.edu
Web Site: http://law.pepperdine.edu
To assist students at Pepperdine University School of Law.
Title of Award: Edward D. Di Loreto-Odell S. McConnell Scholarships **Area, Field, or Subject:** Law. **Level of Education for which Award is Granted:** Undergraduate **Funds Available:** No specific amount.
Eligibility Requirements: Applicants must be Pepperdine University School of Law students with high scholastic standing. **Application Requirements:** Applicants must submit a completed scholarship application form together with a resume and a letter of qualifications. **Deadline for Receipt:** October 31.

4492 ■ PEPPERDINE UNIVERSITY SCHOOL OF LAW
24255 Pacific Coast Highway
Malibu, CA 90263
Tel: (310)506-4611
E-mail: soladmis@pepperdine.edu
Web Site: http://law.pepperdine.edu
To assist students at Pepperdine University School of Law.
Title of Award: R. Wayne Estes Endowed Scholarships **Area, Field, or Subject:** Law. **Level of Education for which Award is Granted:** Undergraduate **Funds Available:** No specific amount.
Eligibility Requirements: Applicants must be Pepperdine University School of Law students. **Application Requirements:** Applicants must submit a completed scholarship application form together with a resume and a letter of qualifications. **Additional Information:** Established by former students, colleagues and friends of Professor Emeritus R. Wayne Estes. **Deadline for Receipt:** October 31.

4493 ■ PEPPERDINE UNIVERSITY SCHOOL OF LAW
24255 Pacific Coast Highway
Malibu, CA 90263
Tel: (310)506-4611
E-mail: soladmis@pepperdine.edu

Web Site: http://law.pepperdine.edu
To assist students at Pepperdine University School of Law.
Title of Award: Judge McIntyre Faries Scholarships **Area, Field, or Subject:** Law. **Level of Education for which Award is Granted:** Undergraduate **Funds Available:** No specific amount.
Eligibility Requirements: Applicants must be Pepperdine University School of Law students. **Application Requirements:** Applicants must submit a completed scholarship application form together with a resume and a letter of qualifications. **Additional Information:** Established by John Herlotz to honor California jurist, Judge McIntyre Faries. **Deadline for Receipt:** October 31.

4494 ■ PEPPERDINE UNIVERSITY SCHOOL OF LAW
24255 Pacific Coast Highway
Malibu, CA 90263
Tel: (310)506-4611
E-mail: soladmis@pepperdine.edu
Web Site: http://law.pepperdine.edu
To assist students at Pepperdine University School of Law.
Title of Award: Froberg-Suess JD/MBA Scholarships **Area, Field, or Subject:** Law. **Level of Education for which Award is Granted:** Undergraduate **Funds Available:** No specific amount.
Eligibility Requirements: Applicants must have successfully completed at least one semester of law school and one semester of business school. **Application Requirements:** Applicants must submit a completed scholarship application form together with a resume and a letter of qualifications. **Additional Information:** Applicants are required to make a moral pledge to give back to the scholarship fund within five years of the date of graduation from Pepperdine's School of Law. **Deadline for Receipt:** October 31.

4495 ■ PEPPERDINE UNIVERSITY SCHOOL OF LAW
24255 Pacific Coast Highway
Malibu, CA 90263
Tel: (310)506-4611
E-mail: soladmis@pepperdine.edu
Web Site: http://law.pepperdine.edu
To assist students at Pepperdine University School of Law.
Title of Award: Gerald Garner Memorial Scholarships **Area, Field, or Subject:** Law. **Level of Education for which Award is Granted:** Undergraduate **Funds Available:** No specific amount.
Eligibility Requirements: Applicants must be Pepperdine University School of Law students. **Application Requirements:** Applicants must submit a completed scholarship application form together with a resume and a letter of qualifications. **Additional Information:** Established in memory of Gerald Garner. **Deadline for Receipt:** October 31.

4496 ■ PEPPERDINE UNIVERSITY SCHOOL OF LAW
24255 Pacific Coast Highway
Malibu, CA 90263
Tel: (310)506-4611
E-mail: soladmis@pepperdine.edu
Web Site: http://law.pepperdine.edu
To assist students at Pepperdine University School of Law.
Title of Award: Terry M. Giles Honor Scholarships **Area, Field, or Subject:** Law. **Level of Education for which Award is Granted:** Undergraduate **Funds Available:** No specific amount.
Eligibility Requirements: Applicants must be third-year students. **Application Requirements:** Applicants must submit a completed scholarship application form together with a resume and a letter of qualifications. **Additional Information:** Sponsored by Terry M. Giles (class of 1974). **Deadline for Receipt:** October 31.

4497 ■ PEPPERDINE UNIVERSITY SCHOOL OF LAW
24255 Pacific Coast Highway
Malibu, CA 90263
Tel: (310)506-4611
E-mail: soladmis@pepperdine.edu
Web Site: http://law.pepperdine.edu
To assist students at Pepperdine University School of Law.
Title of Award: Guy P. Greenwald Jr. Endowed Scholarships **Area, Field, or Subject:** Law. **Level of Education for which Award is Granted:** Undergraduate **Funds Available:** No specific amount.

Eligibility Requirements: Applicants must be Pepperdine University School of Law students. **Application Requirements:** Applicants must submit a completed scholarship application form together with a resume and a letter of qualifications. **Additional Information:** Established by the late Guy P. Greenwald, attorney and Pepperdine friend. **Deadline for Receipt:** October 31.

4498 ■ PEPPERDINE UNIVERSITY SCHOOL OF LAW
24255 Pacific Coast Highway
Malibu, CA 90263
Tel: (310)506-4611
E-mail: soladmis@pepperdine.edu
Web Site: http://law.pepperdine.edu
To assist students at Pepperdine University School of Law.
Title of Award: Warren and Rosalie Gummow Endowed Scholarships **Area, Field, or Subject:** Law. **Level of Education for which Award is Granted:** Undergraduate **Funds Available:** No specific amount.
Eligibility Requirements: Applicants must be Pepperdine University School of Law students. **Application Requirements:** Applicants must submit a completed scholarship application form together with a resume and a letter of qualifications. **Additional Information:** Funded by Rosalie and the late Warren Gummow. **Deadline for Receipt:** October 31.

4499 ■ PEPPERDINE UNIVERSITY SCHOOL OF LAW
24255 Pacific Coast Highway
Malibu, CA 90263
Tel: (310)506-4611
E-mail: soladmis@pepperdine.edu
Web Site: http://law.pepperdine.edu
To assist students at Pepperdine University School of Law.
Title of Award: Mark and Michelle Hiepler Endowed Scholarships **Area, Field, or Subject:** Law. **Level of Education for which Award is Granted:** Undergraduate **Funds Available:** Total of $1,000.
Eligibility Requirements: Applicants must be the writers of the Best Respondent's Brief and Best Petitioner's Brief in the yearly Vincent S. Dalsimer Moot Court Competition. **Application Requirements:** Applicants must submit a completed scholarship application form together with a resume and a letter of qualifications. **Additional Information:** Established by Mark (class of 1988) and Michelle (class of 1989) Hiepler, in memory of Nelene Hiepler Fox. **Deadline for Receipt:** October 31.

4500 ■ PEPPERDINE UNIVERSITY SCHOOL OF LAW
24255 Pacific Coast Highway
Malibu, CA 90263
Tel: (310)506-4611
E-mail: soladmis@pepperdine.edu
Web Site: http://law.pepperdine.edu
To assist students at Pepperdine University School of Law.
Title of Award: JD/MBA Scholarships **Area, Field, or Subject:** Law; Business. **Level of Education for which Award is Granted:** Undergraduate **Funds Available:** No specific amount.
Eligibility Requirements: Applicant must be a student enrolled in the joint JD and MBA program at the School of Law and Graziadio School of Business and Management. Applicant must be in good standing in all areas of the University. **Application Requirements:** Applicants must submit a completed scholarship application form together with a resume and a letter of qualifications. **Deadline for Receipt:** October 31.

4501 ■ PEPPERDINE UNIVERSITY SCHOOL OF LAW
24255 Pacific Coast Highway
Malibu, CA 90263
Tel: (310)506-4611
E-mail: soladmis@pepperdine.edu
Web Site: http://law.pepperdine.edu
To assist students at Pepperdine University School of Law.
Title of Award: JSR Foundation Endowed School of Law Scholarships **Area, Field, or Subject:** Law. **Level of Education for which Award is Granted:** Undergraduate **Funds Available:** No specific amount.
Eligibility Requirements: Applicants must be Pepperdine University School of Law students. **Application Requirements:** Applicants must submit a completed scholarship application form together with a resume and a letter of qualifications. **Additional Information:** Funded by JSR (Joan Stuart Richard) Foundation. **Deadline for Receipt:** October 31.

4502 ■ PEPPERDINE UNIVERSITY SCHOOL OF LAW
24255 Pacific Coast Highway
Malibu, CA 90263
Tel: (310)506-4611
E-mail: soladmis@pepperdine.edu
Web Site: http://law.pepperdine.edu
To assist students at Pepperdine University School of Law.
Title of Award: Woodrow Judkins Endowed Scholarships **Area, Field, or Subject:** Law. **Level of Education for which Award is Granted:** Undergraduate **Funds Available:** No specific amount.
Eligibility Requirements: Applicants must be Pepperdine University School of Law students with good academic standing. **Application Requirements:** Applicants must submit a completed scholarship application form together with a resume and a letter of qualifications. **Deadline for Receipt:** October 31.

4503 ■ PEPPERDINE UNIVERSITY SCHOOL OF LAW
24255 Pacific Coast Highway
Malibu, CA 90263
Tel: (310)506-4611
E-mail: soladmis@pepperdine.edu
Web Site: http://law.pepperdine.edu
To assist students at Pepperdine University School of Law.
Title of Award: Kerrigan Scholarships **Area, Field, or Subject:** Law. **Level of Education for which Award is Granted:** Undergraduate **Funds Available:** No specific amount.
Eligibility Requirements: Applicant must be a single-parent mother at the School of Law. **Application Requirements:** Applicants must submit a completed scholarship application form together with a resume and a letter of qualifications. **Additional Information:** Established by Sharon Kerrigan, 1992 School of Law alumna. **Deadline for Receipt:** October 31.

4504 ■ PEPPERDINE UNIVERSITY SCHOOL OF LAW
24255 Pacific Coast Highway
Malibu, CA 90263
Tel: (310)506-4611
E-mail: soladmis@pepperdine.edu
Web Site: http://law.pepperdine.edu
To assist students at Pepperdine University School of Law.
Title of Award: Krist-Reavley Minority Scholarships **Area, Field, or Subject:** Law. **Level of Education for which Award is Granted:** Undergraduate **Funds Available:** No specific amount.
Eligibility Requirements: Applicant must be an ethnically diverse student. **Application Requirements:** Applicants must submit a completed scholarship application form together with a resume and a letter of qualifications. **Additional Information:** Established by noted trial attorney Ronald D. Krist and his wife, Carole. **Deadline for Receipt:** October 31.

4505 ■ PEPPERDINE UNIVERSITY SCHOOL OF LAW
24255 Pacific Coast Highway
Malibu, CA 90263
Tel: (310)506-4611
E-mail: soladmis@pepperdine.edu
Web Site: http://law.pepperdine.edu
To assist students at Pepperdine University School of Law.
Title of Award: Albert J. and Mae Lee Memorial Scholarships **Area, Field, or Subject:** Law. **Level of Education for which Award is Granted:** Undergraduate **Funds Available:** No specific amount.
Eligibility Requirements: Applicants must be Pepperdine University School of Law students with above average scholastic ability, and who are in need of financial assistance. **Application Requirements:** Applicants must submit a completed scholarship application form together with a resume and a letter of qualifications. **Deadline for Receipt:** October 31.

4506 ■ PEPPERDINE UNIVERSITY SCHOOL OF LAW
24255 Pacific Coast Highway
Malibu, CA 90263
Tel: (310)506-4611
E-mail: soladmis@pepperdine.edu
Web Site: http://law.pepperdine.edu
To assist students at Pepperdine University School of Law.
Title of Award: Greg Matthews Memorial Scholarships **Area, Field, or Subject:** Law. **Level of Education for which Award is Granted:** Undergraduate **Funds Available:** No specific amount.

Eligibility Requirements: Applicants must be Pepperdine University School of Law students. **Application Requirements:** Applicants must submit a completed scholarship application form together with a resume and a letter of qualifications. **Deadline for Receipt:** October 31.

4507 ■ PEPPERDINE UNIVERSITY SCHOOL OF LAW
24255 Pacific Coast Highway
Malibu, CA 90263
Tel: (310)506-4611
E-mail: soladmis@pepperdine.edu
Web Site: http://law.pepperdine.edu
To assist students at Pepperdine University School of Law.
Title of Award: J. McDonald and Judy Williams School of Law Scholarships **Area, Field, or Subject:** Law. **Level of Education for which Award is Granted:** Undergraduate **Funds Available:** No specific amount.
Eligibility Requirements: Applicants must be admitted at Pepperdine University; and must be members of the Church of Christ. **Application Requirements:** Applicants must submit a completed scholarship application form together with a resume, letter of qualifications, and a letter confirming active membership in a local Church of Christ congregation. **Deadline for Receipt:** October 31.

4508 ■ PEPPERDINE UNIVERSITY SCHOOL OF LAW
24255 Pacific Coast Highway
Malibu, CA 90263
Tel: (310)506-4611
E-mail: soladmis@pepperdine.edu
Web Site: http://law.pepperdine.edu
To assist students at Pepperdine University School of Law.
Title of Award: John Merrick Law Scholarships **Area, Field, or Subject:** Law. **Level of Education for which Award is Granted:** Undergraduate **Funds Available:** No specific amount.
Eligibility Requirements: Applicants must be Pepperdine University School of Law students. **Application Requirements:** Applicants must submit a completed scholarship application form together with a resume and a letter of qualifications. **Additional Information:** Established in honor of long-time Malibu judge John Merrick. **Deadline for Receipt:** October 31.

4509 ■ PEPPERDINE UNIVERSITY SCHOOL OF LAW
24255 Pacific Coast Highway
Malibu, CA 90263
Tel: (310)506-4611
E-mail: soladmis@pepperdine.edu
Web Site: http://law.pepperdine.edu
To assist students at Pepperdine University School of Law.
Title of Award: Charles I. Nelson Endowed Scholarships **Area, Field, or Subject:** Law. **Level of Education for which Award is Granted:** Undergraduate **Funds Available:** No specific amount.
Eligibility Requirements: Applicants must be Pepperdine University School of Law students. **Application Requirements:** Applicants must submit a completed scholarship application form together with a resume and a letter of qualifications. **Additional Information:** Established by Kae Brockemeyer in honor of Professor Emeritus Charles I. Nelson. **Deadline for Receipt:** October 31.

4510 ■ PEPPERDINE UNIVERSITY SCHOOL OF LAW
24255 Pacific Coast Highway
Malibu, CA 90263
Tel: (310)506-4611
E-mail: soladmis@pepperdine.edu
Web Site: http://law.pepperdine.edu
To assist students at Pepperdine University School of Law.
Title of Award: Gunnar Nicholson Endowed Scholarships **Area, Field, or Subject:** Law. **Level of Education for which Award is Granted:** Undergraduate **Funds Available:** No specific amount.
Eligibility Requirements: Applicants must be Pepperdine University School of Law students. **Application Requirements:** Applicants must submit a completed scholarship application form together with a resume and a letter of qualifications. **Deadline for Receipt:** October 31.

4511 ■ PEPPERDINE UNIVERSITY SCHOOL OF LAW
24255 Pacific Coast Highway
Malibu, CA 90263

Tel: (310)506-4611
E-mail: soladmis@pepperdine.edu
Web Site: http://law.pepperdine.edu
To assist students at Pepperdine University School of Law.
Title of Award: Pepperdine University Armenian Student Scholarships **Area, Field, or Subject:** Law. **Level of Education for which Award is Granted:** Undergraduate **Funds Available:** No specific amount.
Eligibility Requirements: Applicants must be law students of Armenian heritage; and must be admitted at Pepperdine University School of Law. **Application Requirements:** Applicants must submit a completed application form together with a resume and a letter of qualifications. **Additional Information:** Established by Khajak Kassabian, a 1997 School of Law alum. **Deadline for Receipt:** October 31.

4512 ■ PEPPERDINE UNIVERSITY SCHOOL OF LAW
24255 Pacific Coast Highway
Malibu, CA 90263
Tel: (310)506-4611
E-mail: soladmis@pepperdine.edu
Web Site: http://law.pepperdine.edu
To assist students at Pepperdine University School of Law.
Title of Award: Jamie Phillips Endowed Scholarships **Area, Field, or Subject:** Law. **Level of Education for which Award is Granted:** Undergraduate **Funds Available:** No specific amount.
Eligibility Requirements: Applicants must be Pepperdine University School of Law students. **Application Requirements:** Applicants must submit a completed scholarship application form together with a resume and a letter of qualifications. **Additional Information:** Established in memory of Jamie Phillips, wife of School of Law Dean Emeritus Ronald F. Phillips. **Deadline for Receipt:** October 31.

4513 ■ PEPPERDINE UNIVERSITY SCHOOL OF LAW
24255 Pacific Coast Highway
Malibu, CA 90263
Tel: (310)506-4611
E-mail: soladmis@pepperdine.edu
Web Site: http://law.pepperdine.edu
To assist students at Pepperdine University School of Law.
Title of Award: John Purfield Endowed Scholarships **Area, Field, or Subject:** Law. **Level of Education for which Award is Granted:** Undergraduate **Funds Available:** No specific amount.
Eligibility Requirements: Applicants must be Pepperdine University School of Law students. **Application Requirements:** Applicants must submit a completed scholarship application form together with a resume and a letter of qualifications. **Additional Information:** Established by John Purfield. . **Deadline for Receipt:** October 31.

4514 ■ PEPPERDINE UNIVERSITY SCHOOL OF LAW
24255 Pacific Coast Highway
Malibu, CA 90263
Tel: (310)506-4611
E-mail: soladmis@pepperdine.edu
Web Site: http://law.pepperdine.edu
To assist students at Pepperdine University School of Law.
Title of Award: Barbara A. Shacochis Scholarships **Area, Field, or Subject:** Law. **Level of Education for which Award is Granted:** Undergraduate **Funds Available:** No specific amount.
Eligibility Requirements: Applicants must be Pepperdine University School of Law students and members of the Law Review. **Application Requirements:** Applicants must submit a completed scholarship application form together with a resume and a letter of qualifications. **Deadline for Receipt:** October 31.

4515 ■ PEPPERDINE UNIVERSITY SCHOOL OF LAW
24255 Pacific Coast Highway
Malibu, CA 90263
Tel: (310)506-4611
E-mail: soladmis@pepperdine.edu
Web Site: http://law.pepperdine.edu
To assist students at Pepperdine University School of Law.
Title of Award: Benjamin G. Shatz Scholarships **Area, Field, or Subject:** Law. **Level of Education for which Award is Granted:** Undergraduate **Funds Available:** No specific amount.

Eligibility Requirements: Applicants must be second or third-year students and an active members of the Jewish Law Student Association. **Application Requirements:** Applicants must submit a completed scholarship application form together with a resume and a letter of qualifications. **Additional Information:** Sponsored by Benjamin G. Shatz (class of 1992). **Deadline for Receipt:** October 31.

4516 ■ PEPPERDINE UNIVERSITY SCHOOL OF LAW
24255 Pacific Coast Highway
Malibu, CA 90263
Tel: (310)506-4611
E-mail: soladmis@pepperdine.edu
Web Site: http://law.pepperdine.edu
To assist students at Pepperdine University School of Law.
Title of Award: Stuart Silverman Scholarships **Area, Field, or Subject:** Law. **Level of Education for which Award is Granted:** Undergraduate **Funds Available:** No specific amount.
Eligibility Requirements: Applicants must be Pepperdine University School of Law students pursuing a Juris Doctorate degree at the School of Law; and must have overcome a major tragedy or hardship. **Application Requirements:** Applicants must submit a completed scholarship application form together with a resume and a letter of qualifications. **Deadline for Receipt:** October 31.

4517 ■ PEPPERDINE UNIVERSITY SCHOOL OF LAW
24255 Pacific Coast Highway
Malibu, CA 90263
Tel: (310)506-4611
E-mail: soladmis@pepperdine.edu
Web Site: http://law.pepperdine.edu
To assist students at Pepperdine University School of Law.
Title of Award: Special Law School Scholarships **Area, Field, or Subject:** Law. **Level of Education for which Award is Granted:** Undergraduate **Funds Available:** No specific amount.
Eligibility Requirements: Applicants must be Pepperdine University School of Law students with a special financial need. **Application Requirements:** Applicants must submit a completed scholarship application form together with a resume and a letter of qualifications. **Deadline for Receipt:** October 31.

4518 ■ PEPPERDINE UNIVERSITY SCHOOL OF LAW
24255 Pacific Coast Highway
Malibu, CA 90263
Tel: (310)506-4611
E-mail: soladmis@pepperdine.edu
Web Site: http://law.pepperdine.edu
To assist students at Pepperdine University School of Law.
Title of Award: Honorable Raymond Thompson Endowed Scholarships **Area, Field, or Subject:** Law. **Level of Education for which Award is Granted:** Undergraduate **Funds Available:** No specific amount.
Eligibility Requirements: Applicants must be Pepperdine University School of Law students. **Application Requirements:** Applicants must submit a completed scholarship application form together with a resume and a letter of qualifications. **Additional Information:** Established in memory of Raymond H. Thompson, Superior Court Judge and Professor Emeritus at the School of Law. **Deadline for Receipt:** October 31.

4519 ■ PEPPERDINE UNIVERSITY SCHOOL OF LAW
24255 Pacific Coast Highway
Malibu, CA 90263
Tel: (310)506-4611
E-mail: soladmis@pepperdine.edu
Web Site: http://law.pepperdine.edu
To assist students at Pepperdine University School.
Title of Award: Thomas and Glenna Trimble Endowed Scholarships **Area, Field, or Subject:** Law. **Level of Education for which Award is Granted:** Undergraduate **Funds Available:** No specific amount.
Eligibility Requirements: Applicants must be admitted at Pepperdine University; and must be members of the Church of Christ. **Application Requirements:** Applicants must submit a completed scholarship application form together with a resume, letter of qualifications, and a letter confirming active membership in a local Church of Christ congregation. **Additional Information:** Established by Tom and Glenna Trimble. **Deadline for Receipt:** October 31.

4520 ■ PEPPERDINE UNIVERSITY SCHOOL OF LAW

24255 Pacific Coast Highway
Malibu, CA 90263
Tel: (310)506-4611
E-mail: soladmis@pepperdine.edu
Web Site: http://law.pepperdine.edu
To assist students at Pepperdine University School.
Title of Award: Brian J. White Endowed Law Scholarships **Area, Field, or Subject:** Law. **Level of Education for which Award is Granted:** Undergraduate **Funds Available:** No specific amount.
Eligibility Requirements: Applicants must be practicing Christians committed to pursuing a career in criminal defense; must actively worship with a local congregation and be committed to Christ. **Application Requirements:** Applicants must submit a completed scholarship application form together with a resume, letter of qualifications, and a letter of confirmation from a minister or priest. **Additional Information:** Established by Brian White. **Deadline for Receipt:** October 31.

4521 ■ PEPPERDINE UNIVERSITY SCHOOL OF LAW

24255 Pacific Coast Highway
Malibu, CA 90263
Tel: (310)506-4611
E-mail: soladmis@pepperdine.edu
Web Site: http://law.pepperdine.edu
To assist students at Pepperdine University School of Law.
Title of Award: Howard A. White Endowed Scholarships **Area, Field, or Subject:** Law. **Level of Education for which Award is Granted:** Undergraduate **Funds Available:** No specific amount.
Eligibility Requirements: Applicants must be Pepperdine University School of Law students. **Application Requirements:** Applicants must submit a completed scholarship application form together with a resume and a letter of qualifications. **Additional Information:** Established in honor of Howard A. White, President Emeritus of Pepperdine University. **Deadline for Receipt:** October 31.

4522 ■ PRACTISING LAW INSTITUTE

810 Seventh Ave., 21st Fl.
New York, NY 10019
Tel: (212)824-5700
Fax: (212)824-5733
Web Site: http://www.pli.edu
To provide financial assistance to qualified students who want to pursue their career.
Title of Award: Practising Law Institute Law Student Scholarships **Area, Field, or Subject:** Law. **Level of Education for which Award is Granted:** Undergraduate **Funds Available:** Scholarship award will cover the full or partial tuition cost.
Eligibility Requirements: Applicants must be legal aid and government attorneys, judges, judicial clerks, and employees of nonprofit organizations. **Application Requirements:** Applicants must complete the application forms available online; must have a legible copy of a student ID for the current term; and must complete the Statement of Need on the respective letter head. Application forms other supporting documents must be sent to PLI, 810 7th Ave., New York, NY 10019 or faxed to 888560-4852.

4523 ■ PRIDE FOUNDATION

PO Box 2194, 1122 E Pike St. PMB 1001
Seattle, WA 98112
Tel: (206)323-3318
Free: 800-735-7287
Fax: (206)323-1017
E-mail: prideweb@pridefoundation.org
Web Site: http://www.pridefoundation.org
To provide scholarship to the students who have been stigmatized, isolated or closeted because of sexual identity issues.
Title of Award: Political Leadership Scholarships **Area, Field, or Subject:** Law; Political science; Public Administration. **Level of Education for which Award is Granted:** Undergraduate **Funds Available:** No specific amount.
Eligibility Requirements: Applicant must be studying law, political science, public policy or public administration with the goal of improving rights for LGBT people. Preference is given to students who are self-

identified lesbian, gay, bisexual or transgender (LGBT). **Application Requirements:** Qualified students are asked to submit an application to determine eligibility for scholarships. Applicants may download an application form from the Foundation's website. **Additional Information:** Pride Foundation at the above address.

4524 ■ PUERTO RICAN LEGAL DEFENSE AND EDUCATION FUND

99 Hudson St., 14th Fl.
New York, NY 10013
Tel: (212)219-3360
Free: 800-328-2322
Fax: (212)431-4276
E-mail: info@prldef.org
Web Site: http://www.prldef.org
To protect opportunities for all Latinos to succeed in school and work, fulfill their dreams, and sustain their families and communities.
Title of Award: Puerto Rican Bar Association Scholarships **Area, Field, or Subject:** Law. **Level of Education for which Award is Granted:** Undergraduate **Funds Available:** $1500-$2000. **Duration:** One year.
Eligibility Requirements: Applicants must be first or second year students in a JD degree program at an American Bar Association (ABA) approved law school. **Application Requirements:** Applicants must complete the applications. **Deadline for Receipt:** March 1.

4525 ■ REDLANDS COMMUNITY SCHOLARSHIP FOUNDATION

c/o Kathleen Venegas-Boge, Admin. Asst.
PO Box 1683
Redlands, CA 92373
Tel: (909)307-9892
Fax: (909)307-9892
Web Site: http://www.redlandsscholarships.org
To encourage educational pursuits among Redlands Unified School District graduates by providing educational assistance.
Title of Award: Brian Jimenez Memorial Scholarships **Area, Field, or Subject:** Criminal justice. **Level of Education for which Award is Granted:** Undergraduate **Number Awarded:** 1. **Funds Available:** $500.
Eligibility Requirements: Applicant must be a male senior who has participated in baseball or soccer, has a GPA of 2.5 or higher, and is intending to attend an institution of higher learning on a full-time basis. **Application Requirements:** Applicants must submit a completed application form together with the scantron sheet; cover sheet; student activity and community activity sheets; personal essay; and a copy of unofficial transcript (signed by the counselor). **Additional Information:** No electronic submissions of application will be accepted. Submit two printed copies of the application and use a No. 2 pencil on the scantron sheet. **Deadline for Receipt:** February 20.

4526 ■ REDLANDS COMMUNITY SCHOLARSHIP FOUNDATION

c/o Kathleen Venegas-Boge, Admin. Asst.
PO Box 1683
Redlands, CA 92373
Tel: (909)307-9892
Fax: (909)307-9892
Web Site: http://www.redlandsscholarships.org
To encourage educational pursuits among Redlands Unified School District graduates by providing educational assistance.
Title of Award: Soroptimist International of Redlands Scholarships **Area, Field, or Subject:** Health care services; Law; Engineering; Computer and information sciences; Education; Business. **Level of Education for which Award is Granted:** Undergraduate **Number Awarded:** 1. **Funds Available:** $750.
Eligibility Requirements: Applicant must be a graduating senior who has participated in community service and who will be attending an accredited college on a full-time basis and is planning to major in one of the following fields: health care, law, engineering, computer science, education and/or business administration. **Application Requirements:** Applicants must submit a completed application form together with the scantron sheet; cover sheet; student activity and community activity sheets; personal essay; and a copy of unofficial transcript (signed by the counselor). **Additional Information:** No electronic submissions of application will be accepted. Submit two printed copies of the application and use a No. 2 pencil on the scantron sheet. **Deadline for Receipt:** February 20.

4527 ■ RHODE ISLAND FOUNDATION
One Union Sta.
Providence, RI 02903
Tel: (401)274-4564
Fax: (401)331-8085
Web Site: http://www.rifoundation.org/matriarch/default.asp
To provide tuition support to women with financial need planning to attend graduate school to attain a law degree at an accredited institution.
Title of Award: Marilyn Graboys Wool Scholarships **Area, Field, or Subject:** Law. **Level of Education for which Award is Granted:** Undergraduate **Funds Available:** $2,000. **Duration:** One year.
Eligibility Requirements: Applicants must be females planning to attend or registered in an accredited law school; must be Rhode Island residents; must be accepted into an accredited law school; and must be able to demonstrate financial need. **Application Requirements:** Applicants must complete the application form, available online; must have a copy of their financial aid award letter and a recent official transcript; and must provide one essay, a copy of their Student Aid Report, and letter of recommendation. Application forms and other supporting documents must be sent to Libby Monahan, GFWC Women's Club of South County Scholarship, Rhode Island Foundation, One Union Station, Providence, RI 02903. **Deadline for Receipt:** June 20.

4528 ■ ROANOKE BAR ASSOCIATION
PO Box 18183
Roanoke, VA 24014
Tel: (540)342-4905
Fax: (540)342-1252
E-mail: roanokebar@earthlink.net
Web Site: http://www.roanokebar.com
To provide financial assistance to those deserving law students.
Title of Award: Jane S. Glenn Memorial Endowed Scholarships **Area, Field, or Subject:** Law. **Level of Education for which Award is Granted:** Undergraduate **Funds Available:** No specific amount.
Eligibility Requirements: Applicants must be law students who are enrolled at an accredited law school in the Commonwealth of Virginia; must maintain a minimum 2.5 GPA. **Application Requirements:** Applicants must submit a completed application form. **Additional Information:** Roanoke Bar Association at the above address.

4529 ■ ROANOKE BAR ASSOCIATION
PO Box 18183
Roanoke, VA 24014
Tel: (540)342-4905
Fax: (540)342-1252
E-mail: roanokebar@earthlink.net
Web Site: http://www.roanokebar.com
To provide financial assistance to those students who demonstrate diligence and commitment to their studies, academic excellence and an interest in the pursuit of law.
Title of Award: James N. Kincanon Scholarships **Area, Field, or Subject:** Law. **Level of Education for which Award is Granted:** Undergraduate **Funds Available:** No specific amount.
Eligibility Requirements: Applicants must be residents of the City of Roanoke, the City of Salem, or the County of Roanoke, or graduates of a high school located in those jurisdictions. Applicants must have a grade point average of at least 3.0 during high school (and college or law school, if applicable) and must be accepted, or expect to be accepted prior to the fall semester, into post-secondary training, pursuing education in the law. **Application Requirements:** Applicants must submit a completed application form online. **Deadline for Receipt:** February 1. **Additional Information:** Roanoke Bar Association at the above address.

4530 ■ ROCKY MOUNTAIN MINERAL LAW FOUNDATION
9191 Sheridan Blvd., Ste. 203
Westminster, CO 80031
Tel: (303)321-8100
Fax: (303)321-7657
E-mail: info@rmmlf.org
Web Site: http://www.rmmlf.org
To encourage the study of natural resources law by well-qualified law students who have the potential to make significant contributions to scholarship in natural resources law.

Title of Award: Joe Rudd Scholarships **Area, Field, or Subject:** Law. **Level of Education for which Award is Granted:** Undergraduate **Funds Available:** A total amount of $100,000 per year. **Duration:** One year.
Eligibility Requirements: Applicants must be a law student enrolled at one of the foundation's governing law schools and can demonstrate a commitment to study natural resources law. **Application Requirements:** Applicants must submit the requirements. **Deadline for Receipt:** April 1.

4531 ■ SAFE SCHOOLS COALITION
1002 E Seneca St.
Seattle, WA 98122-4203
Tel: (206)957-1621
Fax: (206)325-2689
Web Site: http://www.safeschoolscoalition.org
To provide financial assistance for transgender-identified students.
Title of Award: Transgender Scholarships and Education Legacy Fund **Area, Field, or Subject:** Social Services; Health Care Services; Religious Education; Teaching; Law. **Level of Education for which Award is Granted:** Undergraduate **Funds Available:** No specific amount.
Eligibility Requirements: Applicants must be students of one of these fields of studies. **Application Requirements:** Applicants must check the contact information for more inquiries. **Additional Information:** The awards are sponsored by the International Foundation for Gender Education. **Deadline for Receipt:** February 1. **Additional Information:** International Foundation for Gender Education (IFGE) TSELF Awards Committee PO Box 540229 Waltham, MA 02454-0229 Phone: 781-899-2212
Fax: 781-899-2212 URL: www.tself.org.

4532 ■ SAFE SCHOOLS COALITION
1002 E Seneca St.
Seattle, WA 98122-4203
Tel: (206)957-1621
Fax: (206)325-2689
Web Site: http://www.safeschoolscoalition.org
To provide financial assistance for a lesbian/gay student beginning his or her final fall semester of law school.
Title of Award: Michael A. Zamperini/W. Clay Burchell Scholarships **Area, Field, or Subject:** Law. **Level of Education for which Award is Granted:** Undergraduate **Funds Available:** The scholarship amount varies, but is typically $1,000 to $2,000.
Eligibility Requirements: Applicants must be enrolled at Golden Gate University School of Law. **Application Requirements:** Applicants must check the available website for the required materials. **Additional Information:** Golden Gate University School of Law; Financial Aid Office at 536 Mission Street San Francisco, CA 94105 Phone: 1-415-442-6635 Fax: 1-415-442-6609.

4533 ■ SERBIAN BAR ASSOCIATION OF AMERICA
1000 N Lake Shore Dr., Unit 2204
Chicago, IL 60611
E-mail: dbalac@aol.com
Web Site: http://www.serbbar.org
To promote the best interests of the Serbian American community.
Title of Award: Serbian Bar Association of America Scholarships **Area, Field, or Subject:** Law. **Level of Education for which Award is Granted:** Undergraduate **Funds Available:** $500-$2000.
Eligibility Requirements: Applicants must be of Serbian birth or ancestry and/or their spouses who are enrolled in an accredited law school in the US. **Application Requirements:** Applicants must submit a typed essay of no more than 250 words detailing how they plan to use their legal education within the Serbian American community and submit a certified copy of their law school transcript. **Deadline for Receipt:** October.

4534 ■ SETON HALL UNIVERSITY SCHOOL OF LAW
1 Newark Ctr.
Newark, NJ 07102
Tel: (973)642-8850; 888-415-7271
Fax: (973)642-8876
E-mail: law_financial@shu.edu
Web Site: http://law.shu.edu
To reward the hard work and academic success of students.
Title of Award: Seton Hall Law School's Merit Scholarship Program **Area, Field, or Subject:** Law. **Level of Education for which Award is**

Granted: Undergraduate **Funds Available:** $4,500 to full tuition. **Duration:** Every semester.
Eligibility Requirements: Prospective recipient must be an incoming law student of the university. **Application Requirements:** All applicants for school admission are considered an applicant for the program. **Additional Information:** No separate application is required. Scholarship is renewable by maintaining a required GPA standard. **Deadline for Receipt:** End of enrollment in fall.

4535 ■ SHORELINE COMMUNITY COLLEGE FOUNDATION
16101 Greenwood Ave. N, Ste. 1005
Shoreline, WA 98133-5696
Tel: (206)546-4755
Fax: (206)546-5826
E-mail: rmanchester@shoreline.edu
Web Site: http://www.shoreline.edu
To increase access and success of Shoreline Community College students.
Title of Award: Carli Edwards Memorial Scholarships **Area, Field, or Subject:** Criminal Justice. **Level of Education for which Award is Granted:** Undergraduate **Funds Available:** $200. **Duration:** One quarter.
Eligibility Requirements: Applicants must be returning or part-time students at Shoreline Community College; must be survivors of domestic abuse; must be Washington State residents for a minimum of one year; must not have previous two or four year college degree; must be criminal justice majors; must earn and maintain a minimum cumulative GPA of 3.0 (GPA of 3.5 in criminal justice coursework); and must not be currently included on the Scholarship Selection Committee or related (first degree) to a person on the Selection Committee. **Application Requirements:** Applicants must complete application form; must submit letter of recommendation from teacher, professor or employer (excluding criminal justice faculty); statement or documentation of income and need; and unofficial SCC transcript.

4536 ■ SOUTHWEST FLORIDA COMMUNITY FOUNDATION
8260 College Pkwy., Ste. 101
Fort Myers, FL 33919
Tel: (239)274-5900
Fax: (239)274-5930
Web Site: http://www.floridacommunity.com
To fund a student who will attend: FGCU, university of Florida/Gainesville, Florida State University/Tallahassee, Flagler College, Stetson University/Deland, University of Miami, University of Tampa, or Embry Riddle Aeronautical University/Daytona Beach.
Title of Award: D&A Florida Scholarships **Area, Field, or Subject:** Architecture; Business; Engineering; International affairs and relations; Journalism; Computer and information sciences; Law; Literature; Medicine; Physics; Chemistry; Political science. **Level of Education for which Award is Granted:** Undergraduate **Funds Available:** $10,000. **Duration:** One year.
Eligibility Requirements: Applicants must have graduated from a public or private high school in Charlotte, Glades, Hendry or Lee County; must pursue a degree in Architecture, Business, Engineering, International affairs and relations, Journalism, Computer and information sciences, Law, Literature, Medicine, Physics, Chemistry, or Political science. **Application Requirements:** Application forms are available online. Applicants must submit a letter of interest and letter of recommendation, a transcript and financial need documentation. **Deadline for Receipt:** February 15.

4537 ■ SOUTHWEST FLORIDA COMMUNITY FOUNDATION
8260 College Pkwy., Ste. 101
Fort Myers, FL 33919
Tel: (239)274-5900
Fax: (239)274-5930
Web Site: http://www.floridacommunity.com
To fund scholarships for students who have completed their first year of course load at an accredited law school.
Title of Award: William L. Graddy Law School Scholarships **Area, Field, or Subject:** Law. **Level of Education for which Award is Granted:** Undergraduate **Funds Available:** $1,000. **Duration:** One year.
Eligibility Requirements: Applicants must have completed first year of law school; must have a GPA of 2.8 or above and be in the top 25% of class; must have been a resident of Charlotte, Collier, Glades, Hendry or

Lee for at least 3 years; and must demonstrate financial need. **Application Requirements:** Application forms are available online. Applicants must submit a letter of interest, letter of recommendation from college instructor, transcript and financial need documentation. **Deadline for Receipt:** March 20.

4538 ■ SOUTHWEST FLORIDA COMMUNITY FOUNDATION
8260 College Pkwy., Ste. 101
Fort Myers, FL 33919
Tel: (239)274-5900
Fax: (239)274-5930
Web Site: http://www.floridacommunity.com
To fund students pursuing degrees or advanced degrees in medicine, law, dentistry, teaching (math and science), ministry, engineering, accounting, architecture and computer science.
Title of Award: John M. and Mary A. Shanley Memorial Scholarships **Area, Field, or Subject:** Medicine; Law; Dentistry; Teaching; Ministry; Engineering; Accounting; Agriculture; Economic aspects; Architecture; Computer and information sciences. **Level of Education for which Award is Granted:** Undergraduate **Funds Available:** $5,000. **Duration:** One year.
Eligibility Requirements: Applicant must be a resident of Charlotte, Hendry or Lee County. **Application Requirements:** Application forms are available online. Applicants must submit a letter of interest, letter of recommendation and transcript. **Deadline for Receipt:** February 15.

4539 ■ STARK COMMUNITY FOUNDATION
400 Market Ave. N, Ste. 200
Canton, OH 44702-2107
Tel: (330)454-3426
Fax: (330)454-5855
Web Site: http://www.starkcommunityfoundation.org
To provide scholarship assistance to qualified individuals who want to pursue their studies.
Title of Award: Sanders J. Mestel Legal Scholarship Fund **Area, Field, or Subject:** Law. **Level of Education for which Award is Granted:** Undergraduate **Funds Available:** No specific amount. **Duration:** One year.
Eligibility Requirements: Applicants must be law students whose residence is in Stark County. **Application Requirements:** Applicants must submit written statement of 250-300 words by the applicant indicating his/her special interest, extracurricular activities and future career aspirations in law. Application form and other supporting documents must be sent to Stark Community Foundation, 400 Market Ave. N, Canton, OH 44702. **Deadline for Receipt:** May 1.

4540 ■ STARK COMMUNITY FOUNDATION
400 Market Ave. N, Ste. 200
Canton, OH 44702-2107
Tel: (330)454-3426
Fax: (330)454-5855
Web Site: http://www.starkcommunityfoundation.org
To provide scholarship assistance to qualified individuals who want to pursue their studies.
Title of Award: Stark County Bar Association Fund **Area, Field, or Subject:** Law. **Level of Education for which Award is Granted:** Undergraduate **Funds Available:** No specific amount. **Duration:** One year.
Eligibility Requirements: Applicants must be law students enrolled at accredited law schools; must be from the Stark County area. **Application Requirements:** Applicants must complete and submit the application form and requirements to Stark County Bar Association, 116 Cleveland Ave. NW, Ste. 400, Canton, OH 44702. **Deadline for Receipt:** April 1.

4541 ■ STRAIGHTFORWARD MEDIA
508 7th St., Ste 202
Rapid City, SD 57701
Tel: (605)348-3042
Fax: (605)348-3043
E-mail: info@straightforwardmedia.com
Web Site: http://www.straightforwardmedia.com
To financially assist students in their educational pursuits.
Title of Award: StraightForward Media's Law School Scholarships **Area, Field, or Subject:** Law. **Level of Education for which Award is Granted:** Undergraduate **Number Awarded:** 4. **Funds Available:** $500.

Eligibility Requirements: Applicant must be a law student. **Application Requirements:** Applicants must complete the scholarship application online. **Additional Information:** Awards are given four times a year. **Deadline for Receipt:** March, June, September, December.

4542 ■ TANANA VALLEY CAMPUS

604 Barnette St.
Fairbanks, AK 99701
Tel: (907)455-2800; 877-882-8827
Web Site: http://www.tvc.uaf.edu
To provide educational support for qualified students intending to pursue their education.

Title of Award: Rachael Patterson Memorial Scholarships **Area, Field, or Subject:** Technology, Criminal justice, Fires and fire prevention. **Level of Education for which Award is Granted:** Undergraduate **Funds Available:** No specific amount. **Duration:** One year.
Eligibility Requirements: Applicants must be sophomores or above; must be enrolled in justice, fire science or office management and technology; must be residents of Alaska (at least two years) and are intending to remain in Alaska. **Application Requirements:** Scholarship applications are available online at uaonline.alaska.edu (to access the scholarship application, applicant must choose "Login to secured area" if they have a UA ID or apply for admission for the new students).

4543 ■ J.L. TURNER LEGAL ASSOCIATION

PO Box 134002
Dallas, TX 75313-4002
Tel: (214)761-1707
Web Site: http://www.jltla.org
To inspire educational pursuits in the field of law among law students.

Title of Award: JLTLA Scholarships **Area, Field, or Subject:** Law. **Level of Education for which Award is Granted:** Undergraduate **Funds Available:** No specific amount.
Eligibility Requirements: Program is open to second or third year law students that are from or attending law school in the Dallas-Fort Worth Metroplex. **Application Requirements:** Applicants must submit the following requirements: application; a short biographical sketch (5-7 sentences, written in third person for inclusion in gala booklet if selected); photograph (3x5 or larger of head and shoulders, photograph should be suitable for inclusion in gala booklet if selected); a certified copy of law school transcript; letters of reference; and a brief essay. Applicants may download an application form at J.L Turner website. **Deadline for Receipt:** September 28. **Additional Information:** Star A. Carter; 214-746-7899; Star.Carter@weil.com.

4544 ■ J.L. TURNER LEGAL ASSOCIATION

PO Box 134002
Dallas, TX 75313-4002
Tel: (214)761-1707
Web Site: http://www.jltla.org
To inspire educational pursuits in the field of law among minority law students.

Title of Award: JLTLA Texas Bar Review Scholarships **Area, Field, or Subject:** Law. **Level of Education for which Award is Granted:** Undergraduate **Funds Available:** No specific amount.
Eligibility Requirements: Applicants must be in their 3L year and must be taking the Texas Bar Examination. **Application Requirements:** Applicants must submit the following requirements: application; financial statement; resume; essay; and letter of reference; certified copy of law school transcript; short biographical sketch (5-7 sentences length, and written in third person); photograph (size 3x5 or larger of head and shoulders only. Photograph should be suitable for inclusion in a professional publication). **Deadline for Receipt:** March 31. **Additional Information:** Star A. Carter; 214-746-7899; Star.Carter@weil.com.

4545 ■ UNIVERSITY OF MEMPHIS

Cecil C. Humphreys School of Law
3715 Central Ave.
Memphis, TN 38152
Tel: (901)678-2421
Fax: (901)678-5210
E-mail: lawadmissions@memphis.edu
Web Site: http://www.law.memphis.edu

To support the education of female law students at the University of Memphis.
Title of Award: Tillie B. Alperin Scholarships **Area, Field, or Subject:** Law. **Level of Education for which Award is Granted:** Undergraduate **Funds Available:** No specific amount.
Eligibility Requirements: Applicant must be a female law student who has successfully completed her first year with a B average; has demonstrated a commitment to the legal profession; and demonstrates financial need. **Application Requirements:** Applicants must complete the online scholarship application form along with a personal statement; resume; scholarship statement; and recommendation letters. Applicants must also complete the FAFSA Form. **Additional Information:** Named in honor of the late Tillie Blen Alperin, a 1935 graduate of the old University of Memphis Law School and one of the first women to practice law in Tennessee. **Deadline for Receipt:** March 15. **Additional Information:** Dr. Sue Ann McClellan, Assistant Dean of Admissions, at 901-678-5403, or smcclell@memphis.edu; Ms. DebraAnn Brown, Assistant Director for Student Financial Aid, at 901-678-3737, or dbrown@memphis.edu.

4546 ■ UNIVERSITY OF MEMPHIS

Cecil C. Humphreys School of Law
3715 Central Ave.
Memphis, TN 38152
Tel: (901)678-2421
Fax: (901)678-5210
E-mail: lawadmissions@memphis.edu
Web Site: http://www.law.memphis.edu
To support the education of law students at the University of Memphis.
Title of Award: Claude T. Coffman Memorial Scholarships **Area, Field, or Subject:** Law. **Level of Education for which Award is Granted:** Undergraduate **Funds Available:** No specific amount.
Eligibility Requirements: Applicant must be admitted at the University of Memphis Cecil C. Humphreys School of Law. **Application Requirements:** Applicants must complete the online scholarship application form along with a personal statement; resume; scholarship statement; and recommendation letters. Applicants must also complete the FAFSA Form. **Additional Information:** The scholarship is named in honor of the late professor and former interim dean of the Cecil C. Humphreys School of Law. **Deadline for Receipt:** March 15. **Additional Information:** Dr. Sue Ann McClellan, Assistant Dean of Admissions, at 901-678-5403, or smcclell@memphis.edu; Ms. DebraAnn Brown, Assistant Director for Student Financial Aid, at 901-678-3737, or dbrown@memphis.edu.

4547 ■ UNIVERSITY OF MEMPHIS

Cecil C. Humphreys School of Law
3715 Central Ave.
Memphis, TN 38152
Tel: (901)678-2421
Fax: (901)678-5210
E-mail: lawadmissions@memphis.edu
Web Site: http://www.law.memphis.edu
To support the education of law students at the University of Memphis.
Title of Award: Cleveland Drennon, Jr. Memorial Scholarships **Area, Field, or Subject:** Law. **Level of Education for which Award is Granted:** Undergraduate **Funds Available:** No specific amount.
Eligibility Requirements: Applicant must be admitted as full-time student at the University of Memphis Cecil C. Humphreys School of Law. **Application Requirements:** Applicants must complete the online scholarship application form along with a personal statement; resume; scholarship statement; and recommendation letters. Applicants must also complete the FAFSA Form. **Additional Information:** Funded by Humphrey E. Folk, Jr. and the Drennon family and friends. **Deadline for Receipt:** March 15. **Additional Information:** Dr. Sue Ann McClellan, Assistant Dean of Admissions, at 901-678-5403, or smcclell@memphis.edu; Ms. DebraAnn Brown, Assistant Director for Student Financial Aid, at 901-678-3737, or dbrown@memphis.edu.

4548 ■ UNIVERSITY OF MEMPHIS

Cecil C. Humphreys School of Law
3715 Central Ave.
Memphis, TN 38152
Tel: (901)678-2421
Fax: (901)678-5210

E-mail: lawadmissions@memphis.edu
Web Site: http://www.law.memphis.edu
To support the education of law students at the University of Memphis.
Title of Award: East Tennessee Foundation Scholarships **Area, Field, or Subject:** Law. **Level of Education for which Award is Granted:** Undergraduate **Number Awarded:** 1. **Funds Available:** No specific amount.
Eligibility Requirements: Applicant must be a second- or third-year student who demonstrates community involvement or commitment to public service. **Application Requirements:** Applicants must complete the online scholarship application form along with a personal statement; resume; scholarship statement; and recommendation letters. Applicants must also complete the FAFSA Form. **Additional Information:** Scholarship is made possible by a grant from the Tennessee Judicial Conference Foundation. The scholarship is awarded every four years, rotating among the other law schools in the state. **Deadline for Receipt:** March 15. **Additional Information:** Dr. Sue Ann McClellan, Assistant Dean of Admissions, at 901-678-5403, or smcclell@memphis.edu; Ms. DebraAnn Brown, Assistant Director for Student Financial Aid, at 901-678-3737, or dbrown@memphis.edu.

4549 ■ UNIVERSITY OF MEMPHIS
Cecil C. Humphreys School of Law
3715 Central Ave.
Memphis, TN 38152
Tel: (901)678-2421
Fax: (901)678-5210
E-mail: lawadmissions@memphis.edu
Web Site: http://www.law.memphis.edu
To support the education of law students at the University of Memphis.
Title of Award: Evans and Petree Law Firm Scholarships **Area, Field, or Subject:** Law. **Level of Education for which Award is Granted:** Undergraduate **Number Awarded:** 1. **Funds Available:** No specific amount.
Eligibility Requirements: Applicant must be an African American law student. **Application Requirements:** Applicants must complete the online scholarship application form along with the personal statement; resume; scholarship statement; and recommendation letters. Applicants must also complete the FAFSA Form. **Additional Information:** Established in Honor of Percy Harvey, Esq. by the Evans and Petree Law Firm. **Deadline for Receipt:** March 15. **Additional Information:** Dr. Sue Ann McClellan, Assistant Dean of Admissions, at 901-678-5403, or smcclell@memphis.edu; Ms. DebraAnn Brown, Assistant Director for Student Financial Aid, at 901-678-3737, or dbrown@memphis.edu.

4550 ■ UNIVERSITY OF MEMPHIS
Cecil C. Humphreys School of Law
3715 Central Ave.
Memphis, TN 38152
Tel: (901)678-2421
Fax: (901)678-5210
E-mail: lawadmissions@memphis.edu
Web Site: http://www.law.memphis.edu
To broaden the Middle District of Tennessee bar through expanded opportunities for law students from all backgrounds.
Title of Award: Federal Court Bench and Bar Scholarships **Area, Field, or Subject:** Law. **Level of Education for which Award is Granted:** Undergraduate **Funds Available:** No specific amount.
Eligibility Requirements: Applicants must be economically disadvantaged law students from the Middle District of Tennessee; in good academic standing at the law school or the most recent school attended; have demonstrated financial need; and must have graduated from a high school in, or resided for the previous three years as a non-full time student in one of the following Tennessee Counties: Cannon, Cheatham, Clay, Cumberland, Davidson, DeKalb, Dickson, Fentress, Giles, Hickman, Houston, Humphreys, Jackson, Lawrence, Lewis, Macon, Marshall, Maury, Montgomery, Overton, Pickett, Putnam, Robertson, Rutherford, Smith, Stewart, Sumner, Trousdale, Wayne, White, Williamson, or Wilson. **Application Requirements:** Applicants must complete the online scholarship application form along with a personal statement; resume; scholarship statement; and recommendation letters. Applicants must also complete the FAFSA Form. **Deadline for Receipt:** March 15. **Additional Information:** Dr. Sue Ann McClellan, Assistant Dean of Admissions, at

901-678-5403, or smcclell@memphis.edu; Ms. DebraAnn Brown, Assistant Director for Student Financial Aid, at 901-678-3737, or dbrown@memphis.edu.

4551 ■ UNIVERSITY OF MEMPHIS
Cecil C. Humphreys School of Law
3715 Central Ave.
Memphis, TN 38152
Tel: (901)678-2421
Fax: (901)678-5210
E-mail: lawadmissions@memphis.edu
Web Site: http://www.law.memphis.edu
To support the education of law students at the University of Memphis.
Title of Award: Wilford Hayes Gowen Scholarships **Area, Field, or Subject:** Law. **Level of Education for which Award is Granted:** Undergraduate **Funds Available:** No specific amount.
Eligibility Requirements: Applicant must be a second- or third-year law student. **Application Requirements:** Applicants must complete the online scholarship application form along with a personal statement; resume; scholarship statement; and recommendation letters. Applicants must also complete the FAFSA Form. **Additional Information:** Established in memory of Wilford Hayes Gowen, through the Community Foundation of Western North Carolina. **Deadline for Receipt:** March 15. **Additional Information:** Dr. Sue Ann McClellan, Assistant Dean of Admissions, at 901-678-5403, or smcclell@memphis.edu; Ms. DebraAnn Brown, Assistant Director for Student Financial Aid, at 901-678-3737, or dbrown@memphis.edu.

4552 ■ UNIVERSITY OF MEMPHIS
Cecil C. Humphreys School of Law
3715 Central Ave.
Memphis, TN 38152
Tel: (901)678-2421
Fax: (901)678-5210
E-mail: lawadmissions@memphis.edu
Web Site: http://www.law.memphis.edu
To support the education of law students at the University of Memphis.
Title of Award: Herbert Herff Presidential Law Scholarships **Area, Field, or Subject:** Law. **Level of Education for which Award is Granted:** Undergraduate **Funds Available:** No specific amount. **Duration:** One year.
Eligibility Requirements: Applicants must be admitted at the University of Memphis Cecil C. Humphreys School of Law; have demonstrated high academic or professional achievement; and show potential for an outstanding law career. **Application Requirements:** Applicants must complete the online scholarship application form along with a personal statement; resume; scholarship statement; and recommendation letters. Applicants must also complete the FAFSA Form. **Additional Information:** Funded by the Herbert Herff Trust. **Deadline for Receipt:** March 15. **Additional Information:** Dr. Sue Ann McClellan, Assistant Dean of Admissions, at 901-678-5403, or smcclell@memphis.edu; Ms. DebraAnn Brown, Assistant Director for Student Financial Aid, at 901-678-3737, or dbrown@memphis.edu.

4553 ■ UNIVERSITY OF MEMPHIS
Cecil C. Humphreys School of Law
3715 Central Ave.
Memphis, TN 38152
Tel: (901)678-2421
Fax: (901)678-5210
E-mail: lawadmissions@memphis.edu
Web Site: http://www.law.memphis.edu
To support the education of law students at the University of Memphis.
Title of Award: Robert and Elaine Hoffman Memorial Scholarships **Area, Field, or Subject:** Law. **Level of Education for which Award is Granted:** Undergraduate **Funds Available:** No specific amount.
Eligibility Requirements: Applicants must be admitted at the University of Memphis Cecil C. Humphreys School of Law. **Application Requirements:** Applicants must complete the online scholarship application form along with a personal statement; resume; scholarship statement; and recommendation letters. Applicants must also complete the FAFSA Form. **Additional Information:** The scholarship is named in honor of the late Chancellor Robert Hoffman and his sister Elaine. **Deadline for Receipt:**

March 15. **Additional Information:** Dr. Sue Ann McClellan, Assistant Dean of Admissions, at 901-678-5403, or smcclell@memphis.edu; Ms. DebraAnn Brown, Assistant Director for Student Financial Aid, at 901-678-3737, or dbrown@memphis.edu.

4554 ■ UNIVERSITY OF MEMPHIS
Cecil C. Humphreys School of Law
3715 Central Ave.
Memphis, TN 38152
Tel: (901)678-2421
Fax: (901)678-5210
E-mail: lawadmissions@memphis.edu
Web Site: http://www.law.memphis.edu
To support the education of law students at the University of Memphis.
Title of Award: Kathryn Hookanson Law Fellowships **Area, Field, or Subject:** Law. **Level of Education for which Award is Granted:** Undergraduate **Funds Available:** No specific amount.
Eligibility Requirements: Applicant must be a student at the University of Memphis. **Application Requirements:** Applicants must complete the online scholarship application form along with a personal statement; resume; scholarship statement; and recommendation letters. Applicants must also complete the FAFSA Form. **Additional Information:** Established by Ms. Hookanson, her family, friends and colleagues. **Deadline for Receipt:** March 15. **Additional Information:** Dr. Sue Ann McClellan, Assistant Dean of Admissions, at 901-678-5403, or smcclell@memphis.edu; Ms. DebraAnn Brown, Assistant Director for Student Financial Aid, at 901-678-3737, or dbrown@memphis.edu.

4555 ■ UNIVERSITY OF MEMPHIS
Cecil C. Humphreys School of Law
3715 Central Ave.
Memphis, TN 38152
Tel: (901)678-2421
Fax: (901)678-5210
E-mail: lawadmissions@memphis.edu
Web Site: http://www.law.memphis.edu
To support the education of law students at the University of Memphis.
Title of Award: John C. "Jack" Hough Memorial Law Scholarships **Area, Field, or Subject:** Law. **Level of Education for which Award is Granted:** Undergraduate **Funds Available:** No specific amount.
Eligibility Requirements: Applicant must be a second- or third-year law student who demonstrates financial need and is working as a volunteer or in a law school externship in the office of the Shelby County Public Defender. **Application Requirements:** Applicants must complete the online scholarship application form along with a personal statement; resume; scholarship statement; and recommendation letters. Applicants must also complete the FAFSA Form. **Additional Information:** Scholarship is named in honor of the late John C. "Jack" Hough, a former member of the Shelby County Public Defender's Office. **Deadline for Receipt:** March 15. **Additional Information:** Dr. Sue Ann McClellan, Assistant Dean of Admissions, at 901-678-5403, or smcclell@memphis.edu; Ms. DebraAnn Brown, Assistant Director for Student Financial Aid, at 901-678-3737, or dbrown@memphis.edu.

4556 ■ UNIVERSITY OF MEMPHIS
Cecil C. Humphreys School of Law
3715 Central Ave.
Memphis, TN 38152
Tel: (901)678-2421
Fax: (901)678-5210
E-mail: lawadmissions@memphis.edu
Web Site: http://www.law.memphis.edu
To support the education of law students at the University of Memphis.
Title of Award: Cecil C. Humphreys Law Fellowships **Area, Field, or Subject:** Law. **Level of Education for which Award is Granted:** Undergraduate **Funds Available:** Free waiver for half the cost of in-state tuition.
Eligibility Requirements: Applicant must be a second- or third-year student. **Application Requirements:** Applicants must complete the online scholarship application form along with a personal statement; resume; scholarship statement; and recommendation letters. Applicants must also complete the FAFSA Form. **Additional Information:** Fellowship is funded through a grant from the Plough Foundation. Humphreys

Fellows are required to work 15 hours per week as a research assistant to faculty members. **Deadline for Receipt:** March 15. **Additional Information:** Dr. Sue Ann McClellan, Assistant Dean of Admissions, at 901-678-5403, or smcclell@memphis.edu; Ms. DebraAnn Brown, Assistant Director for Student Financial Aid, at 901-678-3737, or dbrown@memphis.edu.

4557 ■ UNIVERSITY OF MEMPHIS
Cecil C. Humphreys School of Law
3715 Central Ave.
Memphis, TN 38152
Tel: (901)678-2421
Fax: (901)678-5210
E-mail: lawadmissions@memphis.edu
Web Site: http://www.law.memphis.edu
To support the education of law students at the University of Memphis.
Title of Award: Judge William B. Leffler Scholarships **Area, Field, or Subject:** Law. **Level of Education for which Award is Granted:** Undergraduate **Funds Available:** No specific amount.
Eligibility Requirements: Applicants must be admitted at the University of Memphis Cecil C. Humphreys School of Law. **Application Requirements:** Applicants must complete the online scholarship application form along with the personal statement; resume; scholarship statement; and recommendation letters. Applicants must also complete the FAFSA Form. **Additional Information:** The award is funded through the Leffler family, the donations of friends, and proceeds from the annual bankruptcy law seminar in Judge Leffler's memory. **Deadline for Receipt:** March 15. **Additional Information:** Dr. Sue Ann McClellan, Assistant Dean of Admissions, at 901-678-5403, or smcclell@memphis.edu; Ms. DebraAnn Brown, Assistant Director for Student Financial Aid, at 901-678-3737, or dbrown@memphis.edu.

4558 ■ UNIVERSITY OF MEMPHIS
Cecil C. Humphreys School of Law
3715 Central Ave.
Memphis, TN 38152
Tel: (901)678-2421
Fax: (901)678-5210
E-mail: lawadmissions@memphis.edu
Web Site: http://www.law.memphis.edu
To support the education of law students at the University of Memphis.
Title of Award: H.H. McKnight Memorial Scholarships **Area, Field, or Subject:** Law. **Level of Education for which Award is Granted:** Undergraduate **Number Awarded:** 2. **Funds Available:** No specific amount.
Eligibility Requirements: Applicants must be veterans of the United States Armed Forces interested in pursuing a career in criminal law. **Application Requirements:** Applicants must complete the online scholarship application form along with a personal statement; resume; scholarship statement; and recommendation letters. Applicants must also complete the FAFSA Form. **Deadline for Receipt:** March 15. **Additional Information:** Dr. Sue Ann McClellan, Assistant Dean of Admissions, at 901-678-5403, or smcclell@memphis.edu; Ms. DebraAnn Brown, Assistant Director for Student Financial Aid, at 901-678-3737, or dbrown@memphis.edu.

4559 ■ UNIVERSITY OF MEMPHIS
Cecil C. Humphreys School of Law
3715 Central Ave.
Memphis, TN 38152
Tel: (901)678-2421
Fax: (901)678-5210
E-mail: lawadmissions@memphis.edu
Web Site: http://www.law.memphis.edu
To support the education of law students at the University of Memphis.
Title of Award: Sam A. Myar, Jr. Law Scholarships **Area, Field, or Subject:** Law. **Level of Education for which Award is Granted:** Undergraduate **Funds Available:** No specific amount.
Eligibility Requirements: Applicant must be the Editor-in-Chief and the Managing Editor of the University of Memphis Law Review. **Application Requirements:** Applicants must complete the online scholarship application form along with a personal statement; resume; scholarship statement; and recommendation letters. Applicants must also complete the FAFSA Form. **Additional Information:** Established in 1960. **Deadline for**

Receipt: March 15. **Additional Information:** Dr. Sue Ann McClellan, Assistant Dean of Admissions, at 901-678-5403, or smcclell@memphis.edu; Ms. DebraAnn Brown, Assistant Director for Student Financial Aid, at 901-678-3737, or dbrown@memphis.edu.

4560 ■ UNIVERSITY OF MEMPHIS
Cecil C. Humphreys School of Law
3715 Central Ave.
Memphis, TN 38152
Tel: (901)678-2421
Fax: (901)678-5210
E-mail: lawadmissions@memphis.edu
Web Site: http://www.law.memphis.edu
To support the education of law students at the University of Memphis.
Title of Award: Donald and Susie Polden Dean's Scholarships **Area, Field, or Subject:** Law. **Level of Education for which Award is Granted:** Undergraduate **Funds Available:** No specific amount.
Eligibility Requirements: Applicants must be law students; must be committed to community or public service; and must express a desire to serve the community during or following law school. **Application Requirements:** Applicants must complete the online scholarship application form along with a personal statement; resume; scholarship statement; and recommendation letters. Applicants must also complete the FAFSA Form. **Deadline for Receipt:** March 15. **Additional Information:** Dr. Sue Ann McClellan, Assistant Dean of Admissions, at 901-678-5403, or smcclell@memphis.edu; Ms. DebraAnn Brown, Assistant Director for Student Financial Aid, at 901-678-3737, or dbrown@memphis.edu.

4561 ■ UNIVERSITY OF MEMPHIS
Cecil C. Humphreys School of Law
3715 Central Ave.
Memphis, TN 38152
Tel: (901)678-2421
Fax: (901)678-5210
E-mail: lawadmissions@memphis.edu
Web Site: http://www.law.memphis.edu
To support the education of law students at the University of Memphis.
Title of Award: Ratner and Sugarmon Scholarships **Area, Field, or Subject:** Law. **Level of Education for which Award is Granted:** Undergraduate **Funds Available:** No specific amount.
Eligibility Requirements: Applicants must be second or third year law students. **Application Requirements:** Applicants must complete the online scholarship application form along with a personal statement; resume; scholarship statement; and recommendation letters. Applicants must also complete the FAFSA Form. **Deadline for Receipt:** March 15. **Additional Information:** Dr. Sue Ann McClellan, Assistant Dean of Admissions, at 901-678-5403, or smcclell@memphis.edu; Ms. DebraAnn Brown, Assistant Director for Student Financial Aid, at 901-678-3737, or dbrown@memphis.edu.

4562 ■ UNIVERSITY OF MEMPHIS
Cecil C. Humphreys School of Law
3715 Central Ave.
Memphis, TN 38152
Tel: (901)678-2421
Fax: (901)678-5210
E-mail: lawadmissions@memphis.edu
Web Site: http://www.law.memphis.edu
To support the education of law students at the University of Memphis.
Title of Award: Joseph Henry Shepherd Scholarships **Area, Field, or Subject:** Law. **Level of Education for which Award is Granted:** Undergraduate **Number Awarded:** 3. **Funds Available:** No specific amount.
Eligibility Requirements: Applicant must be admitted at the University of Memphis Cecil C. Humphreys School of Law. **Application Requirements:** Applicants must complete the online scholarship application form along with a personal statement; resume; scholarship statement; and recommendation letters. Applicants must also complete the FAFSA Form. **Additional Information:** Sponsored by Dorothy S. Shepherd. **Deadline for Receipt:** March 15. **Additional Information:** Dr. Sue Ann McClellan, Assistant Dean of Admissions, at 901-678-5403, or smcclell@memphis.edu; Ms. DebraAnn Brown, Assistant Director for Student Financial Aid, at 901-678-3737, or dbrown@memphis.edu.

4563 ■ UNIVERSITY OF MEMPHIS
Cecil C. Humphreys School of Law
3715 Central Ave.
Memphis, TN 38152
Tel: (901)678-2421
Fax: (901)678-5210
E-mail: lawadmissions@memphis.edu
Web Site: http://www.law.memphis.edu
To support the education of law students at the University of Memphis.
Title of Award: Amy E. Spain Memorial Scholarships **Area, Field, or Subject:** Law. **Level of Education for which Award is Granted:** Undergraduate **Number Awarded:** 2. **Funds Available:** No specific amount.
Eligibility Requirements: Applicants must be law students with demonstrated academic merit. **Application Requirements:** Applicants must complete the online scholarship application form along with a personal statement; resume; scholarship statement; and recommendation letters. Applicants must also complete the FAFSA Form. **Additional Information:** Established by the family and friends of Amy Elizabeth Spain, who died at age 30 by a car accident in 1997. **Deadline for Receipt:** March 15. **Additional Information:** Dr. Sue Ann McClellan, Assistant Dean of Admissions, at 901-678-5403, or smcclell@memphis.edu; Ms. DebraAnn Brown, Assistant Director for Student Financial Aid, at 901-678-3737, or dbrown@memphis.edu.

4564 ■ UNIVERSITY OF MEMPHIS
Cecil C. Humphreys School of Law
3715 Central Ave.
Memphis, TN 38152
Tel: (901)678-2421
Fax: (901)678-5210
E-mail: lawadmissions@memphis.edu
Web Site: http://www.law.memphis.edu
To support the education of law students at the University of Memphis.
Title of Award: James F. and Donna Springfield Scholarships **Area, Field, or Subject:** Law. **Level of Education for which Award is Granted:** Undergraduate **Number Awarded:** 1. **Funds Available:** No specific amount.
Eligibility Requirements: Applicant must be a graduate of Rhodes College. **Application Requirements:** Applicants must complete the online scholarship application form along with the personal statement; resume; scholarship statement; and recommendation letters. Applicants must also complete the FAFSA Form. **Additional Information:** Scholarship is made possible by an endowment fund established by Mr. and Mrs. Springfield. **Deadline for Receipt:** March 15. **Additional Information:** Dr. Sue Ann McClellan, Assistant Dean of Admissions, at 901-678-5403, or smcclell@memphis.edu; Ms. DebraAnn Brown, Assistant Director for Student Financial Aid, at 901-678-3737, or dbrown@memphis.edu.

4565 ■ UNIVERSITY OF MEMPHIS
Cecil C. Humphreys School of Law
3715 Central Ave.
Memphis, TN 38152
Tel: (901)678-2421
Fax: (901)678-5210
E-mail: lawadmissions@memphis.edu
Web Site: http://www.law.memphis.edu
To support the education of law students at the University of Memphis.
Title of Award: Tennessee Bar Foundation IOLTA Law School Scholarships **Area, Field, or Subject:** Law. **Level of Education for which Award is Granted:** Undergraduate **Funds Available:** No specific amount.
Eligibility Requirements: Applicants must be Tennessee residents and rising third year students in good standing. **Application Requirements:** Applicants must complete the online scholarship application form along with a personal statement; resume; scholarship statement; and recommendation letters. Applicants must also complete the FAFSA Form. **Additional Information:** Scholarship is funded by the Tennessee Bar Foundation. **Deadline for Receipt:** March 15. **Additional Information:** Dr. Sue Ann McClellan, Assistant Dean of Admissions, at 901-678-5403, or smcclell@memphis.edu; Ms. DebraAnn Brown, Assistant Director for Student Financial Aid, at 901-678-3737, or dbrown@memphis.edu.

4566 ■ UNIVERSITY OF MEMPHIS

Cecil C. Humphreys School of Law
3715 Central Ave.
Memphis, TN 38152
Tel: (901)678-2421
Fax: (901)678-5210
E-mail: lawadmissions@memphis.edu
Web Site: http://www.law.memphis.edu
To support the education of law students at the University of Memphis.
Title of Award: Tennessee Board of Regents Law Scholarships **Area, Field, or Subject:** Law. **Level of Education for which Award is Granted:** Undergraduate **Funds Available:** No specific amount.
Eligibility Requirements: Applicant must be a Tennessee resident. **Application Requirements:** Applicants must complete the online scholarship application form along with a personal statement; resume; scholarship statement; and recommendation letters. Applicants must also complete the FAFSA Form. In addition, attach a separate statement explaining in detail the circumstances that qualify the student to be considered for the scholarship. **Deadline for Receipt:** March 15. **Additional Information:** Dr. Sue Ann McClellan, Assistant Dean of Admissions, at 901-678-5403, or smcclell@memphis.edu; Ms. DebraAnn Brown, Assistant Director for Student Financial Aid, at 901-678-3737, or dbrown@memphis.edu.

4567 ■ UNIVERSITY OF MEMPHIS

Cecil C. Humphreys School of Law
3715 Central Ave.
Memphis, TN 38152
Tel: (901)678-2421
Fax: (901)678-5210
E-mail: lawadmissions@memphis.edu
Web Site: http://www.law.memphis.edu
To support the education of law students at the University of Memphis.
Title of Award: Wyatt, Tarrant and Combs, LLP Scholarships **Area, Field, or Subject:** Law. **Level of Education for which Award is Granted:** Undergraduate **Funds Available:** No specific amount.
Eligibility Requirements: Applicant must be admitted as full-time student at the University of Memphis Cecil C. Humphreys School of Law. **Application Requirements:** Applicants must complete the online scholarship application form along with a personal statement; resume; scholarship statement; and recommendation letters. Applicants must also complete the FAFSA Form. **Additional Information:** Scholarship is made possible by Wyatt, Tarrant & Combs, LLP. The scholarship will be offered every three years. **Deadline for Receipt:** March 15. **Additional Information:** Dr. Sue Ann McClellan, Assistant Dean of Admissions, at 901-678-5403, or smcclell@memphis.edu; Ms. DebraAnn Brown, Assistant Director for Student Financial Aid, at 901-678-3737, or dbrown@memphis.edu.

4568 ■ UNIVERSITY OF NORTH CAROLINA SCHOOL OF JOURNALISM AND MASS COMMUNICATION

University of North Carolina, Carol Hall CB 3365
Chapel Hill, NC 27599-3365
Tel: (919)962-1204
Fax: (919)962-0620
E-mail: jomc@unc.edu
Web Site: http://www.jomc.unc.edu
To educate journalists.
Title of Award: Minority Presence Grant Program for Doctoral Study **Area, Field, or Subject:** General studies. **Level of Education for which Award is Granted:** Undergraduate **Funds Available:** $4,000.
Eligibility Requirements: Applicants must be black residents of North Carolina; applicants must be full-time students pursuing doctoral degrees, law degree, or degrees in veterinary medicine at East Carolina University, Carolina State University, University of North Carolina at Chapel Hill, at Greensboro, or at Charlotte Campus. **Application Requirements:** Applicants must complete the application form. **Deadline for Receipt:** March 1. **Additional Information:** PO Box 1080, Chapel Hill, NC 27514-1080.

4569 ■ WARNER NORCROSS & JUDD LLP

900 Fifth Third Ctr.
111 Lyon St. NW
Grand Rapids, MI 49503-2487
Tel: (616)752-2000

Fax: (616)752-2500
Web Site: http://www.wnj.com
To provide encouragement and financial assistance to students of racial and ethnic minority heritage pursuing a career in Law.
Title of Award: Warner Norcross & Judd LLP Law School Studies Scholarships **Area, Field, or Subject:** Law. **Level of Education for which Award is Granted:** Undergraduate **Funds Available:** $5,000. **Duration:** One academic year.
Eligibility Requirements: Applicants must be currently attending an accredited law school within the United States area; must be former or current residents of Michigan or attend a Michigan Law school; must have a cumulative GPA of 2.5 or above at their college or law school; must demonstrate financial need. **Application Requirements:** Applicants must provide a statement of goals and aspirations related to their studies in the legal profession; must prepare a statement of goals indicating the reason why they choose the legal profession/field as their area of study; must demonstrate financial need; must have two letters of reference. Applicants must complete the application forms available online and send it to 161 Ottawa Ave. NW, Ste. 209-C, Grand Rapids, MI 49503. **Deadline for Receipt:** April 15. **Additional Information:** Ruth Bishop, Scholarship Coordinator at the above address.

4570 ■ WASHBURN UNIVERSITY SCHOOL OF LAW

1700 SW College Ave.
Topeka, KS 66621
Tel: (785)670-1060
Fax: (785)670-3249
Web Site: http://washburnlaw.edu
To financially assist Washburn University students with their education.
Title of Award: Business and Transactional Law Center Scholarships **Area, Field, or Subject:** Law. **Level of Education for which Award is Granted:** Undergraduate **Funds Available:** Maximum of $15,000 per year. **Duration:** Three years.
Eligibility Requirements: Applicants must be admitted to Washburn Law; and must have an interest in business law or transactional law. **Application Requirements:** Applicants must attach a 1-2 paragraph description of interest, background or qualifications related to the scholarship specific area.

4571 ■ WASHBURN UNIVERSITY SCHOOL OF LAW

1700 SW College Ave.
Topeka, KS 66621
Tel: (785)670-1060
Fax: (785)670-3249
Web Site: http://washburnlaw.edu
To financially assist Washburn University students with their education.
Title of Award: Child and Family Advocacy Fellowships **Area, Field, or Subject:** Law. **Level of Education for which Award is Granted:** Undergraduate **Funds Available:** Maximum of $14,000 per year.
Eligibility Requirements: Applicants must be admitted to Washburn Law and must pursue careers in child and family advocacy. **Application Requirements:** Applicants must attach a 1-2 paragraph description of interest, background or qualifications related to the scholarship specific area.

4572 ■ WASHBURN UNIVERSITY SCHOOL OF LAW

1700 SW College Ave.
Topeka, KS 66621
Tel: (785)670-1060
Fax: (785)670-3249
Web Site: http://washburnlaw.edu
To financially assist Washburn University students with their education.
Title of Award: Judge Delmas C. Hill Scholarships **Area, Field, or Subject:** Law. **Level of Education for which Award is Granted:** Undergraduate **Number Awarded:** 1. **Funds Available:** Full-tuition and a stipend of $2,000 per year. **Duration:** Three years.
Eligibility Requirements: Applicants must be admitted as full-time students in Washburn Law; must be in the top ten percent of the class; and must have a 2.5 GPA. **Application Requirements:** Applicants must submit a statement showing: the reason for interest in the law as a profession; public and community service activities; leadership activities; and potential for leadership.

4573 ■ WASHBURN UNIVERSITY SCHOOL OF LAW

1700 SW College Ave.
Topeka, KS 66621
Tel: (785)670-1060
Fax: (785)670-3249
Web Site: http://washburnlaw.edu
To financially assist Washburn University students with their education.
Title of Award: Koch Scholarships **Area, Field, or Subject:** Law. **Level of Education for which Award is Granted:** Undergraduate **Number Awarded:** 1. **Funds Available:** Full-tuition for three years of law school; student fees; and a stipend of $6,000 for the first year of law school and $3,000 per year in the second and third years. **Duration:** Three years.
Eligibility Requirements: Applicants must be admitted as full-time students in Washburn Law; must be in the top ten percent of the class; and must have a 3.0 GPA. **Application Requirements:** Applicants must submit a statement showing: the reason for interest in the law as a profession; public and community service activities; leadership activities; and potential for leadership.

4574 ■ WASHBURN UNIVERSITY SCHOOL OF LAW

1700 SW College Ave.
Topeka, KS 66621
Tel: (785)670-1060
Fax: (785)670-3249
Web Site: http://washburnlaw.edu
To help defray some of the costs of a legal education for a Pittsburg State University student elected to attend Washburn Law.
Title of Award: Pittsburg State University Distinguished Graduate Scholarships **Area, Field, or Subject:** Law. **Level of Education for which Award is Granted:** Undergraduate **Funds Available:** No specific amount.
Eligibility Requirements: Applicants must be PSU students admitted to Washburn Law. **Application Requirements:** PSU applicants admitted to Washburn Law will be automatically considered. **Additional Information:** Established by David Pierce, Washburn Law Professor and Pittsburg State University graduate.

4575 ■ WASHBURN UNIVERSITY SCHOOL OF LAW

1700 SW College Ave.
Topeka, KS 66621
Tel: (785)670-1060
Fax: (785)670-3249
Web Site: http://washburnlaw.edu
To financially assist Washburn University minority students with their education.
Title of Award: Polsinelli Diversity Scholarships **Area, Field, or Subject:** Law. **Level of Education for which Award is Granted:** Undergraduate **Number Awarded:** 1. **Funds Available:** $7,500. **Duration:** Three years.
Eligibility Requirements: Applicants must be incoming first-year minority law students. **Application Requirements:** Applicants admitted to Washburn Law will be automatically considered. **Additional Information:** Created through the contributions of the Polsinelli Shalton Flanigan Suelthause PC law firm.

4576 ■ WASHBURN UNIVERSITY SCHOOL OF LAW

1700 SW College Ave.
Topeka, KS 66621
Tel: (785)670-1060
Fax: (785)670-3249
Web Site: http://washburnlaw.edu
To financially assist Washburn University students with their education.
Title of Award: Shamberg Scholarships **Area, Field, or Subject:** Law. **Level of Education for which Award is Granted:** Undergraduate **Number Awarded:** 3. **Funds Available:** Full-tuition and a $1,000 stipend. **Duration:** Three years.
Eligibility Requirements: Applicants must be admitted to Washburn Law. **Additional Information:** Students admitted to Washburn Law will be automatically considered.

4577 ■ WASHBURN UNIVERSITY SCHOOL OF LAW

1700 SW College Ave.
Topeka, KS 66621
Tel: (785)670-1060

Fax: (785)670-3249
Web Site: http://washburnlaw.edu
To promote excellence in legal education and to encourage the most scholastically qualified students who are long term Kansas residents to remain in or return to Kansas to practice law.
Title of Award: J.L. Weigand, Jr. Legal Education Trust Scholarships **Area, Field, or Subject:** Law. **Level of Education for which Award is Granted:** Undergraduate **Funds Available:** No specific amount.
Eligibility Requirements: Applicants must be admitted full-time to Washburn Law; must be in the top ten percent of the class; and have been a legal resident of Kansas for at least ten years prior to their admission to law school. **Application Requirements:** Applicants admitted to Washburn Law will be automatically considered. **Additional Information:** Established by John L. Weigand, Jr.

4578 ■ THE WASHINGTON GROUP

720 Park Blvd.
PO Box 73
Boise, ID 83729
Tel: (208)386-5000
E-mail: membership@washingtongroup.org
Web Site: http://www.wgint.com
To encourage active participation in Ukrainian community.
Title of Award: The Ivan Shandor Memorial Ukrainian American Bar Association Scholarships **Area, Field, or Subject:** Law. **Level of Education for which Award is Granted:** Undergraduate **Funds Available:** No specific amount.
Eligibility Requirements: Applicants must be enrolled in the masters of law degree program at Georgetown University Law center; must be resident or resided in Ukraine; must be fluent in Ukrainian language; and must demonstrate a desire to promote democracy and uphold the rule of law in Ukraine. **Application Requirements:** Applicants must fill out the application form. **Additional Information:** Scholarships for International Students, Georgetown university Law Center, Office of development, 600 New Jersey Avenue, N.W., Washington, DC 20001; 202-662-9000.

4579 ■ WASHINGTON UNIVERSITY LAW SCHOOL

Campus Box 1120
One Brookings Dr.
St. Louis, MO 63130-4899
Tel: (314)935-6400
E-mail: eckrich@wulaw.wustl.edu
Web Site: http://www.law.wustl.edu
To provide financial assistance to law students.
Title of Award: Buder Scholarship for American Indian Law Students **Area, Field, or Subject:** Law. **Level of Education for which Award is Granted:** Undergraduate **Funds Available:** No specific amount.
Eligibility Requirements: Applicants must be American Indian Law students. **Application Requirements:** Applicants must submit an application letter and other requirements to the office.

4580 ■ WOMEN IN DEFENSE

2111 Wilson Blvd., Ste. 400
Arlington, VA 22201-3061
Tel: (703)247-2552
Fax: (703)522-1885
E-mail: wid@ndia.org
Web Site: http://wid.ndia.org
To provide financial assistance to further educational objectives of women either employed or planning careers in defense or national security areas.
Title of Award: Women In Defense HORIZONS Scholarships **Area, Field, or Subject:** National security; Military history; Government; Engineering; Computer and information sciences; Physics; Mathematics and mathematical sciences; Business; Law; International affairs and relations; Political science; Economics. **Level of Education for which Award is Granted:** Graduate, Undergraduate **Funds Available:** No specific amount.
Eligibility Requirements: Applicant must be currently enrolled at an accredited university/college, either full-time or part-time; must have junior, senior or graduate status; demonstrate interest in pursuing a career related to national security or defense; demonstrate financial need; have a minimum GPA of 3.25. Applicant must be a female citizen of the United States. **Application Requirements:** Applicants must submit a completed

scholarship application form with the essays, recommendations, and transcripts. **Additional Information:** Established in 1988. **Deadline for Receipt:** July 1.

4581 ■ YUKON LAW FOUNDATION
Box 31789
Whitehorse, YT, Canada T1A 6L3
Tel: (867)667-7500
Fax: (867)393-3904
E-mail: lsy@yknet.yk.ca
Web Site: http://www.yukonlawfoundation.com
To provide financial assistance to qualified students who want to pursue their studies.
Title of Award: Yukon Law Foundation Scholarships **Area, Field, or Subject:** Law. **Level of Education for which Award is Granted:** Undergraduate **Funds Available:** $5,000. **Duration:** One year.
Eligibility Requirements: Applicants must be students attending law or law related studies. **Application Requirements:** Applicants must complete the application form available online; submit a transcript of record and two letters of recommendation. Application form and other supporting documents must be sent to Yukon Law Foundation, 202-302 Steele St., Whitehorse, YT CA Y1A 2C5.

Law Enforcement

4582 ■ ALBERTA LEARNING INFORMATION SERVICE - ALBERTA SCHOLARSHIP PROGRAM
Box 28000 Sta. Main
Edmonton, AB, Canada T5J 4R4
Tel: (780)427-8640
Fax: (780)427-1288
E-mail: scholarship@gov.ab.ca
Web Site: http://www.alis.alberta.ca
To provide financial assistance to aboriginal students who have successfully completed the first year of a program relating to criminal justice, criminology or law.
Title of Award: Robert C. Carson Memorial Bursary **Area, Field, or Subject:** Criminal justice; Criminology; Law. **Level of Education for which Award is Granted:** Undergraduate **Funds Available:** $500.
Eligibility Requirements: Applicants must be Alberta residents and full-time students enrolled in the second year of either Law Enforcement or Criminal Justice. The qualifying Alberta institutions are: Lethbridge Community College, Mount Royal College, Grant MacEwan College, the University of Calgary or the University of Alberta. **Application Requirements:** Application forms are available from the Institution's Student Award Office. **Deadline for Receipt:** October 1. **Additional Information:** Alberta Scholarship Program at the above address.

4583 ■ AMERICAN ASSOCIATION OF STATE TROOPERS
1949 Raymond Diehl Rd.
Tallahassee, FL 32308
Tel: (850)385-7904
Free: 800-765-5456
Web Site: http://www.statetroopers.org
To provide financial assistance for the education of students who are dependents of the members of American Association of State Troopers, Inc.
Title of Award: American Association of State Troopers Scholarship Foundation First Scholarships **Area, Field, or Subject:** Law enforcement. **Level of Education for which Award is Granted:** Undergraduate **Funds Available:** $500.
Eligibility Requirements: Applicants must be high school or college students who are sons or daughters of a trooper members by natural birth, legal adoption, step child, or legal guardian. **Application Requirements:** Applicants must submit an official transcripts indicating a minimum 2.5 GPA (4.0 scale) at an accredited school; for high school students: final four-year high school transcripts; for college students: a current official college transcripts indicating all grades earned through the current year which he or she is applying for; letter of acceptance from an accredited college, state university or community college for the academic year; typed essay of 500 words entitled "How my Education Will Advance My Career Plans"; and a small photo attached to the bottom of the application where indicated. **Deadline for Receipt:** July 31.

4584 ■ AMERICAN ASSOCIATION OF STATE TROOPERS
1949 Raymond Diehl Rd.
Tallahassee, FL 32308
Tel: (850)385-7904
Free: 800-765-5456
Web Site: http://www.statetroopers.org
To provide financial assistance for the education of students who are dependents of the members of American Association of State Troopers, Inc.
Title of Award: American Association of State Troopers Scholarship Foundation Second Scholarships **Area, Field, or Subject:** Law enforcement. **Level of Education for which Award is Granted:** Undergraduate **Funds Available:** $1,000.
Eligibility Requirements: Applicants must be a high school or college students who are sons or daughters of trooper members by natural birth, legal adoption, step child, or legal guardian. **Application Requirements:** Applicants must submit an original and official transcript indicating the minimum 3.5 GPA (4.0 scale) maintained during the fall through spring semesters for which the scholarship award was granted; a letter or registration notice as proof of enrollment for the academic year; and a small photo attached to the bottom of the application where indicated. **Deadline for Receipt:** July 31.

4585 ■ AMERICAN ASSOCIATION OF STATE TROOPERS
1949 Raymond Diehl Rd.
Tallahassee, FL 32308
Tel: (850)385-7904
Free: 800-765-5456
Web Site: http://www.statetroopers.org
To provide financial assistance to a student who intends to use his or her education to pursue a career in law enforcement.
Title of Award: V.J. Johnson Memorial Scholarships **Area, Field, or Subject:** Law enforcement. **Level of Education for which Award is Granted:** Undergraduate **Number Awarded:** 1. **Funds Available:** $1,500.
Eligibility Requirements: Applicants must be high school or college students who are sons or a daughters of trooper members by natural birth, legal adoption, step child, or legal guardian (in Florida only). **Application Requirements:** Applicants must submit an original and official transcript indicating, a minimum of 3.8 GPA (4.0 scale) was maintained during the fall through spring semesters for which the second scholarship award was granted; a letter or registration notice as proof of enrollment for the academic year; a typed essay of 500 words entitled "How my Education Will Advance My Plans for a Career in Law Enforcement"; and a small photo attached to the bottom of the application where indicated. **Deadline for Receipt:** July 31.

4586 ■ AMERICAN FEDERATION OF POLICE AND CONCERNED CITIZENS
6350 Horizon Dr.
Titusville, FL 32780
Tel: (321)264-0911
E-mail: policeinfo@aphf.org
Web Site: http://www.afp-cc.org
To assist family members and children of officers killed in the line of duty.
Title of Award: American Federation of Police and Concerned Citizen Scholarships **Area, Field, or Subject:** Law Enforcement. **Level of Education for which Award is Granted:** Undergraduate **Funds Available:** $1,500. **Duration:** 4 years.
Eligibility Requirements: Applicants must be high school graduates attending a traditional four year college, university, technical or vocational educational institutions. **Application Requirements:** Applicants must submit an application form.

4587 ■ COMMUNITY FOUNDATION OF NORTHERN ILLINOIS
946 N 2nd St.
Rockford, IL 61107
Tel: (815)962-2110
Fax: (815)962-2116
Web Site: http://www.cfnil.org
To serve the four county area (Boone, Ogle, Stephenson and Winnebago) through philanthropy; to provide leadership in meeting charitable needs and to be a responsible steward to the Foundation's donors and of the Foundation's endowment.

Title of Award: Louise J. Franchini Rockford Police Department Scholarships **Area, Field, or Subject:** Law Enforcement. **Level of Education for which Award is Granted:** Undergraduate **Funds Available:** No specific amount.
Eligibility Requirements: Applicants must be high school graduates currently enrolled in an accredited law enforcement program or high school seniors who are planning to pursue a career in law enforcement; must reside in Winnebago County. **Application Requirements:** Applicants must submit a completed application form, verification form, an official transcript in a sealed envelope and two letters of recommendation. **Deadline for Receipt:** March 1. **Additional Information:** jpatterson@cfnil.org.

4588 ■ FOUNDATION FOR THE CAROLINAS
217 S Tryon St.
Charlotte, NC 28202
Tel: (704)973-4500
Free: 800-973-7244
Web Site: http://www.fftc.org
To provide financial support for students studying law enforcement at Central Piedmont Community College and the University of North Carolina at Charlotte.
Title of Award: Law Enforcement Memorial Scholarship Fund **Area, Field, or Subject:** Law enforcement. **Level of Education for which Award is Granted:** Undergraduate **Funds Available:** No specific amount.
Eligibility Requirements: Applicants must be students at Central Piedmont Community College or the University of North Carolina at Charlotte who have a 2.5 minimum cumulative grade point average (on a 4.0 scale) and are majoring in a law enforcement field. **Application Requirements:** Applicants must submit all the required application information. **Additional Information:** CPCC Financial Aid Office, 704-330-6942 or the UNC Charlotte Student Financial Aid Office, 704-687-2461.

4589 ■ LAPPER COUNTY COMMUNITY FOUNDATION
220 W Nepressing St., Ste. 202
Lapeer, MI 48446
Tel: (810)664-0691
E-mail: lccf@charterinternet.com
Web Site: http://www.lapeercountycommunityfoundation.org
To support education in the law enforcement fields.
Title of Award: Wayne Hildebrant Police Scholarships Fund **Area, Field, or Subject:** Law enforcement. **Level of Education for which Award is Granted:** Undergraduate **Funds Available:** $500.
Eligibility Requirements: Applicants must be residents of Lapeer County and accepted into an accredited police academy of college/university law enforcement program; must have a cumulative GPA of 3.0 or higher. **Application Requirements:** Applicants must be prepared to participate in a brief interview; must submit a transcript of records, test scores, photos and federal tax return for self or family. **Deadline for Receipt:** April 15.

4590 ■ NATIONAL ASSOCIATION OF SCHOOL SAFETY AND LAW ENFORCEMENT OFFICERS
PO Box 210079
Milwaukee, WI 53221
Tel: (315)529-4858
Fax: 877-282-4860
E-mail: nassleo@nassleo.org
Web Site: http://www.nassleo.org
To provide financial assistance to students who have chosen to further their education and are considering a career in school security and/or law enforcement.
Title of Award: NASSLEO Scholarships **Area, Field, or Subject:** Law Enforcement. **Level of Education for which Award is Granted:** Undergraduate **Funds Available:** $500.
Eligibility Requirements: Applicant must be a senior graduating student from a public high school; will be attending an accredited college or university; has not received a full scholarship; has been outstanding in the area of citizenship and community service. **Application Requirements:** The faculty member must submit the complete nomination form, which can be downloaded at the NASSLEO website. Faculty member must list the individual's accomplishments in the area of citizenship and community

service, what he/she has done to improve safety in the school, the contributions the student has made to his/her school, and any recognition received from his/her peers and/or faculty of the school for personal or academic achievement during this past school year. The narrative report must be limited to a single page. **Deadline for Receipt:** April 1. **Additional Information:** Peter Pochowski, Executive Director at the above address.

4591 ■ NATIONAL BLACK POLICE ASSOCIATION
30 Kennedy St. NW, Ste. 101
Washington, DC 20011
Tel: (202)986-2070
Fax: (202)986-0410
E-mail: nbpanatofc@worldnet.att.net
Web Site: http://www.blackpolice.org
To support students pursuing education in law enforcement, or other related field.
Title of Award: Alphonso Deal Scholarship Awards **Area, Field, or Subject:** Law enforcement. **Level of Education for which Award is Granted:** Undergraduate **Funds Available:** Amount not specified. **Duration:** Two years.
Eligibility Requirements: Applicant must be a high school senior and a U.S. citizen with good character. **Application Requirements:** Applicants must fill up the application form available at the website. Applicant must prepare a recommendation letter (from principal, counselor or teacher); a current high school transcript with picture; and an acceptance letter from a college/university. **Deadline for Receipt:** June 1.

4592 ■ PARK LAW ENFORCEMENT ASSOCIATION
520 N Stevenson
Olathe, KS 66061
Tel: (239)332-6975
E-mail: info@parkranger.com
Web Site: http://www.parkranger.com
To promote park law enforcement.
Title of Award: Newell S. Rand Jr. Memorial Scholarships **Area, Field, or Subject:** Law Enforcement. **Level of Education for which Award is Granted:** Undergraduate **Funds Available:** $500. **Duration:** One year.
Eligibility Requirements: Applicants must be enrolled in a field of study related to park law enforcement. **Application Requirements:** Applicants must submit current resume including education, work experience, and civic activity; a letter showing their interest in the Park Law Enforcement field and explaining why they are worthy of the PLEA Scholarship; a letter of recommendation from an instructor or advisor in their field of study; and proof of enrollment. Applications must be submitted to the PLEA President. **Deadline for Receipt:** October 1.

4593 ■ PORTUGUESE AMERICAN POLICE ASSOCIATION
PO Box 51523
New Bedford, MA 02745-0045
Tel: (508)994-5390
E-mail: info@papamass.org
Web Site: http://www.papamass.org
To provide support for deserving students intending to pursue a career in either Health Care, Social Service, Law Enforcement, or other related fields.
Title of Award: Portuguese American Police Association Scholarships **Area, Field, or Subject:** Health care services, Social work, Law enforcement. **Level of Education for which Award is Granted:** Undergraduate **Number Awarded:** 6. **Funds Available:** $500. **Duration:** One year.
Eligibility Requirements: Applicant must be a Portuguese descent; must be a resident of Massachusetts; must be enrolled full-time in an accredited college or university or a graduating senior applying to full-time status in an accredited or another college or university; must be majoring in either health care, social services, law enforcement or another related field; must maintain a GPA of 2.0 or higher. **Application Requirements:** Application forms are available online. Applicant must submit an essay of no more than three paragraphs stating the reason stating their career goals; must have a high school transcript that includes the class rank; must have the current college/university transcript; must have a letter of reference from each of the following: (1) Guidance counselor or advisor and (2) Personal reference, preferably from someone with whom the applicants have work. Application materials must be sent to: Scholarship

Committee, Portuguese American Police Association, Inc., PO Box 51523, New Bedford, MA 02745-0045. **Deadline for Receipt:** June 1.

4594 ■ REDLANDS COMMUNITY SCHOLARSHIP FOUNDATION

c/o Kathleen Venegas-Boge, Admin. Asst.
PO Box 1683
Redlands, CA 92373
Tel: (909)307-9892
Fax: (909)307-9892
Web Site: http://www.redlandsscholarships.org
To encourage educational pursuits among Redlands Unified School District graduates by providing educational assistance.
Title of Award: Christopher J. Kohlmeier Scholarships **Area, Field, or Subject:** Law enforcement. **Level of Education for which Award is Granted:** Undergraduate **Number Awarded:** 1. **Funds Available:** $300.
Eligibility Requirements: Applicant must be a graduating senior planning to attend a two-year or four-year college or university; must have strong test scores, but whose "C" average in high school could easily have been higher. **Application Requirements:** Applicants must submit a completed application form together with the scantron sheet; cover sheet; student activity and community activity sheets; personal essay; and a copy of unofficial transcript (signed by the counselor). **Additional Information:** No electronic submissions of application will be accepted. Submit two printed copies of the application and use a No. 2 pencil on the scantron sheet. **Deadline for Receipt:** February 20.

4595 ■ THE SAN DIEGO FOUNDATION

2508 Historic Decatur Rd., Ste. 200
San Diego, CA 92106
Tel: (619)235-2300
Fax: (619)239-1710
E-mail: info@sdfoundation.org
Web Site: http://www.sdfoundation.org
To support the education of students from California.
Title of Award: Frederick George James Memorial Scholarships **Area, Field, or Subject:** Law enforcement. **Level of Education for which Award is Granted:** Undergraduate **Number Awarded:** 1. **Funds Available:** $500.
Eligibility Requirements: Applicant must be a graduating senior from Sweetwater Union High School, located in National City, CA; a exemplary member of the National City Police Department Explorer Post No. 2859; have a minimum 2.85 GPA on a 4.0 scale; and have demonstrated a strong desire to achieve a degree in Police Science at an accredited two-year college or four-year university in the U.S. **Application Requirements:** Applicants must submit a completed Common Scholarship Application together with personal statement; two letters of recommendation on official letterhead (written within the last six months); official transcript in an official and sealed envelope; copy of most recent tax form (Form 1040-pages 1 & 2; Form 1040A-pages 1 & 2; Form 1040EZ-page 1); a letter of recommendation from a Sweetwater High School administrator or academic teacher; and another letter of recommendation from an officer affiliated with the National City Police Department Explorers Program. **Additional Information:** Letters must be on official letterhead written within the last six months. **Deadline for Receipt:** January 28. **Additional Information:** Arzo Mansury, Dir. Scholarships at 619-814-1343, or scholarships@sdfoundation.org.

4596 ■ STARK COMMUNITY FOUNDATION

400 Market Ave. N, Ste. 200
Canton, OH 44702-2107
Tel: (330)454-3426
Fax: (330)454-5855
Web Site: http://www.starkcommunityfoundation.org
To provide scholarship assistance to qualified individuals who want to pursue their studies.
Title of Award: Sheriff W. Bruce Umpleby Law Enforcement Scholarship Fund **Area, Field, or Subject:** Law enforcement. **Level of Education for which Award is Granted:** Undergraduate **Funds Available:** No specific amount. **Duration:** One year.
Eligibility Requirements: Applicants must be students who are seniors attending high school either inside or outside Stark County, who will graduate with their class, or are graduates of a high school either inside or outside Stark County; must be enrolled as full-time students; must have

achieved cumulative GPA of at least 3.0 on a 4.0 scale; must have demonstrated outstanding involvement both in academics and extra curricular activities; must have been accepted, into a post secondary institution with plans to major in law enforcement. **Application Requirements:** Applicants must submit a written statement (at least 2 paragraphs) and three letters of recommendations from their teacher and/or teacher. Application form and other supporting documents must be sent to Stark Community Foundation, 400 Market Ave. N, Ste. 200, Canton, OH 44702. **Deadline for Receipt:** March 15.

4597 ■ STEUBEN COUNTY COMMUNITY FOUNDATION

1701 N Wayne St.
Angola, IN 46703
Tel: (260)665-6656
Fax: (260)665-8420
Web Site: http://www.steubenfoundation.org
To provide financial support to those students who are interested in earning a degree in Law Enforcement Education.
Title of Award: John W. Kelley Memorial Scholarships **Area, Field, or Subject:** Law Enforcement. **Level of Education for which Award is Granted:** Undergraduate **Funds Available:** No specific amount.
Eligibility Requirements: Applicants must be residents of Steuben County; must be graduating seniors from any Steuben County High School; must be pursuing a degree in Law Enforcement Education. **Application Requirements:** Applicants must check the website for the application process and required materials. **Deadline for Receipt:** March 15. **Additional Information:** Steuben County Community Foundation at the above address.

4598 ■ STRAIGHTFORWARD MEDIA

508 7th St., Ste 202
Rapid City, SD 57701
Tel: (605)348-3042
Fax: (605)348-3043
E-mail: info@straightforwardmedia.com
Web Site: http://www.straightforwardmedia.com
To financially assist students in their educational pursuits.
Title of Award: StraightForward Media's Law Enforcement Scholarships **Area, Field, or Subject:** Law enforcement. **Level of Education for which Award is Granted:** Professional, Undergraduate **Funds Available:** $500.
Eligibility Requirements: Applicant must be a law enforcement professional or a student studying to become a law enforcement officer. **Application Requirements:** Applicants must complete the Online Scholarship Application. **Additional Information:** Awards are given four times a year. **Deadline for Receipt:** March, February, September, December.

4599 ■ WOMEN IN FEDERAL LAW ENFORCEMENT

2200 Wilson Blvd.
Arlington, VA 22201
Tel: (703)548-9211; (866)399-4353
Fax: (410)451-7373
E-mail: wifle@comcast.net
Web Site: http://www.wifle.org
To provide financial assistance to women interested in law enforcement careers.
Title of Award: The WIFLE Scholarship Fund **Area, Field, or Subject:** Law enforcement. **Level of Education for which Award is Granted:** Graduate, Postdoctoral, Undergraduate **Funds Available:** $2,500.
Eligibility Requirements: Applicants must be U.S. citizens; must be full-time students at an accredited four-year college or university, or a fully accredited community college with the intention of transferring to a four-year degree; must have completed at least one full academic year of college work; must major in Criminal Justice or a related discipline such as social sciences, public administration, computer science, finance, linguistic arts, chemistry, or physics leading to a four-year degree; have a minimum 3.0 overall grade point average (GPA). **Application Requirements:** Applicants must complete the application with a 500-word essay describing the applicant's involvement in a community project and the results or impact of that involvement to the community. If the applicant is currently serving or has served an internship with a law enforcement agency, preferably a federal law enforcement agency, the applicant must provide details including the name of the agency, the dates served and

the value of the experience and the accomplishment through the internship in a 500-word essay. Applicants must have at least one community leader or member of a community or police official sponsor their applications with a written statement of support. **Deadline for Receipt:** May 1.

Political Science

4600 ■ ALBERTA INDIAN INVESTMENT CORPORATION
PO Box 180
Enoch, AB, Canada T7X 3Y3
Tel: (780)470-3600; 888-308-6789
Fax: (780)470-3605
E-mail: info@aiicbusiness.org
Web Site: http://www.aiicbusiness.org
To provide scholarship assistance to qualified individuals who want to pursue their education.
Title of Award: Sam Bull Memorial Scholarships **Area, Field, or Subject:** Law; Political science. **Level of Education for which Award is Granted:** Undergraduate **Funds Available:** $1,000. **Duration:** One year.
Eligibility Requirements: Applicant must be a First Nation native who has resided in Alberta for at least one year; must demonstrate interest in law or political science education. **Application Requirements:** Applicant must prepare a 100 to 200 word statement of personal and academic objectives, which should emphasize how their proposed course of study will contribute to First Nation community development in Canada. Application forms are available online and must be sent together with other supporting documents to General Manager, PO Box 180, Enoch, AB T7X 3Y3. **Deadline for Receipt:** February 15.

4601 ■ ALBERTA INDIAN INVESTMENT CORPORATION
PO Box 180
Enoch, AB, Canada T7X 3Y3
Tel: (780)470-3600; 888-308-6789
Fax: (780)470-3605
E-mail: info@aiicbusiness.org
Web Site: http://www.aiicbusiness.org
To provide scholarship assistance to qualified individuals who want to pursue their education.
Title of Award: Senator James Gladstone Memorial Scholarships **Area, Field, or Subject:** Law; Political science. **Level of Education for which Award is Granted:** Undergraduate **Funds Available:** $750-$1,000. **Duration:** One year.
Eligibility Requirements: Applicant must be a First Nation native who has resided in Alberta for at least one year; must demonstrate interest in law or political science education. **Application Requirements:** Applicant must submit a transcript of record; must prepare a 100 to 200 word statement of personal and academic objectives which should emphasize how their proposed course of study will contribute to First Nation economic and business development in Canada. Application form and other supporting documents must be sent to General Manager, Alberta Indian Investment Corporation, PO Box 180, Enoch, AB T7X 3Y3. **Deadline for Receipt:** February 15.

4602 ■ ARAB AMERICAN INSTITUTE
1600 K St. NW, Ste. 601
Washington, DC 20006
Tel: (202)429-9210
Fax: (202)429-9214
E-mail: aai@aaiusa.org
Web Site: http://www.aaiusa.org
To promote academic excellence and to provide an opportunity for outstanding student to reach their fullest potential.
Title of Award: Ameen Rihani Scholarship Program **Area, Field, or Subject:** Literature; Philosophy; Political science. **Level of Education for which Award is Granted:** Undergraduate **Funds Available:** $1,500.
Eligibility Requirements: Individual must: be a Lebanese or other Arab Descent; be a citizen or legal permanent residents of the United States; have attained a cumulative GPA of 3.25 on a 4.0 scale; enter a college or university as a full-time, degree-seeking freshman in the fall of the year; have demonstrated leadership abilities through participation in community service, extracurricular or other activities. **Application Requirements:** Teachers, counselors, and principals are invited to nominate students with

outstanding academic qualifications, particularly those who would promote success in the fields of literature, philosophy, or political science. **Deadline for Receipt:** May 31. **Additional Information:** Ameen Rihani Scholarship Program, The Ameen Rihani Organization, 1010 Wayne Ave. Ste 420 Silver Spring, MD 20910.

4603 ■ ARMENIAN RELIEF SOCIETY - EASTERN UNITED STATES
80 Bigelow Avenue, Ste. 200
Watertown, MA 02472
Tel: (617)926-3801
Fax: (617)924-7238
E-mail: arseastus@aol.com
Web Site: http://www.arseastus.com
To encourage educational pursuits among undergraduate students of Armenian descent.
Title of Award: ARS Undergraduate Scholarships **Area, Field, or Subject:** Law; History; Political science; Journalism; Government; Economics; Business administration; Medicine; Public service. **Level of Education for which Award is Granted:** Four Year College, Two Year College, Undergraduate **Funds Available:** No specific amount. **Duration:** One year.
Eligibility Requirements: Applicants must be of Armenian descent; must be undergraduate students who have completed at least one semester at an accredited four-year college or university in the United States or must be enrolled in a two-year college and are transferring to a four-year college or university as a full-time student in the Fall. **Application Requirements:** Application must include financial aid forms, recent official transcript, two letters of recommendation and tuition costs. Forward materials to: Scholarship Committee, Armenian Relief Society of Eastern USA, Inc., 80 Bigelow Ave., Ste. 200, Watertown, MA 02472. **Deadline for Receipt:** April 1.

4604 ■ ARMENIAN STUDENTS' ASSOCIATION OF AMERICA
333 Atlantic Ave.
Warwick, RI 02888
Tel: (401)461-6114
E-mail: asa@asainc.org
Web Site: http://www.asainc.org
To provide financial assistance to those students who are in need.
Title of Award: Garikian Scholarship Fund **Area, Field, or Subject:** Armenian Studies; Sociology; Psychology; Political Science; Middle Eastern History; Journalism; Education; Music. **Level of Education for which Award is Granted:** Undergraduate **Funds Available:** $750-$1,000.
Eligibility Requirements: Applicants must have completed their first academic year in college or university in California; must be pursuing one of the above field of studies. **Application Requirements:** Applicants must apply to the Executive Board for application forms and return them, completed, before the deadline. **Deadline for Receipt:** August 31. **Additional Information:** Berj S. Baghdoyan c/o Western Prelacy at 4401 Russell Avenue, Los Angeles, CA 90027.

4605 ■ COASTAL BEND COMMUNITY FOUNDATION
600 Leopard St., Ste. 1716
Corpus Christi, TX 78473
Tel: (361)882-9745
Fax: (361)882-2865
Web Site: http://www.cbcfoundation.org
To provide financial assistance to high school seniors or graduates of a Coastal Bend high school in furthering their college education.
Title of Award: Cecil E. Burney Scholarships **Area, Field, or Subject:** Liberal arts; History; Political science; Music; Education. **Level of Education for which Award is Granted:** High School, Undergraduate **Funds Available:** $2,000.
Eligibility Requirements: Applicants must be high school seniors or graduates of a Coastal Bend high school pursuing a liberal arts degree majoring in history, political science, music or education; have a high school GPA of 90 percent or higher; maintain a college 3.0 GPA or higher and at least 12 hours per semester. **Application Requirements:** Applicants must submit all the required application information. **Deadline for Receipt:** March 14.

4606 ■ THE COMMUNITY FOUNDATION OF MIDDLE TENNESSEE
3833 Cleghorn Ave., Ste. 400
Nashville, TN 37215-2519

Tel: (615)321-4939; 888-540-5200
E-mail: mail@cfmt.org
Web Site: http://www.cfmt.org
To help students in planning their postsecondary education.
Title of Award: George Oliver Benton Memorial Scholarships **Area, Field, or Subject:** General studies. **Level of Education for which Award is Granted:** Undergraduate **Funds Available:** No specific amount.
Eligibility Requirements: Applicants must be students who attend an accredited fouryear college/university in the state of Tennessee. Applicants must be residents of Tennessee. **Application Requirements:** Applicants must complete the application form. Applicants must submit two applicant appraisals; transcript of grades; student essay describing educational plans and how these will help in career goals. Applicants must submit one recent photograph. **Deadline for Receipt:** March 15. **Additional Information:** pcole@cfmt.org

4607 ■ DADE COMMUNITY FOUNDATION, INC.
200 S Biscayne Blvd., Ste. 505
Miami, FL 33131-2343
Tel: (305)371-2711
Fax: (305)371-5342
Web Site: http://www.dadecommunityfoundation.org
To provide financial assistance to students at Miami Springs Senior High School who are enrolled in a college program related to public education, political science, history or social work.
Title of Award: Randy Green Memorial Scholarship Fund **Area, Field, or Subject:** Political science; economics; Social work. **Level of Education for which Award is Granted:** High School **Number Awarded:** 2. **Funds Available:** $1,000. **Duration:** One year.
Eligibility Requirements: Applicants must be permanent residents or citizens of the U.S. and domiciled in South Florida; must have minimum high school grade point average of 3.0; must be Miami Springs high-school seniors demonstrating merit and financial need; must be accepted into accredited university and plan to be enrolled in two year or four year university programs concentrating in public education, political science, history, social work, or other major related to community service. **Application Requirements:** Applicants must submit the completed application form and all other required application information. **Deadline for Receipt:** June 3.

4608 ■ DIRKSEN COGRESSIONAL CENTER
2815 Broadway
Pekin, IL 61554
Tel: (309)347-7113
Fax: (309)347-6432
E-mail: info@dirkcenter.org
Web Site: http://www.dirkcenter.org
To provide financial support for Bradley University juniors who are majoring in a discipline related to The Dirksen Center's purpose and interest or in subjects related to the study of Federal Government.
Title of Award: Ray and Kathy LaHood Scholarships for the Study of American Government **Area, Field, or Subject:** Government. **Level of Education for which Award is Granted:** Undergraduate **Funds Available:** $2,000-$3,500.
Eligibility Requirements: Applicants must be juniors in good standing entering their senior year of study in a field related to the study of the U.S. government; must be attending Bradley University; must have a grade point average (on a four-point scale) of at least 3.0 overall and 3.75 in their major; must agree to write a 250-word evaluation of the impact of their scholarship before the end of their senior year; and must agree to meet with Ray or Kathy LaHood during the second semester of their senior year. **Application Requirements:** Applicants must fill out the required scholarship form. **Additional Information:** Brad McMillan, executive Director at 408 Jobs Hall, Bradley University, 1501 W. Bradley Peoria, IL 61625; 309-677-4408; bmcmillan@bradley.edu.

4609 ■ FLORIDA POLICE CHIEFS ASSOCIATION
924 N Gadsden St.
Tallahassee, FL 32303
Tel: (850)219-3631
Free: 800-332-8117
Fax: (850)219-3640

E-mail: amercer@fpca.com
Web Site: http://www.fpca.org
To promote public safety legislation.
Title of Award: Police Explorer Scholarships Program **Area, Field, or Subject:** Government. **Level of Education for which Award is Granted:** Undergraduate **Funds Available:** $1,000. **Duration:** 2 years.
Eligibility Requirements: Applicants must have been involved in a police explorer post, and have been a member of the post for a minimum of one year by the time of award presentation; must maintain a minimum of a 2.0 overall grade point average and should be completing their senior year in high school, already enrolled in college or planning to attend college. **Application Requirements:** Applicants must submit a completed application form; must submit a 4x5 glossy, black and white or colored headshot photo, in uniform, if possible. **Deadline for Receipt:** April 15.

4610 ■ FOUNDATION FOR ENHANCING COMMUNITIES
200 N Third St., PO Box 678
Harrisburg, PA 17108-0678
Tel: (717)236-5040
Fax: (717)231-4463
E-mail: dawn@tfec.org
Web Site: http://www.ghf.org
To encourage and recognize two senior students from the Mechanicsburg Area School District who demonstrate good citizenship.
Title of Award: Bertha and Byron L. Reppert Scholarship Fund **Area, Field, or Subject:** Political science; Horticulture. **Level of Education for which Award is Granted:** Undergraduate **Funds Available:** No specific amount.
Eligibility Requirements: Applicants must have an interest in political science or horticulture; must be in the top one-third of the graduating class; must be accepted to an accredited college or university; must demonstrate good citizenship within the school and local community; and must complete an essay explaining how they meet the criteria. **Application Requirements:** Application form can be obtained online. Applicants must attach the following documents: official transcript of the complete high school/college record, including GPA, through the first half of the present year, with the raised school seal imprinted; list of extracurricular or non-academic activities; FAFSA Student Aid Report; and an essay describing how they meet the eligibility criteria of this scholarship. **Deadline for Receipt:** March 1. **Additional Information:** Dawn Morris, Program Officer at the above address.

4611 ■ BRYCE HARLOW FOUNDATION
1701 Pennsylvania Ave. NW, Ste. 400
Washington, DC 20006
Tel: (202)654-7812
Fax: (202)638-5178
E-mail: info@bryceharlow.org
Web Site: http://www.bryceharlow.org
To provide financial assistance to students who are pursuing a career in professional advocacy through public affairs, government relations or lobbying.
Title of Award: Bryce Harlow Fellowship Program **Area, Field, or Subject:** Public affairs; Government. **Level of Education for which Award is Granted:** Undergraduate **Funds Available:** $6,000.
Eligibility Requirements: Applicants must be students who have been accepted for admission to a graduate program at a participating university; planning to enroll in part-time graduate studies for credit at the participating university for at least two semesters of the next academic year; demonstrate an interest and strong ability for a career in public affairs, government relations or lobbying; and U.S. citizens. **Application Requirements:** Applicants must download and complete the application and recommendation request form(s). Submit it along with two letters of recommendation from persons familiar with the applicants; and official transcripts from all undergraduate universities. **Deadline for Receipt:** April 18.

4612 ■ HARVARD LAW SCHOOL
1563 Massachusetts Ave.
Cambridge, MA 02138
Tel: (617)496-8214
Fax: (617)496-9179
E-mail: qpquery@law.harvard.edu

Web Site: http://www.law.harvard.edu
To encourage the HLS students to build human rights work and to expand their interest in working in the field.
Title of Award: Henigson Human Rights Fellowships **Area, Field, or Subject:** Human rights. **Level of Education for which Award is Granted:** Undergraduate **Funds Available:** $27,000. **Duration:** One year.
Eligibility Requirements: Applicants must be current and former J.D. students: 3Ls expecting to receive the J.D. degree, as well as J.D graduates who currently clerk for a judge; must be engaged in full-time public interest work; must be active in human rights or public interest work while students at HLS; must be LL.M. students who expect to receive the LL.M. degree and who come from and will return to a country other than the United States. **Application Requirements:** Applicants must submit a curriculum vitae, including information about classes, work and extracurricular activities in public interest and human rights inside and outside of Harvard Law School; a personal statement (500 words maximum) about the applicant's relevant experience, interest, and future aspirations with respect to public interest and human rights work; a project description; a letter and supporting materials from sponsoring organization detailing their purpose, function, and particular interest in the work of the applicant; two or three letters of recommendation including at least one from an HLS professor; and an HLS transcript. **Deadline for Receipt:** March 7.

4613 ■ LEWIS-CLARK STATE COLLEGE
500 8th Ave.
Lewiston, ID 83501
Tel: (208)792-5272
Web Site: http://www.lcsc.edu
To provide financial assistance to students who are majoring in these fields: Accounting, Biology, Business, Communications, Computer Science, Economics, Environmental Science, Engineering, Mathematics, Natural Resources, Political Science, Statistics.
Title of Award: Avista Corporation Minds in Motion Scholarships **Area, Field, or Subject:** Accounting; Biology; Business; Communications; Computer and Information Sciences; Economics; Environmental Science; Engineering; Mathematics; Natural Resources; Political Science; Statistics. **Level of Education for which Award is Granted:** Undergraduate **Number Awarded:** 2. **Funds Available:** No specific Amount.
Eligibility Requirements: Applicants must be full-time students attending LCSC and must have a cumulative GPA of 2.5. **Application Requirements:** Applicants must submit general application. **Deadline for Receipt:** March 1.

4614 ■ LEWIS-CLARK STATE COLLEGE
500 8th Ave.
Lewiston, ID 83501
Tel: (208)792-5272
Web Site: http://www.lcsc.edu
To provide funding for outstanding students who are majoring in social or political science at LCSC.
Title of Award: John Streiff Memorial Scholarships **Area, Field, or Subject:** Political science; Social Sciences. **Level of Education for which Award is Granted:** Undergraduate **Funds Available:** No specific amount.
Eligibility Requirements: Program is open to senior or junior students who have a cumulative GPA of 3.0 and are actively involved in both campus and community. **Application Requirements:** Applicants must accomplish a general application available at the website. **Deadline for Receipt:** March 1.

4615 ■ MINNESOTA ASSOCIATION OF TOWNSHIP
PO Box 267
St. Michael, MN 55376
Tel: (763)497-2330
Free: 800-228-0296
Fax: (763)497-3361
E-mail: info@mntownships.org
Web Site: http://www.mntownships.org
To foster efficient, effective and economical town governmental services and to further awareness and education about the township government.
Title of Award: Minnesota Association of Township Scholarships **Area, Field, or Subject:** Government. **Level of Education for which Award is**

Granted: Undergraduate **Number Awarded:** 4. **Funds Available:** $1,000.
Eligibility Requirements: Applicants must be currently enrolled in the 11th grade and attending a Minnesota public, private, or parochial high school or a home study program and plan to further their education at a college, university, or vocational school. **Application Requirements:** Applicants must complete an application form; a 450-500-word, typed, double-spaced written essay; a current high school transcript; and a letter of recommendation from a high school teacher or counselor. **Deadline for Receipt:** May 1.

4616 ■ NATIONAL FEDERATION OF REPUBLICAN WOMEN
124 N Alfred St.
Alexandria, VA 22314
Tel: (703)548-9688
Fax: (703)548-9836
E-mail: mail@nfrw.org
Web Site: http://www.nfrw.org
To support students with their education.
Title of Award: Betty Rendel Scholarships **Area, Field, or Subject:** Political science; Government; Economics. **Level of Education for which Award is Granted:** Undergraduate **Number Awarded:** 3. **Funds Available:** $1000. **Duration:** Annual.
Eligibility Requirements: Applicant must be an undergraduate student majoring in political science, government or economics; and have completed at least two years of college coursework. **Application Requirements:** Applicants must submit a completed application form together with three letters of recommendation (include contact numbers of the authors); an official copy of recent college transcript; a 1-page typed essay stating why deserve the scholarship; another 1-page typed essay on career goals; a photograph (optional); and State Federation President Certification. **Additional Information:** Established in 1995 in honor of NFRW Past President Betty Rendel's extraordinary leadership skills and dedication to the Republican Party in her home state of Indiana. **Deadline for Receipt:** June 1.

4617 ■ NATIONAL FORUM FOR BLACK PUBLIC ADMINISTRATORS
777 N Capitol St. NE, Ste. 807
Washington, DC 20002
Tel: (202)408-9300
Fax: (202)408-8558
E-mail: webmaster@nfbpa.org
Web Site: http://www.nfbpa.org
To support the education and development of African-American students and prepare them for careers in public administration.
Title of Award: CIGNA Healthcare Undergraduate Scholarships **Area, Field, or Subject:** Public administration; Political science; Urban affairs/design/planning. **Level of Education for which Award is Granted:** Undergraduate **Number Awarded:** 1. **Funds Available:** $1,000.
Eligibility Requirements: Applicants must be full-time students, working towards an undergraduate degree in public administration, political science, urban affairs, public policy, or a related field preferably at an HBCU with excellent interpersonal and analytical abilities, strong oral and written communication skills and a 3.5 or better grade point average for completed 1 full-time college semester and at least 1 full-time academic year. **Application Requirements:** Applicants must submit a cover letter describing your current student status and other relevant information that might be used in evaluating the application (extra-curricular activities, volunteer activities, etc); official copies of all undergraduate transcripts; scores from the American College Testing (ACT) program or the Scholastic Aptitude Test (SAT) administered by the College Entrance Examination Board; a copy of their Application for Federal Student Aid (FASFA); two (2) reference letters (at least one of which should be from a faculty member); three-page essay detailing his/her autobiography and career goals and objectives; three-page essay answering the question: In your opinion, what are the five most critical skills public administrators ought to possess, and why?; and a current resume. **Deadline for Receipt:** February 27.

4618 ■ NATIONAL FORUM FOR BLACK PUBLIC ADMINISTRATORS
777 N Capitol St. NE, Ste. 807
Washington, DC 20002
Tel: (202)408-9300

Fax: (202)408-8558
E-mail: webmaster@nfbpa.org
Web Site: http://www.nfbpa.org
To support the education and development of African-American students and prepare them for careers in public administration.
Title of Award: McKinley Financial Scholarships **Area, Field, or Subject:** Public administration. **Level of Education for which Award is Granted:** Graduate, Undergraduate **Funds Available:** $1,000.
Eligibility Requirements: Applicants must be full-time students, working towards an undergraduate or graduate degree in public administration, political science, urban affairs, public policy or a related field with excellent interpersonal and analytical abilities, strong oral and written communication skills and 3.0 or better grade point average for at least 1 full time remaining semester. **Application Requirements:** Applicants must submit a cover letter describing current student status and other relevant information that might be used in evaluating the application (extra-curricular activities, volunteer activities, etc.); official copies of all graduate (if applicable) and undergraduate transcripts; two reference letters (at least one of which should be from a faculty member); three-page essay detailing his/her autobiography and career goals and objectives; and a current resume. **Deadline for Receipt:** February 27.

4619 ■ NATIONAL IRANIAN AMERICAN COUNCIL

1411 K St. NW, Ste. 600
Washington, DC 20005
Tel: (202)386-6325
Fax: (202)386-6409
Web Site: http://www.niacouncil.org
To provide outstanding Iranian-American college students with internships in political and media organizations.
Title of Award: National Iranian American Council Fellowships **Area, Field, or Subject:** Political science; Economics; International affairs and relations; Journalism. **Level of Education for which Award is Granted:** Graduate, Undergraduate **Funds Available:** Travel expenses covered to and from DC; $500 monthly stipend; $700 monthly towards rent.
Eligibility Requirements: Applicant must be a college junior, senior, and graduate student who is a U.S. citizen or a legal permanent resident of Iranian descent. **Application Requirements:** Applicant must submit the following requirements: a completed application form; three letters of recommendation (two academic and one from an employment supervisor); resume; current college transcript; a 500-word essay answering the question: "How has being Iranian-American influenced your decision to pursue a career in public service or journalism?" **Deadline for Receipt:** February 15. **Additional Information:** NIAC at the above address.

4620 ■ NATIONAL SOCIETY, DAUGHTERS OF THE AMERICAN REVOLUTION

1776 D St. NW
Washington, DC 20006-5303
Tel: (202)628-1776
Web Site: http://www.dar.org
To encourage students to pursue an undergraduate degree.
Title of Award: Enid Hall Griswold Memorial Scholarships **Area, Field, or Subject:** Political science; History; Government; Economics. **Level of Education for which Award is Granted:** Undergraduate **Funds Available:** $1,000. **Duration:** One year.
Eligibility Requirements: Applicants must be juniors or seniors enrolled in an accredited college or university in the United States; pursuing a major in political science, history, government, or economics. **Application Requirements:** Applicants must obtain a letter of sponsorship from their local DAR chapter. Application forms and other supporting documents must be completed correctly and submitted in one package. **Deadline for Receipt:** February 15.

4621 ■ PRIDE FOUNDATION

PO Box 2194, 1122 E Pike St. PMB 1001
Seattle, WA 98112
Tel: (206)323-3318
Free: 800-735-7287
Fax: (206)323-1017
E-mail: prideweb@pridefoundation.org
Web Site: http://www.pridefoundation.org

To provide scholarship to the students who have been stigmatized, isolated or closeted because of sexual identity issues.
Title of Award: Political Leadership Scholarships **Area, Field, or Subject:** Law; Political science; Public Administration. **Level of Education for which Award is Granted:** Undergraduate **Funds Available:** No specific amount.
Eligibility Requirements: Applicant must be studying law, political science, public policy or public administration with the goal of improving rights for LGBT people. Preference is given to students who are self-identified lesbian, gay, bisexual or transgender (LGBT). **Application Requirements:** Qualified students are asked to submit an application to determine eligibility for scholarships. Applicants may download an application form from the Foundation's website. **Additional Information:** Pride Foundation at the above address.

4622 ■ PRIDE FOUNDATION

PO Box 2194, 1122 E Pike St. PMB 1001
Seattle, WA 98112
Tel: (206)323-3318
Free: 800-735-7287
Fax: (206)323-1017
E-mail: prideweb@pridefoundation.org
Web Site: http://www.pridefoundation.org
To provide scholarship to the students who have been stigmatized, isolated or closeted because of sexual identity issues.
Title of Award: Urashi Zen Scholarships **Area, Field, or Subject:** Business administration; Computer and information sciences; Political science. **Level of Education for which Award is Granted:** Undergraduate **Funds Available:** No specific amount.
Eligibility Requirements: Applicant must be a student studying business administration, computer science, or political science. **Application Requirements:** Qualified students are asked to submit an application to determine eligibility for scholarships. Applicants may download an application form from the Foundation's website. **Additional Information:** Pride Foundation at the above address.

4623 ■ REDLANDS COMMUNITY SCHOLARSHIP FOUNDATION

c/o Kathleen Venegas-Boge, Admin. Asst.
PO Box 1683
Redlands, CA 92373
Tel: (909)307-9892
Fax: (909)307-9892
Web Site: http://www.redlandsscholarships.org
To encourage educational pursuits among Redlands Unified School District graduates by providing educational assistance.
Title of Award: Charles and Ruth Ronin Memorial Scholarships **Area, Field, or Subject:** Political science; History; Education. **Level of Education for which Award is Granted:** Undergraduate **Number Awarded:** 1. **Funds Available:** $1,000.
Eligibility Requirements: Applicant must be a graduating senior with a 3.5 or higher GPA who will attend a four-year college/university on a full-time basis in pursuit of a bachelor's degree in political science, history, or education. **Application Requirements:** Applicants must submit a completed application form together with the scantron sheet; cover sheet; student activity and community activity sheets; personal essay; and a copy of unofficial transcript (signed by the counselor). **Additional Information:** No electronic submissions of application will be accepted. Submit two printed copies of the application and use a No. 2 pencil on the scantron sheet. **Deadline for Receipt:** February 20.

4624 ■ SAFE SCHOOLS COALITION

1002 E Seneca St.
Seattle, WA 98122-4203
Tel: (206)957-1621
Fax: (206)325-2689
Web Site: http://www.safeschoolscoalition.org
To provide financial assistance for gay, lesbian, bisexual and transgender students pursuing higher education.
Title of Award: Pride Foundation Scholarships **Area, Field, or Subject:** Business Administration; Computer Science; Political Science; Visual arts. **Level of Education for which Award is Granted:** Undergraduate **Funds Available:** Range from $500 to $10,000.
Eligibility Requirements: Applicants must be gay, lesbian, bisexual and transgendered students in these fields of studies. **Application Require-

ments: Applicants must check the available website for the required materials. **Deadline for Receipt:** January.

4625 ■ THE SAN DIEGO FOUNDATION
2508 Historic Decatur Rd., Ste. 200
San Diego, CA 92106
Tel: (619)235-2300
Fax: (619)239-1710
E-mail: info@sdfoundation.org
Web Site: http://www.sdfoundation.org
To support the education of students from California.

Title of Award: Julie Allen World Classroom Scholarships **Area, Field, or Subject:** International affairs and relations; Business; Economics; Civil rights; Foreign languages. **Level of Education for which Award is Granted:** Undergraduate **Number Awarded:** 1. **Funds Available:** $1,000.

Eligibility Requirements: Applicant must be an undergraduate student enrolled at the University of San Diego, UC San Diego, or San Diego State University; have a minimum 2.50 GPA on a 4.0 scale; demonstrated financial need; planning to study abroad for a minimum of one semester in a Second or Third World Country whose culture, language and customs are different than their own. **Application Requirements:** Applicants must submit a completed Common Scholarship Application together with personal statement; two letters of recommendation on official letterhead (written within the last six months); official transcript in an official and sealed envelope; copy of most recent tax form (Form 1040-pages 1 & 2; Form 1040A-pages 1 & 2; Form 1040EZ-page 1); and an essay (maximum one page, typed, double-spaced) addressing applicant's reason(s) for studying abroad, or coming to San Diego to pursue an education from the student's native country. **Deadline for Receipt:** January 28. **Additional Information:** Arzo Mansury, Dir. Scholarships at 619-814-1343, or scholarships@sdfoundation.org.

4626 ■ SILICON VALLEY COMMUNITY FOUNDATION
2240 W El Camino Real Ste. 300
Mountain View, CA 94040-1498
Tel: (650)450-5400
Fax: (650)450-5401
Web Site: http://www.siliconvalleycf.org
To provide financial assistance to those students who are in need.

Title of Award: Fauneil J. Rinn Scholarships **Area, Field, or Subject:** Political Science; Public Administration. **Level of Education for which Award is Granted:** Undergraduate **Number Awarded:** 1. **Funds Available:** Up to $1,250.

Eligibility Requirements: Applicants must be women who are current students in good standing in the Political Science or Master of Public Administration programs at San Jose State University. **Application Requirements:** Applicants must check the available website for the required materials. **Additional Information:** Contact Terry Christensen, Professor, Department of Political Science, San Jose State University, at 408-924-5565 or at Terry.Christensen@sjsu.edu for more information or an application.

4627 ■ SOUTHWEST FLORIDA COMMUNITY FOUNDATION
8260 College Pkwy., Ste. 101
Fort Myers, FL 33919
Tel: (239)274-5900
Fax: (239)274-5930
Web Site: http://www.floridacommunity.com
To fund a student who will attend: FGCU, university of Florida/Gainesville, Florida State University/Tallahassee, Flagler College, Stetson University/Deland, University of Miami, University of Tampa, or Embry Riddle Aeronautical University/Daytona Beach.

Title of Award: D&A Florida Scholarships **Area, Field, or Subject:** Architecture; Business; Engineering; International affairs and relations; Journalism; Computer and information sciences; Law; Literature; Medicine; Physics; Chemistry; Political science. **Level of Education for which Award is Granted:** Undergraduate **Funds Available:** $10,000. **Duration:** One year.

Eligibility Requirements: Applicants must have graduated from a public or private high school in Charlotte, Glades, Hendry or Lee County; must pursue a degree in Architecture, Business, Engineering, International affairs and relations, Journalism, Computer and information sciences, Law,

Literature, Medicine, Physics, Chemistry, or Political science. **Application Requirements:** Application forms are available online. Applicants must submit a letter of interest and letter of recommendation, a transcript and financial need documentation. **Deadline for Receipt:** February 15.

4628 ■ TURKISH COALITION OF AMERICA
1025 Connecticut Ave. NW, Ste. 1000
Washington, DC 20036
Tel: (202)370-1399
Fax: (202)370-1398
E-mail: info@turkishcoalitionofamerica.org
Web Site: http://www.turkishcoalition.org
To engage and cultivate a new generation of young Turkish American leaders.

Title of Award: TCA Turkish American Scholarships **Area, Field, or Subject:** Public Affairs; Political Science; International Affairs and Relations; Communications; Printing Trades; Public Relations. **Level of Education for which Award is Granted:** Undergraduate **Funds Available:** No specific amount.

Eligibility Requirements: Applicants must meet the following criteria: be a U.S. citizen or permanent resident (green card holder); have, and maintain through the course of the scholarship period, a cumulative minimum 3.3 GPA on a 4.0 scale; evidence of leadership commitment through participation in community service, particularly within the Turkish American community; and be a high school senior applying to an accredited college or university, or college student who plans to continue undergraduate study; or a college senior or graduate enrolled or about to enroll in graduate school. Graduate students who apply for the TCA must plan to pursue studies and a career in public affairs. **Application Requirements:** Applicants must submit three (3) collated, non-stapled, paperclipped copies of each of the following items: (1) Completed Application Form (2) Resume: Each copy should be submitted on one single-sided 8.5" x 11" sheet of paper. (3) Short essay: The essay should not exceed 500 words, must be typed and double-spaced. **Deadline for Receipt:** June 6. **Additional Information:** Turkish Coalition of America at the above address.

4629 ■ UNIVERSITY OF ALASKA ANCHORAGE
3211 Providence Dr.
Anchorage, AK 99508
Tel: (907)786-1800
Web Site: http://www.uaa.alaska.edu
To provide financial assistance for tuition and other educational expenses to students who are formally admitted to a political science or history degree-seeking program or who are members of the Forty-Ninth State Fellows Program at the University of Alaska Anchorage.

Title of Award: UAA Governor William A. Egan Scholarships **Area, Field, or Subject:** Political science; History. **Level of Education for which Award is Granted:** Undergraduate **Funds Available:** $560. **Duration:** One year.

Eligibility Requirements: Applicant must demonstrate motivation, academic and leadership potential; must demonstrate a commitment to their community; must be in good academic standing with a minimum cumulative GPA of 2.0; must be formally admitted to a political science or history degreeseeking program at the University of Alaska Anchorage; must plan on enrolling full-time (12 credits) at the University of Alaska Anchorage; may be an incoming or continuing student at the University of Alaska Anchorage; may be a U.S citizen, non-U.S citizen, Alaska resident, out-of-state resident; must be enrolled in the semester for which the award is made. **Application Requirements:** Applicants must complete the electronic scholarship application available online at www.uaa.alaska.edu/scholarships/egan.cfm. **Deadline for Receipt:** February 15.

4630 ■ UNIVERSITY OF ALASKA ANCHORAGE
3211 Providence Dr.
Anchorage, AK 99508
Tel: (907)786-1800
Web Site: http://www.uaa.alaska.edu
To provide financial assistance for tuition and other educational expenses to students who are in financial need.

Title of Award: UAA Mark A. Beltz Scholarships **Area, Field, or Subject:** Political science; Economics; Business administration; Science technologies. **Level of Education for which Award is Granted:** Graduate, Undergraduate **Funds Available:** $500$1,000.

Eligibility Requirements: Applicants must demonstrate motivation, academic and leadership potential; must be in good academic standing with a minimum cumulative GPA of 2.0 for undergraduates and 3.0 for graduates; must be formally admitted to a political science, economics, business administration, business and corporate law, or science and technology undergraduate, graduate, certificate, and/or vocational degree-seeking program at the University of Alaska Anchorage; must plan on enrolling at least half-time (6 credits) at the University of Alaska Anchorage; may be an incoming or continuing student at the University of Alaska Anchorage; may be a U.S. citizen, nonU.S. citizen, Alaska resident, or out-of-state resident. **Application Requirements:** Applicants must complete the electronics scholarship application available online. **Deadline for Receipt:** February 15.

4631 ■ UNIVERSITY OF ALASKA ANCHORAGE
3211 Providence Dr.
Anchorage, AK 99508
Tel: (907)786-1800
Web Site: http://www.uaa.alaska.edu
To provide financial assistance for tuition and other educational expenses to a full-time student majoring in political science.
Title of Award: UAA Pat Brakke Political Science Scholarships **Area, Field, or Subject:** Political science. **Level of Education for which Award is Granted:** Undergraduate **Funds Available:** $650. **Duration:** One year.
Eligibility Requirements: Applicants must be in good academic standing with a minimum cumulative GPA of 3.0; must be formally admitted to the Political Science program at the University of Alaska Anchorage; must plan on enrolling at least full-time (12 credits) at the University of Alaska Anchorage; may be a U.S. citizen, non-U.S. citizen, Alaska resident, or out-of-state resident; must demonstrate motivation, academic and leadership potential. **Application Requirements:** Applicants must complete the electronic scholarship application available online at www.uaa.alaska.edu/scholarships/pat.cfm. **Deadline for Receipt:** February 15.

4632 ■ WOMEN IN DEFENSE
2111 Wilson Blvd., Ste. 400
Arlington, VA 22201-3061
Tel: (703)247-2552
Fax: (703)522-1885
E-mail: wid@ndia.org
Web Site: http://wid.ndia.org
To provide financial assistance to further educational objectives of women either employed or planning careers in defense or national security areas.
Title of Award: Women In Defense HORIZONS Scholarships **Area, Field, or Subject:** National security; Military history; Government; Engineering; Computer and information sciences; Physics; Mathematics and mathematical sciences; Business; Law; International affairs and relations; Political science; Economics. **Level of Education for which Award is Granted:** Graduate, Undergraduate **Funds Available:** No specific amount.
Eligibility Requirements: Applicant must be currently enrolled at an accredited university/college, either full-time or part-time; must have junior, senior or graduate status; demonstrate interest in pursuing a career related to national security or defense; demonstrate financial need; have a minimum GPA of 3.25. Applicant must be a female citizen of the United States. **Application Requirements:** Applicants must submit a completed scholarship application form with the essays, recommendations, and transcripts. **Additional Information:** Established in 1988. **Deadline for Receipt:** July 1.

Public Administration

4633 ■ AMERICAN INSTITUTE OF POLISH CULTURE
1440 79th St. Causeway, Ste. 117
Miami, FL 33141
Tel: (305)864-2349
Fax: (305)865-5150
E-mail: info@ampolinstitute.org
Web Site: http://www.ampolinstitute.org
To provide financial support American students of Polish descent who wish to continue their education after high school.

Title of Award: Harriet Irsay Scholarships **Area, Field, or Subject:** Communications; Education; Media arts; History; International affairs and relations; Journalism; Liberal arts; Polish studies; Public relations. **Level of Education for which Award is Granted:** Graduate, Undergraduate **Number Awarded:** 10-15. **Funds Available:** $1,000.
Eligibility Requirements: Applicants must be of Polish heritage; an American citizen or permanent resident; full-time graduate or undergraduate students in the field of communication, education, film, history, International Relation, journalism, liberal arts, polish studies, public relations; or graduate student in business programs with a thesis related to Poland, or graduate students with a thesis with Polish subject. **Application Requirements:** Applicants must submit a completed application form; school transcripts; resume; essay (200-400 words) about "Why should I receive the scholarship"; an article about Poland (maximum of 700 words); and 3 signed recommendation letters on a letterhead stationary from teachers or other person knowledgeable about the applicant's academic background. A non-refundable $10 processing fee (check or money order) must also be included. **Deadline for Receipt:** April 20.

4634 ■ AMERICAN PUBLIC WORKS ASSOCIATION-NEVADA
c/o Leslie R. Henley, Pres.
Clark County Public Works
PO Box 554000
Las Vegas, NV 89155
Tel: (702)455-6065
Fax: (702)455-6113
E-mail: lrh@co.clark.nv.us
Web Site: http://www.apwa-nv.org
To promote education in the field of public works, public administration or related field.
Title of Award: Michael Koizumi APWA Scholarships **Area, Field, or Subject:** Public administration. **Level of Education for which Award is Granted:** Undergraduate **Number Awarded:** 4. **Funds Available:** $1000 and $2000.
Eligibility Requirements: Applicant must be a Nevada resident; must plan to enroll in a course of study leading to a career in the field of public works, public administration or a related private enterprise (e.g. business, architecture, science, engineering, etc.); and must be an entering their freshman year or currently enrolled in college. **Application Requirements:** Applicants must submit completed application form together with copy of transcripts, reference, list of experience, a written statement on financial status, and career objectives. **Additional Information:** Northern Branch (All Counties except Clark, Lincoln and Nye), Peter Gulash, Terracon 1360 Greg St., Stes. 111-112 Sparks, NV 89431, P: 775-351-2400, F: 775-351-2423, or pmgulash@terracon.com. Southern Branch (Clark, Lincoln and Nye Counties), Michael B. Holloway, Poggemeyer Design Group, Inc. 2601 North Tenaya Way Las Vegas, NV 89128-0427, P: 702-255-8100, F: 702-255-8375.

4635 ■ AMERICAN SOCIETY OF MILITARY COMPTROLLERS
415 N Alfred
Alexandria, VA 22314
Tel: (703)549-0360
Free: 800-462-5637
Fax: (703)549-3181
E-mail: asmchq@asmconline.org
Web Site: http://www.asmconline.org
To provide financial assistance to seniors to accomplish their future financial management baccalaureate educational goals.
Title of Award: American Society of Military Comptrollers National Scholarship Program **Area, Field, or Subject:** Business Administration, Economics, Public Administration, Accounting, Finance. **Level of Education for which Award is Granted:** Undergraduate **Number Awarded:** One. **Funds Available:** $3,000.
Eligibility Requirements: Applicants must be entering a field of study directly related to financial/resource management. **Application Requirements:** Applicants must have endorsement letters from ASMC chapters. Applicants must submit completed application form and three letters of recommendation from local ASMC chapter president, high school principal, academic dean, or guidance counselor, and a high school teacher. **Deadline for Receipt:** March 31. **Additional Information:** Linda Ryan; 301-227-6341; linda.c.ryan@nga.mil.

4636 ■ AMERICAN UNIVERSITY - SCHOOL OF PUBLIC AFFAIRS
Ward Circle Bldg.
4400 Massachusetts Ave. NW
Washington, DC 20016
Tel: (202)885-2940
Fax: (202)885-2353
E-mail: spagrad@american.edu
Web Site: http://spa.american.edu
To support students with financial disabilities.
Title of Award: Center for Congressional and Presidential Studies
(CPPS) Endowment **Area, Field, or Subject:** Public administration. **Level
of Education for which Award is Granted:** Graduate, Undergraduate
Funds Available: $2,500. **Duration:** One year.
Eligibility Requirements: Applicants must be students attending CPPS
programs. **Application Requirements:** Applicants must submit resume;
1-2 pages letter to the Director of CPPS (the letter should address
academic and professional achievements and future aspirations, with
detailed financial need). **Additional Information:** The Support allocated
to any students account will replace a current financial need. The award
will not necessarily be available as a cash reimbursement from students
account, unless a credit remains on the system after all debts are paid.

4637 ■ ARKANSAS PUBLIC HEALTH ASSOCIATION
4815 W Marketing St., Slot 52
Little Rock, AR 72205
Tel: (501)661-2392
E-mail: catherine.tapp@arkansas.gov
Web Site: http://www.arkpublichealth.org
To provide financial support to Arkansas students.
Title of Award: Arkansas Public Health Association Scholarships **Area,
Field, or Subject:** Public health. **Level of Education for which Award is
Granted:** Undergraduate **Funds Available:** $500-$1,000.
Eligibility Requirements: Applicants must be an Arkansas resident; must
be enrolled, or have plans to enroll, in a field of public health; must be
currently classified as at least a sophomore in college, university or approved Vo-Tech; must have at least 2.5 GPA; must demonstrate financial
need. **Application Requirements:** Application forms are available online.
Applicants must submit official college, university, or Vo-Tech transcripts;
must have a letter of recommendation from major professor; must have a
letter of personal reference; must have a statement/explanation of
financial need; must have an explanation in 150 words or less concerning
their goals and plans with the scholarship, their past and present public
health experiences. Application form and other requirements must be sent
to 447 W Gaines Monticello, AR 71655. **Deadline for Receipt:** March 16.

4638 ■ ARMENIAN RELIEF SOCIETY - EASTERN UNITED STATES
80 Bigelow Avenue, Ste. 200
Watertown, MA 02472
Tel: (617)926-3801
Fax: (617)924-7238
E-mail: arseastus@aol.com
Web Site: http://www.arseastus.com
To encourage educational pursuits among undergraduate students of
Armenian descent.
Title of Award: ARS Undergraduate Scholarships **Area, Field, or
Subject:** Law; History; Political science; Journalism; Government;
Economics; Business administration; Medicine; Public service. **Level of
Education for which Award is Granted:** Four Year College, Two Year
College, Undergraduate **Funds Available:** No specific amount. **Duration:**
One year.
Eligibility Requirements: Applicants must be of Armenian descent; must
be undergraduate students who have completed at least one semester at
an accredited four-year college or university in the United States or must
be enrolled in a two-year college and are transferring to a four-year college or university as a full-time student in the Fall. **Application Requirements:** Application must include financial aid forms, recent official
transcript, two letters of recommendation and tuition costs. Forward
materials to: Scholarship Committee, Armenian Relief Society of Eastern
USA, Inc., 80 Bigelow Ave., Ste. 200, Watertown, MA 02472. **Deadline
for Receipt:** April 1.

4639 ■ ASSOCIATION ON AMERICAN INDIAN AFFAIRS
966 Hungerford Dr., Ste. 12-B
Rockville, MD 20850

Tel: (240)314-7155
Fax: (240)314-7159
E-mail: general.aaia@verizon.net
Web Site: http://indian-affairs.org
To provide financial assistance for helping native people for higher educa-
tion.
Title of Award: Elizabeth and Sherman Asche Memorial Scholarship
Fund **Area, Field, or Subject:** Public health, Science. **Level of Educa-
tion for which Award is Granted:** Graduate, Undergraduate **Funds
Available:** $1,500.
Eligibility Requirements: Applicants must be graduate and undergradu-
ate students pursuing a degree in public health or science. **Application
Requirements:** Students are eligible to apply on a yearly basis. **Deadline
for Receipt:** July 1.

4640 ■ MARCH AND RUTI BELL FOUNDATION
6800 Broken Sound Parkway
Boca Raton, FL 33487
Tel: (561)988-1700
Fax: (561)988-1738
Web Site: http://bellfamily.org
To encourage undergraduates in the College of Arts and Science to
choose careers in public service.
Title of Award: March and Ruti Bell Foundation Scholarships **Area,
Field, or Subject:** Public service. **Level of Education for which Award
is Granted:** Undergraduate **Funds Available:** No specific amount.
Eligibility Requirements: Applicants must be junior and senior high
school students who have declared their majors in the field of public
service; must have a strong sense of their career goals. **Application
Requirements:** Students may submit an application letter together with
other requirements. **Deadline for Receipt:** April 1. **Additional Information:** Matthew S. Santirocco, Dean, College of Arts and Science, New
York University, 100 Washington Square E. New York, NY 10003-6688.
212-998-8100.

4641 ■ COASTAL BEND COMMUNITY FOUNDATION
600 Leopard St., Ste. 1716
Corpus Christi, TX 78473
Tel: (361)882-9745
Fax: (361)882-2865
Web Site: http://www.cbcfoundation.org
To provide financial assistance to further the education of deserving
students in Coastal Bend.
Title of Award: Jim Springer Memorial Scholarships **Area, Field, or
Subject:** Public relations; Marketing and distribution; Advertising; Com-
munications. **Level of Education for which Award is Granted:**
Undergraduate **Number Awarded:** 1. **Funds Available:** $500.
Eligibility Requirements: Applicants must be Coastal Bend residents;
full-time college sophomore, junior or senior students with grade point
average of 2.5; majoring in public relations, marketing, advertising or communications. **Application Requirements:** Applicants must submit all the
required application information. **Deadline for Receipt:** March 14.

4642 ■ FOUNDATION FOR THE CAROLINAS
217 S Tryon St.
Charlotte, NC 28202
Tel: (704)973-4500
Free: 800-973-7244
Web Site: http://www.fftc.org
To provide financial assistance for the children of Charlotte area public
safety personnel.
Title of Award: Rotary Public Safety Scholarship Fund **Area, Field, or
Subject:** Public service. **Level of Education for which Award is
Granted:** Undergraduate **Funds Available:** $1,000. **Duration:** One year.
Eligibility Requirements: Applicants must be high school seniors intend-
ing to enter a two-year or four-year degree program with a minimum of 2.5
cumulative grade point average (on a 4.0 scale), whose mother or father
are full time employees of the Charlotte Fire Department, Charlotte-
Mecklenburg Police Department, Mecklenburg County Sheriff's Office or
MEDIC with minimum of one year of service. **Application Requirements:**
Applicants must submit completed application form; copy of SAR from
FAFSA; official transcripts of academic coursework and grades for at least
the last two years; four recommendation forms (two from instructors or

other school administrators and two from employers or other non-related individuals in the Charlotte-Mecklenburg area); one to two-paged typed statement expressing reasons for applying for the scholarship, qualifications, and educational and career goals; and a copy of estimated expense budget for tuition, room and board, books, etc. at the school the applicant wants to attend. **Deadline for Receipt:** April 1.

4643 ■ GOVERNMENT FINANCE OFFICERS ASSOCIATION OF UNITED STATES AND CANADA
203 N LaSalle St., Ste. 2700
Chicago, IL 60601-1210
Tel: (312)977-9700
Fax: (312)977-4806
Web Site: http://www.gfoa.org
To inspire careers and interest in the efficient and productive investment of public funds.
Title of Award: George A. Nielsen Public Investor Scholarships **Area, Field, or Subject:** Public administration; Finance; Business administration. **Level of Education for which Award is Granted:** Graduate, Undergraduate **Funds Available:** $5,000 (may be two awards of $2,500 each).
Eligibility Requirements: Program is open to employees of a local government or other public entity who are enrolled or plan to enroll in an undergraduate or graduate program in public administration, finance, business administration, or related field. Applicants must be employed at least one year by a state, local government, or special district with significant responsibilities for cash management or treasury activities including a specific focus on the investing of available cash; must be a citizen or permanent resident of the United States or Canada; must have a recommendation by employer; must be enrolled in a graduate or undergraduate program in public administration, finance or business administration before fund is awarded; must be a student who has not been a past winner of a scholarship program administered by the Government Finance Officers Association of the United States and Canada. **Application Requirements:** Applicants must submit an application form; statement describing experience working for a state, local government or other special purpose government entity, proposed plan of study and how it will help career in the public sector; undergraduate and graduate grade transcripts; resume; employer's letter of recommendation; and other letters of recommendation (optional). **Deadline for Receipt:** February 29.

4644 ■ HISPANIC ASSOCIATION OF COLLEGES AND UNIVERSITIES
8415 Datapoint Dr., Ste. 400
San Antonio, TX 78229
Tel: (210)698-3805
Fax: (210)692-0823
E-mail: hacu@hacu.net
Web Site: http://www.hacu.net
To promote the development of member colleges and universities; to improve access to and the quality of post-secondary educational opportunities for Hispanic students; and to meet the needs of business, industry and government through the development and sharing of resources, information and expertise.
Title of Award: Wendell Scott Awards **Area, Field, or Subject:** Business; Engineering; Public Relation; Technology; Management. **Level of Education for which Award is Granted:** Graduate, Undergraduate **Funds Available:** $1,500-undergraduate; $2,000-graduate.
Eligibility Requirements: Applicants must be full-time or part-time, undergraduate and graduate students attending four year institutions; must possess a minimum cumulative GPA of 3.0. Applying graduate students must be attending school at least on a part-time basis and must possess a minimum cumulative GPA of 3.0. **Application Requirements:** Applicants must fill out the application form and must provide any documents showing that they are currently enrolled or accepted by a college, university, or institution. **Deadline for Receipt:** May 23.

4645 ■ HISPANIC SCHOLARSHIP FUND
55 Second St., Ste. 1500
San Francisco, CA 94105
877-473-4636
Fax: (415)808-2302
E-mail: info@hsf.net

Web Site: http://www.hsf.net
To promote academic excellence and to provide an opportunity for outstanding students with significant financial need to reach their fullest potential.
Title of Award: The Gates Millennium Scholars **Area, Field, or Subject:** Mathematics and mathematical sciences; Science; Engineering; Education; Public health; Library and archival sciences. **Level of Education for which Award is Granted:** Undergraduate **Funds Available:** No specific amount.
Eligibility Requirements: Applicants must be African American, American Indian/Alaska Native, Asian pacific Islander American and Hispanic American heritage; a U.S. citizen or legal permanent resident; have a minimum 3.3 GPA on a 4.0 scale; must demonstrate leadership skills; must demonstrate financial need. **Application Requirements:** Applicants must complete all three required forms available at the award site www.gmsp.org. American Indian/Alaska Natives must submit proof of tribal enrollment or a certificate of descent if selected as finalists. **Additional Information:** Established in 1999 and funded by a grant from the Bill and Melinda Gates Foundation. **Deadline for Receipt:** December 31 (paper applications), January 11 (online applications). **Additional Information:** gmsinfo@hsf.nett.

4646 ■ HISPANIC SCHOLARSHIP FUND
55 Second St., Ste. 1500
San Francisco, CA 94105
877-473-4636
Fax: (415)808-2302
E-mail: info@hsf.net
Web Site: http://www.hsf.net
For sophomore students who will be transferring to a four-year college.
Title of Award: HSBC-North America Scholarship Program **Area, Field, or Subject:** Accounting; Actuarial science; Advertising; Public relations; Business; Engineering, Computer; Computer and information sciences; Economics; Finance; International trade; Marketing and distribution; Management. **Level of Education for which Award is Granted:** Undergraduate **Funds Available:** $2,500.
Eligibility Requirements: Applicant must be of Hispanic heritage; U.S. citizen or legal permanent resident with a valid permanent resident card or passport stamped I-551; be a current sophomore or community college student transferring to a four-year college/university and will be a junior status for the upcoming academic year; be enrolled full-time in a degree-seeking program at an accredited institution in the U.S., Puerto Rico, U.S. Virgin Islands or Guam; have a minimum 3.0 GPA on a 4.0 scale or 4.00 on a 5.00 scale; must be majoring in one of the following: Accounting, Actuarial Science, Advertising, Public Relations, Business, Computer Engineering, Computer Information Systems (CIS), Computer Science, Economics, Finance, International Business, Marketing or Management; must submit a resume; have applied for Federal Financial Aid; must be a resident of: Los Angeles, CA (LA, Orange, Riverside, San Bernardino, Ventura); Monterey/Salinas, CA (Salinas); San Diego, CA (San Diego); Tampa, FL (Hernando, Hillsborough, Pasco, Pinella); Jacksonville, FL (Nassau, Duval, Clay, St. Johns); Chicago, IL (Cook, DuPage, Grundy, Kane, Kankakee, Kendall, Lake, LaSalle, Will, McHenry); New York, NY (Bronx, Kings, New York, Queens, Richmond); Las Vegas, NV (Clark); Phoenix, AZ (Phoenix-Mesa); Wilmington, DC (New Castle); Bridgewater, NJ (Sussex); or Chesapeake, VA. Applicants must also submit a resume; must have applied for federal financial aid and must be pursuing his/her first undergraduate degree. **Application Requirements:** Applicants must use the HSF online application system. **Additional Information:** In partnership with HSBC. **Deadline for Receipt:** November 1. **Additional Information:** scholar1@hsf.net.

4647 ■ INTERNATIONAL FOODSERVICE EDITORIAL COUNCIL
PO Box 491
Hyde Park, NY 12538
Tel: (845)229-6973
Fax: (845)229-6993
E-mail: info@ifeconline.com
Web Site: http://www.ifec-is-us.com
To increase awareness and understanding of the career opportunities available in the field of food service communications and to encourage entry of qualified professionals in the field.
Title of Award: International Foodservice Editorial Council Scholarships **Area, Field, or Subject:** Culinary arts; Communications; Food service

careers; Food science and technology; Photography; Hotel, institutional, and restaurant management; Nutrition; Dietetics; Journalism; Public relations; Graphic art and design. **Level of Education for which Award is Granted:** Graduate, Undergraduate **Number Awarded:** Varies. **Funds Available:** $3,750.

Eligibility Requirements: Applicants must be full-time students in a U.S. accredited post-secondary educational institution working towards an associate's, bachelor's or master's degree. **Application Requirements:** Applicants must submit a complete application together with academic transcript and two letters of recommendation. Application requirements must be typewritten and submitted using U.S. Postal Service's Return Receipt Service. **Deadline for Receipt:** March 15.

4648 ■ JAPANESE AMERICAN CITIZENS LEAGUE
1765 Sutter St.
San Francisco, CA 94115
Tel: (415)921-5225
Fax: (415)921-4671
E-mail: jacl@jacl.org
Web Site: http://www.jacl.org
To provide financial assistance for qualified individuals.
Title of Award: Alice Yuriko Endo Memorial Scholarships **Area, Field, or Subject:** Public service. **Level of Education for which Award is Granted:** Undergraduate **Funds Available:** $60,000. **Duration:** One year.

Eligibility Requirements: Applicant must be an active National JACL member at either an individual or student/youth level; must be planning to attend full-time at a college, university, trade school, business school, or any other institution of higher learning within the United States at the undergraduate or graduate school level. Entering freshman applicant must be a high school senior. **Application Requirements:** Application forms are available online at www.jacl.org/join.html. **Deadline for Receipt:** March 1 (entering freshman) and April 1 (all applications excluding entering freshman).

4649 ■ JEWISH VOCATIONAL SERVICE
216 W Jackson Blvd., Ste. 700
Chicago, IL 60606
Tel: (312)673-3400
Fax: (312)553-5544
E-mail: jvs@jvschicago.org
Web Site: http://www.jvschicago.org
To support the education of a Jewish college or graduate student.
Title of Award: Jewish Federation Academic Scholarships **Area, Field, or Subject:** Medicine; Education; Social work; Arts; Public health; Urban affairs/design/planning; Law. **Level of Education for which Award is Granted:** Graduate, Undergraduate **Funds Available:** More than $500,000 each year.

Eligibility Requirements: Applicant must be Jewish; be born or raised in either: Cook County, Chicago metropolitan area, or Northwest Indiana; or have one continuous year of full-time employment in Cook County or Chicago metropolitan area prior to starting professional education; must intend to remain in the Chicago metropolitan area after completing school; must be entering as a full-time student in an accredited professional graduate program or entering as junior or senior undergraduate student at an accredited professional education program; and must be demonstrating career promise in a helping profession. **Application Requirements:** Applicants must submit a completed Application Data Form; Career Statement Form; Budget Worksheet; and Academic Budget form as an attachment to jvsscholarship@jvschicago.org. In addition, applicants must send by mail a Legal Domicility Form; two letter of reference form; IRS Forms; parents' or spouse's IRS; documentation of tuition cost; Release of Information form; and official transcripts. **Deadline for Receipt:** February 15. **Additional Information:** 312-673-3457.

4650 ■ THE LAGRANT FOUNDATION
626 Wilshire Blvd., Ste. 700
Los Angeles, CA 90017-2920
Tel: (323)469-8680
Fax: (323)469-8683
Web Site: http://www.lagrantfoundation.org
To provide financial support for the education of undergraduate students who belong to ethnic groups: African American, Asian Pacific American, Hispanic or Native American or Alaska Native.

Title of Award: The Lagrant Foundation - Undergraduate Students Scholarship **Area, Field, or Subject:** Public relations; Marketing and distribution; Advertising. **Level of Education for which Award is Granted:** Undergraduate **Funds Available:** No amount specified.
Eligibility Requirements: Applicants must be U.S. citizens and full-time students at a four-year, accredited institution, carrying a total of 12 units or more per semester/quarter; must have a minimum of 2.75 GPA; and must major in a field of study that has an emphasis on public relations, marketing or advertising or must minor in communications with desire to pursue a career in public relations, marketing or advertising. **Application Requirements:** Applicants must submit a one- to two-page typewritten essay outlining their career goals and what steps they will take to increase the lack of ethnic representation in the fields of advertising, marketing and public relations (must define the role of advertising, marketing or public relations practitioner depending on emphasis); accomplishments relevant to increasing awareness about diversity in their community; brief paragraph describing any honors and awards that they have received (must put the particular dates); a letter of reference from a college professor or internship advisor. **Additional Information:** If chosen, the applicant must attend the Lagrant Foundation's career development workshop and awards reception to receive the scholarship. **Deadline for Receipt:** February 29.

4651 ■ LEWIS-CLARK STATE COLLEGE
500 8th Ave.
Lewiston, ID 83501
Tel: (208)792-5272
Web Site: http://www.lcsc.edu
To provide 12 awards to Idaho high school seniors planning to attend an Idaho college or university.
Title of Award: Lewis-Clark State College Governor's Cup Scholarships **Area, Field, or Subject:** Public service. **Level of Education for which Award is Granted:** Undergraduate **Funds Available:** No specific amount.
Eligibility Requirements: Applicants must be residents of Idaho; must be graduating seniors of an Idaho high school; must be enrolled as full-time students in an academic or technical program at an Idaho college or university; must have a cumulative GPA of 2.8 or above; and must have documentation of volunteer work, leadership and public service. **Application Requirements:** Applicants must accomplish a general application available at the website.

4652 ■ LOUISIANA ENVIRONMENTAL HEALTH ASSOCIATION
PO Box 2661
Baton Rouge, LA 70821
Tel: (225)219-3242
Fax: (225)219-3310
E-mail: james.miller@la.gov
Web Site: http://www.leha.net
To encourage an outstanding undergraduate student to pursue their education.
Title of Award: Frank L. Dautriel Memorial Scholarships (Undergraduate) **Area, Field, or Subject:** Environmental science; Environmental technology; Public health. **Level of Education for which Award is Granted:** Undergraduate **Funds Available:** $1,000. **Duration:** One year.
Eligibility Requirements: Applicant must be enrolled as a full-time student in an environmental health, environmental science, environmental engineering, or public health related degree program at an accredited university; must be a Louisiana resident; must have maintained an overall 2.75 or higher on a 4.0 point rating system and have a record of good conduct supported by official transcript; must demonstrate a need for a scholarship. **Application Requirements:** Application forms are available online and must be sent to Louisiana Environmental Health Association, PO Box 2661, Baton Rouge, LA 70821. **Deadline for Receipt:** October 31.

4653 ■ NATIONAL FORUM FOR BLACK PUBLIC ADMINISTRATORS
777 N Capitol St. NE, Ste. 807
Washington, DC 20002
Tel: (202)408-9300
Fax: (202)408-8558
E-mail: webmaster@nfbpa.org
Web Site: http://www.nfbpa.org

To support the education and development of African-American students and prepare them for careers in public administration.
Title of Award: CIGNA Healthcare Undergraduate Scholarships **Area, Field, or Subject:** Public administration; Political science; Urban affairs/design/planning. **Level of Education for which Award is Granted:** Undergraduate **Number Awarded:** 1. **Funds Available:** $1,000.
Eligibility Requirements: Applicants must be full-time students, working towards an undergraduate degree in public administration, political science, urban affairs, public policy, or a related field preferably at an HBCU with excellent interpersonal and analytical abilities, strong oral and written communication skills and a 3.5 or better grade point average for completed 1 full-time college semester and at least 1 full-time academic year. **Application Requirements:** Applicants must submit a cover letter describing your current student status and other relevant information that might be used in evaluating the application (extra-curricular activities, volunteer activities, etc); official copies of all undergraduate transcripts; scores from the American College Testing (ACT) program or the Scholastic Aptitude Test (SAT) administered by the College Entrance Examination Board; a copy of their Application for Federal Student Aid (FASFA); two (2) reference letters (at least one of which should be from a faculty member); three-page essay detailing his/her autobiography and career goals and objectives; three-page essay answering the question: In your opinion, what are the five most critical skills public administrators ought to possess, and why?; and a current resume. **Deadline for Receipt:** February 27.

4654 ■ NATIONAL FORUM FOR BLACK PUBLIC ADMINISTRATORS
777 N Capitol St. NE, Ste. 807
Washington, DC 20002
Tel: (202)408-9300
Fax: (202)408-8558
E-mail: webmaster@nfbpa.org
Web Site: http://www.nfbpa.org
To help NFBPA further achieve its mission of attracting the best and brightest African Americans to careers in public service.
Title of Award: Johnnie L. Cochran, Jr./MWH Scholarships **Area, Field, or Subject:** Public service. **Level of Education for which Award is Granted:** Undergraduate **Funds Available:** $5,000.
Eligibility Requirements: Applicants must be full-time students working towards an undergraduate or graduate degree in public administration, political science, urban affairs, public policy, or a related field who have excellent interpersonal and analytical abilities, strong oral and written communication skills and have 3.0 or better GPA for at least 1 full time semester remaining. **Application Requirements:** Applicants must submit cover letter describing current student status and other relevant information that might be used in evaluating application; official copies of all graduate and undergraduate transcripts; two reference letters (at least one of which should be from a faculty member); three-page essay detailing autobiography and career goals and objectives; and current resume.

4655 ■ NATIONAL FORUM FOR BLACK PUBLIC ADMINISTRATORS
777 N Capitol St. NE, Ste. 807
Washington, DC 20002
Tel: (202)408-9300
Fax: (202)408-8558
E-mail: webmaster@nfbpa.org
Web Site: http://www.nfbpa.org
To provide financial assistance for the education of undergraduate students pursuing a career in public service.
Title of Award: The Future Colleagues Scholarships **Area, Field, or Subject:** Public service. **Level of Education for which Award is Granted:** Undergraduate **Funds Available:** $1,000.
Eligibility Requirements: Applicants must be full-time undergraduate students with average academic credentials (2.5 to 3.0) and strong written, oral and analytical abilities, and have at least 1 full-time semester remaining. **Application Requirements:** Applicants must submit a cover letter describing the current student status and other relevant information that might be used in evaluating the application (extra-curricular activities, volunteer activities, etc); a 500-word essay which provides an example of prior public or community service involvement and how it has influenced your future aspirations in public administration; official copies of all undergraduate transcripts; two (2) reference letters (at least one of which should be from a faculty member); and a current resume. **Deadline for Receipt:** February 27.

4656 ■ NATIONAL FORUM FOR BLACK PUBLIC ADMINISTRATORS
777 N Capitol St. NE, Ste. 807
Washington, DC 20002
Tel: (202)408-9300
Fax: (202)408-8558
E-mail: webmaster@nfbpa.org
Web Site: http://www.nfbpa.org
To assist NFBPA to further achieve its mission of grooming the next generation of African Americans for careers in public service.
Title of Award: Willie T. Loud - CH2M Hill Scholarships **Area, Field, or Subject:** Public service. **Level of Education for which Award is Granted:** Undergraduate **Funds Available:** No specific amount.
Eligibility Requirements: Applicants must be full-time students with 3.0 or better GPA who are at least 1 full-time semester remaining or working towards a Bachelor's or Master's degree in Public Administration or a related field and should have strong interpersonal skills, excellent writing, analytical, and oral communication abilities. **Application Requirements:** Applicant must submit a cover letter describing current student status and other relevant information that might be used in evaluating application; official copies of all graduate and undergraduate transcripts; two reference letters (at least one of which should be from a faculty member); three-page essay detailing his/her autobiography and career goals and objectives; and current resume.

4657 ■ NATIONAL FORUM FOR BLACK PUBLIC ADMINISTRATORS
777 N Capitol St. NE, Ste. 807
Washington, DC 20002
Tel: (202)408-9300
Fax: (202)408-8558
E-mail: webmaster@nfbpa.org
Web Site: http://www.nfbpa.org
To support the education and development of African-American students and prepare them for careers in public administration.
Title of Award: McKinley Financial Scholarships **Area, Field, or Subject:** Public administration. **Level of Education for which Award is Granted:** Graduate, Undergraduate **Funds Available:** $1,000.
Eligibility Requirements: Applicants must be full-time students, working towards an undergraduate or graduate degree in public administration, political science, urban affairs, public policy or a related field with excellent interpersonal and analytical abilities, strong oral and written communication skills and 3.0 or better grade point average for at least 1 full time remaining semester. **Application Requirements:** Applicants must submit a cover letter describing current student status and other relevant information that might be used in evaluating the application (extra-curricular activities, volunteer activities, etc.); official copies of all graduate (if applicable) and undergraduate transcripts; two reference letters (at least one of which should be from a faculty member); three-page essay detailing his/her autobiography and career goals and objectives; and a current resume. **Deadline for Receipt:** February 27.

4658 ■ NATIONAL FORUM FOR BLACK PUBLIC ADMINISTRATORS
777 N Capitol St. NE, Ste. 807
Washington, DC 20002
Tel: (202)408-9300
Fax: (202)408-8558
E-mail: webmaster@nfbpa.org
Web Site: http://www.nfbpa.org
To help NFBPA further achieve its mission of attracting the best and brightest African Americans to careers in public service.
Title of Award: NFBPA/CDM Scholarships **Area, Field, or Subject:** Public service. **Level of Education for which Award is Granted:** Undergraduate **Funds Available:** $5,000.
Eligibility Requirements: Applicants must be full-time students working towards an undergraduate or graduate degree in public administration, political science, urban affairs, public policy, or a related field with excellent interpersonal and analytical abilities, strong oral and written communication skills, have 3.0 GPA and/or have at least 1 full time semester remaining. **Application Requirements:** Applicants must submit a cover letter describing current student status and other relevant information that might be used in evaluating application; official copies of all graduate and undergraduate transcripts; two reference letters (at least one of which should be from a faculty member); three-page essay, detailing his/her autobiography and career goals and objectives; and current resume.

4659 ■ NEW YORK WOMEN IN COMMUNICATIONS FOUNDATION
355 Lexington Ave., 15th Fl.
New York, NY 10017-6603
Tel: (212)297-2133
Fax: (212)370-9047
Web Site: http://www.nywici.org
To provide financial assistance for the education of the residents of NY, NJ, CT, or PA.
Title of Award: New York Women in Communications, Inc. Foundation Scholarships **Area, Field, or Subject:** Advertising; Broadcasting; Communications; Media arts; Journalism; Marketing and distribution; Media arts; Public relations. **Level of Education for which Award is Granted:** Graduate, Undergraduate **Funds Available:** No specific amount. **Duration:** One year.
Eligibility Requirements: Applicants must be high school seniors, or college undergraduate or graduate students who are permanent residents of NY, NJ, CT or PA majoring or declaring a major in a communications-related field, including but not limited to advertising, broadcasting, communications, English, film, journalism, marketing, new media, or public relations. Applicants must have an overall GPA of 3.2 or better (or the high school equivalent). **Application Requirements:** Applicants must submit completed application form and all other required application information and materials. **Deadline for Receipt:** January 30.

4660 ■ PRIDE FOUNDATION
PO Box 2194, 1122 E Pike St. PMB 1001
Seattle, WA 98112
Tel: (206)323-3318
Free: 800-735-7287
Fax: (206)323-1017
E-mail: prideweb@pridefoundation.org
Web Site: http://www.pridefoundation.org
To provide scholarship to the students who have been stigmatized, isolated or closeted because of sexual identity issues.
Title of Award: Political Leadership Scholarships **Area, Field, or Subject:** Law; Political science; Public Administration. **Level of Education for which Award is Granted:** Undergraduate **Funds Available:** No specific amount.
Eligibility Requirements: Applicant must be studying law, political science, public policy or public administration with the goal of improving rights for LGBT people. Preference is given to students who are self-identified lesbian, gay, bisexual or transgender (LGBT). **Application Requirements:** Qualified students are asked to submit an application to determine eligibility for scholarships. Applicants may download an application form from the Foundation's website. **Additional Information:** Pride Foundation at the above address.

4661 ■ PUBLIC EDUCATION FOUNDATION
3360 W Sahara Ave., Ste. 160
Las Vegas, NV 89102
Tel: (702)799-1042
Fax: (702)799-5247
E-mail: steelej@ccpef.org
Web Site: http://ccpef.org
To provide educational opportunities for individuals intending to pursue higher studies.
Title of Award: Sheila Tarr-Smith Memorial Scholarships **Area, Field, or Subject:** Public service. **Level of Education for which Award is Granted:** Undergraduate **Number Awarded:** 2. **Funds Available:** $2,500.
Eligibility Requirements: Applicants must be CCSD seniors planning to attend the University of Nevada, Las Vegas, as full-time students; must have a major related to public service; must have a minimum 3.4 unweighted cumulative GPA; and must demonstrate community service and financial need. **Application Requirements:** Applicants must submit a completed application form along with an essay, two letters of recommendation, transcript, and resume of awards. **Deadline for Receipt:** March 7. **Additional Information:** Shana Venenga at 702-799-1042.

4662 ■ PUBLIC EDUCATION FOUNDATION
3360 W Sahara Ave., Ste. 160
Las Vegas, NV 89102
Tel: (702)799-1042

Fax: (702)799-5247
E-mail: steelej@ccpef.org
Web Site: http://ccpef.org
To provide educational opportunities for individuals intending to pursue higher studies.
Title of Award: Judith Warner Memorial Scholarships **Area, Field, or Subject:** General studies. **Level of Education for which Award is Granted:** Undergraduate **Number Awarded:** 1. **Funds Available:** $600.
Eligibility Requirements: Applicants must be Rancho High School seniors planning to attend the University of Nevada, Las Vegas as full-time students; must have a minimum 2.5 cumulative GPA; and must demonstrate financial need. **Application Requirements:** Applicants must submit a completed application form along with an essay, two letters of recommendation, transcript, resume of awards, and letter of admission from UNLV. **Deadline for Receipt:** March 7. **Additional Information:** Shana Venenga at 702-799-1042.

4663 ■ PUBLIC RELATIONS SOCIETY OF AMERICA
33 Maiden Ln., 11th Fl.
New York, NY 10038-5150
Tel: (212)460-1474
Fax: (212)995-0757
E-mail: prssa@prsa.org
Web Site: http://www.prssa.org
To provide educational support for deserving students intending to pursue a career in public relations.
Title of Award: Betsy Plank/PRSSA Scholarships **Area, Field, or Subject:** Public relations. **Level of Education for which Award is Granted:** Undergraduate **Funds Available:** $4,250.
Eligibility Requirements: Program is open to PRSSA members who are enrolled in programs of public relations studies and are in their junior or senior year of undergraduate studies. **Application Requirements:** Application form and other supporting documents must be sent to PRSSA, Betsy Plank/PRSSA Scholarship, 33 Maiden Ln., 11th Fl., New York, NY 10038. **Deadline for Receipt:** June 2.

4664 ■ PUBLIC RELATIONS SOCIETY OF AMERICA
33 Maiden Ln., 11th Fl.
New York, NY 10038-5150
Tel: (212)460-1474
Fax: (212)995-0757
E-mail: prssa@prsa.org
Web Site: http://www.prssa.org
To provide educational assistance for qualified students intending to pursue a career in the field of public relations.
Title of Award: Stephen D. Pisinski Memorial Scholarships **Area, Field, or Subject:** Public relations; Journalism; Communications. **Level of Education for which Award is Granted:** Undergraduate **Funds Available:** $1,500.
Eligibility Requirements: Applicants must be majoring in journalism, communications, or public relations; must be junior or senior level only; must have at least a 3.3 overall GPA on a 4.0 system; must be members of the Public Relations Student Society of America, and leadership positions are a plus. **Application Requirements:** Applicants must submit a resume including any academic honors, special projects, activities and/or work experience or training; an official transcript of all college studies, including grades of the preceding semester; an essay of 1,000 words or less stating your career goals; two strong writing samples; and two letters of academic and/or professional recommendations. Application form and other required items must be sent to PRSSA Headquarters by Stephen D. Pininski Memorial Scholarship, Public Relations Student Society of America, 33 Maiden Ln., 11th Fl., New York, NY 10038. **Deadline for Receipt:** June 2.

4665 ■ PUBLIC RELATIONS SOCIETY OF AMERICA
33 Maiden Ln., 11th Fl.
New York, NY 10038-5150
Tel: (212)460-1474
Fax: (212)995-0757
E-mail: prssa@prsa.org
Web Site: http://www.prssa.org
To provide support to qualified PRSSA members who demonstrate a financial need for the pursuit of higher education in the public relations field.

Title of Award: Gary Yoshimura Scholarships **Area, Field, or Subject:** Public relations. **Level of Education for which Award is Granted:** Undergraduate **Funds Available:** $2,400. **Duration:** One year.
Eligibility Requirements: Applicants must have a minimum GPA of 3.0; must be a PRSSA member. **Application Requirements:** Application forms are available at the website. Applicants must submit an official transcript, a letter of recommendation from an internship supervisor/ employer or faculty advisor; must prepare a 1,000-word essay describing a challenge they have faced, either personally or professionally, and how they overcame it; must complete the statement of intent and financial need section. **Deadline for Receipt:** January 31.

4666 ■ SILICON VALLEY COMMUNITY FOUNDATION

2240 W El Camino Real Ste. 300
Mountain View, CA 94040-1498
Tel: (650)450-5400
Fax: (650)450-5401
Web Site: http://www.siliconvalleycf.org
To provide financial assistance to those students who are in need.
Title of Award: Fauneil J. Rinn Scholarships **Area, Field, or Subject:** Political Science; Public Administration. **Level of Education for which Award is Granted:** Undergraduate **Number Awarded:** 1. **Funds Available:** Up to $1,250.
Eligibility Requirements: Applicants must be women who are current students in good standing in the Political Science or Master of Public Administration programs at San Jose State University. **Application Requirements:** Applicants must check the available website for the required materials. **Additional Information:** Contact Terry Christensen, Professor, Department of Political Science, San Jose State University, at 408-924-5565 or at Terry.Christensen@sjsu.edu for more information or an application.

4667 ■ SOUTH CAROLINA PUBLIC HEALTH ASSOCIATION

1215 Anthony Ave.
Columbia, SC 29201
Tel: (803)540-7531
Fax: (803)254-3773
E-mail: scpha@queencommunicationsllc.com
Web Site: http://www.scpha.com
To protect and promote personal, community and environmental health; to exercise leadership in health policy development and action; to foster scientific and professional development among its members.
Title of Award: South Carolina Public Health Association Scholarships **Area, Field, or Subject:** Public Health. **Level of Education for which Award is Granted:** Undergraduate **Funds Available:** $750.
Eligibility Requirements: Applicants must be students enrolled in an accredited School of Public Health; must be current members in good standing of the South Carolina Public Health Association for at least the year in which the scholarship application is submitted; must have documentation of at least six hours of study remaining before graduation; must demonstrate great academic and professional promise; must achieve and maintain a GPA of 3.5 or better based on the 4.0 scale; must exhibit significant commitment to the public health profession through volunteer and/or professional activity such as involvement in community and scholarly activities and participation in related professional and/or student organizations. **Application Requirements:** Applicants must complete the application form; must write a personal statement of 250 words or less about their career goals and professional aspirations; must include current official transcript of records; must include proof of hours remaining before graduation. **Deadline for Receipt:** March 31. **Additional Information:** 803-545-4464.

4668 ■ TURKISH COALITION OF AMERICA

1025 Connecticut Ave. NW, Ste. 1000
Washington, DC 20036
Tel: (202)370-1399
Fax: (202)370-1398
E-mail: info@turkishcoalitionofamerica.org
Web Site: http://www.turkishcoalition.org
To engage and cultivate a new generation of young Turkish American leaders.
Title of Award: TCA Turkish American Scholarships **Area, Field, or Subject:** Public Affairs; Political Science; International Affairs and Rela-

tions; Communications; Printing Trades; Public Relations. **Level of Education for which Award is Granted:** Undergraduate **Funds Available:** No specific amount.
Eligibility Requirements: Applicants must meet the following criteria: be a U.S. citizen or permanent resident (green card holder); have, and maintain through the course of the scholarship period, a cumulative minimum 3.3 GPA on a 4.0 scale; evidence of leadership commitment through participation in community service, particularly within the Turkish American community; and be a high school senior applying to an accredited college or university, or college student who plans to continue undergraduate study; or a college senior or graduate enrolled or about to enroll in graduate school. Graduate students who apply for the TCA must plan to pursue studies and a career in public affairs. **Application Requirements:** Applicants must submit three (3) collated, non-stapled, paperclipped copies of each of the following items: (1) Completed Application Form (2) Resume: Each copy should be submitted on one single-sided 8.5" x 11" sheet of paper. (3) Short essay: The essay should not exceed 500 words, must be typed and double-spaced. **Deadline for Receipt:** June 6. **Additional Information:** Turkish Coalition of America at the above address.

4669 ■ UNIVERSITY OF ALASKA ANCHORAGE

3211 Providence Dr.
Anchorage, AK 99508
Tel: (907)786-1800
Web Site: http://www.uaa.alaska.edu
To provide financial assistance for tuition and other educational expenses to full-time students who are formally admitted to a degreeseeking program within the College of Business & Public Policy at the UAA.
Title of Award: UAA College of Business & Public Policy Scholarships **Area, Field, or Subject:** Business; Public service. **Level of Education for which Award is Granted:** Graduate, Undergraduate **Number Awarded:** 3. **Funds Available:** $500. **Duration:** One year.
Eligibility Requirements: Applicants must demonstrate motivation, academic and leadership potential; must be in good academic standing with a minimum cumulative GPA of 2.0 for undergraduates and 3.0 for graduates; must be formally admitted to an undergraduate, graduate, certificate, and/or vocational degree-seeking program within the College of Business & Public Policy at the UAA; must plan on enrolling full-time (12 credits for undergraduate and nine credits for graduate) at the UAA; may be an incoming or continuing student at the UAA; may be a U.S. citizen, non-U.S. citizen, Alaska resident, or out-of-state resident. **Application Requirements:** Applicants must complete the electronic scholarship application. **Deadline for Receipt:** February 15.

4670 ■ UNIVERSITY OF CALIFORNIA, BERKELEY

301B Campbell Hall No. 2922
Berkeley, CA 94720-2922
Tel: (510)643-6929
E-mail: scholarships@learning.berkeley.edu
Web Site: http://www.berkeley.edu
To encourage the graduating seniors to pursue the public service career of their choice.
Title of Award: John Gardner Fellowships **Area, Field, or Subject:** Public service. **Level of Education for which Award is Granted:** Undergraduate **Number Awarded:** 3. **Funds Available:** $27,500.
Eligibility Requirements: Applicant must be a senior graduating from the University of California, Berkeley; must be a United States citizen. **Application Requirements:** Applicant must submit one copy of the complete application form (available online); must have a formal resume; must have an official academic transcript; must have three letters of recommendation, at least one of which must be from a faculty member who is familiar with the applicant's university level work. Application materials must be sent to: Institute of Governmental Program, 111 Moses Hall, No. 2370, Berkeley, CA 94720-2370. **Deadline for Receipt:** February 27.

4671 ■ UNIVERSITY OF CALIFORNIA, BERKELEY

301B Campbell Hall No. 2922
Berkeley, CA 94720-2922
Tel: (510)643-6929
E-mail: scholarships@learning.berkeley.edu
Web Site: http://www.berkeley.edu

To encourage junior students to pursue a public service career of their choice.

Title of Award: Donald A. Strauss Scholarships **Area, Field, or Subject:** Public service. **Level of Education for which Award is Granted:** Undergraduate **Funds Available:** $10,000.

Eligibility Requirements: Applicant must be a full-time junior; must be in the upper third class (typically a minimum 3.3 GPA); must have plan to devote significant part of life to public service. **Application Requirements:** Applicant must complete the application form (available online); must have one-page resume that includes work history and community service experience; must have one-page autobiographical statement; must have four-page proposal for a community service project; must have completed the acceptance form; must have two or three letters of recommendation from individuals who are well-acquainted worth the student's academic and/or service work; must have an official copies of all college transcripts. **Deadline for Receipt:** February 15.

4672 ■ UNIVERSITY OF NORTH CAROLINA SCHOOL OF JOURNALISM AND MASS COMMUNICATION
University of North Carolina, Carol Hall CB 3365
Chapel Hill, NC 27599-3365
Tel: (919)962-1204
Fax: (919)962-0620
E-mail: jomc@unc.edu
Web Site: http://www.jomc.unc.edu
To educate journalists.

Title of Award: Rick Brewer Scholarships **Area, Field, or Subject:** Broadcasting; Journalism; Public relations. **Level of Education for which Award is Granted:** Undergraduate **Funds Available:** $1,000.

Eligibility Requirements: Applicants must be undergraduate students with a keen interest in pursuing a career in sports journalism, broadcasting, or public relations. **Application Requirements:** Applicants must complete the application form.

4673 ■ UNIVERSITY OF NORTH CAROLINA SCHOOL OF JOURNALISM AND MASS COMMUNICATION
University of North Carolina, Carol Hall CB 3365
Chapel Hill, NC 27599-3365
Tel: (919)962-1204
Fax: (919)962-0620
E-mail: jomc@unc.edu
Web Site: http://www.jomc.unc.edu
To educate journalists.

Title of Award: Louis M. Connor Jr. Scholarships **Area, Field, or Subject:** Public relations. **Level of Education for which Award is Granted:** Undergraduate **Funds Available:** $3,000.

Eligibility Requirements: Applicants must be enrolled or plan to enroll in university and have an at least 2.9 GPA. **Application Requirements:** Applicants must complete the application form. **Deadline for Receipt:** February 1. **Additional Information:** PO Box 1080, Chapel Hill, NC 27514-1080.

4674 ■ WASHINGTON UNIVERSITY LAW SCHOOL
Campus Box 1120
One Brookings Dr.
St. Louis, MO 63130-4899
Tel: (314)935-6400
E-mail: eckrich@wulaw.wustl.edu
Web Site: http://www.law.wustl.edu
To provide financial assistance to public service students who wish to continue their education.

Title of Award: Walter Moran Farmer Scholarships **Area, Field, or Subject:** Public service. **Level of Education for which Award is Granted:** Undergraduate **Funds Available:** No specific amount.

Eligibility Requirements: Applicants must be the first generation of their families to attend college or graduate school. **Application Requirements:** Applicant must submit an application letter and other requirements.

4675 ■ WASHINGTON UNIVERSITY LAW SCHOOL
Campus Box 1120
One Brookings Dr.
St. Louis, MO 63130-4899

Tel: (314)935-6400
E-mail: eckrich@wulaw.wustl.edu
Web Site: http://www.law.wustl.edu
To provide financial assistance to public service students who wish to continue their education.

Title of Award: Webster Society Scholarships **Area, Field, or Subject:** Public service. **Level of Education for which Award is Granted:** Undergraduate **Funds Available:** Full tuition scholarship.

Eligibility Requirements: Applicants must be entering first-year JD students with exemplary academic credentials and an established commitment to public service. **Application Requirements:** Interested applicants should write a short statement summarizing their involvement in public service activities. **Deadline for Receipt:** February 1.

Social Work

4676 ■ BLACK BUSINESS AND PROFESSIONAL ASSOCIATION
675 King St. W, Ste. 210
Toronto, ON, Canada M5V 1M9
Tel: (416)504-4097
Fax: (416)504-7343
E-mail: bbpa@bellnet.ca
Web Site: http://www.bbpa.org
To provide support for Black Canadian students.

Title of Award: Tropicana Community Services - Robert K. Brown Scholarships **Area, Field, or Subject:** Social work. **Level of Education for which Award is Granted:** Undergraduate **Funds Available:** $1,500. **Duration:** One year.

Eligibility Requirements: Applicant must be enrolled in a course of study in the field of social services; must be a Canadian citizen or a permanent resident; must be 17 to 30 years of age; and must be enrolled in a full-time degree (graduate or undergraduate), diploma or certificate program at a Canadian college or university for the academic year. **Application Requirements:** Applicants must complete the application form and submit along with a letter describing the reasons why they would be worthy recipients of a BBPA National Scholarship; a completed financial information schedule stating their budget for the coming year including information on their expected sources of funding, family income and related information; and a letter of reference from the two individuals named in their application (must be a teacher from their high school, college or university, and an individual who is familiar with their community service). Application form and requirements must be sent to The Board of Trustees, BBPA National Scholarship Fund, 675 King St., W, Ste. 210, Toronto, ON M5V 1M9. **Deadline for Receipt:** May 30.

4677 ■ THE COMMUNITY FOUNDATION OF MIDDLE TENNESSEE
3833 Cleghorn Ave., Ste. 400
Nashville, TN 37215-2519
Tel: (615)321-4939; 888-540-5200
E-mail: mail@cfmt.org
Web Site: http://www.cfmt.org
To help students in planning their postsecondary education.

Title of Award: Maude Keisling/Cumberland County Extension Homemakers Scholarships **Area, Field, or Subject:** Ecology; Education; Social work. **Level of Education for which Award is Granted:** Undergraduate **Funds Available:** No specific amount.

Eligibility Requirements: Applicants must be residents of Cumberland County, Tennessee for a period of four years or more. Applicants must be graduating high school seniors, GED graduates, or current college undergraduates with a GPA of 2.5 or better. Applicants must pursue a field of study such as, but not limited to, human ecology, family and consumer science, education, and social services. **Application Requirements:** Applicants must complete the application form. Applicants must submit two applicant appraisals; transcript of grades; student essay describing educational plans and how these will help in career goals. Applicants must submit one recent photograph. **Deadline for Receipt:** March 15. **Additional Information:** pcole@cfmt.org

4678 ■ DADE COMMUNITY FOUNDATION, INC.
200 S Biscayne Blvd., Ste. 505
Miami, FL 33131-2343

Tel: (305)371-2711
Fax: (305)371-5342
Web Site: http://www.dadecommunityfoundation.org
To provide financial assistance to students at Miami Springs Senior High School who are enrolled in a college program related to public education, political science, history or social work.
Title of Award: Randy Green Memorial Scholarship Fund **Area, Field, or Subject:** Political science; economics; Social work. **Level of Education for which Award is Granted:** High School **Number Awarded:** 2. **Funds Available:** $1,000. **Duration:** One year.
Eligibility Requirements: Applicants must be permanent residents or citizens of the U.S. and domiciled in South Florida; must have minimum high school grade point average of 3.0; must be Miami Springs high-school seniors demonstrating merit and financial need; must be accepted into accredited university and plan to be enrolled in two year or four year university programs concentrating in public education, political science, history, social work, or other major related to community service. **Application Requirements:** Applicants must submit the completed application form and all other required application information. **Deadline for Receipt:** June 3.

4679 ■ FOUNDATION FOR ENHANCING COMMUNITIES
200 N Third St., PO Box 678
Harrisburg, PA 17108-0678
Tel: (717)236-5040
Fax: (717)231-4463
E-mail: dawn@tfec.org
Web Site: http://www.ghf.org
To provide financial assistance for Lebanon County residents pursuing higher education degrees.
Title of Award: Family and Children's Services of Lebanon County Fund **Area, Field, or Subject:** Medicine; Nursing, Social work, Mental health. **Level of Education for which Award is Granted:** Undergraduate **Funds Available:** No specific amount.
Eligibility Requirements: Applicants must be enrolled full-time in schools of advanced education in the fields of medicine, nursing, social work, mental health and other specialized therapies in the treatment of physical and mental disabilities; must demonstrate financial need, academic aptitude and achievement, and commitment to a career in human services; and must be residents of Lebanon County. **Application Requirements:** Applicants may obtain the application online. Applicants must provide the most recent, either a certified high school transcript or a certified college transcript. **Additional Information:** Dawn Morris, Program Officer; 717-236-5040; dawn@tfec.org.

4680 ■ JEWISH VOCATIONAL SERVICE
216 W Jackson Blvd., Ste. 700
Chicago, IL 60606
Tel: (312)673-3400
Fax: (312)553-5544
E-mail: jvs@jvschicago.org
Web Site: http://www.jvschicago.org
To support the education of a Jewish college or graduate student.
Title of Award: Jewish Federation Academic Scholarships **Area, Field, or Subject:** Medicine; Education; Social work; Arts; Public health; Urban affairs/design/planning; Law. **Level of Education for which Award is Granted:** Graduate, Undergraduate **Funds Available:** More than $500,000 each year.
Eligibility Requirements: Applicant must be Jewish; be born or raised in either: Cook County, Chicago metropolitan area, or Northwest Indiana; or have one continuous year of full-time employment in Cook County or Chicago metropolitan area prior to starting professional education; must intend to remain in the Chicago metropolitan area after completing school; must be entering as a full-time student in an accredited professional graduate program or entering as junior or senior undergraduate student at an accredited professional education program; and must be demonstrating career promise in a helping profession. **Application Requirements:** Applicants must submit a completed Application Data Form; Career Statement Form; Budget Worksheet; and Academic Budget form as an attachment to jvsscholarship@jvschicago.org. In addition, applicants must send by mail a Legal Domicility Form; two letter of reference form; IRS Forms; parents' or spouse's IRS; documentation of tuition cost; Release of Information form; and official transcripts. **Deadline for Receipt:** February 15. **Additional Information:** 312-673-3457.

4681 ■ MENTAL HEALTH ASSOCIATION OF TARRANT COUNTY
3136 W St.
Fort Worth, TX 76107
Tel: (817)335-5405
Fax: (817)334-0025
E-mail: mhatc@mhatc.org
Web Site: http://www.mhatc.org
To provide financial support to those students pursuing a degree in the mental health field.
Title of Award: Patricia Pownder Conolly Memorial Scholarships **Area, Field, or Subject:** Psychiatry; Psychology; Sociology; Social work; Counseling; Rehabilitation counseling. **Level of Education for which Award is Granted:** Undergraduate **Funds Available:** No specific amount.
Eligibility Requirements: Applicants must be college students pursuing a degree in the mental health field. **Application Requirements:** Applicants must check the available website to download the application form. **Additional Information:** Mental Health Association of Tarrant County at the above address.

4682 ■ MENTAL HEALTH ASSOCIATION OF TARRANT COUNTY
3136 W St.
Fort Worth, TX 76107
Tel: (817)335-5405
Fax: (817)334-0025
E-mail: mhatc@mhatc.org
Web Site: http://www.mhatc.org
To provide financial support to those students pursuing a degree in the mental health field.
Title of Award: Linda Lyons Memorial Scholarship Fund **Area, Field, or Subject:** Psychiatry; Psychology; Sociology; Social work; Counseling; Rehabilitation counseling. **Level of Education for which Award is Granted:** Undergraduate **Funds Available:** No specific amount.
Eligibility Requirements: Applicants must be college students pursuing a degree in the mental health field. **Application Requirements:** Applicants must check the available website to download the application form. **Additional Information:** Mental Health Association of Tarrant County at the above address.

4683 ■ NATIONAL ASSOCIATION OF BLACK SOCIAL WORKERS
2305 Martin Luther King Ave. SE
Washington, DC 20020
Tel: (202)678-4570
Fax: (202)678-4572
E-mail: nabsw.harambee@verizon.net
Web Site: http://www.nabsw.org
To provide financial assistance for African-American students who are active in community service and planning to work in the field of social work.
Title of Award: Emma and Meloid Algood Tuition Scholarships **Area, Field, or Subject:** Social work. **Level of Education for which Award is Granted:** Undergraduate **Number Awarded:** 1. **Funds Available:** $1,000.
Eligibility Requirements: Applicants must be African-American students who have a 2.5 grade point average on a 4.0 scale; must express research interest in the black community; and must be enrolled for full-time study at an accredited US Bachelors of Social Work program in the semester that the award will be granted. **Application Requirements:** Applicants must submit a purpose letter (two to three pages, double-spaced, typewritten) which must include the following: professional interests, future social work aspirations, previous social work experiences, honors and achievements, research interests within the black community; two letters of recommendation, preferably by a professor, field instructor, or a prestigious community-based leader; financial need statement with a breakdown of students' assets and liabilities; and an official academic transcript from the school.

4684 ■ NATIONAL ASSOCIATION OF BLACK SOCIAL WORKERS
2305 Martin Luther King Ave. SE
Washington, DC 20020
Tel: (202)678-4570
Fax: (202)678-4572
E-mail: nabsw.harambee@verizon.net
Web Site: http://www.nabsw.org

To provide financial assistance for individuals completing graduate work and to develop professional skills and talent to work in the African-American community.

Title of Award: Dr. Joyce Beckett Scholarships **Area, Field, or Subject:** Social work. **Level of Education for which Award is Granted:** Undergraduate **Number Awarded:** 1. **Funds Available:** $1,000.

Eligibility Requirements: Applicants must be African-American students who have a 2.5 GPA on 4.0 scale; must express research interest in the black community; and must be enrolled for full-time study at an accredited US graduate social work program in the semester that the award will be granted. **Application Requirements:** Applicants must submit a purpose letter (two to three pages, double-spaced, typewritten) which must include the following: professional interests, future social work aspirations, previous social work experiences, honors and achievements, research interests within the black community; must submit two letters of recommendation, preferably by a professor, field instructor, or a prestigious community-based leader; financial need statement with a breakdown of students' assets and liabilities; and an official academic transcript from the school.

4685 ■ NATIONAL ASSOCIATION OF BLACK SOCIAL WORKERS

2305 Martin Luther King Ave. SE
Washington, DC 20020
Tel: (202)678-4570
Fax: (202)678-4572
E-mail: nabsw.harambee@verizon.net
Web Site: http://www.nabsw.org

To provide financial assistance for African-American students who are active in community service.

Title of Award: Selena Danette Brown Book Scholarships **Area, Field, or Subject:** Social work. **Level of Education for which Award is Granted:** Undergraduate **Number Awarded:** 4. **Funds Available:** $250.

Eligibility Requirements: Applicants must be active, paid members of NABSW; must be African-American students who have a 2.5 Grade Point Average on a 4.0 scale; must express research interest in the black community; and must be enrolled for full-time study at an accredited US social work program in the semester that the award will be granted. **Application Requirements:** Applicants must submit a purpose letter (two to three pages, double-spaced, and typewritten) which must include the following: professional interests, future social work aspirations, previous social work experiences, honors and achievements, research interests within the black community; must submit two letters of recommendation, preferably by a professor, field instructor, or a prestigious community-based leader; financial need statement with a breakdown of students' assets and liabilities; and an official academic transcript from the school.

4686 ■ NATIONAL ASSOCIATION OF BLACK SOCIAL WORKERS

2305 Martin Luther King Ave. SE
Washington, DC 20020
Tel: (202)678-4570
Fax: (202)678-4572
E-mail: nabsw.harambee@verizon.net
Web Site: http://www.nabsw.org

To provide financial assistance for African-American students who are active in community service and planning to work in the field of social work.

Title of Award: Guynn Family Foundation Book Scholarships **Area, Field, or Subject:** Social work. **Level of Education for which Award is Granted:** Undergraduate **Number Awarded:** 1. **Funds Available:** $750.

Eligibility Requirements: Applicants must be African-American students who have a 3.0 grade point average on a 4.0 scale; must perform 40 hours of community service in an underserved African-American community; must express research interest in the black community; and must be enrolled for full-time study at an accredited US social work program in the semester that the award will be granted. **Application Requirements:** Applicants must submit a purpose letter (two to three pages, double-spaced, typewritten) which must include the following: professional interests, future social work aspirations, previous social work experiences, honors and achievements, research interests within the black community; must submit two letters of recommendation, preferably by a professor, field instructor, or a prestigious community-based leader; financial need statement with a breakdown of students' assets and liabilities; and an official academic transcript from the school.

4687 ■ NATIONAL ASSOCIATION OF BLACK SOCIAL WORKERS

2305 Martin Luther King Ave. SE
Washington, DC 20020
Tel: (202)678-4570
Fax: (202)678-4572
E-mail: nabsw.harambee@verizon.net
Web Site: http://www.nabsw.org

To provide financial assistance for African-American students who are active in community service.

Title of Award: Cenie Jomo Williams Tuition Scholarships **Area, Field, or Subject:** Social work. **Level of Education for which Award is Granted:** Undergraduate **Number Awarded:** 2. **Funds Available:** $2,000.

Eligibility Requirements: Applicants must be active, paid members of NABSW; must be students who have a 2.5 grade point average on a 4.0 scale; must be African-American students with demonstrated community service; must be students who will conduct research of interest to the black community; and must be enrolled for full-time study at an accredited US social work program in the semester that the award will be granted. **Application Requirements:** Applicants must submit a purpose letter (two to three pages, double-spaced, and typewritten) which must include the following: professional interests, future social work aspirations, previous social work experiences, honors and achievements, research interests within the black community; must submit two letters of recommendation, preferably by a professor, field instructor, or a prestigious community-based leader; financial need statement with a breakdown of students' assets and liabilities; and an official academic transcript from the school.

4688 ■ PORTUGUESE AMERICAN POLICE ASSOCIATION

PO Box 51523
New Bedford, MA 02745-0045
Tel: (508)994-5390
E-mail: info@papamass.org
Web Site: http://www.papamass.org

To provide support for deserving students intending to pursue a career in either Health Care, Social Service, Law Enforcement, or other related fields.

Title of Award: Portuguese American Police Association Scholarships **Area, Field, or Subject:** Health care services, Social work, Law enforcement. **Level of Education for which Award is Granted:** Undergraduate **Number Awarded:** 6. **Funds Available:** $500. **Duration:** One year.

Eligibility Requirements: Applicant must be a Portuguese descent; must be a resident of Massachusetts; must be enrolled full-time in an accredited college or university or a graduating senior applying to full-time status in an accredited or another college or university; must be majoring in either health care, social services, law enforcement or another related field; must maintain a GPA of 2.0 or higher. **Application Requirements:** Application forms are available online. Applicant must submit an essay of no more than three paragraphs stating the reason stating their career goals; must have a high school transcript that includes the class rank; must have the current college/university transcript; must have a letter of reference from each of the following: (1) Guidance counselor or advisor and (2) Personal reference, preferably from someone with whom the applicants have work. Application materials must be sent to: Scholarship Committee, Portuguese American Police Association, Inc., PO Box 51523, New Bedford, MA 02745-0045. **Deadline for Receipt:** June 1.

4689 ■ PRIDE FOUNDATION

PO Box 2194, 1122 E Pike St. PMB 1001
Seattle, WA 98112
Tel: (206)323-3318
Free: 800-735-7287
Fax: (206)323-1017
E-mail: prideweb@pridefoundation.org
Web Site: http://www.pridefoundation.org

To provide scholarship to the students who have been stigmatized, isolated or closeted because of sexual identity issues.

Title of Award: Social Work Scholarships **Area, Field, or Subject:** Social work. **Level of Education for which Award is Granted:** Graduate, Undergraduate **Funds Available:** No specific amount.

Eligibility Requirements: Applicants must be gay, lesbian or transgender students enrolled or admitted to a C.S.W.E. accredited bachelors or masters social work degree program or to a doctoral program in social work. Preference given to students of color. **Application Requirements:**

Qualified students are asked to submit an application to determine eligibility for scholarships. Applicants may download an application form from the Foundation's website. **Additional Information:** Pride Foundation at the above address.

4690 ■ SAFE SCHOOLS COALITION
1002 E Seneca St.
Seattle, WA 98122-4203
Tel: (206)957-1621
Fax: (206)325-2689
Web Site: http://www.safeschoolscoalition.org
To provide financial assistance for transgender-identified students.
Title of Award: Transgender Scholarships and Education Legacy Fund **Area, Field, or Subject:** Social Services; Health Care Services; Religious Education; Teaching; Law. **Level of Education for which Award is Granted:** Undergraduate **Funds Available:** No specific amount.
Eligibility Requirements: Applicants must be students of one of these fields of studies. **Application Requirements:** Applicants must check the contact information for more inquiries. **Additional Information:** The awards are sponsored by the International Foundation for Gender Education. **Deadline for Receipt:** February 1. **Additional Information:** International Foundation for Gender Education (IFGE) TSELF Awards Committee PO Box 540229 Waltham, MA 02454-0229 Phone: 781-899-2212
Fax: 781-899-2212 URL: www.tself.org.

4691 ■ UNIVERSITY OF TORONTO
315 Bloor St. W
Toronto, ON, Canada M5S 1A3
Tel: (416)978-2011
E-mail: information.commonsats@utoronto.ca
Web Site: http://www.utoronto.ca
To support students with their educational pursuits.
Title of Award: Joseph McCulley Educational Scholarships **Area, Field, or Subject:** Social work. **Level of Education for which Award is Granted:** Graduate, Undergraduate **Funds Available:** Variable in value, to the total of the annual income.
Eligibility Requirements: Applicant must be a U of T graduate or undergraduate student whose programs of study and career interests lie in the area of public life or social work, emphasizing on penology. **Application Requirements:** Applicants must submit a completed application form together with the required materials and information. **Deadline for Receipt:** November 30.

Urban Affairs

4692 ■ AMERICAN PLANNING ASSOCIATION
122 S Michigan Ave., Ste. 1600
Chicago, IL 60603
Tel: (312)431-9100
Fax: (312)431-9985
E-mail: customerservice@planning.org
Web Site: http://www.planning.org
To provide partial funding for women and minority students.
Title of Award: Judith McManus Price Scholarships **Area, Field, or Subject:** Urban affairs/design/planning. **Level of Education for which Award is Granted:** Graduate, Undergraduate **Funds Available:** $2000-$4000. **Duration:** One year.
Eligibility Requirements: Applicants must be U.S. citizens enrolled in Planning Accreditation Board accredited planning programs. Candidates must also be women members of the following minority groups: African American, Hispanic American or Native American. **Application Requirements:** Applicant must submit a two- to five-page background statement describing how the applicant's graduate education will be applied to career goals and why he/she chose planning as a career path; a completed and signed APA financial aid application; two letters of recommendation; written verification from the school's financial officer indicating the average cost of one academic year; resume; copy of acceptance letter from a PAB-accredited graduate planning school; a notarized statement of financial independence signed by the applicant's parents. **Additional Information:** The award also includes a paid one-year student membership to APA. **Deadline for Receipt:** April 30. **Additional Information:** Kriss Blank at the above address.

4693 ■ JEWISH VOCATIONAL SERVICE
216 W Jackson Blvd., Ste. 700
Chicago, IL 60606
Tel: (312)673-3400
Fax: (312)553-5544
E-mail: jvs@jvschicago.org
Web Site: http://www.jvschicago.org
To support the education of a Jewish college or graduate student.
Title of Award: Jewish Federation Academic Scholarships **Area, Field, or Subject:** Medicine; Education; Social work; Arts; Public health; Urban affairs/design/planning; Law. **Level of Education for which Award is Granted:** Graduate, Undergraduate **Funds Available:** More than $500,000 each year.
Eligibility Requirements: Applicant must be Jewish; be born or raised in either: Cook County, Chicago metropolitan area, or Northwest Indiana; or have one continuous year of full-time employment in Cook County or Chicago metropolitan area prior to starting professional education; must intend to remain in the Chicago metropolitan area after completing school; must be entering as a full-time student in an accredited professional graduate program or entering as junior or senior undergraduate student at an accredited professional education program; and must be demonstrating career promise in a helping profession. **Application Requirements:** Applicants must submit a completed Application Data Form; Career Statement Form; Budget Worksheet; and Academic Budget form as an attachment to jvsscholarship@jvschicago.org. In addition, applicants must send by mail a Legal Domicility Form; two letter of reference form; IRS Forms; parents' or spouse's IRS; documentation of tuition cost; Release of Information form; and official transcripts. **Deadline for Receipt:** February 15. **Additional Information:** 312-673-3457.

4694 ■ NATIONAL FORUM FOR BLACK PUBLIC ADMINISTRATORS
777 N Capitol St. NE, Ste. 807
Washington, DC 20002
Tel: (202)408-9300
Fax: (202)408-8558
E-mail: webmaster@nfbpa.org
Web Site: http://www.nfbpa.org
To support the education and development of African-American students and prepare them for careers in public administration.
Title of Award: CIGNA Healthcare Undergraduate Scholarships **Area, Field, or Subject:** Public administration; Political science; Urban affairs/design/planning. **Level of Education for which Award is Granted:** Undergraduate **Number Awarded:** 1. **Funds Available:** $1,000.
Eligibility Requirements: Applicants must be full-time students, working towards an undergraduate degree in public administration, political science, urban affairs, public policy, or a related field preferably at an HBCU with excellent interpersonal and analytical abilities, strong oral and written communication skills and a 3.5 or better grade point average for completed 1 full-time college semester and at least 1 full-time academic year. **Application Requirements:** Applicants must submit a cover letter describing your current student status and other relevant information that might be used in evaluating the application (extra-curricular activities, volunteer activities, etc); official copies of all undergraduate transcripts; scores from the American College Testing (ACT) program or the Scholastic Aptitude Test (SAT) administered by the College Entrance Examination Board; a copy of their Application for Federal Student Aid (FASFA); two (2) reference letters (at least one of which should be from a faculty member); three-page essay detailing his/her autobiography and career goals and objectives; three-page essay answering the question: In your opinion, what are the five most critical skills public administrators ought to possess, and why?; and a current resume. **Deadline for Receipt:** February 27.

4695 ■ NATIONAL FORUM FOR BLACK PUBLIC ADMINISTRATORS
777 N Capitol St. NE, Ste. 807
Washington, DC 20002
Tel: (202)408-9300
Fax: (202)408-8558
E-mail: webmaster@nfbpa.org
Web Site: http://www.nfbpa.org
To support the education and development of African-American students and prepare them for careers in public administration.
Title of Award: McKinley Financial Scholarships **Area, Field, or Subject:** Public administration. **Level of Education for which Award is Granted:**

Graduate, Undergraduate **Funds Available:** $1,000.
Eligibility Requirements: Applicants must be full-time students, working towards an undergraduate or graduate degree in public administration, political science, urban affairs, public policy or a related field with excellent interpersonal and analytical abilities, strong oral and written communication skills and 3.0 or better grade point average for at least 1 full time remaining semester. **Application Requirements:** Applicants must submit a cover letter describing current student status and other relevant information that might be used in evaluating the application (extra-curricular activities, volunteer activities, etc.); official copies of all graduate (if applicable) and undergraduate transcripts; two reference letters (at least one of which should be from a faculty member); three-page essay detailing his/her autobiography and career goals and objectives; and a current resume. **Deadline for Receipt:** February 27.

General

4696 ■ AMERICAN ASSOCIATION OF TEXTILE CHEMISTS AND COLORISTS
PO Box 12215
Research Triangle Park, NC 27709-2215
Tel: (919)549-8141
Fax: (919)549-8933
Web Site: http://www.aatcc.org
To provide financial assistance to junior or senior students who reside in NC, SC, VA or WV and attend North Carolina State University or Clemson University.
Title of Award: Charles H. Stone Scholarships **Area, Field, or Subject:** Textile science. **Level of Education for which Award is Granted:** Undergraduate **Funds Available:** $5,000. **Duration:** One year.
Eligibility Requirements: Applicants must be U.S. citizens; junior or senior students in an undergraduate program; must have a minimum GPA of 2.85 on a 4.0 scale; must be a Textile Chemistry undergraduate in Dyeing/Fiber Science/Polymers/Color Science; must be Piedmont Section Textile employees. **Application Requirements:** Applicants must submit all the required application information.

4697 ■ AMERICAN INDIAN GRADUATE CENTER SCHOLARS (AIGCS)
4520 Montgomery Blvd., NE, Ste. 1B
Albuquerque, NM 87109
Tel: (505)881-4584
Free: 800-628-1920
Web Site: http://www.aigc.com
To provide financial assistance to American Indian tribe or Alaska Native group in furthering their education.
Title of Award: Wal-Mart Stores, Inc. Fellowships - Graduate **Area, Field, or Subject:** Banking; Gaming industry; Management; Accounting; Finance; Information science and technology; Human resource.s **Level of Education for which Award is Granted:** Undergraduate **Funds Available:** No specific amount.
Eligibility Requirements: Applicants must be enrolled members of a United States federally-recognized American Indian tribe or Alaska Native group; pursuing a career and degree in fields relating to banking, resort management, gaming operations, management and administration, including accounting, finance, information technology, and human resources. Full-time graduate students at U.S. accredited colleges or universities with a cumulative GPA of 3.0 on 4.0 scale at the time of application are eligible. **Application Requirements:** Applicants must submit all the required application information.

4698 ■ AMERICAN RADIO RELAY LEAGUE (ARRL) FOUNDATION
225 Main St.
Newington, CT 06111
Tel: (860)594-0200
Fax: (860)594-0259
E-mail: foundation@arrl.org
Web Site: http://www.arrlf.org
To support the education of students holding a valid FCC-granted Amateur Radio license for post-secondary education.

Title of Award: ARRLF Mississippi Scholarships **Area, Field, or Subject:** Radio and television; Electronics; Communications. **Level of Education for which Award is Granted:** Undergraduate **Number Awarded:** 1. **Funds Available:** $500.
Eligibility Requirements: Applicant must hold an FCC amateur radio license; be a Mississippi resident; be studying in baccalaureate or higher courses of study in electronics, communications or related fields; and be under 30 years of age. **Application Requirements:** Applicants must submit a completed scholarship application form along with a recent high school (or equivalent) or college transcript. **Deadline for Receipt:** February 1.

4699 ■ AMERICAN RADIO RELAY LEAGUE (ARRL) FOUNDATION
225 Main St.
Newington, CT 06111
Tel: (860)594-0200
Fax: (860)594-0259
E-mail: foundation@arrl.org
Web Site: http://www.arrlf.org
To support the education of students holding a valid FCC-granted Amateur Radio license for post-secondary education.
Title of Award: Irvine W. Cook WA0CGS Scholarships **Area, Field, or Subject:** Radio and television; Electronics; Communications. **Level of Education for which Award is Granted:** Undergraduate **Number Awarded:** 1. **Funds Available:** $1,000.
Eligibility Requirements: Applicant must hold an FCC amateur radio license; residency in Kansas; and be studying baccalaureate or higher courses in electronics, communications or a related field. **Application Requirements:** Applicants must submit a completed scholarship application form along with a recent high school (or equivalent) or college transcript. **Deadline for Receipt:** February 1.

4700 ■ AMERICAN RADIO RELAY LEAGUE (ARRL) FOUNDATION
225 Main St.
Newington, CT 06111
Tel: (860)594-0200
Fax: (860)594-0259
E-mail: foundation@arrl.org
Web Site: http://www.arrlf.org
To support the education of students holding a valid FCC-granted Amateur Radio license for post-secondary education.
Title of Award: Charles Clarke Cordle Memorial Scholarships **Area, Field, or Subject:** Radio and television; Electronics; Communications. **Level of Education for which Award is Granted:** Undergraduate **Number Awarded:** 1. **Funds Available:** $1,000.
Eligibility Requirements: Applicant must hold an FCC amateur radio license; be a resident of Georgia or Alabama; have a GPA of 2.5 or higher; and be attending an institution in Georgia or Alabama. **Application Requirements:** Applicants must submit a completed scholarship application form along with a recent high school (or equivalent) or college transcript. **Deadline for Receipt:** February 1.

4701 ■ AMERICAN RADIO RELAY LEAGUE (ARRL) FOUNDATION
225 Main St.
Newington, CT 06111

Tel: (860)594-0200
Fax: (860)594-0259
E-mail: foundation@arrl.org
Web Site: http://www.arrlf.org
To support the education of students holding a valid FCC-granted Amateur Radio license for post-secondary education.
Title of Award: Charles N. Fisher Memorial Scholarships **Area, Field, or Subject:** Radio and television; Electronics; Communications. **Level of Education for which Award is Granted:** Undergraduate **Number Awarded:** 1. **Funds Available:** $1,000.
Eligibility Requirements: Applicant must hold an FCC amateur radio license; must be a resident of ARRL Southwestern Division (AZ, Los Angeles, Orange, San Diego, Santa Barbara); studying in electronics, communications or related fields. **Application Requirements:** Applicants must submit a completed scholarship application form along with a recent high school (or equivalent) or college transcript. **Deadline for Receipt:** February 1.

4702 ■ AMERICAN RADIO RELAY LEAGUE (ARRL) FOUNDATION
225 Main St.
Newington, CT 06111
Tel: (860)594-0200
Fax: (860)594-0259
E-mail: foundation@arrl.org
Web Site: http://www.arrlf.org
To support the education of students holding a valid FCC-granted Amateur Radio license for post secondary-education.
Title of Award: Paul and Helen L. Grauer Scholarships **Area, Field, or Subject:** Radio and television; Electronics; Communications. **Level of Education for which Award is Granted:** Undergraduate **Number Awarded:** 1. **Funds Available:** $1,000.
Eligibility Requirements: Applicant must hold an FCC amateur radio license; be a resident of ARRL Midwest Division (IA, KS, MO, NE); be studying in baccalaureate or higher courses in electronics, communications or related field; and be attending school in the Midwest Division. **Application Requirements:** Applicants must submit a completed scholarship application form along with a recent high school (or equivalent) or college transcript. **Deadline for Receipt:** February 1.

4703 ■ AMERICAN RADIO RELAY LEAGUE (ARRL) FOUNDATION
225 Main St.
Newington, CT 06111
Tel: (860)594-0200
Fax: (860)594-0259
E-mail: foundation@arrl.org
Web Site: http://www.arrlf.org
To support the education of students holding a valid FCC-granted Amateur Radio license for post-secondary education.
Title of Award: IRARC Memorial Joseph P. Rubino WA4MMD Scholarships **Area, Field, or Subject:** Radio and television; Electronics. **Level of Education for which Award is Granted:** Undergraduate **Funds Available:** $750.
Eligibility Requirements: Applicant must hold an FCC amateur radio license; have a minimum 2.5 GPA on a 4.0 scale; and be enrolled in an undergraduate degree or electronic technician certification program at an accredited institution. **Application Requirements:** Applicants must submit a completed scholarship application form along with a recent high school (or equivalent) or college transcript. **Deadline for Receipt:** February 1.

4704 ■ AMERICAN RADIO RELAY LEAGUE (ARRL) FOUNDATION
225 Main St.
Newington, CT 06111
Tel: (860)594-0200
Fax: (860)594-0259
E-mail: foundation@arrl.org
Web Site: http://www.arrlf.org
To support the education of students holding a valid FCC-granted Amateur Radio license for post-secondary education.
Title of Award: Dr. James L. Lawson Memorial Scholarships **Area, Field, or Subject:** Radio and television Electronics; Communications. **Level of Education for which Award is Granted:** Undergraduate **Number Awarded:** 1. **Funds Available:** $500.

Eligibility Requirements: Applicant must hold an FCC amateur radio license; be a resident of one of the New England states (ME, NH, VT, CT, RI) or New York State; and be studying in baccalaureate or higher courses in electronics, communications or related fields. **Application Requirements:** Applicants must submit a completed scholarship application form along with a recent high school (or equivalent) or college transcript. **Deadline for Receipt:** February 1.

4705 ■ AMERICAN RADIO RELAY LEAGUE (ARRL) FOUNDATION
225 Main St.
Newington, CT 06111
Tel: (860)594-0200
Fax: (860)594-0259
E-mail: foundation@arrl.org
Web Site: http://www.arrlf.org
To support the education of students holding a valid FCC-granted Amateur Radio license for post-secondary education.
Title of Award: Fred R. McDaniel Memorial Scholarships **Area, Field, or Subject:** Radio and television; Electronics; Communications. **Level of Education for which Award is Granted:** Undergraduate **Number Awarded:** 1. **Funds Available:** $500.
Eligibility Requirements: Applicant must hold an FCC amateur radio license; be a resident of the FCC 5th call district (TX, OK, AR, LA, MS, NM); be studying in baccalaureate or higher courses of study in electronics, communications or related fields. **Application Requirements:** Applicants must submit a completed scholarship application form along with a recent high school (or equivalent) or college transcript. **Deadline for Receipt:** February 1.

4706 ■ AMERICAN RADIO RELAY LEAGUE (ARRL) FOUNDATION
225 Main St.
Newington, CT 06111
Tel: (860)594-0200
Fax: (860)594-0259
E-mail: foundation@arrl.org
Web Site: http://www.arrlf.org
To support the education of students holding a valid FCC-granted Amateur Radio license for post-secondary education.
Title of Award: L. Phil Wicker Scholarships **Area, Field, or Subject:** Radio and television; Electronics; Communications. **Level of Education for which Award is Granted:** Undergraduate **Number Awarded:** 1. **Funds Available:** $1,000.
Eligibility Requirements: Applicant must hold an FCC amateur radio license; be a resident of ARRL Roanoke Division (NC, SC, VA, WV); enrolled in a baccalaureate or higher course in electronics, communications and related fields. **Application Requirements:** Applicants must submit a completed scholarship application form along with a recent high school (or equivalent) or college transcript. **Deadline for Receipt:** February 1.

4707 ■ AMERICAN SOCIETY FOR NONDESTRUCTIVE TESTING
PO Box 28518
Columbus, OH 43228-0518
Tel: (614)274-6003
Free: 800-222-2768
Fax: (614)274-6899
Web Site: http://www.asnt.org
To assist students who have chosen a career in NDT.
Title of Award: Robert B. Oliver ASNT Scholarships **Area, Field, or Subject:** Materials research/science; Testing, educational/psychological. **Level of Education for which Award is Granted:** Undergraduate **Funds Available:** $2,500.
Eligibility Requirements: Applicants must be enrolled in a course work related to nondestructive testing (NDT) leading to an undergraduate degree, an associate degree or a post-secondary certificate. **Application Requirements:** Applicants must submit one original and 4 copies of student manuscript with original illustrations and photos (maximum of ten). Manuscripts must contain the title, author, complete references and must be limited to 5,000 words. International System of Units or SI is preferred for all measurements. Applicants must also submit a completed application form; student's curriculum; transcript; verification of enrollment letter from an instructor. **Deadline for Receipt:** February 15. **Additional Information:** Lynn Anderson, landerson@asnt.org.

4708 ■ AMERICAN WELDING SOCIETY
550 NW LeJeune Rd.
Miami, FL 33126
Tel: (305)443-9353
Free: 800-443-9353
Fax: (305)443-7559
E-mail: info@aws.org
Web Site: http://www.aws.org
To provide financial assistance to individuals interested in pursuing a career in welding engineering.
Title of Award: Howard E. and Wilma J. Adkins Scholarships **Area, Field, or Subject:** Welding. **Level of Education for which Award is Granted:** Undergraduate **Funds Available:** $2,500.
Eligibility Requirements: Applicants must be undergraduate students pursuing a four-year bachelors degree in welding engineering or welding engineering technology; must be 18 years old and above; must have a minimum of 2.5 overall grade point average; must be a citizen of the United States; and must plan to attend an accredited engineering school within the United States. **Application Requirements:** Applicants must complete the application form and submit it along with a high school diploma and a financial statement. **Deadline for Receipt:** January 15. **Additional Information:** found@aws.org

4709 ■ AMERICAN WELDING SOCIETY
550 NW LeJeune Rd.
Miami, FL 33126
Tel: (305)443-9353
Free: 800-443-9353
Fax: (305)443-7559
E-mail: info@aws.org
Web Site: http://www.aws.org
To provide financial assistance to students preparing for a career in the welding and related joining technologies.
Title of Award: American Welding Society District Scholarships **Area, Field, or Subject:** Welding. **Level of Education for which Award is Granted:** Undergraduate **Funds Available:** No specific amount.
Eligibility Requirements: Applicants must be high school graduates is planning to enroll in a welding course program; must attend a school located in the U.S. or its territories. **Application Requirements:** Applicants must submit a financial statement; transcript of records; personal statement; biography and photo. **Deadline for Receipt:** March 1.

4710 ■ AMERICAN WELDING SOCIETY
550 NW LeJeune Rd.
Miami, FL 33126
Tel: (305)443-9353
Free: 800-443-9353
Fax: (305)443-7559
E-mail: info@aws.org
Web Site: http://www.aws.org
To provide financial assistance to international students who wish to pursue their education in welding and related joining technologies.
Title of Award: American Welding Society International Scholarships **Area, Field, or Subject:** Welding. **Level of Education for which Award is Granted:** Undergraduate **Funds Available:** $2,500.
Eligibility Requirements: Applicants must have completed at least one year of welding or related fields of study at a Baccalaureate degree-granting institution; must be full-time students; and must be U.S. or Canadian citizens. **Application Requirements:** Applicants must submit a copy of the proposed curriculum; verification of enrollment to the institution; two letters of personal reference; two-page professional goal statement with a brief bibliography; transcript of grades or equivalent from each college; proof of country of citizenship; AWS membership number, if member; and financial information regarding tuition fees from the academic institution. **Additional Information:** found@aws.org.

4711 ■ AMERICAN WELDING SOCIETY
550 NW LeJeune Rd.
Miami, FL 33126
Tel: (305)443-9353
Free: 800-443-9353
Fax: (305)443-7559
E-mail: info@aws.org

Web Site: http://www.aws.org
To advance opportunities for students preparing for a career in the welding and related joining technologies.
Title of Award: American Welding Society National Scholarships **Area, Field, or Subject:** Welding. **Level of Education for which Award is Granted:** Undergraduate **Funds Available:** $2,500.
Eligibility Requirements: Applicants must be students pursuing a specific degree at an accredited four-year college or university. **Application Requirements:** Applicants must submit a financial statement; transcript of records; personal statement; biography; and photo. **Deadline for Receipt:** January 15.

4712 ■ AMERICAN WELDING SOCIETY
550 NW LeJeune Rd.
Miami, FL 33126
Tel: (305)443-9353
Free: 800-443-9353
Fax: (305)443-7559
E-mail: info@aws.org
Web Site: http://www.aws.org
To provide financial assistance to individuals interested in pursuing a bachelor's degree in welding engineering, welding engineering technology, or an engineering program with an emphasis in welding.
Title of Award: American Welding Society Past Presidents Scholarships **Area, Field, or Subject:** Welding. **Level of Education for which Award is Granted:** Undergraduate **Funds Available:** $2,500.
Eligibility Requirements: Applicants must be junior, senior, or graduate level students pursuing a degree in Welding Engineering or Welding Engineering Technology. **Application Requirements:** Applicants must complete the application form and submit it along with one or more recommendation letters from community members, local AWS officers, and/or AWS district directors attesting to the applicant's leadership capability; and a 300-500 word essay on the applicant's objectives and aspirations in the field of welding.

4713 ■ AMERICAN WELDING SOCIETY
550 NW LeJeune Rd.
Miami, FL 33126
Tel: (305)443-9353
Free: 800-443-9353
Fax: (305)443-7559
E-mail: info@aws.org
Web Site: http://www.aws.org
To provide financial assistance to individuals interested in pursuing a bachelor's degree in welding engineering, welding engineering technology, or an engineering program with an emphasis in welding.
Title of Award: Jerry Baker Scholarships **Area, Field, or Subject:** Welding. **Level of Education for which Award is Granted:** Undergraduate **Funds Available:** $2,500.
Eligibility Requirements: Applicants must be undergraduate students pursuing a four-year bachelors degree in welding engineering or welding engineering technology; must be 18 years of age or above; must be full-time students as defined by the academic institution; must have at least a 2.8 overall point average with a 3.0 grade point average in engineering courses; must be citizen of the United States or Canada; and plan to attend an institution located within the United States or Canada. **Application Requirements:** Applicants must submit an application form and a high school diploma. **Deadline for Receipt:** January 15.

4714 ■ AMERICAN WELDING SOCIETY
550 NW LeJeune Rd.
Miami, FL 33126
Tel: (305)443-9353
Free: 800-443-9353
Fax: (305)443-7559
E-mail: info@aws.org
Web Site: http://www.aws.org
To provide financial assistance to individuals interested in pursuing a career in welding engineering.
Title of Award: Jack R. Barckhoff Welding Management Scholarships **Area, Field, or Subject:** Welding. **Level of Education for which Award is Granted:** Undergraduate **Funds Available:** $2,500.
Eligibility Requirements: Applicants must be college juniors pursuing a four-year bachelors degree in welding engineering at the Ohio State

University; must be 18 years old and above; must have a minimum of 2.5 overall grade point average; must be a citizen of the United States and plan to attend an accredited engineering school within the United States; must be enrolled and must complete the two-hour credit course in Total Welding Management at the Ohio State University. **Application Requirements:** Applicants must complete the application form and submit it along with a high school diploma and a financial statement. Applicants must also submit a 300-500 word essay on how they see their role once they have graduated in improving the world of welding and the welding industry in the United States, and how they plan to use their education to improve the US competitive position in welding and manufacturing. **Deadline for Receipt:** January 15. **Additional Information:** found@aws.org

4715 ■ AMERICAN WELDING SOCIETY

550 NW LeJeune Rd.
Miami, FL 33126
Tel: (305)443-9353
Free: 800-443-9353
Fax: (305)443-7559
E-mail: info@aws.org
Web Site: http://www.aws.org
To provide financial assistance to individuals interested in pursuing a career in welding engineering.
Title of Award: Edward J. Brady Memorial Scholarships **Area, Field, or Subject:** Welding. **Level of Education for which Award is Granted:** Undergraduate **Funds Available:** $2,500.
Eligibility Requirements: Applicants must be undergraduate students pursuing a four-year bachelors degree in welding engineering or welding engineering technology; must be 18 years old and above; must have a minimum of 2.5 overall grade point average; must be a citizen of the United States; and must plan to attend an accredited engineering school within the United States. **Application Requirements:** Applicants must complete the application form and submit it along with a high school diploma and a financial statement. **Deadline for Receipt:** January 15. **Additional Information:** found@aws.org

4716 ■ AMERICAN WELDING SOCIETY

550 NW LeJeune Rd.
Miami, FL 33126
Tel: (305)443-9353
Free: 800-443-9353
Fax: (305)443-7559
E-mail: info@aws.org
Web Site: http://www.aws.org
To provide financial assistance to individuals interested in pursuing a bachelor's degree in welding engineering, welding engineering technology, or an engineering program with an emphasis in welding.
Title of Award: William A. and Ann M. Brothers Scholarships **Area, Field, or Subject:** Welding. **Level of Education for which Award is Granted:** Undergraduate **Funds Available:** $3,500.
Eligibility Requirements: Applicants must be full-time undergraduate students pursuing a four-year degree in Welding Engineering or Welding Engineering Technology; must have demonstrated leadership abilities; must be 18 years of age or above; must be United States citizens; plan to attend an academic institution within the United States or Canada; and must have at least 2.5 overall grade point average. **Application Requirements:** Applicants must submit an application form and a high school diploma. **Deadline for Receipt:** January 15. **Additional Information:** found@aws.org

4717 ■ AMERICAN WELDING SOCIETY

550 NW LeJeune Rd.
Miami, FL 33126
Tel: (305)443-9353
Free: 800-443-9353
Fax: (305)443-7559
E-mail: info@aws.org
Web Site: http://www.aws.org
To provide financial assistance to individuals interested in pursuing a career in welding engineering.
Title of Award: Donald F. Hastings Scholarships **Area, Field, or Subject:** Welding. **Level of Education for which Award is Granted:** Undergraduate **Funds Available:** $2,500.

Eligibility Requirements: Applicants must be undergraduate students pursuing a bachelors degree in welding engineering or welding engineering technology; must be 18 years of age or above; must have a minimum of 2.5 overall grade point average; must be United States citizens; and plan to attend an accredited engineering school within the United States. Applicants may be enrolled full or part time. **Application Requirements:** Applicants must submit an application; a high school diploma; and a financial statement. **Deadline for Receipt:** January 15.

4718 ■ AMERICAN WELDING SOCIETY

550 NW LeJeune Rd.
Miami, FL 33126
Tel: (305)443-9353
Free: 800-443-9353
Fax: (305)443-7559
E-mail: info@aws.org
Web Site: http://www.aws.org
To provide financial assistance to individuals interested in pursuing a career in welding engineering.
Title of Award: Donald and Shirley Hastings Scholarships **Area, Field, or Subject:** Welding. **Level of Education for which Award is Granted:** Undergraduate **Funds Available:** $2,500.
Eligibility Requirements: Applicants must be undergraduate students pursuing a bachelors degree in welding engineering or welding engineering technology; must be 18 years of age or above; must have a minimum of 2.5 overall grade point average; must be United States citizens; and plan to attend an accredited engineering school within the United States. Applicants may be enrolled full or part time. **Application Requirements:** Applicants must submit an application; a high school diploma; and a financial statement. **Deadline for Receipt:** January 15. **Additional Information:** found@aws.org

4719 ■ AMERICAN WELDING SOCIETY

550 NW LeJeune Rd.
Miami, FL 33126
Tel: (305)443-9353
Free: 800-443-9353
Fax: (305)443-7559
E-mail: info@aws.org
Web Site: http://www.aws.org
To provide financial assistance to individuals interested in pursuing a bachelor's degree in welding engineering, welding engineering technology, or an engineering program with an emphasis in welding.
Title of Award: William B. Howell Scholarships **Area, Field, or Subject:** Welding. **Level of Education for which Award is Granted:** Undergraduate **Funds Available:** $2,500.
Eligibility Requirements: Applicants must be full-time undergraduate students pursuing a four-year degree in Welding Engineering or Welding Engineering Technology; must have demonstrated leadership abilities; be 18 years of age or above; must be United States citizens; plan to attend an academic institution within the United States or Canada; and must have at least 2.5 overall grade point average. **Application Requirements:** Applicants must submit an application form and a high school diploma. **Deadline for Receipt:** January 15. **Additional Information:** found@aws.org

4720 ■ AMERICAN WELDING SOCIETY

550 NW LeJeune Rd.
Miami, FL 33126
Tel: (305)443-9353
Free: 800-443-9353
Fax: (305)443-7559
E-mail: info@aws.org
Web Site: http://www.aws.org
To provide financial assistance to individuals interested in pursuing a career in welding engineering.
Title of Award: ITW Welding Companies Scholarships **Area, Field, or Subject:** Welding. **Level of Education for which Award is Granted:** Undergraduate **Number Awarded:** 2. **Funds Available:** $3,000.
Eligibility Requirements: Applicant must be a senior, full-time undergraduate student working towards a bachelors degree in welding engineering or welding engineering technology; must be 18 years old and above; must have a minimum of 3.0 overall grade point average; must be

a citizen of the United States; and must plan to attend an accredited engineering school within the United States. **Application Requirements:** Applicants must complete the application form and submit it along with a high school diploma and a financial statement. **Deadline for Receipt:** January 15. **Additional Information:** found@aws.org

4721 ■ AMERICAN WELDING SOCIETY
550 NW LeJeune Rd.
Miami, FL 33126
Tel: (305)443-9353
Free: 800-443-9353
Fax: (305)443-7559
E-mail: info@aws.org
Web Site: http://www.aws.org
To provide financial assistance to individuals interested in pursuing a bachelor's degree in welding engineering, welding engineering technology, or an engineering program with an emphasis in welding.
Title of Award: Terry Jarvis Memorial Scholarships **Area, Field, or Subject:** Welding. **Level of Education for which Award is Granted:** Undergraduate **Funds Available:** $2,500.
Eligibility Requirements: Applicants must be undergraduate students pursuing a four-year bachelors degree in welding engineering or welding engineering technology; must be 18 years of age or above; must be full-time students as defined by the academic institution; must have at least a 2.8 overall point average with a 3.0 grade point average in engineering courses; must be citizen of the United States or Canada; and plan to attend an institution located within the United States or Canada. **Application Requirements:** Applicants must submit an application form and a high school diploma. **Deadline for Receipt:** January 15.

4722 ■ AMERICAN WELDING SOCIETY
550 NW LeJeune Rd.
Miami, FL 33126
Tel: (305)443-9353
Free: 800-443-9353
Fax: (305)443-7559
E-mail: info@aws.org
Web Site: http://www.aws.org
To provide financial assistance to individuals interested in pursuing a career in welding engineering.
Title of Award: John C. Lincoln Memorial Scholarships **Area, Field, or Subject:** Welding. **Level of Education for which Award is Granted:** Undergraduate **Funds Available:** $3,500.
Eligibility Requirements: Applicants must be undergraduate students pursuing a four-year Bachelors Degree in a welding program at an accredited university; must have a 2.5 overall grade point average; must be 18 years old and above; must be a citizen of the United States and plan to attend an academic institution located within the United States. **Application Requirements:** Applicants must complete the application form and submit it along with a high school diploma and a financial statement. **Deadline for Receipt:** January 15. **Additional Information:** found@aws.org

4723 ■ AMERICAN WELDING SOCIETY
550 NW LeJeune Rd.
Miami, FL 33126
Tel: (305)443-9353
Free: 800-443-9353
Fax: (305)443-7559
E-mail: info@aws.org
Web Site: http://www.aws.org
To provide financial assistance to individuals interested in pursuing a bachelor's degree in welding engineering, welding engineering technology, or an engineering program with an emphasis in welding.
Title of Award: Miller Electric International WorldSkills Competition Scholarships **Area, Field, or Subject:** Welding. **Level of Education for which Award is Granted:** Undergraduate **Funds Available:** Maximum of $40,000. **Duration:** Four years.
Eligibility Requirements: Applicants must be undergraduate students pursuing a four-year degree program in an accredited university. **Application Requirements:** Applicants must complete the National Skills USA Competition and complete the application form.

4724 ■ AMERICAN WELDING SOCIETY
550 NW LeJeune Rd.
Miami, FL 33126
Tel: (305)443-9353
Free: 800-443-9353
Fax: (305)443-7559
E-mail: info@aws.org
Web Site: http://www.aws.org
To provide financial assistance to individuals interested in pursuing a bachelor's degree in welding engineering, welding engineering technology, or an engineering program with an emphasis in welding.
Title of Award: Robert L. Peaslee-Detroit Brazing and Soldiering Division Scholarships **Area, Field, or Subject:** Welding. **Level of Education for which Award is Granted:** Undergraduate **Funds Available:** $2,500.
Eligibility Requirements: Applicants must be college junior or senior students pursuing a degree in Welding Engineering or Welding Engineering Technology; must have demonstrated leadership abilities; must be 18 years old and above; must be United States citizens and plan to attend an academic institution within the United States or Canada; must at least have a 3.0 overall grade point average; must express an interest in the resistance welding process; must show emphasis on Brazing and Soldiering application in their coursework. **Application Requirements:** Applicants must submit an application form along with a high school diploma. **Deadline for Receipt:** January 15. **Additional Information:** found@aws.org

4725 ■ AMERICAN WELDING SOCIETY
550 NW LeJeune Rd.
Miami, FL 33126
Tel: (305)443-9353
Free: 800-443-9353
Fax: (305)443-7559
E-mail: info@aws.org
Web Site: http://www.aws.org
To provide financial assistance to individuals interested in pursuing a bachelor's degree in welding engineering, welding engineering technology, or an engineering program with an emphasis in welding.
Title of Award: Ronald C. and Joyce Pierce Scholarships **Area, Field, or Subject:** Welding. **Level of Education for which Award is Granted:** Undergraduate **Funds Available:** $2,500.
Eligibility Requirements: Applicants must be college junior or senior students pursuing a degree in Welding Engineering or Welding Engineering Technology. Applicants must have demonstrated leadership abilities; must be 18 years of age or above; must be United States citizens; must plan to attend an academic institution within the United States or Canada; and must have at least 3.0 overall grade point average. Applicants must also express an interest in the resistance welding process and show emphasis on Brazing and Soldiering application in their coursework. **Application Requirements:** Applicants must submit an application form; a high school diploma; two letters of reference; personal statement; transcript of records; statement of the unmet financial need; and verification of enrollment. **Deadline for Receipt:** January 15. **Additional Information:** found@aws.org

4726 ■ AMERICAN WELDING SOCIETY
550 NW LeJeune Rd.
Miami, FL 33126
Tel: (305)443-9353
Free: 800-443-9353
Fax: (305)443-7559
E-mail: info@aws.org
Web Site: http://www.aws.org
To provide financial assistance to individuals interested in pursuing a bachelor's degree in welding engineering, welding engineering technology, or an engineering program with an emphasis in welding.
Title of Award: Praxair International Scholarships **Area, Field, or Subject:** Welding. **Level of Education for which Award is Granted:** Undergraduate **Funds Available:** $2,500.
Eligibility Requirements: Applicants must be undergraduate students pursuing a degree in Welding Engineering or Welding Engineering Technology; must have demonstrated leadership abilities; must be 18 years old and above; must be a citizen of the United States and plan to attend an academic institution within the United States or Canada. **Ap-**

plication Requirements: Applicants must an application form along with a high school diploma. **Deadline for Receipt:** January 15.

4727 ■ AMERICAN WELDING SOCIETY
550 NW LeJeune Rd.
Miami, FL 33126
Tel: (305)443-9353
Free: 800-443-9353
Fax: (305)443-7559
E-mail: info@aws.org
Web Site: http://www.aws.org
To provide financial assistance to individuals interested in pursuing a bachelor's degree in welding engineering, welding engineering technology or an engineering program with an emphasis in welding.
Title of Award: Resistance Welder Manufacturers' Association Scholarships **Area, Field, or Subject:** Welding. **Level of Education for which Award is Granted:** Undergraduate **Funds Available:** $2,500.
Eligibility Requirements: Applicants must be college junior students pursuing a degree in Welding Engineering or Welding Engineering Technology; must have demonstrated leadership abilities; must be 18 years old and above; must be United States citizens and plan to attend an academic institution within the United States or Canada; must at least have a 3.0 overall grade point average; must express an interest in the resistance welding process. **Application Requirements:** Applicants must submit an application form along with a high school diploma and an essay of 500 words or less about why the applicant wishes to become involved in the resistance welding industry. **Deadline for Receipt:** January 15.

4728 ■ AMERICAN WELDING SOCIETY
550 NW LeJeune Rd.
Miami, FL 33126
Tel: (305)443-9353
Free: 800-443-9353
Fax: (305)443-7559
E-mail: info@aws.org
Web Site: http://www.aws.org
To provide financial assistance to individuals interested in pursuing a career in welding engineering.
Title of Award: Jerry Robinson Inweld Corporation Scholarships **Area, Field, or Subject:** Welding. **Level of Education for which Award is Granted:** Undergraduate **Funds Available:** $2,500.
Eligibility Requirements: Applicants must be undergraduate students pursuing a four-year Bachelors Degree in a welding program at an accredited university; must have a 2.5 overall grade point average; must be 18 years old and above; must be a citizen of the United States and plan to attend an academic institution located within the United States. **Application Requirements:** Applicants must complete the application form and submit it along with a high school diploma and a financial statement. **Deadline for Receipt:** January 15. **Additional Information:** found@aws.org

4729 ■ AMERICAN WELDING SOCIETY
550 NW LeJeune Rd.
Miami, FL 33126
Tel: (305)443-9353
Free: 800-443-9353
Fax: (305)443-7559
E-mail: info@aws.org
Web Site: http://www.aws.org
To provide financial assistance to individuals interested in pursuing a career in welding engineering.
Title of Award: James A. Turner, Jr. Memorial Scholarships **Area, Field, or Subject:** Welding. **Level of Education for which Award is Granted:** Undergraduate **Funds Available:** $3,500.
Eligibility Requirements: Applicants must be full-time students pursuing a four-year Bachelor of Business Degree leading to a management career in welding store operations or a welding distributorship. Applicants must be employed for at least ten hours a week at a welding distributorship at the time of application. Applicants must be 18 years old and above. **Application Requirements:** Applicants must complete the application form and submit it along with a high school diploma and a financial statement. **Deadline for Receipt:** January 15. **Additional Information:** found@aws.org

4730 ■ AMERICAN WELDING SOCIETY
550 NW LeJeune Rd.
Miami, FL 33126
Tel: (305)443-9353
Free: 800-443-9353
Fax: (305)443-7559
E-mail: info@aws.org
Web Site: http://www.aws.org
To provide financial assistance to individuals interested in pursuing a career in welding engineering.
Title of Award: Armos and Marilyn Winsand-Detroit Section Named Scholarships **Area, Field, or Subject:** Welding. **Level of Education for which Award is Granted:** Undergraduate **Funds Available:** No specific amount.
Eligibility Requirements: Applicants must be enrolled in a two or four-year program and must be residents of Michigan or attending a Michigan College. **Application Requirements:** Applicants must submit an application form and a high school diploma. **Deadline for Receipt:** January 15.

4731 ■ ASSOCIATION FOR FEDERAL INFORMATION RESOURCES MANAGEMENT
PO Box 2848
Alexandria, VA 22301
Tel: (703)549-1160
Fax: (703)995-4890
E-mail: info@affirm.org
Web Site: http://www.affirm.org
To provide scholarships for undergraduate students to achieve a degree in Information Technology.
Title of Award: AFFIRM University Scholarships **Area, Field, or Subject:** Information science and technology; Technology. **Level of Education for which Award is Granted:** Undergraduate **Funds Available:** No specific amount is given.
Eligibility Requirements: Applicant must be a full-time student (12 credits or more); must be a junior or above; have a minimum of 3.0 cumulative GPA; majoring in some aspect of information technology or related field. **Application Requirements:** Scholarship applications will be provided by the universities; applicants must prepare a letter of reference from a professor.

4732 ■ ASSOCIATION FOR FEDERAL INFORMATION RESOURCES MANAGEMENT
PO Box 2848
Alexandria, VA 22301
Tel: (703)549-1160
Fax: (703)995-4890
E-mail: info@affirm.org
Web Site: http://www.affirm.org
To provide educational assistance for graduates of Edison High School who wish to continue their education in Information Technology.
Title of Award: Lisa Winkler Memorial Scholarships **Area, Field, or Subject:** Information science and technology; Technology. **Level of Education for which Award is Granted:** Undergraduate **Funds Available:** No specific amount.
Eligibility Requirements: Applicant must be a graduating senior who completed two full-years at Edison High School; accepted at an accredited four-year college/university; have a minimum of 3.0 cumulative GPA by the end of the first semester (senior year). **Application Requirements:** Applicant must prepare an essay (maximum of 200) on "Why I would like to pursue a career in information technology in the Federal Government". **Additional Information:** In memory of Lisa Winkler, for her devotion to support of IT education.

4733 ■ BDPA EDUCATION TECHNOLOGY FOUNDATION
4423 Lehigh Rd., No. 277
College Park, MD 20740
Tel: (513)362-2703
Fax: (202)318-2194
E-mail: info@betf.org
Web Site: http://www.betf.org
To provide outstanding minority students financial assistance in pursuing an information technology-related degree at an accredited two or four-year college or university of their choice.
Title of Award: Black Data Processing Associates Scholarships **Area, Field, or Subject:** Information science and technology. **Level of Educa-**

tion for which Award is Granted: High School **Number Awarded:** 6. **Funds Available:** $2,500.
Eligibility Requirements: Applicants must be U.S. citizens or permanent U.S. residents and graduating high school seniors at the time of their application; must be pursuing an information technology-related degree at an accredited two or four-year college or university; must be student members of BDPA and participate in computer training activities. **Application Requirements:** Applicants must submit the completed application form; high school transcript; two 500-word essays explaining why information technology is important and the importance of personal commitment in giving back to your community; and two letters of recommendation. **Deadline for Receipt:** May 28.

4734 ■ BLACK BUSINESS AND PROFESSIONAL ASSOCIATION
675 King St. W, Ste. 210
Toronto, ON, Canada M5V 1M9
Tel: (416)504-4097
Fax: (416)504-7343
E-mail: bbpa@bellnet.ca
Web Site: http://www.bbpa.org
To provide support for Black Canadian students.
Title of Award: Urban Financial Services Coalition Scholarships **Area, Field, or Subject:** Business, Economics, Finance, Information science and technology. **Level of Education for which Award is Granted:** Undergraduate **Number Awarded:** 2. **Funds Available:** $2,000. **Duration:** One year.
Eligibility Requirements: Applicant must be a student pursuing studies in business, economics, finance or information technology; must be a Canadian citizen or a permanent resident; must be 17 to 30 years of age; and must be enrolled in a full-time degree (graduate or undergraduate), diploma or certificate program at a Canadian college or university for the academic year. **Application Requirements:** Applicants must complete the application form and submit along with a letter describing the reasons why they would be worthy recipients of a BBPA National Scholarship; a completed financial information schedule stating their budget for the coming year including information on their expected sources of funding, family income and related information; and a letter of reference from the two individuals named in their application (must be a teacher from their high school, college or university, and an individual who is familiar with their community service). Application form and requirements must be sent to The Board of Trustees, BBPA National Scholarship Fund, 675 King St., W, Ste. 210, Toronto, ON M5V 1M9. **Deadline for Receipt:** May 30.

4735 ■ COMMUNITY FOUNDATION OF NORTHERN ILLINOIS
946 N 2nd St.
Rockford, IL 61107
Tel: (815)962-2110
Fax: (815)962-2116
Web Site: http://www.cfnil.org
To serve the four county area (Boone, Ogle, Stephenson and Winnebago) through philanthropy; to provide leadership in meeting charitable needs and to be a responsible steward to the Foundation's donors and of the Foundation's endowment.
Title of Award: Women of Today's Manufacturing Scholarships **Area, Field, or Subject:** Manufacturing. **Level of Education for which Award is Granted:** Undergraduate **Funds Available:** No specific amount.
Eligibility Requirements: Applicants must be male or female residents of Ogle, Winnebago, Boone, Stephenson or Rock County who are attending or plan to attend a college, university or trade/technical school; must demonstrate how their course work will impact manufacturing technology in the region. **Application Requirements:** Applicants must submit a completed application form, verification form, an official transcript in a sealed envelope and two letters of recommendation. **Deadline for Receipt:** March 1. **Additional Information:** jpatterson@cfnil.org.

4736 ■ DEVELOPMENT FUND FOR BLACK STUDENTS IN SCIENCE AND TECHNOLOGY
2705 Bladensburg Rd. NE
Washington, DC 20018
Tel: (202)635-3604
E-mail: dfbsst_info@dlhjr.com
Web Site: http://www.dfbsst.dlhjr.com
To provide scholarships to African American undergraduate students.

Title of Award: Development Fund for Black Students in Science and Technology Scholarship **Area, Field, or Subject:** Scientific or Technical fields. **Level of Education for which Award is Granted:** Undergraduate **Funds Available:** No specific amount.
Eligibility Requirements: Applicants must meet the following criteria: African-American heritage; undergraduate students majoring (or intending to major) in a technical field of study (i.e., engineering, math, science, etc.); enrollment at one of the predominantly Black colleges or universities; U.S. citizenship or permanent residency. **Application Requirements:** Applicants must submit a completed application form. **Additional Information:** Development Fund for Black Students in Science and Technology at the above address.

4737 ■ FEDERATION OF SOCIETIES FOR COATINGS TECHNOLOGY
492 Norristown Rd.
Blue Bell, PA 19422-2350
Tel: (610)940-0777
Fax: (610)940-0292
E-mail: fsct@coatingstech.org
Web Site: http://www.coatingstech.org
To pursue educational opportunities for coatings career-oriented students.
Title of Award: Joseph A. Vasta Memorial Scholarships **Area, Field, or Subject:** Technology. **Level of Education for which Award is Granted:** Undergraduate **Funds Available:** $2500. **Duration:** Annually.
Eligibility Requirements: Applicants must be an outstanding junior or senior college selected by their respected schools. **Application Requirements:** Fund is awarded to the educational institution on a rotating basis. The schools will select deserving students. **Additional Information:** Established in 1988. **Additional Information:** George M. Schmitz, CIEF President.

4738 ■ FOUNDATION FOR THE CAROLINAS
217 S Tryon St.
Charlotte, NC 28202
Tel: (704)973-4500
Free: 800-973-7244
Web Site: http://www.fftc.org
To provide financial support for undergraduate students who have expressed an interest in business through their service to Junior Achievement in Atlanta, GA.
Title of Award: Bank of America Junior Achievement Scholarship Fund **Area, Field, or Subject:** Business; Technology. **Level of Education for which Award is Granted:** Undergraduate **Funds Available:** No specific amount.
Eligibility Requirements: Applicants must be graduating high school seniors with a minimum cumulative GPA of 3.0 on a 4.0 scale and who have actively participated in Junior Achievement of Georgia and are planning to major in business or computer technology. **Application Requirements:** Applicants must submit all the required application information.

4739 ■ THE FUND FOR AMERICAN STUDIES
1706 New Hampshire Ave.
Washington, DC 20009
Tel: (202)986-0384
Free: 800-741-6964
Fax: (202)986-0390
E-mail: info@tfas.org
Web Site: http://www.tfas.org
To make public policy professionals more competent in both policy advocacy and senior management.
Title of Award: Eben Tisdale Fellowships **Area, Field, or Subject:** Technology. **Level of Education for which Award is Granted:** Graduate, Undergraduate **Number Awarded:** 1. **Funds Available:** $5000.
Eligibility Requirements: Applicant must be a junior or senior student interested in public policy and the high-tech industry, or in a graduate program. **Application Requirements:** Applicants must submit a completed application form; official academic transcripts; evaluation forms from two academic references (in a sealed envelope, author's signature must be across the seal); a 500-word statement on reasons of wanting to be a Tisdale fellow. **Additional Information:** Established after the death of Eben Tisdale, general manager of government affairs for the Hewlett-Packard Company. **Deadline for Receipt:** February 15. **Additional Information:** Jonathan Tilley, 202-986-0384, jtilley@tfas.org.

4740 ■ GRAND HAVEN AREA COMMUNITY FOUNDATION

1 S. Harbor Dr.
Grand Haven, MI 49417
Tel: (616)842-6378
Fax: (616)842-9518
E-mail: bpost@ghacf.org
Web Site: http://www.ghacf.org
To provide encouragement and support to a student who wants to further his/her manufacturing education.
Title of Award: Dake Community Manufacturing Scholarships **Area, Field, or Subject:** Manufacturing. **Level of Education for which Award is Granted:** Undergraduate **Funds Available:** No specific amount.
Eligibility Requirements: Applicants must be from Northwest Ottawa County, Muskegon County or Oceana County; must be high school graduating seniors, current college students or adult students. **Application Requirements:** Applicants must submit: completed application form; current high school or college transcript; Student Aid Report (SAR) from the Free Application for Federal Student Aid (FAFSA), unless applying for scholarships that do not consider financial need; and letter of recommendation. **Deadline for Receipt:** March 7. **Additional Information:** 616-842-6378.

4741 ■ GREAT LAKES COMMISSION

2805 S Industrial Hwy., Ste. 100
Ann Arbor, MI 48104-6791
Tel: (734)971-9135
Fax: (734)971-9150
E-mail: eschmidt@glc.org
Web Site: http://www.glc.org
To recognize outstanding achievement and vision in electronic communications technology.
Title of Award: Carol A. Ratza Memorial Scholarships **Area, Field, or Subject:** Electronics, Communications technologies. **Level of Education for which Award is Granted:** Undergraduate **Funds Available:** $1,000.
Eligibility Requirements: Applicant must be enrolled full-time at a college or university in the Great Lakes states or Canadian provinces; must have a career interest in electronic communication technologies; must have a demonstrated interest in the environmental or economic applications of electronic communications technology, exhibit academic excellence and have a sincere appreciation for the Great Lakes and their protection. **Application Requirements:** Application must be submitted along with essay/original web page; resume; letter of intent; grade transcripts and two letters of recommendation. **Deadline for Receipt:** March 31. **Additional Information:** Christine Manninen.

4742 ■ GREATER DAYTON IT ALLIANCE

900 Kettering Tower
Dayton, OH 45423
Tel: (937)229-0054
E-mail: ahickey@gdita.org
Web Site: http://www.daytonitalliance.org
To provide financial support to those deserving students.
Title of Award: Robert V. McKenna Scholarships **Area, Field, or Subject:** Information science and technology. **Level of Education for which Award is Granted:** Undergraduate **Funds Available:** No specific amount.
Eligibility Requirements: Applicant must have at least sophomore standing (30 semester hours or 45 quarter hours) at his/her respective university or college and currently be enrolled as an undergraduate student as defined by the applicant's institution; must be able to prove that his/her major's relation to the information technology field; must have a minimum cumulative GPA of 2.5 and a minimum major GPA of 3.0 on a 4.0 scale at the date of submission; must have a strong interest in pursuing a career in the Miami Valley IT field; must be a permanent resident of or attend an accredited IT degree-granting college within the 11 county Miami Valley region: Champaign, Clark, Darke, Greene, Logan, Miami, Montgomery, Northern Warren, Northern Butler, Northern Clinton, and Shelby. **Application Requirements:** Applicants must submit a completed application form. **Deadline for Receipt:** March 14. **Additional Information:** Greater Dayton IT Alliance at the above address.

4743 ■ HARTFORD FOUNDATION FOR PUBLIC GIVING

10 Columbus Blvd., 8th Flr.
Hartford, CT 06106
Tel: (860)548-1888
Fax: (860)524-8346
E-mail: hfpg@hfpg.org
Web Site: http://www.hfpg.org
To provide educational assistance for undergraduate students enrolled in a college or university in Connecticut.
Title of Award: Malcolm Baldridge Scholarships **Area, Field, or Subject:** Manufacturing; International trade. **Level of Education for which Award is Granted:** Undergraduate **Number Awarded:** 1-3. **Funds Available:** 4,000.
Eligibility Requirements: Applicant must be an International trade and manufacturing related major; must demonstrate academic excellence; must be studying foreign language, if majoring in International Business; and must be a resident of Connecticut. **Application Requirements:** Applicants may obtain the application materials from the website at www.conncf.org. **Deadline for Receipt:** March 1. **Additional Information:** Connecticut Community Foundation. Tallitha Richardson-Selby, Program/Scholarship Associate, 43 Field St. Waterbury, CT 06702. info@conncf.org. fax: 203-756-3054.

4744 ■ HISPANIC ASSOCIATION OF COLLEGES AND UNIVERSITIES

8415 Datapoint Dr., Ste. 400
San Antonio, TX 78229
Tel: (210)698-3805
Fax: (210)692-0823
E-mail: hacu@hacu.net
Web Site: http://www.hacu.net
To promote the development of member colleges and universities; to improve access to and the quality of post-secondary educational opportunities for Hispanic students; and to meet the needs of business, industry and government through the development and sharing of resources, information and expertise.
Title of Award: Office Depot Scholarships **Area, Field, or Subject:** Business; Marketing and Distribution; Information Science and Technology. **Level of Education for which Award is Granted:** Undergraduate **Funds Available:** $1,000.
Eligibility Requirements: Applicants must be undergraduate students attending four year institutions and must possess a minimum cumulative GPA of 3.0. **Application Requirements:** Applicants must fill out the application form and must provide any documents showing that they are currently enrolled or accepted by a college, university, or institution. **Deadline for Receipt:** May 23.

4745 ■ INTERNATIONAL ASSOCIATION OF LIGHTING DESIGNERS

The Merchandise Mart, Ste. 9-104
Chicago, IL 60654
Tel: (312)527-3677
Fax: (312)527-3680
E-mail: iald@iald.org
Web Site: http://www.iald.org
To promote education in architectural lighting design.
Title of Award: IALD Scholarship Programs **Area, Field, or Subject:** Architecture; Lighting science. **Level of Education for which Award is Granted:** Graduate, Undergraduate **Number Awarded:** One year. **Funds Available:** $500 $5000.
Eligibility Requirements: Applicant must be a graduate or undergraduate student studying in the field of architectural lighting design. **Application Requirements:** Applicants must complete an application form (available at the website) attach a copy of official transcript; resume; two letters of recommendation; statement of personal experience with lighting, reasons for studying lighting or why deserve the scholarship (maximum of 2 pages); and examples of work in 8.5x11 format (maximum of 10 images). Send the application and attachments to: Scholarship Chairman, International Association of lighting Designers, Merchandise Mart, Suite 9-104 200 World Trade Center Chicago, IL 60654. **Deadline for Receipt:** February 15.

4746 ■ INTERNATIONAL BEVERAGE PACKING ASSOCIATION

One Ocean Spray Dr.
Middleboro, MA 02349
Tel: (508)946-1000
E-mail: info@ibpa.org

Web Site: http://www.ibpa.org

To encourage educational pursuits among students involved in packaging curriculum.

Title of Award: Richard F. Heaney Memorial Scholarship Fund **Area, Field, or Subject:** Packaging. **Level of Education for which Award is Granted:** Graduate, Undergraduate **Funds Available:** $500-2,000.

Eligibility Requirements: Scholarship is open to juniors, seniors, and graduate students in packaging curriculums; must be citizens of the United States or Canada. **Application Requirements:** Applicants should send an e-mail to the IBPA representatives to request an application form. **Deadline for Receipt:** October 6.

4747 ■ INTERNATIONAL TECHNOLOGY EDUCATION ASSOCIATION
1914 Association Dr., Ste. 201
Reston, VA 20191-1539
Tel: (703)860-2100
Fax: (703)860-0353
E-mail: itea@iteaconnect.org
Web Site: http://www.iteaconnect.org

To recognize and encourage the integration of a quality technology education program within the school curriculum.

Title of Award: Litherland/FTE Scholarships **Area, Field, or Subject:** Technology. **Level of Education for which Award is Granted:** Undergraduate **Funds Available:** $1,000.

Eligibility Requirements: Applicant must be a member of ITEA; Applicant must not be a senior by application deadline; Applicant must be a current, full-time undergraduate majoring in technology education teacher preparation. **Application Requirements:** Applicants must submit the following requirements: Letter of application that includes statement about personal interest in teaching technology and applicant's address with day and night telephone numbers; Applicant's resume; A photocopy of applicant's college transcript. A grade point average of 2.5 or more is required; Three faculty recommendations. **Deadline for Receipt:** December 1. **Additional Information:** ITEA at the above address.

4748 ■ JAMAICAN CANADIAN ASSOCIATION
995 Arrow Rd.
Toronto, ON, Canada M9M 2Z5
Tel: (416)746-5772
Fax: (416)746-7035
E-mail: info@jcassoc.org
Web Site: http://www.jcassoc.org

To provide financial assistance to students from the Caribbean/ African community, who are pursuing postsecondary studies in Ontario universities/colleges.

Title of Award: Jamaica National Building Society Scholarships **Area, Field, or Subject:** Business; Law; Science; Technology; Nursing. **Level of Education for which Award is Granted:** Undergraduate **Number Awarded:** 2. **Funds Available:** $1,000. **Duration:** One year.

Eligibility Requirements: Applicant must be a Canadian citizen or landed immigrant of Caribbean or African background; must be enrolled as a full-time first-year student at an Ontario university/college or other postsecondary institution; must demonstrate remarkable academic performance or progress in high school; must demonstrate involvement and leadership in campus and/or community activities; must demonstrate financial need. **Application Requirements:** Application forms are available online and must be sent to The Jamaican Canadian Association Center, 995 Arrow Rd., Toronto M9M 2Z5. **Additional Information:** Scholarship is donated by the Jamaica National Building Society, a financial institution that facilitates money transfers from Canada. **Deadline for Receipt:** July 25.

4749 ■ JUNIOR ACHIEVEMENT
One Education Way
Colorado Springs, CO 80906
Tel: (719)540-8000; 888-4JA-ALUM
Fax: (719)540-6299
E-mail: newmedia@ja.org
Web Site: http://www.ja.org

To allow educational advancements by providing financial assistance.

Title of Award: Johnson and Wales University Scholarships **Area, Field, or Subject:** Business; Culinary arts; Technology; Teaching. **Level of Education for which Award is Granted:** Undergraduate **Number**

Awarded: Varies. **Funds Available:** $500 to cover full tuition. **Duration:** One year.

Eligibility Requirements: Program is open to individuals who are majoring in the field of business, culinary arts, hospitality, technology or teacher education. **Application Requirements:** Applicants must submit a completed application form together with other supporting materials. Mail all materials to Johnson and Wales University, 8 Abbott Park Place, Providence, RI 02903. **Deadline for Receipt:** February 1. **Additional Information:** National Student Organizations Office at Johnson and Wales University, 8 Abbott Park Place, Providence, RI 02903, at 800DIAL-JWU x-2345, or nso@jwu.edu.

4750 ■ LEWIS-CLARK STATE COLLEGE
500 8th Ave.
Lewiston, ID 83501
Tel: (208)792-5272
Web Site: http://www.lcsc.edu

To provide educational assistance for students pursuing either the Bachelor of Arts in Applied Technology or the Bachelor of Arts in Applied Science.

Title of Award: Hinman-Jensen Endowed Scholarships **Area, Field, or Subject:** Science; Technology. **Level of Education for which Award is Granted:** Undergraduate **Funds Available:** No specific amount.

Eligibility Requirements: Applicants must be classified as full-time students with a cumulative GPA that is consistent with the minimum required for admission and for progress toward their major. **Application Requirements:** Applicants must accomplish a general application available at the website. **Deadline for Receipt:** March 1.

4751 ■ LEWIS-CLARK STATE COLLEGE
500 8th Ave.
Lewiston, ID 83501
Tel: (208)792-5272
Web Site: http://www.lcsc.edu

To offset educationally-related expenses of Lewis-Clark State College Welding Technology students.

Title of Award: LCSC Welding Club Scholarships **Area, Field, or Subject:** Welding. **Level of Education for which Award is Granted:** Undergraduate **Funds Available:** No specific amount.

Eligibility Requirements: Applicants must have completed at least one semester as full-time students enrolled in the Welding Technology program; must be classified as full-time students with a declared major in Welding Technology; and must have a cumulative GPA of at least 3.0. **Application Requirements:** Applicants must accomplish a general application available at the website. **Deadline for Receipt:** March 1.

4752 ■ LEWIS-CLARK STATE COLLEGE
500 8th Ave.
Lewiston, ID 83501
Tel: (208)792-5272
Web Site: http://www.lcsc.edu

To encourage African-American, Hispanic, and American Indian students to pursue undergraduate college degrees in the chemical sciences and chemical technology.

Title of Award: Lewis-Clark State College/American Chemical Society Scholars Program **Area, Field, or Subject:** Chemistry; Science Technologies; Chemical Engineering. **Level of Education for which Award is Granted:** Undergraduate **Funds Available:** $3,000. **Duration:** One year.

Eligibility Requirements: Applicants must be students who want to enter the fields of chemistry, biochemistry, or chemical engineering, and students seeking a two-year degree in chemical technology; high school seniors planning a science preparatory program of study and college students who are currently from freshmen to juniors who are committed to the study of chemistry, biochemistry, chemical engineering or other chemically related fields such as environmental science, materials science or toxicology and are interested in pursuing careers in one of these fields; students who have strong academic records and show an interest in and potential for careers in the chemical sciences. **Application Requirements:** Applicants must accomplish general application available at the website.

4753 ■ NATIONAL GOVERNMENT PUBLISHING ASSOCIATION
207 Third Ave.
Hattiesburg, MS 39401

Tel: (601)582-3330
Fax: (601)582-3354
E-mail: info@govpublishing.org
Web Site: http://www.govpublishing.org
To promote education in the printing and graphic communications industry.

Title of Award: Don Bailey Scholarships **Area, Field, or Subject:** Printing trades and industries; Graphic art and design. **Level of Education for which Award is Granted:** Undergraduate **Funds Available:** $1,000-$50,000 per academic year. **Duration:** Four years.

Eligibility Requirements: Applicants must be pursuing a career in graphic communications, printing technology, printing management or publishing; must be a high school senior or high school graduate; must be enrolled in a two or four year accredited graphic or printing program at a technical school, college/university in the United States; a full-time student maintaining a cumulative GPA of 3.0 or higher. **Application Requirements:** Applicant must submit a completed application form; a copy of SAT scores; an official transcript; a photocopy of the intended course of study. **Additional Information:** In honor of Donald L. Bailey Sr. **Deadline for Receipt:** March 1 for high school and April 1 for college students.

4754 ■ PEDORTHIC FOOTWEAR ASSOCIATION
2025 M St. NW, Ste. 800
Washington, DC 20036
Tel: (202)367-1145
Free: 800-673-8447
Fax: (202)367-2145
E-mail: info@pedorthics.org
Web Site: http://www.pedorthics.org
For students committed to attending the New York College of Podiatric Medicine/EPI course.

Title of Award: The Eneslow Pedorthic Institute Scholarships **Area, Field, or Subject:** Orthotics prosthetics technology; Pathology. **Level of Education for which Award is Granted:** Undergraduate **Funds Available:** $500-$2,500.

Eligibility Requirements: Applicants must be at least 18 years old and have at least a high school diploma or equivalent; have an experience related to footwear for foot care; must describe their educational plans, including the school(s), the approximate timetable, the approximate date on which they plan to take the pedorthic certification exam (Applicants need not be enrolled in a course at the time of application); must sit for the certification exam within two years of completing course work supported by the Foundation scholarship; must agree in advance that, if selected to receive a scholarship, they will serve as advisors to the Foundation Scholarship Committee for two years immediately after receipt of a scholarship (such service shall not exceed 16 hours of consultation, generally by telephone or e-mail, over the course of those years); must describe their preferred area of concentration in pedorthics. **Application Requirements:** Applicants must submit a completed application form to the Scholarship Review Committee. Applicants must also submit three recommendations from individuals not related to them. **Deadline for Receipt:** January 15.

4755 ■ PEDORTHIC FOOTWEAR ASSOCIATION
2025 M St. NW, Ste. 800
Washington, DC 20036
Tel: (202)367-1145
Free: 800-673-8447
Fax: (202)367-2145
E-mail: info@pedorthics.org
Web Site: http://www.pedorthics.org
To provide financial assistance to students who are interested in a career in pedorthics.

Title of Award: The Dawn Janisse Scholarships **Area, Field, or Subject:** Orthotics prosthetics technology; Pathology. **Level of Education for which Award is Granted:** Undergraduate **Funds Available:** $500-$2,500.

Eligibility Requirements: Applicants must be at least 18 years old and have at least a high school diploma or equivalent; have an experience related to footwear for foot care; must describe their educational plans, including the school(s), the approximate timetable, the approximate date on which they plan to take the pedorthic certification exam (Applicants need not be enrolled in a course at the time of application); must sit for the certification exam within two years of completing course work supported by the Foundation scholarship; must agree in advance that, if selected to receive a scholarship, they will serve as advisors to the Foundation Scholarship Committee for two years immediately after receipt of a scholarship (such service shall not exceed 16 hours of consultation, generally by telephone or e-mail, over the course of those years); must describe their preferred area of concentration in pedorthics. **Application Requirements:** Applicants must submit a completed application form to the Scholarship Review Committee. Applicants must also submit three recommendations from individuals not related to them. **Deadline for Receipt:** January 15.

4756 ■ PEDORTHIC FOOTWEAR ASSOCIATION
2025 M St. NW, Ste. 800
Washington, DC 20036
Tel: (202)367-1145
Free: 800-673-8447
Fax: (202)367-2145
E-mail: info@pedorthics.org
Web Site: http://www.pedorthics.org
To financially assist students interested in a career in pedorthics.

Title of Award: The Aristotle Mirones Scholarships **Area, Field, or Subject:** Orthotics prosthetics technology; Pathology. **Level of Education for which Award is Granted:** Undergraduate **Funds Available:** $500-$2,500.

Eligibility Requirements: Applicants must be at least 18 years old and have at least a high school diploma or equivalent; have an experience related to footwear for foot care; must describe their educational plans, including the school(s), the approximate timetable, the approximate date on which they plan to take the pedorthic certification exam (Applicants need not be enrolled in a course at the time of application); must sit for the certification exam within two years of completing course work supported by the Foundation scholarship; must agree in advance that, if selected to receive a scholarship, they will serve as advisors to the Foundation Scholarship Committee for two years immediately after receipt of a scholarship (such service shall not exceed 16 hours of consultation, generally by telephone or e-mail, over the course of those years); must describe their preferred area of concentration in pedorthics. **Application Requirements:** Applicants must submit a completed application form to the Scholarship Review Committee. Applicants must also submit three recommendations from individuals not related to them. **Additional Information:** In memory of Aristotle Mirones, founder of ARIMED Orthotics, Prosthetics and Pedorthics.

4757 ■ PEDORTHIC FOOTWEAR ASSOCIATION
2025 M St. NW, Ste. 800
Washington, DC 20036
Tel: (202)367-1145
Free: 800-673-8447
Fax: (202)367-2145
E-mail: info@pedorthics.org
Web Site: http://www.pedorthics.org
To students pursuing Fundamentals Course at Oklahoma State University.

Title of Award: The Oklahoma State University at Okmulgee Scholarships **Area, Field, or Subject:** Orthotics prosthetics technology; Pathology. **Level of Education for which Award is Granted:** Undergraduate **Funds Available:** $500-$2,500.

Eligibility Requirements: Applicants must be at least 18 years old and have at least a high school diploma or equivalent; have an experience related to footwear for foot care; must describe their educational plans, including the school(s), the approximate timetable, the approximate date on which they plan to take the pedorthic certification exam (Applicants need not be enrolled in a course at the time of application); must sit for the certification exam within two years of completing course work supported by the Foundation scholarship; must agree in advance that, if selected to receive a scholarship, they will serve as advisors to the Foundation Scholarship Committee for two years immediately after receipt of a scholarship (such service shall not exceed 16 hours of consultation, generally by telephone or e-mail, over the course of those years); must describe their preferred area of concentration in pedorthics. **Application Requirements:** Applicants must submit a completed application form to the Scholarship Review Committee. Applicants must also submit three recommendations from individuals not related to them. **Deadline for Receipt:** January 15.

4758 ■ PEDORTHIC FOOTWEAR ASSOCIATION
2025 M St. NW, Ste. 800
Washington, DC 20036
Tel: (202)367-1145
Free: 800-673-8447
Fax: (202)367-2145
E-mail: info@pedorthics.org
Web Site: http://www.pedorthics.org
To provide financial assistance to students who are interested in a career in pedorthics.
Title of Award: The Sidney M. Pols Scholarships **Area, Field, or Subject:** Orthotics prosthetics technology; Pathology. **Level of Education for which Award is Granted:** Undergraduate **Funds Available:** $500-$2,500.
Eligibility Requirements: Applicants must be at least 18 years old and have at least a high school diploma or equivalent; have an experience related to footwear for foot care; must describe their educational plans, including the school(s), the approximate timetable, the approximate date on which they plan to take the pedorthic certification exam (Applicants need not be enrolled in a course at the time of application); must sit for the certification exam within two years of completing course work supported by the Foundation scholarship; must agree in advance that, if selected to receive a scholarship, they will serve as advisors to the Foundation Scholarship Committee for two years immediately after receipt of a scholarship (such service shall not exceed 16 hours of consultation, generally by telephone or e-mail, over the course of those years); must describe their preferred area of concentration in pedorthics. **Application Requirements:** Applicants must submit a completed application form to the Scholarship Review Committee. Applicants must also submit three recommendations from individuals not related to them. **Additional Information:** Scholarship is created by P.W. Minor and Son, Inc. **Deadline for Receipt:** January 15.

4759 ■ PEDORTHIC FOOTWEAR ASSOCIATION
2025 M St. NW, Ste. 800
Washington, DC 20036
Tel: (202)367-1145
Free: 800-673-8447
Fax: (202)367-2145
E-mail: info@pedorthics.org
Web Site: http://www.pedorthics.org
To students pursuing Basic Course at Finch University.
Title of Award: The Dr. William M. Scholl College of Podiatric Medicine Scholarships **Area, Field, or Subject:** Orthotics prosthetics technology; Pathology. **Level of Education for which Award is Granted:** Undergraduate **Funds Available:** $500-$2,500.
Eligibility Requirements: Applicants must be at least 18 years old and have at least a high school diploma or equivalent; have an experience related to footwear for foot care; must describe their educational plans, including the school(s), the approximate timetable, the approximate date on which they plan to take the pedorthic certification exam (Applicants need not be enrolled in a course at the time of application); must sit for the certification exam within two years of completing course work supported by the Foundation scholarship; must agree in advance that, if selected to receive a scholarship, they will serve as advisors to the Foundation Scholarship Committee for two years immediately after receipt of a scholarship (such service shall not exceed 16 hours of consultation, generally by telephone or e-mail, over the course of those years); must describe their preferred area of concentration in pedorthics. **Application Requirements:** Applicants must submit a completed application form to the Scholarship Review Committee. Applicants must also submit three recommendations from individuals not related to them. **Deadline for Receipt:** January 15.

4760 ■ PEDORTHIC FOOTWEAR ASSOCIATION
2025 M St. NW, Ste. 800
Washington, DC 20036
Tel: (202)367-1145
Free: 800-673-8447
Fax: (202)367-2145
E-mail: info@pedorthics.org
Web Site: http://www.pedorthics.org
To provide financial assistance to students who are interested in a career in pedorthics.
Title of Award: The Xtra Depth University Scholarships **Area, Field, or Subject:** Orthotics prosthetics technology; Pathology. **Level of Education for which Award is Granted:** Undergraduate **Funds Available:** $500-$2,500.
Eligibility Requirements: Applicants must be at least 18 years old and have at least a high school diploma or equivalent; have an experience related to footwear for foot care; must describe their educational plans, including the school(s), the approximate timetable, the approximate date on which they plan to take the pedorthic certification exam (Applicants need not be enrolled in a course at the time of application); must sit for the certification exam within two years of completing course work supported by the Foundation scholarship; must agree in advance that, if selected to receive a scholarship, they will serve as advisors to the Foundation Scholarship Committee for two years immediately after receipt of a scholarship (such service shall not exceed 16 hours of consultation, generally by telephone or e-mail, over the course of those years); must describe their preferred area of concentration in pedorthics. **Application Requirements:** Applicants must submit a completed application form to the Scholarship Review Committee. Applicants must also submit three recommendations from individuals not related to them. **Additional Information:** Scholarship is created by P.W. Minor and Son, Inc. **Deadline for Receipt:** January 15.

4761 ■ PETROLEUM PACKAGING COUNCIL
1219 Ganado
San Clemente, CA 92673
Tel: (949)369-7102
Fax: (949)498-6496
E-mail: ppc@atdmanagement.com
Web Site: http://www.ppcouncil.org
To provide technical leadership and education for the petroleum packaging industry.
Title of Award: Petroleum Packaging Council Scholarships **Area, Field, or Subject:** Packaging. **Level of Education for which Award is Granted:** Undergraduate **Funds Available:** $2,500.
Eligibility Requirements: Must be a member of PPC with good standing. **Application Requirements:** Applications are available online. Applicant must be a member to access the links. **Deadline for Receipt:** April 1. **Additional Information:** Brenda Baker 949-369-7102.

4762 ■ PHI UPSILON OMICRON
PO Box 329
Fairmont, WV 26555
Tel: (304)368-0612
E-mail: info@phiu.org
Web Site: http://www.phiu.org
To promote education in advance family and consumer sciences and related areas.
Title of Award: S. Penny Chappell Scholarships **Area, Field, or Subject:** Fashion design; Textile science. **Level of Education for which Award is Granted:** Undergraduate **Funds Available:** No specific amount.
Eligibility Requirements: Applicant must be a Phi U member; pursuing a baccalaureate degree in fashion design and construction, textile design and development and/or textile preservation. **Application Requirements:** Applicants must submit an application; transcripts; recommendations. Application documents must be assembled in order, clipped together with a paper clip and placed in a 10" x 13" envelope. Enclose a self-addressed stamped postcard. **Additional Information:** Applicants may apply for more than one fellowship. **Deadline for Receipt:** February 1.

4763 ■ PHI UPSILON OMICRON
PO Box 329
Fairmont, WV 26555
Tel: (304)368-0612
E-mail: info@phiu.org
Web Site: http://www.phiu.org
To promote education in advance family and consumer sciences and related areas.
Title of Award: Sutherland/Purdy Scholarships **Area, Field, or Subject:** Fashion design; Textile science. **Level of Education for which Award is Granted:** Undergraduate **Funds Available:** No specific amount.

Eligibility Requirements: Applicant must be a Phi U member; pursuing a baccalaureate degree in clothing and textiles or a related area such as apparel design or fashion merchandising; have held a leadership position in her/his Phi U chapter; and have earned at least a 3.0 out of 4.0 overall point average. **Application Requirements:** Applicants must submit an application; transcripts; recommendations. Application documents must be assembled in order, clipped together with a paper clip and placed in a 10" x 13" envelope. Enclose a self-addressed stamped postcard. **Additional Information:** Applicants may apply for more than one fellowship. **Deadline for Receipt:** February 1.

4764 ■ PORTABLE SANITATION ASSOCIATION INTERNATIONAL
7800 Metro Pkwy., Ste. 104
Bloomington, MN 55425-1514
Tel: (952)854-8300
Free: 800-822-3020
Fax: (952)854-7560
E-mail: info@psai.org
Web Site: http://www.psai.org
To assist individuals intending to pursue higher education.
Title of Award: PSAI Scholarship Funds **Area, Field, or Subject:** Technology. **Level of Education for which Award is Granted:** Undergraduate **Funds Available:** $2,500 to cover college expenses. **Duration:** One year.
Eligibility Requirements: Applicants must be graduating high school students or current undergraduate college students; must be employees of PSAI company or their dependents; must be college undergraduates; must have at least a GPA of 3.0 or above; must demonstrate the importance and value of portable sanitation; must have at least minimum of two (2) years employed by PSAI member company; and must maintain a minimum SAT Score 1000 or ACT 21. **Application Requirements:** Applicants must submit a copy of transcript; a 500 to 1000 word essay; a completed hard copy of application form; and profile sheet with the PSAI office. **Deadline for Receipt:** March 15.

4765 ■ SOCIETY OF MANUFACTURING ENGINEERS EDUCATION FOUNDATION
PO Box 930
Dearborn, MI 48121-0930
Tel: (313)425-3300
Free: 800-733-4763
Fax: (313)425-3411
E-mail: foundation@sme.org
Web Site: http://www.sme.org/cgi-bin/smeefhtml.pl?/foundation/foundation_hp.htm&&&SEF&
To promote higher education to students from New Mexico, Arizona or Southern California.
Title of Award: Walt Bartram Memorial Education Awards (Region 12 and Chapter 119) **Area, Field, or Subject:** Manufacturing. **Level of Education for which Award is Granted:** Undergraduate **Funds Available:** $1,000. Scholarship funds may be used for credit toward books, fees or tuition only.
Eligibility Requirements: Applicant must be a graduating high school senior enrolling as a full-time college or university student; must be a current SME Chapter member (except high school students); must pursue a degree in manufacturing engineering or related field in New Mexico, Arizona or Southern California; have a GPA of 3.5 on a 4.0 scale. **Application Requirements:** Visit the website for the online scholarship application process.

4766 ■ SOCIETY OF MANUFACTURING ENGINEERS EDUCATION FOUNDATION
PO Box 930
Dearborn, MI 48121-0930
Tel: (313)425-3300
Free: 800-733-4763
Fax: (313)425-3411
E-mail: foundation@sme.org
Web Site: http://www.sme.org/cgi-bin/smeefhtml.pl?/foundation/foundation_hp.htm&&&SEF&
To assist high school seniors and undergraduate students in their college education.
Title of Award: Caterpillar Scholars Award **Area, Field, or Subject:** Manufacturing. **Level of Education for which Award is Granted:**

Undergraduate **Funds Available:** $1,000. Scholarship funds may be used for credit toward books, fees or tuition only.
Eligibility Requirements: Applicant must be enrolled as a full-time undergraduate student in a degree program in manufacturing engineering in the U.S. or Canada; must have completed a minimum of 30 college credit hours (minority applicants may apply as incoming freshmen); have GPA of 3.0 on a 4.0 scale. **Application Requirements:** Applicants must contact the Foundation for applications.

4767 ■ SOCIETY OF MANUFACTURING ENGINEERS EDUCATION FOUNDATION
PO Box 930
Dearborn, MI 48121-0930
Tel: (313)425-3300
Free: 800-733-4763
Fax: (313)425-3411
E-mail: foundation@sme.org
Web Site: http://www.sme.org/cgi-bin/smeefhtml.pl?/foundation/foundation_hp.htm&&&SEF&
To promote higher education to students.
Title of Award: Arthur and Gladys Cervenka Scholarships **Area, Field, or Subject:** Manufacturing; Technology. **Level of Education for which Award is Granted:** Undergraduate **Funds Available:** $1,000. Scholarship funds may be used for credit toward books, fees or tuition only.
Eligibility Requirements: Applicant must be an undergraduate student enrolled fulltime in a degree program in manufacturing engineering or technology; have completed a minimum of 30 college credit hours; have a GPA of 3.0 on a 4.0 scale. **Application Requirements:** Visit the website for the online scholarship application process. **Additional Information:** In memory of Arthur and Gladys Cervenka.

4768 ■ SOCIETY OF MANUFACTURING ENGINEERS EDUCATION FOUNDATION
PO Box 930
Dearborn, MI 48121-0930
Tel: (313)425-3300
Free: 800-733-4763
Fax: (313)425-3411
E-mail: foundation@sme.org
Web Site: http://www.sme.org/cgi-bin/smeefhtml.pl?/foundation/foundation_hp.htm&&&SEF&
To financially support students in their education.
Title of Award: Chapter - 6 Fairfield County Scholarships **Area, Field, or Subject:** Manufacturing; Technology. **Level of Education for which Award is Granted:** Undergraduate **Funds Available:** $1,000. Scholarship funds may be used for credit toward books, fees or tuition only.
Eligibility Requirements: Applicants must be undergraduate students enrolled full-time in a degree program in manufacturing, technology, or a closely related field in the U.S. or Canada; have a GPA of 3.0 on a 4.0 scale. **Application Requirements:** Visit the website for the online scholarship application process.

4769 ■ SOCIETY OF MANUFACTURING ENGINEERS EDUCATION FOUNDATION
PO Box 930
Dearborn, MI 48121-0930
Tel: (313)425-3300
Free: 800-733-4763
Fax: (313)425-3411
E-mail: foundation@sme.org
Web Site: http://www.sme.org/cgi-bin/smeefhtml.pl?/foundation/foundation_hp.htm&&&SEF&
To assist high school seniors and undergraduate students in their education.
Title of Award: Chapter 23 - Quad Cities Iowa/Illinois Scholarships **Area, Field, or Subject:** Manufacturing. **Level of Education for which Award is Granted:** Undergraduate **Funds Available:** $1,000. Scholarship funds may be used for credit toward books, fees or tuition only.
Eligibility Requirements: Applicant must be an undergraduate student or entering freshman pursuing a bachelor's degree in manufacturing engineering or related field on an accredited college or university in Iowa or Illinois; have a GPA of 2.5 on a 4.0 scale. **Application Requirements:** Visit the website for the online scholarship application process.

4770 ■ SOCIETY OF MANUFACTURING ENGINEERS EDUCATION FOUNDATION
PO Box 930
Dearborn, MI 48121-0930
Tel: (313)425-3300
Free: 800-733-4763
Fax: (313)425-3411
E-mail: foundation@sme.org
Web Site: http://www.sme.org/cgi-bin/smeefhtml.pl?/foundation/foundation_hp.htm&&&SEF&
To financially support students in their education.
Title of Award: Chapter 63 - Portland James E. Morrow Scholarships **Area, Field, or Subject:** Manufacturing. **Level of Education for which Award is Granted:** Graduate, Undergraduate **Funds Available:** $1,000. Scholarship funds may be used for credit toward books, fees or tuition only.
Eligibility Requirements: Applicant must be a student pursuing a career in manufacturing or any related field; have a GPA of 2.5 on a 4.0 scale. **Application Requirements:** Visit the website for the online scholarship application process.

4771 ■ SOCIETY OF MANUFACTURING ENGINEERS EDUCATION FOUNDATION
PO Box 930
Dearborn, MI 48121-0930
Tel: (313)425-3300
Free: 800-733-4763
Fax: (313)425-3411
E-mail: foundation@sme.org
Web Site: http://www.sme.org/cgi-bin/smeefhtml.pl?/foundation/foundation_hp.htm&&&SEF&
To financially support students in their education.
Title of Award: Chapter 63 - Portland Uncle Bud Smith Scholarships **Area, Field, or Subject:** Manufacturing. **Level of Education for which Award is Granted:** Graduate, Undergraduate **Funds Available:** $1,000. Scholarship funds may be used for credit toward books, fees or tuition only.
Eligibility Requirements: Applicant must be a student pursuing a career in manufacturing or any related field; have a GPA of 2.5 on a 4.0 scale. **Application Requirements:** Visit the website for the online scholarship application process.

4772 ■ SOCIETY OF MANUFACTURING ENGINEERS EDUCATION FOUNDATION
PO Box 930
Dearborn, MI 48121-0930
Tel: (313)425-3300
Free: 800-733-4763
Fax: (313)425-3411
E-mail: foundation@sme.org
Web Site: http://www.sme.org/cgi-bin/smeefhtml.pl?/foundation/foundation_hp.htm&&&SEF&
To assist high school seniors and undergraduate students in New Mexico to attend college.
Title of Award: Chapter 93 - Albuquerque Scholarships **Area, Field, or Subject:** Manufacturing. **Level of Education for which Award is Granted:** Undergraduate **Funds Available:** $1,000. Scholarship funds may be used for credit toward books, fees or tuition only.
Eligibility Requirements: Applicant must be a freshman or undergraduate student pursuing a bachelor's degree in manufacturing engineering or related field at an accredited college or university in New Mexico; have a GPA of 2.5 on a 4.0 scale. **Application Requirements:** Visit the website for the online Scholarship Application Process.

4773 ■ SOCIETY OF MANUFACTURING ENGINEERS EDUCATION FOUNDATION
PO Box 930
Dearborn, MI 48121-0930
Tel: (313)425-3300
Free: 800-733-4763
Fax: (313)425-3411
E-mail: foundation@sme.org

Web Site: http://www.sme.org/cgi-bin/smeefhtml.pl?/foundation/foundation_hp.htm&&&SEF&
To financially support students in their education.
Title of Award: Chapter One - Detroit Founding Chapter Scholarships **Area, Field, or Subject:** Manufacturing. **Level of Education for which Award is Granted:** Graduate, Undergraduate **Number Awarded:** 3. One award for three academic levels (Associates, Baccalaureate, Graduate). **Funds Available:** $1,000. Scholarship funds may be used for credit toward books, fees or tuition only.
Eligibility Requirements: Applicants must be graduate or undergraduate students enrolled full-time or part-time in a manufacturing, manufacturing engineering technology or any related degree or certificate program in the following institutions: Wayne State University, Student Chapter S004; Lawrence Technological University, Student Chapter S011; University of Detroit-Mercy, Student Chapter S081; Focus: Hope, Center for Advanced Technologies, Student Chapter S279; Henry Ford Community College, Student Chapter S331; Macomb Community College, Student Chapter S071; University of Michigan - Dearborn, Student Chapter S326. Applicants must have a minimum GPA of 3.0 on a 4.0 scale; and must demonstrate good character and leadership. **Application Requirements:** Visit the website for the online scholarship application process.

4774 ■ SOCIETY OF MANUFACTURING ENGINEERS EDUCATION FOUNDATION
PO Box 930
Dearborn, MI 48121-0930
Tel: (313)425-3300
Free: 800-733-4763
Fax: (313)425-3411
E-mail: foundation@sme.org
Web Site: http://www.sme.org/cgi-bin/smeefhtml.pl?/foundation/foundation_hp.htm&&&SEF&
To financially support students in their education.
Title of Award: Chapter 116 - Kalamazoo - Roscoe Douglas Scholarships **Area, Field, or Subject:** Manufacturing. **Level of Education for which Award is Granted:** Undergraduate **Funds Available:** $1,000. Scholarship funds may be used for credit toward books, fees or tuition only.
Eligibility Requirements: Applicant must be a full-time undergraduate student at the Western Michigan University; must have completed at least 30 college credit hours; be pursuing a career in manufacturing engineering or manufacturing engineering technology; have a GPA of 3.0 on a 4.0 scale. **Application Requirements:** Visit the website for the online scholarship application process. **Additional Information:** The scholarship is named after the professor of emeritus of mechanical engineering Roscoe H. Douglas at Western Michigan University.

4775 ■ SOCIETY OF MANUFACTURING ENGINEERS EDUCATION FOUNDATION
PO Box 930
Dearborn, MI 48121-0930
Tel: (313)425-3300
Free: 800-733-4763
Fax: (313)425-3411
E-mail: foundation@sme.org
Web Site: http://www.sme.org/cgi-bin/smeefhtml.pl?/foundation/foundation_hp.htm&&&SEF&
To financially support students in their education.
Title of Award: Connie and Robert T. Gunter Scholarships **Area, Field, or Subject:** Manufacturing. **Level of Education for which Award is Granted:** Undergraduate **Funds Available:** $1,000. Scholarship funds may be used for credit toward books, fees or tuition only.
Eligibility Requirements: Applicant must be enrolled as a full-time undergraduate student in a degree program in manufacturing engineering or technology; must have completed a minimum of 30 college credit hours; must have a GPA of 3.5 on a 4.0 scale. **Application Requirements:** Visit the website for the online scholarship application process. **Additional Information:** Started in 1997.

4776 ■ SOCIETY OF MANUFACTURING ENGINEERS EDUCATION FOUNDATION
PO Box 930
Dearborn, MI 48121-0930
Tel: (313)425-3300

Free: 800-733-4763
Fax: (313)425-3411
E-mail: foundation@sme.org
Web Site: http://www.sme.org/cgi-bin/smeefhtml.pl?/foundation/founda-
tion_hp.htm&&&SEF&
To encourage students to attend the "Careers in Technology" event.
Title of Award: Gene Haas Foundation Manufacturing Technology
Scholarships **Area, Field, or Subject:** Manufacturing. **Level of Education for which Award is Granted:** Undergraduate **Funds Available:**
$1,000. Scholarship funds may be used for credit toward books, fees or
tuition only.
Eligibility Requirements: Applicant must be a graduating high school
senior or undergraduate student seeking an associate or baccalaureate
degree in manufacturing engineering, manufacturing engineering technology or a related field; must have a GPA of 2.5 on a 4.0 scale; must attend
the SME Great lakes Advanced Productivity Careers in Technology. **Application Requirements:** Applicants must use the on-line SME-EF
scholarship application process to apply.

4777 ■ SOCIETY OF MANUFACTURING ENGINEERS EDUCATION FOUNDATION

PO Box 930
Dearborn, MI 48121-0930
Tel: (313)425-3300
Free: 800-733-4763
Fax: (313)425-3411
E-mail: foundation@sme.org
Web Site: http://www.sme.org/cgi-bin/smeefhtml.pl?/foundation/founda-
tion_hp.htm&&&SEF&
To financially support students in their education.
Title of Award: Clinton J. Helton Manufacturing Scholarships **Area, Field,
or Subject:** Manufacturing. **Level of Education for which Award is
Granted:** Undergraduate **Funds Available:** No specific amount.
Eligibility Requirements: Applicant must be enrolled as a full-time
undergraduate student in a degree seeking program in manufacturing
engineering, technology or related field at an approved Colorado college
(Colorado State University or University of Colorado); must have
completed a minimum of 30 college credit hours; must have a GPA of 3.0
on a 4.0 scale. **Application Requirements:** Visit the website for the
online scholarship application process. **Additional Information:** Scholarship funds may be used for credit toward books, fees or tuition only.
Established in 1979.

4778 ■ SOCIETY OF MANUFACTURING ENGINEERS EDUCATION FOUNDATION

PO Box 930
Dearborn, MI 48121-0930
Tel: (313)425-3300
Free: 800-733-4763
Fax: (313)425-3411
E-mail: foundation@sme.org
Web Site: http://www.sme.org/cgi-bin/smeefhtml.pl?/foundation/founda-
tion_hp.htm&&&SEF&
To financially support students in their education.
Title of Award: Lucile B. Kaufman Women's Scholarships **Area, Field, or
Subject:** Manufacturing; Technology. **Level of Education for which
Award is Granted:** Undergraduate **Funds Available:** $1,000. Scholar-
ship funds may be used for credit toward books, fees or tuition only.
Eligibility Requirements: Applicants must be enrolled full-time
undergraduate students in a degree program in manufacturing engineering, technology, or related field in the U.S. or Canada; must be female;
have a GPA of 3.0 on a 4.0 scale; have completed at least 30 college
credits; pursuing a career in manufacturing engineering or manufacturing
technology. **Application Requirements:** Visit the website for the online
scholarship application process. **Additional Information:** The scholarship was established by Professor Emeritus of Engineering Lucile B.
Kaufman at Arizona State University.

4779 ■ SOCIETY OF MANUFACTURING ENGINEERS EDUCATION FOUNDATION

PO Box 930
Dearborn, MI 48121-0930
Tel: (313)425-3300

Free: 800-733-4763
Fax: (313)425-3411
E-mail: foundation@sme.org
Web Site: http://www.sme.org/cgi-bin/smeefhtml.pl?/foundation/founda-
tion_hp.htm&&&SEF&
To financially support students in their education.
Title of Award: E. Wayne Kay Co-op Scholarships **Area, Field, or
Subject:** Manufacturing. **Level of Education for which Award is
Granted:** Undergraduate **Funds Available:** $1,000. Scholarship funds
may be used for credit toward books, fees or tuition only.
Eligibility Requirements: Applicant must be enrolled as a full-time
undergraduate student in a manufacturing engineering or technology
degree program in the U.S. or Canada; must be working through a co-op
program in a manufacturing related environment; must have completed a
minimum of 30 college credit hours; have a GPA of 3.0 on a 4.0 scale;
must provide evidence of demonstrated excellence related to manufacturing engineering or technology that may include a project completed for the
applicant's employer. **Application Requirements:** Visit the website for
the online scholarship application process. Applicants must present a letter of recommendation from their employer and a letter of support from a
faculty at their college or university.

4780 ■ SOCIETY OF MANUFACTURING ENGINEERS EDUCATION FOUNDATION

PO Box 930
Dearborn, MI 48121-0930
Tel: (313)425-3300
Free: 800-733-4763
Fax: (313)425-3411
E-mail: foundation@sme.org
Web Site: http://www.sme.org/cgi-bin/smeefhtml.pl?/foundation/founda-
tion_hp.htm&&&SEF&
To assist high school seniors and undergraduate students to attend col-
lege.
Title of Award: E. Wayne Kay Community College Scholarships **Area,
Field, or Subject:** Manufacturing. **Level of Education for which Award
is Granted:** Undergraduate **Funds Available:** $1,000. Scholarship funds
may be used for credit toward books, fees or tuition only.
Eligibility Requirements: Applicant must be a graduating high school
senior or a full-time undergraduate student enrolled in a degree program
in manufacturing or related field at a two year Community College or trade
school in the U.S. or Canada; freshman or sophomore with less than 60
college credit hours completed and pursuing a career in manufacturing
engineering or technology; have a GPA of 3.0 on a 4.0 scale. **Application
Requirements:** Visit the website for the online Scholarship Application
Process.

4781 ■ SOCIETY OF MANUFACTURING ENGINEERS EDUCATION FOUNDATION

PO Box 930
Dearborn, MI 48121-0930
Tel: (313)425-3300
Free: 800-733-4763
Fax: (313)425-3411
E-mail: foundation@sme.org
Web Site: http://www.sme.org/cgi-bin/smeefhtml.pl?/foundation/founda-
tion_hp.htm&&&SEF&
To assist high school seniors to attend college.
Title of Award: E. Wayne Kay High School Scholarships **Area, Field, or
Subject:** Manufacturing. **Level of Education for which Award is
Granted:** Undergraduate **Funds Available:** $1,000. Scholarship funds
may be used for credit toward books, fees or tuition only.
Eligibility Requirements: Applicant must be a graduating high school
senior who commits to enroll as a full-time freshman in a manufacturing
engineering or technology program at an accredited college or university;
have an overall GPA of 3.0 on a 4.0 scale for high school senior year.
Application Requirements: Visit the website for the online Scholarship
Application Process.

4782 ■ SOCIETY OF MANUFACTURING ENGINEERS EDUCATION FOUNDATION

PO Box 930
Dearborn, MI 48121-0930

Tel: (313)425-3300
Free: 800-733-4763
Fax: (313)425-3411
E-mail: foundation@sme.org
Web Site: http://www.sme.org/cgi-bin/smeefhtml.pl?/foundation/foundation_hp.htm&&&SEF&
To financially support students in their education.
Title of Award: Giuliano Mazzetti Scholarships **Area, Field, or Subject:** Manufacturing; Technology. **Level of Education for which Award is Granted:** Undergraduate **Funds Available:** $1,000. Scholarship funds may be used for credit toward books, fees or tuition only.
Eligibility Requirements: Applicants must be enrolled full-time undergraduate students in a degree program in manufacturing engineering, technology, or related field in the U.S. or Canada; must have completed at least 30 college credit hours; must be pursuing a career in manufacturing engineering or technology; must have a GPA of 3.0 on a 4.0 scale. **Application Requirements:** Visit the website for the online scholarship application process.

4783 ■ SOCIETY OF MANUFACTURING ENGINEERS EDUCATION FOUNDATION

PO Box 930
Dearborn, MI 48121-0930
Tel: (313)425-3300
Free: 800-733-4763
Fax: (313)425-3411
E-mail: foundation@sme.org
Web Site: http://www.sme.org/cgi-bin/smeefhtml.pl?/foundation/foundation_hp.htm&&&SEF&
To financially support students in their education.
Title of Award: North Central (Region 9) Scholarships **Area, Field, or Subject:** Manufacturing; Mechanical engineering; Engineering, Industrial. **Level of Education for which Award is Granted:** Undergraduate **Funds Available:** $1,000. Scholarship funds may be used for credit toward books, fees or tuition only.
Eligibility Requirements: Applicant must be an enrolled full-time undergraduate student pursuing a bachelor's degree or associate's degree in manufacturing, mechanical, industrial engineering or industrial engineering or industrial technology at a two- or four-year college/university within the North Central Region (Iowa, Minnesota, Nebraska, North Dakota, South Dakota, Wisconsin and upper peninsula of Michigan); have a GPA of 3.0 on a 4.0 scale. **Application Requirements:** Visit the website for the online scholarship application process.

4784 ■ SOCIETY OF MANUFACTURING ENGINEERS EDUCATION FOUNDATION

PO Box 930
Dearborn, MI 48121-0930
Tel: (313)425-3300
Free: 800-733-4763
Fax: (313)425-3411
E-mail: foundation@sme.org
Web Site: http://www.sme.org/cgi-bin/smeefhtml.pl?/foundation/foundation_hp.htm&&&SEF&
To assist high school seniors and undergraduate students to attend college.
Title of Award: Edward S. Roth Manufacturing Engineering Scholarships **Area, Field, or Subject:** Manufacturing. **Level of Education for which Award is Granted:** Graduate, Undergraduate **Funds Available:** $1,000. Scholarship funds may be used for credit toward books, fees or tuition only.
Eligibility Requirements: Applicant must be a U.S. citizen; must be a graduating high school senior or a current full-time graduate or undergraduate student pursuing a bachelor's or master's degree in manufacturing engineering from an ABET-accredited school (California Polytechnic State University, CA; California State Polytechnic University, CA; University of Miami, FL; Bradley University, IL; Central State University, OH; Miami University, OH; Boston University, MA; Worcester Polytechnic Institute, MA; University of Massachusetts, MA; St. Cloud State University, MN; The University of Texas - Pan American, TX; Brigham Young University, UT; Utah State University, UT); must have a GPA of 3.0 on a 4.0 scale.

4785 ■ SOCIETY OF MANUFACTURING ENGINEERS EDUCATION FOUNDATION

PO Box 930
Dearborn, MI 48121-0930
Tel: (313)425-3300
Free: 800-733-4763
Fax: (313)425-3411
E-mail: foundation@sme.org
Web Site: http://www.sme.org/cgi-bin/smeefhtml.pl?/foundation/foundation_hp.htm&&&SEF&
To financially support students in their education.
Title of Award: Prof. George Schneider, Jr. Manufacturing Technology Education Scholarships **Area, Field, or Subject:** Manufacturing. **Level of Education for which Award is Granted:** Undergraduate **Funds Available:** $1,000. Scholarship funds may be used for credit toward books, fees or tuition only.
Eligibility Requirements: Applicants must be enrolled at least 6 credit hours per semester; pursuing a bachelor's degree in manufacturing engineering, manufacturing engineering technology or related field at the Lawrence Technological University; have a GPA of 2.5 on a 4.0 scale; have completed at least 60 college credit hours. **Application Requirements:** The College of Engineering Dean at Lawrence Technological University will recommend two to three candidates for the scholarship annually. A letter of recommendation for the nominated student is provided by the Chair of the School of Technology at Lawrence Technological University.

4786 ■ SOCIETY OF MANUFACTURING ENGINEERS EDUCATION FOUNDATION

PO Box 930
Dearborn, MI 48121-0930
Tel: (313)425-3300
Free: 800-733-4763
Fax: (313)425-3411
E-mail: foundation@sme.org
Web Site: http://www.sme.org/cgi-bin/smeefhtml.pl?/foundation/foundation_hp.htm&&&SEF&
To financially support students in their education.
Title of Award: SME Directors Scholarships **Area, Field, or Subject:** Manufacturing. **Level of Education for which Award is Granted:** Undergraduate **Funds Available:** $1,000. Scholarship funds may be used for credit toward books, fees or tuition only.
Eligibility Requirements: Applicants must be enrolled full-time undergraduate students in a manufacturing degree program at a U.S. or Canadian college; have completed at least 30 college credit hours; pursuing a career in manufacturing; have a GPA of 3.5 on a 4.0 scale. **Application Requirements:** Visit the website for the online scholarship application process.

4787 ■ SOCIETY OF MANUFACTURING ENGINEERS EDUCATION FOUNDATION

PO Box 930
Dearborn, MI 48121-0930
Tel: (313)425-3300
Free: 800-733-4763
Fax: (313)425-3411
E-mail: foundation@sme.org
Web Site: http://www.sme.org/cgi-bin/smeefhtml.pl?/foundation/foundation_hp.htm&&&SEF&
To support the children or grandchildren of SME members.
Title of Award: SME Education Foundation Family Scholarships **Area, Field, or Subject:** Manufacturing. **Level of Education for which Award is Granted:** Undergraduate **Funds Available:** $1,000.
Eligibility Requirements: Applicant must pursue a degree in manufacturing engineering, manufacturing engineering technology, or a related manufacturing field of study; must be a resident and attending in an accredited institution in the U.S. or Canada; must have at least one parent or grandparent that became an SME member for 2 years in good standing; must be graduating high school senior or undergraduate with up to 30 credit hours completed; enrolling full-time at a college or university; have a GPA of 3.0 on a 4.0 scale; have a minimum 1000 SAT score and/or 21 ACT score. **Application Requirements:** Applicants must complete the Scholarship Application Process; and submit a 300-word student state-

ment letter explaining: career objectives in manufacturing engineering, manufacturing engineering technology, or related fields; educational objectives; how the scholarship will help with the objectives; reason for entering this field. Applicants must also include a 2-page resume; official transcripts; two letters of recommendation from current or former employers or teachers; a copy of SAT or ACT test results; an essay about the applicant's favorite manufacturing engineer. **Deadline for Receipt:** February 1.

4788 ■ SOCIETY OF MANUFACTURING ENGINEERS EDUCATION FOUNDATION

PO Box 930
Dearborn, MI 48121-0930
Tel: (313)425-3300
Free: 800-733-4763
Fax: (313)425-3411
E-mail: foundation@sme.org
Web Site: http://www.sme.org/cgi-bin/smeefhtml.pl?/foundation/foundation_hp.htm&&&SEF&
To financially support students in their education.

Title of Award: Myrtle and Earl Walker Scholarships **Area, Field, or Subject:** Manufacturing; Technology. **Level of Education for which Award is Granted:** Undergraduate **Funds Available:** $1,000. Scholarship funds may be used for credit toward books, fees or tuition only. **Eligibility Requirements:** Applicant must be an enrolled full-time undergraduate student in a degree program in manufacturing engineering or technology in the U.S. or Canada; must have completed at least 15 college credit hours or one semester; must be pursuing a career in manufacturing engineering or technology; must have a GPA of 3.0 on a 4.0 scale. **Application Requirements:** Visit the website for the online scholarship application process.

4789 ■ SOCIETY OF BROADCAST ENGINEERS

9102 North Meridian St., Ste. 150
Indianapolis, IN 46260
Tel: (317)846-9000
Fax: (317)846-9120
E-mail: mclappe@sbe.org
Web Site: http://www.sbe.org
To provide educational fund to deserving candidates who aspire to a career in the technical aspects of broadcasting.

Title of Award: Youth Scholarships **Area, Field, or Subject:** Broadcasting; Engineering. **Level of Education for which Award is Granted:** Undergraduate **Number Awarded:** 3. **Funds Available:** $1000 $3000. **Eligibility Requirements:** Applicants must be high school seniors; planning to enroll at a technical school; pursuing studies leading to a career in broadcasting engineering or related field. **Application Requirements:** Application forms are available at the website. Complete only the B and C sections of the application form and send together with a brief autobiography; a summary of technical changes; and a copy of recent college transcripts (if applicable). **Deadline for Receipt:** July 1.

4790 ■ TECHNOLOGY STUDENT ASSOCIATION

1914 Association Dr.
Reston, VA 20191-1540
Tel: (703)860-9000
Fax: (703)758-4852
Web Site: http://www.tsaweb.org
To provide financial support for the outstanding service in the field of technology to a TSA student who is college or vocational/tech school bound and who is in good academic standing.

Title of Award: William P. Elrod Memorial Scholarships **Area, Field, or Subject:** Technology. **Level of Education for which Award is Granted:** Undergraduate **Funds Available:** $500. **Eligibility Requirements:** Applicants must be: TSA graduating high school seniors or alumni still enrolled in an undergraduate program or vo/tech school with a GPA of 3.0 or better; must have performed services on the local, state and national level and active member of an affiliated TSA chapter; able to express financial need for the scholarship; accepted or enrolled in a four-year college, university, or vo/tech school to receive the funds; and able to describe their future educational goals. **Application Requirements:** Applicants must submit a completed application to the TSA Awards Committee. **Deadline for Receipt:** May 1.

4791 ■ TECHNOLOGY STUDENT ASSOCIATION

1914 Association Dr.
Reston, VA 20191-1540
Tel: (703)860-9000
Fax: (703)758-4852
Web Site: http://www.tsaweb.org
To support the technology education profession by encouraging TSA students to pursue careers as K-12 technology teachers.

Title of Award: TSA Teach Technology Scholarships **Area, Field, or Subject:** Technology. **Level of Education for which Award is Granted:** Undergraduate **Number Awarded:** 1. **Funds Available:** $500. **Eligibility Requirements:** Applicants must have participated in an active TSA chapter for a minimum of two (2) consecutive years; served as a TSA officer at the local, state and/or national level for a minimum of one (1) academic year; attended and participated in at least one (1) TSA conference at the state or national level.Participated in an active TSA chapter for a minimum of two (2) consecutive years; served as a TSA officer at the local, state and/or national level for a minimum of one (1) academic year; attended and participated in at least one (1) TSA conference at the state or national level. **Application Requirements:** Applicants must submit: a signed cover letter that includes the following: a detailed description of the applicant's involvement in TSA, based on the above criteria; SAT score and/or ACT score: high school class rank (indicate how many in the class); no more than three (3) letters of reference, one of which must come from a technology teacher; a single-sided, one-page typed essay on his/her career plans for becoming a teacher in the technology education profession. **Deadline for Receipt:** December 31.

4792 ■ TURKISH COALITION OF AMERICA

1025 Connecticut Ave. NW, Ste. 1000
Washington, DC 20036
Tel: (202)370-1399
Fax: (202)370-1398
E-mail: info@turkishcoalitionofamerica.org
Web Site: http://www.turkishcoalition.org
To engage and cultivate a new generation of young Turkish American leaders.

Title of Award: TCA Turkish American Scholarships **Area, Field, or Subject:** Public Affairs; Political Science; International Affairs and Relations; Communications; Printing Trades; Public Relations. **Level of Education for which Award is Granted:** Undergraduate **Funds Available:** No specific amount. **Eligibility Requirements:** Applicants must meet the following criteria: be a U.S. citizen or permanent resident (green card holder); have, and maintain through the course of the scholarship period, a cumulative minimum 3.3 GPA on a 4.0 scale; evidence of leadership commitment through participation in community service, particularly within the Turkish American community; and be a high school senior applying to an accredited college or university, or college student who plans to continue undergraduate study; or a college senior or graduate enrolled or about to enroll in graduate school. Graduate students who apply for the TCA must plan to pursue studies and a career in public affairs. **Application Requirements:** Applicants must submit three (3) collated, non-stapled, paperclipped copies of each of the following items: (1) Completed Application Form (2) Resume: Each copy should be submitted on one single-sided 8.5" x 11" sheet of paper. (3) Short essay: The essay should not exceed 500 words, must be typed and double-spaced. **Deadline for Receipt:** June 6. **Additional Information:** Turkish Coalition of America at the above address.

4793 ■ UNIVERSITY OF ALASKA ANCHORAGE

3211 Providence Dr.
Anchorage, AK 99508
Tel: (907)786-1800
Web Site: http://www.uaa.alaska.edu
To provide financial assistance for tuition and other educational expenses to students who are in financial need.

Title of Award: UAA Mark A. Beltz Scholarships **Area, Field, or Subject:** Political science; Economics; Business administration; Science technologies. **Level of Education for which Award is Granted:** Graduate, Undergraduate **Funds Available:** $500 $1,000. **Eligibility Requirements:** Applicants must demonstrate motivation, academic and leadership potential; must be in good academic standing with a minimum cumulative GPA of 2.0 for undergraduates and 3.0 for graduates; must be formally admitted to a political science, economics, business administration, business and corporate law, or science and technology undergraduate, graduate, certificate, and/or vocational degree-seeking program at the University of Alaska Anchorage; must plan on enrolling at least half-time (6 credits) at the University of Alaska Anchorage; may be an incoming or continuing student at the University of Alaska Anchorage; may be a U.S. citizen, nonU.S. citizen, Alaska resident, or out-of-state resident. **Application Requirements:** Applicants must complete the electronics scholarship application available online. **Deadline for Receipt:** February 15.

4794 ■ WINSTON-SALEM FOUNDATION

860 W Fifth St.
Winston-Salem, NC 27101-2506
Tel: (336)725-2382
Fax: (336)727-0581
E-mail: info@wsfoundation.org
Web Site: http://www.wsfoundation.org
To award a worthy Forbush High School senior who will go directly to an accredited vocational/technical school, community college, or college/university in pursuit of a certificate, diploma or baccalaureate degree.
Title of Award: Johny Lineberry Memorial Scholarships **Area, Field, or Subject:** General science. **Level of Education for which Award is Granted:** Undergraduate **Funds Available:** $500.
Eligibility Requirements: Applicants must be graduating high school seniors from Forsbush High School in East Bend, N.C.; demonstrate a minimum, cumulative, unweighted GPA of at least 2.5; demonstrate strong character and community involvement; intend to study the field of electronics, preferably. **Application Requirements:** Applications for the scholarship are available in the guidance office at Forbush High School and from The Winston-Salem Foundation's web site. Completed applications should be submitted to the guidance office. **Deadline for Receipt:** March 31. **Additional Information:** WSF Student Aid Department, 336-714-3445.

Aerospace Sciences

4795 ■ ACADEMY OF MODEL AERONAUTICS

5161 E Memorial Dr.
Muncie, IN 47302
Tel: (765)287-1256
Free: 800-435-9262
Fax: (765)289-4248
Web Site: http://www.modelaircraft.org
To assist students in their educational pursuits.
Title of Award: AMA/Charles H. Grant Scholarships **Area, Field, or Subject:** Aeronautics. **Level of Education for which Award is Granted:** Undergraduate **Funds Available:** No specific amount.
Eligibility Requirements: Applicants must be full members of AMA for 36 months prior to applying; high school graduate; accepted by a college/university offering a degree program. **Application Requirements:** Applicants must submit a completed application form. **Deadline for Receipt:** April 30. **Additional Information:** Scholarship Committee Chairman, Bob Underwood.

4796 ■ ACADEMY OF MODEL AERONAUTICS

5161 E Memorial Dr.
Muncie, IN 47302
Tel: (765)287-1256
Free: 800-435-9262
Fax: (765)289-4248
Web Site: http://www.modelaircraft.org
To assist students in their educational pursuits.
Title of Award: Sig Memorial Scholarships **Area, Field, or Subject:** Aeronautics. **Level of Education for which Award is Granted:** Undergraduate **Funds Available:** No specific amount.
Eligibility Requirements: Applicants must be full members of AMA for 36 months prior to applying; high school graduate; accepted by a college/university offering a degree program; and have demonstrated financial need. **Application Requirements:** Applicants must submit a completed application form together with a 1-page statement about the need of

financial support. **Deadline for Receipt:** April 30. **Additional Information:** Scholarship Committee Chairman, Bob Underwood.

4797 ■ ACADEMY OF MODEL AERONAUTICS

5161 E Memorial Dr.
Muncie, IN 47302
Tel: (765)287-1256
Free: 800-435-9262
Fax: (765)289-4248
Web Site: http://www.modelaircraft.org
To assist students in their educational pursuits.
Title of Award: Telford Scholarships **Area, Field, or Subject:** Aeronautics. **Level of Education for which Award is Granted:** Undergraduate **Funds Available:** No Specific amount.
Eligibility Requirements: Applicants must be full members of AMA 36 months prior to applying; high school graduate; accepted by a college/university offering a degree program; and have participated in any of AMA and FAI activities/events. **Application Requirements:** Applicant must submit a Contest Classification form to list competitions that applicant participated in. **Deadline for Receipt:** April 30. **Additional Information:** Scholarship Committee Chairman, Bob Underwood.

4798 ■ AIR FORCE ASSOCIATION

1501 Lee Highway
Arlington, VA 22209-1198
800-727-3337
E-mail: service@afa.org
Web Site: http://www.afa.org
To educate the public about the critical role of aerospace power in the defense of the nation.
Title of Award: AFROTC Scholarships **Area, Field, or Subject:** Aerospace. **Level of Education for which Award is Granted:** Undergraduate **Number Awarded:** 2. **Funds Available:** $5,000.
Eligibility Requirements: Applicants must be current Air Force ROTC cadets in good standing, enrolled full-time as incoming juniors or seniors for the academic year; and must be committed to studying in the fields of science, technology, engineering or math. **Application Requirements:** Applicants must submit complete application package to Captain Douglas Huttenlocker. **Additional Information:** Captain Douglas Huttenlocker; douglas.huttenlocker@maxwell.af.mil.

4799 ■ AIR FORCE ASSOCIATION

1501 Lee Highway
Arlington, VA 22209-1198
800-727-3337
E-mail: service@afa.org
Web Site: http://www.afa.org
To educate the public about the critical role of aerospace power in the defense of the nation.
Title of Award: Air Force Association Excellence Scholarships **Area, Field, or Subject:** Aerospace. **Level of Education for which Award is Granted:** Undergraduate **Number Awarded:** 5. **Funds Available:** $5,000.
Eligibility Requirements: Applicants must be enrolled or planning to enroll, full-time or part-time in an undergraduate or graduate program of studies leading to an associate's, bachelor's or master's degree at an accredited college or university. **Application Requirements:** Applicants must submit completed scholarship application form and three essays to the Air Force Association. **Deadline for Receipt:** April 30. **Additional Information:** Anne Sagle
Free: 800-727-3337 ext. 4869.

4800 ■ AIR FORCE ASSOCIATION

1501 Lee Highway
Arlington, VA 22209-1198
800-727-3337
E-mail: service@afa.org
Web Site: http://www.afa.org
To promote aerospace education, specifically the study of science, mathematics and technology.
Title of Award: Air Force Association/Grantham Scholarships **Area, Field, or Subject:** Aerospace Science. **Level of Education for which Award is Granted:** Undergraduate **Funds Available:** $28,000. **Duration:** Four years.

Eligibility Requirements: Candidates must have a high school diploma or GED and must be members of AFA or their dependents. **Application Requirements:** Applicants must submit a completed application form; a two-page, double-spaced essay describing your academic and career goals and explaining why you are interested in pursuing your degree via an online degree program. Explain why this is the right time in your life and why you would be committed to continuing your education to get a degree; two letters of recommendation (These should be character references with descriptions of your performance and your potential as a student); and proof of GED completion or high school transcripts (or college transcripts if applicable). College transcript(s) and proof of undergraduate degree are required for the graduate programs. Applicants will be required to provide us with information requested on a feedback form six months after the scholarship is awarded.

4801 ■ AIR FORCE ASSOCIATION

1501 Lee Highway
Arlington, VA 22209-1198
800-727-3337
E-mail: service@afa.org
Web Site: http://www.afa.org
To encourage Air Force spouses worldwide to pursue associates/bachelor undergraduate or graduate/postgraduate degrees.
Title of Award: Air Force Association Spouse Scholarships **Area, Field, or Subject:** Aerospace. **Level of Education for which Award is Granted:** Undergraduate **Funds Available:** $2,500.
Eligibility Requirements: Applicants must be spouses of Air Force Active Duty, Air National Guard or Air Force Reserve. Spouses who are themselves Air Force members, or in ROTC, are not eligible. **Application Requirements:** Applicants must include the following in their application: an original or copy of the most recent college/university transcript or a report card from your last semester verifying your minimum 3.5 GPA or higher; proof of acceptance into a regionally accredited community college/ college/ university (this may consist of a short letter on college/ university stationery from either the admissions office or the registrar); a two-page double-spaced essay, describing your academic and career goals and the motivation which led you to this decision and describing how Air Force and other local community activities in which you are involved will enhance your goals; two letters of recommendation (should be character references and descriptions of performance and potential as a student, employee or volunteer); a letter of endorsement from the local AFA Chapter would be welcomed and encouraged. (the two letters must be from the different sources). Letters from previous or present professors, employers and volunteer organizations referencing work you have done are encouraged.

4802 ■ AIR FORCE ASSOCIATION

1501 Lee Highway
Arlington, VA 22209-1198
800-727-3337
E-mail: service@afa.org
Web Site: http://www.afa.org
To provide scholarships for active duty of Air Force, full-time Air National Guard or full-time Air Force Reserve.
Title of Award: Jodi Callahan Memorial Scholarships **Area, Field, or Subject:** Aerospace. **Level of Education for which Award is Granted:** Undergraduate **Funds Available:** $1,000.
Eligibility Requirements: Applicants must be enrolled in the current or upcoming semester with a minimum of 3 credit hours or the equivalent. Proof of acceptance may consist of a short letter on college/university stationery from either the admissions office or the registrar. A minimum Grade Point Average of 3.0 is required. **Application Requirements:** Applicants must complete both online portion and mail required documents by the deadline to be considered: one letter of recommendation from the Air Force supervisor or commander; proof of acceptance into an accredited college/university; and proof of Grade Point Average. Applicants essay should describe the academic goals and how you expect your degree to enhance your service to the Air Force. The letter of recommendation should include a character reference, a description of your performance and an assessment of your potential as an Air Force leader and volunteer. **Deadline for Receipt:** June 30. **Additional Information:** Lynetter Cross 800-727-3337 ext. 4807.

4803 ■ AIR FORCE ASSOCIATION

1501 Lee Highway
Arlington, VA 22209-1198
800-727-3337
E-mail: service@afa.org
Web Site: http://www.afa.org
To provide a one-time grant to selected top USAF enlisted personnel.
Title of Award: Pitsenbarger Awards **Area, Field, or Subject:** Aerospace. **Level of Education for which Award is Granted:** Undergraduate **Funds Available:** $500.
Eligibility Requirements: Applicants must be USAF personnel and graduating from the Community College of the Air Force (CCAF) who plan to pursue a baccalaureate degree. **Application Requirements:** Applicants may download an application form at AFA web site.

4804 ■ AIRCRAFT ELECTRONICS ASSOCIATION

4217 S Hocker
Independence, MO 64055
Tel: (816)373-6565
Fax: (816)478-3100
E-mail: info@aea.net
Web Site: http://www.aea.net
To provide support to the individuals intending to pursue their career in aircraft electronics and aviation maintenance industry.
Title of Award: Aircraft Owners and Pilots Association Scholarships **Area, Field, or Subject:** Aviation. **Level of Education for which Award is Granted:** Undergraduate **Funds Available:** $2,000.
Eligibility Requirements: Applicant must be a high school senior and/or college student who plans to or are attending an accredited school in an avionics or aircraft repair program. **Application Requirements:** For further information about the scholarship, applicants are advice to contact the foundation at Aircraft Electronics Association, 4217 S Hocker, Independence, MO 64055.

4805 ■ AIRCRAFT ELECTRONICS ASSOCIATION

4217 S Hocker
Independence, MO 64055
Tel: (816)373-6565
Fax: (816)478-3100
E-mail: info@aea.net
Web Site: http://www.aea.net
To provide support for individuals intending to pursue their career in aircraft electronics and aviation maintenance industry.
Title of Award: David Arver Memorial Scholarships **Area, Field, or Subject:** Aviation. **Level of Education for which Award is Granted:** Undergraduate **Funds Available:** $1,000.
Eligibility Requirements: Applicant must be a high school senior and/or college students planning to or are attending an accredited school in an avionics or aircraft repair program. **Application Requirements:** For further information about the scholarship, applicants are advised to contact the foundation at Aircraft Electronics Association, 4217 S Hocker, Independence, MO 64055. **Additional Information:** Scholarship given by Dutch and Ginger Arver in memory of their son, David. Dutch Arver was a strong supporter of the AEA for many years and served on the board of Directors until his retirement.

4806 ■ AIRCRAFT ELECTRONICS ASSOCIATION

4217 S Hocker
Independence, MO 64055
Tel: (816)373-6565
Fax: (816)478-3100
E-mail: info@aea.net
Web Site: http://www.aea.net
To provide support to the individuals intending to pursue their career in aircraft electronics and aviation maintenance industry.
Title of Award: Dutch and Ginger Arver Scholarships **Area, Field, or Subject:** Aviation. **Level of Education for which Award is Granted:** Undergraduate **Funds Available:** $1,000.
Eligibility Requirements: Applicant must be a senior and/or college students planning to or are attending an accredited school in an avionics or aircraft repair program. **Application Requirements:** For further information about the scholarship, applicants are advice to contact the foundation at Aircraft Electronics Association, 4217 S Hocker, Independence, MO 64055.

4807 ■ AIRCRAFT ELECTRONICS ASSOCIATION
4217 S Hocker
Independence, MO 64055
Tel: (816)373-6565
Fax: (816)478-3100
E-mail: info@aea.net
Web Site: http://www.aea.net
To provide support to the individuals who wants to pursue their career in aircraft electronics and aviation maintenance industry.
Title of Award: Johnny Davis Memorial Scholarships **Area, Field, or Subject:** Aviation. **Level of Education for which Award is Granted:** Undergraduate **Funds Available:** $1,000.
Eligibility Requirements: Applicant must be a high school senior and/or college student who plans to or are attending an accredited school in an avionics or aircraft repair program. **Application Requirements:** For further information about the scholarship, applicants are advice to contact the foundation at Aircraft Electronics Association, 4217 S Hocker, Independence, MO 64055. **Additional Information:** Scholarship is named in memory of Johnny Davis, president of Dallas Avionics, Dallas, Texas, who supported general aviation for over 30 years and served as an AEA Associate Board Member.

4808 ■ AIRCRAFT ELECTRONICS ASSOCIATION
4217 S Hocker
Independence, MO 64055
Tel: (816)373-6565
Fax: (816)478-3100
E-mail: info@aea.net
Web Site: http://www.aea.net
To provide support to the individuals intending to pursue their career in aircraft electronics and aviation maintenance industry.
Title of Award: Duncan Aviation Scholarships **Area, Field, or Subject:** Aviation. **Level of Education for which Award is Granted:** Undergraduate **Funds Available:** $1,000.
Eligibility Requirements: Applicant must be a high school senior and/or college students who plan to or are attending an accredited school in an avionics or aircraft repair program. **Application Requirements:** For further information about the scholarship, applicants are advice to contact the foundation at Aircraft Electronics Association, 4217 S Hocker, Independence, MO 64055.

4809 ■ AIRCRAFT ELECTRONICS ASSOCIATION
4217 S Hocker
Independence, MO 64055
Tel: (816)373-6565
Fax: (816)478-3100
E-mail: info@aea.net
Web Site: http://www.aea.net
To provide support to the individuals intending to pursue their career in aircraft electronics and aviation maintenance industry.
Title of Award: Field Aviation Co., Inc. Scholarships **Area, Field, or Subject:** Aviation. **Level of Education for which Award is Granted:** Undergraduate **Funds Available:** $1,000.
Eligibility Requirements: Applicant must be a high school senior and/or college students planning to or are attending an accredited college/university in an aircraft repair program. **Application Requirements:** For further information about the scholarship, applicants are advice to contact the foundation at Aircraft Electronics Association, 4217 S Hocker, Independence, MO 64055.

4810 ■ AIRCRAFT ELECTRONICS ASSOCIATION
4217 S Hocker
Independence, MO 64055
Tel: (816)373-6565
Fax: (816)478-3100
E-mail: info@aea.net
Web Site: http://www.aea.net
To provide support to the individuals intending to pursue their career in aircraft electronics and aviation maintenance industry.
Title of Award: Garmin Scholarships **Area, Field, or Subject:** Aviation. **Level of Education for which Award is Granted:** Undergraduate **Funds Available:** $2,000.
Eligibility Requirements: Applicants must be a senior and/or college students who plan to or are attending an accredited school in an avionics

or aircraft repair program. **Application Requirements:** For further information about the scholarship, applicants are advice to contact the foundation at Aircraft Electronics Association, 4217 S Hocker, Independence, MO 64055.

4811 ■ AIRCRAFT ELECTRONICS ASSOCIATION
4217 S Hocker
Independence, MO 64055
Tel: (816)373-6565
Fax: (816)478-3100
E-mail: info@aea.net
Web Site: http://www.aea.net
To provide support to the individuals intending to pursue their career in aircraft electronics and aviation maintenance industry.
Title of Award: Lowell Gaylor Memorial Scholarships **Area, Field, or Subject:** Aviation. **Level of Education for which Award is Granted:** Undergraduate **Funds Available:** $1,000.
Eligibility Requirements: Applicant must be a high school senior and/or college students who plan to or are attending an accredited school in an avionics or aircraft repair program. **Application Requirements:** For further information about the scholarship, applicants are advice to contact the foundation at Aircraft Electronics Association, 4217 S Hocker, Independence, MO 64055. **Additional Information:** Scholarship is named in memory of Lowell Gaylor, president of AvEL Co., Dallas, Texas, who supported general aviation and the AEA for over 25 yrs.

4812 ■ AIRCRAFT ELECTRONICS ASSOCIATION
4217 S Hocker
Independence, MO 64055
Tel: (816)373-6565
Fax: (816)478-3100
E-mail: info@aea.net
Web Site: http://www.aea.net
To provide support for individuals intending to pursue their career in aircraft electronics and aviation maintenance industry.
Title of Award: Bud Glover Memorial Scholarships **Area, Field, or Subject:** Aviation. **Level of Education for which Award is Granted:** Undergraduate **Funds Available:** $1,000.
Eligibility Requirements: Applicant must be a high school senior and/or college students who plan to or are attending an accredited school in an avionics or aircraft repair program. **Application Requirements:** For further information about the scholarship, applicants are advised to contact the foundation at Aircraft Electronics Association, 4217 S Hocker, Independence, MO 64055. **Additional Information:** Scholarship is named in memory of Bud Glover, former vice president of general aviation sales for Bendix/King. Bud was a 25-year contributor to our avionics industry.

4813 ■ AIRCRAFT ELECTRONICS ASSOCIATION
4217 S Hocker
Independence, MO 64055
Tel: (816)373-6565
Fax: (816)478-3100
E-mail: info@aea.net
Web Site: http://www.aea.net
To provide support for individuals intending to pursue a career in aircraft electronics and aviation maintenance industry.
Title of Award: Leon Harris/Les Nichols Memorial Scholarships to Spartan College of Aeronautics & Technology **Area, Field, or Subject:** Aviation. **Level of Education for which Award is Granted:** Undergraduate **Funds Available:** $35,000.
Eligibility Requirements: Applicant must be a student planning to pursue an Associate's Degree in Applied Science in Aviation Electronics (avionics) at Spartan College of Aeronautics and Technology campus in Tulsa, Oklahoma. **Application Requirements:** For further information about the scholarship, applicants are advised to contact the foundation at Aircraft Electronics Association, 4217 S Hocker, Independence, MO 64055. **Additional Information:** Award will cover all tuition expenses for eight quarters or until the recipient completes an Associate's Degree.

4814 ■ AIRCRAFT ELECTRONICS ASSOCIATION
4217 S Hocker
Independence, MO 64055

Tel: (816)373-6565
Fax: (816)478-3100
E-mail: info@aea.net
Web Site: http://www.aea.net
To provide support to the individuals who wants to pursue their career in aircraft electronics and aviation maintenance industry.
Title of Award: Don C. Hawkins Memorial Scholarships **Area, Field, or Subject:** Aviation. **Level of Education for which Award is Granted:** Undergraduate **Funds Available:** $1,000.
Eligibility Requirements: Applicant must be a high school senior and/or college students who plan to or are attending an accredited school in an avionics or aircraft repair program. **Application Requirements:** For further information about the scholarship, applicants are advice to contact the foundation at Aircraft Electronics Association, 4217 S Hocker, Independence, MO 64055. **Additional Information:** Scholarship is named in memory of Don C. Hawkins.

4815 ■ AIRCRAFT ELECTRONICS ASSOCIATION
4217 S Hocker
Independence, MO 64055
Tel: (816)373-6565
Fax: (816)478-3100
E-mail: info@aea.net
Web Site: http://www.aea.net
To provide support to the individuals intending to pursue their career in aircraft electronics and aviation maintenance industry.
Title of Award: Honeywell Avionics Scholarships **Area, Field, or Subject:** Aviation. **Level of Education for which Award is Granted:** Undergraduate **Funds Available:** $1,000.
Eligibility Requirements: Applicant must be a high school, college, or vocational/technical school student planning to or are attending an accredited school in an avionics or aircraft repair program. **Application Requirements:** For further information about the scholarship, applicants are advice to contact the foundation at Aircraft Electronics Association, 4217 S Hocker, Independence, MO 64055.

4816 ■ AIRCRAFT ELECTRONICS ASSOCIATION
4217 S Hocker
Independence, MO 64055
Tel: (816)373-6565
Fax: (816)478-3100
E-mail: info@aea.net
Web Site: http://www.aea.net
To provide support to the individuals intending to pursue their career in aircraft electronics and aviation maintenance industry.
Title of Award: L-3 Avionics Systems Scholarships **Area, Field, or Subject:** Aviation. **Level of Education for which Award is Granted:** Undergraduate **Funds Available:** $2,500.
Eligibility Requirements: Applicant must be a high school, college, or vocational/technical school students planning to or are attending an accredited school in an avionics or aircraft repair program. **Application Requirements:** For further information about the scholarship, applicants are advice to contact the foundation at Aircraft Electronics Association, 4217 S Hocker, Independence, MO 64055.

4817 ■ AIRCRAFT ELECTRONICS ASSOCIATION
4217 S Hocker
Independence, MO 64055
Tel: (816)373-6565
Fax: (816)478-3100
E-mail: info@aea.net
Web Site: http://www.aea.net
To provide support to the individuals intending to pursue their career in aircraft electronics and aviation maintenance industry.
Title of Award: Mid-Continent Instrument Scholarships **Area, Field, or Subject:** Aviation. **Level of Education for which Award is Granted:** Undergraduate **Funds Available:** $1,000.
Eligibility Requirements: Applicant must be a high school senior and/or college students planning to or are attending an accredited school in an avionics or aircraft repair program. **Application Requirements:** For further information about the scholarship, applicants are advice to contact the foundation at Aircraft Electronics Association, 4217 S Hocker, Independence, MO 64055.

4818 ■ AIRCRAFT ELECTRONICS ASSOCIATION
4217 S Hocker
Independence, MO 64055
Tel: (816)373-6565
Fax: (816)478-3100
E-mail: info@aea.net
Web Site: http://www.aea.net
To provide support to the individuals intending to pursue their career in aircraft electronics and aviation maintenance industry.
Title of Award: Monte R. Mitchell Global Scholarships **Area, Field, or Subject:** Aviation. **Level of Education for which Award is Granted:** Undergraduate **Funds Available:** $1,000.
Eligibility Requirements: Applicant must be a European student pursuing a degree in aviation maintenance technology, avionics or aircraft repair at an accredited school located in Europe or the United States. **Application Requirements:** For further information about the scholarship, applicants are advised to contact the foundation at Aircraft Electronics Association, 4217 S Hocker, Independence, MO 64055.

4819 ■ AIRCRAFT ELECTRONICS ASSOCIATION
4217 S Hocker
Independence, MO 64055
Tel: (816)373-6565
Fax: (816)478-3100
E-mail: info@aea.net
Web Site: http://www.aea.net
To recognize the importance of management skills.
Title of Award: Chuck Peacock Memorial Scholarships **Area, Field, or Subject:** Aviation. **Level of Education for which Award is Granted:** Undergraduate **Funds Available:** $1,000.
Eligibility Requirements: Applicant must be high school seniors and/or college students who plan to or are attending an accredited school in an aviation management program. **Application Requirements:** For further information about the scholarship, applicants are advised to contact the foundation at Aircraft Electronics Association, 4217 S Hocker, Independence, MO 64055. **Additional Information:** Scholarship is given by Wanda Peacock in memory of her late husband Chuck. As the founder of the Aircraft Electronics Association, Chuck credited his aviation and business management skills as the cornerstones for his success in the industry.

4820 ■ AIRCRAFT ELECTRONICS ASSOCIATION
4217 S Hocker
Independence, MO 64055
Tel: (816)373-6565
Fax: (816)478-3100
E-mail: info@aea.net
Web Site: http://www.aea.net
Title of Award: Plane and Pilot Magazine/Garmin Scholarships **Level of Education for which Award is Granted:** Undergraduate **Funds Available:** $2,000.
Eligibility Requirements: Applicant must be a high school, college or vocational/ technical school students who plan to or are attending an accredited vocational/technical school in an avionics or aircraft repair program. **Application Requirements:** For further information about the scholarship, applicants are advised to contact the foundation at Aircraft Electronics Association, 4217 S Hocker, Independence, MO 64055.

4821 ■ AIRCRAFT ELECTRONICS ASSOCIATION
4217 S Hocker
Independence, MO 64055
Tel: (816)373-6565
Fax: (816)478-3100
E-mail: info@aea.net
Web Site: http://www.aea.net
To provide support to the individuals intending to pursue their career in aircraft electronics and aviation maintenance industry.
Title of Award: Rockwell Collins Scholarships **Area, Field, or Subject:** Aviation. **Level of Education for which Award is Granted:** Undergraduate **Funds Available:** $1,000.
Eligibility Requirements: Applicants must be a high school senior and/or college students planning to or are attending an accredited school in an avionics or aircraft repair program. **Application Requirements:** For

further information about the scholarship, applicants are advice to contact the foundation at Aircraft Electronics Association, 4217 S Hocker, Independence, MO 64055.

4822 ■ AIRCRAFT ELECTRONICS ASSOCIATION
4217 S Hocker
Independence, MO 64055
Tel: (816)373-6565
Fax: (816)478-3100
E-mail: info@aea.net
Web Site: http://www.aea.net
To provide support for individuals intending to pursue their career in aircraft electronics and aviation maintenance industry.
Title of Award: Thomas J. Slocum Memorial Scholarships to Westwood College of Aviation Technology **Area, Field, or Subject:** Aviation. **Level of Education for which Award is Granted:** Undergraduate **Number Awarded:** 3. **Funds Available:** $6,000.
Eligibility Requirements: Applicant must be a student who plans to attend Westwood College of Aviation Technology in Broomfield, Colorado, in the avionics program. **Application Requirements:** For further information about the scholarship, applicants are advised to contact the foundation at Aircraft Electronics Association, 4217 S Hocker, Independence, MO 64055.

4823 ■ AIRCRAFT ELECTRONICS ASSOCIATION
4217 S Hocker
Independence, MO 64055
Tel: (816)373-6565
Fax: (816)478-3100
E-mail: info@aea.net
Web Site: http://www.aea.net
Title of Award: Southeast Aerospace Inc. Scholarships **Level of Education for which Award is Granted:** Undergraduate **Funds Available:** $1,000.
Eligibility Requirements: Applicant must be a high school senior and/or college students who plan to or are attending an accredited school in an avionics or aircraft repair program. **Application Requirements:** For further information about the scholarship, applicants are advice to contact the foundation at Aircraft Electronics Association, 4217 S Hocker, Independence, MO 64055.

4824 ■ AIRCRAFT ELECTRONICS ASSOCIATION
4217 S Hocker
Independence, MO 64055
Tel: (816)373-6565
Fax: (816)478-3100
E-mail: info@aea.net
Web Site: http://www.aea.net
To provide support to the individuals intending to pursue their career in aircraft electronics and aviation maintenance industry.
Title of Award: Sporty's Pilot Shop/Cincinnati Avionics Scholarships **Area, Field, or Subject:** Aviation. **Level of Education for which Award is Granted:** Undergraduate **Funds Available:** $2,000.
Eligibility Requirements: Applicant must be a high school, college, or vocational/technical school students planning to or are attending an accredited school in an avionics or aircraft repair program. **Application Requirements:** For further information about the scholarship, applicants are advice to contact the foundation at Aircraft Electronics Association, 4217 S Hocker, Independence, MO 64055.

4825 ■ AIRCRAFT ELECTRONICS ASSOCIATION
4217 S Hocker
Independence, MO 64055
Tel: (816)373-6565
Fax: (816)478-3100
E-mail: info@aea.net
Web Site: http://www.aea.net
To provide support to the individuals intending to pursue their career in aircraft electronics and aviation maintenance industry.
Title of Award: Kei Takemoto Memorial Scholarships **Area, Field, or Subject:** Aviation. **Level of Education for which Award is Granted:** Undergraduate **Funds Available:** $500.
Eligibility Requirements: Applicant must be a high school senior and/or college students who plan to or are attending an accredited school in an

avionics or aircraft repair program. **Application Requirements:** For further information about the scholarship, applicants are advice to contact the foundation at Aircraft Electronics Association, 4217 S Hocker, Independence, MO 64055. **Additional Information:** Scholarship is named in memory of Kei Takemoto whose technical expertise, engineering skill and passion for customer service was an inspiration to the avionics industry for many years.

4826 ■ AIRCRAFT ELECTRONICS ASSOCIATION
4217 S Hocker
Independence, MO 64055
Tel: (816)373-6565
Fax: (816)478-3100
E-mail: info@aea.net
Web Site: http://www.aea.net
To provide support for individuals intending to pursue a career in aircraft electronics and aviation maintenance industry.
Title of Award: Lee Tarbox Memorial Scholarships **Area, Field, or Subject:** Aviation. **Level of Education for which Award is Granted:** Undergraduate **Funds Available:** $2,500.
Eligibility Requirements: Applicant must be a high school senior and/or college students planning to or are attending an accredited school in an avionics or aircraft repair program. **Application Requirements:** For further information about the scholarship, applicants are advised to contact the foundation at Aircraft Electronics Association, 4217 S Hocker, Independence, MO 64055. **Additional Information:** Scholarship is given by Pacific Southwest Instruments.

4827 ■ AIRCRAFT ELECTRONICS ASSOCIATION
4217 S Hocker
Independence, MO 64055
Tel: (816)373-6565
Fax: (816)478-3100
E-mail: info@aea.net
Web Site: http://www.aea.net
To encourage young individuals to pursue study in Applied Science or in Aviation Maintenance Technology.
Title of Award: Tom Taylor Memorial Scholarships to Spartan College of Aeronautics and Technology **Area, Field, or Subject:** Aviation. **Level of Education for which Award is Granted:** Undergraduate **Funds Available:** $35,000.
Eligibility Requirements: Applicant must be an individual who wants to pursue their Associates Degree in Applied Science or a diploma in Aviation Maintenance Technology at Spartan College of Aeronautics & Technology's campus in Tulsa, Oklahoma. **Application Requirements:** For further information about the scholarship, applicants are advice to contact the foundation at Aircraft Electronics Association, 4217 S Hocker, Independence, MO 64055.

4828 ■ AIRCRAFT ELECTRONICS ASSOCIATION
4217 S Hocker
Independence, MO 64055
Tel: (816)373-6565
Fax: (816)478-3100
E-mail: info@aea.net
Web Site: http://www.aea.net
To provide support to the individuals intending to pursue their career in aircraft electronics and aviation maintenance industry.
Title of Award: Texas State Technical College Scholarships **Area, Field, or Subject:** Aviation. **Level of Education for which Award is Granted:** Undergraduate **Funds Available:** $1,000.
Eligibility Requirements: Applicant must be students intending to pursue an associate's degree in avionics. **Application Requirements:** For further information about the scholarship, applicants are advice to contact the foundation at Aircraft Electronics Association, 4217 S Hocker, Independence, MO 64055.

4829 ■ AIRPORT MINORITY ADVISORY COUNCIL EDUCATIONAL AND SCHOLARSHIP PROGRAM
Ronald Reagan Washington National Airport
Washington, DC 20001
Tel: (703)417-2622
Fax: (703)417-2620

E-mail: amac.manager@verizon.net
Web Site: http://amac-org.com
To provide financial assistance for education and outreach to full-time college students interested in pursuing aviation careers.
Title of Award: AMACESP Student Scholarships **Area, Field, or Subject:** Aviation. **Level of Education for which Award is Granted:** Undergraduate **Funds Available:** No amount mentioned.
Eligibility Requirements: Applicant must be a U.S. citizen admitted by an accredited school or university for the current school term in which he/she is applying for a scholarship with a cumulative 3.0 GPA and demonstrates involvement in community activities and extracurricular activities and interest and desire to pursue a career in the aviation/airport industry and seeking a degree in aviation, business administration, accounting, architecture, engineering or finance. **Application Requirements:** Applicants must complete current Scholarship Application; enclose transcripts to show proof of 3.0 GPA; and a one-page essay on career goals and why he/she have chosen his/her particular field of study.

4830 ■ ALASKA AIRMEN ASSOCIATION
4200 Floatplane Dr.
Anchorage, AK 99502
Tel: (907)245-1251
Free: 800-464-7030
Fax: (907)245-1259
E-mail: info@alaskaairmen.org
Web Site: http://www.alaskaairmen.org
To promote development in aviation careers.
Title of Award: John P. Culhane Memorial Scholarships **Area, Field, or Subject:** Aviation. **Level of Education for which Award is Granted:** Undergraduate **Funds Available:** $2,500.
Eligibility Requirements: Applicants must be enrolled in an aviation-related program at an accredited college, university, trade school or approved training center or be in current training with a certified Flight Instructor or A&P Mechanic; must have completed one year of a commercial aviation training program or at least 25% of the work toward it; must maintain a minimum GPA of 3.0 if enrolled in an accredited college, university or trade school program; must be legal U.S. residents and have no felony convictions. **Application Requirements:** Applicants must provide a letter of recommendation from one of their current instructors attesting to the commitment of the applicant to the program; must submit a completed application form; school transcripts; proof of U.S. citizenship. **Deadline for Receipt:** May 31. **Additional Information:** Erin Hall Meade, Merrill Lynch, 3601 C. St., Penthouse Anchorage, AK 99503-5996.

4831 ■ ALASKA AIRMEN ASSOCIATION
4200 Floatplane Dr.
Anchorage, AK 99502
Tel: (907)245-1251
Free: 800-464-7030
Fax: (907)245-1259
E-mail: info@alaskaairmen.org
Web Site: http://www.alaskaairmen.org
To promote development in aviation careers.
Title of Award: F. Atlee Dodge Maintenance Scholarships **Area, Field, or Subject:** Aviation. **Level of Education for which Award is Granted:** Undergraduate **Funds Available:** $2,500.
Eligibility Requirements: Applicants must be enrolled in an aviation-related program at an accredited college, university, trade school, approved training center or be in current training with a certified Flight Instructor or A&P Mechanic; must have completed one year of a commercial aviation training program or at least 25% of the work; must maintain a minimum GPA of 3.0 if enrolled in an accredited college, university or trade school program; must be legal U.S. residents and have no felony convictions. **Application Requirements:** Applicants must provide a letter of recommendation from one of their current instructors attesting to the commitment of the applicant to the program; must submit a completed application form; school transcripts; proof of U.S. citizenship. **Deadline for Receipt:** May 31. **Additional Information:** Erin Hall Meade, Merrill Lynch, 3601 C. St., Penthouse Anchorage, AK 99503-5996.

4832 ■ ALASKA AIRMEN ASSOCIATION
4200 Floatplane Dr.
Anchorage, AK 99502

Tel: (907)245-1251
Free: 800-464-7030
Fax: (907)245-1259
E-mail: info@alaskaairmen.org
Web Site: http://www.alaskaairmen.org
To promote development in aviation careers.
Title of Award: Bob Reeve Professional Aviation Management Scholarships **Area, Field, or Subject:** Aviation. **Level of Education for which Award is Granted:** Undergraduate **Funds Available:** $2,500.
Eligibility Requirements: Applicants must be enrolled in an aviation-related program with an accredited college, university, trade school, approved training center or be in current training with a certified Flight Instructor or A&P Mechanic; must have completed one year of a commercial aviation training program or at least 25% of the work; must maintain a minimum GPA of 3.0 if enrolled in an accredited college, university or trade school program; must be legal U.S. residents and have no felony convictions. **Application Requirements:** Applicants must provide a letter of recommendation from one of their current instructors attesting to the commitment of the applicant to the program; must submit a completed application form; school transcripts; proof of U.S. citizenship. **Deadline for Receipt:** May 31. **Additional Information:** Erin Hall Meade, Merrill Lynch, 3601 C. St., Penthouse Anchorage, AK 99503-5996.

4833 ■ AMERICAN INSTITUTE OF AERONAUTICS AND ASTRONAUTICS FOUNDATION
1801 Alexander Bell Drive, Ste. 500
Reston, VA 20194-4344
Tel: (703)264-7500
Free: 800-639-AIAA
Fax: (703)264-7551
E-mail: ceciliac@aiaa.org
Web Site: http://www.aiaa.org
To advance the arts, sciences, and technology of aeronautics and astronautics.
Title of Award: AIAA Foundation Scholarship Program **Area, Field, or Subject:** Aeronautics; Astronautics. **Level of Education for which Award is Granted:** Undergraduate **Funds Available:** No specific amount.
Eligibility Requirements: Applicant must: have completed at least one academic quarter or semester of full-time college work; have a college GPA of not less than the equivalent of a 3.3 on a 4.0 scale; be enrolled in an accredited college or university. Applicant does not have to be an AIAA student member in good standing to apply, but must become one before receiving a scholarship. Applicant's scholarship plan shall be such as to provide entry into some field of science or engineering encompassed by the technical activities of AIAA. Applicants shall not have, or subsequently receive, any other scholarship/award which, when combined with the AIAA Foundation award covers more than the cost of tuition. Applicant may be students of any nationality, not restricted by the US State Department, in full-time study at any accredited college or university within the United States. **Application Requirements:** The completed application must be received on or before the deadline. Students submitting their applications should include the essay and also make arrangements to have their official college transcripts sent directly to AIAA. Sophomore and junior students who have received one of these scholarship awards and wish to be considered for continuation of this award should arrange to have transcripts of their college academic record, and letters of recommendation from their faculty members and others supporting their continuance in the program sent to AIAA. **Deadline for Receipt:** January 31.

4834 ■ ARIZONA AIRPORT ASSOCIATION
4697 S Golden Arrow Dr.
Green Valley, AZ 85622
Tel: (520)398-6287
E-mail: mcovalt@cox.net
Web Site: http://www.azairports.org
To enhance careers in the aviation industry.
Title of Award: Marty Rosness Student Scholarships **Area, Field, or Subject:** Aviation. **Level of Education for which Award is Granted:** Undergraduate **Funds Available:** $3,000.
Eligibility Requirements: Applicants must be enrolled in bachelor's or master's degree programs in the state of Arizona. **Application Requirements:** Applicants must submit a completed application form; must

submit a brief statement of their interest in the scholarship; must write an at least one page brief autobiography of their aviation education, experience and background. **Additional Information:** 480-312-8475.

4835 ■ ASSOCIATION OF FLIGHT ATTENDANTS
501 3rd St., NW
Washington, DC 20001
Tel: (202)434-1300
E-mail: afatalk@afanet.org
Web Site: http://www.afanet.org
To further the education of promising young men and women who are dependents of AFA members in good standing to have the opportunity for higher education.
Title of Award: Association of Flight Attendants Scholarship Fund **Area, Field, or Subject:** Aviation. **Level of Education for which Award is Granted:** Undergraduate **Number Awarded:** 1. **Funds Available:** $5,000 for the cost of tuition, room, board and book expenses. **Duration:** One year.
Eligibility Requirements: Applicants must be dependent of AFA members in good standing seeking to further education at an accredited college or university. **Application Requirements:** Applicants must submit a completed application form (available at the website), 300-word essay, three references and transcript, if applicable. **Deadline for Receipt:** April 10.

4836 ■ COLLEGIATE SOARING ASSOCIATION
4671 Kipling St., No. 68
Wheat Ridge, CO 80033
Tel: (303)432-2137
E-mail: president.jhpc@hotmail.com
Web Site: http://www.coloradosoaring.org
To support young people in school, primarily college students, from first flight through advanced soaring.
Title of Award: Gogos Scholarships **Area, Field, or Subject:** Aviation. **Level of Education for which Award is Granted:** Undergraduate **Number Awarded:** 1. **Funds Available:** $2,000. **Duration:** Three years.
Eligibility Requirements: Applicant must be a U.S. citizen or permanent resident student, age 14-25 nominated by an FAI soaring badge holder within a sponsoring Soaring Club or Operator. **Application Requirements:** Applicants must submit complete application form. **Deadline for Receipt:** March 31.

4837 ■ DAEDALIAN FOUNDATION
PO Box 249
Randolph AFB, TX 78148-0249
Tel: (210)945-2113
Fax: (210)945-2112
E-mail: foundationchairman@daedalians.org
Web Site: http://www.daedalians.org
To encourage the youth to become military pilots.
Title of Award: Descendant Scholarships **Area, Field, or Subject:** Aerospace sciences. **Level of Education for which Award is Granted:** Undergraduate **Funds Available:** No specific amount.
Eligibility Requirements: Applicants must be direct-line descendants of Daedalians. **Application Requirements:** Applicants must submit a completed application form together with a 3" x 5" photograph and a letter stating the rank, name and number of their sponsoring Daeldalian to the Chairman, Daedalian Foundation, PO Box 249 Randolph AFB, TX 78148-0249.

4838 ■ DAEDALIAN FOUNDATION
PO Box 249
Randolph AFB, TX 78148-0249
Tel: (210)945-2113
Fax: (210)945-2112
E-mail: foundationchairman@daedalians.org
Web Site: http://www.daedalians.org
To encourage the youth to become military pilots.
Title of Award: John and Alice Egan Multi-Year Mentioning Scholarships **Area, Field, or Subject:** Aerospace sciences. **Level of Education for which Award is Granted:** Undergraduate **Funds Available:** $2000. **Duration:** 3-4 years.
Eligibility Requirements: Applicants must be a college/university student pursuing a career as a military aviator. Freshmen are not quali-

fied. **Application Requirements:** Applicants must submit a completed application form together with a 3" x 5" photograph; complete transcripts (sent directly by the educational institution); a copy of FAA medical certificate and annotated copy of the Flight Physical Standards Questionnaire to the Chairman, Daedalian Foundation, PO Box 249 Randolph AFB, TX 78148-0249. **Additional Information:** The scholarship is not tied to the Matching Program, students may apply for both programs. **Deadline for Receipt:** August 1.

4839 ■ DAEDALIAN FOUNDATION
PO Box 249
Randolph AFB, TX 78148-0249
Tel: (210)945-2113
Fax: (210)945-2112
E-mail: foundationchairman@daedalians.org
Web Site: http://www.daedalians.org
To encourage the youth to become military pilots.
Title of Award: Matching Scholarships Program **Area, Field, or Subject:** Aerospace sciences. **Level of Education for which Award is Granted:** Undergraduate **Funds Available:** No specific amount.
Eligibility Requirements: Applicants must be a college/university student pursuing a career as a military aviator. **Application Requirements:** Applicants must submit a completed application form together with a 3" x 5" photograph to the Chairman, Daedalian Foundation, PO Box 249 Randolph AFB, TX 78148-0249.

4840 ■ DAEDALIAN FOUNDATION
PO Box 249
Randolph AFB, TX 78148-0249
Tel: (210)945-2113
Fax: (210)945-2112
E-mail: foundationchairman@daedalians.org
Web Site: http://www.daedalians.org
To encourage the youth to become military pilots.
Title of Award: Navy, Army or Air Force ROTC Scholarship Program **Area, Field, or Subject:** Aerospace sciences. **Level of Education for which Award is Granted:** Undergraduate **Funds Available:** No specific amount.
Eligibility Requirements: Applicants must be a college/university student pursuing a career as a military aviator. **Application Requirements:** Candidates must be nominated by their local commanders.

4841 ■ DELTA ZETA SORORITY
202 E Church St.
Oxford, OH 45056
Tel: (513)523-7597
Web Site: http://www.deltazeta.org
To provide financial assistance to all qualified undergraduate students.
Title of Award: Arlene Davis Scholarships **Area, Field, or Subject:** Aviation. **Level of Education for which Award is Granted:** Undergraduate **Funds Available:** $1,000-$2,500. **Duration:** One academic year.
Eligibility Requirements: Applicant must be an initiated, active, continuing member entering her sophomore or junior year, who is enrolled in courses showing an interest in aviation; must have a 3.0 grade average. **Application Requirements:** Scholarship applications are available on the website and must be completed properly. Applicant must have the FAFSA reply form. **Deadline for Receipt:** February 15.

4842 ■ DISTINGUISHED FLYING CROSS SOCIETY
PO Box 530250
San Diego, CA 92153
(866)332-6332
Web Site: http://www.dfcsociety.org
To support dependents of DFC Society members in the pursuit of continuing higher education.
Title of Award: Distinguished Flying Cross Society Scholarship **Area, Field, or Subject:** Aviation. **Level of Education for which Award is Granted:** Undergraduate **Funds Available:** No amount mentioned.
Eligibility Requirements: Applicants must be descendants (or legally adopted children) of a DFC Society member. **Application Requirements:** Applicants must provide 500-word essay on why they deserve a DFCS Scholarship, SAT/SCAT scores, official high school transcript, and a letter from DFCS member attesting that he/she is a descendant of a DFCS member. **Deadline for Receipt:** November 15.

4843 ■ GENERAL AVIATION MANUFACTURERS ASSOCIATION

1400 K St. NW, Ste. 801
Washington, DC 20005
Tel: (202)393-1500
Fax: (202)842-4063
E-mail: webmaster@gama.aero
Web Site: http://www.gama.aero
To support a college student attending a National Intercollegiate Flying Association member college or university program.
Title of Award: Dr. Harold S. Wood Award for Excellence **Area, Field, or Subject:** Aviation. **Level of Education for which Award is Granted:** Undergraduate **Number Awarded:** 1. **Funds Available:** $1,000. **Duration:** One year.
Eligibility Requirements: Candidate for the award must be an enrolled college student and have completed a semester at a NIFA participating institution with GPA of 3.0 on a 4.0 scale or better and must have rendered service to NIFA, aviation clubs or aviation-related activities or non-aviation extra-curricular service and contribution to school and community. **Application Requirements:** Applicants must submit transcript and letters of recommendation with the application. **Deadline for Receipt:** March 21.

4844 ■ GRAND RAPIDS COMMUNITY FOUNDATION

161 Ottawa Ave. NW
Ste. 209-C Waters Bldg.
Grand Rapids, MI 49503
Tel: (616)454-1751
Fax: (616)454-6455
E-mail: grfound@grfoundation.org
Web Site: http://www.grfoundation.org
To provide financial support to those students who study flight science.
Title of Award: Joshua Esch Mitchell Aviation Scholarships **Area, Field, or Subject:** Aviation. **Level of Education for which Award is Granted:** Undergraduate **Funds Available:** No specific amount.
Eligibility Requirements: Applicants must be U.S citizens. Must be enrolled full or part-time at a college or university in the United States providing an accredited flight science curriculum. Applicants must be second year students or above with a minimum of 2.75 GPA; must be pursuing studies in the field of professional piloting with an emphasis in General Aviation, Aviation Management, or Aviation Safety. **Application Requirements:** Applicants must check the available website for the required materials. **Additional Information:** Grand Rapids Community Foundation at the above address

4845 ■ HARTFIELD COALITION

PO Box 4742
Morgantown, WV 26504-4742
E-mail: hfcoalition@email.com
Web Site: http://www.hartfieldcoalition.org
To create aviation education and training scholarship opportunities to benefit the youth in Appalachia.
Title of Award: Scholarship Challenge Flight **Area, Field, or Subject:** Aviation. **Level of Education for which Award is Granted:** Undergraduate **Funds Available:** No specific amount.
Eligibility Requirements: Applicants must be youth from Appalachia. **Application Requirements:** Applicants must check the available website for the required materials. **Additional Information:** Hartfield Coalition at the above address.

4846 ■ INTERNATIONAL SOCIETY OF AIR SAFETY INVESTIGATORS

107 E Holly Ave., Ste. 11
Sterling, VA 20164
Tel: (703)430-9668
Fax: (703)430-4970
E-mail: isasi@erols.com
Web Site: http://www.isasi.org
To encourage and assist college-level students interested in the field of aviation safety and aircraft occurrence investigation.
Title of Award: The ISASI Rudolf Kapustin Memorial Scholarships **Area, Field, or Subject:** Aviation. **Level of Education for which Award is Granted:** Undergraduate **Funds Available:** $1500.
Eligibility Requirements: Applicant must be a member of ISASI enrolled as full-time student in a recognized education program, which includes courses in aircraft engineering and/or operations, aviation psychology, aviation safety or aircraft occurrence investigation, etc., with major or minor subjects that focus on aviation safety/investigation. **Application Requirements:** Applicants must submit a the application form and a 1000 word paper in English addressing "the challenges for air safety investigators". Paper must be countersigned by applicant's tutor/academic supervisor as authentic, original work.

4847 ■ NATIONAL BUSINESS AVIATION ASSOCIATION

1200 18th St. NW, Ste. 400
Washington, DC 20036-9000
Tel: (202)783-9000
Fax: (202)331-8364
E-mail: info@nbaa.org
Web Site: http://www.nbaa.org
To promote professional development and business aviation careers and to benefit individuals seeking to become NBAA Certified Aviation Managers(CAMs).
Title of Award: Donald A. Baldwin Sr. Business Aviation Management Scholarships **Area, Field, or Subject:** Aviation. **Level of Education for which Award is Granted:** Undergraduate **Funds Available:** No specific amount.
Eligibility Requirements: Applicants must be eligible to take the CAM Exam within two years of the date of the scholarship award; must meet the minimum qualifications to take the CAM Exam; must be U.S. citizens; and must have a grade point average of 3.0 or above on a 4.0 scale. **Application Requirements:** Applicants must submit a completed application form; an official transcript of record; a 250-word, typed, double-spaced essay describing the applicant's interest in and goals for a career in the business aviation industry; two letters of recommendation from those who can comment on the career aspirations and qualifications of the applicant; and current resume. **Deadline for Receipt:** November 1. **Additional Information:** Jay Evans at the above address.

4848 ■ NATIONAL BUSINESS AVIATION ASSOCIATION

1200 18th St. NW, Ste. 400
Washington, DC 20036-9000
Tel: (202)783-9000
Fax: (202)331-8364
E-mail: info@nbaa.org
Web Site: http://www.nbaa.org
To promote professional development and business aviation careers.
Title of Award: Janice K. Barden Aviation Scholarships **Area, Field, or Subject:** Aviation. **Level of Education for which Award is Granted:** Undergraduate **Number Awarded:** 5. **Funds Available:** $5,000.
Eligibility Requirements: Applicants must be undergraduate sophomores, juniors, or seniors enrolled in an aviation-related two-year, four-year, or postgraduate degree program; must have a GPA of at least 3.0 on a 4.0 scale; and must be U.S. citizens. **Application Requirements:** Applicants must submit completed application form; a typed, double-spaced essay of 250 words, describing the applicant's interest and goals for a career in the business aviation industry; a letter of recommendation from a member of the aviation department faculty at the institution in which the applicant is currently enrolled; two professional letters of recommendation; and a current resume. **Deadline for Receipt:** November 1. **Additional Information:** Jay Evans at the above address.

4849 ■ NATIONAL BUSINESS AVIATION ASSOCIATION

1200 18th St. NW, Ste. 400
Washington, DC 20036-9000
Tel: (202)783-9000
Fax: (202)331-8364
E-mail: info@nbaa.org
Web Site: http://www.nbaa.org
To promote professional development and business aviation careers.
Title of Award: Alan H. Conklin Business Aviation Management Scholarships **Area, Field, or Subject:** Aviation. **Level of Education for which Award is Granted:** Undergraduate **Funds Available:** No specific amount.
Eligibility Requirements: Applicants must be full-time undergraduate sophomore, junior, or senior students; officially enrolled or accepted for enrollment in an aviation management program; U.S. citizens; and must have a grade point average of 3.0 or above on a 4.0 scale. **Application**

Requirements: Applicants must submit completed application form; an official transcript of record; a 500-word, typed, double-spaced essay describing the applicant's interest in and goals for a career in business aviation; two letters of recommendation from those qualified to comment on the career aspirations and qualifications of the applicant especially as they relate to business aviation; and current resume. **Deadline for Receipt:** August 1. **Additional Information:** Jay Evans at the above address.

4850 ■ NATIONAL BUSINESS AVIATION ASSOCIATION
1200 18th St. NW, Ste. 400
Washington, DC 20036-9000
Tel: (202)783-9000
Fax: (202)331-8364
E-mail: info@nbaa.org
Web Site: http://www.nbaa.org
To benefit a student intending to pursue a career in journalism, preferably with an aviation focus. **Title of Award:** David E. Ewald Journalism Scholarships **Area, Field, or Subject:** Aviation; Journalism. **Level of Education for which Award is Granted:** Undergraduate **Funds Available:** $1,000.
Eligibility Requirements: Applicants must be either enrolled or accepted for enrollment in an accredited college or university program in journalism or a related area and must be U.S. citizens. **Application Requirements:** Applicants must submit a completed application form; an official transcript of record; a proof of enrollment or acceptance, prior to the distribution of award; a 500-1,000-word, typed, double-spaced essay describing the applicant's interest in and goals for a career in journalism; two letters of recommendation from either a faculty member or other individual who is familiar with the applicant's capabilities; and a current resume. **Deadline for Receipt:** August 15. **Additional Information:** Jay Evans at the above address.

4851 ■ NATIONAL BUSINESS AVIATION ASSOCIATION
1200 18th St. NW, Ste. 400
Washington, DC 20036-9000
Tel: (202)783-9000
Fax: (202)331-8364
E-mail: info@nbaa.org
Web Site: http://www.nbaa.org
To promote professional development and business aviation careers. **Title of Award:** William M. Fanning Maintenance Scholarships **Area, Field, or Subject:** Aviation. **Level of Education for which Award is Granted:** Undergraduate **Number Awarded:** 2. **Funds Available:** $2,500.
Eligibility Requirements: Applicants must be students who are currently enrolled in an accredited airframe and powerplant program at an approved FAR Part 147 school or an individual who is not currently enrolled but has been accepted for enrollment in an A&P program; must be U.S. citizens; and must have a grade point average of 3.0 or above on a 4.0 scale. **Application Requirements:** Applicants must submit a complete application form; an official transcript of record; a 250-word, typed, double-spaced essay describing the applicant's interest in and goals for a career in the aviation maintenance field; two letters of recommendation from a member or other individual who is familiar with the applicant's capabilities; and current resume. **Deadline for Receipt:** August 1. **Additional Information:** Jay Evans at the above address.

4852 ■ NATIONAL BUSINESS AVIATION ASSOCIATION
1200 18th St. NW, Ste. 400
Washington, DC 20036-9000
Tel: (202)783-9000
Fax: (202)331-8364
E-mail: info@nbaa.org
Web Site: http://www.nbaa.org
To promote education and training as a means for business aviation flight attendants and flight technicians to enhance their professional careers. **Title of Award:** Flight Attendants/Flight Technician Scholarships **Area, Field, or Subject:** Aviation. **Level of Education for which Award is Granted:** Undergraduate **Funds Available:** No specific amount.
Eligibility Requirements: Applicants must be flight attendants or flight technicians. **Application Requirements:** Applicants must submit a completed application form; one signed aviation or leadership-related let-

ter of recommendation, dated within the last two years; a typed, 100-word essay answering the required question; and a current, one-page resume. **Deadline for Receipt:** March 31. **Additional Information:** Jay Evans at the above address.

4853 ■ NATIONAL BUSINESS AVIATION ASSOCIATION
1200 18th St. NW, Ste. 400
Washington, DC 20036-9000
Tel: (202)783-9000
Fax: (202)331-8364
E-mail: info@nbaa.org
Web Site: http://www.nbaa.org
To recognize individuals who have demonstrated honesty, integrity, and selflessness in their dealings with others.
Title of Award: Lawrence Ginocchio Aviation Scholarships **Area, Field, or Subject:** Aviation. **Level of Education for which Award is Granted:** Undergraduate **Number Awarded:** 5. **Funds Available:** $25,000.
Eligibility Requirements: Applicants must be full-time undergraduate sophomore, junior, or senior students officially enrolled or accepted for enrollment in an aviation related two-year, four-year or postgraduate degree program; must be U.S. citizens; and must have a grade point average of 3.0 or above on a 4.0 scale. **Application Requirements:** Applicants must submit a complete application form; must submit an official transcript of record; a 500-to 1,000-word, typed, double-spaced essay describing the applicant's interest in and goals for a career in the business aviation industry and demonstrating the applicant's strength of character; two letters of recommendation from those qualified to comment on the career aspirations and qualifications of the applicant especially as they relate to business aviation; and current resume. **Deadline for Receipt:** August 1. **Additional Information:** Jay Evans at the above address.

4854 ■ NATIONAL BUSINESS AVIATION ASSOCIATION
1200 18th St. NW, Ste. 400
Washington, DC 20036-9000
Tel: (202)783-9000
Fax: (202)331-8364
E-mail: info@nbaa.org
Web Site: http://www.nbaa.org
To promote professional development and business aviation careers. **Title of Award:** NORDAM Dee Howard/Etienne Fage Scholarships **Area, Field, or Subject:** Aviation; Aeronautics. **Level of Education for which Award is Granted:** Undergraduate **Number Awarded:** 5. **Funds Available:** $25,000.
Eligibility Requirements: Applicants must be full-time undergraduate sophomore, junior, or senior students enrolled in the aerospace engineering or aeronautical systems maintenance engineering major at Embry-Riddle Aeronautical University; must be U.S. citizens; and must have a grade point average of 3.0 or above on a 4.0 scale. **Application Requirements:** Applicants must submit a completed application form; an official transcript of record; a 250-word, typed, double-spaced essay describing the applicant's interest in and goals for a career in the business aviation industry; two letters of recommendation from an Embry-Riddle faculty member who is familiar with the applicant's capabilities; and current resume. **Deadline for Receipt:** August 1. **Additional Information:** Jay Evans at the above address.

4855 ■ NATIONAL BUSINESS AVIATION ASSOCIATION
1200 18th St. NW, Ste. 400
Washington, DC 20036-9000
Tel: (202)783-9000
Fax: (202)331-8364
E-mail: info@nbaa.org
Web Site: http://www.nbaa.org
To promote technical education and professional development as a means for business aviation maintenance technicians to enhance their careers.
Title of Award: Maintenance Technical Reward and Career Scholarships **Area, Field, or Subject:** Aviation. **Level of Education for which Award is Granted:** Undergraduate **Funds Available:** No specific amount.
Eligibility Requirements: Applicants must be current holder of an airframe and powerplant certificate; currently employed in general aviation; must either be currently enrolled in either an accredited A&P program or an approved FAR Part 147 school. **Application Requirements:** Ap-

plicants must submit completed application form; a 250-word, typed, double-spaced essay describing the applicant's interest in and goals for a career in the business aviation maintenance field; current resume; and a letter of recommendation from either a supervisor, faculty member or other individual who is familiar with the applicant's capabilities. **Deadline for Receipt:** February 15. **Additional Information:** Jay Evans at the above address.

4856 ■ NATIONAL BUSINESS AVIATION ASSOCIATION
1200 18th St. NW, Ste. 400
Washington, DC 20036-9000
Tel: (202)783-9000
Fax: (202)331-8364
E-mail: info@nbaa.org
Web Site: http://www.nbaa.org
To promote professional development and business aviation careers.
Title of Award: U.S. Aircraft Insurance Group Professional Development Program Scholarships **Area, Field, or Subject:** Aviation. **Level of Education for which Award is Granted:** Undergraduate **Funds Available:** $1,000.

Eligibility Requirements: Applicants must be full-time undergraduate sophomore, junior, or senior students in academic year enrolled in an aviation-related two-year, four-year, or postgraduate degree program that incorporates the NBAA PDP; must be U.S. citizens; and must have a grade point average of 3.0 or above on a 4.0 scale. **Application Requirements:** Applicants must submit a completed application form; an official transcript of record; a 250-word, typed, double-spaced essay describing the applicant's interest in and goals for a career in business aviation flight department; two letters of recommendation from a member of aviation department faculty at the institution where the applicant is currently enrolled; and current resume. **Deadline for Receipt:** August 1. **Additional Information:** Jay Evans at the above address.

4857 ■ NATIONAL GAY PILOTS ASSOCIATION
PO Box 7271
Dallas, TX 75209-0271
Tel: (214)336-0873
Fax: (214)350-0447
Web Site: http://www.ngpa.org
To provide educational assistance to students pursuing aviation careers as professional pilots.
Title of Award: NGPA Education Fund Scholarships **Area, Field, or Subject:** Aviation. **Level of Education for which Award is Granted:** Undergraduate **Number Awarded:** Varies. **Funds Available:** $2,000.
Eligibility Requirements: Applicants must be pursuing a career in the field of aviation; must be accepted or enrolled in an accredited college or university with an aviation related curriculum (aerospace; aerodynamics; engineering and airport management) in pursuit of a degree leading to a career as a professional pilot or undergoing a course of study in recognized professional pilot aviation training program in an institution of higher learning, aviation technical school or government approved flight school; must have demonstrated community involvement, including support of the gay, lesbian, bi-sexual and transgender (GLBT) community. **Application Requirements:** Applicants must submit a formal application; academic records; list of work experience, extra curricular activities and or/community activities/honors/awards; proof of financial need; letter of recommendation; and essay on personal goals. Further instructions can be found in the NGPA website. **Deadline for Receipt:** March 1.

4858 ■ NINETY-NINES, INTERNATIONAL ORGANIZATION OF WOMEN PILOTS
4300 Amelia Earhart Rd.
Oklahoma City, OK 73159
Tel: (405)685-7969
Free: 800-994-1929
Fax: (405)685-7985
E-mail: 99s@ninety-nines.org
Web Site: http://www.ninety-nines.org
To provide financial assistance for students pursuing education in the field of aviation and aerospace
Title of Award: Amelia Earhart Memorial Academic Scholarships **Area, Field, or Subject:** Aviation. **Level of Education for which Award is Granted:** Undergraduate **Funds Available:** $5,000.

Eligibility Requirements: Applicant must be currently enrolled in a degree seeking institution in the field of aerospace and aviation; must be a member of The Ninety-Nines Inc. Associates and bachelor degree students must have a cumulative GPA of 3.0 or better on a 4.0 scale, or equivalent; and must demonstrate financial need. **Application Requirements:** Applicant must complete the application form (please visit website) on an 8 1/2x11 paper (clipped or stapled) and submit it to Section AE Scholarship Chairman or to Section Governor. **Additional Information:** Joy Parker-Blackwood, AEMSF Chairman aechair@ninety-nines.org, 905-841-7930.

4859 ■ PROFESSIONAL AVIATION MAINTENANCE ASSOCIATION
400 Commonwealth Dr.
Warrendale, PA 15096
Tel: (724)772-4092; (866)865-7262
Fax: (724)772-4064
E-mail: hq@pama.org
Web Site: http://www.pama.org
To provide educational assistance as a reward and recognition to qualified students pursuing careers in aviation maintenance.
Title of Award: PAMA Foundation Scholarship Program **Area, Field, or Subject:** Aviation; Aeronautics. **Level of Education for which Award is Granted:** Graduate, Undergraduate **Funds Available:** $1,000.
Eligibility Requirements: Applicants who are applying individually must be enrolled in a FAR Part 147 certificated educational institution in pursuit of an Airframe and Powerplant (A&P) license or a degree in aerospace maintenance and management; must have completed 25 percent of the required curriculum; must have a B average or equivalent; and must have a need for financial assistance. Applicants pursuing a Chapter application must be active; and not a relative of any PAMA board member. The chapter must also be recognized by PAMA. **Application Requirements:** Individual applicants must submit a certificate of current enrollment or avionics certification; completed Form SS-APP-880(typewritten and signed) and letter(s) of reference(s); Chapter applicants must submit completed Form CH-APP-880 (typewritten and signed) and are encouraged to present CH-APP-880 Forms of students awarded the previous year (if applicable). All requirements must be forwarded to PAMA Foundation Scholarships, 400 Commonwealth Dr. Warrendale, PA 15096. **Deadline for Receipt:** October 31.

4860 ■ THE SAN DIEGO FOUNDATION
2508 Historic Decatur Rd., Ste. 200
San Diego, CA 92106
Tel: (619)235-2300
Fax: (619)239-1710
E-mail: info@sdfoundation.org
Web Site: http://www.sdfoundation.org
To support the education of students from California.
Title of Award: San Diego Regional Aviation Association Scholarships **Area, Field, or Subject:** Aviation. **Level of Education for which Award is Granted:** Undergraduate **Funds Available:** No specific amount.
Eligibility Requirements: Applicant must be a Southern California resident enrolled at an accredited two-year college or four-year university in Southern California, studying aviation-related curricula. Student must have a minimum 2.50 GPA on a 4.0 scale. **Application Requirements:** Applicants must submit a completed scholarship application form, along with a typed personal statement (maximum of two pages); two letters of recommendation on official letterhead (one letter must come from a member of the aviation community or aviation department faculty at the institution in which the applicant is currently enrolled); a official transcripts in a sealed envelope; and a copy of most recent tax form(s) used to complete financial information (Form 1040-pages 1 & 2; Form 1040A-pages 1 & 2: Form 1040EZ-page 1). **Deadline for Receipt:** March 21. **Additional Information:** 619-814-1343 or scholarships@sdfoundation.org.

4861 ■ TAILHOOK ASSOCIATION
9696 Businesspark Ave.
San Diego, CA 92131
Tel: (858)689-9223
Free: 800-322-4665
E-mail: thookassn@aol.com
Web Site: http://www.tailhook.org

To educate the public with the history and present day activities of US navy carrier aviation.

Title of Award: Tailhook Educational Foundation Scholarships Program **Area, Field, or Subject:** Aviation. **Level of Education for which Award is Granted:** Undergraduate **Funds Available:** $2000-$10000.

Eligibility Requirements: Applicants must be high school graduates and dependents of current or former (US Navy/US Marines Corps/US Coast Guards) Naval Aviators, Naval Flight Officers, or Naval Aircrewmen; must be dependents of individuals who are serving or have served on board as US Navy Aircraft carriers. **Application Requirements:** Application forms are available at the website. Applicants must complete the application form together with a certified copy of high school transcript; documentation of SAT or ACT score; an essay on career goals (1 page); endorsement letter; letter of acceptance at a college/university; and an aircrew designation letter (if applicable). Mail application and other supporting materials to: The Tailhook Educational Foundation, Scholarship Applications 9696 Businesspark Ave. San Diego, CA 92131-1643. **Deadline for Receipt:** March 17.

4862 ■ U.S. AIR FORCE ROTC

551 E Maxwell Blvd.
Maxwell AFB, AL 36112-5917
Tel: (334)953-6167
Fax: (866)423-7682
Web Site: http://www.afrotc.com

To provide financial assistance for college students enrolled in specific fields.

Title of Award: U.S. Air Force ROTC Express Scholarships **Area, Field, or Subject:** Engineering; Aerospace sciences; Aeronautics; Atmospheric sciences. **Level of Education for which Award is Granted:** Undergraduate **Funds Available:** $15,000.

Eligibility Requirements: Applicants must be United States citizens by the end of the projected term of activation; must pass the Air Force Officer Qualifying Test; must pass the Air Force ROTC Physical Fitness Test; must have at least a 2.5 cumulative college grade point average; must a physical examination and be certified; must not be a contracted scholarship recipient; and must meet the age, moral and other scholarship eligibility requirements for Air force ROTC. **Application Requirements:** Applications for the Express Scholarship are processed and approved at the detachment level. Applicant must contact the detachment serving the school that he/she wishes to attend and the school will work to nominate the student for the appropriate scholarship program.

4863 ■ UNIVERSITY AVIATION ASSOCIATION

3410 Skyway Dr.
Auburn, AL 36830-6444
Tel: (334)844-2434
Web Site: http://www.uaa.aero

To encourage a high level of achievement in aviation studies through education assistance.

Title of Award: Joseph Frasca Excellence in Aviation Scholarships **Area, Field, or Subject:** Aviation. **Level of Education for which Award is Granted:** Undergraduate **Number Awarded:** 2. **Funds Available:** 1,500.

Eligibility Requirements: Applicants must have a minimum of 3.0 GPA; must have Federal Aviation Administration certification in either aviation maintenance or flight; a member of at least one Aviation organization; and juniors or seniors currently enrolled in a UAA member institution. **Application Requirements:** Applicants must submit five copies of completed application form; a brief essay; transcript; FAA certificates; one letter of reference; documents about financial status and other supporting documents. **Deadline for Receipt:** April 4.

4864 ■ UNIVERSITY AVIATION ASSOCIATION

3410 Skyway Dr.
Auburn, AL 36830-6444
Tel: (334)844-2434
Web Site: http://www.uaa.aero

To encourage careers in aviation and other related fields through educational assistance.

Title of Award: Eugene S. Kropf Scholarships **Area, Field, or Subject:** Aviation. **Level of Education for which Award is Granted:** Undergraduate **Funds Available:** $500.

Eligibility Requirements: Applicants must be U.S. citizens; enrolled in or planning to pursue two- or four-year degrees in the field of aviation; must

be officially enrolled in a UAA member institution; and have a 3.0 GPA. **Application Requirements:** Applicants must submit application form; proof of enrollment; transcript; an essay (250 words typewritten, double-spaced) on "How Can I Improve Aviation Education". **Deadline for Receipt:** May 31. **Additional Information:** Kevin R. Kuhlmann, Professor of Aviation and Aerospace Science, Metropolitan State College of Denver, Campus Box 30, PO Box 173362, Denver, CO 802173362.

4865 ■ UNIVERSITY AVIATION ASSOCIATION

3410 Skyway Dr.
Auburn, AL 36830-6444
Tel: (334)844-2434
Web Site: http://www.uaa.aero

To promote educational pursuits in the field of aviation or space-related fields through financial assistance.

Title of Award: Paul A. Whelan Aviation Scholarships **Area, Field, or Subject:** Aviation. **Level of Education for which Award is Granted:** Undergraduate **Number Awarded:** 1. **Funds Available:** $2,000.

Eligibility Requirements: Applicants must be U.S. citizens; sophomore, junior, senior or graduate students; enrolled in a UAA member institution; and must have 2.5 overall GPA and 3.0 in Aviation. **Application Requirements:** Applicants must submit original copies and five copies of application form; official transcript; and recommendation letter from the institution. **Additional Information:** Established in memory of Paul A. Whelan, an aviation educator. **Deadline for Receipt:** May 15. **Additional Information:** Dr. David A. NewMyer, Chair, University Aviation Association Scholarship Committee, Southern Illinois University Carbondale, 1365 Douglas Drive, ASA Carbondale, IL 62901-6623.

4866 ■ XAVIER UNIVERSITY

3800 Victory Pky.
Cincinnati, OH 45207
Tel: (513)745-3000
Free: 800-344-GOXU
Web Site: http://www.xavier.edu

To financially support students with their education.

Title of Award: Xavier University ROTC Scholarships - Air Force ROTC **Area, Field, or Subject:** Aerospace sciences. **Level of Education for which Award is Granted:** Undergraduate **Funds Available:** Covers the cost of remaining tuition, room and board.

Eligibility Requirements: Applicants must be high school students pursuing an Air Force ROTC or college freshmen and sophomores pursuing an in-college Air Force ROTC. **Application Requirements:** Applicants must contact the Detachment 665 Unit Admission Officer for the application process. **Additional Information:** 513-556-2237.

Applied Science

4867 ■ ALBUQUERQUE COMMUNITY FOUNDATION

PO Box 36960
Albuquerque, NM 87176-6960
Tel: (505)883-6240
Fax: (505)883-3629
E-mail: foundation@albuquerquefoundation.org
Web Site: http://www.swcp.com

To support students of exceptional promise in the fields of science and math.

Title of Award: Woodcock Family Education Scholarship Program **Area, Field, or Subject:** Math; Science. **Level of Education for which Award is Granted:** Undergraduate **Funds Available:** $11,000. **Duration:** 4 years.

Eligibility Requirements: Applicants must be Albuquerque graduating high school seniors; with strong math and/or science credentials; must attend a college or university full time; must have a minimum GPA of 3.8; **Application Requirements:** Applicants must attach these to their application packet: career goals in personal statement MUST include those in the field of math or science; one reference from a math or science teacher; one or more references from other teachers, internship or work programs, or community services. **Additional Information:** Albuquerque Community Foundation at the above address

4868 ■ ALLIANCE OF TECHNOLOGY AND WOMEN

25 Highland Park Vill., No. 100-393
Dallas, TX 75205

888-895-1566
E-mail: info@atwinternational.org
Web Site: http://www.atwinternational.org
To provide financial assistance to women whose academic and professional goals include work in science, math, engineering or technology.
Title of Award: GREAT MINDS Collegiate Scholarship Program **Area, Field, or Subject:** Science; Math; Engineering; Technology. **Level of Education for which Award is Granted:** Undergraduate **Funds Available:** No specific amount.
Eligibility Requirements: Applicants must be first-time students or adult learners returning to school to pursue a new career; must be enrolled in an Associate's or Bachelor's Degree program; may have diverse levels of life experience, academic merit, age, race and religion. **Application Requirements:** Applicants must submit a completed application form. **Additional Information:** Alliance of Technology and Women at the above address.

4869 ■ AMERICAN SOCIETY FOR QUALITY - STATISTIC DIVISION

611 E Wisconsin Ave.
PO Box 3005
Milwaukee, WI 53201-3005
E-mail: contact@asqstatdiv.org
Web Site: http://www.asqstatdiv.org
To provide financial assistance to deserving students who are in applied statistics and/or quality management field.
Title of Award: Ellis R. Ott Scholarships **Area, Field, or Subject:** Statistics; Quality assurance and control. **Level of Education for which Award is Granted:** Graduate, Undergraduate **Number Awarded:** 3. **Funds Available:** No specific amount.
Eligibility Requirements: Applicants must be students who are planning to enroll or currently enrolled in a masters degree or higher level US or Canadian program that has concentration in applied statistics and/or quality management. **Application Requirements:** Applicants must submit completed application form; resume; undergraduate transcript; graduate transcript, for students who have graduate school experience; essay of no longer than one page, typewritten, no smaller than 10-point type, stating qualifications, career goals, reasons for seeking the scholarship; two letters of recommendation from professors in the current or intended field of study. **Deadline for Receipt:** April 1.

4870 ■ AMERICAN STATISTICAL ASSOCIATION

732 N Washington St.
Alexandria, VA 22314-1943
Tel: (703)684-1221; 888-231-3473
Fax: (703)684-2037
E-mail: asainfo@amstat.org
Web Site: http://www.amstat.org
To provide financial assistance for students who are in need; to honor the memory and distinguished career of Sam by honoring contributions (either recent or past) to the advancement of scientific or technical knowledge, ingenious application of existing knowledge, or successful activity in the fostering of cooperative scientific efforts that have been directly involved in matters of national defense or public interest.
Title of Award: Wilks Memorial Awards **Area, Field, or Subject:** Statistics. **Level of Education for which Award is Granted:** Undergraduate **Funds Available:** No specific amount.
Eligibility Requirements: Applicants must demonstrate financial need. **Application Requirements:** Applicants may check website for scholarship instructions and information. **Additional Information:** American Statistical Association at the above address.

4871 ■ ARMED FORCES COMMUNICATIONS AND ELECTRONICS ASSOCIATION

4400 Fair Lakes Court
Fairfax, VA 22033
Tel: (703)631-6141
Free: 800-336-4583
Fax: (703)631-4693
Web Site: http://www.afcea.org
To provide scholarship for the general public.
Title of Award: AFCEA Distance Learning/Online Scholarships **Area, Field, or Subject:** Engineering; Mathematics; Physics; Communications; Electronics. **Level of Education for which Award is Granted:** Undergraduate **Funds Available:** $1,500.

Eligibility Requirements: Applicants must be U.S. citizens currently enrolled full time pursuing either a Bachelor of Science or Master's of Science degree through distance learning or online program (only a few second-year students only will be accepted). **Application Requirements:** Applicants may apply online at AFFECT website. Applicants must also submit two letters of recommendation printed in school stationery and with signature from field-of-study professors. **Deadline for Receipt:** June 1. **Additional Information:** Norma Corrales; 703-631-6149.

4872 ■ ARMED FORCES COMMUNICATIONS AND ELECTRONICS ASSOCIATION

4400 Fair Lakes Court
Fairfax, VA 22033
Tel: (703)631-6141
Free: 800-336-4583
Fax: (703)631-4693
Web Site: http://www.afcea.org
To provide scholarship to the general public.
Title of Award: AFCEA General John A. Wickham Scholarships **Area, Field, or Subject:** Engineering; Mathematics; Physics; Communications; Electronics. **Level of Education for which Award is Granted:** Undergraduate **Funds Available:** $2,000.
Eligibility Requirements: Applicants must be US citizens; must have GPA of 3.5 on 4.0 scale. **Application Requirements:** Applicants may apply at AFCEA web site. Applicants must also submit two letters of recommendation printed in school stationery and with signature from field-of-study professors. **Deadline for Receipt:** May 1. **Additional Information:** Norma Corrales; 703-631-6149.

4873 ■ ARMED FORCES COMMUNICATIONS AND ELECTRONICS ASSOCIATION

4400 Fair Lakes Court
Fairfax, VA 22033
Tel: (703)631-6141
Free: 800-336-4583
Fax: (703)631-4693
Web Site: http://www.afcea.org
To provide scholarship for the general public.
Title of Award: William E. "Buck" Bragunier Scholarships **Area, Field, or Subject:** Engineering; Mathematics; Physics; Communications; Electronics. **Level of Education for which Award is Granted:** Undergraduate **Funds Available:** $2,000.
Eligibility Requirements: Applicants must be at least second year college students; must be enrolled full time as sophomores or juniors at the time of application; must have an outstanding record of demonstrated leadership within university or local community. **Application Requirements:** Applicants may apply online at AFFECT website. Applicants must also submit two letters of recommendation printed in school stationery and with signature from field-of-study professors. **Deadline for Receipt:** May 1. **Additional Information:** Norma Corrales; 703-631-6149.

4874 ■ ARMED FORCES COMMUNICATIONS AND ELECTRONICS ASSOCIATION

4400 Fair Lakes Court
Fairfax, VA 22033
Tel: (703)631-6141
Free: 800-336-4583
Fax: (703)631-4693
Web Site: http://www.afcea.org
To provide scholarships to students connected to the US Military.
Title of Award: LT.G. Douglas D. Buchholz Memorial Scholarships **Area, Field, or Subject:** Engineering; Mathematics; Physics; Communications. **Level of Education for which Award is Granted:** Undergraduate **Funds Available:** $2,000.
Eligibility Requirements: Applicants must be currently active enlisted soldiers assigned to Fort Gordon, Georgia; must have completed a minimum of 15 semester hours/25 quarter hours; must be currently enrolled either full or part time in an accredited US college; and must have a minimum GPA of 2.5 on a 4.0 scale. **Application Requirements:** Students may apply online at the AFCEA web site. **Deadline for Receipt:** November 15. **Additional Information:** Mr. Joseph S. Yavorsky, President; president@afcea-augusta.org.

4875 ■ ARMED FORCES COMMUNICATIONS AND ELECTRONICS ASSOCIATION
4400 Fair Lakes Court
Fairfax, VA 22033
Tel: (703)631-6141
Free: 800-336-4583
Fax: (703)631-4693
Web Site: http://www.afcea.org
To provide educational incentives, opportunities and assistance for people engaged in information management, communications and intelligence efforts and fostering excellence in education particularly in the "hard science" disciplines related to C4ISR.
Title of Award: Disabled War Veterans Scholarships **Area, Field, or Subject:** Engineering; Mathematics; Physics; Communications. **Level of Education for which Award is Granted:** Undergraduate **Funds Available:** $2,500.
Eligibility Requirements: Applicants must be currently enrolled and attending either a two year or four year in an accredited college or university in the United States; must be enrolled in an accredited distance learning or online degree granting program affiliated with major, accredited two year or four year college or university in the United States. **Application Requirements:** Applicants may apply online at AFFECT website. Applicants must also submit two letters of recommendation printed on school stationery and with signature from field-of-study professors. **Deadline for Receipt:** November 1. **Additional Information:** Norma Corrales; 703-631-6149.

4876 ■ ARMED FORCES COMMUNICATIONS AND ELECTRONICS ASSOCIATION
4400 Fair Lakes Court
Fairfax, VA 22033
Tel: (703)631-6141
Free: 800-336-4583
Fax: (703)631-4693
Web Site: http://www.afcea.org
To provide scholarship to the general public.
Title of Award: Lockheed Martin IT Scholarships **Area, Field, or Subject:** Engineering; Mathematics; Physics; Communications. **Level of Education for which Award is Granted:** Undergraduate **Funds Available:** $3,000.
Eligibility Requirements: Applicants must be at least second year college students, must be enrolled full time as sophomores or juniors at the time of application. **Application Requirements:** Applicants may apply online. Applicants must also submit two letters of recommendation printed in school stationery and with signature from field-of-study professors; and official transcript of all college level study. **Deadline for Receipt:** May 1. **Additional Information:** Norma Corrales; 703-631-6149.

4877 ■ ARMED FORCES COMMUNICATIONS AND ELECTRONICS ASSOCIATION
4400 Fair Lakes Court
Fairfax, VA 22033
Tel: (703)631-6141
Free: 800-336-4583
Fax: (703)631-4693
Web Site: http://www.afcea.org
To provide scholarships to students connected to the US Military.
Title of Award: AFCEA General Emmett Paige Scholarships **Area, Field, or Subject:** Engineering; Mathematics; Physics; Communications. **Level of Education for which Award is Granted:** Undergraduate **Funds Available:** $2,000.
Eligibility Requirements: Applicants must be US citizens; must have a minimum GPA of 3.0 on 4.0 scale. **Application Requirements:** Applicants may apply online at the AFCEA web site. Applicants must also submit a copy of Certificate of Service, Discharge From DD214, or facsimile of current Department of Defense or Coast Guard Identification Card; and two letters of recommendation printed in school stationery and with signature from field-of-study professors. **Deadline for Receipt:** March 1. **Additional Information:** Norma Corrales; 703-631-6149.

4878 ■ ARMED FORCES COMMUNICATIONS AND ELECTRONICS ASSOCIATION
4400 Fair Lakes Court
Fairfax, VA 22033

Tel: (703)631-6141
Free: 800-336-4583
Fax: (703)631-4693
Web Site: http://www.afcea.org
To provide scholarships to students connected to the US military.
Title of Award: Veterans of Enduring Freedom (Afghanistan) and Iraqi Freedom Scholarships **Area, Field, or Subject:** Engineering; Mathematics; Physics; Communications. **Level of Education for which Award is Granted:** Undergraduate **Funds Available:** $2,500. **Duration:** One year.
Eligibility Requirements: Applicants must be currently enrolled and attending either a two year accredited college or university in the United States. **Application Requirements:** Applicants may apply online at AFCEA web site. **Additional Information:** The AFCEA Educational Foundation is pleased to co-sponsor this scholarship opportunity for U.S. War Veterans. **Deadline for Receipt:** April 1 and November 1. **Additional Information:** Norma Corrales 703-631-6149.

4879 ■ ARMED FORCES COMMUNICATIONS AND ELECTRONICS ASSOCIATION
4400 Fair Lakes Court
Fairfax, VA 22033
Tel: (703)631-6141
Free: 800-336-4583
Fax: (703)631-4693
Web Site: http://www.afcea.org
To provide scholarships to students connected with the US Military.
Title of Award: Marine Corps Sgt. Jeannette L. Winters Memorial Scholarships **Area, Field, or Subject:** Engineering; Mathematics; Physics; Communications. **Level of Education for which Award is Granted:** Undergraduate **Funds Available:** $2,000.
Eligibility Requirements: Applicants must be enrolled full time in a Bachelor of Science degree program in accredited colleges or universities in the United States; and must have a minimum GPA of 3.0 on 4.0 scale. Majors directly related to the support of US Intelligence enterprises or national security with relevance to the mission of AFCEA are also eligible. **Application Requirements:** Applicants may apply online at the AFCEA web site. Applicants must also submit two letters of recommendation printed in school stationery and with signature from field-of-study professors. **Deadline for Receipt:** September 1. **Additional Information:** Norma Corrales; 703-631-6149.

4880 ■ ASSOCIATION FOR WOMEN IN SCIENCE
1200 New York Ave. NW, Ste. 650
Washington, DC 20005
Tel: (202)326-8940
Fax: (202)326-8960
E-mail: awis@awis.org
Web Site: http://www.awis.org
To promote education in science.
Title of Award: AWIS College Scholarships **Area, Field, or Subject:** Astronomy and astronomical sciences; Geosciences; Biology; Mathematics and mathematical sciences; Chemistry; Physics; Computer and information sciences; Engineering; Psychology. **Level of Education for which Award is Granted:** Undergraduate **Number Awarded:** 2-5. **Funds Available:** No specific amount.
Eligibility Requirements: Applicant must be a female high school senior; U.S. citizen or permanent resident; have at least 3.75 GPA; at least 1200 score in SAT or a composite score of 25 in ACT; planning to study in any field of Astronomy, Geoscience, Biology, Mathematics, Chemistry, Physics, Computer and Information Science, Engineering, Psychology; planning to become a researcher or teacher. **Application Requirements:** Applicants must send five copies of: summary form; essay describing research experience; resume; two recommendation letters from science or research teachers; high school transcript and score of standardized test if available. **Deadline for Receipt:** January 17.

4881 ■ CAMDEN COUNTY COLLEGE
200 N Broadway
Camden, NJ 08102-1185
Tel: (856)338-1817
Web Site: http://www.camdencc.edu
To provide opportunity to qualified students to pursue an education at CCC.

Title of Award: Diane Basilone-Engle Memorial Scholarships **Area, Field, or Subject:** Theater arts; Secretarial sciences; Veterinary science and medicine; Education. **Level of Education for which Award is Granted:** Undergraduate **Funds Available:** No specific amount. **Duration:** One academic year.
Eligibility Requirements: Applicants must be students who want to continue their degree or certificate in theater, secretariat science, veterinary science or education. **Application Requirements:** Applicants must submit one recommendation from a faculty member or administrator at Camden County College. Application forms are available online and must be sent to Camden County College Foundation, PO Box 200, College Dr., Blackwood, NJ 08012. **Deadline for Receipt:** February 18.

4882 ■ CATCHING THE DREAM
8200 Mountain Rd. NE., Ste. 203
Albuquerque, NM 87110
Tel: (505)262-2351
E-mail: nscholarships@aol.com
Web Site: http://www.catchingthedream.org
To support the education of Native Schools.
Title of Award: MESBEC Scholarships **Area, Field, or Subject:** Mathematics and mathematical sciences; Engineering; Science; Business; Education; Computer and information sciences. **Level of Education for which Award is Granted:** Undergraduate **Funds Available:** $500-$5000. **Duration:** One academic year.
Eligibility Requirements: Applicants must be 1/4 or more degree Native American; an enrolled member of a "U.S. tribe"; attending or planning to attend a college/university within the U.S. on a full-time basis that is fully accredited; studying in the field of business, finance, management, economics, banking, hotel management, and related field; have excellent grades; high ACT or SAT scores; and have a strong commitment to their Native American community. **Application Requirements:** Applicants must submit a completed application form (available at the website); financial need analysis; a copy of the IRS 1040 Federal Tax Return for the previous year; Certificate of Native American Blood; an essay explaining career goals; three letters of recommendation; official transcripts; a copy of standardized test scores; copy of letter of admission from an accredited college or university or graduate school and degree program in the US; and a photograph (2X3) of head and shoulders. **Deadline for Receipt:** March 15, April 15, and September 15.

4883 ■ EAST TENNESSEE FOUNDATION
625 Market St., Ste. 1400
Knoxville, TN 37902
Tel: (865)524-1223; 877-524-1223
Fax: (865)637-6039
Web Site: http://www.easttennesseefoundation.org
To benefit graduating high school seniors wishing to pursue careers in science, math or pre-engineering related fields.
Title of Award: B&W Y-12 Scholarship Fund **Area, Field, or Subject:** Science; math; Engineering. **Level of Education for which Award is Granted:** Undergraduate **Number Awarded:** 1. **Funds Available:** $1,500.
Eligibility Requirements: Applicants must be enrolled as full-time students at either Roane State Community College or Pellissippi State Technical College; must be U.S citizens; must have a minimum GPA of at least 3.0. **Application Requirements:** Applicants must check the application process online. **Deadline for Receipt:** March 14. **Additional Information:** East Tennessee Foundation at the above address

4884 ■ FIRST COMMUNITY FOUNDATION OF PENNSYLVANIA, WILLIAMSPORT-LYCOMING
330 Pine St., Suite 401
Williamsport, PA 17701
Tel: (570)321-1500; (866)901-2372
Fax: (570)321-6434
E-mail: fcfpa@fcfpa.org
Web Site: http://www.wlfoundation.org
To provide financial assistance for Danville Area High School seniors who have been accepted into a full-time undergraduate program.
Title of Award: Jane Hood Memorial Fund **Area, Field, or Subject:** Visual arts; Mathematics and mathematical science; Science; Engineering. **Level of Education for which Award is Granted:** Undergraduate **Funds Available:** No specific amount.

Eligibility Requirements: Applicants must be accepted in a full-time undergraduate program at an institution of higher education to study graphic-visual arts, math and/or science (including engineering). Applicants must have exhibited good citizenship and community involvement. **Application Requirements:** Applicants may request an application to the Guidance Counselor of Danville Area School District. **Additional Information:** Gary Grozier, Guidance Counselor of Danville Area School District, 600 Walnut St., Danville, PA 17821; 570-271-3268 ext. 2006; ggrozier@danville.k12.pa.us.

4885 ■ FOUNDATION FOR THE CAROLINAS
217 S Tryon St.
Charlotte, NC 28202
Tel: (704)973-4500
Free: 800-973-7244
Web Site: http://www.fftc.org
To provide scholarships for college-bound students from North and South Carolina who are pursuing a major in engineering, math, science, computer science, accounting, finance or business administration.
Title of Award: African American Network - Carolinas Scholarship Fund **Area, Field, or Subject:** Engineering; Mathematics and mathematical sciences; Science; Computer and information sciences; Accounting; Finance; Business administration. **Level of Education for which Award is Granted:** Undergraduate **Number Awarded:** 2. **Funds Available:** No specific amount. **Duration:** One year.
Eligibility Requirements: Applicants must be graduating seniors at a North or South Carolina high school; must attend a four-year college or university located in North or South Carolina; must plan to major in engineering, computer science, the sciences, accounting, finance or business administration. **Application Requirements:** Applicants must submit all the required application information.

4886 ■ FOUNDATION FOR ENHANCING COMMUNITIES
200 N Third St., PO Box 678
Harrisburg, PA 17108-0678
Tel: (717)236-5040
Fax: (717)231-4463
E-mail: dawn@tfec.org
Web Site: http://www.ghf.org
To provide educational assistance for students attending Greenwood High School, Newport High School, Susquenita High School and West Perry High School.
Title of Award: Carie and George Lyter Scholarship Fund **Area, Field, or Subject:** Education, Elementary; Science; Mathematics and mathematical sciences. **Level of Education for which Award is Granted:** Undergraduate **Funds Available:** No specific amount.
Eligibility Requirements: Applicants must have a desire to pursue a career in elementary or middle school education with emphasis in science or mathematics; an academic achievement of a cumulative GPA of 2.5 to 3.0 on a 4.0 scale in their junior/senior year; demonstrated talent for leadership; a high moral character (must have attended and be involved in church activities); and must demonstrate financial need. **Application Requirements:** Applicants must submit the following required attachments: completed student background sheet; official high school transcript with raised school seal; FAFSA student aid report; completed student 300-word essay identifying their interest in Elementary or Middle School Education with an emphasis in science and mathematics (include professional goals); and two personal reference letters. One letter should be from a teacher and the other letter should be from an employer or a supervisor of a community service volunteer agency. Letters of reference may not be from a family member. **Deadline for Receipt:** April 24. **Additional Information:** Dawn Morris, Program Officer at the above address.

4887 ■ FOUNDATION FOR ENHANCING COMMUNITIES
200 N Third St., PO Box 678
Harrisburg, PA 17108-0678
Tel: (717)236-5040
Fax: (717)231-4463
E-mail: dawn@tfec.org
Web Site: http://www.ghf.org
To encourage educational pursuits by providing financial assistance.
Title of Award: Anil and Neema Thakrar Family Fund **Area, Field, or Subject:** Mathematics and mathematical science; Science; Engineering.

Level of Education for which Award is Granted: Undergraduate **Number Awarded:** 2. **Funds Available:** No specific amount. **Duration:** Annual.
Eligibility Requirements: Program is open to students, intending to study Math, Science and Engineering, from the City of Harrisburg School District and Sci-Tech High School, or to high school students in Dauphin, Cumberland and Perry Counties intending to study in a medical-related discipline. Applicants must have a minimum of 2.5 GPA on a 4.0 scale. **Application Requirements:** Applicants must complete and submit the application and other required attachments on or before the deadline. Applicants must provide the following attachments: official transcript of complete high school/college record, including GPA, through the first half of the present year, with the raised school seal imprinted; list of most significant extracurricular or nonacademic activities, emphasizing work experience and community service. Attach a 300-word essay on the following statement: "What was my biggest life challenge and what did I learn form the experience." **Deadline for Receipt:** March 31. **Additional Information:** Dawn Morris, Program Officer at the above address.

4888 ■ GOLDEN KEY INTERNATIONAL HONOUR SOCIETY
621 Noeth Ave. NE., Ste. C-100
Atlanta, GA 30308
Tel: (404)377-2400
Free: 800-377-2401
Fax: (678)420-6757
E-mail: memberservices@goldenkey.org
Web Site: http://www.goldenkey.org
To financially assist students studying math.
Title of Award: Golden Key Math Scholarships **Area, Field, or Subject:** Mathematics and mathematical sciences. **Level of Education for which Award is Granted:** Undergraduate **Number Awarded:** 2. **Funds Available:** $10000.
Eligibility Requirements: Applicant must be undergraduate member majoring in math and currently enrolled in classes at a degree-granting program. **Application Requirements:** Applicants must register their scholarship application online. Print the cover page from the online registration and use it as a cover for the entire application and attach a math related paper/report (maximum of 10 pages), an essay (maximum of 500 words), a letter of recommendation, and a current comprehensive official academic transcript. **Additional Information:** Applicants can apply for more than one scholarship. **Deadline for Receipt:** April 15. **Additional Information:** awards@goldenkey.org.

4889 ■ GRAND HAVEN AREA COMMUNITY FOUNDATION
1 S. Harbor Dr.
Grand Haven, MI 49417
Tel: (616)842-6378
Fax: (616)842-9518
E-mail: bpost@ghacf.org
Web Site: http://www.ghacf.org
To improve and enhance the quality of life in the Tri-Cities area by serving as a leader, catalyst and resource for philanthropy; to strive for community improvement through strategic grantmaking in such fields as the arts, education, health, environment, youth, social services and other human needs.
Title of Award: Kevin Ernst Memorial Scholarship Fund **Area, Field, or Subject:** Mathematics and mathematical sciences. **Level of Education for which Award is Granted:** Undergraduate **Funds Available:** No specific amount.
Eligibility Requirements: Applicants must be students in the Foundation's service area who wish to continue their education in the field of mathematics. **Application Requirements:** Applicants must submit: completed application form; current high school or college transcript; Student Aid Report (SAR) from the Free Application for Federal Student Aid (FAFSA), unless applying for scholarships that do not consider financial need; and letter of recommendation. **Deadline for Receipt:** March 7. **Additional Information:** 616-842-6378.

4890 ■ GRAND HAVEN AREA COMMUNITY FOUNDATION
1 S. Harbor Dr.
Grand Haven, MI 49417
Tel: (616)842-6378
Fax: (616)842-9518

E-mail: bpost@ghacf.org
Web Site: http://www.ghacf.org
To improve and enhance the quality of life in the Tri-Cities area by serving as a leader, catalyst and resource for philanthropy; to strive for community improvement through strategic grantmaking in such fields as arts, education, health, environment, youth, social services and other human needs.
Title of Award: Leo Zupin Memorial Scholarship Fund **Area, Field, or Subject:** Mathematics and mathematical sciences. **Level of Education for which Award is Granted:** Undergraduate **Funds Available:** No specific amount.
Eligibility Requirements: Applicants must plan to attend any Michigan two-to-four year accredited public college, university, vocational or technology training and/or certification institution; must be students wishing to pursue a degree in mathematics. **Application Requirements:** Applicants must submit: completed application form; current high school or college transcript; Student Aid Report (SAR) from the Free Application for Federal Student Aid (FAFSA), unless applying for scholarships that do not consider financial need; and letter of recommendation. **Deadline for Receipt:** March 7. **Additional Information:** 616-842-6378.

4891 ■ HISPANIC SCHOLARSHIP FUND
55 Second St., Ste. 1500
San Francisco, CA 94105
877-473-4636
Fax: (415)808-2302
E-mail: info@hsf.net
Web Site: http://www.hsf.net
To promote academic excellence and to provide an opportunity for outstanding students with significant financial need to reach their fullest potential.
Title of Award: The Gates Millennium Scholars **Area, Field, or Subject:** Mathematics and mathematical sciences; Science; Engineering; Education; Public health; Library and archival sciences. **Level of Education for which Award is Granted:** Undergraduate **Funds Available:** No specific amount.
Eligibility Requirements: Applicants must be African American, American Indian/Alaska Native, Asian pacific Islander American and Hispanic American heritage; a U.S. citizen or legal permanent resident; have a minimum 3.3 GPA on a 4.0 scale; must demonstrate leadership skills; must demonstrate financial need. **Application Requirements:** Applicants must complete all three required forms available at the award site www.gmsp.org. American Indian/Alaska Natives must submit proof of tribal enrollment or a certificate of descent if selected as finalists. **Additional Information:** Established in 1999 and funded by a grant from the Bill and Melinda Gates Foundation. **Deadline for Receipt:** December 31 (paper applications), January 11 (online applications). **Additional Information:** gmsinfo@hsf.nett.

4892 ■ IDAHO COMMUNITY FOUNDATION
210 W State St.
Boise, ID 83702
Tel: (208)342-3535
Free: 800-657-5357
Fax: (208)342-3577
E-mail: info@idcomfdn.org
Web Site: http://www.idcomfdn.org
To assist Idaho students who are interested in pursuing math and science degrees at Idaho college and universities.
Title of Award: Mike Crapo Math and Science Scholarship Fund **Area, Field, or Subject:** Mathematics and mathematical sciences. **Level of Education for which Award is Granted:** Undergraduate **Funds Available:** No specific amount.
Eligibility Requirements: Applicants must be students pursuing math and science degrees at Idaho colleges and universities. **Application Requirements:** Applicants must submit a "300-word or less" original essay discussing the value of math and science to an individual and society as a whole; most recent certified transcript from high school and higher education institution; two letters of reference from teacher/professor of math or science and from two members of the community who are not relatives and ACT/SAT Assessment Report. **Deadline for Receipt:** April 30.

4893 ■ INDIANA STATE ALUMNI ASSOCIATION

200 N 7th St.
Terre Haute, IN 47809-9989
800-GO-TO-ISU
Web Site: http://www.indstate.edu/alum/alum_assoc.htm
To support educational pursuit of students.

Title of Award: Noyce Scholarships for Secondary Math and Science Education **Area, Field, or Subject:** Education, Secondary; Science; Mathematics and mathematical sciences. **Level of Education for which Award is Granted:** Undergraduate **Funds Available:** $10,000. **Duration:** One year.

Eligibility Requirements: Applicant must be a transfer student with a GPA of 2.75 in all science and mathematics work. **Application Requirements:** Applicants must submit a signed urban teaching commitment and a scholarship application checklist. **Additional Information:** Dr. Jay D. Gatrell, project director, 812-237-2785 or jgatrell@indstate.edu.

4894 ■ INTERNATIONAL ASSOCIATION OF LAW ENFORCEMENT INTELLIGENCE ANALYSTS

PO box 13857
Richmond, VA 23225
Tel: (804)565-2059
Fax: (804)565-2059
E-mail: admin@ialeia.org
Web Site: http://www.ialeia.org
To strive for professionalism in the intelligence field by promoting career development and continued education.

Title of Award: Jorge Espejal Contreras Memorial Scholarships **Area, Field, or Subject:** Intelligence Service; Statistics; Criminal Justice. **Level of Education for which Award is Granted:** Graduate, Undergraduate **Number Awarded:** 2. **Funds Available:** $1,000.

Eligibility Requirements: Program is open to active IALEIA members or immediate family members enrolled in an intelligence, analysis, criminal justice, or other related undergraduate or graduate program at an accredited academic institution; must be based on full-time or part-time enrollment in an accredited college/university and can be on campus or via distance-learning. **Application Requirements:** Applicants should download application from the IALEIA website and submit to the IALEIA Training, Education, and Career Development Committee. Eligible submissions must be provided in English. Applicants must submit their work electronically to the attention of the TE&CD Director and a signed original copy to be mailed. Application must include a mandatory 1,000-1,500 word essay on: The Future of Law Enforcement Intelligence as a Profession. Mail application package to: IALEIA Scholarship Program, Attn: IALEIA TE&CD, 705 Somerset Drive, El Paso, Texas 79912, USA. **Deadline for Receipt:** May 16.

4895 ■ LAKSELAGET

c/o Ingeborg Sorensen
1235 Yale Place, No. 1305
Minneapolis, MN 55403
E-mail: president@lakselaget.org
Web Site: http://www.lakselaget.org
To promote the international connections between Norway and Minnesota, and learn, teach and share knowledge that will benefit women in their complex roles in today's society.

Title of Award: Lakselaget Foundation Scholarships **Area, Field, or Subject:** Biology; Mathematics and mathematical sciences; Science. **Level of Education for which Award is Granted:** Graduate, Undergraduate **Number Awarded:** Varies. **Funds Available:** $1,000.

Eligibility Requirements: Applicant must be female; an American citizen residing in Minnesota, enrolled in undergraduate or graduate studies at an accredited Minnesota college or university or at the University of North Dakota, Grand Forks and wish to study in Norway; or must be a Norwegian citizen attending undergraduate or graduate studies at an accredited Norwegian college or university, who wishes to study at a Minnesota college or university or at the University of North Dakota, Grand Forks. Study areas may include, but are not limited to, non-traditional women's studies such as biotechnology, mathematics, and the sciences. Applicants must be full-time undergraduates who have completed at least one year or full-time graduate students. American students should have a GPA of 3.0 or better, Norwegians the equivalent. **Application Requirements:** Applicant must submit a completed application form with official

transcripts, two letters or recommendation, a letter from an individual who can assess the applicant's Norwegian language skills (if an American), and a 1000-word essay. **Deadline for Receipt:** March 15. **Additional Information:** scholarships@lakselaget.org.

4896 ■ LEWIS-CLARK STATE COLLEGE

500 8th Ave.
Lewiston, ID 83501
Tel: (208)792-5272
Web Site: http://www.lcsc.edu
To provide financial assistance to students who are majoring in these fields: Accounting, Biology, Business, Communications, Computer Science, Economics, Environmental Science, Engineering, Mathematics, Natural Resources, Political Science, Statistics.

Title of Award: Avista Corporation Minds in Motion Scholarships **Area, Field, or Subject:** Accounting; Biology; Business; Communications; Computer and Information Sciences; Economics; Environmental Science; Engineering; Mathematics; Natural Resources; Political Science; Statistics. **Level of Education for which Award is Granted:** Undergraduate **Number Awarded:** 2. **Funds Available:** No specific Amount.

Eligibility Requirements: Applicants must be full-time students attending LCSC and must have a cumulative GPA of 2.5. **Application Requirements:** Applicants must submit general application. **Deadline for Receipt:** March 1.

4897 ■ LEWIS-CLARK STATE COLLEGE

500 8th Ave.
Lewiston, ID 83501
Tel: (208)792-5272
Web Site: http://www.lcsc.edu
To provide educational assistance for students intending to pursue a career in the area of Computer Science.

Title of Award: Jimmy Guild Memorial Scholarships **Area, Field, or Subject:** Mathematics and Mathematical Sciences; Computer and Information Sciences. **Level of Education for which Award is Granted:** Undergraduate **Number Awarded:** 1. **Funds Available:** $1,000. **Duration:** One year.

Eligibility Requirements: Applicants must be full-time students who are majoring in mathematics; must have interest in Computer science; and must have a cumulative GPA of 3.0. **Application Requirements:** Preference will be given to graduating students from local high schools who are affiliated with a member of the United Paperworkers International Union. **Deadline for Receipt:** May 19.

4898 ■ LEWIS-CLARK STATE COLLEGE

500 8th Ave.
Lewiston, ID 83501
Tel: (208)792-5272
Web Site: http://www.lcsc.edu
To inspire educational pursuits among less capable individuals by providing financial assistance.

Title of Award: Lewis-Clark State College Presidential Technical Out-of-State Scholarships **Area, Field, or Subject:** Chemistry; Computer Science; Engineering; Information Systems Analysis; Industrial Electronics; Biology; Earth Information Systems; Radiology; Heating/Air Conditioning; Automated Manufacturing Technology; Mathematics; Printing Technology; Graphic Arts or Web Development. **Level of Education for which Award is Granted:** Undergraduate **Funds Available:** No specific amount.

Eligibility Requirements: Applicants must be new non-resident high school or transfer students who have at least 14 transferable semester credits. **Application Requirements:** Applicants must accomplish a general application available in the website. **Deadline for Receipt:** March 1 for Fall enrollment or November 1 for Spring enrollment.

4899 ■ MATANUSKA-SUSITNA COLLEGE

PO Box 2889
Palmer, AK 99645
Tel: (907)745-9774
Fax: (907)745-9711
E-mail: info@matsu.alaska.edu
Web Site: http://www.matsu.alaska.edu
To provide support to deserving students in Alaska who want to pursue an education in any campus of the University of Alaska.

Title of Award: Alaska Aerospace Development Corporation Scholarships **Area, Field, or Subject:** Applied mathematics; Physics; Engineering; Business; Technical communications. **Level of Education for which Award is Granted:** Undergraduate **Funds Available:** $5,000.
Eligibility Requirements: Applicant must be a freshman student majoring in mathematics, physics, engineering, business, or a technical science field such as computer science who has graduated from the Kodiak Island Borough School District; must be a full-time student enrolled in 14 credits and in good academic standing. **Application Requirements:** Applicants must submit a written statement verifying that he/she has not been convicted of a crime other than a minor traffic violation; must complete the application forms available at the website; must attach a personal essay, two letters of recommendation, and current transcripts. **Deadline for Receipt:** February 15.

4900 ■ MATANUSKA-SUSITNA COLLEGE
PO Box 2889
Palmer, AK 99645
Tel: (907)745-9774
Fax: (907)745-9711
E-mail: info@matsu.alaska.edu
Web Site: http://www.matsu.alaska.edu
To provide support to deserving students in Alaska who want to pursue an education in any campus of the University of Alaska.
Title of Award: Bill & Nell Biggs Scholarships **Area, Field, or Subject:** Accounting; Business administration; Engineering; Science; Mathematics and mathematical sciences. **Level of Education for which Award is Granted:** Undergraduate **Funds Available:** $500.
Eligibility Requirements: Applicants must be graduates of Juneau-Douglas High School or Juneau residents who have completed a high school equivalency program. **Application Requirements:** Applicant must complete the application forms available at the website; must attach a personal essay, two letters of recommendation, and current transcripts. **Deadline for Receipt:** February 15.

4901 ■ NATIONAL COMMISSION FOR COOPERATIVE EDUCATION
360 Huntington Ave., 384 CP
Boston, MA 02115-5096
Tel: (617)373-3770
Fax: (617)373-3463
E-mail: ncce@neu.edu
Web Site: http://www.co-op.edu
To assist students pursuing education in science, mathematics, engineering and technology.
Title of Award: National Co-op Scholarship Program **Area, Field, or Subject:** Mathematics and mathematical sciences; Science; Engineering. **Level of Education for which Award is Granted:** Undergraduate **Funds Available:** No specific amount.
Eligibility Requirements: Applicants must be have a high school GPA of 3.5 (B+) or better. **Application Requirements:** Applicants must complete the National Co-op Scholarship program application including a typed one-page essay. Application materials and must be sent directly to the applicant's college or university. **Deadline for Receipt:** February 15.

4902 ■ PENNSYLVANIA STATE SYSTEM OF HIGHER EDUCATION FOUNDATION
2986 N 2nd St.
Harrisburg, PA 17110
Tel: (717)720-4086
Fax: (717)720-7082
Web Site: http://www.thepafoundation.org
To provide financial assistance to increase the number of basic education teachers with strong content knowledge in science, technology, engineering, and mathematics (STEM).
Title of Award: Robert Noyce Scholarship Program **Area, Field, or Subject:** Science; Technology; Engineering; Mathematics and mathematical sciences. **Level of Education for which Award is Granted:** Undergraduate **Funds Available:** $10,000. **Duration:** One year.
Eligibility Requirements: Applicants must have a qualifying cumulative GPA of 3.00, with preference for those with a GPA of 3.5 or higher; must be transfer students or post-baccalaureates who completed a semester or more of coursework at a State System university to establish the qualifying GPA of 3.00; must be full-time students during each semester for which the award is received. **Application Requirements:** Applicants must submit completed application form; official transcripts from all institutions attended; a two page essay describing personal and professional goals, commitment to teaching and personal philosophy of teaching; three letters of recommendation that must address, but are not limited to: a) the scholarship of the applicant, b) the character of the applicant, c) the interpersonal skills of the applicant relative to teaching, and d) the general interpersonal skills of the applicant; and a resume. **Deadline for Receipt:** April 20.

4903 ■ PRIDE FOUNDATION
PO Box 2194, 1122 E Pike St. PMB 1001
Seattle, WA 98112
Tel: (206)323-3318
Free: 800-735-7287
Fax: (206)323-1017
E-mail: prideweb@pridefoundation.org
Web Site: http://www.pridefoundation.org
To provide scholarship to the students who have been stigmatized, isolated or closeted because of sexual identity issues.
Title of Award: True North Land Surveying Scholarships **Area, Field, or Subject:** Mathematics and mathematical sciences. **Level of Education for which Award is Granted:** Undergraduate **Funds Available:** No specific amount.
Eligibility Requirements: Applicant must be a student pursuing a career in Land Surveying (Geomatics) or majoring in mathematics. **Application Requirements:** Qualified students are asked to submit an application to determine eligibility for scholarships. Applicants may download an application form from the Foundation's website. **Additional Information:** Pride Foundation at the above address.

4904 ■ PUBLIC EDUCATION FOUNDATION
3360 W Sahara Ave., Ste. 160
Las Vegas, NV 89102
Tel: (702)799-1042
Fax: (702)799-5247
E-mail: steelej@ccpef.org
Web Site: http://ccpef.org
To promote education in the field of mathematics.
Title of Award: Dr. Virginia Gilbert Memorial Scholarships **Area, Field, or Subject:** Mathematics and mathematical sciences. **Level of Education for which Award is Granted:** Undergraduate **Number Awarded:** 2. **Funds Available:** $10,000.
Eligibility Requirements: Applicants must be CCSD seniors who have demonstrated an interest in mathematics and planning to attend a Southern Nevada accredited college/university. **Application Requirements:** Applicants must submit a completed application form together with an essay, a recommendation letter, and a transcript. **Deadline for Receipt:** March 7. **Additional Information:** Shana Venenga at 702-799-1042.

4905 ■ PUBLIC EDUCATION FOUNDATION
3360 W Sahara Ave., Ste. 160
Las Vegas, NV 89102
Tel: (702)799-1042
Fax: (702)799-5247
E-mail: steelej@ccpef.org
Web Site: http://ccpef.org
To provide educational opportunities for individuals intending to pursue higher studies.
Title of Award: Josef Princ Memorial Scholarships **Area, Field, or Subject:** Engineering; Mathematics and mathematical sciences. **Level of Education for which Award is Granted:** Undergraduate **Number Awarded:** 3. **Funds Available:** $2,000.
Eligibility Requirements: Applicants must be CCSD male seniors of European descent; must be maintaining a minimum 3.5 cumulative GPA; must be demonstrating financial need; and must be planning to attend an accredited post-secondary college/university majoring in engineering, mathematics or science. **Application Requirements:** Applicants must submit a completed application form along with an essay, two letters of recommendation, transcript, and resume of awards. **Deadline for Receipt:** March 7. **Additional Information:** Shana Venenga at 702-799-1042.

4906 ■ THE SAN DIEGO FOUNDATION

2508 Historic Decatur Rd., Ste. 200
San Diego, CA 92106
Tel: (619)235-2300
Fax: (619)239-1710
E-mail: info@sdfoundation.org
Web Site: http://www.sdfoundation.org
To support the education of students from California.
Title of Award: AeA Scholarships **Area, Field, or Subject:** Mathematics and mathematical sciences; Science; Engineering; Computer and information sciences. **Level of Education for which Award is Granted:** Undergraduate **Number Awarded:** 2. **Funds Available:** $1000.
Eligibility Requirements: Applicant must be a resident of San Diego County (military personnel and dependents are exempt); a citizen or legal resident of the United States; attend an accredited two-year college, four-year university or licensed trade and vocational school in the U.S.; a full-time student (unless otherwise noted); have a measure of academic and civic achievement; be of good moral and personal character; graduate from a San Diego County public high school; have a minimum 3.75 GPA on a 4.0 scale; and be majoring in math, science, engineering, or computers. **Application Requirements:** Applicants must submit a completed Common Scholarship Application together with personal statement; two letters of recommendation on official letterhead (written within the last six months); official transcript in an official and sealed envelope; copy of 2006 or most recent tax form (Form 1040-pages 1 & 2; Form 1040A-pages 1 & 2; Form 1040EZ-page 1); and an unofficial copy of SAT score results. **Deadline for Receipt:** January 28. **Additional Information:** Arzo Mansury, Dir. Scholarships at 619-814-1343, or scholarships@sdfoundation.org.

4907 ■ THE SAN DIEGO FOUNDATION

2508 Historic Decatur Rd., Ste. 200
San Diego, CA 92106
Tel: (619)235-2300
Fax: (619)239-1710
E-mail: info@sdfoundation.org
Web Site: http://www.sdfoundation.org
To support the education of students from California.
Title of Award: Reuben H. Fleet Memorial Scholarships **Area, Field, or Subject:** Science; Engineering; Mathematics and mathematical sciences. **Level of Education for which Award is Granted:** Undergraduate **Number Awarded:** 3. **Funds Available:** $5,000.
Eligibility Requirements: Applicant must be a college student pursuing an undergraduate degree in science, engineering or math. Students must have completed 54 semester units or 72 quarter units; maintained a minimum 3.0 GPA on a 4.0 scale; enrolled at a four-year university in San Diego County; or be a San Diego County resident attending a four-year university in the U.S. **Application Requirements:** Applicants must submit a completed Common Scholarship Application together with personal statement; two letters of recommendation on official letterhead (written within the last six months); official transcript in an official and sealed envelope; and a copy of most recent tax form (Form 1040-pages 1 & 2; Form 1040A-pages 1 & 2; Form 1040EZ-page 1). If attending a two-year college, applicants must submit a letter of acceptance on official letterhead from the four-year university which the applicant will be transferring. **Deadline for Receipt:** January 28. **Additional Information:** Arzo Mansury, Dir. Scholarships at 619-814-1343, or scholarships@sdfoundation.org.

4908 ■ THE SAN DIEGO FOUNDATION

2508 Historic Decatur Rd., Ste. 200
San Diego, CA 92106
Tel: (619)235-2300
Fax: (619)239-1710
E-mail: info@sdfoundation.org
Web Site: http://www.sdfoundation.org
To support the education of students from California.
Title of Award: SDF Community College Transfer Scholarships for Math and Science **Area, Field, or Subject:** Science; Engineering; Mathematics and mathematical sciences. **Level of Education for which Award is Granted:** Undergraduate **Number Awarded:** 5. **Funds Available:** $2,500.
Eligibility Requirements: Applicant must be a San Diego Community College student transferring to an accredited four-year university in the U.S.; majoring in science, engineering, or mathematics; and have a minimum 3.0 GPA on a 4.0 scale in community college work. **Application Requirements:** Applicants must submit a completed Common Scholarship Application together with personal statement; two letters of recommendation on official letterhead (written within the last six months); official transcript in an official and sealed envelope; copy of 2006 or most recent tax form (Form 1040-pages 1 & 2; Form 1040A-pages 1 & 2; Form 1040EZ-page 1); and s letter of acceptance on official letterhead from the accredited four-year university. **Deadline for Receipt:** January 28. **Additional Information:** Arzo Mansury, Dir. Scholarships at 619-814-1343, or scholarships@sdfoundation.org

4909 ■ SHORELINE COMMUNITY COLLEGE FOUNDATION

16101 Greenwood Ave. N, Ste. 1005
Shoreline, WA 98133-5696
Tel: (206)546-4755
Fax: (206)546-5826
E-mail: rmanchester@shoreline.edu
Web Site: http://www.shoreline.edu
To increase access and success of Shoreline Community College students.
Title of Award: Dr. Bill Johnson Scholarships **Area, Field, or Subject:** Mathematics and mathematical science. **Level of Education for which Award is Granted:** Undergraduate **Funds Available:** No specific amount.
Eligibility Requirements: Applicants must be full-time or part-time students at the Shoreline/Lake Forest Park area who are enrolling at SCC. **Application Requirements:** Applicants must complete the application form.

4910 ■ SHORELINE COMMUNITY COLLEGE FOUNDATION

16101 Greenwood Ave. N, Ste. 1005
Shoreline, WA 98133-5696
Tel: (206)546-4755
Fax: (206)546-5826
E-mail: rmanchester@shoreline.edu
Web Site: http://www.shoreline.edu
To increase access and success of Shoreline Community College students; to assist promising students to continue their studies in Mathematics at an accredited four year college or university.
Title of Award: Joseph Wood Rogers Memorial Scholarships **Area, Field, or Subject:** Mathematics and mathematical science. **Level of Education for which Award is Granted:** Undergraduate **Funds Available:** No specific amount.
Eligibility Requirements: Applicants must be part-time or full-time students who are currently enrolled at Shoreline Community College. **Application Requirements:** Applicants must complete the application form.

4911 ■ SHORELINE COMMUNITY COLLEGE FOUNDATION

16101 Greenwood Ave. N, Ste. 1005
Shoreline, WA 98133-5696
Tel: (206)546-4755
Fax: (206)546-5826
E-mail: rmanchester@shoreline.edu
Web Site: http://www.shoreline.edu
To increase access and success of Shoreline Community College students; to assist promising students to continue their studies in mathematics at an accredited four year college or university.
Title of Award: Margaret Svec Scholarships **Area, Field, or Subject:** Mathematics and mathematical science. **Level of Education for which Award is Granted:** Undergraduate **Funds Available:** No specific amount.
Eligibility Requirements: Applicants must be part-time or full-time students who are currently enrolled at Shoreline Community College. **Application Requirements:** Applicants must complete the application form.

4912 ■ SOCIETY OF ALLIED WEIGHT ENGINEERS

PO Box 60024, Terminal Annex
Los Angeles, CA 90060
Tel: (562)596-2873
Fax: (562)596-2874
Web Site: http://www.sawe.org

To provide financial assistance for the education of the dependents of SAWE members.

Title of Award: Frank Fong Scholarships **Area, Field, or Subject:** Engineering; Physics; Mathematics and mathematical sciences; Computer and information sciences. **Level of Education for which Award is Granted:** Undergraduate **Number Awarded:** 5. **Funds Available:** $1000. **Duration:** One year.

Eligibility Requirements: Applicants must be children or grandchildren of SAWE members; must be aged 25 or below; full-time undergraduate students; pursuing a technical course of study (engineering, physics, mathematics, computer sciences, etc.). **Application Requirements:** Application forms are available at the website. Applicants must submit completed application form and send together with a complete transcript of grades. **Deadline for Receipt:** April. **Additional Information:** Ginny Miller, Scholarship Management Services, Telephone: (507)931-1682, Toll-free: (800)537-4180.

4913 ■ STARK COMMUNITY FOUNDATION
400 Market Ave. N, Ste. 200
Canton, OH 44702-2107
Tel: (330)454-3426
Fax: (330)454-5855
Web Site: http://www.starkcommunityfoundation.org
To provide scholarship assistance to qualified individuals who want to pursue their studies.

Title of Award: Margaret S. Gilbert Scholarship Fund **Area, Field, or Subject:** Natural sciences; Mathematics and mathematical sciences; History. **Level of Education for which Award is Granted:** Undergraduate **Number Awarded:** 2. **Funds Available:** $37,000. **Duration:** One year.

Eligibility Requirements: Applicants must be Stark County public high school female graduates who attend or will attend Oberlin College; must have a major in one of the natural sciences, mathematics, or history; must have extracurricular activities, especially those demonstrating interest in science; must demonstrate diligent effort, responsibility and financial need. **Application Requirements:** Applicants must have academic record; must submit the application form and requirements at 400 Market Ave. N, Ste. 200, Canton, OH 44702. **Deadline for Receipt:** May 1.

4914 ■ U.S. DEPARTMENT OF HOMELAND SECURITY
12th & C St. SW
Washington, DC 20024
Tel: (202)245-2499
E-mail: dhsed@orau.org
Web Site: http://www.orau.gov/dhsed
To pursue basic science and technology innovations that can be applied to the DHS mission.

Title of Award: The Homeland Security Undergraduate Scholarships **Area, Field, or Subject:** Science technologies; Engineering; Mathematics and mathematical sciences. **Level of Education for which Award is Granted:** Undergraduate **Funds Available:** $1,000; **Duration:** 9 months. **Eligibility Requirements:** Applicants must be a U.S. citizen as of the application deadline; applicants must have a cumulative undergraduate GPA of 3.30 or higher on a 4.00 scale; applicants must be majoring in a homeland security science, technology, engineering or mathematics field with interest in a homeland security research area; applicants must be in second year of college if been attending college full-time; applicants must have completed a total of at least 45 but not more than 60 semester hours if been attending on a part-time, or combination or part-time and full-time basis. **Application Requirements:** Applicants must complete the online application form; applicants must submit two online reference report forms; applicants must submit official academic transcript from all postsecondary institutions attended. **Deadline for Receipt:** January 7 for online application form; January 14 for documents.

4915 ■ UNIVERSITY OF WISCONSIN-MADISON
432 N Murray St.
Madison, WI 53706-1496
Tel: (608)262-3060
Fax: (608)262-9068
E-mail: askbucky@uwmad.wisc.edu
Web Site: http://www.wisc.edu
To provide financial assistance to mathematics, science, and engineering students who wish to pursue their education.

Title of Award: Barry M. Goldwater Scholarships **Area, Field, or Subject:** Mathematics and mathematical sciences; Science; Engineering. **Level of Education for which Award is Granted:** Undergraduate **Number Awarded:** 300. **Funds Available:** $7500.

Eligibility Requirements: Applicants must be full-time juniors or seniors with outstanding potential for a career in mathematics, science, or engineering; have at least a B average; rank in the upper quarter of the high schools class; be U.S. citizens or U.S. nationals; and nominated by UW-Madison. **Application Requirements:** Applicants must contact the Office of Undergraduate Academic Awards for information about the scholarship. **Deadline for Receipt:** November. **Additional Information:** Office of Undergraduate Academic Awards, Julie Stubbs, at 608-890-0370, or stubbs@wisc.edu.

4916 ■ VIRGINIA FOUNDATION FOR INDEPENDENT COLLEGES
8010 Ridge Rd., Ste. B
Richmond, VA 23229-7288
Tel: (804)288-6609
Free: 800-230-6757
Fax: (804)282-4635
E-mail: info@vfic.org
Web Site: http://www.vfic.org
To provide financial assistance to students who will be juniors at a VFIC member college.

Title of Award: Hilb, Rogal and Hobbs Scholarships **Area, Field, or Subject:** Marketing and distribution; Business; Economics; Finance; Mathematics and Mathematical sciences. **Level of Education for which Award is Granted:** Undergraduate **Funds Available:** $2,500.

Eligibility Requirements: Applicants must be full-time students at one of the fifteen private colleges/universities associated with the Virginia Foundation for Independent Colleges; must be first-semester juniors at the time of application with a cumulative grade point average of at least 3.0 on a 4.0 scale, who have declared, or intend to declare a major in one of the following disciplines: marketing, business, economics, finance, mathematics or related fields; must be U.S. citizens. **Application Requirements:** Applicants must submit all the required application information. **Deadline for Receipt:** November 1.

4917 ■ WASHINGTON HIGHER EDUCATION COORDINATING BOARD
PO Box 43430
Olympia, WA 98504-3430
Tel: (360)753-7800
E-mail: info@hecb.wa.gov
Web Site: http://www.hecb.wa.gov
To support low-income and middle-income high school students with top math and science test scores to apply college for free.

Title of Award: GET Ready for Math and Science Conditional Scholarships **Area, Field, or Subject:** Mathematics and mathematical sciences; Science. **Level of Education for which Award is Granted:** Four Year College, Two Year College, Undergraduate **Funds Available:** Full-tuition. **Eligibility Requirements:** Applicants must score a 4 on the math or science section of the high school WASL or score above the 95th percentile on the math section of the SAT or ACT; have a family income at or below 125 percent of the state median family income at the time of application; a Washington state resident; agrees to earn a bachelor's degree in a qualified math or science program at an eligible Washington college/university; and agree to work full-time in a math or science occupation in Washington for at least three years following college graduation. **Application Requirements:** Applications will be available April 2009. **Additional Information:** In partnership with the Office of the Superintendent of Public Instruction and the College Success Foundation. **Deadline for Receipt:** June.

4918 ■ WINSTON-SALEM FOUNDATION
860 W Fifth St.
Winston-Salem, NC 27101-2506
Tel: (336)725-2382
Fax: (336)727-0581
E-mail: info@wsfoundation.org
Web Site: http://www.wsfoundation.org
To encourage students to pursue careers in the Mathematics field.

Title of Award: Sam L. Booke, Sr. Scholarships **Area, Field, or Subject:** Mathematics and mathematical sciences. **Level of Education for which**

Award is Granted: Undergraduate **Funds Available:** No specific amount.

Eligibility Requirements: Applicants must be graduating seniors from public high schools in the Winston-Salem/Forsyth County School; must demonstrate interest in Mathematics. **Application Requirements:** Applicants must complete online application form. Applicants must also submit one teacher recommendation from math teacher; and official high school grade transcript (through at least first semester of the 12th grade and including SAT scores and class rank). **Deadline for Receipt:** March 31. **Additional Information:** Winston-Salem Foundation at the above address.

4919 ■ WINSTON-SALEM FOUNDATION
860 W Fifth St.
Winston-Salem, NC 27101-2506
Tel: (336)725-2382
Fax: (336)727-0581
E-mail: info@wsfoundation.org
Web Site: http://www.wsfoundation.org
To assist graduating high school seniors of Mt. Tabor High School.
Title of Award: Wes Burton Memorial Scholarships **Area, Field, or Subject:** Mathematics and mathematical science; Computer and information sciences; Business administration; Engineering. **Level of Education for which Award is Granted:** Undergraduate **Funds Available:** No specific amount.

Eligibility Requirements: Applicants must have a minimum GPA of 3.5; must demonstrate community and school service; must have an intent to pursue a career in Mathematics, Computer Science, Business Administration, or Engineering; demonstrate financial need (award is not restricted to lowest family incomes). **Application Requirements:** Student must complete the application in its entirety and include supplemental items and information requested in the various sections of the application. The supplemental items include: an interview with the Foundation; a grade transcript; a resume or list of student activities; one letter of recommendation from a math teacher, business teacher, or computer science teacher. **Deadline for Receipt:** March 31. **Additional Information:** WSF Student Aid Department, 336-714-3445.

4920 ■ WINSTON-SALEM FOUNDATION
860 W Fifth St.
Winston-Salem, NC 27101-2506
Tel: (336)725-2382
Fax: (336)727-0581
E-mail: info@wsfoundation.org
Web Site: http://www.wsfoundation.org
To award scholarship to worthy graduating high school seniors from Elkin High School who are US citizens.
Title of Award: Claude B. Hart Memorial Scholarships **Area, Field, or Subject:** Mathematics and mathematical sciences; Engineering. **Level of Education for which Award is Granted:** Undergraduate **Funds Available:** No specific amount.

Eligibility Requirements: Applicants must demonstrate significant promise in academics, leadership, community service and school service and intend to major in mathematics (accounting, computer science, business administration) and/or engineering (mechanical, civil, chemical, etc.) in college. Demonstration of financial need is preferred, but award is not restricted to lowest family incomes. Renewal of the award after the first year will require that the student be a full-time undergraduate student at an accredited four-year institution, maintain a minimum cumulative grade point average of 2.5, and continue to major in mathematics or engineering. **Application Requirements:** Scholarship applications will be provided in the guidance office at Elkin High School. Student must complete the application, requested transcripts, and financial information before being considered by the Elkin High School Scholarship Committee. The Scholarship Committee will submit up to 5 candidates to The Winston-Salem Foundation for review by the Elkin Advisory Committee or its appointed sub-committee. **Additional Information:** WSF Student Aid Department, 336-714-3445.

4921 ■ WOMEN IN DEFENSE
2111 Wilson Blvd., Ste. 400
Arlington, VA 22201-3061
Tel: (703)247-2552
Fax: (703)522-1885
E-mail: wid@ndia.org
Web Site: http://wid.ndia.org
To provide financial assistance to further educational objectives of women either employed or planning careers in defense or national security areas.
Title of Award: Women In Defense HORIZONS Scholarships **Area, Field, or Subject:** National security; Military history; Government; Engineering; Computer and information sciences; Physics; Mathematics and mathematical sciences; Business; Law; International affairs and relations; Political science; Economics. **Level of Education for which Award is Granted:** Graduate, Undergraduate **Funds Available:** No specific amount.

Eligibility Requirements: Applicant must be currently enrolled at an accredited university/college, either full-time or part-time; must have junior, senior or graduate status; demonstrate interest in pursuing a career related to national security or defense; demonstrate financial need; have a minimum GPA of 3.25. Applicant must be a female citizen of the United States. **Application Requirements:** Applicants must submit a completed scholarship application form with the essays, recommendations, and transcripts. **Additional Information:** Established in 1988. **Deadline for Receipt:** July 1.

4922 ■ XAVIER UNIVERSITY
3800 Victory Pky.
Cincinnati, OH 45207
Tel: (513)745-3000
Free: 800-344-GOXU
Web Site: http://www.xavier.edu
To financially support students with their education.
Title of Award: Xavier University Departmental Scholarships **Area, Field, or Subject:** Chemistry; Classical studies; History; Mathematics and mathematical sciences; Modern languages; Physics. **Level of Education for which Award is Granted:** Undergraduate **Funds Available:** $2500.

Eligibility Requirements: Applicant must top the score in either of the six departmental exams (chemistry, classics (Latin), history, mathematics, modern languages (French, German or Spanish) and physics). Student must major in the area for which the scholarship is awarded. **Application Requirements:** Participants will take an exam in the appropriate subject area and have an opportunity to speak with faculty and learn more about the department.

Computer Science

4923 ■ AMERICAN RADIO RELAY LEAGUE (ARRL) FOUNDATION
225 Main St.
Newington, CT 06111
Tel: (860)594-0200
Fax: (860)594-0259
E-mail: foundation@arrl.org
Web Site: http://www.arrlf.org
To support the education of students holding a valid FCC-granted Amateur Radio license for post-secondary education.
Title of Award: William R. Goldfarb Memorial Scholarships **Area, Field, or Subject:** Radio and television; Business; Computer and information sciences; Medicine; Nursing; Engineering; Science. **Level of Education for which Award is Granted:** Undergraduate **Number Awarded:** 1. **Funds Available:** No specific amount.

Eligibility Requirements: Applicant must hold an FCC amateur radio license; must be studying baccalaureate courses in business-related, computers, medical, nursing, engineering or sciences; be a high school senior; and must demonstrate financial need. **Application Requirements:** Applicants must submit a completed scholarship application form along with a recent high school (or equivalent) or college transcript, and the Free Application for Federal Student Aid (FAFSA) or Student Aid Report (SAR). **Deadline for Receipt:** February 1.

4924 ■ AMERICAN RADIO RELAY LEAGUE (ARRL) FOUNDATION
225 Main St.
Newington, CT 06111
Tel: (860)594-0200
Fax: (860)594-0259
E-mail: foundation@arrl.org

Web Site: http://www.arrlf.org

To support the education of students holding a valid FCC-granted Amateur Radio license for post-secondary education.

Title of Award: Ray, NORP and Katie, WOKTE Pautz Scholarships **Area, Field, or Subject:** Radio and television; Electronics; Computer and information sciences. **Level of Education for which Award is Granted:** Undergraduate **Number Awarded:** 1. **Funds Available:** $500-$1,000.

Eligibility Requirements: Applicant must hold an FCC amateur radio license; be a resident of the ARRL Midwest Division (IA, KS, MO, NE); be enrolled in electronics, computer science or related field at an accredited 4-year college/university; and be an ARRL member. **Application Requirements:** Applicants must submit a completed scholarship application form along with a recent high school (or equivalent) or college transcript. **Deadline for Receipt:** February 1.

4925 ■ AMERICAN RADIO RELAY LEAGUE (ARRL) FOUNDATION

225 Main St.
Newington, CT 06111
Tel: (860)594-0200
Fax: (860)594-0259
E-mail: foundation@arrl.org
Web Site: http://www.arrlf.org

To support the education of students holding a valid FCC-granted Amateur Radio license for post-secondary education.

Title of Award: PHD ARA Scholarships **Area, Field, or Subject:** Radio and television; Journalism; Computer and information sciences; Electronics. **Level of Education for which Award is Granted:** Undergraduate **Number Awarded:** 1. **Funds Available:** $500.

Eligibility Requirements: Applicant must hold an FCC amateur radio license; be a resident of ARRL Midwest Division (IA, KS, MO, NE); with course sof study in journalism, computer science or electronic engineering; and be the child of a deceased radio amateur. **Application Requirements:** Applicants must submit a completed scholarship application form along with a recent high school (or equivalent) or college transcript. **Deadline for Receipt:** February 1.

4926 ■ ARMED FORCES COMMUNICATIONS AND ELECTRONICS ASSOCIATION

4400 Fair Lakes Court
Fairfax, VA 22033
Tel: (703)631-6141
Free: 800-336-4583
Fax: (703)631-4693
Web Site: http://www.afcea.org

To support students working full time.

Title of Award: Vice Adm. Jerry O. Tuttle, USN (Ret.) and Mrs. Barbara A. Tuttle Science and Technology Scholarships **Area, Field, or Subject:** Engineering; Computer and Information Sciences. **Level of Education for which Award is Granted:** Undergraduate **Funds Available:** $2,000.

Eligibility Requirements: Applicants must be U.S. citizens enrolled full time with majoring in technology; and must be sophomores and juniors at the time of application. **Application Requirements:** Applicants may apply online. Applicants must also submit two letters of recommendation printed in school stationery and with signature from field-of-study professors; and official transcript of all college level study. **Deadline for Receipt:** November 1. **Additional Information:** Norma Corrales; 703-631-6149.

4927 ■ ASSOCIATION OF INDEPENDENT COLLEGES AND UNIVERSITIES OF PENNSYLVANIA

101 N Front St.
Harrisburg, PA 17101-1405
Tel: (717)232-8649
Fax: (717)233-8574
E-mail: duck@aicup.org
Web Site: http://www.aicup.org

To promote the engineering and information technology profession to individuals from groups historically underrepresented in engineering.

Title of Award: Air Products and Chemicals, Inc. Scholarships **Area, Field, or Subject:** Chemical engineering; Mechanical, Engineering; Computer and information sciences. **Level of Education for which Award is Granted:** Undergraduate **Funds Available:** $7,500.

Eligibility Requirements: Applicants must: be full-time undergraduate students majoring only in Chemical engineering, Mechanical engineering,

Information technology (computer science, management information systems, IST); be enrolled as a junior in fall; have a minimum GPA of 3.0; be women and/or members of the following minority groups: American Indian or Alaska Native, Asian, Black or African American, Hispanic or Latino, Native Hawaiian or other Pacific Islander. Student must be accepted at, or currently attending, one of 84 member colleges and universities of the Association of Independent Colleges and Universities of Pennsylvania. **Application Requirements:** Application forms are available at the Financial Aid office; applicant must submit complete application materials to Mary Maronic, Foundation Associate, Association of Independent Colleges and Universities of Pennsylvania. A complete application consists of a completed, signed application form, a copy of the student's transcript, a resume and an essay; the candidate may submit a letter of recommendation. **Deadline for Receipt:** April 29. **Additional Information:** Mary Maronic, 717-232-8649 ext. 232; maronic@aicup.org.

4928 ■ ASSOCIATION FOR WOMEN IN SCIENCE

1200 New York Ave. NW, Ste. 650
Washington, DC 20005
Tel: (202)326-8940
Fax: (202)326-8960
E-mail: awis@awis.org
Web Site: http://www.awis.org

To promote education in science.

Title of Award: AWIS College Scholarships **Area, Field, or Subject:** Astronomy and astronomical sciences; Geosciences; Biology; Mathematics and mathematical sciences; Chemistry; Physics; Computer and information sciences; Engineering; Psychology. **Level of Education for which Award is Granted:** Undergraduate **Number Awarded:** 2-5. **Funds Available:** No specific amount.

Eligibility Requirements: Applicant must be a female high school senior; U.S. citizen or permanent resident; have at least 3.75 GPA; at least 1200 score in SAT or a composite score of 25 in ACT; planning to study in any field of Astronomy, Geoscience, Biology, Mathematics, Chemistry, Physics, Computer and Information Science, Engineering, Psychology; planning to become a researcher or teacher. **Application Requirements:** Applicants must send five copies of: summary form; essay describing research experience; resume; two recommendation letters from science or research teachers; high school transcript and score of standardized test if available. **Deadline for Receipt:** January 17.

4929 ■ BLACK WOMEN IN SISTERHOOD FOR ACTION

PO Box 1592
Washington, DC 20013
Tel: (202)543-6013
Fax: (202)543-5719
E-mail: info@bisa-hq.org
Web Site: http://www.bisa-hq.org

To provide financial assistance to offset the cost of education for qualified students who have been accepted by an accredited college or university.

Title of Award: Richard Gregory Freeland, II Educational Scholarships **Area, Field, or Subject:** Computer and information sciences; Engineering; Telecommunications systems; Business administration. **Level of Education for which Award is Granted:** High School **Funds Available:** $500 to $2,500.

Eligibility Requirements: Applicants must be graduating high school students of African American ethnicity; reside in Maryland, Washington, DC or the Northern Virginia area; hold a grade point average of 2.5 or above; be pursuing a degree in the areas of computer science, information management, engineering, telecommunications, business management/administration or another technology-related field. **Application Requirements:** Applicants must submit all the required application information. **Deadline for Receipt:** May 5.

4930 ■ CANADIAN ENGINEERING MEMORIAL FOUNDATION

PO Box 370
Renfrew, ON, Canada K7V 4A6
(866)883-2363
Fax: (613)432-6840
E-mail: info@cemf.ca
Web Site: http://www.cemf.ca

To provide financial assistance to qualified individuals who want to pursue their studies.

Title of Award: IBM Canada Undergraduate Scholarships **Area, Field, or Subject:** Electrical engineering; Engineering, Computer. **Level of Education for which Award is Granted:** Undergraduate **Funds Available:** $2,500. **Duration:** One year.
Eligibility Requirements: Applicants must be Canadian women who are pursuing their undergraduate engineering studies in either electrical or computer engineering. **Application Requirements:** For further information and requirements about the scholarship, applicants are advised to contact the Canadian Engineering Memorial Foundation at PO Box 370, Refrew, ON K7V 4A6.

4931 ■ CATCHING THE DREAM
8200 Mountain Rd. NE., Ste. 203
Albuquerque, NM 87110
Tel: (505)262-2351
E-mail: nscholarships@aol.com
Web Site: http://www.catchingthedream.org
To support the education of Native Schools.

Title of Award: MESBEC Scholarships **Area, Field, or Subject:** Mathematics and mathematical sciences; Engineering; Science; Business; Education; Computer and information sciences. **Level of Education for which Award is Granted:** Undergraduate **Funds Available:** $500-$5000. **Duration:** One academic year.
Eligibility Requirements: Applicants must be 1/4 or more degree Native American; an enrolled member of a "U.S. tribe"; attending or planning to attend a college/university within the U.S. on a full-time basis that is fully accredited; studying in the field of business, finance, management, economics, banking, hotel management, and related field; have excellent grades; high ACT or SAT scores; and have a strong commitment to their Native American community. **Application Requirements:** Applicants must submit a completed application form (available at the website); financial need analysis; a copy of the IRS 1040 Federal Tax Return for the previous year; Certificate of Native American Blood; an essay explaining career goals; three letters of recommendation; official transcripts; a copy of standardized test scores; copy of letter of admission from an accredited college or university or graduate school and degree program in the US; and a photograph (2X3) of head and shoulders. **Deadline for Receipt:** March 15, April 15, and September 15.

4932 ■ COASTAL BEND COMMUNITY FOUNDATION
600 Leopard St., Ste. 1716
Corpus Christi, TX 78473
Tel: (361)882-9745
Fax: (361)882-2865
Web Site: http://www.cbcfoundation.org
To provide financial assistance to high school seniors who are planning to pursue a career in computer/electrical engineering.
Title of Award: Zachary Barriger Memorial Scholarships **Area, Field, or Subject:** Engineering, Computer; Engineering, Electrical. **Level of Education for which Award is Granted:** High School **Number Awarded:** 1. **Funds Available:** $500.
Eligibility Requirements: Applicants must be seniors at Tuloso-Midway High School; must be attending an accredited two or four-year college in Texas; must demonstrate interest in pursuing studies in the field of engineering or medicine; and must excel academically with A/B Honor Roll status and honor classes. **Application Requirements:** Applicants must submit all the required application information. **Deadline for Receipt:** March 14.

4933 ■ ELECTRONIC DOCUMENT SYSTEMS FOUNDATION
1845 Precinct Ln. Rd., Ste. 212
Hurst, TX 76054
Tel: (817)849-1145
Fax: (817)849-1185
E-mail: info@edsf.org
Web Site: http://www.edsf.org
To recognize and support the next generation of professionals for the document management and communication companies worldwide.
Title of Award: Electronic Document Systems Foundation Scholarships **Area, Field, or Subject:** Computer and information sciences; engineering; Communications technologies. **Level of Education for which Award is Granted:** Undergraduate **Funds Available:** No specific amount.
Eligibility Requirements: Applicants must be full-time students who are committed to pursuing careers in document management and com-

munications marketplace which include computer science and engineering, graphic and media communications and those students interested in Business in the document management and communications industry; must have a minimum GPA of 3.0 or a 'B' average; must be technical, trade school, community college, undergraduate and advanced-degree students in the U.S. and/or diploma or tertiary students outside of the U.S. may be considered for scholarships; must be students who are attending full-time, an accredited college or university. **Application Requirements:** Applicants must submit all the required application information.

4934 ■ ENTERTAINMENT SOFTWARE ASSOCIATION
575 7th St. NW, Ste. 300
Washington, DC 20004
Tel: (202)223-2400
E-mail: esa@theesa.com
Web Site: http://www.theesa.com
To assist women and minority students who plan to continue their education in fields supporting Video Game Development.
Title of Award: ESA Foundation Computer and Video Game Scholarship Program **Area, Field, or Subject:** Graphic Arts and Design; Computer and Information Sciences. **Level of Education for which Award is Granted:** Undergraduate **Number Awarded:** 15. **Funds Available:** $3,000.
Eligibility Requirements: Applicants must be enrolled full time study in an accredited four year colleges and universities. **Application Requirements:** Applicants must complete online application form. Applicants must provide proof that he/she is currently enrolled in a college, university, or institution. **Deadline for Receipt:** April 15.

4935 ■ FOUNDATION FOR THE CAROLINAS
217 S Tryon St.
Charlotte, NC 28202
Tel: (704)973-4500
Free: 800-973-7244
Web Site: http://www.fftc.org
To provide scholarships for college-bound students from North and South Carolina who are pursuing a major in engineering, math, science, computer science, accounting, finance or business administration.
Title of Award: African American Network - Carolinas Scholarship Fund **Area, Field, or Subject:** Engineering; Mathematics and mathematical sciences; Science; Computer and information sciences; Accounting; Finance; Business administration. **Level of Education for which Award is Granted:** Undergraduate **Number Awarded:** 2. **Funds Available:** No specific amount. **Duration:** One year.
Eligibility Requirements: Applicants must be graduating seniors at a North or South Carolina high school; must attend a four-year college or university located in North or South Carolina; must plan to major in engineering, computer science, the sciences, accounting, finance or business administration. **Application Requirements:** Applicants must submit all the required application information.

4936 ■ FOUNDATION FOR THE CAROLINAS
217 S Tryon St.
Charlotte, NC 28202
Tel: (704)973-4500
Free: 800-973-7244
Web Site: http://www.fftc.org
To provide financial assistance for students at Clemson University and the University of North Carolina at Charlotte who are preparing for a career in a technological field appropriate to meet the requirements of the U.S. Patent Office as a patent agent or attorney.
Title of Award: Julian E. Carnes Scholarship Fund **Area, Field, or Subject:** Engineering; Chemistry; Physics; Biology; Computer and information sciences. **Level of Education for which Award is Granted:** Undergraduate **Funds Available:** No specific amount.
Eligibility Requirements: Applicants must be legal residents of North or South Carolina; must be rising juniors or seniors at Clemson University or UNC Charlotte whose academic major is appropriate to meet the requirements of the U.S. Patent Office for admission as a patent agent or attorney (including but not limited to engineering, chemistry, physics, biology and computer science); and must have at least a 3.0 cumulative grade point average (on a 4.0 scale). **Application Requirements:** Applicants must submit all the required application information. **Additional**

Information: Clemson University Office of Student Financial Aid, 864-656-2280 or the UNC Charlotte Student Financial Aid Office, 704-687-2461.

4937 ■ FOUNDATION FOR ENHANCING COMMUNITIES
200 N Third St., PO Box 678
Harrisburg, PA 17108-0678
Tel: (717)236-5040
Fax: (717)231-4463
E-mail: dawn@tfec.org
Web Site: http://www.ghf.org
To provide educational assistance for students of Chambersburg High School and Fannett-Metal High School.
Title of Award: Chambersburg/Fannett-Metal School District Scholarship Fund **Area, Field, or Subject:** Engineering, computer; Computer and information sciences. **Level of Education for which Award is Granted:** Undergraduate **Funds Available:** No specific amount.
Eligibility Requirements: Applicants must have a desire to pursue a career in computer engineering or computer science and must have an academic achievement of a cumulative GPA of 2.0 or higher on a 4.0 scale. **Application Requirements:** Applicants must have the following required attachments: completed student background sheet; official high school transcript with raised school seal; 1st and 2nd page of parent's and student's IRS 1040 and/or 1040 A forms; completed student essay (not to exceed 300 words); two personal letters (one letter should be from a teacher and the other letter should be from an employer or a supervisor of a community service volunteer agency). Letters of reference may not be from a family member. Students must return their completed application to their high school guidance counselor. **Additional Information:** Established in 1999. **Deadline for Receipt:** March 22. **Additional Information:** Dawn Morris, Program Officer; 717-236-5040; dawn@tfec.org.

4938 ■ GRAND HAVEN AREA COMMUNITY FOUNDATION
1 S. Harbor Dr.
Grand Haven, MI 49417
Tel: (616)842-6378
Fax: (616)842-9518
E-mail: bpost@ghacf.org
Web Site: http://www.ghacf.org
To improve and enhance the quality of life in the Tri-Cities area by serving as a leader, catalyst and resource for philanthropy; to strive for community improvement through strategic grantmaking in such fields as arts, education, health, environment, youth, social services and other human needs.
Title of Award: Henry D. and Ruth G. Swartz Family Scholarship Fund **Area, Field, or Subject:** Computer and Information Sciences. **Level of Education for which Award is Granted:** Undergraduate **Funds Available:** No specific amount.
Eligibility Requirements: Applicants must be graduating high school seniors from Grand Haven High School, Spring Lake High School, Holland Christian High School or Western Michigan Christian High School in North Ottawa County; must be pursuing a career in engineering, computer science, pre-law or medicine. **Application Requirements:** Applicants must submit: completed application form; current high school or college transcript; Student Aid Report (SAR) from the Free Application for Federal Student Aid (FAFSA); and letter of recommendation. **Deadline for Receipt:** March 7. **Additional Information:** 616-842-6378.

4939 ■ HISPANIC SCHOLARSHIP FUND
55 Second St., Ste. 1500
San Francisco, CA 94105
877-473-4636
Fax: (415)808-2302
E-mail: info@hsf.net
Web Site: http://www.hsf.net
For sophomore students who will be transferring to a four-year college.
Title of Award: HSBC-North America Scholarship Program **Area, Field, or Subject:** Accounting; Actuarial science; Advertising; Public relations; Business; Engineering, Computer; Computer and information sciences; Economics; Finance; International trade; Marketing and distribution; Management. **Level of Education for which Award is Granted:** Undergraduate **Funds Available:** $2,500.
Eligibility Requirements: Applicant must be of Hispanic heritage; U.S. citizen or legal permanent resident with a valid permanent resident card or

passport stamped I-551; be a current sophomore or community college student transferring to a four-year college/university and will be a junior status for the upcoming academic year; be enrolled full-time in a degree-seeking program at an accredited institution in the U.S., Puerto Rico, U.S. Virgin Islands or Guam; have a minimum 3.0 GPA on a 4.0 scale or 4.00 on a 5.00 scale; must be majoring in one of the following: Accounting, Actuarial Science, Advertising, Public Relations, Business, Computer Engineering, Computer Information Systems (CIS), Computer Science, Economics, Finance, International Business, Marketing or Management; must submit a resume; have applied for Federal Financial Aid; must be a resident of: Los Angeles, CA (LA, Orange, Riverside, San Bernardino, Ventura); Monterey/Salinas, CA (Salinas); San Diego, CA (San Diego); Tampa, FL (Hernando, Hillsborough, Pasco, Pinella); Jacksonville, FL (Nassau, Duval, Clay, St. Johns); Chicago, IL (Cook, DuPage, Grundy, Kane, Kankakee, Kendall, Lake, LaSalle, Will, McHenry); New York, NY (Bronx, Kings, New York, Queens, Richmond); Las Vegas, NV (Clark); Phoenix, AZ (Phoenix-Mesa); Wilmington, DC (New Castle); Bridgewater, NJ (Sussex); or Chesapeake, VA. Applicants must also submit a resume; must have applied for federal financial aid and must be pursuing his/her first undergraduate degree. **Application Requirements:** Applicants must use the HSF online application system. **Additional Information:** In partnership with HSBC. **Deadline for Receipt:** November 1. **Additional Information:** scholar1@hsf.net.

4940 ■ HISPANIC SCHOLARSHIP FUND
55 Second St., Ste. 1500
San Francisco, CA 94105
877-473-4636
Fax: (415)808-2302
E-mail: info@hsf.net
Web Site: http://www.hsf.net
To provide financial assistance to minority students.
Title of Award: HSF/Hewlett Packard (HP) Diversity in Education Scholarship Program **Area, Field, or Subject:** Computer and information sciences; Engineering, Computer; Engineering, Electrical. **Level of Education for which Award is Granted:** Undergraduate **Funds Available:** $3,000 per year. **Duration:** Four years.
Eligibility Requirements: Applicants must be graduating high school seniors enrolling as a fulltime first-year student or a community college student transferring into University of California, Los Angeles, North Carolina AT&T, Morgan State University or University of Washington; plan to major in computer engineering, computer science or electrical engineering; must be African American, Latino or American Indian; be able to legally work full time in the United States at the time of application. **Application Requirements:** Applicants must download application forms from the award site website www.hp.com/scholars. **Additional Information:** In partnership with HP Development Company. **Deadline for Receipt:** March 15. **Additional Information:** highschool@hsf.net.

4941 ■ HISPANIC SCHOLARSHIP FUND
55 Second St., Ste. 1500
San Francisco, CA 94105
877-473-4636
Fax: (415)808-2302
E-mail: info@hsf.net
Web Site: http://www.hsf.net
To provide financial assistance to students of Hispanic heritage.
Title of Award: HSF/Wal-Mart Stores Inc. Scholarship Program **Area, Field, or Subject:** Marketing and distribution; Accounting; Business; Finance; Management; Computer and information sciences; Information science and technology; Civil engineering; Construction; Electrical engineering; Geology; Engineering, Industrial; Fashion design; Law; **Level of Education for which Award is Granted:** Graduate, Undergraduate **Funds Available:** $2,500.
Eligibility Requirements: Applicant must be of Hispanic heritage; U.S. citizen or legal permanent resident with a valid permanent resident card or passport stamped I-551; enrolled as sophomore, junior, senior undergraduate or First or Second year Master student in a full-time degree-seeking program at an accredited U.S. institution in the U.S., Puerto Rico, U.S. Virgin Islands or Guam; have a minimum 3.0 GPA on a 4.0 scale or 4.00 on a 5.00 scale; must apply for Federal Financing Aid; pursuing his/her first undergraduate or graduate degree. Undergraduate students must be majoring in: Marketing, Accounting, Business, Finance, Management,

Computer Science, Computer Programming, Information Technology (IT), Civil Engineering, Construction, Electrical Engineering, Environmental/ Geological Engineering, Industrial Engineering, and Fashion. Master's students must be majoring in: Business, Finance, Marketing, Civil Engineering, Construction, Electrical Engineering, Environmental/ Geological Engineering and Law. **Application Requirements:** Applications must be submitted using the HSF online application system. **Additional Information:** In partnership with Wal-Mart Stores, Inc. **Deadline for Receipt:** March 15. **Additional Information:** scholar1@hsf.net.

4942 ■ HISPANIC SCHOLARSHIP FUND
55 Second St., Ste. 1500
San Francisco, CA 94105
877-473-4636
Fax: (415)808-2302
E-mail: info@hsf.net
Web Site: http://www.hsf.net
To provide financial resources to assist outstanding Latino high school graduates.

Title of Award: Toyota High School Scholarship Program **Area, Field, or Subject:** Accounting; Actuarial science; Advertising; Architecture; Automotive technology; Bioengineering; Business; Chemical engineering; Civil engineering; Engineering, Computer; Electronics; Computer and information sciences; Construction; Drafting; Economics; Education; Education, Bilingual and cross-cultural; Education, Early childhood; Education, Special; Counseling/Guidance; Electrical engineering; Engineering; Environmental design; Environmental science; Geology; Educational administration; Education-Curricula; Personnel administration/human resources; Industrial design; Engineering, Industrial; Information science and technology; Management; Marketing and distribution; International trade; Manufacturing; Mechanical engineering; Engineering, Nuclear; Public administration; Public relations; Transportation. **Level of Education for which Award is Granted:** Undergraduate **Funds Available:** $5,000.

Eligibility Requirements: Applicant must be of Hispanic heritage; U.S. citizen or legal permanent resident with a valid permanent resident card or passport stamped I-551; have a minimum GPA of 3.0 on a 4.0 scale or equivalent; must apply for federal financing aid using the Free Application for Federal Student Aid (FAFSA) at www.fafsa.ed.gov; enrolling as full-time freshman at: Arizona State University; Central Missouri University; Colorado State University, Pueblo; Cornell University; Ferris State; Florida International University; Harvard University; Indiana University; Massachusetts Institute of Technology; New York University; Northwestern University; Pennsylvania Tech College; Pittsburg State University; Southern Illinois University; Stanford University; Texas A&M University; University of Arizona; University of California, Berkeley; University of California, Davis; University of California, Los Angeles; University of California, San Diego; University of Florida; University of Houston; University of Illinois at Chicago; University of Illinois at Urbana-Champaign; University of Michigan; University of New Mexico; University of Pennsylvania; University of Southern California; University of Texas at Austin; University of Texas at El Paso; University of Texas at San Antonio; University of Texas, Pan American; or Weber State University. Applicants must pursue a degree in: Accounting; Actuarial Science; Advertising; Architecture; Automotive Technology; Bio-Engineering; Business; Chemical Engineering; Civil Engineering; Computer Electronics; Computer Engineering; Computer Information Systems (CIS); Computer Programming; Computer Science; Construction; Drafting/CAD; Economics; Education Admin./Leadership; Education/Teaching; Education: Bilingual; Education: Early Childhood/ Elementary; Education: Special; Educational Counseling; Electrical Engineering; Engineering; Environmental Design/ Landscaping; Environmental Management/Science; Environmental/ Geological Engineering; Human Resource Management; Industrial Design; Industrial Engineering; Information Technology (IT); International Business; Management; Management Information Systems (MIS); Manufacturing Engineering; Marketing; Materials/ Manufacturing; Mechanical Engineering; Network Administration; Non-Profit Management; Nuclear Engineering; Office Administration; Public Administration; Public Relations; Supply Chain Management; or Transportation. **Application Requirements:** Applications must be submitted using the HSF online application system. **Additional Information:** In partnership with Toyota Motor Sales, USA. **Deadline for Receipt:** July 16. **Additional Information:** highschool@hsf.net.

4943 ■ HISPANIC SCHOLARSHIP FUND
55 Second St., Ste. 1500
San Francisco, CA 94105
877-473-4636
Fax: (415)808-2302
E-mail: info@hsf.net
Web Site: http://www.hsf.net
To provide financial assistance to college students of Hispanic heritage.

Title of Award: Verizon Scholarship Program **Area, Field, or Subject:** Accounting; Business; Economics; Finance; Personnel administration/ human resources; Marketing and distribution; Engineering, Computer; Information science and technology; Computer and information sciences; Civil engineering; Electrical engineering; Engineering, Industrial; Engineering, Mechanical. **Level of Education for which Award is Granted:** Undergraduate **Funds Available:** $5,000.

Eligibility Requirements: Applicant must be of Hispanic heritage; U.S. citizen or legal permanent resident with a valid permanent resident card or passport stamped I-551; enrolled as sophomore, junior or senior in a full-time degree-seeking program at an accredited U.S. institution in the U.S., Puerto Rico, U.S. Virgin Islands or Guam; have a minimum 3.0 GPA on a 4.0 scale or 4.00 on a 5.00 scale; must apply for federal financing aid using the Free Application for Federal Student Aid (FAFSA) at www.fafsa. ed.gov; must submit a resume with application; must be pursuing his/her first undergraduate degree; must be majoring in: Accounting, Business, Economics, Finance, Human Resource Management, Marketing, Computer Science, Computer Engineering, Computer Programming, Computer Electronics, Information Technology (IT), Management Information Systems (MIS), Network Administration, Computer Information Systems (CIS), Civil, Electrical, Industrial, or Mechanical Engineering; must be a resident of: (NY counties) Bronx, Kings, New York, Queens, and Richmond; (NJ) Town of Basking Ridge in Somerset County; (PA Counties) Bucks, Montgomery, Chester, Delaware, Philadelphia; (FL counties) Hernando, Hillsborough, Pasco, and Pinella; (MA counties) Essex, Middlesex, Plymouth, Suffolk; (TX counties) Collin, Dallas, Denton, Dexar, Dorris, Ellis, Henderson, Hood, Hunt, Johnson, Kaufman, Parker, Rockwall, and Tarrant; (VA county) Arlington, Loudoun; (DC) Washington; (Southern CA counties) Los Angeles, Orange, Riverside, San Bernardino, Ventura; Maine, New Hampshire, Washington State. **Application Requirements:** Applications must be submitted using the HSF online application system. **Additional Information:** In partnership with Verizon. **Deadline for Receipt:** March 15. **Additional Information:** scholar1@hsf. net.

4944 ■ INFORMATION TECHNOLOGY INDUSTRY ALLIANCE OF NOVA SCOTIA
PO Box 9410 Sta. A
Halifax, NS, Canada B3K 5S3
Tel: (902)423-5332
Fax: (902)484-5094
E-mail: info@itans.ns.ca
Web Site: http://www.itans.ns.ca
To provide financial assistance for qualified individuals.

Title of Award: Dr. Stan Heaps Memorial Scholarships **Area, Field, or Subject:** Computer and information sciences. **Level of Education for which Award is Granted:** Undergraduate **Number Awarded:** 2. **Funds Available:** $2,000. **Duration:** One year.

Eligibility Requirements: Applicant must be a student about to enter his or her junior or senior year at a 4-year Nova Scotia university program leading to a degree with specialization in computer studies; must have achieved a minimum overall GPA of 2.67; must be a Canadian citizen or landed immigrant. **Application Requirements:** applicants must complete and submit the scholarship application form available at the CIPS Bluenose website and must also submit any additional information supporting their application. **Deadline for Receipt:** May 30.

4945 ■ JAMAICAN CANADIAN ASSOCIATION
995 Arrow Rd.
Toronto, ON, Canada M9M 2Z5
Tel: (416)746-5772
Fax: (416)746-7035
E-mail: info@jcassoc.org
Web Site: http://www.jcassoc.org

To provide financial assistance to students from the Caribbean or African community, who are pursuing postsecondary studies in Ontario universities/colleges. **Title of Award:** Dr. Ezra Nesbeth Scholarships **Area, Field, or Subject:** Business; Technology; Computer and information sciences; Health sciences. **Level of Education for which Award is Granted:** Undergraduate **Funds Available:** $2,000. **Duration:** One year.

Eligibility Requirements: Applicants must be college or university students studying business, technology, computer science or health science; must have a high academic standing; must demonstrate leadership; must have completed at least one year of college or university in Canada; must demonstrate strong oral and written communication skills; must have an involvement in extracurricular activities within the university, AfroCanadian community, or wider Canadian community; must have landed immigrant or Canadian citizenship; must not be receiving more than one other award of equal or greater value in the receiving year; must have a good understanding of the importance of economic self-sufficiency and entrepreneurship to the success of African Canadians in the Greater Toronto Area and elsewhere in Canada. **Application Requirements:** Application forms are available online and must be sent to The Jamaican Canadian Association Center, 995 Arrow Rd., Toronto M9M 2Z5. **Additional Information:** Sponsored by Dr. Ezra Nesbeth, a graduate of the University of Waterloo and the University of Toronto with varied and extensive experience in community and health programs. **Deadline for Receipt:** July 25.

4946 ■ LEWIS-CLARK STATE COLLEGE
500 8th Ave.
Lewiston, ID 83501
Tel: (208)792-5272
Web Site: http://www.lcsc.edu
To provide financial assistance to students who are majoring in these fields: Accounting, Biology, Business, Communications, Computer Science, Economics, Environmental Science, Engineering, Mathematics, Natural Resources, Political Science, Statistics.

Title of Award: Avista Corporation Minds in Motion Scholarships **Area, Field, or Subject:** Accounting; Biology; Business; Communications; Computer and Information Sciences; Economics; Environmental Science; Engineering; Mathematics; Natural Resources; Political Science; Statistics. **Level of Education for which Award is Granted:** Undergraduate **Number Awarded:** 2. **Funds Available:** No specific Amount.

Eligibility Requirements: Applicants must be full-time students attending LCSC and must have a cumulative GPA of 2.5. **Application Requirements:** Applicants must submit general application. **Deadline for Receipt:** March 1.

4947 ■ LEWIS-CLARK STATE COLLEGE
500 8th Ave.
Lewiston, ID 83501
Tel: (208)792-5272
Web Site: http://www.lcsc.edu
To provide educational assistance for students intending to pursue a career in the area of Computer Science.

Title of Award: Jimmy Guild Memorial Scholarships **Area, Field, or Subject:** Mathematics and Mathematical Sciences; Computer and Information Sciences. **Level of Education for which Award is Granted:** Undergraduate **Number Awarded:** 1. **Funds Available:** $1,000. **Duration:** One year.

Eligibility Requirements: Applicants must be full-time students who are majoring in mathematics; must have interest in Computer science; and must have a cumulative GPA of 3.0. **Application Requirements:** Preference will be given to graduating students from local high schools who are affiliated with a member of the United Paperworkers International Union. **Deadline for Receipt:** May 19.

4948 ■ LEWIS-CLARK STATE COLLEGE
500 8th Ave.
Lewiston, ID 83501
Tel: (208)792-5272
Web Site: http://www.lcsc.edu
To inspire educational pursuits among less capable individuals by providing financial assistance.

Title of Award: Lewis-Clark State College Presidential Technical Out-of-State Scholarships **Area, Field, or Subject:** Chemistry; Computer Science; Engineering; Information Systems Analysis; Industrial Electronics; Biology; Earth Information Systems; Radiology; Heating/Air Conditioning; Automated Manufacturing Technology; Mathematics; Printing Technology; Graphic Arts or Web Development. **Level of Education for which Award is Granted:** Undergraduate **Funds Available:** No specific amount.

Eligibility Requirements: Applicants must be new non-resident high school or transfer students who have at least 14 transferable semester credits. **Application Requirements:** Applicants must accomplish a general application available in the website. **Deadline for Receipt:** March 1 for Fall enrollment or November 1 for Spring enrollment.

4949 ■ LEXINGTON COMMUNITY FOUNDATION
607 Washington St.
PO Box 422
Lexington, NE 68850
Tel: (308)324-6704
E-mail: lexfoundation@alltel.net
Web Site: http://www.lexfoundation.org
To promote community philanthropy by working with individuals, families and organizations to develop tailored giving plans that effectively meet the charitable goals and financial circumstances.

Title of Award: Edsel Newman Scholarship **Area, Field, or Subject:** Engineering; Computer and information sciences. **Level of Education for which Award is Granted:** Undergraduate **Funds Available:** $2,000.

Eligibility Requirements: Applicants must be graduating seniors who are planning to pursue a career in the field of engineering an/or computer science; must have ranked in the upper 1/3 of their class and must be U.S. citizens. **Application Requirements:** Applicants must submit a completed application form; must provide three letters of recommendation and must attach a recent photo.

4950 ■ MATANUSKA-SUSITNA COLLEGE
PO Box 2889
Palmer, AK 99645
Tel: (907)745-9774
Fax: (907)745-9711
E-mail: info@matsu.alaska.edu
Web Site: http://www.matsu.alaska.edu
To provide an incentive for Alaska's middle and high school students to achieve academic excellence, and to encourage the top high school graduates from every community in Alaska to attend the University of Alaska.

Title of Award: Snodgrass Scholarships **Area, Field, or Subject:** Accounting; Engineering, Architectural; Computer and information sciences; Fires and fire prevention; Heating, air conditioning, and refrigeration; Business administration; Telecommunications systems. **Level of Education for which Award is Granted:** Undergraduate **Funds Available:** $500-$2,000. **Duration:** One academic year.

Eligibility Requirements: Applicant must be admitted to the given Matanuska-Susitna College degree programs; must be a continuing student at Matanuska-Susitna College who has earned at least 20 credit hours; must have a cumulative GPA of 3.0 or higher; must exhibit good moral character and conduct; must be registered for eight or more credit hours. **Application Requirements:** Applicants must complete the MSC scholarship application and attach a resume showing their work experience; must compose an essay of 500 words or less describing their educational and career goals and how they plan to attain them; must have two letters of recommendation, written within the last two years. Application form and other supporting documents must be sent to Snodgrass Scholarships, Matanuska-Susitna College, Student Service, FSM 102, Palmer, AK 99645. **Deadline for Receipt:** May 31.

4951 ■ MATANUSKA-SUSITNA COLLEGE
PO Box 2889
Palmer, AK 99645
Tel: (907)745-9774
Fax: (907)745-9711
E-mail: info@matsu.alaska.edu
Web Site: http://www.matsu.alaska.edu
To provide support to deserving students in Alaska who want to pursue an education in any campus of the University of Alaska.

Title of Award: Ralph Yetka Memorial Scholarships **Area, Field, or Subject:** Engineering; Education, Elementary; Education, Secondary;

Computer and information sciences. **Level of Education for which Award is Granted:** Undergraduate **Funds Available:** $750. **Eligibility Requirements:** Applicants must be full-time students and graduates of Ketchikan or Revilla High School with a minimum GPA of 2.5; must be majoring in engineering, elementary or secondary education, computer science or aviation. **Application Requirements:** Applicant must complete the application forms available at the website; must attach a personal essay, two letters of recommendation, and current transcripts. **Deadline for Receipt:** February 15.

4952 ■ PARKERSBURG AREA COMMUNITY FOUNDATION
501 Avery St.
Parkersburg, WV 26101
Tel: (304)428-4438; (866)428-4438
Fax: (304)428-1200
E-mail: info@pacfwv.com
Web Site: http://www.pacfwv.com
To provide financial assistance for qualified individuals intending to pursue their undergraduate degree.
Title of Award: William (Billbo) Boston Scholarships **Area, Field, or Subject:** Computer and information sciences. **Level of Education for which Award is Granted:** Undergraduate **Funds Available:** $450.
Eligibility Requirements: Applicants must be graduating seniors or current undergraduates who previously graduated from a Wood County high school and are pursuing undergraduate degree in computer science at an accredited post-secondary school in West Virginia or Ohio with a minimum of 3.0 GPA. **Application Requirements:** Applicants must submit a cover sheet (3 pages) and application form (4 pages); a personal essay; a high school and/or post-secondary transcript; a letter of recommendation; a signed copy of the page of their or their parent's most recent tax return that indicates adjusted gross income; and a Student Aid Report, showing estimated family contribution, from FAFSA. Application form and other supporting documents must be sent to Our Community's Foundation, P.O Box 1762, Parkersburg, WV 26102. **Deadline for Receipt:** March 20.

4953 ■ PRIDE FOUNDATION
PO Box 2194, 1122 E Pike St. PMB 1001
Seattle, WA 98112
Tel: (206)323-3318
Free: 800-735-7287
Fax: (206)323-1017
E-mail: prideweb@pridefoundation.org
Web Site: http://www.pridefoundation.org
To provide scholarship to the students who have been stigmatized, isolated or closeted because of sexual identity issues.
Title of Award: Urashi Zen Scholarships **Area, Field, or Subject:** Business administration; Computer and information sciences; Political science. **Level of Education for which Award is Granted:** Undergraduate **Funds Available:** No specific amount.
Eligibility Requirements: Applicant must be a student studying business administration, computer science, or political science. **Application Requirements:** Qualified students are asked to submit an application to determine eligibility for scholarships. Applicants may download an application form from the Foundation's website. **Additional Information:** Pride Foundation at the above address.

4954 ■ PUBLIC EDUCATION FOUNDATION
3360 W Sahara Ave., Ste. 160
Las Vegas, NV 89102
Tel: (702)799-1042
Fax: (702)799-5247
E-mail: steelej@ccpef.org
Web Site: http://ccpef.org
To provide educational opportunities for individuals intending to pursue higher studies.
Title of Award: Edwin F. Wiegand Science and Technology Scholarships **Area, Field, or Subject:** Computer and information sciences. **Level of Education for which Award is Granted:** Undergraduate **Number Awarded:** 2. **Funds Available:** $1,250. **Duration:** One year.
Eligibility Requirements: Applicants must be CCSD seniors pursuing a degree in science, technology, computer science or related field at the University of Nevada, Las Vegas, or the University of Nevada, or Reno,

with a minimum of 3.0 cumulative GPA. **Application Requirements:** Applicants must submit a completed application form along with an essay, two letters of recommendation, transcript, and a resume of awards. **Deadline for Receipt:** March 7. **Additional Information:** Shana Venenga at 702-799-1042.

4955 ■ REDLANDS COMMUNITY SCHOLARSHIP FOUNDATION
c/o Kathleen Venegas-Boge, Admin. Asst.
PO Box 1683
Redlands, CA 92373
Tel: (909)307-9892
Fax: (909)307-9892
Web Site: http://www.redlandsscholarships.org
To encourage educational pursuits among Redlands Unified School District graduates by providing educational assistance.
Title of Award: Soroptimist International of Redlands Scholarships **Area, Field, or Subject:** Health care services; Law; Engineering; Computer and information sciences; Education; Business. **Level of Education for which Award is Granted:** Undergraduate **Number Awarded:** 1. **Funds Available:** $750.
Eligibility Requirements: Applicant must be a graduating senior who has participated in community service and who will be attending an accredited college on a full-time basis and is planning to major in one of the following fields: health care, law, engineering, computer science, education and/or business administration. **Application Requirements:** Applicants must submit a completed application form together with the scantron sheet; cover sheet; student activity and community activity sheets; personal essay; and a copy of unofficial transcript (signed by the counselor). **Additional Information:** No electronic submissions of application will be accepted. Submit two printed copies of the application and use a No. 2 pencil on the scantron sheet. **Deadline for Receipt:** February 20.

4956 ■ SAFE SCHOOLS COALITION
1002 E Seneca St.
Seattle, WA 98122-4203
Tel: (206)957-1621
Fax: (206)325-2689
Web Site: http://www.safeschoolscoalition.org
To provide financial assistance for gay, lesbian, bisexual and transgender students pursuing higher education.
Title of Award: Pride Foundation Scholarships **Area, Field, or Subject:** Business Administration; Computer Science; Political Science; Visual arts. **Level of Education for which Award is Granted:** Undergraduate **Funds Available:** Range from $500 to $10,000.
Eligibility Requirements: Applicants must be gay, lesbian, bisexual and transgendered students in these fields of studies. **Application Requirements:** Applicants must check the available website for the required materials. **Deadline for Receipt:** January.

4957 ■ THE SAN DIEGO FOUNDATION
2508 Historic Decatur Rd., Ste. 200
San Diego, CA 92106
Tel: (619)235-2300
Fax: (619)239-1710
E-mail: info@sdfoundation.org
Web Site: http://www.sdfoundation.org
To support the education of students from California.
Title of Award: AeA Scholarships **Area, Field, or Subject:** Mathematics and mathematical sciences; Science; Engineering; Computer and information sciences. **Level of Education for which Award is Granted:** Undergraduate **Number Awarded:** 2. **Funds Available:** $1000.
Eligibility Requirements: Applicant must be a resident of San Diego County (military personnel and dependents are exempt); a citizen or legal resident of the United States; attend an accredited two-year college, four-year university or licensed trade and vocational school in the U.S.; a full-time student (unless otherwise noted); have a measure of academic and civic achievement; be of good moral and personal character; graduate from a San Diego County public high school; have a minimum 3.75 GPA on a 4.0 scale; and be majoring in math, science, engineering, or computers. **Application Requirements:** Applicants must submit a completed Common Scholarship Application together with personal statement; two letters of recommendation on official letterhead (written within the last six months); official transcript in an official and sealed envelope; copy of 2006

or most recent tax form (Form 1040-pages 1 & 2; Form 1040A-pages 1 & 2; Form 1040EZ-page 1); and an unofficial copy of SAT score results. **Deadline for Receipt:** January 28. **Additional Information:** Arzo Mansury, Dir. Scholarships at 619-814-1343, or scholarships@ sdfoundation.org.

4958 ■ THE SAN DIEGO FOUNDATION

2508 Historic Decatur Rd., Ste. 200
San Diego, CA 92106
Tel: (619)235-2300
Fax: (619)239-1710
E-mail: info@sdfoundation.org
Web Site: http://www.sdfoundation.org
To support the education of students from California.
Title of Award: Helm Family Scholarships **Area, Field, or Subject:** Biology; Computer and information sciences; Chemistry; Technology; Engineering; Physics. **Level of Education for which Award is Granted:** Undergraduate **Number Awarded:** 2. **Funds Available:** $5,00.
Eligibility Requirements: Applicant must be an entering junior or senior student at San Diego State University or the University of California, San Diego; have declared a major in mathematics or a scientific field such as, but not limited to, biology, computer science, chemistry, technology, engineering, physics, etc.; have a minimum 3.0 GPA on a 4.0 scale; and have demonstrated financial need. **Application Requirements:** Applicants must submit a completed Common Scholarship Application together with personal statement; two letters of recommendation on official letterhead (written within the last six months); official transcript in an official and sealed envelope; and a copy of most recent tax form (Form 1040-pages 1 & 2; Form 1040Apages 1 & 2; Form 1040EZ-page 1). **Deadline for Receipt:** January 28. **Additional Information:** Arzo Mansury, Dir. Scholarships at 619-814-1343, or scholarships@ sdfoundation.org.

4959 ■ SOCIETY OF ALLIED WEIGHT ENGINEERS

PO Box 60024, Terminal Annex
Los Angeles, CA 90060
Tel: (562)596-2873
Fax: (562)596-2874
Web Site: http://www.sawe.org
To provide financial assistance for the education of the dependents of SAWE members.
Title of Award: Frank Fong Scholarships **Area, Field, or Subject:** Engineering; Physics; Mathematics and mathematical sciences; Computer and information sciences. **Level of Education for which Award is Granted:** Undergraduate **Number Awarded:** 5. **Funds Available:** $1000. **Duration:** One year.
Eligibility Requirements: Applicants must be children or grandchildren of SAWE members; must be aged 25 or below; full-time undergraduate students; pursuing a technical course of study (engineering, physics, mathematics, computer sciences, etc.). **Application Requirements:** Application forms are available at the website. Applicants must submit completed application form and send together with a complete transcript of grades. **Deadline for Receipt:** April. **Additional Information:** Ginny Miller, Scholarship Management Services, Telephone: (507)931-1682, Toll-free: (800)537-4180.

4960 ■ SOUTHWEST FLORIDA COMMUNITY FOUNDATION

8260 College Pkwy., Ste. 101
Fort Myers, FL 33919
Tel: (239)274-5900
Fax: (239)274-5930
Web Site: http://www.floridacommunity.com
To fund a student who will attend: FGCU, university of Florida/ Gainesville, Florida State University/Tallahassee, Flagler College, Stetson University/Deland, University of Miami, University of Tampa, or Embry Riddle Aeronautical University/Daytona Beach.
Title of Award: D&A Florida Scholarships **Area, Field, or Subject:** Architecture; Business; Engineering; International affairs and relations; Journalism; Computer and information sciences; Law; Literature; Medicine; Physics; Chemistry; Political science. **Level of Education for which Award is Granted:** Undergraduate **Funds Available:** $10,000. **Duration:** One year.
Eligibility Requirements: Applicants must have graduated from a public or private high school in Charlotte, Glades, Hendry or Lee County; must

pursue a degree in Architecture, Business, Engineering, International affairs and relations, Journalism, Computer and information sciences, Law, Literature, Medicine, Physics, Chemistry, or Political science. **Application Requirements:** Application forms are available online. Applicants must submit a letter of interest and letter of recommendation, a transcript and financial need documentation. **Deadline for Receipt:** February 15.

4961 ■ SOUTHWEST FLORIDA COMMUNITY FOUNDATION

8260 College Pkwy., Ste. 101
Fort Myers, FL 33919
Tel: (239)274-5900
Fax: (239)274-5930
Web Site: http://www.floridacommunity.com
To fund scholarships for female students pursuing a career in technical studies, court reporting, computer training or nursing.
Title of Award: Faye Lynn Roberts Educational Scholarships **Area, Field, or Subject:** Technical training; Computer and information sciences; Nursing. **Level of Education for which Award is Granted:** Undergraduate **Funds Available:** $5,000. **Duration:** One year.
Eligibility Requirements: Applicants must be 21 years of age or older; must be residents of Lee County; and must demonstrate financial need. **Application Requirements:** Application forms are available online. Applicants must submit a personal essay, financial need documentation, high school/college transcript and letter of recommendation. **Deadline for Receipt:** March 20.

4962 ■ SOUTHWEST FLORIDA COMMUNITY FOUNDATION

8260 College Pkwy., Ste. 101
Fort Myers, FL 33919
Tel: (239)274-5900
Fax: (239)274-5930
Web Site: http://www.floridacommunity.com
To fund students pursuing degrees or advanced degrees in medicine, law, dentistry, teaching (math and science), ministry, engineering, accounting, architecture and computer science.
Title of Award: John M. and Mary A. Shanley Memorial Scholarships **Area, Field, or Subject:** Medicine; Law; Dentistry; Teaching; Ministry; Engineering; Accounting; Agriculture; Economic aspects; Architecture; Computer and information sciences. **Level of Education for which Award is Granted:** Undergraduate **Funds Available:** $5,000. **Duration:** One year.
Eligibility Requirements: Applicant must be a resident of Charlotte, Hendry or Lee County. **Application Requirements:** Application forms are available online. Applicants must submit a letter of interest, letter of recommendation and transcript. **Deadline for Receipt:** February 15.

4963 ■ UNIVERSITY OF TORONTO

315 Bloor St. W
Toronto, ON, Canada M5S 1A3
Tel: (416)978-2011
E-mail: information.commonsats@utoronto.ca
Web Site: http://www.utoronto.ca
To support students with their educational pursuits.
Title of Award: Stephanie Ali Memorial Scholarships **Area, Field, or Subject:** General studies. **Level of Education for which Award is Granted:** Undergraduate **Funds Available:** Approximately $200.
Eligibility Requirements: Applicant must be a student of U of T; in financial need; and have demonstrated commitment to community work or participation in charitable activities. **Application Requirements:** Applicants must submit a completed Stephanie Ali Memorial Scholarships application form along with the required materials and information. **Deadline for Receipt:** March 28.

4964 ■ UNIVERSITY OF TORONTO

315 Bloor St. W
Toronto, ON, Canada M5S 1A3
Tel: (416)978-2011
E-mail: information.commonsats@utoronto.ca
Web Site: http://www.utoronto.ca
To support students with their educational pursuits.
Title of Award: University of Toronto Accenture Scholarships **Area, Field, or Subject:** Engineering; Computer and information sciences. **Level of Education for which Award is Granted:** Undergraduate **Funds Available:** $1500.

Eligibility Requirements: Applicant must be a student of U of T; enrolled in an Engineering, Computer Science or Bachelor of Commerce Degree; a third year student entering the final year of study; have maintained a strong academic background - minimum GPA of 3.0; and actively involved in two or more extracurricular activities. **Application Requirements:** Applicants must submit a completed Accenture Scholarship application form along with the required materials and information. **Deadline for Receipt:** April 25.

4965 ■ UPSILON PI EPSILON ASSOCIATION

158 Wetlands Edge Rd.
American Canyon, CA 94503
Tel: (530)518-8488
Fax: (707)647-3560
Web Site: http://upe.acm.org
To encourage academic excellence for students in the computing discipline. To raise the importance of academic achievement and professional commitment in our future computer professionals.
Title of Award: UPE/ACM Scholarship Awards **Area, Field, or Subject:** Computer and information sciences. **Level of Education for which Award is Granted:** Graduate, Undergraduate **Funds Available:** $1,000. **Duration:** One year.
Eligibility Requirements: Applicant must be a graduate or undergraduate students, who are ACM members and members of the ACM student chapter at their academic institution. **Application Requirements:** Applicant must submit a three letter of recommendation (one letter indicating class rank from Department Chair or Advisor); must have a certificate copy of the three years (minimum) official academic transcripts; must have a statement of your participation in the ACM student chapter at their academic institution. Application forms are available in the website address and must be sent together with the other application materials to: ACM Local Activities, 1515 Broadway, New York, NY 10036.

4966 ■ UPSILON PI EPSILON ASSOCIATION

158 Wetlands Edge Rd.
American Canyon, CA 94503
Tel: (530)518-8488
Fax: (707)647-3560
Web Site: http://upe.acm.org
To promote computing sciences and to encourage its contribution to the enhancement of knowledge.
Title of Award: UPE Scholarship Awards **Area, Field, or Subject:** Computer and information sciences. **Level of Education for which Award is Granted:** Graduate, Undergraduate **Funds Available:** No specific amount.
Eligibility Requirements: Applicant must be in graduate or undergraduate student levels. **Application Requirements:** Application forms are available in the website address and must be sent to: Upsilon Pi Epsilon, California State University, Chico, 158 Wetlands Edge Rd., American Canyon, CA, 94503. **Deadline for Receipt:** June 15.

4967 ■ VIRGINIA FOUNDATION FOR INDEPENDENT COLLEGES

8010 Ridge Rd., Ste. B
Richmond, VA 23229-7288
Tel: (804)288-6609
Free: 800-230-6757
Fax: (804)282-4635
E-mail: info@vfic.org
Web Site: http://www.vfic.org
To provide financial assistance for the students in their junior year at a VFIC college or university.
Title of Award: Phillip Morris USA Scholarships **Area, Field, or Subject:** Accounting; Biology; Business; Chemistry; Computer and information sciences; Economics; Engineering; Finance; Physics. **Level of Education for which Award is Granted:** Undergraduate **Funds Available:** $5,000.
Eligibility Requirements: Applicants must be U.S. citizens and current full-time sophomores attending a VFIC college or university (students from underrepresented populations are encouraged to apply); have minimum of 3.5 cumulative GPA; committed to applying for an internship with Phillip Morris USA for the summer after junior year; have declared, or intend to declare, a major in one of the following disciplines: accounting, biology, business, chemistry, computer science, economics, engineering, finance, or physics. **Application Requirements:** Applicants must submit

completed application form along with two letters of recommendation and other required application information. **Deadline for Receipt:** November 1.

4968 ■ WINSTON-SALEM FOUNDATION

860 W Fifth St.
Winston-Salem, NC 27101-2506
Tel: (336)725-2382
Fax: (336)727-0581
E-mail: info@wsfoundation.org
Web Site: http://www.wsfoundation.org
To assist graduating high school seniors of Mt. Tabor High School.
Title of Award: Wes Burton Memorial Scholarships **Area, Field, or Subject:** Mathematics and mathematical science; Computer and information sciences; Business administration; Engineering. **Level of Education for which Award is Granted:** Undergraduate **Funds Available:** No specific amount.
Eligibility Requirements: Applicants must have a minimum GPA of 3.5; must demonstrate community and school service; must have an intent to pursue a career in Mathematics, Computer Science, Business Administration, or Engineering; demonstrate financial need (award is not restricted to lowest family incomes). **Application Requirements:** Student must complete the application in its entirety and include supplemental items and information requested in the various sections of the application. The supplemental items include: an interview with the Foundation; a grade transcript; a resume or list of student activities; one letter of recommendation from a math teacher, business teacher, or computer science teacher. **Deadline for Receipt:** March 31. **Additional Information:** WSF Student Aid Department, 336-714-3445.

4969 ■ WOMEN IN DEFENSE

2111 Wilson Blvd., Ste. 400
Arlington, VA 22201-3061
Tel: (703)247-2552
Fax: (703)522-1885
E-mail: wid@ndia.org
Web Site: http://wid.ndia.org
To provide financial assistance to further educational objectives of women either employed or planning careers in defense or national security areas.
Title of Award: Women In Defense HORIZONS Scholarships **Area, Field, or Subject:** National security; Military history; Government; Engineering; Computer and information sciences; Physics; Mathematics and mathematical sciences; Business; Law; International affairs and relations; Political science; Economics. **Level of Education for which Award is Granted:** Graduate, Undergraduate **Funds Available:** No specific amount.
Eligibility Requirements: Applicant must be currently enrolled at an accredited university/college, either full-time or part-time; must have junior, senior or graduate status; demonstrate interest in pursuing a career related to national security or defense; demonstrate financial need; have a minimum GPA of 3.25. Applicant must be a female citizen of the United States. **Application Requirements:** Applicants must submit a completed scholarship application form with the essays, recommendations, and transcripts. **Additional Information:** Established in 1988. **Deadline for Receipt:** July 1.

Engineering

4970 ■ AIR FORCE ASSOCIATION

1501 Lee Highway
Arlington, VA 22209-1198
800-727-3337
E-mail: service@afa.org
Web Site: http://www.afa.org
To provide educational assistance for graduating high school students.
Title of Award: Lt. Col. Romeo and Josephine Bass Ferretti Scholarships **Area, Field, or Subject:** Science; Technology; Engineering. **Level of Education for which Award is Granted:** Undergraduate **Number Awarded:** 2. **Funds Available:** $2,500.
Eligibility Requirements: Applicants must be in their final year of high school and must be entering an accredited institute of higher learning. Applicants must state an intent to study in the area of science, technology,

engineering or math. **Application Requirements:** Students must submit an application to Douglas J. Huttenlocker, Capt., USAF. **Additional Information:** Douglas J. Huttenlocker, Capt., USAF; Chief, Operations and Support Branch, HQ AFROTC/DOS; 334-953-6396; douglas. huttenlocker@maxwell.af.mil.

4971 ■ ALBERTA LEARNING INFORMATION SERVICE - ALBERTA SCHOLARSHIP PROGRAM
Box 28000 Sta. Main
Edmonton, AB, Canada T5J 4R4
Tel: (780)427-8640
Fax: (780)427-1288
E-mail: scholarship@gov.ab.ca
Web Site: http://www.alis.alberta.ca
To recognize and reward the academic and leadership accomplishments of three students graduating from Sexsmith Secondary School who are entering post-secondary studies.
Title of Award: Dr. Robert and Anna Shaw Scholarships **Area, Field, or Subject:** Agriculture; Engineering; Art industries and trade; Fine arts. **Level of Education for which Award is Granted:** Undergraduate **Funds Available:** $500.
Eligibility Requirements: Applicants must be Alberta residents and plan to enroll full-time in a post-secondary program related to agriculture, engineering/trades or fine arts. **Application Requirements:** Applicants may obtain application form from Alberta Scholarship Programs and from the Counseling Office at Sexsmith Secondary School. **Deadline for Receipt:** June 1. **Additional Information:** Alberta Scholarship Programs at the above address.

4972 ■ ALBUQUERQUE COMMUNITY FOUNDATION
PO Box 36960
Albuquerque, NM 87176-6960
Tel: (505)883-6240
Fax: (505)883-3629
E-mail: foundation@albuquerquefoundation.org
Web Site: http://www.swcp.com
To provide financial assistance to those students who are in need.
Title of Award: Barnes W. Rose, Jr. and Eva Rose Nichol Scholarship Fund **Area, Field, or Subject:** Engineering. **Level of Education for which Award is Granted:** Undergraduate **Funds Available:** No specific amount.
Eligibility Requirements: Applicants must demonstrate math and/or science interest and skill through SAT/ACF scores and/or strong grades in appropriate high school classes; must have a minimum of 3.6 GPA; must demonstrate financial need; must attend a college or university in pursuit of an engineering degree. **Application Requirements:** Applicants must submit a completed application form and a minimum of one reference from an Albuquerque High School Math or Science teacher. **Additional Information:** Albuquerque Community Foundation at the above address

4973 ■ ALLIANCE OF TECHNOLOGY AND WOMEN
25 Highland Park Vill., No. 100-393
Dallas, TX 75205
888-895-1566
E-mail: info@atwinternational.org
Web Site: http://www.atwinternational.org
To provide financial assistance to women whose academic and professional goals include work in science, math, engineering or technology.
Title of Award: GREAT MINDS Collegiate Scholarship Program **Area, Field, or Subject:** Science; Math; Engineering; Technology. **Level of Education for which Award is Granted:** Undergraduate **Funds Available:** No specific amount.
Eligibility Requirements: Applicants must be first-time students or adult learners returning to school to pursue a new career; must be enrolled in an Associate's or Bachelor's Degree program; may have diverse levels of life experience, academic merit, age, race and religion. **Application Requirements:** Applicants must submit a completed application form. **Additional Information:** Alliance of Technology and Women at the above address.

4974 ■ AMERICAN ASSOCIATION FOR THE ADVANCEMENT OF SCIENCE
1200 New York Ave. NW
Washington, DC 20005
Tel: (202)326-6400
E-mail: webmaster@aaas.org
Web Site: http://www.aaas.org
To increase public understanding of science and technology.
Title of Award: AAAS Mass Media Science and Engineering Fellowships **Area, Field, or Subject:** Media Art; Science Technologies; Engineering. **Level of Education for which Award is Granted:** Graduate, Postgraduate, Undergraduate **Funds Available:** $450.
Eligibility Requirements: Applicants must be undergraduates in their senior year; must be graduate or post-graduate students. **Application Requirements:** Applicants must fill out the application form. Applicants must submit a copy of resume including honors, awards and relevant activities; one brief sample of their writing (two-to-three pages on any subjects written in terms appropriate for the general public); journal articles; three letters of recommendation; transcript of the undergraduate and graduate work. **Deadline for Receipt:** January 15.

4975 ■ AMERICAN CERAMIC SOCIETY
600 N Cleveland Ave., Ste. 210
Westerville, OH 43082
Tel: (866)721-3322
Fax: (301)206-9789
E-mail: customerservice@ceramics.org
Web Site: http://www.ceramics.org
To encourage academic interest and excellence among undergraduate students.
Title of Award: Electronics Division Lewis C. Hoffman Scholarships **Area, Field, or Subject:** Materials research/science; Engineering, Materials. **Level of Education for which Award is Granted:** Undergraduate **Funds Available:** $2,000. **Duration:** One year.
Eligibility Requirements: Applicant must be a junior-year student, or a student who has recently completed his or her junior year; must have acquired a total of 70 or more semester credits or equivalent quarter credits; must have extracurricular activities. **Application Requirements:** Applicants must submit a recommendation letter from a faculty member in the department; must have a 500 word essay on the year's topic. Application form and materials must be sent to Dr. Quanxi Jia, MS 763, Materials Physics and Application Division, Los Alamos National Laboratory, Los Alamos, NM 87545. **Deadline for Receipt:** July 18.

4976 ■ AMERICAN COUNCIL OF ENGINEERING COMPANIES OF ILLINOIS
5221 S 6th Rd., Ste. 120
Springfield, IL 62703
Tel: (217)529-7430
Fax: (217)529-2742
E-mail: acec-il@acec-il.org
Web Site: http://www.acec-il.org
To assist engineering students of Illinois in reaching their goals of higher education.
Title of Award: American Council of Engineering Companies of Illinois Scholarships **Area, Field, or Subject:** Engineering. **Level of Education for which Award is Granted:** Doctorate, Graduate, Undergraduate **Number Awarded:** 13. **Funds Available:** $1,500. **Duration:** One year.
Eligibility Requirements: Applicants must be U.S. citizens, specifically, Illinois engineering students currently enrolled and pursuing a bachelor's, master's or PhD degree in an Accreditation Board for Engineering and Technology (ABET)-accredited engineering program or in an accredited land surveying program located in the state of Illinois; may be students entering their junior, senior, fifth, master's or graduate year in the fall. **Application Requirements:** Applicants must submit the completed application form along with student's GPA; work experience; extracurricular college activities; recommendation from a professor, consulting engineering or land surveyor; and an essay. **Deadline for Receipt:** December.

4977 ■ AMERICAN INDIAN EDUCATION FOUNDATION
2401 Eglin St.
Rapid City, SD 57703
Tel: (866)866-8642; (866)866-8642
Fax: (605)342-4113
E-mail: info@programs.org
Web Site: http://www.nrcprograms.org

To give American Indian students the tools, resources and opportunities to learn and succeed.

Title of Award: Catching the Dream Scholarship **Area, Field, or Subject:** Education; Business; Science; Engineering. **Level of Education for which Award is Granted:** Graduate, Undergraduate **Funds Available:** $500-$5,000.

Eligibility Requirements: Applicants must be enrolled members of a federally recognized tribe; both undergraduate and graduate students may apply. **Application Requirements:** Applicants may submit an application to the Scholarship Affairs Office of Catching the Dream. **Deadline for Receipt:** March 15-Summer; April 15-Fall; September 15-spring. **Additional Information:** Catching the Dream 8200 Mountain Rd. NE Ste. 203 Albuquerque, NM 87110; 505-262-2351 x 116; nscholarsh@aol.com.

4978 ■ AMERICAN INDIAN GRADUATE CENTER SCHOLARS (AIGCS)

4520 Montgomery Blvd., NE, Ste. 1B
Albuquerque, NM 87109
Tel: (505)881-4584
Free: 800-628-1920
Web Site: http://www.aigc.com

To provide financial assistance to undergraduate and graduate American Indians in furthering their education.

Title of Award: Accenture American Indian Scholarship Program **Area, Field, or Subject:** Technology; Engineering; Medicine; Law; Business. **Level of Education for which Award is Granted:** Graduate, Undergraduate **Funds Available:** No specific amount.

Eligibility Requirements: Applicants must be American Indians who are incoming freshmen with a cumulative GPA of 3.25 or greater on a 4.0 scale at the end of the seventh semester of high school or graduates/professionals who have attained a cumulative GPA of 3.25 or greater on a 4.0 scale, as measured by undergraduate transcripts; must be enrolled members of a U.S. federally-recognized American Indian tribe or Alaska Native group; must be seeking a degree and career in fields of study including technology, engineering, medicine, law, and business. **Application Requirements:** Applicants must submit completed application form; copy of certificate of Indian Blood (CIB); unofficial undergraduate and/or graduate academic transcripts; biographical data and/or resume; essay describing their character, personal merit and commitment to community and heritage; two personal letters of recommendation (one must come from an education professional who is familiar with their academic work and the other one must come from an individual having knowledge of their leadership and community service activities); and financial aid award letter from the institution they will attend. **Deadline for Receipt:** June 2.

4979 ■ AMERICAN INSTITUTE OF CHEMICAL ENGINEERS

3 Park Ave.
New York, NY 10016-5991
Tel: (203)702-7660
Free: 800-242-4363
Fax: (203)775-5177
Web Site: http://www.aiche.org

To provide financial assistance for AIChE national student members for their undergraduate education in chemical engineering.

Title of Award: AIChE/Donald F. and Mildred Topp Othmer National Scholarship Awards **Area, Field, or Subject:** Engineering, Chemical. **Level of Education for which Award is Granted:** Undergraduate **Funds Available:** $15,000.

Eligibility Requirements: Nominees must be AIChE national student members at the time of the nomination. **Application Requirements:** Nominators must submit completed nomination form; letter of nomination from the AIChE Student Chapter Advisor containing, but not limited to, the following: a) verification of the nominees' GPAs and projected completion date; b) an evaluation of the nominees' academic performance and participation in AIChE Student Chapter and other professional activities; statement from the nominees (not to exceed 300 words) outlining their career plans and objectives in chemical engineering and including, but not limited to, the following: a) immediate plans after graduation and area(s) of chemical engineering of most interest; b) long-range career objectives. **Deadline for Receipt:** May 16.

4980 ■ AMERICAN INSTITUTE OF CHEMICAL ENGINEERS

3 Park Ave.
New York, NY 10016-5991
Tel: (203)702-7660
Free: 800-242-4363
Fax: (203)775-5177
Web Site: http://www.aiche.org

To provide financial assistance for chemical engineering undergraduate students planning a career in the chemical engineering process industries.

Title of Award: John J. McKetta Undergraduate Scholarships **Area, Field, or Subject:** Engineering, Chemical. **Level of Education for which Award is Granted:** Undergraduate **Funds Available:** $5,000.

Eligibility Requirements: Nominees must be national student members of AIChE attending an ABET accredited schools in the US, Canada or Mexico who are in their junior or senior year of a 4-year program in Chemical Engineering or equivalent for a 5-year co-op program. Nominees must have maintained a minimum of 3.0/4.0 GPA. **Application Requirements:** Nominees must submit a maximum two-page essay outlining career goals in the chemical engineering process industries (2 single-sided, single-spaced typed pages) and nominations must be accompanied by a minimum of two letters of recommendation, one from AIChE student advisor and the other from either a departmental faculty member or technical work supervisor. **Deadline for Receipt:** May 30.

4981 ■ AMERICAN INSTITUTE OF CHEMICAL ENGINEERS

3 Park Ave.
New York, NY 10016-5991
Tel: (203)702-7660
Free: 800-242-4363
Fax: (203)775-5177
Web Site: http://www.aiche.org

To provide educational assistance for chemical engineering undergraduate students.

Title of Award: Minority Scholarship Awards for College Students **Area, Field, or Subject:** Engineering, Chemical. **Level of Education for which Award is Granted:** Undergraduate **Number Awarded:** 10. **Funds Available:** No specific amount. **Duration:** One year.

Eligibility Requirements: Applicants must be AIChE national student members at the time of application. **Application Requirements:** Nominations must be submitted containing the following items: from the students: a) a completed application form; b) a career essay not to exceed 300 words outlining the following: immediate plans after graduation and area(s) of chemical engineering of most interest; long-range career objectives; official transcript of college grades. Nominations from the college financial aid office must contain: a letter indicating that the student is eligible for financial aid based on their records; a letter of recommendation from the AIChE student chapter advisor, department chair, or chemical engineering faculty member containing, but not limited to, the following: verification of nominee's GPA and projected completion date; evaluation of the student's academic performance and participation in AIChE and other professional or civic activities. **Deadline for Receipt:** May 15.

4982 ■ AMERICAN INSTITUTE OF CHEMICAL ENGINEERS

3 Park Ave.
New York, NY 10016-5991
Tel: (203)702-7660
Free: 800-242-4363
Fax: (203)775-5177
Web Site: http://www.aiche.org

To provide educational assistance for chemical engineering college freshmen.

Title of Award: Minority Scholarship Awards for Incoming College Freshmen **Area, Field, or Subject:** Engineering, Chemical. **Level of Education for which Award is Granted:** Undergraduate **Number Awarded:** 10. **Funds Available:** $1,000. **Duration:** One year.

Eligibility Requirements: Applicants must be members of a minority group (i.e. African-American, Hispanic, Native American, or Alaskan Native) that is underrepresented in chemical engineering; must be high school graduates during the previous academic year and plan to enroll during the following academic year in a four-year university offering a science/engineering degree. **Application Requirements:** Nominations must be submitted containing the following items from the student: a) completed application form; b) career essay not to exceed 300 words outlining the following: (1) college or university chosen to attend, (2) reasons for choosing science/engineering, (3) possible career choices that may be of interest; c) official transcript of high school grades. Nominations must also include documents from the parent/guardian which should contain a letter verifying financial need which includes a list of financial resources for educational support; and a letter of recommendation from the high school counselor, math teacher or science teacher containing, but not limited to, the following: a) verification of student's GPA and graduation date; b) verification of high school senior class average grade (if confidential, high school counselor statement is required); c) confirmation of minority group of student; d) information about the student's school, job and/or other activities. **Deadline for Receipt:** May 15.

4983 ■ AMERICAN INSTITUTE OF STEEL CONSTRUCTION

1 E Wacker Dr., Ste. 700
Chicago, IL 60601-1802
Tel: (312)670-5408
Fax: (312)670-5403
Web Site: http://www.aisc.org
To encourage greater interest in structural steel design.
Title of Award: AISC/Carolina Steel Scholarships **Area, Field, or Subject:** Civil engineering; Architectural engineering. **Level of Education for which Award is Granted:** Undergraduate **Number Awarded:** 1. **Funds Available:** $3,000. **Duration:** One year.
Eligibility Requirements: Applicants must be full-time civil or architectural engineering students of U.S. Citizenship entering their 3rd or 4th year of study from a university in Alabama, North Carolina, South Carolina and Virginia. **Application Requirements:** Applicants must submit an official transcript; a reference and optional letter of reference; a short essay on overall career objective and an original sample steel design analysis/design solution with calculations. **Deadline for Receipt:** April 9. **Additional Information:** Fromy Rosenburg at the above address.

4984 ■ AMERICAN INSTITUTE OF STEEL CONSTRUCTION

1 E Wacker Dr., Ste. 700
Chicago, IL 60601-1802
Tel: (312)670-5408
Fax: (312)670-5403
Web Site: http://www.aisc.org
To provide financial assistance to those studying civil engineering.
Title of Award: AISC/Fred R. Havens Fellowships **Area, Field, or Subject:** Civil engineering; Architectural engineering. **Level of Education for which Award is Granted:** Graduate, Undergraduate **Number Awarded:** 1. **Funds Available:** $5,000.
Eligibility Requirements: Applicants must be U.S. citizens studying civil or architectural engineering full-time at universities in Missouri, Kansas or at MIT. Applicants must be graduate or undergraduate students who have completed one steel design course. **Application Requirements:** Undergraduate applicants must submit an official transcript; a reference and optional letter of reference; a two-page essay on his/her interest in steel structures and an original sample steel design analysis/design solution with calculations. In addition to the mentioned requirements, graduate students applying must submit an official transcript; a reference and optional letter of reference; and a one-page detailed answers to the following: (a) Demonstrate concentration on steel related course work and/or thesis with a strong steel orientation, or (b) Demonstrate proposed course work and proposed thesis concentration in structural steel. **Deadline for Receipt:** April 9. **Additional Information:** Fromy Rosenberg at the above address.

4985 ■ AMERICAN INSTITUTE OF STEEL CONSTRUCTION

1 E Wacker Dr., Ste. 700
Chicago, IL 60601-1802
Tel: (312)670-5408
Fax: (312)670-5403
Web Site: http://www.aisc.org
To encourage greater interest in structural steel design.
Title of Award: AISC/Southern Association of Steel Fabricators Scholarships **Area, Field, or Subject:** Civil engineering; Architectural engineering. **Level of Education for which Award is Granted:** Undergraduate **Number Awarded:** 1. **Funds Available:** $2,500. **Duration:** One year.

Eligibility Requirements: Applicants must be full-time civil or architectural engineering students who are U.S. Citizens entering their 3rd or 4th year of study with an interest in structural steel from a university in Alabama, Arkansas, Florida, Georgia, Kentucky, Louisiana, Mississippi and Tennessee. **Application Requirements:** Applicants must submit an official transcript; a reference and optional letter of reference; and a short essay on overall career objective. **Deadline for Receipt:** April 9. **Additional Information:** Fromy Rosenberg at the above address.

4986 ■ AMERICAN NUCLEAR SOCIETY

555 N Kensington Ave.
La Grange Park, IL 60526
Tel: (708)352-6611
Free: 800-323-3044
Fax: (708)352-0499
Web Site: http://www.ans.org
To assist students complete their post-secondary education and prepare for careers in nuclear science and technology (NS&T).
Title of Award: American Nuclear Society Incoming Freshman Scholarships **Area, Field, or Subject:** Engineering, Nuclear. **Level of Education for which Award is Granted:** High School **Number Awarded:** 4. **Funds Available:** $1,000 for each recipient.
Eligibility Requirements: Applicants must be graduating high school seniors who have the intention to pursue a degree in nuclear engineering. **Application Requirements:** Applicants must submit all the required application information. **Deadline for Receipt:** April 1.

4987 ■ AMERICAN NUCLEAR SOCIETY

555 N Kensington Ave.
La Grange Park, IL 60526
Tel: (708)352-6611
Free: 800-323-3044
Fax: (708)352-0499
Web Site: http://www.ans.org
To help students complete their post-secondary education and prepare for careers in nuclear science and technology (NS&T).
Title of Award: American Nuclear Society Undergraduates Scholarships **Area, Field, or Subject:** Nuclear science; Engineering, Nuclear. **Level of Education for which Award is Granted:** Undergraduate **Funds Available:** No specific amount.
Eligibility Requirements: Applicants must be students who have completed at least one year in a course of study leading to a degree in nuclear science, nuclear engineering, or a nuclear-related field. **Application Requirements:** Applicants must submit all the required application information.

4988 ■ AMERICAN PUBLIC WORKS ASSOCIATION

2345 Grand Blvd., Ste. 700
Kansas City, MO 64108-2625
Tel: (816)472-6100
Free: 800-848-APWA
Fax: (816)472-1610
E-mail: pking@apwa.net
Web Site: http://www.apwa.net
To provide financial assistance for the students taking up civil engineering.
Title of Award: APWA Engineering Scholarships **Area, Field, or Subject:** Civil engineering. **Level of Education for which Award is Granted:** Undergraduate **Funds Available:** $500-$1,500.
Eligibility Requirements: Applicants must be students pursuing a career in civil engineering or a related field within the Antelope Valley, Santa Clarita, and Victor Valley areas. **Application Requirements:** Applicants must submit all the required application information. **Deadline for Receipt:** March 15. **Additional Information:** Brian Glidden, 42138 10th St. West, Lancaster, CA 93534.

4989 ■ AMERICAN PUBLIC WORKS ASSOCIATION-NEVADA

c/o Leslie R. Henley, Pres.
Clark County Public Works
PO Box 554000
Las Vegas, NV 89155
Tel: (702)455-6065
Fax: (702)455-6113
E-mail: lrh@co.clark.nv.us

Web Site: http://www.apwa-nv.org
To support minority students studying engineering.
Title of Award: Lari Ann Vest Memorial Scholarships **Area, Field, or Subject:** Engineering. **Level of Education for which Award is Granted:** Undergraduate **Funds Available:** No specific amount.
Eligibility Requirements: Applicant must be a minority student majoring in engineering. **Application Requirements:** Applicants may contact APWA-Nevada for more information about the scholarships. **Additional Information:** Established in memory of Lari Anne Vest. **Additional Information:** Vanessa Pestka, 702-278-0911, or vanessa@pestilenthen. com. Derek Pendergraft, 702-743-7049, or dereko66@hotmail.com.

4990 ■ AMERICAN RADIO RELAY LEAGUE (ARRL) FOUNDATION
225 Main St.
Newington, CT 06111
Tel: (860)594-0200
Fax: (860)594-0259
E-mail: foundation@arrl.org
Web Site: http://www.arrlf.org
To support the education of students holding a valid FCC-granted Amateur Radio license for post-secondary education.
Title of Award: Henry Broughton, K2AE Memorial Scholarships **Area, Field, or Subject:** Radio and television; Engineering; Science. **Level of Education for which Award is Granted:** Undergraduate **Number Awarded:** 1. **Funds Available:** $1,000.
Eligibility Requirements: Applicant must hold an FCC amateur radio license; reside within 70 miles of Schenectady NY; studying in baccalaureate or higher courses of study in engineering, sciences or a similar field in an accredited four-year college/university. **Application Requirements:** Applicants must submit a completed scholarship application form along with a recent high school (or equivalent) or college transcript. **Deadline for Receipt:** February 1.

4991 ■ AMERICAN RADIO RELAY LEAGUE (ARRL) FOUNDATION
225 Main St.
Newington, CT 06111
Tel: (860)594-0200
Fax: (860)594-0259
E-mail: foundation@arrl.org
Web Site: http://www.arrlf.org
To support the education of students holding a valid FCC-granted Amateur Radio license for post-secondary education.
Title of Award: William R. Goldfarb Memorial Scholarships **Area, Field, or Subject:** Radio and television; Business; Computer and information sciences; Medicine; Nursing; Engineering; Science. **Level of Education for which Award is Granted:** Undergraduate **Number Awarded:** 1. **Funds Available:** No specific amount.
Eligibility Requirements: Applicant must hold an FCC amateur radio license; must be studying baccalaureate courses in business-related, computers, medical, nursing, engineering or sciences; be a high school senior; and must demonstrate financial need. **Application Requirements:** Applicants must submit a completed scholarship application form along with a recent high school (or equivalent) or college transcript, and the Free Application for Federal Student Aid (FAFSA) or Student Aid Report (SAR). **Deadline for Receipt:** February 1.

4992 ■ AMERICAN RADIO RELAY LEAGUE (ARRL) FOUNDATION
225 Main St.
Newington, CT 06111
Tel: (860)594-0200
Fax: (860)594-0259
E-mail: foundation@arrl.org
Web Site: http://www.arrlf.org
To support the education of students holding a valid FCC-granted Amateur Radio license for post-secondary education.
Title of Award: Perry F. Hadlock Memorial Scholarships **Area, Field, or Subject:** Radio and television; Technology; Engineering, Electrical. **Level of Education for which Award is Granted:** Undergraduate **Number Awarded:** 1. **Funds Available:** $2,000.
Eligibility Requirements: Applicant must hold an FCC amateur radio license; must be studying in baccalaureate or higher courses in a technology-related field; preference to electrical and electronics engineering. **Application Requirements:** Applicants must submit a completed

scholarship application form along with a recent high school (or equivalent) or college transcript. **Deadline for Receipt:** February 1.

4993 ■ AMERICAN RADIO RELAY LEAGUE (ARRL) FOUNDATION
225 Main St.
Newington, CT 06111
Tel: (860)594-0200
Fax: (860)594-0259
E-mail: foundation@arrl.org
Web Site: http://www.arrlf.org
To support the education of students holding a valid FCC-granted Amateur Radio license for post-secondary education.
Title of Award: Edmond A. Metzger Scholarships **Area, Field, or Subject:** Radio and television; Electrical engineering. **Level of Education for which Award is Granted:** Undergraduate **Number Awarded:** 1. **Funds Available:** $500.
Eligibility Requirements: Applicant must hold an FCC amateur radio license; be a resident of ARRL Central Division (IL, IN, WI); be studying in baccalaureate or higher courses of study in electrical engineering; be an ARRL member; and attending school in the Central Division. **Application Requirements:** Applicants must submit a completed scholarship application form along with a recent high school (or equivalent) or college transcript. **Deadline for Receipt:** February 1.

4994 ■ AMERICAN RADIO RELAY LEAGUE (ARRL) FOUNDATION
225 Main St.
Newington, CT 06111
Tel: (860)594-0200
Fax: (860)594-0259
E-mail: foundation@arrl.org
Web Site: http://www.arrlf.org
To support the education of students holding a valid FCC-granted Amateur Radio license for post-secondary education.
Title of Award: Gary Wagner, K3OMI Scholarships **Area, Field, or Subject:** Radio and television; Engineering. **Level of Education for which Award is Granted:** Undergraduate **Number Awarded:** 1. **Funds Available:** $1,000.
Eligibility Requirements: Applicant must hold an FCC amateur radio license; be a resident of NC, VA, WV, MD or TN; enrolled in an accredited four-year college/university (NC, VA, WV, MD, or TN) working towards a Bachelor's of Science in any field of engineering; and have financial need. **Application Requirements:** Applicants must submit a completed scholarship application form along with a recent high school (or equivalent) or college transcript. **Deadline for Receipt:** February 1.

4995 ■ AMERICAN RADIO RELAY LEAGUE (ARRL) FOUNDATION
225 Main St.
Newington, CT 06111
Tel: (860)594-0200
Fax: (860)594-0259
E-mail: foundation@arrl.org
Web Site: http://www.arrlf.org
To support the education of students holding a valid FCC-granted Amateur Radio license for post-secondary education.
Title of Award: Yasme Foundation Scholarships **Area, Field, or Subject:** Radio and television; Science; Engineering. **Level of Education for which Award is Granted:** Undergraduate **Number Awarded:** 5 in 2006. **Funds Available:** $2,000.
Eligibility Requirements: Applicant must hold an FCC amateur radio license, and be enrolled in a science or engineering course at an accredited four-year college/university. **Application Requirements:** Applicants must submit a completed scholarship application form along with a recent high school (or equivalent) or college transcript. **Deadline for Receipt:** February 1.

4996 ■ AMERICAN RAILWAY ENGINEERING AND MAINTENANCE-OF-WAY ASSOCIATION
10003 Derekwood Ln., Ste. 210
Lanham, MD 20706
Tel: (301)459-3200
Fax: (301)459-8077
E-mail: chemely@arema.org
Web Site: http://www.arema.org

To support the education of an engineering student who has a potential interest in railway engineering careers.

Title of Award: AREMA Committee Scholarships 18 - Light Density & Short Line Railways **Area, Field, or Subject:** Engineering. **Level of Education for which Award is Granted:** Undergraduate **Number Awarded:** 2. **Funds Available:** $1000. **Duration:** One academic year.

Eligibility Requirements: Applicant must be enrolled full-time in a four or five year program leading to a Bachelor's degree in Engineering or Engineering Technology in a curriculum accredited by the Accreditation Board of Engineering and Technology; have completed at least one quarter or semester in college prior to the application; and have a GPA of 2.00. **Application Requirements:** Applicants must submit completed AREMA data form together with a cover letter (maximum of 350 words); a resume; two letters of recommendation, one from a faculty member, and another from a present employer, AREMA member, or other responsible person; and a transcript from the schools attended, and courses currently enrolled in. **Additional Information:** Staple application materials in the upper left hand corner and do not include any photos. **Deadline for Receipt:** March 14.

4997 ■ AMERICAN RAILWAY ENGINEERING AND MAINTENANCE-OF-WAY ASSOCIATION
10003 Derekwood Ln., Ste. 210
Lanham, MD 20706
Tel: (301)459-3200
Fax: (301)459-8077
E-mail: chemely@arema.org
Web Site: http://www.arema.org
To support the education of an engineering student who has a potential interest in railway engineering careers.

Title of Award: AREMA Committee Scholarships 24 - Education and Training **Area, Field, or Subject:** Engineering. **Level of Education for which Award is Granted:** Undergraduate **Number Awarded:** 1. **Funds Available:** $1000. **Duration:** One academic year.

Eligibility Requirements: Applicant must be enrolled full-time in a four or five year program leading to a Bachelor's degree in Engineering or Engineering Technology in a curriculum accredited by the Accreditation Board of Engineering and Technology; have completed at least one quarter or semester in college prior to the application; and have a GPA of 2.00. **Application Requirements:** Applicants must submit completed AREMA data form together with a cover letter (maximum of 350 words); a resume; two letters of recommendation, one from a faculty member, and another from a present employer, AREMA member, or other responsible person; and a transcript from the schools attended, and courses currently enrolled in. **Additional Information:** Staple application materials in the upper left hand corner and do not include any photos. **Deadline for Receipt:** March 14.

4998 ■ AMERICAN RAILWAY ENGINEERING AND MAINTENANCE-OF-WAY ASSOCIATION
10003 Derekwood Ln., Ste. 210
Lanham, MD 20706
Tel: (301)459-3200
Fax: (301)459-8077
E-mail: chemely@arema.org
Web Site: http://www.arema.org
To support the education of an engineering student who has a potential interest in railway engineering careers.

Title of Award: AREMA Committee Scholarships 33 - Electric Energy Utilization **Area, Field, or Subject:** Engineering. **Level of Education for which Award is Granted:** Undergraduate **Number Awarded:** 1. **Funds Available:** $1000. **Duration:** One academic year.

Eligibility Requirements: Applicant must be enrolled full-time in a four or five year program leading to a Bachelor's degree in Engineering or Engineering Technology in a curriculum accredited by the Accreditation Board of Engineering and Technology; have completed at least one quarter or semester in college prior to the application; and have a GPA of 2.00. **Application Requirements:** Applicants must submit completed AREMA data form together with a cover letter (maximum of 350 words); a resume; two letters of recommendation, one from a faculty member, and another from a present employer, AREMA member, or other responsible person; and a transcript from the schools attended, and courses currently enrolled in. **Additional Information:** Staple application materials in the

upper left hand corner and do not include any photos. **Deadline for Receipt:** March 14.

4999 ■ AMERICAN RAILWAY ENGINEERING AND MAINTENANCE-OF-WAY ASSOCIATION
10003 Derekwood Ln., Ste. 210
Lanham, MD 20706
Tel: (301)459-3200
Fax: (301)459-8077
E-mail: chemely@arema.org
Web Site: http://www.arema.org
To support the education of a female engineering student with a potential interest in railway engineering careers.

Title of Award: AREMA Presidential Spouse Scholarships **Area, Field, or Subject:** Engineering. **Level of Education for which Award is Granted:** Undergraduate **Number Awarded:** 1. **Funds Available:** $1000. **Duration:** One academic year.

Eligibility Requirements: Applicant must be an enrolled full-time female student in a four or five year program leading to a Bachelor's degree in Engineering or Engineering Technology in a curriculum accredited by the Accreditation Board of Engineering and Technology; have completed at least one quarter or semester prior to the application; and have a minimum GPA of 2.0. **Application Requirements:** Applicants must submit completed AREMA data form together with a cover letter (maximum of 350 words); a resume; two letters of recommendation, one from a faculty member, and another from a present employer, AREMA member, or other responsible person; and a transcript from the schools attended, and courses currently enrolled in. **Additional Information:** Staple application materials in the upper left hand corner and do not include any photos. **Deadline for Receipt:** March 14.

5000 ■ AMERICAN RAILWAY ENGINEERING AND MAINTENANCE-OF-WAY ASSOCIATION
10003 Derekwood Ln., Ste. 210
Lanham, MD 20706
Tel: (301)459-3200
Fax: (301)459-8077
E-mail: chemely@arema.org
Web Site: http://www.arema.org
To support the education of undergraduate engineering student who has potential interest in railway engineering careers.

Title of Award: AREMA Scholarships **Area, Field, or Subject:** Engineering. **Level of Education for which Award is Granted:** Undergraduate **Number Awarded:** 1. **Funds Available:** $1000.

Eligibility Requirements: Applicant must be enrolled as a full-time undergraduate student in a four or five year program leading to a Bachelor's degree in Engineering or Engineering Technology in a curriculum accredited by the Accreditation Board of Engineering and Technology; have completed at least one quarter or semester prior to the application; interest in railway engineering; and maintaining a minimum GPA of 2.0. **Application Requirements:** Applicants must submit completed AREMA data form together with a cover letter (maximum of 350 words); a resume; two letters of recommendation, one from a faculty member, and another from a present employer, AREMA member, or other responsible person; and a transcript from the schools attended, and courses currently enrolled in. **Additional Information:** Staple application materials in the upper left hand corner and do not include any photos. **Deadline for Receipt:** March 14.

5001 ■ AMERICAN RAILWAY ENGINEERING AND MAINTENANCE-OF-WAY ASSOCIATION
10003 Derekwood Ln., Ste. 210
Lanham, MD 20706
Tel: (301)459-3200
Fax: (301)459-8077
E-mail: chemely@arema.org
Web Site: http://www.arema.org
To support the education of undergraduate engineering student who has potential interest in railway engineering careers.

Title of Award: AREMA Staff Scholarships **Area, Field, or Subject:** Engineering. **Level of Education for which Award is Granted:** Undergraduate **Number Awarded:** 1. **Funds Available:** $1000.

Eligibility Requirements: Applicant must be enrolled full-time undergraduate student in a four or five year program leading to a Bachelor's degree in Engineering or Engineering Technology in a curriculum accredited by the Accreditation Board of Engineering and Technology; have completed at least one quarter or semester prior to the application; interest in railway engineering; and maintaining a minimum GPA of 2.0. **Application Requirements:** Applicants must submit completed AREMA data form together with a cover letter (maximum of 350 words); a resume; two letters of recommendation, one from a faculty member, and another from a present employer, AREMA member, or other responsible person; and a transcript from the schools attended, and courses currently enrolled in. **Additional Information:** Staple application materials in the upper left hand corner and do not include any photos. **Deadline for Receipt:** March 14.

5002 ■ AMERICAN RAILWAY ENGINEERING AND MAINTENANCE-OF-WAY ASSOCIATION
10003 Derekwood Ln., Ste. 210
Lanham, MD 20706
Tel: (301)459-3200
Fax: (301)459-8077
E-mail: chemely@arema.org
Web Site: http://www.arema.org
To support education of railway-engineering students at the University of Illinois in the Engineering Department at Urbana-Champaign.
Title of Award: Paul I. and Elena H. Cohen Scholarships **Area, Field, or Subject:** Engineering. **Level of Education for which Award is Granted:** Graduate, Undergraduate **Number Awarded:** 1. **Funds Available:** $2000.
Eligibility Requirements: Applicant must be a student at the University of Illinois at Urbana-Champaign; have at least 2.0 GPA; an undergraduate or graduate student in the Engineering Department; and interested in railwayengineering. **Application Requirements:** Applicants must submit completed AREMA data form together with a cover letter (maximum of 350 words); a resume; two letters of recommendation, one from a faculty member, and another from a present employer, AREMA member, or other responsible person; and a transcript from the schools attended, and courses currently enrolled in. **Additional Information:** Staple application materials in the upper left hand corner and do not include any photos. **Deadline for Receipt:** March 14.

5003 ■ AMERICAN RAILWAY ENGINEERING AND MAINTENANCE-OF-WAY ASSOCIATION
10003 Derekwood Ln., Ste. 210
Lanham, MD 20706
Tel: (301)459-3200
Fax: (301)459-8077
E-mail: chemely@arema.org
Web Site: http://www.arema.org
To support the education of a student who is also working full-time in the railway industry.
Title of Award: Committee 12 - Rail Transit Scholarships **Area, Field, or Subject:** Engineering. **Level of Education for which Award is Granted:** Undergraduate **Number Awarded:** 1. **Funds Available:** $1000. **Duration:** One academic year.
Eligibility Requirements: Applicant must be enrolled as full-time student, or part-time working as full-time in the railway industry, in a four or five year program leading to a Bachelor's degree in Engineering or Engineering Technology in a curriculum accredited by the Accreditation Board of Engineering and Technology; have completed at least one quarter or semester in college prior to the application; and have a GPA of 2.00. **Application Requirements:** Applicants must submit completed AREMA data form together with a cover letter (maximum of 350 words); a resume; two letters of recommendation, one from a faculty member, and another from a present employer, AREMA member, or other responsible person; and a transcript from the schools attended, and courses currently enrolled in. **Additional Information:** Staple application materials in the upper left hand corner and do not include any photos. **Deadline for Receipt:** March 14.

5004 ■ AMERICAN RAILWAY ENGINEERING AND MAINTENANCE-OF-WAY ASSOCIATION
10003 Derekwood Ln., Ste. 210
Lanham, MD 20706
Tel: (301)459-3200

Fax: (301)459-8077
E-mail: chemely@arema.org
Web Site: http://www.arema.org
To support the education of an engineering student.
Title of Award: Committee 27 - Maintenance-of-Way Work Equipment Scholarships **Area, Field, or Subject:** Engineering. **Level of Education for which Award is Granted:** Undergraduate **Number Awarded:** 1. **Funds Available:** $1000. **Duration:** One academic year.
Eligibility Requirements: Applicant must be enrolled full-time student in a four or five year program leading to a Bachelor's degree in Engineering or Engineering Technology in a curriculum accredited by the Accreditation Board of Engineering and Technology; have completed at least one quarter or semester in college prior to the application; and have a GPA of 2.00. **Application Requirements:** Applicants must submit completed AREMA data form together with a cover letter (maximum of 350 words); a resume; two letters of recommendation, one from a faculty member, and another from a present employer, AREMA member, or other responsible person; and a transcript from the schools attended, and courses currently enrolled in. **Additional Information:** Staple application materials in the upper left hand corner and do not include any photos. **Deadline for Receipt:** March 14.

5005 ■ AMERICAN RAILWAY ENGINEERING AND MAINTENANCE-OF-WAY ASSOCIATION
10003 Derekwood Ln., Ste. 210
Lanham, MD 20706
Tel: (301)459-3200
Fax: (301)459-8077
E-mail: chemely@arema.org
Web Site: http://www.arema.org
To support the education of an undergraduate engineering student who has potential interest in railway engineering careers.
Title of Award: CSX Scholarships **Area, Field, or Subject:** Engineering. **Level of Education for which Award is Granted:** Undergraduate **Number Awarded:** 1. **Funds Available:** $2500.
Eligibility Requirements: Applicant must be enrolled full-time as an undergraduate student in a four or five year program leading to a Bachelor's degree in Engineering or Engineering Technology in a curriculum accredited by the Accreditation Board of Engineering and Technology; have completed at least one quarter or semester prior to the application; interest in railway engineering; and maintaining a minimum GPA of 2.0. **Application Requirements:** Applicants must submit completed AREMA data form together with a cover letter (maximum of 350 words); a resume; two letters of recommendation, one from a faculty member, and another from a present employer, AREMA member, or other responsible person; and a transcript from the schools attended, and courses currently enrolled in. **Additional Information:** Staple application materials in the upper left hand corner and do not include any photos. **Deadline for Receipt:** March 14.

5006 ■ AMERICAN RAILWAY ENGINEERING AND MAINTENANCE-OF-WAY ASSOCIATION
10003 Derekwood Ln., Ste. 210
Lanham, MD 20706
Tel: (301)459-3200
Fax: (301)459-8077
E-mail: chemely@arema.org
Web Site: http://www.arema.org
To support the education of student in a professional field that has direct applications in the passenger rail sector.
Title of Award: John J. Cunningham Memorial Scholarships **Area, Field, or Subject:** Engineering. **Level of Education for which Award is Granted:** Undergraduate **Number Awarded:** 1. **Funds Available:** $1000. **Duration:** One academic year.
Eligibility Requirements: Applicant must be an enrolled full-time Junior or Senior student in a four or five year program leading to an undergraduate degree in a professional field that has direct applications in the passenger rail sector; and have a GPA of 2.00. **Application Requirements:** Applicants must submit completed AREMA data form together with a cover letter (maximum of 350 words); a resume; two letters of recommendation, one from a faculty member, and another from a present employer, AREMA member, or other responsible person; and a transcript from the schools attended, and courses currently enrolled in. **Additional**

Information: Staple application materials in the upper left hand corner and do not include any photos. Sponsored jointly by Committees 11 and 17. **Deadline for Receipt:** March 14.

5007 ■ AMERICAN RAILWAY ENGINEERING AND MAINTENANCE-OF-WAY ASSOCIATION
10003 Derekwood Ln., Ste. 210
Lanham, MD 20706
Tel: (301)459-3200
Fax: (301)459-8077
E-mail: chemely@arema.org
Web Site: http://www.arema.org
To support education of railway engineering students at the University of Illinois in the Engineering Department at Urbana-Champaign.
Title of Award: Larry L. Etherton Scholarships **Area, Field, or Subject:** Engineering. **Level of Education for which Award is Granted:** Graduate, Undergraduate **Number Awarded:** 1. **Funds Available:** $1500.
Eligibility Requirements: Applicant must be a student at the University of Illinois at Urbana-Champaign; have at least 2.0 GPA; an undergraduate or graduate student in the Engineering Department; and interested in railway engineering. **Application Requirements:** Applicants must submit completed AREMA data form together with a cover letter (maximum of 350 words); a resume; two letters of recommendation, one from a faculty member, and another from a present employer, AREMA member, or other responsible person; and a transcript from the schools attended, and courses currently enrolled in. **Additional Information:** Staple application materials in the upper left hand corner and do not include any photos. **Deadline for Receipt:** March 14.

5008 ■ AMERICAN RAILWAY ENGINEERING AND MAINTENANCE-OF-WAY ASSOCIATION
10003 Derekwood Ln., Ste. 210
Lanham, MD 20706
Tel: (301)459-3200
Fax: (301)459-8077
E-mail: chemely@arema.org
Web Site: http://www.arema.org
To support education of railway engineering students at the University of Illinois in the Engineering Department at Urbana-Champaign.
Title of Award: Michael W. and Jean D. Franke Family Foundation Scholarships **Area, Field, or Subject:** Engineering. **Level of Education for which Award is Granted:** Graduate, Undergraduate **Number Awarded:** 1. **Funds Available:** $5000.
Eligibility Requirements: Applicant must be a student at the University of Illinois at Urbana-Champaign; have at least 2.0 GPA; an undergraduate or graduate student in the Engineering Department; and interested in railwayengineering. **Application Requirements:** Applicants must submit completed AREMA data form together with a cover letter (maximum of 350 words); a resume; two letters of recommendation, one from a faculty member, and another from a present employer, AREMA member, or other responsible person; and a transcript from the schools attended, and courses currently enrolled in. **Additional Information:** Staple application materials in the upper left hand corner and do not include any photos. **Deadline for Receipt:** March 14.

5009 ■ AMERICAN RAILWAY ENGINEERING AND MAINTENANCE-OF-WAY ASSOCIATION
10003 Derekwood Ln., Ste. 210
Lanham, MD 20706
Tel: (301)459-3200
Fax: (301)459-8077
E-mail: chemely@arema.org
Web Site: http://www.arema.org
To support education of students pursuing a degree in Electrical Engineering at Carnegie Mellon University.
Title of Award: Belknap Freeman Carnegie Mellon Scholarships **Area, Field, or Subject:** Engineering, Electrical. **Level of Education for which Award is Granted:** Undergraduate **Number Awarded:** 1. **Funds Available:** $10,000.
Eligibility Requirements: Applicant must be a student of Carnegie Mellon University; pursuing an Electrical Engineering degree; and interested in railway engineering and have a goal of obtaining a "Professional Engineering" license. **Application Requirements:** Applicants must

submit completed AREMA data form together with a cover letter (maximum of 350 words); a resume; and a transcript from the schools attended, and courses currently enrolled in. **Additional Information:** Staple application materials in the upper left hand corner and do not include any photos. **Deadline for Receipt:** March 14.

5010 ■ AMERICAN RAILWAY ENGINEERING AND MAINTENANCE-OF-WAY ASSOCIATION
10003 Derekwood Ln., Ste. 210
Lanham, MD 20706
Tel: (301)459-3200
Fax: (301)459-8077
E-mail: chemely@arema.org
Web Site: http://www.arema.org
To support the education of an engineering student, especially two students already married or supporting a family.
Title of Award: Michael and Gina Garcia Rail Engineering Scholarships **Area, Field, or Subject:** Engineering. **Level of Education for which Award is Granted:** Undergraduate **Funds Available:** $2000. **Duration:** One academic year.
Eligibility Requirements: Applicant must be enrolled in a four or five year program leading to a Bachelor's degree in Engineering or Engineering Technology. **Application Requirements:** Applicants must submit completed AREMA data form together with a cover letter (maximum of 350 words); a resume; two letters of recommendation, one from a faculty member, and another from a present employer, AREMA member, or other responsible person; and a transcript from the schools attended, and courses currently enrolled in. **Additional Information:** Staple application materials in the upper left hand corner and do not include any photos. **Deadline for Receipt:** March 14.

5011 ■ AMERICAN RAILWAY ENGINEERING AND MAINTENANCE-OF-WAY ASSOCIATION
10003 Derekwood Ln., Ste. 210
Lanham, MD 20706
Tel: (301)459-3200
Fax: (301)459-8077
E-mail: chemely@arema.org
Web Site: http://www.arema.org
To support the education of a railway-engineering student at Clarkson University.
Title of Award: Chris Harding Scholarships **Area, Field, or Subject:** Engineering. **Level of Education for which Award is Granted:** Undergraduate **Funds Available:** $1000. **Duration:** One academic year.
Eligibility Requirements: Applicant must be enrolled full-time in a four or five year program leading to a Bachelor's degree in Engineering or Engineering Technology in a curriculum accredited by the Accreditation Board of Engineering and Technology; have completed at least one quarter or semester in college prior to the application; and have a GPA of 2.00. **Application Requirements:** Applicants must submit completed AREMA data form together with a cover letter (maximum of 350 words); a resume; two letters of recommendation, one from a faculty member, and another from a present employer, AREMA member, or other responsible person; and a transcript from the schools attended, and courses currently enrolled in. **Additional Information:** Staple application materials in the upper left hand corner and do not include any photos. **Deadline for Receipt:** March 14.

5012 ■ AMERICAN RAILWAY ENGINEERING AND MAINTENANCE-OF-WAY ASSOCIATION
10003 Derekwood Ln., Ste. 210
Lanham, MD 20706
Tel: (301)459-3200
Fax: (301)459-8077
E-mail: chemely@arema.org
Web Site: http://www.arema.org
To support the education of an engineering student at Michigan Technological University.
Title of Award: Michigan Tech Alumni Scholarships **Area, Field, or Subject:** Engineering. **Level of Education for which Award is Granted:** Undergraduate **Funds Available:** $1000.
Eligibility Requirements: Applicant must be an engineering student at Michigan Tech University and interested in railway engineering. **Applica-**

tion Requirements: Applicants must submit completed AREMA data form together with a cover letter (maximum of 350 words); a resume; two letters of recommendation, one from a faculty member, and another from a present employer, AREMA member, or other responsible person; and a transcript from the schools attended, and courses currently enrolled in. **Additional Information:** Staple application materials in the upper left hand corner and do not include any photos. **Deadline for Receipt:** March 14.

5013 ■ AMERICAN RAILWAY ENGINEERING AND MAINTENANCE-OF-WAY ASSOCIATION

10003 Derekwood Ln., Ste. 210
Lanham, MD 20706
Tel: (301)459-3200
Fax: (301)459-8077
E-mail: chemely@arema.org
Web Site: http://www.arema.org
To support the education of an engineering student.
Title of Award: Norfolk Southern Foundation Scholarships **Area, Field, or Subject:** Engineering. **Level of Education for which Award is Granted:** Undergraduate **Number Awarded:** 1. **Funds Available:** $1000. **Duration:** One academic year.
Eligibility Requirements: Applicant must be enrolled full-time in a four or five year undergraduate program in Engineering or Engineering Technology; institution must be located in Norfolk Southern; service area (22 states, the District of Columbia and Ontario, Canada); have completed at least one quarter or semester in college prior to the application; and have a GPA of 2.00. **Application Requirements:** Applicants must submit completed AREMA data form together with a cover letter (maximum of 350 words); a resume; two letters of recommendation, one from a faculty member, and another from a present employer, AREMA member, or other responsible person; and a transcript from the schools attended, and courses currently enrolled in. **Additional Information:** Staple application materials in the upper left hand corner and do not include any photos. **Deadline for Receipt:** March 14.

5014 ■ AMERICAN RAILWAY ENGINEERING AND MAINTENANCE-OF-WAY ASSOCIATION

10003 Derekwood Ln., Ste. 210
Lanham, MD 20706
Tel: (301)459-3200
Fax: (301)459-8077
E-mail: chemely@arema.org
Web Site: http://www.arema.org
To support the education of an undergraduate engineering student who have potential interest in railway engineering careers.
Title of Award: PB Rail Engineering Scholarships **Area, Field, or Subject:** Engineering. **Level of Education for which Award is Granted:** Undergraduate **Number Awarded:** 1. **Funds Available:** $2000.
Eligibility Requirements: Applicant must be enrolled full-time as an undergraduate student in a four or five year program leading to a Bachelor's degree in Engineering or Engineering Technology in a curriculum accredited by the Accreditation Board of Engineering and Technology; have completed at least one quarter or semester prior to the application; interest in railway engineering; and maintaining a minimum GPA of 2.0. **Application Requirements:** Applicants must submit completed AREMA data form together with a cover letter (maximum of 350 words); a resume; two letters of recommendation, one from a faculty member, and another from a present employer, AREMA member, or other responsible person; and a transcript from the schools attended, and courses currently enrolled in. **Additional Information:** Staple application materials in the upper left hand corner and do not include any photos. **Deadline for Receipt:** March 14.

5015 ■ AMERICAN RAILWAY ENGINEERING AND MAINTENANCE-OF-WAY ASSOCIATION

10003 Derekwood Ln., Ste. 210
Lanham, MD 20706
Tel: (301)459-3200
Fax: (301)459-8077
E-mail: chemely@arema.org
Web Site: http://www.arema.org

To support the education of an undergraduate engineering student who has potential interest in railway engineering careers.
Title of Award: REMSA Scholarships **Area, Field, or Subject:** Engineering. **Level of Education for which Award is Granted:** Undergraduate **Number Awarded:** 1. **Funds Available:** $1000.
Eligibility Requirements: Applicant must be enrolled full-time as an undergraduate student in a four or five year program leading to a Bachelor's degree in Engineering or Engineering Technology in a curriculum accredited by the Accreditation Board of Engineering and Technology; have completed at least one quarter or semester prior to the application; interest in railway engineering; and maintaining a minimum GPA of 2.0. **Application Requirements:** Applicants must submit completed AREMA data form together with a cover letter (maximum of 350 words); a resume; two letters of recommendation, one from a faculty member, and another from a present employer, AREMA member, or other responsible person; and a transcript from the schools attended, and courses currently enrolled in. **Additional Information:** Staple application materials in the upper left hand corner and do not include any photos. **Deadline for Receipt:** March 14.

5016 ■ AMERICAN RESEARCH INSTITUTE IN TURKEY

3260 S St.
Philadelphia, PA 19104-6324
Tel: (215)898-3474
Fax: (215)898-0657
E-mail: leinwand@sas.upenn.edu
Web Site: http://www.ccat.sas.upenn.edu
To expand the number of Americans studying and mastering critical need foreign languages.
Title of Award: Critical Language Scholarships for Intensive Summer Institutes **Area, Field, or Subject:** Business; Engineering; Science; Social Sciences; Humanities. **Level of Education for which Award is Granted:** Graduate, Undergraduate **Funds Available:** no stated amount.
Eligibility Requirements: Applicants must be U.S. citizens; must be currently enrolled in a degree-granting program at the undergraduate or graduate level; must have graduated from an undergraduate or graduate program no more than two-years ago; undergraduate students must have completed at least one year of general college course-work by program start date (one year is defined as two semesters or three quarters); or students in all disciplines including business, engineering, science, the social sciences and humanities are encourage to apply. **Application Requirements:** Applicants must submit completed application form; transcript of records; and letters of recommendation. **Deadline for Receipt:** January 25.

5017 ■ AMERICAN SOCIETY OF CERTIFIED ENGINEERING TECHNICIANS

PO Box 1536
Brandon, MS 39043
Tel: (601)824-8991
Web Site: http://www.ascet.org
To diminish the cost of tuition, books, and lab fees for students.
Title of Award: Joseph C. Johnson Memorial Grants **Area, Field, or Subject:** Engineering. **Level of Education for which Award is Granted:** Undergraduate **Funds Available:** $750. **Duration:** One academic year.
Eligibility Requirements: Applicant must be an American citizen or a legal resident, a student, certified, regular, registered or associate member of ASCET; full or part-time student in an Engineering Technology program (students in a two year program should apply in the first year to receive the grant for their second year. Students in a four year program who apply in the third year may receive the grant for their fourth year); and qualified for financial aid under the Federal College Work Study Program. Applicant must meet the following grade requirements: 2 points on a 3 point system, 3 points on a 4 point system, 4 points on a 5 point system, or 5 points on a 6 point system. **Application Requirements:** Applicants must submit the fully accomplished printed or typewritten application form available online; a letter of recommendation from a faculty member of the Engineering Technology Department indicating the motivation, progress, achievements, and an evaluation of the applicant's potential in the field of Engineering Technology; letters of recommendation from two personal acquaintances, employers or former employers, outlining association, motivation and potential for success; a copy of transcript of records and be sure to pass all the requirements on time.

5018 ■ AMERICAN SOCIETY OF CERTIFIED ENGINEERING TECHNICIANS

PO Box 1536
Brandon, MS 39043
Tel: (601)824-8991
Web Site: http://www.ascet.org
To diminish the cost of tuition, books, and lab fees for students.
Title of Award: Joseph M. Parish Memorial Grants **Area, Field, or Subject:** Engineering. **Level of Education for which Award is Granted:** Undergraduate **Number Awarded:** 1. **Funds Available:** $500. **Duration:** Annually.
Eligibility Requirements: Applicants must meet the following minimum grade points average: 2 points on a 3 point system, 3 points on a 4 point system, 4 points on a 5 point system, or 5 points on a 6 point system. Applicant must be an American citizen or a legal resident; a student member of ASCET; a full time student in an Engineering Technology program; qualified for financial aid under the Federal Work Study Program. **Application Requirements:** Applicants must submit a fully accomplished printed or typewritten application form available online; a letter of recommendation from a faculty member of the Engineering Technology Department indicating the motivation, progress, achievements, and an evaluation of the applicant's potential in the field of Engineering Technology; letters of recommendation from two personal acquaintances, employers or former employers, outlining association, motivation and potential for success; a copy of transcript of records and be sure to pass all the requirements on time.

5019 ■ AMERICAN SOCIETY OF CERTIFIED ENGINEERING TECHNICIANS

PO Box 1536
Brandon, MS 39043
Tel: (601)824-8991
Web Site: http://www.ascet.org
To offset the cost of educational expenses as desired.
Title of Award: Small Cash Grants **Area, Field, or Subject:** Engineering. **Level of Education for which Award is Granted:** Undergraduate **Funds Available:** $100.
Eligibility Requirements: Applicants must either be a student, certified, regular, registered, or associate member of ASCET; a high school senior in the last five months of the academic year who will be enrolled in an Engineering Technology curriculum no later than six months following selection for award; achieved passing grades in their present curriculum. **Application Requirements:** Applicants must provide a copy of transcript; a letter of recommendation from a personal acquaintance, faculty member, or employer outlining motivation, progress, outstanding achievements, and an evaluation of the applicant's potential in the field of Engineering Technology.

5020 ■ AMERICAN SOCIETY FOR ENGINEERING EDUCATION

1818 N St. NW, Ste. 600
Washington, DC 20036-2479
Tel: (202)331-3500
E-mail: aseeexec@asee.org
Web Site: http://www.asee.org
To provide financial assistance for rising undergraduate students entering their third year of education at a college or university.
Title of Award: NASA Aeronautics Scholarship Undergraduate Program **Area, Field, or Subject:** Engineering, Mechanical; Engineering, Electrical. **Level of Education for which Award is Granted:** Undergraduate **Number Awarded:** 20. **Funds Available:** $1,500. **Duration:** Two years.
Eligibility Requirements: Applicants must be citizens or nationals of the United States with at least two years of full time study left to complete at an accredited U.S. college or university as of fall. **Application Requirements:** Applicants must submit all the required application information electronically at www.asee.org. **Deadline for Receipt:** March 24.

5021 ■ AMERICAN SOCIETY OF HEATING, REFRIGERATING AND AIR-CONDITIONING ENGINEERS

1791 Tullie Circle NE
Atlanta, GA 30329
Tel: (404)636-8400
Free: 800-527-4723
Fax: (404)321-5478

E-mail: ashrae@ashrae.org
Web Site: http://www.ashrae.org
To help reduce the financial burdens of obtaining an engineering education.
Title of Award: Henry Adams Scholarships **Area, Field, or Subject:** Engineering. **Level of Education for which Award is Granted:** Undergraduate **Funds Available:** $3,000.
Eligibility Requirements: Applicants must be full-time undergraduates in ABET-accredited Engineering Technology program leading to Bachelors of Science or Engineering degree; must have cumulative GPA of at least 3.0 on a scale where 4.0 is the highest. **Application Requirements:** Applicants must submit an official transcript of college grades; letter of recommendation; and evaluation form from three references including professor or faculty advisor. **Deadline for Receipt:** December 1.

5022 ■ AMERICAN SOCIETY OF HEATING, REFRIGERATING AND AIR-CONDITIONING ENGINEERS

1791 Tullie Circle NE
Atlanta, GA 30329
Tel: (404)636-8400
Free: 800-527-4723
Fax: (404)321-5478
E-mail: ashrae@ashrae.org
Web Site: http://www.ashrae.org
To help reduce the financial burdens of obtaining an engineering education.
Title of Award: American Society of Heating, Refrigerating, and Air-Conditioning Memorial Scholarships **Area, Field, or Subject:** Engineering. **Level of Education for which Award is Granted:** Undergraduate **Funds Available:** $3,000.
Eligibility Requirements: Applicants must be full-time undergraduates in an ABET-accredited Engineering Technology program leading to a Bachelor of Science or Engineering Degree and must have cumulative GPA of at least 3.0 on a 4.0 scale. **Application Requirements:** Applicants must submit an official transcript of college grades; a letter of recommendation; and an evaluation form from three references including professor or faculty advisor. **Deadline for Receipt:** December 1.

5023 ■ AMERICAN SOCIETY OF HEATING, REFRIGERATING AND AIR-CONDITIONING ENGINEERS

1791 Tullie Circle NE
Atlanta, GA 30329
Tel: (404)636-8400
Free: 800-527-4723
Fax: (404)321-5478
E-mail: ashrae@ashrae.org
Web Site: http://www.ashrae.org
To help reduce the financial burdens of obtaining an engineering education.
Title of Award: American Society of Heating, Refrigerating, and Air-Conditioning Undergraduate Scholarships **Area, Field, or Subject:** Engineering. **Level of Education for which Award is Granted:** Undergraduate **Funds Available:** $3,000.
Eligibility Requirements: Applicants must be full-time undergraduate in an ABET-accredited Engineering Technology program leading to a Bachelor of Science or Engineering Degree and must have cumulative GPA of at least 3.0 on a 4.0 scale. **Application Requirements:** Applicants must submit an official transcript of college grades; a letter of recommendation; and an evaluation form from three references including professor or faculty advisor. **Deadline for Receipt:** December 1.

5024 ■ AMERICAN SOCIETY OF HEATING, REFRIGERATING AND AIR-CONDITIONING ENGINEERS

1791 Tullie Circle NE
Atlanta, GA 30329
Tel: (404)636-8400
Free: 800-527-4723
Fax: (404)321-5478
E-mail: ashrae@ashrae.org
Web Site: http://www.ashrae.org
To help reduce the financial burdens of obtaining an engineering education.
Title of Award: Willis H. Carrier Scholarships **Area, Field, or Subject:** Engineering. **Level of Education for which Award is Granted:** Undergraduate **Funds Available:** $10,000.

Eligibility Requirements: Applicants must be full-time undergraduates in an ABET-accredited Engineering Technology program leading to a Bachelor of Science or Engineering Degree; must have cumulative GPA of at least 3.0 on a 4.0 scale. **Application Requirements:** Applicants must submit an official transcript of college grades; a letter of recommendation; and an evaluation form from three references including professor or faculty advisor. **Deadline for Receipt:** December 1.

5025 ■ AMERICAN SOCIETY OF HEATING, REFRIGERATING AND AIR-CONDITIONING ENGINEERS
1791 Tullie Circle NE
Atlanta, GA 30329
Tel: (404)636-8400
Free: 800-527-4723
Fax: (404)321-5478
E-mail: ashrae@ashrae.org
Web Site: http://www.ashrae.org
To help reduce the financial burdens of obtaining the engineering education.

Title of Award: Frank M. Coda Scholarships **Area, Field, or Subject:** Engineering. **Level of Education for which Award is Granted:** Undergraduate **Funds Available:** $5,000.
Eligibility Requirements: Applicants must be full-time undergraduates in an ABET-accredited Engineering Technology program leading to a Bachelor of Science or Engineering Degree and must have cumulative GPA of at least 3.0 on a 4.0 scale. **Application Requirements:** Applicants must submit an official transcript of college grades; a letter of recommendation and an evaluation form from three references including professor or faculty advisor. **Deadline for Receipt:** December 1.

5026 ■ AMERICAN SOCIETY OF HEATING, REFRIGERATING AND AIR-CONDITIONING ENGINEERS
1791 Tullie Circle NE
Atlanta, GA 30329
Tel: (404)636-8400
Free: 800-527-4723
Fax: (404)321-5478
E-mail: ashrae@ashrae.org
Web Site: http://www.ashrae.org
To help reduce the financial burdens of obtaining an engineering education.

Title of Award: Duane Hanson Scholarships **Area, Field, or Subject:** Engineering. **Level of Education for which Award is Granted:** Undergraduate **Funds Available:** $3,000.
Eligibility Requirements: Applicants must be full-time undergraduates in ABET-accredited Engineering Technology program leading to Bachelors of Science or Engineering degree; must have cumulative GPA of at least 3.0 on a scale where 4.0 is the highest. **Application Requirements:** Applicants must submit an official transcript of college grades; letter of recommendation; and evaluation form from three references including professor or faculty advisor. **Deadline for Receipt:** December 1.

5027 ■ AMERICAN SOCIETY OF HEATING, REFRIGERATING AND AIR-CONDITIONING ENGINEERS
1791 Tullie Circle NE
Atlanta, GA 30329
Tel: (404)636-8400
Free: 800-527-4723
Fax: (404)321-5478
E-mail: ashrae@ashrae.org
Web Site: http://www.ashrae.org
To help reduce the financial burdens of obtaining an engineering education.

Title of Award: Alwin B. Newton Scholarships **Area, Field, or Subject:** Engineering. **Level of Education for which Award is Granted:** Undergraduate **Funds Available:** $3,000.
Eligibility Requirements: Applicants must be full-time undergraduates in an ABET-accredited Engineering Technology program leading to a Bachelors of Science or Engineering degree; must have cumulative GPA of at least 3.0 on a scale of 4.0. **Application Requirements:** Applicants must submit official transcripts of college grades; a letter of recommendation; and an evaluation form from three references including a professor or faculty advisor. **Deadline for Receipt:** December 1.

5028 ■ AMERICAN SOCIETY OF HEATING, REFRIGERATING AND AIR-CONDITIONING ENGINEERS
1791 Tullie Circle NE
Atlanta, GA 30329
Tel: (404)636-8400
Free: 800-527-4723
Fax: (404)321-5478
E-mail: ashrae@ashrae.org
Web Site: http://www.ashrae.org
To help reduce the financial burdens of obtaining the engineering education.

Title of Award: Donald E. Nichols Scholarships **Area, Field, or Subject:** Engineering. **Level of Education for which Award is Granted:** Undergraduate **Funds Available:** $3,000.
Eligibility Requirements: Applicants must be full-time undergraduates in an ABET-accredited Engineering Technology program leading to a Bachelor of Science or Engineering Degree; must have cumulative GPA of at least 3.0 on a 4.0 scale. **Application Requirements:** Applicants must submit an official transcript of college grades; a letter of recommendation; and an evaluation form from three references including professor or faculty advisor. **Deadline for Receipt:** December 1.

5029 ■ AMERICAN SOCIETY OF HEATING, REFRIGERATING AND AIR-CONDITIONING ENGINEERS
1791 Tullie Circle NE
Atlanta, GA 30329
Tel: (404)636-8400
Free: 800-527-4723
Fax: (404)321-5478
E-mail: ashrae@ashrae.org
Web Site: http://www.ashrae.org
To help reduce the financial burdens of obtaining the engineering education.

Title of Award: Reuben Trane Scholarships **Area, Field, or Subject:** Engineering. **Level of Education for which Award is Granted:** Undergraduate **Funds Available:** $10,000.
Eligibility Requirements: Applicants must be full-time undergraduates in an ABET-accredited Engineering Technology program leading to a Bachelor of Science or Engineering Degree; must have cumulative GPA of at least 3.0 on a 4.0 scale. **Application Requirements:** Applicants must submit an official transcript of college grades; a letter of recommendation; and an evaluation form from three references including professor or faculty advisor. **Deadline for Receipt:** December 1.

5030 ■ AMERICAN SOCIETY OF MECHANICAL ENGINEERS
Three Park Ave.
New York, NY 10016-5990
Tel: (212)591-7733
Free: 800-843-2763
Fax: (212)591-7739
E-mail: infocentral@asme.org
Web Site: http://www.asme.org
To provide scholarships and new developments in Mechanical Engineering. To honor students who demonstrate outstanding personal and academic characteristics.

Title of Award: Auxiliary Undergraduate Scholarships **Area, Field, or Subject:** Mechanical engineering. **Level of Education for which Award is Granted:** Undergraduate **Number Awarded:** 1. **Funds Available:** $2,000 Cash scholarship used for one academic year. **Duration:** One year.
Eligibility Requirements: Applicants must be a full-time students seeking either Mechanical Engineering courses or any related field of study engineering; must be a U.S citizen. **Application Requirements:** Applicants must be enrolled in U.S. school in an ABET accredited Mechanical Engineering Department; Applicants must submit letter of recommendation by the Head of The Mechanical Engineering Faculty Advisor; Applicants must file a letter from a non-academic reference; Applicants should have a letter from any other person will not fulfill the requirement; Applicants must prepare letter of recommendation from an instructor, preferably in the Engineering School; Applicants must submit Official transcript with academic record; Applicants should have Completed Application Form; Guidelines and application form are available from the ASME scholarship office or can be downloaded from the ASME website.

Deadline for Receipt: March 15. **Additional Information:** Alverta E. Cover 5425 Caldwell Mill Rd. Birmingham, AL 35242; 205-991-6109 at the above address.

5031 ■ AMERICAN SOCIETY OF MECHANICAL ENGINEERS
Three Park Ave.
New York, NY 10016-5990
Tel: (212)591-7733
Free: 800-843-2763
Fax: (212)591-7739
E-mail: infocentral@asme.org
Web Site: http://www.asme.org
To promote art, science and practice of mechanical and multidisciplinary engineering and allied sciences through educational assistance.
Title of Award: Lucy and Charles W.E. Clarke Scholarships **Area, Field, or Subject:** Mechanical engineering. **Level of Education for which Award is Granted:** Undergraduate **Funds Available:** $6,000 (for the winning schools).
Eligibility Requirements: Scholarship is open to schools accredited by the Accreditation Board for Engineering and Technology or substantially equivalent mechanical engineering technology departments who directly choose incoming freshmen beginning engineering studies in the fall to receive the scholarship. **Application Requirements:** Applications for deserving schools are made by the AMSE Student Section as endorsed by the mechanical engineering technology department; Necessary forms are available in the website also indicating other instructions. **Deadline for Receipt:** October 20. **Additional Information:** Marcelle Austin, tel: 212-591-7733, fax: 212-591-7739, email: austinm@asme.org.

5032 ■ AMERICAN WELDING SOCIETY
550 NW LeJeune Rd.
Miami, FL 33126
Tel: (305)443-9353
Free: 800-443-9353
Fax: (305)443-7559
E-mail: info@aws.org
Web Site: http://www.aws.org
To provide financial assistance to individuals interested in pursuing a career in either welding engineering or the application of the art of welding in civil and structural engineering.
Title of Award: Arsham Amirikian Engineering Scholarships **Area, Field, or Subject:** Welding; Civil Engineering. **Level of Education for which Award is Granted:** Undergraduate **Funds Available:** $2,500.
Eligibility Requirements: Applicants must be undergraduate students pursuing a bachelors degree in civil engineering or welding related degree at an accredited university; must be 18 years of age or above; must have a minimum of 3.0 grade point average; must be citizens of the United States; and plan to attend an accredited engineering school within the United States. Applicants must have a minimum of 3.0 grade point average throughout the academic year. **Application Requirements:** Applicants must submit an application; a high school diploma; and a financial statement. **Deadline for Receipt:** January 15.

5033 ■ ARKANSAS ENVIRONMENTAL FEDERATION
1400 W Markham St., Ste. 302
Little Rock, AR 72201
Tel: (501)374-0263
Fax: (501)374-8752
Web Site: http://www.environmentark.org
To provide financial assistance for selected students from Arkansas universities.
Title of Award: Larry Wilson Scholarships for Undergraduate Civil Engineering Students **Area, Field, or Subject:** Engineering, Civil. **Level of Education for which Award is Granted:** Undergraduate **Funds Available:** No specific amount.
Eligibility Requirements: Applicants must be U.S. citizens who are residents of Arkansas; must be undergraduate students who have Civil Engineering as a degree goal; must be full-time students at time of application and for year scholarship is awarded; must have a minimum of 2.8 cumulative grade point average based on 4.0 system; and must be nominated by a faculty member. **Application Requirements:** Applicants must submit a completed application form along with current official transcript(s) and letters. **Deadline for Receipt:** April 11.

5034 ■ ARMED FORCES COMMUNICATIONS AND ELECTRONICS ASSOCIATION
4400 Fair Lakes Court
Fairfax, VA 22033
Tel: (703)631-6141
Free: 800-336-4583
Fax: (703)631-4693
Web Site: http://www.afcea.org
To provide scholarship for the general public.
Title of Award: AFCEA Distance Learning/Online Scholarships **Area, Field, or Subject:** Engineering; Mathematics; Physics; Communications; Electronics. **Level of Education for which Award is Granted:** Undergraduate **Funds Available:** $1,500.
Eligibility Requirements: Applicants must be U.S. citizens currently enrolled full time pursuing either a Bachelor of Science or Master's of Science degree through distance learning or online program (only a few second-year students only will be accepted). **Application Requirements:** Applicants may apply online at AFFECT website. Applicants must also submit two letters of recommendation printed in school stationery and with signature from field-of-study professors. **Deadline for Receipt:** June 1. **Additional Information:** Norma Corrales; 703-631-6149.

5035 ■ ARMED FORCES COMMUNICATIONS AND ELECTRONICS ASSOCIATION
4400 Fair Lakes Court
Fairfax, VA 22033
Tel: (703)631-6141
Free: 800-336-4583
Fax: (703)631-4693
Web Site: http://www.afcea.org
To provide scholarship to the general public.
Title of Award: AFCEA General John A. Wickham Scholarships **Area, Field, or Subject:** Engineering; Mathematics; Physics; Communications; Electronics. **Level of Education for which Award is Granted:** Undergraduate **Funds Available:** $2,000.
Eligibility Requirements: Applicants must be US citizens; must have GPA of 3.5 on 4.0 scale. **Application Requirements:** Applicants may apply at AFCEA web site. Applicants must also submit two letters of recommendation printed in school stationery and with signature from field-of-study professors. **Deadline for Receipt:** May 1. **Additional Information:** Norma Corrales; 703-631-6149.

5036 ■ ARMED FORCES COMMUNICATIONS AND ELECTRONICS ASSOCIATION
4400 Fair Lakes Court
Fairfax, VA 22033
Tel: (703)631-6141
Free: 800-336-4583
Fax: (703)631-4693
Web Site: http://www.afcea.org
To provide scholarship for the general public.
Title of Award: William E. "Buck" Bragunier Scholarships **Area, Field, or Subject:** Engineering; Mathematics; Physics; Communications; Electronics. **Level of Education for which Award is Granted:** Undergraduate **Funds Available:** $2,000.
Eligibility Requirements: Applicants must be at least second year college students; must be enrolled full time as sophomores or juniors at the time of application; must have an outstanding record of demonstrated leadership within university or local community. **Application Requirements:** Applicants may apply online at AFFECT website. Applicants must also submit two letters of recommendation printed in school stationery and with signature from field-of-study professors. **Deadline for Receipt:** May 1. **Additional Information:** Norma Corrales; 703-631-6149.

5037 ■ ARMED FORCES COMMUNICATIONS AND ELECTRONICS ASSOCIATION
4400 Fair Lakes Court
Fairfax, VA 22033
Tel: (703)631-6141
Free: 800-336-4583
Fax: (703)631-4693
Web Site: http://www.afcea.org
To provide scholarships to students connected to the US Military.
Title of Award: LT.G. Douglas D. Buchholz Memorial Scholarships **Area, Field, or Subject:** Engineering; Mathematics; Physics; Communications.

Level of Education for which Award is Granted: Undergraduate **Funds Available:** $2,000.

Eligibility Requirements: Applicants must be currently active enlisted soldiers assigned to Fort Gordon, Georgia; must have completed a minimum of 15 semester hours/25 quarter hours; must be currently enrolled either full or part time in an accredited US college; and must have a minimum GPA of 2.5 on a 4.0 scale. **Application Requirements:** Students may apply online at the AFCEA web site. **Deadline for Receipt:** November 15. **Additional Information:** Mr. Joseph S. Yavorsky, President; president@afcea-augusta.org.

5038 ■ ARMED FORCES COMMUNICATIONS AND ELECTRONICS ASSOCIATION
4400 Fair Lakes Court
Fairfax, VA 22033
Tel: (703)631-6141
Free: 800-336-4583
Fax: (703)631-4693
Web Site: http://www.afcea.org

To provide educational incentives, opportunities and assistance for people engaged in information management, communications and intelligence efforts and fostering excellence in education particularly in the "hard science" disciplines related to C4ISR.

Title of Award: Disabled War Veterans Scholarships **Area, Field, or Subject:** Engineering; Mathematics; Physics; Communications. **Level of Education for which Award is Granted:** Undergraduate **Funds Available:** $2,500.

Eligibility Requirements: Applicants must be currently enrolled and attending either a two year or four year in an accredited college or university in the United States; must be enrolled in an accredited distance learning or online degree granting program affiliated with major, accredited two year or four year college or university in the United States. **Application Requirements:** Applicants may apply online at AFFECT website. Applicants must also submit two letters of recommendation printed on school stationery and with signature from field-of-study professors. **Deadline for Receipt:** November 1. **Additional Information:** Norma Corrales; 703-631-6149.

5039 ■ ARMED FORCES COMMUNICATIONS AND ELECTRONICS ASSOCIATION
4400 Fair Lakes Court
Fairfax, VA 22033
Tel: (703)631-6141
Free: 800-336-4583
Fax: (703)631-4693
Web Site: http://www.afcea.org

To provide scholarship to the general public.

Title of Award: Lockheed Martin IT Scholarships **Area, Field, or Subject:** Engineering; Mathematics; Physics; Communications. **Level of Education for which Award is Granted:** Undergraduate **Funds Available:** $3,000.

Eligibility Requirements: Applicants must be at least second year college students, must be enrolled full time as sophomores or juniors at the time of application. **Application Requirements:** Applicants may apply online. Applicants must also submit two letters of recommendation printed in school stationery and with signature from field-of-study professors; and official transcript of all college level study. **Deadline for Receipt:** May 1. **Additional Information:** Norma Corrales; 703-631-6149.

5040 ■ ARMED FORCES COMMUNICATIONS AND ELECTRONICS ASSOCIATION
4400 Fair Lakes Court
Fairfax, VA 22033
Tel: (703)631-6141
Free: 800-336-4583
Fax: (703)631-4693
Web Site: http://www.afcea.org

To provide scholarships to students connected to the US Military.

Title of Award: AFCEA General Emmett Paige Scholarships **Area, Field, or Subject:** Engineering; Mathematics; Physics; Communications. **Level of Education for which Award is Granted:** Undergraduate **Funds Available:** $2,000.

Eligibility Requirements: Applicants must be US citizens; must have a minimum GPA of 3.0 on 4.0 scale. **Application Requirements:** Ap-

plicants may apply online at the AFCEA web site. Applicants must also submit a copy of Certificate of Service, Discharge From DD214, or facsimile of current Department of Defense or Coast Guard Identification Card; and two letters of recommendation printed in school stationery and with signature from field-of-study professors. **Deadline for Receipt:** March 1. **Additional Information:** Norma Corrales; 703-631-6149.

5041 ■ ARMED FORCES COMMUNICATIONS AND ELECTRONICS ASSOCIATION
4400 Fair Lakes Court
Fairfax, VA 22033
Tel: (703)631-6141
Free: 800-336-4583
Fax: (703)631-4693
Web Site: http://www.afcea.org

To support students working full time.

Title of Award: Vice Adm. Jerry O. Tuttle, USN (Ret.) and Mrs. Barbara A. Tuttle Science and Technology Scholarships **Area, Field, or Subject:** Engineering; Computer and Information Sciences. **Level of Education for which Award is Granted:** Undergraduate **Funds Available:** $2,000.

Eligibility Requirements: Applicants must be U.S. citizens enrolled full time with majoring in technology; and must be sophomores and juniors at the time of application. **Application Requirements:** Applicants may apply online. Applicants must also submit two letters of recommendation printed in school stationery and with signature from field-of-study professors; and official transcript of all college level study. **Deadline for Receipt:** November 1. **Additional Information:** Norma Corrales; 703-631-6149.

5042 ■ ARMED FORCES COMMUNICATIONS AND ELECTRONICS ASSOCIATION
4400 Fair Lakes Court
Fairfax, VA 22033
Tel: (703)631-6141
Free: 800-336-4583
Fax: (703)631-4693
Web Site: http://www.afcea.org

To provide scholarships to students connected to the US military.

Title of Award: Veterans of Enduring Freedom (Afghanistan) and Iraqi Freedom Scholarships **Area, Field, or Subject:** Engineering; Mathematics; Physics; Communications. **Level of Education for which Award is Granted:** Undergraduate **Funds Available:** $2,500. **Duration:** One year.

Eligibility Requirements: Applicants must be currently enrolled and attending either a two year accredited college or university in the United States. **Application Requirements:** Applicants may apply online at AFCEA web site. **Additional Information:** The AFCEA Educational Foundation is pleased to co-sponsor this scholarship opportunity for U.S. War Veterans. **Deadline for Receipt:** April 1 and November 1. **Additional Information:** Norma Corrales 703-631-6149.

5043 ■ ARMED FORCES COMMUNICATIONS AND ELECTRONICS ASSOCIATION
4400 Fair Lakes Court
Fairfax, VA 22033
Tel: (703)631-6141
Free: 800-336-4583
Fax: (703)631-4693
Web Site: http://www.afcea.org

To provide scholarships to students connected with the US Military.

Title of Award: Marine Corps Sgt. Jeannette L. Winters Memorial Scholarships **Area, Field, or Subject:** Engineering; Mathematics; Physics; Communications. **Level of Education for which Award is Granted:** Undergraduate **Funds Available:** $2,000.

Eligibility Requirements: Applicants must be enrolled full time in a Bachelor of Science degree program in accredited colleges or universities in the United States; and must have a minimum GPA of 3.0 on 4.0 scale. Majors directly related to the support of US Intelligence enterprises or national security with relevance to the mission of AFCEA are also eligible. **Application Requirements:** Applicants may apply online at the AFCEA web site. Applicants must also submit two letters of recommendation printed in school stationery and with signature from field-of-study professors. **Deadline for Receipt:** September 1. **Additional Information:** Norma Corrales; 703-631-6149.

5044 ■ ASCE SAN DIEGO SECTION

PO Box 1028
El Cajon, CA 92022
Tel: (619)588-0641
Fax: (619)749-2188
E-mail: sdcivil@asce-sd.org
Web Site: http://www.asce-sd.org

To provide financial assistance for students pursuing Construction Management, Construction Engineering and/or Construction Practices as a career goal.

Title of Award: Charles McMahon Memorial Construction Management/Engineering Scholarship Awards **Area, Field, or Subject:** Construction, Engineering. **Level of Education for which Award is Granted:** Undergraduate **Funds Available:** No specific amount.

Eligibility Requirements: Applicant must be a freshman, sophomore, junior or senior level ASCE student member in good standing at one of the local San Diego universities and must have a minimum 2.5 overall grade point average. **Application Requirements:** Applicants must submit application package that must include a filled out scholarship application form and proof of ASCE Student Membership. **Deadline for Receipt:** March 3.

5045 ■ ASCE SAN DIEGO SECTION

PO Box 1028
El Cajon, CA 92022
Tel: (619)588-0641
Fax: (619)749-2188
E-mail: sdcivil@asce-sd.org
Web Site: http://www.asce-sd.org

To provide financial assistance for student members of ASCE intending to continue their education in college.

Title of Award: Charles Smith Memorial Scholarship Awards **Area, Field, or Subject:** Engineering, Civil. **Level of Education for which Award is Granted:** Undergraduate **Funds Available:** No specific amount.

Eligibility Requirements: Applicant must be a freshman, sophomore, junior or senior ASCE student member in good standing at one of the local San Diego universities who has a minimum 2.5 overall grade point average. **Application Requirements:** Applicants must submit application package which includes a filled out scholarship application form and proof of ASCE Student Membership. **Deadline for Receipt:** March 3.

5046 ■ ASSOCIATION FOR THE ADVANCEMENT OF COST ENGINEERING

209 Prairie Ave., Ste. 100
Morgantown, WV 26501-5934
Tel: (304)296-8444
Free: 800-858-2678
Fax: (304)291-5728
E-mail: president@aacei.org
Web Site: http://www.aacei.org

To advance the study of cost engineering and cost management through the integrative process of total cost management.

Title of Award: AACE International Competitive Scholarships **Area, Field, or Subject:** Engineering. **Level of Education for which Award is Granted:** Undergraduate **Funds Available:** $2,000-$8,000.

Eligibility Requirements: Applicants must be full-time students pursuing a related degree in engineering and other related courses. **Application Requirements:** Applicants must fill out the application form. **Deadline for Receipt:** February 17. **Additional Information:** AACE International at the above address.

5047 ■ ASSOCIATION OF DESK AND DERRICK CLUBS

5153 E 51st St., Ste. 107
Tulsa, OK 74135
Tel: (918)622-1749
Fax: (918)622-1675
E-mail: adotulsa@swbell.net
Web Site: http://www.addc.org

To provide financial assistance to college students planning a career in the petroleum energy or allied industries.

Title of Award: Association of Desk and Derrick Clubs Education Trust Scholarships **Area, Field, or Subject:** Geology; Geophysics; Engineering, Petroleum; Engineering, Nuclear; Engineering, Mechanical; Energy-related areas. **Level of Education for which Award is Granted:** Undergraduate **Funds Available:** $1,500.

Eligibility Requirements: Applicant must have completed at least two years or be currently enrolled in the second year of undergraduate study at an accredited college or university; be a U.S. or Canadian citizen; maintain a GPA of 3.2 or above on a 4.0 scale; be pursuing a career in the field of petroleum, energy or allied industry. **Application Requirements:** Applicants must submit a completed application form to Desk and Derrick Educational Trust, 5153 E 51st St., Ste. 107, Tulsa, OK 74135. **Deadline for Receipt:** April 1.

5048 ■ ASSOCIATION OF ENVIRONMENTAL AND ENGINEERING GEOLOGISTS

PO Box 460518
Denver, CO 80246
Tel: (303)757-2926
Fax: (303)757-2969
E-mail: aeg@aegweb.org
Web Site: http://www.aegweb.org

To provide scholarships to those outstanding students in the field of geological engineering.

Title of Award: Marliave Scholarship Fund **Area, Field, or Subject:** Geological Engineering. **Level of Education for which Award is Granted:** Undergraduate **Funds Available:** No specific amount.

Eligibility Requirements: Applicants must be outstanding students in geological engineering. **Application Requirements:** Applicants must submit a completed application form. **Additional Information:** The Marliave Scholarship Fund was established in 1968 by the Association of Environmental & Engineering Geologists (AEG). The fund name honors an eminent family of engineering geologists: Chester E. Marliave (1888-1958), and his sons Elmer C. Marliave (1910-1967) and Burton H. Marliave (1917-199), who were pioneers in the profession. **Additional Information:** Association of Environmental and Engineering Geologists at the above address

5049 ■ ASSOCIATION OF ENVIRONMENTAL AND ENGINEERING GEOLOGISTS

PO Box 460518
Denver, CO 80246
Tel: (303)757-2926
Fax: (303)757-2969
E-mail: aeg@aegweb.org
Web Site: http://www.aegweb.org

To provide financial support to those students who are in need.

Title of Award: Martin L. Stout Scholarships **Area, Field, or Subject:** Geological Engineering. **Level of Education for which Award is Granted:** Undergraduate **Funds Available:** No specific amount.

Eligibility Requirements: Applicants must be students who are pursuing geological engineering; must be in good academic standing; must have financial need. **Application Requirements:** Applicants must submit a completed application form. **Additional Information:** Association of Environmental and Engineering Geologists at the above address

5050 ■ ASSOCIATION GENERAL CONTRACTORS OF AMERICA, NEW YORK STATE CHAPTER

10 Airline Dr., Ste. 203
Albany, NY 12205
Tel: (518)456-1134
Fax: (518)456-1198
E-mail: agcadmin@agcnys.org
Web Site: http://www.agcnys.org

To provide financial assistance to college students working toward a degree in Civil Engineering or Construction Technology at a college or university.

Title of Award: AGC New York State Chapter Scholarship Program **Area, Field, or Subject:** Civil engineering. **Level of Education for which Award is Granted:** Undergraduate **Funds Available:** $2,500. **Duration:** One year.

Eligibility Requirements: Applicant must be entering the 2nd, 3rd or 4th year of a two or four-year college; seriously intent upon a career in the highway construction industry. Applicant must pursue a Bachelor or Associate degree in construction or civil engineering and have at least a 2.50 GPA. **Application Requirements:** Applicant must submit a signed, completed five-page application; three evaluation forms: one completed by a college faculty advisor, and two completed by adults not related to the applicant and preferably in the industry; and, official transcript of all college grades. **Deadline for Receipt:** May 15.

5051 ■ ASSOCIATION OF INDEPENDENT COLLEGES AND UNIVERSITIES OF PENNSYLVANIA
101 N Front St.
Harrisburg, PA 17101-1405
Tel: (717)232-8649
Fax: (717)233-8574
E-mail: duck@aicup.org
Web Site: http://www.aicup.org
To promote the engineering and information technology profession to individuals from groups historically underrepresented in engineering.
Title of Award: Air Products and Chemicals, Inc. Scholarships **Area, Field, or Subject:** Chemical engineering; Mechanical, Engineering; Computer and information sciences. **Level of Education for which Award is Granted:** Undergraduate **Funds Available:** $7,500.
Eligibility Requirements: Applicants must: be full-time undergraduate students majoring only in Chemical engineering, Mechanical engineering, Information technology (computer science, management information systems, IST); be enrolled as a junior in fall; have a minimum GPA of 3.0; be women and/or members of the following minority groups: American Indian or Alaska Native, Asian, Black or African American, Hispanic or Latino, Native Hawaiian or other Pacific Islander. Student must be accepted at, or currently attending, one of 84 member colleges and universities of the Association of Independent Colleges and Universities of Pennsylvania. **Application Requirements:** Application forms are available at the Financial Aid office; applicant must submit complete application materials to Mary Maronic, Foundation Associate, Association of Independent Colleges and Universities of Pennsylvania. A complete application consists of a completed, signed application form, a copy of the student's transcript, a resume and an essay; the candidate may submit a letter of recommendation. **Deadline for Receipt:** April 29. **Additional Information:** Mary Maronic, 717-232-8649 ext. 232; maronic@aicup.org.

5052 ■ ASSOCIATION OF INDEPENDENT COLLEGES AND UNIVERSITIES OF PENNSYLVANIA
101 N Front St.
Harrisburg, PA 17101-1405
Tel: (717)232-8649
Fax: (717)233-8574
E-mail: duck@aicup.org
Web Site: http://www.aicup.org
To promote the engineering and information technology profession to individuals from groups historically underrepresented in engineering.
Title of Award: Michael Baker Corporation Scholarship Program **Area, Field, or Subject:** Civil engineering; Architectural engineering. **Level of Education for which Award is Granted:** Undergraduate **Number Awarded:** 1. **Funds Available:** $2,500.
Eligibility Requirements: Applicant must be: full-time undergraduate students majoring in Civil, Environmental or Architectural Engineering only; enrolled as juniors in the fall; maintaining a minimum GPA of 3.0; women and/or members of the following minority groups: American Indians or Alaska Natives, Asians, Black or African Americans, Hispanics or Latinos or Other Pacific Islanders. Student must be accepted at, or currently attending, one of 84 member colleges and universities of the Association of Independent Colleges and Universities of Pennsylvania. **Application Requirements:** Application forms are available at the Financial Aid office. Applicant must submit complete application to Mary Maronic, Foundation Associate, Association of Independent Colleges and Universities of Pennsylvania. A complete application consists of a completed, signed application form, a copy of the student's transcript, a resume and an essay; the candidate may submit a letter of recommendation. **Deadline for Receipt:** April 29. **Additional Information:** Mary Maronic, 717-232-8649 ext. 232; maronic@aicup.org.

5053 ■ ASSOCIATION OF INDEPENDENT COLLEGES AND UNIVERSITIES OF PENNSYLVANIA
101 N Front St.
Harrisburg, PA 17101-1405
Tel: (717)232-8649
Fax: (717)233-8574
E-mail: duck@aicup.org

Web Site: http://www.aicup.org
To promote the engineering and information technology profession to individuals from groups historically underrepresented in engineering.
Title of Award: HDR Engineering, Inc. Scholarship for Diversity in Engineering **Area, Field, or Subject:** Civil engineering; Architectural engineering; Engineering, Geological. **Level of Education for which Award is Granted:** Undergraduate **Funds Available:** $2,500.
Eligibility Requirements: Applicants must: be full-time undergraduate students majoring only in civil engineering, structural engineering or geotechnical engineering; be enrolled as juniors in fall; have a minimum GPA of 3.0; be women and/or members of one of the following minority groups: American Indian or Alaska Native, Asian, Black or African American, Hispanic or Latino, Native Hawaiian or Other Pacific Islander. Applicants must be accepted at, or currently attending, one of 84 member colleges and universities of the Association of Independent Colleges and Universities of Pennsylvania. **Application Requirements:** Application forms are available at the Financial Aid office. Applicant must submit complete application materials to Mary Maronic, Foundation Associate, Association of Independent Colleges and Universities of Pennsylvania. A complete application consists of a completed, signed application form, a copy of the student's transcript, a resume and an essay; the candidate may submit a letter of recommendation. **Deadline for Receipt:** April 29. **Additional Information:** Mary Maronic, 717-232-8649 ext. 232; maronic@aicup.org.

5054 ■ ASSOCIATION FOR IRON AND STEEL TECHNOLOGY
186 Thorn Hill Rd.
Warrendale, PA 15086-7528
Tel: (724)776-6040
Fax: (724)776-1880
E-mail: info@aist.org
Web Site: http://www.aist.org
To enhance education and careers in engineering or metallurgy.
Title of Award: AIST Baltimore Chapter Scholarships **Area, Field, or Subject:** Engineering; Metallurgy. **Level of Education for which Award is Granted:** Undergraduate **Number Awarded:** 1. **Funds Available:** $1,500. **Duration:** One year.
Eligibility Requirements: Applicant must be a dependent or a spouse of a commendable member of the AIST Baltimore Chapter Scholarship; must be attending an eligible, full-time course in the field of engineering at an institution; demonstrate interest towards a career in the field of iron and steel industry. **Application Requirements:** Applicants must submit an application form available at the website; a resume; a copy of SAT/ACT scores; copy of transcripts; two essays about the applicant's accomplishments, and the applicant's interest/involvement in the steel and iron industry. Send all documents to: AIST Baltimore Chapter Scholarships, Thomas J. Russo, 1430 Sparrows Point Blvd. Sparrows Point, MD 21219-1014. **Deadline for Receipt:** April 30. **Additional Information:** Thomas J. Russo, 410-388-4337, tom.russo@mittalsteel.com.

5055 ■ ASSOCIATION FOR IRON AND STEEL TECHNOLOGY
186 Thorn Hill Rd.
Warrendale, PA 15086-7528
Tel: (724)776-6040
Fax: (724)776-1880
E-mail: info@aist.org
Web Site: http://www.aist.org
To enhance education and careers in the iron and steel-related industry.
Title of Award: AIST Detroit Chapter Scholarships **Area, Field, or Subject:** Engineering; Metallurgy. **Level of Education for which Award is Granted:** Undergraduate **Number Awarded:** 2. **Funds Available:** $2,500. **Duration:** One year.
Eligibility Requirements: Applicant must be a dependent of an AIST Detroit Chapter member in good standing for two or more consecutive years; have a minimum cumulative GPA of 3.0 on a 4.0 scale; must be enrolled full-time as an undergraduate student majoring in engineering, metallurgy or materials science program at an accredited North American university; demonstrate interest towards a career in the field of iron and steel industry. **Application Requirements:** Applicant must submit an application form available at the website; a resume; three letters of recommendation (addressing character, academic status, leadership potential and career commitment) from a high school counselor or college academic advisor, teacher/professor or a previous employer; copy of SAT/

ACT scores; copy of current transcripts; an essay (maximum of 2 pages) about the applicant's professional goals, interest in a career in the iron and steel industry, and how the applicant's skills could be applied to enhance the industry. Requirements must be sent to: AIST Detroit Member Chapter Scholarships, c/o Judith A. Quinn, Chapter Secretary 41158 Savage Road Belleville, MI 48111. **Deadline for Receipt:** April 30. **Additional Information:** Judith Quinn, 313-319-2815, judieqn@aol.com.

5056 ■ ASSOCIATION FOR IRON AND STEEL TECHNOLOGY
186 Thorn Hill Rd.
Warrendale, PA 15086-7528
Tel: (724)776-6040
Fax: (724)776-1880
E-mail: info@aist.org
Web Site: http://www.aist.org
To enhance education and careers in the field of engineering.
Title of Award: AIST Northwest Chapter Scholarships **Area, Field, or Subject:** Engineering. **Level of Education for which Award is Granted:** Undergraduate **Number Awarded:** 2. **Funds Available:** $1,000.
Eligibility Requirements: Applicant must be a relative of a member of the AIST Northwest Member Chapter; must be a Pacific Northwest student; must demonstrate great interest in the iron and steel profession. Chemistry, metallurgy, mathematics, engineering and physics students are also qualified for the scholarships. **Application Requirements:** Applicants must submit an application form available at the website; a resume; a recommendation/evaluation from a counselor, teacher or professor; copy of SAT/ACT scores; copy of transcripts; and an essay (maximum of 2 pages) with one of the topics: Purpose in going to college; beneficial experience during the last two summers; most significant experiences and effect on future plans; accomplishments providing the greatest satisfaction; reason why the applicant should be chosen as the recipient of the award. Requirements must be sent to: Gerardo L. Giraldo, Quality Assurance Manager Nucor Steel Seattle, Inc. Washington Steel Division 2424 SW Andover St., Seattle, Washington 98106-1100. **Deadline for Receipt:** April 30. **Additional Information:** Gerardo L. Giraldo at gerry.giraldo@nucor-seattle.com 206-933-2245.

5057 ■ ASSOCIATION FOR IRON AND STEEL TECHNOLOGY
186 Thorn Hill Rd.
Warrendale, PA 15086-7528
Tel: (724)776-6040
Fax: (724)776-1880
E-mail: info@aist.org
Web Site: http://www.aist.org
To enhance education and careers iron and steel-related industries.
Title of Award: AIST Ronald E. Lincoln Memorial Scholarships **Area, Field, or Subject:** Engineering; Metallurgy. **Level of Education for which Award is Granted:** Undergraduate **Number Awarded:** 2. **Funds Available:** $3,000. **Duration:** One year.
Eligibility Requirements: Applicant must be enrolled full-time in an engineering, metallurgy or materials science program at an accredited North American university; have a minimum cumulative GPA of 3.0 on a 4.0 scale; demonstrate interest toward a career in the field of iron and steel industry. **Application Requirements:** Applicants must submit an application form available at the website; a resume; three letters of recommendation (addressing character, academic status, leadership potential and career commitment) from a college academic advisor, professor and previous employer; transcripts; an essay (maximum of 2 pages) about the applicant's professional goals, interest in a career in the iron and steel industry, and how the applicant's skills could be applied to enhance the industry. **Additional Information:** Established by Chaparral Steel. **Deadline for Receipt:** March 2. **Additional Information:** Lori Wharrey lwharrey@aist.org or 724-776-6040 ext.621.

5058 ■ ASSOCIATION FOR IRON AND STEEL TECHNOLOGY
186 Thorn Hill Rd.
Warrendale, PA 15086-7528
Tel: (724)776-6040
Fax: (724)776-1880
E-mail: info@aist.org
Web Site: http://www.aist.org
To enhance education and careers in iron and steel-related industries.
Title of Award: AIST William E. Schwabe Memorial Scholarships **Area, Field, or Subject:** Engineering; Metallurgy. **Level of Education for**

which **Award is Granted:** Undergraduate **Number Awarded:** 1. **Funds Available:** $3,000. **Duration:** One year.
Eligibility Requirements: Applicant must be enrolled full-time in an engineering, metallurgy or materials science program at an accredited North American university; have a minimum cumulative GPA of 3.0 on a 4.0 scale; demonstrate interest in a career in the iron and steel industry. **Application Requirements:** Applicants must submit an application form available at the website; a resume; three letters of recommendation (addressing character, academic status, leadership potential and career commitment) from a college academic advisor, professor and previous employer; transcripts; an essay (maximum of 2 pages) about the applicant's professional goals, interest in a career in the iron and steel industry, and how the applicant's skills could be applied to enhance the industry. **Additional Information:** Established in 2005 by the Steel Manufacturers Association (SMA). **Deadline for Receipt:** March 2. **Additional Information:** Lori Wharrey at lwharrey@aist.org or 724-776-6040, ext. 621.

5059 ■ ASSOCIATION FOR IRON AND STEEL TECHNOLOGY
186 Thorn Hill Rd.
Warrendale, PA 15086-7528
Tel: (724)776-6040
Fax: (724)776-1880
E-mail: info@aist.org
Web Site: http://www.aist.org
To enhance education and careers in iron and steel-related industry.
Title of Award: AIST Willy Korf Memorial Fund **Area, Field, or Subject:** Engineering; Metallurgy. **Level of Education for which Award is Granted:** Undergraduate **Number Awarded:** 3. **Funds Available:** $3,000. **Duration:** One year.
Eligibility Requirements: Applicant must be enrolled full-time in an engineering, metallurgy or materials science program at an accredited North American university; have a minimum cumulative GPA of 3.0 on a 4.0 scale; demonstrate interest in a career in the iron and steel industry. **Application Requirements:** Applicants must submit an application form available at the website; a resume; three letters of recommendation which address the applicant's character, academic status, leadership potential and career commitment from a college academic advisor, professor and previous employer; transcripts; and an essay (maximum of 2 pages) about the applicant's professional goals, interest in a career in the iron and steel industry, and how the applicant's skills could be applied to enhance the industry. **Additional Information:** Established by Korf Lurgi Steeltec, Inc. **Deadline for Receipt:** March 2. **Additional Information:** Lori Wharrey lwharrey@aist.org or 724-776-6040, ext. 621.

5060 ■ ASSOCIATION FOR IRON AND STEEL TECHNOLOGY
186 Thorn Hill Rd.
Warrendale, PA 15086-7528
Tel: (724)776-6040
Fax: (724)776-1880
E-mail: info@aist.org
Web Site: http://www.aist.org
To enhance education and careers in the iron and steel-related industries.
Title of Award: AIST Benjamin F. Fairless Scholarships (AIME) **Area, Field, or Subject:** Engineering; Metallurgy. **Level of Education for which Award is Granted:** Undergraduate **Number Awarded:** 11. **Funds Available:** $2,000. **Duration:** One year.
Eligibility Requirements: Applicant must be enrolled full-time in an engineering, metallurgy or materials science program at an accredited North American university; have a minimum GPA of 3.0 on a 4.0 scale; demonstrate interest toward a career in the field of iron and steel industry. **Application Requirements:** Applicant must submit an application form available at the website; a resume; an essay (maximum of 2 pages) about the applicant's professional goals, interest in a career in the steel industry, and how the applicant's skills could be applied to enhance the industry; three letters of recommendation (addressing the character, academic status, leadership potential and career commitment) from a college academic advisor, professor and previous employer; and transcripts. **Additional Information:** Established in 1954. **Deadline for Receipt:** March 2. **Additional Information:** Lori Wharrey at lwharrey@aist.org or 724-776-6040 ext. 621.

5061 ■ ASSOCIATION FOR IRON AND STEEL TECHNOLOGY

186 Thorn Hill Rd.
Warrendale, PA 15086-7528
Tel: (724)776-6040
Fax: (724)776-1880
E-mail: info@aist.org
Web Site: http://www.aist.org
To provide educational assistance to engineering students.

Title of Award: Midwest Chapter Scholarships - Betty McKern **Area, Field, or Subject:** Engineering. **Level of Education for which Award is Granted:** Undergraduate **Number Awarded:** 1. **Funds Available:** $3,000. **Duration:** One year.

Eligibility Requirements: Applicant must be a graduating female high school student or a full-time freshman, sophomore or junior student in good academic standing from an accredited institution. **Application Requirements:** Applicants must submit an application form available at the website; a resume; a recommendation/evaluation from a counselor, teacher or professor; copy of SAT/ACT scores; transcripts; and an essay (maximum of 2 pages) describing the applicant's objectives for college and career. Requirements should be sent to: AIST Midwest Member Chapter Scholarships c/o Barry Felton 250 W US Highway 12 Burns Harbor, IN 46304. **Deadline for Receipt:** March 15. **Additional Information:** Barry Felton barry.felton@arcelormittal, 219-787-4280.

5062 ■ ASSOCIATION FOR IRON AND STEEL TECHNOLOGY

186 Thorn Hill Rd.
Warrendale, PA 15086-7528
Tel: (724)776-6040
Fax: (724)776-1880
E-mail: info@aist.org
Web Site: http://www.aist.org
To provide educational assistance to engineering students.

Title of Award: Midwest Chapter Scholarships - Don Nelson **Area, Field, or Subject:** Engineering. **Level of Education for which Award is Granted:** Undergraduate **Number Awarded:** 1. **Funds Available:** $3,000. **Duration:** One year.

Eligibility Requirements: Applicant must be a graduating high school student or a full-time freshman, sophomore or junior student in good academic standing from an accredited institution. **Application Requirements:** Applicants must submit an application form available at the website; a resume; a recommendation/evaluation from a counselor, teacher or professor; copy of SAT/ACT scores; copy of transcripts; and an essay (maximum of 2 pages) describing the applicant's objectives for college and career. Requirements should be sent to: AIST Midwest Member Chapter Scholarships c/o Barry Felton 250 W US Highway 12 Burns Harbor, IN 46304. **Deadline for Receipt:** March 15. **Additional Information:** Barry Felton barry.felton@arcelormittal, 219-787-4280.

5063 ■ ASSOCIATION FOR IRON AND STEEL TECHNOLOGY

186 Thorn Hill Rd.
Warrendale, PA 15086-7528
Tel: (724)776-6040
Fax: (724)776-1880
E-mail: info@aist.org
Web Site: http://www.aist.org
To provide educational assistance to engineering students.

Title of Award: Midwest Chapter Scholarships - Engineering **Area, Field, or Subject:** Engineering. **Level of Education for which Award is Granted:** Undergraduate **Number Awarded:** 2. **Funds Available:** $1,500. **Duration:** One year.

Eligibility Requirements: Applicant must be a graduating high school student or a full-time freshman, sophomore or junior student in good academic standing from an accredited institution. **Application Requirements:** Applicants must submit an application form available at the website; a resume; a recommendation/evaluation from a counselor, teacher or professor; copy of SAT/ACT scores; a copy of transcripts; and an essay (maximum of 2 pages) describing the applicant's objectives for college and career. Requirements should be sent to: AIST Midwest Member Chapter Scholarships c/o Barry Felton 250 W US Highway 12 Burns Harbor, IN 46304. **Deadline for Receipt:** March 15. **Additional Information:** Barry Felton barry.felton@arcelormittal, 219-787-4280.

5064 ■ ASSOCIATION FOR IRON AND STEEL TECHNOLOGY

186 Thorn Hill Rd.
Warrendale, PA 15086-7528
Tel: (724)776-6040
Fax: (724)776-1880
E-mail: info@aist.org
Web Site: http://www.aist.org
To provide educational assistance to engineering students.

Title of Award: Midwest Chapter Scholarships - Jack Gill **Area, Field, or Subject:** Engineering. **Level of Education for which Award is Granted:** Undergraduate **Number Awarded:** 1. **Funds Available:** $3,000. **Duration:** One year.

Eligibility Requirements: Applicant must be a graduating high school student or a full-time freshman, sophomore or junior student in good academic standing from an accredited institution. **Application Requirements:** Applicants must submit an application form available at the website; a resume; a recommendation/evaluation from a counselor, teacher or professor; copy of SAT/ACT scores; copy of transcripts; and an essay (maximum of 2 pages) describing the applicant's objectives for college and career. Requirements should be sent to: AIST Midwest Member Chapter Scholarships c/o Barry Felton 250 W US Highway 12 Burns Harbor, IN 46304. **Deadline for Receipt:** March 15. **Additional Information:** Barry Felton barry.felton@arcelormittal, 219-787-4280.

5065 ■ ASSOCIATION FOR IRON AND STEEL TECHNOLOGY

186 Thorn Hill Rd.
Warrendale, PA 15086-7528
Tel: (724)776-6040
Fax: (724)776-1880
E-mail: info@aist.org
Web Site: http://www.aist.org
To provide educational assistance to engineering students.

Title of Award: Midwest Chapter Scholarships - Mel Nickel **Area, Field, or Subject:** Engineering. **Level of Education for which Award is Granted:** Undergraduate **Number Awarded:** 1. **Funds Available:** $3,000. **Duration:** One year.

Eligibility Requirements: Applicant must be a graduating high school student or a full-time freshman, sophomore or junior student in good academic standing from an accredited institution. **Application Requirements:** Applicants must submit an application form available at the website; a resume; a recommendation/evaluation from a counselor, teacher or professor; copy of SAT/ACT scores; copy of transcripts; and an essay (maximum of 2 pages) describing the applicant's objectives for college and career. Requirements should be sent to: AIST Midwest Member Chapter Scholarships c/o Barry Felton 250 W US Highway 12 Burns Harbor, IN 46304. **Deadline for Receipt:** March 15. **Additional Information:** Barry Felton barry.felton@arcelormittal, 219-787-4280.

5066 ■ ASSOCIATION FOR IRON AND STEEL TECHNOLOGY

186 Thorn Hill Rd.
Warrendale, PA 15086-7528
Tel: (724)776-6040
Fax: (724)776-1880
E-mail: info@aist.org
Web Site: http://www.aist.org
To provide educational assistance to students who wish to pursue their education and career in engineering and metallurgy.

Title of Award: Northeastern Ohio Chapter Scholarships - Alfred B. Glossbrenner and John Klusch Scholarships **Area, Field, or Subject:** Engineering; Metallurgy. **Level of Education for which Award is Granted:** Undergraduate **Number Awarded:** 1. **Funds Available:** $2,000. **Duration:** One year.

Eligibility Requirements: Applicant must be a dependent of an at least two-year member of the Association for Iron and Steel Technology, which must be a U.S. citizen or a U.S landed immigrant. Applicant should also be a full-time student from an accredited North American University; pursuing education in the field of engineering or metallurgy. Chemistry, geology, mathematics or physics students are also qualified for the scholarships. **Application Requirements:** Applicants must submit an application form available at the website; a resume; a recommendation/ evaluation from a counselor, teacher or professor; copy of SAT/ACT scores; copy of transcripts; and an essay (maximum of 2 pages) with one of the topics: Purpose in going to college; beneficial experience during the last two summers; most significant experiences and effect on future plans; accomplishments providing the greatest satisfaction; reason why the applicant should be chosen as the recipient of the award. All documents and application should be sent to: Richard J. Kurz, Chapter Secretary AIST Northeastern Ohio Chapter 22831 East State Street, Rte. 62 Alliance, Ohio 44601. **Deadline for Receipt:** April 30. **Additional Information:** Richard J. Kurz at rkurz@eohiomach.com, 330-821-7198 ext.109.

5067 ■ ASSOCIATION FOR IRON AND STEEL TECHNOLOGY
186 Thorn Hill Rd.
Warrendale, PA 15086-7528
Tel: (724)776-6040
Fax: (724)776-1880
E-mail: info@aist.org
Web Site: http://www.aist.org
To enhance education and careers in engineering, metallurgy, physical science, computer technology or an engineering technology field.
Title of Award: Ohio Valley Chapter Scholarships **Area, Field, or Subject:** Engineering; Metallurgy; Physical sciences. **Level of Education for which Award is Granted:** Undergraduate **Number Awarded:** 2. **Funds Available:** $1,000. **Duration:** One year.
Eligibility Requirements: Applicant must be a dependent or member of Ohio Valley Chapter of the AIST; planning to attend or currently enrolled full-time curriculum at an accredited university or college; pursuing a degree in Mechanical Engineering, Electrical Engineering, Engineering/Engineering Technology, Environmental Engineering/Sciences, Metallurgy, Physical Sciences, Computer Technology, Computer Programming, Information Systems Technology, Chemistry, Biology/Microbiology, Physics, other engineering-related fields, or other related fields approved by the committee. **Application Requirements:** Applicants must submit an application form available at the website; a resume; a recommendation/evaluation from a counselor and teacher or professor; copy of SAT/ACT scores; copy of transcripts; an essay (maximum of 2 pages) with either one of the topics: purpose in going to college; beneficial experience during the last two summers; most significant experiences and effect on future plans; accomplishments providing the greatest satisfaction; reasons why he/she should be chosen as the recipient of the award. All requirements must be sent to: Jeff McKain, 11451 Reading Road Cincinnati, OH 45241. Or thru email, Attn: AIST Scholarship, E-mail subject: AIST Scholarship to jeff.mckain@xtek.com. **Deadline for Receipt:** March 31. **Additional Information:** Jeff Mckain 513-200-3000.

5068 ■ ASSOCIATION FOR IRON AND STEEL TECHNOLOGY
186 Thorn Hill Rd.
Warrendale, PA 15086-7528
Tel: (724)776-6040
Fax: (724)776-1880
E-mail: info@aist.org
Web Site: http://www.aist.org
To provide financial support for Canadian students who are pursuing a career in engineering.
Title of Award: AIST David H. Samson Scholarships **Area, Field, or Subject:** Engineering. **Level of Education for which Award is Granted:** Undergraduate **Number Awarded:** 1. **Funds Available:** $2,000.
Eligibility Requirements: Applicant must be a dependent of a Canadian citizen or an immigrant who is a commendable member of the Association for Iron and Steel Technology; must be attending full-time engineering course at an accredited Canadian university or college. Chemistry, geology, mathematics or physics students are also welcome for the scholarships. **Application Requirements:** Applicant must submit an application form available at the website; a resume; a recommendation/evaluation (from a counselor, teacher or professor); a copy of SAT/ACT scores; a copy of current transcripts; an essay (1-2 pages) with either one of the topics: purpose in going to college; beneficial experience during the last two summers, most significant experiences and effect on future plans; accomplishments providing the greatest satisfaction; reasons why he/she should be chosen as the recipient of the award. All requirements should be sent to: Robert Kneale, AIST Northern Member Chapter, David H. Samson Canadian Scholarship PO Box 1734 Cambridge, ON NIR7G8 Canada. **Additional Information:** Managed by the AIST Northern Member Chapter. **Deadline for Receipt:** June 30. **Additional Information:** Robert Kneale at 519-740-2488, bkneale@gerdauameristeel.com.

5069 ■ ASSOCIATION FOR IRON AND STEEL TECHNOLOGY
186 Thorn Hill Rd.
Warrendale, PA 15086-7528
Tel: (724)776-6040
Fax: (724)776-1880
E-mail: info@aist.org
Web Site: http://www.aist.org
To provide educational assistance to students who are planning a career in Engineering or the sciences.
Title of Award: Southeast Member Chapter Scholarships **Area, Field, or Subject:** Engineering. **Level of Education for which Award is Granted:** Undergraduate **Number Awarded:** 1. **Funds Available:** $1,500. **Duration:** One year.
Eligibility Requirements: Applicant must be a Southeast Chapter student; planning to take up courses in engineering, sciences or other majors related to iron and steel production. **Application Requirements:** Applicants must submit an application form available at the website; a resume; a recommendation/evaluation from a counselor, teacher or professor; copy of SAT/ACT scores; copy of transcripts; and an essay (maximum of 250 words) discussing the applicant's involvement in high school and the reason why the applicant deserves the scholarship. All documents together with the application should be sent to: AIST Southeast Chapter Mike Hutson, Secretary 803 Floyd St., Kings Mountain, NC, 29086. **Deadline for Receipt:** April 30. **Additional Information:** Mike Hutson at mike@johnhutsoncompany.com.

5070 ■ ASSOCIATION OF STATE DAM SAFETY OFFICIALS
450 Old Vine St.
Lexington, KY 40507
Tel: (859)257-5140
Fax: (859)323-1958
E-mail: info@damsafety.org
Web Site: http://www.damsafety.org
To promote the study of civil engineering and related fields as a career.
Title of Award: ASDSO Undergraduate Scholarships **Area, Field, or Subject:** Engineering, Civil. **Level of Education for which Award is Granted:** Undergraduate **Funds Available:** A maximum of $10,000. **Duration:** One year.
Eligibility Requirements: Applicant must be a U.S. citizen; enrolled in a civil engineering program and in their senior year; pursuing a career in hydraulics, hydrology or geotechnical disciplines or related to design, construction and operation of dams; have 2.5 GPA for the first three years in college and recommended by advisor. **Application Requirements:** Applicant must send application form; transcript; three letters of recommendation; essay about what is ASDSO and why is dam safety important and include proposed curriculum study. **Deadline for Receipt:** March29.

5071 ■ ASSOCIATION FOR WOMEN IN SCIENCE
1200 New York Ave. NW, Ste. 650
Washington, DC 20005
Tel: (202)326-8940
Fax: (202)326-8960
E-mail: awis@awis.org
Web Site: http://www.awis.org
To promote education in science.
Title of Award: AWIS College Scholarships **Area, Field, or Subject:** Astronomy and astronomical sciences; Geosciences; Biology; Mathematics and mathematical sciences; Chemistry; Physics; Computer and information sciences; Engineering; Psychology. **Level of Education for which Award is Granted:** Undergraduate **Number Awarded:** 2-5. **Funds Available:** No specific amount.
Eligibility Requirements: Applicant must be a female high school senior; U.S. citizen or permanent resident; have at least 3.75 GPA; at least 1200 score in SAT or a composite score of 25 in ACT; planning to study in any field of Astronomy, Geoscience, Biology, Mathematics, Chemistry, Physics, Computer and Information Science, Engineering, Psychology; planning to become a researcher or teacher. **Application Requirements:** Applicants must send five copies of: summary form; essay describing research experience; resume; two recommendation letters from science or research teachers; high school transcript and score of standardized test if available. **Deadline for Receipt:** January 17.

5072 ■ ASTRONAUT SCHOLARSHIP FOUNDATION
6225 Vectorspace Blvd.
Titusville, FL 32780
Fax: (321)264-9176
Web Site: http://www.astronautscholarship.org
To support the promising students who want to pursue their masters in the fields of science and engineering.
Title of Award: Astronaut Scholarship Foundation Scholarships **Area, Field, or Subject:** Science; Engineering; Applied mathematics. **Level of Education for which Award is Granted:** Undergraduate **Funds Available:** No specific amount. **Duration:** One year.
Eligibility Requirements: Applicants must be nominated by faculty members; must be U.S citizens; must be engineering or natural or applied science majors, or mathematics students intending to pursue research or advance their field upon completion of their final degree; must be junior, senior or master's students; must have shown initiative, creativity, and excellence in their chosen field. **Application Requirements:** For further information, applicants are advised to contact the Astronaut Scholarship Foundation, 6225 Vectorspace Blvd., Titusville, FL 32780.

5073 ■ AUDIO ENGINEERING SOCIETY
60 E 42nd St., Ste. 2520
New York, NY 10165
Tel: (212)661-8528
Fax: (212)682-0477
E-mail: hq@aes.org
Web Site: http://www.aes.org
To encourage entry of talented students into the profession of audio engineering and related fields.
Title of Award: Audio Engineering Society Educational Foundation Scholarships **Area, Field, or Subject:** Engineering. **Level of Education for which Award is Granted:** Undergraduate **Funds Available:** No specific amount.
Eligibility Requirements: Applicants must have successfully completed an undergraduate degree program (typically four years) at a recognized college or university; a demonstrated commitment to audio engineering or related fields as a career choice; acceptance or a pending application for graduate studies leading to a masters or higher degree, or an internationally recognized equivalent. **Application Requirements:** Applicants must submit two current letters of recommendation (one must be from major professor or academic advisors); a cover page; essays on past achievements and future plans; and list of references. **Deadline for Receipt:** March 15.

5074 ■ AUTOMOTIVE AFTERMARKET INDUSTRY ASSOCIATION
7101 Wisconsin Ave., Ste. 1300
Bethesda, MD 20814-3415
Tel: (301)654-6664
Fax: (301)654-3299
E-mail: aaia@aftermarket.org
Web Site: http://www.aftermarket.org
To further promote quality and high standards through education within the automotive aftermarket industry.
Title of Award: APSAIL's Ralph Silverman Memorial Scholarships **Area, Field, or Subject:** Automotive technology. **Level of Education for which Award is Granted:** Undergraduate **Number Awarded:** 6. **Funds Available:** $500. **Duration:** 4 years.
Eligibility Requirements: Applicants must be students who intend to pursue a career in the automotive aftermarket industry. **Application Requirements:** Applicants must submit a complete application form. **Deadline for Receipt:** June 30.

5075 ■ AUTOMOTIVE AFTERMARKET INDUSTRY ASSOCIATION
7101 Wisconsin Ave., Ste. 1300
Bethesda, MD 20814-3415
Tel: (301)654-6664
Fax: (301)654-3299
E-mail: aaia@aftermarket.org
Web Site: http://www.aftermarket.org
To develop quality technicians, managers, and shop owners.
Title of Award: AVI Scholarships **Area, Field, or Subject:** Automotive technology. **Level of Education for which Award is Granted:** Undergraduate **Funds Available:** $1,000.

Eligibility Requirements: Applicants must be 21 years of age; must have a minimum of two years work experience in the mechanical repair industry; must demonstrate an interest in self-improvement through education and training. If an applicant is not a business owner, he/she must be recommended by a business owner. **Application Requirements:** Applicants must submit a complete application form. **Deadline for Receipt:** August 17.

5076 ■ AUTOMOTIVE AFTERMARKET INDUSTRY ASSOCIATION
7101 Wisconsin Ave., Ste. 1300
Bethesda, MD 20814-3415
Tel: (301)654-6664
Fax: (301)654-3299
E-mail: aaia@aftermarket.org
Web Site: http://www.aftermarket.org
To provide and promote practical business management service.
Title of Award: Florida Automotive Industry Scholarships **Area, Field, or Subject:** Automotive technology. **Level of Education for which Award is Granted:** Undergraduate **Funds Available:** No specific amount.
Eligibility Requirements: Applicants must be high school seniors, or high school graduates, or persons possessing a GED. **Application Requirements:** Applicants must submit a complete application form. **Additional Information:** 813-962-4445.

5077 ■ AUTOMOTIVE AFTERMARKET INDUSTRY ASSOCIATION
7101 Wisconsin Ave., Ste. 1300
Bethesda, MD 20814-3415
Tel: (301)654-6664
Fax: (301)654-3299
E-mail: aaia@aftermarket.org
Web Site: http://www.aftermarket.org
To provide and promote practical business management service.
Title of Award: Sloan Northwood Heavy-Duty Scholarships **Area, Field, or Subject:** Automotive technology. **Level of Education for which Award is Granted:** Undergraduate **Funds Available:** No specific amount.
Eligibility Requirements: Applicants must be enrolled in the university's Automotive Aftermarket Management curriculum, Heavy Duty Management program or the Heavy Duty Vehicle Technology program; must be U.S. citizens and maintain a 2.5 cumulative grade point average. **Application Requirements:** Applicants must submit a complete application form. **Additional Information:** 616-395-5620.

5078 ■ AUTOMOTIVE HALL OF FAME
21400 Oakwood Blvd.
Dearborn, MI 48124
Tel: (313)240-4000
Fax: (313)240-8641
Web Site: http://www.automotivehalloffame.org
To financially support students pursuing education in an automotive related career.
Title of Award: Larry H. Averill Memorial Scholarships **Area, Field, or Subject:** Automotive technology; Engineering, Automotive. **Level of Education for which Award is Granted:** Undergraduate **Funds Available:** No specific amount.
Eligibility Requirements: Applicant must be an upper level undergraduate; interested in careers in automotive; have a 3.0 GPA; enrolled full-time at an accredited college or university; and have demonstrated financial need. **Application Requirements:** Application form is available at the website or send a letter of request with a self-addressed stamped envelope. Applicants must submit a completed application form; an official transcript; two recommendation letters; and a letter of acceptance for an associate, bachelor or masters program. Send all materials to: Automotive Hall of Fame, Scholarship Programs 21400 Oakwood Blvd. Dearborn, MI 48124. **Deadline for Receipt:** May 30.

5079 ■ AUTOMOTIVE HALL OF FAME
21400 Oakwood Blvd.
Dearborn, MI 48124
Tel: (313)240-4000
Fax: (313)240-8641
Web Site: http://www.automotivehalloffame.org

To financially support students pursuing education in an automotive related career.
Title of Award: Harold Dieckmann Draper, Sr. Scholarships **Area, Field, or Subject:** Automotive technology; Engineering, Automotive. **Level of Education for which Award is Granted:** Undergraduate **Funds Available:** No specific amount.
Eligibility Requirements: Applicant must be an upper level undergraduate; interested in careers in automotive; have a 3.4 GPA; enrolled full-time at an accredited college or university; and have demonstrated financial need. **Application Requirements:** Application form is available at the website or send a letter of request with a self-addressed stamped envelope. Applicants must submit a completed application form; an official transcript; two recommendation letters; and a letter of acceptance for an associate, bachelor or masters program. Send all materials to: Automotive Hall of Fame, Scholarship Programs 21400 Oakwood Blvd. Dearborn, MI 48124. **Deadline for Receipt:** May 30.

5080 ■ AUTOMOTIVE HALL OF FAME
21400 Oakwood Blvd.
Dearborn, MI 48124
Tel: (313)240-4000
Fax: (313)240-8641
Web Site: http://www.automotivehalloffame.org
To financially support students pursuing education in an automotive related career.
Title of Award: John E. Echlin Memorial Scholarships **Area, Field, or Subject:** Automotive technology; Engineering, Automotive. **Level of Education for which Award is Granted:** Undergraduate **Funds Available:** No specific amount.
Eligibility Requirements: Applicant must be an upper level undergraduate; interested in careers in automotive; have a 3.0 GPA; enrolled full-time at an accredited college or university; and have demonstrated financial need. **Application Requirements:** Application form is available at the website or send a letter of request with a self-addressed stamped envelope. Applicants must submit a completed application form; an official transcript; two recommendation letters; and a letter of acceptance for an associate, bachelor or masters program. Send all materials to: Automotive Hall of Fame, Scholarship Programs 21400 Oakwood Blvd. Dearborn, MI 48124. **Deadline for Receipt:** May 30.

5081 ■ AUTOMOTIVE HALL OF FAME
21400 Oakwood Blvd.
Dearborn, MI 48124
Tel: (313)240-4000
Fax: (313)240-8641
Web Site: http://www.automotivehalloffame.org
To financially support students pursuing education in an automotive related career.
Title of Award: Carlyle Fraser/Wilton Looney Scholarships **Area, Field, or Subject:** Automotive technology; Engineering, Automotive. **Level of Education for which Award is Granted:** Undergraduate **Funds Available:** No specific amount.
Eligibility Requirements: Applicant must be an upper level undergraduate; interested in careers in automotive; have a 3.4 GPA; enrolled full-time at an accredited college or university; and have demonstrated financial need. **Application Requirements:** Application form is available at the website or send a letter of request with a self-addressed stamped envelope. Applicants must submit a completed application form; an official transcript; two recommendation letters; and a letter of acceptance for an associate, bachelor or masters program. Send all materials to: Automotive Hall of Fame, Scholarship Programs 21400 Oakwood Blvd. Dearborn, MI 48124. **Deadline for Receipt:** May 30.

5082 ■ AUTOMOTIVE HALL OF FAME
21400 Oakwood Blvd.
Dearborn, MI 48124
Tel: (313)240-4000
Fax: (313)240-8641
Web Site: http://www.automotivehalloffame.org
To financially support students pursuing education in an automotive related career.
Title of Award: John Goerlich Memorial Scholarships **Area, Field, or Subject:** Automotive technology; Engineering, Automotive. **Level of**

Education for which Award is Granted: Undergraduate **Funds Available:** No specific amount.
Eligibility Requirements: Applicant must be an upper level undergraduate; interested in careers in automotive; have a 3.4 GPA; enrolled full-time at an accredited college or university; and have demonstrated financial need. **Application Requirements:** Application form is available at the website or send a letter of request with a self-addressed stamped envelope. Applicants must submit a completed application form; an official transcript; two recommendation letters; and a letter of acceptance for an associate, bachelor or masters program. Send all materials to: Automotive Hall of Fame, Scholarship Programs 21400 Oakwood Blvd. Dearborn, MI 48124. **Deadline for Receipt:** May 30.

5083 ■ AUTOMOTIVE HALL OF FAME
21400 Oakwood Blvd.
Dearborn, MI 48124
Tel: (313)240-4000
Fax: (313)240-8641
Web Site: http://www.automotivehalloffame.org
To financially support students pursuing education in an automotive related career.
Title of Award: Charles V. Hagler Scholarships **Area, Field, or Subject:** Automotive technology; Engineering, Automotive. **Level of Education for which Award is Granted:** Undergraduate **Funds Available:** No specific amount.
Eligibility Requirements: Applicant must be an interested in careers in automotive; have a 3.0 GPA; enrolled full-time at an accredited college or university; and have demonstrated financial need. **Application Requirements:** Application form is available at the website or send a letter of request with a self-addressed stamped envelope. Applicants must submit a completed application form; an official transcript; two recommendation letters; and a letter of acceptance for an associate, bachelor or masters program. Send all materials to: Automotive Hall of Fame, Scholarship Programs 21400 Oakwood Blvd. Dearborn, MI 48124. **Deadline for Receipt:** May 30.

5084 ■ AUTOMOTIVE HALL OF FAME
21400 Oakwood Blvd.
Dearborn, MI 48124
Tel: (313)240-4000
Fax: (313)240-8641
Web Site: http://www.automotivehalloffame.org
To financially support students pursuing education in an automotive related career.
Title of Award: Zenon C.R. Hansen Memorial Scholarships **Area, Field, or Subject:** Automotive technology; Engineering, Automotive. **Level of Education for which Award is Granted:** Undergraduate **Funds Available:** No specific amount.
Eligibility Requirements: Applicant must be an upper level undergraduate; interested in careers in automotive/trucking; have a 3.4 GPA; enrolled full-time at an accredited college or university; and have demonstrated financial need. **Application Requirements:** Application form is available at the website or send a letter of request with a self-addressed stamped envelope. Applicants must submit a completed application form; an official transcript; two recommendation letters; and a letter of acceptance for an associate, bachelor or masters program. Send all materials to: Automotive Hall of Fame, Scholarship Programs 21400 Oakwood Blvd. Dearborn, MI 48124. **Deadline for Receipt:** May 30.

5085 ■ AUTOMOTIVE HALL OF FAME
21400 Oakwood Blvd.
Dearborn, MI 48124
Tel: (313)240-4000
Fax: (313)240-8641
Web Site: http://www.automotivehalloffame.org
To financially support students pursuing education in an automotive related career.
Title of Award: John W. Koons, Sr. Memorial Scholarships **Area, Field, or Subject:** Automotive technology; Engineering, Automotive. **Level of Education for which Award is Granted:** Undergraduate **Funds Available:** No specific amount.
Eligibility Requirements: Applicant must be an upper level undergraduate; interested in careers in automotive; have a 3.4 GPA; enrolled full-time

at an accredited college or university; and have demonstrated financial need. **Application Requirements:** Application form is available at the website or send a letter of request with a self-addressed stamped envelope. Applicants must submit a completed application form; an official transcript; two recommendation letters; and a letter of acceptance for an associate, bachelor or masters program. Send all materials to: Automotive Hall of Fame, Scholarship Programs 21400 Oakwood Blvd. Dearborn, MI 48124. **Deadline for Receipt:** May 30.

5086 ■ AUTOMOTIVE HALL OF FAME
21400 Oakwood Blvd.
Dearborn, MI 48124
Tel: (313)240-4000
Fax: (313)240-8641
Web Site: http://www.automotivehalloffame.org
To financially support students pursuing education in an automotive related career.
Title of Award: Ken Krum/Bud Kouts Memorial Scholarships **Area, Field, or Subject:** Automotive technology; Engineering, Automotive. **Level of Education for which Award is Granted:** Undergraduate **Funds Available:** No specific amount.
Eligibility Requirements: Applicant must be an upper level undergraduate; interested in careers in automotive; have a 3.0 GPA; enrolled full-time at an accredited college or university; and have demonstrated financial need. **Application Requirements:** Application form is available at the website or send a letter of request with a self-addressed stamped envelope. Applicants must submit a completed application form; an official transcript; two recommendation letters; and a letter of acceptance for an associate, bachelor or masters program. Send all materials to: Automotive Hall of Fame, Scholarship Programs 21400 Oakwood Blvd. Dearborn, MI 48124. **Deadline for Receipt:** May 30.

5087 ■ AUTOMOTIVE HALL OF FAME
21400 Oakwood Blvd.
Dearborn, MI 48124
Tel: (313)240-4000
Fax: (313)240-8641
Web Site: http://www.automotivehalloffame.org
To financially support students pursuing education in an automotive related career.
Title of Award: Brouwer D. McIntyre Memorial Scholarships **Area, Field, or Subject:** Automotive technology; Engineering, Automotive. **Level of Education for which Award is Granted:** Undergraduate **Funds Available:** No specific amount.
Eligibility Requirements: Applicant must be an upper level undergraduate; interested in careers in automotive replacement parts industry; have a 3.0 GPA; enrolled full-time at Northwood University; and have demonstrated financial need. **Application Requirements:** Application form is available at the website or send a letter of request with a self-addressed stamped envelope. Applicants must submit a completed application form; an official transcript; two recommendation letters; and a letter of acceptance for an associate, bachelor or masters program. Send all materials to: Automotive Hall of Fame, Scholarship Programs 21400 Oakwood Blvd. Dearborn, MI 48124. **Deadline for Receipt:** May 30.

5088 ■ AUTOMOTIVE HALL OF FAME
21400 Oakwood Blvd.
Dearborn, MI 48124
Tel: (313)240-4000
Fax: (313)240-8641
Web Site: http://www.automotivehalloffame.org
To financially support students pursuing education in an automotive related career.
Title of Award: Jim Moran Scholarships **Area, Field, or Subject:** Automotive technology; Engineering, Automotive. **Level of Education for which Award is Granted:** Undergraduate **Funds Available:** No specific amount.
Eligibility Requirements: Applicant must have a 2.7 GPA; enrolled full-time at Northwood University majoring in Automotive Marketing or Automotive Aftermarket; and have demonstrated financial need. **Application Requirements:** Application form is available at the website or send a letter of request with a self-addressed stamped envelope. Applicants must submit a completed application form; an official transcript; two recom-

mendation letters; and a letter of acceptance for an associate, bachelor or masters program. Send all materials to: Automotive Hall of Fame, Scholarship Programs 21400 Oakwood Blvd. Dearborn, MI 48124. **Deadline for Receipt:** May 30.

5089 ■ AUTOMOTIVE HALL OF FAME
21400 Oakwood Blvd.
Dearborn, MI 48124
Tel: (313)240-4000
Fax: (313)240-8641
Web Site: http://www.automotivehalloffame.org
To financially support students pursuing education in an automotive related career.
Title of Award: Dorothy M. Ross Memorial Scholarships **Area, Field, or Subject:** Automotive technology; Engineering, Automotive. **Level of Education for which Award is Granted:** Undergraduate **Funds Available:** No specific amount.
Eligibility Requirements: Applicant must be an undergraduate student; interested in careers in automotive; have a 3.0 GPA; and enrolled full-time at an accredited college or university. **Application Requirements:** Application form is available at the website or send a letter of request with a self-addressed stamped envelope. Applicants must submit a completed application form; an official transcript; two recommendation letters; and a letter of acceptance for an associate, bachelor or masters program. Send all materials to: Automotive Hall of Fame, Scholarship Programs 21400 Oakwood Blvd. Dearborn, MI 48124. **Deadline for Receipt:** May 30.

5090 ■ AUTOMOTIVE HALL OF FAME
21400 Oakwood Blvd.
Dearborn, MI 48124
Tel: (313)240-4000
Fax: (313)240-8641
Web Site: http://www.automotivehalloffame.org
To financially support students pursuing education in an automotive related career.
Title of Award: Stuart H. Snyder Memorial Scholarships **Area, Field, or Subject:** Automotive technology; Engineering, Automotive. **Level of Education for which Award is Granted:** Undergraduate **Funds Available:** No specific amount.
Eligibility Requirements: Applicant must be an undergraduate student; interested in careers in automotive/trucking; have a 3.0 GPA; enrolled full-time at an accredited college/university; and have demonstrated financial need. **Application Requirements:** Application form is available at the website or send a letter of request with a self-addressed stamped envelope. Applicants must submit a completed application form; an official transcript; two recommendation letters; and a letter of acceptance for an associate, bachelor or masters program. Send all materials to: Automotive Hall of Fame, Scholarship Programs 21400 Oakwood Blvd. Dearborn, MI 48124. **Deadline for Receipt:** May 30.

5091 ■ AUTOMOTIVE HALL OF FAME
21400 Oakwood Blvd.
Dearborn, MI 48124
Tel: (313)240-4000
Fax: (313)240-8641
Web Site: http://www.automotivehalloffame.org
To financially support students pursuing education in an automotive related career.
Title of Award: Society of Automotive Analyst Scholarships **Area, Field, or Subject:** Automotive technology; Engineering, Automotive; Economics; Finance; Business administration; Marketing and distribution. **Level of Education for which Award is Granted:** Undergraduate **Funds Available:** No specific amount.
Eligibility Requirements: Applicant must be an undergraduate student; interested in careers in automotive analysis; have a 3.0 GPA; and enrolled full-time at an accredited college or university majoring in economics, finance, business administration, or marketing management. **Application Requirements:** Application form is available at the website or send a letter of request with a self-addressed stamped envelope. Applicants must submit a completed application form; an official transcript; two recommendation letters; and a letter of acceptance for an associate, bachelor or masters program. Send all materials to: Automotive Hall of Fame, Scholarship Programs 21400 Oakwood Blvd. Dearborn, MI 48124. **Deadline for Receipt:** May 30.

5092 ■ AUTOMOTIVE HALL OF FAME
21400 Oakwood Blvd.
Dearborn, MI 48124
Tel: (313)240-4000
Fax: (313)240-8641
Web Site: http://www.automotivehalloffame.org
To financially support students pursuing education in an automotive related career.
Title of Award: Walter W. Stillman Scholarships **Area, Field, or Subject:** Automotive technology; Engineering, Automotive. **Level of Education for which Award is Granted:** Undergraduate **Funds Available:** No specific amount.
Eligibility Requirements: Applicant must be an upper level undergraduate; interested in careers in automotive; have a 3.0 GPA; enrolled full-time at Northwood University; and have demonstrated financial need. **Application Requirements:** Application form is available at the website or send a letter of request with a self-addressed stamped envelope. Applicants must submit a completed application form; an official transcript; two recommendation letters; and a letter of acceptance for an associate, bachelor or masters program. Send all materials to: Automotive Hall of Fame, Scholarship Programs 21400 Oakwood Blvd. Dearborn, MI 48124.
Deadline for Receipt: May 30.

5093 ■ AUTOMOTIVE HALL OF FAME
21400 Oakwood Blvd.
Dearborn, MI 48124
Tel: (313)240-4000
Fax: (313)240-8641
Web Site: http://www.automotivehalloffame.org
To financially support students pursuing education in an automotive related career.
Title of Award: TRW Foundation Scholarships **Area, Field, or Subject:** Automotive technology; Engineering, Automotive. **Level of Education for which Award is Granted:** Undergraduate **Funds Available:** No specific amount.
Eligibility Requirements: Applicant must be an undergraduate student; interested in careers in automotive; have a 3.0 GPA; enrolled full-time at an accredited college or university; a U.S. citizen; and have demonstrated financial need. **Application Requirements:** Application form is available at the website or send a letter of request with a self-addressed stamped envelope. Applicants must submit a completed application form; an official transcript; two recommendation letters; and a letter of acceptance for an associate, bachelor or masters program. Send all materials to: Automotive Hall of Fame, Scholarship Programs 21400 Oakwood Blvd. Dearborn, MI 48124. **Deadline for Receipt:** May 30.

5094 ■ AUTOMOTIVE HALL OF FAME
21400 Oakwood Blvd.
Dearborn, MI 48124
Tel: (313)240-4000
Fax: (313)240-8641
Web Site: http://www.automotivehalloffame.org
To financially support students pursuing education in an automotive related career.
Title of Award: Universal Underwriters Scholarships **Area, Field, or Subject:** Automotive technology; Engineering, Automotive. **Level of Education for which Award is Granted:** Undergraduate **Funds Available:** No specific amount.
Eligibility Requirements: Applicant must be an upper level undergraduate; interested in careers in automotive; have a 3.0 GPA; enrolled full-time Northwood University; and have demonstrated financial need. **Application Requirements:** Application form is available at the website or send a letter of request with a self-addressed stamped envelope. Applicants must submit a completed application form; an official transcript; two recommendation letters; and a letter of acceptance for an associate, bachelor or masters program. Send all materials to: Automotive Hall of Fame, Scholarship Programs 21400 Oakwood Blvd. Dearborn, MI 48124.
Deadline for Receipt: May 30.

5095 ■ AUTOMOTIVE HALL OF FAME
21400 Oakwood Blvd.
Dearborn, MI 48124
Tel: (313)240-4000

Fax: (313)240-8641
Web Site: http://www.automotivehalloffame.org
To financially support students pursuing education in an automotive related career.
Title of Award: J. Irving Whalley Memorial Scholarships **Area, Field, or Subject:** Automotive technology; Engineering, Automotive. **Level of Education for which Award is Granted:** Undergraduate **Funds Available:** No specific amount.
Eligibility Requirements: Applicant must be an upper level undergraduate; interested in careers in automotive; have a 3.0 GPA; enrolled full-time Northwood University; and have demonstrated financial need. **Application Requirements:** Application form is available at the website or send a letter of request with a self-addressed stamped envelope. Applicants must submit a completed application form; an official transcript; two recommendation letters; and a letter of acceptance for an associate, bachelor or masters program. Send all materials to: Automotive Hall of Fame, Scholarship Programs 21400 Oakwood Blvd. Dearborn, MI 48124.
Deadline for Receipt: May 30.

5096 ■ AUTOMOTIVE HALL OF FAME
21400 Oakwood Blvd.
Dearborn, MI 48124
Tel: (313)240-4000
Fax: (313)240-8641
Web Site: http://www.automotivehalloffame.org
To financially support students pursuing education in an automotive related career.
Title of Award: M.H. Yager Memorial Scholarships **Area, Field, or Subject:** Automotive technology; Engineering, Automotive. **Level of Education for which Award is Granted:** Undergraduate **Funds Available:** No specific amount.
Eligibility Requirements: Applicant must be an upper level undergraduate; interested in careers in automotive; have a 3.4 GPA; enrolled full-time at an accredited college or university; and have demonstrated financial need. **Application Requirements:** Application form is available at the website or send a letter of request with a self-addressed stamped envelope. Applicants must submit a completed application form; an official transcript; two recommendation letters; and a letter of acceptance for an associate, bachelor or masters program. Send all materials to: Automotive Hall of Fame, Scholarship Programs 21400 Oakwood Blvd. Dearborn, MI 48124. **Deadline for Receipt:** May 30.

5097 ■ AUTOMOTIVE INDUSTRIES ASSOCIATION OF CANADA
1272 Wellington St. W
Ottawa, ON, Canada K1Y 3A7
Tel: 800-808-2920
Fax: (613)728-6021
E-mail: info.aia@aiacanada.com
Web Site: http://www.aiacanada.com
To financially support deserving secondary, college and university students intending to pursue a career in automotive aftermarket.
Title of Award: AIA and the Global Automotive Aftermarket Symposium Scholarships **Area, Field, or Subject:** Automotive technology. **Level of Education for which Award is Granted:** Undergraduate **Funds Available:** $1,000. **Duration:** One year.
Eligibility Requirements: Applicants must be graduating high school senior or have graduated from high school within the past two years; must be enrolled in a college-level program, university or an accredited automotive technical program through either a CAMPE college or a CARS-approved institute; must be attending a full-time program in Canada or the United States. **Application Requirements:** Application forms are available at the website. Applicants must prepare a copy of the current school transcript with official school seal; must submit an essay (at least 250 words in length, no longer than one page, double-spaced); letter of recommendation (from a non-family member, preferably an employer, teacher or someone other than a family friend). **Deadline for Receipt:** June 15.

5098 ■ AUTOMOTIVE WOMEN'S ALLIANCE FOUNDATION
PO Box 4305
Troy, MI 48099
Tel: (248)643-6590
Fax: (248)643-9685

Web Site: http://www.automotivewomensalliance.com
To support the advancement of automotive professionals and motivate current and future students studying an automotive related field.
Title of Award: Automotive Women's Alliance Foundation Scholarships **Area, Field, or Subject:** Automotive technology. **Level of Education for which Award is Granted:** Undergraduate **Funds Available:** $2,000.
Eligibility Requirements: Candidates must be high school seniors preparing to enter college, current college students, those starting postgraduate work, or women in the workforce looking to enhance their current positions through additional education. **Application Requirements:** Candidates must submit complete application letter.

5099 ■ BLACK WOMEN IN SISTERHOOD FOR ACTION

PO Box 1592
Washington, DC 20013
Tel: (202)543-6013
Fax: (202)543-5719
E-mail: info@bisa-hq.org
Web Site: http://www.bisa-hq.org
To provide financial assistance to offset the cost of education for qualified students who have been accepted by an accredited college or university.
Title of Award: Richard Gregory Freeland, II Educational Scholarships **Area, Field, or Subject:** Computer and information sciences; Engineering; Telecommunications systems; Business administration. **Level of Education for which Award is Granted:** High School **Funds Available:** $500 to $2,500.
Eligibility Requirements: Applicants must be graduating high school students of African American ethnicity; reside in Maryland, Washington, DC or the Northern Virginia area; hold a grade point average of 2.5 or above; be pursuing a degree in the areas of computer science, information management, engineering, telecommunications, business management/administration or another technology-related field. **Application Requirements:** Applicants must submit all the required application information. **Deadline for Receipt:** May 5.

5100 ■ CAMECO CORPORATION

2121-11th St. W
Saskatoon, SK, Canada S7M 1J3
Tel: (306)956-6290
Fax: (306)956-6201
Web Site: http://www.cameco.com
To provide financial support to a Saskatchewan aboriginal student who wants to pursue their studies.
Title of Award: Bernard Michel Scholarships **Area, Field, or Subject:** Engineering; Liberal arts. **Level of Education for which Award is Granted:** Undergraduate **Funds Available:** $20,000. **Duration:** One year.
Eligibility Requirements: Applicant must be a Saskatchewan aboriginal student entering his or her first or second year of study within the Colleges of Engineering, Commerce, or Arts and Science at the University of Saskatchewan. **Application Requirements:** Applicant must complete the application form available online and must be sent to University of Saskatchewan, 105 Administration Place, Saskatoon, SK S7N 5A2. **Deadline for Receipt:** June 1.

5101 ■ CANADIAN ENGINEERING MEMORIAL FOUNDATION

PO Box 370
Renfrew, ON, Canada K7V 4A6
(866)883-2363
Fax: (613)432-6840
E-mail: info@cemf.ca
Web Site: http://www.cemf.ca
To provide financial assistance to qualified individuals who want to pursue their studies.
Title of Award: AMEC Aboriginal Undergraduate Scholarships **Area, Field, or Subject:** Engineering. **Level of Education for which Award is Granted:** Undergraduate **Funds Available:** $5,000. **Duration:** One year.
Eligibility Requirements: Applicants must be women who are pursuing their studies in an accredited university engineering program. **Application Requirements:** For further information and requirements about the scholarship, applicants are advised to contact the Canadian Engineering Memorial Foundation at PO Box 370, Refrew, ON K7V 4A6.

5102 ■ CANADIAN ENGINEERING MEMORIAL FOUNDATION

PO Box 370
Renfrew, ON, Canada K7V 4A6
(866)883-2363
Fax: (613)432-6840
E-mail: info@cemf.ca
Web Site: http://www.cemf.ca
To provide financial assistance to qualified individuals who want to pursue their studies.
Title of Award: CEMF Undergraduate Engineering Scholarships **Area, Field, or Subject:** Engineering. **Level of Education for which Award is Granted:** Undergraduate **Funds Available:** $5,000. **Duration:** One year.
Eligibility Requirements: Applicants must be Canadian women in engineering in either their 1st, 2nd, or 3rd year of study in an accredited program in Canada. **Application Requirements:** For further information and requirements about the scholarship, applicants are advised to contact the Canadian Engineering Memorial Foundation at PO Box 370, Refrew, ON K7V 4A6.

5103 ■ CANADIAN ENGINEERING MEMORIAL FOUNDATION

PO Box 370
Renfrew, ON, Canada K7V 4A6
(866)883-2363
Fax: (613)432-6840
E-mail: info@cemf.ca
Web Site: http://www.cemf.ca
To provide financial assistance to qualified individuals who want to pursue their studies.
Title of Award: Hewlett-Packard Undergraduate Scholarships **Area, Field, or Subject:** Engineering. **Level of Education for which Award is Granted:** Undergraduate **Funds Available:** $2,500. **Duration:** One year.
Eligibility Requirements: Applicants must be women in Canada who are pursuing their studies in engineering. **Application Requirements:** For further information and requirements about the scholarship, applicants are advised to contact the Canadian Engineering Memorial Foundation at PO Box 370, Refrew, ON K7V 4A6.

5104 ■ CANADIAN ENGINEERING MEMORIAL FOUNDATION

PO Box 370
Renfrew, ON, Canada K7V 4A6
(866)883-2363
Fax: (613)432-6840
E-mail: info@cemf.ca
Web Site: http://www.cemf.ca
To provide financial assistance to qualified individuals who want to pursue their studies.
Title of Award: IBM Canada Undergraduate Scholarships **Area, Field, or Subject:** Electrical engineering; Engineering, Computer. **Level of Education for which Award is Granted:** Undergraduate **Funds Available:** $2,500. **Duration:** One year.
Eligibility Requirements: Applicants must be Canadian women who are pursuing their undergraduate engineering studies in either electrical or computer engineering. **Application Requirements:** For further information and requirements about the scholarship, applicants are advised to contact the Canadian Engineering Memorial Foundation at PO Box 370, Refrew, ON K7V 4A6.

5105 ■ CATCHING THE DREAM

8200 Mountain Rd. NE., Ste. 203
Albuquerque, NM 87110
Tel: (505)262-2351
E-mail: nscholarships@aol.com
Web Site: http://www.catchingthedream.org
To support the education of Native Schools.
Title of Award: MESBEC Scholarships **Area, Field, or Subject:** Mathematics and mathematical sciences; Engineering; Science; Business; Education; Computer and information sciences. **Level of Education for which Award is Granted:** Undergraduate **Funds Available:** $500-$5000. **Duration:** One academic year.
Eligibility Requirements: Applicants must be 1/4 or more degree Native American; an enrolled member of a "U.S. tribe"; attending or planning to attend a college/university within the U.S. on a full-time basis that is fully accredited; studying in the field of business, finance, management,

economics, banking, hotel management, and related field; have excellent grades; high ACT or SAT scores; and have a strong commitment to their Native American community. **Application Requirements:** Applicants must submit a completed application form (available at the website); financial need analysis; a copy of the IRS 1040 Federal Tax Return for the previous year; Certificate of Native American Blood; an essay explaining career goals; three letters of recommendation; official transcripts; a copy of standardized test scores; copy of letter of admission from an accredited college or university or graduate school and degree program in the US; and a photograph (2X3) of head and shoulders. **Deadline for Receipt:** March 15, April 15, and September 15.

5106 ■ COASTAL BEND COMMUNITY FOUNDATION

600 Leopard St., Ste. 1716
Corpus Christi, TX 78473
Tel: (361)882-9745
Fax: (361)882-2865
Web Site: http://www.cbcfoundation.org
To provide financial assistance to high school seniors who are planning to pursue a career in computer/electrical engineering.
Title of Award: Zachary Barriger Memorial Scholarships **Area, Field, or Subject:** Engineering, Computer; Engineering, Electrical. **Level of Education for which Award is Granted:** High School **Number Awarded:** 1. **Funds Available:** $500.
Eligibility Requirements: Applicants must be seniors at Tuloso-Midway High School; must be attending an accredited two or four-year college in Texas; must demonstrate interest in pursuing studies in the field of engineering or medicine; and must excel academically with A/B Honor Roll status and honor classes. **Application Requirements:** Applicants must submit all the required application information. **Deadline for Receipt:** March 14.

5107 ■ COASTAL BEND COMMUNITY FOUNDATION

600 Leopard St., Ste. 1716
Corpus Christi, TX 78473
Tel: (361)882-9745
Fax: (361)882-2865
Web Site: http://www.cbcfoundation.org
To provide financial assistance to Coastal Bend students who intend to study engineering in college.
Title of Award: John R. Eidson Jr., Scholarships **Area, Field, or Subject:** Engineering. **Level of Education for which Award is Granted:** Undergraduate **Number Awarded:** 1. **Funds Available:** $1,000.
Eligibility Requirements: Applicants must be students who are in good standing with the Engineering Department; must be sophomores or higher; must exhibit academic potential; must have participated in professional and social societies; and maintained full-time status and a GPA of 3.0 higher. **Application Requirements:** Applicants must obtain application form from the financial aid office at Texas A&M University in College Station.

5108 ■ COMMUNITY FOUNDATION OF THE EASTERN SHORE

1324 Belmont Ave.
Salisbury, MD 21804
Tel: (410)742-9911
Fax: (410)742-6638
E-mail: info@cfes.org
Web Site: http://www.cfes.org
To empower donors to make a profound difference in the quality of life in Maryland's Lower Eastern Shore; to provide community leadership through grants, non-profit support programs, charitable partnerships and local initiatives in Somerset, Wicomico and Worcester counties.
Title of Award: Herb Fincher Memorial Scholarship **Area, Field, or Subject:** Engineering. **Level of Education for which Award is Granted:** Undergraduate **Funds Available:** $6,000.
Eligibility Requirements: Applicants must be graduates of the four public high schools in Wicomico County, Maryland who have been accepted into a course of study for either math or engineering; must have a reputation of good character and be well-rounded young citizens who participated in extra-curricular school or community activities. **Application Requirements:** Applicants must submit a completed application form, an official high school transcript of grades, letter of acceptance from college or university and two letters of recommendation from non-family members. **Deadline for Receipt:** April 1.

5109 ■ COMMUNITY FOUNDATION OF NORTHERN ILLINOIS

946 N 2nd St.
Rockford, IL 61107
Tel: (815)962-2110
Fax: (815)962-2116
Web Site: http://www.cfnil.org
To serve the four county area (Boone, Ogle, Stephenson and Winnebago) through philanthropy; to provide leadership in meeting charitable needs and to be a responsible steward to the Foundation's donors and of the Foundation's endowment.
Title of Award: William Pigott Memorial Scholarship **Area, Field, or Subject:** Engineering. **Level of Education for which Award is Granted:** Undergraduate **Funds Available:** No specific amount.
Eligibility Requirements: Applicants must be graduating senior students from McHenry, Boone or Winnebago county majoring in engineering. **Application Requirements:** Applicants must submit a completed application form, verification form, an official transcript in a sealed envelope and two letters of recommendation. **Deadline for Receipt:** March 1. **Additional Information:** jpatterson@cfnil.org.

5110 ■ COMPOSITE PANEL ASSOCIATION

19465 Deerfield Ave., Ste. 306
Leesburg, VA 20176
Tel: (703)724-1128
Fax: (703)724-1588
Web Site: http://www.pbmdf.com
To provide financial assistance to students pursuing a career in the composite panel and affiliated industries.
Title of Award: Robert E. Dougherty Scholarships **Area, Field, or Subject:** Forestry; Chemistry; Engineering. **Level of Education for which Award is Granted:** Undergraduate **Number Awarded:** 8. **Funds Available:** 5,000.
Eligibility Requirements: Applicant must be North American citizen; and nominated by a member of the Robert E. Dougherty Education Foundation. **Application Requirements:** Scholarship Application forms can be downloaded at the website and must be filled out and returned to the Foundation. **Deadline for Receipt:** March 21.

5111 ■ EAST TENNESSEE FOUNDATION

625 Market St., Ste. 1400
Knoxville, TN 37902
Tel: (865)524-1223; 877-524-1223
Fax: (865)637-6039
Web Site: http://www.easttennesseefoundation.org
To benefit graduating high school seniors wishing to pursue careers in science, math or pre-engineering related fields.
Title of Award: B&W Y-12 Scholarship Fund **Area, Field, or Subject:** Science; math; Engineering. **Level of Education for which Award is Granted:** Undergraduate **Number Awarded:** 1. **Funds Available:** $1,500.
Eligibility Requirements: Applicants must be enrolled as full-time students at either Roane State Community College or Pellissippi State Technical College; must be U.S citizens; must have a minimum GPA of at least 3.0. **Application Requirements:** Applicants must check the application process online. **Deadline for Receipt:** March 14. **Additional Information:** East Tennessee Foundation at the above address

5112 ■ EDIS COMPANY

PO Box 2697
Wilmington, DE 19805
Tel: (302)421-5700
Fax: (302)421-5715
Web Site: http://www.ediscompany.com
To recognize members of the community who played a part in the growth of EDiS.
Title of Award: Gen III Scholarships **Area, Field, or Subject:** Architecture; Engineering; Business. **Level of Education for which Award is Granted:** Undergraduate **Number Awarded:** 2. **Funds Available:** $1,000 renewable. **Duration:** One year.
Eligibility Requirements: Applicant must be a resident within the community in which EDiS is currently working; must not be any employee of an EDiS Company or a relative of an employee of an EDiS Company; must be pursuing either an Associate's degree or Bachelor's degree; field

of study is limited to business or construction-related degrees; and must have a cumulative GPA of 2.5 or greater for renewal. **Application Requirements:** Applicants must submit a completed scholarship application together with official transcript (from current institution), and a copy of best SAT score. **Deadline for Receipt:** May 2. **Additional Information:** Ms. Cyndi Slothour.

5113 ■ ELECTRONIC DOCUMENT SYSTEMS FOUNDATION

1845 Precinct Ln. Rd., Ste. 212
Hurst, TX 76054
Tel: (817)849-1145
Fax: (817)849-1185
E-mail: info@edsf.org
Web Site: http://www.edsf.org
To recognize and support the next generation of professionals for the document management and communication companies worldwide.
Title of Award: Electronic Document Systems Foundation Scholarships **Area, Field, or Subject:** Computer and information sciences; engineering; Communications technologies. **Level of Education for which Award is Granted:** Undergraduate **Funds Available:** No specific amount.
Eligibility Requirements: Applicants must be full-time students who are committed to pursuing careers in document management and communications marketplace which include computer science and engineering, graphic and media communications and those students interested in Business in the document management and communications industry; must have a minimum GPA of 3.0 or a 'B' average; must be technical, trade school, community college, undergraduate and advanced-degree students in the U.S. and/or diploma or tertiary students outside of the U.S. may be considered for scholarships; must be students who are attending full-time, an accredited college or university. **Application Requirements:** Applicants must submit all the required application information.

5114 ■ FABRICATORS AND MANUFACTURERS ASSOCIATION FOUNDATION

833 Featherstone Rd.
Rockford, IL 61107-6302
Tel: (815)399-8700; 888-394-4362
E-mail: foundation@fmanet.org
Web Site: http://www.fmafoundation.com
To award scholarships to students in courses of study that may lead to careers in manufacturing.
Title of Award: College and Trade/Technical School Scholarships **Area, Field, or Subject:** Manufacturing; Engineering. **Level of Education for which Award is Granted:** Undergraduate **Funds Available:** College Scholarships $2,500 for non-members; $5,000 for members. **Duration:** One year.
Eligibility Requirements: Applicant must be a full-time with a minimum cumulative 3.0 GPA for a college scholarship or cumulative 2.0 GPA for a trade/technical school scholarship, and enrolled in a manufacturing-related course of study, or a trade or technical program, that may lead to a career in manufacturing. Applicant must be a member or a non-member of the Association, students must plan to major in an engineering, trade school or manufacturing-related program that may lead to a career in manufacturing and must be accepted in an institution of higher learning college/university/technical school for the fall semester as a full-time student, FMA Foundation will verify acceptance before the award is made. **Application Requirements:** Applicants may apply online. The Association will investigate any possible misuse of funds and may withhold disbursement of scholarship awards and seek recovery of disbursement funds if misuse of funds is discovered. Recovered funds will be dedicated for charitable purposes. **Deadline for Receipt:** April 4. **Additional Information:** Fabricators and Manufacturers Association Foundation at the above address.

5115 ■ FIRST COMMUNITY FOUNDATION OF PENNSYLVANIA, WILLIAMSPORT-LYCOMING

330 Pine St., Suite 401
Williamsport, PA 17701
Tel: (570)321-1500; (866)901-2372
Fax: (570)321-6434
E-mail: fcfpa@fcfpa.org
Web Site: http://www.wlfoundation.org

To provide scholarship awards for students enrolled in a Civil Engineering curriculum.
Title of Award: Warren E. "Whitey" Cole American Society of Highway Engineers Scholarships **Area, Field, or Subject:** Civil engineering. **Level of Education for which Award is Granted:** Undergraduate **Funds Available:** No specific amount.
Eligibility Requirements: Applicants must be enrolled in a civil engineering, civil engineering technology or civil technology curriculum; have completed at least the sophomore year of a four-year curriculum or the freshman year of a two-year curriculum; be either enrolled at Pennsylvania State University, Bucknell University or Pennsylvania College of Technology or have residence in the counties of Bradford, Columbia, Lycoming, Montour, Northumberland, Snyder, Sullivan, Tioga or Union and attend another college. **Application Requirements:** Candidates must complete the application and submit it along with any requested additional information to the Williamsport-Lycoming Community Foundation. **Additional Information:** Ken Klingerman, American Society of Highway Engineers, 570-368-4231.

5116 ■ FIRST COMMUNITY FOUNDATION OF PENNSYLVANIA, WILLIAMSPORT-LYCOMING

330 Pine St., Suite 401
Williamsport, PA 17701
Tel: (570)321-1500; (866)901-2372
Fax: (570)321-6434
E-mail: fcfpa@fcfpa.org
Web Site: http://www.wlfoundation.org
To provide financial assistance for Danville Area High School seniors who have been accepted into a full-time undergraduate program.
Title of Award: Jane Hood Memorial Fund **Area, Field, or Subject:** Visual arts; Mathematics and mathematical science; Science; Engineering. **Level of Education for which Award is Granted:** Undergraduate **Funds Available:** No specific amount.
Eligibility Requirements: Applicants must be accepted in a full-time undergraduate program at an institution of higher education to study graphic-visual arts, math and/or science (including engineering). Applicants must have exhibited good citizenship and community involvement. **Application Requirements:** Applicants may request an application to the Guidance Counselor of Danville Area School District. **Additional Information:** Gary Grozier, Guidance Counselor of Danville Area School District, 600 Walnut St., Danville, PA 17821; 570-271-3268 ext. 2006; ggrozier@danville.k12.pa.us.

5117 ■ FIRST COMMUNITY FOUNDATION OF PENNSYLVANIA, WILLIAMSPORT-LYCOMING

330 Pine St., Suite 401
Williamsport, PA 17701
Tel: (570)321-1500; (866)901-2372
Fax: (570)321-6434
E-mail: fcfpa@fcfpa.org
Web Site: http://www.wlfoundation.org
To provide financial support for Danville Area High School seniors who are pursuing their studies in the field of engineering or science.
Title of Award: Gerald J. Levandoski Memorial Scholarship Fund **Area, Field, or Subject:** Engineering. **Level of Education for which Award is Granted:** Undergraduate **Funds Available:** No specific amount.
Eligibility Requirements: Applicants must have exhibited good citizenship and community involvement. **Application Requirements:** Applicants may request an application from the guidance counselor of Danville Area School District. **Additional Information:** Gary Grozier, Guidance Counselor of Danville Area School District, 600 Walnut St., Danville, PA 17821; 570-271-3268 ext. 2006; ggrozier@danville.k12.pa.us.

5118 ■ FIRST COMMUNITY FOUNDATION OF PENNSYLVANIA, WILLIAMSPORT-LYCOMING

330 Pine St., Suite 401
Williamsport, PA 17701
Tel: (570)321-1500; (866)901-2372
Fax: (570)321-6434
E-mail: fcfpa@fcfpa.org
Web Site: http://www.wlfoundation.org
To provide financial assistance for Montgomery Area High School students intending to pursue higher education in finance, engineering, business or science.

Title of Award: Robert E. and Judy More Scholarship Fund **Area, Field, or Subject:** Finance; Engineering; Business; Science. **Level of Education for which Award is Granted:** Undergraduate **Funds Available:** No specific amount.
Eligibility Requirements: Candidates must exhibit leadership qualities, academic excellence and a cooperative spirit. **Application Requirements:** Candidates must complete and submit the application. Scholarship application can be requested from Montgomery Area High School or may be downloaded from the Foundation's web site. **Deadline for Receipt:** April 15. **Additional Information:** Tara Bozella, Guidance Counselor, Montgomery Area High School, 120 Penn Street, Montgomery, PA 17752, 570-547-1608 ext. 116, tbozella@montasd.org.

5119 ■ THE FLEXIBLE PACKAGING ASSOCIATION
971 Corporate Blvd., Ste. 403
Linthicum, MD 21090
Tel: (410)694-0800
Fax: (410)694-0900
E-mail: fpa@flexpack.org
Web Site: http://www.flexpack.org
To provide a learning experience on the flexible packaging industry.
Title of Award: Flexible Packaging Academic Scholarships & Summer Internship Program **Area, Field, or Subject:** Industrial design; Industrial education. **Level of Education for which Award is Granted:** Undergraduate **Funds Available:** $3,000. **Duration:** One summer.
Eligibility Requirements: Applicants must be enrolled in an AA, BA, BS or MS degree program; have a 2.7 GPA; have 24 credit hours, 9 credits of which are in packaging, printing or other areas in the converting industry. **Application Requirements:** Applicants are advised to visit the website for the online application system. Prepare a recommendation letter from a faculty member; and an essay (maximum of 500 words). Send all materials to: Flexible Packaging Association, Attn: Lauren Kinard, 971 Corporate Blvd., Ste. 403, Linthicum, MD 21090, email to: fpa@flexpack.org. **Additional Information:** Introduced in 2005.

5120 ■ FLORIDA ENGINEERING SOCIETY
PO Box 750
Tallahassee, FL 32302-0750
Tel: (850)224-7121
Fax: (850)222-4349
E-mail: fes@fleng.org
Web Site: http://www.fleng.org
To encourage and assist students in pursuing engineering careers; to educate the public about engineering; and to promote and enhance engineering education in Florida in order to position ther state as a technological leader in global economy.
Title of Award: Cesar A. Calas/FES Miami Chapter Scholarships **Area, Field, or Subject:** Engineering. **Level of Education for which Award is Granted:** Undergraduate **Funds Available:** $1,000.
Eligibility Requirements: Applicants must be attending an accredited college of higher learning and enrolled in an engineering program approved by the Florida Engineering Society Scholarship Committee; must have at least 3.0 GPA; must maintain 12 credit hours per semester; and must be permanent residents of Miami-Dade or Monroe County. **Application Requirements:** Applicants must submit completed application form; an official transcript; and letter of recommendation from any appropriate source.

5121 ■ FLORIDA ENGINEERING SOCIETY
PO Box 750
Tallahassee, FL 32302-0750
Tel: (850)224-7121
Fax: (850)222-4349
E-mail: fes@fleng.org
Web Site: http://www.fleng.org
To encourage and assist students in pursuing engineering careers; to educate the public about engineering; and to promote and enhance engineering education in Florida in order to position the state as a technological leader in global economy.
Title of Award: Fecon Scholarships **Area, Field, or Subject:** Engineering. **Level of Education for which Award is Granted:** Undergraduate **Funds Available:** $1,000.
Eligibility Requirements: Applicant must be currently enrolled or accepted into a Florida university engineering program; must be in or entering his/her junior or senior year; must have at least 3.0 average on a 4.0 scale; must be recommended by an engineering faculty member; and must be interested in pursuing a career in the field of construction. **Application Requirements:** Applicants must submit a complete application form and an official transcript. **Deadline for Receipt:** February 15. **Additional Information:** 850-224-7121.

5122 ■ FLORIDA ENGINEERING SOCIETY
PO Box 750
Tallahassee, FL 32302-0750
Tel: (850)224-7121
Fax: (850)222-4349
E-mail: fes@fleng.org
Web Site: http://www.fleng.org
To encourage and assist students in pursuing engineering careers; to educate the public about engineering; and to promote and enhance engineering education in Florida in order to position the state as a technological leader in global economy.
Title of Award: FICE Scholarships **Area, Field, or Subject:** Engineering. **Level of Education for which Award is Granted:** Undergraduate **Funds Available:** $5,000.
Eligibility Requirements: Applicants must be U.S. citizens pursuing a bachelor's degree in an Accreditation Board Engineering and Technology (ABET) program and must be entering their junior, senior, or fifth year of college. **Application Requirements:** Applicants must submit completed application form and an official transcript. **Deadline for Receipt:** February 1.

5123 ■ FLORIDA ENGINEERING SOCIETY
PO Box 750
Tallahassee, FL 32302-0750
Tel: (850)224-7121
Fax: (850)222-4349
E-mail: fes@fleng.org
Web Site: http://www.fleng.org
To encourage and assist students in pursuing engineering careers; to educate the public about engineering; and to promote and enhance engineering education in Florida in order to position the state as a technological leader in global economy.
Title of Award: Florida Engineering Society Junior College Scholarships **Area, Field, or Subject:** Engineering. **Level of Education for which Award is Granted:** Undergraduate **Funds Available:** $1,000.
Eligibility Requirements: Applicants must be enrolled in the final year of a pre-engineering program in a Florida Junior Community College; must have at least 3.0 grade point average on a 4.0 scale; must be recommended by an engineering faculty member; and must be United States citizen or resident of Florida. **Application Requirements:** Applicants must submit a completed application form; an official transcript; and letter of recommendation from any appropriate source.

5124 ■ FLORIDA ENGINEERING SOCIETY
PO Box 750
Tallahassee, FL 32302-0750
Tel: (850)224-7121
Fax: (850)222-4349
E-mail: fes@fleng.org
Web Site: http://www.fleng.org
To encourage and assist students in pursuing engineering careers; to educate the public about engineering; and to promote and enhance engineering education in Florida in order to position the state as a technological leader in global economy.
Title of Award: Florida Engineering Society University Scholarships **Area, Field, or Subject:** Engineering. **Level of Education for which Award is Granted:** Undergraduate **Funds Available:** $30,000.
Eligibility Requirements: Applicant must be entering his or her junior or senior year in the Florida University Engineering Program; must have at least 3.0 grade point average on a 4.0 scale; must be recommended by an engineering faculty member; and must be a U.S. citizen or resident of Florida. **Application Requirements:** Applicants must submit a completed application form; an official transcript; and letter of recommendation from an engineering faculty member.

5125 ■ FLORIDA ENGINEERING SOCIETY
PO Box 750
Tallahassee, FL 32302-0750

Tel: (850)224-7121
Fax: (850)222-4349
E-mail: fes@fleng.org
Web Site: http://www.fleng.org

To encourage and assist students in pursuing engineering careers; to educate the public about engineering; and to promote and enhance engineering education in Florida in order to position the state as a technological leader in global economy.

Title of Award: David F. Ludovici Scholarships **Area, Field, or Subject:** Engineering. **Level of Education for which Award is Granted:** Undergraduate **Funds Available:** $1,000.

Eligibility Requirements: Applicants must be enrolled in an ABET accredited Florida engineering school and must be interested in civil, structural, or consulting engineering. **Application Requirements:** Applicants must submit completed application form; an official transcript; and letter of recommendation from any appropriate source.

5126 ■ FLORIDA ENGINEERING SOCIETY

PO Box 750
Tallahassee, FL 32302-0750
Tel: (850)224-7121
Fax: (850)222-4349
E-mail: fes@fleng.org
Web Site: http://www.fleng.org

To encourage and assist students in pursuing engineering careers; to educate the public about engineering; and to promote and enhance engineering education in Florida in order to position the state as a technological leader in global economy.

Title of Award: Raymond W. Miller, PE and Alice E. Miller Scholarships **Area, Field, or Subject:** Engineering. **Level of Education for which Award is Granted:** Undergraduate **Funds Available:** $1,000.

Eligibility Requirements: Applicants must be enrolled in an ABET accredited Florida engineering school and must plan to attend the University of Florida. **Application Requirements:** Applicants must submit completed application form; an official transcript; and letter of recommendation from any appropriate source.

5127 ■ FLORIDA ENGINEERING SOCIETY

PO Box 750
Tallahassee, FL 32302-0750
Tel: (850)224-7121
Fax: (850)222-4349
E-mail: fes@fleng.org
Web Site: http://www.fleng.org

To encourage and assist students in pursuing engineering careers; to educate the public about engineering; and to promote and enhance engineering education in Florida in order to position the state as a technological leader in global economy.

Title of Award: Raymond W. Miller, PE Scholarships **Area, Field, or Subject:** Engineering. **Level of Education for which Award is Granted:** Undergraduate **Funds Available:** $2,500.

Eligibility Requirements: Applicants must be enrolled in an ABET accredited Florida engineering school and must plan to attend the University of Florida. **Application Requirements:** Applicants must submit a complete application form; an official transcript; and letter of recommendation from any appropriate source.

5128 ■ FLORIDA ENGINEERING SOCIETY

PO Box 750
Tallahassee, FL 32302-0750
Tel: (850)224-7121
Fax: (850)222-4349
E-mail: fes@fleng.org
Web Site: http://www.fleng.org

To encourage and assist students in pursuing engineering careers; to educate the public about engineering; and to promote and enhance engineering education in Florida in order to position the state as a technological leader in global economy.

Title of Award: Eric Primavera Memorial Scholarships **Area, Field, or Subject:** Engineering. **Level of Education for which Award is Granted:** Undergraduate **Funds Available:** $1,000.

Eligibility Requirements: Applicants must be enrolled in an ABET accredited Florida engineering school and plan to attend the Florida Institute of Technology. **Application Requirements:** Applicants must submit completed application form; an official transcript; and letter of recommendation from any appropriate source.

5129 ■ FMA FOUNDATION

833 Featherstone Rd.
Rockford, IL 61107-6302
Tel: (815)399-8700; 888-394-4362
E-mail: foundation@fmanet.org
Web Site: http://www.fmafoundation.com

To provide financial support to students in courses of study that may lead to careers in manufacturing.

Title of Award: FMA Foundation Scholarships **Area, Field, or Subject:** Engineering; manufacturing. **Level of Education for which Award is Granted:** Undergraduate **Funds Available:** $2,500 up to $5,000.

Eligibility Requirements: Applicants must be full-time students with a minimum 3.0 GPA (for a college scholarship) or a 2.0 GPA (for a trade/technical school scholarship), enrolled in an engineering or manufacturing-related course of study, or a trade or technical program, that may lead to a career in manufacturing; or a member of FMA, TPA, or OPC the employee of a member company; or the child of a member; or the child of a member company's employee. **Application Requirements:** Applicants must submit completed online application form and other materials by the application deadline. **Deadline for Receipt:** April 4.

5130 ■ FOUNDATION FOR THE CAROLINAS

217 S Tryon St.
Charlotte, NC 28202
Tel: (704)973-4500
Free: 800-973-7244
Web Site: http://www.fftc.org

To provide scholarships for college-bound students from North and South Carolina who are pursuing a major in engineering, math, science, computer science, accounting, finance or business administration.

Title of Award: African American Network - Carolinas Scholarship Fund **Area, Field, or Subject:** Engineering; Mathematics and mathematical sciences; Science; Computer and information sciences; Accounting; Finance; Business administration. **Level of Education for which Award is Granted:** Undergraduate **Number Awarded:** 2. **Funds Available:** No specific amount. **Duration:** One year.

Eligibility Requirements: Applicants must be graduating seniors at a North or South Carolina high school; must attend a four-year college or university located in North or South Carolina; must plan to major in engineering, computer science, the sciences, accounting, finance or business administration. **Application Requirements:** Applicants must submit all the required application information.

5131 ■ FOUNDATION FOR THE CAROLINAS

217 S Tryon St.
Charlotte, NC 28202
Tel: (704)973-4500
Free: 800-973-7244
Web Site: http://www.fftc.org

To provide financial assistance for students at Clemson University and the University of North Carolina at Charlotte who are preparing for a career in a technological field appropriate to meet the requirements of the U.S. Patent Office as a patent agent or attorney.

Title of Award: Julian E. Carnes Scholarship Fund **Area, Field, or Subject:** Engineering; Chemistry; Physics; Biology; Computer and information sciences. **Level of Education for which Award is Granted:** Undergraduate **Funds Available:** No specific amount.

Eligibility Requirements: Applicants must be legal residents of North or South Carolina; must be rising juniors or seniors at Clemson University or UNC Charlotte whose academic major is appropriate to meet the requirements of the U.S. Patent Office for admission as a patent agent or attorney (including but not limited to engineering, chemistry, physics, biology and computer science); and must have at least a 3.0 cumulative grade point average (on a 4.0 scale). **Application Requirements:** Applicants must submit all the required application information. **Additional Information:** Clemson University Office of Student Financial Aid, 864-656-2280 or the UNC Charlotte Student Financial Aid Office, 704-687-2461.

5132 ■ FOUNDATION FOR ENHANCING COMMUNITIES
200 N Third St., PO Box 678
Harrisburg, PA 17108-0678
Tel: (717)236-5040
Fax: (717)231-4463
E-mail: dawn@tfec.org
Web Site: http://www.ghf.org
To assist students with college tuition expenses.
Title of Award: Ken and Romaine Kauffman Scholarship Fund **Area, Field, or Subject:** Automotive technology. **Level of Education for which Award is Granted:** Undergraduate **Funds Available:** No specific amount.
Eligibility Requirements: Students must be residents of Cumberland Perry Counties pursuing a degree in the mechanical or technical field. **Application Requirements:** Students must complete and return the application and attachments to the Foundation before the deadline. Application form can be obtained online. **Deadline for Receipt:** April 14. **Additional Information:** Dawn Morris, Program Officer at the above address.

5133 ■ FOUNDATION FOR ENHANCING COMMUNITIES
200 N Third St., PO Box 678
Harrisburg, PA 17108-0678
Tel: (717)236-5040
Fax: (717)231-4463
E-mail: dawn@tfec.org
Web Site: http://www.ghf.org
To assist students with their college tuition expenses.
Title of Award: Leon I. Lock and Barbara R. Lock Scholarship Fund **Area, Field, or Subject:** Automotive technology. **Level of Education for which Award is Granted:** Undergraduate **Funds Available:** No specific amount.
Eligibility Requirements: Applicants must be graduating seniors of a high school in the Harrisburg School District (including Bishop McDevitt High School) who will attend Harrisburg Area Community College, or Penn State, or students who have graduated from one of the two high schools in no more than five years before the year of application. **Application Requirements:** Students must complete and return the application and attachments to the Foundation before the deadline. Application form can be obtained online. **Deadline for Receipt:** April 3. **Additional Information:** Dawn Morris, Program Officer at the above address.

5134 ■ FOUNDATION FOR ENHANCING COMMUNITIES
200 N Third St., PO Box 678
Harrisburg, PA 17108-0678
Tel: (717)236-5040
Fax: (717)231-4463
E-mail: dawn@tfec.org
Web Site: http://www.ghf.org
To encourage educational pursuits by providing financial assistance.
Title of Award: Anil and Neema Thakrar Family Fund **Area, Field, or Subject:** Mathematics and mathematical science; Science; Engineering. **Level of Education for which Award is Granted:** Undergraduate **Number Awarded:** 2. **Funds Available:** No specific amount. **Duration:** Annual.
Eligibility Requirements: Program is open to students, intending to study Math, Science and Engineering, from the City of Harrisburg School District and Sci-Tech High School, or to high school students in Dauphin, Cumberland and Perry Counties intending to study in a medical-related discipline. Applicants must have a minimum of 2.5 GPA on a 4.0 scale. **Application Requirements:** Applicants must complete and submit the application and other required attachments on or before the deadline. Applicants must provide the following attachments: official transcript of complete high school/college record, including GPA, through the first half of the present year, with the raised school seal imprinted; list of most significant extracurricular or nonacademic activities, emphasizing work experience and community service. Attach a 300-word essay on the following statement: "What was my biggest life challenge and what did I learn form the experience." **Deadline for Receipt:** March 31. **Additional Information:** Dawn Morris, Program Officer at the above address.

5135 ■ GEORGIA ENGINEERING FOUNDATION
233 Peachtree St. Harris Tower, Ste. 700
Atlanta, GA 30303
Tel: (404)521-2324
Fax: (404)521-0283
Web Site: http://www.gefinc.org
To provide financial assistance to those students who are in need.
Title of Award: Georgia Engineering Foundation Scholarships **Area, Field, or Subject:** Engineering. **Level of Education for which Award is Granted:** Undergraduate **Funds Available:** Ranging from $1,000-$5,000.
Eligibility Requirements: Applicants must be Georgia students who are preparing for a career in engineering or engineering technology; must be U.S citizens; must be enrolled in an engineering or engineering technology ABET-accredited program leading to a B.S or graduate degree. **Application Requirements:** Applicants must check the available website for the required materials. **Deadline for Receipt:** August 29. **Additional Information:** Georgia Engineering Foundation at the above address

5136 ■ GOLDEN KEY INTERNATIONAL HONOUR SOCIETY
621 Noeth Ave. NE., Ste. C-100
Atlanta, GA 30308
Tel: (404)377-2400
Free: 800-377-2401
Fax: (678)420-6757
E-mail: memberservices@goldenkey.org
Web Site: http://www.goldenkey.org
To financially assist students studying engineering.
Title of Award: Boeing Engineering Scholarships **Area, Field, or Subject:** Engineering. **Level of Education for which Award is Granted:** Undergraduate **Number Awarded:** 4. **Funds Available:** $10000.
Eligibility Requirements: Applicant must be a U.S. undergraduate member currently enrolled in classes at a degree-granting program. **Application Requirements:** Applicants must submit a letter of recommendation from a professor in the discipline; and a current, comprehensive official academic transcript. Submit materials to awards@goldenkey.org. **Additional Information:** Applicants can apply for more than one scholarship. **Deadline for Receipt:** May 15.

5137 ■ GRAND HAVEN AREA COMMUNITY FOUNDATION
1 S. Harbor Dr.
Grand Haven, MI 49417
Tel: (616)842-6378
Fax: (616)842-9518
E-mail: bpost@ghacf.org
Web Site: http://www.ghacf.org
To improve and enhance the quality of life in the Tri-Cities area by serving as a leader, catalyst and resource for philanthropy; to strive for community improvement through strategic grantmaking in such fields as the arts, education, health, environment, youth, social services and other human needs.
Title of Award: Gautier Family Scholarships Fund **Area, Field, or Subject:** Engineering. **Level of Education for which Award is Granted:** Undergraduate **Funds Available:** No specific amount.
Eligibility Requirements: Applicants must be high school students from the Tri-Cities area who wish to pursue studies in mechanical or electrical engineering at Michigan Technical Institute. **Application Requirements:** Applicants must submit: completed application form; current high school or college transcript; Student Aid Report (SAR) from the Free Application for Federal Student Aid (FAFSA), unless applying for scholarships that do not consider financial need; and letter of recommendation. **Deadline for Receipt:** March 7. **Additional Information:** 616-842-6378.

5138 ■ GRAND HAVEN AREA COMMUNITY FOUNDATION
1 S. Harbor Dr.
Grand Haven, MI 49417
Tel: (616)842-6378
Fax: (616)842-9518
E-mail: bpost@ghacf.org
Web Site: http://www.ghacf.org
To improve and enhance the quality of life in the Tri-Cities area by serving as a leader, catalyst and resource for philanthropy; to strive for community improvement through strategic grantmaking in such fields as the arts, education, health, environment, youth, social services and other human needs.
Title of Award: Marion A. and Ruth K. Sherwood Family Fund Engineering Scholarships **Area, Field, or Subject:** Engineering. **Level of Education for which Award is Granted:** Undergraduate **Funds Available:** No specific amount.

Eligibility Requirements: Applicants must be students planning to pursue a career in the field of engineering. **Application Requirements:** Applicants must submit: completed application form; current high school or college transcript; Student Aid Report (SAR) from the Free Application for Federal Student Aid (FAFSA), unless applying for scholarships that do not consider financial need; and letter of recommendation. **Deadline for Receipt:** March 7. **Additional Information:** 616-842-6378.

5139 ■ GRAND RAPIDS COMMUNITY FOUNDATION
161 Ottawa Ave. NW
Ste. 209-C Waters Bldg.
Grand Rapids, MI 49503
Tel: (616)454-1751
Fax: (616)454-6455
E-mail: grfound@grfoundation.org
Web Site: http://www.grfoundation.org
To provide financial support to those students who are in need.
Title of Award: Patricia & Armen Oumedian Scholarships **Area, Field, or Subject:** Engineering. **Level of Education for which Award is Granted:** Undergraduate **Funds Available:** No specific amount.
Eligibility Requirements: Applicants must be second year or above full-time engineering students at Kettering or transferring from GRCC to Kettering. Applicants must be residents of Kent, Ottawa, or Muskegon County. Applicants must have demonstrated financial need and must have a minimum of 3.0 GPA. **Application Requirements:** Applicants must check the available website for the required materials. **Additional Information:** Grand Rapids Community Foundation at the above address

5140 ■ THE GREATER TACOMA COMMUNITY FOUNDATION
PO Box 1995
Tacoma, WA 98401
Tel: (253)383-5622
Web Site: http://www.tacomafoundation.org
To foster generosity by connecting people who care with causes that matter.
Title of Award: Fuchs-Harden Educational Scholarships Fund **Area, Field, or Subject:** Engineering; Business Administration; Social sciences. **Level of Education for which Award is Granted:** Undergraduate **Funds Available:** No specific amount.
Eligibility Requirements: Applicant must be an African American residing in the legal limits of the city of Tacoma, Washington; must be enrolled in and maintain a satisfactory GPA at a college or university in the courses for Business Administration, Engineering, Applied Physics, Dentistry, Medicine, Law, Sociology, Journalism or Home Economics. **Application Requirements:** Applicants must submit a completed application form available through R. Merle Palmer Minority Scholarship Fund. **Additional Information:** PO Box 7119, Tacoma, WA 98406-0119.

5141 ■ HAMILTON INDUSTRIAL ENVIRONMENTAL ASSOCIATION
PO Box 35545
Hamilton, ON, Canada L8H 7S6
Tel: (905)561-4432
E-mail: info@hiea.org
Web Site: http://www.hiea.org
To provide financial assistance to those students who are in need.
Title of Award: Hamilton Industrial Environmental Association Bursaries-Mohawk College **Area, Field, or Subject:** Engineering Technology; Environmental Technology. **Level of Education for which Award is Granted:** Undergraduate **Funds Available:** No specific amount.
Eligibility Requirements: Applicants must be 2nd year students in their final semester; must have been raised in Hamilton or graduated from Hamilton High School. **Application Requirements:** Applicants must check the available website for more information. **Additional Information:** Hamilton Industrial Environmental Association at the above address.

5142 ■ HARTFORD FOUNDATION FOR PUBLIC GIVING
10 Columbus Blvd., 8th Flr.
Hartford, CT 06106
Tel: (860)548-1888
Fax: (860)524-8346
E-mail: hfpg@hfpg.org
Web Site: http://www.hfpg.org

To provide scholarship for graduating high school seniors, undergraduate, or graduate students.
Title of Award: Connecticut Building Congress Scholarships **Area, Field, or Subject:** Engineering; Architecture. **Level of Education for which Award is Granted:** Undergraduate **Funds Available:** $500-$2,000.
Eligibility Requirements: Applicants must be attending two or four-year college or university; must demonstrate financial need, academic excellence and community service; must be residents of Connecticut. **Application Requirements:** Applicants may obtain application materials from Connecticut Bldg. Congress Scholarship Fund, Inc. 10 Westgate Rd. Columbia, CT 06237. Phone: 2032281387 Fax: 203228-2296. info@cbc-ct.org. **Deadline for Receipt:** March 15.

5143 ■ HELLENIC UNIVERSITY CLUB OF PHILADELPHIA
PO Box 42199
Philadelphia, PA 19101-2199
Tel: (215)483-7440
E-mail: hucphila@yahoo.com
Web Site: http://www.hucphila.org
To provide financial assistance for qualified students pursuing a degree in the fields of Architecture and/or Engineering.
Title of Award: Dimitri J. Ververelli Memorial Scholarships **Area, Field, or Subject:** Architecture; Engineering. **Level of Education for which Award is Granted:** Undergraduate **Funds Available:** $2,000.
Eligibility Requirements: Applicants must be of Greek descent; must be U.S. citizens; and must be pursuing a degree in the fields of Architecture and/or Engineering. **Application Requirements:** Application form can be obtained from the HUCPhila website. Applicants must complete the application form and mail to Scholarship Chairman. Applicants must also provide one letter of recommendation and scholastic transcripts. **Deadline for Receipt:** April 21. **Additional Information:** Scholarship Chairman at the above address.

5144 ■ HISPANIC ASSOCIATION OF COLLEGES AND UNIVERSITIES
8415 Datapoint Dr., Ste. 400
San Antonio, TX 78229
Tel: (210)698-3805
Fax: (210)692-0823
E-mail: hacu@hacu.net
Web Site: http://www.hacu.net
To promote the development of member colleges and universities; to improve access to and the quality of post-secondary educational opportunities for Hispanic students; and to meet the needs of business, industry and government through the development and sharing of resources, information and expertise.
Title of Award: Wendell Scott Awards **Area, Field, or Subject:** Business; Engineering; Public Relation; Technology; Management. **Level of Education for which Award is Granted:** Graduate, Undergraduate **Funds Available:** $1,500-undergraduate; $2,000-graduate.
Eligibility Requirements: Applicants must be full-time or part-time, undergraduate and graduate students attending four year institutions; must possess a minimum cumulative GPA of 3.0. Applying graduate students must be attending school at least on a part-time basis and must possess a minimum cumulative GPA of 3.0. **Application Requirements:** Applicants must fill out the application form and must provide any documents showing that they are currently enrolled or accepted by a college, university, or institution. **Deadline for Receipt:** May 23.

5145 ■ HISPANIC NATIONAL BAR ASSOCIATION
1111 Pennsylvania Ave. NW
Washington, DC 20004
Tel: (202)223-4777
Web Site: http://www.hnba.com
To support and help the nation's top college students to pursue their careers.
Title of Award: Hispanic College Fund Scholarship Programs **Area, Field, or Subject:** Business, Finance, Engineering, Science. **Level of Education for which Award is Granted:** Undergraduate **Funds Available:** $500-$5,000.
Eligibility Requirements: Applicant must be of Hispanic descent and a U.S. citizen or a permanent resident; must be studying at an accredited university in the U.S. or Puerto Rico; must be enrolled full-time as an

undergraduate student for the upcoming academic year; must have earned and maintain a grade point of no less than 3.0 on a 4.0 scale; must demonstrate financial need. **Application Requirements:** Applicants must submit an official transcript, proof of family income, proof of citizenship status, essay, resume, and financial verification (if chosen as semi finalist only). **Deadline for Receipt:** March 22.

5146 ■ HISPANIC SCHOLARSHIP FUND
55 Second St., Ste. 1500
San Francisco, CA 94105
877-473-4636
Fax: (415)808-2302
E-mail: info@hsf.net
Web Site: http://www.hsf.net
To promote academic excellence and to provide an opportunity for outstanding students with significant financial need to reach their fullest potential.
Title of Award: The Gates Millennium Scholars **Area, Field, or Subject:** Mathematics and mathematical sciences; Science; Engineering; Education; Public health; Library and archival sciences. **Level of Education for which Award is Granted:** Undergraduate **Funds Available:** No specific amount.
Eligibility Requirements: Applicants must be African American, American Indian/Alaska Native, Asian pacific Islander American and Hispanic American heritage; a U.S. citizen or legal permanent resident; have a minimum 3.3 GPA on a 4.0 scale; must demonstrate leadership skills; must demonstrate financial need. **Application Requirements:** Applicants must complete all three required forms available at the award site www.gmsp.org. American Indian/Alaska Natives must submit proof of tribal enrollment or a certificate of descent if selected as finalists. **Additional Information:** Established in 1999 and funded by a grant from the Bill and Melinda Gates Foundation. **Deadline for Receipt:** December 31 (paper applications), January 11 (online applications). **Additional Information:** gmsinfo@hsf.nett.

5147 ■ HISPANIC SCHOLARSHIP FUND
55 Second St., Ste. 1500
San Francisco, CA 94105
877-473-4636
Fax: (415)808-2302
E-mail: info@hsf.net
Web Site: http://www.hsf.net
To provide financial resources to outstanding Latinos pursuing degrees in engineering and business.
Title of Award: HSF/General Motors Scholarship Program **Area, Field, or Subject:** Electrical engineering; Engineering, Industrial; Manufacturing; Mechanical engineering; Accounting; Business administration; Economics; Finance; Personnel administration/human resources. **Level of Education for which Award is Granted:** Undergraduate **Funds Available:** $2,500.
Eligibility Requirements: Applicants must be of Hispanic heritage; U.S. citizens or legal permanent residents with a valid permanent resident card or passport stamped I-551; enrolled full-time in a degree-seeking program at any four-year U.S. accredited institution in the U.S., Puerto Rico, U.S. Virgin Islands or Guam; have a minimum 3.0 GPA on a 4.0 scale or the equivalent; pursue degrees in Engineering, Business or Human Resources; must apply for federal financing aid using the Free Application for Federal Student Aid (FAFSA) at www.fafsa.ed.gov. For semi-finalists, applicants must complete the GM Online Assessment. **Application Requirements:** Applicants must use the HSF online application system. **Additional Information:** Given in partnership with General Motors (GM). **Deadline for Receipt:** June 30. **Additional Information:** scholar1@hsf.net.

5148 ■ HISPANIC SCHOLARSHIP FUND
55 Second St., Ste. 1500
San Francisco, CA 94105
877-473-4636
Fax: (415)808-2302
E-mail: info@hsf.net
Web Site: http://www.hsf.net
To provide financial assistance to minority students.
Title of Award: HSF/Hewlett Packard (HP) Diversity in Education Scholarship Program **Area, Field, or Subject:** Computer and information sciences; Engineering, Computer; Engineering, Electrical. **Level of Education for which Award is Granted:** Undergraduate **Funds Available:** $3,000 per year. **Duration:** Four years.
Eligibility Requirements: Applicants must be graduating high school seniors enrolling as a fulltime first-year student or a community college student transferring into University of California, Los Angeles, North Carolina AT&T, Morgan State University or University of Washington; plan to major in computer engineering, computer science or electrical engineering; must be African American, Latino or American Indian; be able to legally work full time in the United States at the time of application. **Application Requirements:** Applicants must download application forms from the award site website www.hp.com/scholars. **Additional Information:** In partnership with HP Development Company. **Deadline for Receipt:** March 15. **Additional Information:** highschool@hsf.net.

5149 ■ HISPANIC SCHOLARSHIP FUND
55 Second St., Ste. 1500
San Francisco, CA 94105
877-473-4636
Fax: (415)808-2302
E-mail: info@hsf.net
Web Site: http://www.hsf.net
To support outstanding Community College Transfer Students.
Title of Award: HSF/Nissan Community College Transfer Scholarship Program **Area, Field, or Subject:** Business; Engineering; Communications; Media arts. **Level of Education for which Award is Granted:** Undergraduate **Funds Available:** $2,500.
Eligibility Requirements: Applicant must be of Hispanic heritage; U.S. citizen or legal permanent resident with a valid permanent resident card or passport stamped I-551; currently enrolled part-time or full-time at a community college; planning to transfer and enroll full-time in a degree-seeking program at a four-year U.S. accredited institution; must reside or transfer to a four-year institution in Atlanta, Georgia; Chicago Illinois; Greater Dallas/Forth Worth, Texas; Jackson/Canton, Mississippi; Los Angeles, California; Nashville, Tennessee; Northern California; New York City/New Jersey; be pursuing a degree in Business, Engineering, Communications or Media Arts; have a minimum GPA of 3.0 on a 4.0 scale; must apply for federal financing aid using the Free Application for Federal Student Aid (FAFSA) at www.fafsa.ed.gov. **Application Requirements:** Applications must be submitted using the HSF online application system. **Additional Information:** In partnership with Nissan North America, Inc. **Deadline for Receipt:** March 15. **Additional Information:** cctransfer@hsf.net.

5150 ■ HISPANIC SCHOLARSHIP FUND
55 Second St., Ste. 1500
San Francisco, CA 94105
877-473-4636
Fax: (415)808-2302
E-mail: info@hsf.net
Web Site: http://www.hsf.net
To provide financial assistance to students of Hispanic heritage.
Title of Award: HSF/Wal-Mart Stores Inc. Scholarship Program **Area, Field, or Subject:** Marketing and distribution; Accounting; Business; Finance; Management; Computer and information sciences; Information science and technology; Civil engineering; Construction; Electrical engineering; Geology; Engineering, Industrial; Fashion design; Law; **Level of Education for which Award is Granted:** Graduate, Undergraduate **Funds Available:** $2,500.
Eligibility Requirements: Applicant must be of Hispanic heritage; U.S. citizen or legal permanent resident with a valid permanent resident card or passport stamped I-551; enrolled as sophomore, junior, senior undergraduate or First or Second year Master student in a full-time degree-seeking program at an accredited U.S. institution in the U.S., Puerto Rico, U.S. Virgin Islands or Guam; have a minimum 3.0 GPA on a 4.0 scale or 4.00 on a 5.00 scale; must apply for Federal Financing Aid; pursuing his/her first undergraduate or graduate degree. Undergraduate students must be majoring in: Marketing, Accounting, Business, Finance, Management, Computer Science, Computer Programming, Information Technology (IT), Civil Engineering, Construction, Electrical Engineering, Environmental/Geological Engineering, Industrial Engineering, and Fashion. Master's students must be majoring in: Business, Finance, Marketing, Civil Engineering, Construction, Electrical Engineering, Environmental/

Geological Engineering and Law. **Application Requirements:** Applications must be submitted using the HSF online application system. **Additional Information:** In partnership with Wal-Mart Stores, Inc. **Deadline for Receipt:** March 15. **Additional Information:** scholar1@hsf.net.

5151 ■ HISPANIC SCHOLARSHIP FUND
55 Second St., Ste. 1500
San Francisco, CA 94105
877-473-4636
Fax: (415)808-2302
E-mail: info@hsf.net
Web Site: http://www.hsf.net
To provide financial assistance to those who are studying engineering.
Title of Award: Marathon Oil Corporation College Scholarship Program **Area, Field, or Subject:** Chemical engineering; Civil engineering; Electrical engineering; Mechanical engineering; Petroleum engineering; Geology; Geophysics; Accounting; Marketing and distribution; Land management; Transportation; Logistics; Engineering, Petroleum **Level of Education for which Award is Granted:** Graduate, Undergraduate **Funds Available:** $20,000. **Duration:** Two academic years.
Eligibility Requirements: Applicant must be of Hispanic American, African American, Asian Pacific Islander American or American Indian/Alaskan Native heritage; U.S. citizen or legal permanent resident with a valid Social Security Number and a permanent resident card or passport stamped I-551; have a minimum 3.0 GPA on a 4.0 scale; a sophomore majoring in chemical engineering, civil engineering, electrical engineering, mechanical engineering, petroleum engineering, geology, geophysics, accounting, marketing, global procurement or supply chain management, environmental health & safety, energy management or petroleum land management, transportation & logistics or geotechnical engineering; or a senior pursuing a Masters degree in geology or geophysics; must participate in a possible paid summer internship opportunity in Marathon Oil Corporation; must apply for federal financing aid using the Free Application for Federal Student Aid (FAFSA) at www.fafsa.ed.gov. **Application Requirements:** Applications must be submitted using the HSF online application system. **Additional Information:** Scholars will be paired with a Marathon Oil Corporation employee as a professional mentor. **Deadline for Receipt:** November 1. **Additional Information:** scholar1@hsf.net.

5152 ■ HISPANIC SCHOLARSHIP FUND
55 Second St., Ste. 1500
San Francisco, CA 94105
877-473-4636
Fax: (415)808-2302
E-mail: info@hsf.net
Web Site: http://www.hsf.net
To provide financial resources to assist outstanding Latino high school graduates.
Title of Award: Toyota High School Scholarship Program **Area, Field, or Subject:** Accounting; Actuarial science; Advertising; Architecture; Automotive technology; Bioengineering; Business; Chemical engineering; Civil engineering; Engineering, Computer; Electronics; Computer and information sciences; Construction; Drafting; Economics; Education; Education, Bilingual and cross-cultural; Education, Early childhood; Education, Special; Counseling/Guidance; Electrical engineering; Engineering; Environmental design; Environmental science; Geology; Educational administration; Education-Curricula; Personnel administration/human resources; Industrial design; Engineering, Industrial; Information science and technology; Management; Marketing and distribution; International trade; Manufacturing; Mechanical engineering; Engineering, Nuclear; Public administration; Public relations; Transportation. **Level of Education for which Award is Granted:** Undergraduate **Funds Available:** $5,000.
Eligibility Requirements: Applicant must be of Hispanic heritage; U.S. citizen or legal permanent resident with a valid permanent resident card or passport stamped I-551; have a minimum GPA of 3.0 on a 4.0 scale or equivalent; must apply for federal financing aid using the Free Application for Federal Student Aid (FAFSA) at www.fafsa.ed.gov; enrolling as full-time freshman at: Arizona State University; Central Missouri University; Colorado State University, Pueblo; Cornell University; Ferris State; Florida International University; Harvard University; Indiana University; Massachusetts Institute of Technology; New York University; Northwestern University; Pennsylvania Tech College; Pittsburg State University;

Southern Illinois University; Stanford University; Texas A&M University; University of Arizona; University of California, Berkeley; University of California, Davis; University of California, Los Angeles; University of California, San Diego; University of Florida; University of Houston; University of Illinois at Chicago; University of Illinois at Urbana-Champaign; University of Michigan; University of New Mexico; University of Pennsylvania; University of Southern California; University of Texas at Austin; University of Texas at El Paso; University of Texas at San Antonio; University of Texas, Pan American; or Weber State University. Applicants must pursue a degree in: Accounting; Actuarial Science; Advertising; Architecture; Automotive Technology; Bio-Engineering; Business; Chemical Engineering; Civil Engineering; Computer Electronics; Computer Engineering; Computer Information Systems (CIS); Computer Programming; Computer Science; Construction; Drafting/CAD; Economics; Education Admin./Leadership; Education/Teaching; Education: Bilingual; Education: Early Childhood/ Elementary; Education: Special; Educational Counseling; Electrical Engineering; Engineering; Environmental Design/Landscaping; Environmental Management/Science; Environmental/Geological Engineering; Human Resource Management; Industrial Design; Industrial Engineering; Information Technology (IT); International Business; Management; Management Information Systems (MIS); Manufacturing Engineering; Marketing; Materials/ Manufacturing; Mechanical Engineering; Network Administration; Non-Profit Management; Nuclear Engineering; Office Administration; Public Administration; Public Relations; Supply Chain Management; or Transportation. **Application Requirements:** Applications must be submitted using the HSF online application system. **Additional Information:** In partnership with Toyota Motor Sales, USA. **Deadline for Receipt:** July 16. **Additional Information:** highschool@hsf.net.

5153 ■ HISPANIC SCHOLARSHIP FUND
55 Second St., Ste. 1500
San Francisco, CA 94105
877-473-4636
Fax: (415)808-2302
E-mail: info@hsf.net
Web Site: http://www.hsf.net
To provide financial assistance to college students of Hispanic heritage.
Title of Award: Verizon Scholarship Program **Area, Field, or Subject:** Accounting; Business; Economics; Finance; Personnel administration/human resources; Marketing and distribution; Engineering, Computer; Information science and technology; Computer and information sciences; Civil engineering; Electrical engineering; Engineering, Industrial; Engineering, Mechanical. **Level of Education for which Award is Granted:** Undergraduate **Funds Available:** $5,000.
Eligibility Requirements: Applicant must be of Hispanic heritage; U.S. citizen or legal permanent resident with a valid permanent resident card or passport stamped I-551; enrolled as sophomore, junior or senior in a full-time degree-seeking program at an accredited U.S. institution in the U.S., Puerto Rico, U.S. Virgin Islands or Guam; have a minimum 3.0 GPA on a 4.0 scale or 4.00 on a 5.00 scale; must apply for federal financing aid using the Free Application for Federal Student Aid (FAFSA) at www.fafsa.ed.gov; must submit a resume with application; must be pursuing his/her first undergraduate degree; must be majoring in: Accounting, Business, Economics, Finance, Human Resource Management, Marketing, Computer Science, Computer Engineering, Computer Programming, Computer Electronics, Information Technology (IT), Management Information Systems (MIS), Network Administration, Computer Information Systems (CIS), Civil, Electrical, Industrial, or Mechanical Engineering; must be a resident of: (NY counties) Bronx, Kings, New York, Queens, and Richmond; (NJ) Town of Basking Ridge in Somerset County; (PA Counties) Bucks, Montgomery, Chester, Delaware, Philadelphia; (FL counties) Hernando, Hillsborough, Pasco, and Pinella; (MA counties) Essex, Middlesex, Plymouth, Suffolk; (TX counties) Collin, Dallas, Denton, Dexar, Dorris, Ellis, Henderson, Hood, Hunt, Johnson, Kaufman, Parker, Rockwall, and Tarrant; (VA county) Arlington, Loudoun; (DC) Washington; (Southern CA counties) Los Angeles, Orange, Riverside, San Bernardino, Ventura; Maine, New Hampshire, Washington State. **Application Requirements:** Applications must be submitted using the HSF online application system. **Additional Information:** In partnership with Verizon. **Deadline for Receipt:** March 15. **Additional Information:** scholar1@hsf.net.

5154 ■ ILLINOIS SOCIETY OF PROFESSIONAL ENGINEERS

600 S 2nd St., Ste. 403
Springfield, IL 62704
Tel: (217)544-7424
Fax: (217)528-6545
E-mail: info@illinoisengineer.com
Web Site: http://www.illinoisengineer.com
To provide financial assistance for the education of students for the advancement and betterment of human welfare and the engineering profession.
Title of Award: ISPE/M.E. Amstutz Memorial Award **Area, Field, or Subject:** Engineering. **Level of Education for which Award is Granted:** Undergraduate **Funds Available:** $1,500.
Eligibility Requirements: Applicants must be enrolled in an ABETaccredited engineering program, be at least a junior maintaining a B average or better, and demonstrate financial need. **Application Requirements:** Applicants must submit official transcripts of all college and university work; two letters of reference from the department chair or department faculty member; from past employer or other character reference; and a typewritten essay in 200 words or less discussing why they want to become a professional engineer. **Deadline for Receipt:** January 31.

5155 ■ ILLINOIS SOCIETY OF PROFESSIONAL ENGINEERS

600 S 2nd St., Ste. 403
Springfield, IL 62704
Tel: (217)544-7424
Fax: (217)528-6545
E-mail: info@illinoisengineer.com
Web Site: http://www.illinoisengineer.com
To provide financial assistance for the education of students who are sons or daughters of ISPE members; for the advancement and betterment of human welfare and the engineering profession.
Title of Award: ISPE Advantage Award/Foundation Scholarships **Area, Field, or Subject:** Engineering. **Level of Education for which Award is Granted:** Undergraduate **Funds Available:** $1,200.
Eligibility Requirements: Applicants must be attending an Illinois university; enrolled in an engineering program accredited by the Accreditation Board of Engineering and Technology (ABET); have at least junior standing; a B average or better in courses which are credited toward the engineering degree. **Application Requirements:** Applicants must submit official transcripts of all college and university work; two letters of reference from the department chair or department faculty member; from past employer or other character reference; and typewritten essay in 200 words or less discussing why they want to become a professional engineer. **Deadline for Receipt:** January 31.

5156 ■ INSTITUTE OF INDUSTRIAL ENGINEERS

3577 Parkway Ln., Ste. 200
Norcross, GA 30092
Tel: (770)449-0460
Free: 800-494-0460
Fax: (770)441-3295
E-mail: cs@iienet.org
Web Site: http://www.iienet2.org
To recognize undergraduate industrial engineering students for academic excellence and campus leadership.
Title of Award: Dwight D. Gardner Scholarships **Area, Field, or Subject:** Engineering, Industrial. **Level of Education for which Award is Granted:** Undergraduate **Number Awarded:** 2. **Funds Available:** $1,000.
Eligibility Requirements: Candidates must be undergraduate students enrolled in any school in the United States and its territories, Canada and Mexico, provided that the school's engineering program or equivalent is accredited by an agency or organization recognized by IIE and the student is pursuing a course of study in industrial engineering. Candidates must be active Institute members and have an overall average of 3.40 on a scale of 0-4.00. **Application Requirements:** Candidates must be nominated by IE department heads and mailed to the Institute headquarters by November 15. After the review of nominations, eligible candidates will receive an application package that must be completed and sent back to IIE. **Deadline for Receipt:** February 1.

5157 ■ INSTITUTE OF INDUSTRIAL ENGINEERS

3577 Parkway Ln., Ste. 200
Norcross, GA 30092
Tel: (770)449-0460
Free: 800-494-0460
Fax: (770)441-3295
E-mail: cs@iienet.org
Web Site: http://www.iienet2.org
To recognize outstanding academic scholarship and leadership at the undergraduate level.
Title of Award: IIE Council of Fellows Undergraduate Scholarships **Area, Field, or Subject:** Engineering, Industrial. **Level of Education for which Award is Granted:** Undergraduate **Number Awarded:** 2. **Funds Available:** $1,000 each.
Eligibility Requirements: Candidates must be undergraduate students enrolled in any school in the United States and its territories, Canada and Mexico, provided that the school's industrial engineering program or equivalent is accredited by an agency or organization recognized by IIE and the student is pursuing a course of study in industrial engineering. **Application Requirements:** Candidates must request an application packet from the scholarship coordinator and submit the completed form to IIE headquarters. **Deadline for Receipt:** February 1. **Additional Information:** Bonnie Cameron at the above address.

5158 ■ INSTITUTE OF INDUSTRIAL ENGINEERS

3577 Parkway Ln., Ste. 200
Norcross, GA 30092
Tel: (770)449-0460
Free: 800-494-0460
Fax: (770)441-3295
E-mail: cs@iienet.org
Web Site: http://www.iienet2.org
To recognize industrial engineering students for academic excellence and campus leadership.
Title of Award: John L. Imhoff Scholarships **Area, Field, or Subject:** Engineering, Industrial. **Level of Education for which Award is Granted:** Graduate, Undergraduate **Number Awarded:** 1. **Funds Available:** $1,000.
Eligibility Requirements: Candidates must be pursuing a BS in an accredited IE program, or have a BS in IE and pursuing a master's or doctorate degree in an accredited IE program. **Application Requirements:** Candidates must submit a completed application form; a written essay describing candidate's international contributions to, or experience in, industrial engineering; and three references reinforcing applicant's contributions to the industrial engineering profession through international understanding. **Deadline for Receipt:** August 31. **Additional Information:** Bonnie Cameron at the above address.

5159 ■ INSTITUTE OF INDUSTRIAL ENGINEERS

3577 Parkway Ln., Ste. 200
Norcross, GA 30092
Tel: (770)449-0460
Free: 800-494-0460
Fax: (770)441-3295
E-mail: cs@iienet.org
Web Site: http://www.iienet2.org
To recognize undergraduate industrial engineering students for academic excellence and noteworthy contribution to the development of the industrial engineering profession.
Title of Award: Harold and Inge Marcus Scholarships **Area, Field, or Subject:** Engineering, Industrial. **Level of Education for which Award is Granted:** Undergraduate **Number Awarded:** 1. **Funds Available:** $1,000.
Eligibility Requirements: Candidates must be undergraduate students enrolled in any school in the United States, provided that the school's engineering program is accredited by an agency recognized by IIE and the student is pursuing a course of study in industrial engineering. Candidates must be active Institute members and have an overall average of 3.40 on a scale of 0-4.00. **Application Requirements:** Candidates must be nominated by IE department heads. Nominations must be mailed to the Institute headquarters by November 15. Candidates must submit a completed application package to IIE. **Deadline for Receipt:** February 1.

5160 ■ INSTITUTE OF INDUSTRIAL ENGINEERS
3577 Parkway Ln., Ste. 200
Norcross, GA 30092
Tel: (770)449-0460
Free: 800-494-0460
Fax: (770)441-3295
E-mail: cs@iienet.org
Web Site: http://www.iienet2.org
To recognize undergraduate industrial engineering students for academic excellence and campus leadership.
Title of Award: Marvin Mundel Memorial Scholarships **Area, Field, or Subject:** Engineering, Industrial. **Level of Education for which Award is Granted:** Undergraduate **Number Awarded:** 1. **Funds Available:** $600. **Duration:** One year.
Eligibility Requirements: Candidates must be undergraduate students enrolled in any school in the United States and its territories, Canada and Mexico, provided that the school's industrial engineering program or its equivalent is accredited by an agency or organization recognized by IIE and the student is pursuing a course of study in industrial engineering. **Application Requirements:** Candidates must be nominated by IE department heads. Nominations must be mailed to the Institute headquarters by November 15. Candidates must submit a completed application package to IIE. **Deadline for Receipt:** February 1.

5161 ■ INSTITUTE OF INDUSTRIAL ENGINEERS
3577 Parkway Ln., Ste. 200
Norcross, GA 30092
Tel: (770)449-0460
Free: 800-494-0460
Fax: (770)441-3295
E-mail: cs@iienet.org
Web Site: http://www.iienet2.org
To recognize excellence in scholarly activities and leadership of the industrial engineering profession.
Title of Award: Presidents Scholarships **Area, Field, or Subject:** Engineering, Industrial. **Level of Education for which Award is Granted:** Undergraduate **Funds Available:** To be determined.
Eligibility Requirements: Candidates must be undergraduate students pursuing a course of study in industrial engineering. Candidates must be active Institute members and have an overall average of 3.40 on a scale of 0-4.00. **Application Requirements:** Candidates must be nominated by IE department heads and mailed to the Institute headquarters by November 15. After review of nominations, eligible candidates will receive an application package that must be completed and sent back to IIE. **Deadline for Receipt:** February 1.

5162 ■ INSTITUTE OF INDUSTRIAL ENGINEERS
3577 Parkway Ln., Ste. 200
Norcross, GA 30092
Tel: (770)449-0460
Free: 800-494-0460
Fax: (770)441-3295
E-mail: cs@iienet.org
Web Site: http://www.iienet2.org
To recognize undergraduate industrial engineering students for academic excellence and campus leadership.
Title of Award: A.O. Putnam Memorial Scholarships **Area, Field, or Subject:** Engineering, Industrial. **Level of Education for which Award is Granted:** Undergraduate **Number Awarded:** 1. **Funds Available:** $600.
Eligibility Requirements: Candidates must be undergraduate students enrolled in any school in the United States and its territories, Canada and Mexico, provided that the school's industrial engineering program or equivalent is accredited by an agency or organization recognized by IIE and the student is pursuing a course of study in industrial engineering. Candidates must be active Institute members and have an overall average of 3.40 on a scale of 0-4.00. **Application Requirements:** Candidates must be nominated by IE department heads and mailed to the Institute headquarters by November 15. After the review of nominations, eligible candidates will receive an application package that must be completed and sent back to IIE. **Deadline for Receipt:** February 1.

5163 ■ INSTITUTE OF INDUSTRIAL ENGINEERS
3577 Parkway Ln., Ste. 200
Norcross, GA 30092

Tel: (770)449-0460
Free: 800-494-0460
Fax: (770)441-3295
E-mail: cs@iienet.org
Web Site: http://www.iienet2.org
To recognize undergraduate industrial engineering students for academic excellence and campus leadership.
Title of Award: United Parcel Service Scholarship for Female Students **Area, Field, or Subject:** Engineering, Industrial. **Level of Education for which Award is Granted:** Undergraduate **Number Awarded:** 1. **Funds Available:** $4,000. **Duration:** One year.
Eligibility Requirements: Candidates must be undergraduate students enrolled in any school in the United States and its territories, Canada and Mexico, provided that the school's industrial engineering program or its equivalent is accredited by an agency or organization recognized by IIE and the student is pursuing a course of study in industrial engineering. **Application Requirements:** Candidates must be nominated by IE department heads. Nominations must be mailed to the Institute headquarters by November 15. Candidates must submit a completed application package to IIE. **Deadline for Receipt:** February 1.

5164 ■ INSTITUTE OF INDUSTRIAL ENGINEERS
3577 Parkway Ln., Ste. 200
Norcross, GA 30092
Tel: (770)449-0460
Free: 800-494-0460
Fax: (770)441-3295
E-mail: cs@iienet.org
Web Site: http://www.iienet2.org
To recognize undergraduate industrial engineering students for academic excellence and campus leadership.
Title of Award: United Parcel Service Scholarship for Minority Students **Area, Field, or Subject:** Engineering, Industrial. **Level of Education for which Award is Granted:** Undergraduate **Number Awarded:** 1. **Funds Available:** $4,000. **Duration:** One year.
Eligibility Requirements: Candidates must be undergraduate students enrolled in any school in the United States and its territories, Canada and Mexico, provided that the school's industrial engineering program or its equivalent is accredited by an agency or organization recognized by IIE and the student is pursuing a course of study in industrial engineering. **Application Requirements:** Candidates must be nominated by IE department heads. Nominations must be mailed to the Institute headquarters by November 15. Candidates must submit a completed application package to IIE. **Deadline for Receipt:** February 1.

5165 ■ INSTITUTE OF INDUSTRIAL ENGINEERS
3577 Parkway Ln., Ste. 200
Norcross, GA 30092
Tel: (770)449-0460
Free: 800-494-0460
Fax: (770)441-3295
E-mail: cs@iienet.org
Web Site: http://www.iienet2.org
To recognize excellence in scholarly activities and leadership related to the industrial engineering profession on campus.
Title of Award: Lisa Zaken Award For Excellence **Area, Field, or Subject:** Engineering, Industrial. **Level of Education for which Award is Granted:** Graduate, Undergraduate **Number Awarded:** 1. **Funds Available:** $600. **Duration:** One year.
Eligibility Requirements: Candidates must be undergraduate and graduate students enrolled in any school, and pursuing a course of study in industrial engineering. Candidates must be active in a student chapter, must have demonstrated leadership and promoted IIE involvement on campus. Candidates must have an overall grade point average of 3.00 on a scale of 0-4.00. **Application Requirements:** Candidates must submit a nomination letter, along with an official transcript to IIE. **Deadline for Receipt:** August 31. **Additional Information:** Bonnie Cameron at the above address.

5166 ■ ISA (INSTRUMENTATION, SYSTEMS, AND AUTOMATION)
67 Alexander Dr.
Research Triangle Park, NC 27709
Tel: (919)549-8411

Fax: (919)549-8288
E-mail: info@isa.org
Web Site: http://www.isa.org
To promote education in an instrumentation, systems, or automation discipline.
Title of Award: ISA Aerospace Industries Division - William H. Atkinson Scholarships **Area, Field, or Subject:** Systems engineering; Automotive technology. **Level of Education for which Award is Granted:** Graduate, Undergraduate **Funds Available:** Varies.
Eligibility Requirements: Applicant must be currently enrolled in a graduate or undergraduate program in an instrumentation, systems, or automation discipline (2-year program or 4-year baccalaureate program or its equivalent). Two-year program applicants must have completed at least one academic semester or its equivalent. Four-year degree program applicants must be in sophomore year or higher at the time of application. Applicants must be full-time students in an educational institution and have at least an overall GPA of 3.0 on a 4.0 scale. **Application Requirements:** Applicants must submit completed application (with Department Head Signature); two reference letters; original transcript (with raised seal); list of awards and honors; extracurricular activities; employment history; and an essay. Mail the original and ten copies of the complete application with attachments unfolded in an envelope. **Deadline for Receipt:** February 15. **Additional Information:** Randy Buchanan at randy.buchanan@usm.edu.

5167 ■ ISA (INSTRUMENTATION, SYSTEMS, AND AUTOMATION)
67 Alexander Dr.
Research Triangle Park, NC 27709
Tel: (919)549-8411
Fax: (919)549-8288
E-mail: info@isa.org
Web Site: http://www.isa.org
To promote education in an instrumentation, systems, or automation discipline.
Title of Award: Norman E. Huston Scholarships **Area, Field, or Subject:** Systems engineering; Automotive technology. **Level of Education for which Award is Granted:** Graduate, Undergraduate **Funds Available:** Varies.
Eligibility Requirements: Applicant must be currently enrolled in a graduate or undergraduate program in an instrumentation, systems, or automation discipline (2-year program or 4-year baccalaureate program or its equivalent). Two-year program applicants must have completed at least one academic semester or its equivalent. Four-year degree program applicants must be in sophomore year or higher at the time of application. Applicants must be full-time students in an educational institution who have at least an overall GPA of 3.0 on a 4.0 scale. **Application Requirements:** Applicants must submit a completed application (with Department Head Signature); two reference letters; original transcript (with raised seal); list of awards and honors; extracurricular activities; employment history; and an essay. Mail the original and ten copies of the complete application with attachments unfolded in an envelope. **Additional Information:** Funds were provided by the family of Norman E. Huston. **Deadline for Receipt:** February 15.

5168 ■ ISA (INSTRUMENTATION, SYSTEMS, AND AUTOMATION)
67 Alexander Dr.
Research Triangle Park, NC 27709
Tel: (919)549-8411
Fax: (919)549-8288
E-mail: info@isa.org
Web Site: http://www.isa.org
To promote education in an instrumentation, systems, or automation discipline.
Title of Award: ISA Educational Foundation Scholarships **Area, Field, or Subject:** Systems engineering; Automotive technology. **Level of Education for which Award is Granted:** Graduate, Undergraduate **Funds Available:** No specific amount.
Eligibility Requirements: Applicant must be a full-time college/university student in either a graduate, undergraduate, or 2-year degree program; must have an overall GPA of at least 3.0 on a 4.0 scale; and must be enrolled in a program in automation and control or a closely related field. **Application Requirements:** Applicants must submit completed application (with Department Head Signature); two reference letters; original

transcript (with raised seal); list of awards and honors and extracurricular activities; employment history; and an essay. Mail the original and ten copies of the complete application with attachments unfolded in an envelope. **Deadline for Receipt:** February 15.

5169 ■ ISA (INSTRUMENTATION, SYSTEMS, AND AUTOMATION)
67 Alexander Dr.
Research Triangle Park, NC 27709
Tel: (919)549-8411
Fax: (919)549-8288
E-mail: info@isa.org
Web Site: http://www.isa.org
To promote education in an instrumentation, systems, or automation discipline.
Title of Award: ISA Executive Board Scholarships **Area, Field, or Subject:** Systems engineering; Automotive technology. **Level of Education for which Award is Granted:** Graduate, Undergraduate **Funds Available:** Varies.
Eligibility Requirements: Applicant must be currently enrolled in a graduate or undergraduate program in an instrumentation, systems, or automation discipline (2-year program or 4 year baccalaureate program or its equivalent). Two-year program applicants must have completed at least one academic semester. Four-year degree program applicants must be in sophomore year or higher at the time of application. Applicant must be a full-time student in an educational institution who have at least an overall GPA of 3.0 on a 4.0 scale. **Application Requirements:** Applicants must submit a completed application (with Department Head Signature); two reference letters; original transcript (with raised seal); list of awards and honors; extracurricular activities; employment history; and an essay. Mail the original and ten copies of the complete application with attachments unfolded in an envelope. **Additional Information:** Funds were provided by past and present members of ISA's Executive Board. **Deadline for Receipt:** February 15.

5170 ■ ISA (INSTRUMENTATION, SYSTEMS, AND AUTOMATION)
67 Alexander Dr.
Research Triangle Park, NC 27709
Tel: (919)549-8411
Fax: (919)549-8288
E-mail: info@isa.org
Web Site: http://www.isa.org
To promote education in an instrumentation, systems, or automation discipline.
Title of Award: ISA Section and District Scholarships - Birmingham **Area, Field, or Subject:** Systems engineering; Automotive technology. **Level of Education for which Award is Granted:** Graduate, Undergraduate **Funds Available:** Varies.
Eligibility Requirements: Applicant must be currently enrolled in a graduate or undergraduate program in an instrumentation, systems, or automation discipline (2-year program or 4-year baccalaureate program or its equivalent). Two-year program applicants must have completed at least one academic semester or its equivalent. Four-year degree program applicants must be in sophomore year or higher at the time of application. Applicants must be full-time students in an educational institution and have at least an overall GPA of 3.0 on a 4.0 scale. **Application Requirements:** Applicants must submit completed application (with Department Head Signature); two reference letters; original transcript (with raised seal); list of awards and honors; extracurricular activities; employment history; and an essay. Mail the original and ten copies of the complete application with attachments unfolded in an envelope. **Deadline for Receipt:** February 15. **Additional Information:** Catherine Anrews at candrews@hilealabama.com.

5171 ■ ISA (INSTRUMENTATION, SYSTEMS, AND AUTOMATION)
67 Alexander Dr.
Research Triangle Park, NC 27709
Tel: (919)549-8411
Fax: (919)549-8288
E-mail: info@isa.org
Web Site: http://www.isa.org
To promote education in an instrumentation, systems, or automation discipline.
Title of Award: ISA Section and District Scholarships - Houston **Area, Field, or Subject:** Systems engineering; Automotive technology. **Level of

Education for which Award is Granted: Graduate, Undergraduate **Funds Available:** Varies.
Eligibility Requirements: Applicant must be currently enrolled in a graduate or undergraduate program in an instrumentation, systems, or automation discipline (2-year program or 4-year baccalaureate program or its equivalent). Two-year program applicants must have completed at least one academic semester or its equivalent. Four-year degree program applicants must be in sophomore year or higher at the time of application. Applicants must be full-time students in an educational institution and have at least an overall GPA of 3.0 on a 4.0 scale. **Application Requirements:** Applicants must submit completed application (with Department Head Signature); two reference letters; original transcript (with raised seal); list of awards and honors; extracurricular activities; employment history; and an essay. Mail the original and ten copies of the complete application with attachments unfolded in an envelope. **Deadline for Receipt:** February 15. **Additional Information:** Chan Miller at cmiller@technip.com.

5172 ■ ISA (INSTRUMENTATION, SYSTEMS, AND AUTOMATION)
67 Alexander Dr.
Research Triangle Park, NC 27709
Tel: (919)549-8411
Fax: (919)549-8288
E-mail: info@isa.org
Web Site: http://www.isa.org
To promote education in an instrumentation, systems, or automation discipline.
Title of Award: ISA Section and District Scholarships - Lehigh Valley **Area, Field, or Subject:** Systems engineering; Automotive technology. **Level of Education for which Award is Granted:** Graduate, Undergraduate **Funds Available:** Varies.
Eligibility Requirements: Applicant must be currently enrolled in a graduate or undergraduate program in an instrumentation, systems, or automation discipline (2-year program or 4-year baccalaureate program or its equivalent). Two-year program applicants must have completed at least one academic semester or its equivalent. Four-year degree program applicants must be in sophomore year or higher at the time of application. Applicants must be full-time students in an educational institution and have at least an overall GPA of 3.0 on a 4.0 scale. **Application Requirements:** Applicants must submit completed application (with Department Head Signature); two reference letters; original transcript (with raised seal); list of awards and honors; extracurricular activities; employment history; and an essay. Mail the original and ten copies of the complete application with attachments unfolded in an envelope. **Deadline for Receipt:** February 15. **Additional Information:** Ronald Christman at christr2@apci.com.

5173 ■ ISA (INSTRUMENTATION, SYSTEMS, AND AUTOMATION)
67 Alexander Dr.
Research Triangle Park, NC 27709
Tel: (919)549-8411
Fax: (919)549-8288
E-mail: info@isa.org
Web Site: http://www.isa.org
To promote education in an instrumentation, systems, or automation discipline.
Title of Award: ISA Section and District Scholarships - New Jersey **Area, Field, or Subject:** Systems engineering; Automotive technology. **Level of Education for which Award is Granted:** Graduate, Undergraduate **Funds Available:** Varies.
Eligibility Requirements: Applicant must be currently enrolled in a graduate or undergraduate program in an instrumentation, systems, or automation discipline (2-year program or 4-year baccalaureate program or its equivalent). Two-year program applicants must have completed at least one academic semester or its equivalent. Four-year degree program applicants must be in sophomore year or higher at the time of application. Applicants must be full-time students in an educational institution and have at least an overall GPA of 3.0 on a 4.0 scale. **Application Requirements:** Applicants must submit completed application (with Department Head Signature); two reference letters; original transcript (with raised seal); list of awards and honors; extracurricular activities; employment history; and an essay. Mail the original and ten copies of the complete application with attachments unfolded in an envelope. **Deadline for

Receipt:** February 15. **Additional Information:** Bob Linder at boblindner@aol.com.

5174 ■ ISA (INSTRUMENTATION, SYSTEMS, AND AUTOMATION)
67 Alexander Dr.
Research Triangle Park, NC 27709
Tel: (919)549-8411
Fax: (919)549-8288
E-mail: info@isa.org
Web Site: http://www.isa.org
To promote education in an instrumentation, systems, or automation discipline.
Title of Award: ISA Section and District Scholarships - Niagara Frontier **Area, Field, or Subject:** Systems engineering; Automotive technology. **Level of Education for which Award is Granted:** Graduate, Undergraduate **Funds Available:** Varies.
Eligibility Requirements: Applicant must be currently enrolled in a graduate or undergraduate program in an instrumentation, systems, or automation discipline (2-year program or 4-year baccalaureate program or its equivalent). Two-year program applicants must have completed at least one academic semester or its equivalent. Four-year degree program applicants must be in sophomore year or higher at the time of application. Applicants must be full-time students in an educational institution and have at least an overall GPA of 3.0 on a 4.0 scale. **Application Requirements:** Applicants must submit completed application (with Department Head Signature); two reference letters; original transcript (with raised seal); list of awards and honors; extracurricular activities; employment history; and an essay. Mail the original and ten copies of the complete application with attachments unfolded in an envelope. **Deadline for Receipt:** February 15. **Additional Information:** Maxwell Bennett at maxwell33@adelphia.net.

5175 ■ ISA (INSTRUMENTATION, SYSTEMS, AND AUTOMATION)
67 Alexander Dr.
Research Triangle Park, NC 27709
Tel: (919)549-8411
Fax: (919)549-8288
E-mail: info@isa.org
Web Site: http://www.isa.org
To promote education in an instrumentation, systems, or automation discipline.
Title of Award: ISA Section and District Scholarships - Northern California **Area, Field, or Subject:** Systems engineering; Automotive technology. **Level of Education for which Award is Granted:** Graduate, Undergraduate **Funds Available:** Varies.
Eligibility Requirements: Applicant must be currently enrolled in a graduate or undergraduate program in an instrumentation, systems, or automation discipline (2-year program or 4-year baccalaureate program or its equivalent). Two-year program applicants must have completed at least one academic semester or its equivalent. Four-year degree program applicants must be in sophomore year or higher or its equivalent at the time of application. Applicants must be full-time students in an educational institution and have at least an overall GPA of 3.0 on a 4.0 scale. **Application Requirements:** Applicants must submit completed application (with Department Head Signature); two reference letters; original transcript (with raised seal); list of awards and honors; extracurricular activities; employment history; and an essay. Mail the original and ten copies of the complete application with attachments unfolded in an envelope. **Deadline for Receipt:** February 15. **Additional Information:** Terry Molloy at tvmolloy@cmes.net.

5176 ■ ISA (INSTRUMENTATION, SYSTEMS, AND AUTOMATION)
67 Alexander Dr.
Research Triangle Park, NC 27709
Tel: (919)549-8411
Fax: (919)549-8288
E-mail: info@isa.org
Web Site: http://www.isa.org
To promote education in an instrumentation, systems, or automation discipline.
Title of Award: ISA Section and District Scholarships - Richmond (Hopewell) **Area, Field, or Subject:** Systems engineering; Automotive technology. **Level of Education for which Award is Granted:** Graduate, Undergraduate **Funds Available:** Varies.

Eligibility Requirements: Applicant must be currently enrolled in a graduate or undergraduate program in an instrumentation, systems, or automation discipline (2-year program or 4-year baccalaureate program or its equivalent). Two-year program applicants must have completed at least one academic semester or its equivalent. Four-year degree program applicants must be in sophomore year or higher at the time of application. Applicants must be full-time students in an educational institution and have at least an overall GPA of 3.0 on a 4.0 scale. **Application Requirements:** Applicants must submit completed application (with Department Head Signature); two reference letters; original transcript (with raised seal); list of awards and honors; extracurricular activities; employment history; and an essay. Mail the original and ten copies of the complete application with attachments unfolded in an envelope. **Deadline for Receipt:** February 15. **Additional Information:** Bill Sneddon at bill. sneddon@qimonda.com.

5177 ■ ISA (INSTRUMENTATION, SYSTEMS, AND AUTOMATION)
67 Alexander Dr.
Research Triangle Park, NC 27709
Tel: (919)549-8411
Fax: (919)549-8288
E-mail: info@isa.org
Web Site: http://www.isa.org
To promote education in an instrumentation, systems, or automation discipline.
Title of Award: ISA Section and District Scholarships - Savannah River **Area, Field, or Subject:** Systems engineering; Automotive technology. **Level of Education for which Award is Granted:** Graduate, Undergraduate **Funds Available:** Varies.
Eligibility Requirements: Applicant must be currently enrolled in a graduate or undergraduate program in an instrumentation, systems, or automation discipline (2-year program or 4-year baccalaureate program or its equivalent). Two-year program applicants must have completed at least one academic semester or its equivalent. Four-year degree program applicants must be in sophomore year or higher at the time of application. Applicants must be full-time students in an educational institution and have at least an overall GPA of 3.0 on a 4.0 scale. **Application Requirements:** Applicants must submit completed application (with Department Head Signature); two reference letters; original transcript (with raised seal); list of awards and honors; extracurricular activities; employment history; and an essay. Mail the original and ten copies of the complete application with attachments unfolded in an envelope. **Deadline for Receipt:** February 15. **Additional Information:** Lance Brown at ltbrown1@comcast.net.

5178 ■ ISA (INSTRUMENTATION, SYSTEMS, AND AUTOMATION)
67 Alexander Dr.
Research Triangle Park, NC 27709
Tel: (919)549-8411
Fax: (919)549-8288
E-mail: info@isa.org
Web Site: http://www.isa.org
To promote education in an instrumentation, systems, or automation discipline.
Title of Award: ISA Section and District Scholarships - Southwestern Wyoming **Area, Field, or Subject:** Systems engineering; Automotive technology. **Level of Education for which Award is Granted:** Graduate, Undergraduate **Funds Available:** Varies.
Eligibility Requirements: Applicant must be currently enrolled in a graduate or undergraduate program in an instrumentation, systems, or automation discipline (2-year program or 4-year baccalaureate program or its equivalent). Two-year program applicants must have completed at least one academic semester or its equivalent. Four-year degree program applicants must be in sophomore year or higher at the time of application. Applicants must be full-time students in an educational institution and have at least an overall GPA of 3.0 on a 4.0 scale. **Application Requirements:** Applicants must submit completed application (with Department Head Signature); two reference letters; original transcript (with raised seal); list of awards and honors; extracurricular activities; employment history; and an essay. Mail the original and ten copies of the complete application with attachments unfolded in an envelope. **Deadline for Receipt:** February 15. **Additional Information:** Tom Kottenstette at swwyoisa@hotmail.com.

5179 ■ ISA (INSTRUMENTATION, SYSTEMS, AND AUTOMATION)
67 Alexander Dr.
Research Triangle Park, NC 27709
Tel: (919)549-8411
Fax: (919)549-8288
E-mail: info@isa.org
Web Site: http://www.isa.org
To promote education in an instrumentation, systems, or automation discipline.
Title of Award: ISA Section and District Scholarships - Texas, Louisiana and Mississippi **Area, Field, or Subject:** Systems engineering; Automotive technology. **Level of Education for which Award is Granted:** Graduate, Undergraduate **Funds Available:** Varies.
Eligibility Requirements: Applicant must be currently enrolled in a graduate or undergraduate program in an instrumentation, systems, or automation discipline (2 year program or 4 year baccalaureate program or its equivalent). Two-year program applicants must have completed at least one academic semester or its equivalent. Four-year degree program applicants must be in sophomore year or higher at the time of application. Applicants must be full-time students in an educational institution who have at least an overall GPA of 3.0 on a 4.0 scale. **Application Requirements:** Applicants must submit a completed application (with Department Head Signature); two reference letters; original transcript (with raised seal); list of awards and honors; extracurricular activities; employment history; and an essay. Mail the original and ten copies of the complete application with attachments unfolded in an envelope. **Deadline for Receipt:** February 15. **Additional Information:** Victor Carbajal at viccarba@aol.com.

5180 ■ ISA (INSTRUMENTATION, SYSTEMS, AND AUTOMATION)
67 Alexander Dr.
Research Triangle Park, NC 27709
Tel: (919)549-8411
Fax: (919)549-8288
E-mail: info@isa.org
Web Site: http://www.isa.org
To promote education in an instrumentation, systems, or automation discipline.
Title of Award: ISA Section and District Scholarships - Wilmington **Area, Field, or Subject:** Systems engineering; Automotive technology. **Level of Education for which Award is Granted:** Graduate, Undergraduate **Funds Available:** Varies.
Eligibility Requirements: Applicant must be currently enrolled in a graduate or undergraduate program in an instrumentation, systems, or automation discipline (2-year program or 4-year baccalaureate program or its equivalent). Two-year program applicants must have completed at least one academic semester or its equivalent. Four-year degree program applicants must be in sophomore year or higher at the time of application. Applicants must be full-time students in an educational institution and have at least an overall GPA of 3.0 on a 4.0 scale. **Application Requirements:** Applicants must submit completed application (with Department Head Signature); two reference letters; original transcript (with raised seal); list of awards and honors; extracurricular activities; employment history; and an essay. Mail the original and ten copies of the complete application with attachments unfolded in an envelope. **Deadline for Receipt:** February 15. **Additional Information:** Bill Balascio at w_balascio@carewassoc.com, or George Bentinck at george.c.bentinck-2@usa.dupont.com.

5181 ■ ISA (INSTRUMENTATION, SYSTEMS, AND AUTOMATION)
67 Alexander Dr.
Research Triangle Park, NC 27709
Tel: (919)549-8411
Fax: (919)549-8288
E-mail: info@isa.org
Web Site: http://www.isa.org
To promote education in an instrumentation, systems, or automation discipline.
Title of Award: ISA Technical Division Scholarships - Analysis Division **Area, Field, or Subject:** Systems engineering; Automotive technology. **Level of Education for which Award is Granted:** Graduate, Undergraduate **Funds Available:** Varies.
Eligibility Requirements: Applicant must be currently enrolled in a graduate or undergraduate program in an instrumentation, systems, or

automation discipline (2-year program or 4-year baccalaureate program or its equivalent). Two-year program applicants must have completed at least one academic semester or its equivalent. Four-year degree program applicants must be in sophomore year or higher at the time of application. Applicants must be full-time students in an educational institution who have at least an overall GPA of 3.0 on a 4.0 scale. **Application Requirements:** Applicants must submit completed application (with Department Head Signature); two reference letters; original transcript (with raised seal); list of awards and honors; extracurricular activities; employment history; and an essay. Mail the original and ten copies of the complete application with attachments unfolded in an envelope. **Deadline for Receipt:** February 15. **Additional Information:** Mike Chaney at mwchaney@msn.com, or Don Nettles at dnettles@chevron.com.

5182 ■ ISA (INSTRUMENTATION, SYSTEMS, AND AUTOMATION)
67 Alexander Dr.
Research Triangle Park, NC 27709
Tel: (919)549-8411
Fax: (919)549-8288
E-mail: info@isa.org
Web Site: http://www.isa.org
To promote education in an instrumentation, systems, or automation discipline.
Title of Award: ISA Technical Division Scholarships - Chemical and Petroleum Industries Division **Area, Field, or Subject:** Systems engineering; Automotive technology. **Level of Education for which Award is Granted:** Graduate, Undergraduate **Funds Available:** Varies.
Eligibility Requirements: Applicant must be currently enrolled in a graduate or undergraduate program in an instrumentation, systems, or automation discipline (2-year program or 4-year baccalaureate program or its equivalent). Two-year program applicants must have completed at least one academic semester or its equivalent. Four-year degree program applicants must be in sophomore year or higher at the time of application. Applicants must be full-time students in an educational institution who have at least an overall GPA of 3.0 on a 4.0 scale. **Application Requirements:** Applicants must submit completed application (with Department Head Signature); two reference letters; original transcript (with raised seal); list of awards and honors; extracurricular activities; employment history; and an essay. Mail the original and ten copies of the complete application with attachments unfolded in an envelope. **Deadline for Receipt:** February 15. **Additional Information:** at the above address.

5183 ■ ISA (INSTRUMENTATION, SYSTEMS, AND AUTOMATION)
67 Alexander Dr.
Research Triangle Park, NC 27709
Tel: (919)549-8411
Fax: (919)549-8288
E-mail: info@isa.org
Web Site: http://www.isa.org
To promote education in an instrumentation, systems, or automation discipline.
Title of Award: ISA Technical Division Scholarships - Computer Technology Division **Area, Field, or Subject:** Systems engineering; Automotive technology. **Level of Education for which Award is Granted:** Graduate, Undergraduate **Funds Available:** Varies.
Eligibility Requirements: Applicant must be currently enrolled in a graduate or undergraduate program in an instrumentation, systems, or automation discipline (2-year program or 4-year baccalaureate program or its equivalent). Two-year program applicants must have completed at least one academic semester or its equivalent. Four-year degree program applicants must be in sophomore year or higher at the time of application. Applicants must be full-time students in an educational institution who have at least an overall GPA of 3.0 on a 4.0 scale. **Application Requirements:** Applicants must submit completed application (with Department Head Signature); two reference letters; original transcript (with raised seal); list of awards and honors; extracurricular activities; employment history; and an essay. Mail the original and ten copies of the complete application with attachments unfolded in an envelope. **Deadline for Receipt:** February 15. **Additional Information:** F. Mike Johnson at mike.johnson@veco.com.

5184 ■ ISA (INSTRUMENTATION, SYSTEMS, AND AUTOMATION)
67 Alexander Dr.
Research Triangle Park, NC 27709

Tel: (919)549-8411
Fax: (919)549-8288
E-mail: info@isa.org
Web Site: http://www.isa.org
To promote education in an instrumentation, systems, or automation discipline.
Title of Award: ISA Technical Division Scholarships - Food and Pharmaceutical Industries Division **Area, Field, or Subject:** Systems engineering; Automotive technology. **Level of Education for which Award is Granted:** Graduate, Undergraduate **Funds Available:** Varies.
Eligibility Requirements: Applicant must be currently enrolled in a graduate or undergraduate program in an instrumentation, systems, or automation discipline (2-year program or 4-year baccalaureate program or its equivalent). Two-year program applicants must have completed at least one academic semester or 12 semester hours or its equivalent. Four-year degree program applicants must be in sophomore year or higher at the time of application. Applicants must be full-time students in an educational institution and have an at least 3.0 GPA on a 4.0 scale. **Application Requirements:** Applicants must submit completed application (with Department Head Signature); two reference letters; original transcript (with raised seal); list of awards and honors; extracurricular activities; employment history; and an essay. Mail the original and ten copies of the complete application with attachments unfolded in an envelope. **Deadline for Receipt:** February 15. **Additional Information:** James Bouchard at jboucha@cpcca.jnj.com.

5185 ■ ISA (INSTRUMENTATION, SYSTEMS, AND AUTOMATION)
67 Alexander Dr.
Research Triangle Park, NC 27709
Tel: (919)549-8411
Fax: (919)549-8288
E-mail: info@isa.org
Web Site: http://www.isa.org
To promote education in an instrumentation, systems, or automation discipline.
Title of Award: ISA Technical Division Scholarships - Power Industry Division **Area, Field, or Subject:** Systems engineering; Automotive technology. **Level of Education for which Award is Granted:** Graduate, Undergraduate **Funds Available:** Varies.
Eligibility Requirements: Applicant must be currently enrolled in a graduate or undergraduate program in an instrumentation, systems, or automation discipline (2-year program or 4-year baccalaureate program or its equivalent). Two-year program applicants must have completed at least one academic semester or 12 semester hours or its equivalent. Four-year degree program applicants must be in sophomore year or higher at the time of application. Applicants must be full-time students in an educational institution who have an overall GPA of 3.0 on a 4.0 scale. **Application Requirements:** Applicants must submit completed application (with Department Head Signature); two reference letters; original transcript (with raised seal); list of awards and honors; extracurricular activities; employment history; and an essay. Mail the original and ten copies of the complete application with attachments unfolded in an envelope. **Deadline for Receipt:** February 15. **Additional Information:** Mike Skoncey at mskoncey@firstenergy.corp.com.

5186 ■ ISA (INSTRUMENTATION, SYSTEMS, AND AUTOMATION)
67 Alexander Dr.
Research Triangle Park, NC 27709
Tel: (919)549-8411
Fax: (919)549-8288
E-mail: info@isa.org
Web Site: http://www.isa.org
To promote education in an instrumentation, systems, or automation discipline.
Title of Award: ISA Technical Division Scholarships - Process Measurement and Control Division **Area, Field, or Subject:** Systems engineering; Automotive technology. **Level of Education for which Award is Granted:** Graduate, Undergraduate **Funds Available:** Varies.
Eligibility Requirements: Applicant must be currently enrolled in a graduate or undergraduate program in an instrumentation, systems, or automation discipline (2-year program or 4-year baccalaureate program or its equivalent). Two-year program applicants must have completed at least one academic semester or 12 semester hours or its equivalent.

Four-year degree program applicants must be in sophomore year or higher at the time of application. Applicants must be full-time students in an educational institution who have at least an overall GPA of 3.0 on a 4.0 scale. **Application Requirements:** Applicants must submit completed application (with Department Head Signature); two reference letters; original transcript (with raised seal); list of awards and honors; extracurricular activities; employment history; and an essay. Mail the original and ten copies of the complete application with attachments unfolded in an envelope. **Deadline for Receipt:** February 15. **Additional Information:** Robert Carrell at bcarrell@hofferflow.com.

5187 ■ ISA (INSTRUMENTATION, SYSTEMS, AND AUTOMATION)
67 Alexander Dr.
Research Triangle Park, NC 27709
Tel: (919)549-8411
Fax: (919)549-8288
E-mail: info@isa.org
Web Site: http://www.isa.org
To promote education in an instrumentation, systems, or automation discipline.
Title of Award: ISA Technical Division Scholarships - Pulp and Paper Industry Division **Area, Field, or Subject:** Systems engineering; Automotive technology. **Level of Education for which Award is Granted:** Graduate, Undergraduate **Funds Available:** Varies.
Eligibility Requirements: Applicant must be currently enrolled in a graduate or undergraduate program in an instrumentation, systems, or automation discipline (2-year program or 4-year baccalaureate program or its equivalent). Two-year program applicants must have completed at least one academic semester, or 12 semester hours, or its equivalent. Four-year degree program applicants must be in sophomore year or higher at the time of application. Applicants must be full-time students in an educational institution who have an overall GPA of 3.0 on a 4.0 scale. **Application Requirements:** Applicants must submit completed application (with Department Head Signature); two reference letters; original transcript (with raised seal); list of awards and honors; extracurricular activities; employment history; and an essay. Mail the original and ten copies of the complete application with attachments unfolded in an envelope. **Deadline for Receipt:** February 15. **Additional Information:** Brad Carlberg at brad.carlberg@bsc-engineering.com.

5188 ■ ISA (INSTRUMENTATION, SYSTEMS, AND AUTOMATION)
67 Alexander Dr.
Research Triangle Park, NC 27709
Tel: (919)549-8411
Fax: (919)549-8288
E-mail: info@isa.org
Web Site: http://www.isa.org
To promote education in an instrumentation, systems, or automation discipline.
Title of Award: ISA Technical Division Scholarships - Test Measurement Division **Area, Field, or Subject:** Systems engineering; Automotive technology. **Level of Education for which Award is Granted:** Graduate, Undergraduate **Funds Available:** Varies.
Eligibility Requirements: Applicant must be currently enrolled in a graduate or undergraduate program in an instrumentation, systems, or automation discipline (2-year program or 4-year baccalaureate program or its equivalent). Two-year program applicants must have completed at least one academic semester, or 12 semester hours, or its equivalent. Four-year degree program applicants must be in sophomore year or higher at the time of application. Applicants must be full-time students in an educational institution and have at least an overall GPA of 3.0 on a 4.0 scale. **Application Requirements:** Applicants must submit completed application (with Department Head Signature); two reference letters; original transcript (with raised seal); list of awards and honors; extracurricular activities; employment history; and an essay. Mail the original and ten copies of the complete application with attachments unfolded in an envelope. **Deadline for Receipt:** February 15. **Additional Information:** Susan Reel at reelsj@y12.doe.gov.

5189 ■ ISA (INSTRUMENTATION, SYSTEMS, AND AUTOMATION)
67 Alexander Dr.
Research Triangle Park, NC 27709
Tel: (919)549-8411

Fax: (919)549-8288
E-mail: info@isa.org
Web Site: http://www.isa.org
To promote education in an instrumentation, systems, or automation discipline.
Title of Award: ISA Technical Division Scholarships - Water and Wastewater Industries Division **Area, Field, or Subject:** Systems engineering; Automotive technology. **Level of Education for which Award is Granted:** Graduate, Undergraduate **Funds Available:** Varies.
Eligibility Requirements: Applicant must be currently enrolled in a graduate or undergraduate program in an instrumentation, systems, or automation discipline (2-year program or 4-year baccalaureate program or its equivalent). Two-year program applicants must have completed at least one academic semester, or 12 semester hours, or its equivalent. Four-year degree program applicants must be in sophomore year or higher at the time of application. Applicants must be full-time students in an educational institution and have at least an overall GPA of 3.0 on a 4.0 scale. **Application Requirements:** Applicants must submit completed application (with Department Head Signature); two reference letters; original transcript (with raised seal); list of awards and honors; extracurricular activities; employment history; and an essay. Mail the original and ten copies of the complete application with attachments unfolded in an envelope. **Deadline for Receipt:** February 15. **Additional Information:** Steve Valdez at stevenvaldez@member.isa.org.

5190 ■ ISA (INSTRUMENTATION, SYSTEMS, AND AUTOMATION)
67 Alexander Dr.
Research Triangle Park, NC 27709
Tel: (919)549-8411
Fax: (919)549-8288
E-mail: info@isa.org
Web Site: http://www.isa.org
To promote education in an instrumentation, systems, or automation discipline.
Title of Award: Bob and Mary Ives Scholarships **Area, Field, or Subject:** Systems engineering; Automotive technology. **Level of Education for which Award is Granted:** Graduate, Undergraduate **Funds Available:** Varies.
Eligibility Requirements: Applicant must be currently enrolled in a graduate or undergraduate program in an instrumentation, systems, or automation discipline (2 year program or 4 year baccalaureate program or its equivalent). Two-year program applicants must have completed at least one academic semester or its equivalent. Four-year degree program applicants must be in sophomore year or higher at the time of application. Applicants must be full-time students in an educational institution who have at least an overall GPA of 3.0 on a 4.0 scale. **Application Requirements:** Applicants must submit a completed application (with Department Head Signature); two reference letters; original transcript (with raised seal); list of awards and honors; extracurricular activities; employment history; and an essay. Mail the original and ten copies of the complete application with attachments unfolded in an envelope. **Additional Information:** Funds provided by Executive Board action in honor of Robert P. Ives, President of ISA in 2003. **Deadline for Receipt:** February 15.

5191 ■ JACKSON COUNTY COMMUNITY FOUNDATION
One Jackson Square, 100 E Michigan Ave., Ste. 308
Jackson, MI 49201-1406
Tel: (517)787-1321
Fax: (517)787-4333
E-mail: jcf@jacksoncf.org
Web Site: http://www.jacksoncf.org
To provide deserving young students who might otherwise be unable to afford the opportunity to attend a smaller Michigan college.
Title of Award: Dorothy and Dick Burgess Scholarship **Area, Field, or Subject:** Engineering. **Level of Education for which Award is Granted:** Undergraduate **Funds Available:** $4,000.
Eligibility Requirements: Applicants must have plan to pursue a course of study that leads to a degree in earth science, engineering, premedical or Christian ministry; must have plan to complete a baccalaureate within four consecutive years; must have a cumulative GPA of 3.0 or above; must have demonstrated good citizenship, high moral character and potential for leadership and academic success. **Application Requirements:** Applicants must submit a completed application form and must provide a proof of financial need.

5192 ■ JACKSON COUNTY COMMUNITY FOUNDATION
One Jackson Square, 100 E Michigan Ave., Ste. 308
Jackson, MI 49201-1406
Tel: (517)787-1321
Fax: (517)787-4333
E-mail: jcf@jacksoncf.org
Web Site: http://www.jacksoncf.org
To help students who desire to make the automobile business their career.
Title of Award: Bob and Dawn Hardy Automotive Scholarship **Area, Field, or Subject:** Automotive technology. **Level of Education for which Award is Granted:** Undergraduate **Funds Available:** $1,500.
Eligibility Requirements: Applicants must be currently enrolled full- or part-time at Jackson Community College in Automotive Service Technology, Toyota Technical Education Network, Ford Maintenance and Light Repair Associate in Applied Science program or Automotive Service Technology; must have 2.0 GPA or higher. **Application Requirements:** Applicants must submit a completed application form.

5193 ■ JACKSON COUNTY COMMUNITY FOUNDATION
One Jackson Square, 100 E Michigan Ave., Ste. 308
Jackson, MI 49201-1406
Tel: (517)787-1321
Fax: (517)787-4333
E-mail: jcf@jacksoncf.org
Web Site: http://www.jacksoncf.org
To assist all citizens of greater Jackson in improving the quality of their lives; to support its work as a community grantmaker and community leader.
Title of Award: The John and Marion Selby Engineering Scholarship **Area, Field, or Subject:** Engineering. **Level of Education for which Award is Granted:** Undergraduate **Funds Available:** $3,500.
Eligibility Requirements: Applicants must intend to pursue an engineering degree in an accredited (ABET) program at a Michigan College or university; must be accepted by a college or university with a GPA of 3.0 or higher. **Application Requirements:** Applicants must submit a completed application form.

5194 ■ LAM RESEARCH CORPORATION
4650 Cushing Pkwy.
Fremont, CA 94538
Tel: (510)572-0200
E-mail: ehshelpdesk@lamresearch.com
Web Site: http://www.lamresearch.com
To further the education of students who exemplify the core values of the company.
Title of Award: Carl A. Kountz Engineering Scholarships **Area, Field, or Subject:** Engineering. **Level of Education for which Award is Granted:** Undergraduate **Number Awarded:** 2. **Funds Available:** $2,500.
Eligibility Requirements: Applicants must students pursuing study in the area of engineering. **Application Requirements:** Applicants may contact the Community Affairs department for more information about the scholarship. **Additional Information:** Lam Research Corporation Core Values: Achievement; Honesty and integrity; Innovation and continuous improvement; Mutual trust and respect; Open communication; Ownership and accountability; and Teamwork. **Additional Information:** communityaffairs@lamrc.com.

5195 ■ LAM RESEARCH CORPORATION
4650 Cushing Pkwy.
Fremont, CA 94538
Tel: (510)572-0200
E-mail: ehshelpdesk@lamresearch.com
Web Site: http://www.lamresearch.com
To further the education of students who exemplify the core values of the company.
Title of Award: Lam Research Corporation - San Jose State University Scholarships **Area, Field, or Subject:** Engineering. **Level of Education for which Award is Granted:** Undergraduate **Number Awarded:** 4. **Funds Available:** No specific amount. **Duration:** Four years.
Eligibility Requirements: Applicants must be students pursuing study in the area of engineering. **Application Requirements:** Applicants may contact the Community Affairs department for more information about the

scholarship. **Additional Information:** Lam Research Corporation Core Values: Achievement; Honesty and integrity; Innovation and continuous improvement; Mutual trust and respect; Open communication; Ownership and accountability; and Teamwork. **Additional Information:** communityaffairs@lamrc.com.

5196 ■ LEWIS-CLARK STATE COLLEGE
500 8th Ave.
Lewiston, ID 83501
Tel: (208)792-5272
Web Site: http://www.lcsc.edu
To provide financial assistance to students who are majoring in these fields: Accounting, Biology, Business, Communications, Computer Science, Economics, Environmental Science, Engineering, Mathematics, Natural Resources, Political Science, Statistics.
Title of Award: Avista Corporation Minds in Motion Scholarships **Area, Field, or Subject:** Accounting; Biology; Business; Communications; Computer and Information Sciences; Economics; Environmental Science; Engineering; Mathematics; Natural Resources; Political Science; Statistics. **Level of Education for which Award is Granted:** Undergraduate **Number Awarded:** 2. **Funds Available:** No specific Amount.
Eligibility Requirements: Applicants must be full-time students attending LCSC and must have a cumulative GPA of 2.5. **Application Requirements:** Applicants must submit general application. **Deadline for Receipt:** March 1.

5197 ■ LEWIS-CLARK STATE COLLEGE
500 8th Ave.
Lewiston, ID 83501
Tel: (208)792-5272
Web Site: http://www.lcsc.edu
To provide educational assistance for students enrolled in the Diesel Mechanic program at Lewis-Clark State College.
Title of Award: Caterpillar Scholarships in Diesel Mechanics **Area, Field, or Subject:** Mechanics and repairs. **Level of Education for which Award is Granted:** Undergraduate **Funds Available:** No specific amount.
Eligibility Requirements: Applicants must register for 12 or more credits; must be students of LCSC majoring in Diesel mechanic. **Application Requirements:** Applicants must accomplish a general application available in the website. **Deadline for Receipt:** December 21.

5198 ■ LEWIS-CLARK STATE COLLEGE
500 8th Ave.
Lewiston, ID 83501
Tel: (208)792-5272
Web Site: http://www.lcsc.edu
To provide financial assistance for individuals intending to pursue educational goals.
Title of Award: Rob Copeland Memorial Scholarships **Area, Field, or Subject:** Automotive technology. **Level of Education for which Award is Granted:** Undergraduate **Funds Available:** No specific amount.
Eligibility Requirements: Applicants must be full-time students who are majoring in Auto Mechanics Technology. **Application Requirements:** Applicants must accomplish a general application available in the website. **Deadline for Receipt:** March 1.

5199 ■ LEWIS-CLARK STATE COLLEGE
500 8th Ave.
Lewiston, ID 83501
Tel: (208)792-5272
Web Site: http://www.lcsc.edu
To inspire educational pursuits among less capable individuals by providing financial assistance.
Title of Award: Lewis-Clark State College Presidential Technical Out-of-State Scholarships **Area, Field, or Subject:** Chemistry; Computer Science; Engineering; Information Systems Analysis; Industrial Electronics; Biology; Earth Information Systems; Radiology; Heating/Air Conditioning; Automated Manufacturing Technology; Mathematics; Printing Technology; Graphic Arts or Web Development. **Level of Education for which Award is Granted:** Undergraduate **Funds Available:** No specific amount.
Eligibility Requirements: Applicants must be new non-resident high school or transfer students who have at least 14 transferable semester

credits. **Application Requirements:** Applicants must accomplish a general application available in the website. **Deadline for Receipt:** March 1 for Fall enrollment or November 1 for Spring enrollment.

5200 ■ LEWIS-CLARK STATE COLLEGE

500 8th Ave.
Lewiston, ID 83501
Tel: (208)792-5272
Web Site: http://www.lcsc.edu
To provide educational assistance for eligible students who are enrolled full-time in the Auto Body Repair Program at LCSC.
Title of Award: Kenneth Rogers Memorial Scholarships **Area, Field, or Subject:** Automotive Technology. **Level of Education for which Award is Granted:** Undergraduate **Funds Available:** No specific amount.
Eligibility Requirements: Applicants must have a GPA consistent with the minimum required for Admission and for progress toward completion of the Associates degree or certificate and must be enrolled full-time in the Auto Body Repair Program at LCSC. **Application Requirements:** Applicants must accomplish a general application available at the website. **Deadline for Receipt:** March 1.

5201 ■ LEXINGTON COMMUNITY FOUNDATION

607 Washington St.
PO Box 422
Lexington, NE 68850
Tel: (308)324-6704
E-mail: lexfoundation@alltel.net
Web Site: http://www.lexfoundation.org
To promote community philanthropy by working with individuals, families and organizations to develop tailored giving plans that effectively meet the charitable goals and financial circumstances.
Title of Award: Edsel Newman Scholarship **Area, Field, or Subject:** Engineering; Computer and information sciences. **Level of Education for which Award is Granted:** Undergraduate **Funds Available:** $2,000.
Eligibility Requirements: Applicants must be graduating seniors who are planning to pursue a career in the field of engineering an/or computer science; must have ranked in the upper 1/3 of their class and must be U.S. citizens. **Application Requirements:** Applicants must submit a completed application form; must provide three letters of recommendation and must attach a recent photo.

5202 ■ MARINE CORPS ENGINEER ASSOCIATION

PO Box 322
Ashville, NY 14710
Tel: (716)763-5655
E-mail: frantzkd@alltel.net
Web Site: http://www.marcorengasn.org
To provide financial assistance for the education of the members of the United States Marine Corp's engineer and explosive ordinance disposal communities and their families or for members of the United States Armed Forces who have served with or been attached to Marine Corps Air Ground Task Force engineer or EOD units.
Title of Award: Marine Corps Engineer Association Assistance Fund **Area, Field, or Subject:** Engineering. **Level of Education for which Award is Granted:** Graduate, High School, Undergraduate **Funds Available:** No specified amount.
Eligibility Requirements: Program is open to citizens of the United States over the age of 18 years old seeking for financial assistance to further education beyond high school at an accredited college, university or higher technical trade school up to a maximum of four years. They can also be individuals who are already enrolled in a post-secondary curriculum. Neither graduate study request nor applications at the high school or prep school level are acceptable. **Application Requirements:** Applicants must complete and submit the application form and enclose all items requested in the application; name and address; and have the application and attachment notarized. **Deadline for Receipt:** June 30.

5203 ■ MARINE TECHNOLOGY SOCIETY

5565 Sterrett Pl., Ste. 108
Columbia, MD 21044
Tel: (410)884-5330
Fax: (410)884-9060
E-mail: membership@mtsociety.org
Web Site: http://www.mtsociety.org
To help students achieve success.
Title of Award: Marine Technology Society Student Scholarships for Two-year Technical, Engineering and Community College Students **Area, Field, or Subject:** Marine; Marine Engineering. **Level of Education for which Award is Granted:** Undergraduate **Funds Available:** $2,000.
Eligibility Requirements: Applicants must be enrolled in a two-year technical, engineering or community college in a marine-related field. **Application Requirements:** Applicants must submit a written recommendation from a current teacher or counselor in a marine-related field; a written letter of reference from someone who is not a teacher or counselor; an official sealed transcript. For high school seniors, proof of acceptance to a two-year or four-year academic program must be submitted. **Additional Information:** scholarships@mtsociety.org.

5204 ■ MASSACHUSETTS ASSOCIATION OF LAND SURVEYORS AND CIVIL ENGINEERS

50 Depot St.
Dalton, MA 01226-1806
Tel: (413)684-0925
Fax: (413)684-0267
E-mail: mcorcoran@hillengineers.com
Web Site: http://www.malsce.org
To provide support for qualified individuals intending to pursue their studies.
Title of Award: MALSE Scholarships **Area, Field, or Subject:** Surveying; Civil engineering. **Level of Education for which Award is Granted:** Undergraduate **Funds Available:** No specific amount. **Duration:** One year.
Eligibility Requirements: Applicants must be enrolled full-time in a college, university, junior college, technical institute or community college; must be residents of Massachusetts or attending an out-of-state school; and must be majoring in surveying, civil or environmental engineering. **Application Requirements:** Applicants must write/call the chairman for an application; must complete the application form available online; must have a letter of recommendation; and must submit a transcript of grades. Application form and other supporting materials must be sent to MALSE Scholarship Chair, 50 Depot St., Dalton, MA 01226-1806. **Deadline for Receipt:** July. **Additional Information:** Mary Ann Corcoran at the above address.

5205 ■ MASSACHUSETTS STATE AUTOMOBILE DEALERS ASSOCIATION

59 Temple Pl., Ste. 505
Boston, MA 02111
Tel: (617)451-1051
Fax: (617)451-9309
E-mail: spoikail@msada.org
Web Site: http://www.msada.org
To enrich the lives of auto tech students through scholarships.
Title of Award: Automotive Technician Scholarship Program **Area, Field, or Subject:** Automotive technology. **Level of Education for which Award is Granted:** Undergraduate **Number Awarded:** 17. **Funds Available:** $6,000.
Eligibility Requirements: Applicants must be retraining for a career change or a recent high school graduate. Applicants must be enrolled in an automotive program at an accredited college. **Application Requirements:** Applicants must submit a curriculum vitae; the complete application form; a three-page applicant's appraisal; and complete transcript of record. **Additional Information:** 617-451-9309.

5206 ■ MATANUSKA-SUSITNA COLLEGE

PO Box 2889
Palmer, AK 99645
Tel: (907)745-9774
Fax: (907)745-9711
E-mail: info@matsu.alaska.edu
Web Site: http://www.matsu.alaska.edu
To provide support to deserving students in Alaska who want to pursue an education in any campus of the University of Alaska.
Title of Award: Alaska Aerospace Development Corporation Scholarships **Area, Field, or Subject:** Applied mathematics; Physics; Engineering; Business; Technical communications. **Level of Education for which Award is Granted:** Undergraduate **Funds Available:** $5,000.

Eligibility Requirements: Applicant must be a freshman student majoring in mathematics, physics, engineering, business, or a technical science field such as computer science who has graduated from the Kodiak Island Borough School District; must be a full-time student enrolled in 14 credits and in good academic standing. **Application Requirements:** Applicants must submit a written statement verifying that he/she has not been convicted of a crime other than a minor traffic violation; must complete the application forms available at the website; must attach a personal essay, two letters of recommendation, and current transcripts. **Deadline for Receipt:** February 15.

5207 ■ MATANUSKA-SUSITNA COLLEGE
PO Box 2889
Palmer, AK 99645
Tel: (907)745-9774
Fax: (907)745-9711
E-mail: info@matsu.alaska.edu
Web Site: http://www.matsu.alaska.edu
To provide financial support for deserving students in Alaska intending to pursue an education in any campus of the University of Alaska.
Title of Award: Alaska Support Industry Alliance Scholarships **Area, Field, or Subject:** Resource management, Biology, Wildlife conservation, management, and science, Petroleum engineering. **Level of Education for which Award is Granted:** Undergraduate **Funds Available:** $500.
Eligibility Requirements: Applicants must be full-time students and Alaska residents who have at least 3.0 GPA majoring in a field that will support the industry growth in Alaska and at the same time showing concern for the environment and how industry is developed. **Application Requirements:** Applicants must complete the application forms available in the website; must attach a personal essay, two letters of recommendation, and their current transcripts. **Deadline for Receipt:** February 15.

5208 ■ MATANUSKA-SUSITNA COLLEGE
PO Box 2889
Palmer, AK 99645
Tel: (907)745-9774
Fax: (907)745-9711
E-mail: info@matsu.alaska.edu
Web Site: http://www.matsu.alaska.edu
To provide support to deserving students in Alaska who want to pursue an education in any campus of the University of Alaska.
Title of Award: Amos Joe Alter ASCE Section Alaska Section Scholarships **Area, Field, or Subject:** Civil engineering. **Level of Education for which Award is Granted:** Undergraduate **Funds Available:** $1,000.
Eligibility Requirements: Applicant must be a full-time student attending the University of Alaska at Anchorage or the University of Alaska at Fairbanks, and must be a civil engineering major. **Application Requirements:** Applicant must complete the application forms available at the website; must attach a personal essay, two letters of recommendation, and current transcripts. **Deadline for Receipt:** February 15.

5209 ■ MATANUSKA-SUSITNA COLLEGE
PO Box 2889
Palmer, AK 99645
Tel: (907)745-9774
Fax: (907)745-9711
E-mail: info@matsu.alaska.edu
Web Site: http://www.matsu.alaska.edu
To provide support to deserving students in Alaska who want to pursue an education in any campus of the University of Alaska.
Title of Award: Mike Ardaw Scholarships **Area, Field, or Subject:** Science; Education; Engineering. **Level of Education for which Award is Granted:** Undergraduate **Funds Available:** $1,000.
Eligibility Requirements: Applicant must be a full-time student and have a minimum GPA of 2.5. **Application Requirements:** Applicant must complete the application forms available at the website; must attach a personal essay, two letters of recommendation, and current transcripts. **Deadline for Receipt:** February 15.

5210 ■ MATANUSKA-SUSITNA COLLEGE
PO Box 2889
Palmer, AK 99645
Tel: (907)745-9774

Fax: (907)745-9711
E-mail: info@matsu.alaska.edu
Web Site: http://www.matsu.alaska.edu
To provide support to deserving students in Alaska who want to pursue an education in any campus of the University of Alaska.
Title of Award: Charles E. Behlke Engineering Memorial Scholarships **Area, Field, or Subject:** Engineering. **Level of Education for which Award is Granted:** Undergraduate **Funds Available:** $1,000.
Eligibility Requirements: Applicants must be full-time students entering their sophomore, junior, or senior year; must be engineering majors; must be in good academic standing with a minimum GPA of 2.5. **Application Requirements:** Applicant must complete the application forms available at the website; must attach a personal essay, two letters of recommendation, and current transcripts. **Deadline for Receipt:** February 15.

5211 ■ MATANUSKA-SUSITNA COLLEGE
PO Box 2889
Palmer, AK 99645
Tel: (907)745-9774
Fax: (907)745-9711
E-mail: info@matsu.alaska.edu
Web Site: http://www.matsu.alaska.edu
To provide support to deserving students in Alaska who want to pursue an education in any campus of the University of Alaska.
Title of Award: Bill & Nell Biggs Scholarships **Area, Field, or Subject:** Accounting; Business administration; Engineering; Science; Mathematics and mathematical sciences. **Level of Education for which Award is Granted:** Undergraduate **Funds Available:** $500.
Eligibility Requirements: Applicants must be graduates of Juneau-Douglas High School or Juneau residents who have completed a high school equivalency program. **Application Requirements:** Applicant must complete the application forms available at the website; must attach a personal essay, two letters of recommendation, and current transcripts. **Deadline for Receipt:** February 15.

5212 ■ MATANUSKA-SUSITNA COLLEGE
PO Box 2889
Palmer, AK 99645
Tel: (907)745-9774
Fax: (907)745-9711
E-mail: info@matsu.alaska.edu
Web Site: http://www.matsu.alaska.edu
To provide support to deserving students in Alaska who want to pursue an education in any campus of the University of Alaska.
Title of Award: Ralph Yetka Memorial Scholarships **Area, Field, or Subject:** Engineering; Education, Elementary; Education, Secondary; Computer and information sciences. **Level of Education for which Award is Granted:** Undergraduate **Funds Available:** $750.
Eligibility Requirements: Applicants must be full-time students and graduates of Ketchikan or Revilla High School with a minimum GPA of 2.5; must be majoring in engineering, elementary or secondary education, computer science or aviation. **Application Requirements:** Applicant must complete the application forms available at the website; must attach a personal essay, two letters of recommendation, and current transcripts. **Deadline for Receipt:** February 15.

5213 ■ MICHIGAN SOCIETY OF PROFESSIONAL ENGINEERS
PO Box 5276
Lansing, MI 48901
Tel: (517)487-9388
Fax: (517)487-0635
E-mail: mspe@voyager.net
Web Site: http://www.michiganspe.org
To encourage high school seniors with the talent and commitment to pursue an engineering degree.
Title of Award: Michigan Society of Professional Engineers Scholarships **Area, Field, or Subject:** Engineering. **Level of Education for which Award is Granted:** Undergraduate **Funds Available:** No specific amount.
Eligibility Requirements: Applicants must be accepted at a Michigan ABET accredited college or university and enroll in an engineering program; must be high school seniors, residents of Michigan and U.S. citizens at the time of application; must have at least 3.0 GPA based on

4.0 scale for the 10th and 11th grades; and must attain a minimum composite test score of 26 on the American College Testing (ACT Exam). **Application Requirements:** Applicants must submit a completed application form which can be obtained from a guidance counselor, local chapters or the MSPE Headquarters; a list of senior classes being taken; and a documented high school transcript and ACT test scores. **Additional Information:** mspe@voyager.net.

5214 ■ MOLINE FOUNDATION
817 11th Ave.
Moline, IL 61265
Tel: (309)736-3800
Fax: (309)736-3721
E-mail: molinefoundation@gconline.com
Web Site: http://www.molinefoundation.org
To provide grants to health, human services, education, community development, the arts, and other charitable organizations which benefit the citizens of Moline Foundations. To encourage engineering as a career and provide an incentive for young college graduates to return to live and work in Quad cities.
Title of Award: Engineers for Tomorrow Scholarships Program **Area, Field, or Subject:** Engineering. **Level of Education for which Award is Granted:** Undergraduate **Funds Available:** $16,000.
Eligibility Requirements: Applicants must be graduating high school seniors, or community college students preparing to transfer to four-year colleges. Applicants must intend to pursue a bachelor's degree on a full-time basis. Applicants must demonstrate financial need. Applicants must have achieved high school scholastic performance in the upper one-third of their class, or community college grade performance of 2.5 on a 4.0 scale, or equivalent. **Application Requirements:** Applicants must complete the application form. **Additional Information:** 309-736-3800.

5215 ■ MONTANA BROADCASTERS ASSOCIATION
HC 70, Box 90
Bonner, MT 59823
Tel: (406)244-4622
Fax: (406)244-5518
E-mail: mba@mtbroadcasters.org
Web Site: http://www.mtbroadcasters.org
To promote the values of local, free over-the-air broadcasting to the business community, governmental bodies and the general public in Montana; and to support the Montana broadcasting industry by providing services, information, continuing education, recruitment and a strong unified voice.
Title of Award: Montana Broadcasters Association Engineers' Scholarships **Area, Field, or Subject:** Broadcasting; Engineering. **Level of Education for which Award is Granted:** Undergraduate **Funds Available:** No specific amount.
Eligibility Requirements: Applicants must be second year students, majoring in Engineering at the UM College of Technology, and interested in pursuing a career in Broadcast Engineering. **Application Requirements:** Applicants must submit completed application form.

5216 ■ NATIONAL ASSOCIATION OF MULTICULTURAL ENGINEERING PROGRAM ADVOCATES
341 N Maitland Ave., Ste. 130
Maitland, FL 32751-4761
Tel: (407)647-8839
Fax: (407)629-2502
E-mail: namepa@namepa.org
Web Site: http://www.namepa.org
To support students who have demonstrated potential and interest in pursuing an undergraduate degree in engineering.
Title of Award: Beginning Freshmen Awards **Area, Field, or Subject:** Engineering. **Level of Education for which Award is Granted:** Undergraduate **Funds Available:** $1,000.
Eligibility Requirements: Applicants must be African American, Latino, and American Indian students who have been approved for admission as engineering majors. Applicants must also have a minimum cumulative grade point average of 2.70-4.00 and minimum cumulative scores on either the ACT/SAT college entrance examination of 25-1000. Students must attend a NAMEPA member institution. **Application Requirements:** Applicants must submit the following: an official copy of high school transcript and test scores; a one-page essay expressing their reasons for choosing engineering, why they think they should be selected, and an overview of their future aspirations as an engineer; resume; and a completed recommendation form. The application and recommendation forms are available from the website. **Deadline for Receipt:** May 15.

5217 ■ NATIONAL ASSOCIATION OF MULTICULTURAL ENGINEERING PROGRAM ADVOCATES
341 N Maitland Ave., Ste. 130
Maitland, FL 32751-4761
Tel: (407)647-8839
Fax: (407)629-2502
E-mail: namepa@namepa.org
Web Site: http://www.namepa.org
For students who have demonstrated potential and interest in pursuing an undergraduate degree in engineering.
Title of Award: Transfer Engineering Student Awards **Area, Field, or Subject:** Engineering. **Level of Education for which Award is Granted:** Undergraduate **Funds Available:** $1,000.
Eligibility Requirements: Applicants must be African American, Latino, and American Indian students admitted as transfer students from either a junior college, community college or three/two dual-degree program; must have a minimum grade point average of 2.70-4.00. **Application Requirements:** Applicants must submit a complete application package including a completed application and recommendation form available from the website; an official copy of college transcripts; a one-page essay expressing their reasons for choosing engineering, why they think they should be selected, and an overview of their future aspirations as an engineer; and a resume. **Deadline for Receipt:** May 15.

5218 ■ NATIONAL COMMISSION FOR COOPERATIVE EDUCATION
360 Huntington Ave., 384 CP
Boston, MA 02115-5096
Tel: (617)373-3770
Fax: (617)373-3463
E-mail: ncce@neu.edu
Web Site: http://www.co-op.edu
To assist students pursuing education in science, mathematics, engineering and technology.
Title of Award: National Co-op Scholarship Program **Area, Field, or Subject:** Mathematics and mathematical sciences; Science; Engineering. **Level of Education for which Award is Granted:** Undergraduate **Funds Available:** No specific amount.
Eligibility Requirements: Applicants must be have a high school GPA of 3.5 (B+) or better. **Application Requirements:** Applicants must complete the National Co-op Scholarship program application including a typed one-page essay. Application materials and must be sent directly to the applicant's college or university. **Deadline for Receipt:** February 15.

5219 ■ NATIONAL EAGLE SCOUT ASSOCIATION
PO Box 152079
Irving, TX 75015-2079
Tel: (972)580-2114
E-mail: eagletter@netbsa.org
Web Site: http://www.nesa.org
To assist the education of an Eagle Scout student.
Title of Award: Lamar University College of Engineering Scholarships **Area, Field, or Subject:** Engineering. **Level of Education for which Award is Granted:** Undergraduate **Funds Available:** $5000 per year.
Eligibility Requirements: Applicant must be a Lamar University undergraduate student, including entering freshmen, majoring in chemical, civil, electrical, industrial, or mechanical engineering. **Application Requirements:** Applicants must submit a completed Scholarship application form. **Additional Information:** Award is given by Lamar University College of Engineering, Beaumont, Texas. **Deadline for Receipt:** February 1. **Additional Information:** Ron Peevy, Director of Recruiting and Cooperative Education, Lamar University College of Engineering P.O. Box 10057 Beaumont, TX 77710, at 409-880-7870, or ronald.peevy@lamar.edu START HERE...

5220 ■ NATIONAL FEDERATION OF THE BLIND
1800 Johnson St.
Baltimore, MD 21230
Tel: (410)659-9314

Fax: (410)685-5653

Web Site: http://www.nfb.org

To recognize achievement of blind scholars and to create opportunity for all blind people.

Title of Award: Howard B. Rickard Scholarships **Area, Field, or Subject:** Law; Medicine; Engineering; Architecture; Natural Science. **Level of Education for which Award is Granted:** Undergraduate **Funds Available:** $3,000.

Eligibility Requirements: All applicants must be legally blind; he/she must be pursuing or planning to study in the field of law, medicine, engineering, architecture or the natural science; he/she must be participant in NFB national convention and in all scheduled scholarship program activities. **Application Requirements:** Applicant must fill out the application form; he/she must submit two letters of recommendation from individuals that can describe the academic ability, leadership skills, and/or community involvement; copies of transcript of record and a photocopy of score reports for all standardized tests taken for college admission (ACT, SAT or other); an applicant must provide a letter of proof of legal blindness from a qualified professional; and an affiliate President's letter. **Deadline for Receipt:** March 31.

5221 ■ NATIONAL FORUM FOR BLACK PUBLIC ADMINISTRATORS

777 N Capitol St. NE, Ste. 807

Washington, DC 20002

Tel: (202)408-9300

Fax: (202)408-8558

E-mail: webmaster@nfbpa.org

Web Site: http://www.nfbpa.org

To provide financial assistance for the education and development of public administrators serving in the engineering and information technology field.

Title of Award: RA Consulting Service Maria Riley Scholarships **Area, Field, or Subject:** Engineering. **Level of Education for which Award is Granted:** Graduate, Undergraduate **Funds Available:** $1,500.

Eligibility Requirements: Applicants must be full-time students, working towards an undergraduate or graduate degree in engineering or information technology with excellent interpersonal and analytical abilities, strong oral and written communication skills and a 3.0 or better grade point average for at least 1 remaining full time semester. **Application Requirements:** Applicants must submit cover letter describing current student status, and other relevant information that might be used in evaluating your application (extra-curricula activities, volunteer activities, etc); official copies of all graduate (if applicable) and undergraduate transcripts (transcripts must be included in application package, not sent separately); two reference letters (at least one of which should be from a faculty member); three-page essay detailing his/her autobiography and career goals and objectives; and a current resume. **Deadline for Receipt:** February 27.

5222 ■ NATIONAL SPACE CLUB

2025 M St. NW, Ste. 800

Washington, DC 20006

Tel: (202)973-8661

E-mail: info@spaceclub.org

Web Site: http://www.spaceclub.org

To stimulate the interest of students in the opportunity to advance scientific knowledge through space research and exploration.

Title of Award: Dr. Robert H. Goddard Memorial Scholarships **Area, Field, or Subject:** Engineering; Science. **Level of Education for which Award is Granted:** Graduate, Undergraduate **Number Awarded:** 1. **Funds Available:** $10,000. **Duration:** One year.

Eligibility Requirements: Applicant must be a U.S. citizen, in at least the junior year of an accredited university, and have the intention of pursuing undergraduate or graduate studies in science or engineering during the interval of the scholarship. **Application Requirements:** Applicants must submit an official transcript of college record; letters of recommendation from faculty; accomplishments demonstrating personal qualities of creativity and leadership; scholastic plans that would lead to future participation in some phase of the aerospace sciences and technology; and past research and participation in space-related science and engineering. **Deadline for Receipt:** January 6.

5223 ■ NEW HAMPSHIRE AUTOMOTIVE DEALERS ASSOCIATION

PO Box 2337, 507 S St.

Concord, NH 03302-2337

Tel: (603)224-2369

Free: 800-852-3372

Fax: (603)225-4895

E-mail: pmcnamara@nhada.com

Web Site: http://www.nhada.com

To assist individuals who are interested in attending accredited vocational or technical programs; to improve the workforce skills, especially in areas of need, in the state of New Hampshire.

Title of Award: The Medallion Fund Scholarships **Area, Field, or Subject:** Automotive technology. **Level of Education for which Award is Granted:** Undergraduate **Funds Available:** No specific amount.

Eligibility Requirements: Applicants must be legal residents of New Hampshire; must have a keen desire to work in a vocational/technical career. **Application Requirements:** Applicants must submit a completed application form, high school or college transcript, a signed letter of recommendation from an Automotive Technology or other technical instructor and a signed letter of recommendation from a high school math, science or English teacher, verifying applicants' ability to do satisfactory academic work at the postsecondary level. **Additional Information:** 37 Pleasant St., concord, NH 03301-4005.

5224 ■ PENNSYLVANIA SOCIETY OF PROFESSIONAL ENGINEERS

908 N 2nd St.

Harrisburg, PA 17102

Tel: (717)441-6051

Fax: (717)236-2046

E-mail: pspeinfo@pspe.org

Web Site: http://www.pspe.org

To provide financial assistance for freshmen students to pursue their academic goals in the engineering field of study.

Title of Award: Pennsylvania Society of Professional Engineers Scholarships **Area, Field, or Subject:** Engineering. **Level of Education for which Award is Granted:** Undergraduate **Number Awarded:** 6. **Funds Available:** $4,000.

Eligibility Requirements: Applicants must be freshmen attending their first semester of college at an ABET-accredited engineering School in the Commonwealth of Pennsylvania. **Application Requirements:** Applicants must submit all the required application information.

5225 ■ PENNSYLVANIA STATE SYSTEM OF HIGHER EDUCATION FOUNDATION

2986 N 2nd St.

Harrisburg, PA 17110

Tel: (717)720-4086

Fax: (717)720-7082

Web Site: http://www.thepafoundation.org

To provide financial assistance to increase the number of basic education teachers with strong content knowledge in science, technology, engineering, and mathematics (STEM).

Title of Award: Robert Noyce Scholarship Program **Area, Field, or Subject:** Science; Technology; Engineering; Mathematics and mathematical sciences. **Level of Education for which Award is Granted:** Undergraduate **Funds Available:** $10,000. **Duration:** One year.

Eligibility Requirements: Applicants must have a qualifying cumulative GPA of 3.00, with preference for those with a GPA of 3.5 or higher; must be transfer students or post-baccalaureates who completed a semester or more of coursework at a State System university to establish the qualifying GPA of 3.00; must be full-time students during each semester for which the award is received. **Application Requirements:** Applicants must submit completed application form; official transcripts from all institutions attended; a two page essay describing personal and professional goals, commitment to teaching and personal philosophy of teaching; three letters of recommendation that must address, but are not limited to: a) the scholarship of the applicant, b) the character of the applicant, c) the interpersonal skills of the applicant relative to teaching, and d) the general interpersonal skills of the applicant; and a resume. **Deadline for Receipt:** April 20.

5226 ■ PINNACLE WEST CAPITAL CORPORATION

PO Box 53999

Phoenix, AZ 85072-3999

Tel: (602)250-1000
Free: 800-457-2983
Web Site: http://www.pinnaclewest.com
To provide financial assistance to qualified individuals who want to pursue their career.
Title of Award: APS/ASU Scholarships **Area, Field, or Subject:** Chemical engineering; Electrical engineering; Mechanical engineering; Civil engineering; Construction; Telecommunications systems; Accounting; Finance; Economics; Information science and technology; Education, Elementary; Education, Secondary; Special education; Nursing. **Level of Education for which Award is Granted:** Undergraduate **Number Awarded:** 10. **Funds Available:** $2,000. **Duration:** One year.
Eligibility Requirements: Applicant must be an Arizona resident; must have a cumulative GPA of at least 3.0; must demonstrate financial need.
Application Requirements: Applicant must complete the application form available online and send it to ASU Scholarship Office, Arizona State University, PO Box 470412, Tempe, AZ 85287-0412. **Deadline for Receipt:** March 1. **Additional Information:** Louise Moskowitz at louise. moskowitz@aps.com.

5227 ■ PINNACLE WEST CAPITAL CORPORATION
PO Box 53999
Phoenix, AZ 85072-3999
Tel: (602)250-1000
Free: 800-457-2983
Web Site: http://www.pinnaclewest.com
To provide financial assistance to qualified individuals who want to pursue their career.
Title of Award: APS/Maricopa County Community Colleges Scholarships **Area, Field, or Subject:** Mechanical engineering; Electrical engineering; Civil engineering; Chemical engineering; Trades training; Information science and technology; Marketing and distribution; Accounting; Finance; Economics; Management; Education; Health care services. **Level of Education for which Award is Granted:** Undergraduate **Number Awarded:** 25. **Funds Available:** $1,000. **Duration:** One year.
Eligibility Requirements: Applicant must be an Arizona resident; must have a cumulative GPA of at least 3.0; must demonstrate financial need; must be a high school senior or current Maricopa Community College student; must be enrolled in a minimum of nine credit hours per semester.
Application Requirements: Applicant must complete the application form available online and must be sent to ASU Scholarship Office, Arizona State University, PO Box 470412, Tempe, AZ 85287-0412. **Additional Information:** Louise Moskowitz at louise.moskowitz@aps.com.

5228 ■ POLISH AMERICAN ENGINEERS ASSOCIATION
5835 W Irving Park Rd.
Chicago, IL 60634
E-mail: contact@polishengineers.org
Web Site: http://www.polishengineers.org
To provide financial assistance for qualified engineering students.
Title of Award: Ralph Modjeski Scholarships **Area, Field, or Subject:** Engineering. **Level of Education for which Award is Granted:** Graduate, Undergraduate **Funds Available:** No specific amount.
Eligibility Requirements: Applicant must be an engineering student at 4-year college or university or can also be a graduate engineering who demonstrates excellent academic achievements and proven commitment to engineering. **Application Requirements:** Applicants must complete the application form, available online; must submit an official transcript, 200-word letter describing the student's short and long term goals with any other information deemed pertinent; and must have three references with addresses and telephone numbers. Application form and requirements must be sent to Polish American Engineers Association, 5835 W Irving Park Rd., Chicago, IL 60634. **Deadline for Receipt:** June 30.

5229 ■ PROFESSIONAL CONSTRUCTION ESTIMATORS ASSOCIATION OF AMERICA
PO Box 680336
Charlotte, NC 28216
Tel: (704)489-1494; 877-521-7232
Fax: (704)489-1495
E-mail: pcea@pcea.org
Web Site: http://www.pcea.org

To provide financial assistance to those who plan to further their education in the construction industry.
Title of Award: Ted C. Wilson Memorial Scholarships **Area, Field, or Subject:** Engineering; Construction. **Level of Education for which Award is Granted:** Undergraduate **Funds Available:** $1,500. **Duration:** One year.
Eligibility Requirements: Applicant must be a high school senior, college freshman, sophomore or junior student planning to further his/her education in the construction industry. Applicant must be a resident of, or plan to attend a school or university in North Carolina, South Carolina, Virginia, Georgia and Florida where PCEA has an established chapter. **Application Requirements:** Applicants must submit a completed application form; one evaluation form completed by the high school Guidance Counselor or College Faculty Advisor, whichever is applicable at time of application; one evaluation form completed by an adult not related to the applicant; official transcript of high school/college grades and latest S.A.T. scores if available. Finalists may be interviewed by the Scholarship Committee. **Additional Information:** Established in May 21, 1988 in memory of Ted Wilson (1932-1987), the first National Executive Director of the PCEA. **Deadline for Receipt:** March 15.

5230 ■ PUBLIC EDUCATION FOUNDATION
3360 W Sahara Ave., Ste. 160
Las Vegas, NV 89102
Tel: (702)799-1042
Fax: (702)799-5247
E-mail: steelej@ccpef.org
Web Site: http://ccpef.org
To promote education in the field of nuclear science.
Title of Award: American Nuclear Society Nevada Section Scholarships **Area, Field, or Subject:** Engineering, Nuclear; Nuclear science. **Level of Education for which Award is Granted:** Undergraduate **Number Awarded:** 2. **Funds Available:** $1,000.
Eligibility Requirements: Applicants must be CCSD seniors planning to major in nuclear engineering or a nuclear science related field at UNLV with a minimum 3.8 cumulative GPA. **Application Requirements:** Applicants must submit a completed application form together with an essay, two letters of recommendation, transcript and a resume of awards. **Deadline for Receipt:** March 7. **Additional Information:** Shana Venenga at 702-799-1042.

5231 ■ PUBLIC EDUCATION FOUNDATION
3360 W Sahara Ave., Ste. 160
Las Vegas, NV 89102
Tel: (702)799-1042
Fax: (702)799-5247
E-mail: steelej@ccpef.org
Web Site: http://ccpef.org
To promote education in the field of engineering or science.
Title of Award: National Security Technologies Engineering and Science Scholarships **Area, Field, or Subject:** Engineering; Science. **Level of Education for which Award is Granted:** Undergraduate **Number Awarded:** Up to 10. **Funds Available:** $5,000.
Eligibility Requirements: Applicants must be CCSD seniors planning to major in engineering or science at a four-year institution with a minimum 3.5 cumulative GPA. **Application Requirements:** Applicants must submit a completed application form along with an essay, transcript, and three letters of recommendation. **Deadline for Receipt:** March 7. **Additional Information:** Shana Venenga at 702-799-1042.

5232 ■ PUBLIC EDUCATION FOUNDATION
3360 W Sahara Ave., Ste. 160
Las Vegas, NV 89102
Tel: (702)799-1042
Fax: (702)799-5247
E-mail: steelej@ccpef.org
Web Site: http://ccpef.org
To provide educational opportunities for individuals intending to pursue higher studies.
Title of Award: Pardee Community Building Scholarships **Area, Field, or Subject:** Business; Civil engineering; Architecture; Construction. **Level of Education for which Award is Granted:** Undergraduate **Number Awarded:** 10. **Funds Available:** $1,500. **Duration:** One year.

Eligibility Requirements: Applicants must be CCSD seniors who have demonstrated an interest in home building and community development; must be planning to attend a Nevada accredited college or university; must be pursuing studies in areas of business, civil engineering, architecture or landscape architecture and construction management; and must have a minimum 2.8 cumulative GPA. **Application Requirements:** Applicants must submit a completed application form along with an essay, two letters of recommendation, transcript, and resume of awards. **Deadline for Receipt:** March 7. **Additional Information:** Shana Venenga at 702-799-1042.

5233 ■ PUBLIC EDUCATION FOUNDATION

3360 W Sahara Ave., Ste. 160
Las Vegas, NV 89102
Tel: (702)799-1042
Fax: (702)799-5247
E-mail: steelej@ccpef.org
Web Site: http://ccpef.org
To provide educational opportunities for individuals intending to pursue higher studies.
Title of Award: Josef Princ Memorial Scholarships **Area, Field, or Subject:** Engineering; Mathematics and mathematical sciences. **Level of Education for which Award is Granted:** Undergraduate **Number Awarded:** 3. **Funds Available:** $2,000.
Eligibility Requirements: Applicants must be CCSD male seniors of European descent; must be maintaining a minimum 3.5 cumulative GPA; must be demonstrating financial need; and must be planning to attend an accredited post-secondary college/university majoring in engineering, mathematics or science. **Application Requirements:** Applicants must submit a completed application form along with an essay, two letters of recommendation, transcript, and resume of awards. **Deadline for Receipt:** March 7. **Additional Information:** Shana Venenga at 702-799-1042.

5234 ■ REDLANDS COMMUNITY SCHOLARSHIP FOUNDATION

c/o Kathleen Venegas-Boge, Admin. Asst.
PO Box 1683
Redlands, CA 92373
Tel: (909)307-9892
Fax: (909)307-9892
Web Site: http://www.redlandsscholarships.org
To encourage educational pursuits among Redlands Unified School District graduates by providing educational assistance.
Title of Award: Harold Leeming Memorial Scholarships **Area, Field, or Subject:** Engineering; Physical sciences. **Level of Education for which Award is Granted:** Undergraduate **Number Awarded:** 2. **Funds Available:** $1,000.
Eligibility Requirements: Applicant must be a graduating senior who has an interest in engineering or physical science; must have played an active part in school and community activities; and must be enrolled in engineering or physical science courses. **Application Requirements:** Applicants must submit a completed application form together with the scantron sheet; cover sheet; student activity and community activity sheets; personal essay; and a copy of unofficial transcript (signed by the counselor). **Additional Information:** No electronic submissions of application will be accepted. Submit two printed copies of the application and use a No. 2 pencil on the scantron sheet. **Deadline for Receipt:** February 20.

5235 ■ REDLANDS COMMUNITY SCHOLARSHIP FOUNDATION

c/o Kathleen Venegas-Boge, Admin. Asst.
PO Box 1683
Redlands, CA 92373
Tel: (909)307-9892
Fax: (909)307-9892
Web Site: http://www.redlandsscholarships.org
To encourage educational pursuits among Redlands Unified School District graduates by providing educational assistance.
Title of Award: Soroptimist International of Redlands Scholarships **Area, Field, or Subject:** Health care services; Law; Engineering; Computer and information sciences; Education; Business. **Level of Education for which Award is Granted:** Undergraduate **Number Awarded:** 1. **Funds Available:** $750.

Eligibility Requirements: Applicant must be a graduating senior who has participated in community service and who will be attending an accredited college on a full-time basis and is planning to major in one of the following fields: health care, law, engineering, computer science, education and/or business administration. **Application Requirements:** Applicants must submit a completed application form together with the scantron sheet; cover sheet; student activity and community activity sheets; personal essay; and a copy of unofficial transcript (signed by the counselor). **Additional Information:** No electronic submissions of application will be accepted. Submit two printed copies of the application and use a No. 2 pencil on the scantron sheet. **Deadline for Receipt:** February 20.

5236 ■ ROCKY MOUNTAIN COAL MINING INSTITUTE

8057 S Yukon Way
Littleton, CO 80128-5510
Tel: (303)948-3300
Fax: (303)948-1132
E-mail: mail@rmcmi.org
Web Site: http://www.rmcmi.org
To provide financial aid to junior and senior year students who are career-pathed in mining related industries.
Title of Award: Rocky Mountain Coal Mining Institute Engineering/Geology Scholarships **Area, Field, or Subject:** Engineering, Geological; Engineering. **Level of Education for which Award is Granted:** Undergraduate **Number Awarded:** 1 candidate from each state. **Funds Available:** $2,000. **Duration:** One up to two years.
Eligibility Requirements: Applicant must be a full-time college sophomore or junior at the time of selection; both a U.S. citizen and a legal resident of one of the Rocky Mountain Coal Mining Institute member states Arizona, Colorado, Montana, New Mexico, North Dakota, Texas, Utah, or Wyoming; pursuing a degree in a mining-related field or in the engineering disciplines; interested in coal as a career path. **Application Requirements:** Applicants must submit a completed application form that can be downloaded from www.rmcmi.org. **Additional Information:** Established in 1984. **Deadline for Receipt:** February 1. **Additional Information:** Karen Inzano, RMCMI Executive Director, or Beth Coen.

5237 ■ RUBBER DIVISION AMERICAN CHEMICAL SOCIETY

PO Box 499
Akron, OH 44309-0499
Tel: (330)972-7814
Fax: (330)972-5269
Web Site: http://www.rubber.org
To provide financial assistance to students pursuing a college degree related to rubber technology, polymer science or the chemical profession.
Title of Award: Rubber Division American Chemical Society Scholarships **Area, Field, or Subject:** Chemistry; Physics; Chemical engineering; Mechanical engineering. **Level of Education for which Award is Granted:** Undergraduate **Funds Available:** $5,000. **Duration:** One academic year.
Eligibility Requirements: Applicants must be enrolled in an accredited university or college where rubber division has a partner organization; must be students majoring in chemistry, physics, chemical engineering, mechanical engineering, polymer science or any other field related to the rubber industry. **Application Requirements:** Applicants must send application form; two nomination letters; and transcript mailed by school registrar via regular mail. **Deadline for Receipt:** March. **Additional Information:** Christie Robinson, Education & Publications Manager, 330-972-7815.

5238 ■ THE SAN DIEGO FOUNDATION

2508 Historic Decatur Rd., Ste. 200
San Diego, CA 92106
Tel: (619)235-2300
Fax: (619)239-1710
E-mail: info@sdfoundation.org
Web Site: http://www.sdfoundation.org
To support the education of students from California.
Title of Award: AeA Scholarships **Area, Field, or Subject:** Mathematics and mathematical sciences; Science; Engineering; Computer and information sciences. **Level of Education for which Award is Granted:** Undergraduate **Number Awarded:** 2. **Funds Available:** $1000.
Eligibility Requirements: Applicant must be a resident of San Diego County (military personnel and dependents are exempt); a citizen or legal

resident of the United States; attend an accredited two-year college, four-year university or licensed trade and vocational school in the U.S.; a full-time student (unless otherwise noted); have a measure of academic and civic achievement; be of good moral and personal character; graduate from a San Diego County public high school; have a minimum 3.75 GPA on a 4.0 scale; and be majoring in math, science, engineering, or computers. **Application Requirements:** Applicants must submit a completed Common Scholarship Application together with personal statement; two letters of recommendation on official letterhead (written within the last six months); official transcript in an official and sealed envelope; copy of 2006 or most recent tax form (Form 1040-pages 1 & 2; Form 1040A-pages 1 & 2; Form 1040EZ-page 1); and an unofficial copy of SAT score results. **Deadline for Receipt:** January 28. **Additional Information:** Arzo Mansury, Dir. Scholarships at 619-814-1343, or scholarships@ sdfoundation.org.

5239 ■ THE SAN DIEGO FOUNDATION
2508 Historic Decatur Rd., Ste. 200
San Diego, CA 92106
Tel: (619)235-2300
Fax: (619)239-1710
E-mail: info@sdfoundation.org
Web Site: http://www.sdfoundation.org
To support the education of students from California.
Title of Award: Marvin Arnold and Irene Jaquetta Heye Scholarships **Area, Field, or Subject:** Engineering. **Level of Education for which Award is Granted:** Undergraduate **Number Awarded:** 1. **Funds Available:** $17,500.
Eligibility Requirements: Applicant must be a graduating high school senior planning to attend California Polytechnic State University or current student attending California Polytechnic State University. Student must be majoring in engineering; have a minimum 3.33 grade point average on a 4.0 scale; have a demonstrated financial need; and be actively involved in extra-curricular activities, community service, or work experience. **Application Requirements:** Applicants may obtain a copy of the Marvin Arnold and Irene Jaquetta Heye Scholarship Application by sending through e-mail the applicant's name and address to scholarships@ sdfoundation.org. **Additional Information:** 619-814-1343 or scholarships@sdfoundation.org.

5240 ■ THE SAN DIEGO FOUNDATION
2508 Historic Decatur Rd., Ste. 200
San Diego, CA 92106
Tel: (619)235-2300
Fax: (619)239-1710
E-mail: info@sdfoundation.org
Web Site: http://www.sdfoundation.org
To support the education of students from California.
Title of Award: Biocom Scholarships **Area, Field, or Subject:** Biology; Chemistry; Biomedical engineering. **Level of Education for which Award is Granted:** Undergraduate **Number Awarded:** 5. **Funds Available:** $1,500. **Duration:** One year.
Eligibility Requirements: Applicant must be a graduating high school senior with a minimum 3.50 GPA on a 4.0 scale; planning to attend an accredited two-year college or four-year university in the U.S.; must demonstrate a likelihood of achieving academic success with primary emphasis in biology, chemistry, physical and computational biosciences or biomedical engineering; committed in serving San Diego life sciences community; maintain a minimum 3.20 cumulative GPA on a 4.0 scale while in college; and exhibit the traits modeled by BIOCOM co-founder, James McGraw (leadership, passion for life sciences, integrity, and community service). **Application Requirements:** Applicants must submit a completed Common Scholarship Application together with personal statement; two letters of recommendation on official letterhead (written within the last six months); official transcript in an official and sealed envelope; and copy of most recent tax form (Form 1040-pages 1 & 2; Form 1040A-pages 1 & 2; Form 1040EZ-page 1). **Additional Information:** In memory of James McGraw. **Deadline for Receipt:** January 28. **Additional Information:** Arzo Mansury, Dir. Scholarships at 619-814-1343, or scholarships@sdfoundation.org.

5241 ■ THE SAN DIEGO FOUNDATION
2508 Historic Decatur Rd., Ste. 200
San Diego, CA 92106

Tel: (619)235-2300
Fax: (619)239-1710
E-mail: info@sdfoundation.org
Web Site: http://www.sdfoundation.org
To support the education of students from California.
Title of Award: Reuben H. Fleet Memorial Scholarships **Area, Field, or Subject:** Science; Engineering; Mathematics and mathematical sciences. **Level of Education for which Award is Granted:** Undergraduate **Number Awarded:** 3. **Funds Available:** $5,000.
Eligibility Requirements: Applicant must be a college student pursuing an undergraduate degree in science, engineering or math. Students must have completed 54 semester units or 72 quarter units; maintained a minimum 3.0 GPA on a 4.0 scale; enrolled at a four-year university in San Diego County; or be a San Diego County resident attending a four-year university in the U.S. **Application Requirements:** Applicants must submit a completed Common Scholarship Application together with personal statement; two letters of recommendation on official letterhead (written within the last six months); official transcript in an official and sealed envelope; and a copy of most recent tax form (Form 1040-pages 1 & 2; Form 1040A-pages 1 & 2; Form 1040EZ-page 1). If attending a two-year college, applicants must submit a letter of acceptance on official letterhead from the four-year university which the applicant will be transferring. **Deadline for Receipt:** January 28. **Additional Information:** Arzo Mansury, Dir. Scholarships at 619-814-1343, or scholarships@ sdfoundation.org.

5242 ■ THE SAN DIEGO FOUNDATION
2508 Historic Decatur Rd., Ste. 200
San Diego, CA 92106
Tel: (619)235-2300
Fax: (619)239-1710
E-mail: info@sdfoundation.org
Web Site: http://www.sdfoundation.org
To support the education of students from California.
Title of Award: Helm Family Scholarships **Area, Field, or Subject:** Biology; Computer and information sciences; Chemistry; Technology; Engineering; Physics. **Level of Education for which Award is Granted:** Undergraduate **Number Awarded:** 2. **Funds Available:** $5,00.
Eligibility Requirements: Applicant must be an entering junior or senior student at San Diego State University or the University of California, San Diego; have declared a major in mathematics or a scientific field such as, but not limited to, biology, computer science, chemistry, technology, engineering, physics, etc.; have a minimum 3.0 GPA on a 4.0 scale; and have demonstrated financial need. **Application Requirements:** Applicants must submit a completed Common Scholarship Application together with personal statement; two letters of recommendation on official letterhead (written within the last six months); official transcript in an official and sealed envelope; and a copy of most recent tax form (Form 1040-pages 1 & 2; Form 1040Apages 1 & 2; Form 1040EZ-page 1). **Deadline for Receipt:** January 28. **Additional Information:** Arzo Mansury, Dir. Scholarships at 619-814-1343, or scholarships@ sdfoundation.org.

5243 ■ THE SAN DIEGO FOUNDATION
2508 Historic Decatur Rd., Ste. 200
San Diego, CA 92106
Tel: (619)235-2300
Fax: (619)239-1710
E-mail: info@sdfoundation.org
Web Site: http://www.sdfoundation.org
To support the education of students from California.
Title of Award: Stuart L. Noderer Memorial Scholarships **Area, Field, or Subject:** Science; Engineering; Architecture. **Level of Education for which Award is Granted:** Undergraduate **Number Awarded:** 2. **Funds Available:** $1,000.
Eligibility Requirements: Applicant must be graduating senior from Mission Bay High School; planning to attend an accredited four-year university in the U.S.; have a minimum 3.50 GPA on a 4.0 scale; and will major in science, engineering or architecture. **Application Requirements:** Applicants must submit a completed Common Scholarship Application together with personal statement; two letters of recommendation on official letterhead (written within the last six months); official transcript in an official and sealed envelope; and a copy of 2006 or most recent tax

form (Form 1040-pages 1 & 2; Form 1040Apages 1 & 2; Form 1040EZ-page 1). **Deadline for Receipt:** January 28. **Additional Information:** Arzo Mansury, Dir. Scholarships at 619-814-1343, or scholarships@ sdfoundation.org.

5244 ■ THE SAN DIEGO FOUNDATION
2508 Historic Decatur Rd., Ste. 200
San Diego, CA 92106
Tel: (619)235-2300
Fax: (619)239-1710
E-mail: info@sdfoundation.org
Web Site: http://www.sdfoundation.org
To support the education of students from California.
Title of Award: SDF Community College Transfer Scholarships for Math and Science **Area, Field, or Subject:** Science; Engineering; Mathematics and mathematical sciences. **Level of Education for which Award is Granted:** Undergraduate **Number Awarded:** 5. **Funds Available:** $2,500.
Eligibility Requirements: Applicant must be a San Diego Community College student transferring to an accredited four-year university in the U.S.; majoring in science, engineering, or mathematics; and have a minimum 3.0 GPA on a 4.0 scale in community college work. **Application Requirements:** Applicants must submit a completed Common Scholarship Application together with personal statement; two letters of recommendation on official letterhead (written within the last six months); official transcript in an official and sealed envelope; copy of 2006 or most recent tax form (Form 1040-pages 1 & 2; Form 1040A-pages 1 & 2; Form 1040EZ-page 1); and s letter of acceptance on official letterhead from the accredited four-year university. **Deadline for Receipt:** January 28. **Additional Information:** Arzo Mansury, Dir. Scholarships at 619-814-1343, or scholarships@sdfoundation.org

5245 ■ SHELL OIL COMPANY
PO Box 2463
Houston, TX 77252
Tel: (713)241-6161; 888-467-4355
E-mail: shellcustomercare@shell.com
Web Site: http://www.shell.com
To offer scholarships to selected students pursuing two and four-year college degrees in certain engineering or geosciences disciplines at certain colleges.
Title of Award: Shell Incentive Scholarships Fund **Area, Field, or Subject:** Engineering; Geosciences. **Level of Education for which Award is Granted:** Undergraduate **Funds Available:** $5,000.
Eligibility Requirements: Applicants must be underrepresented students pursuing a four-year degree in a specific technical field of study at certain colleges. **Application Requirements:** Applicants must submit a completed application form.

5246 ■ SHELL OIL COMPANY
PO Box 2463
Houston, TX 77252
Tel: (713)241-6161; 888-467-4355
E-mail: shellcustomercare@shell.com
Web Site: http://www.shell.com
To help students who seek an education to obtain employment in the industries that use and control mechanical, physical or chemical processes to produce a final product.
Title of Award: Shell Process Technology Scholarships **Area, Field, or Subject:** Engineering; Geosciences. **Level of Education for which Award is Granted:** Undergraduate **Funds Available:** $2,000.
Eligibility Requirements: Applicants must be currently enrolled or planning to enroll in the Process Technology two-year degree program. **Application Requirements:** Applicants must submit a completed application form.

5247 ■ SHELL OIL COMPANY
PO Box 2463
Houston, TX 77252
Tel: (713)241-6161; 888-467-4355
E-mail: shellcustomercare@shell.com
Web Site: http://www.shell.com

To offer scholarships to selected students pursuing two and four-year college degrees in certain engineering or geosciences disciplines at certain colleges.
Title of Award: Shell Technical Scholarships **Area, Field, or Subject:** Engineering; Geosciences. **Level of Education for which Award is Granted:** Undergraduate **Funds Available:** $5,000. **Duration:** 4 years.
Eligibility Requirements: Applicants must be students pursuing a four-year college degree in certain engineering or geosciences disciplines at certain colleges. **Application Requirements:** Applicants must submit a completed application form.

5248 ■ SHORELINE COMMUNITY COLLEGE FOUNDATION
16101 Greenwood Ave. N, Ste. 1005
Shoreline, WA 98133-5696
Tel: (206)546-4755
Fax: (206)546-5826
E-mail: rmanchester@shoreline.edu
Web Site: http://www.shoreline.edu
To increase access and success of Shoreline Community College students.
Title of Award: Boeing Company Scholarships **Area, Field, or Subject:** Manufacturing; Engineering; Information Science and Technology. **Level of Education for which Award is Granted:** Undergraduate **Number Awarded:** 2. **Funds Available:** $500.
Eligibility Requirements: Applicants must be full-time or part-time students at the Shoreline/Lake Forest Park area who are enrolling at SCC. **Application Requirements:** Applicants must complete the application form.

5249 ■ SHORELINE COMMUNITY COLLEGE FOUNDATION
16101 Greenwood Ave. N, Ste. 1005
Shoreline, WA 98133-5696
Tel: (206)546-4755
Fax: (206)546-5826
E-mail: rmanchester@shoreline.edu
Web Site: http://www.shoreline.edu
To increase access and success of Shoreline Community College students; to provide financial assistance to women in the automotive program.
Title of Award: Friends of Mary Automotive Scholarships **Area, Field, or Subject:** Automotive technology. **Level of Education for which Award is Granted:** Undergraduate **Funds Available:** No specific amount.
Eligibility Requirements: Applicants must be full-time or part-time students at the Shoreline/Lake Forest Park area who are enrolling at SCC. **Application Requirements:** Applicants must complete the application form.

5250 ■ SOCIETY OF ALLIED WEIGHT ENGINEERS
PO Box 60024, Terminal Annex
Los Angeles, CA 90060
Tel: (562)596-2873
Fax: (562)596-2874
Web Site: http://www.sawe.org
To provide financial assistance for the education of the dependents of SAWE members.
Title of Award: Frank Fong Scholarships **Area, Field, or Subject:** Engineering; Physics; Mathematics and mathematical sciences; Computer and information sciences. **Level of Education for which Award is Granted:** Undergraduate **Number Awarded:** 5. **Funds Available:** $1000. **Duration:** One year.
Eligibility Requirements: Applicants must be children or grandchildren of SAWE members; must be aged 25 or below; full-time undergraduate students; pursuing a technical course of study (engineering, physics, mathematics, computer sciences, etc.). **Application Requirements:** Application forms are available at the website. Applicants must submit completed application form and send together with a complete transcript of grades. **Deadline for Receipt:** April. **Additional Information:** Ginny Miller, Scholarship Management Services, Telephone: (507)931-1682, Toll-free: (800)537-4180.

5251 ■ SOCIETY OF MANUFACTURING ENGINEERS EDUCATION FOUNDATION
PO Box 930
Dearborn, MI 48121-0930

Tel: (313)425-3300
Free: 800-733-4763
Fax: (313)425-3411
E-mail: foundation@sme.org
Web Site: http://www.sme.org/cgi-bin/smeefhtml.pl?/foundation/foundation_hp.htm&&&SEF&
To assist high school seniors and undergraduate students to continue their education.
Title of Award: Chapter 4 - Lawrence A. Wacker Memorial Awards **Area, Field, or Subject:** Manufacturing; Mechanical engineering; Engineering, Industrial. **Level of Education for which Award is Granted:** Undergraduate **Number Awarded:** 2. One to a graduating senior, and another to a current undergraduate student. **Funds Available:** $1,000. Scholarship funds may be used for credit toward books, fees or housing only.
Eligibility Requirements: Applicant must pursue a bachelor's degree in manufacturing, mechanical or industrial engineering; have a GPA of 3.0 on a 4.0 scale; must reside and attend an accredited institution in the U.S. or Canada. **Application Requirements:** Visit the website for the Scholarship Application Process.

5252 ■ SOCIETY OF MANUFACTURING ENGINEERS EDUCATION FOUNDATION
PO Box 930
Dearborn, MI 48121-0930
Tel: (313)425-3300
Free: 800-733-4763
Fax: (313)425-3411
E-mail: foundation@sme.org
Web Site: http://www.sme.org/cgi-bin/smeefhtml.pl?/foundation/foundation_hp.htm&&&SEF&
To financially support students who wish to pursue their education.
Title of Award: Chapter 17 - St. Louis Scholarships **Area, Field, or Subject:** Manufacturing; Engineering, Industrial. **Level of Education for which Award is Granted:** Undergraduate **Funds Available:** $1,000. Scholarship funds may be used for credit toward books, fees or tuition only.
Eligibility Requirements: Applicants must be enrolled full-time or part-time undergraduate in a manufacturing engineering, industrial technology or other manufacturing related degree program; have a GPA of 2.5 on a 4.0 scale. **Application Requirements:** Visit the website for the online scholarship application process.

5253 ■ SOCIETY OF MANUFACTURING ENGINEERS EDUCATION FOUNDATION
PO Box 930
Dearborn, MI 48121-0930
Tel: (313)425-3300
Free: 800-733-4763
Fax: (313)425-3411
E-mail: foundation@sme.org
Web Site: http://www.sme.org/cgi-bin/smeefhtml.pl?/foundation/foundation_hp.htm&&&SEF&
To financially support students in their education.
Title of Award: Chapter 31 - Peoria Endowed Scholarships **Area, Field, or Subject:** Manufacturing; Engineering, Industrial. **Level of Education for which Award is Granted:** Undergraduate **Funds Available:** $1,000. Scholarship funds may be used for credit toward books, fees or tuition only.
Eligibility Requirements: Applicants must be pursuing a bachelor's degree in manufacturing engineering, industrial engineering, manufacturing technology or a manufacturing related degree program at Bradley University (Peoria, Illinois) or Illinois University (Normal, Illinois); have a GPA of 3.0 on a 4.0 scale. **Application Requirements:** Visit the website for the online scholarship application process.

5254 ■ SOCIETY OF MANUFACTURING ENGINEERS EDUCATION FOUNDATION
PO Box 930
Dearborn, MI 48121-0930
Tel: (313)425-3300
Free: 800-733-4763
Fax: (313)425-3411
E-mail: foundation@sme.org

Web Site: http://www.sme.org/cgi-bin/smeefhtml.pl?/foundation/foundation_hp.htm&&&SEF&
To financially support students in their education.
Title of Award: Chapter 52 - Wichita Scholarships **Area, Field, or Subject:** Manufacturing; Engineering, Industrial. **Level of Education for which Award is Granted:** Graduate, Undergraduate **Funds Available:** $1,000. Scholarship funds may be used for credit toward books, fees or tuition only.
Eligibility Requirements: Applicants must pursue an associate's degree, bachelor's degree or graduate degree in manufacturing, mechanical or industrial engineering, engineering technology or industrial technology at an accredited public or private college or university in Kansas, Oklahoma or Missouri; have a GPA of 2.5 on a 4.0 scale. **Application Requirements:** Visit the website for the online scholarship application process.

5255 ■ SOCIETY OF MANUFACTURING ENGINEERS EDUCATION FOUNDATION
PO Box 930
Dearborn, MI 48121-0930
Tel: (313)425-3300
Free: 800-733-4763
Fax: (313)425-3411
E-mail: foundation@sme.org
Web Site: http://www.sme.org/cgi-bin/smeefhtml.pl?/foundation/foundation_hp.htm&&&SEF&
To financially support students in their education.
Title of Award: Chapter 56 - Fort Wayne Scholarships **Area, Field, or Subject:** Manufacturing; Engineering, Industrial. **Level of Education for which Award is Granted:** Graduate, Undergraduate **Funds Available:** $1,000. Scholarship funds may be used for credit toward books, fees or tuition only.
Eligibility Requirements: Applicant must pursue an associate's degree, bachelor's degree or graduate degree in manufacturing, mechanical or industrial engineering, engineering technology or industrial technology at an accredited public or private college or university in Indiana; have a GPA of 2.5 on a 4.0 scale. **Application Requirements:** Visit the website for the online scholarship application process.

5256 ■ SOCIETY OF MANUFACTURING ENGINEERS EDUCATION FOUNDATION
PO Box 930
Dearborn, MI 48121-0930
Tel: (313)425-3300
Free: 800-733-4763
Fax: (313)425-3411
E-mail: foundation@sme.org
Web Site: http://www.sme.org/cgi-bin/smeefhtml.pl?/foundation/foundation_hp.htm&&&SEF&
To assist high school seniors and undergraduate students to continue college.
Title of Award: Chapter 67 - Phoenix Scholarships **Area, Field, or Subject:** Manufacturing; Engineering, Industrial. **Level of Education for which Award is Granted:** Undergraduate **Funds Available:** $1,000. Scholarship funds may be used for credit toward books, fees or housing only.
Eligibility Requirements: Applicant must be a high school senior planning to enroll in a manufacturing program technology course; or an undergraduate student currently enrolled in a manufacturing engineering technology, manufacturing technology, industrial technology or related program at an accredited college or university in Arizona; have a GPA of 2.5 on a 4.0 scale. **Application Requirements:** Visit the website for the Scholarship Application Process.

5257 ■ SOCIETY OF MANUFACTURING ENGINEERS EDUCATION FOUNDATION
PO Box 930
Dearborn, MI 48121-0930
Tel: (313)425-3300
Free: 800-733-4763
Fax: (313)425-3411
E-mail: foundation@sme.org
Web Site: http://www.sme.org/cgi-bin/smeefhtml.pl?/foundation/foundation_hp.htm&&&SEF&

To financially support students in their education.
Title of Award: Chapter 198 - Downriver Detroit Scholarships **Area, Field, or Subject:** Manufacturing; Mechanical engineering; Industrial engineering. **Level of Education for which Award is Granted:** Graduate, Undergraduate **Funds Available:** $1,000. Scholarship funds may be used for credit toward books, fees or tuition only.
Eligibility Requirements: Applicant must be enrolled full-time seeking an associate's degree, bachelor's degree or graduate degree in manufacturing, mechanical or industrial engineering, engineering technology, or industrial technology at an accredited public or private college/university in the state of Michigan; have a GPA of 2.5 on a 4.0 scale. **Application Requirements:** Visit the website for the online scholarship application process.

5258 ■ SOCIETY OF MANUFACTURING ENGINEERS EDUCATION FOUNDATION
PO Box 930
Dearborn, MI 48121-0930
Tel: (313)425-3300
Free: 800-733-4763
Fax: (313)425-3411
E-mail: foundation@sme.org
Web Site: http://www.sme.org/cgi-bin/smeefhtml.pl?/foundation/foundation_hp.htm&&&SEF&
To assist high school seniors and undergraduate students in Michigan to attend college.
Title of Award: Chapter 311 - Tri City Scholarships **Area, Field, or Subject:** Manufacturing; Engineering, Industrial. **Level of Education for which Award is Granted:** Undergraduate **Funds Available:** $1,000. Scholarship funds may be used for credit toward books, fees and tuition only.
Eligibility Requirements: Applicants must pursue a bachelor's degree in manufacturing engineering, industrial engineering, manufacturing technology engineering or related field; have a GPA of 3.0 on a 4.0 scale. **Application Requirements:** Visit the website for the online Scholarship Application Process.

5259 ■ SOCIETY OF MANUFACTURING ENGINEERS EDUCATION FOUNDATION
PO Box 930
Dearborn, MI 48121-0930
Tel: (313)425-3300
Free: 800-733-4763
Fax: (313)425-3411
E-mail: foundation@sme.org
Web Site: http://www.sme.org/cgi-bin/smeefhtml.pl?/foundation/foundation_hp.htm&&&SEF&
To financially support students in their education.
Title of Award: Future Leaders of Manufacturing Scholarships **Area, Field, or Subject:** Manufacturing; Engineering; Engineering, Industrial. **Level of Education for which Award is Granted:** Graduate, Undergraduate **Funds Available:** $1,000. Scholarship funds may be used for credit toward books, fees or tuition only.
Eligibility Requirements: Candidates must be SME Student Chapter members; must be nominated by their faculty advisors; must be enrolled full-time undergraduate or graduate students; must be in manufacturing engineering, engineering technology, industrial technology, technical or related majors. **Application Requirements:** Candidates must submit a completed Nomination/Application form; a recommendation letter from the faculty advisor; a resume; transcripts. **Deadline for Receipt:** February 1. **Additional Information:** SME Foundation at 313-425-3300.

5260 ■ SOCIETY OF MANUFACTURING ENGINEERS EDUCATION FOUNDATION
PO Box 930
Dearborn, MI 48121-0930
Tel: (313)425-3300
Free: 800-733-4763
Fax: (313)425-3411
E-mail: foundation@sme.org
Web Site: http://www.sme.org/cgi-bin/smeefhtml.pl?/foundation/foundation_hp.htm&&&SEF&

To assist high school seniors and undergraduate students to attend college.
Title of Award: Henry Ford Academy Scholarships **Area, Field, or Subject:** Engineering; Technology. **Level of Education for which Award is Granted:** Undergraduate **Funds Available:** $1,000. Scholarship funds may be used for credit toward books, fees or tuition only.
Eligibility Requirements: Applicants must be graduating high school seniors from Henry Ford Academy pursuing a bachelor/associate degree in engineering or technology at an accredited college or university in the U.S.; have a GPA of 3.0 on a 4.0 scale. **Application Requirements:** Applicants must submit two reference letters, one from a Henry Ford Academy instructor. **Additional Information:** Renewal of scholarship requires a GPA of 3.0.

5261 ■ SOCIETY OF MANUFACTURING ENGINEERS EDUCATION FOUNDATION
PO Box 930
Dearborn, MI 48121-0930
Tel: (313)425-3300
Free: 800-733-4763
Fax: (313)425-3411
E-mail: foundation@sme.org
Web Site: http://www.sme.org/cgi-bin/smeefhtml.pl?/foundation/foundation_hp.htm&&&SEF&
To financially support students in their education.
Title of Award: Clarence and Josephine Myers Scholarships **Area, Field, or Subject:** Manufacturing; Mechanical engineering; Industrial engineering. **Level of Education for which Award is Granted:** Graduate, Undergraduate **Funds Available:** $1,000; Scholarship funds may be used for credit toward books, fees or tuition only.
Eligibility Requirements: Applicant must be a graduate or undergraduate student pursuing an associate, bachelor or graduate degree in manufacturing, machinable or industrial engineering in the state of Indiana; have a GPA of 3.0 on a 4.0 scale. **Application Requirements:** Visit the website for the online scholarship application process. **Additional Information:** In memory of Josephine and Clarence J. Myers.

5262 ■ SOCIETY OF MANUFACTURING ENGINEERS EDUCATION FOUNDATION
PO Box 930
Dearborn, MI 48121-0930
Tel: (313)425-3300
Free: 800-733-4763
Fax: (313)425-3411
E-mail: foundation@sme.org
Web Site: http://www.sme.org/cgi-bin/smeefhtml.pl?/foundation/foundation_hp.htm&&&SEF&
To assist high school seniors and undergraduate students in their college education.
Title of Award: SME Ford PAS Scholarships **Area, Field, or Subject:** Engineering; Technology. **Level of Education for which Award is Granted:** Undergraduate **Funds Available:** $1,000. Scholarship funds may be used for credit toward books, fees or tuition only.
Eligibility Requirements: Applicant must be a current or former student of a Ford PAS program at their high school or in a Ford PAS after-school/weekend/summer/college program; must be pursuing a bachelor/associate degree in engineering or technology at an accredited college or university in the U.S.; have a GPA of 3.0 on a 4.0 scale. **Application Requirements:** Applicants must submit two reference letters, one from a Ford PAS instructor. **Additional Information:** Renewal of scholarship requires a GPA of 3.0.

5263 ■ SOCIETY OF MANUFACTURING ENGINEERS EDUCATION FOUNDATION
PO Box 930
Dearborn, MI 48121-0930
Tel: (313)425-3300
Free: 800-733-4763
Fax: (313)425-3411
E-mail: foundation@sme.org
Web Site: http://www.sme.org/cgi-bin/smeefhtml.pl?/foundation/foundation_hp.htm&&&SEF&

To assist high school seniors and undergraduate students in their college education.
Title of Award: Allen and Loureena Weber Scholarships **Area, Field, or Subject:** Manufacturing; Mechanical engineering; Engineering; Industrial Engineering. **Level of Education for which Award is Granted:** Undergraduate **Funds Available:** $1,000. Scholarship funds may be used for credit toward books, fees or tuition only.
Eligibility Requirements: Applicant must be a student of the University of Northern Kentucky or pursuing an associate's degree or bachelor's degree in manufacturing, mechanical, industrial engineering, engineering technology or industrial technology with a satisfactory GPA; should reflect the interest of the donor in "individuals who possess technical aptitude and desire for education and practical learning". **Application Requirements:** Visit the website for the scholarship application process.

5264 ■ SOCIETY OF MANUFACTURING ENGINEERS EDUCATION FOUNDATION

PO Box 930
Dearborn, MI 48121-0930
Tel: (313)425-3300
Free: 800-733-4763
Fax: (313)425-3411
E-mail: foundation@sme.org
Web Site: http://www.sme.org/cgi-bin/smeefhtml.pl?/foundation/foundation_hp.htm&&&SEF&
To financially support students in their education.
Title of Award: William E. Weisel Scholarships **Area, Field, or Subject:** Engineering; Technology. **Level of Education for which Award is Granted:** Undergraduate **Funds Available:** $1,000. Scholarship funds may be used for credit toward books, fees or tuition only.
Eligibility Requirements: Applicants must be U.S. citizens; enrolled full-time undergraduate students in an engineering or technology program in the U.S or Canada; have completed at least 30 college credit hours; have a GPA of 3.0 on a 4.0 scale. **Application Requirements:** Visit the website for the online scholarship application process. **Additional Information:** The scholarship is a living tribute to the memory of William E. Weisel's career in manufacturing.

5265 ■ SOCIETY OF MANUFACTURING ENGINEERS EDUCATION FOUNDATION

PO Box 930
Dearborn, MI 48121-0930
Tel: (313)425-3300
Free: 800-733-4763
Fax: (313)425-3411
E-mail: foundation@sme.org
Web Site: http://www.sme.org/cgi-bin/smeefhtml.pl?/foundation/foundation_hp.htm&&&SEF&
To assist high school seniors and undergraduate students in their education.
Title of Award: Albert E. Wischmeyer Memorial Scholarships **Area, Field, or Subject:** Manufacturing; Mechanical engineering. **Level of Education for which Award is Granted:** Undergraduate **Funds Available:** $1,000. Scholarship funds may be used for credit toward books, fees or tuition only.
Eligibility Requirements: Applicants must be graduating high school seniors or undergraduates pursuing a degree in manufacturing engineering, manufacturing engineering technology, or mechanical technology; attending an accredited institution in New York State; must be residents of Western New York; have a GPA of 2.5 on a 4.0 scale. **Application Requirements:** Students must write for applications. **Additional Information:** In memory of Albert E. Wischmeyer.

5266 ■ SOCIETY OF NAVAL ARCHITECTS AND MARINE ENGINEERS

601 Pavonia Ave.
Jersey City, NJ 07306
Tel: (201)798-4800
Free: 800-798-2188
Fax: (201)798-4975
E-mail: ldavis@sname.org
Web Site: http://www.sname.org

To encourage study in naval architecture, marine engineering, ocean engineering or marine industry-related fields.
Title of Award: Mandell and Lester Rosenblatt and Robert N. Herbert Undergraduate Scholarships **Area, Field, or Subject:** Architecture, Naval; Marine engineering; Ocean engineering. **Level of Education for which Award is Granted:** Undergraduate **Funds Available:** $6,000.
Eligibility Requirements: Applicants must be U.S. or Canadian citizens who are actively involved with SNAME and other professional organizations. **Application Requirements:** Applicants must complete the application form; Applicants must provide an evidence of sound academic achievement; a 500-600 word application essay; three letters of professional recommendations in which the two must be NA/ME/OE faculty who have had the student in class and at least two of whom are SNAME members. **Deadline for Receipt:** June 1. **Additional Information:** efaustino@sname.org.

5267 ■ SOCIETY OF NAVAL ARCHITECTS AND MARINE ENGINEERS

601 Pavonia Ave.
Jersey City, NJ 07306
Tel: (201)798-4800
Free: 800-798-2188
Fax: (201)798-4975
E-mail: ldavis@sname.org
Web Site: http://www.sname.org
To encourage study in naval architecture, marine engineering, ocean engineering or marine industry-related fields.
Title of Award: Society of Naval Architects and Marine Engineers Undergraduate Scholarships **Area, Field, or Subject:** Architecture, Naval; Marine engineering; Ocean engineering. **Level of Education for which Award is Granted:** Undergraduate **Funds Available:** $2,000.
Eligibility Requirements: Applicants must be planning to study in the U.S. or Canada; applicants must study toward a degree in naval architecture, marine engineering, ocean engineering or marine industry related fields at an accredited school; applicants must be entering junior or senior year. **Application Requirements:** Applicants must complete the online application form; applicants must submit a transcript of records or any proof that he/she is currently enrolled or have been accepted by the school, colleges, or universities. **Additional Information:** efaustino@sname.org.

5268 ■ SOCIETY OF PLASTICS ENGINEERS

14 Fairfield Dr.
Brookfield, CT 06804-0403
Tel: (203)775-0471
Fax: (203)775-8490
E-mail: info@4spe.org
Web Site: http://www.4spe.org
To promote scientific and engineering knowledge relating to plastics.
Title of Award: Blow Molding Division Memorial Scholarships **Area, Field, or Subject:** Science; Engineering. **Level of Education for which Award is Granted:** Graduate, Undergraduate **Number Awarded:** 2. **Funds Available:** $8,000.
Eligibility Requirements: Applicants must be undergraduate and graduate students in institutions, colleges, or universities; applicants must have demonstrated or expressed interest in the plastic industry; applicants must be in good academic standing. **Application Requirements:** Applicants must complete the application form; applicants must submit three letters of recommendation, two of which are from a teacher or school official and one from an employer or non-relative; a high school and/or college transcript for the past two years; a list of current and past school activities, community activities, and honors; a listing of employment history; a one-to-two-page typewritten statement telling why they are applying for the scholarship, qualifications, educational and career goals in the plastic industry. **Deadline for Receipt:** January 15. **Additional Information:** foundation@4spe.org.

5269 ■ SOCIETY OF PLASTICS ENGINEERS

14 Fairfield Dr.
Brookfield, CT 06804-0403
Tel: (203)775-0471
Fax: (203)775-8490
E-mail: info@4spe.org

Web Site: http://www.4spe.org
To promote scientific and engineering knowledge relating to plastics.
Title of Award: Robert E. Cramer Scholarships **Area, Field, or Subject:** Science; Engineering. **Level of Education for which Award is Granted:** Graduate, Undergraduate **Number Awarded:** 1. **Funds Available:** $1,000.
Eligibility Requirements: Applicants must be undergraduate and graduate students in institutions, colleges, or universities; applicants must have demonstrated or expressed interest in the plastic industry; applicants must be in good academic standing. **Application Requirements:** Applicants must complete the application form; applicants must submit three letters of recommendation, two of which are from a teacher or school official and one from an employer or non-relative; a high school and/or college transcript for the past two years; a list of current and past school activities, community activities, and honors; A listing of employment history; a one-to-two-page typewritten statement telling why they are applying for the scholarship, qualifications, educational and career goals in the plastic industry. **Deadline for Receipt:** January 15. **Additional Information:** foundation@4spe.org

5270 ■ SOCIETY OF PLASTICS ENGINEERS
14 Fairfield Dr.
Brookfield, CT 06804-0403
Tel: (203)775-0471
Fax: (203)775-8490
E-mail: info@4spe.org
Web Site: http://www.4spe.org
To promote scientific and engineering knowledge relating to plastics.
Title of Award: Robert G. Dailey Scholarships **Area, Field, or Subject:** Science; Engineering. **Level of Education for which Award is Granted:** Graduate, Undergraduate **Number Awarded:** 1. **Funds Available:** $4,000.
Eligibility Requirements: Applicants must be undergraduate and graduate students in institutions, colleges, or universities; Applicants must have demonstrated or expressed interest in the plastic industry; applicants must be in good academic standing. **Application Requirements:** Applicants must complete the application form; applicants must submit three letters of recommendation, two of which are from a teacher or school official and one from an employer or non-relative; a high school and/or college transcript for the past two years; a list of current and past school activities, community activities, and honors; a listing of employment history; a one-to-two-page typewritten statement telling why they are applying for the scholarship, qualifications, educational and career goals in the plastic industry. **Deadline for Receipt:** January 15. **Additional Information:** foundation@4spe.org

5271 ■ SOCIETY OF PLASTICS ENGINEERS
14 Fairfield Dr.
Brookfield, CT 06804-0403
Tel: (203)775-0471
Fax: (203)775-8490
E-mail: info@4spe.org
Web Site: http://www.4spe.org
To promote scientific and engineering knowledge relating to plastics.
Title of Award: Fleming/Blaszcak Scholarships **Area, Field, or Subject:** Science; Engineering. **Level of Education for which Award is Granted:** Graduate, Undergraduate **Number Awarded:** 1. **Funds Available:** $2,000.
Eligibility Requirements: Applicants must be undergraduate and graduate students in institutions, colleges, or universities; applicants must have demonstrated or expressed interest in the plastic industry; applicants must be in good academic standing; applicants must be of Mexican descent and citizens or legal residents of the United States. **Application Requirements:** Applicants must complete the application form; applicants must submit three letters of recommendation, two of which are from a teacher or school official and one from an employer or non-relative; a high school and/or college transcript for the past two years; a list of current and past school activities, community activities, and honors; a listing of employment history; a one-to-two-page typewritten statement telling why they are applying for the scholarship, qualifications, educational and career goals in the plastic industry; applicants must provide a documentation of their Mexican heritage and their citizenship status such as a birth certificate or a U.S. passport. **Deadline for Receipt:** January 15. **Additional Information:** foundation@4spe.org

5272 ■ SOCIETY OF PLASTICS ENGINEERS
14 Fairfield Dr.
Brookfield, CT 06804-0403
Tel: (203)775-0471
Fax: (203)775-8490
E-mail: info@4spe.org
Web Site: http://www.4spe.org
To promote scientific and engineering knowledge relating to plastics.
Title of Award: Harold Giles Scholarships **Area, Field, or Subject:** Science; Engineering. **Level of Education for which Award is Granted:** Graduate, Undergraduate **Number Awarded:** 1. **Funds Available:** $1,000.
Eligibility Requirements: Applicants must be undergraduate and graduate students in institutions, colleges, or universities; applicants must have demonstrated or expressed interest in the plastic industry; applicants must be in good academic standing; applicants must have experience in the composites industry such as courses taken, research conducted, or jobs held. **Application Requirements:** Applicants must complete the application form; applicants must submit three letters of recommendation, two of which are from a teacher or school official and one from an employer or non-relative; a high school and/or college transcript for the past two years; a list of current and past school activities, community activities, and honors; a listing of employment history; a one-to-two-page typewritten statement telling why they are applying for the scholarship, qualifications, educational and career goals in the plastic industry. **Deadline for Receipt:** January 15. **Additional Information:** foundation@4spe.org

5273 ■ SOCIETY OF PLASTICS ENGINEERS
14 Fairfield Dr.
Brookfield, CT 06804-0403
Tel: (203)775-0471
Fax: (203)775-8490
E-mail: info@4spe.org
Web Site: http://www.4spe.org
To promote scientific and engineering knowledge relating to plastics.
Title of Award: Gulf Coast Hurricane Scholarships **Area, Field, or Subject:** Science; Engineering. **Level of Education for which Award is Granted:** Graduate, Undergraduate **Number Awarded:** 1. **Funds Available:** $6,000 for four-year university; $2,000 for two-year junior college. **Duration:** 4 years; 2 years.
Eligibility Requirements: Applicants must be undergraduate and graduate students in institutions, colleges, or universities; Applicants must have demonstrated or expressed interest in the plastic industry; applicants must be in good academic standing; applicants must maintain a 2.0 GPA and enroll in at least six credit hours per semester. **Application Requirements:** Applicants must complete the application form; applicants must submit three letters of recommendation, two of which are from a teacher or school official and one from an employer or non-relative; a high school and/or college transcript for the past two years; a list of current and past school activities, community activities, and honors; a listing of employment history; a one-to-two-page typewritten statement telling why they are applying for the scholarship, qualifications, educational and career goals in the plastic industry; applicants must provide proof of residence in a Gulf Coast County declared a national disaster area by the President. **Deadline for Receipt:** January 15. **Additional Information:** foundation@4spe.org

5274 ■ SOCIETY OF PLASTICS ENGINEERS
14 Fairfield Dr.
Brookfield, CT 06804-0403
Tel: (203)775-0471
Fax: (203)775-8490
E-mail: info@4spe.org
Web Site: http://www.4spe.org
To promote scientific and engineering knowledge relating to plastics.
Title of Award: Injection Molding Division Scholarships **Area, Field, or Subject:** Science; Engineering. **Level of Education for which Award is Granted:** Graduate, Undergraduate **Funds Available:** $3,000.
Eligibility Requirements: Applicants must be undergraduate and graduate students in institutions, colleges, or universities; applicants must have demonstrated or expressed interest in the plastic industry; applicants must be in good academic standing; applicants must have experience in

the molding industry such as courses taken, research conducted or jobs held. **Application Requirements:** Applicants must complete the application form; Applicants must submit three letters of recommendation, two of which are from a teacher or school official and one from an employer or non-relative; a high school and/or college transcript for the past two years; a list of current and past school activities, community activities, and honors; a listing of employment history; a one-to-two-page typewritten statement telling why they are applying for the scholarship, qualifications, educational and career goals in the plastic industry. **Deadline for Receipt:** January 15. **Additional Information:** foundation@4spe.org

5275 ■ SOCIETY OF PLASTICS ENGINEERS
14 Fairfield Dr.
Brookfield, CT 06804-0403
Tel: (203)775-0471
Fax: (203)775-8490
E-mail: info@4spe.org
Web Site: http://www.4spe.org
To promote scientific and engineering knowledge relating to plastics.
Title of Award: Erwin Lew Memorial Scholarships **Area, Field, or Subject:** Science; Engineering. **Level of Education for which Award is Granted:** Graduate, Undergraduate **Number Awarded:** 1. **Funds Available:** $2,500.
Eligibility Requirements: Applicants must be undergraduate and graduate students in institutions, colleges, or universities; applicants must have demonstrated or expressed interest in the plastic industry; applicants must be in good academic standing in their respective schools; applicants must be working on a senior or MS project which the scholarship will support. **Application Requirements:** Applicants must complete the application form; three letters of recommendation, two of which are from a teacher or school official and one from an employer or non-relative; a high school and/or college transcript for the past two years; a list of current and past school activities, community activities, and honors; a listing of employment history; a one-to-two-page typewritten statement telling why they are applying for the scholarship, qualifications, educational and career goals in the plastic industry. **Deadline for Receipt:** January 15. **Additional Information:** foundation@4spe.org

5276 ■ SOCIETY OF PLASTICS ENGINEERS
14 Fairfield Dr.
Brookfield, CT 06804-0403
Tel: (203)775-0471
Fax: (203)775-8490
E-mail: info@4spe.org
Web Site: http://www.4spe.org
To promote scientific and engineering knowledge relating to plastics.
Title of Award: James I. MacKenzie Memorial Scholarships **Area, Field, or Subject:** Science; Engineering. **Level of Education for which Award is Granted:** Graduate, Undergraduate **Number Awarded:** 1. **Funds Available:** $2,500.
Eligibility Requirements: Applicants must be undergraduate and graduate students in institutions, colleges, or universities. Applicants must have demonstrated or expressed interest in the plastic industry; applicants must be in good academic standing; applicants must have experience in the thermoplastic elastomers industry, such as courses taken, research conducted, or jobs held. **Application Requirements:** Applicants must complete the application form; applicants must submit three letters of recommendation, two of which are from a teacher or school official and one from an employer or non-relative; a high school and/or college transcript for the past two years; a list of current and past school activities, community activities, and honors; a listing of employment history; a one-to-two-page typewritten statement telling why they are applying for the scholarship, qualifications, educational and career goals in the plastic industry; applicants must include a statement detailing their exposure to the thermoses industry. **Deadline for Receipt:** January 15. **Additional Information:** foundation@4spe.org

5277 ■ SOCIETY OF PLASTICS ENGINEERS
14 Fairfield Dr.
Brookfield, CT 06804-0403
Tel: (203)775-0471
Fax: (203)775-8490
E-mail: info@4spe.org

Web Site: http://www.4spe.org
To promote scientific and engineering knowledge relating to plastics.
Title of Award: Ted and Ruth Neward Scholarships **Area, Field, or Subject:** Science; Engineering. **Level of Education for which Award is Granted:** Graduate, Undergraduate **Number Awarded:** 3. **Funds Available:** $3,000.
Eligibility Requirements: Applicants must be undergraduate and graduate students in institutions, colleges, or universities; applicants must have demonstrated or expressed interest in the plastic industry; applicants must be in good academic standing. **Application Requirements:** Applicants must complete the application form; applicants must submit three letters of recommendation, two of which are from a teacher or school official and one from an employer or non-relative; a high school and/or college transcript for the past two years; a list of current and past school activities, community activities, and honors; a listing of employment history; a one-to-two-page typewritten statement telling why they are applying for the scholarship, qualifications, educational and career goals in the plastic industry. **Deadline for Receipt:** January 15. **Additional Information:** foundation@4spe.org

5278 ■ SOCIETY OF PLASTICS ENGINEERS
14 Fairfield Dr.
Brookfield, CT 06804-0403
Tel: (203)775-0471
Fax: (203)775-8490
E-mail: info@4spe.org
Web Site: http://www.4spe.org
To promote scientific and engineering knowledge relating to plastics.
Title of Award: Plastics Pioneers Association Scholarships **Area, Field, or Subject:** Science; Engineering. **Level of Education for which Award is Granted:** Graduate, Undergraduate **Funds Available:** $3,000.
Eligibility Requirements: Applicants must be undergraduate and graduate students in institutions, colleges, or universities including those enrolled in associate degree or technical degree programs who are committed to becoming hands-on workers in the plastics industry and who are dedicated to careers as plastics technicians or engineers. Applicants must have demonstrated or expressed interest in the plastic industry; applicants must be in good academic standing. **Application Requirements:** Applicants must complete the application form; applicants must submit three letters of recommendation, two of which are from a teacher or school official and one from an employer or non-relative; a high school and/or college transcript for the past two years; a list of current and past school activities, community activities, and honors; a listing of employment history; A one-to-two-page typewritten statement telling why they are applying for the scholarship, qualifications, educational and career goals in the plastic industry. **Deadline for Receipt:** January 15. **Additional Information:** foundation@4spe.org

5279 ■ SOCIETY OF PLASTICS ENGINEERS
14 Fairfield Dr.
Brookfield, CT 06804-0403
Tel: (203)775-0471
Fax: (203)775-8490
E-mail: info@4spe.org
Web Site: http://www.4spe.org
To promote scientific and engineering knowledge relating to plastics.
Title of Award: Polymer Modifiers and Additives Division Scholarships **Area, Field, or Subject:** Science; Engineering. **Level of Education for which Award is Granted:** Graduate, Undergraduate **Number Awarded:** 3. **Funds Available:** $4,000.
Eligibility Requirements: Applicants must be undergraduate and graduate students in institutions, colleges, or universities; applicants must have demonstrated or expressed interest in the plastic industry; applicants must be in good academic standing. **Application Requirements:** Applicants must complete the application form; applicants must submit three letters of recommendation, two of which are from a teacher or school official and one from an employer or non-relative; a high school and/or college transcript for the past two years; a list of current and past school activities, community activities, and honors; a listing of employment history; a one-to-two-page typewritten statement telling why they are applying for the scholarship, qualifications, educational and career goals in the plastic industry. **Deadline for Receipt:** January 15. **Additional Information:** foundation@4spe.org

5280 ■ SOCIETY OF PLASTICS ENGINEERS

14 Fairfield Dr.
Brookfield, CT 06804-0403
Tel: (203)775-0471
Fax: (203)775-8490
E-mail: info@4spe.org
Web Site: http://www.4spe.org
To promote scientific and engineering knowledge relating to plastics.
Title of Award: Society of Plastics Engineers General Scholarships **Area, Field, or Subject:** Science; Engineering. **Level of Education for which Award is Granted:** Graduate, Undergraduate **Funds Available:** $4,000. **Duration:** One year.
Eligibility Requirements: Applicants must be undergraduate and graduate students in institutions, colleges, or universities; applicants must have demonstrated or expressed interest in the plastic industry; applicants must be in good academic standing. **Application Requirements:** Applicants must complete the application form; applicants must submit three letters of recommendation, two of which are from a teacher or school official and one from an employer or non-relative; a high school and/or college transcript for the past two years; a list of current and past school activities, community activities, and honors; a listing of employment history; a one-to-two-page typewritten statement telling why they are applying for the scholarship, qualifications, educational and career goals in the plastic industry. **Deadline for Receipt:** January 15. **Additional Information:** foundation@4spe.org

5281 ■ SOCIETY OF PLASTICS ENGINEERS

14 Fairfield Dr.
Brookfield, CT 06804-0403
Tel: (203)775-0471
Fax: (203)775-8490
E-mail: info@4spe.org
Web Site: http://www.4spe.org
To promote scientific and engineering knowledge relating to plastics.
Title of Award: Society of Plastics Engineers Pittsburgh Scholarships **Area, Field, or Subject:** Science; Engineering. **Level of Education for which Award is Granted:** Graduate, Undergraduate **Number Awarded:** 2. **Funds Available:** $2,000.
Eligibility Requirements: Applicants must be undergraduate and graduate students in institutions, colleges, or universities; applicants must have demonstrated or expressed interest in the plastic industry; applicants must be in good academic standing; **Application Requirements:** Applicants must complete the application form; applicants must submit three letters of recommendation, two of which are from a teacher or school official and one from an employer or non-relative; a high school and/or college transcript for the past two years; a list of current and past school activities, community activities, and honors; a listing of employment history; A one-to-two-page typewritten statement telling why they are applying for the scholarship, qualifications, educational and career goals in the plastic industry; applicants must provide proof of graduation from high school. **Deadline for Receipt:** January 15. **Additional Information:** foundation@4spe.org

5282 ■ SOCIETY OF PLASTICS ENGINEERS

14 Fairfield Dr.
Brookfield, CT 06804-0403
Tel: (203)775-0471
Fax: (203)775-8490
E-mail: info@4spe.org
Web Site: http://www.4spe.org
To promote scientific and engineering knowledge relating to plastics.
Title of Award: Thermoforming Scholarships **Area, Field, or Subject:** Science; Engineering. **Level of Education for which Award is Granted:** Graduate, Undergraduate **Funds Available:** $7,500.
Eligibility Requirements: Applicants must be undergraduate and graduate students in institutions, colleges, or universities including those enrolled in associate degree or technical degree programs who are committed to becoming hands-on workers in the plastics industry and who are dedicated to careers as plastics technicians or engineers. Applicants must have demonstrated or expressed interest in the plastic industry; applicants must be in good academic standing; applicants must have experience in the thermoplastic elastomers industry, such as courses taken, research conducted, or jobs held. **Application Requirements:** Applicants

must complete the application form; applicants must submit three letters of recommendation, two of which are from a teacher or school official and one from an employer or non-relative; a high school and/or college transcript for the past two years; a list of current and past school activities, community activities, and honors; a listing of employment history; a one-to-two-page typewritten statement telling why they are applying for the scholarship, qualifications, educational and career goals in the plastic industry. **Deadline for Receipt:** January 15. **Additional Information:** foundation@4spe.org

5283 ■ SOCIETY OF PLASTICS ENGINEERS

14 Fairfield Dr.
Brookfield, CT 06804-0403
Tel: (203)775-0471
Fax: (203)775-8490
E-mail: info@4spe.org
Web Site: http://www.4spe.org
To promote scientific and engineering knowledge relating to plastics.
Title of Award: Thermoplastic Materials and Foams Division Scholarships **Area, Field, or Subject:** Science; Engineering. **Level of Education for which Award is Granted:** Graduate, Undergraduate **Number Awarded:** 1. **Funds Available:** $1,000.
Eligibility Requirements: Applicants must be undergraduate and graduate students in institutions, colleges, or universities; applicants must have demonstrated or expressed interest in the plastic industry; applicants must be in good academic standing. **Application Requirements:** Applicants must complete the application form; applicants must submit three letters of recommendation, two of which are from a teacher or school official and one from an employer or non-relative; a high school and/or college transcript for the past two years; a list of current and past school activities, community activities, and honors; a listing of employment history; a one-to-two-page typewritten statement telling why they are applying for the scholarship, qualifications, educational and career goals in the plastic industry. **Deadline for Receipt:** January 15. **Additional Information:** foundation@4spe.org

5284 ■ SOCIETY OF PLASTICS ENGINEERS

14 Fairfield Dr.
Brookfield, CT 06804-0403
Tel: (203)775-0471
Fax: (203)775-8490
E-mail: info@4spe.org
Web Site: http://www.4spe.org
To promote scientific and engineering knowledge relating to plastics.
Title of Award: Thermoplastics Elastomers Special Interest Group Scholarships **Area, Field, or Subject:** Science; Engineering. **Level of Education for which Award is Granted:** Graduate, Undergraduate **Number Awarded:** 1. **Funds Available:** $1,000.
Eligibility Requirements: Applicants must be undergraduate and graduate students in institutions, colleges, or universities. Applicants must have demonstrated or expressed interest in the plastic industry; applicants must be in good academic standing; applicants must have experience in the thermoplastic elastomers industry, such as courses taken, research conducted, or jobs held. **Application Requirements:** Applicants must complete the application form; applicants must submit three letters of recommendation, two of which are from a teacher or school official and one from an employer or non-relative; a high school and/or college transcript for the past two years; a list of current and past school activities, community activities, and honors; a listing of employment history; a one-to-two-page typewritten statement telling why they are applying for the scholarship, qualifications, educational and career goals in the plastic industry. **Deadline for Receipt:** January 15. **Additional Information:** foundation@4spe.org

5285 ■ SOCIETY OF PLASTICS ENGINEERS

14 Fairfield Dr.
Brookfield, CT 06804-0403
Tel: (203)775-0471
Fax: (203)775-8490
E-mail: info@4spe.org
Web Site: http://www.4spe.org
To promote scientific and engineering knowledge relating to plastics.
Title of Award: Vinyl Plastics Division Scholarships **Area, Field, or Subject:** Science; Engineering. **Level of Education for which Award is

Granted: Graduate, Undergraduate **Number Awarded:** 1. **Funds Available:** $3,000.

Eligibility Requirements: Applicants must be undergraduate and graduate students in institutions, colleges, or universities; applicants must have demonstrated or expressed interest in the plastic industry; applicants must be in good academic standing. **Application Requirements:** Applicants must complete the application form; applicants must submit three letters of recommendation, two of which are from a teacher or school official and one from an employer or non-relative; a high school and/or college transcript for the past two years; a list of current and past school activities, community activities, and honors; a listing of employment history; a one-to-two-page typewritten statement telling why they are applying for the scholarship, qualifications, educational and career goals in the plastic industry. **Deadline for Receipt:** January 15. **Additional Information:** foundation@4spe.org

5286 ■ SOCIETY OF WOMEN ENGINEERS
230 East Ohio St., Ste. 400
Chicago, IL 60611
Tel: (312)596-5223
E-mail: hq@swe.org
Web Site: http://www.swe.org
To help individuals achieve full potential in careers as engineers and leaders; to expand the image of the engineering profession as a positive force improving the quality of life; to demonstrate the value of diversity.
Title of Award: Society of Women Engineers Scholarships **Area, Field, or Subject:** Engineering. **Level of Education for which Award is Granted:** Undergraduate **Funds Available:** $400,000.
Eligibility Requirements: Applicants must be incoming freshmen women who are accepted for enrollment in a baccalaureate ABET/CSAB accredited engineering or computer science degree program; must have a minimum GPA of 3.5/4.0 scale for freshmen applicants; must not be the current recipients of a renewable SWE Scholarship; must be full-time students; must be U.S. citizens or permanent residents of the US for some scholarships; and must not be receiving full funding for education from another organization. **Application Requirements:** Applicants must fill out the online application form; send a current school stamp and signature official transcript from high school or where you have taken courses; a copy of letter of acceptance from ABET accredited college or university indicating acceptance into an engineering or computer science curriculum for the coming academic year; and two letters of recommendation of which one must be from a high school teacher and the other must be from a person who has known the applicant for two or more years and who is not a relative or member of the applicant's family. **Deadline for Receipt:** May 15. **Additional Information:** Society of Women Engineers at the above address.

5287 ■ SOLID WASTE ASSOCIATION OF NORTH AMERICA
1100 Wayne Ave., Ste. 700
Silver Spring, MD 20910
Tel: 800-467-9262
Fax: (301)589-7068
Web Site: http://www.swana.org
To promote education and professional development by providing financial aid.
Title of Award: Grant H. Flint International Scholarships - Category II **Area, Field, or Subject:** Environmental Science; Engineering. **Level of Education for which Award is Granted:** Undergraduate **Number Awarded:** 1. **Funds Available:** $2,000. **Duration:** Annual.
Eligibility Requirements: Applicants can be SWANA student members who are currently enrolled full-time students and/or entering their junior or senior undergraduate year; must be pursuing a degree in environmental science, engineering, or other suitable major related to solid waste management. **Application Requirements:** Application forms and instructions are available at SWANA website. **Deadline for Receipt:** May 1. **Additional Information:** Kathy Callaghan, Staff Administrator, at the above address tel 240-494-2248, email: kcallaghan@swana.org.

5288 ■ SONS OF NORWAY FOUNDATION
1455 W Lake St.
Minneapolis, MN 55408-2666
Tel: (612)827-3611
Fax: (612)827-0658

E-mail: foundation@sofn.com
Web Site: http://www.sofn.com
To promote the heritage and the culture of Norway. To encourage young women to enter the field of science and engineering.
Title of Award: Nancy Lorraine Jensen Memorial Scholarships **Area, Field, or Subject:** Science; Engineering. **Level of Education for which Award is Granted:** Undergraduate **Number Awarded:** 3. **Funds Available:** No specific amount.
Eligibility Requirements: Applicant must be an American citizen not younger than 17 and not older than 35 on the date the scholarship application is submitted. Applicant must be a current female member or the daughter or granddaughter of a current member of the Sons of Norway, and have held such membership for at least three years duration, on the date the application is submitted. Applicants must be full-time undergraduates who have completed at least one term (quarter, semester) of her studies. **Application Requirements:** Applicants must submit an application form. Applicants must send SAT or ACT scores; a 500-word essay giving proof of their accomplishments and describing how they intend to pursue their career; sealed, official copy of their latest grade transcript; and three sealed letters of recommendation. **Deadline for Receipt:** April 1.

5289 ■ SONS OF NORWAY FOUNDATION
1455 W Lake St.
Minneapolis, MN 55408-2666
Tel: (612)827-3611
Fax: (612)827-0658
E-mail: foundation@sofn.com
Web Site: http://www.sofn.com
To support students who attend Oslo International Summer School.
Title of Award: Sons of Norway Foundation Scholarships to Oslo International School **Area, Field, or Subject:** Engineering; Science. **Level of Education for which Award is Granted:** Undergraduate **Number Awarded:** 2. **Funds Available:** $1,500.
Eligibility Requirements: Applicants must be admitted to Oslo International Summer School. Applicants must be current members of the Sons of Norway, or the children or grandchildren of current members. **Application Requirements:** Applicants must submit an application form; essay; letters of recommendation. **Deadline for Receipt:** March 1.

5290 ■ SOUTHWEST FLORIDA COMMUNITY FOUNDATION
8260 College Pkwy., Ste. 101
Fort Myers, FL 33919
Tel: (239)274-5900
Fax: (239)274-5930
Web Site: http://www.floridacommunity.com
To fund a student who will attend: FGCU, university of Florida/Gainesville, University of Florida/Tallahassee, Flagler College, Stetson University/Deland, University of Miami, University of Tampa, or Embry Riddle Aeronautical University/Daytona Beach.
Title of Award: D&A Florida Scholarships **Area, Field, or Subject:** Architecture; Business; Engineering; International affairs and relations; Journalism; Computer and information sciences; Law; Literature; Medicine; Physics; Chemistry; Political science. **Level of Education for which Award is Granted:** Undergraduate **Funds Available:** $10,000. **Duration:** One year.
Eligibility Requirements: Applicants must have graduated from a public or private high school in Charlotte, Glades, Hendry or Lee County; must pursue a degree in Architecture, Business, Engineering, International affairs and relations, Journalism, Computer and information sciences, Law, Literature, Medicine, Physics, Chemistry, or Political science. **Application Requirements:** Application forms are available online. Applicants must submit a letter of interest and letter of recommendation, a transcript and financial need documentation. **Deadline for Receipt:** February 15.

5291 ■ SOUTHWEST FLORIDA COMMUNITY FOUNDATION
8260 College Pkwy., Ste. 101
Fort Myers, FL 33919
Tel: (239)274-5900
Fax: (239)274-5930
Web Site: http://www.floridacommunity.com
To fund students pursuing degrees or advanced degrees in medicine, law, dentistry, teaching (math and science), ministry, engineering, accounting, architecture and computer science.

Title of Award: John M. and Mary A. Shanley Memorial Scholarships **Area, Field, or Subject:** Medicine; Law; Dentistry; Teaching; Ministry; Engineering; Accounting; Agriculture; Economic aspects; Architecture; Computer and information sciences. **Level of Education for which Award is Granted:** Undergraduate **Funds Available:** $5,000. **Duration:** One year.

Eligibility Requirements: Applicant must be a resident of Charlotte, Hendry or Lee County. **Application Requirements:** Application forms are available online. Applicants must submit a letter of interest, letter of recommendation and transcript. **Deadline for Receipt:** February 15.

5292 ■ SPECIALTY EQUIPMENT MARKET ASSOCIATION

PO Box 4910
Diamond Bar, CA 91765-0910
Tel: (909)396-0289
Fax: (909)860-1709
E-mail: sema@sema.org
Web Site: http://www.sema.org
To foster industry leadership by supporting the education of students pursuing careers in the automotive aftermarket.
Title of Award: Loan Forgiveness Scholarships **Area, Field, or Subject:** Automotive technology. **Level of Education for which Award is Granted:** Undergraduate **Funds Available:** $1,000.

Eligibility Requirements: Applicants must be post-graduate students with one year minimum employment by a SEMA member company. **Application Requirements:** Applicants must submit a completed application form; resume; official, sealed transcripts for all college or post-secondary course work completed through the first quarter or semester of the current year; must provide documentation of outstanding student loans; personal essay; two letters of recommendation from professors, career counselors, or employers; must submit a current photo for publication and promotional use. **Additional Information:** education@sema.org.

5293 ■ SPECIALTY EQUIPMENT MARKET ASSOCIATION

PO Box 4910
Diamond Bar, CA 91765-0910
Tel: (909)396-0289
Fax: (909)860-1709
E-mail: sema@sema.org
Web Site: http://www.sema.org
To foster industry leadership by supporting the education of students pursuing careers in the automotive aftermarket; to foster leadership in the specialty equipment marketplace and to support educational goals for students pursuing careers in the automotive aftermarket.
Title of Award: Specialty Equipment Market Association Scholarships **Area, Field, or Subject:** Automotive technology. **Level of Education for which Award is Granted:** Undergraduate **Number Awarded:** 4. **Funds Available:** Varies.

Eligibility Requirements: Applicants must be graduates, or undergraduate sophomores, juniors or seniors, in a vocational or technical degree program in a two-to-four year accredited university or college in the United States or Canada. Applicants must have a minimum 2.5 grade point average; must be pursuing studies leading to a career in the automotive aftermarket or a related field. **Application Requirements:** Applicants must submit a completed application form; must submit a personal essay outlining reasons the applicant wants to pursue a career in the automotive aftermarket or related fields; must submit an official sealed transcript from all college or post-secondary course work completed; two letters of recommendation from a non-family member on company letterhead. **Deadline for Receipt:** April 20.

5294 ■ SPIE (THE INTERNATIONAL SOCIETY FOR OPTICAL ENGINEERING)

PO Box 10
Bellingham, WA 98227-0010
Tel: (360)676-3290; 888-504-8171
Fax: (360)647-1445
E-mail: customerservice@spie.org
Web Site: http://www.spie.org
To provide education assistance to students in field of microlithography.
Title of Award: BACUS Scholarships **Area, Field, or Subject:** Optical engineering; Optics. **Level of Education for which Award is Granted:** Graduate, Undergraduate **Number Awarded:** 2. **Funds Available:** $4000.

Eligibility Requirements: Applicants must be student members of SPIE; must be enrolled full-time, undergraduate or graduate students in the field of microlithography emphasizing on optical tooling or semiconductor manufacturing technologies. **Application Requirements:** Applicants must submit a completed scholarship application form (available at the website); a 450-word essay; and two letters of recommendation sent separately by the recommender. Application materials must not exceed more than ten pages. **Additional Information:** Scholarships are sponsored by BACUS, the International Technical Group of SPIE dedicated to the advancement of photomask technology. **Deadline for Receipt:** January 11. **Additional Information:** scholarships@spie.org.

5295 ■ SPIE (THE INTERNATIONAL SOCIETY FOR OPTICAL ENGINEERING)

PO Box 10
Bellingham, WA 98227-0010
Tel: (360)676-3290; 888-504-8171
Fax: (360)647-1445
E-mail: customerservice@spie.org
Web Site: http://www.spie.org
To promote education in laser technology, engineering, or applications.
Title of Award: Laser Technology, Engineering and Applications Scholarships **Area, Field, or Subject:** Engineering; Technology. **Level of Education for which Award is Granted:** Graduate, Undergraduate **Funds Available:** $4000. **Duration:** One year.

Eligibility Requirements: Applicants must be student members of SPIE; must be enrolled full-time in an optics photonics imaging or optoelectronics program or related discipline at an accredited school; must be in high school or secondary school, undergraduate or post-secondary school, or graduate school. **Application Requirements:** Applicants must submit a completed scholarship application form (available at the website); a 450-word essay; and two letters of recommendation sent separately by the recommender. Application materials must not exceed more than ten pages. **Additional Information:** Sponsored in part by a gift from the former Forum for Military Applications of Directed Energy. **Deadline for Receipt:** January 11. **Additional Information:** scholarships@spie.org.

5296 ■ SPIE (THE INTERNATIONAL SOCIETY FOR OPTICAL ENGINEERING)

PO Box 10
Bellingham, WA 98227-0010
Tel: (360)676-3290; 888-504-8171
Fax: (360)647-1445
E-mail: customerservice@spie.org
Web Site: http://www.spie.org
To provide education assistance to a student in optical design.
Title of Award: D.J. Lovell Scholarships **Area, Field, or Subject:** Optics; Optical engineering. **Level of Education for which Award is Granted:** Graduate, Undergraduate **Funds Available:** $11,000. **Duration:** One year.

Eligibility Requirements: Applicants must be student members of SPIE; must be enrolled full-time in an optics photonics imaging or optoelectronics program or related discipline at an accredited school; must be in high school or secondary school, undergraduate or post-secondary school, or graduate school. **Application Requirements:** Applicants must submit a completed scholarship application form (available at the website); a 450-word essay; and two letters of recommendation sent separately by the recommender. Application materials must not exceed more than ten pages. **Additional Information:** The scholarship is sponsored in part by SPIE with contributions from Labsphere Inc. **Deadline for Receipt:** January 11. **Additional Information:** scholarships@spie.org.

5297 ■ SPIE (THE INTERNATIONAL SOCIETY FOR OPTICAL ENGINEERING)

PO Box 10
Bellingham, WA 98227-0010
Tel: (360)676-3290; 888-504-8171
Fax: (360)647-1445
E-mail: customerservice@spie.org
Web Site: http://www.spie.org
To provide education assistance to a student in optical design.
Title of Award: William H. Price Scholarships **Area, Field, or Subject:** Optical engineering; Optics. **Level of Education for which Award is Granted:** Graduate, Undergraduate **Funds Available:** $3000.

Eligibility Requirements: Applicants must be student members of SPIE; must be enrolled full-time, undergraduate or graduate in an optical design and engineering. **Application Requirements:** Applicants must submit a completed scholarship application form (available at the website); a 450-word essay; and two letters of recommendation sent separately by the recommender. Application materials must not exceed more than ten pages. **Additional Information:** Established in 1985 in honor of Bill Price, a well-respected member of the SPIE technical community. **Deadline for Receipt:** January 11. **Additional Information:** scholarships@spie.org.

5298 ■ SPIE (THE INTERNATIONAL SOCIETY FOR OPTICAL ENGINEERING)
PO Box 10
Bellingham, WA 98227-0010
Tel: (360)676-3290; 888-504-8171
Fax: (360)647-1445
E-mail: customerservice@spie.org
Web Site: http://www.spie.org
To supplement travel support for students presenting a paper at any of SPIE's meetings.
Title of Award: Student Travel Grants **Area, Field, or Subject:** Optical engineering; Optics. **Level of Education for which Award is Granted:** Graduate, Undergraduate **Funds Available:** Covers travel expenses.
Eligibility Requirements: Applicants must be fulltime student members of SPIE; must be authors of an accepted paper presented at the conference; and must have not received any SPIE funding in the past 12 months. **Application Requirements:** Applicant must submit a student travel grant application form (available at the website); a letter of recommendation from faculty advisor or head department; and a written support from the chair of the conference which the paper will be presented.

5299 ■ STARK COMMUNITY FOUNDATION
400 Market Ave. N, Ste. 200
Canton, OH 44702-2107
Tel: (330)454-3426
Fax: (330)454-5855
Web Site: http://www.starkcommunityfoundation.org
To provide scholarship assistance to qualified individuals who want to pursue their studies.
Title of Award: John G. and Betty J. Mick Scholarship Fund **Area, Field, or Subject:** Engineering. **Level of Education for which Award is Granted:** Undergraduate **Funds Available:** No specific amount. **Duration:** One year.
Eligibility Requirements: Applicants must be seniors attending a high school in Stark County, OH; must have been accepted as a full-time students in Stark State College of Technology engineering Program for a two year degree program which will also transfer to a four year degree program at another university at the discretion of the students; must have been accepted as full-time students into the Engineering program at any university or college in the State of Ohio; nontraditional students furthering their education after entering the workforce will be considered secondarily; must have cumulative GPA of at least 2.0 on a 4.0 scale. **Application Requirements:** Applicants must complete and submit the application form and requirements to Stark Community Foundation, 400 Market Ave. N, Ste. 200, Canton, OH 44702. **Deadline for Receipt:** April 15.

5300 ■ STRAIGHTFORWARD MEDIA
508 7th St., Ste 202
Rapid City, SD 57701
Tel: (605)348-3042
Fax: (605)348-3043
E-mail: info@straightforwardmedia.com
Web Site: http://www.straightforwardmedia.com
To financially assist students in their educational pursuits.
Title of Award: StraightForward Media's Engineering Scholarships **Area, Field, or Subject:** Engineering. **Level of Education for which Award is Granted:** Undergraduate **Funds Available:** $500.
Eligibility Requirements: Applicant must be an engineering student. **Application Requirements:** Applicants must complete the Online Scholarship Application. **Additional Information:** Awards are given four times a year. **Deadline for Receipt:** March, June, September, December.

5301 ■ TAG AND LABEL MANUFACTURERS INSTITUTE
40 Shuman Blvd., Ste. 295
Naperville, IL 60563

Tel: (630)357-9222
Free: 800-533-8564
Fax: (630)357-0192
E-mail: office@tlmi.com
Web Site: http://www.tlmi.com
To promote education in the flexographic industry.
Title of Award: TLMI Scholarships - Two-Year Colleges **Area, Field, or Subject:** Industrial design. **Level of Education for which Award is Granted:** Undergraduate **Number Awarded:** 4. **Funds Available:** $1,000.
Eligibility Requirements: Applicants must be enrolled full-time in a flexographic printing program at a two-year college or technical program that grants degrees; and must maintain a 3.00 or higher GPA. **Application Requirements:** Application forms are available at the website. Committee will not accept applications direct from a student, applicants must present the application form together with an official college transcript and a personal statement to his/her educator for submission to the TLMI. Educators must forward complete application package to TLMI **Deadline for Receipt:** January 1-March 31. **Additional Information:** Karen Planzat, 800-533-8564.

5302 ■ TEXAS SOCIETY OF PROFESSIONAL ENGINEERS
PO Box 2145
Austin, TX 78768
Tel: (512)472-9286
Free: 800-580-8973
Fax: (512)472-2934
E-mail: trishb@tspe.org
Web Site: http://www.tspe.org
To provide financial assistance to students studying to become engineers in an engineering program at an ABET-accredited college or university.
Title of Award: Texas Society of Professional Engineers Scholarships **Area, Field, or Subject:** Engineering. **Level of Education for which Award is Granted:** Undergraduate **Funds Available:** No specific amount.
Eligibility Requirements: Applicants must be United States citizens; high school seniors with a 3.0 or higher GPA entering college in the coming school year; have scored at least 600 in math, 550 in critical reading and 500 in writing on the SAT, or a 29 in math and 25 in English on the ACT; and enrolled in an ABET program. **Application Requirements:** Applicants must submit the completed application form; essay; two recommendations from non-relatives (high school teachers preferred); and an official transcript. **Deadline for Receipt:** January 21.

5303 ■ TRANSPORTATION ASSOCIATION OF CANADA
2323 St., Laurent Blvd.
Ottawa, ON, Canada K1G 4J8
Tel: (613)736-1350
Fax: (613)736-1395
E-mail: secretariat@tac-act.ca
Web Site: http://www.tac-atc.ca
To encourage engineering students to focus on the vital aspects of Canada's landscape.
Title of Award: TAC Foundation-Armtec Scholarships **Area, Field, or Subject:** Civil engineering; Transportation. **Level of Education for which Award is Granted:** Undergraduate **Funds Available:** $5,000. **Duration:** One year.
Eligibility Requirements: Applicant must be entering third or fourth year studies; must intend to pursue a career in some aspect of the transportation field and meet the conditions of the scholarships; must have achieved an overall B level or equivalent average mark in their previous academic year. **Application Requirements:** Applicant must complete the application form (available online); must provide academic references and relevant employment information; must have an electronic version of their transcript of record. Application form and requirements must be sent to the TAC Foundation. **Deadline for Receipt:** March 3.

5304 ■ U.S. AIR FORCE ROTC
551 E Maxwell Blvd.
Maxwell AFB, AL 36112-5917
Tel: (334)953-6167
Fax: (866)423-7682
Web Site: http://www.afrotc.com

To provide financial assistance for college students enrolled in specific fields.

Title of Award: U.S. Air Force ROTC Express Scholarships **Area, Field, or Subject:** Engineering; Aerospace sciences; Aeronautics; Atmospheric sciences. **Level of Education for which Award is Granted:** Undergraduate **Funds Available:** $15,000.

Eligibility Requirements: Applicants must be United States citizens by the end of the projected term of activation; must pass the Air Force Officer Qualifying Test; must pass the Air Force ROTC Physical Fitness Test; must have at least a 2.5 cumulative college grade point average; must a physical examination and be certified; must not be a contracted scholarship recipient; and must meet the age, moral and other scholarship eligibility requirements for Air force ROTC. **Application Requirements:** Applications for the Express Scholarship are processed and approved at the detachment level. Applicant must contact the detachment serving the school that he/she wishes to attend and the school will work to nominate the student for the appropriate scholarship program.

5305 ■ U.S. DEPARTMENT OF HOMELAND SECURITY

12th & C St. SW
Washington, DC 20024
Tel: (202)245-2499
E-mail: dhsed@orau.org
Web Site: http://www.orau.gov/dhsed

To pursue basic science and technology innovations that can be applied to the DHS mission.

Title of Award: The Homeland Security Undergraduate Scholarships **Area, Field, or Subject:** Science technologies; Engineering; Mathematics and mathematical sciences. **Level of Education for which Award is Granted:** Undergraduate **Funds Available:** $1,000; **Duration:** 9 months.

Eligibility Requirements: Applicants must be a U.S. citizen as of the application deadline; applicants must have a cumulative undergraduate GPA of 3.30 or higher on a 4.00 scale; applicants must be majoring in a homeland security science, technology, engineering or mathematics field with interest in a homeland security research area; applicants must be in second year of college if been attending college full-time; applicants must have completed a total of at least 45 but not more than 60 semester hours if been attending on a part-time, or combination or part-time and full-time basis. **Application Requirements:** Applicants must complete the online application form; applicants must submit two online reference report forms; applicants must submit official academic transcript from all postsecondary institutions attended. **Deadline for Receipt:** January 7 for online application form; January 14 for documents.

5306 ■ UNIVERSITY OF ALASKA ANCHORAGE

3211 Providence Dr.
Anchorage, AK 99508
Tel: (907)786-1800
Web Site: http://www.uaa.alaska.edu

To provide financial assistance for tuition and other related educational expenses to full-time students of the University of Alaska Anchorage who are formally admitted to an undergraduate engineering or music degree-seeking program.

Title of Award: Alaska Community Foundation Sven E. & Lorraine Eriksson Scholarships **Area, Field, or Subject:** Engineering; Music. **Level of Education for which Award is Granted:** Undergraduate **Funds Available:** No specific amount. **Duration:** One academic year.

Eligibility Requirements: Applicant must demonstrate motivation, academic and leadership potential; must be an Alaskan resident who has graduated from an Alaskan high school; must be a United States citizen; must be an incoming college freshman must have a minimum high school GPA of 2.5; must have a minimum cumulative grade point average of 3.0 from college and have had a 2.5 GPA from high school; must be formally admitted to an undergraduate engineering or music degree-seeking program at the University of Alaska Anchorage; must demonstrate financial need; must be an incoming or continuing student at the University of Alaska Anchorage. **Application Requirements:** Applicants must complete the application form available online. **Deadline for Receipt:** February 15.

5307 ■ UNIVERSITY OF ALASKA ANCHORAGE

3211 Providence Dr.
Anchorage, AK 99508

Tel: (907)786-1800
Web Site: http://www.uaa.alaska.edu

To encourage students to choose non-traditional study destinations abroad, especially those outside of Western Europe and Australia; to support students who have been traditionally under-represented in study abroad, including but not limited to, students with high financial need, community college students, students in under-represented fields such as the sciences and engineering, students with diverse ethnic backgrounds, and students with disabilities.

Title of Award: Benjamin A. Gilman International Scholarship **Area, Field, or Subject:** Engineering; Science; General studies. **Level of Education for which Award is Granted:** Undergraduate **Funds Available:** Award amounts will vary depending on length of study and student need, with the average award being $4,000.

Eligibility Requirements: Applicants must be U.S. citizen undergraduate students who are receiving Federal Pell Grant funding at a 2-year or 4-year college or university to participate in study abroad programs worldwide; must be receiving a Federal Pell Grant or provide proof that he/she will be receiving a Pell Grant at the time of application or during the term of their study abroad; must be applying to or has been accepted into a study abroad program eligible for credit by the student's accredited institution of higher education in the U.S; must be studying abroad for at least 4 weeks in one country; must be studying abroad in any country except Cuba or a country on the State Department's current travel warning list; must be studying in the fall, spring, or academic year terms including winter inter-sessions. **Application Requirements:** Applicants must submit a completed application form with other requirements or supporting documents. **Deadline for Receipt:** April and September.

5308 ■ UNIVERSITY OF ALASKA ANCHORAGE

3211 Providence Dr.
Anchorage, AK 99508
Tel: (907)786-1800
Web Site: http://www.uaa.alaska.edu

To provide financial assistance for tuition and other educational expenses to full-time students who are formally admitted to a journalism, engineering, or education degree-seeking program at the University of Alaska Anchorage.

Title of Award: Sturgulewski Family Scholarships **Area, Field, or Subject:** Journalism; Engineering; Education. **Level of Education for which Award is Granted:** Graduate, Undergraduate **Funds Available:** $500.

Eligibility Requirements: Applicants must demonstrate motivation, academic and leadership potential; must be in good academic standing with a minimum cumulative GPA of 2.0 for undergraduates and 3.0 for graduates; must be formally admitted to a journalism, engineering, or education undergraduate, graduate, certificate, and/or vocational degree-seeking program at the University of Alaska Anchorage; must have plan on enrolling full-time (12 credits for undergraduates and 9 for graduates) at the University of Alaska Anchorage; may be an incoming or continuing student at the University of Alaska Anchorage; may be a U.S citizen, non-US citizen, Alaska resident, or out-of-state resident; must be enrolled in the semester for which the award is made. **Application Requirements:** Applicants must complete the electronic scholarship application available online at www.uaa.alaska.edu/scholarships/sturgulewski_family. cfm. **Deadline for Receipt:** February 15.

5309 ■ UNIVERSITY OF ALASKA ANCHORAGE

3211 Providence Dr.
Anchorage, AK 99508
Tel: (907)786-1800
Web Site: http://www.uaa.alaska.edu

To provide financial assistance for tuition and other educational expenses to full-time or part-time students who are formally admitted to an engineering or science degree-seeking program at the University of Alaska Anchorage and who are of Alaska Native ethnicity.

Title of Award: UAA Quanterra Scholarships **Area, Field, or Subject:** Engineering; Science. **Level of Education for which Award is Granted:** Undergraduate **Funds Available:** No specific amount.

Eligibility Requirements: Applicants must demonstrate motivation, academic and leadership potential; must be in good academic standing with a minimum cumulative GPA of 2.5 for undergraduate and 3.0 for graduate; must be formally admitted to a engineering or science degree-seeking program at the University of Alaska Anchorage by the start of the semester of the award; may also be in the Masters of Civil Engineering Program, Master of Science Program; Associate of Applied Science Program for Petroleum Engineering Aide or Petroleum Technology, or working toward a Petroleum Technology Certificate; must plan on enrolling at least half-time (6 credits) at the University of Alaska Anchorage; must be able to demonstrate financial need; must be enrolled in the semester for which the award is made; must be Alaska Native ethnicity; must provide proof of Native Corporation Affiliation and Lineage Verification; may be an incoming or continuing student at the University of Alaska Anchorage. **Application Requirements:** Applicant must provide a proof of Native Corporation Affiliation and Lineage Verification. **Deadline for Receipt:** February 15.

5310 ■ UNIVERSITY OF NEW HAMPSHIRE
Office of Admission
4 Garrison Ave.
Durham, NH 03824
Tel: (603)862-1360
Fax: (603)862-0077
E-mail: admission@unh.edu
Web Site: http://www.unh.edu
To provide financial assistance to students who want to continue their education at UNH.
Title of Award: CEPS-Tyco Scholarships **Area, Field, or Subject:** Engineering; Physical sciences. **Level of Education for which Award is Granted:** Undergraduate **Number Awarded:** 2. **Funds Available:** $10,000. **Duration:** One year.
Eligibility Requirements: Applicants must be high school seniors admitted to the University's College of Engineering and Physical Sciences. **Application Requirements:** Applicants must have an application for admission to a major within the College of Engineering and Physical Sciences at the University of New Hampshire; must have official high school transcripts, including the first marking period of senior year; must have the official test scores for either the SAT Reasoning Test or ACT with writing test; must submit an additional scholarship essay through the online form; must submit a Free Application for Federal Student Aid (FAFSA) form. Application form and other supporting documents must be sent to University of New Hampshire, Office of Admission/CEPS-Tyco Scholarship, Grant House, 4 Garrison Ave., Durham, NH 03824. **Deadline for Receipt:** November 15.

5311 ■ UNIVERSITY OF TORONTO
315 Bloor St. W
Toronto, ON, Canada M5S 1A3
Tel: (416)978-2011
E-mail: information.commonsats@utoronto.ca
Web Site: http://www.utoronto.ca
To support students with their educational pursuits.
Title of Award: Stephanie Ali Memorial Scholarships **Area, Field, or Subject:** General studies. **Level of Education for which Award is Granted:** Undergraduate **Funds Available:** Approximately $200.
Eligibility Requirements: Applicant must be a student of U of T; in financial need; and have demonstrated commitment to community work or participation in charitable activities. **Application Requirements:** Applicants must submit a completed Stephanie Ali Memorial Scholarships application form along with the required materials and information. **Deadline for Receipt:** March 28.

5312 ■ UNIVERSITY OF TORONTO
315 Bloor St. W
Toronto, ON, Canada M5S 1A3
Tel: (416)978-2011
E-mail: information.commonsats@utoronto.ca
Web Site: http://www.utoronto.ca
To support students with their educational pursuits.
Title of Award: Nortel Institute Undergraduate Scholarships **Area, Field, or Subject:** Applied art; Engineering. **Level of Education for which Award is Granted:** Undergraduate **Funds Available:** Approximately $5000.
Eligibility Requirements: Applicant must be a U of T student and a Canadian citizen or landed immigrant and a resident of Ontario; must be in the second or third year in the Faculty of Applied Science and Engineer-

ing, the Faculty of Arts and Science, University of Toronto Mississauga and University of Toronto Scarborough. **Application Requirements:** Applicants must submit a completed application form together with the required materials and information. **Deadline for Receipt:** November 1.

5313 ■ UNIVERSITY OF TORONTO
315 Bloor St. W
Toronto, ON, Canada M5S 1A3
Tel: (416)978-2011
E-mail: information.commonsats@utoronto.ca
Web Site: http://www.utoronto.ca
To support students with their educational pursuits.
Title of Award: University of Toronto Accenture Scholarships **Area, Field, or Subject:** Engineering; Computer and information sciences. **Level of Education for which Award is Granted:** Undergraduate **Funds Available:** $1500.
Eligibility Requirements: Applicant must be a student of U of T; enrolled in an Engineering, Computer Science or Bachelor of Commerce Degree; a third year student entering the final year of study; have maintained a strong academic background - minimum GPA of 3.0; and actively involved in two or more extracurricular activities. **Application Requirements:** Applicants must submit a completed Accenture Scholarship application form along with the required materials and information. **Deadline for Receipt:** April 25.

5314 ■ UNIVERSITY OF WISCONSIN-MADISON
432 N Murray St.
Madison, WI 53706-1496
Tel: (608)262-3060
Fax: (608)262-9068
E-mail: askbucky@uwmad.wisc.edu
Web Site: http://www.wisc.edu
To support UW-Madison students in their education.
Title of Award: Engineering Departmental Scholarships **Area, Field, or Subject:** Engineering. **Level of Education for which Award is Granted:** Undergraduate **Number Awarded:** Varies. **Funds Available:** Varies.
Eligibility Requirements: Applicants must be UW-Madison students admitted into a degree-granting department. **Application Requirements:** Students must contact the specific department office about the application process. **Deadline for Receipt:** March 15. **Additional Information:** College of Engineering, Engineering Student Services Office, at 608-262-2473, or hansen@engr.wisc.edu.

5315 ■ UNIVERSITY OF WISCONSIN-MADISON
432 N Murray St.
Madison, WI 53706-1496
Tel: (608)262-3060
Fax: (608)262-9068
E-mail: askbucky@uwmad.wisc.edu
Web Site: http://www.wisc.edu
To provide financial assistance to mathematics, science, and engineering students who wish to pursue their education.
Title of Award: Barry M. Goldwater Scholarships **Area, Field, or Subject:** Mathematics and mathematical sciences; Science; Engineering. **Level of Education for which Award is Granted:** Undergraduate **Number Awarded:** 300. **Funds Available:** $7500.
Eligibility Requirements: Applicants must be full-time juniors or seniors with outstanding potential for a career in mathematics, science, or engineering; have at least a B average; rank in the upper quarter of the high schools class; be U.S. citizens or U.S. nationals; and nominated by UW-Madison. **Application Requirements:** Applicants must contact the Office of Undergraduate Academic Awards for information about the scholarship. **Deadline for Receipt:** November. **Additional Information:** Office of Undergraduate Academic Awards, Julie Stubbs, at 608-890-0370, or stubbs@wisc.edu.

5316 ■ VIRGINIA FOUNDATION FOR INDEPENDENT COLLEGES
8010 Ridge Rd., Ste. B
Richmond, VA 23229-7288
Tel: (804)288-6609
Free: 800-230-6757
Fax: (804)282-4635
E-mail: info@vfic.org

Web Site: http://www.vfic.org
To provide financial assistance for the students in their junior year at a VFIC college or university.
Title of Award: Phillip Morris USA Scholarships **Area, Field, or Subject:** Accounting; Biology; Business; Chemistry; Computer and information sciences; Economics; Engineering; Finance; Physics. **Level of Education for which Award is Granted:** Undergraduate **Funds Available:** $5,000.
Eligibility Requirements: Applicants must be U.S. citizens and current full-time sophomores attending a VFIC college or university (students from underrepresented populations are encouraged to apply); have minimum of 3.5 cumulative GPA; committed to applying for an internship with Phillip Morris USA for the summer after junior year; have declared, or intend to declare, a major in one of the following disciplines: accounting, biology, business, chemistry, computer science, economics, engineering, finance, or physics. **Application Requirements:** Applicants must submit completed application form along with two letters of recommendation and other required application information. **Deadline for Receipt:** November 1.

5317 ■ WINSTON-SALEM FOUNDATION
860 W Fifth St.
Winston-Salem, NC 27101-2506
Tel: (336)725-2382
Fax: (336)727-0581
E-mail: info@wsfoundation.org
Web Site: http://www.wsfoundation.org
To assist graduating high school seniors of Mt. Tabor High School.
Title of Award: Wes Burton Memorial Scholarships **Area, Field, or Subject:** Mathematics and mathematical science; Computer and information sciences; Business administration; Engineering. **Level of Education for which Award is Granted:** Undergraduate **Funds Available:** No specific amount.
Eligibility Requirements: Applicants must have a minimum GPA of 3.5; must demonstrate community and school service; must have an intent to pursue a career in Mathematics, Computer Science, Business Administration, or Engineering; demonstrate financial need (award is not restricted to lowest family incomes). **Application Requirements:** Student must complete the application in its entirety and include supplemental items and information requested in the various sections of the application. The supplemental items include: an interview with the Foundation; a grade transcript; a resume or list of student activities; one letter of recommendation from a math teacher, business teacher, or computer science teacher. **Deadline for Receipt:** March 31. **Additional Information:** WSF Student Aid Department, 336-714-3445.

5318 ■ WINSTON-SALEM FOUNDATION
860 W Fifth St.
Winston-Salem, NC 27101-2506
Tel: (336)725-2382
Fax: (336)727-0581
E-mail: info@wsfoundation.org
Web Site: http://www.wsfoundation.org
To award scholarship to worthy graduating high school seniors from Elkin High School who are US citizens.
Title of Award: Claude B. Hart Memorial Scholarships **Area, Field, or Subject:** Mathematics and mathematical sciences; Engineering. **Level of Education for which Award is Granted:** Undergraduate **Funds Available:** No specific amount.
Eligibility Requirements: Applicants must demonstrate significant promise in academics, leadership, community service and school service and intend to major in mathematics (accounting, computer science, business administration) and/or engineering (mechanical, civil, chemical, etc.) in college. Demonstration of financial need is preferred, but award is not restricted to lowest family incomes. Renewal of the award after the first year will require that the student be a full-time undergraduate student at an accredited four-year institution, maintain a minimum cumulative grade point average of 2.5, and continue to major in mathematics or engineering. **Application Requirements:** Scholarship applications will be provided in the guidance office at Elkin High School. Student must complete the application, requested transcripts, and financial information before being considered by the Elkin High School Scholarship Committee. The Scholarship Committee will submit up to 5 candidates to The Winston-Salem Foundation for review by the Elkin Advisory Committee or

its appointed sub-committee. **Additional Information:** WSF Student Aid Department, 336-714-3445.

5319 ■ WOMEN IN DEFENSE
2111 Wilson Blvd., Ste. 400
Arlington, VA 22201-3061
Tel: (703)247-2552
Fax: (703)522-1885
E-mail: wid@ndia.org
Web Site: http://wid.ndia.org
To provide financial assistance to further educational objectives of women either employed or planning careers in defense or national security areas.
Title of Award: Women In Defense HORIZONS Scholarships **Area, Field, or Subject:** National security; Military history; Government; Engineering; Computer and information sciences; Physics; Mathematics and mathematical sciences; Business; Law; International affairs and relations; Political science; Economics. **Level of Education for which Award is Granted:** Graduate, Undergraduate **Funds Available:** No specific amount.
Eligibility Requirements: Applicant must be currently enrolled at an accredited university/college, either full-time or part-time; must have junior, senior or graduate status; demonstrate interest in pursuing a career related to national security or defense; demonstrate financial need; have a minimum GPA of 3.25. Applicant must be a female citizen of the United States. **Application Requirements:** Applicants must submit a completed scholarship application form with the essays, recommendations, and transcripts. **Additional Information:** Established in 1988. **Deadline for Receipt:** July 1.

Fire Science

5320 ■ INTERNATIONAL ASSOCIATION OF ARSON INVESTIGATORS
2151 Priest Bridge Dr., Ste. 25
Crofton, MD 21114
Tel: (410)451-3473
Fax: (410)451-9049
E-mail: aclark@gmrc.com
Web Site: http://www.firearson.com
To foster, support and promote fire prevention and arson awareness through education and training.
Title of Award: John Charles Wilson Scholarships **Area, Field, or Subject:** Fires and fire prevention. **Level of Education for which Award is Granted:** Undergraduate **Funds Available:** Varies.
Eligibility Requirements: Applicants must be enrolled in a two or four-year accredited college or university that offers courses in police or fire science including fire investigation and related subjects. **Application Requirements:** Applicants must submit completed application form. **Deadline for Receipt:** February 15.

5321 ■ MAINE CHAPTER OF THE INTERNATIONAL ASSOCIATION OF ARSON INVESTIGATORS
PO Box 1101
Auburn, ME 04211-1101
E-mail: rshepar1@maine.rr.com
Web Site: http://www.maineiaai.com
To provide financial support for individuals pursuing studies in the field of Fire Science Degree programs.
Title of Award: Joseph C. Menezes Scholarships **Area, Field, or Subject:** Fires and fire prevention. **Level of Education for which Award is Granted:** Undergraduate **Funds Available:** No specific amount.
Eligibility Requirements: Applicants must be student enrolled in Fire Science Degree programs and must desire becoming involved in fire investigation. **Application Requirements:** Applicants must submit a completed application form along with the supporting documents. **Additional Information:** Rick Shepard.

5322 ■ MATANUSKA-SUSITNA COLLEGE
PO Box 2889
Palmer, AK 99645
Tel: (907)745-9774
Fax: (907)745-9711

E-mail: info@matsu.alaska.edu
Web Site: http://www.matsu.alaska.edu
To provide an incentive for Alaska's middle and high school students to achieve academic excellence, and to encourage the top high school graduates from every community in Alaska to attend the University of Alaska.
Title of Award: Snodgrass Scholarships **Area, Field, or Subject:** Accounting; Engineering, Architectural; Computer and information sciences; Fires and fire prevention; Heating, air conditioning, and refrigeration; Business administration; Telecommunications systems. **Level of Education for which Award is Granted:** Undergraduate **Funds Available:** $500-$2,000. **Duration:** One academic year.
Eligibility Requirements: Applicant must be admitted to the given Matanuska-Susitna College degree programs; must be a continuing student at Matanuska-Susitna College who has earned at least 20 credit hours; must have a cumulative GPA of 3.0 or higher; must exhibit good moral character and conduct; must be registered for eight or more credit hours. **Application Requirements:** Applicants must complete the MSC scholarship application and attach a resume showing their work experience; must compose an essay of 500 words or less describing their educational and career goals and how they plan to attain them; must have two letters of recommendation, written within the last two years. Application form and other supporting documents must be sent to Snodgrass Scholarships, Matanuska-Susitna College, Student Service, FSM 102, Palmer, AK 99645. **Deadline for Receipt:** May 31.

5323 ■ NATIONAL VOLUNTEER FIRE COUNCIL
7852 Walker Dr., Ste. 450
Greenbelt, MD 20770
Tel: (202)887-5700
Fax: (202)887-5291
E-mail: nvfcoffice@nvfc.org
Web Site: http://www.nvfc.org
To provide resources on how to establish a program, a network for connecting with other program, and to increase recruitment and retention to junior firefighters.
Title of Award: Junior Firefighter Scholarships **Area, Field, or Subject:** Fires and fire prevention. **Level of Education for which Award is Granted:** Undergraduate **Number Awarded:** 10. **Funds Available:** $5,000.
Eligibility Requirements: Applicant must be a high school senior, or a high school graduate within the past three years who is enrolled or will be enrolled in the following school year at an accredited two- or four-year institution of higher learning, a trade school or a certification program; be a pat or current junior firefighter in a department that is registered with the NVFC National Junior Firefighter Program. Applicants must also have proven to be an active and vital member of a junior firefighter program for at least one year and currently be active either as a junior firefighter or in some other capacity. Applicants must also have demonstrated intent to pursue emergency services. **Application Requirements:** Applicants must complete the scholarship application form; must submit an official transcript from the institution most recently attended; complete a 250-word essay outlining how being a junior firefighter has impacted the applicant's life, how the scholarship will further field of study, and plans for the future involvement in emergency services; must submit two letters of recommendation; recent photo to be used for NVFC newsletter, website if selected; fire department must submit a 250-word essay outlining its current junior firefighter program and how a $5,000 grant would benefit the department. **Deadline for Receipt:** May 15. **Additional Information:** nvfcoffice@nvfc.org.

5324 ■ PENNSYLVANIA ASSOCIATION OF ARSON INVESTIGATORS
RR2 Box 195
Martinsburg, PA 16662
Tel: (717)278-4854
E-mail: cjpi77@aol.com
Web Site: http://www.paai.org
To support members of the association with their educational pursuits.
Title of Award: Pennsylvania Association of Arson Investigators Scholarships **Area, Field, or Subject:** Fires and fire prevention. **Level of Education for which Award is Granted:** Undergraduate **Funds Available:** No specific amount.
Eligibility Requirements: Applicants must be paid-up members in good standing or an immediate family of paid-up member in good standing or

children of deceased members; must be enrolled, or planning to enroll, in the next scheduled semester of a two- or four-year accredited college/university that offers courses in police or fire sciences including, fire investigation and related subjects. **Application Requirements:** Applicants must submit a completed application form with the required materials to the Chairman of the Scholarship Committee, Thomas W. Dolan, Jr., 2 Luke Lane, Carlisle PA 17013. **Deadline for Receipt:** May 15. **Additional Information:** Thomas W. Dolan.

5325 ■ TANANA VALLEY CAMPUS
604 Barnette St.
Fairbanks, AK 99701
Tel: (907)455-2800; 877-882-8827
Web Site: http://www.tvc.uaf.edu
To provide educational support for qualified students intending to pursue their education.
Title of Award: Rachael Patterson Memorial Scholarships **Area, Field, or Subject:** Technology, Criminal justice, Fires and fire prevention. **Level of Education for which Award is Granted:** Undergraduate **Funds Available:** No specific amount. **Duration:** One year.
Eligibility Requirements: Applicants must be sophomores or above; must be enrolled in justice, fire science or office management and technology; must be residents of Alaska (at least two years) and are intending to remain in Alaska. **Application Requirements:** Scholarship applications are available online at uaonline.alaska.edu (to access the scholarship application, applicant must choose "Login to secured area" if they have a UA ID or apply for admission for the new students).

Food Service and Food Science

5326 ■ ALL STAR ASSOCIATION
PO Box 911050
Lexington, KY 40591-1050
Tel: (859)255-3644
Free: 800-930-3644
Fax: (859)255-3647
Web Site: http://www.allstardairy.com
To provide support for dependents of association members.
Title of Award: John D. Utterback Undergraduate Scholarships **Area, Field, or Subject:** Food science and technology. **Level of Education for which Award is Granted:** Undergraduate **Number Awarded:** 5. **Funds Available:** $1,000. **Duration:** One year.
Eligibility Requirements: Applicant must be a high school or college student enrolled in food science, marketing, business, nutrition, packaging, or AG education programs. **Application Requirements:** Applicants must complete and print the online questionnaire; must have the official transcript from all high schools, colleges, and universities attended; must submit a request letter of recommendation from a faculty member familiar with the applicant's scholastic performance; must have a recent photograph. Application form and other supporting documents must be sent to: All Star Dairy Association, Inc., 1050 Monarch St., Ste. No, 101, Lexington, KY 40513. **Deadline for Receipt:** April 1.

5327 ■ AMERICAN ASSOCIATION OF CANDY TECHNOLOGISTS
175 Rock Rd.
Glen Rock, NJ 07452
Tel: (201)652-2655; (201)652-3419
E-mail: aactinfo@gomc.com
Web Site: http://www.aactcandy.org
To provide support for individuals pursuing their career.
Title of Award: National Candy Technologist Scholarship Program **Area, Field, or Subject:** Food science and technology, Biological and clinical sciences. **Level of Education for which Award is Granted:** Undergraduate **Funds Available:** $5,000.
Eligibility Requirements: Applicants must be Sophomore, Junior, or Senior Status; have demonstrated interest in confectionery technology; attend an accredited four-year college or university within North America; be majoring in a food science, chemical science, biological science, or related area; minimum 3.0 GPA required (or equivalent on another scale). **Application Requirements:** Applicants must submit a complete application with short statement of personal and professional goals; must attach the academic activities including those relating to confectionery technol-

ogy; must have the current copy of college transcript and a recommendation letter. Application must be mailed to: Warrell Corp., 1250 Slate Hill Rd., Camp Hill, PA 17011. **Deadline for Receipt:** April 18. **Additional Information:** Mr. Karen Silva at the above address.

5328 ■ AMERICAN INSTITUTE OF BAKING

PO Box 3999
Manhattan, KS 66505-3999
Tel: (785)537-4750
Fax: (785)537-1493
Web Site: http://www.aibonline.org
To support self-sponsored students in attending AIB's 20-week Baking Science and Technology course and/or its 11-week Maintenance Engineering course.
Title of Award: American Institute of Baking Scholarships **Area, Field, or Subject:** Food science and technology. **Level of Education for which Award is Granted:** Undergraduate **Funds Available:** $500.
Eligibility Requirements: Applicants must be company-sponsored or self-sponsored students. **Application Requirements:** Applicant must submit a complete application form and three letters of recommendation.

5329 ■ INSTITUTE OF FOOD TECHNOLOGISTS

525 W Van Buren, Ste. 1000
Chicago, IL 60607
Tel: (312)782-8424
Free: 800-438-3663
Fax: (312)782-8348
E-mail: info@ift.org
Web Site: http://www.ift.org
To encourage and support undergraduate students intending to pursue a career in the field of food science/technology and in other related areas.
Title of Award: Institute of Food Technologists Junior/Senior Scholarships **Area, Field, or Subject:** Food Technology. **Level of Education for which Award is Granted:** Undergraduate **Funds Available:** Varies.
Eligibility Requirements: Program is open to sophomores, juniors or seniors with a 3.0 GPA or above, pursuing a curriculum in food science or food technology in an educational institution having an IFT approved degree program. **Application Requirements:** Applicants must submit an application form including name and contact information, degree and department where the study will be conducted; Statement outlining students career objectives; List of extracurricular activities and hobbies; List of awards, honors and scholarship received; Summary of work experience; Applicants must submit an official transcript of all college courses completed; Applicants must submit a letter of recommendation from a faculty member who is familiar with the applicant. **Deadline for Receipt:** February 1. **Additional Information:** Institute of Food Technologists at the above address.

5330 ■ INSTITUTE OF FOOD TECHNOLOGISTS

525 W Van Buren, Ste. 1000
Chicago, IL 60607
Tel: (312)782-8424
Free: 800-438-3663
Fax: (312)782-8348
E-mail: info@ift.org
Web Site: http://www.ift.org
To inspire careers in the field of food science/technology.
Title of Award: Institute of Food Technologists Sophomore Scholarships **Area, Field, or Subject:** Food Science and Technology. **Level of Education for which Award is Granted:** Undergraduate **Number Awarded:** 15. **Funds Available:** $1,000.
Eligibility Requirements: Applicants must be freshmen students intending to enroll in an approved food science/technology program and who have maintained at least 3.0 GPA for the first term of study and are recommended by the department head. **Application Requirements:** Applicants must complete the application form; must submit an official transcript of record; letter of recommendation from a faculty member in the food science/food technology department who is familiar with the applicant's eligibility; a one-page essay stating why they desire to continue their studies in food science and/or food technology. **Deadline for Receipt:** March 1. **Additional Information:** Institute of Food Technologists at the above address.

5331 ■ INTERNATIONAL DAIRY-DELI-BAKERY ASSOCIATION

PO Box 5528
Madison, WI 53705-0528
Tel: (608)310-5000
Fax: (608)238-6330
Web Site: http://www.iddba.org
To support employees of IDDBA-member companies.
Title of Award: International Dairy-Deli-Bakery Association Undergraduate Scholarships **Area, Field, or Subject:** Culinary arts; Food service careers; Business. **Level of Education for which Award is Granted:** Graduate, Undergraduate **Funds Available:** $1,000. May be prorated among applicants. **Duration:** One semester.
Eligibility Requirements: Applicants must have an academic field of study in a food-related field such as culinary arts, baking/pastry arts or food science, business or marketing program. Applicants must also have a 2.5 grade-point average on a 4.0 scale, or equivalent which may be waived for first-time returning adult students. **Application Requirements:** Applicants must submit a completed application form together with at least one letter of reference on letterhead from a department/store manager and/or professional academic contact. Incomplete or illegible applications will not be considered. **Deadline for Receipt:** January 1, April 1, July 1, October 1. **Additional Information:** Karen Peckham at the above address.

5332 ■ INTERNATIONAL FLIGHT SERVICES ASSOCIATION

1100 Johnson Ferry Rd., Ste. 300
Atlanta, GA 30342
Tel: (404)252-3663
Fax: (404)252-0774
E-mail: ifsa@kellencompany.com
Web Site: http://www.ifsanet.com
To support students preparing for careers in the industry as well as opportunities for established professionals to further their career in onboard food services.
Title of Award: Harvey and Laura Alpert Scholarship Award **Area, Field, or Subject:** Service food careers. **Level of Education for which Award is Granted:** Undergraduate **Funds Available:** $5,000.
Eligibility Requirements: Applicants must be currently enrolled at or transferring to Michigan State University ultimately receiving a degree from that institution; must have completed a minimum of 32 credit hours or in sophomore level of course study in a post-secondary, hospitality management program and must be in good standing. **Application Requirements:** Applicants must submit a completed application form; must provide three letters of recommendation preferably from high school counselors, college professors or employers and transcript for all high school and post-secondary studies. **Deadline for Receipt:** May 15. **Additional Information:** Olena Eaton at the above address.

5333 ■ INTERNATIONAL FLIGHT SERVICES ASSOCIATION

1100 Johnson Ferry Rd., Ste. 300
Atlanta, GA 30342
Tel: (404)252-3663
Fax: (404)252-0774
E-mail: ifsa@kellencompany.com
Web Site: http://www.ifsanet.com
To provide opportunity for students involved in food science programs at the University of Guelph and Laval to further their education.
Title of Award: Delta Daily Food (Canada) Inc. Scholarships **Area, Field, or Subject:** Food science and technology. **Level of Education for which Award is Granted:** Undergraduate **Funds Available:** $2,250.
Eligibility Requirements: Applicants must be currently enrolled as full-time students in food science program; must have completed a minimum of three semesters of course study in food science program; must have a "good" academic standing with an average of 75% or better. **Application Requirements:** Applicants must submit a completed application form and official transcript for all post-secondary, college and university studies at an accredited institution. **Deadline for Receipt:** May 15. **Additional Information:** Olena Eaton at the above address.

5334 ■ INTERNATIONAL FOODSERVICE EDITORIAL COUNCIL

PO Box 491
Hyde Park, NY 12538
Tel: (845)229-6973

Fax: (845)229-6993
E-mail: info@ifeconline.com
Web Site: http://www.ifec-is-us.com
To increase awareness and understanding of the career opportunities available in the field of food service communications and to encourage entry of qualified professionals in the field.
Title of Award: International Foodservice Editorial Council Scholarships **Area, Field, or Subject:** Culinary arts; Communications; Food service careers; Food science and technology; Photography; Hotel, institutional, and restaurant management; Nutrition; Dietetics; Journalism; Public relations; Graphic art and design. **Level of Education for which Award is Granted:** Graduate, Undergraduate **Number Awarded:** Varies. **Funds Available:** $3,750.
Eligibility Requirements: Applicants must be full-time students in a U.S. accredited post-secondary educational institution working towards an associate's, bachelor's or master's degree. **Application Requirements:** Applicants must submit a complete application together with academic transcript and two letters of recommendation. Application requirements must be typewritten and submitted using U.S. Postal Service's Return Receipt Service. **Deadline for Receipt:** March 15.

5335 ■ MARYLAND HOSPITALITY EDUCATION FOUNDATION
6301 Hillside Ct.
Columbia, MD 21046
Tel: (410)290-6800
Free: 800-874-1313
Fax: (410)290-6882
E-mail: webmaster@mhef.org
Web Site: http://www.mhef.org
To support students in the restaurant and food service industry.
Title of Award: Marcia S. Harris Legacy Fund Scholarships **Area, Field, or Subject:** Service food careers. **Level of Education for which Award is Granted:** Undergraduate **Funds Available:** No specific amount.
Eligibility Requirements: Applicants must be high school or college students, or high school or postsecondary instructors who teach culinary arts or hospitality management courses. Applicants must be enrolled in a postsecondary or professional development course; applicants must be pursuing hospitality-related coursework in culinary arts, hospitality management, or bartending academy programs. **Application Requirements:** High school or college students must submit a photocopy of college curriculum vitae; supervisor's or employer's letter of recommendation; teacher's letter of recommendation. Applicants for industry must submit pay stub from employer documenting 2,000 hours or two years of industry experience; letter of support and employment from immediate supervisor or owner; two letters of recommendation. **Deadline for Receipt:** March 14.

5336 ■ MARYLAND HOSPITALITY EDUCATION FOUNDATION
6301 Hillside Ct.
Columbia, MD 21046
Tel: (410)290-6800
Free: 800-874-1313
Fax: (410)290-6882
E-mail: webmaster@mhef.org
Web Site: http://www.mhef.org
To support students in the restaurant and food service industry.
Title of Award: The Erika A. Hayes Scholarships **Area, Field, or Subject:** Service food careers. **Level of Education for which Award is Granted:** Undergraduate **Funds Available:** No specific amount.
Eligibility Requirements: Applicants must be high school or college students; enrolled in postsecondary or professional development courses; pursuing hospitality-related coursework in culinary arts, hospitality managements, or a bartending academy program. **Application Requirements:** High school or college students must submit a photocopy of college curriculum vitae; supervisor's or employer's letter of recommendation; teacher's letter of recommendation. Applicants for industry must submit pay stub from employer documenting 2,000 hours or two years of industry experience; letter of support and employment from immediate supervisor or owner; two letters of recommendation. **Deadline for Receipt:** March 14.

5337 ■ MARYLAND HOSPITALITY EDUCATION FOUNDATION
6301 Hillside Ct.
Columbia, MD 21046

Tel: (410)290-6800
Free: 800-874-1313
Fax: (410)290-6882
E-mail: webmaster@mhef.org
Web Site: http://www.mhef.org
To support students in the restaurant and food service industry.
Title of Award: Maryland Hospitality Education Foundation Co-Branded Scholarships **Area, Field, or Subject:** Service food careers. **Level of Education for which Award is Granted:** Undergraduate **Funds Available:** No specific amount.
Eligibility Requirements: Applicants must be high school seniors having an average GPA of 2.75 on a 4.0 scale or equivalent, verified by a transcript from each high school attended. Applicants must have a minimum of 250 hours of restaurant or food service-related work experience, verified by copies of paycheck stubs or letters from employers stipulating numbers of hours worked. **Application Requirements:** Applicants must complete the application form. Applicants must submit a transcript of records; essays; signed letters of recommendation from current or previous employers; copy of college acceptance letter. **Deadline for Receipt:** April 11.

5338 ■ NATIONAL POULTRY AND FOOD DISTRIBUTORS ASSOCIATION
958 McEver Rd. Ext., Unit B-8
Gainesville, GA 30504
Tel: (770)535-9901; 877-845-1545
Fax: (770)535-7385
E-mail: info@npfda.org
Web Site: http://www.npfda.org
To help build "people resources" for the poultry and food industries.
Title of Award: National Poultry and Food Distributors Association Scholarships **Area, Field, or Subject:** Poultry Science; Food science and technology; Dietetics; Agribusiness; Agricultural economics; Agriculture, Economic aspects; Agricultural sciences. **Level of Education for which Award is Granted:** Undergraduate **Number Awarded:** 5. Cash prizes will go to the top four; the fifth student chosen will be the alternate student should one of the award recipients not use all of his/her funds (early graduation). **Funds Available:** $2,000. **Duration:** Entire length of study.
Eligibility Requirements: Applicant must be a full time junior or senior at a U.S. institution for the upcoming award year, and must be pursuing a poultry or related agricultural degree. **Application Requirements:** Applicant must submit an application form; official transcript; letter of recommendation from his/her Dean; and a one-page letter describing his/her goals and aspirations. **Additional Information:** This scholarship foundation was established in 1979. **Deadline for Receipt:** May 31.

5339 ■ NATIONAL RESTAURANT ASSOCIATION EDUCATIONAL FOUNDATION
175 W Jackson Blvd., Ste. 1500
Chicago, IL 60604-2702
Tel: (312)715-1010
Free: 800-765-2122
E-mail: info@nraef.org
Web Site: http://www.nraef.org
To support post-secondary students with strong entrepreneurial commitment who are dedicated to furthering their education and enhancing their careers in the restaurant and food service industry.
Title of Award: Al Schuman Ecolab Undergraduate Entrepreneurial Scholarships **Area, Field, or Subject:** Food service careers. **Level of Education for which Award is Granted:** Undergraduate **Number Awarded:** 3. **Funds Available:** Bronze - $3,500; Silver $5,500; Gold - $7,500. **Duration:** One year.
Eligibility Requirements: Applicant must be a citizen or a permanent resident of the United States of America or be a resident of American Samoa, Guam, Puerto Rico or the U.S. Virgin Islands; must be pursuing a degree in the restaurant and food service industry; must be accepted or enrolled in the following schools: California State Polytechnic University - Pomona, Cornell University, Culinary Institute of America, Johnson and Wales University, Kendall College, Lynn University, Michigan State University, New York University, Pennsylvania State University, Purdue University, University of Denver, University of Houston, University of Nevada (Las Vegas) or University of Massachusetts-Amherst. Applicant must have a minimum grade point average of 3.0 on a 4.0 scale, or a

GED average standard score of 470 or higher. Applicant must also be enrolled for two consecutive semesters and not entering his/her last term before graduating. **Application Requirements:** Applicants must submit an application packet which includes completed online application, an entrepreneurial project as described in the application, a copy of college curriculum with the number of credit hours detailed, transcript from current school or a copy of the GED certificate and three letters of recommendation from current or previous employer(s) in the restaurant and/or food service industries, current teachers/professors or personal references. **Deadline for Receipt:** March 7.

5340 ■ NEW ENGLAND CLUB MANAGERS ASSOCIATION

300 Arnold Palmer Blvd., Ste. 227
Norton, MA 02766-1365
Tel: (774)430-9050
Fax: (774)430-9051
E-mail: necma@necma.org
Web Site: http://www.necma.org
To support students of hospitality studies and those interested in the club management profession.
Title of Award: Hospitality Food Service Scholarships **Area, Field, or Subject:** Service food careers. **Level of Education for which Award is Granted:** Undergraduate **Funds Available:** No specific amount. **Eligibility Requirements:** Applicants must be full-time students in a degree program with a minimum 3.0 GPA; must be currently working in the club industry and demonstrate an interest in continuing to work in the field. **Application Requirements:** Applicants must submit a completed and neat application form; a transcript; references; and an essay. **Deadline for Receipt:** September 14.

5341 ■ NEW YORK SCHOOL NUTRITION ASSOCIATION

125 Wolf Rd.
Albany, NY 12205
Tel: (518)446-9061
Fax: (518)446-0113
E-mail: suzanne@nyssfsa.org
Web Site: http://www.nyssfsa.org
To help defray the cost of food service education for students; to provide means of recognition for the school food service department.
Title of Award: Jeff Siegel Scholarships **Area, Field, or Subject:** Service food careers. **Level of Education for which Award is Granted:** Undergraduate **Funds Available:** No specific amount.
Eligibility Requirements: Applicants must be recommended by a NYSNA member who has been an active member for at least one year; must be high school graduating students in the year the scholarship is awarded, from the school where the Director is employed; must have been accepted at a college with a program in food service and intend to pursue a career in the food service industry. **Application Requirements:** Applicants must attach a letter of recommendation from the NYSNA member who submitted their name for the award; must attach a 200 word essay on how/why they chose food service as their future career; must attach a letter of recommendation from a school official, guidance counselor, principal etc.; must attach a copy of letter of acceptance from college; must submit a copy of high school transcript, including first semester of the senior year; must attach any additional comments or information that will be helpful. **Deadline for Receipt:** May 1. **Additional Information:** 125 Wolf Rd., Ste. 315, Albany, NY 12205.

5342 ■ PMCA: AN INTERNATIONAL ASSOCIATION OF CONFECTIONERS

2980 Linden St., Ste. E3
Bethlehem, PA 18017
Tel: (610)625-4655
Fax: (610)625-4567
E-mail: info@pmca.com
Web Site: http://www.pmca.com
To foster education students involved in confectionery technology.
Title of Award: AACT Undergraduate Scholarships **Area, Field, or Subject:** Food science and technology; Chemistry; Biology. **Level of Education for which Award is Granted:** Undergraduate **Funds Available:** $5,000 (two $2,500 installments). **Duration:** One year.
Eligibility Requirements: Applicants must be sophomores, juniors or seniors majoring in food science, chemical science, biological science, or related field at an accredited four-year college or university in North America; must have a GPA of 3.0; and must be interested in confectionery technology. **Application Requirements:** Applicants must submit a completed application form together with a letter of recommendation; copy of college transcript; and a list of academic activities, experience, other activities, honors and awards, and a short statement of personal and professional goals. Send materials to Kevin Silva, Warrell Corp. 2150 Slate Hill Road Camp Hill, PA 17011. **Deadline for Receipt:** April 18. **Additional Information:** Kevin Silva, kevins@warrellcorp.com

5343 ■ THE SAN DIEGO FOUNDATION

2508 Historic Decatur Rd., Ste. 200
San Diego, CA 92106
Tel: (619)235-2300
Fax: (619)239-1710
E-mail: info@sdfoundation.org
Web Site: http://www.sdfoundation.org
To support the education of students from California.
Title of Award: California Association of Family and Consumer Sciences (CAFCS)-San Diego Chapter Scholarships **Area, Field, or Subject:** Food science and technology; Diabetes; Nutrition; Food service careers; Home Economics; Fashion design; Textile science; Housing; Management. **Level of Education for which Award is Granted:** Graduate, Undergraduate **Number Awarded:** To be determined. **Funds Available:** To be determined.
Eligibility Requirements: Applicant must be a graduating high school senior, current college student, or graduate student majoring in Food Sciences; Dietetics; Nutrition; Food Services; Hospitality; Human, Child and Family Development; Apparel, Fashion and Textile Services; Housing and Interiors; Consumer Economics; Management and Resources; or Family and Consumer Science Education. Student must have a minimum 2.50 GPA on a 4.0 scale; planning to attend an accredited two-year college, four-year university, or licensed trade-vocational school in the U.S. Undergraduate student must be enrolled in school full-time (12 units per semester or 9 per quarter). Graduate student may be enrolled full-time or part-time with awards allocated appropriately based upon enrollment units. **Application Requirements:** Applicants must submit a completed Common Scholarship Application together with personal statement; two letters of recommendation on official letterhead (written within the last six months); official transcript in an official and sealed envelope; copy of 2006 or most recent tax form (Form 1040-pages 1 & 2; Form 1040A-pages 1 & 2; Form 1040EZ -page 1); and a letter of recommendation on official letterhead from an instructor or professional indicating the applicant's interest in pursing one of the above listed fields. **Deadline for Receipt:** January 28. **Additional Information:** Arzo Mansury, Dir. Scholarships at 619-814-1343, or scholarships@sdfoundation.org.

5344 ■ SCHOOL NUTRITION ASSOCIATION

700 South Washington St., Ste. 300
Alexandria, VA 22314
Tel: (703)739-3900
Free: 800-877-8822
Fax: (703)739-3915
E-mail: servicecenter@schoolnutrition.org
Web Site: http://www.schoolnutrition.org/Index.aspx?id=1075
To provide School Nutrition Association members with the opportunity to explore higher education options with the help of financial assistance.
Title of Award: Schwan's Food Service Scholarships **Area, Field, or Subject:** Food service careers. **Level of Education for which Award is Granted:** Undergraduate **Funds Available:** No specific amount. **Duration:** One academic year.
Eligibility Requirements: Applicant must be a member or dependent of a member of SNA for at least one year; pursuing a school foodservicerelated field; accepted at technical/vocational institution or university/ college; have a satisfactory academic record; and must express the desire to make school foodservice a career. **Application Requirements:** Applicants must submit a completed application along with the required materials and information. **Additional Information:** Funded by Schwan's Food Service. **Deadline for Receipt:** April 15.

5345 ■ SCHOOL NUTRITION ASSOCIATION

700 South Washington St., Ste. 300
Alexandria, VA 22314

Tel: (703)739-3900
Free: 800-877-8822
Fax: (703)739-3915
E-mail: servicecenter@schoolnutrition.org
Web Site: http://www.schoolnutrition.org/Index.aspx?id=1075
To provide School Nutrition Association members with the opportunity to explore higher education options with the help of financial assistance.
Title of Award: SNF Professional Growth Scholarships **Area, Field, or Subject:** Food service careers. **Level of Education for which Award is Granted:** Graduate, Undergraduate **Funds Available:** No specific amount. **Duration:** One academic year.
Eligibility Requirements: Applicant must be a member or dependent of a member of SNA for at least one year; pursuing undergraduate or graduate studies; have a satisfactory academic record; and must express the desire to make school foodservice a career. **Application Requirements:** Applicants must submit a completed application along with the required materials and information. **Deadline for Receipt:** April 15.

5346 ■ SCHOOL NUTRITION ASSOCIATION
700 South Washington St., Ste. 300
Alexandria, VA 22314
Tel: (703)739-3900
Free: 800-877-8822
Fax: (703)739-3915
E-mail: servicecenter@schoolnutrition.org
Web Site: http://www.schoolnutrition.org/Index.aspx?id=1075
To provide School Nutrition Association members with the opportunity to explore higher education options with the help of financial assistance.
Title of Award: Winston Scholarships **Area, Field, or Subject:** Food service careers. **Level of Education for which Award is Granted:** Graduate, Undergraduate **Funds Available:** $2500.
Eligibility Requirements: Applicant must be employed as a School Food Service Professional; or a the dependent of an employee, employed as a School Food Service Professional; a registered, or have plans to attend an accredited college, university or vocational/technical institution. **Application Requirements:** Applicants must submit a completed Winston Scholarship application form along with the required materials and information. **Deadline for Receipt:** April 15.

5347 ■ SIGMA KAPPA FOUNDATION
8733 Founder Rd.
Indianapolis, IN 46268
Tel: (317)872-3275
E-mail: alewis@sigmakappa.org
Web Site: http://www.sigmakappafoundation.org
To encourage and support the scholastic development of the collegiate and alumnae sisters of the foundation.
Title of Award: Margaret J. Andrew Memorial Scholarships **Area, Field, or Subject:** Food science and technology. **Level of Education for which Award is Granted:** Undergraduate **Number Awarded:** 2. **Funds Available:** $750.
Eligibility Requirements: Applicants must be in good standing as a junior, senior, or graduate student; must be studying food science/food technology or a related major (nutrition, dietetics); must have a minimum cumulative GPA: 3.0. **Application Requirements:** Application forms are available online. Applicant must submit the transcript and recommendation letter through online. **Deadline for Receipt:** March 1.

5348 ■ STARK COMMUNITY FOUNDATION
400 Market Ave. N, Ste. 200
Canton, OH 44702-2107
Tel: (330)454-3426
Fax: (330)454-5855
Web Site: http://www.starkcommunityfoundation.org
To provide scholarship assistance to qualified individuals who want to pursue their studies.
Title of Award: Stark County Dairy Promoters Scholarships **Area, Field, or Subject:** Dairy science; Animal science and behavior; Medicine, Veterinary; Nutrition; Food science and technology. **Level of Education for which Award is Granted:** Undergraduate **Funds Available:** No specific amount. **Duration:** One year.
Eligibility Requirements: Applicants must be residents of Stark County, OH; must be pursuing college-level study in the field of dairy science,

animal science, veterinary medicine, human nutrition, or food science; must have 2.5 high school GPA; must have demonstrated financial need.
Application Requirements: Applicants must complete and submit the application form and requirements to Stark County Diary Promoters Scholarship Committee, Stark Community Foundation, 400 Market Ave. N, Ste. 200, Canton, OH 44702. **Deadline for Receipt:** April 15.

5349 ■ WISCONSIN ASSOCIATION FOR FOOD PROTECTION
PO Box 329
Sun Prairie, WI 53590
Tel: (608)833-6181
E-mail: info@wafp-wi.org
Web Site: http://www.wafp-wi.org
To promote and sustain interest in fields of study that may lead to a career in dairy, food, or environmental sanitation.
Title of Award: E.H. Marth Food and Environmental Scholarships **Area, Field, or Subject:** Food science and technology. **Level of Education for which Award is Granted:** Undergraduate **Funds Available:** No specific amount.
Eligibility Requirements: Applicants must be accepted or enrolled in an accredited post high school undergraduate degree or diploma program (university, college, or technical college) in Wisconsin or an out-of-state school with a reciprocal enrollment agreement with Wisconsin. They must be full-time students enrolled in a dairy science, food science, environmental sanitation or closely related major who are residents of Wisconsin.
Application Requirements: Applicants must submit a complete application form; a copy of official transcript; recommendation of advisor or instructor which should address scholastic ability, professional potential, applicable work experience, extra-curricular activities, financial need and other relevant information. **Additional Information:** nelsong@uwstout.edu.

Home Economics

5350 ■ THE SAN DIEGO FOUNDATION
2508 Historic Decatur Rd., Ste. 200
San Diego, CA 92106
Tel: (619)235-2300
Fax: (619)239-1710
E-mail: info@sdfoundation.org
Web Site: http://www.sdfoundation.org
To support the education of students from California.
Title of Award: California Association of Family and Consumer Sciences (CAFCS)-San Diego Chapter Scholarships **Area, Field, or Subject:** Food science and technology; Diabetes; Nutrition; Food service careers; Home Economics; Fashion design; Textile science; Housing; Management. **Level of Education for which Award is Granted:** Graduate, Undergraduate **Number Awarded:** To be determined. **Funds Available:** To be determined.
Eligibility Requirements: Applicant must be a graduating high school senior, current college student, or graduate student majoring in Food Sciences; Dietetics; Nutrition; Food Services; Hospitality; Human, Child and Family Development; Apparel, Fashion and Textile Services; Housing and Interiors; Consumer Economics; Management and Resources; or Family and Consumer Science Education. Student must have a minimum 2.50 GPA on a 4.0 scale; planning to attend an accredited two-year college, four-year university, or licensed trade-vocational school in the U.S. Undergraduate student must be enrolled in school full-time (12 units per semester or 9 per quarter). Graduate student may be enrolled full-time or part-time with awards allocated appropriately based upon enrollment units. **Application Requirements:** Applicants must submit a completed Common Scholarship Application together with personal statement; two letters of recommendation on official letterhead (written within the last six months); official transcript in an official and sealed envelope; copy of 2006 or most recent tax form (Form 1040-pages 1 & 2; Form 1040A-pages 1 & 2; Form 1040EZ -page 1); and a letter of recommendation on official letterhead from an instructor or professional indicating the applicant's interest in pursing one of the above listed fields. **Deadline for Receipt:** January 28. **Additional Information:** Arzo Mansury, Dir. Scholarships at 619-814-1343, or scholarships@sdfoundation.org.

Military Science

5351 ■ BETA THETA PI
PO Box 6277
Oxford, OH 45056
Tel: (513)523-7591
Free: 800-800-BETA
E-mail: beta@betathetapi.org
Web Site: http://www.betathetapi.org
To financially assist students in their pursuit of academic achievement.
Title of Award: Burton L. Gerber Scholarships **Area, Field, or Subject:** Military science and education; International affairs and relations. **Level of Education for which Award is Granted:** Graduate, Undergraduate **Number Awarded:** 1. **Funds Available:** $1025. **Duration:** One academic year.
Eligibility Requirements: Applicant must be undergraduate or graduate student; a member of Beta Theta Pi enrolled as full-time student; and a senior pursuing a career in military or international affairs. Previous recipients are not qualified. **Application Requirements:** Applicants must submit a completed standard application form along with transcript of grades and a passport type photo (head and shoulders, wallet size, in coat and tie). **Deadline for Receipt:** April 1.

5352 ■ CATCHING THE DREAM
8200 Mountain Rd. NE., Ste. 203
Albuquerque, NM 87110
Tel: (505)262-2351
E-mail: nscholarships@aol.com
Web Site: http://www.catchingthedream.org
To support American Indian students in their education.
Title of Award: Sergeant Douglas and Charlotte DeHorse Scholarships **Area, Field, or Subject:** Military science and education. **Level of Education for which Award is Granted:** Undergraduate **Funds Available:** No specific amount.
Eligibility Requirements: Applicants must be American Indian students who have completed one year of any Army, Navy, or Air Force Junior Reserve Officer Training program; enrolled in an Army, Navy, or Air Force Reserve Officer Training Program; a veteran of the United States Army, Navy, Air Force, Merchant Marine or Coast Guard; and enrolled in undergraduate or graduate program of study. **Application Requirements:** Applicants must submit a completed application; letters of recommendation; personal essay; and high school transcripts. **Additional Information:** The First Sergeant Douglas and Charlotte DeHorse Scholarship was established in 2007 to honor the American Indian veterans. **Deadline for Receipt:** April and September 15.

5353 ■ MCRD MUSEUM HISTORICAL SOCIETY
PO Box 400085 Bldg. 26
San Diego, CA 92140-0085
Tel: (619)524-4426
Web Site: http://mcrdmuseumhistoricalsociety.org
To provide educational assistance for MCRD San Diego enlisted marines or sailors, and their dependents, who are enrolled in an accredited graduate or undergraduate college program.
Title of Award: Colonel Nate Smith Memorial Scholarships **Area, Field, or Subject:** Military science and education. **Level of Education for which Award is Granted:** Graduate, Undergraduate **Number Awarded:** 3. **Funds Available:** No specific amount.
Eligibility Requirements: Applicants must be enlisted active duty marines or sailors currently assigned to MCRD San Diego/Western Recruiting Region or their dependents; must be high school graduates and must provide proof of enrollment in a postsecondary program, or have previously attended college. **Application Requirements:** Applicants must submit all the required application information. **Deadline for Receipt:** July 3.

5354 ■ NATIONAL MILITARY INTELLIGENCE ASSOCIATION
PO Box 479
Hamilton, VA 20159
Tel: (540)338-1143
E-mail: admin@nmia.org
Web Site: http://www.nmia.org

To support the growth of professional studies in the field of military intelligence and to recognize and reward excellence in the development and transfer of knowledge about military and associated intelligence disciplines.
Title of Award: NMIA Scholarship Program **Area, Field, or Subject:** Military science and education. **Level of Education for which Award is Granted:** Undergraduate **Number Awarded:** 3. **Funds Available:** $1,000.
Eligibility Requirements: Applicants must be dependents of NMIA active members, mobilized reserve and national guard personnel, and other reserve or National Guard members, eligible for college entrance in the class of 2011. **Application Requirements:** Applicants must submit application form, supporting transcripts and SAT or ACT scores. **Deadline for Receipt:** August 1.

5355 ■ UNIVERSITY OF WISCONSIN-MADISON
432 N Murray St.
Madison, WI 53706-1496
Tel: (608)262-3060
Fax: (608)262-9068
E-mail: askbucky@uwmad.wisc.edu
Web Site: http://www.wisc.edu
To support UW-Madison students in their education.
Title of Award: Reserve Officers Training Corps (ROTC) Scholarships **Area, Field, or Subject:** Military science and education. **Level of Education for which Award is Granted:** Undergraduate **Number Awarded:** Varies. **Funds Available:** Full tuition and fees, book allowance, and a monthly tax-free stipend.
Eligibility Requirements: Applicants must be U.S. citizens enrolled in ROTC programs. **Application Requirements:** Applicants may contact Air Force Aerospace Studies, Air Force ROTC; Military Science, Army ROTC; Naval Sciences, Navy ROTC for more information about the program. **Deadline for Receipt:** December 1. **Additional Information:** Air Force Aerospace Studies, Air Force ROTC at 608-262-3440; Military Science, Army ROTC, at 608-262-3411; Naval Sciences, Navy ROTC, at 608-262-3794 or 800-443-2672.

5356 ■ XAVIER UNIVERSITY
3800 Victory Pky.
Cincinnati, OH 45207
Tel: (513)745-3000
Free: 800-344-GOXU
Web Site: http://www.xavier.edu
To financially support students with their education.
Title of Award: Xavier University ROTC Scholarships - Army ROTC **Area, Field, or Subject:** Military science and education. **Level of Education for which Award is Granted:** Undergraduate **Funds Available:** Full-tuition, $900 yearly book allowance and a monthly stipend starting at $350/month during the academic school year. **Duration:** Oné to Four years.
Eligibility Requirements: Applicant may be a freshman, sophomore, junior, or senior student pursuing military science at Xavier University. Nursing students can also compete for an Army ROTC nursing scholarship and upon graduation become an Army Nurse. **Application Requirements:** High School students may apply online for an Army ROTC Scholarship at www.goarmy.com/rotc. **Deadline for Receipt:** March 1. **Additional Information:** Major Tim Diley, at 513-745-1062.

Mining and Metallurgy

5357 ■ AMERICAN SOCIETY OF MINING AND RECLAMATION
3134 Montavesta Rd.
Lexington, KY 40502
Tel: (859)351-9032
Fax: (859)335-6529
E-mail: asmr@insightbb.com
Web Site: http://ces.ca.uky.edu/asmr/
To grant deserving undergraduate students from academic institutions.
Title of Award: American Society of Mining and Reclamation Memorial Scholarships **Area, Field, or Subject:** Mining. **Level of Education for which Award is Granted:** Undergraduate **Number Awarded:** 3. **Funds Available:** $750-undergraduate; $1,000-masters; $1,500-Ph.D.

Eligibility Requirements: Applicants must have completed at least sophomore year of curriculum in a science discipline directly relating to and leading to a profession in reclamation; must be full time students; and must have an adequate grade point of average, carry the curriculum required hours and participated in other curricular activities. **Application Requirements:** Applicants must complete the application form found at ASMR website. Applicants must submit a letter containing education and career goals; three reference letters with two academic (one from advisor); college transcripts; and resume with list of awards, honors and extracurricular activities listed. **Deadline for Receipt:** March 14. **Additional Information:** Robert W. Naim, UASMR Memorial Scholarship Chair, University of Oklahoma, 202 W. Boyd St., Rm. 334, Norman OK 73019; 405-325-3354; 405-325-4217; naim@ou.edu.

5358 ■ ASSOCIATION FOR IRON AND STEEL TECHNOLOGY

186 Thorn Hill Rd.
Warrendale, PA 15086-7528
Tel: (724)776-6040
Fax: (724)776-1880
E-mail: info@aist.org
Web Site: http://www.aist.org
To enhance education and careers in engineering or metallurgy.
Title of Award: AIST Baltimore Chapter Scholarships **Area, Field, or Subject:** Engineering; Metallurgy. **Level of Education for which Award is Granted:** Undergraduate **Number Awarded:** 1. **Funds Available:** $1,500. **Duration:** One year.
Eligibility Requirements: Applicant must be a dependent or a spouse of a commendable member of the AIST Baltimore Chapter Scholarship; must be attending an eligible, full-time course in the field of engineering at an institution; demonstrate interest towards a career in the field of iron and steel industry. **Application Requirements:** Applicants must submit an application form available at the website; a resume; a copy of SAT/ACT scores; copy of transcripts; two essays about the applicant's accomplishments, and the applicant's interest/involvement in the steel and iron industry. Send all documents to: AIST Baltimore Chapter Scholarships, Thomas J. Russo, 1430 Sparrows Point Blvd. Sparrows Point, MD 21219-1014. **Deadline for Receipt:** April 30. **Additional Information:** Thomas J. Russo, 410-388-4337, tom.russo@mittalsteel.com.

5359 ■ ASSOCIATION FOR IRON AND STEEL TECHNOLOGY

186 Thorn Hill Rd.
Warrendale, PA 15086-7528
Tel: (724)776-6040
Fax: (724)776-1880
E-mail: info@aist.org
Web Site: http://www.aist.org
To enhance education and careers in the iron and steel-related industry.
Title of Award: AIST Detroit Chapter Scholarships **Area, Field, or Subject:** Engineering; Metallurgy. **Level of Education for which Award is Granted:** Undergraduate **Number Awarded:** 2. **Funds Available:** $2,500. **Duration:** One year.
Eligibility Requirements: Applicant must be a dependent of an AIST Detroit Chapter member in good standing for two or more consecutive years; have a minimum cumulative GPA of 3.0 on a 4.0 scale; must be enrolled full-time as an undergraduate student majoring in engineering, metallurgy or materials science program at an accredited North American university; demonstrate interest towards a career in the field of iron and steel industry. **Application Requirements:** Applicant must submit an application form available at the website; a resume; three letters of recommendation (addressing character, academic status, leadership potential and career commitment) from a high school counselor or college academic advisor, teacher/professor or a previous employer; copy of SAT/ACT scores; copy of current transcripts; an essay (maximum of 2 pages) about the applicant's professional goals, interest in a career in the iron and steel industry, and how the applicant's skills could be applied to enhance the industry. Requirements must be sent to: AIST Detroit Member Chapter Scholarships, c/o Judith A. Quinn, Chapter Secretary 41158 Savage Road Belleville, MI 48111. **Deadline for Receipt:** April 30. **Additional Information:** Judith Quinn, 313-319-2815, judieqn@aol.com.

5360 ■ ASSOCIATION FOR IRON AND STEEL TECHNOLOGY

186 Thorn Hill Rd.
Warrendale, PA 15086-7528

Tel: (724)776-6040
Fax: (724)776-1880
E-mail: info@aist.org
Web Site: http://www.aist.org
To enhance education and careers iron and steel-related industries.
Title of Award: AIST Ronald E. Lincoln Memorial Scholarships **Area, Field, or Subject:** Engineering; Metallurgy. **Level of Education for which Award is Granted:** Undergraduate **Number Awarded:** 2. **Funds Available:** $3,000. **Duration:** One year.
Eligibility Requirements: Applicant must be enrolled full-time in an engineering, metallurgy or materials science program at an accredited North American university; have a minimum cumulative GPA of 3.0 on a 4.0 scale; demonstrate interest toward a career in the field of iron and steel industry. **Application Requirements:** Applicants must submit an application form available at the website; a resume; three letters of recommendation (addressing character, academic status, leadership potential and career commitment) from a college academic advisor, professor and previous employer; transcripts; an essay (maximum of 2 pages) about the applicant's professional goals, interest in a career in the iron and steel industry, and how the applicant's skills could be applied to enhance the industry. **Additional Information:** Established by Chaparral Steel. **Deadline for Receipt:** March 2. **Additional Information:** Lori Wharrey lwharrey@aist.org or 724-776-6040 ext.621.

5361 ■ ASSOCIATION FOR IRON AND STEEL TECHNOLOGY

186 Thorn Hill Rd.
Warrendale, PA 15086-7528
Tel: (724)776-6040
Fax: (724)776-1880
E-mail: info@aist.org
Web Site: http://www.aist.org
To enhance education and careers in iron and steel-related industries.
Title of Award: AIST William E. Schwabe Memorial Scholarships **Area, Field, or Subject:** Engineering; Metallurgy. **Level of Education for which Award is Granted:** Undergraduate **Number Awarded:** 1. **Funds Available:** $3,000. **Duration:** One year.
Eligibility Requirements: Applicant must be enrolled full-time in an engineering, metallurgy or materials science program at an accredited North American university; have a minimum cumulative GPA of 3.0 on a 4.0 scale; demonstrate interest in a career in the iron and steel industry. **Application Requirements:** Applicants must submit an application form available at the website; a resume; three letters of recommendation (addressing character, academic status, leadership potential and career commitment) from a college academic advisor, professor and previous employer; transcripts; an essay (maximum of 2 pages) about the applicant's professional goals, interest in a career in the iron and steel industry, and how the applicant's skills could be applied to enhance the industry. **Additional Information:** Established in 2005 by the Steel Manufacturers Association (SMA). **Deadline for Receipt:** March 2. **Additional Information:** Lori Wharrey at lwharrey@aist.org or 724-776-6040, ext. 621.

5362 ■ ASSOCIATION FOR IRON AND STEEL TECHNOLOGY

186 Thorn Hill Rd.
Warrendale, PA 15086-7528
Tel: (724)776-6040
Fax: (724)776-1880
E-mail: info@aist.org
Web Site: http://www.aist.org
To enhance education and careers in iron and steel-related industry.
Title of Award: AIST Willy Korf Memorial Fund **Area, Field, or Subject:** Engineering; Metallurgy. **Level of Education for which Award is Granted:** Undergraduate **Number Awarded:** 3. **Funds Available:** $3,000. **Duration:** One year.
Eligibility Requirements: Applicant must be enrolled full-time in an engineering, metallurgy or materials science program at an accredited North American university; have a minimum cumulative GPA of 3.0 on a 4.0 scale; demonstrate interest in a career in the iron and steel industry. **Application Requirements:** Applicants must submit an application form available at the website; a resume; three letters of recommendation which address the applicant's character, academic status, leadership potential and career commitment from a college academic advisor, professor and previous employer; transcripts; and an essay (maximum of 2 pages)

about the applicant's professional goals, interest in a career in the iron and steel industry, and how the applicant's skills could be applied to enhance the industry. **Additional Information:** Established by Korf Lurgi Steeltec, Inc. **Deadline for Receipt:** March 2. **Additional Information:** Lori Wharrey lwharrey@aist.org or 724-776-6040, ext. 621.

5363 ■ ASSOCIATION FOR IRON AND STEEL TECHNOLOGY
186 Thorn Hill Rd.
Warrendale, PA 15086-7528
Tel: (724)776-6040
Fax: (724)776-1880
E-mail: info@aist.org
Web Site: http://www.aist.org
To enhance education and careers in the iron and steel-related industries.
Title of Award: AIST Benjamin F. Fairless Scholarships (AIME) **Area, Field, or Subject:** Engineering; Metallurgy. **Level of Education for which Award is Granted:** Undergraduate **Number Awarded:** 11. **Funds Available:** $2,000. **Duration:** One year.
Eligibility Requirements: Applicant must be enrolled full-time in an engineering, metallurgy or materials science program at an accredited North American university; have a minimum GPA of 3.0 on a 4.0 scale; demonstrate interest toward a career in the field of iron and steel industry. **Application Requirements:** Applicant must submit an application form available at the website; a resume; an essay (maximum of 2 pages) about the applicant's professional goals, interest in a career in the steel industry, and how the applicant's skills could be applied to enhance the industry; three letters of recommendation (addressing the character, academic status, leadership potential and career commitment) from a college academic advisor, professor and previous employer; and transcripts. **Additional Information:** Established in 1954. **Deadline for Receipt:** March 2. **Additional Information:** Lori Wharrey at lwharrey@aist.org or 724-776-6040 ext. 621.

5364 ■ ASSOCIATION FOR IRON AND STEEL TECHNOLOGY
186 Thorn Hill Rd.
Warrendale, PA 15086-7528
Tel: (724)776-6040
Fax: (724)776-1880
E-mail: info@aist.org
Web Site: http://www.aist.org
To enhance education and careers in the iron and steel-related industry.
Title of Award: Globe-Trotters Chapter Scholarships **Area, Field, or Subject:** Metallurgy. **Level of Education for which Award is Granted:** Undergraduate **Number Awarded:** 5. **Funds Available:** $2,500. **Duration:** One year.
Eligibility Requirements: Applicant must be a dependent of a member (Globe-Trotters member must also be a current member of AIST); be currently enrolled in an accredited college or university. Postgraduate students are also qualified for the scholarships. **Application Requirements:** Applicants must submit an application form available at the website; resume; copy of SAT/ACT scores; a copy of transcripts; an essay (maximum of 300 words) about the reason the applicant has selected the particular field of study, and an explanation on how the scholarship will be applied, such as tuition, books, etc. All required documents, together with the application, must be sent to: Globe-Trotter Scholarships Dennis Foster Day Melter Nucor Steel Texas PO Box 126 Jewett, TX 75846. **Deadline for Receipt:** April 30. **Additional Information:** Dennis Foster at dennis.foster@nstexas.com, Phone: 903-626-4461 ext. 606, Fax: 903-626-6295.

5365 ■ ASSOCIATION FOR IRON AND STEEL TECHNOLOGY
186 Thorn Hill Rd.
Warrendale, PA 15086-7528
Tel: (724)776-6040
Fax: (724)776-1880
E-mail: info@aist.org
Web Site: http://www.aist.org
To provide educational assistance to students who wish to pursue their education and career in engineering and metallurgy.
Title of Award: Northeastern Ohio Chapter Scholarships - Alfred B. Glossbrenner and John Klusch Scholarships **Area, Field, or Subject:** Engineering; Metallurgy. **Level of Education for which Award is Granted:** Undergraduate **Number Awarded:** 1. **Funds Available:** $2,000. **Duration:** One year.

Eligibility Requirements: Applicant must be a dependent of an at least two-year member of the Association for Iron and Steel Technology, which must be a U.S. citizen or a U.S landed immigrant. Applicant should also be a full-time student from an accredited North American University; pursuing education in the field of engineering or metallurgy. Chemistry, geology, mathematics or physics students are also qualified for the scholarships. **Application Requirements:** Applicants must submit an application form available at the website; a resume; a recommendation/ evaluation from a counselor, teacher or professor; copy of SAT/ACT scores; copy of transcripts; and an essay (maximum of 2 pages) with one of the topics: Purpose in going to college; beneficial experience during the last two summers; most significant experiences and effect on future plans; accomplishments providing the greatest satisfaction; reason why the applicant should be chosen as the recipient of the award. All documents and application should be sent to: Richard J. Kurz, Chapter Secretary AIST Northeastern Ohio Chapter 22831 East State Street, Rte. 62 Alliance, Ohio 44601. **Deadline for Receipt:** April 30. **Additional Information:** Richard J. Kurz at rkurz@eohiomach.com, 330-821-7198 ext.109.

5366 ■ ASSOCIATION FOR IRON AND STEEL TECHNOLOGY
186 Thorn Hill Rd.
Warrendale, PA 15086-7528
Tel: (724)776-6040
Fax: (724)776-1880
E-mail: info@aist.org
Web Site: http://www.aist.org
To enhance education and careers in engineering, metallurgy, physical science, computer technology or an engineering technology field.
Title of Award: Ohio Valley Chapter Scholarships **Area, Field, or Subject:** Engineering; Metallurgy; Physical sciences. **Level of Education for which Award is Granted:** Undergraduate **Number Awarded:** 2. **Funds Available:** $1,000. **Duration:** One year.
Eligibility Requirements: Applicant must be a dependent or member of Ohio Valley Chapter of the AIST; planning to attend or currently enrolled full-time curriculum at an accredited university or college; pursuing a degree in Mechanical Engineering, Electrical Engineering, Engineering/ Engineering Technology, Environmental Engineering/Sciences, Metallurgy, Physical Sciences, Computer Technology, Computer Programming, Information Systems Technology, Chemistry, Biology/Microbiology, Physics, other engineering-related fields, or other related fields approved by the committee. **Application Requirements:** Applicants must submit an application form available at the website; a resume; a recommendation/ evaluation from a counselor and teacher or professor; copy of SAT/ACT scores; copy of transcripts; an essay (maximum of 2 pages) with either one of the topics: purpose in going to college; beneficial experience during the last two summers; most significant experiences and effect on future plans; accomplishments providing the greatest satisfaction; reasons why he/she should be chosen as the recipient of the award. All requirements must be sent to: Jeff McKain, 11451 Reading Road Cincinnati, OH 45241. Or thru email, Attn: AIST Scholarship, E-mail subject: AIST Scholarship to jeff.mckain@xtek.com. **Deadline for Receipt:** March 31. **Additional Information:** Jeff Mckain 513-200-3000.

5367 ■ THE GREATER TACOMA COMMUNITY FOUNDATION
PO Box 1995
Tacoma, WA 98401
Tel: (253)383-5622
Web Site: http://www.tacomafoundation.org
To foster generosity by connecting people who care with causes that matter.
Title of Award: Dayton E. Finnigan Scholarship **Area, Field, or Subject:** Metallurgy. **Level of Education for which Award is Granted:** Undergraduate **Funds Available:** No specific amount.
Eligibility Requirements: Applicants must be students enrolled in the sheet metal program at Bates Technical College. **Application Requirements:** Applicants must request an application form at the guidance office of Bates Technical College.

5368 ■ MATERIALS INFORMATION SOCIETY
9639 Kinsman Rd.
Novelty, OH 44073
Tel: (440)338-5151
Free: 800-966-4867

Fax: (440)338-4634
E-mail: customerservice@asminternational.org
Web Site: http://asmcommunity.asminternational.org
To encourage and support capable students with interest and potential in
the field of metallurgy/materials engineering and related careers.
Title of Award: Edward J. Dulis Scholarships **Area, Field, or Subject:**
Metallurgy. **Level of Education for which Award is Granted:** Undergraduate **Funds Available:** $1,500. **Duration:** One year.
Eligibility Requirements: Applicants must be material advantage
members. Applicants must have an intended major in metallurgy or material science engineering. Applicants must have completed at least one
year of college. **Application Requirements:** Applicants must complete
the application form. Applicants must write a personal statement
(maximum of two pages). Applicants must submit a resume; a copy of the
current academic transcript; a completed undergraduate scholarship
recommendation form. Applicants must include a photograph for publication. Applicants must complete the personal statement with a financial officer contact. **Deadline for Receipt:** May 1. **Additional Information:**
asmif@asmiinternational.org

5369 ■ MATERIALS INFORMATION SOCIETY
9639 Kinsman Rd.
Novelty, OH 44073
Tel: (440)338-5151
Free: 800-966-4867
Fax: (440)338-4634
E-mail: customerservice@asminternational.org
Web Site: http://asmcommunity.asminternational.org
To encourage and support capable students with interest and potential in
the field of metallurgy/materials engineering and related careers.
Title of Award: Nicholas J. Grant Scholarships **Area, Field, or Subject:**
Metallurgy. **Level of Education for which Award is Granted:** Under-
graduate **Funds Available:** No specific amount. **Duration:** 1 year.
Eligibility Requirements: Applicants must be material advantage
members. Applicants must have an intended major in metallurgy or material science engineering. Applicants must have completed at least one
year of college. **Application Requirements:** Applicants must complete
the application form. Applicants must write a personal statement
(maximum of two pages). Applicants must submit a resume; a copy of the
current academic transcript; a completed undergraduate scholarship
recommendation form. Applicants must include a photograph for publication. Applicants must complete the personal statement with a financial officer contact. **Deadline for Receipt:** May 1. **Additional Information:**
asmif@asmiinternational.org

5370 ■ MATERIALS INFORMATION SOCIETY
9639 Kinsman Rd.
Novelty, OH 44073
Tel: (440)338-5151
Free: 800-966-4867
Fax: (440)338-4634
E-mail: customerservice@asminternational.org
Web Site: http://asmcommunity.asminternational.org
To encourage and support capable students with interest and potential in
the field of metallurgy/materials engineering and related careers.
Title of Award: John M. Haniak Scholarships **Area, Field, or Subject:**
Metallurgy. **Level of Education for which Award is Granted:** Under-
graduate **Number Awarded:** 1. **Funds Available:** $1,500.
Eligibility Requirements: Applicants must be material advantage
members. Applicants must have an intended major in metallurgy or material science engineering. Applicants must have completed at least one
year of college. **Application Requirements:** Applicants must complete
the application form. Applicants must write a personal statement
(maximum of two pages). Applicants must submit a resume; a copy of the
current academic transcript; a completed undergraduate scholarship
recommendation form. Applicants must include a photograph for publication. Applicants must complete the personal statement with a financial officer contact. **Deadline for Receipt:** May 1. **Additional Information:**
asmif@asmiinternational.org

5371 ■ MATERIALS INFORMATION SOCIETY
9639 Kinsman Rd.
Novelty, OH 44073

Tel: (440)338-5151
Free: 800-966-4867
Fax: (440)338-4634
E-mail: customerservice@asminternational.org
Web Site: http://asmcommunity.asminternational.org
To encourage and support capable students with interest and potential in
the field of metallurgy/materials engineering and related careers.
Title of Award: Materials Information Society National Merit Scholarships
Area, Field, or Subject: Metallurgy. **Level of Education for which
Award is Granted:** Undergraduate **Funds Available:** $1,000.
Eligibility Requirements: Applicants must be material advantage
members. Applicants must have an intended major in metallurgy or material science engineering. Applicants must have completed at least one
year of college. **Application Requirements:** Applicants must complete
the application form. Applicants must write a personal statement,
maximum of two pagesn Applicants must submit a resume; a copy of the
current academic transcript; a completed undergraduate scholarship
recommendation form. Applicants must include a photograph for publication. Applicants must complete the personal statement with a financial officer contact. **Deadline for Receipt:** May 1. **Additional Information:**
asmif@asmiinternational.org

5372 ■ MATERIALS INFORMATION SOCIETY
9639 Kinsman Rd.
Novelty, OH 44073
Tel: (440)338-5151
Free: 800-966-4867
Fax: (440)338-4634
E-mail: customerservice@asminternational.org
Web Site: http://asmcommunity.asminternational.org
To encourage and support capable students with interest and potential in
the field of metallurgy/materials engineering and related careers.
Title of Award: William Park Woodside Founder's Scholarships **Area,
Field, or Subject:** Metallurgy. **Level of Education for which Award is
Granted:** Undergraduate **Funds Available:** Maximum amount of
$10,000. **Duration:** 1 year.
Eligibility Requirements: Applicants must be material advantage
members. Applicants must have an intended major in metallurgy or material science engineering. Applicants must have completed at least one
year of college. **Application Requirements:** Applicants must complete
the application form. Applicants must write a two-page personal statement. Applicants must submit a resume; a copy of the current academic
transcript; a completed undergraduate scholarship recommendation form.
Applicants must include a photograph for publication. Applicants must
complete the personal statement with a financial officer contact. **Deadline
for Receipt:** May 1. **Additional Information:** asmif@asmiinternational.
org

5373 ■ MATERIALS INFORMATION SOCIETY
9639 Kinsman Rd.
Novelty, OH 44073
Tel: (440)338-5151
Free: 800-966-4867
Fax: (440)338-4634
E-mail: customerservice@asminternational.org
Web Site: http://asmcommunity.asminternational.org
To encourage and support capable students with interest and potential in
the field of metallurgy/materials engineering and related careers.
Title of Award: George A. Roberts Scholarships **Area, Field, or Subject:**
Metallurgy. **Level of Education for which Award is Granted:** Under-
graduate **Number Awarded:** 7. **Funds Available:** $6,000.
Eligibility Requirements: Applicants must be material advantage
members. Applicants must have an intended major in metallurgy or material science engineering. Applicants must have completed at least one
year of college. **Application Requirements:** Applicants must complete
the application form. Applicants must write a two-page personal statement. Applicants must submit a resume; a copy of the current academic
transcript; a completed undergraduate scholarship recommendation form.
Applicants must include a photograph for publication. Applicants must
complete the personal statement with a financial officer contact. **Deadline
for Receipt:** May 1. **Additional Information:** asmif@asmiinternational.
org

5374 ■ MATERIALS INFORMATION SOCIETY

9639 Kinsman Rd.
Novelty, OH 44073
Tel: (440)338-5151
Free: 800-966-4867
Fax: (440)338-4634
E-mail: customerservice@asminternational.org
Web Site: http://asmcommunity.asminternational.org
To encourage and support capable students with interest and potential in the field of metallurgy/materials engineering and related careers.
Title of Award: Lucille and Charles A. Wert Scholarships **Area, Field, or Subject:** Metallurgy. **Level of Education for which Award is Granted:** Undergraduate **Funds Available:** $10,000. **Duration:** 1 year.
Eligibility Requirements: Applicants must be material advantage members. Applicants must have an intended major in metallurgy or material science engineering. Applicants must have completed at least one year of college. **Application Requirements:** Applicants must complete the application form. Applicants must write a personal statement (maximum of two pages). Applicants must submit a resume; a copy of the current academic transcript; a completed undergraduate scholarship recommendation form. Applicants must include a photograph for publication. Applicants must complete the personal statement with a financial officer contact. **Deadline for Receipt:** May 1. **Additional Information:** asmif@asmiinternational.org

5375 ■ NATIONAL STONE SAND AND GRAVEL ASSOCIATION

1605 King St.
Alexandria, VA 22314
Tel: (703)525-8788
Web Site: http://www.nssga.org
To provide scholarships to students pursuing a career in the crushed stone industry.
Title of Award: Samuel C. Kraus, Jr. Memorial Scholarships **Area, Field, or Subject:** Engineering, Mining and Mineral; Geology. **Level of Education for which Award is Granted:** Undergraduate **Funds Available:** No specific amount. **Duration:** One year.
Eligibility Requirements: Applicant must be a mining engineering or geology student at the University of Missouri Rolla. **Application Requirements:** Contact the School of Mines and Metallurgy, University of Missouri Rolla for the application procedures. **Additional Information:** 64501-0249.

5376 ■ RHODE ISLAND FOUNDATION

One Union Sta.
Providence, RI 02903
Tel: (401)274-4564
Fax: (401)331-8085
Web Site: http://www.rifoundation.org/matriarch/default.asp
To provide financial assistance for qualified students enrolled at colleges, universities, or nonprofit technical schools on the post-secondary level in the US.
Title of Award: MJSA Educational Foundation Jewelry Scholarships **Area, Field, or Subject:** Metallurgy. **Level of Education for which Award is Granted:** Undergraduate **Funds Available:** No specific amount.
Eligibility Requirements: Applicant must be a student enrolled in toolmaking, design, metals fabrication, or other jewelry-related courses. **Application Requirements:** Applicants must complete and submit the application form and materials to www.callforentry.org. **Deadline for Receipt:** May 14.

5377 ■ SHEET METAL AND AIR CONDITIONING CONTRACTORS' NATIONAL ASSOCIATION

4201 Lafayette Center Dr.
Chantilly, VA 20151-1209
Tel: (703)803-2980
Fax: (703)803-3732
E-mail: info@smacna.org
Web Site: http://www.smacna.org
To provide financial assistance for the discovery, interpretation, and dissemination of new knowledge that promotes leadership development and personal growth.
Title of Award: SMACNA College of Fellows Scholarships **Area, Field, or Subject:** Metallurgy. **Level of Education for which Award is Granted:** Undergraduate **Number Awarded:** 3. **Funds Available:** $2,000.

Eligibility Requirements: Applicants must be students seeking to further their education in an undergraduate course of study in an accredited institution of higher education; must be planning to pursue any course of study, however, studies in a field related to the sheet metal industry are preferred. Entering freshmen and undergraduate students seeking a degree from an accredited four-year program, college, or university are eligible. **Application Requirements:** Applicants must submit all the required application information. **Deadline for Receipt:** April 30.

5378 ■ SOCIETY FOR MINING, METALLURGY AND EXPLORATION

8307 Shaffer Pkwy.
Littleton, CO 80127-4102
Tel: (303)973-9550
Free: 800-763-3132
Fax: (303)973-3845
E-mail: estrada@smenet.org
Web Site: http://www.smenet.org
To provide support to students seeking advanced education in the minerals industry profession and field.
Title of Award: SME Coal and Energy Division Scholarships **Area, Field, or Subject:** Metallurgy; Mineralogy; Mining; Engineering, Mining and Mineral. **Level of Education for which Award is Granted:** Undergraduate **Number Awarded:** 15. **Funds Available:** $1,500. **Duration:** One year.
Eligibility Requirements: Applicants must be junior or senior students majoring in mining or mineral engineering programs that are accredited by the Accreditation Board for Engineering and Technology (ABET). Applicants must be a student member of SME and must have a minimum cumulative 2.50 GPA. Applicants who have received a previous Coal and Energy Division Scholarship may, upon submitting a new application, be granted a scholarship, subject to the recommendations of the college or university the recipient is attending and review by the Scholarship Committee. **Application Requirements:** Applicants must submit a completed application form, transcript and two letters of recommendation, one of which must be from the Program Chair or Department Head. Application form should include a brief outline of the applicant's participation in mining industry-related activities (such as the student chapter or local section of SME), coal industry employment or employment commitment, scholastic achievements and an explanation why the applicant is interested in a career in coal and is deserving of Coal and Energy Division support. **Deadline for Receipt:** October 30. **Additional Information:** Ann Marie Estrada at the above address.

5379 ■ SOCIETY FOR MINING, METALLURGY AND EXPLORATION

8307 Shaffer Pkwy.
Littleton, CO 80127-4102
Tel: (303)973-9550
Free: 800-763-3132
Fax: (303)973-3845
E-mail: estrada@smenet.org
Web Site: http://www.smenet.org
To provide support to students seeking advanced education in the minerals industry profession and field.
Title of Award: SME Environmental Division Scholarships **Area, Field, or Subject:** Metallurgy; Mineralogy; Mining; Engineering, Mining and Mineral. **Level of Education for which Award is Granted:** Undergraduate **Funds Available:** $2,000. **Duration:** One academic year.
Eligibility Requirements: Candidates must be promising college students who desire to develop their skills related to mining and the environment. Candidates must be of good character and must have demonstrated scholastic aptitude; must be a member of SME, attending a college or university of his or her choice that provides a curriculum leading to an undergraduate degree related to mining and the environment and a faculty advisor with special interests in an environmentally oriented program. **Application Requirements:** Applicants must submit a completed application form, transcript and two references from faculty members, people from industry, or others who can write about his/her academic potential and professional interests. **Deadline for Receipt:** October 30. **Additional Information:** Ann Marie Estrada at the above address.

5380 ■ UNIVERSITY OF TORONTO

315 Bloor St. W
Toronto, ON, Canada M5S 1A3

Tel: (416)978-2011
E-mail: information.commonsats@utoronto.ca
Web Site: http://www.utoronto.ca
To support students with their educational pursuits. **Title of Award:** J.P. Bickell Mining Scholarships **Area, Field, or Subject:** Geology; Geophysics; Earth sciences; Mining; Environmental science. **Level of Education for which Award is Granted:** Undergraduate **Funds Available:** Approximately $2000.
Eligibility Requirements: Applicant must be a student of U of T; an undergraduate student in second or higher years studying mining (including the geological and geophysical fields as well as environmental sciences, geological sciences, earth science programs and mining engineering); have a minimum GPA of B or better and have demonstrated interest in the mining industry or field. **Application Requirements:** Applicants must submit a letter of application together with a letter outlining the interest in the mining industry. **Deadline for Receipt:** October 31.

Naval Science

5381 ■ AMERICAN SOCIETY OF NAVAL ENGINEERS
1452 Duke St.
Alexandria, VA 22314-3458
Tel: (703)836-6727
Fax: (703)836-7491
E-mail: asnehq@navalengineers.org
Web Site: http://www.navalengineers.org
To improve and promote the profession of naval engineering.
Title of Award: ASNE Scholarships **Area, Field, or Subject:** Naval engineering. **Level of Education for which Award is Granted:** Graduate, Undergraduate **Funds Available:** $3,000 for undergraduate students; $4,000 for graduate students. **Duration:** One year.
Eligibility Requirements: Applicant must be a U.S. citizen; undergraduate full-time student in the last year of undergraduate program at an accredited college or university; or graduate student on a full graduate program leading to an engineering or physical science degree at an accredited university; be members of ASNE. **Application Requirements:** Applicants must submit a completed application form. **Additional Information:** Inaugurated in 1979. **Deadline for Receipt:** February 15.

5382 ■ SOCIETY OF NAVAL ARCHITECTS AND MARINE ENGINEERS
601 Pavonia Ave.
Jersey City, NJ 07306
Tel: (201)798-4800
Free: 800-798-2188
Fax: (201)798-4975
E-mail: ldavis@sname.org
Web Site: http://www.sname.org
To encourage study in naval architecture, marine engineering, ocean engineering or marine industry-related fields.
Title of Award: Mandell and Lester Rosenblatt and Robert N. Herbert Undergraduate Scholarships **Area, Field, or Subject:** Architecture, Naval; Marine engineering; Ocean engineering. **Level of Education for which Award is Granted:** Undergraduate **Funds Available:** $6,000.
Eligibility Requirements: Applicants must be U.S. or Canadian citizens who are actively involved with SNAME and other professional organizations. **Application Requirements:** Applicants must complete the application form; Applicants must provide an evidence of sound academic achievement; a 500-600 word application essay; three letters of professional recommendations in which the two must be NA/ME/OE faculty who have had the student in class and at least two of whom are SNAME members. **Deadline for Receipt:** June 1. **Additional Information:** efaustino@sname.org.

5383 ■ SOCIETY OF NAVAL ARCHITECTS AND MARINE ENGINEERS
601 Pavonia Ave.
Jersey City, NJ 07306
Tel: (201)798-4800
Free: 800-798-2188
Fax: (201)798-4975
E-mail: ldavis@sname.org

Web Site: http://www.sname.org
To encourage study in naval architecture, marine engineering, ocean engineering or marine industry-related fields.
Title of Award: Society of Naval Architects and Marine Engineers Undergraduate Scholarships **Area, Field, or Subject:** Architecture, Naval; Marine engineering; Ocean engineering. **Level of Education for which Award is Granted:** Undergraduate **Funds Available:** $2,000.
Eligibility Requirements: Applicants must be planning to study in the U.S. or Canada; applicants must study toward a degree in naval architecture, marine engineering, ocean engineering or marine industry related fields at an accredited school; applicants must be entering junior or senior year. **Application Requirements:** Applicants must complete the online application form; applicants must submit a transcript of records or any proof that he/she is currently enrolled or have been accepted by the school, colleges, or universities. **Additional Information:** efaustino@sname.org.

Photography

5384 ■ AMERICAN SOCIETY FOR PHOTOGRAMMETRY AND REMOTE SENSING
5410 Grosvenor Ln., Ste. 210
Bethesda, MD 20814-2160
Tel: (301)493-0290
Fax: (301)493-0208
E-mail: asprs@asprs.org
Web Site: http://www.asprs.org
To promote education in the theoretical aspects of photogrammetry.
Title of Award: Robert E. Altenhofen Memorial Scholarships **Area, Field, or Subject:** Photogrammetry. **Level of Education for which Award is Granted:** Graduate, Undergraduate **Funds Available:** $2,000 and a certificate.
Eligibility Requirements: Applicants must be undergraduate or graduate student members of ASPRS. **Application Requirements:** Applicants must submit an application form; a statement (2 pages) regarding plans for continuing studies in theoretical photogrammetry; evidence of capabilities of the applicant in these fields; and academic transcripts. **Additional Information:** Funded by the estate of Mrs. Helen Altenhofen as a memorial to her husband and the past president of ASPRS, Robert E. Altenhofen.

5385 ■ AMERICAN SOCIETY FOR PHOTOGRAMMETRY AND REMOTE SENSING
5410 Grosvenor Ln., Ste. 210
Bethesda, MD 20814-2160
Tel: (301)493-0290
Fax: (301)493-0208
E-mail: asprs@asprs.org
Web Site: http://www.asprs.org
To promote study in surveying and photogrammetry leading to a career in the geospatial mapping profession.
Title of Award: Francis H. Moffitt Memorial Scholarships **Area, Field, or Subject:** Remote sensing; Photogrammetry. **Level of Education for which Award is Granted:** Graduate, Undergraduate **Funds Available:** $2,500.
Eligibility Requirements: Applicants must be students currently enrolled or planning to enroll in a college/university in the United States or Canada; pursuing a program of study in surveying or photogrammetry. **Application Requirements:** Applicants must submit an application form; a listing of courses taken and/or those to be taken in surveying and photogrammetry and other related geospatial information technologies; a transcript of all college/university level courses completed; a listing of internships, special projects or work experience; two letters of recommendation or reference form; a statement (maximum of 2 pages) detailing the applicant's educational and research goals. **Additional Information:** Established in memory of Frank Moffitt for his lifetime contributions to the photogrammetric surveying profession. **Deadline for Receipt:** December 3.

5386 ■ AMERICAN SOCIETY FOR PHOTOGRAMMETRY AND REMOTE SENSING
5410 Grosvenor Ln., Ste. 210
Bethesda, MD 20814-2160

Tel: (301)493-0290
Fax: (301)493-0208
E-mail: asprs@asprs.org
Web Site: http://www.asprs.org
To encourage students to enter the profession of surveying, mapping and photogrammetry or geospatial information and technology.
Title of Award: The Kenneth J. Osborn Memorial Scholarships **Area, Field, or Subject:** Photogrammetry. **Level of Education for which Award is Granted:** Undergraduate **Funds Available:** $1,500.
Eligibility Requirements: Applicant must be an undergraduate student enrolled or planning to enroll in a college/university in the U.S. **Application Requirements:** Applicants must submit an application form; a listing of courses taken in surveying; mapping; photogrammetry and geospatial information and technology and the academic grades received; a transcript of all college or university level courses completed; two letters of recommendation from faculty members or professionals; evidence materials of the applicant's capabilities in this field; a statement of work experience; and a personal statement (maximum of 2 pages). **Additional Information:** Established as a tribute to Kenneth J. Osborn.

5387 ■ ALLISON E. FISHER MEMORIAL FUND
PO Box 43402
Baltimore, MD 21236
Tel: (410)679-0595
E-mail: fishers@verizon.net
Web Site: http://www.allisonfisherfund.org
To provide financial assistance to students who are attending an accredited four-year university.
Title of Award: Allison E. Fisher Scholarships **Area, Field, or Subject:** Journalism; Photography; Radio and television. **Level of Education for which Award is Granted:** Undergraduate **Funds Available:** $2,500.
Eligibility Requirements: Applicants must be any foreign or U.S. students who are majoring in journalism-print, photography or radio and television or planning a career in one of those fields; must be currently attending accredited four-year university; must have cumulative grade point average of 3.0 and be enrolled in undergraduate or graduate school during the award year. **Application Requirements:** Applicants must submit all the required application information.

5388 ■ INTERNATIONAL FOODSERVICE EDITORIAL COUNCIL
PO Box 491
Hyde Park, NY 12538
Tel: (845)229-6973
Fax: (845)229-6993
E-mail: info@ifeconline.com
Web Site: http://www.ifec-is-us.com
To increase awareness and understanding of the career opportunities available in the field of food service communications and to encourage entry of qualified professionals in the field.
Title of Award: International Foodservice Editorial Council Scholarships **Area, Field, or Subject:** Culinary arts; Communications; Food service careers; Food science and technology; Photography; Hotel, institutional, and restaurant management; Nutrition; Dietetics; Journalism; Public relations; Graphic art and design. **Level of Education for which Award is Granted:** Graduate, Undergraduate **Number Awarded:** Varies. **Funds Available:** $3,750.
Eligibility Requirements: Applicants must be full-time students in a U.S. accredited post-secondary educational institution working towards an associate's, bachelor's or master's degree. **Application Requirements:** Applicants must submit a complete application together with academic transcript and two letters of recommendation. Application requirements must be typewritten and submitted using U.S. Postal Service's Return Receipt Service. **Deadline for Receipt:** March 15.

5389 ■ NATIONAL PRESS PHOTOGRAPHERS ASSOCIATION
3200 Croasdaile Dr., Ste. 306
Durham, NC 27705
Tel: (919)383-7246
Fax: (919)383-7261
E-mail: info@nppa.org
Web Site: http://www.nppa.org
To improve and facilitate the administration of press photography. To promote the study of press photography and research therein, and to continue the education of press photographers.

Title of Award: Bob Baxter Scholarships **Area, Field, or Subject:** Photography. **Level of Education for which Award is Granted:** Undergraduate **Funds Available:** $1,000.
Eligibility Requirements: Applicants must be full-time students at a school in the United States and intend to pursue a career in photojournalism. **Application Requirements:** Applicants must submit a portfolio; six or more photos; picture editors must send three tearsheets. Video journalists must submit a tape of three short but complete stories. **Deadline for Receipt:** March 1. **Additional Information:** richards@northjersey.com

5390 ■ NATIONAL PRESS PHOTOGRAPHERS ASSOCIATION
3200 Croasdaile Dr., Ste. 306
Durham, NC 27705
Tel: (919)383-7246
Fax: (919)383-7261
E-mail: info@nppa.org
Web Site: http://www.nppa.org
To improve and facilitate the administration of press photography. To promote the study of press photography and research therein, and to continue the education of press photographers.
Title of Award: Reid Blackburn Scholarships **Area, Field, or Subject:** Photography. **Level of Education for which Award is Granted:** Undergraduate **Funds Available:** No specific amount.
Eligibility Requirements: Applicants must have completed one year at a recognized four-year college or university with courses in photojournalism and must be continuing in a program leading to bachelor's degree. Applicants must have at least one half year of undergraduate schooling remaining at time of award. **Application Requirements:** Applicants must submit a portfolio; six or more photos; picture editors must send three tearsheets. Video journalists must submit a tape of three short but complete stories. Applicants must submit an essay stating the philosophy and goals of their work. **Deadline for Receipt:** March 1. **Additional Information:** fay.blackburn@columbian.com

5391 ■ NATIONAL PRESS PHOTOGRAPHERS ASSOCIATION
3200 Croasdaile Dr., Ste. 306
Durham, NC 27705
Tel: (919)383-7246
Fax: (919)383-7261
E-mail: info@nppa.org
Web Site: http://www.nppa.org
To improve and facilitate the administration of press photography. To promote the study of press photography and research therein, and to continue the education of press photographers.
Title of Award: Bob East Scholarships **Area, Field, or Subject:** Photography. **Level of Education for which Award is Granted:** Undergraduate **Funds Available:** $2,000.
Eligibility Requirements: Applicants must either be undergraduates in the first three-and-a-half years of college, or planning to pursue postgraduate work and able to offer some indication of acceptance in such program. **Application Requirements:** Applicants must submit a five-single-image portfolio; six or more photos. Picture editors must send three tearsheets. Video journalists must submit a tape of three short but complete stories. **Deadline for Receipt:** March 1. **Additional Information:** 305-376-2015

5392 ■ NATIONAL PRESS PHOTOGRAPHERS ASSOCIATION
3200 Croasdaile Dr., Ste. 306
Durham, NC 27705
Tel: (919)383-7246
Fax: (919)383-7261
E-mail: info@nppa.org
Web Site: http://www.nppa.org
To improve and facilitate the administration of press photography. To promote the study of press photography and research therein, and to continue the education of press photographers.
Title of Award: Still Photographer Scholarships **Area, Field, or Subject:** Photography. **Level of Education for which Award is Granted:** Undergraduate **Funds Available:** $2,000.
Eligibility Requirements: Applicants must have completed one year at a recognized four-year college or university with courses in photojournalism and must be continuing in a program leading to a bachelor's degree. Applicants must have at least one half of undergraduate schooling remaining

at the time of award. **Application Requirements:** Applicants must submit a portfolio with six or more photos and state their goals and philosophy relating to documentary photojournalism. Picture editors must send three tearsheets. Video journalists must submit a tape of three short but complete stories. **Deadline for Receipt:** March 1. **Additional Information:** wsanders@citizen-times.com

5393 ■ NATIONAL PRESS PHOTOGRAPHERS ASSOCIATION
3200 Croasdaile Dr., Ste. 306
Durham, NC 27705
Tel: (919)383-7246
Fax: (919)383-7261
E-mail: info@nppa.org
Web Site: http://www.nppa.org
To improve and facilitate the administration of press photography. To promote the study of press photography and research therein, and to continue the education of press photographers.
Title of Award: Television News Scholarships **Area, Field, or Subject:** Photography. **Level of Education for which Award is Granted:** Undergraduate **Funds Available:** $1,000.
Eligibility Requirements: Applicants must be enrolled in a recognized four-year college or university with courses in TV news photojournalism. Applicants must be continuing in a program leading to a bachelor's degree. Applicants must be in their junior or senior year at the time award is given. **Application Requirements:** Applicants must submit a portfolio with six or more photos. Picture editors must send three tearsheets. Video journalists must submit a tape of three short but complete stories. Applicants must complete the entry form and submit it along with a videotape containing examples of his or her work. Applicants must include a one-page biographical sketch including a personal statement addressing their professional goals. **Deadline for Receipt:** March 1. **Additional Information:** dooks@verizon.net

5394 ■ PUBLIC EDUCATION FOUNDATION
3360 W Sahara Ave., Ste. 160
Las Vegas, NV 89102
Tel: (702)799-1042
Fax: (702)799-5247
E-mail: steelej@ccpef.org
Web Site: http://ccpef.org
To promote education related in photography.
Title of Award: Donald Franklin Bradley Memorial Scholarships **Area, Field, or Subject:** Photography. **Level of Education for which Award is Granted:** Undergraduate **Number Awarded:** 1. **Funds Available:** $1,000.
Eligibility Requirements: Applicants must be CCSD seniors planning to attend the University of Nevada, Las Vegas as full-time students for a major related to photography; must have a minimum 3.0 cumulative GPA (weighted or unweighted). **Application Requirements:** Applicants must submit a completed application form together with an essay, transcript, a letter of recommendation, and copies of best photographs taken. **Deadline for Receipt:** March 31. **Additional Information:** Shana Venenga at 702-799-1042.

5395 ■ PUBLIC EDUCATION FOUNDATION
3360 W Sahara Ave., Ste. 160
Las Vegas, NV 89102
Tel: (702)799-1042
Fax: (702)799-5247
E-mail: steelej@ccpef.org
Web Site: http://ccpef.org
To promote education in photography and journalism.
Title of Award: Don English Memorial Scholarships **Area, Field, or Subject:** Photography; Journalism. **Level of Education for which Award is Granted:** Undergraduate **Number Awarded:** 1. **Funds Available:** $4,100.
Eligibility Requirements: Applicants must be CCSD seniors planning to attend an accredited college, university, or institute as full-time students in the field of photography, media arts, or journalism; must have a minimum 3.0 cumulative GPA. **Application Requirements:** Applicants must submit a completed application form together with an essay, two letters of recommendation, transcript, and resume of awards. **Deadline for Receipt:** March 7. **Additional Information:** Shana Venenga at 702-799-1042.

5396 ■ STARK COMMUNITY FOUNDATION
400 Market Ave. N, Ste. 200
Canton, OH 44702-2107
Tel: (330)454-3426
Fax: (330)454-5855
Web Site: http://www.starkcommunityfoundation.org
To provide scholarship assistance to qualified individuals who want to pursue their studies.
Title of Award: Manzer-Keener-Wefler Scholarships **Area, Field, or Subject:** Photography; Visual arts. **Level of Education for which Award is Granted:** Undergraduate **Funds Available:** No specific amount.
Eligibility Requirements: Applicants must have been accepted by, or are currently attending, a two-year or four-year college or university or art institute within the United States; that their chosen field of study is in the field of or related to photography or visual arts; either seniors attending a high school in Stark County, OH, or counties contiguous to Stark, who will graduate the year the scholarship is awarded or college undergraduate students originally from Stark County, OH, or counties contiguous to Stark, who are currently attending a two-year or four-year college or university or art institute full time or non-traditional college students originally from Stark County, OH, or counties contiguous to Stark, who are currently attending a two-year or four-year college or university or art institute part-time; and first time applicants must have a minimum GPA of at least 2.5 on a 4.0. **Application Requirements:** Applicants must submit a two letters of recommendation letter. Application from and other supporting documents must be sent to Stark Community Foundation, 400 Market Ave. N, Ste. 200, Canton, OH 44702. **Deadline for Receipt:** May 1.

5397 ■ UNIVERSITY OF ALASKA ANCHORAGE
3211 Providence Dr.
Anchorage, AK 99508
Tel: (907)786-1800
Web Site: http://www.uaa.alaska.edu
To provide financial assistance for tuition and other related educational expenses to full-time students at the University of Alaska Anchorage with a declared major in art or journalism & public communications.
Title of Award: UAA Kimura Scholarship Fund (Photography Scholarships) **Area, Field, or Subject:** Art; Journalism; Photography. **Level of Education for which Award is Granted:** Undergraduate **Number Awarded:** 2. **Funds Available:** No specific amount.
Eligibility Requirements: Applicant must be a full-time student attending the University of Alaska Anchorage with a declared major in art or with a declared major in journalism & public communication with an emphasis in photography; must be in their junior year and has completed at least nine credits in studio photography classes at the 200 level or above; must be in good academic standing with at least a 3.0 GPA. **Application Requirements:** Applicants must submit a proof of their photography work. Application documents and other supporting documents must submit to UAA Office of Student Financial Assistance, Kimura Scholarships, PO Box 141608, Anchorage, AK 99514. **Deadline for Receipt:** February 15.

Vocational-Technical

5398 ■ AMERICAN RENTAL ASSOCIATION FOUNDATION
1900 19th St.
Moline, IL 61265
800-334-2177
Fax: (309)764-1533
E-mail: arafoundation@ararental.org
Web Site: http://www.ararental.org/Foundation
To provide scholarships to promising young students looking to enter the rental industry.
Title of Award: American Rental Association Foundation Scholarships **Area, Field, or Subject:** Industrial education. **Level of Education for which Award is Granted:** Undergraduate **Number Awarded:** 23. **Funds Available:** $37,000. **Duration:** One year.
Eligibility Requirements: Applicants must be students pursuing a field of study they will use while working in the rental industry or completing a rental-related vocational or certification program. **Application Requirements:** For further information, applicants are advised to contact the ARA Foundation at 1900 19th St., Moline, IL 61265.

5399 ■ AMERICAN RENTAL ASSOCIATION FOUNDATION
1900 19th St.
Moline, IL 61265
800-334-2177
Fax: (309)764-1533
E-mail: arafoundation@ararental.org
Web Site: http://www.ararental.org/Foundation
To provide scholarships to promising young students looking to enter the rental industry.
Title of Award: Ron Marshall Scholarships **Area, Field, or Subject:** Industrial education. **Level of Education for which Award is Granted:** Undergraduate **Number Awarded:** 2. **Funds Available:** $500. **Duration:** One year.
Eligibility Requirements: Applicants must be pursuing an education applicable to the rental industry. **Application Requirements:** Applicants are advised to contact the ARA Foundation at 1900 19th St., Moline, IL 61265. **Additional Information:** Ron Marshall was the owner of Reading Rentals in Reading, Pa., until his death in October 1995. He was active in the Keystone Rental Association and ARA's Region Two.

5400 ■ AMERICAN RENTAL ASSOCIATION FOUNDATION
1900 19th St.
Moline, IL 61265
800-334-2177
Fax: (309)764-1533
E-mail: arafoundation@ararental.org
Web Site: http://www.ararental.org/Foundation
To provide scholarships to promising young students looking to enter the rental industry.
Title of Award: Dorothy Wellnitz Canadian Scholarships **Area, Field, or Subject:** Industrial education. **Level of Education for which Award is Granted:** Undergraduate **Funds Available:** $1,000. **Duration:** One year.
Eligibility Requirements: Applicants must be pursuing an education program applicable to the rental industry. **Application Requirements:** For further information, applicants are advised to contact the ARA Foundation at 1900 19th St., Moline, IL 61265. **Additional Information:** Scholarship is named for Dorothy Wellnitz, former executive director of the Canadian Rental Association and is administered by the ARA Foundation.

5401 ■ THE FLEXIBLE PACKAGING ASSOCIATION
971 Corporate Blvd., Ste. 403
Linthicum, MD 21090
Tel: (410)694-0800
Fax: (410)694-0900
E-mail: fpa@flexpack.org
Web Site: http://www.flexpack.org
To provide a learning experience on the flexible packaging industry.
Title of Award: Flexible Packaging Academic Scholarships & Summer Internship Program **Area, Field, or Subject:** Industrial design; Industrial education. **Level of Education for which Award is Granted:** Undergraduate **Funds Available:** $3,000. **Duration:** One summer.
Eligibility Requirements: Applicants must be enrolled in an AA, BA, BS or MS degree program; have a 2.7 GPA; have 24 credit hours, 9 credits of which are in packaging, printing or other areas in the converting industry. **Application Requirements:** Applicants are advised to visit the website for the online application system. Prepare a recommendation letter from a faculty member; and an essay (maximum of 500 words). Send all materials to: Flexible Packaging Association, Attn: Lauren Kinard, 971 Corporate Blvd., Ste. 403, Linthicum, MD 21090, email to: fpa@flexpack.org. **Additional Information:** Introduced in 2005.

5402 ■ INDUSTRIAL SUPPLY ASSOCIATION
100 N 20th St., 4th Fl.
Philadelphia, PA 19103
Tel: (215)320-3862; (866)460-2360
Fax: (215)564-2175
E-mail: info@isapartners.org
Web Site: http://www.isapartners.org
To recognize members who embody the values postered by Gary L. Buffington while performing his duty for the industry.
Title of Award: Gary L. Buffington Memorial Scholarships **Area, Field, or Subject:** Industrial. **Level of Education for which Award is Granted:** Undergraduate **Funds Available:** $10,000.

Eligibility Requirements: Applicant must be a rising senior in an established college or university industrial distribution channel. **Application Requirements:** Applicants must submit complete application.

5403 ■ LEWIS-CLARK STATE COLLEGE
500 8th Ave.
Lewiston, ID 83501
Tel: (208)792-5272
Web Site: http://www.lcsc.edu
To encourage promising students from Timberline High School, Clearwater County to continue their education.
Title of Award: Bus and Mary Ellen Durant Timberline High School Endowed Scholarships **Area, Field, or Subject:** Nursing; Technical; Industrial. **Level of Education for which Award is Granted:** Undergraduate **Funds Available:** No specific amount.
Eligibility Requirements: Applicants must be alumni of Timberline High School or their successor in Clearwater County, Idaho; must be enrolled full-time who majoring in any other discipline offered at LCSC. **Application Requirements:** Applicants must accomplish a general application available in the website. **Deadline for Receipt:** March 1.

5404 ■ LEWIS-CLARK STATE COLLEGE
500 8th Ave.
Lewiston, ID 83501
Tel: (208)792-5272
Web Site: http://www.lcsc.edu
To inspire educational pursuits among less capable individuals by providing financial assistance.
Title of Award: Lewis-Clark State College Presidential Technical Out-of-State Scholarships **Area, Field, or Subject:** Chemistry; Computer Science; Engineering; Information Systems Analysis; Industrial Electronics; Biology; Earth Information Systems; Radiology; Heating/Air Conditioning; Automated Manufacturing Technology; Mathematics; Printing Technology; Graphic Arts or Web Development. **Level of Education for which Award is Granted:** Undergraduate **Funds Available:** No specific amount.
Eligibility Requirements: Applicants must be new non-resident high school or transfer students who have at least 14 transferable semester credits. **Application Requirements:** Applicants must accomplish a general application available in the website. **Deadline for Receipt:** March 1 for Fall enrollment or November 1 for Spring enrollment.

5405 ■ MATERIAL HANDLING INSTITUTE OF AMERICA
8720 Red Oak Blvd., Ste. 201
Charlotte, NC 28217-3992
Tel: (704)676-1190
Fax: (704)676-1199
Web Site: http://www.mhia.org
To promote the study of material handling and to expose as many students as possible to the material handling industry, including the vast array of equipment, systems and technologies represented by the industry; the role material handling in a productive enterprise; and the many career paths available within the supplier, distributor and end-user (applications) sides of the industry.
Title of Award: Material Handling Institute of America Scholarships **Area, Field, or Subject:** Industrial. **Level of Education for which Award is Granted:** Graduate, Undergraduate **Funds Available:** No amount mentioned.
Eligibility Requirements: Applicants must be enrolled, or intending to enroll, in either an undergraduate, four (4) year baccalaureate program or a post graduate program leading to a masters or Ph.D. degree at a pre-qualified institution. Undergraduates must have completed a minimum of two (2) years of their undergraduate education. Students from junior and community colleges or other two (2) year post secondary institutions are also encouraged to apply if they have been accepted as a transfer student to a four (4) year program; have maintained a "B" overall grade point average and be full-time students; enrolled with courses like Civil, Electrical, Industrial, and Mechanical Engineering (and Engineering Technology); computer engineering; computer science; and business administration with an emphasis in production management, industrial distribution and/or logistics and in an accredited and pre-qualified program of study with the resources and means to support the study of material handling and material handling related subjects either through formal course work, independent study, summer work or coop experience, industry internships

or some combination of same. **Application Requirements:** Applicants must name a primary faculty contact willing to assist in the preparation and submission of the scholarship application; must sent three letters of recommendation; official transcripts of all academic work completed beyond high school; and completed scholarship application. **Deadline for Receipt:** March 1.

5406 ■ NATIONAL ORGANIZATION OF INDUSTRIAL TRADE UNIONS

148-06 Hillside Ave.
Jamaica, NY 11435
Tel: (718)291-3434
Fax: (718)526-2920
Web Site: http://www.noitu.org
To provide financial assistance to sons and daughters of the Union.

Title of Award: Daniel Lasky Scholarship Fund **Area, Field, or Subject:** Industrial. **Level of Education for which Award is Granted:** Undergraduate **Funds Available:** No amount mentioned.
Eligibility Requirements: Applicants must be sons or daughters of a NOITU member who will graduate from high school this year and planning to attend an accredited college in the coming fall term. **Application Requirements:** Applicants must submit the following requirements: a) Scholastic Aptitude Test (SAT I) scores; b) verification of acceptance by a college or university approved by the Federation of Regional Accrediting commission of Higher Education; c) letters of recommendation from (2) faculty members in the high school you are attending; high school transcript (showing final grades of the graduating year); and the name and address of the college applicants will be attending. **Deadline for Receipt:** July 1.

4321, 4324, 4325, 4344, 4523, 4536, 4580, 4600, 4601, 4602, 4603, 4604, 4605, 4607, 4610, 4613, 4614, 4616, 4617, 4618, 4619, 4620, 4621, 4622, 4623, 4624, 4626, 4627, 4628, 4629, 4630, 4631, 4632, 4638, 4653, 4657, 4660, 4666, 4668, 4678, 4694, 4695, 4792, 4793, 4896, 4921, 4946, 4953, 4956, 4960, 4969, 5196, 5290, 5319

Poultry science – 3021, 3552, 5338

Printing trades and industries – 2691, 4063, 4319, 4628, 4668, 4753, 4792

Printmaking – 2686, 2726, 3059, 3240, 3654, 4898, 4948, 5199, 5404

Psychiatry – 3602, 3603, 3610, 3611, 3767, 3768, 4681, 4682

Psychology – 2454, 2472, 2492, 2733, 2891, 3050, 3596, 3597, 3598, 3599, 3600, 3601, 3602, 3603, 3604, 3605, 3606, 3607, 3608, 3609, 3610, 3611, 3650, 3688, 3767, 3768, 4123, 4233, 4479, 4604, 4681, 4682, 4880, 4928, 5071

Public administration – 3782, 4523, 4617, 4618, 4621, 4626, 4634, 4635, 4636, 4643, 4653, 4657, 4660, 4666, 4694, 4695

Public affairs – 2819, 2820, 3717, 3726, 3748, 3750, 4063, 4319, 4611, 4628, 4668, 4792

Public health – 2506, 2555, 3381, 4184, 4198, 4445, 4637, 4639, 4645, 4649, 4652, 4667, 4680, 4693, 4891, 5146

Public relations – 2473, 2681, 2727, 2771, 2788, 2800, 2827, 3550, 3793, 3822, 3824, 3838, 3862, 3942, 4024, 4037, 4046, 4063, 4070, 4114, 4294, 4312, 4319, 4628, 4633, 4641, 4644, 4646, 4647, 4650, 4659, 4663, 4664, 4665, 4668, 4672, 4673, 4792, 4939, 5144, 5334, 5388

Public service – 2732, 3353, 3783, 3919, 4295, 4344, 4603, 4638, 4640, 4642, 4648, 4651, 4654, 4655, 4656, 4658, 4661, 4662, 4669, 4670, 4671, 4674, 4675

Quality assurance and control – 4869

Radio and television – 2447, 2688, 2729, 2749, 2757, 2893, 3350, 3407, 3780, 3943, 3944, 3945, 3946, 3947, 3948, 3949, 3950, 3951, 3952, 3953, 3954, 3955, 3956, 3957, 3958, 3959, 3960, 3961, 3962, 3963, 3964, 3965, 3966, 3967, 3968, 3969, 3970, 3971, 3972, 3973, 3974, 3975, 3976, 3977, 3978, 3979, 3980, 3981, 3982, 3983, 3984, 3985, 3986, 3987, 3988, 3989, 3990, 3991, 4006, 4013, 4030, 4035, 4047, 4698, 4699, 4700, 4701, 4702, 4703, 4704, 4705, 4706, 4923, 4924, 4925, 4990, 4991, 4992, 4993, 4994, 4995, 5387

Radiology – 2686, 2726, 3059, 3193, 3194, 3202, 3203, 3204, 3205, 3240, 3296, 3654, 4898, 4948, 5199, 5404

Real estate – 1156, 1249, 1358, 1682, 2345, 2494, 3819

Rehabilitation, Physical/Psychological – 3602, 3603, 3610, 3611, 3767, 3768, 4681, 4682

Religion – 188, 1634, 2105, 2243, 2244, 2299, 2625, 2816, 3034, 3342, 3390, 3391, 3523, 4064, 4261, 4538, 4962, 5291

Remote sensing – 3613, 5385

Resource management – 2534, 3086, 5207

Risk management – 1143

Secretarial sciences – 2649, 3206, 4132, 4881

Science – 34, 108, 794, 799, 966, 973, 1322, 1332, 1679, 2067, 2089, 2102, 2186, 2213, 2471, 2542, 2560, 2574, 2622, 2647, 2678, 2680, 2717, 2756, 2867, 2875, 3057, 3350, 3407, 3495, 3776, 3780, 3781, 3790, 3806, 3823, 3835, 3910, 3950, 3962, 3991, 4113, 4134, 4160, 4172, 4184, 4194, 4205, 4442, 4639, 4645, 4736, 4748, 4750, 4867, 4868, 4882, 4883, 4884, 4885, 4886, 4887, 4891, 4893, 4895, 4900, 4901, 4902, 4906, 4907, 4908, 4915, 4917, 4923, 4931, 4935, 4957, 4970, 4973, 4977, 4990, 4991, 4995, 5016, 5072, 5105, 5111, 5116, 5118, 5130, 5134, 5145, 5146, 5209, 5211, 5218, 5222, 5225, 5231, 5238, 5241, 5243, 5244, 5268, 5269, 5270, 5271, 5272, 5273, 5274, 5275, 5276, 5277, 5278, 5279, 5280, 5281, 5282, 5283, 5284, 5285, 5288, 5289, 5307, 5309, 5315

Science technologies – 2541, 3653, 3922, 4630, 4752, 4793, 4914, 4974, 5305

Scottish studies – 2462

Sculpture – 2693, 2718, 2957

Sexuality – 2090

Social sciences – 2539, 2542, 2572, 3254, 3716, 3720, 3722, 3751, 3752, 3769, 3781, 4334, 4614, 5016, 5140

Social work – 2532, 2555, 3276, 3286, 3367, 3381, 3476, 3602, 3603, 3610, 3611, 3767, 3768, 3798, 4140, 4198, 4255, 4445, 4531, 4593, 4607, 4649, 4676, 4677, 4678, 4679, 4680, 4681, 4682, 4683, 4684, 4685, 4686, 4687, 4688, 4689, 4690, 4691, 4693

Sociology – 2454, 2472, 2733, 2891, 3598, 3602, 3603, 3610, 3611, 3749, 3751, 3767, 3768, 4123, 4604, 4681, 4682

Spanish studies – 2442

Speech, Debate, and Forensics – 2554

Speech and language pathology/audiology – 2540, 2548, 2549, 3223, 3309

Sports studies – 3718, 3723, 3742, 3746

Sports writing – 2750, 2782, 4007

Statistics – 2505, 3058, 3839, 4027, 4436, 4613, 4869, 4870, 4894, 4896, 4946, 5196

Surgery – 3289, 3344, 3398

Swedish studies – 2459, 2460, 2461

Systems engineering – 5166, 5167, 5168, 5169, 5170, 5171, 5172, 5173, 5174, 5175, 5176, 5177, 5178, 5179, 5180, 5181, 5182, 5183, 5184, 5185, 5186, 5187, 5188, 5189, 5190

Taxonomy – 2985

Teaching – 2625, 3034, 3286, 3342, 3391, 3526, 3837, 3908, 4115, 4129, 4180, 4181, 4186, 4188, 4199, 4206, 4225, 4234, 4250, 4251, 4255, 4256, 4261, 4262, 4272, 4289, 4531, 4538, 4690, 4749, 4962, 5291

Technical communications – 3690, 3845, 4052, 4789, 4899, 5206

Technology – 3090, 3238, 3349, 3495, 3658, 3704, 3777, 3807, 3822, 3835, 3836, 3837, 3965, 4199, 4337, 4442, 4542, 4644, 4731, 4732, 4736, 4737, 4738, 4739, 4747, 4748, 4749, 4750, 4764, 4767,

4768, 4778, 4782, 4788, 4790, 4791, 4868, 4902, 4945, 4958, 4970, 4973, 4978, 4992, 5144, 5225, 5242, 5260, 5262, 5264, 5295, 5325

Telecommunications systems – 2615, 3518, 3892, 4005, 4011, 4029, 4036, 4043, 4053, 4054, 4055, 4056, 4057, 4058, 4235, 4929, 4950, 5099, 5226, 5322

Testing, educational/psychological – 4707

Textile science – 2696, 2697, 2704, 3555, 4696, 4762, 4763, 5343, 5350

Theater arts – 2646, 2648, 2649, 2653, 2655, 2663, 2667, 2677, 2679, 2690, 2694, 2700, 2701, 2702, 2703, 2706, 2707, 2708, 2769, 2865, 2869, 2873, 2892, 2910, 2915, 2922, 2932, 3206, 4033, 4132, 4148, 4193, 4881

Theology – 2968

Toxicology – 3591, 3592, 3594, 3595

Transportation – 13, 14, 114, 116, 117, 119, 120, 795, 1432, 1433, 2079, 2129, 2130, 2217, 2218, 2219, 2220, 2221, 2222, 2223, 2224, 2225, 2226, 2227, 2228, 2229, 2230, 2231, 2232, 2233, 2234, 2235, 2423, 2424, 2425, 2503, 3669, 3675, 3829, 3864, 5151, 5303

Travel and tourism – 116, 117, 119, 120, 221, 222, 223, 224, 225, 226, 227, 228, 229, 230, 231, 479, 480, 481, 923, 931, 968, 1118, 1303, 1606, 2273, 2378, 2379, 2380, 2439

Turfgrass management – 1893, 3045, 3136

Ukrainian studies – 2456, 2457

Urban affairs/design/planning – 2555, 3381, 4198, 4445, 4617, 4618, 4649, 4653, 4657, 4680, 4692, 4693, 4694, 4695

Veterinary science and medicine – 2649, 2728, 2765, 3002, 3035, 3047, 3170, 3173, 3174, 3175, 3176, 3177, 3196, 3206, 3226, 3253, 3259, 3260, 3261, 3294, 3302, 3359, 3406, 3556, 4017, 4116, 4132, 4881, 5348

Video – 2573

Vietnamese studies – 2484, 2485

Visual arts – 2646, 2694, 2701, 2865, 2866, 2867, 2868, 2869, 2870, 2871, 2872, 2873, 2874, 2875, 2876, 2877, 2878, 2892, 2932, 2941, 3277, 3743, 3910, 4624, 4884, 4956, 5116, 5396

Visual impairment – 290

Viticulture – 192

Water resources – 238, 284, 285, 486

Water supply industry – 1362, 1464

Welding – 4708, 4709, 4710, 4711, 4712, 4713, 4714, 4715, 4716, 4717, 4718, 4719, 4720, 4721, 4722, 4723, 4724, 4725, 4726, 4727, 4728, 4729, 4730, 4751, 5032

Wildlife conservation, management, and science – 2529, 2530, 2531, 2533, 2534, 2535, 2536, 2537, 3001, 3055, 3086, 3094, 3095, 3129, 3168, 5207

Women's studies – 2491, 2492, 2493, 3607

Writing – 2676, 2767, 2768, 2795, 2815, 2921, 2949, 4021, 4307

Zoology – 2531, 3051, 3129, 3167, 3168, 3310, 3357, 3418

High School

Postdoctoral

Postgraduate

Professional

Two Year College

Undergraduate

American Academy of Neurology – 3172

American Advertising Federation-Cleveland – 3773, 3774

American Architectural Foundation – 2579

American Association for the Advancement of Science – 2541, 3048, 3649, 4974

American Association of Ambulatory Care Nursing – 3399

American Association of Attorney-Certified Public Accountants – 4328

American Association of Blacks in Energy – 107

American Association of Bovine Practitioners – 3173, 3174, 3175, 3176

American Association of Candy Technologists – 2970, 5327

American Association of Colleges of Nursing – 3400, 3401

American Association of Colleges of Osteopathic Medicine – 3562

American Association of Critical-Care Nurses – 3402

American Association of Equine Practitioners – 3177

American Association of Family and Consumer Sciences – 108

American Association for Health Education – 2880, 4111

American Association of Healthcare Administrative Management – 109

American Association for the Improvement of Boxing – 110

American Association for Justice – 4329, 4330, 4331, 4332

American Association of Neurological Surgeons – 3178, 3179

American Association of Neuroscience Nurses – 3396, 3403

American Association of Occupational Health Nurses – 111

American Association of People with Disabilities – 112

American Association of Physics Teachers – 3677

American Association of Police Polygraphists – 113

American Association of Professional Apiculturists – 2971

American Association of Railroad Superintendents – 114

American Association of School Administrators – 115

American Association of State Troopers – 4583, 4584, 4585

American Association of Stratigraphic Palynologists – 2972, 3663

American Association of Textile Chemists and Colorists – 4696

American Association for Thoracic Surgery – 3347, 3348

American Bar Association – 4333

American Bar Foundation – 4334

American Birding Association – 3042, 3043, 3044

American Board of Funeral Service Education – 3163

American Bus Association – 116, 117, 118, 119, 120

American Business Travel Association – 121

American Ceramic Society – 4975

American Clan Gregor Society – 122

The American Classical League – 2627, 2628, 2629

American College of Healthcare Executives – 3180, 3181

American College of Nurse-Midwives Foundation – 3404

American College of Nursing Practitioners – 3405

American Composites Manufacturers Association – 123, 124

American Congress on Surveying and Mapping – 125, 126, 127, 128, 129, 130, 131, 132, 133, 134, 135

American Conifer Society – 3100

American Copy Editors Society – 136

American Council of Engineering Companies of Illinois – 4976

American Council on Exercise – 3182, 3183, 3184

American Council of Independent Laboratories – 3612

American Counsel Association – 4335

American Criminal Justice Association – 4336

American Culinary Federation – 137, 138, 139, 143, 144

American Dental Association – 3319, 3320, 3321, 3322, 3323

American Division Veterans Association – 4293

American Federation of Police and Concerned Citizens – 4586

American Floral Endowment – 3101, 3102, 3103, 3104, 3105, 3106, 3107, 3108, 3109, 3110, 3111, 3112, 3113, 3114, 3115, 3116, 3117, 3118, 3119, 3120, 3121, 3122, 3123

American Floral Industry Association – 145

American Foreign Service Association – 146

American GI Forum of San Jose – 147

American Handel Society – 148

American Hotel and Lodging Educational Foundation – 149, 150, 151, 152, 153, 154, 155, 156

American Indian College Fund – 157, 158, 159, 160, 161, 162, 163, 164, 165, 3775

American Indian Education Foundation – 166, 167, 168, 169, 170, 171, 3185, 3776, 4112, 4113, 4977

American Indian Graduate Center Scholars (AIGCS) – 3349, 3777, 3778, 4337, 4697, 4978

American Institute of Aeronautics and Astronautics Foundation – 4833

American Institute of Baking – 5328

American Institute of Chemical Engineers – 4979, 4980, 4981, 4982

American Institute for Paralegal Studies – 4338, 4339, 4340

American Institute of Polish Culture – 2473, 2727, 3942, 4114, 4294, 4312, 4633

American Institute of Steel Construction – 2580, 2581, 2582, 4983, 4984, 4985

American Intellectual Property Law Education Foundation – 4341

American Jersey Cattle Association – 172, 173

The American Legion – 174, 175, 176

American Marketing Association Foundation – 3779

American Medical Association – 3186, 3187, 3188

American Military Retirees Association – 177

American Montessori Society – 4115

American Musicological Society – 2881

American Nuclear Society – 4987

American Osteopathic Foundation – 3563, 3564, 3565, 3566, 3567

American Paint Horse Foundation – 178

American Pet Products Manufacturers Association – 179

American Physical Society – 3678

American Planning Association – 4692

American Polygraph Association – 180

American Psychiatric Association Alliance – 181

American Psychiatric Publishing Inc. – 3596

American Psychological Association of Graduate Students – 3597

American Public Power Association – 182

American Public Works Association – 4988

American Public Works Association-Nevada – 4634, 4989

American Quarter Horse Youth Association – 2728, 3406, 4116

American Radio Relay League (ARRL) Foundation – 2729, 3350, 3407, 3780, 3943, 3944, 3945, 3946, 3947, 3948, 3949, 3950, 3951, 3952, 3953, 3954, 3955, 3956, 3957, 3958, 3959, 3960, 3961, 3962, 3963, 3964, 3965, 3966, 3967, 3968, 3969, 3970, 3971, 3972, 3973, 3974, 3975, 3976, 3977, 3978, 3979, 3980, 3981, 3982, 3983, 3984, 3985, 3986, 3987, 3988, 3989, 3990, 3991, 4698, 4699, 4700, 4701, 4702, 4703, 4704, 4705, 4706, 4923, 4924, 4925, 4990, 4991, 4992, 4993, 4994, 4995

American Railway Engineering and Maintenance-of-Way Association – 4996, 4997, 4998, 4999, 5000, 5001, 5002, 5003, 5004, 5005, 5006, 5007, 5008, 5009, 5010, 5011, 5012, 5013, 5014, 5015

American Red Cross – 3408

American Rental Association Foundation – 5398, 5399, 5400

American Research Institute in Turkey – 183, 2542, 3781, 5016

American Risk and Insurance Association – 184

American Road and Transportation Builders Association – 185

American Romanian Orthodox Youth – 186, 187, 188, 189

American School Health Association – 3324, 3325, 3351, 3352, 3409, 3410, 3547, 3548, 3573, 3574, 3759, 3760, 4117, 4118

American Small Businesses Association – 190

American Society of Brewing Chemists – 191

American Society of Certified Engineering Technicians – 5017, 5018, 5019

American Society for Clinical Laboratory Science – 3189, 3190

American Society of Composers, Authors and Publishers (ASCAP) Foundation – 2636, 2883, 2884, 2885, 2886, 2887, 2888, 2889, 2890

American Society of Echocardiography – 3191

American Society for Engineering Education – 5020

American Society for Enology and Viticulture – 192

American Society of Heating, Refrigerating and Air-Conditioning Engineers – 5021, 5022, 5023, 5024, 5025, 5026, 5027, 5028, 5029

American Society for Horticultural Science – 3124, 3125, 3126

American Society of Landscape Architects – 2583, 2584, 2585, 2586, 2587, 2588, 2589, 2590, 2591, 3127

American Society for Legal History – 2448

American Society of Mechanical Engineers – 5030, 5031

American Society for Microbiology – 193, 3049, 4119

American Society of Military Comptrollers – 3782, 4635

American Society of Mining and Reclamation – 5357

American Society of Naval Engineers – 5381

American Society for Nondestructive Testing – 4707

American Society for Photogrammetry and Remote Sensing – 3613, 5384, 5385, 5386

American Society of Podiatric Medical Assistants – 3192

American Society for Quality - Statistic Division – 4869

American Society of Radiologic Technologists – 3193, 3194

American Society of Safety Engineers – 194, 195, 196, 197, 198, 199, 200, 201, 202, 203, 204, 205, 206, 207, 208, 209, 210, 211, 212, 213, 214, 215, 216, 217, 218, 219, 220

American Society of Travel Agents – 221, 222, 223, 224, 225, 226, 227, 228, 229, 230, 231

American Society of Women Accountants – 232, 233

American Sokol – 3614, 4120

American Statistical Association – 4870

American Swedish Institute – 2459, 2460, 2461

American University - School of Public Affairs – 3717, 4636

American Veterans – 234, 235, 236, 237

American Water Resources Association – 238

American Water Ski Educational Foundation – 239

American Welding Society – 4708, 4709, 4710, 4711, 4712, 4713, 4714, 4715, 4716, 4717, 4718, 4719, 4720, 4721, 4722, 4723, 4724, 4725, 4726, 4727, 4728, 4729, 4730, 5032

Americans for Informed Democracy – 240

Anaheim Police Association – 241

Wilbur H. Anderson Memorial Scholarship Foundation, Inc. – 242

Appalachian School of Law – 4342

Appraisal Institute Education Trust – 2494

Arab American Institute – 2730, 2731, 2967, 4602

Archaeological Institute of America – 2578

Architectural Precast Association – 2592

Arent Fox LLP – 4343

Arizona Airport Association – 4834

Arizona Association of Student Financial Aid Administrators – 243, 244, 245, 246

Arizona Christian School Tuition Organization – 247

Arizona Nursery Association – 3128

Arizona Nurses Association – 3411

Arizona Parks and Recreation Association – 248

Arkansas Environmental Federation – 2495, 2496, 2973, 4121, 5033

Arkansas Public Health Association – 2497, 4637

Armed Forces Communications and Electronics Association – 3679, 3680, 3681, 3682, 3683,

Keith Gilmore Foundation – 2765, 3002, 3226, 4017
Gleaner Life Insurance Association – 953
Godparents for Tanzania – 954
Golden Key International Honour Society – 955, 956, 957, 958, 3811, 4888, 5136
Gonja Association of North America – 959
Gonzaga University School of Law – 4420
Goodman and Company, LLP – 960
Government Finance Officers Association of United States and Canada – 961, 4643
Grand Haven Area Community Foundation – 962, 963, 964, 965, 966, 967, 968, 969, 970, 971, 972, 973, 974, 975, 976, 977, 978, 979, 980, 981, 982, 983, 984, 985, 2500, 2501, 2668, 2980, 3134, 3483, 3812, 3813, 3814, 3815, 3816, 4174, 4175, 4176, 4177, 4178, 4421, 4422, 4740, 4889, 4890, 4938, 5137, 5138
Grand Rapids Community Foundation – 986, 987, 988, 989, 990, 991, 992, 993, 994, 995, 996, 997, 998, 999, 1000, 1001, 1002, 1003, 1004, 1005, 1006, 1007, 1008, 1009, 1010, 1011, 1012, 1013, 1014, 1015, 2669, 2670, 2917, 2918, 3374, 3375, 3817, 4018, 4844, 5139
Grandmothers for Peace International – 1016
Granger Business Association – 1017
Great Lakes Commission – 4741
Great Seattle Business Association – 1018
Greater Dayton IT Alliance – 4742
Greater Philadelphia Law Library Association – 4423
The Greater Tacoma Community Foundation – 1019, 1020, 1021, 3135, 3484, 3722, 5140, 5367
Green Knight Economic Development Corporation – 1022
Griffin Foundation – 1023
Gulf and Caribbean Fisheries Institute – 3056
Hamilton Industrial Environmental Association – 2502, 5141
Handweavers Guild of America – 2671, 2672
Bryce Harlow Foundation – 4611
Harness Horse Youth Foundation – 1025, 1026, 1027
Harness Tracks of America – 1028
Hartfield Coalition – 4845
Hartford Foundation for Public Giving – 1029, 1030, 1031, 1032, 1033, 1034, 1035, 1036, 1037, 1038, 1039, 1040, 1041, 1042, 1043, 1044, 1045, 1046, 1047, 1048, 1049, 1050, 1051, 1052, 1053, 1054, 1055, 1056, 1057, 1058, 1059, 1060, 1061, 1062, 1063, 1064, 1065, 1066, 1067, 1068, 1069, 1070, 1071, 1072, 1073, 1074, 1075, 1076, 1077, 1078, 1079, 1080, 1081, 1082, 1083, 1084, 2450, 2466, 2468, 2474, 2551, 2599, 2600, 2766, 2919, 2920, 3003, 3045, 3098, 3136, 3227, 3228, 3314, 3332, 3333, 3376, 3377, 3378, 3485, 3486, 3487, 3488, 3489, 3765, 3818, 3819, 3820, 4019, 4179, 4180, 4181, 4182, 4424, 4425, 4743, 5142
Harvard Law School – 4612
Hawaii Hotel and Lodging Association – 1085, 1086, 1087
Health Resources and Services Administration - Bureau of Health Professions – 3229, 3490
Hellenic News of America – 1088
Hellenic University Club of Philadelphia – 1089, 1090, 1091, 1092, 1093, 2552, 2601, 5143
Hemophilia Federation of America – 3230
The Herb Society of America – 3137, 3138, 3139, 3140, 3141
Hillel Montreal – 1094, 1095, 1096, 2673, 3231, 3379, 4183
Hispanic Association of Colleges and Universities – 1097, 1098, 1099, 1100, 2674, 3821, 3822, 4644, 4744, 5144
Hispanic Association on Corporate Responsibility – 1101, 1102
Hispanic Faculty Staff Association – 1103
Hispanic Lawyers Association of Illinois – 4426, 4427, 4428
Hispanic National Bar Association – 1104, 3823, 4429, 4430, 4431, 4432, 5145
Hispanic Scholarship Fund – 1105, 1106, 1107, 1108, 1109, 1110, 1111, 1112, 1113, 2503, 2553, 2602, 2675, 2676, 2767, 2921, 3668, 3669, 3675, 3766, 3824, 3825, 3826, 3827, 3828, 3829, 3830, 3831, 3832, 4020, 4021, 4184, 4185, 4433, 4645,

4646, 4891, 4939, 4940, 4941, 4942, 4943, 5146, 5147, 5148, 5149, 5150, 5151, 5152, 5153
Holocaust and Human Rights Center of Maine – 1114
Herbert Hoover Presidential Library Association – 1115
Hormel Foods Corporation – 1116
Hospitality Association of South Carolina – 1117, 1118, 1119
Human Race Theatre Company – 2677
Human Resources Research Management – 3601
Hungarian American Coalition – 1121
Huntington's Disease Society of America – 3232
Hydrocephalus Association – 1122, 1123, 1124, 1125, 1126, 1127
Ice Skating Institute of America – 1128
Idaho Community Foundation – 1129, 1130, 1131, 1132, 2768, 3491, 4892
Idaho Nursery and Landscape Association – 3142
Illinois Landscape Contractors Association – 3143
Illinois Society of Professional Engineers – 5154, 5155
Illinois Student Assistance Commission – 1133, 1134, 3233, 3234, 3492, 3493, 4186, 4187, 4188
Imagine America Foundation – 1135, 4189, 4190, 4191, 4192
Immune Deficiency Foundation – 3235
Independent Lubricant Manufacturers Association – 1136
Independent Order of Foresters – 1137
Independent Professional Seed Association – 3004, 3005
Indiana Broadcasters Association – 4022, 4023
Indiana Library Federation – 1138, 1139, 1140
Indiana State Alumni Association – 1141, 1142, 1143, 1144, 1145, 1146, 1147, 1148, 1149, 1150, 1151, 1152, 1153, 2678, 2679, 2680, 2769, 2922, 4193, 4194, 4893
Indigenous Bar Association – 4434
Industrial Supply Association – 5402
Information Technology Industry Alliance of Nova Scotia – 4944
Institute of Food Technologists – 5329, 5330
Institute of Industrial Engineers – 5156, 5157, 5158, 5159, 5160, 5161, 5162, 5163, 5164, 5165
Institute of Management Accountants – 1154, 1155
Institute of Real Estate Management – 1156
Institute of Turkish Studies – 1157
Insurance Scholarship Foundation of America – 1158, 1159
Intellectual Property Owners Association – 4435
Inter American Press Association – 2770
Intermediaries and Reinsurance Underwriters Association – 1160
International Alumni Association of Shri Mahavir Jain Vidyalaya – 1161
International Association of Administrative Professionals – 3833
International Association of Arson Investigators – 5320
International Association of Black Actuaries – 1162
International Association for Dental Research – 3334
International Association of Emergency Managers – 1163
International Association of Law Enforcement Intelligence Analysts – 4436, 4894
International Association of Lighting Designers – 2603, 4745
International Association of Workforce Professionals – 1164
International Beverage Packing Association – 4746
International Brotherhood of Electrical Workers – 1165
International Center for Not-for-Profit Law – 4437, 4438
International Code Council Foundation – 1166, 1167, 3006, 3007, 3008
International Dairy-Deli-Bakery Association – 3834, 5331
International Door Association – 1168
International Executive House Keepers Association – 1169, 1170
International Flight Services Association – 1171, 1172, 5332, 5333

International Foodservice Editorial Council – 2681, 2771, 3550, 4024, 4647, 5334, 5388
International Franchise Association – 1173, 4439
International Furnishings and Design Association – 2604, 2682, 2683
International Grenfell Association – 1174, 1175, 1176
International Harvester Collectors – 1177
International Horn Society – 2923
International Military Community Executives Association – 1178, 1179
International Radio and Television Society Foundation – 1180
International Safety Equipment Association – 1181
International Society of Air Safety Investigators – 4846
International Society of Air Safety Investigators – 4846
International Technology Education Association – 4747
International Transportation Management Association – 1182
International Union of Bricklayers and Allied Craftworkers – 1183, 1184
Iowa Court Reporters Association – 4025
Iowa Newspaper Association – 2772, 2773, 2774, 4026
Iranian American Bar Association – 4440
ISA (Instrumentation, Systems, and Automation) – 5166, 5167, 5168, 5169, 5170, 5171, 5172, 5173, 5174, 5175, 5176, 5177, 5178, 5179, 5180, 5181, 5182, 5183, 5184, 5185, 5186, 5187, 5188, 5189, 5190
Island Resources Foundation – 2504
Italian American Lawyers Association – 4441
Jack and Jill of America Foundation – 1185
Jackson County Community Foundation – 1186, 1187, 1188, 1189, 1190, 1191, 1192, 1193, 1194, 1195, 1196, 3236, 3237, 3494, 3723, 4195, 4196, 4197, 5191, 5192, 5193
Jamaican Canadian Association – 1197, 1198, 1199, 1200, 1201, 1202, 1203, 1204, 1205, 1206, 1207, 2684, 3238, 3495, 3835, 3836, 4442, 4748, 4945
Japan Foundation, New York – 2482
Japanese American Bar Association – 4443
Japanese American Citizens League – 2554, 2775, 3009, 3010, 4444, 4648
Jewish Foundation for Education of Women – 1208, 3315, 3335, 3380, 3496, 3584
Jewish Guild for the Blind – 1209
Jewish Vocational Service – 2555, 3381, 4198, 4445, 4649, 4680, 4693
Jewish War Veterans of the United States of America – 1210
Journalism Education Association – 2776
Journyx – 1211
Junior Achievement – 1212, 1213, 2685, 3837, 4199, 4749
Kappa Kappa Gamma – 1214
Kappa Omicron Nu – 1215
Kappa Omicron Nu Honor Society – 1216
Kegler, Brown, Hill and Ritter – 4446
Kellogg Community College Foundation – 1217, 1218, 1219, 1220, 1221
Kentucky Fried Chicken Foundation – 1222
Kentucky Paralegal Association – 4447
Alden Kindred of America – 1223
Susan G. Komen Breast Cancer Foundation – 1224
Korean American Scholarship Foundation – 1225, 1226, 1227
Kosciuszko Foundation – 2475, 2476, 2477, 2478, 2479, 2480
The Lagrant Foundation – 3838, 4650
Lakselaget – 3057, 4895
Lam Research Corporation – 1228, 1229, 5194, 5195
Lambda Iota Tau – 1230
Landscape Architecture Foundation – 2605, 2606, 2607, 2608, 2609, 2610, 2611, 2612, 2613, 2614, 3144
Lane Powell PC – 4448
Lanier Technical College – 1231, 1232, 1233, 1234, 1235
Lapper County Community Foundation – 1236, 1237, 1238, 3239, 4589
Latin American Educational Foundation – 2486
Law Foundation of British Columbia – 4449
Law Society of Prince Edward Island – 4450

American Osteopathic Foundation – 3563, 3564, 3565, 3566, 3567

American Paint Horse Foundation – 178

American Pet Products Manufacturers Association – 179

American Physical Society – 3678

American Planning Association – 4692

American Polygraph Association – 180

American Psychiatric Association Alliance – 181

American Psychiatric Publishing Inc. – 3596

American Psychological Association of Graduate Students – 3597

American Public Power Association – 182

American Public Works Association – 4988

American Public Works Association-Nevada – 4634, 4989

American Quarter Horse Youth Association – 2728, 3406, 4116

American Radio Relay League (ARRL) Foundation – 2729, 3350, 3407, 3780, 3943, 3944, 3945, 3946, 3947, 3948, 3949, 3950, 3951, 3952, 3953, 3954, 3955, 3956, 3957, 3958, 3959, 3960, 3961, 3962, 3963, 3964, 3965, 3966, 3967, 3968, 3969, 3970, 3971, 3972, 3973, 3974, 3975, 3976, 3977, 3978, 3979, 3980, 3981, 3982, 3983, 3984, 3985, 3986, 3987, 3988, 3989, 3990, 3991, 4698, 4699, 4700, 4701, 4702, 4703, 4704, 4705, 4706, 4923, 4924, 4925, 4990, 4991, 4992, 4993, 4994, 4995

American Railway Engineering and Maintenance-of-Way Association – 4996, 4997, 4998, 4999, 5000, 5001, 5002, 5003, 5004, 5005, 5006, 5007, 5008, 5009, 5010, 5011, 5012, 5013, 5014, 5015

American Red Cross – 3408

American Rental Association Foundation – 5398, 5399, 5400

American Research Institute in Turkey – 183, 2542, 3781, 5016

American Risk and Insurance Association – 184

American Road and Transportation Builders Association – 185

American Romanian Orthodox Youth – 186, 187, 188, 189

American School Health Association – 3324, 3325, 3351, 3352, 3409, 3410, 3547, 3548, 3573, 3574, 3759, 3760, 4117, 4118

American Small Businesses Association – 190

American Society of Brewing Chemists – 191

American Society of Certified Engineering Technicians – 5017, 5018, 5019

American Society for Clinical Laboratory Science – 3189, 3190

American Society of Composers, Authors and Publishers (ASCAP) Foundation – 2636, 2882, 2883, 2884, 2885, 2886, 2887, 2888, 2889, 2890

American Society of Echocardiography – 3191

American Society for Engineering Education – 5020

American Society for Enology and Viticulture – 192

American Society of Heating, Refrigerating and Air-Conditioning Engineers – 5021, 5022, 5023, 5024, 5025, 5026, 5027, 5028, 5029

American Society for Horticultural Science – 3124, 3125, 3126

American Society of Landscape Architects – 2583, 2584, 2585, 2586, 2587, 2588, 2589, 2590, 2591, 3127

American Society for Legal History – 2448

American Society of Mechanical Engineers – 5030, 5031

American Society for Microbiology – 193, 3049, 4119

American Society of Military Comptrollers – 3782, 4635

American Society of Mining and Reclamation – 5357

American Society of Naval Engineers – 5381

American Society for Nondestructive Testing – 4707

American Society for Photogrammetry and Remote Sensing – 3613, 5384, 5385, 5386

American Society of Podiatric Medical Assistants – 3192

American Society for Quality - Statistic Division – 4869

American Society of Radiologic Technologists – 3193, 3194

American Society of Safety Engineers – 194, 195,

196, 197, 198, 199, 200, 201, 202, 203, 204, 205, 206, 207, 208, 209, 210, 211, 212, 213, 214, 215, 216, 217, 218, 219, 220

American Society of Travel Agents – 221, 222, 223, 224, 225, 226, 227, 228, 229, 230, 231

American Society of Women Accountants – 232, 233

American Sokol – 3614, 4120

American Statistical Association – 4870

American Swedish Institute – 2459, 2460, 2461

American University - School of Public Affairs – 3717, 4636

American Veterans – 234, 235, 236, 237

American Water Resources Association – 238

American Water Ski Educational Foundation – 239

American Welding Society – 4708, 4709, 4710, 4711, 4712, 4713, 4714, 4715, 4716, 4717, 4718, 4719, 4720, 4721, 4722, 4723, 4724, 4725, 4726, 4727, 4728, 4729, 4730, 5032

Americans for Informed Democracy – 240

Anaheim Police Association – 241

Wilbur H. Anderson Memorial Scholarship Foundation, Inc. – 242

Appalachian School of Law – 4342

Appraisal Institute Education Trust – 2494

Arab American Institute – 2730, 2731, 2967, 4602

Archaeological Institute of America – 2578

Architectural Precast Association – 2592

Arent Fox LLP – 4343

Arizona Airport Association – 4834

Arizona Association of Student Financial Aid Administrators – 243, 244, 245, 246

Arizona Christian School Tuition Organization – 247

Arizona Nursery Association – 3128

Arizona Nurses Association – 3411

Arizona Parks and Recreation Association – 248

Arkansas Environmental Federation – 2495, 2496, 2973, 4121, 5033

Arkansas Public Health Association – 2497, 4637

Armed Forces Communications and Electronics Association – 3679, 3680, 3681, 3682, 3683, 3684, 3685, 3686, 3687, 3992, 3993, 3994, 3995, 3996, 3997, 3998, 3999, 4000, 4871, 4872, 4873, 4874, 4875, 4876, 4877, 4878, 4879, 4926, 5034, 5035, 5036, 5037, 5038, 5039, 5040, 5041, 5042, 5043

Armenian Educational Foundation – 249

Armenian Relief Society - Eastern United States – 2732, 3353, 3783, 4295, 4344, 4603, 4638

Armenian Scholarship Foundation – 250, 251, 252

Armenian Students' Association of America – 253, 254, 255, 256, 257, 258, 259, 260, 261, 262, 263, 264, 265, 266, 267, 268, 269, 270, 271, 272, 2453, 2454, 2455, 2472, 2733, 2891, 2968, 3354, 3598, 4122, 4123, 4604

Army Aviation Association of America – 273

Army Nurse Corps Association – 3412

Army Scholarship Foundation – 274, 275, 276, 277

Aaron Arnoldsen Memorial Scholarship Fund – 278

Art Institute of Colorado – 2637, 2638, 2639, 2640, 2641, 2642, 2643, 2644, 2645

ASCE San Diego Section – 5044, 5045

Ashburn Institute – 4313

Asian American Bar Association – 4345, 4346

Asian American Journalists Association – 2734, 2735, 2736, 4001, 4002

Asian American Lawyers Association of Massachusetts – 4347

Asian/Pacific Bar Association of Sacramento – 4348

Asian and Pacific Islander American Scholarship Fund – 279

ASIS International – 280

Associated Locksmiths of America – 4124

Association for the Advancement of Cost Engineering – 5046

Association of American Geographers – 281, 282, 283

Association on American Indian Affairs – 2449, 4639

Association of American Indian Physicians – 4125

Association of American Medical Colleges – 3195

Association for Applied and Therapeutic Humor – 2543, 2544

Association of Black Women Physicians – 3355

Association of California Water Agencies – 284, 285

Association of College Unions International – 286

Association of College and University Auditors – 287

Association for Compensatory Educators of Texas – 288, 289

Association of Desk and Derrick Clubs – 3664, 3674, 5047

Association for Education and Rehabilitation of the Blind and Visually Impaired – 290

Association of Electronic Journalists – 2737, 2738, 2739, 2740, 2741, 2742, 2743, 2744, 2745, 2746, 2747, 2748

Association of Energy Engineers Foundation – 291

Association of Environmental and Engineering Geologists – 5048, 5049

Association of Family Practice Physician Assistants – 3356

Association for Federal Information Resources Management – 4731, 4732

Association for Financial Technology – 292

Association of Flight Attendants – 4835

Association of Food and Drug Officials – 293, 294

Association of Former Intelligence Officers – 295, 296

Association General Contractors of America, New York State Chapter – 5050

Association of Independent Colleges and Universities of Pennsylvania – 297, 2593, 2594, 3413, 4927, 5051, 5052, 5053

Association for International Training – 298, 3784

Association for Iron and Steel Technology – 299, 300, 301, 3615, 5054, 5055, 5056, 5057, 5058, 5059, 5060, 5061, 5062, 5063, 5064, 5065, 5066, 5067, 5068, 5069, 5358, 5359, 5360, 5361, 5362, 5363, 5364, 5365, 5366

Association of Jewish Libraries – 302

Association of Occupational Health Professionals in Healthcare – 303

Association of PeriOperative Registered Nurses – 3414

Association for Psychological Science – 3599

Association of Rehabilitation Nurses – 3415, 3416

Association of School Business Officials of Maryland and the District of Columbia – 304

Association of Seventh-Day Adventist Librarians – 305, 3785

Association of State Dam Safety Officials – 5070

Association of Universities and Colleges of Canada – 306

Association for Women in Architecture – 2595

Association for Women Geoscientists – 3616, 3617, 3618, 3619, 3620

Association for Women in Science – 3050, 3600, 3650, 3688, 4880, 4928, 5071

Association for Women in Sports Media – 2545

Association of Zoo Veterinary Technicians (AZVT) – 3196

Astronaut Scholarship Foundation – 5072

Athletic Equipment Managers Association – 307

Atlantic Provinces Library Association – 308

Audio Engineering Society – 5073

Autism Society of America – 3197

Automotive Aftermarket Industry Association – 5074, 5075, 5076, 5077

Automotive Hall of Fame – 3786, 5078, 5079, 5080, 5081, 5082, 5083, 5084, 5085, 5086, 5087, 5088, 5089, 5090, 5091, 5092, 5093, 5094, 5095, 5096

Automotive Industries Association of Canada – 5097

Automotive Recyclers Association – 3787, 4126

Automotive Women's Alliance Foundation – 5098

The Bailey Family Foundation – 4127, 4349

Howard Baker Foundation – 3417

Baltimore City College – 309, 310

Banner & Witcoff, Ltd. – 4350

Bar Association of San Francisco – 4351

Barrientos Scholarship Foundation – 311, 2646, 2865, 2892

Bat Conservation International – 2521

John Bayliss Broadcast Foundation – 4003, 4004

BDPA Education Technology Foundation – 4733

Beacon of Hope Scholarship Foundation – 312

BECA Foundation – 313, 314, 3198

Alexander Graham Bell Association for the Deaf and Hard of Hearing – 3199, 3200

March and Ruti Bell Foundation – 4640

Ben Meadows – 2529, 2530, 3094, 3095

North American Interfraternal Foundation – 1550, 1551

North Carolina American Water Works Association – 2510, 2511

North Carolina Association of Health Care Recruiters – 3258

North Carolina Commercial Flower Growers Association – 3148

North Carolina Nursery and Landscape Association – 2618, 3149

North Carolina Simmental Association – 3024

North Carolina Vending Association – 3863

North Dakota Farmers Union – 1552, 1553, 1554, 1555, 1556, 1557, 3025

North Dakota Veterinary Medical Association – 3259, 3260, 3261

Northampton County Medical Society Alliance – 3513, 3702

Northern Arizona Native-American Foundation – 1558

Northern Indiana Community Foundation – 4472

Northwest Michigan Home Builders Association – 1559

Northwest-Shoals Community College – 1560, 1561, 1562, 1563, 1564, 1565, 1566, 1567, 1568, 1569, 1570, 1571, 1572, 1573, 1574, 1575, 1576, 1577, 1578, 1579, 1580, 1581, 1582, 1583, 1584, 1585, 1586, 2558, 2559, 2931, 4221

Occupational Physicians Scholarship Fund – 1587

Office Products Wholesaler Association – 1588

Ohio Association of Broadcasters – 4038, 4039

Ohio Farm Bureau Federation – 3026

Ohio Newspaper Association – 2790, 2791, 2792, 2793

Oklahoma Association for the Improvement of Developmental Education – 1589

Oklahoma City University School of Law – 4473, 4474, 4475

Olympia Tumwater Foundation – 1590, 1591

Omaha Education Association – 1592

Ontario Trucking Association – 1593, 1594, 1595, 1596, 3864

Operation Homefront – 4222

Orange County Association of Educational Office Professionals – 1597

Orange County Community Foundation – 1598, 1599, 1600, 1601, 1602, 1603, 1604, 1605, 1606, 1607, 1608, 1609, 1610, 2694, 2794, 2869, 2932, 4223

Order Sons of Italy in America – 1611, 1612, 1613

Oregon Association of Broadcasters – 4040

Oregon Association of Nurseries – 3150, 3151, 3152, 3153, 3154, 3155, 3156, 3157, 3158, 3159, 3160, 3161

Oregon Farm Bureau – 3027, 3028, 3029, 3030, 3031

Oregon Medical Association – 3386

Organization of American States – 1614, 1615, 1616, 1617, 2471, 2560

Organization of Chinese Americans – 1618

Orphan Foundation of America – 3262

Ottawa Centre for Research and Innovation – 1619, 1620, 1621, 1622, 1623, 1624, 1625, 1626

Outdoor Power Equipment Aftermarket Association – 1627

Outdoor Writers Association of America – 2795

Outward Bound – 1628, 1629

Owner-Operator Independent Drivers Association – 1630

Pacific Legal Foundation – 4476

Painting and Decorating Contractors of America – 4224

Palos Fine Arts Association – 2695

Paper Stock Industries – 1631

Paper Stock Industries Chapter of ISRI – 1632

Parapsychology Foundation – 3604, 3605

Park Law Enforcement Association – 4592

Parkersburg Area Community Foundation – 1633, 1634, 1635, 1636, 1637, 1638, 1639, 1640, 1641, 1642, 1643, 1644, 1645, 1646, 1647, 1648, 1649, 1650, 1651, 1652, 1653, 1654, 1655, 1656, 1657, 1658, 1659, 1660, 1661, 1662, 1663, 1664, 1665, 1666, 1667, 1668, 1669, 1670, 1671, 1672, 1673, 1674, 1675, 1676, 2796, 2797, 2933, 2934, 2935, 3032, 3033, 3263, 3264, 3265, 3266, 3316, 3514,

3515, 3865, 3866, 3867, 4041, 4042, 4225, 4226, 4227, 4228, 4229, 4230, 4231, 4232, 4304, 4477, 4478, 4952

Patient Advocate Foundation – 3267

PBR Forces Veterans Association – 2485

Pediatric Endocrinology Nursing Society – 3516, 3517

Pedorthic Footwear Association – 3268, 3269, 3270, 3271, 3272, 3273, 3274, 4754, 4755, 4756, 4757, 4758, 4759, 4760

Penndelphia Scholarship Foundation – 1677

Pennsylvania Association of Arson Investigators – 5324

Pennsylvania Land Surveyors Foundation – 1678

Pennsylvania Library Association – 1679

Pennsylvania Society of Professional Engineers – 5224

Pennsylvania State System of Higher Education Foundation – 1680, 1681, 3868, 4902, 5225

Pension Real Estate Association – 1682

People To People International – 1683

Pepperdine University School of Law – 3606, 3869, 4233, 4479, 4480, 4481, 4482, 4483, 4484, 4485, 4486, 4487, 4488, 4489, 4490, 4491, 4492, 4493, 4494, 4495, 4496, 4497, 4498, 4499, 4500, 4501, 4502, 4503, 4504, 4505, 4506, 4507, 4508, 4509, 4510, 4511, 4512, 4513, 4514, 4515, 4516, 4517, 4518, 4519, 4520, 4521

Petroleum Packaging Council – 4761

Phi Chi Theta – 3870, 3871

Phi Kappa Phi – 1684

Phi Kappa Sigma – 1685, 1686

Phi Sigma Epsilon – 3872, 3873, 3874, 3875, 3876, 3877, 3878, 3879, 3880, 3881, 3882, 3883, 3884, 3885, 3886, 3887, 3888, 3889, 3890, 3891

Phi Sigma Pi National Honor Fraternity – 1687

Phi Upsilon Omicron – 2696, 2697, 3553, 3554, 3727, 3728, 3729, 3730, 3731, 3732, 3733, 3734, 3735, 3736, 3737, 3738, 3739, 3740, 3741, 4762, 4763

Philanthropic Educational Organization – 1688, 1689

The Phillips Foundation – 1690

PHS Commissioned Officers Foundation – 1691

Pierce College District 11 – 1692, 1693, 4234

Pinnacle West Capital Corporation – 3275, 3518, 3892, 3893, 4043, 4235, 4236, 5226, 5227

Plumbing-Heating-Cooling Contractors Association – 3894, 3895, 3896, 3897, 3898, 3899, 3900

Plus Foundation – 1694, 1695

PMCA: An International Association of Confectioners – 3087, 3655, 5342

Point Foundation – 1696, 1697, 1698, 1699, 1700, 1701, 1702, 1703, 1704, 1705, 1706, 1707, 1708, 2698

Polish American Engineers Association – 5228

Polish Falcons of America – 1709, 1710, 2481

Portable Sanitation Association International – 4764

Portuguese American Leadership Council of the United States – 1711, 1712

Portuguese American Police Association – 3276, 4593, 4688

Practising Law Institute – 4522

Prescott Fine Arts Association – 2561

Pride Foundation – 1713, 1714, 1715, 1716, 1717, 1718, 1719, 1720, 1721, 1722, 1723, 1724, 1725, 1726, 1727, 1728, 1729, 1730, 1731, 2699, 2700, 2701, 2870, 2871, 2872, 2873, 2936, 2937, 3277, 3278, 3279, 3742, 3743, 3744, 4237, 4238, 4523, 4621, 4622, 4660, 4689, 4903, 4953

Professional Aviation Maintenance Association – 4859

Professional Construction Estimators Association of America – 5229

Professional Institute of the Public Service of Canada – 1732

Public Agency Risk Managers Association – 1733

Public Education Foundation – 1734, 1735, 1736, 1737, 1738, 1739, 1740, 1741, 1742, 1743, 1744, 1745, 1746, 1747, 1748, 1749, 1750, 1751, 1752, 1753, 1754, 1755, 1756, 1757, 1758, 1759, 1760, 1761, 1762, 1763, 1764, 1765, 1766, 1767, 1768, 1769, 1770, 1771, 1772, 1773, 2512, 2562, 2619, 2620, 2702, 2798, 2799, 3280, 3281, 3745, 3901, 3902, 3903, 3904, 3905, 3906, 4044, 4045, 4239,

4240, 4241, 4242, 4243, 4244, 4245, 4246, 4247, 4248, 4661, 4662, 4904, 4905, 4954, 5230, 5231, 5232, 5233, 5394, 5395

Public Relations Society of America – 2800, 4046, 4663, 4664, 4665

Puerto Rican Legal Defense and Education Fund – 4524

Quality Function Deployment (QFD) Institute – 4249

Quarter Century Wireless Association – 4047

Quill and Scroll Society – 2801

Railway Tie Association – 1774

Jeannette Rankin Foundation – 1775

Raytheon Company – 1776

Reach Out for Youth with Ileitis and Colitis – 3282

Redlands Community Scholarship Foundation – 1777, 1778, 1779, 1780, 1781, 1782, 1783, 1784, 1785, 1786, 1787, 1788, 1789, 1790, 1791, 1792, 1793, 1794, 1795, 1796, 1797, 1798, 1799, 1800, 1801, 1802, 1803, 1804, 1805, 1806, 1807, 1808, 1809, 1810, 1811, 1812, 1813, 1814, 1815, 1816, 1817, 1818, 1819, 1820, 1821, 1822, 1823, 1824, 1825, 1826, 1827, 1828, 1829, 1830, 1831, 1832, 1833, 1834, 1835, 1836, 1837, 1838, 1839, 1840, 1841, 1842, 1843, 1844, 1845, 1846, 1847, 1848, 1849, 1850, 1851, 1852, 1853, 1854, 1855, 1856, 1857, 1858, 1859, 1860, 1861, 1862, 1863, 1864, 1865, 1866, 1867, 1868, 1869, 1870, 1871, 2621, 2703, 2938, 2939, 2986, 3088, 3283, 3519, 3637, 3907, 3908, 3909, 4250, 4251, 4252, 4253, 4305, 4525, 4526, 4594, 4623, 4955, 5234, 5235

Registry of Interpreters for the Deaf – 3284, 3285

Reserve Officers Association of the United States – 1872, 1873, 1874

Retail Packaging Association – 1875

Retired League Postmasters of the National League of Postmasters – 1876

Rhode Island Foundation – 1877, 1878, 1879, 1880, 1881, 1882, 2563, 2874, 2940, 2941, 4527, 5376

Roanoke Bar Association – 4528, 4529

Jackie Robinson Foundation – 1883

Rocky Mountain Coal Mining Institute – 4254, 5236

Rocky Mountain Mineral Law Foundation – 4530

Roofing Industry Alliance for Progress – 1884

Roothbert Fund – 1885

The Rotary Foundation – 1886

Rowan Business Alliance – 1887

Royal Bank of Canada – 1888, 2875, 3338, 3910

Royal Canadian Golf Association – 1889, 1890, 1891, 1892, 1893, 1894, 3746

Rubber Division American Chemical Society – 3656, 3703, 5237

Rural Telephone Company – 1895

Russian Brotherhood Organization of the USA – 1896

SACHS Foundation – 1897

Safe Schools Coalition – 1898, 1899, 1900, 1901, 1902, 1903, 1904, 1905, 1906, 1907, 1908, 1909, 1910, 1911, 1912, 1913, 1914, 1915, 1916, 1917, 1918, 1919, 1920, 1921, 1922, 1923, 1924, 1925, 1926, 1927, 1928, 1929, 1930, 1931, 1932, 1933, 1934, 1935, 1936, 1937, 1938, 1939, 1940, 1941, 1942, 1943, 1944, 1945, 2802, 2803, 2876, 3286, 4048, 4255, 4531, 4532, 4624, 4690, 4956

Saint Andrew's Society of the State of New York – 1946

Saint Paul University Canada – 1947, 1948

Sallie Mae Fund – 1949, 1950, 1951, 1952, 1953

The San Diego Foundation – 1954, 1955, 1956, 1957, 1958, 1959, 1960, 1961, 1962, 1963, 1964, 1965, 1966, 1967, 1968, 1969, 1970, 1971, 1972, 1973, 1974, 1975, 1976, 1977, 1978, 1979, 1980, 1981, 1982, 1983, 1984, 1985, 1986, 1987, 1988, 1989, 1990, 1991, 1992, 1993, 1994, 1995, 1996, 1997, 1998, 1999, 2000, 2001, 2002, 2003, 2004, 2005, 2006, 2007, 2008, 2009, 2010, 2011, 2012, 2013, 2014, 2564, 2565, 2566, 2622, 2704, 2804, 2942, 3089, 3090, 3287, 3288, 3387, 3520, 3555, 3657, 3658, 3704, 3911, 4049, 4256, 4317, 4595, 4625, 4860, 4906, 4907, 4908, 4957, 4958, 5238, 5239, 5240, 5241, 5242, 5243, 5244, 5343, 5350

Santa Barbara Dance Alliance – 2943

Bert Saperstein Communications Scholarship Fund – 4050

Saskatchewan Trucking Association – 2015

Scholarship Foundation of Santa Barbara – 2016, 2567

Sponsoring Organization Index

Banner Bank Business Scholarships – 3840

Donald W. Banner Corporate Intern Scholarships – 4435

Donald W. Banner Diversity Scholarship for Law Students – 4350

Banner Health System - McKee Medical Center, Loveland: Nightingale Scholarships – 3436

Banner Health System - North Colorado Medical Center, Greeley: Nightingale Scholarships – 3437

Bernice Barabash Sports Scholarship – 3723

Joe Barbarow Memorial Scholarships – 1635

Lewis B. Barber Memorial Scholarships – 2105

Barbri Scholarships for Bar Preparation – 4426

Jack R. Barckhoff Welding Management Scholarships – 4714

Janice K. Barden Aviation Scholarships – 4848

Gina L. Barnhart Memorial Scholarship Fund – 4156

Robbie Baron Memorial Scholarships – 920

Zachary Barriger Memorial Scholarships – 4932, 5106

Laura Beckley Barsotti Memorial Scholarships – 1124

Leon and Talin Barsoumian Scholarships – 251

Barta-Lehman Musical Scholarships – 2942

Avery Bayle Barth Scholarships – 4149

William E. Barto Scholarships – 2866

Elsa Barton Educational Scholarships Fund – 181

Walt Bartram Memorial Education Awards (Region 12 and Chapter 119) – 4765

Bascom Hill Society Scholarships – 2325

Basic Midwifery Student Scholarship Program – 3404

Diane Basilone-Engle Memorial Scholarships – 2649, 3206, 4132, 4881

Helen Bassett Commemorative Scholarships – 4469

Charles A. Bassett Endowed Memorial Scholarship Fund – 962

Bat Conservation International Student Research Scholarships – 2521

William H. Bates Oxford Cup Scholarships – 322

Jim Batten Community Newspaper Internships – 2825, 4068

Lewis and Gurry Batten Scholarships – 1636

Hazel Reed Baumeister Scholarship Program – 2063

Jeannette Bautista Memorial Scholarships – 4239

Bob Baxter Scholarships – 5389

Bay Area Minority Law Student Scholarships – 4351

Lawrence Bayer Business Administration Scholarships – 1305

Timothy Baylink Good Fellowship Awards – 1785

John Bayliss Broadcast Foundation Internship Programs – 4003

Bayly-Tiffany Scholarships – 2317

BBM Canada Scholarships – 4008

BCA Ethnic Minority Postgraduate Scholarships for Careers in Athletics – 3718

BCCC Foundation Scholarships – 309

BCCC Foundation Workforce Scholarships – 310

BCEN Undergraduate Scholarships – 3466

Beacon of Hope Scholarships – 312

James Beard Foundation/Art Institute of Colorado Scholarships – 2639

Beau Gunn Redlands Baseball For Youth Scholarships – 1786

Suzanne Beauregard Scholarships – 1889

Sally Beauty Scholarships for High School Graduates – 1428

Beaver Medical Clinic-Glen Adams Scholarship Awards – 1787

Beaver Medical Clinic-H.E.A.R.T. Scholarship Awards – 1788

Beaver Medical Clinic-Premed Scholarship Awards – 1789

Don C. Beaver Memorial Scholarship – 408

BECA Foundation-CUSM Scholarships – 313

BECA Foundation General Scholarships Fund – 314

Bechtel Group Foundation Scholarship for Safety & Health – 197

Stephen D. Bechtel Oxford Cup Scholarships – 323

Stan Beck Fellowships – 3052

O.J. Beck, Jr. Memorial Scholarships – 588

Dennis J. Beck Memorial Scholarship – 1186

Beck-Pfann Memorial Scholarships – 4480

Garvin L. Beck Scholarships – 1790

Dr. Joyce Beckett Scholarships – 4684

Beecroft Family Scholarships – 589

Beef Industry Scholarships – 3016

Raymond and Donald Beeler Memorial Scholarships – 1791

Notah Begay III Scholarship Program – 58

Beginning Freshmen Awards – 5216

Behavioral Sciences Student Fellowships – 3397, 3764

Charles E. Behlke Engineering Memorial Scholarships – 5210

Norbert J. Beihoff Scholarships – 2899

Beinecke Brothers Memorial Scholarships – 2572, 3752

N.S. Beinstock Fellowships – 2738

March and Ruti Bell Foundation Scholarships – 4640

John Bell and Lawrence Thornton Scholarship Fund – 1034

Ray and Mary Bell Memorial Scholarships – 1960

Bellevue PFLAG Scholarships – 1715

Belmont University Commercial Music Scholarships – 2905

David Beltran Memorial Scholarships – 2703

Benchwarmers of Redlands-Jess Mercado Football Scholarships – 1792

Richard W. Bendicksen Memorial Scholarships – 3948

Bill Bendiner and Doug Morgenson Scholarships – 2870, 3277, 3743

Dr. Francis Anthony Beneventi Medical Scholarships – 1035

Louise Bennett-Coverley Scholarships – 375

Bertram W. Bennett Memorial Scholarships – 324

Reverend E.F. Bennett Scholarships – 590

Casey Bennett Scholarships – 3624

William Bennett W7PHO Memorial Scholarships – 3949

Pete and Ellen Bensley Memorial Scholarship Fund – 2759, 4015

Marcy and Bruce Benson: Nightingale Scholarships – 3438

Elizabeth Benson Scholarship Awards – 3284

George Oliver Benton Memorial Scholarships – 4606

Linn Benton Scholarships – 3386

Charlotte V. Bergen Scholarships – 2883

Bergman Scholarships – 1552

Richard L. Bernardi Memorial Scholarship – 700

Peggy Bernheim Memorial Scholarships – 4356

Donald H. Bernstein/John B. Talbert, Jr. Scholarship Fund – 891

The Bernsten International Scholarships in Surveying Technology – 128

James R. and Geraldine F. Bertelsen Scholarships – 1961

Beta Gamma Memorial Scholarship Fund – 769

Beta Nu/Caryl Cordis D'hondt Scholarships – 2030

Beta Omega Scholarships – 2031

Beta Sigma Phi-VCT Scholarships – 2705

Beta Sigma Scholarships – 2032

Bethune-Cookman University Excelsior Scholarships – 366

Bethune-Cookman University Presidential Scholarships – 367

Betsy Plank/PRSSA Scholarships – 4663

Harold Bettinger Scholarships – 3104

Leonard Bettinger Scholarships – 3105

Beverly Estate Scholarships – 4373

Dr. Noorali & Sabiya Bharwani Endowment – 3420

Hussein Jina Bharwani Memorial Endowment – 3421

BIA Higher Education Grants – 243

J.P. Bickell Mining Scholarships – 2518, 2989, 3673, 3676, 5380

BIGALA (Bisexual Gay and Lesbian Alliance) Scholarships – 1903

Bill & Nell Biggs Scholarships – 4900, 5211

Frank and Ruth Bila Scholarships – 1598

James Bilder Scholarships – 2106

Biocom Scholarships – 3089, 3657, 5240

BioQuip Scholarships – 3053

BioRx/Hemophilia of North Carolina Educational Scholarships – 1493

Birks Family Foundation Scholarships – 3424

Birmingham-Southern College Eagle Scout Scholarships – 1437

Birmingham Student Scholarship Fund Association – 371

BISA's Scholarship Assistance Program – 391

BISA's Scholarships Assistance Program – 392

Bishop State Community College Scholarships – 3165

Bison Transport Scholarships – 3864

Lebbeus F. Bissell Scholarships – 1036

Mary E. Bivins Foundation Religious Scholarship Program – 4130

Norman Blachford Point Scholarships – 1697

Black Canadian Scholarships – 1619

Black Data Processing Associates Scholarships – 4733

Black Student Fund – 373

Black Women Lawyers Association of Los Angeles Scholarships – 4354

Reid Blackburn Scholarships – 5390

William T. Blackwell Scholarship Fund – 1487

Beatrice K. Blair Scholarships – 3317

Joan Blend Scholarship Fund – 3527

Bloch-Selinger Education Fund – 863

F.A. and Charlotte Blount Scholarships – 2387

Blow Molding Division Memorial Scholarships – 5268

Blues Ambassador Scholarships – 1737

Jordan ABDO/Michael Bluett Memorial Scholarships – 2107

Harry and Edith Blunt Scholarships – 122

BMO Financial Group Scholarships – 376

David and Camille Boatwright Endowed Scholarships – 4481

Sandra Bobbitt Continuing Education Scholarships – 303

Boeing Business Scholarships – 3811

Boeing Company Scholarships – 5248

Boeing Engineering Scholarships – 5136

Hagop Bogigian Scholarship Fund – 258

Therese and David Bohbot Scholarship – 1094

Bolick Foreign Student Scholarships – 1306

Dorothy M. Bolyard Memorial Scholarships – 1962

BOMA/NY Scholarships – 403

Carol Bond College Scholarships – 2510

Carol Bond University Scholarships – 2511

Lorne and Ruby Bonnell Scholarships – 725

Barbara Bonnema Memorial Scholarships – 1793

Anne-Marie Bonner Scholarships – 2684

Ellis J. Bonner Scholarships – 3250

Scott Bonners Memorial Scholarships – 455

Sam L. Booke, Sr. Scholarships – 4918

Admiral Mike Boorda Scholarship Program – 1535

T. Frank Booth Memorial Scholarship Fund – 892

Diane Booth Memorial Scholarships – 864

Tom Boots Memorial Scholarships – 1541

David L. Boren Undergraduate Scholarships – 295

Maria Borrero Scholarships – 3227

Geraldine Geistert Boss Scholarships – 987

Tom Bost Scholarships – 2826, 4069

William (Billbo) Boston Scholarships – 4952

Dr. George T. Bottomley Scholarships – 1339

Miranda Bouldin General Scholarships – 1291

Emma L. Bowen Foundation Scholarships for Minority Interests in Media work/study Program – 2361

William R. Bowen Scholarship – 636

Billy Bowling Memorial Scholarships – 1561

Boy Scouts of America General Scholarships – 1037

Boy Scouts of America Troop 3 Scholarships - Art Till/Nathan E. Smith Memorial Scholarships – 1794

Elizabeth W. Boyce Scholarships – 2900

Dr. Betty J. Boyd-Beu & Edwin G. Beu, Jr. Scholarships – 1307

Dody Boyd Scholarships – 667

Verna Curry Boyer Scholarships – 2168

Eugene Boyko Scholarships – 2996

Charles Bradley Memorial Scholarships – 1025

Donald Franklin Bradley Memorial Scholarships – 5394

Ed Bradley Scholarships – 2739

Edward J. Brady Memorial Scholarships – 4715

W. Philip Braender and Nancy Coleman Braender Scholarships – 1038

Ivan Braga Scholarships – 3289

Susan Brager Occupational Education Scholarships – 4240
William E. "Buck" Bragunier Scholarships – 3681, 3994, 4873, 5036
George and Mary Brammer Scholarships – 4374
Marlene Brand Memorial Scholarship – 1095
Breakthrough to Nursing Scholarships – 3479
Ann Marie Bredefeld Scholarships – 4482
Kenneth H. Breeden Scholarships – 1231
Marion Luna Brem/Pat McNeil Teen Parent Scholarships – 591
Lee Brennan Memorial Scholarships – 1599
Breslauer Family Scholarships – 1963
Hilda E. Bretzlaff Foundation Scholarships – 396
Rick Brewer Scholarships – 2827, 4070, 4672
Mary Ann Brichta Scholarships – 4282
James Bridenbaugh Memorial Scholarship – 3106
Phil Brimhall Memorial Scholarships – 1363
Donald J. Bristow Memorial Scholarship Program – 3849
Broadcast News Management Fellowships – 2740
Margaret Martin Brock Scholarships in Law – 4483
Kae and Kay Brockermeyer Endowed Scholarships – 4484
Louise A. Broderick San Diego County Scholarships – 1964
Ross P. Broesamle Educational Scholarships Fund – 1237
John G. Brokaw Scholarships – 1528
Shirley J. Brooke Endowed Scholarships – 4485
George M. Brooker Collegiate Scholarships for Minorities – 1156
Seth R. and Corrine H. Brooks Memorial Scholarships – 325
Carl E. Brooks Scholarships – 2108
Dorothy B. Brothers Executive Scholarship Program – 2419
William A. and Ann M. Brothers Scholarships – 4716
Henry Broughton, K2AE Memorial Scholarships – 3950, 4990
The Allen E. Broussard Scholarships – 4333
Selena Danette Brown Book Scholarships – 4685
Brown and Caldwell Minority Scholarships – 2362
Brown Dental Scholarships – 1197
Diana Brown Endowed Scholarships – 1243
Brown Foundation Academic Scholarships – 4131
Brown Foundation College Scholarship – 4112
Ruby A. Brown Memorial Scholarships – 3465
Quincy Brown Memorial Scholarships – 4250
Jesse Brown Memorial Youth Scholarship Program – 810
JoAhn Brown-Nash Memorial Scholarships – 668
Edward M. Brown Oxford Cup Memorial Scholarships – 326
Ron Brown Scholars Program – 401
James W. Jr.and Jane T. Brown Scholarship Fund – 963
Jack H. Brown Scholarship – 409
Charles S. Brown Scholarships in Physics – 3694
Warren K. Brown Scholarships – 198
Mary Lou Brown Scholarships – 3951
Mary L. Brown Scholarships – 4025
Robert Browning Scholarships – 3278
Chester H. Bruce Memorial Scholarships – 1637
Sheriff W. Bruce Umpleby Law Enforcement Scholarship Fund – 4596
Gregory Brunk Scholarships – 4375
The Robert W. Brunsman Memorial Scholarships – 1178
Bernard and Mary Brusin Scholarships – 813
William and Clara Bryan Scholarships – 669
Joe Q. Bryant American Council on Exercise Educational Scholarships – 3182
Bryce-Lietzke Martin Scholarships – 1638
Patricia Buchanan Memorial Scholarships – 4283
LT.G. Douglas D. Buchholz Memorial Scholarships – 3682, 3995, 4874, 5037
John and Elisabeth Buck Endowed Scholarships – 3060
Buder Scholarship for American Indian Law Students – 4579
Susan Thompson Buffett Foundation Scholarships – 402
Gary L. Buffington Memorial Scholarships – 5402
Tien Bui Memorial Scholarships – 2388

Builders Association of Northeast Indiana (BANI) Scholarships – 2169
Bujea Memorial Scholarships – 188
Sam Bull Memorial Scholarships – 4324, 4600
Armen H. Bululian Scholarships – 259
Charles E. Bunnell Scholarships – 1308
William T. Burbage Family Memorial Scholarship – 637
C. Lalor Burdick Scholarships – 3061
George M. Burditt Scholarships – 293
Adam S. Burford Memorial Scholarships – 327
Freda Burge Scholarships – 1639
Max M. Burger Endowed Scholarships in Embryology – 3062
Dorothy and Dick Burgess Scholarship – 5191
Eleanor McWilliams Burke Fund – 3311, 3364, 3469, 3549, 3582
Loyal D. Burkett Memorial Scholarships – 1309
Cecil E. Burney Scholarships – 2903, 4137, 4296, 4605
Wes Burton Memorial Scholarships – 4919, 4968, 5317
Kathy Bush Memorial Scholarships – 1795
Business and Transactional Law Center Scholarships – 4570
Lindsay Buster Memorial Scholarship – 701
Nellie Love Butcher Scholarships – 2919
Donald C. and Doris K. Byers Scholarships – 4376
Leon C. Bynoe Memorial Scholarships – 2306
Joe Bynum/Raymond James Investment Services Technical Excellence Scholarships Fund – 621
byourself Scholarship Fund – 3462
Robert C. Byrd Honors Scholarships – 1133
Thad Byrne Memorial Scholarships – 328
George J. Bysiewicz Scholarship Fund – 656
Johnston Cabaniss Scholarships – 4323
Cabrillo Clubs of California Scholarships – 1711
Dr. Aurelio M. Caccomo Family Foundation Memorial Scholarships – 237
Cadmus Communications Corporation Graphics Scholarship Endowment Fund – 2665
Cal State San Macros Alumna Scholarships – 430
Cesar A. Calas/FES Miami Chapter Scholarships – 5120
Tese Caldarelli Memorial Scholarships – 1400
Joseph R. Calder, Jr., MD Scholarship Fund – 3365, 3470, 3583
J.E. Caldwell Centennial Scholarships – 4302
Calhoun County Auburn University Scholarships – 622
Calhoun Scholarships – 405
Hermoine Grant Calhoun Scholarships – 1455
California Association of Family and Consumer Sciences (CAFCS)-San Diego Chapter Scholarships – 2704, 3555, 5343, 5350
California Association of Private Postsecondary Schools Scholarships – 406
California Bar Foundation Diversity Scholarships – 4345
California Bar Law Foundation Scholarships – 4346
California Community Service Scholarships - Bay Area – 3384
California Community Service Scholarships – 3383
California Groundwater Association Scholarships – 424
California Landscape Contractors Association Scholarships – 2596
California Scottish Rite Foundation Scholarships – 429
California Shopping Cart Retrieval Corporation Inc. Scholarships – 410
Calista Scholarships – 432
Harry D. Callahan Educational Trust – 2134
Jodi Callahan Memorial Scholarships – 4802
Calvin Alumni Association Arizona Central Chapter Scholarships – 433
Calvin Alumni Association-Black Alumni Chapter Scholarships – 434
Calvin Alumni Association British Columbia Scholarships – 435
Calvin Alumni Association California- Bay Area Scholarships – 436
Calvin Alumni Association Colorado Chapter Scholarships – 437
Calvin Alumni Association Florida-Gulf Coast Scholarships – 438

Calvin Alumni Association-Illinois Scholarships – 439
Calvin Alumni Association-Iowa/Pella Scholarships – 440
Calvin Alumni Association-Maryland/Baltimore Scholarships – 441
Calvin Alumni Association-Michigan Lakeshore Scholarships – 442
Calvin Alumni Association-Michigan, Lansing Scholarships – 443
Calvin Alumni Association-New Jersey Scholarships – 444
Calvin Alumni Association-New York, Rochester Scholarships – 445
Calvin Alumni Association-South Florida Scholarships – 446
Calvin Alumni Association-South Florida Sophomore Scholarships – 447
Calvin Alumni Association-Southeast Michigan Scholarships – 448
Calvin Alumni Association-Southeastern Wisconsin Scholarships – 449
Calvin Alumni Association Southern California Chapter Scholarships – 450
Calvin Alumni Association-Southwest Michigan, Kalamazoo Scholarships – 451
Calvin Alumni Association-Washington, D.C. Scholarships – 452
Calvin Alumni Association-Washington, Lynden Scholarships – 453
Calvin Alumni Association-Washington-Seattle/Tacoma Scholarships – 454
Camden County College Employee Memorial Scholarships – 456
Camden County College Foundation Scholarships – 457
Camden County Retired Educators Association Scholarships – 458
Cameco Corporation Scholarships in the Geological Sciences - Continuing Students – 3665
Cameco Corporation Scholarships in the Geological Sciences - Entering Students – 3666
Cameco Northern Scholarships - Technical Institute – 468
Cameco Northern Scholarships - University – 469
Stuart Cameron and Margaret McLeod Memorial Scholarships (SCMS) – 1154
Wesley C. Cameron Scholarships – 1529
Lois Campbell Scholarship Award – 1171
Theodore R. Campbell Scholarship – 35
Robert G. Campbell Scholarships – 1796
Canada Millennium Bursary – 36
Canada Millennium Scholarship Foundation Millennium Bursary Award – 470
Canada Study Grant for the Accommodation of Students with Permanent Disabilities – 1239
Canada-Ukraine Parliamentary Program (CUPP) Internship Scholarships – 2365
Canadian Aboriginal Science and Technology Society Scholarships – 3621
Canadian Federation of University Women Etobicoke Bursary – 2307
Canadian Hard of Hearing Association Scholarships – 476
Canadian Hospitality Foundation College Entrance Scholarships – 480
Canadian Hospitality Foundation University Entrance Scholarships – 481
Canadian Macedonian Federation Scholarships – 2308
Canadian Nurses Foundation Northern Scholarships – 3425
Canadian Nurses Foundation Scholarships – 3426
Canadian Parking Association Scholarships – 483
Canadian Sanitation Supply Association Scholarships – 484
Canadian Seniors Golf Association Scholarships – 1890
Canadian Society of Petroleum Geologists Regional Undergraduate Scholarships – 2978
Cancer Survivors' Fund Scholarships – 487
John Cannon Memorial Scholarships – 4035
Agustin Cano Memorial Scholarships – 1738
John Caoile Memorial Scholarships – 1739

Northwest-Shoals Community College Applied Technology Scholarships – 4221

Northwest-Shoals Community College Athletic Scholarships – 1575

Northwest-Shoals Community College Bank Independent Scholarships – 1576

Northwest-Shoals Community College Fine Arts Scholarships - Art – 2558

Northwest-Shoals Community College Fine Arts Scholarships - Drama – 2559

Northwest-Shoals Community College Fine Arts Scholarships - Music – 2931

Northwest-Shoals Community College High School Academic Scholarships – 1577

Northwest-Shoals Community College Independent Computer Scholarships – 1578

Northwest-Shoals Community College Student Activities Scholarships – 1579

Northwestern Mutual Financial Network Scholarships – 3880

Notre Dame Club of Canton Scholarships – 2153

Mike and Flo Novovesky Scholarships – 3115

Robert Noyce Scholarship Program – 4902, 5225

Noyce Scholarships for Secondary Math and Science Education – 4194, 4893

NPM Program Scholarships – 2928

NSA Scholarship Program – 4468

NSHSS Academic Paper Awards – 1507

NSHSS National Scholar Awards – 1508

NSPS Board of Governors Scholarships – 133

The NSPS Scholarships – 134

NSSA/NSCA Collegiate Scholarships – 1514

Nu-Gro Corporation Turfgrass Scholarships (Undergraduate) – 1893

Nurseries Foundation Scholarship Awards – 3157

Nursing Scholarship Program – 3490

NW-SCC/American Cancer Society College Scholarships – 1580

NW-SCC American Legion Scholarships - Florence/Lauderdale Post No. 11 – 1581

NWF's Women for Sustainable Development (WSD) Scholarships – 2027

NYNEX Diversity Scholarship Awards – 1929

Obrzut Ling Scholarships – 1722

Katharine H. Obye Scholarship Award – 715

OCA Scholarships – 1618

OCAEOP Community Service Scholarship Program – 1597

Occupational Physicians Scholarship Fund – 1587

John O'Connor Memorial Scholarship Fund – 1519

Odd Fellows Lodge No. 8 Endowed Scholarships – 1273

Captain Jennifer Shafer Odom Memorial Scholarships - Children of Soldiers – 276

Captain Jennifer Shafer Odom Memorial Scholarships - Spouses of Soldiers – 277

Don & Jan O'Dowd/SWAA Scholarships – 1323

Office Depot Scholarships – 3821, 4744

Ohio Association of Broadcaster's Kids Scholarships – 4038

Ohio Association of Broadcasters Scholarships – 4039

Ohio Newspaper Association Minority Scholarships – 2791

Ohio Newspaper Association University Journalism Scholarships – 2792

Ohio Newspaper Association Women's Scholarships – 2793

Ohio Valley Chapter Scholarships – 3615, 5067, 5366

Ohio War Orphan Scholarships – 2431

Lawrence "Bud" Ohlman Memorial Scholarships – 3116

O'Jays Scholarship Fund – 2154

OKAIDE Scholarships – 1589

Oklahoma City University Merit Scholarships – 4474

The Oklahoma State University at Okmulgee Scholarships – 3271, 4757

Robert B. Oliver ASNT Scholarships – 4707

Roy C. and Dorothy Jean Olson Memorial Scholarships – 1179

Olympia Tumwater Foundation Traditional Scholarships – 1590

Olympia Tumwater Foundation Transitional (non-traditional) Scholarships – 1591

O'Meara Foundation Scholarships – 1075

Charlie O'Meilia Scholarships – 1167

Eloise Pitts O'More Scholarships – 2652

Ontario Hockey Association War Memorial Scholarships – 2314

Operation Homefront Scholarships – 4222

Sheldon Oppenheim Memorial Scholarships – 1930

Dwight D. Opperman Scholarships – 4402

Optimist Club Of Redlands - Ralph Maloof Scholarships – 1833

Optimist Club of Redlands - Virginia Elliott Scholarships – 1834

OPWA Educational Scholarships – 1588

Orange County Centennial Academic Scholarships – 1604

Orange County Centennial Arts Scholarships – 2694, 2869, 2932

Orange County Centennial Certification Scholarships – 1605

Orange County Tourism Council Scholarships – 1606

Orchard-Hoyman Fund for GLBT Student Scholarships – 850

Order Sons of Italy Foundation General Scholarships – 1612

Oregon Association of Broadcasters Scholarships – 4040

Oregon Association of Nurseries Scholarship Program – 3158

Oregon Community Credit Union Scholarships – 2300

Oregon Farm Bureau Memorial Scholarships – 3028

Oregon Logging Conference Scholarships – 1274

Organization of American States Academic Scholarships – 1614

Organization of American States AOS-Placed Scholarships – 1615

Organization of American States Graduate Scholarships – 1616

Organization of American States Self-Placed Scholarships – 1617

Orin Carver Scholarships – 726

Orthopaedic Specialists Nursing Scholarships – 3543

The Kenneth J. Osborn Memorial Scholarships – 5386

Margaret E. Oser Scholarships for Women – 1607

OSU Gay, Lesbian, Bisexual and Transgender Alumni Society (PFLAG Scholarships) – 1931

OTA Education Foundation Scholarships – 1596

Alvin G. Ott Fish and Wildlife Scholarships – 1324

Ellis R. Ott Scholarships – 4869

Ottawa Police 150th Anniversary Scholarships – 4355

Patricia & Armen Oumedian Scholarships – 5139

Ted H. Ousley Scholarship Fund – 908

Outstanding Undergraduate Scholarships (SOAR) – 2293

Outward Bound Wilderness Leadership Awards – 1629

Helen M. Overly Memorial Scholarships – 2425

Charles and Melva T. Owen Memorial Scholarships – 1458

Owner-Operator Independent Drivers Association Scholarships – 1630

Ozarks Division Scholarships – 1372

PACE/Columbian Lawyers Association of Westchester County Endowed Scholarships – 4364

The Arthur J. Packard Memorial Scholarship Competition – 154

Laurie Page-Peck Scholarships Fund – 3196

Raymond E. Page Scholarships – 2587

AFCEA General Emmett Paige Scholarships – 3685, 3998, 4877, 5040

Paleontological Society Student Research Grants – 2972, 3663

E. William Palmer Memorial Scholarships – 353

Palo Verde High School Faculty Follies Scholarships – 2702

Palos Fine Arts Association Scholarships – 2695

PAMA Foundation Scholarship Program – 4859

The PanHellenic Scholarships – 1088

Panther Cafe Scholarships – 1762

Paper Stock Industries Chapter of ISRI Scholarship Program – 1632

Paper Stock Industries/RRF Scholarships – 1631

Pardee Community Building Scholarships – 2620, 3905, 5232

Parents Scholarships – 4192

Joseph M. Parish Memorial Grants – 5018

William Park Woodside Founder's Scholarships – 5372

Cissy McDaniel Parker Scholarships – 781

E.U. Parker Scholarships – 1459

Parking Industry Institute Scholarship Program – 1496

Fitzroy and Mildred Parkinson Memorial Scholarships – 1076

Sylvia Parkinson Scholarships – 3377

PARMA Scholarships – 1733

The Paros-Digiquartz Scholarships – 3085

Pathways to Success Scholarships – 4418

Patient Advocate Foundations Scholarships – 3267

James H. Patrenos Memorial Scholarships – 2078

Gail Patrick Charitable Trust Scholarships – 803

Marvin R. and Pearl E. Patterson Family Scholarships Fund – 2668

Rachael Patterson Memorial Scholarships – 4542, 5325

Alice Conger Patterson Scholarships – 2405

Paul and Inger Friend 4-H Scholarships – 2176

Courtland Paul Scholarships – 2612

Ray, NORP and Katie, WOKTE Pautz Scholarships – 3975, 4924

Kenyon T. Payne Outstanding Student Awards – 1369

PB Rail Engineering Scholarships – 5014

PCH Architects/Steven J. Lehnhof Memorial Architectural Scholarships – 2621

PDC Scholarships – 213

Chuck Peacock Memorial Scholarships – 4819

Charles S. Pearce Scholarships – 2333

Minnie Pearl Scholarship Program – 833

Pearman Family Scholarships – 1992

Robert L. Peaslee-Detroit Brazing and Soldiering Division Scholarships – 4724

Laura Ann Peck Memorial Endowed Scholarships – 2981

Pediatric Endocrinology Nursing Society Academic Education Scholarships – 3516

Pediatric Endocrinology Nursing Society Continuing Education Scholarships – 3517

Peierls Rising Star Scholarship Program – 1109

Pellegrini Scholarships – 2195

Margaret Pemberton Scholarships – 3423

Dorothy E. Hofmann Pembroke Scholarships – 1077

Robert B. and Dorothy Pence Scholarships – 2122

Penn-Bird Family Memorial Scholarships – 4246

Penndelphia Scholarships Foundation – 1677

Pennsboro Alumni Scholarship Fund – 1666

Pennsylvania Association of Arson Investigators Scholarships – 5324

Pennsylvania Heartland Unit Scholarships – 3138

Pennsylvania Land Surveyors Foundation Scholarships – 1678

Pennsylvania Library Association Scholarships for MLS Students – 1679

Pennsylvania Society of Professional Engineers Scholarships – 5224

Pension Real Estate Association Scholarships – 1682

P.E.O. Chapter Scholarship Fund – 975

PEO Educational Loan Funds – 1689

Peoria Area Amateur Radio Club Scholarships – 3976

Pepperdine University Armenian Student Scholarships – 4511

Pepsi Escribe tu Futuro Scholarships – 2490

Pepsi Scholarships – 155

Pepsi Wood County Technical/Caperton Center Scholarship Fund – 1667

Pepsico Scholarships – 2265

Joe Perdue Scholarships – 583

Joaquin Pereira Memorial Scholarships – 1293

Rudy Perez Songwriting Scholarships – 2890

Peridian International, Inc./Rae L. Price, FASLA Scholarships – 2613

The A.W. Perigard Fund – 4054

Sanky Perlowin Memorial Scholarships – 3803

Zoe Gore Perrin Scholarships – 782

James L. Warner Scholarships – 1609
John R. and Joan F. Warren Scholarship Fund – 2164
Washington College Bound Scholarships – 2368
Washington County Farm Bureau Scholarships – 3029
Washington Group International Safety Scholarships – 220
Washington Higher Education Coordinating Board Educational Opportunity Grants – 2369
Washington Higher Education Coordinating Board Health Professional Scholarships – 3343, 3540, 3593, 3713
Washington Higher Education Coordinating Board State Need Grants – 2370
Washington Metropolitan Scholarships – 2371
Washington Reciprocity Out-of-State Scholarships – 1278
Washington Scholarship Fund Signature Scholarships Program – 2373
Stand Watie Scholarships – 2093
Watson-Brown Scholarships – 2375
Thomas S. Watson, Jr. Memorial Scholarships – 3856
Watsontown Volunteer Fire Company Scholarships – 467
The Wax Company Scholarships – 2995
Wayne County Bank Scholarships – 1586
Wayne-Meador-Elliott Scholarships – 1676
Monica M. Weaver Memorial Fund – 3312
Faye and Rendell Webb Scholarships – 4138
Art and Dannie Weber Scholarships – 4290
Allen and Loureena Weber Scholarships – 5263
Lester and Eleanor Webster Charitable Trust Fund – 2165
Webster Society Scholarships – 4675
Kenneth G. Weckel Scholarships – 3012
J.L. Weigand, Jr. Legal Education Trust Scholarships – 4577
Frank L. Weil Memorial Eagle Scout Scholarships – 1453
William E. Weisel Scholarships – 5264
Weissbuch Family Scholarships – 2013
Edward Kent Welch Memorial Scholarships – 2415
Welch Scholars Grants – 3567
Sue Marsh Weller Memorial Scholarships – 1140
Dorothy Wellnitz Canadian Scholarships – 5400
Wells Fargo Scholarship Program – 3832
Wells Fargo Scholarships – 1728
Donald M. Wells Scholarships – 1014
Teri Wenglein-Callender Undergraduate Scholarships – 790
Francis X. Weninger Scholarships – 2434
Lucille and Charles A. Wert Scholarships – 5374
West Indian Migrant Farm Workers Memorial Scholarships – 1083
West Michigan Nursery and Landscape Association Scholarships Fund – 3134
West Virginia Educational Foundation Hospitality Business Alliance Scholarships – 2379
West Virginia Hospitality and Travel Association General Scholarships – 2380
West Virginia Nurses Association District No. 3 Scholarships – 3515
West Virginia PTA Scholarships – 2377
Redlands Evening Lions Club - Barbara Westen Scholarships – 1871
Western Governors University Scholarship Program – 1113
Western Michigan Greenhouse Association Scholarships – 3123
Western Reserve Herb Society Scholarships – 3140
Robert B. Westover Scholarships – 947
Dr. William "Tim" Whalen Memorial Scholarship – 3261
J. Irving Whalley Memorial Scholarships – 5095
Whan Memorial Scholarships – 3890
Haemer Wheatcraft Scholarships – 4408
Wheelchair Success Foundation Scholarships – 613
Seitlin Franklin E. Wheeler Scholarship Fund – 3802
Paul A. Whelan Aviation Scholarships – 4865
Whidbey Island Giving Circle Scholarships – 1729
Whitaker-Minard Memorial Scholarships – 3266
Brian J. White Endowed Law Scholarships – 4520
Howard A. White Endowed Scholarships – 4521

Mary Kean White Memorial Scholarship Fund – 4270
White Rose Scholarships – 1944
Portia White Scholarships – 389
Bradford White Scholarships – 3900
Herbert W. Whiteman, Jr. Scholarships – 3927
Robert B. and Sophia Whiteside Scholarships – 832
Ann Cook Whitman Scholarships for Perry High School – 843
Ann Cook Whitman Washington, DC Scholarships – 844
Donna Axum Whitworth Scholarships – 791
Dwight Whylie Scholarships – 390
David Julian Wichard Scholarships – 2858, 4106
Louise Wachter Wichman Scholarship Fund – 4178
Alice Hersey Wick Scholarships – 2061
Tom Wicker Scholarships – 2859
L. Phil Wicker Scholarships – 3989
Tom Wicker Scholarships – 4107
L. Phil Wicker Scholarships – 4706
Wicomico High School Class of '55 Scholarships – 652
Ethyl and Armin Wiebke Memorial Scholarships – 3755
Barbara Wiedner and Dorothy Vandercook Memorial Peace Scholarships – 1016
Edwin F. Wiegand Science and Technology Scholarships – 4954
Elmo Wierenga Alumni Scholarships – 1015
The WIFLE Scholarship Fund – 4599
Fred C. Wikoff, Jr. Scholarship Fund – 916
Teddy Wilburn Scholarships – 698
WildBird/Clements Memorial Scholarships – 3044
Wiley Publishing Inc. Scholarships – 1518
Wilkinson & Company LLP Secondary School Scholarships – 3935
Wilks Memorial Awards – 4870
Andrea Will Memorial Scholarships – 2062
Willa Beach-Porter Music Scholarships – 2895
Willamette Chapter Scholarship Awards – 3160
Willamette Valley AG Association Scholarships – 3030
M. William and Frances J. Tilghman Scholarship – 653
William Goldberg Diamond Corp. Scholarships – 3636
Williams Foundation Scholarships – 1773
Sidney B. Williams, Jr. Scholarships – 4341
Rodney Williams Legacy Scholarships – 2294
James Elliott Williams Scholarship Fund – 2485
John G. Williams Scholarships Fund – 2384
CSM Virgil R. Williams Scholarships – 846
Randy Williams Scholarships – 2014
Elizabeth T. Williams Scholarships – 2416
Leon Williams Scholarships – 3288
Dr. Dana Williams Scholarships – 4139
Cenie Jomo Williams Tuition Scholarships – 4687
Edwin H. and Louise N. Williamson Endowed Scholarships – 2417
Mary Katherine "Kathy" Williamson Scholarship Fund – 635
Williamsville High School Class of 1970 Scholarship Fund – 884
Williamsport-Lycoming Community Foundation - Benjamin Franklin Scholarships – 885
Gary S. Wilmer RAMI Music Scholarship – 2909
The Wilmore Scholarship Fund – 4169
Glenn Wilson Broadcast Journalism Scholarships – 2797, 3867, 4042
Larry Wilson for Environmental Studies Scholarships – 2496
Pete Wilson Journalism Scholarships – 2748
Saul T. Wilson, Jr. Scholarships – 3302
Bob Wilson Legacy Scholarship – 423
The Arthur N. Wilson, MD, Scholarships – 3188
William S. Wilson Memorial Scholarship – 1332
Ted C. Wilson Memorial Scholarships – 5229
Larry Wilson Scholarships for Undergraduate Civil Engineering Students –.5033
John Charles Wilson Scholarships – 5320
Ross A. Wilson Science Scholarships – 2213
Harriet Barnhart Wimmer Scholarships – 2590
Lisa Winkler Memorial Scholarships – 4732
Armos and Marilyn Winsand-Detroit Section Named Scholarships – 4730
Winston-Salem Foundation Scholarships – 4291

Winston Scholarships – 5346
Marine Corps Sgt. Jeannette L. Winters Memorial Scholarships – 3687, 4000, 4879, 5043
Albert E. Wischmeyer Memorial Scholarships – 5265
Wisconsin Broadcasters Association Scholarships – 4110
Wisconsin High School Scholarships – 2344
Wisconsin-Madison Journalism Scholarships – 2861
Wisconsin-Madison Music Clinic Scholarships – 2961
Wisconsin Region Student Leadership Scholarships – 1408
Witt Mares Scholarships – 2360
WKIX Alumni Association Scholarships – 4108
WMA Memorial Scholarships – 3756
WOCN Accredited Nursing Education Scholarships – 3544
WOCN Advanced Education Scholarships – 3545
Woksape Oyate: "Wisdom of the People" Distinguished Scholars Award – 165
Milton Wolf Scholarships – 948
The Wolf Trap Internship Program – 2965
Deborah Partridge Wolfe International Fellowships – 2440
Charles H. and Ethel E. Wolfe Scholarships – 1610
Tim Wolfred Scholarships – 1945
Eleanor M. Wolfson Memorial Scholarship Fund – 2664
Wendy Y. Wolfson Memorial Scholarship Fund – 2912
Lee Womack Scholarships Fund – 4213
Woman In Rural Electrification Scholarships – 2101
Woman's Club of Grand Haven Scholarships Fund – 984
The Woman's Club of Nashville Scholarships – 699
Women In Defense HORIZONS Scholarships – 2575, 3714, 3936, 4310, 4321, 4580, 4632, 4921, 4969, 5319
Women In Need Scholarships – 840
Women In Transition Scholarships – 841
Women of Today's Manufacturing Scholarships – 4735
Women's Army Corps Veterans Association Scholarships – 2418
Women's Independence Scholarship Programs – 2190
Women's Jewelry Association Scholarships – 2724
Women's Leadership in Agriculture Scholarship Program – 3026
Women's Overseas and Service League Scholarships for Women – 2422
Carolyn Wones Recruitment Scholarships Grant – 722
Charles Fred Wonson Scholarships – 2322
Dr. Harold S. Wood Award for Excellence – 4843
Wood County Bar Association Memorial Scholarships – 4478
Mary and Elliot Wood Foundation Undergraduate Scholarship Fund – 917
Ed Wood Memorial Scholarship Awards – 3161
Hugh and Helen Wood Nepales Scholarship – 321
Geofrey H. Wood Scholarships – 4133
Woodcock Family Education Scholarship Program – 4867
Guy A. Woodings Scholarships – 2983
Betsy B. Woodward Scholarships – 294
Marilyn Graboys Wool Scholarships – 4527
David T. Woolsey Scholarships – 2591
Patty Wooten Scholarships – 2544
Worcester District Medical Society Scholarship Fund – 3394
John W. Work III Memorial Foundation Scholarships – 2907
Working for Farmers' Success Scholarships – 3038
The Working Press Internships – 2808
Workshop, Inc. and Stark MRDD Fostering Diversity Through Special Needs Scholarship Fund – 4271
James and Colin Lee Wozumi Scholarships – 1730
Jean Wright-Elson Scholarships – 3520
Audrey L. Wright Scholarships – 4018
Writers of Passage Scholarship Program – 1953
WTVD Endowment Scholarships – 2860, 4109
Wyatt, Tarrant and Combs, LLP Scholarships – 4567
Margaret Wyeth Scholarship – 723

Title of Awards Index